The College Blue Book®

34th Edition

Scholarships, Fellowships, Grants, and Loans

The College Blue Book®

34th Edition

Scholarships, Fellowships, Grants, and Loans

MACMILLAN REFERENCE USA

An imprint of Thomson Gale, a part of The Thomson Corporation

THOMSON

GALE ™

Detroit • New York • San Francisco • New Haven, Conn. • Waterville, Maine • London

THOMSON
GALE

The College Blue Book, 34th Edition
Volume 5

Project Editors
Bohdan Romaniuk, Verne Thompson

Editorial
Jessica Boguslawski, Kim Hunt-Lowrance, Amanda Sams, Kristy Swartout

Editorial Support Services
Wayne Fong

Imaging and Multimedia
Randy Bassett, Lezlie Light, Mike Logusz, Dan Newell

Rights and Acquisitions
Dean Dauphinais

Composition and Electronic Prepress
Gary Leach, Evi Seoud

Manufacturing
Rhonda Dover

Product Manager
Jennifer F. Bernardelli

ISBN-13:
978-0-02-866006-6 (set)
978-0-02-866011-0 (vol. 5)

ISBN-10:
0-02-866006-4 (set)
0-02-866011-0 (vol. 5)

ISSN 0198-8409

This book is also available as an e-book
ISBN 13: 978-0-02-866084-4 (set)   ISBN 10: 0-02-866084-6 (set)
Contact your Thomson Gale sales representative for ordering information.

Printed in the United States of America
10 9 8 7 6 5 4 3 2 1

Contents

The College Blue Book has been a standard, professional reference on higher education since it was first published in 1923. New features have been added during the intervening years to keep pace with the changing needs for information about our educational facilities. The information, especially in the areas of tuition, room and board, enrollment figures, library holdings, is constantly changing. It is difficult to maintain up-to-date figures in these areas, as many schools change tuition and related costs on an ongoing basis. We therefore urge our readers to check directly with the schools for the most current cost information.

CONTENTS OF EACH VOLUME

Volume 1: Narrative Descriptions

More than 4,100 colleges in the United States and Canada are fully described. Entrance requirements are detailed and campus facilities and costs are described. A map of each U.S. state and Canadian province is included and each college has a grid index fore easy location. Web sites are also listed.

Volume 2: Tabular Data

Colleges are listed alphabetically by state or province. Information about costs, accreditation, enrollment figures, faculty, and names of the chief administrative officers are given for each school.

Volume 3: Degrees Offered by College and Subject

In Part I, the name of each college is listed alphabetically by state or province, with a list of the subject areas for which degrees are offered. Part II includes an alphabetical listing of subject areas for which degrees are granted by one or more institutions of higher education.

Volume 4: Occupational Education

More than 5,600 schools in the United States that provide occupational or technical training are fully described, offering such information as tuition costs, enrollment figures, and entrance requirements. Two indexes are provided: an alphabetical listing of schools in the "Index of Occupational Education Schools," in addition to the "Curricula and Areas of Instruction" index.

Volume 5: Scholarships, Fellowships, Grants, and Loans

This volume provides a listing of almost 3,500 different sources of financial aid for students wishing to further their education. Split alphabetically into eight broad subject areas (each containing several more specialized concentrations of study), as well as a general section, each listing provides basic information about a specific award, including eligibility requirements, amount of award, and application deadlines.

Volume 6: Distance Learning Programs

Responding to this rapidly growing trend in postsecondary education, this volume features comprehensive profiles of nearly 900 institutions offering distance learning programs within the United States and Canada, providing both basic information as well as in-depth descriptions of certain institutions.

For More Information

We are always open to suggestions and recommendations for improvement of *The College Blue Book* from our readers and from the educational professions. Please write or call:

Editor, *The College Blue Book*

Macmillan Reference USA

27500 Drake Rd.

Farmington Hills, MI 48331-3535

Phone: (248)699-4253

Toll-free: 800-347-GALE

Fax: (248)699-8075

Email: blue.book@thomson.com

Web site: www.gale.com

The value of higher education, including highly specialized education in technical and vocational fields, has proved to be an absolute necessity. Through this edition of *Scholarships, Fellowships, Grants, and Loans,* students, counselors, and parents will find a wide variety of sources committed to funding all phases of postsecondary education. Those seeking financial help should make use of as many sources of information as possible, including the Internet, but should be aware that many scholarships and other sources of funding are available in their local area or through the institution they plan to attend.

Scholarships, Fellowships, Grants, and Loans is divided into eight broad subject areas. These are preceded by a "General" section, listing sponsors who do not restrict their awards to the study of a specific subject. Each of the eight categories is then divided into more specific areas of interest within that field. Under these more specific headings are the award entries, listed alphabetically by sponsoring organization. These entries assume a standard format throughout this volume.

All the information in the entry should be studied carefully; it is submitted directly by the sponsoring organization. If, under "Eligibility Requirements," only female descendants of Confederate soldiers are ruled eligible for the award, it is a waste of time for others to apply. On the other hand, if there is some indication of eligibility, prospective applicants should inquire further. You will speed the process of getting information if you enclose a stamped, self-addressed envelope. Some organizations will not respond unless they receive a stamped, self- addressed envelope.

The broad subject area listings are followed by four comprehensive indexes: "Title Index," "Sponsoring Organization," "Level of Education," and "Subject Index." By using the first index, the reader can locate specific awards with which they are already familiar. The second index lists sponsoring organizations and all the awards given by them. The "Level of Education Index" groups the awards by the various levels for which the funds are allocated. The "Subject Index" enables prospective applicants to determine awards that are given in specific subject areas.

Although *Scholarships, Fellowships, Grants, and Loans* lists, for the most part, private sources of financial aid, much assistance is still provided by the federal government, the states, and increasingly, the schools involved.

Federal aid, in the form of scholarships, outright grants, work study and various guaranteed loan programs has declined during the past decade; however, all postsecondary students should order an extremely useful publication, *The Student Guide,* from:

ED Pubs

PO Box 1398

Jessup, MD 20794-1398

877-4-ED-PUBS

http://www.edpubs.org

Applications for federal student aid (FAFSA) are available from high schools, colleges, career schools, or The Federal Student Aid Information Center (800-433-3243). The FAFSA is also available on the web at: http://www.fafsa.ed.gov/

State governments are also sources of scholarships, grants and guaranteed loans, and students should contact their state department of education for details of what is offered. Programs and education budgets vary considerably from state to state.

Finally, the schools are themselves a major source of aid. Their financial aid programs have become as innovative as their curricula. Usually, all forms of aid are available, from outright grants to loans and work-study.

In determining need, most schools require an independent assessment of the student's, or if dependent, the family's, ability to help finance tuition and living costs. The College Board provides the CSS/Financial Aid PROFILE, a financial aid application service. PROFILE is required by select private colleges and some public institutions. All students should file the FAFSA (Free Application for Federal Student Aid). FAFSA is necessary to receive consideration for federal aid, many state grants, college scholarships, and other private aid programs. For specific filing requirements, the financial aid officer of the student's college of choice should be contacted.

The College Board

45 Columbus Ave.

New York, NY 10023-6992

(212)713-8000

www.collegeboard.com

Many civic, fraternal, educational, and business groups give scholarships in their local communities. Sometimes these are limited to a specific high school, but more often they are given to a local area which includes several high schools. These awards can be of significant help to graduating high school seniors. While one award may be as low as $250-$500, the student is usually eligible for more than one award.

Finally, students should be aware that many scholarships are also awarded (nationally) only to those that are already in college and entering their sophomore, junior, or senior year.

Scholarships, Fellowships, Grants, and Loans is both a key and a stepping stone to financing higher education which has become almost a necessity in the United States. Despite budget cuts and an increase in competition for scarce financial resources, funds are available to the enterprising student determined to explore every avenue in pursuit of an education.

1 ■ 7TH GENERATION COMMUNITY SERVICE CORPORATION
Attn: Scholarship Program
4495 South Hopkins Avenue, Suite A
Titusville, FL 32780
Tel: (321)385-0207; 888-385-0207
Fax: (321)385-1586
E-mail: Info@7thGeneration.org
Web Site: http://www.7thgeneration.org
To provide financial assistance to Native American students entering college for the first time.
Title of Award: 7th Generation Community Service Corporation Scholarship Program **Area, Field, or Subject:** General studies/Field of study not specified **Level of Education for which Award is Granted:** Undergraduate **Number Awarded:** 1 each year. **Funds Available:** Stipends depend on the need of the recipient, to a maximum of $20,000. **Duration:** 1 year; may be renewed up to 3 additional years if the recipient maintains a GPA of 2.5 or higher.
Eligibility Requirements: This program is open to Native Americans who are under 21 years of age and graduating high school seniors or entering a 2-year or 4-year college or university as a full-time student for the first time. Applicants must be tribally enrolled or have a Certificate of Degree of Indian Blood (CDIB) card. They must rank in the top quarter of their high school class and have a GPA of 3.25 or higher. Selection is based primarily on financial need. Applications are accepted beginning in mid-October of each year. Only the first 350 that are received are considered. **Deadline for Receipt:** January of each year. **Additional Information:** This program is administered by Scholarship Management Services of Scholarship America, One Scholarship Way, P.O. Box 297, St. Peter, MN 56082, (507) 931-1682, (800) 537-4180, Fax: (507) 931-9168, E-mail: smsinfo@csfa.org.

2 ■ 10TH MOUNTAIN DIVISION DESCENDANTS, INC.
c/o Val Rios
6816 South Maple
Fresno, CA 93725
Tel: (559)834-6230
E-mail: vrios913@aol.com
Web Site: http://www.10thmtndivdesc.org/scolarship.htm
To provide financial assistance for college to descendants of former members of the 10th Mountain Division.
Title of Award: 10th Mountain Division Descendant Merit Scholarship **Area, Field, or Subject:** General studies/Field of study not specified **Level of Education for which Award is Granted:** Undergraduate **Number Awarded:** 1 each year. **Funds Available:** The stipend is $1,000. **Duration:** 1 year.
Eligibility Requirements: Eligible to apply for these scholarships are the descendants of veterans who served in the 10th Mountain Division during World War II. Applicants must be entering their first year of college. Selection is based on service to the World War II 10th Mountain Division (e.g., assisting at local chapter functions, involved in activities that support the legacy of the division, assisting at memorial services to the division, visiting veterans and/or wives or widows in nursing or private homes). Financial need is not considered. Membership in 10th Mountain Division Descendants, Inc. is not required, but it is recommended that the applicant or a parent be a member. **Deadline for Receipt:** May of each year.

3 ■ 11TH ARMORED CAVALRY VETERANS OF VIETNAM AND CAMBODIA
c/o Gene Johnson, Scholarship Committee Chair
3335 Casey Drive, Number 6-101
Las Vegas, NV 89120-1183
Tel: (702)456-3218
E-mail: gene677@aol.com
Web Site: http://www.11thcavnam.com/scholar.html
To provide financial assistance to members of the 11th Armored Cavalry Veterans of Vietnam and Cambodia (ACVVC) and to their dependents.
Title of Award: 11th Armored Cavalry Veterans of Vietnam and Cambodia Scholarship **Area, Field, or Subject:** General studies/Field of study not specified **Level of Education for which Award is Granted:** Undergraduate **Number Awarded:** Varies each year; recently, 25 of these scholarships were awarded. **Funds Available:** The stipend is $3,000; funds are paid directly to the recipient's school, in 2 equal installments. **Duration:** 1 year; nonrenewable.
Eligibility Requirements: This program is open to 11th ACVVC members and to their dependents. In addition, dependents of deceased troopers who served with the 11th Armored Cavalry in Vietnam or Cambodia may apply (a copy of the father's obituary must be supplied). Affiliation with the cavalry must be documented. Applicants must submit brief essays on 1) the field of study they plan to enter and why; and 2) why they would be a worthy recipient of this scholarship. Selection is based on the essays and grades; financial need is no longer considered. Priority is given to children of members who were killed in action or died of wounds. **Deadline for Receipt:** May of each year. **Additional Information:** Recipients must use the awarded money within 20 months of being notified.

4 ■ THE 13TH REGIONAL CORPORATION
Attn: The 13th Regional Heritage Foundation
1156 Industry Drive
Seattle, WA 98188
Tel: (206)575-6229
Fax: (206)575-6283
E-mail: info@the13thregion.com
Web Site: http://www.the13thregion.com/Scholarships
To provide financial assistance for college or graduate school to Alaska Natives who are shareholders of The 13th Regional Corporation or their dependent children or grandchildren.
Title of Award: The 13th Regional Heritage Foundation Scholarships **Area, Field, or Subject:** General studies/Field of study not specified **Level of Education for which Award is Granted:** Graduate, Undergraduate **Number Awarded:** Varies each year. **Funds Available:** The stipend depends on the need of the recipient and the availability of funds. Funds are disbursed directly to the school to be used for tuition, books, board, or laboratory fees. **Duration:** 1 year; may be renewed.
Eligibility Requirements: This program is open to 1) original shareholders of The 13th Regional Corporation, and 2) their dependent children and grandchildren who are also Alaska Natives. Applicants must be accepted to or enrolled in an accredited community college, university, college, or vocational/trade school as an undergraduate, graduate, or vocational student. Along with their application, they must submit an essay of 500 to 1,000 words on their personal history, special talents and abilities, community involvement, plans for the future, philosophy of life, why they wish

to attend college or graduate school, educational objective, major and minor field of interest, and school they plan to attend. Selection is based on leadership and initiative (20%), academic achievement (20%), educational goals (20%), completeness and neatness of application (20%), and financial need (20%). **Deadline for Receipt:** February of each year for spring and summer terms; June of each year for fall and winter terms. **Additional Information:** The 13th Regional Corporation was established under provisions of the Alaska Native Claims Settlement Act of 1971. Its shareholders are Alaska Natives who no longer live in Alaska.

5 ■ 25TH INFANTRY DIVISION ASSOCIATION

P.O. Box 7
Flourtown, PA 19031-0007
E-mail: TropicLtn@aol.com
Web Site: http://www.25thida.com/associat.html
To provide financial assistance for college to the children of veterans and current members of the 25th Infantry Division Association.
Title of Award: 25th Infantry Division Association Educational Memorial Scholarship Award **Area, Field, or Subject:** General studies/Field of study not specified **Level of Education for which Award is Granted:** Four Year College **Number Awarded:** Varies each year. **Funds Available:** Stipends up to $1,500 are available. **Duration:** Each grant is a 1-time award, which may be spent over any period of time.
Eligibility Requirements: This program is open to 1) children and grandchildren of active members of the association; 2) children of former members of the division deceased during active combat with the division or as a result of it; and 3) active members of an association chapter with the division who are scheduled for release from active service or discharge on or before December 31 of the award year. Applicants must be enrolling in the freshman year of an accredited 4-year college or university and intending to work toward a baccalaureate degree by enrolling in at least 12 semester hours of study each semester. They must submit 1) a personal letter describing the reasons for their request, future plans, school interests and activities, and financial situation; 2) a transcript of high school credits; 3) most recent ACT or SAT scores; 4) 3 letters of recommendation; 5) a letter of acceptance from the institution they plan to attend; and 6) a photograph. **Deadline for Receipt:** March of each year. **Additional Information:** Information is also available from the Scholarship Committee Chairman, 3930 South Bridlewood Drive, Bountiful, UT 84010. This program includes the George and Rosemary Murray Scholarship Award.

6 ■ 43D INFANTRY DIVISION VETERANS ASSOCIATION

c/o Howie Brown, Secretary/Treasurer
150 Lakedell Drive
East Greenwich, RI 02818-4716
Tel: (401)884-7052
E-mail: Brownhowieb@aol.com
Web Site: http://www.geocities.com/Pentagon/Quarters/9543/scholarships.htm
To provide financial assistance for college to members of the 43d Infantry Division Veterans Association and their families.
Title of Award: 43d Infantry Division Veterans Association Scholarships **Area, Field, or Subject:** General studies/Field of study not specified **Level of Education for which Award is Granted:** Undergraduate **Number Awarded:** At least 5 each year. **Funds Available:** A stipend is awarded (amount not specified). **Duration:** 1 year.
Eligibility Requirements: This program is open to members of the association; the wives, children, grandchildren, and great-grandchildren of members; and the widows, children, grandchildren, and great-grandchildren of deceased members who were in good standing at the time of their death. Descendants of members of the 43d Infantry Division who died on active duty with the division during World War II are also eligible. Financial need is considered in the selection process.

7 ■ 82ND AIRBORNE DIVISION ASSOCIATION

Attn: President, Educational Fund
P.O. Box 65089
Fayetteville, NC 28306-5089
Tel: (919)822-4534
E-mail: abn82dassn@aol.com
Web Site: http://www.82ndassociation.org

To provide financial assistance for college to members of the 82d Airborne Division Association and their dependent children.
Title of Award: 82nd Airborne Division Association Awards **Area, Field, or Subject:** General studies/Field of study not specified **Level of Education for which Award is Granted:** Undergraduate **Number Awarded:** Varies each year; recently, $87,000 in scholarships was awarded. **Funds Available:** The stipend is $1,500 per year. Funds are paid to the recipient's college or university. **Duration:** 1 semester (the second in a school year); recipients may reapply for up to 3 additional annual awards.
Eligibility Requirements: Eligible to apply for this award are 1) dependent children of 82nd Airborne Division Association voting members; 2) dependent children of 82nd Airborne servicemen killed in combat; 3) dependent children of deceased Life or All American members of the 82nd Airborne Division Association; and 4) former active-duty 82nd Airborne Division troopers who are association members, are within 2 years of honorable discharge, and served no more than 2 enlistments. Applicants must be enrolled in an accredited university or college. Selection is based on academic achievement and financial need. **Deadline for Receipt:** October of each year. **Additional Information:** In years when a suitable candidate applies, 1 of these awards is designated the General Mathew B. Ridgeway Scholarship. Membership in the association is open to anyone who ever served in the 82nd Airborne Division, anyone who is currently serving on active duty in jump status, and anyone who has ever served in any of the uniformed services on either jump or glider status and was honorably discharged.

8 ■ 100 BLACK MEN OF AMERICA, INC.

Attn: Scholarship Administrator
141 Auburn Avenue
Atlanta, GA 30303
Tel: (404)688-5100
Free: 800-598-3411
Fax: (404)688-1028
Web Site: http://www.100blackmen.org
To provide financial assistance for college to high school seniors and current undergraduates who submit essays on topics related to African Americans, particularly African American males.
Title of Award: 100 Black Men of America National Scholarship Program **Area, Field, or Subject:** General studies/Field of study not specified **Level of Education for which Award is Granted:** Undergraduate **Number Awarded:** Varies each year. **Funds Available:** Stipends range from $1,000 to $3,000 and are paid directly to the institution. **Duration:** 1 year.
Eligibility Requirements: This program is open to high school seniors and undergraduates who are attending or planning to attend an accredited postsecondary institution as a full-time student. Applicants must submit a 600-word essay on 1 of the following topics: 1) what is the state of the African American male; 2) why are the academic results of African American youth in grades K-12 in the areas of reading and mathematics below the national average and what strategies do they believe school systems should implement to improve those statistics; 3) how should the African American community address the nation's current economic slow down; or 4) how would they define and address the current problem of race relations in America. They must have a GPA of 2.5 or higher and have completed at least 50 hours of active community service within the past 12 months. Financial need is not considered in the selection process. **Deadline for Receipt:** February of each year.

9 ■ 100TH INFANTRY BATTALION VETERANS CLUB

Attn: Scholarship Committee
520 Kamoku Street
Honolulu, HI 96826
Tel: (808)732-5216
E-mail: daisyy@hgea.net
Web Site: http://emedia.leeward.hawaii.edu/mnakano
To provide financial assistance to high school seniors and college students from Hawaii who attend mainland institutions and exemplify the sponsor's motto of "Continuing Service."
Title of Award: Mr. and Mrs. Moichi Okazaki Scholarship **Area, Field, or Subject:** General studies/Field of study not specified **Level of Education for which Award is Granted:** Undergraduate **Number Awarded:** 1 each year. **Funds Available:** The stipend is $1,000. **Duration:** 1 year; nonrenewable.

Eligibility Requirements: This program is open to high school seniors planning to attend an institution of higher learning on the mainland and full-time undergraduate students at mainland community colleges, vocational/trade schools, 4-year colleges, and universities. Applicants must have a GPA of 2.5 or higher and be able to demonstrate civic responsibility and community service. Along with their application, they must submit a 4-page essay on how their postsecondary education at an out-of-state school will benefit them, their community, and their state. Selection is based on that essay and the applicant's demonstration that he or she can effectively promote the legacy of the 100th Infantry Battalion and its motto of "Continuing Service." Financial need is not considered. **Deadline for Receipt:** April of each year.

10 ■ 100TH INFANTRY BATTALION VETERANS CLUB

Attn: Scholarship Committee
520 Kamoku Street
Honolulu, HI 96826
Tel: (808)732-5216
E-mail: daisyy@hgea.net
Web Site: http://emedia.leeward.hawaii.edu/mnakano
To provide financial assistance for college to family members of veterans who served in the 100th Infantry Battalion of World War II.
Title of Award: One Puka Puka Scholarship **Area, Field, or Subject:** General studies/Field of study not specified **Level of Education for which Award is Granted:** Undergraduate **Number Awarded:** 1 each year. **Funds Available:** The stipend is $2,000. **Duration:** 1 year; nonrenewable.
Eligibility Requirements: This program is open to direct family members and descendants of 100th Infantry Battalion World War II veterans. Applicants must be high school seniors planning to attend an institution of higher learning or full-time undergraduate students at community colleges, vocational/trade schools, 4-year colleges, and universities. Along with their application, they must submit a 4-page essay that reviews the experience of Nisei men who fought in the racially-segregated 100th Infantry Battalion during World War II and asks, in the light of that experience and the meaning of democracy, if American troops should continue fighting in Iraq. Selection is based on that essay, academic achievement, extracurricular activities, and community service. Financial need is not considered. **Deadline for Receipt:** April of each year.

11 ■ 100TH INFANTRY BATTALION VETERANS CLUB

Attn: Scholarship Committee
520 Kamoku Street
Honolulu, HI 96826
Tel: (808)732-5216
E-mail: daisyy@hgea.net
Web Site: http://emedia.leeward.hawaii.edu/mnakano
To provide financial assistance to high school seniors and college students who exemplify the sponsor's motto of "Continuing Service."
Title of Award: Warren Fencl Scholarships **Area, Field, or Subject:** General studies/Field of study not specified **Level of Education for which Award is Granted:** Undergraduate **Number Awarded:** 2 each year. **Funds Available:** The stipend is $1,000. **Duration:** 1 year; nonrenewable.
Eligibility Requirements: This program is open to high school seniors planning to attend an institution of higher learning and full-time undergraduate students at community colleges, vocational/trade schools, 4-year colleges, and universities. Applicants must have a GPA of 2.5 or higher and be able to demonstrate civic responsibility and community service. Along with their application, they must submit a 4-page essay that explains how valuing a diversity of different opinions, cultures, and lifestyles affects a nation that is challenged with resolving complex issues. Selection is based on that essay and the applicant's demonstration that he or she can effectively promote the legacy of the 100th Infantry Battalion and its motto of "Continuing Service." Financial need is not considered. **Deadline for Receipt:** April of each year. **Additional Information:** This scholarship is named in honor of a World War II veteran of the 34th Infantry Division who fought alongside the Japanese

American soldiers of the 100th Infantry Battalion and subsequently campaigned to correct the injustices committed against Japanese Americans during the war.

12 ■ 101ST AIRBORNE DIVISION ASSOCIATION

2703 Michigan Avenue
P.O. Box 929
Fort Campbell, KY 42223-0929
Tel: (270)439-0445
Fax: (270)439-6645
E-mail: assn101abn@aol.com
Web Site: http://www.screamingeagle.org
To provide financial assistance for college to the spouses, children, and grandchildren of members of the 101st Airborne Division Association.
Title of Award: Chappie Hall Memorial Scholarship Program **Area, Field, or Subject:** General studies/Field of study not specified **Level of Education for which Award is Granted:** Undergraduate **Number Awarded:** At least 1 each year. **Funds Available:** The amount awarded varies, depending upon the needs of the recipient and the funds available.
Eligibility Requirements: Eligible to apply for these scholarships are individuals who maintained a GPA of 2.0 or higher during the preceding school year and whose parent, grandparent, or spouse is (or, if deceased, was) a regular (not associate) member of the 101st Airborne Division. Selection is based on career objectives, academic record, and financial need. **Deadline for Receipt:** May of each year.

13 ■ 531 GRAY GHOST SQUADRON ASSOCIATION

c/o Marine Corps Scholarship Foundation
P.O. Box 3008
Princeton, NJ 08543-3008
Tel: (609)921-3534
Free: 800-292-7777
Fax: (609)452-2259
E-mail: mcsfnj@mcsf.org
Web Site: http://www.marine-scholars.org
To provide financial assistance for college to the grandchildren of veterans who served with the 531 Gray Ghost Squadron of Marines.
Title of Award: 531 Gray Ghost Squadron Association Scholarship **Area, Field, or Subject:** General studies/Field of study not specified **Level of Education for which Award is Granted:** Undergraduate **Number Awarded:** Varies each year. **Funds Available:** Stipends depend on the need of the recipient and the availability of funds. **Duration:** 1 year; may be renewed for up to 3 additional years.
Eligibility Requirements: This program is open to grandchildren of veterans who served with the 531 Gray Ghost Squadron and are or were members of its association. Applicants must submit academic transcripts, a copy of their grandparent's honorable discharge, and a 300-word essay on topics that change periodically. Recently, they were invited to write on the topic, "What is the most valuable lesson you have learned and who was responsible for teaching it?" Only undergraduate study is supported. The family income of applicants must be less than $63,000 per year. **Deadline for Receipt:** April of each year.

14 ■ ACACIA FRATERNITY

Attn: Acacia Fraternity Foundation
8777 Purdue Road, Suite 130
Indianapolis, IN 46268
Tel: (317)872-8210; 888-345-1904
Fax: (317)872-8213
Web Site: http://www.acacia.org/aff_scholarship_app.pdf
To provide financial assistance to undergraduate members of Acacia Fraternity.
Title of Award: Acacia Fraternity Foundation Scholarships **Area, Field, or Subject:** General studies/Field of study not specified **Level of Education for which Award is Granted:** Undergraduate **Number Awarded:** Varies each year; recently, 47 of these scholarships were awarded: 1 at $3,500, 4 at $1,000, 40 at $500, and 2 at $100. **Funds Available:** Stipends range from $100 to $3,500. Funds are paid directly to the bursar at the recipient's institution. **Duration:** 1 year.
Eligibility Requirements: This program is open to brothers of the fraternity in good standing who have a GPA of 2.5 or higher. Applicants must be planning to continue their undergraduate education as full-time students at an accredited institution. Selection is based on scholarship,

leadership, citizenship, and financial need. **Deadline for Receipt:** June of each year.

15 ■ ACADEMY OF MODEL AERONAUTICS

Attn: Education Coordinator
5161 East Memorial Drive
Muncie, IN 47302-9252
Tel: (765)287-1256
Fax: (765)289-4248
Web Site: http://www.buildandfly.com/AMAchgrantscholarship.asp
To provide financial assistance for college to members of the Academy of Model Aeronautics (AMA).
Title of Award: Charles H. Grant Scholarship **Area, Field, or Subject:** General studies/Field of study not specified **Level of Education for which Award is Granted:** Undergraduate **Number Awarded:** Varies each year; a total of $20,000 is available for this program annually. **Funds Available:** The stipend depends on the number of recipients. **Duration:** 1 year; nonrenewable.
Eligibility Requirements: Applicants must be graduating high school seniors who have been AMA members for the last full 36 months prior to applying. They must have been accepted by a college or university offering a certificate or degree program. Along with their application, they must submit a 1-page statement on why they are applying for this scholarship. Selection is based on that statement, academic achievement (class rank, GPA, test scores), school and community activities, work experience, and modeling experience. Financial need is not considered. **Deadline for Receipt:** April of each year.

16 ■ ACADEMY OF MODEL AERONAUTICS

Attn: Education Coordinator
5161 East Memorial Drive
Muncie, IN 47302-9252
Tel: (765)287-1256
Fax: (765)289-4248
Web Site: http://www.buildandfly.com/AMAchgrantscholarship.asp
To provide financial assistance for college to members of the Academy of Model Aeronautics (AMA).
Title of Award: Sig Memorial Scholarship **Area, Field, or Subject:** General studies/Field of study not specified **Level of Education for which Award is Granted:** Undergraduate **Number Awarded:** Varies each year. **Funds Available:** The stipend depends on the number of recipients. **Duration:** 1 year; nonrenewable.
Eligibility Requirements: Applicants must be graduating high school seniors who have been AMA members for the last full 36 months prior to applying. They must have been accepted by a college or university offering a certificate or degree program. Along with their application, they must submit a 1-page statement on why they are applying for this scholarship. Selection is based on that statement, financial need, school and community activities, work experience, and modeling experience. Academic achievement is not considered. **Deadline for Receipt:** April of each year.

17 ■ ACCEL/EXCHANGE NETWORK

c/o Fiserv
255 Fiserv Drive
P.O. Box 979
Brookfield, WI 53008-0979
Tel: (262)879-5966
Free: 800-872-7882
Fax: (262)879-5013
E-mail: general_info@fiserv.com
Web Site: http://www.fiserv.com
To provide financial assistance for college to needy high school seniors.
Title of Award: Education Exchange College Grant Program **Area, Field, or Subject:** General studies/Field of study not specified **Level of Education for which Award is Granted:** Four Year College **Number Awarded:** 34 each year: 4 at $5,000 and 30 at $1,000. **Funds Available:** Stipends are either $5,000 or $1,000. A total of $100,000 is distributed annually. **Duration:** 1 year.
Eligibility Requirements: This program is open to seniors graduating from high school who have been accepted at an accredited 4-year college or university. Students must pick up an application at a participating Exchange member institution (primarily banks and credit unions). For a list of financial institutions that will have applications, write to the sponsor

or visit their web site. U.S. citizenship is required. Selection is based on extracurricular activities, character, leadership, financial need, and a required essay. **Deadline for Receipt:** March of each year. **Additional Information:** This program was established in 1994.

18 ■ ACTUARIAL FOUNDATION

Attn: Actuarial Education and Research Fund Committee
475 North Martingale Road, Suite 800
Schaumburg, IL 60173-2226
Tel: (847)706-3565
Fax: (847)706-3599
E-mail: scholarships@actfnd.org
Web Site: http://www.aerf.org/research_edu/prize_award.htm
To provide financial assistance to undergraduate students who are preparing for a career in actuarial science.
Title of Award: John Culver Wooddy Scholarships **Area, Field, or Subject:** Actuarial science; Insurance and insurance-related fields **Level of Education for which Award is Granted:** Four Year College **Number Awarded:** Varies each year; recently, 4 of these scholarships were awarded. **Funds Available:** The stipend is $2,000 per academic year. Funds are paid directly to the recipient's school. **Duration:** 1 year.
Eligibility Requirements: Eligible to be nominated are undergraduate students who will have senior standing in the semester after receiving the scholarship. Applicants must rank in the top quartile of their class and have successfully completed 1 actuarial examination. Each university may nominate only 1 student. Preference is given to candidates who have demonstrated leadership potential by participating in extracurricular activities. Financial need is not considered in the selection process. **Deadline for Receipt:** June of each year. **Additional Information:** This program was established in 1996.

19 ■ ADELANTE! U.S. EDUCATION LEADERSHIP FUND

8415 Datapoint Drive, Suite 400
San Antonio, TX 78229
Tel: (210)692-1971; 877-692-1971
Fax: (210)692-1951
E-mail: info@adelantefund.org
Web Site: http://www.adelantefund.org
To provide financial aid, internships, and leadership training to upper-division Hispanic students enrolled in Hispanic Serving Institutions (HSIs).
Title of Award: Adelante! Fund Scholarship Program **Area, Field, or Subject:** General studies/Field of study not specified **Level of Education for which Award is Granted:** Four Year College **Number Awarded:** Varies each year; recently, 22 students received scholarships. **Funds Available:** The maximum stipend is $3,000 per year. **Duration:** 1 year.
Eligibility Requirements: This program is open to Hispanic students currently enrolled in HSIs. Applicants must have a GPA of 3.0 or higher, be eligible to receive financial aid, be juniors or seniors in college, agree to attend the Adelante Leadership Institute, be eligible to participate in a summer internship, exhibit leadership, and provide 2 letters of recommendation. Most recipients are the first in their families to complete a college education. **Additional Information:** This fund was established by the Hispanic Association of Colleges and Universities in 1997 and became a separate organization in 1999. Recipients must participate in a summer internship and the Adelante Leadership Institute.

20 ■ ADIRONDACK SPINTACULAR

Attn: Scholarship Panel
485 Bunker Hill Road
Mayfield, NY 12117
Tel: (518)863-2668
E-mail: Iamspintacular@aol.com
Web Site: http://www.adirondackspintacular.com/pages/scholarship.html
To provide financial assistance for college to high school seniors who have a bleeding disorder or other chronic disorder.
Title of Award: Lawrence Madeiros Scholarship **Area, Field, or Subject:** General studies/Field of study not specified **Level of Education for which Award is Granted:** Undergraduate **Number Awarded:** Varies each year; recently, 5 of these scholarships were awarded. **Funds Available:** The stipend is $1,000. **Duration:** 1 year.
Eligibility Requirements: This program is open to seniors graduating from high school who have been accepted at an accredited college or university. Applicants must be diagnosed with a bleeding disorder or other

chronic disorder. Along with their application, they must submit brief essays on 1) how living with or around a chronic disorder has impacted their life; 2) their goals and aspirations in life; and 3) their passion. Financial need may also be considered. **Deadline for Receipt:** June of each year. **Additional Information:** This program, established in 2001, is supported by the Adirondack Spintacular, a charity event in which volunteers cycle, walk, or run to raise money. Other chronic disorders have included muscular dystrophy, diabetes, autism, and Aspergers Syndrome.

21 ■ ADJUTANT GENERAL'S DEPARTMENT

Attn: ONG Scholarship Program Office
2825 West Dublin Granville Road
Columbus, OH 43235-2789
Tel: (614)336-7032; 888-400-6484
Fax: (614)336-7410
E-mail: ongsp@ongsp.org
Web Site: http://www.ongsp.org
To provide financial assistance to members of the Ohio National Guard interested in working on a college degree.

Title of Award: Ohio National Guard Scholarship Program **Area, Field, or Subject:** General studies/Field of study not specified **Level of Education for which Award is Granted:** Undergraduate **Number Awarded:** Grants are limited to the annual average student load of 4,000 full-time equivalent students per term. **Funds Available:** The program covers 100% of the tuition and general fee charges at state-assisted 2- and 4-year colleges and universities in Ohio. **Duration:** The grant is limited to 12 quarters or 8 semesters and participants must remain enrolled as a full-time undergraduate student for that time. Enrollment in the institution of higher education must begin not later than 12 months after the completion of Initial Active Duty for Training (IADT), or date of reenlistment, or date of extension of current enlistment.

Eligibility Requirements: This program is open to members of the Ohio Army and Air National Guard attending a 2- or 4-year public college or university. Applicants must commit to and/or complete a 6-year enlistment in the Ohio Guard. New enlistees must complete basic training and obtain a military job skill. **Deadline for Receipt:** June for fall term; October for winter quarter or spring semester; January for spring quarter; and March for summer term. **Additional Information:** This program was established in 1999. Grant assistance is not available for an additional baccalaureate degree, for postgraduate courses, or for courses not applicable to a degree.

22 ■ AFRICAN METHODIST EPISCOPAL CHURCH

Attn: CMSWW Organization
c/o Ora L. Easley, President
5981 Hitching Post Lane
Nashville, TN 37211
Tel: (615)833-6936
Fax: (615)833-3781
E-mail: Amespouses1@aol.com
Web Site: http://www.amemswwpk.org
To provide financial assistance for college to children of ministers in the African Methodist Episcopal (AME) Church.

Title of Award: AME Preacher's Kid Scholarship **Area, Field, or Subject:** General studies/Field of study not specified **Level of Education for which Award is Granted:** Undergraduate **Number Awarded:** 2 or 3 each year. **Funds Available:** The stipend is $1,000. **Duration:** 1 year.
Eligibility Requirements: This program is open to dependent children under 21 years of age whose parent or legal guardian is an AME minister. Applicants must be a member of the AME Church, have a satisfactory score on the SAT or ACT, rank in the top 50% of their high school class, and have a cumulative GPA of 2.3 or higher. Along with their application, they must submit a 300-word essay on how the AME Church has made a difference in their life and what they will do to support their church. Their minister parent must be a member of the Connectional AME Ministers' Spouses, Widows and Widowers Organization. **Deadline for Receipt:** April of each year.

23 ■ AHF, INC.

31 Moody Road
P.O. Box 985
Enfield, CT 06083-0985
800-243-4621

Fax: (860)763-7022
E-mail: info@ahfinfo.com
Web Site: http://www.ahfinfo.com/ahfinfo/bc_mem_scholarship.html
To provide financial assistance to college to students who have a bleeding disorder.

Title of Award: Beth Carew Memorial Scholarships **Area, Field, or Subject:** General studies/Field of study not specified **Level of Education for which Award is Granted:** Undergraduate **Number Awarded:** 5 each year. **Funds Available:** The stipend is $2,000. **Duration:** 1 year.
Eligibility Requirements: This program is open to high school seniors and college freshmen, sophomores, and juniors who have hemophilia, von Willebrand Disease, or another related inherited bleeding disorder. Applicants must be attending or planning to attend an accredited college or university in the United States as a full-time student. As part of their application, they must submit essays on their academic goals, why they would be a good choice for this scholarship, their participation in volunteer community activities, their greatest challenge as a person living with a bleeding disorder, examples of choices they have made that demonstrate good and bad judgment on their part, and other financial assistance they are or may be receiving. **Deadline for Receipt:** April of each year. **Additional Information:** This program was established in 2002 to honor Beth Carew, who died in 1994 as 1 of the very few women to have hemophilia A.

24 ■ AIR FORCE AID SOCIETY

Attn: Education Assistance Department
241 18th Street South, Suite 202
Arlington, VA 22202-3409
Tel: (703)607-3072
Free: 800-429-9475
Web Site: http://www.afas.org/Education/body_grant.cfm
To provide financial assistance for college to dependents of active-duty, retired, or deceased Air Force personnel.

Title of Award: General Henry H. Arnold Education Grant Program **Area, Field, or Subject:** General studies/Field of study not specified **Level of Education for which Award is Granted:** Undergraduate **Number Awarded:** Varies each year. **Funds Available:** The stipend is $1,500. **Duration:** 1 year; may be renewed if the recipient maintains a GPA of 2.0 or higher.
Eligibility Requirements: This program is open to 1) dependent children of Air Force personnel who are either active duty, Reservists on extended active duty, retired due to length of active-duty service or disability, or deceased while on active duty or in retired status; 2) spouses of active-duty Air Force members and Reservists on extended active duty; and 3) surviving spouses of Air Force members who died while on active duty or in retired status. Applicants must be enrolled or planning to enroll as full-time undergraduate students in an accredited college, university, or vocational/trade school. Spouses must be attending school within the 48 contiguous states. Selection is based on family income and education costs. **Deadline for Receipt:** April of each year. **Additional Information:** Since this program was established in the 1988-89 academic year, it has awarded more than 70,000 grants.

25 ■ AIR FORCE ASSOCIATION

Attn: Awards and Scholarships
1501 Lee Highway
Arlington, VA 22209-1198
Tel: (703)247-5839
Free: 800-727-3337, ext. 5801
Fax: (703)247-5853
E-mail: AFAStaff@AFA.org
Web Site: http://www.afa.org/aef/aid/spouse.asp
To provide financial assistance for undergraduate or graduate study to spouses of Air Force members.

Title of Award: AEF Air Force Spouse Scholarships **Area, Field, or Subject:** General studies/Field of study not specified **Level of Education for which Award is Granted:** Graduate, Undergraduate **Number Awarded:** 10 each year: 1 for each Air Force Major Air Command (MAJCOM). **Funds Available:** The stipend is $1,000 per year; funds are sent to the recipients' schools to be used for any reasonable cost related to working on a degree. **Duration:** 1 year; nonrenewable.
Eligibility Requirements: This program is open to spouses of Air Force active duty, Air National Guard, or Air Force Reserve members. Spouses

who are themselves military members or in ROTC are not eligible. Applicants must have a GPA of 3.5 or higher in college (or high school if entering college for the first time) and be able to provide proof of acceptance into an accredited undergraduate or graduate degree program. They must submit a 2-page essay on their academic and career goals, the motivation that led them to that decision, and how Air Force and other local community activities in which they are involved will enhance their goals. Selection is based on the essay and 2 letters of recommendation. **Deadline for Receipt:** April of each year. **Additional Information:** This program was established in 1995. Previously, it was sponsored by the Aerospace Education Foundation which, in 2006, merged with the Air Force Association.

26 ■ AIR FORCE OFFICERS' WIVES' CLUB OF WASHINGTON, D.C.
Attn: AFOWC Scholarship Committee
50 Theisen Street
Bolling Air Force Base
Washington, DC 20032-5411
To provide financial assistance for undergraduate or graduate education to the dependents of Air Force members in the Washington, D.C. area.
Title of Award: Air Force Officers' Wives' Club of Washington, D.C. Continuing Education Scholarships for Air Force Dependents **Area, Field, or Subject:** General studies/Field of study not specified **Level of Education for which Award is Granted:** Graduate, Undergraduate **Number Awarded:** Varies each year. **Funds Available:** A stipend is awarded (amount not specified). Funds may be used only for payment of tuition or academic fees. **Duration:** 1 year.
Eligibility Requirements: This program is open to the dependents of Air Force members residing in the Washington, D.C. metropolitan area in the following categories: active duty, retired, MIA/POW, or deceased. Dependents whose Air Force sponsor is assigned remote from the area or reassigned during the current school year and the student has remained behind to continue education are also eligible. Applicants must be currently enrolled full time at an accredited college or university with a GPA of 3.0 or higher. Along with their application, they must submit a 500-word essay 0n their interests, goals, and how being an Air Force dependent has affected their life. Selection is based on academic and citizenship achievements; financial need is not considered. Applicants who receive an appointment to a service academy are not eligible. **Deadline for Receipt:** February of each year.

27 ■ AIR FORCE OFFICERS' WIVES' CLUB OF WASHINGTON, D.C.
Attn: AFOWC Scholarship Committee
50 Theisen Street
Bolling Air Force Base
Washington, DC 20032-5411
To provide financial assistance for undergraduate or graduate education to the non-military spouses of Air Force members in the Washington, D.C. area.
Title of Award: Air Force Officers' Wives' Club of Washington, D.C. Continuing Education Scholarships for Non-Military Air Force Spouses **Area, Field, or Subject:** General studies/Field of study not specified **Level of Education for which Award is Granted:** Graduate, Undergraduate **Number Awarded:** Varies each year. **Funds Available:** A stipend is awarded (amount not specified). Funds may be used only for payment of tuition or academic fees. **Duration:** 1 year.
Eligibility Requirements: This program is open to the non-military spouses of Air Force members residing in the Washington, D.C. metropolitan area in the following categories: active duty, retired, MIA/POW, or deceased. Spouses whose Air Force sponsor is assigned remote from the area or reassigned during the current school year and the student has remained behind to continue education are also eligible. Applicants must be enrolled or planning to enroll as an undergraduate or graduate student. Along with their application, they must submit a 500-word essay on their experiences, interests, goals, and how being an Air Force spouse has affected their life. Selection is based on academic and citizenship achievements; financial need is not considered. **Deadline for Receipt:** February of each year.

28 ■ AIR FORCE OFFICERS' WIVES' CLUB OF WASHINGTON, D.C.
Attn: AFOWC Scholarship Committee
50 Theisen Street
Bolling Air Force Base
Washington, DC 20032-5411

To provide financial assistance for college to high school seniors who are dependents of Air Force members in the Washington, D.C. area.
Title of Award: Air Force Officers' Wives' Club of Washington, D.C. High School Scholarships for Air Force Dependents **Area, Field, or Subject:** General studies/Field of study not specified **Level of Education for which Award is Granted:** Undergraduate **Number Awarded:** Varies each year. **Funds Available:** A stipend is awarded (amount not specified). Funds may be used only for payment of tuition or academic fees. **Duration:** 1 year.
Eligibility Requirements: This program is open to high school seniors residing in the Washington, D.C. metropolitan area who are dependents of Air Force members in the following categories: active duty, retired, MIA/POW, or deceased. Also eligible are dependents whose Air Force sponsor is assigned remote from the area or reassigned during the current school year and the student has remained behind to graduate. Applicants must be 1) college-bound high school seniors planning to work full time on an accredited undergraduate degree; 2) high school seniors planning to attend a vocational or trade school; or 3) high school seniors with a learning disability who plan to work full time on an undergraduate degree. Along with their application, they must submit a 500-word essay on why they should be awarded this scholarship. Selection is based on academic and citizenship achievements; financial need is not considered. Applicants who receive an appointment to a service academy are not eligible. **Deadline for Receipt:** February of each year.

29 ■ AIR FORCE SERGEANTS ASSOCIATION
Attn: Scholarship Coordinator
P.O. Box 50
Temple Hills, MD 20757
Tel: (301)899-3500
Free: 800-638-0594
Fax: (301)899-8136
E-mail: staff@amf.org
Web Site: http://www.afsahq.org/body_education06.htm
To provide financial assistance to members of the Air Force Sergeants Association (AFSA) Auxiliary who wish to gain further training.
Title of Award: Air Force Sergeants Association Auxiliary Education Grants **Area, Field, or Subject:** General studies/Field of study not specified **Level of Education for which Award is Granted:** Undergraduate **Number Awarded:** Varies each year. Since the program began, it has awarded grants for more than $75,000. **Funds Available:** Stipends up to $2,000 per year are available. Funds are sent directly to the recipient's school to be used for tuition, room and board, fees, books, supplies, child care, meals, and transportation. **Duration:** 1 year; may be renewed if the student maintains full-time enrollment.
Eligibility Requirements: Applicants must have been AFSA Auxiliary members for at least 1 year and must remain members for 2 additional years. They must be 21 years of age or older, able to demonstrate financial need, and accepted at an accredited institution. At the conclusion of the course, class, or program for which they are applying, they must receive a certificate, diploma, or degree. They must show that they are acquiring or enhancing marketable skills that will increase their economic security, and at the end of their studies they must enter or rejoin the work force. Along with their application, they must include a description of their career goals and how the training will help them accomplish those goals. **Deadline for Receipt:** Applications may be submitted at any time. **Additional Information:** This program began in 1990. Requests for applications must be accompanied by a stamped self-addressed envelope.

30 ■ AIR FORCE SERGEANTS ASSOCIATION
Attn: Scholarship Coordinator
P.O. Box 50
Temple Hills, MD 20757
Tel: (301)899-3500
Free: 800-638-0594
Fax: (301)899-8136
E-mail: staff@amf.org
Web Site: http://www.afsahq.org/body_education01.htm
To provide financial assistance for undergraduate education to the dependent children of Air Force enlisted personnel.
Title of Award: Air Force Sergeants Association Scholarships **Area, Field, or Subject:** General studies/Field of study not specified **Level of Education for which Award is Granted:** Undergraduate **Number**

Awarded: Varies each year. Recently, 17 of these scholarships were awarded, including the Frank C. Fini, the Hardy B. Abbott, and the Claude Klobus Scholarships (each at $2,500), 3 at $2,000, 10 at $1,500, and 1 at $1,000. Since the program began, it has awarded 429 scholarships worth $568,600. **Funds Available:** Stipends range from $1,000 to $2,500 per year. Scholarships may be used for tuition, room and board, fees, books, supplies, and transportation. **Duration:** 1 year; may be renewed if the student maintains full-time enrollment.

Eligibility Requirements: This program is open to the unmarried children (including stepchildren and legally adopted children) of active-duty, retired, or veteran members of the U.S. Air Force, Air National Guard, or Air Force Reserves. Applicants must be younger than 23 years of age and dependent upon the parent or guardian for more than half of their support. Their parent must be a member of the Air Force Sergeants Association or its auxiliary. Selection is based on academic ability (ACT score of 24 or higher or SAT equivalent and GPA of 3.5 or higher), character, leadership, writing ability, and potential for success. Financial need is not a consideration. **Deadline for Receipt:** March of each year. **Additional Information:** This program began in 1968. Requests for applications must be accompanied by a stamped self-addressed envelope.

31 ■ AIR FORCE SERGEANTS ASSOCIATION

Attn: Scholarship Coordinator
P.O. Box 50
Temple Hills, MD 20757
Tel: (301)899-3500
Free: 800-638-0594
Fax: (301)899-8136
E-mail: staff@amf.org
Web Site: http://www.afsahq.org/body_education01.htm
To provide financial assistance for college to the dependent children of enlisted Air Force personnel.
Title of Award: Airmen Memorial Foundation Scholarship Program **Area, Field, or Subject:** General studies/Field of study not specified **Level of Education for which Award is Granted:** Undergraduate **Number Awarded:** 20 each year: the Sharon L. Piccoli Memorial Scholarship at $1,500 and 19 others at $1,000 each. Since this program began, it has awarded more than $295 in financial aid. **Funds Available:** The stipend is $1,500 or $1,000; funds may be used for tuition, room and board, fees, books, supplies, and transportation. **Duration:** 1 year; may be renewed if the recipient maintains full-time enrollment.

Eligibility Requirements: This program is open to the unmarried children (including stepchildren and legally adopted children) of active-duty, retired, or veteran members of the U.S. Air Force, Air National Guard, or Air Force Reserves. Applicants must be younger than 23 years of age and dependent upon the parent or guardian for more than half of their support. Selection is based on academic ability (ACT score of 24 or higher or SAT equivalent and GPA of 3.5 or higher), character, leadership, writing ability, and potential for success. Financial need is not a consideration. **Deadline for Receipt:** March of each year. **Additional Information:** The Air Force Sergeants Association administers this program on behalf of the Airmen Memorial Foundation. The highest ranked applicant receives the Sharon L. Piccoli Memorial Scholarship. This program began in 1987. Requests for applications must be accompanied by a stamped self-addressed envelope.

32 ■ AIR FORCE SERGEANTS ASSOCIATION

Attn: Scholarship Coordinator
P.O. Box 50
Temple Hills, MD 20757
Tel: (301)899-3500
Free: 800-638-0594
Fax: (301)899-8136
E-mail: staff@amf.org
Web Site: http://www.afsahq.org/body_education01.htm
To provide financial assistance for college to the dependent children of enlisted Air Force personnel.
Title of Award: Chief Master Sergeants of the Air Force Scholarships **Area, Field, or Subject:** General studies/Field of study not specified **Level of Education for which Award is Granted:** Undergraduate **Number Awarded:** 11 each year: 1 at $3,000, 2 at $2,000, and 8 at $1,000. Since this program began, it has awarded more than $200,000 in scholarships. **Funds Available:** Stipends are $3,000, $2,000, or $1,000;

funds may be used for tuition, room and board, fees, books, supplies, and transportation. **Duration:** 1 year; may be renewed if the recipient maintains full-time enrollment.

Eligibility Requirements: This program is open to the unmarried children (including stepchildren and legally adopted children) of active-duty, retired, or veteran members of the U.S. Air Force, Air National Guard, or Air Force Reserves. Applicants must be younger than 23 years of age and dependent upon the parent or guardian for more than half of their support. Selection is based on academic ability (ACT score of 24 o4 higher or SAT equivalent and GPA of 3.5 or higher), character, leadership, writing ability, and potential for success. Financial need is not a consideration. A unique aspect of these scholarships is that applicants may supply additional information regarding circumstances that entitle them to special consideration; examples of such circumstances include student disabilities, financial hardships, parent disabled and unable to work, parent missing in action/killed in action/prisoner of war, or other unusual extenuating circumstances. **Deadline for Receipt:** March of each year. **Additional Information:** The Air Force Sergeants Association administers this program on behalf of the Airmen Memorial Foundation. It was established in 1987 and named in honor of CMSAF Richard D. Kisling, the late third Chief Master Sergeant of the Air Force. In 1997, following the deaths of CMSAF's (Retired) Andrews and Harlow, it was given its current name. Requests for applications must be accompanied by a stamped self-addressed envelope.

33 ■ AIRCRAFT ELECTRONICS ASSOCIATION

Attn: AEA Educational Foundation
4217 South Hocker Drive
Independence, MO 64055-4723
Tel: (816)373-6565
Fax: (816)478-3100
E-mail: info@aea.net
Web Site: http://www.aea.net
To provide financial assistance for college in the United States or abroad to members of the Aircraft Electronics Association (AEA) and their relatives.
Title of Award: Aircraft Electronics Association Members Scholarship Program **Area, Field, or Subject:** General studies/Field of study not specified **Level of Education for which Award is Granted:** Undergraduate **Number Awarded:** 2 each year. **Funds Available:** The stipend is $1,500; funds must be used for tuition. **Duration:** 1 year.

Eligibility Requirements: This program is open to high school seniors, high school graduates, and currently-enrolled college students who are either members or the children, grandchildren, or other dependents of members of the association. Applicants must be planning to work on a college degree in any field of study at an accredited U.S. postsecondary institution or international equivalent institution. Along with their application, they must submit a transcript of high school or college grades (GPA of 2.5 or higher), a letter of recommendation, and a 300-word essay on why they believe they have talent or ability related to their academic major and career goal. Financial need is not considered. **Deadline for Receipt:** February of each year. **Additional Information:** This program includes the following named scholarships: the Chuck Peacock Honorary Scholarship, the Gene Baker Memorial Scholarship, and the Jim Cook Honorary Scholarship.

34 ■ AIRPORTS COUNCIL INTERNATIONAL-NORTH AMERICA

1775 K Street, N.W., Suite 500
Washington, DC 20006
Tel: (202)293-8500
Fax: (202)331-1362
Web Site: http://www.aci-na.org
To provide financial support for college or graduate school to students preparing for a career in airport management or airport administration.
Title of Award: ACI-NA Commissioners Committee Scholarship **Area, Field, or Subject:** Management; Transportation **Level of Education for which Award is Granted:** Graduate, Undergraduate **Funds Available:** The stipend is $3,000. **Duration:** 1 year; recipients may reapply.

Eligibility Requirements: This program is open to students enrolled in a program that focuses on airport management or airport administration at an accredited college or university that is a member of the University Aviation Association (UAA). Students interested in a flight-related major are not eligible. Applicants must have earned at least a 3.0 GPA in college, and they must reside and attend school in the United States, Canada, Saipan (Northern Marianas), the U.S. Virgin Islands, or Guam. Along with their application, they must submit a personal statement (from 250 to 300 words) on their interest in airport management or airport operations. Undergraduates may be majoring in other fields if their goal of a career in airport management can be demonstrated through work experience or the personal essay. Students planning graduate work must provide proof of acceptance to a graduate school and intention to study courses related to airport management and/or operations. Financial need must be demonstrated. Preference is given to students in their junior or senior year of undergraduate study. **Deadline for Receipt:** December of each year. **Additional Information:** Further information is also available from Gregory Schwab, CM, Indiana State University, Department of Aerospace Technology, Myers Technology Building, Room 216, 650 Cherry Street, Terre Haute, IN 47809.

35 ■ ALABAMA BANKERS ASSOCIATION

Attn: Scholarship Applications
534 Adams Avenue
Montgomery, AL 36104
Tel: (334)834-1890
Free: 800-239-5521
Fax: (334)834-4443
E-mail: info@alabamabankers.org
Web Site: http://www.alabamabankers.org
To provide financial assistance for college to high school seniors in Alabama whose parents are employed in a bank.
Title of Award: Dr. Donald L. Moak Scholarship **Area, Field, or Subject:** General studies/Field of study not specified **Level of Education for which Award is Granted:** Undergraduate **Number Awarded:** 1 or more each year. **Funds Available:** The stipend is $1,000. **Duration:** 1 year.
Eligibility Requirements: This program is open to seniors graduating from high schools in Alabama whose parents are employed full time at a bank in the state. Applicants must be planning to enroll in a college or university as a full-time student. Along with their application, they must submit a statement about themselves and their college plans, transcripts, and their ACT or SAT scores. Selection is based on academic record, character, leadership, potential for development, and financial need. **Deadline for Receipt:** February of each year. **Additional Information:** This program was established in 2004.

36 ■ ALABAMA COMMISSION ON HIGHER EDUCATION

Attn: Grants and Scholarships Department
100 North Union Street
P.O. Box 302000
Montgomery, AL 36130-2000
Tel: (334)242-2274
Fax: (334)242-0268
E-mail: wwall@ache.state.al.us
Web Site: http://www.ache.state.al.us/StudentAsst/Programs.htm
To provide financial assistance to entering junior college students in Alabama.
Title of Award: Alabama 2-Year College Academic Scholarships **Area, Field, or Subject:** General studies/Field of study not specified **Level of Education for which Award is Granted:** Two Year College **Number Awarded:** Varies each year. **Funds Available:** Scholarships are available to cover the cost of in-state tuition and books. **Duration:** 1 year; may be renewed if the recipient maintains a high level of academic achievement.
Eligibility Requirements: Eligible are students who have been accepted for enrollment at any Alabama public 2-year postsecondary educational institution. Selection is based on academic merit. Preference is given to Alabama residents.

37 ■ ALABAMA COMMISSION ON HIGHER EDUCATION

Attn: Grants and Scholarships Department
100 North Union Street
P.O. Box 302000
Montgomery, AL 36130-2000
Tel: (334)242-2274
Fax: (334)242-0268
E-mail: wwall@ache.state.al.us
Web Site: http://www.ache.state.al.us/StudentAsst/Programs.htm

To provide financial assistance to athletes in Alabama interested in attending a junior or community college.
Title of Award: Alabama Junior and Community College Athletic Scholarships **Area, Field, or Subject:** General studies/Field of study not specified **Level of Education for which Award is Granted:** Two Year College **Number Awarded:** Varies each year. **Funds Available:** Awards cover the cost of tuition and books. **Duration:** Scholarships are available as long as the recipient continues to participate in the designated sport or activity.
Eligibility Requirements: Eligible are full-time students enrolled in public junior and community colleges in Alabama. Selection is based on athletic ability as determined through try-outs. **Additional Information:** Interested students must contact a coach, athletic director, or financial aid officer at their junior or community college.

38 ■ ALABAMA COMMISSION ON HIGHER EDUCATION

Attn: Grants and Scholarships Department
100 North Union Street
P.O. Box 302000
Montgomery, AL 36130-2000
Tel: (334)242-2274
Fax: (334)242-0268
E-mail: wwall@ache.state.al.us
Web Site: http://www.ache.state.al.us/StudentAsst/Programs.htm
To provide financial assistance for college or graduate school to members of the Alabama National Guard.
Title of Award: Alabama National Guard Educational Assistance Program **Area, Field, or Subject:** General studies/Field of study not specified **Level of Education for which Award is Granted:** Graduate, Undergraduate **Number Awarded:** Varies each year; awards are determined on a first-in, first-out basis as long as funds are available. **Funds Available:** Scholarships cover tuition, educational fees, books, and supplies, up to a maximum of $1,000 per year. All Alabama Student Grant program proceeds for which the student is eligible are deducted from this award. **Duration:** Up to 12 years after the date of the first grant payment to the student through this program.
Eligibility Requirements: This program is open to Alabama residents who are enrolled in an associate, baccalaureate, master's, or doctoral program at a public college, university, community college, technical college, or junior college in the state; are making satisfactory academic progress as determined by the eligible institution; and are members in good standing of the Alabama National Guard who have completed basic training and advanced individual training. Applicants may be receiving federal veterans benefits, but they must show a cost less aid amount of at least $25. **Deadline for Receipt:** July of each year. **Additional Information:** Information is also available from the Alabama National Guard, RRO-ISR, P.O. Box 3711, Montgomery, AL 36109-0711, (334) 271-7442, (800) 392-1947 (within AL), Fax: (334) 271-7296.

39 ■ ALABAMA COMMISSION ON HIGHER EDUCATION

Attn: Grants and Scholarships Department
100 North Union Street
P.O. Box 302000
Montgomery, AL 36130-2000
Tel: (334)242-2274
Fax: (334)242-0268
E-mail: wwall@ache.state.al.us
Web Site: http://www.ache.state.al.us/StudentAsst/Programs.htm
To provide financial assistance for college to the spouses and dependents of police officers and fire fighters killed in Alabama.
Title of Award: Alabama Police Officers' and Fire Fighters' Survivors' Educational Assistance Program **Area, Field, or Subject:** General studies/Field of study not specified **Level of Education for which Award is Granted:** Undergraduate **Number Awarded:** Varies each year. **Funds Available:** Grants are offered to cover tuition, fees, books, and supplies. There is no limit on the amount awarded to recipients. **Duration:** 1 year; may be renewed.
Eligibility Requirements: This program is open to the unremarried spouses and children of police officers and fire fighters killed in the line of duty in Alabama. Applicants may be high school seniors or currently-

enrolled undergraduates in Alabama. **Additional Information:** Recipients must attend public institutions in Alabama.

40 ■ ALABAMA COMMISSION ON HIGHER EDUCATION

Attn: Grants and Scholarships Department
100 North Union Street
P.O. Box 302000
Montgomery, AL 36130-2000
Tel: (334)242-2274
Fax: (334)242-0268
E-mail: wwall@ache.state.al.us
Web Site: http://www.ache.state.al.us/StudentAsst/Programs.htm
To provide financial assistance to undergraduate students who are residents of Alabama.
Title of Award: Alabama Student Assistance Program **Area, Field, or Subject:** General studies/Field of study not specified **Level of Education for which Award is Granted:** Undergraduate **Funds Available:** Stipends range from $300 to $2,500 per academic year. **Duration:** 1 year; may be renewed.
Eligibility Requirements: This program is open to residents of Alabama who are attending or planning to attend eligible Alabama institutions (nearly 80 schools participate in this program). Applicants must be able to demonstrate financial need. Eligible students are required to submit the Free Application for Federal Student Aid (FAFSA).

41 ■ ALABAMA COMMISSION ON HIGHER EDUCATION

Attn: Grants and Scholarships Department
100 North Union Street
P.O. Box 302000
Montgomery, AL 36130-2000
Tel: (334)242-2274
Fax: (334)242-0268
E-mail: wwall@ache.state.al.us
Web Site: http://www.ache.state.al.us/StudentAsst/Programs.htm
To provide financial assistance to undergraduates at private colleges or universities in Alabama.
Title of Award: Alabama Student Grant Program **Area, Field, or Subject:** General studies/Field of study not specified **Level of Education for which Award is Granted:** Undergraduate **Number Awarded:** Varies each year. **Funds Available:** Stipends up to $1,200 per year are available.
Eligibility Requirements: Eligible are undergraduate students who are attending 1 of 14 designated private colleges or universities in Alabama on at least a half-time basis. Alabama residency is required, but financial need is not considered. **Deadline for Receipt:** Each participating institution sets its own deadline date. **Additional Information:** The participating schools are Birmingham-Southern College, Concordia College, Faulkner University, Huntingdon College, Judson College, Miles College, Oakwood College, Samford University, Selma University, Southeastern Bible College, Southern Vocational College, Spring Hill College, Stillman College, and the University of Mobile.

42 ■ ALABAMA DEPARTMENT OF REHABILITATION SERVICES

Attn: Debra Culver
7 Bemiston Avenue
Talladega, AL 35160
Tel: (256)362-0638
Free: 800-441-7607
Fax: (256)362-6841
E-mail: dculver@rehab.state.al.us
Web Site: http://www.rehab.state.al.us/Home/default.aspx?url=/Home/Main
To provide financial assistance for college to students whose blind parents are residents of Alabama.
Title of Award: Alabama Scholarships for Dependents of Blind Parents **Area, Field, or Subject:** General studies/Field of study not specified **Level of Education for which Award is Granted:** Undergraduate **Number Awarded:** Varies each year. **Funds Available:** Eligible students receive free tuition, waiver of fees, and necessary textbooks at any Alabama state-supported postsecondary institution. **Duration:** Up to 36 months at an institution of higher education, or for the period required to complete a course of study at a trade school.
Eligibility Requirements: Eligible to apply are seniors or recent graduates of Alabama high schools whose family head of household is blind

and whose annual family income is limited (less than $9,000 for a family with 1 child, $12,000 with 2 children, $15,000 with 3 children, or $18,000 with 4 or more children). Applicants must 1) have been permanent residents of Alabama for at least 5 years, 2) apply within 2 years after graduation from high school, and 3) be under 23 years of age. **Additional Information:** Recipients must complete their course of study within 5 years (unless interrupted by military service), but at least prior to the age of 30.

43 ■ ALABAMA DEPARTMENT OF VETERANS AFFAIRS

770 Washington Avenue, Suite 530
P.O. Box 1509
Montgomery, AL 36102-1509
Tel: (334)242-5077
Fax: (334)242-5102
E-mail: willie.moore@va.state.al.us
Web Site: http://www.va.state.al.us/scholarship.htm
To provide educational benefits to the dependents of disabled, deceased, and other Alabama veterans.
Title of Award: Alabama G.I. Dependents' Scholarship Program **Area, Field, or Subject:** General studies/Field of study not specified **Level of Education for which Award is Granted:** Graduate, Undergraduate **Number Awarded:** Varies each year. **Funds Available:** Eligible dependents may attend any state-supported Alabama institution of higher learning or enroll in a prescribed course of study at any Alabama state-supported trade school without payment of any tuition, book fees, or laboratory charges. **Duration:** This is an entitlement program for 4 years of full-time undergraduate or graduate study or part-time equivalent. Spouses and unremarried widow(er)s whose veteran spouse is rated between 20 and 90% disabled, or 100% disabled but not permanently so, may attend only 2 standard academic years.
Eligibility Requirements: Eligible are spouses, children, stepchildren, and unremarried widow(er)s of veterans who served honorably for 90 days or more and 1) are currently rated as 20% or more service-connected disabled or were so rated at time of death; 2) were a former prisoner of war; 3) have been declared missing in action; 4) died as the result of a service-connected disability; or 5) died while on active military duty in the line of duty. The veteran must have been a permanent civilian resident of Alabama for at least 1 year prior to entering active military service; veterans who were not Alabama residents at the time of entering active military service may also qualify if they have a 100% disability and were permanent residents of Alabama for at least 5 years prior to filing the application for this program or prior to death, if deceased. Children and stepchildren must be under the age of 26, but spouses and unremarried widow(er)s may be of any age. **Deadline for Receipt:** Applications may be submitted at any time. **Additional Information:** Benefits for children, spouses, and unremarried widow(er)s are available in addition to federal government benefits. Assistance is not provided for noncredit courses, placement testing, GED preparation, continuing educational courses, pretechnical courses, or state board examinations.

44 ■ ALABAMA FUNERAL DIRECTORS ASSOCIATION

Attn: Executive Director
P.O. Box 241281
Montgomery, AL 36124-1281
Tel: (334)277-9565
Fax: (334)277-8028
To provide financial assistance to residents of Alabama who are attending an accredited mortuary science school.
Title of Award: Alabama Funeral Directors Association Scholarship **Area, Field, or Subject:** Mortuary science **Level of Education for which Award is Granted:** Undergraduate **Number Awarded:** 2 each year. **Funds Available:** The stipend is $1,000. Funds are paid directly to the school the recipient attends. **Duration:** 1 year.
Eligibility Requirements: This program is open to residents of Alabama who have completed at least 30 credit hours in an accredited mortuary science school in any state with a grade of at least "C" in all required mortuary science classes and have an overall GPA of 2.5 or higher. Applicants must be sponsored by an active member of the Alabama Funeral Directors Association (AFDA) and must submit a 500-word essay on "A Career in Funeral Service." They must be planning to return to Alabama to serve the public in their chosen profession. Selection is based on academic record and evaluation of the required essay; financial need is

not considered. **Deadline for Receipt:** April of each year.

45 ■ ALABAMA GOLF COURSE SUPERINTENDENTS ASSOCIATION

Attn: Scholarship Committee
P.O. Box 661214
Birmingham, AL 35266-1214
Tel: (205)967-0397
Fax: (205)967-1466
E-mail: agcsa@charter.net
Web Site: http://www.agcsa.org/scholarshipprogram.htm
To provide financial assistance to students from Alabama who are majoring in turfgrass management in college.
Title of Award: Donnie Arthur Memorial Turfgrass Scholarship **Area, Field, or Subject:** Turfgrass management **Level of Education for which Award is Granted:** Undergraduate **Number Awarded:** 2 each year. **Funds Available:** The stipend is $1,000. Funds are paid directly to the recipient. **Duration:** 1 year.
Eligibility Requirements: This program is open to residents of Alabama who are currently enrolled full time in an agricultural program emphasizing turfgrass management. Applicants must have a GPA of 2.0 or higher. Along with their application, they must submit a description of themselves that covers their academic ability, dependability, work habits, potential for leadership, and thoughts on what a superintendent needs in the 21st century to be successful. **Deadline for Receipt:** October of each year.

46 ■ ALABAMA INDIAN AFFAIRS COMMISSION

770 South McDonough Street
Montgomery, AL 36104
Tel: (334)242-2831
Free: 800-436-8261
Fax: (334)240-3408
E-mail: aiac@midspring.com
Web Site: http://www.aiac.state.al.us/Scholarship%20Page.htm
To provide financial assistance for college to American Indians residing in Alabama.
Title of Award: AIAC Scholarships **Area, Field, or Subject:** General studies/Field of study not specified **Level of Education for which Award is Granted:** Undergraduate **Number Awarded:** Varies each year. **Funds Available:** A stipend is awarded (amount not specified). **Duration:** 1 year; recipients may reapply.
Eligibility Requirements: This program is open to residents of Alabama who have a tribal roll card in a state- or federally-recognized Indian tribe. Applicants must attend or plan to attend an academic institution in the state, unless their chosen program of study is not offered in an Alabama school. Both merit and need-based scholarships are awarded.

47 ■ ALABAMA LAW FOUNDATION

415 Dexter Avenue
P.O. Box 671
Montgomery, AL 36101
Tel: (334)269-1515
E-mail: info@alfinc.org
Web Site: http://www.alfinc.org/kidschance.cfm
To provide financial assistance for college to Alabama residents whose parent was killed or disabled on the job.
Title of Award: Kids' Chance Scholarship Fund **Area, Field, or Subject:** General studies/Field of study not specified **Level of Education for which Award is Granted:** Undergraduate **Number Awarded:** Varies each year; recently, 28 of these scholarships were awarded. **Funds Available:** Stipends range from $500 to $3,000 but do not exceed the cost of tuition and books at the most expensive public university in Alabama.
Eligibility Requirements: This program is open to high school seniors and college students (including students at technical colleges) in Alabama whose parent was killed or permanently and totally disabled in an on-the-job accident. Financial need is considered in the selection process. **Deadline for Receipt:** April of each year. **Additional Information:** This program was established in 1992 by the Workers' Compensation Section of the Alabama State Bar and is currently administered by the Alabama Law Foundation.

48 ■ ALASKA COMMISSION ON POSTSECONDARY EDUCATION

Attn: AlaskAdvantage Programs
3030 Vintage Boulevard
Juneau, AK 99801-7100
Tel: (907)465-2962
Free: 800-441-2962
Fax: (907)465-5316
E-mail: customer_service@acpe.ak.us
Web Site: http://alaskaadvantage.state.ak.us/page/253
To provide low-interest loans to Alaska residents who wish to borrow on behalf of their children or other dependents to help meet their educational costs.
Title of Award: Alaska Family Education Loan Program **Area, Field, or Subject:** General studies/Field of study not specified **Level of Education for which Award is Granted:** Graduate, Undergraduate **Funds Available:** The annual maximum loan is $8,500 for undergraduate students, $5,500 for vocational school students, or $9,500 for graduate students. The maximum that may be borrowed is $42,500 for undergraduate study, $47,000 for graduate study, or $60,000 for all study combined. An origination fee of 3% is deducted from the eligible loan amount. The interest rate is 5%. **Duration:** Loans may be made for up to 5 years of undergraduate study and up to 5 years of graduate study but not more than 8 years of combined study. Repayment begins the first of the month after the loan is disbursed. Repayment must be completed within 10 years.
Eligibility Requirements: The family member requesting the loan must meet Alaska residency requirements: 1 year of physical presence at the time of initial application. Continuing eligibility for loans requires continued Alaska residency by the family member making the loan and maintenance of full-time study in good standing by the student. Loans will not be granted to either the borrower or the student if they are past due on prior loan payments or child support payments. U.S. citizenship or permanent resident status is required. **Deadline for Receipt:** May of each year. **Additional Information:** This program provides an alternative to the AlaskAdvantage PLUS Loan Program. The program enables a student's family to share the cost of the student's education and thus reduce the level of indebtedness faced by the student upon completion of schooling or training. Loans may be used for attendance at any regionally or nationally approved institution. Loans may not be received under this program and the Alaska Student Loan Program for the same student during the same loan year.

49 ■ ALASKA COMMISSION ON POSTSECONDARY EDUCATION

Attn: AlaskAdvantage Programs
3030 Vintage Boulevard
Juneau, AK 99801-7109
Tel: (907)465-2962
Free: 800-441-2962
Fax: (907)465-5316
E-mail: customer_service@acpe.ak.us
Web Site: http://alaskaadvantage.state.ak.us/page/251
To provide low-interest loans to Alaskans interested in studying on the undergraduate or graduate school level.
Title of Award: Alaska Supplemental Education Loan Program **Area, Field, or Subject:** General studies/Field of study not specified **Level of Education for which Award is Granted:** Graduate, Undergraduate **Funds Available:** The annual maximum loan is $8,500 for undergraduate students, $6,500 for vocational school students, or $9,500 for graduate students. The maximum that may be borrowed is $42,500 for undergraduate study, $47,000 for graduate study, or $60,000 for all study combined. An origination fee of 3% is deducted from the eligible loan amount. The interest rate is set each year, based on interest rates paid by the Alaska Student Loan Corporation on its bonds and the cost of administering the program. Recently, the rate was 5.8%, but students who complied with special provisions (remaining Alaska residents during the repayment period, using a direct payment procedure, making timely repayments for 48 months) lowered the rate to 4.3% while in school and 2.55% during the repayment period. **Duration:** Loans may be made for up to 5 years of undergraduate study and up to 5 years of graduate study but not more than 8 years of combined study. Repayment begins 6 months after the borrower ceases to be a full-time student. Repayment must be completed within 10 years.
Eligibility Requirements: This program is open to residents of Alaska attending school anywhere and to students physically present in Alaska and attending an Alaska institution. Applicants must be enrolled at least half time in an accredited career vocational/technical program or an associate, baccalaureate, or graduate degree program. They must be able to demonstrate academic good standing, a satisfactory credit history, and

U.S. citizenship or permanent resident status. **Deadline for Receipt:** May of each year. **Additional Information:** This program replaced the Alaska Student Loan Program in 2002. Loans are not granted for more than the difference between the costs of education and the student's sources to cover these expenses.

50 ■ ALASKA COMMISSION ON POSTSECONDARY EDUCATION

Attn: AlaskAdvantage Programs
3030 Vintage Boulevard
Juneau, AK 99801-7109
Tel: (907)465-2962
Free: 800-441-2962
Fax: (907)465-5316
E-mail: customer_service@acpe.ak.us
Web Site: http://www.eed.state.ak.us/gearup/scholarship.html
To provide financial assistance for college to Alaska residents who participated in federal GEAR UP programs while in middle school.
Title of Award: GEAR UP Alaska Scholarship Program **Area, Field, or Subject:** General studies/Field of study not specified **Level of Education for which Award is Granted:** Undergraduate **Number Awarded:** Varies each year. **Funds Available:** The maximum stipend is $7,000 per year for full-time study or $3,500 per year for half-time study. **Duration:** 1 year; may be renewed up to 3 additional years.
Eligibility Requirements: This program is open to residents of Alaska who are high school seniors or graduates or recipients of a GED. Applicants must be younger than 22 years of age and able to demonstrate financial need. They must have participated in a federal GEAR UP program during grades 6-8 and met other academic milestones. They must be planning to attend an approved postsecondary institution. **Deadline for Receipt:** May of each year. **Additional Information:** This program was established in the 2000-01 academic year. It is administered by the Alaska Commission on Postsecondary Education (ACPE) on behalf of the Alaska Department of Education and Early Development. Funding is provided by the U.S. Department of Education as part of its Gaining Early Awareness and Readiness for Undergraduate Programs (GEAR UP).

51 ■ ALASKA INDEPENDENT BLIND

1102 West International Airport Road
Anchorage, AK 99518
Tel: (907)563-2121
Free: 800-478-9998
Fax: (907)276-0066
Web Site: http://www.acb.org/alaska
To provide financial assistance for college to individuals in Alaska whose lives have been dramatically changed by their blindness.
Title of Award: Louise Rude Scholarship **Area, Field, or Subject:** General studies/Field of study not specified **Level of Education for which Award is Granted:** Undergraduate **Number Awarded:** 3 each year. **Funds Available:** Stipends are $2,000, $1,500, or $1,000. **Duration:** 1 year; recipients may reapply.
Eligibility Requirements: Eligible to apply for this assistance are high school seniors and currently-enrolled college students in Alaska who are blind or visually impaired. Their lives must have been dramatically changed by their blindness. To apply, students must submit a completed application form (including a certification of visual status), 2 education and/or employment reference letters, and 2 personal reference letters. Selection is based on scholastic aptitude (60%), volunteer and community service (20%), and employment record (20%). **Deadline for Receipt:** May of each year. **Additional Information:** The scholarship may be used at any accredited college, university, technical school, or vocational institute.

52 ■ ALASKA NATIONAL GUARD

Attn: Education Services Officer
P.O. Box 5800
Fort Richardson, AK 99505-5800
Tel: (907)428-6477
Fax: (907)428-6929
E-mail: jerry.kidrick@ak.ngb.army.mil
Web Site: http://www.ak-prepared.com/dmva/education.htm
To provide financial assistance to members of the Alaska National Guard who wish to attend a college or university in the state other than the University of Alaska.

Title of Award: Alaska National Guard State Tuition Assistance Program **Area, Field, or Subject:** General studies/Field of study not specified **Level of Education for which Award is Granted:** Master's, Undergraduate **Number Awarded:** Varies each year. **Funds Available:** Recipients are entitled to reimbursement of 100% of the cost of tuition and fees, to a maximum of $2,000 per fiscal year. **Duration:** 1 semester; may be renewed.
Eligibility Requirements: This program is open to members of the Alaska National Guard (Air and Army) and Naval Militia who are attending a university program in Alaska, other than the University of Alaska. Applicants may be working on their first or second associate degree, first or second bachelor's degree, first master's degree, or an enrichment course. Non-prior service members must complete Initial Active Duty for Training (IADT); prior service members are eligible immediately. **Deadline for Receipt:** Applications may be submitted at any time.

53 ■ ALASKA NATIONAL GUARD

Attn: Education Services Officer
P.O. Box 5800
Fort Richardson, AK 99505-5800
Tel: (907)428-6477
Fax: (907)428-6929
E-mail: jerry.kidrick@ak.ngb.army.mil
Web Site: http://www.ak-prepared.com/dmva/education.htm
To provide financial assistance to members of the Alaska National Guard who wish to take classes at a campus or branch of the University of Alaska.
Title of Award: Alaska National Guard University of Alaska Tuition Scholarships **Area, Field, or Subject:** General studies/Field of study not specified **Level of Education for which Award is Granted:** Master's, Undergraduate **Number Awarded:** Varies each year. **Funds Available:** Recipients are entitled to reimbursement of 100% of the cost of tuition and fees, to a maximum of 15 undergraduate course units per semester or 9 graduate course units per semester. **Duration:** 1 semester; may be renewed as long as undergraduates maintain a GPA of 2.0 or higher and graduate students maintain a GPA of 3.0 or higher.
Eligibility Requirements: This program is open to members of the Alaska National Guard (Air and Army) and Naval Militia who are interested in attending any institution within the University of Alaska system to work on an associate, bachelor's, or master's degree. Applicants must have completed Initial Active Duty for Training (IADT). **Deadline for Receipt:** August of each year for fall semester; December of each year for spring semester.

54 ■ ALBUQUERQUE COMMUNITY FOUNDATION

Attn: Scholarship Program
3301 Menaul N.E., Suite 2
P.O. Box 36960
Albuquerque, NM 87176-6960
Tel: (505)883-6240
E-mail: acf@albuquerquefoundation.org
Web Site: http://www.albuquerquefoundation.org/scholar/scholar.htm
To provide financial assistance for college to residents of New Mexico who live in mobile homes.
Title of Award: New Mexico Manufactured Housing Scholarship Fund **Area, Field, or Subject:** General studies/Field of study not specified **Level of Education for which Award is Granted:** Undergraduate **Number Awarded:** 1 or more each year. **Funds Available:** The stipend is $1,000. **Duration:** 1 year.
Eligibility Requirements: This program is open to graduating seniors who reside in mobile/manufactured housing in New Mexico. Applicants must be able to demonstrate financial need and have a high school GPA of 3.0 or higher. **Deadline for Receipt:** March of each year. **Additional Information:** This scholarship was first awarded in 1998. Recipients must attend a 2-year or 4-year college, university, or vocational institution in New Mexico.

55 ■ ALBUQUERQUE COMMUNITY FOUNDATION

Attn: Scholarship Program
3301 Menaul N.E., Suite 2
P.O. Box 36960
Albuquerque, NM 87176-6960
Tel: (505)883-6240

E-mail: acf@albuquerquefoundation.org
Web Site: http://www.albuquerquefoundation.org/scholar/scholar.htm
To provide financial assistance to undergraduate students from New Mexico.

Title of Award: Sussman-Miller Educational Assistance Fund **Area, Field, or Subject:** General studies/Field of study not specified **Level of Education for which Award is Granted:** Undergraduate **Number Awarded:** Varies each year. **Funds Available:** The minimum stipend is $500 per year. The maximum stipend is 20% of the student's total budget or $2,500, whichever is less. **Duration:** 1 year; may be renewed up to 3 additional years.

Eligibility Requirements: Applicants must have been residents of New Mexico for at least 1 year and be able to demonstrate financial need. They may be either graduating high school seniors (who apply during the spring semester of their senior year) or current undergraduate students (who apply after completing 1 semester of undergraduate study). U.S. citizenship or permanent resident status is required. High school applicants must have a GPA of 3.0 or higher in academic subjects; current college students must have a GPA of 2.5 or higher. Selection is based primarily on financial need. **Deadline for Receipt:** April of each year for high school seniors planning to attend college outside New Mexico or in-state private schools; June of each year for current undergraduate students and high school seniors planning to attend public schools in New Mexico.

56 ■ HORATIO ALGER ASSOCIATION OF DISTINGUISHED AMERICANS, INC.

99 Canal Center Plaza
Alexandria, VA 22314
Tel: (703)684-9444
Fax: (703)684-9445
E-mail: horatioaa@aol.com
Web Site: http://www.horatioalger.com/scholarships_military
To provide financial assistance for college to veterans who served in the Iraq/Afghanistan theater.

Title of Award: Horatio Alger Military Veterans Scholarship **Area, Field, or Subject:** General studies/Field of study not specified **Level of Education for which Award is Granted:** Undergraduate **Number Awarded:** 1 or more each year. **Funds Available:** A stipend is awarded (amount not specified). **Duration:** Up to 4 years.

Eligibility Requirements: This program is open to veterans who served in the U.S. military in the Iraq/Afghanistan theater beginning in 2001 or later. Applicants must be planning to enter college to work on a bachelor's degree at an accredited institution (they may begin at a 2-year college and then transfer to a 4-year college or university). They must be U.S. citizens or in the process of becoming a citizen, demonstrate critical financial need ($50,000 or less adjusted gross income per family is preferred), have a GPA of 2.0 or higher, and evidence integrity and perseverance in the face of adversity. Along with their application, they must submit 3 essays: 1) explaining how their current financial situation qualifies them for financial assistance to attend college (50 to 100 words); 2) describing the adversities they have faced in detail and what they have done to overcome and cope with those obstacles (250 to 350 words); and 3) a personal statement (150 to 200 words). Selection is based on integrity, perseverance in overcoming adversity, strength of character, academic record, commitment to pursue a college education, desire to contribute to society, and financial need. **Deadline for Receipt:** August of each year. **Additional Information:** This program was established in 2005.

57 ■ HORATIO ALGER ASSOCIATION OF DISTINGUISHED AMERICANS, INC.

99 Canal Center Plaza
Alexandria, VA 22314
Tel: (703)684-9444
Fax: (703)684-9445
E-mail: horatioaa@aol.com
Web Site: http://www.horatioalger.com/scholarships/
program_national_finalist.cfm
To provide financial assistance for college to students who have demonstrated academic achievement as well as tenacity and courage in overcoming obstacles.

Title of Award: Horatio Alger National Scholarship Finalist Program **Area, Field, or Subject:** General studies/Field of study not specified **Level of Education for which Award is Granted:** Undergraduate **Number

Awarded: 200 each year. **Funds Available:** The stipend is $1,000. **Duration:** 1 year.

Eligibility Requirements: This program is open to seniors at high schools in states that do not currently have a state scholarship program of the Horatio Alger Association of Distinguished Americans. Applicants must be planning to enter college in the fall following graduation and work on a bachelor's degree at an accredited institution (they may begin at a 2-year college and then transfer to a 4-year college or university). They must be U.S. citizens or in the process of becoming a citizen, demonstrate critical financial need ($50,000 or less adjusted gross income per family is preferred), have a GPA of 2.0 or higher, and evidence perseverance in the face of adversity. Examples of adversity include having been in foster care or a ward of the state; having been homeless; experiencing the death, incarceration, or abandonment of a parent or guardian; living in a household where alcohol or drugs are or were abused; having a physical or mental disability or serious illness; or suffering from physical or mental abuse. Along with their application, they must submit 3 essays: 1) explaining how their current financial situation qualifies them for financial assistance to attend college (50 to 100 words); 2) describing the adversities they have faced in detail and what they have done to overcome and cope with those obstacles (250 to 350 words); and 3) selecting a member of the Horatio Alger Association and explaining how and why they intend to apply the virtues and principles exemplified in the life of that member to reach their personal goals (150 to 200 words). **Deadline for Receipt:** The end of September for applications submitted on paper; mid-October for applications submitted online. **Additional Information:** The states in which the association currently does not have a state scholarship program are Alabama, Alaska, Arizona, Arkansas, Colorado, Connecticut, Georgia, Hawaii, Illinois, Kansas, Maine, Massachusetts, Michigan, Mississippi, Nevada, New Hampshire, New Jersey, New Mexico, New York, North Carolina, North Dakota, Ohio, Oklahoma, Oregon, Rhode Island, South Carolina, South Dakota, Tennessee, Utah, Vermont, Washington, West Virginia, Wisconsin, and Wyoming.

58 ■ HORATIO ALGER ASSOCIATION OF DISTINGUISHED AMERICANS, INC.

99 Canal Center Plaza
Alexandria, VA 22314
Tel: (703)684-9444
Fax: (703)684-9445
E-mail: horatioaa@aol.com
Web Site: http://www.horatioalger.com/scholarships/
program_national.cfm
To provide financial assistance for college to students who have demonstrated academic achievement as well as tenacity and courage in overcoming obstacles.

Title of Award: Horatio Alger National Scholarship Program **Area, Field, or Subject:** General studies/Field of study not specified **Level of Education for which Award is Granted:** Undergraduate **Number Awarded:** 100 each year. **Funds Available:** The stipend is $10,000, distributed over 4 years. **Duration:** 4 years.

Eligibility Requirements: This program is open to seniors at high schools in all fifty states, the District of Columbia, and Puerto Rico. Applicants must be planning to enter college in the fall following graduation and work on a bachelor's degree at an accredited institution (they may begin at a 2-year college and then transfer to a 4-year college or university). They must be U.S. citizens or in the process of becoming a citizen, demonstrate critical financial need ($50,000 or less adjusted gross income per family is preferred), have a GPA of 2.0 or higher, and evidence perseverance in the face of adversity. Examples of adversity include having been in foster care or a ward of the state; having been homeless; experiencing the death, incarceration, or abandonment of a parent or guardian; living in a household where alcohol or drugs are or were abused; having a physical or mental disability or serious illness; or suffering from physical or mental abuse. Along with their application, they must submit 3 essays: 1) explaining how their current financial situation qualifies them for financial assistance to attend college (50 to 100 words); 2) describing the adversities they have faced in detail and what they have done to overcome and cope with those obstacles (250 to 350 words); and 3) selecting a member of the Horatio Alger Association and explaining how and why they intend to apply the virtues and principles exemplified in the life of that member to reach their personal goals (150 to 200 words). **Deadline for Receipt:** The end of September for applications submitted on paper; mid-October for applications submitted online. **Additional Information:** This program was established in 1984.

59 ■ HORATIO ALGER ASSOCIATION OF DISTINGUISHED AMERICANS, INC.

99 Canal Center Plaza
Alexandria, VA 22314
Tel: (703)684-9444
Fax: (703)684-9445
E-mail: horatioaa@aol.com
Web Site: http://www.horatioalger.com/scholarships/program_calif.cfm
To provide financial assistance for college to students in California who have "exhibited integrity and perseverance in overcoming personal adversity and who aspire to pursue higher education."
Title of Award: California Scholarships of the Horatio Alger Association **Area, Field, or Subject:** General studies/Field of study not specified **Level of Education for which Award is Granted:** Undergraduate **Number Awarded:** 200 each year. **Funds Available:** The stipend is $2,500. **Duration:** 1 year.
Eligibility Requirements: This program is open to seniors graduating from high schools in California. Applicants must be planning to enter college in the fall following graduation and work on a bachelor's degree at an accredited institution (they may begin at a 2-year college and then transfer to a 4-year college or university). They must be U.S. citizens or in the process of becoming a citizen, demonstrate critical financial need ($50,000 or less adjusted gross income per family is preferred), have a GPA of 2.0 or higher, and have a record of involvement in co-curricular and community activities. Along with their application, they must submit 3 essays: 1) explaining how their current financial situation qualifies them for financial assistance to attend college (50 to 100 words); 2) describing the adversities they have faced in detail and what they have done to overcome and cope with those obstacles (250 to 350 words); and 3) selecting a member of the Horatio Alger Association and explaining how and why they intend to apply the virtues and principles exemplified in the life of that member to reach their personal goals (150 to 200 words). Examples of adversity include having been in foster care or a ward of the state; having been homeless; experiencing the death, incarceration, or abandonment of a parent or guardian; living in a household where alcohol or drugs are or were abused; having a physical or mental or mental disability or serious illness; or suffering from physical or mental abuse.
Deadline for Receipt: The end of September for applications submitted on paper; mid-October for applications submitted online. **Additional Information:** This program is funded by Horatio Alger Association members George L. Argyros and Arthur A. Ciocca.

60 ■ HORATIO ALGER ASSOCIATION OF DISTINGUISHED AMERICANS, INC.

99 Canal Center Plaza
Alexandria, VA 22314
Tel: (703)684-9444
Fax: (703)684-9445
E-mail: horatioaa@aol.com
Web Site: http://www.horatioalger.com/scholarships/
program_delaware.cfm
To provide financial assistance for college to students in Delaware who have "exhibited integrity and perseverance in overcoming personal adversity and who aspire to pursue higher education."
Title of Award: Delaware Scholarships of the Horatio Alger Association **Area, Field, or Subject:** General studies/Field of study not specified **Level of Education for which Award is Granted:** Undergraduate **Number Awarded:** 100 each year. **Funds Available:** The stipend is $2,500. **Duration:** 1 year.
Eligibility Requirements: This program is open to seniors graduating from high schools in Delaware. Applicants must be planning to enter college in the fall following graduation and work on a bachelor's degree at an accredited institution (they may begin at a 2-year college and then transfer to a 4-year college or university). They must be U.S. citizens or in the process of becoming a citizen, demonstrate critical financial need ($50,000 or less adjusted gross income per family is preferred), have a GPA of 2.0 or higher, and have a record of involvement in co-curricular and community activities. Along with their application, they must submit 3 essays: 1) explaining how their current financial situation qualifies them for financial assistance to attend college (50 to 100 words); 2) describing

the adversities they have faced in detail and what they have done to overcome and cope with those obstacles (250 to 350 words); and 3) selecting a member of the Horatio Alger Association and explaining how and why they intend to apply the virtues and principles exemplified in the life of that member to reach their personal goals (150 to 200 words). Examples of adversity include having been in foster care or a ward of the state; having been homeless; experiencing the death, incarceration, or abandonment of a parent or guardian; living in a household where alcohol or drugs are or were abused; having a physical or mental or mental disability or serious illness; or suffering from physical or mental abuse.
Deadline for Receipt: April of each year. **Additional Information:** This program is funded by the MBNA Education Foundation.

61 ■ HORATIO ALGER ASSOCIATION OF DISTINGUISHED AMERICANS, INC.

99 Canal Center Plaza
Alexandria, VA 22314
Tel: (703)684-9444
Fax: (703)684-9445
E-mail: horatioaa@aol.com
Web Site: http://www.horatioalger.com/scholarships/program_metro.cfm
To provide financial assistance for college to students in the Washington, D.C. metropolitan area who have "exhibited integrity and perseverance in overcoming personal adversity and who aspire to pursue higher education."
Title of Award: District of Columbia, Maryland, and Virginia Scholarships of the Horatio Alger Association **Area, Field, or Subject:** General studies/Field of study not specified **Level of Education for which Award is Granted:** Undergraduate **Number Awarded:** 100 each year. **Funds Available:** The stipend is $2,500. **Duration:** 1 year.
Eligibility Requirements: This program is open to seniors graduating from high schools in the Washington, D.C. metropolitan area. Applicants must be planning to enter a college or university in the fall following graduation and work on a bachelor's degree at an accredited institution (they may begin at a 2-year college and then transfer to a 4-year college or university). They must be U.S. citizens or in the process of becoming a citizen, demonstrate critical financial need ($50,000 or less adjusted gross income per family is preferred), have a GPA of 2.0 or higher, and have a record of involvement in co-curricular and community activities. Along with their application, they must submit 3 essays: 1) explaining how their current financial situation qualifies them for financial assistance to attend college (50 to 100 words); 2) describing the adversities they have faced in detail and what they have done to overcome and cope with those obstacles (250 to 350 words); and 3) selecting a member of the Horatio Alger Association and explaining how and why they intend to apply the virtues and principles exemplified in the life of that member to reach their personal goals (150 to 200 words). Examples of adversity include having been in foster care or a ward of the state; having been homeless; experiencing the death, incarceration, or abandonment of a parent or guardian; living in a household where alcohol or drugs are or were abused; having a physical or mental or mental disability or serious illness; or suffering from physical or mental abuse. **Deadline for Receipt:** The end of September for applications submitted on paper; mid-October for applications submitted online. **Additional Information:** This program is funded by Horatio Alger Association member Anthony Welters and his wife Beatrice. The Washington D.C. metropolitan area is defined to include the District of Columbia; the Maryland counties of Anne Arundel, Charles, Frederick, Howard, Montgomery, and Prince George's; the Virginia counties of Arlington, Fairfax, and Prince William; and the independent Virginia cities of Alexandria, Fairfax, Falls Church, Manassas, and Manassas Park.

62 ■ HORATIO ALGER ASSOCIATION OF DISTINGUISHED AMERICANS, INC.

99 Canal Center Plaza
Alexandria, VA 22314
Tel: (703)684-9444
Fax: (703)684-9445
E-mail: horatioaa@aol.com
Web Site: http://www.horatioalger.com/scholarships/program_texas.cfm
To provide financial assistance for college to students in Texas who have "exhibited integrity and perseverance in overcoming personal adversity and who aspire to pursue higher education."

Title of Award: Education is Freedom/Horatio Alger Texas Scholarship Program **Area, Field, or Subject:** General studies/Field of study not specified **Level of Education for which Award is Granted:** Undergraduate **Number Awarded:** 50 each year. **Funds Available:** The stipend is $2,500. **Duration:** 1 year.

Eligibility Requirements: This program is open to seniors graduating from high schools in Kentucky. Applicants must be planning to enter college in the fall following graduation and work on a bachelor's degree at an accredited institution (they may begin at a 2-year college and then transfer to a 4-year college or university). They must be U.S. citizens or in the process of becoming a citizen, demonstrate critical financial need ($50,000 or less adjusted gross income per family is preferred), have a GPA of 2.0 or higher, and have a record of involvement in co-curricular and community activities. Along with their application, they must submit 3 essays: 1) explaining how their current financial situation qualifies them for financial assistance to attend college (50 to 100 words); 2) describing the adversities they have faced in detail and what they have done to overcome and cope with those obstacles (250 to 350 words); and 3) selecting a member of the Horatio Alger Association and explaining how and why they intend to apply the virtues and principles exemplified in the life of that member to reach their personal goals (150 to 200 words). Examples of adversity include having been in foster care or a ward of the state; having been homeless; experiencing the death, incarceration, or abandonment of a parent or guardian; living in a household where alcohol or drugs are or were abused; having a physical or mental or mental disability or serious illness; or suffering from physical or mental abuse. **Deadline for Receipt:** The end of September for applications submitted on paper; mid-October for applications submitted online. **Additional Information:** This program is funded by the Education is Freedom Foundation and 7-Eleven, Inc.

63 ■ HORATIO ALGER ASSOCIATION OF DISTINGUISHED AMERICANS, INC.

99 Canal Center Plaza
Alexandria, VA 22314
Tel: (703)684-9444
Fax: (703)684-9445
E-mail: horatioaa@aol.com
Web Site: http://www.horatioalger.com/scholarships/program_indiana.cfm
To provide financial assistance for college to students in Indiana who have "exhibited integrity and perseverance in overcoming personal adversity and who aspire to pursue higher education."

Title of Award: Indiana Scholarships of the Horatio Alger Association **Area, Field, or Subject:** General studies/Field of study not specified **Level of Education for which Award is Granted:** Undergraduate **Number Awarded:** 16 each year. **Funds Available:** The stipend is $2,500. **Duration:** 1 year.

Eligibility Requirements: This program is open to seniors graduating from high schools in Indiana. Applicants must be planning to enter college in the fall following graduation and work on a bachelor's degree at an accredited institution (they may begin at a 2-year college and then transfer to a 4-year college or university). They must be U.S. citizens or in the process of becoming a citizen, demonstrate critical financial need ($50,000 or less adjusted gross income per family is preferred), have a GPA of 2.0 or higher, and have a record of involvement in co-curricular and community activities. Along with their application, they must submit 3 essays: 1) explaining how their current financial situation qualifies them for financial assistance to attend college (50 to 100 words); 2) describing the adversities they have faced in detail and what they have done to overcome and cope with those obstacles (250 to 350 words); and 3) selecting a member of the Horatio Alger Association and explaining how and why they intend to apply the virtues and principles exemplified in the life of that member to reach their personal goals (150 to 200 words). Examples of adversity include having been in foster care or a ward of the state; having been homeless; experiencing the death, incarceration, or abandonment of a parent or guardian; living in a household where alcohol or drugs are or were abused; having a physical or mental or mental disability or serious illness; or suffering from physical or mental abuse. **Deadline for Receipt:** The end of September for applications submitted on paper; mid-October for applications submitted online. **Additional**

Information: This program is funded by Horatio Alger Association member Jack Gill and his wife Linda.

64 ■ HORATIO ALGER ASSOCIATION OF DISTINGUISHED AMERICANS, INC.

99 Canal Center Plaza
Alexandria, VA 22314
Tel: (703)684-9444
Fax: (703)684-9445
E-mail: horatioaa@aol.com
Web Site: http://www.horatioalger.com/scholarships/program_kentucky.cfm
To provide financial assistance for college to students in Kentucky who have "exhibited integrity and perseverance in overcoming personal adversity and who aspire to pursue higher education."

Title of Award: Kentucky Scholarships of the Horatio Alger Association **Area, Field, or Subject:** General studies/Field of study not specified **Level of Education for which Award is Granted:** Undergraduate **Number Awarded:** 16 each year. **Funds Available:** The stipend is $2,500. **Duration:** 1 year.

Eligibility Requirements: This program is open to seniors graduating from high schools in Kentucky. Applicants must be planning to enter college in the fall following graduation and work on a bachelor's degree at an accredited institution (they may begin at a 2-year college and then transfer to a 4-year college or university). They must be U.S. citizens or in the process of becoming a citizen, demonstrate critical financial need ($50,000 or less adjusted gross income per family is preferred), have a GPA of 2.0 or higher, and have a record of involvement in co-curricular and community activities. Along with their application, they must submit 3 essays: 1) explaining how their current financial situation qualifies them for financial assistance to attend college (50 to 100 words); 2) describing the adversities they have faced in detail and what they have done to overcome and cope with those obstacles (250 to 350 words); and 3) selecting a member of the Horatio Alger Association and explaining how and why they intend to apply the virtues and principles exemplified in the life of that member to reach their personal goals (150 to 200 words). Examples of adversity include having been in foster care or a ward of the state; having been homeless; experiencing the death, incarceration, or abandonment of a parent or guardian; living in a household where alcohol or drugs are or were abused; having a physical or mental or mental disability or serious illness; or suffering from physical or mental abuse. **Deadline for Receipt:** The end of September for applications submitted on paper; mid-October for applications submitted online. **Additional Information:** This program is funded by Horatio Alger Association member Jack Gill and his wife Linda.

65 ■ HORATIO ALGER ASSOCIATION OF DISTINGUISHED AMERICANS, INC.

99 Canal Center Plaza
Alexandria, VA 22314
Tel: (703)684-9444
Fax: (703)684-9445
E-mail: horatioaa@aol.com
Web Site: http://www.horatioalger.com/scholarships/program_louisiana.cfm
To provide financial assistance for college to students in Louisiana who have "exhibited integrity and perseverance in overcoming personal adversity and who aspire to pursue higher education."

Title of Award: Louisiana Scholarships of the Horatio Alger Association **Area, Field, or Subject:** General studies/Field of study not specified **Level of Education for which Award is Granted:** Undergraduate **Number Awarded:** 50 each year. **Funds Available:** The stipend is $7,000. **Duration:** 1 year.

Eligibility Requirements: This program is open to seniors graduating from high schools in Louisiana. Applicants must be planning to enter a Louisiana college or university in the fall following graduation and work on a bachelor's degree at an accredited institution (they may begin at a 2-year college and then transfer to a 4-year college or university). They must be U.S. citizens or in the process of becoming a citizen, demonstrate critical financial need ($50,000 or less adjusted gross income per family is preferred), have a GPA of 2.0 or higher, and have a record of involvement in co-curricular and community activities. Along with their application, they must submit 3 essays: 1) explaining how their current financial situation qualifies them for financial assistance to attend college (50 to 100 words); 2) describing the adversities they have faced in detail and what they have done to overcome and cope with those obstacles (250 to 350 words); and 3) selecting a member of the Horatio Alger Association and explaining how and why they intend to apply the virtues and principles exemplified in the life of that member to reach their personal goals (150 to 200 words). Examples of adversity include having been in foster care or a ward of the state; having been homeless; experiencing the death, incarceration, or abandonment of a parent or guardian; living in a household where alcohol or drugs are or were abused; having a physical or mental or mental disability or serious illness; or suffering from physical or mental abuse. **Deadline for Receipt:** The end of September for applications submitted on paper; mid-October for applications submitted online. **Additional Information:** This program is funded by Horatio Alger Association member William Dore.

66 ■ HORATIO ALGER ASSOCIATION OF DISTINGUISHED AMERICANS, INC.

99 Canal Center Plaza
Alexandria, VA 22314
Tel: (703)684-9444
Fax: (703)684-9445
E-mail: horatioaa@aol.com
Web Site: http://www.horatioalger.com/scholarships/
program_missouri.cfm
To provide financial assistance for college to students in Missouri who have "exhibited integrity and perseverance in overcoming personal adversity and who aspire to pursue higher education."
Title of Award: Missouri Scholarships of the Horatio Alger Association **Area, Field, or Subject:** General studies/Field of study not specified **Level of Education for which Award is Granted:** Undergraduate **Number Awarded:** 100 each year. **Funds Available:** The stipend is $2,500. **Duration:** 1 year.
Eligibility Requirements: This program is open to seniors graduating from high schools in Missouri. Applicants must be planning to enter college in the fall following graduation and work on a bachelor's degree at an accredited institution (they may begin at a 2-year college and then transfer to a 4-year college or university). They must be U.S. citizens or in the process of becoming a citizen, demonstrate critical financial need ($50,000 or less adjusted gross income per family is preferred), have a GPA of 2.0 or higher, and have a record of involvement in co-curricular and community activities. Along with their application, they must submit 3 essays: 1) explaining how their current financial situation qualifies them for financial assistance to attend college (50 to 100 words); 2) describing the adversities they have faced in detail and what they have done to overcome and cope with those obstacles (250 to 350 words); and 3) selecting a member of the Horatio Alger Association and explaining how and why they intend to apply the virtues and principles exemplified in the life of that member to reach their personal goals (150 to 200 words). Examples of adversity include having been in foster care or a ward of the state; having been homeless; experiencing the death, incarceration, or abandonment of a parent or guardian; living in a household where alcohol or drugs are or were abused; having a physical or mental or mental disability or serious illness; or suffering from physical or mental abuse. **Deadline for Receipt:** April of each year.

67 ■ HORATIO ALGER ASSOCIATION OF DISTINGUISHED AMERICANS, INC.

99 Canal Center Plaza
Alexandria, VA 22314
Tel: (703)684-9444
Fax: (703)684-9445
E-mail: horatioaa@aol.com
Web Site: http://www.horatioalger.com/scholarships/
program_montana.cfm
To provide financial assistance for college to students in Montana who have "exhibited integrity and perseverance in overcoming personal adversity and who aspire to pursue higher education."
Title of Award: Montana Scholarships of the Horatio Alger Association **Area, Field, or Subject:** General studies/Field of study not specified **Level of Education for which Award is Granted:** Undergraduate **Number Awarded:** 100 each year. **Funds Available:** The stipend is $2,500. Each school has agreed to match that stipend, so total support is $5,000. **Duration:** 1 year.

Eligibility Requirements: This program is open to seniors graduating from high schools in Montana. Applicants must be planning to enter a designated Montana college or university in the fall following graduation and work on a bachelor's degree at an accredited institution (they may begin at a 2-year college and then transfer to a 4-year college or university). They must be U.S. citizens or in the process of becoming a citizen, demonstrate critical financial need ($50,000 or less adjusted gross income per family is preferred), have a GPA of 2.0 or higher, and have a record of involvement in co-curricular and community activities. Along with their application, they must submit 3 essays: 1) explaining how their current financial situation qualifies them for financial assistance to attend college (50 to 100 words); 2) describing the adversities they have faced in detail and what they have done to overcome and cope with those obstacles (250 to 350 words); and 3) selecting a member of the Horatio Alger Association and explaining how and why they intend to apply the virtues and principles exemplified in the life of that member to reach their personal goals (150 to 200 words). Examples of adversity include having been in foster care or a ward of the state; having been homeless; experiencing the death, incarceration, or abandonment of a parent or guardian; living in a household where alcohol or drugs are or were abused; having a physical or mental or mental disability or serious illness; or suffering from physical or mental abuse. **Deadline for Receipt:** April of each year. **Additional Information:** This program, established in 2003, is funded by the Dennis and Phyllis Washington Foundation. The participating schools are the University of Montana, the University of Montana-Western, the University of Montana-Missoula College of Technology, Helena College of Technology of The University of Montana, and Montana Tech of The University of Montana.

68 ■ HORATIO ALGER ASSOCIATION OF DISTINGUISHED AMERICANS, INC.

99 Canal Center Plaza
Alexandria, VA 22314
Tel: (703)684-9444
Fax: (703)684-9445
E-mail: horatioaa@aol.com
Web Site: http://www.horatioalger.com/scholarships/
program_nebraska.cfm
To provide financial assistance for college to students in Nebraska who have "exhibited integrity and perseverance in overcoming personal adversity and who aspire to pursue higher education."
Title of Award: Nebraska Scholarships of the Horatio Alger Association **Area, Field, or Subject:** General studies/Field of study not specified **Level of Education for which Award is Granted:** Undergraduate **Number Awarded:** 100 each year. **Funds Available:** The stipend is $2,500. **Duration:** 1 year.
Eligibility Requirements: This program is open to seniors graduating from high schools in Nebraska. Applicants must be planning to enter college in the fall following graduation and work on a bachelor's degree at an accredited institution (they may begin at a 2-year college and then transfer to a 4-year college or university). They must be U.S. citizens or in the process of becoming a citizen, demonstrate critical financial need ($50,000 or less adjusted gross income per family is preferred), have a GPA of 2.0 or higher, and have a record of involvement in co-curricular and community activities. Along with their application, they must submit 3 essays: 1) explaining how their current financial situation qualifies them for financial assistance to attend college (50 to 100 words); 2) describing the adversities they have faced in detail and what they have done to overcome and cope with those obstacles (250 to 350 words); and 3) selecting a member of the Horatio Alger Association and explaining how and why they intend to apply the virtues and principles exemplified in the life of that member to reach their personal goals (150 to 200 words). Examples of adversity include having been in foster care or a ward of the state; having been homeless; experiencing the death, incarceration, or abandonment of a parent or guardian; living in a household where alcohol or drugs are or were abused; having a physical or mental or mental disability or serious illness; or suffering from physical or mental abuse. **Deadline for Receipt:** The end of September for applications submitted on paper; mid-October for applications submitted online. **Additional Information:** This program, established in 1999, is funded by Horatio

Alger Association member Walter Scott, Jr. through the generosity of the Suzanne and Walter Scott Foundation.

69 ■ HORATIO ALGER ASSOCIATION OF DISTINGUISHED AMERICANS, INC.

99 Canal Center Plaza
Alexandria, VA 22314
Tel: (703)684-9444
Fax: (703)684-9445
E-mail: horatioaa@aol.com
Web Site: http://www.horatioalger.com/scholarships/program_penn.cfm
To provide financial assistance for college to students in Pennsylvania who have "exhibited integrity and perseverance in overcoming personal adversity and who aspire to pursue higher education."
Title of Award: Pennsylvania Scholarships of the Horatio Alger Association **Area, Field, or Subject:** General studies/Field of study not specified **Level of Education for which Award is Granted:** Undergraduate **Number Awarded:** 100 each year. **Funds Available:** The stipend is $2,500. **Duration:** 1 year.
Eligibility Requirements: This program is open to seniors graduating from high schools in Pennsylvania. Applicants must be planning to enter college in the fall following graduation and work on a bachelor's degree at an accredited institution (they may begin at a 2-year college and then transfer to a 4-year college or university). They must be U.S. citizens or in the process of becoming a citizen, demonstrate critical financial need ($50,000 or less adjusted gross income per family is preferred), have a GPA of 2.0 or higher, and have a record of involvement in co-curricular and community activities. Along with their application, they must submit 3 essays: 1) explaining how their current financial situation qualifies them for financial assistance to attend college (50 to 100 words); 2) describing the adversities they have faced in detail and what they have done to overcome and cope with those obstacles (250 to 350 words); and 3) selecting a member of the Horatio Alger Association and explaining how and why they intend to apply the virtues and principles exemplified in the life of that member to reach their personal goals (150 to 200 words). Examples of adversity include having been in foster care or a ward of the state; having been homeless; experiencing the death, incarceration, or abandonment of a parent or guardian; living in a household where alcohol or drugs are or were abused; having a physical or mental or mental disability or serious illness; or suffering from physical or mental abuse.
Deadline for Receipt: April of each year. **Additional Information:** This program is funded by Horatio Alger Association member Joseph Neubauer and his wife Jeanette through the generosity of the Neubauer Family Foundation.

70 ■ ALL-AMERICAN SOAP BOX DERBY

P.O. Box 7225
Akron, OH 44306-7233
Tel: (330)733-8723
Fax: (330)733-1370
E-mail: Soapbox@aasbd.org
Web Site: http://www.allamericansoapboxderby.com
To provide financial aid for college to winners of a racing car competition.
Title of Award: All-American Soap Box Derby Competition **Area, Field, or Subject:** General studies/Field of study not specified **Level of Education for which Award is Granted:** Undergraduate **Number Awarded:** 18 scholarships are awarded each year: 3 in each division (stock, super stock, and master's) for both the All-American and the rally programs.
Funds Available: For the All-American program in all divisions (stock, super stock, and master's), prizes are scholarships of $5,000 for first place, $3,000 for second place, and $2,000 for third place. For the rally program in all divisions, first place is a $3,000 scholarship, second place is a $2,000 scholarship, and third place is a $1,500 scholarship. Funds may be used only for the payment of college tuition and fees. **Duration:** Competitions are held annually.
Eligibility Requirements: This competition is open to boys and girls who construct (from kits provided by the Derby) their own cars as coasters propelled by gravity. Local winners compete in the All-American national competition in Akron, Ohio. In addition, the country is divided into 9 geographical districts; drivers who accumulate the most points in their district qualify for the rally program. All competitions are held in 3 divisions: 1) stock, for competitors aged 8 through 17; 2) super stock, for competitors aged 8 through 17 who build from a more advanced kit; and

3) masters, for entrants aged 10 through 17 who may either purchase and build a master's kit or build their own car design from scratch. **Deadline for Receipt:** The national races are usually held in the second week in August. **Additional Information:** Corporate sponsors include Levi Strauss Signature for first place in the stock, super stock, and master's divisions; OMNOVA Solutions, Inc. for second and third places in the stock and super stock divisions and second place in the rally program; Goodyear Tire and Rubber Company for second place in the master's division; the POWERade Division of the Coca-Cola Company for third place in the master's division; the Dodge Division of DaimlerChrysler Corporation for third place in the master's division; the Robert O. Orr & Anna Mae Orr Family Foundation for first place in the rally program; Nintendo of America, Inc. for second and third place in the rally program; and the Gertrude F. Orr Trust Advised Fund for third place in the rally program.

71 ■ ALLIANCE OF BLACK TELECOMMUNICATIONS EMPLOYEES, INC.-NATION'S CAPITAL CHAPTER

Attn: Scholarships
P.O. Box 8386
Silver Spring, MD 20907
To provide financial assistance for college to African American high school seniors in the metropolitan Washington, D.C. area.
Title of Award: Nation's Capital Alliance Scholarship **Area, Field, or Subject:** General studies/Field of study not specified **Level of Education for which Award is Granted:** Four Year College **Number Awarded:** 1 or more each year. **Funds Available:** The stipend is $1,000. **Duration:** 1 year; nonrenewable.
Eligibility Requirements: This program is open to African American seniors graduating from high schools in the metropolitan Washington, D.C. area. Applicants must have been accepted as full-time students at an accredited 4-year college or university. They must have a GPA of 3.0 or higher. Along with their application, they must submit a personal statement outlining their educational and career goals and the impact the scholarship would have on them. Special consideration is given to students with demonstrated community involvement. Financial need is also considered in the selection process. **Deadline for Receipt:** March of each year.

72 ■ ALLIANZ GLOBAL INVESTORS DISTRIBUTORS LLC

Attn: CollegeAccess 529
2187 Atlantic Street
Stamford, CT 06902
(866)529-7462
Web Site: http://www.collegeaccess529.com/benefits.html
To provide financial assistance to high school seniors in South Dakota who plan to attend a college or university in the state.
Title of Award: Allianz South Dakota Scholarship Program **Area, Field, or Subject:** General studies/Field of study not specified **Level of Education for which Award is Granted:** Undergraduate **Number Awarded:** 70 each year. **Funds Available:** The stipend is $2,000 per year. **Duration:** 1 year; may be renewed up to 3 additional years, provided the recipient maintains a GPA of 3.0 or higher.
Eligibility Requirements: This program is open to seniors graduating from high schools in South Dakota who plan to attend a 2-year or 4-year college or university in the state. Applicants must have an ACT score of at least 27 and be on track to complete the Regent Scholar curriculum. Financial need is not considered in the selection process. **Deadline for Receipt:** March of each year. **Additional Information:** This program was formerly known as the PIMCO South Dakota Scholarship Program. It is sponsored by Allianz Global Investors Distributors LLC which currently manages the CollegeAccess 529 Plan in South Dakota. Applicants for scholarships are not required to be investors in the 529 program. Information is also available from Allianz South Dakota Scholarship Program, 4009 West 49th Street, Suite 300, Sioux Falls, SD 57106.

73 ■ ALPHA CHI OMEGA FOUNDATION

Attn: Foundation Programs Coordinator
5939 Castle Creek Parkway North Drive
Indianapolis, IN 46250-4343
Tel: (317)579-5050
Fax: (317)579-5051
E-mail: foundation@alphachiomega.org

Web Site: http://www.alphachiomega.org

To provide financial assistance for college to undergraduate and alumnae members of Alpha Chi Omega in Texas.

Title of Award: Donna Smith Chereck Scholarship **Area, Field, or Subject:** General studies/Field of study not specified **Level of Education for which Award is Granted:** Graduate, Undergraduate **Number Awarded:** 1 each year. **Funds Available:** A stipend is awarded (amount not specified). **Duration:** 1 year.

Eligibility Requirements: This program is open to full-time women undergraduate and graduate students in Texas who are members of Alpha Chi Omega. Preference is given to members of Alpha Phi Chapter (University of Texas at Austin). If there is no qualified applicant from that chapter, the scholarship is open to members of any other chapter in the state of Texas. Selection is based on chapter involvement, campus and community service, academic achievement, and financial need. **Deadline for Receipt:** March of each year.

74 ■ ALPHA CHI OMEGA FOUNDATION

Attn: Foundation Programs Coordinator
5939 Castle Creek Parkway North Drive
Indianapolis, IN 46250-4343
Tel: (317)579-5050
Fax: (317)579-5051
E-mail: foundation@alphachiomega.org
Web Site: http://www.alphachiomega.org/foundation/main.asp

To provide financial assistance for college to undergraduate and alumnae members of Alpha Chi Omega in Colorado.

Title of Award: Nu Nu Alumnae Chapter Fund **Area, Field, or Subject:** General studies/Field of study not specified **Level of Education for which Award is Granted:** Graduate, Undergraduate **Number Awarded:** 1 each year. **Funds Available:** A stipend is awarded (amount not specified). **Duration:** 1 year.

Eligibility Requirements: This program is open to full-time women undergraduate and graduate who are members of Alpha Chi Omega. Applicants must be living or attending school in Colorado. Selection is based on chapter involvement, campus and community service, academic achievement, and financial need. **Deadline for Receipt:** March of each year.

75 ■ ALPHA CHI OMEGA FOUNDATION

Attn: Foundation Programs Coordinator
5939 Castle Creek Parkway North Drive
Indianapolis, IN 46250-4343
Tel: (317)579-5050
Fax: (317)579-5051
E-mail: foundation@alphachiomega.org
Web Site: http://www.alphachiomega.org/foundation/main.asp

To provide financial assistance for college to undergraduate and alumnae members of Alpha Chi Omega in Kansas.

Title of Award: Omicron Centennial Scholarship **Area, Field, or Subject:** General studies/Field of study not specified **Level of Education for which Award is Granted:** Graduate, Undergraduate **Number Awarded:** 1 each year. **Funds Available:** A stipend is awarded (amount not specified). **Duration:** 1 year.

Eligibility Requirements: This program is open to full-time women undergraduate and graduate students in Kansas who are members of Alpha Chi Omega. Preference is given to members of Omicron Chapter (Baker University), but all qualified alumnae members in the state are considered. Selection is based on chapter involvement, campus and community service, academic achievement, and financial need. **Deadline for Receipt:** March of each year.

76 ■ ALPHA EPSILON PHI FOUNDATION, INC.

c/o Executive Director
11 Lake Avenue Extension, Suite 1A
Danbury, CT 06811
Tel: (203)748-0029
Fax: (203)748-0039
E-mail: execdir@aephi.org
Web Site: http://www.aephi.org

To provide financial assistance for undergraduate or graduate education to Alpha Epsilon Phi members or alumnae.

Title of Award: Alpha Epsilon Phi Foundation Scholarship **Area, Field, or Subject:** General studies/Field of study not specified **Level of Education**

for which Award is Granted: Graduate, Undergraduate **Number Awarded:** Several each year. **Funds Available:** Stipends range from $1,000 to $2,000 per year. **Duration:** 1 year; may be renewed.

Eligibility Requirements: Current members or alumnae of the sorority are eligible to apply if they need financial assistance to pursue or continue studies at the undergraduate or graduate level. Selection is based on scholastic standing, university citizenship, activities in the sorority, and financial need. **Deadline for Receipt:** April of each year. **Additional Information:** This program includes the following named scholarships: the Judith Resnik Memorial Scholarship, the Anne Klauber Berson Memorial Scholarship, the Edith Hirsch Miller Memorial Scholarship (preference given to Jewish applicants), the Irma Loeb Cohen Scholarship (for students who are attending Ohio State University or Cleveland State University or who are residents of Ohio), the Ruth Rosenbaum Goldfeder Memorial Scholarship (preference given to residents of Los Angeles or Colorado), the Alpha Iota Scholarship (preference given to residents of Minnesota), the Constance Bauman Abraham Scholarship, and the Shonnette Meyer Kahn Scholarship (preference given to students at Ohio State University or Tulane University). Recipients must be willing to remain active in the sorority and live in the sorority house (if any) for the entire year the scholarship covers.

77 ■ ALPHA OMICRON PI FOUNDATION

Attn: Scholarship Committee
5390 Virginia Way
P.O. Box 395
Brentwood, TN 37024-0395
Tel: (615)370-0920
Fax: (615)370-4424
E-mail: foundation@alphaomicronpi.org
Web Site: http://www.aoiifoundation.org

To provide financial assistance for college or graduate school to collegiate and alumnae members of Alpha Omicron Pi.

Title of Award: Alpha Omicron Pi Scholarships **Area, Field, or Subject:** General studies/Field of study not specified **Level of Education for which Award is Granted:** Graduate, Undergraduate **Number Awarded:** Varies each year. **Funds Available:** A stipend is awarded (amount not specified). **Duration:** 1 year.

Eligibility Requirements: This program is open to collegiate members of Alpha Omicron Pi who wish to continue their undergraduate education and alumnae members who wish to work on a graduate degree. Applicants must submit 50-word essays on the following topics: 1) the circumstances that have created their need for this scholarship, and 2) their immediate and long-term life objectives. Selection is based on academic excellence, dedication to serving the community and Alpha Omicron Pi, and financial need. **Deadline for Receipt:** February of each year. **Additional Information:** This program was established in 1962. Undergraduate recipients must enroll full time, but graduate recipients may enroll part time.

78 ■ ALPHA OMICRON PI FOUNDATION

Attn: Scholarship Committee
5390 Virginia Way
P.O. Box 395
Brentwood, TN 37024-0395
Tel: (615)370-0920
Fax: (615)370-4424
E-mail: foundation@alphaomicronpi.org
Web Site: http://www.aoiifoundation.org

To provide financial assistance for college or graduate school to collegiate and alumnae members of Alpha Omicron Pi.

Title of Award: Alpha Tau Chapter Scholarship **Area, Field, or Subject:** General studies/Field of study not specified **Level of Education for which Award is Granted:** Graduate, Undergraduate **Number Awarded:** 1 each year. **Funds Available:** A stipend is awarded (amount not specified). **Duration:** 1 year.

Eligibility Requirements: This program is open to collegiate members of Alpha Omicron Pi who wish to continue their undergraduate education and alumnae members who wish to work on a graduate degree. Applicants must submit 50-word essays on the following topics: 1) the circumstances that have created their need for this scholarship, and 2) their immediate and long-term life objectives. Selection is based on academic excellence, dedication to serving the community and Alpha

Omicron Pi, and financial need. Preference is given to legacies. **Deadline for Receipt:** February of each year. **Additional Information:** Undergraduate recipients must enroll full time, but graduate recipients may enroll part time.

79 ■ ALPHA OMICRON PI FOUNDATION

Attn: Scholarship Committee
5390 Virginia Way
P.O. Box 395
Brentwood, TN 37024-0395
Tel: (615)370-0920
Fax: (615)370-4424
E-mail: foundation@alphaomicronpi.org
Web Site: http://www.aoiifoundation.org
To provide financial assistance for college to collegiate members of Alpha Omicron Pi from California or the West Coast.
Title of Award: Angels of Kappa Theta Memorial Scholarship **Area, Field, or Subject:** General studies/Field of study not specified **Level of Education for which Award is Granted:** Undergraduate **Number Awarded:** 1 each year. **Funds Available:** A stipend is awarded (amount not specified). **Duration:** 1 year.
Eligibility Requirements: This program is open to collegiate members of Alpha Omicron Pi who are members of an active chapter in southern California. If no southern California chapter member applies, the award is available to a member of an active California chapter. If no California member applies, the award is available to a collegian at an active West Coast chapter. Applicants must submit 50-word essays on the following topics: 1) the circumstances that have created their need for this scholarship, and 2) their immediate and long-term life objectives. Selection is based on academic excellence (GPA of 2.5 or higher), dedication to serving the community and Alpha Omicron Pi, and financial need. **Deadline for Receipt:** February of each year. **Additional Information:** Undergraduate recipients must enroll full time, but graduate recipients may enroll part time.

80 ■ ALPHA OMICRON PI FOUNDATION

Attn: Scholarship Committee
5390 Virginia Way
P.O. Box 395
Brentwood, TN 37024-0395
Tel: (615)370-0920
Fax: (615)370-4424
E-mail: foundation@alphaomicronpi.org
Web Site: http://www.aoiifoundation.org
To provide financial assistance for college or graduate school to collegiate and alumnae members of Alpha Omicron Pi from Indiana.
Title of Award: Jo Ann Gibbons Scholarship **Area, Field, or Subject:** General studies/Field of study not specified **Level of Education for which Award is Granted:** Graduate, Undergraduate **Number Awarded:** 1 each odd-numbered year. **Funds Available:** A stipend is awarded (amount not specified). **Duration:** 1 year.
Eligibility Requirements: This program is open to collegiate and alumnae members of Alpha Omicron Pi who wish to continue their undergraduate or graduate education. Applicants must be Kappa Alpha chapter members who can demonstrate service to their chapter and have a GPA of 2.5 or higher. If no Kappa Alpha chapter member applies, sisters from other Indiana chapters may be considered. Applicants must submit 50-word essays on the following topics: 1) the circumstances that have created their need for this scholarship, and 2) their immediate and long-term life objectives. Selection is based on academic excellence, dedication to serving the community and Alpha Omicron Pi, and financial need.
Deadline for Receipt: February of each odd-numbered year. **Additional Information:** Undergraduate recipients must enroll full time, but graduate recipients may enroll part time.

81 ■ ALPHA OMICRON PI FOUNDATION

Attn: Scholarship Committee
5390 Virginia Way
P.O. Box 395
Brentwood, TN 37024-0395
Tel: (615)370-0920
Fax: (615)370-4424
E-mail: foundation@alphaomicronpi.org

Web Site: http://www.aoiifoundation.org
To provide financial assistance for college to members of Alpha Omicron Pi from Indiana.
Title of Award: Carey Griner Memorial Scholarship **Area, Field, or Subject:** General studies/Field of study not specified **Level of Education for which Award is Granted:** Four Year College **Number Awarded:** 1 each year. **Funds Available:** A stipend is awarded (amount not specified). **Duration:** 1 year.
Eligibility Requirements: This program is open to juniors and seniors who are members of Alpha Omicron Pi and wish to continue their undergraduate education. Applicants must be Kappa Kappa chapter members who hold a leadership position (e.g., officer, committee chair, event chair) and have a GPA of 2.5 or higher. If no Kappa Kappa chapter member applies, sisters from other Indiana chapters may be considered. Applicants must submit 50-word essays on the following topics: 1) the circumstances that have created their need for this scholarship, and 2) their immediate and long-term life objectives. Selection is based on academic excellence, dedication to serving the community and Alpha Omicron Pi, and financial need. **Deadline for Receipt:** February of each year.

82 ■ ALPHA OMICRON PI FOUNDATION

Attn: Scholarship Committee
5390 Virginia Way
P.O. Box 395
Brentwood, TN 37024-0395
Tel: (615)370-0920
Fax: (615)370-4424
E-mail: foundation@alphaomicronpi.org
Web Site: http://www.aoiifoundation.org
To provide financial assistance for college to members of Alpha Omicron Pi from Georgia, especially those majoring in actuarial science or a related field.
Title of Award: Kerri Keith Memorial Scholarship **Area, Field, or Subject:** Actuarial science; General studies/Field of study not specified; Insurance and insurance-related fields **Level of Education for which Award is Granted:** Four Year College **Number Awarded:** 1 each year. **Funds Available:** A stipend is awarded (amount not specified). **Duration:** 1 year.
Eligibility Requirements: This program is open to juniors and seniors who are members of Alpha Omicron Pi and wish to continue their undergraduate education. Applicants must be Gamma Sigma chapter members who exhibit high involvement in the fraternity and have a GPA of 3.0 or higher. Special attention is given to applicants working on a degree in actuarial science or a related field. If no Gamma Sigma chapter member applies, sisters from other Georgia chapters may be considered. Applicants must submit 50-word essays on the following topics: 1) the circumstances that have created their need for this scholarship, and 2) their immediate and long-term life objectives. Selection is based on academic excellence, dedication to serving the community and Alpha Omicron Pi, and financial need. **Deadline for Receipt:** February of each year.

83 ■ ALPHA OMICRON PI FOUNDATION

Attn: Scholarship Committee
5390 Virginia Way
P.O. Box 395
Brentwood, TN 37024-0395
Tel: (615)370-0920
Fax: (615)370-4424
E-mail: foundation@alphaomicronpi.org
Web Site: http://www.aoiifoundation.org
To provide financial assistance for college or graduate school to collegiate and alumnae members of Alpha Omicron Pi.
Title of Award: Robert and Eleanore MacCurdy Scholarship **Area, Field, or Subject:** General studies/Field of study not specified **Level of Education for which Award is Granted:** Graduate, Undergraduate **Number Awarded:** 1 each year. **Funds Available:** A stipend is awarded (amount not specified). **Duration:** 1 year.
Eligibility Requirements: This program is open to collegiate members of Alpha Omicron Pi who wish to continue their undergraduate education and alumnae members who wish to work on a graduate degree. Applicants must submit 50-word essays on the following topics: 1) the

circumstances that have created their need for this scholarship, and 2) their immediate and long-term life objectives. Selection is based on academic excellence, dedication to serving the community and Alpha Omicron Pi, and financial need. **Deadline for Receipt:** February of each year. **Additional Information:** Undergraduate recipients must enroll full time, but graduate recipients may enroll part time.

84 ■ ALPHA OMICRON PI FOUNDATION
Attn: Scholarship Committee
5390 Virginia Way
P.O. Box 395
Brentwood, TN 37024-0395
Tel: (615)370-0920
Fax: (615)370-4424
E-mail: foundation@alphaomicronpi.org
Web Site: http://www.aoiifoundation.org
To provide financial assistance for college or graduate school to collegiate and alumnae members of Alpha Omicron Pi.
Title of Award: Laura McDowell Scholarship **Area, Field, or Subject:** General studies/Field of study not specified **Level of Education for which Award is Granted:** Graduate, Undergraduate **Number Awarded:** 1 each even-numbered year. **Funds Available:** A stipend is awarded (amount not specified). **Duration:** 1 year.
Eligibility Requirements: This program is open to collegiate members of Alpha Omicron Pi who wish to continue their undergraduate education and alumnae members who wish to work on a graduate degree. Applicants must submit 50-word essays on the following topics: 1) the circumstances that have created their need for this scholarship, and 2) their immediate and long-term life objectives. Selection is based on academic excellence, dedication to serving the community and Alpha Omicron Pi, and financial need. **Deadline for Receipt:** February of each even-numbered year. **Additional Information:** Undergraduate recipients must enroll full time, but graduate recipients may enroll part time.

85 ■ ALPHA OMICRON PI FOUNDATION
Attn: Scholarship Committee
5390 Virginia Way
P.O. Box 395
Brentwood, TN 37024-0395
Tel: (615)370-0920
Fax: (615)370-4424
E-mail: foundation@alphaomicronpi.org
Web Site: http://www.aoiifoundation.org
To provide financial assistance for college to collegiate members of Alpha Omicron Pi.
Title of Award: Muriel T. McKinney Scholarship **Area, Field, or Subject:** General studies/Field of study not specified **Level of Education for which Award is Granted:** Undergraduate **Number Awarded:** 1 each year. **Funds Available:** A stipend is awarded (amount not specified). **Duration:** 1 year.
Eligibility Requirements: This program is open to collegiate members of Alpha Omicron Pi who wish to continue their undergraduate education. Applicants must submit 50-word essays on the following topics: 1) the circumstances that have created their need for this scholarship, and 2) their immediate and long-term life objectives. Selection is based on academic excellence, dedication to serving the community and Alpha Omicron Pi, and financial need. The award is presented to the highest-ranked undergraduate applicant. **Deadline for Receipt:** February of each year. **Additional Information:** Recipients must enroll full time in college after receiving the award.

86 ■ ALPHA OMICRON PI FOUNDATION
Attn: Scholarship Committee
5390 Virginia Way
P.O. Box 395
Brentwood, TN 37024-0395
Tel: (615)370-0920
Fax: (615)370-4424
E-mail: foundation@alphaomicronpi.org
Web Site: http://www.aoiifoundation.org
To provide financial assistance for college to members of Alpha Omicron Pi in Indiana.
Title of Award: Martha McKinney Wilhoite Scholarship **Area, Field, or Subject:** General studies/Field of study not specified **Level of Education**

for which Award is Granted: Four Year College **Number Awarded:** 1 each year. **Funds Available:** A stipend is awarded (amount not specified). **Duration:** 1 year.
Eligibility Requirements: This program is open to juniors and seniors who are members of Alpha Omicron Pi and wish to continue their undergraduate education. Applicants must be Theta chapter members who have a GPA of 2.5 or higher. If no Theta chapter member applies, sisters from other Indiana chapters may be considered. Applicants must submit 50-word essays on the following topics: 1) the circumstances that have created their need for this scholarship, and 2) their immediate and long-term life objectives. Selection is based on academic excellence, dedication to serving the community and Alpha Omicron Pi, and financial need. **Deadline for Receipt:** February of each year.

87 ■ ALPHA OMICRON PI FOUNDATION
Attn: Scholarship Committee
5390 Virginia Way
P.O. Box 395
Brentwood, TN 37024-0395
Tel: (615)370-0920
Fax: (615)370-4424
E-mail: foundation@alphaomicronpi.org
Web Site: http://www.aoiifoundation.org
To provide financial assistance for college or graduate school to collegiate and alumnae members of Alpha Omicron Pi at 4-year schools in Texas.
Title of Award: Pi Kappa Scholarship **Area, Field, or Subject:** General studies/Field of study not specified **Level of Education for which Award is Granted:** Four Year College, Graduate **Number Awarded:** 1 each odd-numbered year. **Funds Available:** A stipend is awarded (amount not specified). **Duration:** 1 year.
Eligibility Requirements: This program is open to collegiate members of Alpha Omicron Pi who wish to continue their undergraduate education and alumnae members who wish to work on a graduate degree. Applicants must be attending a 4-year college or university in Texas. They must submit 50-word essays on the following topics: 1) the circumstances that have created their need for this scholarship, and 2) their immediate and long-term life objectives. Selection is based on academic excellence, dedication to serving the community and Alpha Omicron Pi, and financial need. **Deadline for Receipt:** February of each odd-numbered year. **Additional Information:** Undergraduate recipients must enroll full time, but graduate recipients may enroll part time.

88 ■ ALPHA OMICRON PI FOUNDATION
Attn: Scholarship Committee
5390 Virginia Way
P.O. Box 395
Brentwood, TN 37024-0395
Tel: (615)370-0920
Fax: (615)370-4424
E-mail: foundation@alphaomicronpi.org
Web Site: http://www.aoiifoundation.org
To provide financial assistance for college or graduate school to collegiate and alumnae members of Alpha Omicron Pi.
Title of Award: Rho Chapter Scholarship **Area, Field, or Subject:** General studies/Field of study not specified **Level of Education for which Award is Granted:** Graduate, Undergraduate **Number Awarded:** 1 each even-numbered year. **Funds Available:** A stipend is awarded (amount not specified). **Duration:** 1 year.
Eligibility Requirements: This program is open to collegiate members of Alpha Omicron Pi who wish to continue their undergraduate education and alumnae members who wish to work on a graduate degree. Applicants must submit 50-word essays on the following topics: 1) the circumstances that have created their need for this scholarship, and 2) their immediate and long-term life objectives. Selection is based on academic excellence, dedication to serving the community and Alpha Omicron Pi, and financial need. **Deadline for Receipt:** February of each even-numbered year. **Additional Information:** Undergraduate recipients must enroll full time, but graduate recipients may enroll part time.

89 ■ ALPHA OMICRON PI FOUNDATION
Attn: Scholarship Committee
5390 Virginia Way
P.O. Box 395
Brentwood, TN 37024-0395

Tel: (615)370-0920

Fax: (615)370-4424

E-mail: foundation@alphaomicronpi.org

Web Site: http://www.aoiifoundation.org

To provide financial assistance for college or graduate school to collegiate and alumnae members of Alpha Omicron Pi in Tennessee.

Title of Award: Rho Omicron Chapter Scholarship **Area, Field, or Subject:** General studies/Field of study not specified **Level of Education for which Award is Granted:** Graduate, Undergraduate **Number Awarded:** 1 each year. **Funds Available:** A stipend is awarded (amount not specified). **Duration:** 1 year.

Eligibility Requirements: This program is open to collegiate members of Rho Omicron chapter of Alpha Omicron Pi who wish to continue their undergraduate education. If no collegiate member applies or is qualified, they the award is available to an alumna member who is working on an advanced degree. If no Rho Omicron chapter member applies, then the award is available to any member who lives or attend school in Tennessee. Applicants must submit 50-word essays on the following topics: 1) the circumstances that have created their need for this scholarship, and 2) their immediate and long-term life objectives. Selection is based on academic excellence, dedication to serving the community and Alpha Omicron Pi, and financial need. **Deadline for Receipt:** February of each year. **Additional Information:** Undergraduate recipients must enroll full time, but graduate recipients may enroll part time.

90 ■ ALPHA OMICRON PI FOUNDATION

Attn: Scholarship Committee

5390 Virginia Way

P.O. Box 395

Brentwood, TN 37024-0395

Tel: (615)370-0920

Fax: (615)370-4424

E-mail: foundation@alphaomicronpi.org

Web Site: http://www.aoiifoundation.org

To provide financial assistance for college or graduate school to collegiate and alumnae members of Alpha Omicron Pi.

Title of Award: Karen Tucker Centennial Scholarship **Area, Field, or Subject:** General studies/Field of study not specified **Level of Education for which Award is Granted:** Graduate, Undergraduate **Number Awarded:** 1 each year. **Funds Available:** A stipend is awarded (amount not specified). **Duration:** 1 year.

Eligibility Requirements: This program is open to collegiate members of Alpha Omicron Pi who wish to continue their undergraduate education and alumnae members who wish to work on a graduate degree. Applicants must submit 50-word essays on the following topics: 1) the circumstances that have created their need for this scholarship, and 2) their immediate and long-term life objectives. Selection is based on academic excellence, dedication to serving the community and Alpha Omicron Pi, and financial need. **Deadline for Receipt:** February of each year. **Additional Information:** Undergraduate recipients must enroll full time, but graduate recipients may enroll part time.

91 ■ ALPHA PHI ALPHA FRATERNITY, INC.

Attn: Assistant Director of Membership Services

2313 St. Paul Street

Baltimore, MD 21218-5234

Tel: (410)554-0040

Fax: (410)554-0054

Web Site: http://www.alphaphialpha.net

To provide financial assistance for college or graduate school to brothers of Alpha Phi Alpha Fraternity.

Title of Award: Alpha Phi Alpha Fraternity Scholarships **Area, Field, or Subject:** General studies/Field of study not specified **Level of Education for which Award is Granted:** Graduate, Undergraduate **Number Awarded:** 15 each year: 3 in each of the fraternity's 5 geographic regions. **Funds Available:** The stipend is $1,500. **Duration:** 1 year.

Eligibility Requirements: This program is open to brothers of the fraternity who either 1) are working on an degree, or 2) have been admitted to a graduate or professional program. Applicants must have a GPA of 3.0 or higher. Along with their application, they must submit a resume, a list of their involvement in the fraternity's national programs and special projects, an official transcript, 3 letters of recommendation, and an essay on their career ambitions, goals, and why they should be awarded the

scholarship. **Deadline for Receipt:** June of each year. **Additional Information:** Alpha Phi Alpha is the first collegiate fraternity established primarily for African American men. The first chapter was established at Cornell University in 1906; there are now more than 700 chapters around the world.

92 ■ AMALGAMATED TRANSIT UNION

Attn: Scholarship Program Office

5025 Wisconsin Avenue, N.W.

Washington, DC 20016-4139

Tel: (202)537-1645

Fax: (202)244-7824

E-mail: dispatch@atu.org

Web Site: http://www.atu.org

To provide financial assistance for college to members or children of members of the Amalgamated Transit Union (ATU).

Title of Award: Sydney W. Hare Scholarship Competition **Area, Field, or Subject:** General studies/Field of study not specified **Level of Education for which Award is Granted:** Undergraduate **Number Awarded:** 5 each year. **Funds Available:** The stipend is $2,000. **Duration:** 1 year.

Eligibility Requirements: This program is open to high school students or graduates who are planning to enter college, trade school, or vocational school for the first time. Applicants must be a member of the union in good standing, or the child, stepchild, or legally adopted child of a union member in good standing, or the child of a deceased person who was a retired member in good standing at the time of death; spouses and grandchildren of members are not eligible. Selection is based on a biographical questionnaire and an essay of at least 500 words on "Organized Labor's Contribution to the Welfare of the People of the United States or Canada." Essays may be written in French, English, or Spanish. **Deadline for Receipt:** January of each year.

93 ■ AMERICAL DIVISION VETERANS ASSOCIATION

P.O. Box 1381

Boston, MA 02104

Web Site: http://www.americal.org/scholar.shtml

To provide financial assistance for college to the dependents of members of the Americal Division Veterans Association.

Title of Award: Americal Division Veterans Association Scholarship **Area, Field, or Subject:** General studies/Field of study not specified **Level of Education for which Award is Granted:** Undergraduate **Number Awarded:** Varies each year. Recently, 36 of these scholarships were available: 1 at $3,000, 1 at $2,500, 1 at $2,000, 2 at $1,500, 9 at $1,000, 21 at $500, and 1 at $250. **Funds Available:** Stipends range from $250 to $3,000 per year. **Duration:** 1 year; recipients may reapply.

Eligibility Requirements: This program is open to the children and grandchildren of members of the Americal Division Veterans Association and to the children of Americal Division veterans who were killed in action or died while on active duty with the Division. Applicants must submit an essay of 200 to 300 words on subjects pertaining to Americal Division history, national pride, loyalty to the nation, patriotism, or a related topic. Financial need is not considered in the selection process. **Deadline for Receipt:** April of each year. **Additional Information:** Information is also available from the Scholarship Foundation Chair, Bob Short, 3839 Old Savannah Drive, Kalamazoo, MI 49009, (269) 372-2192, E-mail: c146thinf@aol.com.

94 ■ AMERICAN ACADEMY OF ALLERGY, ASTHMA & IMMUNOLOGY

555 East Wells Street, Suite 1100

Milwaukee, WI 53202-3823

Tel: (414)272-6071

Free: 800-822-2762

Fax: (414)272-6070

E-mail: info@aaaai.org

Web Site: http://www.aaaai.org/members/associates/asthmascholarship

To provide financial assistance for college to high school seniors who have asthma.

Title of Award: Award of Excellence Asthma Scholarships **Area, Field, or Subject:** General studies/Field of study not specified **Level of Education for which Award is Granted:** Undergraduate **Number Awarded:** At least 30 scholarships and 30 merit awards are presented each year. **Funds Available:** The scholarship stipend is $1,000 per year. Merit awards are $100. **Duration:** 1 year; nonrenewable.

Eligibility Requirements: This program is open to U.S. citizens who are graduating high school seniors with asthma. Applicants must submit a high school transcript, a letter of recommendation from a principal or guidance counselor, and a 1-page essay on how they have achieved their educational goals while coping with asthma. Selection is based on academic achievement, extracurricular activities, and community service. **Deadline for Receipt:** December of each year. **Additional Information:** This program, established in 1982, includes 1 scholarship designated as the Tanner McQuiston Memorial Scholarship. Support is provided by an unrestricted educational grant from Sanofi-Aventis.

95 ■ AMERICAN ATHEISTS

P.O. Box 5733
Parsippany, NJ 07054-6733
Tel: (908)276-7300
Fax: (908)276-7402
E-mail: info@atheists.org
Web Site: http://www.atheists.org/family/temp/scholarship
To provide financial assistance for college to gay and lesbian students who identify themselves as atheists.
Title of Award: Dr. Richard Chinn Scholarship **Area, Field, or Subject:** General studies/Field of study not specified **Level of Education for which Award is Granted:** Undergraduate **Number Awarded:** 1 each year. **Funds Available:** The stipend is $1,000 **Duration:** 1 year.
Eligibility Requirements: This program is open to college-bound high school seniors and current college students. Applicants must be lesbian or gay, be atheists, and have a cumulative GPA of 2.5 or higher. Selection is based on activism, with special attention given to students who show activism in their schools (e.g., starting atheist/freethinker groups, fighting against violations of the separation of church and state in the school). **Deadline for Receipt:** January of each year. **Additional Information:** Information is also available from the American Atheists Scholarship Fund, 1308 Centennial Avenue, Suite 101, Piscataway, NJ 08854. The scholarship is also designated the American Atheists Gay/Lesbian College Scholarship (AAGLCS). The funding includes $500 donated by Dr. Richard Chinn and $500 in matching funds from American Atheists.

96 ■ AMERICAN ATHEISTS

P.O. Box 5733
Parsippany, NJ 07054-6733
Tel: (908)276-7300
Fax: (908)276-7402
E-mail: info@atheists.org
Web Site: http://www.atheists.org/family/temp/scholarship
To provide financial assistance for college to students who identify themselves as atheists.
Title of Award: Life Members' Scholarship **Area, Field, or Subject:** General studies/Field of study not specified **Level of Education for which Award is Granted:** Undergraduate **Number Awarded:** 1 each year. **Funds Available:** The stipend is $2,000 **Duration:** 1 year.
Eligibility Requirements: This program is open to college-bound high school seniors and current college students. Applicants must be atheists and have a cumulative GPA of 2.5 or higher. Selection is based on activism, with special attention given to students who show activism in their schools (e.g., starting atheist/freethinker groups, fighting against violations of the separation of church and state in the school). **Deadline for Receipt:** January of each year. **Additional Information:** Information is also available from the American Atheists Scholarship Fund, 1308 Centennial Avenue, Suite 101, Piscataway, NJ 08854. The scholarship is also designated the American Atheists College Scholarship (AACS). The funding includes $1,000 donated by 5 life members of American Atheists and $1,000 in matching funds from the organization.

97 ■ AMERICAN BRAHMAN BREEDERS ASSOCIATION

Attn: Youth Activities Director
3003 South Loop West, Suite 140
Houston, TX 77054
Tel: (713)349-0854
Fax: (713)349-9795
E-mail: abba@brahman.org
Web Site: http://www.brahman.org

To provide financial assistance for college to members of the American Junior Brahman Association (AJBA).
Title of Award: American Junior Brahman Association Scholarships **Area, Field, or Subject:** General studies/Field of study not specified **Level of Education for which Award is Granted:** Undergraduate **Number Awarded:** Varies each year. Recently, 9 of these scholarships were awarded: 4 at $1,000, 3 at $500, and 2 at $250. **Funds Available:** Stipends are $1,000, $500, or $250 per year. **Duration:** 1 year.
Eligibility Requirements: Applicants must be active members of AJBA (the youth division of the American Brahman Breeders Association) who are graduating high school seniors. Selection is based on involvement and contribution in AJBA (20 points); involvement and contribution in other agricultural organizations (5 points); involvement in school, civic, and church groups (5 points); experience and knowledge of the livestock industry (5 points); industry leadership potential and goals (20 points); academic achievements (40 points); and general effect (5 points). **Deadline for Receipt:** May of each year. **Additional Information:** This program includes the following named scholarships: the Barry Bryant Memorial Scholarship, the Betty Goudeau Memorial Scholarship, the John Joyce Memorial Scholarship, the Jesse Leggett Memorial Scholarship, and the Leon Locke Memorial Scholarship. Recipients must enroll in college full time.

98 ■ AMERICAN BUSINESS WOMEN'S ASSOCIATION

9100 Ward Parkway
P.O. Box 8728
Kansas City, MO 64114-0728
Tel: (816)361-6621
Free: 800-228-0007
Fax: (816)361-4991
E-mail: abwa@abwahq.org
Web Site: http://www.abwahq.org
To provide financial assistance to women undergraduate and graduate students who are members of the American Business Women's Association (ABWA) or part of a member's household.
Title of Award: Stephen Bufton Memorial Education Fund Grants **Area, Field, or Subject:** General studies/Field of study not specified **Level of Education for which Award is Granted:** Four Year College, Graduate **Number Awarded:** Varies each year; since the inception of this program, it has awarded more than $13.5 million to more than 13,700 students. **Funds Available:** The maximum grant is $1,200. Funds are paid directly to the recipient's institution to be used only for tuition, books, and fees. **Duration:** 1 year. Grants are not automatically renewed, but recipients may reapply.
Eligibility Requirements: ABWA members or individuals who are part of an ABWA member's household may apply for these grants if they are entering at least the junior year of college and have a cumulative GPA of 2.5 or higher. They must be sponsored by an ABWA chapter that has contributed to the fund in the previous chapter year. U.S. citizenship is required. **Deadline for Receipt:** May of each year. **Additional Information:** This program was established in 1953. The ABWA does not provide the names and addresses of local chapters; it recommends that applicants check with their local Chamber of Commerce, library, or university to see if any chapter has registered a contact's name and number.

99 ■ AMERICAN CANCER SOCIETY-CALIFORNIA DIVISION

1710 Webster Street
Oakland, CA 94612
Tel: (510)893-7900
Free: 800-877-1710
Fax: (510)835-8656
E-mail: tony.daquipa@cancer.org
Web Site: http://www.cancer.org
To provide financial assistance for college to residents of California who have been diagnosed as having cancer.
Title of Award: California Young Cancer Survivor Scholarship Program **Area, Field, or Subject:** General studies/Field of study not specified **Level of Education for which Award is Granted:** Undergraduate **Number Awarded:** Varies each year; recently, 45 of these scholarships were awarded. **Funds Available:** Stipends range up to $5,000 per year, depending on the need of the recipient. Funds are paid directly to the recipient's institution. **Duration:** 1 year.
Eligibility Requirements: This program is open to residents of California who were diagnosed with cancer before the age of 18. Applicants must be

currently younger than 25 years of age and attending or planning to attend an accredited 2-year or 4-year institution of higher education in California. Along with their application, they must submit 3 essays (250 words each) on their goals, life experiences, and community service. Selection is based on financial need; determination, motivation, and educational goals; GPA (2.5 or higher); and community service. **Deadline for Receipt:** April of each year. **Additional Information:** Recipients are expected to serve a minimum of 25 volunteer hours with the American Cancer Society.

100 ■ AMERICAN CANCER SOCIETY-FLORIDA DIVISION

3709 West Jetton Avenue
Tampa, FL 33629-5146
Tel: (813)253-0541
Free: 800-444-1410
Fax: (813)254-5857
E-mail: marilyn.westley@cancer.org
Web Site: http://www.cancer.org
To provide financial assistance for college to students diagnosed with cancer in Florida.

Title of Award: R.O.C.K. College Scholarship Program **Area, Field, or Subject:** General studies/Field of study not specified **Level of Education for which Award is Granted:** Undergraduate **Number Awarded:** Varies each year; recently, 154 of these scholarships were awarded. **Funds Available:** Stipends provide up to $2,000 per year for tuition plus $300 per year for textbooks. **Duration:** Scholarships are limited to a maximum of 130 semester hours.
Eligibility Requirements: This program is open to Florida residents who have been diagnosed with cancer before the age of 21, are under 21 at the time of application, are high school seniors or graduates, and have been accepted at an accredited 2-year or 4-year college or university in Florida. Consideration is also given to students planning to enroll in a regionally-accredited vocational/technical school. Applicants must submit a completed application form, 3 letters of recommendation (including 1 from a physician), their financial aid form, an official transcript, their standardized test scores, and a 500-word essay on their philosophical, educational, and occupational goals. Selection is based on financial need, academic record, leadership ability, and community service. **Deadline for Receipt:** April of each year. **Additional Information:** These scholarships were first awarded in 1992 as part of the Florida division's Reaching Out to Cancer Kids (R.O.C.K.) program.

101 ■ AMERICAN CANCER SOCIETY-GREAT LAKES DIVISION

Attn: College Scholarship Program
1755 Abbey Road
East Lansing, MI 48823-1907
Tel: (517)332-2222
Free: 800-723-0360
Fax: (517)333-4656
Web Site: http://www.cancer.org
To provide financial assistance for college to students from Michigan and Indiana who have a history of cancer.

Title of Award: Great Lakes Division College Scholarship **Area, Field, or Subject:** General studies/Field of study not specified **Level of Education for which Award is Granted:** Undergraduate **Number Awarded:** Varies each year; recently, 71 of these scholarships were awarded. **Funds Available:** The stipend is $1,000. Funds must be used for tuition. **Duration:** 1 year; may be renewed up to 3 additional years.
Eligibility Requirements: This program is open to Michigan and Indiana residents who are U.S. citizens and have had a diagnosis of cancer before age 21. Applicants must be attending an accredited college or university in either of the 2 states. Along with their application, they must submit a 500-word essay on their philosophical, educational, and occupational goals. Selection is based on the essay, 2 letters of recommendation, grades, and financial need. **Deadline for Receipt:** April of each year. **Additional Information:** This program was established in 1997.

102 ■ AMERICAN CANCER SOCIETY-GREAT WEST DIVISION

P.O. Box 19140
Seattle, WA 98109
800-729-1151
Fax: (206)285-5108

E-mail: jennifer.kohler@cancer.org
Web Site: http://www.cancer.org
To provide financial assistance for college to high school seniors in selected western states who have been diagnosed as having cancer.
Title of Award: Great West Division College Scholarship Program **Area, Field, or Subject:** General studies/Field of study not specified **Level of Education for which Award is Granted:** Undergraduate **Number Awarded:** Varies each year. **Funds Available:** The stipend is $2,500 per year. **Duration:** 4 years, provided the recipient remains enrolled full time with a GPA of 2.5 or higher and volunteers with the American Cancer Society for at least 12 hours per academic term.
Eligibility Requirements: This program is open to U.S. citizens who are residents of Alaska, Arizona, Colorado, Idaho, Montana, North Dakota, New Mexico, Nevada, Oregon, Utah, Washington, and Wyoming. Applicants must have had a diagnosis of cancer before the age of 21 and have been accepted as a continuing or entering full-time student at an accredited community college, university, college, or vocational/technical school. They must have a GPA of 2.5 or higher. Along with their application, they must submit a 500-word essay on how this scholarship will help further their academic career, including their educational, occupational, and personal goals. Selection is based on financial need (50%), community service of 12 hours of volunteer service to the American Cancer Society per academic term (25%), and the essay (25%). **Deadline for Receipt:** April of each year.

103 ■ AMERICAN CANCER SOCIETY-HEARTLAND DIVISION

4207 Lindell Boulevard
St. Louis, MO 63108
Tel: (314)286-8100
Free: 800-842-7144
Fax: (314)286-8160
E-mail: Joyce.Watson@cancer.org
Web Site: http://www.cancer.org
To provide financial assistance for college or graduate school to cancer patients and survivors in Kansas, Missouri, Nebraska, and Oklahoma.
Title of Award: Heartland Cancer Survivors' Scholarship Program **Area, Field, or Subject:** General studies/Field of study not specified **Level of Education for which Award is Granted:** Graduate, Undergraduate **Number Awarded:** Varies each year; recently, 70 of these scholarships were awarded. **Funds Available:** The stipend is $1,000 per year. Funds are paid directly to the academic institution. **Duration:** 1 year.
Eligibility Requirements: This program is open to residents of Kansas, Missouri, Nebraska, and Oklahoma who have had a cancer diagnosis before age 21. Applicants must be accepted at or attending an accredited university, graduate school, community college, or vocational/technical school. They must be 25 years of age or younger at the time of applying. Students already in college must have a GPA of 2.0 or higher; no minimum GPA requirement applies to high school seniors. Along with their application, they must submit 2 recommendations (including 1 from a physician verifying diagnosis), an acceptance letter from an academic institution, documentation of financial need, academic transcripts, and an essay describing their life experiences and future goals.

104 ■ AMERICAN CANCER SOCIETY-MID-SOUTH DIVISION

1100 Ireland Way, Suite 300
Birmingham, AL 35205-7014
Tel: (205)930-8860
Free: 800-ACS-2345
Fax: (205)930-8877
Web Site: http://www.cancer.org
To provide financial assistance for college to residents of designated southern states who have been diagnosed as having cancer.
Title of Award: Mid-South Division College Scholarships **Area, Field, or Subject:** General studies/Field of study not specified **Level of Education for which Award is Granted:** Undergraduate **Number Awarded:** Varies each year; recently, 175 of these scholarships were awarded. **Funds Available:** The stipend is $1,000. **Duration:** 1 year.
Eligibility Requirements: This program is open to residents of Alabama, Arkansas, Kentucky, Louisiana, Mississippi, and Tennessee. Applicants must be younger than 25 years of age, have had a cancer diagnosis before age 21, have a GPA of 2.5 or higher, and have been accepted at an accredited school. Selection is based on academic achievement, leadership, community service, and financial need. **Deadline for Receipt:** February of each year.

105 ■ AMERICAN CANCER SOCIETY-MIDWEST DIVISION

8364 Hickman Road, Suite D
Des Moines, IA 50325
Tel: (515)253-0147
Fax: (515)253-0806
Web Site: http://www.cancer.org
To provide financial assistance for college to residents of selected midwestern states who have been diagnosed as having cancer.
Title of Award: Midwest Division Youth Scholarship Program **Area, Field, or Subject:** General studies/Field of study not specified **Level of Education for which Award is Granted:** Undergraduate **Number Awarded:** Varies each year; recently, 40 of these scholarships were awarded. **Funds Available:** The stipend is $1,000. Funds are paid directly to the recipient's institution. **Duration:** 1 year.
Eligibility Requirements: This program is open to residents (for at least 1 year) of Iowa, Minnesota, South Dakota, and Wisconsin who were diagnosed with cancer before the age of 21 and are currently younger than 21 years of age. Applicants must have maintained a GPA above the average level and be attending or planning to attend an accredited 2- or 4-year college or university or a vocational/technical school. Along with their application, they must submit an essay on how cancer has impacted their life and how they plan to use that experience in their future. Selection is based on their commitment to academic or vocational goals, leadership and community service, and financial need. **Deadline for Receipt:** March of each year. **Additional Information:** Information is also available from the Youth Scholarship Program, P.O. Box 902, Pewaukee, WI 53072-0902, (262) 523-5572.

106 ■ AMERICAN CANCER SOCIETY-OHIO DIVISION

Attn: Youth Survivor Scholarship Review Committee
5555 Frantz Road
Dublin, OH 43017
Tel: (614)889-9565; 888-ACS-OHIO
Fax: (614)889-6578
E-mail: OhioACS@cancer.org
Web Site: http://www.cancer.org/ohiogrants
To provide financial assistance for college to residents of Ohio who have been diagnosed as having cancer.
Title of Award: Ohio Scholarships for Young Cancer Survivors **Area, Field, or Subject:** General studies/Field of study not specified **Level of Education for which Award is Granted:** Undergraduate **Number Awarded:** Approximately 100 each year. **Funds Available:** The stipend is $1,000 per year. **Duration:** 1 year; recipients are encouraged to reapply.
Eligibility Requirements: This program is open to residents of Ohio who were diagnosed with cancer before the age of 21. Applicants must be U.S. citizens, currently younger than 25 years of age, who plan to attend or are attending an accredited university or community college in the United States. Along with their application, they must submit an essay on their reasons for applying for this scholarship. Selection is based on academic performance, community service, and leadership. **Deadline for Receipt:** January of each year. **Additional Information:** This program was established in 2000.

107 ■ AMERICAN CANCER SOCIETY-SOUTH ATLANTIC DIVISION

128 Stonemark Lane
Columbia, SC 29210
Tel: (803)750-1693
Free: 800-ACS-2345
E-mail: Henry.well@cancer.org
Web Site: http://www.cancer.org
To provide financial assistance for college to residents of designated South Atlantic states who have been diagnosed as having cancer.
Title of Award: Terry Zahn Memorial Scholarships **Area, Field, or Subject:** General studies/Field of study not specified **Level of Education for which Award is Granted:** Undergraduate **Number Awarded:** Varies each year; recently, 52 of these scholarships were awarded. **Funds Available:** The first-year stipend is $1,000; renewal stipends are $500. **Duration:** 1 year; may be renewed up to 3 additional years.
Eligibility Requirements: This program is open to U.S. citizens who are residents of Delaware, the District of Columbia, Georgia, Maryland, North Carolina, South Carolina, Virginia, and West Virginia. Applicants must be younger than 25 years of age and have had a cancer diagnosis before the age of 19. They must be attending or planning to attend an accredited

institution of higher education. **Deadline for Receipt:** March of each year.

108 ■ AMERICAN COUNCIL OF THE BLIND

Attn: Coordinator, Scholarship Program
1155 15th Street, N.W., Suite 1004
Washington, DC 20005
Tel: (202)467-5081
Free: 800-424-8666
Fax: (202)467-5085
E-mail: info@acb.org
Web Site: http://www.acb.org
To provide financial assistance for college to blind high school seniors.
Title of Award: Duane Buckley Memorial Scholarship **Area, Field, or Subject:** General studies/Field of study not specified **Level of Education for which Award is Granted:** Undergraduate **Number Awarded:** 1 each year. **Funds Available:** The stipend is $1,000. In addition, the winner receives a Kurzweil-1000 Reading System. **Duration:** 1 year.
Eligibility Requirements: Eligible to apply for this scholarship are legally blind U.S. citizens or resident aliens who are college-bound high school seniors. Applicants must be able to demonstrate that they strive to overcome extraordinary challenges. In addition to letters of recommendation and copies of academic transcripts, they must submit an autobiographical sketch. A cumulative GPA of 3.3 or higher is generally required. Selection is based on demonstrated academic record, involvement in extracurricular and civic activities, and academic objectives. The severity of the applicant's visual impairment and his/her study methods are also taken into account. **Deadline for Receipt:** February of each year. **Additional Information:** The scholarship winner is expected to be present at the council's annual national convention; the council will cover all reasonable costs connected with convention attendance.

109 ■ AMERICAN COUNCIL OF THE BLIND

Attn: Coordinator, Scholarship Program
1155 15th Street, N.W., Suite 1004
Washington, DC 20005
Tel: (202)467-5081
Free: 800-424-8666
Fax: (202)467-5085
E-mail: info@acb.org
Web Site: http://www.acb.org
To provide financial assistance to blind students entering their freshman year of college.
Title of Award: Dr. Mae Davidow Memorial Scholarship **Area, Field, or Subject:** General studies/Field of study not specified **Level of Education for which Award is Granted:** Undergraduate **Number Awarded:** 1 each year. **Funds Available:** The stipend is $1,500. In addition, the winner receives a Kurzweil-1000 Reading System. **Duration:** 1 year.
Eligibility Requirements: This program is open to entering freshmen in academic programs who are legally blind. They must be U.S. citizens. In addition to letters of recommendation and copies of academic transcripts, applications must include an autobiographical sketch. A cumulative GPA of 3.3 or higher is generally required. Selection is based on demonstrated academic record, involvement in extracurricular and civic activities, and academic objectives. The severity of the applicant's visual impairment and his/her study methods are also taken into account. **Deadline for Receipt:** February of each year. **Additional Information:** This scholarship is sponsored by the Pennsylvania Council of the Blind, an affiliate of the American Council of the Blind. Scholarship winners are expected to be present at the council's annual conference; the council will cover all reasonable expenses connected with convention attendance.

110 ■ AMERICAN COUNCIL OF THE BLIND

Attn: Coordinator, Scholarship Program
1155 15th Street, N.W., Suite 1004
Washington, DC 20005
Tel: (202)467-5081
Free: 800-424-8666
Fax: (202)467-5085
E-mail: info@acb.org
Web Site: http://www.acb.org
To provide financial assistance to outstanding blind undergraduates.
Title of Award: Dr. Nicholas S. DiCaprio Scholarship **Area, Field, or Subject:** General studies/Field of study not specified **Level of Education**

for which **Award is Granted:** Undergraduate **Number Awarded:** 1 each year. **Funds Available:** The stipend is $2,500. In addition, the winner receives a Kurzweil-1000 Reading System. **Duration:** 1 year.
Eligibility Requirements: Eligible to apply for this scholarship are legally blind U.S. citizens or resident aliens who are undergraduate students. In addition to letters of recommendation and copies of academic transcripts, applications must include an autobiographical sketch. A cumulative GPA of 3.3 or higher is generally required. Selection is based on demonstrated academic record, involvement in extracurricular and civic activities, and academic objectives. The severity of the applicant's visual impairment and his/her study methods are also taken into account. **Deadline for Receipt:** February of each year. **Additional Information:** The scholarship winner is expected to be present at the council's annual national convention; the council will cover all reasonable costs connected with convention attendance.

111 ■ AMERICAN COUNCIL OF THE BLIND
Attn: Coordinator, Scholarship Program
1155 15th Street, N.W., Suite 1004
Washington, DC 20005
Tel: (202)467-5081
Free: 800-424-8666
Fax: (202)467-5085
E-mail: info@acb.org
Web Site: http://www.acb.org
To provide financial assistance to outstanding blind undergraduates.
Title of Award: Eunice Fiorito Memorial Scholarship **Area, Field, or Subject:** General studies/Field of study not specified **Level of Education for which Award is Granted:** Undergraduate **Number Awarded:** 1 each year. **Funds Available:** The stipend is $2,000. In addition, the winner receives a Kurzweil-1000 Reading System. **Duration:** 1 year.
Eligibility Requirements: This program is open to legally blind U.S. citizens or resident aliens who are undergraduate students. Applicants must be planning to enter the advocacy/disability field. In addition to letters of recommendation and copies of academic transcripts, they must include an autobiographical sketch. A cumulative GPA of 3.3 or higher is generally required. Preference is given to students with little or no vision. Selection is based on demonstrated academic record, involvement in extracurricular and civic activities, and academic objectives. The severity of the applicant's visual impairment and his/her study methods are also taken into account. **Deadline for Receipt:** February of each year. **Additional Information:** The scholarship winner is expected to be present at the council's annual national convention; the council will cover all reasonable costs connected with convention attendance.

112 ■ AMERICAN COUNCIL OF THE BLIND
Attn: Coordinator, Scholarship Program
1155 15th Street, N.W., Suite 1004
Washington, DC 20005
Tel: (202)467-5081
Free: 800-424-8666
Fax: (202)467-5085
E-mail: info@acb.org
Web Site: http://www.acb.org
To provide financial assistance to students who are blind and working on an undergraduate or graduate degree in business or management.
Title of Award: NIB Grant M. Mack Memorial Scholarship **Area, Field, or Subject:** Business administration; Management **Level of Education for which Award is Granted:** Graduate, Undergraduate **Number Awarded:** 1 each year. **Funds Available:** The stipend is $2,000. In addition, the winner receives a Kurzweil-1000 Reading System. **Duration:** 1 year.
Eligibility Requirements: All legally blind persons who are majoring in business or management (undergraduate or graduate) and are U.S. citizens or resident aliens are eligible to apply. In addition to letters of recommendation and copies of academic transcripts, applications must include an autobiographical sketch. A cumulative GPA of 3.3 or higher is generally required. Selection is based on demonstrated academic record, involvement in extracurricular and civic activities, and academic objectives. The severity of the applicant's visual impairment and his/her study methods are also taken into account. **Deadline for Receipt:** February of each year. **Additional Information:** This scholarship is sponsored by National Industries for the Blind (NIB) in honor of a dedicated leader of the American Council of the Blind. Scholarship winners are expected to be

present at the council's annual conference; the council will cover all reasonable expenses connected with convention attendance.

113 ■ AMERICAN COUNCIL OF THE BLIND
Attn: Coordinator, Scholarship Program
1155 15th Street, N.W., Suite 1004
Washington, DC 20005
Tel: (202)467-5081
Free: 800-424-8666
Fax: (202)467-5085
E-mail: info@acb.org
Web Site: http://www.acb.org
To provide financial assistance for undergraduate or graduate study to outstanding blind students.
Title of Award: Ross N. and Patricia Pangere Foundation Scholarships **Area, Field, or Subject:** General studies/Field of study not specified **Level of Education for which Award is Granted:** Graduate, Undergraduate **Number Awarded:** 1 each year. **Funds Available:** A stipend is awarded (amount not specified). In addition, the winner receives a Kurzweil-1000 Reading System. **Duration:** 1 year.
Eligibility Requirements: Eligible to apply for this scholarship are legally blind U.S. citizens or resident aliens who are undergraduate or graduate students. In addition to letters of recommendation and copies of academic transcripts, applications must include an autobiographical sketch. A cumulative GPA of 3.3 or higher is generally required. Selection is based on demonstrated academic record, involvement in extracurricular and civic activities, and academic objectives. The severity of the applicant's visual impairment and his/her study methods are also taken into account. **Deadline for Receipt:** February of each year. **Additional Information:** The scholarship winner is expected to be present at the council's annual national convention; the council will cover all reasonable costs connected with convention attendance.

114 ■ AMERICAN COUNCIL OF THE BLIND
Attn: Coordinator, Scholarship Program
1155 15th Street, N.W., Suite 1004
Washington, DC 20005
Tel: (202)467-5081
Free: 800-424-8666
Fax: (202)467-5085
E-mail: info@acb.org
Web Site: http://www.acb.org
To provide financial assistance to undergraduate and graduate students who are blind.
Title of Award: Floyd Qualls Memorial Scholarships **Area, Field, or Subject:** General studies/Field of study not specified **Level of Education for which Award is Granted:** Graduate, Undergraduate **Number Awarded:** Up to 8 each year: 2 in each of the 4 categories. **Funds Available:** The stipend is $2,500. In addition, the winners receive a Kurzweil-1000 Reading System. **Duration:** 1 year.
Eligibility Requirements: Students who are legally blind may apply for these scholarships. Recipients are selected in each of 4 categories: entering freshmen in academic programs, undergraduates (sophomores, juniors, and seniors) in academic programs, graduate students in academic programs, and vocational school students or students working on an associate's degree from a community college. In addition to letters of recommendation and copies of academic transcripts, applications must include an autobiographical sketch. A cumulative GPA of 3.3 or higher is generally required. Selection is based on demonstrated academic record, involvement in extracurricular and civic activities, and academic objectives. The severity of the applicant's visual impairment and his/her study methods are also taken into account. **Deadline for Receipt:** February of each year. **Additional Information:** Scholarship winners are expected to be present at the council's annual conference; the council will cover all reasonable expenses connected with convention attendance.

115 ■ AMERICAN FLINT GLASS WORKERS UNION
Attn: Assistant Secretary
1440 South Byrne Road
Toledo, OH 43614-2398
Tel: (419)385-6687
Fax: (419)385-8839

To provide financial assistance for college to dependents of members of the American Flint Glass Workers Union (AFGWU).

Title of Award: AIL/AFGWU Lawrence Bankowski Scholarship Awards **Area, Field, or Subject:** General studies/Field of study not specified **Level of Education for which Award is Granted:** Undergraduate **Number Awarded:** 5 each year. **Funds Available:** The awards are $1,000. **Duration:** 1 year; nonrenewable.

Eligibility Requirements: This program is open to graduating high school seniors who are the children, stepchildren, or legally adopted children of members of the union (continuous membership for at least 1 year is required). Children are also eligible if their parent died within the preceding year and at the time of death had been a member for at least 1 year or if the parent is on sick leave or layoff with contractual rights to return to work and at the beginning of the sick leave or layoff had been a member for at least 1 year. All applicants must submit an essay of at least 500 words on a topic chosen annually. Selection of recipients is based on a lottery. **Deadline for Receipt:** July of each year.

116 ■ AMERICAN FOUNDATION FOR THE BLIND

Attn: Scholarship Committee
11 Penn Plaza, Suite 300
New York, NY 10001
Tel: (212)502-7661
Free: 800-AFB-LINE
Fax: (212)502-7771
E-mail: afbinfo@afb.net
Web Site: http://www.afb.org/scholarships.asp

To provide financial assistance for college or graduate school to blind students in the United States.

Title of Award: Ferdinand Torres Scholarship **Area, Field, or Subject:** General studies/Field of study not specified **Level of Education for which Award is Granted:** Graduate, Undergraduate **Number Awarded:** 1 each year. **Funds Available:** The stipend is $1,500. **Duration:** 1 year.

Eligibility Requirements: Applicants must be legally blind and reside in the United States, although U.S. citizenship is not necessary. They must present evidence of economic need, legal blindness, and acceptance into a full-time undergraduate or graduate program. Preference is given to residents of New York City. Along with their application, they must submit an essay that includes the field of study they are pursuing and why they have chosen it; their educational and personal goals; their work experience; any extracurricular activities with which they have been involved, including those in school, religious organizations, and the community; and how they intend to use scholarship monies that may be awarded. **Deadline for Receipt:** April of each year.

117 ■ AMERICAN GI FORUM-MILE HIGH CHAPTER

c/o Chairperson, Education Committee
1717 Federal Boulevard
Denver, CO 80204
Web Site: http://www.agifmh.org/EduCommPurpose.html

To provide financial assistance for college to Hispanic residents of Colorado.

Title of Award: Mile High Chapter Scholarship Awards Program **Area, Field, or Subject:** General studies/Field of study not specified **Level of Education for which Award is Granted:** Undergraduate **Number Awarded:** Up to 10 each year. **Funds Available:** A stipend is awarded (amount not specified). **Duration:** 1 year.

Eligibility Requirements: This program is open to Colorado residents who are high school seniors, high school graduates, GED recipients, or continuing college students. Applicants must be of Hispanic background or involved with the Hispanic community or veteran's organizations. Along with their application, they must submit an essay of 250 to 500 words on their educational and career goals, their financial need, their association with the Mile High Chapter of the American GI Forum, how they have contributed to the Hispanic community or veteran's organizations through their activities or services; and why they should be selected to receive a scholarship award. Selection is based on that essay, academic potential, community service and extracurricular activities, association with the Mile High Chapter, and financial need. **Deadline for Receipt:** June of each

year. **Additional Information:** Recipients must provide 4 hours of volunteer service to the Mile High Chapter during the year they receive the award.

118 ■ AMERICAN HELLENIC EDUCATIONAL PROGRESSIVE ASSOCIATION

Attn: AHEPA Educational Foundation
1909 Q Street, N.W., Suite 500
Washington, DC 20009
Tel: (202)232-6300
Fax: (202)232-2140
Web Site: http://www.ahepa.org/ahepa

To provide financial assistance for college to students who apply through district foundations or committees of the American Hellenic Educational Progressive Association (AHEPA).

Title of Award: AHEPA District Scholarship Awards **Area, Field, or Subject:** General studies/Field of study not specified **Level of Education for which Award is Granted:** Undergraduate **Number Awarded:** Varies each year; recently, 20 of these scholarships were awarded. **Funds Available:** The stipend is $1,000 per year. **Duration:** 1 year.

Eligibility Requirements: This program is open to students who are enrolled or planning to enroll in a college or university. Recipients are selected by AHEPA districts that qualify to receive funding from the national foundation. Districts establish their own requirements, but they may follow procedures similar to those of the national organization: applicants must be members in good standing of the Order of Ahepa, Daughters of Penelope, Sons of Pericles, or Maids of Athena, or the children of Order of Ahepa or Daughters of Penelope members in good standing. High school seniors must submit their most recent official transcript as well as SAT or ACT scores; college freshmen and sophomores must submit high school transcripts, SAT or ACT scores, and their most recent college transcript; college juniors and seniors must submit their most recent college transcript. Selection is based on academic achievement, extracurricular activities, athletic achievements, work experience, and community service. Financial need is not considered. **Deadline for Receipt:** Recommendation forms must be submitted to the national office by June of each year. **Additional Information:** This program includes the following named scholarships: the Sam Nakos Scholarship, the Nicholas Kounaris Scholarship, the P.A. Margaronis Scholarship, the Carlos T. Touris Scholarship, and the William P. Thomas Scholarship. Applications for this scholarship must be submitted to the AHEPA local district scholarship committee chair, who then selects the recipients.

119 ■ AMERICAN HELLENIC EDUCATIONAL PROGRESSIVE ASSOCIATION

Attn: AHEPA Educational Foundation
1909 Q Street, N.W., Suite 500
Washington, DC 20009
Tel: (202)232-6300
Fax: (202)232-2140
Web Site: http://www.ahepa.org/ahepa

To provide financial assistance for college to students with a connection to the American Hellenic Educational Progressive Association (AHEPA).

Title of Award: George Chirgotis Scholarship **Area, Field, or Subject:** General studies/Field of study not specified **Level of Education for which Award is Granted:** Undergraduate **Number Awarded:** Varies each year; recently, 1 of these scholarships was awarded. **Funds Available:** Stipends range from $500 to $2,000 per year. **Duration:** 1 year.

Eligibility Requirements: This program is open to 1) members in good standing of the Order of Ahepa, Daughters of Penelope, Sons of Pericles, or Maids of Athena, and 2) the children of Order of Ahepa or Daughters of Penelope members in good standing. Applicants must be currently enrolled or planning to enroll in a college or university. High school seniors must submit their most recent official transcript as well as SAT or ACT scores; college freshmen and sophomores must submit high school transcripts, SAT or ACT scores, and their most recent college transcript; college juniors and seniors must submit their most recent college transcript. Selection is based on academic achievement, extracurricular activities, athletic achievements, work experience, and community service. Financial need is not considered. **Deadline for Receipt:** March of each year. **Additional Information:** A processing fee of $20 must accompany each application.

120 ■ AMERICAN HELLENIC EDUCATIONAL PROGRESSIVE ASSOCIATION

Attn: AHEPA Educational Foundation
1909 Q Street, N.W., Suite 500
Washington, DC 20009
Tel: (202)232-6300
Fax: (202)232-2140
Web Site: http://www.ahepa.org/ahepa
To provide financial assistance for college to students with a connection to the American Hellenic Educational Progressive Association (AHEPA).
Title of Award: Sam Dakis Scholarship **Area, Field, or Subject:** General studies/Field of study not specified **Level of Education for which Award is Granted:** Undergraduate **Number Awarded:** Varies each year; recently, 1 of these scholarships was awarded. **Funds Available:** Stipends range from $500 to $2,000 per year. **Duration:** 1 year.
Eligibility Requirements: This program is open to 1) members in good standing of the Order of Ahepa, Daughters of Penelope, Sons of Pericles, or Maids of Athena, and 2) the children of Order of Ahepa or Daughters of Penelope members in good standing. Applicants must be currently enrolled or planning to enroll in a college or university. High school seniors must submit their most recent official transcript as well as SAT or ACT scores; college freshmen and sophomores must submit high school transcripts, SAT or ACT scores, and their most recent college transcript; college juniors and seniors must submit their most recent college transcript. Selection is based on academic achievement, extracurricular activities, athletic achievements, work experience, and community service. Financial need is not considered. **Deadline for Receipt:** March of each year. **Additional Information:** A processing fee of $20 must accompany each application.

121 ■ AMERICAN HELLENIC EDUCATIONAL PROGRESSIVE ASSOCIATION

Attn: AHEPA Educational Foundation
1909 Q Street, N.W., Suite 500
Washington, DC 20009
Tel: (202)232-6300
Fax: (202)232-2140
Web Site: http://www.ahepa.org/ahepa
To provide financial assistance to undergraduate and graduate students of Hellenic heritage.
Title of Award: P.A. Margaronis Scholarships **Area, Field, or Subject:** General studies/Field of study not specified **Level of Education for which Award is Granted:** Graduate, Undergraduate **Number Awarded:** Varies each year. Recently, 14 of these scholarships were awarded: 6 to graduate students and 8 to undergraduates. **Funds Available:** Stipends range from $500 to $2,000 per year. **Duration:** 1 year.
Eligibility Requirements: Applicants must be of Hellenic heritage (although their ancestry does not need to be 100% Greek) and currently enrolled or planning to enroll as undergraduate or graduate students. High school seniors must submit their most recent official transcript as well as SAT or ACT scores; college freshmen and sophomores must submit high school transcripts, SAT or ACT scores, and their most recent college transcript; college juniors and seniors must submit their most recent college transcript; graduate students must submit college transcripts, GRE or MCAT scores (if available), and their most recent graduate school transcript. Selection is based on academic achievement, extracurricular activities, athletic achievements, work experience, community service, and financial need. **Deadline for Receipt:** March of each year. **Additional Information:** A processing fee of $20 must accompany each application.

122 ■ AMERICAN HELLENIC EDUCATIONAL PROGRESSIVE ASSOCIATION

Attn: AHEPA Educational Foundation
1909 Q Street, N.W., Suite 500
Washington, DC 20009
Tel: (202)232-6300
Fax: (202)232-2140
Web Site: http://www.ahepa.org/ahepa
To provide financial assistance to incoming college freshmen who are members of the Sons of Pericles.
Title of Award: Stergios B. Milonas Scholarship **Area, Field, or Subject:** General studies/Field of study not specified **Level of Education for which Award is Granted:** Undergraduate **Number Awarded:** 1 each year. **Funds Available:** Stipends range from $500 to $2,000 per year. **Duration:** 1 year.
Eligibility Requirements: This program is open to incoming college freshmen who are members of the Sons of Pericles. Applicants must submit their most recent high school transcript as well as SAT or ACT scores. In addition to the transcripts and test scores, selection is based on extracurricular activities, athletic achievements, work and community service, and a 500-word essay on past achievements and future goals.
Deadline for Receipt: March of each year. **Additional Information:** A processing fee of $20 must accompany each application.

123 ■ AMERICAN HELLENIC EDUCATIONAL PROGRESSIVE ASSOCIATION

Attn: AHEPA Educational Foundation
1909 Q Street, N.W., Suite 500
Washington, DC 20009
Tel: (202)232-6300
Fax: (202)232-2140
Web Site: http://www.ahepa.org/ahepa
To provide financial assistance to undergraduate and graduate students with a connection to the American Hellenic Educational Progressive Association (AHEPA).
Title of Award: Nick Cost Scholarships **Area, Field, or Subject:** General studies/Field of study not specified **Level of Education for which Award is Granted:** Graduate, Undergraduate **Number Awarded:** Varies each year; recently, 2 of these scholarships were awarded. **Funds Available:** Stipends range from $500 to $2,000 per year. **Duration:** 1 year.
Eligibility Requirements: This program is open to 1) members in good standing of the Order of Ahepa, Daughters of Penelope, Sons of Pericles, or Maids of Athena, and 2) the children of Order of Ahepa or Daughters of Penelope members in good standing. Applicants must be currently enrolled or planning to enroll as undergraduate or graduate students. High school seniors must submit their most recent official transcript as well as SAT or ACT scores; college freshmen and sophomores must submit high school transcripts, SAT or ACT scores, and their most recent college transcript; college juniors and seniors must submit their most recent college transcript; graduate students must submit college transcripts, GRE or MCAT scores (if available), and their most recent graduate school transcript. Selection is based on academic achievement, extracurricular activities, athletic achievements, work experience, and community service. Financial need is not considered. **Deadline for Receipt:** March of each year. **Additional Information:** A processing fee of $20 must accompany each application.

124 ■ AMERICAN HELLENIC EDUCATIONAL PROGRESSIVE ASSOCIATION

Attn: AHEPA Educational Foundation
1909 Q Street, N.W., Suite 500
Washington, DC 20009
Tel: (202)232-6300
Fax: (202)232-2140
Web Site: http://www.ahepa.org/ahepa
To provide financial assistance for college to students with a connection to the American Hellenic Educational Progressive Association (AHEPA).
Title of Award: Chris Gustav Rallis Scholarship **Area, Field, or Subject:** General studies/Field of study not specified **Level of Education for which Award is Granted:** Undergraduate **Number Awarded:** Varies each year; recently, 1 of these scholarships was awarded. **Funds Available:** Stipends range from $500 to $2,000 per year. **Duration:** 1 year.
Eligibility Requirements: This program is open to 1) members in good standing of the Order of Ahepa, Daughters of Penelope, Sons of Pericles, or Maids of Athena, and 2) the children of Order of Ahepa or Daughters of Penelope members in good standing. Applicants must be currently enrolled or planning to enroll in a college or university. High school seniors must submit their most recent official transcript as well as SAT or ACT scores; college freshmen and sophomores must submit high school transcripts, SAT or ACT scores, and their most recent college transcript; college juniors and seniors must submit their most recent college transcript. Selection is based on academic achievement, extracurricular activities, athletic achievements, work experience, community service, and financial need. **Deadline for Receipt:** March of each year. **Additional Information:** A processing fee of $20 must accompany each application.

125 ■ AMERICAN HELLENIC EDUCATIONAL PROGRESSIVE AS-SOCIATION

Attn: AHEPA Educational Foundation
1909 Q Street, N.W., Suite 500
Washington, DC 20009
Tel: (202)232-6300
Fax: (202)232-2140
Web Site: http://www.ahepa.org/ahepa
To provide financial assistance to undergraduate students who are members of the Sons of Pericles.

Title of Award: Sons of Pericles Undergraduate Scholarships **Area, Field, or Subject:** General studies/Field of study not specified **Level of Education for which Award is Granted:** Undergraduate **Number Awarded:** 1 each year. **Funds Available:** Stipends range from $500 to $2,000 per year. **Duration:** 1 year.
Eligibility Requirements: This program is open to current undergraduates who are members of the Sons of Pericles. Freshmen and sophomores must submit a complete high school transcript, SAT or ACT scores, and their most recent college transcript. Juniors and seniors must submit their most recent college transcript. In addition to the transcripts and test scores, selection is based on extracurricular activities, athletic achievements, work and community service, and a 500-word essay on past achievements and future goals. **Deadline for Receipt:** March of each year. **Additional Information:** This program includes the George Kaloudis Memorial Scholarship and the John Katsimatides Memorial Scholarship. A processing fee of $20 must accompany each application.

126 ■ AMERICAN HELLENIC EDUCATIONAL PROGRESSIVE AS-SOCIATION

Attn: AHEPA Educational Foundation
1909 Q Street, N.W., Suite 500
Washington, DC 20009
Tel: (202)232-6300
Fax: (202)232-2140
Web Site: http://www.ahepa.org/ahepa
To provide financial assistance to undergraduate and graduate students with a connection to the American Hellenic Educational Progressive Association (AHEPA).

Title of Award: Dr. John C. Yavis Scholarships **Area, Field, or Subject:** General studies/Field of study not specified **Level of Education for which Award is Granted:** Graduate, Undergraduate **Number Awarded:** Varies each year; recently, 2 of these scholarships were awarded. **Funds Available:** Stipends range from $500 to $2,000 per year. **Duration:** 1 year.
Eligibility Requirements: This program is open to 1) members in good standing of the Order of Ahepa, Daughters of Penelope, Sons of Pericles, or Maids of Athena, and 2) the children of Order of Ahepa or Daughters of Penelope members in good standing. Applicants must be currently enrolled or planning to enroll as undergraduate or graduate students. High school seniors must submit their most recent official transcript as well as SAT or ACT scores; college freshmen and sophomores must submit high school transcripts, SAT or ACT scores, and their most recent college transcript; college juniors and seniors must submit their most recent college transcript; graduate students must submit college transcripts, GRE or MCAT scores (if available), and their most recent graduate school transcript. Selection is based on academic achievement, extracurricular activities, athletic achievements, work experience, and community service. Financial need is not considered. **Deadline for Receipt:** March of each year. **Additional Information:** A processing fee of $20 must accompany each application.

127 ■ AMERICAN HELLENIC EDUCATIONAL PROGRESSIVE ASSOCIATION-DISTRICT 1

Attn: Family District 1 Educational Fund, Inc.
c/o Melva Zinaich, Co-Chair
P.O. Box 1011
Charleston, SC 29402
To provide financial assistance for college or graduate school to residents of designated southeastern states.

Title of Award: Family District 1 Scholarships **Area, Field, or Subject:** General studies/Field of study not specified **Level of Education for which Award is Granted:** Graduate, Undergraduate **Number Awarded:** Varies each year. **Funds Available:** Stipends range from $500 to $1,500. **Duration:** 1 year.

Eligibility Requirements: This program is open to residents of Alabama, Florida, Georgia, Mississippi, South Carolina, and Tennessee who are high school seniors or graduates or current undergraduate or graduate students. Applicants must be attending or planning to attend an accredited college or university as a full-time student. They must submit a 500-word essay on the topic, "How has your family history, culture, or environment influenced who you are?" High school seniors must also submit an official transcript and SAT or ACT scores. College freshmen and sophomores must submit an official high school transcript, SAT and ACT scores, and their most recent college transcript. College juniors and seniors must submit their most recent college transcript. Graduate students must submit undergraduate and graduate transcripts and GRE scores. Consideration is also given to extracurricular activities, athletic achievements, work, and community service. Students who also demonstrate financial need are considered in a separate selection process. **Deadline for Receipt:** December of each year.

128 ■ AMERICAN HELLENIC EDUCATIONAL PROGRESSIVE ASSOCIATION-DISTRICT 4

c/o Angelo Pournaras, Scholarship Committee Chair
1027 Spruce Street
Ambridge, PA 15003
Tel: (724)266-9160
E-mail: atpournaras@msn.com
Web Site: http://www.ahepa.org/district4
To provide financial assistance for college to residents of Pennsylvania who are affiliated with the American Hellenic Educational Progressive Association (AHEPA).

Title of Award: Power District 4 Scholarship Fund **Area, Field, or Subject:** General studies/Field of study not specified **Level of Education for which Award is Granted:** Undergraduate **Number Awarded:** Varies each year; recently, 45 of these scholarships were awarded. **Funds Available:** A stipend is awarded (amount not specified). Funds are paid directly to the student. **Duration:** 1 year.
Eligibility Requirements: This program is open to Pennsylvania residents who are members of an AHEPA family organization (Order of Ahepa, Daughters of Penelope, Sons of Pericles, Maids of Athena) or the child of a member of Order of Ahepa or Daughters of Penelope. Applicants must be college-bound high school seniors or students at an accredited institution of higher learning. They must have a GPA of 2.5 or higher. Admission to the pool of potential recipients is based solely on scholastic achievement. Individual grants are then awarded to members of the pool who demonstrate the greatest financial need, with the most needy student receiving the largest grant. **Deadline for Receipt:** April of each year.

129 ■ AMERICAN HELLENIC EDUCATIONAL PROGRESSIVE ASSOCIATION-DISTRICT 10

Attn: District 10 Educational Foundation
c/o Milton A. Gust, Executive Secretary/Treasurer
1628 Crimson Drive
Troy, MI 48083
Tel: (248)689-4156
Fax: (248)689-3802
E-mail: mgust@ahepamichigan.org
Web Site: http://www.ahepamichigan.org
To provide financial assistance for college to high school seniors from Michigan who have an affiliation with the American Hellenic Educational Progressive Association (AHEPA).

Title of Award: Order of Ahepa District 10 Scholarships **Area, Field, or Subject:** General studies/Field of study not specified **Level of Education for which Award is Granted:** Undergraduate **Number Awarded:** 1 or more each year. **Funds Available:** A stipend is awarded (amount not specified). **Duration:** 1 year.
Eligibility Requirements: This program is open to college-bound seniors graduating from high schools in Michigan who are of Greek descent. Applicants must be 1) the child or grandchild of a current member of the Order of Ahepa or Daughters of Penelope, or 2) a member of Sons of Pericles or Maids of Athena. They must submit an essay of no more than 500 words on "What Hellenism means to me." Selection is based on character and intelligence, capacity in chosen field as reflected in school work, scope of interest as reflected in extracurricular activities, leadership, and some financial need. **Deadline for Receipt:** April of each year. **Ad-**

ditional Information: This program includes the Chris and Betty Baryames Scholarship for students who can demonstrate great financial need.

130 ■ AMERICAN HELLENIC EDUCATIONAL PROGRESSIVE ASSOCIATION-DISTRICT 11

Attn: Buckeye District 11 Scholarship Foundation
1125 Brittany Hills Drive
Dayton, OH 45459
Tel: (937)434-3751
Web Site: http://www.ahepa.org/district11/foundations/scholarship.html
To provide financial assistance for college to members and families of members of organizations affiliated with the American Hellenic Educational Progressive Association (AHEPA) in its District 11 (Kentucky, Ohio, and parts of Pennsylvania and West Virginia).
Title of Award: Buckeye District 11 Scholarships **Area, Field, or Subject:** General studies/Field of study not specified **Level of Education for which Award is Granted:** Undergraduate **Number Awarded:** Varies each year; recently, 37 of these scholarships were awarded. **Funds Available:** Stipends are $1,000 or $1,250. Funds are sent directly to the college or university to be used for tuition, books, laboratory fees, or other related school expenses. **Duration:** 1 year.
Eligibility Requirements: This program is open to residents of Kentucky, Ohio, and parts of Pennsylvania and West Virginia who are 1) members of the Order of Ahepa, Daughters of Penelope, Sons of Pericles, or Maids of Athena, or 2) children of members of the senior orders. Applicants must be high school seniors planning to enter college in the following fall or already enrolled in a college or university as an undergraduate. Selection is based on academic ability, class rank, leadership potential, and financial need. **Deadline for Receipt:** April of each year.

131 ■ AMERICAN HELLENIC EDUCATIONAL PROGRESSIVE ASSOCIATION-DISTRICT 13

Attn: District 13 Scholarship Foundation, Inc.
P.O. Box 6117
Chicago, IL 60680
Web Site: http://www.ahepafamily.org/d13
To provide financial assistance for college to members of the American Hellenic Educational Progressive Association's (AHEPA) District 13 or to students of Greek descent in Illinois and Wisconsin.
Title of Award: Blue Ribbon District 13 Scholarships **Area, Field, or Subject:** General studies/Field of study not specified **Level of Education for which Award is Granted:** Undergraduate **Number Awarded:** Varies each year; recently, 26 of these scholarships were awarded. **Funds Available:** The stipend is $1,000 per year. **Duration:** 1 year; nonrenewable.
Eligibility Requirements: This program is open to high school seniors and college freshmen, sophomores, and juniors (seniors are ineligible) who reside within AHEPA's District 13 (Illinois and Wisconsin). The applicant or the parent of the applicant must be either 1) a member in good standing in a AHEPA family chapter for at least 2 years immediately preceding submission of the application, or 2) a member of the Greek community (lineage must go back to and include the grandparents). Financial need and a GPA of 3.0 or higher are required. Applications must be accompanied by a certified transcript, 2 recommendations, a certified copy of SAT or ACT test scores, an acceptance letter, and a photograph. **Deadline for Receipt:** March of each year. **Additional Information:** Information is also available from Gerald J. Garbis, Director of Philanthropy, 2718 Helen Drive, Glenview, IL 60025, (847) 966-0413.

132 ■ AMERICAN HELLENIC EDUCATIONAL PROGRESSIVE ASSOCIATION-DISTRICT 16

Attn: District 16 Scholarship Board
c/o Steve G. Kirkikis, Chair
310 Orleans Drive
Shreveport, LA 71106-6224
Tel: (318)861-1582
Fax: (318)219-0753
Web Site: http://www.ahepad16.org/scholarships.html
To provide financial assistance to college students from Arkansas, Louisiana, and Texas who have an affiliation with the American Hellenic Educational Progressive Association (AHEPA).
Title of Award: Delta District 16 Scholarships **Area, Field, or Subject:** General studies/Field of study not specified **Level of Education for**

which **Award is Granted:** Undergraduate **Number Awarded:** Varies each year; recently, 14 of these scholarships were awarded. **Funds Available:** The stipend is $1,000. **Duration:** 1 year; may be renewed.
Eligibility Requirements: This program is open to residents of AHEPA District 16 (Arkansas, Louisiana, and Texas) who have completed at least 2 semesters of full-time college study. Applicants must be 1) a member of the Order of Ahepa, Daughters of Penelope, Sons of Pericles, or Maids of Athena and under 25 years of age, or 2) the child of a member of the Order of Ahepa or Daughters of Penelope. If they wish financial need to be considered in the selection process, they must have a GPA of 2.25 or higher. If they wish selection to be based only on academic achievement, they must have a GPA of 3.0 or higher. **Deadline for Receipt:** May of each year. **Additional Information:** This program includes the Mary M. Verges Scholarship and the Nick C. Demeris Scholarship.

133 ■ AMERICAN HELLENIC EDUCATIONAL PROGRESSIVE ASSOCIATION-DISTRICT 20

Attn: El Camino Real Scholarship Foundation
c/o Christine Haidos, Secretary
4317 Miraleste Drive
Rancho Palos Verdes, CA 90275-6530
Tel: (310)832-1459
Fax: (310)832-4154
E-mail: alekhaidos1459@msn.com
Web Site: http://www.ahepa20.org/scholarship
To provide financial assistance for college to members and families of members of organizations affiliated with the American Hellenic Educational Progressive Association (AHEPA) in its District 20 (Arizona, southern California, parts of Nevada, and parts of Utah).
Title of Award: El Camino Real District 20 Scholarships **Area, Field, or Subject:** General studies/Field of study not specified **Level of Education for which Award is Granted:** Undergraduate **Number Awarded:** Varies each year; recently, 15 of these scholarships were awarded. **Funds Available:** A stipend is awarded (amount not specified). **Duration:** 1 year; may be renewed up to 3 additional years.
Eligibility Requirements: This program is open to residents of Arizona, southern California, parts of Nevada, and parts of Utah who are 1) members of the Sons of Pericles or Maids of Athena, or 2) children of members of the Order of Ahepa or Daughters of Penelope. Applicants must be high school seniors planning to enter college in the following fall or already enrolled in a college or university with at least 12 semester hours completed for an undergraduate degree. They must have a GPA of 3.5 or higher. Along with their application, they must submit an essay of 500 words or less describing their career aspirations, honors classes or activities, extracurricular or community activities, and participation in AHEPA family or church-related activities. Financial need is not considered in the selection process. **Deadline for Receipt:** February of each year. **Additional Information:** This foundation began awarding scholarships in 1963. It includes the following named scholarships: the George Brotsis Memorial Scholarship, the John Dratos Memorial Scholarship, the Lt. Col. William L. Kokenes, USMC (Ret) Scholarship, the James Panousis Memorial Scholarship, the Peter John Peterson Memorial Scholarship, the Sam Platis Memorial Scholarship, the Frank Rhodes Scholarship, and the Peter Stevens Memorial Scholarship.

134 ■ AMERICAN HELLENIC EDUCATIONAL PROGRESSIVE ASSOCIATION-DISTRICT 22

Attn: Northwest AHEPA Family Educational Foundation
c/o St. Nicholas Greek Orthodox Church
1523 South Yakima Avenue
Tacoma, WA 98405-4460
Tel: (206)243-5881
E-mail: xeniag13@aol.com
Web Site: http://www.ahepafamily.org/d22/sch/index.html
To provide financial assistance to undergraduate and graduate student members and families of members of organizations affiliated with the American Hellenic Educational Progressive Association (AHEPA) in its District 22 (Oregon and Washington).
Title of Award: Firwood District 22 Scholarships **Area, Field, or Subject:** General studies/Field of study not specified **Level of Education for which Award is Granted:** Graduate, Undergraduate **Number Awarded:** Varies each year. **Funds Available:** A stipend is awarded (amount not specified). **Duration:** 1 year; recipients are eligible to receive a maximum of 2 undergraduate scholarships and 1 graduate scholarship.

Eligibility Requirements: This program is open to District 22 (Oregon and Washington) members of the Order of Ahepa, the Daughters of Penelope, the Maids of Athena, or the Sons of Pericles who were inducted as members at least 1 year prior to applying for the scholarship. Children of members of the Order of Ahepa or Daughters of Penelope are also eligible. Applicants must be high school seniors, technical/vocational school students, undergraduates, or graduate students, Selection is based on academic achievement; school activities, honors, and awards; and AHEPA family, Greek community, and other civic activities. Financial need is also considered for students who complete a supplemental application. **Deadline for Receipt:** April of each year.

135 ■ AMERICAN HOTEL & LODGING EDUCATIONAL FOUNDATION

Attn: Manager of Foundation Programs
1201 New York Avenue, N.W., Suite 600
Washington, DC 20005-3931
Tel: (202)289-3181
Fax: (202)289-3199
E-mail: ahlef@ahlef.org
Web Site: http://www.ahlef.org/scholarships_hyatt_hotel.asp
To provide financial assistance to minority college students working on a degree in hotel management.
Title of Award: Hyatt Hotels Fund for Minority Lodging Management Students **Area, Field, or Subject:** Hotel, institutional, and restaurant management **Level of Education for which Award is Granted:** Four Year College **Number Awarded:** Varies each year; recently, 18 of these scholarships were awarded. **Funds Available:** The stipend is $2,000. **Duration:** 1 year.
Eligibility Requirements: Applicants must be attending a 4-year college or university that is a member of the Council on Hotel, Restaurant and Institutional Education. They must be minorities and majoring in hotel management. Each member university may nominate 1 student. The most outstanding students receive this scholarship. **Deadline for Receipt:** March of each year. **Additional Information:** Funding for this program is provided by Hyatt Hotels & Resorts.

136 ■ AMERICAN HOTEL & LODGING EDUCATIONAL FOUNDATION

Attn: Manager of Foundation Programs
1201 New York Avenue, N.W., Suite 600
Washington, DC 20005-3931
Tel: (202)289-3181
Fax: (202)289-3199
E-mail: ahlef@ahlef.org
Web Site: http://www.ahlef.org/scholarships_rama.asp
To provide financial assistance to minority college students working on a degree in hotel management at designated schools.
Title of Award: Rama Scholarship for the American Dream **Area, Field, or Subject:** Hotel, institutional, and restaurant management **Level of Education for which Award is Granted:** Four Year College **Number Awarded:** Varies each year; recently, 24 of these scholarships were awarded. **Funds Available:** The stipend varies at each of the participating schools. **Duration:** 1 year.
Eligibility Requirements: Applicants must be attending 1 of 15 designated hospitality management schools, which select the recipients. Preference is given to students of Asian-Indian descent and other minority groups and to JHM Hotel employees. **Additional Information:** The participating institutions are Bethune-Cookman College, California State Polytechnic University at Pomona, Cornell University, Florida International University, Georgia State University, Greenville Technical College, Howard University, Johnson & Wales University (Charleston, South Carolina), Johnson & Wales University (Providence, Rhode Island), Michigan State University, New York University, University of Central Florida, University of Houston, University of South Carolina, and Virginia Polytechnic Institute and State University. This program is funded by JHM Hotels, Inc.

137 ■ AMERICAN INDIAN CHAMBER OF COMMERCE OF CALIFORNIA

Attn: AICC Scholarship
555 West Fifth Street, 31st Floor
Los Angeles, CA 90017
E-mail: info@aiccsocal.org
Web Site: http://www.aiccsocal.org/scholarship.htm

To provide financial assistance for college or graduate school to American Indians who live or attend school in California.
Title of Award: American Indian Chamber of Commerce of California Scholarship **Area, Field, or Subject:** Business administration; General studies/Field of study not specified **Level of Education for which Award is Granted:** Graduate, Undergraduate **Number Awarded:** 2 each year. **Funds Available:** The stipend is $1,000. **Duration:** 1 year.
Eligibility Requirements: This program is open to American Indians who 1) are on a federal- or state-recognized tribal roll and identified by a tribal enrollment card; or 2) have an official letter from a federal- or state-recognized tribe or agency verifying tribal membership or Indian blood. Applicants must be full-time degree candidates at an accredited institution of higher learning (junior college, trade/vocational school, 4-year university, graduate school) in California or residents of California attending an institution of higher learning elsewhere in the United States. Along with their application, they must submit an educational commitment essay describing their chosen field of study, educational goals, career goals, involvement in the Indian community, and how this scholarship will help in furthering their education. Selection is based on transcripts (30 points), a letter of recommendation (20 points), the educational commitment essay (50 points), and major in business (bonus 10 points). **Deadline for Receipt:** October of each year.

138 ■ AMERICAN INDIAN COLLEGE FUND

Attn: Scholarship Department
8333 Greenwood Boulevard
Denver, CO 80221
Tel: (303)426-8900
Free: 800-776-FUND
Fax: (303)426-1200
E-mail: info@collegefund.org
Web Site: http://www.collegefund.org/scholarships/main.html
To provide financial assistance to American Indian students who are attending tribal colleges in California, Minnesota, and New Mexico.
Title of Award: General Mills Tribal College Scholarship Program **Area, Field, or Subject:** General studies/Field of study not specified **Level of Education for which Award is Granted:** Undergraduate **Number Awarded:** 25 each year. **Funds Available:** The stipend is $2,000. **Duration:** 1 year.
Eligibility Requirements: Eligible to apply are American Indians or Alaska Natives working full time on an associate or bachelor's degree at an accredited tribal college or university in California, Minnesota, or New Mexico. Applicants must be able to demonstrate exceptional academic achievement (GPA of 3.0 or higher), as well as leadership, service, and commitment to the American Indian community. Along with their application, they must submit official college transcripts; a personal essay (500 words or less) on their personal and academic background, career goals, and how this scholarship will help them achieve those goals; a statement regarding any financial hardship they have; 2 letters of recommendation; tribal enrollment information; and a color photograph. **Deadline for Receipt:** April of each year. **Additional Information:** This scholarship is sponsored by the General Mills Foundation in partnership with the American Indian College Fund.

139 ■ AMERICAN INDIAN COLLEGE FUND

Attn: Scholarship Department
8333 Greenwood Boulevard
Denver, CO 80221
Tel: (303)426-8900
Free: 800-776-FUND
Fax: (303)426-1200
E-mail: info@collegefund.org
Web Site: http://www.collegefund.org/scholarships/main.html
To provide financial assistance to American Indian students in an associate degree program at a tribal college who will be transferring to a bachelor's degree program at a tribal or mainstream college.
Title of Award: Nissan North America, Inc. Tribal College Transfer Program **Area, Field, or Subject:** General studies/Field of study not specified **Level of Education for which Award is Granted:** Four Year College **Number Awarded:** 20 each year. **Funds Available:** The stipend is $2,000 per year, starting in the recipient's sophomore year. **Duration:** 1 year; may be renewed up to 2 additional years.
Eligibility Requirements: Eligible to apply are American Indians or Alaska Natives enrolled full time in an associate degree program at a

tribal college or university (juniors and seniors are ineligible to apply) who are planning to transfer to a bachelor's degree program at a tribal college or a mainstream institution. Applicants must be able to demonstrate exceptional academic achievement, as well as leadership, service, and commitment to the American Indian community. Along with their application, they must submit official college transcripts; a personal essay (500 words or less) on their personal and academic background, career goals, and how this scholarship will help them achieve those goals; a statement regarding any financial hardship they have; 2 letters of recommendation; tribal enrollment information; and a color photograph. **Deadline for Receipt:** April of each year. **Additional Information:** This scholarship is sponsored by Nissan North America, Inc., in partnership with the American Indian College Fund.

140 ■ AMERICAN INDIAN EDUCATION FOUNDATION

10029 S.W. Nimbus Avenue, Suite 200
Beaverton, OR 97008
(866)866-8642
Fax: (503)641-0495
E-mail: scholarships@nrc1.org
Web Site: http://www.aiefprograms.org/program_scholarshipfund.htm
To provide financial assistance for college to American Indian and Alaskan Native students.

Title of Award: American Indian Education Foundation Scholarship Program **Area, Field, or Subject:** General studies/Field of study not specified **Level of Education for which Award is Granted:** Undergraduate **Number Awarded:** More than 200 each year. **Funds Available:** Freshman scholarships are $3,000 per school year. Undergraduate scholarships are $1,500 per school year. The amounts of the 2 memorial scholarships vary each year. **Duration:** 1 year; undergraduate scholarships may be renewed.

Eligibility Requirements: This program is open to full-time students of Native American or Alaskan Native descent who are currently residing on a federally-recognized reservation and attending or planning to attend a 2-year college, a 4-year college or university, or a vocational/technical school. Applicants may be either graduating high school seniors or undergraduates who are entering, continuing, or returning to school and are not high school seniors. They must submit an essay in which they describe themselves as a student, their ultimate career goals, their plans for working in or with the Indian community, and their participation in leadership and/or community service activities. An ACT score of 14 or higher is desirable. Financial need is considered in the selection process. All finalists are considered for the Paul Francis Memorial Scholarship and the Josephine Nipper Memorial Scholarship; priority for those awards is given to applicants who demonstrate true commitment to bettering their community. **Deadline for Receipt:** April of each year.

141 ■ AMERICAN INDIAN HERITAGE FOUNDATION

P.O. Box 6301
Falls Church, VA 22040
Tel: (703)819-0979
E-mail: PaleMoon@indians.org
Web Site: http://www.indians.org/Programs/MIUSApro/miusapro.html
To recognize and reward the most beautiful and talented Indian women.

Title of Award: Miss Indian USA Scholarship Program **Area, Field, or Subject:** General studies/Field of study not specified **Level of Education for which Award is Granted:** Undergraduate **Number Awarded:** 1 winner and 4 runners-up are selected each year. **Funds Available:** Miss Indian USA receives an academic scholarship of $4,000 plus a cash grant of $6,500, a wardrobe allowance of $2,000, appearance fees of $3,000, a professional photo shoot worth $500, gifts worth more than $4,000, honoring gifts worth more than $2,000, promotional materials worth more than $2,000, and travel to Washington, D.C. with a value of approximately $2,000; the total value of the prize is more than $26,000. Members of her court receive scholarships of $2,000 for the first runner-up, $1,500 for the second runner-up, $1,000 for the third runner-up, and $500 for the fourth runner-up. **Duration:** This competition is held annually.

Eligibility Requirements: American Indian women between the ages of 18 and 26 are eligible to enter this national contest if they are high school graduates and have never been married, cohabited with the opposite sex, been pregnant, or had children. U.S. citizenship is required. Selection is based on public appearance (20%), a traditional interview (15%), a contemporary interview (15%), beauty of spirit (15%), a cultural presentation (10%), scholastic achievement (10%), a platform question (10%), and a finalist question (5%). **Deadline for Receipt:** May of each year. **Additional Information:** The program involves a week-long competition in the Washington, D.C. metropolitan area that includes seminars, interviews, cultural presentations, and many public appearances. The application fee is $100 if submitted prior to mid-April or $200 if submitted later. In addition, a candidate fee of $750 is required.

142 ■ AMERICAN INDIAN SERVICES

1902 North Canyon Road, Suite 100
Provo, UT 84604
Tel: (801)375-1777; 888-227-4120
Fax: (801)375-1643
Web Site: http://www.americanindianservices.org/students.html
To provide financial assistance for college to needy Native Americans.

Title of Award: American Indian Services Scholarship Program **Area, Field, or Subject:** General studies/Field of study not specified **Level of Education for which Award is Granted:** Undergraduate **Number Awarded:** Recently, more than 1,500 of these scholarships were awarded. **Funds Available:** Students are expected to arrange for payment of half their tuition, and this program pays the other half. **Duration:** 1 semester; may be renewed if the recipient maintains a GPA of 2.25 or higher.

Eligibility Requirements: This program is open to undergraduate students who have completed no more than 150 semester credits at a university, college, junior college, or technical school with a GPA of 2.25 or higher. Applicants must be of at least one-quarter northern Native American Indian blood. Along with their application, they must submit a 1-page letter about themselves, including their tribe and home area, the school they are attending, their area of study, their educational goals and future plans, and why they need this scholarship. **Deadline for Receipt:** February of each year for classes starting in April or May; January of each year for classes starting in June; August of each year for classes starting in August or September; November of each year for classes starting in January.

143 ■ AMERICAN INSTITUTE OF CERTIFIED PUBLIC ACCOUNTANTS

Attn: Academic and Career Development Division
1211 Avenue of the Americas
New York, NY 10036-8775
Tel: (212)596-6223
Fax: (212)596-6292
E-mail: educat@aicpa.org
Web Site: http://www.aicpa.org/members/div/career/mini/smas.htm
To provide financial assistance to underrepresented minorities interested in studying accounting at the undergraduate or graduate school level.

Title of Award: Scholarships for Minority Accounting Students **Area, Field, or Subject:** Accounting **Level of Education for which Award is Granted:** Master's, Undergraduate **Number Awarded:** Varies each year; recently, 157 students received funding through this program. **Funds Available:** The maximum stipend is $5,000 per year. **Duration:** 1 year; may be renewed, if recipients are making satisfactory progress toward graduation.

Eligibility Requirements: Undergraduate applicants must be minority students who are enrolled full time, have completed at least 30 semester hours of college work (including at least 6 semester hours in accounting), be majoring in accounting with an overall GPA of 3.3 or higher, and be U.S. citizens or permanent residents. Minority students who are interested in a graduate degree must be 1) in the final year of a 5-year accounting program; 2) an undergraduate accounting major currently accepted or enrolled in a master's-level accounting, business administration, finance, or taxation program; or 3) any undergraduate major currently accepted in a master's-level accounting program. Selection is based primarily on merit (academic and personal achievement); financial need is evaluated as a secondary criteria. For purposes of this program, the American Institute of Certified Public Accountants (AICPA) considers minority students to be those of Black, Native American/Alaskan Native, or Hispanic ethnic origin.

Deadline for Receipt: May of each year. **Additional Information:** These scholarships are granted by the institute's Minority Educational Initiatives Committee.

144 ■ AMERICAN INSTITUTE OF WINE & FOOD-PACIFIC NORTHWEST CHAPTER

c/o Ken Rudee, Scholarship Chair
Barnes & Watson Fine Teas
P.O. Box 24061
Seattle, WA 98124
Tel: (206)625-9435
E-mail: Krudee@barnesandwatson.com
Web Site: http://www.aiwf.org/site/scholarships.html
To provide financial assistance to students in Washington state working on a degree in the culinary arts.
Title of Award: John Schwartz Scholarship **Area, Field, or Subject:** Culinary arts **Level of Education for which Award is Granted:** Undergraduate **Number Awarded:** 1 each year. **Funds Available:** The stipend is $1,000. **Duration:** 1 year.
Eligibility Requirements: This program is open to Washington residents who have been enrolled for at least 2 quarters in a culinary arts program in the state. Applicants must submit an essay that explains why they think they qualify for a scholarship, including their 2-year and 5-year professional goals. Selection is based on merit, including the essay, a resume, 2 letters of reference, and GPA (must be at least 3.0). **Additional Information:** The recipient is given a 1-year membership in the American Institute of Wine & Food. Recipients must prepare an article for publication in the Pacific Northwest newsletter 6 months into their school year discussing their program and success.

145 ■ AMERICAN LEGION

Attn: Americanism and Children & Youth Division
P.O. Box 1055
Indianapolis, IN 46206-1055
Tel: (317)630-1249
Fax: (317)630-1223
E-mail: acy@legion.org
Web Site: http://www.legion.org
To provide financial assistance for college to children of U.S. military personnel killed on active duty on or after September 11, 2001.
Title of Award: American Legacy Scholarships **Area, Field, or Subject:** General studies/Field of study not specified **Level of Education for which Award is Granted:** Undergraduate **Number Awarded:** Varies each year. **Funds Available:** The stipend depends on the availability of funds. **Duration:** 1 year; may be renewed.
Eligibility Requirements: This program is open to the children (including adopted children and stepchildren) of active-duty U.S. military personnel (including federalized National Guard and Reserve members) who died on active duty on or after September 11, 2001. Applicants must be high school seniors or graduates planning to enroll full time at an accredited institution of higher education in the United States. Selection is based on academic achievement, school and community activities, leadership skills, and financial need. **Deadline for Receipt:** April of each year. **Additional Information:** This program was established in 2003.

146 ■ AMERICAN LEGION

Attn: Americanism and Children & Youth Division
P.O. Box 1055
Indianapolis, IN 46206-1055
Tel: (317)630-1249
Fax: (317)630-1223
E-mail: acy@legion.org
Web Site: http://www.legion.org
To provide college scholarships to the top competitors in the American Legion Junior Position Air Rifle Tournament.
Title of Award: American Legion Junior Air Rifle National Championship Scholarships **Area, Field, or Subject:** General studies/Field of study not specified **Level of Education for which Award is Granted:** Undergraduate **Number Awarded:** 2 each year: 1 in the precision category and 1 in the sporter category. **Funds Available:** The awards are $1,000 college scholarships. **Duration:** The awards are presented annually.
Eligibility Requirements: This program is open to students between the ages of 14 and 20 who compete in air rifle tournaments sponsored by

local posts of the American Legion. Based on posted scores in the precision and sporter categories, the top 30 competitors and state and regional champions compete in a qualification round, also a postal tournament. The top 15 shooters then participate in a shoulder-to-shoulder match in August at the Olympic Training Center, Colorado Springs, Colorado.

147 ■ AMERICAN LEGION

Attn: Department of Arkansas
702 Victory Street
P.O. Box 3280
Little Rock, AR 72203
Tel: (501)375-1104; 877-243-9799
Fax: (501)375-4236
E-mail: alegion@swbell.net
Web Site: http://www.arlegion.org/Scholarship.html
To provide financial assistance for college to descendants of members of the American Legion in Arkansas.
Title of Award: Arkansas Legion Scholarships **Area, Field, or Subject:** General studies/Field of study not specified **Level of Education for which Award is Granted:** Undergraduate **Number Awarded:** 4 each year: 1 in each of the 4 areas of the state. **Funds Available:** A stipend is awarded (amount not specified).
Eligibility Requirements: Eligible are the children, grandchildren, and great-grandchildren of living or deceased members of the American Legion. They must be high school seniors under 21 years of age and residents of Arkansas. Applicants must sign a drug free pledge and a declaration of support for the Preamble to the Constitution of the American Legion. Selection is based on American spirit, character, leadership quality, scholastic endeavor, and financial need. **Deadline for Receipt:** March of each year.

148 ■ AMERICAN LEGION

Attn: Department of Wyoming
c/o Julie A. Rust, Adjutant
1320 Hugur Avenue
Cheyenne, WY 82001
Tel: (307)634-3035
Fax: (307)635-7093
E-mail: wylegion@qwest.net
To provide financial assistance for college to the children and grandchildren of Wyoming Legionnaires.
Title of Award: E.A. Blackmore Scholarship **Area, Field, or Subject:** General studies/Field of study not specified **Level of Education for which Award is Granted:** Undergraduate **Number Awarded:** 1 each year. **Funds Available:** The stipend is $1,000 per year. Funds, paid directly to the recipient's school, may be used for tuition, room and board, textbooks, and other fees. **Duration:** 1 year; may be renewed up to 3 additional years.
Eligibility Requirements: Eligible to apply for this scholarship are children and grandchildren of members and deceased members of the American Legion in Wyoming. Applicants must rank in the top 20% of their high school graduating class and be able to demonstrate financial need. **Deadline for Receipt:** May of each year.

149 ■ AMERICAN LEGION

Attn: Department of Massachusetts
State House
24 Beacon Street, Suite 546-2
Boston, MA 02133-1044
Tel: (617)727-2966
Fax: (617)727-2969
To provide financial assistance for college to the children and grandchildren of members of the American Legion in Massachusetts.
Title of Award: Edward and Helen DelPozzo Family Scholarship **Area, Field, or Subject:** General studies/Field of study not specified **Level of Education for which Award is Granted:** Undergraduate **Number Awarded:** 1 or more each year. **Funds Available:** The stipend is $1,000. **Duration:** 1 year.
Eligibility Requirements: Eligible to apply are the children and grandchildren of members in good standing in the American Legion's Department of Massachusetts (or who were members in good standing at the time of death). Applicants must be entering their freshman year of college. **Deadline for Receipt:** March of each year.

150 ■ AMERICAN LEGION

Attn: Americanism and Children & Youth Division
P.O. Box 1055
Indianapolis, IN 46206-1055
Tel: (317)630-1249
Fax: (317)630-1223
E-mail: acy@legion.org
Web Site: http://www.legion.org
To provide financial assistance for college to outstanding Eagle Scouts whose parent is a member of the American Legion.

Title of Award: Eagle Scout of the Year **Area, Field, or Subject:** General studies/Field of study not specified **Level of Education for which Award is Granted:** Undergraduate **Number Awarded:** 1 Scout of the Year and 3 runners-up each year. **Funds Available:** The Scout of the Year receives $10,000; each runner-up receives $2,500. **Duration:** 4 years; recipients are eligible to receive their scholarships immediately upon graduation from an accredited high school and must utilize the award within 4 years of their graduation date.

Eligibility Requirements: Applicants for this award must be either 1) a registered, active member of a Boy Scout Troop, Varsity Scout Team, or Venturing Crew chartered to an American Legion Post, Auxiliary Unit, or Sons of the American Legion Squadron, or 2) a registered active member of a Boy Scout Troop, Varsity Scout Team, or Venturing Crew and also the son or grandson of a member of the American Legion or American Legion Auxiliary. Candidates must also 1) have received the Eagle Scout Award; 2) be active members of their religious institution and have received the appropriate religious emblem; 3) have demonstrated practical citizenship in church, school, Scouting, and community; 4) be at least 15 years of age and enrolled in high school; and 5) submit at least 4 letters of recommendation, including 1 each from leaders of their religious institution, school, community, and Scouting. **Deadline for Receipt:** Nominations must be received by the respective department headquarters by the end of February of each year and by the national headquarters before the end of March. **Additional Information:** The recipients may use the scholarships at any school of their choice, provided it is accredited for education above the high school level and located within the United States or its possessions.

151 ■ AMERICAN LEGION

Attn: Department of Florida
1912 Lee Road
P.O. Box 547859
Orlando, FL 32854-7859
Tel: (407)295-2631
Fax: (407)299-0901
E-mail: fal@fllegion.newsouth.net
Web Site: http://www.floridalegion.org/programs/scholarships/scholarship.html
To provide financial assistance for college to the descendants of American Legion members in Florida.

Title of Award: Florida American Legion Scholarships **Area, Field, or Subject:** General studies/Field of study not specified **Level of Education for which Award is Granted:** Undergraduate **Number Awarded:** 3 each year. **Funds Available:** Stipends are $2,500, $1,500, or $1,000. **Duration:** 1 year; nonrenewable.

Eligibility Requirements: This program is open to the direct descendants (children, grandchildren, great-grandchildren, and legally adopted children) of a member of the American Legion's Department of Florida or of a deceased U.S. veteran who would have been eligible for membership in the American Legion. Applicants must be seniors attending a Florida high school and planning to attend an accredited U.S. college or university. **Deadline for Receipt:** February of each year.

152 ■ AMERICAN LEGION

Attn: Department of Florida
1912 Lee Road
P.O. Box 547859
Orlando, FL 32854-7859
Tel: (407)295-2631
Fax: (407)299-0901
E-mail: fal@fllegion.newsouth.net
Web Site: http://www.floridalegion.org/programs/scholarships/schol.html

To provide financial assistance for college to the descendants of veterans who participate in Florida Boys State.

Title of Award: Florida Boys State Scholarship **Area, Field, or Subject:** General studies/Field of study not specified **Level of Education for which Award is Granted:** Undergraduate **Number Awarded:** 1 each year. **Funds Available:** The stipend is $1,000. **Duration:** 1 year; nonrenewable.

Eligibility Requirements: This program is open to the direct descendants (sons, grandsons, great-grandsons, and legally adopted sons) of American war veterans who are selected as delegates to Florida Boys State. **Additional Information:** In addition to this scholarship that can be used at the college or university of the recipient's choice, Tallahassee Community College (TCC) and Florida State University (FSU) offer 5 scholarships to Boys State delegates who attend TCC for 2 years followed by 2 years at FSU.

153 ■ AMERICAN LEGION

Attn: Department of Florida
1912 Lee Road
P.O. Box 547859
Orlando, FL 32854-7859
Tel: (407)295-2631
Fax: (407)299-0901
E-mail: fal@fllegion.newsouth.net
Web Site: http://www.floridalegion.org/programs/rotc/rotc.htm
To recognize and reward, with college scholarships outstanding cadets who participate in the Junior ROTC program in Florida.

Title of Award: Florida JROTC Cadet of the Year Scholarships **Area, Field, or Subject:** General studies/Field of study not specified **Level of Education for which Award is Granted:** Undergraduate **Number Awarded:** 4 each year. **Funds Available:** The cadet selected as most outstanding in Florida receives a $2,000 scholarship, the runner-up a $1,000 scholarship, and third and fourth places $500 scholarships. **Duration:** 1 year; nonrenewable.

Eligibility Requirements: Each high school JROTC program in Florida may nominate its outstanding cadet to receive these scholarships. **Deadline for Receipt:** February of each year.

154 ■ AMERICAN LEGION

Attn: Department of Missouri
P.O. Box 179
Jefferson City, MO 65102-0179
Tel: (573)893-2353
Free: 800-846-9023
Fax: (573)893-2980
E-mail: info@missourilegion.org
Web Site: http://www.missourilegion.org/programs/scholarships/index.htm
To provide financial assistance for college to descendants of Missouri veterans who have participated in specified American Legion programs.

Title of Award: Lillie Lois Ford Scholarships **Area, Field, or Subject:** General studies/Field of study not specified **Level of Education for which Award is Granted:** Undergraduate **Number Awarded:** 2 each year: 1 is set aside specifically for a girl who attended Missouri Girls State or Missouri Cadet Patrol Academy and 1 for a boy who attended Missouri Boys State or Missouri Cadet Patrol Academy. **Funds Available:** The stipend is $1,000. **Duration:** 1 year (the first year of college).

Eligibility Requirements: This program is open to the unmarried children, grandchildren, and great-grandchildren under 21 years of age of honorably-discharged Missouri veterans who served at least 90 days on active duty. Applicants must have attended a complete session of Missouri Boys State, Girls State, or Cadet Patrol Academy. They must be enrolled or planning to enroll at an accredited college or university as a full-time student. Financial need is considered in the selection process. Girls and boys compete separately. **Deadline for Receipt:** April of each year. **Additional Information:** Information is also available from the Education and Scholarship Committee Chairman, John Doane, (417) 924-8186.

155 ■ AMERICAN LEGION

Attn: Department of Pennsylvania
Attn: Scholarship Secretary
P.O. Box 2324
Harrisburg, PA 17105-2324

Tel: (717)730-9100
Fax: (717)975-2836
E-mail: hq@pa-legion.com
Web Site: http://www.pa-legion.com
To provide financial assistance for college to the children of Pennsylvania Legionnaires.
Title of Award: Joseph P. Gavenonis Scholarships **Area, Field, or Subject:** General studies/Field of study not specified **Level of Education for which Award is Granted:** Four Year College **Number Awarded:** 1 or more each year. **Funds Available:** The stipend is $1,000 per year. **Duration:** 4 years, provided a satisfactory GPA is maintained at the end of each semester.
Eligibility Requirements: This program is open to seniors at high schools in Pennsylvania who are planning to attend a 4-year college or university in the state. Applicants must be children of members of an American Legion Post in Pennsylvania. First preference is given to the children of Legion members who are deceased, killed in action, or missing in action. **Deadline for Receipt:** May of each year.

156 ■ AMERICAN LEGION
Attn: Department of New Jersey
Attn: State Baseball Chairman
135 West Hanover Street
Trenton, NJ 08618
Tel: (609)695-5418
Fax: (609)394-1532
E-mail: newjersey@legion.org
Web Site: http://www.nj.legion.org
To provide financial assistance for college to outstanding participants in the New Jersey American Legion Baseball Program.
Title of Award: David C. Goodwin Memorial Scholarship **Area, Field, or Subject:** General studies/Field of study not specified **Level of Education for which Award is Granted:** Undergraduate **Number Awarded:** 2 each year: 1 at $1,000 per year and 1 at $500 per year. **Funds Available:** Stipends are $1,000 or $500 per year. **Duration:** 4 years.
Eligibility Requirements: High school juniors who participate in the New Jersey American Legion Baseball Program are eligible to apply for this scholarship. The American Legion Baseball Committee of the Department of New Jersey selects the recipients. **Deadline for Receipt:** August of each year.

157 ■ AMERICAN LEGION
Attn: Department of New Hampshire
State House Annex
25 Capitol Street, Room 431
Concord, NH 03301-6312
Tel: (603)271-5338
Fax: (603)271-5352
To provide financial assistance for college to the sons of members of the New Hampshire Department of the American Legion or American Legion Auxiliary.
Title of Award: John A. High Child Welfare Scholarship Endowment Fund **Area, Field, or Subject:** General studies/Field of study not specified **Level of Education for which Award is Granted:** Undergraduate **Number Awarded:** 1 each year. **Funds Available:** The stipend is $1,000. **Duration:** 1 year.
Eligibility Requirements: Eligible to apply for this scholarship are boys in their senior year in high school who are able to demonstrate financial need and whose parents have been members of the American Legion or the American Legion Auxiliary in New Hampshire for 3 continuous years. Selection is based on academic record, Americanism, financial need, and character. **Deadline for Receipt:** April of each year.

158 ■ AMERICAN LEGION
Attn: Department of Idaho
901 Warren Street
Boise, ID 83706-3825
Tel: (208)342-7061
Fax: (208)342-1964
E-mail: idlegion@mindspring.com
To provide financial support for college to the children and grandchildren of members of the American Legion or American Legion Auxiliary in Idaho.
Title of Award: Idaho Legion Scholarships **Area, Field, or Subject:** General studies/Field of study not specified **Level of Education for**

which **Award is Granted:** Undergraduate **Number Awarded:** Varies each year. **Funds Available:** The stipend is determined annually. **Duration:** 1 year.
Eligibility Requirements: This program is open to the children and grandchildren of members of the American Legion or American Legion Auxiliary in Idaho who have been members for at least 2 consecutive years. Applicants must be Idaho residents and high school seniors who plan to attend accredited colleges, universities, or vocational/technical schools within the state. **Deadline for Receipt:** June of each year.

159 ■ AMERICAN LEGION
Attn: Department of Illinois
2720 East Lincoln Street
P.O. Box 2910
Bloomington, IL 61702-2910
Tel: (309)663-0361
Fax: (309)663-5783
E-mail: hdqs@illegion.org
Web Site: http://www.illegion.org/scholarship.html
To provide financial assistance for college to Illinois residents who participate in American Legion baseball.
Title of Award: Illinois Legion Baseball Scholarships **Area, Field, or Subject:** General studies/Field of study not specified **Level of Education for which Award is Granted:** Undergraduate **Number Awarded:** 5 each year: 1 in each division of the Illinois American Legion. The Illinois player of the year also receives a $1,000 scholarship from the national American Legion. **Funds Available:** The stipend is $1,000. **Duration:** 1 year.
Eligibility Requirements: This program is open to residents of Illinois who have played on a baseball team that is sponsored or affiliated with an American Legion post. Applicants must have graduated from high school or be a college freshman; students still in high school are not eligible. They must be planning to attend college in the fall. Selection is based on leadership, scholarship, character, citizenship, and financial need.

160 ■ AMERICAN LEGION
Attn: Department of Illinois
2720 East Lincoln Street
P.O. Box 2910
Bloomington, IL 61702-2910
Tel: (309)663-0361
Fax: (309)663-5783
E-mail: hdqs@illegion.org
Web Site: http://www.illegion.org/scholarship.html
To provide financial assistance for college to Scouts in Illinois.
Title of Award: Illinois Legion Boy Scout Scholarships **Area, Field, or Subject:** General studies/Field of study not specified **Level of Education for which Award is Granted:** Undergraduate **Number Awarded:** 5 each year: 1 at $1,000 and 4 runners-up at $200 each. **Funds Available:** Awards are $1,000 or $200. **Duration:** 1 year.
Eligibility Requirements: Applicants must be residents of Illinois, high school seniors, and qualified Scouts or Venturers. Both males and females are eligible. Selection is based on a 500-word essay on the American Legion, Americanism, and Scouting. **Deadline for Receipt:** April of each year.

161 ■ AMERICAN LEGION
Attn: Department of Illinois
2720 East Lincoln Street
P.O. Box 2910
Bloomington, IL 61702-2910
Tel: (309)663-0361
Fax: (309)663-5783
E-mail: hdqs@illegion.org
Web Site: http://www.illegion.org/scholarship.html
To provide financial assistance for college to the children and grandchildren of members of the American Legion in Illinois.
Title of Award: Illinois Legion Scholarships **Area, Field, or Subject:** General studies/Field of study not specified **Level of Education for which Award is Granted:** Undergraduate **Number Awarded:** 20 each year: 4 in each of the Illinois department's 5 divisions. **Funds Available:** The stipend is $1,000. **Duration:** 1 year; nonrenewable.
Eligibility Requirements: This program is open to students graduating from high schools in Illinois who plan to further their education at an ac-

credited college, university, vocational school, or trade school. Applicants must be the children or grandchildren of members of American Legion posts in Illinois. Selection is based on academic performance and financial need. **Deadline for Receipt:** March of each year.

162 ■ AMERICAN LEGION

Attn: Department of Iowa
720 Lyon Street
Des Moines, IA 50309-5481
Tel: (515)282-5068
Fax: (515)282-7583
E-mail: programs@ialegion.org
Web Site: http://www.ialegion.org/eagle_scout_of_the_year.htm
To provide financial assistance for college to outstanding Eagle Scouts in Iowa.
Title of Award: Iowa Legion Eagle Scout of the Year Scholarship **Area, Field, or Subject:** General studies/Field of study not specified **Level of Education for which Award is Granted:** Undergraduate **Number Awarded:** 3 each year. **Funds Available:** The first-place winner receives a $2,000 scholarship, second a $1,500 scholarship, and third a $1,000 scholarship. All awards must be used for payment of tuition at the recipient's college or university. **Duration:** 1 year.
Eligibility Requirements: Members of the Boy Scouts in Iowa who have received the Eagle Scout Award are eligible to receive this scholarship. The Boy Scout Committee of the American Legion selects the recipient on the basis of outstanding service to his religious institution, school, and community.

163 ■ AMERICAN LEGION

Attn: Department of Iowa
720 Lyon Street
Des Moines, IA 50309-5481
Tel: (515)282-5068
Fax: (515)282-7583
E-mail: boysstate@ialegion.org
Web Site: http://www.ialegion.org/boys_state.htm
To provide financial assistance for college to the outstanding citizen at Iowa American Legion Boys State.
Title of Award: Iowa Legion Foundation Outstanding Citizen of Boys State Scholarship **Area, Field, or Subject:** General studies/Field of study not specified **Level of Education for which Award is Granted:** Undergraduate **Number Awarded:** 1 each year. **Funds Available:** The stipend is $2,500. **Duration:** 1 year.
Eligibility Requirements: Boys who have completed their junior year at a high school in Iowa are chosen to attend the Iowa American Legion Boys State. The staff at Boys State selects the outstanding citizen to receive this scholarship. The recipient must be planning to attend a college or university in Iowa.

164 ■ AMERICAN LEGION

Attn: Department of Iowa
720 Lyon Street
Des Moines, IA 50309-5481
Tel: (515)282-5068
Fax: (515)282-7583
E-mail: programs@ialegion.org
Web Site: http://www.ialegion.org/baseball.htm
To provide financial assistance for college to outstanding participants in the Iowa American Legion Senior Baseball Tournament.
Title of Award: Iowa Legion Foundation Outstanding Senior Baseball Player Scholarship **Area, Field, or Subject:** General studies/Field of study not specified **Level of Education for which Award is Granted:** Undergraduate **Number Awarded:** 1 each year. **Funds Available:** The award is $1,500. **Duration:** 1 year.
Eligibility Requirements: Boys who participate in the Iowa American Legion Senior Baseball Tournament are eligible to receive this scholarship. The State Baseball Committee selects the recipient on the basis of outstanding sportsmanship, team play, athletic ability, and proven academic achievements.

165 ■ AMERICAN LEGION

Attn: Department of Pennsylvania
Attn: Keystone Boys State

P.O. Box 2324
Harrisburg, PA 17105-2324
Tel: (717)730-9100
Fax: (717)975-2836
E-mail: hq@pa-legion.com
Web Site: http://www.pa-legion.com/boysstate.shtml
To provide financial assistance for college to outstanding participants at Keystone Boys State, sponsored by the Department of Pennsylvania of the American Legion.
Title of Award: Keystone Boys State Scholarships **Area, Field, or Subject:** General studies/Field of study not specified **Level of Education for which Award is Granted:** Undergraduate **Number Awarded:** 3 each year. **Funds Available:** The stipend is $1,000. **Duration:** 1 year.
Eligibility Requirements: Keystone Boys State is open to male students who have completed their junior year of high school in Pennsylvania. Staff at Boys State select scholarship recipients on the basis of loyalty to our nation, an interest in government, character, ambition, leadership ability, and communication skills. **Deadline for Receipt:** May of each year.

166 ■ AMERICAN LEGION

Attn: Department of Kansas
1314 S.W. Topeka Boulevard
Topeka, KS 66612-1886
Tel: (785)232-9315
Fax: (785)232-1399
Web Site: http://www.ksamlegion.org/programs.htm
To provide financial assistance for college to the children of members of the Kansas American Legion or American Legion Auxiliary.
Title of Award: Albert M. Lappin Scholarship **Area, Field, or Subject:** General studies/Field of study not specified **Level of Education for which Award is Granted:** Undergraduate **Number Awarded:** 1 each year. **Funds Available:** The stipend is $1,000. **Duration:** 1 year.
Eligibility Requirements: Applicants must be high school seniors who plan to attend an approved Kansas college, university, or trade school; freshmen or sophomores at those schools are also eligible. At least 1 of their parents must be a veteran and a member of an American Legion post or Auxiliary in Kansas for the past 3 consecutive years. Along with their application, they must submit an essay of 250 to 500 words on "Why I Want to Go to College." Financial need is also considered in the selection process. **Deadline for Receipt:** February of each year.

167 ■ AMERICAN LEGION

Attn: Department of New Jersey
Attn: Scholarship Judges
135 West Hanover Street
Trenton, NJ 08618
Tel: (609)695-5418
Fax: (609)394-1532
E-mail: newjersey@legion.org
Web Site: http://www.nj.legion.org
To provide financial assistance for college to the descendants of members of the New Jersey Department of the American Legion.
Title of Award: Lawrence Luterman Memorial Scholarships **Area, Field, or Subject:** General studies/Field of study not specified **Level of Education for which Award is Granted:** Undergraduate **Number Awarded:** 7 each year: 2 for 4 years, 3 for 2 years, and 2 for 1 year. **Funds Available:** The stipend is $1,000 per year. **Duration:** These scholarships are for 4 years, 2 years, or 1 year.
Eligibility Requirements: This program is open to high school seniors who are the natural or adopted descendants of members of the American Legion's New Jersey Department. Selection is based on character (20%), Americanism (20%), leadership (20%), scholarship (20%), and financial need (20%). **Deadline for Receipt:** February of each year.

168 ■ AMERICAN LEGION

Attn: Department of New Hampshire
State House Annex
25 Capitol Street, Room 431
Concord, NH 03301-6312
Tel: (603)271-2211
To provide financial assistance for college to the children of members of the New Hampshire Department of the American Legion or American Legion Auxiliary.
Title of Award: Albert T. Marcoux Memorial Scholarship **Area, Field, or Subject:** General studies/Field of study not specified **Level of Education

for which Award is Granted: Undergraduate Number Awarded: 1 each year. Funds Available: The stipend is $1,000. Duration: 1 year.
Eligibility Requirements: Applicants must submit evidence of 1) a parent's current membership in a New Hampshire post of the American Legion or unit of the American Legion Auxiliary, 2) residence in New Hampshire for at least 3 years, 3) acceptance to an accredited college or university, 4) a GPA of 3.0 or higher in their junior and senior high school years, and 5) financial need. Deadline for Receipt: April of each year.

169 ■ AMERICAN LEGION
Attn: Department of Massachusetts
State House
24 Beacon Street, Suite 546-2
Boston, MA 02133-1044
Tel: (617)727-2966
Fax: (617)727-2969
To provide financial assistance for college to the children and grandchildren of members of the American Legion in Massachusetts.
Title of Award: Massachusetts Legion Department General Scholarships Area, Field, or Subject: General studies/Field of study not specified Level of Education for which Award is Granted: Undergraduate Number Awarded: 18 each year: 8 at $1,000 and 10 at $500. Funds Available: Stipends are $1,000 or $500. Duration: 1 year.
Eligibility Requirements: Eligible to apply are the children and grandchildren of members in good standing in the American Legion's Department of Massachusetts (or who were members in good standing at the time of death). Applicants must be entering their freshman year of college. Deadline for Receipt: March of each year.

170 ■ AMERICAN LEGION
Attn: Department of Indiana
777 North Meridian Street
Indianapolis, IN 46204
Tel: (317)630-1264
Fax: (317)630-1277
Web Site: http://www.indlegion.org
To provide financial assistance for college to outstanding participants in Hoosier Boys State.
Title of Award: Frank W. McHale Memorial Scholarships Area, Field, or Subject: General studies/Field of study not specified Level of Education for which Award is Granted: Undergraduate Number Awarded: 3 each year. Funds Available: The amount of the awards depends on the availability of funds; recently, stipends were $1,650.
Eligibility Requirements: High school juniors in Indiana who attend Hoosier Boys State are eligible for these scholarships, but only in the year they attend Boys State. Recipients are selected by the staff of Hoosier Boys State. The delegate elected as the B.W. Breedlove Outstanding Citizen by the staff of Hoosier Boys State receives the Col. Frank R. Kossa Scholarship.

171 ■ AMERICAN LEGION
Attn: Department of New Hampshire
State House Annex
25 Capitol Street, Room 431
Concord, NH 03301-6312
Tel: (603)271-2211
Fax: (603)271-5352
To provide financial assistance for college to outstanding participants in New Hampshire Boys State.
Title of Award: New Hampshire Boys State Scholarship Area, Field, or Subject: General studies/Field of study not specified Level of Education for which Award is Granted: Undergraduate Number Awarded: 1 each year. Funds Available: The amount of the award varies.
Eligibility Requirements: This scholarship is awarded at graduation from New Hampshire Boys State. The recipient is selected by the staff from Boys State participants entering their senior year in a New Hampshire high school.

172 ■ AMERICAN LEGION
Attn: Department of New Hampshire
State House Annex
25 Capitol Street, Room 431
Concord, NH 03301-6312

Tel: (603)271-2211
Fax: (603)271-5352
To provide financial assistance for college to students in New Hampshire.
Title of Award: New Hampshire Legion Department Scholarship Area, Field, or Subject: General studies/Field of study not specified Level of Education for which Award is Granted: Undergraduate Number Awarded: 2 each year. Funds Available: The stipend is $1,000. Duration: 1 year.
Eligibility Requirements: Students who are or will be graduates of a New Hampshire high school and have been New Hampshire residents for at least 3 years may apply for this scholarship if they are entering their first year of college. Deadline for Receipt: April of each year.

173 ■ AMERICAN LEGION
Attn: Department of New Hampshire
State House Annex
25 Capitol Street, Room 431
Concord, NH 03301-6312
Tel: (603)271-2211
Fax: (603)271-5352
To provide financial assistance for vocational education to students in New Hampshire.
Title of Award: New Hampshire Legion Department Vocational Scholarship Area, Field, or Subject: General studies/Field of study not specified Level of Education for which Award is Granted: Vocational/Occupational Number Awarded: 1 each year. Funds Available: The stipend is $1,000. Duration: 1 year.
Eligibility Requirements: Students who are or will be graduates of a New Hampshire high school and have been New Hampshire residents for at least 3 years may apply for this scholarship if they are entering their first year of higher education in a vocational field. Deadline for Receipt: April of each year.

174 ■ AMERICAN LEGION
Attn: Department of New York
112 State Street, Suite 400
Albany, NY 12207
Tel: (518)463-2215
Fax: (518)427-8443
E-mail: newyork@legion.org
Web Site: http://www.ny.legion.org/scouting_.htm
To provide financial assistance for college to outstanding Eagle Scouts in New York.
Title of Award: New York American Legion Eagle Scout of the Year Scholarship Area, Field, or Subject: General studies/Field of study not specified Level of Education for which Award is Granted: Undergraduate Number Awarded: 1 each year. Funds Available: The award is $1,000. Duration: 1 year.
Eligibility Requirements: The New York nominee for American Legion Scout of the Year receives this scholarship. Applicants must be either 1) registered, active members of a Boy Scout Troop or Varsity Scout Team sponsored by an American Legion Post in Vermont or Auxiliary Unit in Vermont, or 2) registered, active members of a duly chartered Boy Scout Troop or Varsity Scout Team and the sons or grandsons of American Legion or Auxiliary members. They must be active members of their religious institution; have received the appropriate religious emblem; have demonstrated practical citizenship in church, school, Scouting, and community; have received the Eagle Scout award; be between 15 and 19 years of age; and be enrolled in high school. Deadline for Receipt: February of each year. Additional Information: Information is also available from Robert J. Colucci, Department Scouting Vice-Chair, 111 Orlando Avenue, Albany, NY 12203, (518) 459-1030, E-mail: bclooch@yahoo.com.

175 ■ AMERICAN LEGION
Attn: Department of Ohio
60 Big Run Road
P.O. Box 8007
Delaware, OH 43015
Tel: (740)362-7478
Fax: (740)362-1429
E-mail: ohlegion@iwaynet.net
Web Site: http://www.ohioamericanlegion.org/scholars.htm

To provide financial assistance for college to Ohio Legionnaires, their spouses, and their descendants.

Title of Award: Ohio Legion Scholarships **Area, Field, or Subject:** General studies/Field of study not specified **Level of Education for which Award is Granted:** Undergraduate **Number Awarded:** Varies each year; recently, 18 of these scholarships were awarded. **Funds Available:** Stipends are at least $2,000. **Duration:** 1 year.

Eligibility Requirements: Eligible to apply for these scholarships are residents of Ohio who are Legionnaires, direct descendants of living or deceased Legionnaires, and surviving spouses or children of deceased U.S. military personnel who died on active duty or of injuries received on active duty. All applicants must be attending or planning to attend colleges, universities, or other approved postsecondary schools in Ohio. Selection is based on academic achievement as measured by course grades, scholastic test scores, difficulty of curriculum, participation in outside activities, and the judging committee's general impression. **Deadline for Receipt:** April of each year.

176 ■ AMERICAN LEGION

Attn: Department of Kansas
1314 S.W. Topeka Boulevard
Topeka, KS 66612-1886
Tel: (785)232-9315
Fax: (785)232-1399
Web Site: http://www.ksamlegion.org/programs.htm

To provide financial assistance for college to the children of members of the Kansas American Legion or American Legion Auxiliary.

Title of Award: Rosedale Post 346 Scholarship Fund **Area, Field, or Subject:** General studies/Field of study not specified **Level of Education for which Award is Granted:** Undergraduate **Number Awarded:** 2 each year. **Funds Available:** The stipend is $1,500. **Duration:** 1 year; nonrenewable.

Eligibility Requirements: Applicants must be high school seniors who plan to attend an approved Kansas college, university, junior college, or trade school; freshmen or sophomores at those schools are also eligible. At least 1 of their parents must be a veteran and a member of an American Legion post or Auxiliary in Kansas for at least 3 consecutive years. Along with their application, they must submit an essay of 250 to 500 words on "Why I Want to Go to College." Financial need is also considered in the selection process. **Deadline for Receipt:** February of each year.

177 ■ AMERICAN LEGION

Attn: Americanism and Children & Youth Division
P.O. Box 1055
Indianapolis, IN 46206-1055
Tel: (317)630-1249
Fax: (317)630-1223
E-mail: acy@legion.org
Web Site: http://www.legion.org

To provide financial assistance for college to children and grandchildren of veterans who participate in Girls State or Boys State.

Title of Award: Samsung American Legion Scholarships **Area, Field, or Subject:** General studies/Field of study not specified **Level of Education for which Award is Granted:** Undergraduate **Number Awarded:** Varies each year; recently, 7 scholarships at $20,000 and 91 at $1,000 were awarded. **Funds Available:** Stipends are $20,000 or $1,000. **Duration:** 4 years.

Eligibility Requirements: This program is open to students entering their senior year of high school who are selected to participate in Girls State or Boys State, sponsored by the American Legion Auxiliary or American Legion in their state. If they are also the child, grandchild, or great-grandchild of a veteran who saw active-duty service during World War I, World War II, Korea, Vietnam, Lebanon/Grenada, Panama, or the Persian Gulf War, they are eligible for these scholarships. Finalists are chosen at each participating Girls and Boys State, and they are then nominated for the national awards. Selection is based on academic record, community service, involvement in school and community activities, and financial need. Special consideration is given to descendants of U.S. veterans of the Korean War. **Additional Information:** These scholarships were first presented in 1996, following a gift in July 1995 to the American Legion from Samsung Corporation of Korea, as an act of appreciation for U.S. involvement in the Korean War.

178 ■ AMERICAN LEGION

Attn: Department of Wisconsin
Attn: Scholarship Chairperson
2930 American Legion Drive
P.O. Box 388
Portage, WI 53901-0388
Tel: (608)745-1090
Fax: (608)745-0179
E-mail: info@wilegion.org
Web Site: http://www.wilegion.org/scholarships/
schneider_emanuel_scholarship_body.htm

To provide financial assistance for college to members of the American Legion in Wisconsin and their children.

Title of Award: Schneider-Emanuel American Legion Scholarships **Area, Field, or Subject:** General studies/Field of study not specified **Level of Education for which Award is Granted:** Undergraduate **Number Awarded:** 3 each year. **Funds Available:** The stipend is $1,000. **Duration:** 1 year.

Eligibility Requirements: This program is open to seniors and graduates from accredited Wisconsin high schools. Applicants must be at least 1 of the following 1) a child whose father, mother, or legal guardian is a member of the Department of Wisconsin of the American Legion, American Legion Auxiliary, or Sons of the American Legion; 2) a grandchild whose grandfather, grandmother, or legal guardian is a member of the Department of Wisconsin of the American Legion, American Legion Auxiliary, or Sons of the American Legion; 3) a member of the Sons of the American Legion, American Legion Auxiliary, or Junior American Legion Auxiliary; or 4) a veteran and an American Legion member in Wisconsin. They must have participated in Legion and Auxiliary youth programs. Selection is based on moral character, scholastic excellence (GPA of 3.0 or higher), participation in American Legion activities, and general extracurricular activities. **Deadline for Receipt:** February of each year. **Additional Information:** Recipients must have graduated from an accredited Wisconsin high school but may attend a college or university anywhere in the United States.

179 ■ AMERICAN LEGION

Attn: Department of South Dakota
P.O. Box 67
Watertown, SD 57201-0067
Tel: (605)886-3604
Fax: (605)886-2870
E-mail: sdlegion@dailypost.com

To provide loans for college to children of South Dakota veterans.

Title of Award: South Dakota Legion Educational Loan **Area, Field, or Subject:** General studies/Field of study not specified **Level of Education for which Award is Granted:** Undergraduate **Funds Available:** Loans are available up to $1,500 per year. Repayment begins 90 days after the student leaves school, with interest at 3%. **Duration:** 1 year; the lifetime maximum that may be borrowed is $3,000.

Eligibility Requirements: Applicants must be the children of South Dakota veteran residents and interested in attending a South Dakota college or vocational school.

180 ■ AMERICAN LEGION

Attn: Department of New Jersey
Attn: Scholarship Judges
135 West Hanover Street
Trenton, NJ 08618
Tel: (609)695-5418
Fax: (609)394-1532
E-mail: newjersey@legion.org
Web Site: http://www.nj.legion.org

To provide financial assistance for college to the children of members of the American Legion's New Jersey Department.

Title of Award: Stutz Memorial Scholarship **Area, Field, or Subject:** General studies/Field of study not specified **Level of Education for which Award is Granted:** Undergraduate **Number Awarded:** 1 each year. **Funds Available:** The stipend is $1,000 per year. **Duration:** 4 years.

Eligibility Requirements: This program is open to graduating high school seniors who are the natural or adopted children of members of the American Legion's New Jersey Department. Selection is based on character (20%), Americanism (20%), leadership (20%), scholarship (20%), and financial need (20%). **Deadline for Receipt:** February of each year.

181 ■ AMERICAN LEGION
Attn: Department of North Dakota
722 First Avenue North
Fargo, ND 58102
Tel: (701)293-3120
Fax: (701)293-9951
E-mail: adjutant@ndlegion.org
Web Site: http://www.ndlegion.org
To provide financial assistance for college to high school seniors in North Dakota who are direct descendants of veterans.
Title of Award: Hattie Tedrow Memorial Fund Scholarship **Area, Field, or Subject:** General studies/Field of study not specified **Level of Education for which Award is Granted:** Undergraduate **Number Awarded:** 1 each year. **Funds Available:** The stipend is $2,000. **Duration:** 1 year; nonrenewable.
Eligibility Requirements: This program is open to college bound seniors graduating from high schools in North Dakota. Applicants must be the children, grandchildren, or great-grandchildren of veterans who served honorably in the U.S. armed forces. **Additional Information:** Information is also available from the American Legion, Attn: Hattie Tedrow Memorial Fund Scholarship, P.O. Box 1055, Indianapolis, IN 46206.

182 ■ AMERICAN LEGION
Attn: Department of Tennessee
215 Eighth Avenue North
Nashville, TN 37203-3583
Tel: (615)254-0568
Fax: (615)255-1551
E-mail: tnamerleg@datatek.com
To provide financial assistance for college to outstanding Eagle Scouts in Tennessee.
Title of Award: Tennessee Legion Eagle Scout of the Year Scholarship **Area, Field, or Subject:** General studies/Field of study not specified **Level of Education for which Award is Granted:** Undergraduate **Number Awarded:** 1 each year. **Funds Available:** The award is $1,500. **Duration:** 1 year.
Eligibility Requirements: The Tennessee nominee for American Legion Scout of the Year receives this scholarship. Applicants must be 1) registered, active members of a Boy Scout Troop or Varsity Scout Team sponsored by an American Legion Post in Tennessee or Auxiliary Unit in Tennessee, or 2) registered, active members of a duly chartered Boy Scout Troop or Varsity Scout Team and the sons or grandsons of American Legion or Auxiliary members. Candidates must also 1) be active members of their religious institution and have received the appropriate religious emblem; 2) have demonstrated practical citizenship in church, school, Scouting, and community; 3) be at least 15 years of age and enrolled in high school. **Additional Information:** Funds may be used to attend any postsecondary institution in the United States.

183 ■ AMERICAN LEGION
Attn: Department of Vermont
P.O. Box 396
Montpelier, VT 05601-0396
Tel: (802)223-7131
Fax: (802)223-7131
E-mail: alvt@adelphia.net
To provide financial assistance for college to outstanding Eagle Scouts in Vermont.
Title of Award: Vermont American Legion Eagle Scout of the Year Scholarship **Area, Field, or Subject:** General studies/Field of study not specified **Level of Education for which Award is Granted:** Undergraduate **Number Awarded:** 1 each year. **Funds Available:** The award is $1,000. **Duration:** 1 year.
Eligibility Requirements: The Vermont nominee for American Legion Scout of the Year receives this scholarship. Applicants must be either 1) registered, active members of a Boy Scout Troop or Varsity Scout Team sponsored by an American Legion Post in Vermont or Auxiliary Unit in Vermont, or 2) registered, active members of a duly chartered Boy Scout Troop or Varsity Scout Team and the sons or grandsons of American

Legion or Auxiliary members. They must be active members of their religious institution; have received the appropriate religious emblem; have demonstrated practical citizenship in church, school, Scouting, and community; have received the Eagle Scout award; be between 15 and 19 years of age; and be enrolled in high school. **Deadline for Receipt:** February of each year.

184 ■ AMERICAN LEGION
Attn: Department of Washington
3600 Ruddell Road S.E.
P.O. Box 3917
Lacey, WA 98509-3917
Tel: (360)491-4373
Fax: (360)491-7442
E-mail: tomal@qwest.net
Web Site: http://www.walegion.org
To provide financial assistance for college to the children of members of the American Legion or American Legion Auxiliary in Washington.
Title of Award: Washington Legion Children and Youth Scholarships **Area, Field, or Subject:** General studies/Field of study not specified **Level of Education for which Award is Granted:** Undergraduate **Number Awarded:** 2 each year: 1 at $2,500 and 1 at $1,500. **Funds Available:** The scholarships are either $2,500 or $1,500, payable in equal amounts per semester. **Duration:** 1 year.
Eligibility Requirements: Applicants must be the sons or daughters of Washington Legionnaires or Auxiliary members, living or deceased, who are high school seniors in need of financial assistance to attend an accredited institution of higher education, trade, or vocational school in the state of Washington. **Deadline for Receipt:** March of each year.

185 ■ AMERICAN LEGION
Attn: Department of Wisconsin
Attn: Scholarship Chairperson
2930 American Legion Drive
P.O. Box 388
Portage, WI 53901-0388
Tel: (608)745-1090
Fax: (608)745-0179
E-mail: info@wilegion.org
Web Site: http://www.wilegion.org/scholarships/
eagle_scout_award_body.htm
To provide financial assistance for college to outstanding Boy Scouts in Wisconsin.
Title of Award: Wisconsin American Legion Eagle Scout of the Year **Area, Field, or Subject:** General studies/Field of study not specified **Level of Education for which Award is Granted:** Undergraduate **Number Awarded:** 1 each year. **Funds Available:** The state award is a $1,000 scholarship. **Duration:** 1 year.
Eligibility Requirements: The Wisconsin nominee for American Legion Scout of the Year receives this scholarship. Applicants must be 1) a registered, active members of a Boy Scout Troop, Varsity Scout Team, or Explorer Post chartered to an American Legion Post in Wisconsin or Auxiliary Unit in Wisconsin, or 2) a registered, active member of a Boy Scout Troop, Varsity Scout Team, or Venturing Crew and the son or grandson of an American Legion or Auxiliary member. They must have received the Eagle Scout award; be an active member of their religious institution and have received the appropriate Boy Scout religious emblem; have demonstrated practical citizenship in church, school, Scouting, and community; have reached their 15th birthday; and be enrolled in high school. **Deadline for Receipt:** February of each year.

186 ■ AMERICAN LEGION
Attn: Department of Wisconsin
Attn: Scholarship Chairperson
2930 American Legion Drive
P.O. Box 388
Portage, WI 53901-0388
Tel: (608)745-1090
Fax: (608)745-0179
E-mail: info@wilegion.org
Web Site: http://www.wilegion.org/scholarships/shooting_sports_body.htm
To provide financial assistance for college to outstanding participants in the American Legion air rifle program in Wisconsin.
Title of Award: Wisconsin American Legion Shooting Sports Scholarship **Area, Field, or Subject:** General studies/Field of study not specified

Level of Education for which Award is Granted: Undergraduate **Number Awarded:** 1 each year. **Funds Available:** The award is a $1,000 scholarship.

Eligibility Requirements: Candidates must have participated in the current American Legion regional or Wisconsin state championship, junior position air rifle tournament. **Deadline for Receipt:** May of each year.

187 ■ AMERICAN LEGION AUXILIARY

Attn: Department of Illinois
2720 East Lincoln Street
P.O. Box 1426
Bloomington, IL 61702-1426
Tel: (309)663-9366
Fax: (309)663-5827
E-mail: ilala@ilala.org
Web Site: http://illegion.org/auxiliary/scholar.html
To provide financial assistance for college to the children of Illinois veterans.

Title of Award: Ada Mucklestone Memorial Scholarships **Area, Field, or Subject:** General studies/Field of study not specified **Level of Education for which Award is Granted:** Undergraduate **Number Awarded:** Varies each year. **Funds Available:** The first winner receives a scholarship of $1,200, the second winner a scholarship of $1,000, and several other winners each receive $800. **Duration:** 1 year.

Eligibility Requirements: Eligible to apply for these scholarships are Illinois residents. Applicants must be the children or grandchildren of veterans who served during eligibility dates for membership in the American Legion. They must be high school seniors or high school graduates who have not yet attended an institution of higher learning. They must be sponsored by their local American Legion Auxiliary unit. Winners are selected on the basis of character, Americanism, leadership, scholarship, and need. **Deadline for Receipt:** March of each year.

188 ■ AMERICAN LEGION AUXILIARY

Attn: Department of Alaska
Secretary/Treasurer
1392 Sixth Avenue
Fairbanks, AK 99701
Tel: (907)455-4420
Fax: (907)474-3040
E-mail: akaladep@ptialaska.net
Web Site: http://www.alada.net
To provide financial assistance for college to veterans' children in Alaska.

Title of Award: Alaska Legion Auxiliary Scholarship **Area, Field, or Subject:** General studies/Field of study not specified **Level of Education for which Award is Granted:** Undergraduate **Number Awarded:** 1 each year. **Funds Available:** The stipend is $1,000, half of which is payable each semester toward tuition, matriculation, laboratory, or similar fees. **Duration:** 1 year.

Eligibility Requirements: This program is open to the children of veterans who served during eligibility dates for membership in the American Legion. Applicants must be between 17 and 24 years of age, high school seniors or graduates who have not yet attended an institution of higher learning, and residents of Alaska. **Deadline for Receipt:** March of each year.

189 ■ AMERICAN LEGION AUXILIARY

Attn: Department of Arkansas
1415 West Seventh Street
Little Rock, AR 72201-2903
Tel: (501)374-5836
E-mail: arkaux@juno.com
To provide financial assistance for college to children of veterans who are residents of Arkansas.

Title of Award: American Legion Auxiliary Department of Arkansas Academic Scholarship **Area, Field, or Subject:** General studies/Field of study not specified **Level of Education for which Award is Granted:** Undergraduate **Number Awarded:** 1 each year. **Funds Available:** The stipend is $1,000; funds are paid in 2 equal installments. **Duration:** 1 year.

Eligibility Requirements: Eligible to apply for this scholarship are children of veterans in Arkansas who served during eligibility dates for membership in the American Legion. Both the student and the parent

must be residents of Arkansas. The student must be a high school senior or graduate who has not yet attended an institution of higher learning. Selection is based on character (15%), Americanism (15%), leadership (15%), financial need (15%), and scholarship (40%). **Deadline for Receipt:** February of each year.

190 ■ AMERICAN LEGION AUXILIARY

777 North Meridian Street, Third Floor
Indianapolis, IN 46204-1189
Tel: (317)955-3845
Fax: (317)955-3884
E-mail: alahq@legion-aux.org
Web Site: http://www.legion-aux.org/AboutUs/AuxiliaryPrograms/index.aspx
To provide funding to members of the American Legion Auxiliary who are facing temporary emergency needs.

Title of Award: American Legion Auxiliary Emergency Fund **Area, Field, or Subject:** General studies/Field of study not specified **Level of Education for which Award is Granted:** Undergraduate, Other **Number Awarded:** Varies each year. **Funds Available:** The maximum grant is $2,400. Payments may be made directly to the member or to the mortgage company or utility. Educational grants may be paid directly to the educational institution. **Duration:** Grants are expended over no more than 3 months.

Eligibility Requirements: This program is open to members of the American Legion Auxiliary who have maintained their membership for the immediate past 2 consecutive years and have paid their dues for the current year. Applicants must need emergency assistance for the following purposes: 1) food, shelter, and utilities during a time of financial crisis; 2) food and shelter for victims of weather-related emergencies and natural disasters; or 3) educational training for members who, because of changes in their life (such as death of a spouse, divorce, or separation), have become the main source of support for their family. They must have exhausted all other sources of financial assistance, including funds and/or services available through the local Post and/or Unit, appropriate community welfare agencies, or state and federal financial aid for education. Grants are not available to settle already existing or accumulated debts, handle catastrophic illness, resettle disaster victims, or other similar problems. **Deadline for Receipt:** Applications may be submitted at any time. **Additional Information:** This program was established in 1969. In 1981, it was expanded to include the Displaced Homemaker Fund (although that term is no longer used).

191 ■ AMERICAN LEGION AUXILIARY

777 North Meridian Street, Third Floor
Indianapolis, IN 46204-1189
Tel: (317)955-3845
Fax: (317)955-3884
E-mail: alahq@legion-aux.org
Web Site: http://www.legion-aux.org/Scholarships/NationalPresident/index.aspx
To provide financial assistance for college to the children of war veterans.

Title of Award: American Legion Auxiliary National President's Scholarship **Area, Field, or Subject:** General studies/Field of study not specified **Level of Education for which Award is Granted:** Undergraduate **Number Awarded:** 15 each year: in each of the 5 divisions of the Auxiliary, 1 scholarship at $2,500, 1 at $2,000, and 1 at $1,000 are awarded. **Funds Available:** Stipends are $2,500, $2,000, or $1,000. Funds are paid directly to the recipient's school. **Duration:** 1 year; recipients may not reapply.

Eligibility Requirements: This program is open to children of veterans who served in World War I, World War II, Korea, Vietnam, Grenada, Lebanon, Panama, or the Persian Gulf. Applicants must be high school seniors who have completed at least 50 hours of volunteer service within the community. Each Department (state) organization of the American Legion Auxiliary nominates 1 candidate for the National President's Scholarship annually. Nominees must submit a 1,000-word essay on a topic that changes annually; recently, students were asked to write on "My Role in Sustaining Our Freedoms." Selection is based on the essay (20%), character and leadership (20%), scholarship, (40%), and financial need (20%). **Deadline for Receipt:** March of each year. **Additional Information:** Applications are available from the local Unit or from the Department Secretary or Department Education Chair of the state in which the applicant resides.

192 ■ AMERICAN LEGION AUXILIARY

777 North Meridian Street, Third Floor
Indianapolis, IN 46204-1189
Tel: (317)955-3845
Fax: (317)955-3884
E-mail: alahq@legion-aux.org
Web Site: http://www.legion-aux.org/Scholarships/NonTraditionalStudent/index.aspx
To provide financial assistance for college to nontraditional students affiliated with the American Legion.

Title of Award: American Legion Auxiliary Non-Traditional Student Scholarships **Area, Field, or Subject:** General studies/Field of study not specified **Level of Education for which Award is Granted:** Undergraduate **Number Awarded:** 5 each year: 1 in each division of the American Legion Auxiliary. **Funds Available:** The scholarship is $1,000 per year, paid directly to the school. **Duration:** 1 year.

Eligibility Requirements: This program is open to members of the American Legion, American Legion Auxiliary, or Sons of the American Legion who have paid dues for the 2 preceding years and the calendar year in which application is being made. Applicants must be 1) nontraditional students returning to school after some period of time during which their formal education was interrupted or 2) students who have had at least 1 year of college and are working on an undergraduate degree. Along with their application, they must submit a statement explaining why they are entering college at this time, why their education was interrupted, and why they feel they should be selected for this scholarship. Selection is based on scholastic standing and academic achievement (25%), character and leadership (25%), initiative and goals (25%), and financial need (25%). **Deadline for Receipt:** Applications must be submitted to the unit president by March. **Additional Information:** Applications are available from the president of the candidate's own unit or from the secretary or education chair of the department.

193 ■ AMERICAN LEGION AUXILIARY

Attn: Department of New Hampshire
State House Annex
25 Capitol Street, Room 432
Concord, NH 03301-6312
Tel: (603)271-2212
Fax: (603)271-5352
E-mail: sankenj@comcast.net
To provide financial assistance for college to New Hampshire residents.

Title of Award: Marion J. Bagley Scholarship **Area, Field, or Subject:** General studies/Field of study not specified **Level of Education for which Award is Granted:** Undergraduate **Number Awarded:** 1 each year. **Funds Available:** The stipend is $1,000. **Duration:** 1 year.

Eligibility Requirements: This program is open to New Hampshire residents who are high school seniors, high school graduates or equivalent, or attending a school of higher learning. Applicants must submit 3 letters of recommendation; a list of school, church, and community activities or organizations in which they have participated; transcripts; and a 1,000-word essay on "My obligations as an American." Financial need is considered in the selection process. **Deadline for Receipt:** April of each year. **Additional Information:** Requests for applications must be accompanied by a self-addressed stamped envelope.

194 ■ AMERICAN LEGION AUXILIARY

Attn: Department of Virginia
1708 Commonwealth Avenue
Richmond, VA 23230
Tel: (804)355-6410
Fax: (804)353-1940
To provide financial assistance for college to Virginia residents who are children of veterans or of members of the American Legion Auxiliary.

Title of Award: Dr. Kate Waller Barrett Grant **Area, Field, or Subject:** General studies/Field of study not specified **Level of Education for which Award is Granted:** Undergraduate **Number Awarded:** 1 each year. **Funds Available:** The stipend is $1,000. **Duration:** 1 year.

Eligibility Requirements: This program is open to the children of veterans or of members of the American Legion Auxiliary who are high school seniors in Virginia planning to attend an accredited educational institution in the state. Along with their application, they must submit a 500-word essay on their responsibilities as a citizen of the United States.

Selection is based on citizenship (20%), leadership (20%), scholarship (40%), and financial need (20%). **Deadline for Receipt:** March of each year.

195 ■ AMERICAN LEGION AUXILIARY

Attn: Department of Kentucky
105 North Public Square
P.O. Box 189
Greensburg, KY 42743-1530
Tel: (270)932-7533
Fax: (270)932-7672
E-mail: secretarykyala@aol.com
To provide financial assistance for college to descendants of veterans in Kentucky.

Title of Award: Laura Blackburn Memorial Scholarship **Area, Field, or Subject:** General studies/Field of study not specified **Level of Education for which Award is Granted:** Undergraduate **Number Awarded:** 1 each year. **Funds Available:** The stipend is $1,000. **Duration:** 1 year.

Eligibility Requirements: This program is open to the children, grandchildren, and great-grandchildren of veterans who served in the armed forces during eligibility dates for membership in the American Legion. Applicants must be Kentucky residents enrolled in their senior year at an accredited high school. **Deadline for Receipt:** March of each year. **Additional Information:** Further information is also available from the Education Chair, Michelle Elmore, 1166 Blanton Road, New Haven, KY 40051, E-mail: melmore@bardstown.com.

196 ■ AMERICAN LEGION AUXILIARY

Attn: Department of California
Veterans War Memorial Building
401 Van Ness Avenue, Room 113
San Francisco, CA 94102-4586
Tel: (415)861-5092
Fax: (415)861-8365
E-mail: calegionaux@calegionaux.org
Web Site: http://www.calegionaux.org/scholarships.html
To provide financial assistance to California residents who are the children of veterans and require assistance to continue their education.

Title of Award: California Legion Auxiliary Educational Assistance **Area, Field, or Subject:** General studies/Field of study not specified **Level of Education for which Award is Granted:** Undergraduate **Number Awarded:** 11 each year: 1 at $1,000 that may be renewed, 5 at $1,000 that are nonrenewable, and 5 at $500 that are nonrenewable. **Funds Available:** Stipends are $1,000 or $500 per year. **Duration:** 1 year; 1 of the scholarships may be renewed 1 additional year.

Eligibility Requirements: This program is open to California residents who are the children of veterans of World War I, World War II, Korea, Vietnam, Grenada/Lebanon, Panama, or Desert Shield/Desert Storm. Applicants must be high school seniors or graduates planning to continue their education at a college, university, or business/trade school in California. Financial need is considered in the selection process. Each high school in California may nominate only 1 student for these scholarships; the faculty selects the nominee if more than 1 student wishes to apply. Selection is based on financial need (30%), character (20%), scholastic merit (20%), Americanism (20%), and leadership (10%). **Deadline for Receipt:** March of each year.

197 ■ AMERICAN LEGION AUXILIARY

Attn: Department of California
Veterans War Memorial Building
401 Van Ness Avenue, Room 113
San Francisco, CA 94102-4586
Tel: (415)861-5092
Fax: (415)861-8365
E-mail: calegionaux@calegionaux.org
Web Site: http://www.calegionaux.org/scholarships.html
To provide financial assistance for college to the daughters of California veterans who are active in the American Legion Junior Auxiliary.

Title of Award: California Legion Auxiliary Past Department President's Junior Scholarship **Area, Field, or Subject:** General studies/Field of study not specified **Level of Education for which Award is Granted:** Undergraduate **Number Awarded:** 1 each year. **Funds Available:** The stipend depends on the availability of funds but ranges from $300 to $1,000. **Duration:** 1 year.

Eligibility Requirements: This program is open to the daughters, grand-daughters, and great-granddaughters of veterans who served in World War I, World War II, Korea, Vietnam, Grenada/Lebanon, Panama, or Desert Shield/Desert Storm. Applicants must be in their senior year at an accredited high school, must have been members of the Junior Auxiliary for at least 3 consecutive years, and must be residents of California (if eligibility for Junior Auxiliary membership is by a current member of the American Legion or Auxiliary in California, the applicant may reside elsewhere). Selection is based on scholastic merit (20%); active participation in Junior Auxiliary (15%); record of service or volunteerism within the applicant's community, school, and/or unit (35%); a brief description of the applicant's desire to pursue a higher education (15%); and 3 letters of reference (15%). **Deadline for Receipt:** April of each year. **Additional Information:** The recipient must attend college in California.

198 ■ AMERICAN LEGION AUXILIARY

Attn: Department of California
Veterans War Memorial Building
401 Van Ness Avenue, Room 113
San Francisco, CA 94102-4586
Tel: (415)861-5092
Fax: (415)861-8365
E-mail: calegionaux@calegionaux.org
Web Site: http://www.calegionaux.org/scholarships.html
To provide financial assistance to California residents who are the children of veterans and require assistance to continue their education.
Title of Award: California Legion Auxiliary Scholarships for Continuing and/or Reentry Students **Area, Field, or Subject:** General studies/Field of study not specified **Level of Education for which Award is Granted:** Undergraduate **Number Awarded:** 2 each year. **Funds Available:** The stipend is $1,000. **Duration:** 1 year.
Eligibility Requirements: This program is open to California residents who are the children of veterans of World War I, World War II, Korea, Vietnam, Grenada/Lebanon, Panama, or Desert Shield/Desert Storm. Applicants must be continuing or reentry students at a college, university, or business/trade school in California. Financial need is considered in the selection process. **Deadline for Receipt:** March of each year.

199 ■ AMERICAN LEGION AUXILIARY

Attn: Department of Florida
1912 Lee Road
P.O. Box 547917
Orlando, FL 32854-7917
Tel: (407)293-7411
Fax: (407)299-6522
E-mail: alaflorida@aol.com
To provide financial assistance for college to the children of Florida veterans.
Title of Award: Florida Legion Auxiliary Department Scholarship **Area, Field, or Subject:** General studies/Field of study not specified **Level of Education for which Award is Granted:** Undergraduate **Number Awarded:** Varies each year, depending on the availability of funds. **Funds Available:** The stipends are up to $1,000 for a 4-year university or up to $500 for a junior college or technical-vocational school. All funds are paid directly to the institution. **Duration:** 1 year; may be renewed if the recipient needs further financial assistance and has maintained a GPA of 2.5 or higher.
Eligibility Requirements: This program is open to children of honorably-discharged veterans who are Florida residents. Applicants must be attending a postsecondary school in the state on a full-time basis. **Deadline for Receipt:** December of each year.

200 ■ AMERICAN LEGION AUXILIARY

Attn: Department of Florida
1912 Lee Road
P.O. Box 547917
Orlando, FL 32854-7917
Tel: (407)293-7411
Fax: (407)299-6522
E-mail: alaflorida@aol.com
To provide financial assistance for college to members and female dependents of members of the Florida American Legion Auxiliary.
Title of Award: Florida Legion Auxiliary Memorial Scholarship **Area, Field, or Subject:** General studies/Field of study not specified **Level of**

Education for which Award is Granted: Undergraduate **Number Awarded:** Varies each year, depending on the availability of funds. **Funds Available:** The stipends are up to $1,000 for a 4-year university or up to $500 for a junior college or technical-vocational school. All funds are paid directly to the institution. **Duration:** 1 year; may be renewed if the recipient needs further financial assistance and has maintained at least a 2.5 GPA.
Eligibility Requirements: Applicants must be members of the Florida Auxiliary or daughters or granddaughters of members who have at least 3 years of continuous membership. They must be sponsored by their local units, be Florida residents, and be attending Florida schools. Selection is based on academic record and financial need. **Deadline for Receipt:** December of each year. **Additional Information:** Recipients must attend a Florida college, university, or technical school. All awards are for full-time study and are to be used for 2 semesters of the school year.

201 ■ AMERICAN LEGION AUXILIARY

Attn: Department of Virginia
1708 Commonwealth Avenue
Richmond, VA 23230
Tel: (804)355-6410
Fax: (804)353-1940
To provide financial assistance for college to junior members of the American Legion Auxiliary in Virginia.
Title of Award: Anna Gear Junior Scholarship **Area, Field, or Subject:** General studies/Field of study not specified **Level of Education for which Award is Granted:** Undergraduate **Number Awarded:** 1 each year. **Funds Available:** The stipend is $1,000. **Duration:** 1 year.
Eligibility Requirements: This program is open to seniors at accredited high schools in Virginia. Applicants must have held junior membership in the American Legion Auxiliary for the 3 previous years. They must have completed at least 30 hours of volunteer service within their community and submit a 500-word article on "The Value of Volunteering in the Community." **Deadline for Receipt:** March of each year.

202 ■ AMERICAN LEGION AUXILIARY

Attn: Department of Georgia
3035 Mt. Zion Road
Stockbridge, GA 30281-4101
Tel: (678)289-8446
E-mail: amlegaux@bellsouth.net
To provide financial assistance for college to the children of Georgia veterans.
Title of Award: Georgia Legion Auxiliary Past Department Presidents Scholarship **Area, Field, or Subject:** General studies/Field of study not specified **Level of Education for which Award is Granted:** Undergraduate **Number Awarded:** 2 each year. **Funds Available:** The stipend is $1,000. **Duration:** 1 year.
Eligibility Requirements: This program is open to residents of Georgia who are high school seniors and children of veterans. Preference is given to children of deceased veterans. Applicants must be sponsored by a local unit of the American Legion Auxiliary in Georgia. Selection is based on a statement explaining why they want to further their education and their need for a scholarship. **Deadline for Receipt:** May of each year.

203 ■ AMERICAN LEGION AUXILIARY

777 North Meridian Street, Third Floor
Indianapolis, IN 46204-1189
Tel: (317)955-3845
Fax: (317)955-3884
E-mail: alahq@legion-aux.org
Web Site: http://www.legion-aux.org/Scholarships/GirlScoutAward/index.aspx
To provide financial assistance for college to members of the Girl Scouts.
Title of Award: Girl Scout Achievement Award **Area, Field, or Subject:** General studies/Field of study not specified **Level of Education for which Award is Granted:** Undergraduate **Number Awarded:** 1 each year. **Funds Available:** The stipend is $1,000. **Duration:** 1 year; the award must be utilized within 1 year of high school graduation.
Eligibility Requirements: Candidates must belong to the Girl Scouts; have received the Gold Award; be an active member of a religious institution (and have received the appropriate religious emblem); have demonstrated practical citizenship in her religious institution, school,

Scouting, and community; and submit at least 4 letters of recommendation, with 1 letter required from each of the following group leaders: religious institution, school, community, and Scouting. Candidates must be nominated at the local level; those selected at the state level compete at the national level. **Deadline for Receipt:** Local nominations must be submitted no later than February of each year. **Additional Information:** The scholarship must be used to attend an accredited school in the United States.

204 ■ AMERICAN LEGION AUXILIARY

Attn: Department of New York
112 State Street, Suite 1310
Albany, NY 12207
Tel: (518)463-1162
Free: 800-421-6348
Fax: (518)449-5406
E-mail: alanyhdqtrs@worldnet.att.net
Web Site: http://www.deptny.org/Scholarships.htm
To provide financial assistance for college to New York residents who are the children or grandchildren of veterans.

Title of Award: Helen Klimek Student Scholarship **Area, Field, or Subject:** General studies/Field of study not specified **Level of Education for which Award is Granted:** Undergraduate **Number Awarded:** 1 each year. **Funds Available:** The stipend is $1,000. **Duration:** 1 year.
Eligibility Requirements: This program is open to residents of New York who are the children grandchildren, or great grandchildren of veterans of World War II, the Korean Conflict, the Vietnam War, Grenada/Lebanon, Panama, or the Persian Gulf. Applicants must be high school seniors or graduates younger than 20 years of age. They must be interested in attending an accredited college or university. Along with their application they must submit a 700-word statement on the significance or value of volunteerism as a resource towards the positive development of the applicant's personal and professional future. Selection is based on character (20%), Americanism (15%), volunteer involvement (20%), leadership (15%), scholarship (15%), and financial need (15%). **Deadline for Receipt:** February of each year.

205 ■ AMERICAN LEGION AUXILIARY

Attn: Department of Illinois
2720 East Lincoln Street
P.O. Box 1426
Bloomington, IL 61702-1426
Tel: (309)663-9366
Fax: (309)663-5827
E-mail: ilala@ilala.org
Web Site: http://illegion.org/auxiliary/scholar.html
To provide financial assistance for college or graduate school to Illinois veterans and their children.

Title of Award: Mildred R. Knoles Opportunity Scholarships **Area, Field, or Subject:** General studies/Field of study not specified **Level of Education for which Award is Granted:** Graduate, Undergraduate **Number Awarded:** Varies; each year 1 scholarship at $1,200 and several at $800 are awarded. **Funds Available:** Stipends are $1,200 or $800. **Duration:** 1 year.
Eligibility Requirements: Eligible to apply for these scholarships are veterans or children and grandchildren of veterans of World War I, World War II, Korea, Vietnam, Grenada/Lebanon, Panama, or Desert Storm who have begun college but need financial assistance to complete their college or graduate education. Applicants must have resided in Illinois for at least 3 years prior to application. Selection is based on character, Americanism, leadership, financial need, and academic record. **Deadline for Receipt:** March of each year. **Additional Information:** Applications may be obtained only from a local unit of the American Legion Auxiliary.

206 ■ AMERICAN LEGION AUXILIARY

Attn: Department of New York
112 State Street, Suite 1310
Albany, NY 12207
Tel: (518)463-1162
Free: 800-421-6348
Fax: (518)449-5406
E-mail: alanyhdqtrs@worldnet.att.net
Web Site: http://www.deptny.org/Scholarships.htm

To provide financial assistance for college to members of the American Legion Auxiliary in New York.

Title of Award: First Lieutenant Michael L. Lewis, Jr. Memorial Fund Scholarship **Area, Field, or Subject:** General studies/Field of study not specified **Level of Education for which Award is Granted:** Undergraduate **Number Awarded:** 2 each year: 1 to a junior member and 1 to a senior member. If no senior members apply, both scholarships are awarded to junior members. **Funds Available:** The stipend is $1,000. **Duration:** 1 year.
Eligibility Requirements: This program is open to 1) junior members of the New York Department of the American Legion Auxiliary who are high school seniors or graduates younger than 20 years of age; and 2) senior members who are continuing their education to further their studies or update their job skills. Applicants must submit a 200-word essay on "Why a college education is important to me," or "Why I want to continue my post high school education in a business or trade school." Selection is based on character (25%), Americanism (25%), leadership (25%), and scholarship (25%). **Deadline for Receipt:** March of each year.

207 ■ AMERICAN LEGION AUXILIARY

Attn: Department of Wisconsin
2930 American Legion Drive
P.O. Box 140
Portage, WI 53901-0140
Tel: (608)745-0124; (866)664-3863
Fax: (608)745-1947
E-mail: alawi@amlegionauxwi.org
Web Site: http://www.amlegionauxwi.org
To provide financial assistance for undergraduate or graduate study to Wisconsin residents who are related to veterans or members of the American Legion Auxiliary.

Title of Award: H.S. and Angeline Lewis Scholarships **Area, Field, or Subject:** General studies/Field of study not specified **Level of Education for which Award is Granted:** Graduate, Undergraduate **Number Awarded:** 6 each year: 1 to a graduate student and 5 to undergraduates. **Funds Available:** The stipend is $1,000. **Duration:** 1 year; nonrenewable.
Eligibility Requirements: This program is open to the children, wives, and widows of veterans who are high school seniors or graduates with a GPA of 3.2 or higher. Granddaughters as well as great-granddaughters of veterans are eligible if they are members of the American Legion Auxiliary. Applicants must be able to demonstrate financial need, be interested in working on an undergraduate or graduate degree, and be residents of Wisconsin. They do not need to attend a college in the state. Along with their application, they must submit a 300-word essay on "Education-An Investment in the Future." **Deadline for Receipt:** March of each year. **Additional Information:** Information is also available from the Education Chair, Renae Allen, 206 West Fremont Street, Darien, WI 53114-1540, (262) 724-5059.

208 ■ AMERICAN LEGION AUXILIARY

Attn: Department of Michigan
212 North Verlinden Street
Lansing, MI 48915
Tel: (517)371-4720
Fax: (517)371-2401
E-mail: michalaux@voyager.net
Web Site: http://www.michalaux.org/Scholarships.htm
To provide financial assistance for college to children of veterans in Michigan.

Title of Award: Michigan Legion Auxiliary National President's Scholarship **Area, Field, or Subject:** General studies/Field of study not specified **Level of Education for which Award is Granted:** Undergraduate **Number Awarded:** 1 each year. **Funds Available:** The stipend ranges from $1,000 to $2,500. **Duration:** 1 year.
Eligibility Requirements: This program is open to Michigan residents who are the children of veterans who served in World War I, World War II, Korea, Vietnam, Grenada/Lebanon, Panama, or Desert Shield/Desert Storm. Applicants must be in their senior year or graduates of an accredited high school and may not yet have attended an institution of higher learning. Selection is based on scholarship, character, leadership, Americanism, and financial need. The winner competes for the American Legion National President's Scholarship. If the Michigan winners are not

awarded the national scholarship, then they receive this departmental scholarship. **Deadline for Receipt:** March of each year.

209 ■ AMERICAN LEGION AUXILIARY

Attn: Department of New York
112 State Street, Suite 1310
Albany, NY 12207
Tel: (518)463-1162
Free: 800-421-6348
Fax: (518)449-5406
E-mail: alanyhdqtrs@worldnet.att.net
Web Site: http://www.deptny.org/Scholarships.htm
To provide financial assistance for college to New York residents who are the descendants of veterans.
Title of Award: Maryann K. Murtha Memorial Scholarship **Area, Field, or Subject:** General studies/Field of study not specified **Level of Education for which Award is Granted:** Undergraduate **Number Awarded:** 1 each year. **Funds Available:** The stipend is $1,000. **Duration:** 1 year.
Eligibility Requirements: This program is open to residents of New York who are the children, grandchildren, or great grandchildren of veterans of World War II, the Korean Conflict, the Vietnam War, Grenada/Lebanon, Panama, or the Persian Gulf. Applicants must be high school seniors or graduates younger than 20 years of age. They must be interested in attending an accredited college or university. Along with their application, they must submit a 700-word article describing their plans and goals for the future and how they hope to use their talent and education to help others. Selection is based on character (20%), Americanism (15%), community involvement (15%), leadership (15%), scholarship (20%), and financial need (15%). **Deadline for Receipt:** March of each year.

210 ■ AMERICAN LEGION AUXILIARY

Attn: Department of New Jersey
c/o Lucille M. Miller, Secretary, Treasurer
1540 Kuser Road, Suite A-8
Hamilton, NJ 08619
Tel: (609)581-9580
Fax: (609)581-8429
To provide financial assistance for college to the children or grandchildren of veterans in New Jersey.
Title of Award: New Jersey Legion Auxiliary Department Scholarships **Area, Field, or Subject:** General studies/Field of study not specified **Level of Education for which Award is Granted:** Undergraduate **Number Awarded:** Several each year. **Funds Available:** The amount awarded varies, depending upon the needs of the recipient and the money available. **Duration:** 1 year.
Eligibility Requirements: This program is open to the children or grandchildren of honorably discharged veterans of the U.S. armed forces. Applicants must have resided in New Jersey for at least 2 years and be members of a New Jersey senior high school graduating class. **Deadline for Receipt:** March of each year.

211 ■ AMERICAN LEGION AUXILIARY

Attn: Department of New York
112 State Street, Suite 1310
Albany, NY 12207
Tel: (518)463-1162
Free: 800-421-6348
Fax: (518)449-5406
E-mail: alanyhdqtrs@worldnet.att.net
Web Site: http://www.deptny.org/Scholarships.htm
To provide financial assistance for college to New York residents who are the descendants of deceased veterans.
Title of Award: New York Legion Auxiliary Department Scholarship **Area, Field, or Subject:** General studies/Field of study not specified **Level of Education for which Award is Granted:** Undergraduate **Number Awarded:** 1 each year. **Funds Available:** The stipend is $1,000. **Duration:** 1 year.
Eligibility Requirements: This program is open to residents of New York who are the children, grandchildren, or great grandchildren of deceased veterans of World War I, World War II, the Korean Conflict, the Vietnam War, Grenada/Lebanon, Panama, or the Persian Gulf. Applicants must be high school seniors or graduates younger than 20 years of age. They must be interested in attending an accredited college or university. Along

with their application, they must submit a 500-word essay on a subject of their choice. Selection is based on character (20%), Americanism (20%), leadership (20%), scholarship (15%), and financial need (25%). **Deadline for Receipt:** February of each year.

212 ■ AMERICAN LEGION AUXILIARY

Attn: Department of New York
112 State Street, Suite 1310
Albany, NY 12207
Tel: (518)463-1162
Free: 800-421-6348
Fax: (518)449-5406
E-mail: alanyhdqtrs@worldnet.att.net
Web Site: http://www.deptny.org/Scholarships.htm
To provide financial assistance to descendants of veterans in New York who are interested in attending college.
Title of Award: New York Legion Auxiliary District Scholarships **Area, Field, or Subject:** General studies/Field of study not specified **Level of Education for which Award is Granted:** Undergraduate **Number Awarded:** 10 each year: 1 in each of the 10 judicial districts in New York state. **Funds Available:** The stipend is $1,000. **Duration:** 1 year.
Eligibility Requirements: This program is open to residents of New York who are the children, grandchildren, or great grandchildren of veterans (living or deceased) of World War I, World War II, the Korean Conflict, the Vietnam War, Grenada/Lebanon, Panama, or the Persian Gulf. Applicants must be high school seniors or graduates younger than 20 years of age. They must be interested in attending an accredited college or university. Along with their application they must submit a 500-word essay on "Why I choose to further my education." Selection is based on character (30%), Americanism (20%), leadership (10%), scholarship (20%), and financial need (20%). **Deadline for Receipt:** March of each year.

213 ■ AMERICAN LEGION AUXILIARY

Attn: Department of North Carolina
P.O. Box 25726
Raleigh, NC 27611-5726
Tel: (919)832-4051
Fax: (919)832-1888
E-mail: ala_nc@bellsouth.net
To provide financial assistance for college to members of the American Legion Auxiliary in North Carolina and their children and grandchildren.
Title of Award: Nannie W. Norfleet Scholarship **Area, Field, or Subject:** General studies/Field of study not specified **Level of Education for which Award is Granted:** Undergraduate **Number Awarded:** 1 each year. **Funds Available:** The stipend is $2,000 per year. **Duration:** 1 year.
Eligibility Requirements: This program is open to North Carolina residents who are either adult members of the American Legion Auxiliary or high school seniors (with preference to the children and grandchildren of members). Applicants must be able to demonstrate financial need. **Deadline for Receipt:** March of each year.

214 ■ AMERICAN LEGION AUXILIARY

Attn: Department of Ohio
1100 Brandywine Boulevard, Building D
P.O. Box 2760
Zanesville, OH 43702-2760
Tel: (740)452-8245
Fax: (740)452-2620
E-mail: ala_pam@rrohio.com
To provide financial assistance for college to the descendants of veterans in Ohio.
Title of Award: Ohio Legion Auxiliary Department Scholarship **Area, Field, or Subject:** General studies/Field of study not specified **Level of Education for which Award is Granted:** Undergraduate **Number Awarded:** 2 each year: 1 at $2,000 and 1 at $1,500. **Funds Available:** Awards are $2,000 or $1,500. Funds are paid to the recipient's school. **Duration:** 1 year.
Eligibility Requirements: This program is open to the children, grandchildren, and great-grandchildren of living or deceased veterans of World War I, World War II, Korea, Vietnam, Lebanon/Grenada, Panama, or Desert Storm. Applicants must be residents of Ohio, seniors at an accredited high school, and sponsored by an American Legion Auxiliary Unit. Applications must include an original article (up to 500 words) written

by the applicant on "What the American Flag Represents to Me." The winner is selected on the basis of character, Americanism, leadership, scholarship, and financial need. **Deadline for Receipt:** February of each year.

215 ■ AMERICAN LEGION AUXILIARY

Attn: Department of New Jersey
c/o Lucille M. Miller, Secretary, Treasurer
1540 Kuser Road, Suite A-8
Hamilton, NJ 08619
Tel: (609)581-9580
Fax: (609)581-8429
To provide financial assistance for college to New Jersey residents who are the children or grandchildren of veterans.

Title of Award: Claire Oliphant Memorial Scholarships **Area, Field, or Subject:** General studies/Field of study not specified **Level of Education for which Award is Granted:** Undergraduate **Number Awarded:** 1 each year. **Funds Available:** The stipend is $1,800. **Duration:** 1 year.

Eligibility Requirements: This program is open to the children and grandchildren of living, deceased, or divorced honorably-discharged veterans of the U.S. armed forces. Applicants must have been residents of New Jersey for at least 2 years and be members of the current graduating class of a senior high school or equivalent. **Deadline for Receipt:** March of each year. **Additional Information:** Rules and applications are distributed to all New Jersey senior high school guidance departments.

216 ■ AMERICAN LEGION AUXILIARY

Attn: Department of Oregon
30450 S.W. Parkway Avenue
P.O. Box 1730
Wilsonville, OR 97070-1730
Tel: (503)682-3162
Fax: (503)685-5008
E-mail: pcalhoun@pcez.com
To provide financial assistance for college to the dependents of Oregon veterans.

Title of Award: Oregon Legion Auxiliary Department Scholarships **Area, Field, or Subject:** General studies/Field of study not specified **Level of Education for which Award is Granted:** Undergraduate **Number Awarded:** 3 each year; 1 of these is to be used for vocational or business school. **Funds Available:** The stipend is $1,000. It must be used for college, university, business school, vocational school, or any other accredited postsecondary school in the state of Oregon. **Duration:** The awards are offered each year. They are nonrenewable.

Eligibility Requirements: This program is open to Oregon residents who are children or wives of disabled veterans or widows of veterans. Applicants must be interested in obtaining education beyond the high school level. Selection is based on ability, aptitude, character, seriousness of purpose, and financial need. **Deadline for Receipt:** March of each year.

217 ■ AMERICAN LEGION AUXILIARY

Attn: Department of Oregon
30450 S.W. Parkway Avenue
P.O. Box 1730
Wilsonville, OR 97070-1730
Tel: (503)682-3162
Fax: (503)685-5008
E-mail: pcalhoun@pcez.com
To provide financial assistance for college to junior members of the American Legion Auxiliary in Oregon.

Title of Award: Oregon Legion Auxiliary Department Spirit of Youth Scholarship **Area, Field, or Subject:** General studies/Field of study not specified **Level of Education for which Award is Granted:** Undergraduate **Number Awarded:** 1 each year. **Funds Available:** The stipend is $1,000. **Duration:** 1 year; nonrenewable.

Eligibility Requirements: Applicants for this scholarship must be Oregon residents who are junior members of the Auxiliary and have been members for at least 3 years. They must be children (including stepchildren), grandchildren, or great-grandchildren of veterans and in

their senior year of high school. **Deadline for Receipt:** March of each year. **Additional Information:** The scholarship may be used at the college of the recipient's choice.

218 ■ AMERICAN LEGION AUXILIARY

Attn: Department of Oregon
30450 S.W. Parkway Avenue
P.O. Box 1730
Wilsonville, OR 97070-1730
Tel: (503)682-3162
Fax: (503)685-5008
E-mail: pcalhoun@pcez.com
To provide financial assistance for college to the children of war veterans in Oregon.

Title of Award: Oregon Legion Auxiliary National President's Scholarship **Area, Field, or Subject:** General studies/Field of study not specified **Level of Education for which Award is Granted:** Undergraduate **Number Awarded:** 2 each year. **Funds Available:** The first-place award is $2,000 and the second-place award is $1,500. **Duration:** The awards are offered each year. They are nonrenewable.

Eligibility Requirements: This program is open to Oregon residents who are the children of veterans who served in World War I, World War II, Korea, Vietnam, Grenada, Lebanon, Panama, or the Persian Gulf. They must be high school seniors or graduates who have not yet attended an institution of higher learning. Selection is based on character, Americanism, leadership, scholarship, and financial need. The winner then competes for the American Legion Auxiliary National President's Scholarship. If the Oregon winner is not awarded a national scholarship, then he or she receives the first-place award and the second winner receives the second-place award; if the Oregon winner is also a national winner, then the second-place winner in Oregon receives the first-place award and the alternate receives the second-place award. **Deadline for Receipt:** March of each year. **Additional Information:** The awards may be used at any college of the recipient's choice.

219 ■ AMERICAN LEGION AUXILIARY

777 North Meridian Street, Third Floor
Indianapolis, IN 46204-1189
Tel: (317)955-3845
Fax: (317)955-3884
E-mail: alahq@legion-aux.org
Web Site: http://www.legion-aux.org/Scholarships/SpiritofYouth/index.aspx
To provide financial assistance for college to junior members of the American Legion Auxiliary.

Title of Award: Spirit of Youth Scholarship for Junior Members **Area, Field, or Subject:** General studies/Field of study not specified **Level of Education for which Award is Granted:** Undergraduate **Number Awarded:** 5 each year; 1 in each division of the American Legion Auxiliary. **Funds Available:** The scholarship is $1,000 per year, to be used at an accredited institution of higher learning or a professional or technical school that awards a certificate upon completion of an accredited course. **Duration:** 4 years.

Eligibility Requirements: Applicants for this scholarship must have been junior members of the Auxiliary for at least the past 3 years. They must be seniors at an accredited high school in the United States and have earned a GPA of 3.0 or higher. Each unit of the Auxiliary may select a candidate for application to the department level, and each department submits a candidate for the national award. Nominees must submit a 1,000-word essay on a topic that changes annually; a recent topic was "My Vision of Freedom." Selection is based on character and leadership (30%), the essay (30%) and academic record (40%). **Deadline for Receipt:** Applications must be submitted to the unit president by March of each year. **Additional Information:** Applications are available from the president of the candidate's own unit or from the secretary or education chair of the department. The awardees must enroll for a minimum of 12 semester hours of work or its equivalent.

220 ■ AMERICAN LEGION AUXILIARY

Attn: Department of Utah
B-61 State Capitol Building
Salt Lake City, UT 84114
Tel: (801)538-1014

Fax: (801)537-9191
E-mail: utaux@aol.com
To provide financial assistance for college to children of veterans in Utah.
Title of Award: Utah Legion Auxiliary National President's Scholarship
Area, Field, or Subject: General studies/Field of study not specified
Level of Education for which Award is Granted: Undergraduate
Number Awarded: 2 each year: 1 at $2,000 and 1 at $1,500. **Funds
Available:** Stipends are $2,000 or $1,500. **Duration:** 1 year.
Eligibility Requirements: This program is open to Utah residents who
are the children of veterans who served in World War I, World War II,
Korea, Vietnam, Grenada, Lebanon, Panama, or the Persian Gulf. They
must be high school seniors or graduates who have not yet attended an
institution of higher learning. Selection is based on character, Americanism, leadership, scholarship, and financial need. The winners then
compete for the American Legion Auxiliary National President's Scholarship. If the Utah winners are not awarded a national scholarship, then they
receive these departmental scholarships. **Deadline for Receipt:** February
of each year.

221 ■ AMERICAN LEGION AUXILIARY

Attn: Department of Wisconsin
2930 American Legion Drive
P.O. Box 140
Portage, WI 53901-0140
Tel: (608)745-0124; (866)664-3863
Fax: (608)745-1947
E-mail: alawi@amlegionauxwi.org
Web Site: http://www.amlegionauxwi.org
To provide financial assistance for college to Wisconsin residents who are
members or children of members of the American Legion Auxiliary.
Title of Award: Della Van Deuren Memorial Scholarships **Area, Field, or
Subject:** General studies/Field of study not specified **Level of Education
for which Award is Granted:** Undergraduate **Number Awarded:** 2 each
year. **Funds Available:** The stipend is $1,000. **Duration:** 1 year;
nonrenewable.
Eligibility Requirements: This program is open to members and children
of members of the American Legion Auxiliary. Applicants must be high
school seniors or graduates with a GPA of 3.2 or higher and be able to
demonstrate financial need. They must be Wisconsin residents, although
they are not required to attend school in the state. Along with their application, they must submit a 300-word essay on "Education-An Investment in
the Future." **Deadline for Receipt:** March of each year. **Additional
Information:** Information is also available from the Education Chair,
Renae Allen, 206 West Fremont Street, Darien, WI 53114-1540, (262)
724-5059.

222 ■ AMERICAN LEGION AUXILIARY

Attn: Department of New York
112 State Street, Suite 1310
Albany, NY 12207
Tel: (518)463-1162
Free: 800-421-6348
Fax: (518)449-5406
E-mail: alanyhdqtrs@worldnet.att.net
Web Site: http://www.deptny.org/Scholarships.htm
To provide financial assistance for college to New York residents who are
the descendants of veterans.
Title of Award: Raymond T. Wellington, Jr. Memorial Scholarship **Area,
Field, or Subject:** General studies/Field of study not specified **Level of
Education for which Award is Granted:** Undergraduate **Number
Awarded:** 1 each year. **Funds Available:** The stipend is $1,000. **Dura-
tion:** 1 year.
Eligibility Requirements: This program is open to residents of New York
who are the children, grandchildren, or great grandchildren of veterans of
World War II, the Korean Conflict, the Vietnam War, Grenada/Lebanon,
Panama, or the Persian Gulf. Applicants must be high school seniors or
graduates younger than 20 years of age. They must be interested in attending an accredited college or university. Along with their application,
they must submit a 700-word autobiography that includes their interests,
experiences, long-range plans, and goals. Selection is based on character
(15%), Americanism (15%), community involvement (15%), leadership
(15%), scholarship (20%), and financial need (20%). **Deadline for
Receipt:** March of each year.

223 ■ AMERICAN LEGION AUXILIARY

Attn: Department of Wisconsin
2930 American Legion Drive
P.O. Box 140
Portage, WI 53901-0140
Tel: (608)745-0124; (866)664-3863
Fax: (608)745-1947
E-mail: alawi@amlegionauxwi.org
Web Site: http://www.amlegionauxwi.org
To provide financial assistance for college to Wisconsin residents who are
the children or spouses of veterans.
Title of Award: Wisconsin Legion Auxiliary Merit and Memorial Scholar-
ships **Area, Field, or Subject:** General studies/Field of study not speci-
fied **Level of Education for which Award is Granted:** Undergraduate
Number Awarded: 6 each year. **Funds Available:** The stipend is $1,000.
Duration: 1 year; nonrenewable.
Eligibility Requirements: This program is open to the children, wives,
and widows of veterans who are high school seniors or graduates with a
GPA of 3.2 or higher. Grandchildren and great-grandchildren of veterans
are eligible if they are members of the American Legion Auxiliary. Applicants must be able to demonstrate financial need and be residents of
Wisconsin, although they do not need to attend college in the state. Along
with their application, they must submit a 300-word essay on
"Education-An Investment in the Future." **Deadline for Receipt:** March of
each year. **Additional Information:** Information is also available from the
Education Chair, Renae Allen, 206 West Fremont Street, Darien, WI
53114-1540, (262) 724-5059 This program includes the following named
scholarships: the Harriet Hass Scholarship, the Adalin Macauley Scholarship, the Eleanor Smith Scholarship, the Pearl Behrend Scholarship, and
the Barbara Kranig Scholarship.

224 ■ AMERICAN LEGION AUXILIARY

Attn: Department of Wisconsin
2930 American Legion Drive
P.O. Box 140
Portage, WI 53901-0140
Tel: (608)745-0124; (866)664-3863
Fax: (608)745-1947
E-mail: alawi@amlegionauxwi.org
Web Site: http://www.amlegionauxwi.org
To provide financial assistance for college to members or the children of
members of the American Legion Auxiliary in Wisconsin.
Title of Award: Wisconsin Legion Auxiliary State President's Scholarship
Area, Field, or Subject: General studies/Field of study not specified
Level of Education for which Award is Granted: Undergraduate
Number Awarded: 3 each year. **Funds Available:** The stipend is $1,000.
Duration: 1 year.
Eligibility Requirements: Eligible are the members or children of
members of the American Legion Auxiliary who are in need of financial aid
to continue their education and are high school seniors or graduates with
a GPA of 3.2 or higher. Applicants must be Wisconsin residents, but they
are not required to attend college in the state. Along with their application,
they must submit a 300-word essay on "Education-An Investment in the
Future." **Deadline for Receipt:** March of each year. **Additional Information:** Information is also available from the Education Chair, Renae Allen,
206 West Fremont Street, Darien, WI 53114-1540, (262) 724-5059.

225 ■ AMERICAN LEGION BASEBALL

700 North Pennsylvania Street
Indianapolis, IN 46204
Tel: (317)630-1249
Fax: (317)630-1223
E-mail: acy@legion.org
Web Site: http://www.baseball.legion.org/awards.htm
To recognize and reward outstanding participants in the American Legion
baseball program.
Title of Award: American Legion Baseball Scholarship **Area, Field, or
Subject:** General studies/Field of study not specified **Level of Education
for which Award is Granted:** Graduate, Undergraduate **Number
Awarded:** 51 each year: 1 in each state and Puerto Rico. **Funds Avail-
able:** The award is a $1,000 scholarship. Funds are disbursed jointly to
the winner and the school. **Duration:** Students have 8 years to utilize the
scholarship funds from the date of the award, excluding any time spent on
active military duty.

Eligibility Requirements: This program is open to participants in the American Legion baseball program who are high school graduates or college freshmen; students still in high school are not eligible. In each of the 50 states and Puerto Rico, candidates may be nominated by a team manager or head coach. The department baseball committee selects a player who demonstrates outstanding leadership, citizenship, character, scholarship, and financial need. **Deadline for Receipt:** July of each year. **Additional Information:** The scholarship may be used at any accredited school above the high school level.

226 ■ AMERICAN LEGION BASEBALL
700 North Pennsylvania Street
Indianapolis, IN 46204
Tel: (317)630-1249
Fax: (317)630-1223
E-mail: acy@legion.org
Web Site: http://www.baseball.legion.org/awards.htm
To recognize and reward, with college scholarships, participants in the American Legion baseball program who demonstrate outstanding academic achievement.
Title of Award: ECI Scholarships **Area, Field, or Subject:** General studies/Field of study not specified **Level of Education for which Award is Granted:** Undergraduate **Number Awarded:** 9 each year. **Funds Available:** The awards are $1,000 scholarships. **Duration:** The awards are presented annually.
Eligibility Requirements: This program is open to participants in the American Legion baseball regional tournaments and the American Legion World Series. Candidates must be high school seniors or graduates who will be entering college as a freshman in the fall; students still in high school are not eligible. Selection is based on academic achievement. **Additional Information:** These awards are funded by the ECI Scholarship Foundation of Educational Communications Inc.

227 ■ AMERICAN LEGION BASEBALL
700 North Pennsylvania Street
Indianapolis, IN 46204
Tel: (317)630-1249
Fax: (317)630-1223
E-mail: acy@legion.org
Web Site: http://www.baseball.legion.org/awards.htm
To recognize and reward, with college scholarships, participants in the American Legion baseball program who demonstrate outstanding leadership.
Title of Award: Gatorade Leadership Awards **Area, Field, or Subject:** General studies/Field of study not specified **Level of Education for which Award is Granted:** Undergraduate **Number Awarded:** 8 winners in regional tournaments receive $1,000 scholarships; 1 of those receives an additional scholarship as the George W. Rulon American Legion Player of the Year. **Funds Available:** The outstanding participants in the regional tournaments receive $1,000 scholarships; the outstanding participant in the American Legion World Series receives an additional $2,000 scholarship. **Duration:** The awards are presented annually.
Eligibility Requirements: This program is open to participants in the American Legion baseball regional tournaments and the American Legion World Series. Candidates must be high school seniors or graduates who will be entering college as a freshman in the fall; students still in high school are not eligible. Selection is based on integrity, mental attitude, cooperation, citizenship, sportsmanship, scholastic aptitude, and general good conduct. **Additional Information:** These awards, first presented in 1986, are funded by Stokely-Van Camp, the maker of Gatorade. The player selected at the World Series is also designated as the George W. Rulon American Legion Play of the Year.

228 ■ AMERICAN MILITARY RETIREES ASSOCIATION, INC.
Attn: Scholarship Committee
5436 Peru Street, Suite 1
Plattsburgh, NY 12901
Tel: (518)563-9479
Free: 800-424-2969
Fax: (518)324-5204
E-mail: info@amra1973.org
Web Site: http://www.amra1973.org/scholarship.html

To provide financial assistance for college to members of the American Military Retirees Association (AMRA) and their dependents.
Title of Award: Sergeant Major Douglas R. Drum Memorial Scholarship **Area, Field, or Subject:** General studies/Field of study not specified **Level of Education for which Award is Granted:** Undergraduate **Number Awarded:** Varies each year. Recently, 13 of these scholarships were awarded: 1 at $1,000, 1 at $800, 2 at $500, and 9 at $300. **Funds Available:** Stipends range from $300 to $1,000. **Duration:** 1 year.
Eligibility Requirements: This program is open to current members of AMRA and their dependents, children, and grandchildren. Applicants must be working on a degree at an accredited college or university. Selection is based on academic achievement, leadership abilities, character, citizenship, and financial need. **Deadline for Receipt:** April of each year. **Additional Information:** Membership in AMRA is open to all retired members of the armed forces, regardless of rank.

229 ■ AMERICAN MILITARY SPOUSE EDUCATION FOUNDATION
9912 Great Oaks Way
Fairfax, VA 22030
Tel: (703)591-8444
Fax: (703)591-8333
E-mail: garybottorff@aol.com
Web Site: http://
To provide financial assistance for undergraduate study to spouses of military personnel.
Title of Award: American Military Spouse Education Foundation Scholarships **Area, Field, or Subject:** General studies/Field of study not specified **Level of Education for which Award is Granted:** Undergraduate **Number Awarded:** Varies each year. **Funds Available:** Stipends range up to $3,000 per year. **Duration:** 1 year; may be renewed.
Eligibility Requirements: This program is open to spouses of U.S. uniformed military service members (active-duty, Reserve, National Guard, and retired). Applicants must be enrolled in an undergraduate degree program. Spouses who are also uniformed military service members are ineligible. Within each category of military service (active-duty, Reserve, National Guard, retired), applicants with the lowest rank receive the highest priority. Ties are broken by date of rank. Special consideration is given to spouses whose military member was 1) killed while serving on active duty, or 2) wounded while serving on active duty and has received a disability rating of 50% or higher. **Deadline for Receipt:** Applications may be submitted at any time.

230 ■ AMERICAN POSTAL WORKERS UNION
Attn: Secretary-Treasurer
1300 L Street, N.W.
Washington, DC 20005
Tel: (202)842-4268
Fax: (202)842-8530
Web Site: http://www.apwu.org/dept/sec-treas/stscholarships.htm
To provide financial assistance for vocational education to children of members of the American Postal Workers Union (APWU).
Title of Award: American Postal Workers Union Vocational Scholarship Program **Area, Field, or Subject:** General studies/Field of study not specified **Level of Education for which Award is Granted:** Vocational/Occupational **Number Awarded:** 1 each year. **Funds Available:** The stipend is $1,000 per year. **Duration:** 1 year; may be renewed up to 2 additional years or until completion of the program.
Eligibility Requirements: Eligible are the children, stepchildren, or legally adopted children of active or deceased members of the APWU who have been in good standing for at least 1 year or were members for 1 year immediately preceding death. Applicants must be high school seniors who plan to attend an accredited trade, technical, industrial, or vocational school. Selection is based on school records, personal qualifications, evidence of a commitment to an occupation, response to contemporary questions, and a 500-word essay on "What the Union Way of Life Means to Me." **Deadline for Receipt:** February of each year.

231 ■ AMERICAN POSTAL WORKERS UNION
Attn: Secretary-Treasurer
1300 L Street, N.W.
Washington, DC 20005
Tel: (202)842-4268
Fax: (202)842-8530

Web Site: http://www.apwu.org/dept/sec-treas/stscholarships.htm
To provide financial assistance for college to children of members of the American Postal Workers Union (APWU).

Title of Award: E.C. Hallbeck Memorial Scholarship Program **Area, Field, or Subject:** General studies/Field of study not specified **Level of Education for which Award is Granted:** Undergraduate **Number Awarded:** 5 each year: 1 in each of the union's 5 areas. **Funds Available:** The stipend is $1,000 per year. **Duration:** 4 years.

Eligibility Requirements: Eligible are the children, grandchildren, stepchildren, and legally adopted children of active or deceased members of the union who have been in good standing for at least 1 year or were members for 1 year immediately preceding death. Applicants must be high school seniors who plan to attend an accredited college, university, or community college as full-time students. Selection is based on school records, personal qualifications, SAT or ACT scores, responses to questions on contemporary issues, and an essay (up to 500 words) on "What the union way of life means to me." **Deadline for Receipt:** February of each year. **Additional Information:** This program was established in 1969.

232 ■ AMERICAN PUBLIC POWER ASSOCIATION

Attn: DEED Administrator
2301 M Street, N.W.
Washington, DC 20037-1484
Tel: (202)467-2960
Fax: (202)467-2910
E-mail: deed@appanet.org
Web Site: http://www.appanet.org
To recognize and reward undergraduate and graduate students who develop and demonstrate outstanding projects related to energy innovation.

Title of Award: DEED Technical Design Project **Area, Field, or Subject:** Energy-related areas **Level of Education for which Award is Granted:** Graduate, Undergraduate **Number Awarded:** 1 each year. **Funds Available:** The grant is $5,000. An additional $3,000 is available to pay for travel expenses to attend the engineering and operations technical conference of the American Public Power Association (ARPA) and present their project. If more than 1 student is involved in a project, the award funds are split among all participants. **Duration:** This competition is held annually.

Eligibility Requirements: Eligible are undergraduate and graduate students in energy-related disciplines at accredited colleges and universities in the United States and Canada. Applicants must complete a technical design project and submit a final report on the project, describing activities, cost, sources used, achievements, problems, results, and recommendations. The project must relate to energy innovation, improving efficiencies, and lowering the cost of providing energy services to the customers of publicly owned electric utilities. Selection is based on the applicability of benefits to public power systems, the applicant's major in an academic field related to the electric power or energy service industries, academic performance, generalizable methodologies, and promotion of energy efficiency. **Deadline for Receipt:** October of each year. **Additional Information:** The APPA is the national trade organization representing approximately 2,000 publicly-owned electric utilities. Its research project, the Demonstration of Energy-Efficient Developments (DEED), was established in 1980.

233 ■ AMERICAN RADIO RELAY LEAGUE

Attn: ARRL Foundation
225 Main Street
Newington, CT 06111
Tel: (860)594-0397
Fax: (860)594-0259
E-mail: foundation@arrl.org
Web Site: http://www.arrl.org/arrlf/scholgen.html
To provide financial assistance to licensed radio amateurs who are interested in working on an undergraduate or graduate degree.

Title of Award: American Radio Relay League General Fund Scholarships **Area, Field, or Subject:** General studies/Field of study not specified **Level of Education for which Award is Granted:** Graduate, Undergraduate **Number Awarded:** Varies each year; recently, 4 of these scholarships were awarded. **Funds Available:** The stipend is $1,000. **Duration:** 1 year.

Eligibility Requirements: This program is open to undergraduate or graduate students at accredited institutions in any subject area who are licensed radio amateurs (any class). Applicants must submit an essay on the role amateur radio has played in their lives and provide documentation of financial need. **Deadline for Receipt:** January of each year.

234 ■ AMERICAN RADIO RELAY LEAGUE

Attn: ARRL Foundation
225 Main Street
Newington, CT 06111
Tel: (860)594-0397
Fax: (860)594-0259
E-mail: foundation@arrl.org
Web Site: http://www.arrl.org/arrlf/scholgen.html
To provide financial assistance to licensed radio amateurs, particularly from designated states, who are interested in working on an undergraduate or graduate degree.

Title of Award: Mary Lou Brown Scholarships **Area, Field, or Subject:** General studies/Field of study not specified **Level of Education for which Award is Granted:** Graduate, Undergraduate **Number Awarded:** 1 or more each year. **Funds Available:** The stipend is $2,500. **Duration:** 1 year.

Eligibility Requirements: This program is open to undergraduate or graduate students at accredited institutions who are licensed radio amateurs of general class. Preference is given to students residing in Alaska, Idaho, Montana, Oregon, or Washington and attending school in those states. Applicants must have a GPA of 3.0 or better and a demonstrated interest in promoting the Amateur Radio Service. They must submit an essay on the role amateur radio has played in their lives and provide documentation of financial need. **Deadline for Receipt:** January of each year.

235 ■ AMERICAN RADIO RELAY LEAGUE

Attn: ARRL Foundation
225 Main Street
Newington, CT 06111
Tel: (860)594-0397
Fax: (860)594-0259
E-mail: foundation@arrl.org
Web Site: http://www.arrl.org/arrlf/scholgen.html
To provide financial assistance to licensed radio amateurs, particularly from Texas or Oklahoma, who are interested in working on an undergraduate degree.

Title of Award: Tom and Judith Comstock Scholarship **Area, Field, or Subject:** General studies/Field of study not specified **Level of Education for which Award is Granted:** Undergraduate **Number Awarded:** 1 each year. **Funds Available:** The stipend is $1,000. **Duration:** 1 year.

Eligibility Requirements: This program is open to high school seniors who 1) have been accepted at a 2-year or 4-year college and 2) are licensed radio amateurs of any class. Preference is given to residents of Texas or Oklahoma. Applicants must submit an essay on the role amateur radio has played in their lives and provide documentation of financial need. **Deadline for Receipt:** January of each year.

236 ■ AMERICAN RADIO RELAY LEAGUE

Attn: ARRL Foundation
225 Main Street
Newington, CT 06111
Tel: (860)594-0397
Fax: (860)594-0259
E-mail: foundation@arrl.org
Web Site: http://www.arrl.org/arrlf/scholgen.html
To provide financial assistance to licensed radio amateurs, particularly from Georgia or Alabama, who are interested in working on an undergraduate degree.

Title of Award: Charles Clarke Cordle Memorial Scholarship **Area, Field, or Subject:** General studies/Field of study not specified **Level of Education for which Award is Granted:** Undergraduate **Number Awarded:** 1 each year. **Funds Available:** The stipend is $1,000. **Duration:** 1 year.

Eligibility Requirements: This program is open to licensed radio amateurs of any class who are working on an undergraduate degree. Preference is given to residents of Georgia and Alabama who are attending college in those states and have a GPA of 2.5 or higher. Applicants must submit an essay on the role amateur radio has played in their lives and provide documentation of financial need. **Deadline for Receipt:** January of each year.

237 ■ AMERICAN RADIO RELAY LEAGUE
Attn: ARRL Foundation
225 Main Street
Newington, CT 06111
Tel: (860)594-0397
Fax: (860)594-0259
E-mail: foundation@arrl.org
Web Site: http://www.arrl.org/arrlf/scholgen.html
To provide financial assistance to licensed radio amateurs who are high school seniors planning to attend college.
Title of Award: Dayton Amateur Radio Association Scholarships **Area, Field, or Subject:** General studies/Field of study not specified **Level of Education for which Award is Granted:** Undergraduate **Number Awarded:** 2 each year. **Funds Available:** The stipend is $1,000 per year. **Duration:** 1 year.
Eligibility Requirements: This program is open to undergraduate students at accredited institutions in any subject area who are licensed radio amateurs (any class). Applicants must submit an essay on the role amateur radio has played in their lives and provide documentation of financial need. **Deadline for Receipt:** January of each year. **Additional Information:** This program is sponsored by the Dayton Amateur Radio Association, P.O. Box 44, Dayton, OH 45401, (937) 237-8440.

238 ■ AMERICAN RADIO RELAY LEAGUE
Attn: ARRL Foundation
225 Main Street
Newington, CT 06111
Tel: (860)594-0397
Fax: (860)594-0259
E-mail: foundation@arrl.org
Web Site: http://www.arrl.org/arrlf/scholgen.html
To provide financial assistance to licensed radio amateurs who are interested in working on an undergraduate or graduate degree.
Title of Award: K2TEO Martin J. Green, Sr. Memorial Scholarship **Area, Field, or Subject:** General studies/Field of study not specified **Level of Education for which Award is Granted:** Graduate, Undergraduate **Number Awarded:** 1 each year. **Funds Available:** The stipend is $1,000. **Duration:** 1 year.
Eligibility Requirements: This program is open to undergraduate or graduate students in any field who are enrolled at accredited institutions and are licensed radio amateurs of general class. Applicants must submit an essay on the role amateur radio has played in their lives and provide documentation of financial need. Preference is given to students whose parents, grandparents, siblings, or other relatives are also ham radio operators. **Deadline for Receipt:** January of each year.

239 ■ AMERICAN RADIO RELAY LEAGUE
Attn: ARRL Foundation
225 Main Street
Newington, CT 06111
Tel: (860)594-0397
Fax: (860)594-0259
E-mail: foundation@arrl.org
Web Site: http://www.arrl.org/arrlf/scholgen.html
To provide funding for college to licensed radio amateurs.
Title of Award: NCDXF Scholarship **Area, Field, or Subject:** General studies/Field of study not specified **Level of Education for which Award is Granted:** Undergraduate **Number Awarded:** 1 each year. **Funds Available:** The stipend is $1,000. **Duration:** 1 year.
Eligibility Requirements: This program is open to licensed radio amateurs who plan to seek a degree at a junior college, 4-year college or university, or trade school in the United States. There is no restriction on the field of study. Applicants must have at least a technician class license; preference is given to students indicating an interest and activity in DXing. Financial need is considered in the selection process. **Deadline for Receipt:** January of each year. **Additional Information:** This program is sponsored by the Northern California DX Foundation (NCDXF), Inc., P.O. Box 1328, Los Altos, CA 94023-1328, (707) 794-9801, Fax: (707) 794-8033, E-mail: ww6d@arrl.net.

240 ■ AMERICAN RADIO RELAY LEAGUE
Attn: ARRL Foundation
225 Main Street
Newington, CT 06111
Tel: (860)594-0397
Fax: (860)594-0259
E-mail: foundation@arrl.org
Web Site: http://www.arrl.org/arrlf/scholgen.html
To provide financial assistance to licensed radio amateurs who are interested in working on an undergraduate or graduate degree.
Title of Award: New England FEMARA Scholarships **Area, Field, or Subject:** General studies/Field of study not specified **Level of Education for which Award is Granted:** Graduate, Undergraduate **Number Awarded:** Varies, depending upon the availability of funds; recently, 5 of these scholarships were awarded per year. **Funds Available:** The stipend is $1,000. **Duration:** 1 year.
Eligibility Requirements: This program is open to undergraduate or graduate students at accredited institutions who are licensed radio amateurs of technician class. Applicants must submit an essay on the role amateur radio has played in their lives and provide documentation of financial need. Preference is given to applicants from the 6 New England states. **Deadline for Receipt:** January of each year.

241 ■ AMERICAN RADIO RELAY LEAGUE
Attn: ARRL Foundation
225 Main Street
Newington, CT 06111
Tel: (860)594-0397
Fax: (860)594-0259
E-mail: foundation@arrl.org
Web Site: http://www.arrl.org/arrlf/scholgen.html
To provide financial assistance to licensed radio amateurs who are interested in working on an undergraduate or graduate degree.
Title of Award: Scholarship Honoring Senator Barry Goldwater, K7UGA **Area, Field, or Subject:** General studies/Field of study not specified **Level of Education for which Award is Granted:** Graduate, Undergraduate **Number Awarded:** 1 each year. **Funds Available:** The stipend is $5,000. **Duration:** 1 year.
Eligibility Requirements: This program is open to undergraduate or graduate students at accredited institutions who are licensed radio amateurs at the novice level or higher. Applicants must submit an essay on the role amateur radio has played in their lives and provide documentation of financial need. **Deadline for Receipt:** January of each year.

242 ■ AMERICAN RADIO RELAY LEAGUE
Attn: ARRL Foundation
225 Main Street
Newington, CT 06111
Tel: (860)594-0397
Fax: (860)594-0259
E-mail: foundation@arrl.org
Web Site: http://www.arrl.org/arrlf/scholgen.html
To provide financial assistance to members of the American Radio Relay League (ARRL), particularly from Pennsylvania, who are interested in working on an undergraduate or graduate degree.
Title of Award: "You've Got a Friend in Pennsylvania" Scholarship **Area, Field, or Subject:** General studies/Field of study not specified **Level of Education for which Award is Granted:** Graduate, Undergraduate **Number Awarded:** 1 each year. **Funds Available:** The stipend is $1,000. **Duration:** 1 year.
Eligibility Requirements: This program is open to undergraduate or graduate students at accredited institutions who are licensed radio amateurs of general class and ARRL members. Applicants must submit an essay on the role amateur radio has played in their lives and provide documentation of financial need. Preference is given to residents of Pennsylvania. **Deadline for Receipt:** January of each year.

243 ■ AMERICAN RED CROSS
c/o Scholarship America
Attn: Scholarship Management Services
One Scholarship Way
P.O. Box 297
St. Peter, MN 56082

Tel: (507)931-1682
Free: 800-537-4180
Fax: (507)931-9168
E-mail: smsinfo@csfa.org
To provide financial assistance for college to persons with hemophilia and their children.
Title of Award: HemAspheres University Scholarship Fund **Area, Field, or Subject:** General studies/Field of study not specified **Level of Education for which Award is Granted:** Undergraduate **Number Awarded:** 3 each year: 2 to students with hemophilia and 1 to the child of a parent with hemophilia. **Funds Available:** The stipend is $5,000 per year. Funds may be used for tuition, fees, books, and room and board. **Duration:** 1 year; may be renewed 1 additional year.
Eligibility Requirements: To be eligible, candidates must be high school seniors, high school graduates, or college students already enrolled in full-time study. Applicants must either be receiving treatment for hemophilia or have a parent receiving treatment for hemophilia. They must be planning to enroll full time at an accredited 2- or 4-year college, university, or vocational/technical school. Selection is based on academic performance, leadership ability, school and community activities, work experience, educational and career goals, and personal or family financial circumstances. **Deadline for Receipt:** February of each year. **Additional Information:** This program is managed by Scholarship America and sponsored by the American Red Cross. Recipients must attend an accredited college or university in the continental United States. Scholarships are awarded for undergraduate study only.

244 ■ AMERICAN ROAD AND TRANSPORTATION BUILDERS ASSOCIATION

Attn: Transportation Development Foundation
1219 28th Street, N.W.
Washington, DC 20007-3389
Tel: (202)289-4434
E-mail: rbritton@artba.org
Web Site: http://www.artba.org/foundation/hwy_worker_scholarship.htm
To provide financial assistance for college to children of highway workers killed or disabled on the job.
Title of Award: Highway Worker Memorial Scholarship Program **Area, Field, or Subject:** General studies/Field of study not specified **Level of Education for which Award is Granted:** Undergraduate **Number Awarded:** Varies each year; recently, 12 of these scholarships were awarded. **Funds Available:** The stipend is $2,000. Funds are paid directly to the recipient's institution to be used for tuition, books, or required fees, but not for room and board. **Duration:** 1 year.
Eligibility Requirements: This program is open to the sons, daughters, and legally adopted children of highway workers who die or have become permanently disabled in roadway construction zone accidents. Applicants must be attending or planning to attend an accredited 4-year college or university, 2-year college, or vocational/technical school. Their parent must have been employed by a transportation construction firm or a transportation public agency at the time of death or disabling injury. Selection is based on academic performance (GPA of 2.5 or higher), a 200-word statement from the applicant on reasons for wanting to continue education, letters of recommendation, and financial need. **Deadline for Receipt:** March of each year. **Additional Information:** This program began in 1999.

245 ■ AMERICAN SOCIETY OF HEATING, REFRIGERATING AND AIR-CONDITIONING ENGINEERS, INC.

Attn: Scholarship Administrator
1791 Tullie Circle, N.E.
Atlanta, GA 30329-2305
Tel: (404)636-8400
Fax: (404)321-5478
E-mail: benedict@ashrae.org
Web Site: http://www.ashrae.org
To provide financial assistance to undergraduate engineering students interested in heating, ventilating, air conditioning, and refrigeration (HVAC&R).
Title of Award: Henry Adams Scholarship **Area, Field, or Subject:** Heating, air conditioning, and refrigeration **Level of Education for which Award is Granted:** Four Year College **Number Awarded:** 1 each year.
Funds Available: The stipend is $3,000 per year. **Duration:** 1 year.

Eligibility Requirements: This program is open to undergraduate engineering students working on a bachelor's degree in a program recognized as accredited by the American Society of Heating, Refrigerating and Air-Conditioning Engineers (ASHRAE). Applicants must be enrolled full time in a course of study that has traditionally been preparatory for the profession of HVAC&R. They must have a GPA of 3.0 or higher and at least 1 full year of undergraduate study remaining. Selection is based on potential service to the HVAC&R profession, financial need, leadership ability, recommendations from instructors, and character. **Deadline for Receipt:** November of each year.

246 ■ AMERICAN SOCIETY OF HEATING, REFRIGERATING AND AIR-CONDITIONING ENGINEERS, INC.

Attn: Scholarship Administrator
1791 Tullie Circle, N.E.
Atlanta, GA 30329-2305
Tel: (404)636-8400
Fax: (404)321-5478
E-mail: benedict@ashrae.org
Web Site: http://www.ashrae.org
To provide financial assistance to undergraduate engineering students interested in heating, ventilating, air conditioning, and refrigeration (HVAC&R).
Title of Award: ASHRAE Memorial Scholarship **Area, Field, or Subject:** Heating, air conditioning, and refrigeration **Level of Education for which Award is Granted:** Four Year College **Number Awarded:** 1 each year. **Funds Available:** The stipend is $3,000 per year. **Duration:** 1 year.
Eligibility Requirements: This program is open to undergraduate engineering students working on a bachelor's degree in a program recognized as accredited by the American Society of Heating, Refrigerating and Air-Conditioning Engineers (ASHRAE). Applicants must be enrolled full time in a course of study that has traditionally been preparatory for the profession of HVAC&R. They must have a GPA of 3.0 or higher and at least 1 full year of undergraduate study remaining. Selection is based on potential service to the HVAC&R profession, financial need, leadership ability, recommendations from instructors, and character. **Deadline for Receipt:** November of each year.

247 ■ AMERICAN SOCIETY OF HEATING, REFRIGERATING AND AIR-CONDITIONING ENGINEERS, INC.

Attn: Scholarship Administrator
1791 Tullie Circle, N.E.
Atlanta, GA 30329-2305
Tel: (404)636-8400
Fax: (404)321-5478
E-mail: benedict@ashrae.org
Web Site: http://www.ashrae.org
To provide financial assistance to undergraduate engineering students at schools in selected states who are interested in heating, ventilating, air conditioning, and refrigeration (HVAC&R).
Title of Award: ASHRAE Region IV Benny Bootle Scholarship **Area, Field, or Subject:** Heating, air conditioning, and refrigeration **Level of Education for which Award is Granted:** Undergraduate **Number Awarded:** 1 each year. **Funds Available:** The stipend is $3,000 per year. **Duration:** 1 year.
Eligibility Requirements: This program is open to undergraduate engineering students working on a bachelor's degree in an ABET-accredited program in Georgia, North Carolina, or South Carolina. Applicants must be enrolled full time in a course of study that has traditionally been preparatory for the profession of HVAC&R. They must have a GPA of 3.0 or higher and at least 1 full year of undergraduate study remaining. Selection is based on potential service to the HVAC&R profession, financial need, leadership ability, recommendations from instructors, and character. **Deadline for Receipt:** November of each year.

248 ■ AMERICAN SOCIETY OF HEATING, REFRIGERATING AND AIR-CONDITIONING ENGINEERS, INC.

Attn: Scholarship Administrator
1791 Tullie Circle, N.E.
Atlanta, GA 30329-2305
Tel: (404)636-8400
Fax: (404)321-5478
E-mail: benedict@ashrae.org

Web Site: http://www.ashrae.org

To provide financial assistance to undergraduate engineering students at schools in selected areas who are interested in heating, ventilating, air conditioning, and refrigeration (HVAC&R).

Title of Award: ASHRAE Region VIII Scholarship **Area, Field, or Subject:** Heating, air conditioning, and refrigeration **Level of Education for which Award is Granted:** Four Year College **Number Awarded:** 1 each year. **Funds Available:** The stipend is $3,000 per year. **Duration:** 1 year.

Eligibility Requirements: This program is open to undergraduate engineering students working on a bachelor's degree in an ABET-accredited program in Arkansas, Louisiana, Mexico, Oklahoma, or Texas. Applicants must be enrolled full time in a course of study that has traditionally been preparatory for the profession of HVAC&R. They must have a GPA of 3.0 or higher and at least 1 full year of undergraduate study remaining. Selection is based on potential service to the HVAC&R profession, financial need, leadership ability, recommendations from instructors, and character. **Deadline for Receipt:** November of each year.

249 ■ AMERICAN SOCIETY OF HEATING, REFRIGERATING AND AIR-CONDITIONING ENGINEERS, INC.

Attn: Scholarship Administrator
1791 Tullie Circle, N.E.
Atlanta, GA 30329-2305
Tel: (404)636-8400
Fax: (404)321-5478
E-mail: benedict@ashrae.org
Web Site: http://www.ashrae.org

To provide financial assistance to undergraduate engineering students interested in heating, ventilating, air conditioning, and refrigeration (HVAC&R).

Title of Award: ASHRAE Scholarships **Area, Field, or Subject:** Heating, air conditioning, and refrigeration **Level of Education for which Award is Granted:** Four Year College **Number Awarded:** 2 each year. **Funds Available:** The stipend is $3,000 per year. **Duration:** 1 year.

Eligibility Requirements: This program is open to undergraduate engineering students working on a bachelor's degree in a program recognized as accredited by the American Society of Heating, Refrigerating and Air-Conditioning Engineers (ASHRAE). Applicants must be enrolled full time in a course of study that has traditionally been preparatory for the profession of HVAC&R. They must have a GPA of 3.0 or higher and at least 1 full year of undergraduate study remaining. Selection is based on potential service to the HVAC&R profession, financial need, leadership ability, recommendations from instructors, and character. **Deadline for Receipt:** November of each year.

250 ■ AMERICAN SOCIETY OF HEATING, REFRIGERATING AND AIR-CONDITIONING ENGINEERS, INC.

Attn: Scholarship Administrator
1791 Tullie Circle, N.E.
Atlanta, GA 30329-2305
Tel: (404)636-8400
Fax: (404)321-5478
E-mail: benedict@ashrae.org
Web Site: http://www.ashrae.org

To provide financial assistance to undergraduate engineering students interested in heating, ventilating, air conditioning, and refrigeration (HVAC&R).

Title of Award: Willis H. Carrier Scholarships **Area, Field, or Subject:** Heating, air conditioning, and refrigeration **Level of Education for which Award is Granted:** Four Year College **Number Awarded:** 2 each year. **Funds Available:** The stipend is $10,000. **Duration:** 1 year.

Eligibility Requirements: This program is open to undergraduate engineering students working on a bachelor's degree in a program recognized as accredited by the American Society of Heating, Refrigerating and Air-Conditioning Engineers (ASHRAE). Applicants must be enrolled full time in a course of study that has traditionally been preparatory for the profession of HVAC&R. They must have a GPA of 3.0 or higher and at least 2 full years of undergraduate study remaining. Selection is based on potential service to the HVAC&R profession, financial

need, leadership ability, recommendations from instructors, and character. **Deadline for Receipt:** November of each year.

251 ■ AMERICAN SOCIETY OF HEATING, REFRIGERATING AND AIR-CONDITIONING ENGINEERS, INC.

Attn: Scholarship Administrator
1791 Tullie Circle, N.E.
Atlanta, GA 30329-2305
Tel: (404)636-8400
Fax: (404)321-5478
E-mail: benedict@ashrae.org
Web Site: http://www.ashrae.org

To provide financial assistance to undergraduate engineering students interested in heating, ventilating, air conditioning, and refrigeration (HVAC&R).

Title of Award: Frank M. Coda Scholarship **Area, Field, or Subject:** Heating, air conditioning, and refrigeration **Level of Education for which Award is Granted:** Four Year College **Number Awarded:** 1 each year. **Funds Available:** The stipend is $5,000. **Duration:** 1 year.

Eligibility Requirements: This program is open to undergraduate engineering students working on a bachelor's degree in a program recognized as accredited by the American Society of Heating, Refrigerating and Air-Conditioning Engineers (ASHRAE). Applicants must be enrolled full time in a course of study that has traditionally been preparatory for the profession of HVAC&R. They must have a GPA of 3.0 or higher and at least 2 full years of undergraduate study remaining. Selection is based on potential service to the HVAC&R profession, financial need, leadership ability, recommendations from instructors, and character. **Deadline for Receipt:** November of each year.

252 ■ AMERICAN SOCIETY OF HEATING, REFRIGERATING AND AIR-CONDITIONING ENGINEERS, INC.

Attn: Scholarship Administrator
1791 Tullie Circle, N.E.
Atlanta, GA 30329-2305
Tel: (404)636-8400
Fax: (404)321-5478
E-mail: benedict@ashrae.org
Web Site: http://www.ashrae.org

To provide financial assistance to undergraduate engineering students interested in heating, ventilating, air conditioning, and refrigeration (HVAC&R).

Title of Award: Duane Hanson Scholarship **Area, Field, or Subject:** Heating, air conditioning, and refrigeration **Level of Education for which Award is Granted:** Four Year College **Number Awarded:** 1 each year. **Funds Available:** The stipend is $3,000 per year. **Duration:** 1 year.

Eligibility Requirements: This program is open to undergraduate engineering students working on a bachelor's degree in a program recognized as accredited by the American Society of Heating, Refrigerating and Air-Conditioning Engineers (ASHRAE). Applicants must be enrolled full time in a course of study that has traditionally been preparatory for the profession of HVAC&R. They must have a GPA of 3.0 or higher and at least 1 full year of undergraduate study remaining. Selection is based on potential service to the HVAC&R profession, financial need, leadership ability, recommendations from instructors, and character. **Deadline for Receipt:** November of each year.

253 ■ AMERICAN SOCIETY OF HEATING, REFRIGERATING AND AIR-CONDITIONING ENGINEERS, INC.

Attn: Scholarship Administrator
1791 Tullie Circle, N.E.
Atlanta, GA 30329-2305
Tel: (404)636-8400
Fax: (404)321-5478
E-mail: benedict@ashrae.org
Web Site: http://www.ashrae.org

To provide financial assistance to undergraduate engineering students interested in heating, ventilating, air conditioning, and refrigeration (HVAC&R).

Title of Award: Alwin B. Newton Scholarship **Area, Field, or Subject:** Heating, air conditioning, and refrigeration **Level of Education for which Award is Granted:** Four Year College **Number Awarded:** 1 each year. **Funds Available:** The stipend is $3,000 per year. **Duration:** 1 year.

Eligibility Requirements: This program is open to undergraduate engineering students working on a bachelor's degree in a program recognized as accredited by the American Society of Heating, Refrigerating and Air-Conditioning Engineers (ASHRAE). Applicants must be enrolled full time in a course of study that has traditionally been preparatory for the profession of HVAC&R. They must have a GPA of 3.0 or higher and at least 1 full year of undergraduate study remaining. Selection is based on potential service to the HVAC&R profession, financial need, leadership ability, recommendations from instructors, and character. **Deadline for Receipt:** November of each year.

254 ■ AMERICAN SOCIETY OF HEATING, REFRIGERATING AND AIR-CONDITIONING ENGINEERS, INC.

Attn: Scholarship Administrator
1791 Tullie Circle, N.E.
Atlanta, GA 30329-2305
Tel: (404)636-8400
Fax: (404)321-5478
E-mail: benedict@ashrae.org
Web Site: http://www.ashrae.org
To provide financial assistance to undergraduate engineering students interested in heating, ventilating, air conditioning, and refrigeration (HVAC&R).

Title of Award: Reuben Trane Scholarships **Area, Field, or Subject:** Heating, air conditioning, and refrigeration **Level of Education for which Award is Granted:** Four Year College **Number Awarded:** 4 each year. **Funds Available:** The stipend is $5,000 per year. **Duration:** 2 years, provided the recipient maintains full-time status and satisfactory academic standing.

Eligibility Requirements: This program is open to undergraduate engineering students working on a bachelor's degree in a program recognized as accredited by the American Society of Heating, Refrigerating and Air-Conditioning Engineers (ASHRAE). Applicants must be enrolled full time in a course of study that has traditionally been preparatory for the profession of HVAC&R. They must have a GPA of 3.0 or higher and at least 2 full years of undergraduate study remaining. Selection is based on potential service to the HVAC&R profession, financial need, leadership ability, recommendations from instructors, and character. **Deadline for Receipt:** November of each year.

255 ■ AMERICAN SOCIETY FOR QUALITY

Attn: Food, Drug and Cosmetic Division
600 North Plankinton Avenue
P.O. Box 3005
Milwaukee, WI 53201-3005
Tel: (414)272-8575
Free: 800-248-1946
Fax: (414)272-1734
E-mail: cs@asqu.org
Web Site: http://www.asq.org/fdc/awards/index.html
To provide financial assistance to members and family members of the Food, Drug and Cosmetic (FD&C) division of the American Society for Quality (ASQ) who are interested in working on a college degree.

Title of Award: FD&C Founders Scholarship **Area, Field, or Subject:** General studies/Field of study not specified **Level of Education for which Award is Granted:** Four Year College **Number Awarded:** 1 each year. **Funds Available:** The stipend is $1,000 per year. **Duration:** 4 years.

Eligibility Requirements: This program is open to FD&C members and their immediate family members who have been accepted at a 4-year college or university. Applicants must have a high school GPA of 2.5 or higher. Along with their application, they must submit a 10-page article on what quality means to them. Selection is based on that article, academic achievement as measured by GPA and SAT or ACT scores, honors and awards, extracurricular activities, and paid and volunteer employment experience. **Additional Information:** Information is also available from Barbara Dixon, FD&C Scholarship Chair, c/o Telik, Inc., 3165 Porter Drive, Palo Alto, CA 94304, E-mail: bdixon@telik.com.

256 ■ AMERICAN SOCIETY FOR QUALITY

Attn: Service Quality Division
600 North Plankinton Avenue
P.O. Box 3005
Milwaukee, WI 53201-3005

Tel: (414)272-8575
Free: 800-248-1946
Fax: (414)272-1734
E-mail: cs@asqu.org
Web Site: http://www.asq.org/service/scholarship/index.html
To provide financial assistance for college to members of the Service Quality Division (SQD) of the American Society for Quality (ASQ), their families, and people they sponsor.

Title of Award: A.C. Rosander Service Quality Scholarship **Area, Field, or Subject:** General studies/Field of study not specified **Level of Education for which Award is Granted:** Undergraduate **Number Awarded:** Varies each year. **Funds Available:** The stipend is at least $1,500 per year. Funds are paid directly to the university for tuition, books, and associated fees. **Duration:** 1 year.

Eligibility Requirements: This program is open to students entering or enrolled in an accredited university. Applicants may be current members of SQD, the family of a member, or sponsored by a member, although SQD members receive priority. An essay, from 3 to 5 pages in length on the topic "Leveraging Innovation in Service Quality," must accompany each application. Selection of scholarship recipients is based on the essay (40 points), the application (30 points), academic achievement (20 points), and SQD membership (10 points). **Deadline for Receipt:** May of each year. **Additional Information:** This program began in 2004. Information is also available from Nicole Van Hill, Allstate Insurance Company, 3100 Sanders Road, Suite J2A, Northbrook, IL 60062, (847) 402-0442, E-mail: nvan2@allstate.com.

257 ■ AMERICAN SOCIETY OF SAFETY ENGINEERS-NEW JERSEY CHAPTER

c/o New Jersey State Safety Council
6 Commerce Drive
Cranford, NJ 07016
Tel: (732)269-7683
Web Site: http://www.njasse.org/scholarships.htm
To provide financial assistance to undergraduate and graduate students who are relatives of members of the New Jersey chapter of the American Society of Safety Engineers (ASSE).

Title of Award: Joyce Cunningham Scholarship **Area, Field, or Subject:** General studies/Field of study not specified **Level of Education for which Award is Granted:** Graduate, Undergraduate **Number Awarded:** 1 or more each year. **Funds Available:** The stipend is $1,000.

Eligibility Requirements: This program is open to undergraduate and graduate students who are the children, nieces, nephews, and grandchildren of members of the New Jersey ASSE chapter. Applicants must be residents of New Jersey, although they may be enrolled at a college or university in any state. They must have a GPA of 2.5 or higher. Selection is based on GPA; leadership skills as demonstrated by participation in extracurricular activities; involvement in professional organizations, communication skills; and awards and honors. Financial need is not considered. **Deadline for Receipt:** February, May, August, or November of each year.

258 ■ AMERICAN SOCIETY OF WOMEN ACCOUNTANTS-ST. LOUIS CHAPTER

c/o Kimberly Temme
Maryville University
13550 Conway Road
St. Louis, MO 63141
Tel: (314)529-9639
E-mail: ktemme@maryville.edu
Web Site: http://www.aswastlouis.org/scholarships/geninfo.html
To provide financial assistance to accounting students at colleges and universities in Missouri and eastern Illinois.

Title of Award: Darthe F. Nay Scholarships **Area, Field, or Subject:** Accounting **Level of Education for which Award is Granted:** Four Year College **Number Awarded:** Up to 4 each year: 2 at $1,000 and 2 at $500. **Funds Available:** Stipends are $1,000 or $500. Funds are paid to the university or college. **Duration:** 1 year.

Eligibility Requirements: This program is open to students majoring in accounting at a college or university in Missouri or eastern Illinois. Applicants must have completed 60 semester hours with at least 12 hours in accounting and a GPA of 3.0 or higher. Selection is based on leadership potential, financial need, and classroom attendance. **Deadline for Receipt:** February of each year.

259 ■ AMERICAN WATER SKI EDUCATIONAL FOUNDATION
Attn: Director
1251 Holy Cow Road
Polk City, FL 33868-8200
Tel: (863)324-2472
Fax: (863)324-3996
E-mail: awsefhalloffame@cs.com
Web Site: http://www.waterskihalloffame.com
To provide financial assistance to currently-enrolled college students who participate in water skiing.
Title of Award: American Water Ski Educational Foundation Scholarships **Area, Field, or Subject:** General studies/Field of study not specified **Level of Education for which Award is Granted:** Undergraduate **Number Awarded:** 6 each year. **Funds Available:** The stipend is $1,500 per year. **Duration:** 1 year; may be renewed for up to 2 additional years. **Eligibility Requirements:** Applicants must be full-time students at 2-year or 4-year accredited colleges. They must have completed at least their freshmen year and be active members of a sport division within USA Water Ski (AWSA, ABC, AKA, WSDA, NSSA, NCWSA, NWSRA, and AWA). U.S. citizenship is required. Along with their application, they must submit a 500-word essay on a topic that changes annually but relates to water skiing; recently, the topic was, "How can USA Water Ski create tournaments so that the competing is more enjoyable and more fun for the athletes participating?" Selection is based on the essay, academic record, leadership, extracurricular involvement, letters of recommendation, AWSA membership activities, and financial need. **Deadline for Receipt:** March of each year. **Additional Information:** This program includes the following named scholarships: the Jennifer Odom Scholarship, the AWSEF Scholarship, the William D. Clifford Scholarship, the Barbara Bolding/Jim Grew Scholarship, the Elmer Stalling/Southern Region Scholarship, and the "Big" Al Wagner/Western Region Scholarship.

260 ■ AMERICAN WATER SKI EDUCATIONAL FOUNDATION
Attn: Director
1251 Holy Cow Road
Polk City, FL 33868-8200
Tel: (863)324-2472
Fax: (863)324-3996
E-mail: awsefhalloffame@cs.com
Web Site: http://www.waterskihalloffame.com
To provide financial assistance and work experience to upper-division and graduate students who are interested in water skiing.
Title of Award: Nancie Rideout-Robertson Bonus Internship Scholarship **Area, Field, or Subject:** General studies/Field of study not specified **Level of Education for which Award is Granted:** Four Year College, Graduate **Number Awarded:** 1 each year. **Funds Available:** The stipend is $2,500. **Duration:** 1 year, including at least 4 weeks (during semester breaks, spring break, summer) at AWSEF headquarters in Polk City, Florida. **Eligibility Requirements:** This program is open to upper-division and graduate students who are members of the United States Water Ski Association (USWSA) and the American Water Ski Educational Foundation (AWSEF). Applicants must have participated in the sport of water skiing as a skier, official, and/or volunteer worker and be able to demonstrate leadership potential. They must have a GPA of at least "B+" overall and an "A" average in their major field of study. Along with their application, they must submit 1) a 500-word personal statement on why they wish to be awarded this scholarship and serve as an intern at AWSEF; and 2) an internship proposal, covering their learning goals and how they want to apply the skills and knowledge related to their program of study in college or graduate school to their internship, the kinds of contributions they think they can make toward the goals of AWSEF, how they would allocate their time toward their internship activities, when they could complete their "onsite" requirement, and the kinds of skills and knowledge of people with whom they might like to work during their internship. **Deadline for Receipt:** January of each year. **Additional Information:** This program was established in 2004.

261 ■ AMVETS-DEPARTMENT OF ILLINOIS
2200 South Sixth Street
Springfield, IL 62703
Tel: (217)528-4713
Free: 800-638-VETS

Fax: (217)528-9896
Web Site: http://www.amvets.com/scholarship.htm
To provide financial assistance for college to high school seniors in Illinois who have participated in Junior ROTC (JROTC), especially children and grandchildren of veterans.
Title of Award: Illinois AMVETS Junior ROTC Scholarships **Area, Field, or Subject:** General studies/Field of study not specified **Level of Education for which Award is Granted:** Undergraduate **Number Awarded:** 1 or more each year. **Funds Available:** The stipend is $1,000 per year. **Duration:** 4 years. **Eligibility Requirements:** This program is open to seniors graduating from high schools in Illinois who have taken the ACT or SAT and have participated in the JROTC program. Financial need is considered in the selection process. Priority is given to children and grandchildren of veterans. **Deadline for Receipt:** February of each year.

262 ■ AMVETS-DEPARTMENT OF ILLINOIS
2200 South Sixth Street
Springfield, IL 62703
Tel: (217)528-4713
Free: 800-638-VETS
Fax: (217)528-9896
Web Site: http://www.amvets.com/scholarship.htm
To provide financial assistance for college to high school seniors in Illinois, especially children and grandchildren of veterans.
Title of Award: Illinois AMVETS Service Foundation Scholarships **Area, Field, or Subject:** General studies/Field of study not specified **Level of Education for which Award is Granted:** Undergraduate **Number Awarded:** Up to 30 each year. **Funds Available:** The stipend is $1,000 per year. **Duration:** 4 years. **Eligibility Requirements:** This program is open to seniors graduating from high schools in Illinois who have taken the ACT or SAT. Financial need is considered in the selection process. Priority is given to children and grandchildren of veterans. **Deadline for Receipt:** February of each year.

263 ■ AMVETS-DEPARTMENT OF ILLINOIS
2200 South Sixth Street
Springfield, IL 62703
Tel: (217)528-4713
Free: 800-638-VETS
Fax: (217)528-9896
Web Site: http://www.amvets.com/scholarship.htm
To provide financial assistance to high school seniors in Illinois, especially children and grandchildren of veterans, who are interested in attending trade school.
Title of Award: Illinois AMVETS Trade School Scholarships **Area, Field, or Subject:** General studies/Field of study not specified **Level of Education for which Award is Granted:** Vocational/Occupational **Number Awarded:** 1 or more each year. **Funds Available:** The stipend is $1,000 per year. **Duration:** 2 years. **Eligibility Requirements:** This program is open to seniors graduating from high schools in Illinois who have been accepted at an approved trade school. Financial need is considered in the selection process. Priority is given to children and grandchildren of veterans. **Deadline for Receipt:** February of each year.

264 ■ AMVETS LADIES AUXILIARY
Attn: National Scholarship Officer
4647 Forbes Boulevard
Lanham, MD 20706-4380
Tel: (301)459-6255
Fax: (301)459-5403
E-mail: auxiliary@amvets.org
Web Site: http://amvetsaux.org/programs.htm
To provide financial assistance to members and certain dependents of members of AMVETS Auxiliary who are already enrolled in college.
Title of Award: AMVETS National Ladies Auxiliary Scholarships **Area, Field, or Subject:** General studies/Field of study not specified **Level of Education for which Award is Granted:** Undergraduate **Number Awarded:** Up to 7 each year: 2 at $1,000 and 5 at $750. **Funds Available:** Scholarships are $1,000 or $750 each. **Duration:** 1 year. **Eligibility Requirements:** Applicants must belong to AMVETS Auxiliary or be the child or grandchild of a member. They must be in at least the

second year of undergraduate study at an accredited college or university. Applications must include 3 letters of recommendation and an essay (from 200 to 500 words) about their past accomplishments, career and educational goals, and objectives for the future. Selection is based on the letters of reference (15%), academic record (25%), the essay (25%), and financial need (35%). **Deadline for Receipt:** May of each year.

265 ■ AMVETS NATIONAL HEADQUARTERS

Attn: Scholarships
4647 Forbes Boulevard
Lanham, MD 20706-3807
Tel: (301)459-9600; 877-7-AMVETS
Fax: (301)459-7924
E-mail: amvets@amvets.org
Web Site: http://www.amvets.org
To provide financial assistance for college to the children and grandchildren of members of AMVETS who have participated in Junior Reserve Officers' Training Corps (JROTC) in high school.
Title of Award: AMVETS JROTC Scholarships **Area, Field, or Subject:** General studies/Field of study not specified **Level of Education for which Award is Granted:** Undergraduate **Number Awarded:** 1 each year. **Funds Available:** The stipend is $1,000 per year. **Duration:** 1 year; nonrenewable.

Eligibility Requirements: This program is open to graduating high school seniors who are JROTC cadets and the children or grandchildren of an AMVETS member or of a deceased veteran who would have been eligible to be an AMVETS member. U.S. citizenship is required. Applicants must be interested in working full time on an undergraduate degree at an accredited college, university, or technical/trade school. Selection is based on financial need, academic promise (GPA of 3.0 or higher), involvement in extracurricular activities, and an essay of 50 to 100 words on "What a Higher Education Means to Me." **Deadline for Receipt:** April of each year. **Additional Information:** Requests for applications must be accompanied by a self-addressed stamped envelope.

266 ■ AMVETS NATIONAL HEADQUARTERS

Attn: Scholarships
4647 Forbes Boulevard
Lanham, MD 20706-3807
Tel: (301)459-9600; 877-7-AMVETS
Fax: (301)459-7924
E-mail: amvets@amvets.org
Web Site: http://www.amvets.org
To provide financial assistance to the children and grandchildren of members of AMVETS who are entering college.
Title of Award: AMVETS National Scholarships for Entering College Freshmen **Area, Field, or Subject:** General studies/Field of study not specified **Level of Education for which Award is Granted:** Undergraduate **Number Awarded:** 6 each year (1 in each AMVETS national district). **Funds Available:** The stipend is $1,000 per year. **Duration:** 4 years (provided the recipient maintains a GPA of 2.0 or higher).

Eligibility Requirements: This program is open to graduating high school seniors who are the children or grandchildren of an AMVETS member or of a deceased veteran who would have been eligible to be an AMVETS member. U.S. citizenship is required. Selection is based on financial need, academic promise (GPA of 3.0 or higher), involvement in extracurricular activities, and an essay of 50 to 100 words on "What a Higher Education Means to Me." **Deadline for Receipt:** April of each year. **Additional Information:** Requests for applications must be accompanied by a self-addressed stamped envelope.

267 ■ AMVETS NATIONAL HEADQUARTERS

Attn: Scholarships
4647 Forbes Boulevard
Lanham, MD 20706-3807
Tel: (301)459-9600; 877-7-AMVETS
Fax: (301)459-7924
E-mail: amvets@amvets.org
Web Site: http://www.amvets.org
To provide financial assistance for college or graduate school to certain veterans who are members of AMVETS.
Title of Award: AMVETS National Scholarships for Veterans **Area, Field, or Subject:** General studies/Field of study not specified **Level of Educa-**

tion for which Award is Granted: Graduate, Undergraduate **Number Awarded:** 3 each year. **Funds Available:** The stipend is $1,000 per year. **Duration:** Up to 4 years.
Eligibility Requirements: This program is open to AMVETS members who are veterans and U.S. citizens. Applicants must be interested in working full time on an undergraduate degree, graduate degree, or certification from an accredited technical/trade school. Selection is based on financial need, academic promise, military duty and awards, volunteer activities, community services, jobs held during the past 4 years, and an essay of 50 to 100 words on "What a Higher Education Means to Me." **Deadline for Receipt:** April of each year. **Additional Information:** Requests for applications must be accompanied by a self-addressed stamped envelope.

268 ■ ANCHOR SCHOLARSHIP FOUNDATION

P.O. Box 9535
Norfolk, VA 23505
Tel: (757)374-3769
E-mail: cnslschf@erols.com
Web Site: http://www.anchorscholarship.com
To provide financial assistance for college to dependents of active-duty or retired personnel serving in the Naval Surface Forces.
Title of Award: Anchor Scholarship Foundation Award **Area, Field, or Subject:** General studies/Field of study not specified **Level of Education for which Award is Granted:** Four Year College **Number Awarded:** Varies each year; recently, 35 of these scholarships, worth $60,000, were awarded. **Funds Available:** Stipends range up to $2,000. **Duration:** 1 year; may be renewed.
Eligibility Requirements: This program is open to dependents of active-duty or retired personnel who have served at least 6 years (need not be consecutive) in a unit under the administrative control of Commanders, Naval Surface Forces, U.S. Atlantic Fleet, or U.S. Pacific Fleet. Applicants must be attending or planning to attend an accredited 4-year college or university to work on a bachelor's degree as a full-time student. Selection is based on academic proficiency, extracurricular activities, character, all-around ability, and financial need. **Deadline for Receipt:** March of each year. **Additional Information:** This foundation was established in 1980 and limited to personnel who had served in the Atlantic Fleet. Its program was originally known as the SURFLANT Scholarship Foundation Award. In 2004, the program was expanded to include those who served in the Pacific Fleet and the current name was adopted. Requests for applications must be accompanied by a self-addressed stamped envelope.

269 ■ ARABIAN HORSE ASSOCIATION

Attn: Sweepstakes Scholarships
10805 East Bethany Drive
Aurora, CO 80014
Tel: (303)696-4500
Fax: (303)696-4599
Web Site: http://www.arabianhorses.org/education/education_scholarships_foundation.asp
To provide financial assistance for college to high school seniors who are members of the Arabian Horse Association (AHA).
Title of Award: International Arabian Breeders Sweepstakes Scholarships **Area, Field, or Subject:** General studies/Field of study not specified **Level of Education for which Award is Granted:** Undergraduate **Number Awarded:** 40 each year. **Funds Available:** The stipend is $2,500. **Duration:** 1 year.
Eligibility Requirements: This program is open to AHA members who are graduating from high school and planning to attend an accredited college or university as a full-time student. Applicants must have competed at the regional or national level on a sweepstakes nominated horse. Along with their application, they must submit their most recent high school transcript, a list of sweepstakes horses and the regional or national competitions where they have shown, a description of their extracurricular activities and leadership roles, a list of any honors or academic distinctions they have received, a description of their specific equine involvement over the past 2 years, and a brief essay on their future career goals. Selection is based on merit. **Deadline for Receipt:** June of each year.

Additional Information: Funding for this program, which began in 2002, is provided by the International Arabian Breeders Sweepstakes Commission.

270 ■ ARABIAN HORSE FOUNDATION
Attn: Scholarship Office
Ten Farnham Park Drive
Houston, TX 77024-7501
Tel: (713)952-7081
Fax: (713)977-9883
E-mail: jean@parkwaychevrolet.com
Web Site: http://pages.sbcglobal.net/jvenhaus/horse/Scholar/scholar.html
To provide financial assistance to undergraduate and graduate students who have a record of equine involvement.
Title of Award: Arabian Horse Foundation General Scholarships **Area, Field, or Subject:** General studies/Field of study not specified **Level of Education for which Award is Granted:** Graduate, Undergraduate **Number Awarded:** 1 or more each year. **Funds Available:** A stipend is awarded (amount not specified). **Duration:** 1 year; may be renewed if the recipient maintains a GPA of 2.5 or higher with no grade below a "D."
Eligibility Requirements: This program is open to students who have a record of involvement with horses. Applicants must be enrolled or planning to enroll as a full-time undergraduate or graduate student at an accredited college or university. High school seniors must have a GPA of "B" or higher; college students must have at least a 3.5 GPA. Along with their application, they must submit information on their financial need, honors or academic awards, extracurricular activities and offices, leadership role, career goal, and equine involvement for the past 2 years. **Deadline for Receipt:** January of each year.

271 ■ ARABIAN HORSE FOUNDATION
Attn: Scholarship Office
Ten Farnham Park Drive
Houston, TX 77024-7501
Tel: (713)952-7081
Fax: (713)977-9883
E-mail: jean@parkwaychevrolet.com
Web Site: http://pages.sbcglobal.net/jvenhaus/horse/Scholar/scholar.html
To provide financial assistance to undergraduate and graduate students who have a record of equine involvement.
Title of Award: Arabian Horse Foundation Regional Scholarships **Area, Field, or Subject:** General studies/Field of study not specified **Level of Education for which Award is Granted:** Graduate, Undergraduate **Number Awarded:** 18 each year: 1 in each region of the Arabian Horse Association. **Funds Available:** A stipend is awarded (amount not specified). **Duration:** 1 year; may be renewed if the recipient maintains of GPA of 2.5 or higher with no grade below a "D."
Eligibility Requirements: This program is open to students who have a record of involvement with horses. Applicants must be enrolled or planning to enroll as a full-time undergraduate or graduate student at an accredited college or university. High school seniors must have a GPA of "B" or higher; college students must have at least a 3.5 GPA. Along with their application, they must submit information on their financial need, honors or academic awards, extracurricular activities and offices, leadership role, career goal, and equine involvement for the past 2 years. **Deadline for Receipt:** January of each year.

272 ■ ARABIAN HORSE FOUNDATION
Attn: Scholarship Office
Ten Farnham Park Drive
Houston, TX 77024-7501
Tel: (713)952-7081
Fax: (713)977-9883
E-mail: jean@parkwaychevrolet.com
Web Site: http://pages.sbcglobal.net/jvenhaus/horse/Scholar/scholar.html
To provide financial assistance to undergraduate and graduate students who have a record of equine involvement.
Title of Award: Jon Oostermeyer Memorial Scholarship **Area, Field, or Subject:** General studies/Field of study not specified **Level of Education for which Award is Granted:** Graduate, Undergraduate **Number Awarded:** 1 or more each year. **Funds Available:** A stipend is awarded (amount not specified). **Duration:** 1 year; may be renewed if the recipient maintains a GPA of 2.5 or higher with no grade below a "D."

Eligibility Requirements: This program is open to students who have a record of involvement with horses. Applicants must be enrolled or planning to enroll as a full-time undergraduate or graduate student at an accredited college or university. High school seniors must have a GPA of "B" or higher; college students must have at least a 3.5 GPA. Along with their application, they must submit information on their financial need, honors or academic awards, extracurricular activities and offices, leadership role, career goal, and equine involvement for the past 2 years. **Deadline for Receipt:** January of each year.

273 ■ ARABIAN HORSE FOUNDATION
Attn: Scholarship Office
Ten Farnham Park Drive
Houston, TX 77024-7501
Tel: (713)952-7081
Fax: (713)977-9883
E-mail: jean@parkwaychevrolet.com
Web Site: http://pages.sbcglobal.net/jvenhaus/horse/Scholar/scholar.html
To provide financial assistance for college to high school students who have a record of equine involvement.
Title of Award: Spirit of a Winner Scholarship **Area, Field, or Subject:** General studies/Field of study not specified **Level of Education for which Award is Granted:** Undergraduate **Number Awarded:** 7 each year. **Funds Available:** The stipend is $2,000 per year. **Duration:** 1 year.
Eligibility Requirements: This program is open to students who have a record of involvement with horses. Applicants must be juniors or seniors in high school who have shown at the Youth Nationals of the Arabian Horse Association. They must have a GPA of "B" or higher. Along with their application, they must submit information on their financial need, honors or academic awards, extracurricular activities and offices, leadership role, career goal, and equine involvement for the past 2 years. **Deadline for Receipt:** January of each year.

274 ■ ARABIAN HORSE FOUNDATION
Attn: Scholarship Office
Ten Farnham Park Drive
Houston, TX 77024-7501
Tel: (713)952-7081
Fax: (713)977-9883
E-mail: jean@parkwaychevrolet.com
Web Site: http://pages.sbcglobal.net/jvenhaus/horse/Scholar/scholar.html
To provide financial assistance to undergraduate and graduate students who have a record of equine involvement.
Title of Award: Don Thompson Memorial Scholarship **Area, Field, or Subject:** General studies/Field of study not specified **Level of Education for which Award is Granted:** Graduate, Undergraduate **Number Awarded:** 1 or more each year. **Funds Available:** A stipend is awarded (amount not specified). **Duration:** 1 year; may be renewed if the recipient maintains a GPA of 2.5 or higher with no grade below a "D."
Eligibility Requirements: This program is open to students who have a record of involvement with horses. Applicants must be enrolled or planning to enroll as a full-time undergraduate or graduate student at an accredited college or university. Preference is given to students who have a GPA between 2.8 and 3.25, whose financial resources are modest, and who are attending a school with relatively low tuition. Along with their application, they must submit information on their financial need, honors or academic awards, extracurricular activities and offices, leadership role, career goal, and equine involvement for the past 2 years. **Deadline for Receipt:** January of each year.

275 ■ ARABIAN HORSE TRUST
12000 Zuni Street
Westminster, CO 80234-2300
Tel: (303)450-4710
Fax: (303)450-4707
Web Site: http://www.imh.org/imh/bw/arabian.html
To provide financial assistance to high school seniors who have been involved with horses and are interested in attending college.
Title of Award: William Zekan Memorial Scholarship **Area, Field, or Subject:** General studies/Field of study not specified **Level of Education for which Award is Granted:** Undergraduate **Number Awarded:** At least 1 each year. **Funds Available:** The stipend is $2,500. **Duration:** 1 year; nonrenewable.

Eligibility Requirements: Applicants must be high school seniors, be able to demonstrate financial need, and have an ongoing interest in and commitment to Arabian horses. Selection is based on both need and achievement. **Deadline for Receipt:** January of each year. **Additional Information:** The fund was established in 1992.

276 ■ ARIZONA ARMY NATIONAL GUARD

Soldier Support Center
Attn: Education
5636 East McDowell Road
Phoenix, AZ 85008-3495
Tel: (602)267-2885
Fax: (602)267-2912
Web Site: http://www.az.ngb.army.mil
To provide financial assistance for college to members of the Arizona Army or Air National Guard.
Title of Award: Arizona National Guard State Education Reimbursement Program **Area, Field, or Subject:** General studies/Field of study not specified **Level of Education for which Award is Granted:** Undergraduate **Number Awarded:** Varies each year. **Funds Available:** Recipients are reimbursed for the actual cost of completed education, to a maximum of $250 per semester hour or $6,500 per state fiscal year. **Duration:** 1 year; may be renewed if the recipient maintains satisfactory drill performance.
Eligibility Requirements: This program is open to members of the Arizona Army and Air National Guard who have completed Initial Active Duty for Training (IADT). Applicants must have attended annual training or equivalent training and may not have any AWOLs. They must be working on a college degree or certification at an Arizona institution. **Deadline for Receipt:** Applications for reimbursement must be submitted no later than 15 calendar days after the start of school.

277 ■ ARIZONA COMMISSION FOR POSTSECONDARY EDUCATION

2020 North Central Avenue, Suite 550
Phoenix, AZ 85004-4503
Tel: (602)258-2435
Fax: (602)258-2483
E-mail: toni@azhighered.org
Web Site: http://www.azhighered.org
To provide financial assistance to undergraduate and graduate students in Arizona who can demonstrate financial need.
Title of Award: Arizona Leveraging Educational Assistance Partnership Grants **Area, Field, or Subject:** General studies/Field of study not specified **Level of Education for which Award is Granted:** Graduate, Undergraduate **Number Awarded:** Varies each year. **Funds Available:** Awards range from $100 to $2,500 per year. **Duration:** 1 year; may be renewed.
Eligibility Requirements: This program is open to Arizona residents who are attending or planning to attend a participating Arizona postsecondary educational institution as either a full-time or part-time undergraduate or graduate student. Applicants must be able to demonstrate financial need. **Deadline for Receipt:** Each participating institution in Arizona sets its own deadline. **Additional Information:** This program was formerly known as the Arizona State Student Incentive Grant Program.

278 ■ ARIZONA COMMISSION FOR POSTSECONDARY EDUCATION

2020 North Central Avenue, Suite 550
Phoenix, AZ 85004-4503
Tel: (602)258-2435
Fax: (602)258-2483
E-mail: toni@azhighered.org
Web Site: http://www.azhighered.org
To provide financial assistance to graduates of Arizona community colleges who wish to attend a private postsecondary institution in the state.
Title of Award: Arizona Private Postsecondary Education Student Financial Assistance Program **Area, Field, or Subject:** General studies/Field of study not specified **Level of Education for which Award is Granted:** Four Year College **Number Awarded:** Varies; grants are awarded on a priority of receipt basis. **Funds Available:** The award is $1,500 per year. Participants must agree when they accept the award to repay the full amount if they do not graduate with their bachelor's degree within 3 years of the initial receipt of the award. **Duration:** 2 years.
Eligibility Requirements: This program is open to students who have graduated or are about to graduate from a public community college in

Arizona with an associate degree. Applicants must be planning to attend a private baccalaureate degree-granting institution in Arizona and be enrolled in a bachelor's degree program on a full-time basis. They must be able to demonstrate financial need. **Deadline for Receipt:** Applications are accepted throughout the year to accommodate the various enrollment periods for the different private postsecondary institutions. **Additional Information:** This program was formerly known as the Arizona Postsecondary Education Voucher Program.

279 ■ ARIZONA FRIENDS OF FOSTER CHILDREN FOUNDATION

Attn: Scholarships
P.O. Box 36233
Phoenix, AZ 85067-6233
Tel: (602)252-9445
Fax: (602)264-6802
E-mail: info@affcf.org
Web Site: http://www.affcf.org/scholar.html
To provide financial assistance for college to Arizona residents who have been foster children.
Title of Award: AFFCF Scholarships **Area, Field, or Subject:** General studies/Field of study not specified **Level of Education for which Award is Granted:** Undergraduate **Number Awarded:** Varies each year. **Funds Available:** The stipend depends on the need of the recipient. **Duration:** 1 year; may be renewed.
Eligibility Requirements: This program is open to current and former wards of the state of Arizona who are enrolled at or accepted into a school, college, course of study, or other educational program. Applicants must be able to demonstrate financial need. Awards are presented on a first-come, first-served basis, with preference to students applying to renew their scholarship. **Deadline for Receipt:** Applications may be submitted at any time.

280 ■ ARIZONA KIDNEY FOUNDATION

Attn: Patient Services Director
4203 East Indian School Road, Suite 140
Phoenix, AZ 85018
Tel: (602)840-1644
Fax: (602)840-2360
E-mail: glennas@azkidney.org
Web Site: http://www.azkidney.org
To provide financial assistance for college to kidney patients in Arizona.
Title of Award: Peter and Bruce Bidstrup Scholarship Fund **Area, Field, or Subject:** General studies/Field of study not specified **Level of Education for which Award is Granted:** Undergraduate **Number Awarded:** Varies each year. **Funds Available:** This scholarship pays the tuition fees at schools in Arizona.
Eligibility Requirements: This program is open to students in Arizona who are undergoing dialysis treatment or have received kidney transplants. Applicants must be attending or planning to attend a college, community college, or technical school in Arizona. Financial need is considered in the selection process. **Additional Information:** This scholarship fund was established in 1985 to honor Peter and Bruce Bidstrup, who did not survive kidney disease. Its selection committee is chaired by their mother, Carol Bidstrup. Recipients must attend school in Arizona.

281 ■ ARKANSAS COMMUNITY FOUNDATION

700 South Rock Street
Little Rock, AR 72202
Tel: (501)372-1116
Free: 800-220-ARCF
Fax: (501)372-1166
E-mail: acf@arcf.org
Web Site: http://www.arcf.org
To provide financial assistance for college to children of deceased veterans or other government officials in Arkansas.
Title of Award: Arkansas Service Memorial Fund **Area, Field, or Subject:** General studies/Field of study not specified **Level of Education for which Award is Granted:** Undergraduate **Number Awarded:** Varies each year; since this program was established, it has awarded 115 scholarships worth $125,000. **Funds Available:** Stipends range from $500 to $5,000 per year. **Duration:** 1 year; may be renewed as long as the recipient is making satisfactory progress toward a degree.

Eligibility Requirements: This program is open to seniors graduating from high schools in Arkansas whose parent died in service to the community, state, or nation. Applicants must be planning to attend an accredited 2- or 4-year college in Arkansas on a full-time basis. Selection is based on such factors as academics, school activities, community service, future goals, faculty and advisor recommendations, and financial need. **Deadline for Receipt:** April of each year. **Additional Information:** This program was established in 1984.

282 ■ ARKANSAS COMMUNITY FOUNDATION

700 South Rock Street
Little Rock, AR 72202
Tel: (501)372-1116
Free: 800-220-ARCF
Fax: (501)372-1166
E-mail: acf@arcf.org
Web Site: http://www.arcf.org
To provide financial assistance for college to minorities graduating from high schools in Arkansas.
Title of Award: SBC L.C. and Daisy Bates Memorial Scholarship **Area, Field, or Subject:** General studies/Field of study not specified **Level of Education for which Award is Granted:** Four Year College **Number Awarded:** Varies each year; since this program was established, it has awarded more than $875,000 to more than 100 Arkansas high school students. **Funds Available:** The stipend is $2,500 per year. Funds are paid directly to the recipient's school and may be used for any legitimate educational expense, such as tuition, fees, books, room, and board. **Duration:** 1 year.
Eligibility Requirements: Applicants must be minority high school seniors, U.S. citizens, and residents of Arkansas. They must be planning to attend an accredited 4-year college in Arkansas on a full-time basis. Along with their application, they must submit an essay, up to 500 words, on their plans as they relate to their educational and career objectives and long-term goals. Selection is based on such factors as academics, school activities, community service, future goals, faculty and advisor recommendations, and financial need. **Deadline for Receipt:** March of each year. **Additional Information:** This program, which began in 1987, is funded by the SBC Foundation.

283 ■ ARKANSAS DEPARTMENT OF HIGHER EDUCATION

Attn: Financial Aid Division
114 East Capitol Avenue
Little Rock, AR 72201-3818
Tel: (501)371-2050
Free: 800-54-STUDY
Fax: (501)371-2001
E-mail: finaid@adhe.arknet.edu
Web Site: http://www.arkansashighered.com/challenge.html
To provide financial assistance to undergraduate students in Arkansas.
Title of Award: Arkansas Academic Challenge Scholarship **Area, Field, or Subject:** General studies/Field of study not specified **Level of Education for which Award is Granted:** Undergraduate **Number Awarded:** Varies each year; recently, 8,728 of these scholarships were awarded. **Funds Available:** The maximum stipend is $3,500 per year. **Duration:** 1 year; may be renewed up to 3 additional years if the recipient maintains full-time enrollment and a GPA of 2.75 or higher.
Eligibility Requirements: This program is open to Arkansas residents who are graduating high school seniors, are planning to attend an approved Arkansas 2- or 4-year public or private college or university, and can demonstrate financial need. The maximum family income is $60,000 for a family with 1 dependent child; it increases $5,000 for each additional dependent child and another $10,000 for each additional dependent child in college full time. Eligibility depends on a correlation between ACT scores, GPA, and whether the applicant wishes to attend a 2-year or a 4-year institution. Students with an ACT score of 15 to 18 must have a GPA of 3.25 or higher if they wish to attend a 4-year school or 3.0 for a 2-year school. Students with an ACT score of 19 must have a GPA of 3.0 or higher if they wish to attend a 4-year school or 2.75 for a 2-year school. Students with an ACT score of 20 to 24 must have a GPA of 2.75 or higher if they wish to attend a 4-year school or 2.5 for a 2-year school. Students with an ACT score of 25 to 36 must have a GPA of 2.5 or higher if they wish to attend a 4-year school or 2.25 for a 2-year school. **Deadline for Receipt:** May of each year. **Additional Information:** This program was established in 1991.

284 ■ ARKANSAS DEPARTMENT OF HIGHER EDUCATION

Attn: Financial Aid Division
114 East Capitol Avenue
Little Rock, AR 72201-3818
Tel: (501)371-2050
Free: 800-54-STUDY
Fax: (501)371-2001
E-mail: finaid@adhe.arknet.edu
Web Site: http://www.arkansashighered.com/governorscholars.html
To provide financial assistance to exceptional high school seniors in Arkansas.
Title of Award: Arkansas Governor's Distinguished Scholars Program **Area, Field, or Subject:** General studies/Field of study not specified **Level of Education for which Award is Granted:** Undergraduate **Number Awarded:** Up to 250 each year. **Funds Available:** Stipends up to $10,000 per year are provided. **Duration:** 1 year; may be renewed for up to 3 additional years provided the recipient maintains a cumulative GPA of 3.25 or higher and completes at least 30 semester hours each year.
Eligibility Requirements: This program is open to high school seniors who are U.S. citizens or permanent residents, are residents of Arkansas, can demonstrate leadership, and are planning to enroll in a college or university in Arkansas. Applicants must have an SAT score of 1410 or higher, have an ACT score of 32 or higher, be a National Merit Finalist or a National Achievement Scholar, or have a GPA of 3.5 or higher. Selection is based on high school GPA, class rank, ACT or SAT score, school leadership, and community leadership. **Deadline for Receipt:** January of each year. **Additional Information:** This program was established in 1997.

285 ■ ARKANSAS DEPARTMENT OF HIGHER EDUCATION

Attn: Financial Aid Division
114 East Capitol Avenue
Little Rock, AR 72201-3818
Tel: (501)371-2050
Free: 800-54-STUDY
Fax: (501)371-2001
E-mail: finaid@adhe.arknet.edu
Web Site: http://www.arkansashighered.com/governorscholars.html
To provide financial assistance to outstanding high school seniors in Arkansas.
Title of Award: Arkansas Governor's Scholars Program **Area, Field, or Subject:** General studies/Field of study not specified **Level of Education for which Award is Granted:** Undergraduate **Number Awarded:** Up to 75 each year. **Funds Available:** The stipend is $4,000 per year. **Duration:** 1 year; may be renewed for up to 3 additional years provided the recipient maintains a 3.0 cumulative GPA and completes at least 30 semester hours each year.
Eligibility Requirements: This program is open to high school seniors who are U.S. citizens or permanent residents, are residents of Arkansas, can demonstrate leadership, and are planning to enroll in a college or university in the state. Applicants must have an SAT score of 1220 or higher, an ACT score of 27 or higher, or a GPA of 3.5 or higher in academic courses. Selection is based on high school GPA, class rank, ACT or SAT score, school leadership, and community leadership. **Deadline for Receipt:** January of each year. **Additional Information:** This program was established in 1983.

286 ■ ARKANSAS DEPARTMENT OF HIGHER EDUCATION

Attn: Financial Aid Division
114 East Capitol Avenue
Little Rock, AR 72201-3818
Tel: (501)371-2050
Free: 800-54-STUDY
Fax: (501)371-2001
E-mail: finaid@adhe.arknet.edu
Web Site: http://www.arkansashighered.com/lawenforcement.html
To provide financial assistance for undergraduate education to the dependents of deceased or disabled Arkansas law enforcement officers, fire fighters, or other designated public employees.
Title of Award: Arkansas Law Enforcement Officers' Dependents' Scholarships **Area, Field, or Subject:** General studies/Field of study not specified **Level of Education for which Award is Granted:** Undergradu-

ate **Number Awarded:** Varies each year. **Funds Available:** The scholarship covers tuition, on-campus room charges, and fees (but not books, school supplies, food, materials, or dues for extracurricular activities) at any state-supported college or university in Arkansas. **Duration:** Up to 8 semesters, as long as the student is working on a baccalaureate or associate degree.

Eligibility Requirements: This program is open to the spouses and/or children (natural, adopted, or step) of Arkansas residents who were killed or permanently disabled in the line of duty as law enforcement officers, municipal police officers, sheriffs and deputy sheriffs, constables, state correction employees, game wardens, state park employees who are commissioned law enforcement officers or emergency response employees, full-time or volunteer fire fighters, state forestry employees engaged in fighting forest fires, certain Arkansas Highway and Transportation Department employees, and public school teachers. Children must be less than 23 years of age. Spouses may not have remarried. All applicants must have been Arkansas residents for at least 6 months. **Deadline for Receipt:** July of each year for fall term, November of each year for spring or winter term, April of each year for first summer session, or June of each year for second summer session.

287 ■ ARKANSAS DEPARTMENT OF HIGHER EDUCATION

Attn: Financial Aid Division
114 East Capitol Avenue
Little Rock, AR 72201-3818
Tel: (501)371-2050
Free: 800-54-STUDY
Fax: (501)371-2001
E-mail: finaid@adhe.arknet.edu
Web Site: http://www.arkansashighered.com/miakia.html
To provide financial assistance for educational purposes to dependents of Arkansas veterans who were killed in action or became POWs or MIAs after January 1, 1960.

Title of Award: Arkansas Missing in Action/Killed in Action Dependents' Scholarship Program **Area, Field, or Subject:** General studies/Field of study not specified **Level of Education for which Award is Granted:** Graduate, Undergraduate **Number Awarded:** Varies each year; recently, 4 of these scholarships were awarded. **Funds Available:** The program pays for tuition, general registration fees, special course fees, activity fees, room and board (if provided in campus facilities), and other charges associated with earning a degree or certificate. **Duration:** 1 year; undergraduates may obtain renewal as long as they make satisfactory progress toward a baccalaureate degree; graduate students may obtain renewal as long as they maintain a minimum GPA of 2.5 and make satisfactory progress toward a degree.

Eligibility Requirements: This program is open to the natural children, adopted children, stepchildren, and spouses of Arkansas residents who became a prisoner of war, killed in action, missing in action, or killed on ordnance delivery after January 1, 1960. Applicants may be working or planning to work 1) on an undergraduate degree in Arkansas or 2) on a graduate or professional degree in Arkansas if their undergraduate degree was not received in Arkansas. Applicants need not be current Arkansas residents, but their parents or spouses must have been an Arkansas resident at the time of entering military service or at the time they were declared a prisoner of war, killed in action, or missing in action. **Deadline for Receipt:** July of each year for the fall term; November of each year for the spring term; April of each year for summer term I; June of each year for summer term II. **Additional Information:** Return or reported death of the veteran will not alter benefits. Applications must be submitted to the financial aid director at an Arkansas state-supported institution of higher education or state-supported technical/vocational school.

288 ■ ARKANSAS DEPARTMENT OF HIGHER EDUCATION

Attn: Financial Aid Division
114 East Capitol Avenue
Little Rock, AR 72201-3818
Tel: (501)371-2050
Free: 800-54-STUDY
Fax: (501)371-2001
E-mail: finaid@adhe.arknet.edu
Web Site: http://www.arkansashighered.com/secondeffort.html
To provide financial assistance for undergraduate study to students in Arkansas who have earned a General Educational Development (GED) certificate.

Title of Award: Arkansas Second Effort Scholarship **Area, Field, or Subject:** General studies/Field of study not specified **Level of Education for which Award is Granted:** Undergraduate **Number Awarded:** 10 each year. **Funds Available:** The stipend is $1,000 per year or the cost of tuition, whichever is less. **Duration:** 1 year; may be renewed for an additional 3 years (or equivalent for part-time students) or until completion of a baccalaureate degree, provided the recipient maintains a GPA of 2.5 or higher.

Eligibility Requirements: This program is open to Arkansas residents who did not graduate from high school but completed their GED certificate in the previous year. Applicants must be attending or planning to attend an approved Arkansas 2 or 4-year public or private postsecondary institution. They must be at least 18 years of age or a former member of a high school class that has graduated. The students who received the highest GED scores are awarded this scholarship. Financial need is not considered. Students do not apply for this award; eligible candidates are contacted directly by the Arkansas Department of Higher Education if they achieve the highest scores.

289 ■ ARKANSAS SINGLE PARENT SCHOLARSHIP FUND

614 East Emma Avenue, Suite 119
Springdale, AR 72764
Tel: (479)927-1402
Fax: (479)751-1110
E-mail: rnesson@jtlshop.jonesnet.org
Web Site: http://www.aspsf.org
To provide financial assistance for college to single parents in Arkansas.

Title of Award: Arkansas Single Parent Scholarships **Area, Field, or Subject:** General studies/Field of study not specified **Level of Education for which Award is Granted:** Undergraduate **Number Awarded:** Varies each year. **Funds Available:** Up to $6,000 in matching funds is provided to affiliates that raise money for scholarships on a local basis. Seed grants of $1,000 are available for start-up costs in newly affiliated counties.

Eligibility Requirements: Eligible to apply are single parents in Arkansas. Applicants must reside in 1 of the counties in which a Single Parent Scholarship Fund has been established; for a list of these counties, contact the sponsor. **Additional Information:** This program was established in 1990.

290 ■ ARKANSAS STUDENT LOAN AUTHORITY

101 East Capitol Avenue, Suite 401
Little Rock, AR 72201
800-443-6030
Web Site: http://www.asla.info/collegeplanning/woodruffscholarship.aspx
To provide financial assistance for college to residents of Arkansas or students attending a postsecondary institution in the state.

Title of Award: R. Preston Woodruff, Jr. Scholarships **Area, Field, or Subject:** General studies/Field of study not specified **Level of Education for which Award is Granted:** Undergraduate **Number Awarded:** 20 each year. **Funds Available:** The stipend is $1,000. Funds are mailed to the financial aid office at the designated school. **Duration:** 1 year; of the scholarships awarded each year, 1 may be renewed up to 3 additional years but the others are nonrenewable.

Eligibility Requirements: This program is open to 1) residents of Arkansas, who may be attending a postsecondary institution in or out of the state, and 2) residents of other states attending a postsecondary institution in Arkansas. Postsecondary educational institutions include 2-year colleges, 4-year colleges and universities, and technical and trade schools. Applicants may enter online or by submitting a postcard with their name, address, telephone number, and name of their educational institution. Winners are selected at random. **Deadline for Receipt:** March of each year.

291 ■ ARMED FORCES COMMUNICATIONS AND ELECTRONICS ASSOCIATION

Attn: AFCEA Educational Foundation
4400 Fair Lakes Court
Fairfax, VA 22033-3899
Tel: (703)631-6149
Free: 800-336-4583
Fax: (703)631-4693
E-mail: scholarship@afcea.org

Web Site: http://www.afcea.org/education/scholarships/rotc/
MedalofHonor.asp
To provide financial assistance to ROTC cadets who demonstrate outstanding leadership performance and potential.
Title of Award: Medal of Honor AFCEA ROTC Scholarships **Area, Field, or Subject:** General studies/Field of study not specified **Level of Education for which Award is Granted:** Four Year College **Number Awarded:** 4 each year: 1 each for Army, Navy, Marine Corps, and Air Force ROTC students. **Funds Available:** The stipend is $3,000. **Duration:** 1 year.
Eligibility Requirements: This program is open to ROTC cadets enrolled full time at an accredited degree-granting 4-year college or university in the United States. Applicants must be sophomores or juniors at the time of application and have a GPA of 3.0 or higher with a major in an academic discipline. Selection is based on demonstrated leadership performance and potential and strong commitment to serve in the U.S. armed forces. **Deadline for Receipt:** March of each year. **Additional Information:** This program, established in 2005, is sponsored by the Congressional Medal of Honor Foundation in partnership with the Armed Forces Communications and Electronics Association (AFCEA) Educational Foundation.

292 ■ ARMY AVIATION ASSOCIATION OF AMERICA

Attn: AAAA Scholarship Foundation
755 Main Street, Suite 4D
Monroe, CT 06468-2830
Tel: (203)268-2450
Fax: (203)268-5870
E-mail: aaaa@quad-a.org
Web Site: http://www.quad-a.org/scholarship.htm
To provide educational loans to members of the Army Aviation Association of America (AAAA) and their relatives.
Title of Award: Army Aviation Association of America Loan Program **Area, Field, or Subject:** General studies/Field of study not specified **Level of Education for which Award is Granted:** Graduate, Undergraduate **Number Awarded:** Varies each year. **Funds Available:** The maximum loan is $1,000 per year. All loans are interest free. **Duration:** Up to 4 years.
Eligibility Requirements: This program is open to AAAA members and their spouses, unmarried siblings, and unmarried children. Applicants must be enrolled or accepted for enrollment as an undergraduate or graduate student at an accredited college or university. **Deadline for Receipt:** April of each year.

293 ■ ARMY AVIATION ASSOCIATION OF AMERICA SCHOLARSHIP FOUNDATION

Attn: AAAA Scholarship Foundation
755 Main Street, Suite 4D
Monroe, CT 06468-2830
Tel: (203)268-2450
Fax: (203)268-5870
E-mail: aaaa@quad-a.org
Web Site: http://www.quad-a.org/scholarship.htm
To provide financial aid for undergraduate or graduate study to members of the Army Aviation Association of America (AAAA) and their relatives.
Title of Award: Army Aviation Association of America Scholarships **Area, Field, or Subject:** General studies/Field of study not specified **Level of Education for which Award is Granted:** Graduate, Undergraduate **Number Awarded:** Varies each year; since the program began in 1963, the foundation has awarded more than $2.2 million to more than 1,300 qualified applicants. **Funds Available:** Stipends range from $1,000 to $4,000. **Duration:** Scholarships may be for 1 year, 2 years, or 4 years.
Eligibility Requirements: This program is open to AAAA members and their spouses, unmarried siblings, unmarried children, and unmarried grandchildren. Applicants must be enrolled or accepted for enrollment as an undergraduate or graduate student at an accredited college or university. Graduate students must include a 250-word essay on their life experiences, work history, and aspirations. Some scholarships are specifically reserved for enlisted, warrant officer, company grade, and Department of the Army civilian members. Selection is based on academic merit and personal achievement. **Deadline for Receipt:** April of each year.

294 ■ ARMY EMERGENCY RELIEF

200 Stovall Street
Alexandria, VA 22332-0600

Tel: (703)428-0000; (866)878-0000
Fax: (703)325-7183
E-mail: Education@aerhq.org
Web Site: http://www.aerhq.org/
education_dependentchildren_MGJames.asp
To provide financial assistance for college to the dependent children of Army personnel.
Title of Award: MG James Ursano Scholarship Fund **Area, Field, or Subject:** General studies/Field of study not specified **Level of Education for which Award is Granted:** Undergraduate **Number Awarded:** Varies each year; recently, 2,165 of these scholarships, with a value of $3,923,000 were awarded. **Funds Available:** The amount varies, depending on the needs of the recipient, but ranges from $900 to $1,900 per academic year. **Duration:** 1 year; may be renewed for up to 3 additional years if the recipient maintains a GPA of 2.0 or higher.
Eligibility Requirements: This program is open to dependent children under 22 years of age (including stepchildren and legally adopted children) of soldiers on active duty, retired, or deceased while on active duty or after retirement. Applicants must be unmarried and enrolled, accepted, or pending acceptance as full-time students in accredited postsecondary educational institutions. Selection is based primarily on financial need, but academic achievements and individual accomplishments are also considered. **Deadline for Receipt:** February of each year. **Additional Information:** Army Emergency Relief is a private nonprofit organization dedicated to "helping the Army take care of its own." Its primary mission is to provide financial assistance to Army people and their dependents in time of valid emergency need; its educational program was established as a secondary mission to meet a need of Army people for their dependents to pursue vocational training, preparation for acceptance by service academies, or an undergraduate education.

295 ■ ARMY ENGINEER ASSOCIATION

P.O. Box 30260
Alexandria, VA 22310-8260
Tel: (703)428-7084
Fax: (703)428-6043
E-mail: DCOps@armyengineer.com
Web Site: http://www.armyengineer.com/Scholarships.htm
To provide financial assistance for college to children and spouses of members of the Army Engineer Association (AEA).
Title of Award: Colonel Harold M. Beardslee Memorial Scholarship Awards **Area, Field, or Subject:** General studies/Field of study not specified **Level of Education for which Award is Granted:** Undergraduate **Number Awarded:** 5 each year. At least 1 scholarship is awarded to a graduating high school senior who is the child of an active-duty or civilian AEA member; at least 1 is awarded to a graduating high school senior who is the child of an Army Reserve or Army National Guard AEA member; at least 1 is awarded to a child or spouse of an AEA member who is entering their second, third, or fourth year of a baccalaureate degree program. **Funds Available:** The stipend is $1,000. **Duration:** 1 year; nonrenewable.
Eligibility Requirements: This program is open to spouses and children of AEA members. Applicants must be attending or planning to attend a college or university as a full-time student. They must submit an essay on their reasons for seeking this award. Selection is based on the essay, scholastic aptitude, and letters of recommendation. **Deadline for Receipt:** April of each year.

296 ■ ARMY ENGINEER ASSOCIATION

P.O. Box 30260
Alexandria, VA 22310-8260
Tel: (703)428-7084
Fax: (703)428-6043
E-mail: DCOps@armyengineer.com
Web Site: http://www.armyengineer.com/Scholarships.htm
To provide financial assistance for college to active-duty and Reservist enlisted members of the Army Engineer Association (AEA).
Title of Award: CSM Robert W. Elkey Award **Area, Field, or Subject:** General studies/Field of study not specified **Level of Education for which Award is Granted:** Undergraduate **Number Awarded:** 3 each year. **Funds Available:** The stipend is $1,000. **Duration:** 1 year.
Eligibility Requirements: This program is open to active and Reserve component junior enlisted soldiers at the rank of staff sergeant or lower.

Applicants must be AEA members interested in additional college training. Selection is based primarily on financial need, although potential for academic success and standards of conduct as supported by personal references are also considered. **Deadline for Receipt:** June of each year.

297 ■ ARMY ENGINEER ASSOCIATION

P.O. Box 30260
Alexandria, VA 22310-8260
Tel: (703)428-7084
Fax: (703)428-6043
E-mail: DCOps@armyengineer.com
Web Site: http://www.armyengineer.com/Scholarships.htm
To provide financial assistance for college to civilian members of the Army Engineer Association (AEA).
Title of Award: Saul Horowitz Award **Area, Field, or Subject:** General studies/Field of study not specified **Level of Education for which Award is Granted:** Undergraduate **Number Awarded:** 1 or 2 each year. **Funds Available:** The stipend is $1,000. **Duration:** 1 year.
Eligibility Requirements: This program is open to Department of the Army civilian engineers at the grade level of GS-9 and below. Applicants must be AEA members interested in additional college training. Selection is based primarily on financial need, although potential for academic success and standards of conduct as supported by personal references are also considered. **Deadline for Receipt:** June of each year.

298 ■ ARMY ENGINEER ASSOCIATION

P.O. Box 30260
Alexandria, VA 22310-8260
Tel: (703)428-7084
Fax: (703)428-6043
E-mail: DCOps@armyengineer.com
Web Site: http://www.armyengineer.com/Scholarships.htm
To provide financial assistance for college to members of the Army Engineer Association (AEA) who are commissioned or warrant officers.
Title of Award: MG Leif J. Sverdrup Award **Area, Field, or Subject:** General studies/Field of study not specified **Level of Education for which Award is Granted:** Undergraduate **Number Awarded:** 1 or 2 each year. **Funds Available:** The stipend is $1,000. **Duration:** 1 year.
Eligibility Requirements: This program is open to active and Reserve component junior grade officers at rank of captain or lower and warrant officers at rating of WO-2 or lower. Applicants must be AEA members interested in additional college training. Selection is based primarily on financial need, although potential for academic success and standards of conduct as supported by personal references are also considered. **Deadline for Receipt:** June of each year.

299 ■ ARMY ENGINEER OFFICERS WIVES CLUB

Attn: Treasurer
P.O. Box 6332
Alexandria, VA 22306-6332
Tel: (703)569-5627
E-mail: lcaver@juno.com
Web Site: http://www.aeowc.com/scholarships.htm
To provide financial assistance for college to the children of officers who served in the Army Corps of Engineers.
Title of Award: Army Engineer Memorial Awards **Area, Field, or Subject:** General studies/Field of study not specified **Level of Education for which Award is Granted:** Undergraduate **Number Awarded:** Varies each year. Recently, 4 of these scholarships were awarded: 1 at $2,000 and 3 at $1,000. **Funds Available:** Stipends are $2,000 or $1,000. **Duration:** 1 year.
Eligibility Requirements: This program is open to children of U.S. Army Corps of Engineers officers who are currently on active duty, retired, or deceased while on active duty. Applicants must be high school seniors planning to attend a college, university, or technical/vocational school. Selection is based on academic and extracurricular achievement during high school. **Deadline for Receipt:** February of each year. **Additional Information:** This program was established in 1973.

300 ■ ARMY OFFICERS' WIVES' CLUB OF THE GREATER WASHINGTON AREA

c/o Sandy Oujiri, Scholarship Committee Chair
7753 Jewelweed Court
Springfield, VA 22152
E-mail: aowcgwascScholarship@fmthriftshop.org
Web Site: http://www.fmthriftshop.org/scholarshippage.html
To provide financial assistance for college to the children and spouses of U.S. Army personnel and veterans in the Washington, D.C. metropolitan area.
Title of Award: AOWCGWA Scholarship Program **Area, Field, or Subject:** General studies/Field of study not specified **Level of Education for which Award is Granted:** Undergraduate **Number Awarded:** 1 or more each year. **Funds Available:** The stipend is at least $2,000. **Duration:** 1 year.
Eligibility Requirements: This program is open to 1) high school seniors who are children of Army personnel, 2) college students under 22 years of age who are children of Army personnel; and 3) spouses of Army personnel. High school seniors and spouses must reside with their sponsor in the Washington metropolitan area; the sponsor of college students must reside in that area. Sponsors may be active-duty, retired, or deceased, and officer or enlisted. Applicants must submit a 500-word statement on their personal ambitions and goals; a list of extracurricular activities, honors, church activities, community service, and employment; an official transcript that includes (for high school seniors) their SAT or ACT scores; and a letter of recommendation. Students who plan to attend a service academy or receive another full scholarship are not eligible. Selection is based on scholastic merit and community involvement; financial need is not considered. **Deadline for Receipt:** March of each year. **Additional Information:** The Washington metropolitan area is defined to include the Virginia cities of Alexandria, Fairfax, Falls Church, Manassas, and Manassas Park; the Virginia counties of Arlington, Fairfax, Fauquier, Loudoun, Prince William, and Stafford; the Maryland counties of Calvert, Charles, Frederick, Montgomery, and Prince George's; and the District of Columbia. This program is supported in part by the First Command Educational Foundation.

301 ■ ARTHRITIS FOUNDATION-SOUTHERN NEW ENGLAND CHAPTER

Attn: Scholarship Chair
35 Cold Spring Road, Suite 411
Rocky Hill, CT 06067
Tel: (860)563-1177
Free: 800-541-8350
Fax: (860)563-6018
E-mail: info.sne@arthritis.org
Web Site: http://www.arthritis.org
To provide financial assistance for college to high school seniors from southern New England who have arthritis or rheumatic disease.
Title of Award: Juvenile Arthritis Scholarships **Area, Field, or Subject:** General studies/Field of study not specified **Level of Education for which Award is Granted:** Undergraduate **Number Awarded:** 3 to 5 each year. **Funds Available:** The stipend is $1,000. **Duration:** 1 year.
Eligibility Requirements: This program is open to seniors graduating from high schools in Connecticut, Massachusetts, New Hampshire, Rhode Island, and Vermont who have arthritis or rheumatic disease. Applicants must be interested in attending a college or university. Selection is based on academic record and financial need. **Deadline for Receipt:** April of each year.

302 ■ ASANTEWAA

P.O. Box 432
Glenwood, IL 60425
To provide financial assistance for college to African Americans in Illinois who are single mothers.
Title of Award: Asantewaa Scholarship **Area, Field, or Subject:** General studies/Field of study not specified **Level of Education for which Award is Granted:** Undergraduate **Number Awarded:** 1 each year. **Funds Available:** The stipend is $2,000. **Duration:** 1 year; may be renewed.
Eligibility Requirements: This program is open to African American residents of Illinois who are single mothers, are in college or have applied to college, are in need of financial assistance, and are struggling to make something of their lives. Selection is based on demonstrated ability to succeed through self-motivation, financial need, and overall commitment to the good of the community. **Deadline for Receipt:** January of each year. **Additional Information:** The sponsor consists of a group of African American flight attendants. The scholarship is also sponsored by Delta Sigma Theta, Inc., the Tuskegee Airmen, and the Urban League.

Recipients must attend school in Illinois.

303 ■ ASIAN & PACIFIC ISLANDER AMERICAN SCHOLARSHIP FUND

1628 16th Street, N.W., Suite 400
Washington, DC 20009
Tel: (202)986-6892; 877-808-7032
Fax: (202)667-6449
E-mail: scholarshipquestions@apiasf.org
Web Site: http://www.apiasf.org
To provide financial assistance to Asian and Pacific Islander Americans who are entering college for the first time.
Title of Award: Asian & Pacific Islander American Scholarships **Area, Field, or Subject:** General studies/Field of study not specified **Level of Education for which Award is Granted:** Undergraduate **Number Awarded:** Varies each year; recently, 165 of these scholarships were awarded. **Funds Available:** The stipend is $2,000. **Duration:** 1 year.
Eligibility Requirements: This program is open to U.S. citizens, nationals, permanent residents, and citizens of the Freely Associated States who are first-time incoming college students and of Asian or Pacific Islander heritage. Applicants must be enrolling full time in an accredited 2-year or 4-year college or university in the United States, Guam, American Samoa, or the Commonwealth of the Northern Mariana Islands. They must have a GPA of 2.7 or higher or the GED equivalent. Along with their application, they must submit an essay of 275 words or less that describes an experience in their life that either demonstrates their character or helped to shape it. Selection is based on the essay, academic record, academic plans and career goals, community service, a letter of recommendation, and financial need. **Deadline for Receipt:** February of each year. **Additional Information:** These scholarships were first offered in 2005. Support for this program is provided by such sponsors as the AT&T Foundation, Wells Fargo and Company, the Coca-Cola Company, Wal-Mart Stores, Hilton Hotels Foundation, General Mills Foundation, and the Asian McDonald's Owners/Operators Association.

304 ■ ASSOCIATED COLLEGES OF ILLINOIS

Attn: Executive Director
20 North Wacker Drive, Suite 1456
Chicago, IL 60606
Tel: (312)263-2391
Fax: (312)263-3424
E-mail: aci@acifund.org
Web Site: http://www.acifund.org/pages/programs/scholarships_app.htm
To provide financial assistance to students attending or planning to attend an academic institution affiliated with the Associated Colleges of Illinois (ACI).
Title of Award: Associated Colleges of Illinois Scholarship Program **Area, Field, or Subject:** General studies/Field of study not specified **Level of Education for which Award is Granted:** Four Year College **Number Awarded:** Varies each year; since 1990, this program has awarded more than $2 million in financial aid to 1,600 students. **Funds Available:** Awards depend on the availability of funds and the need of the recipient. **Duration:** 1 year; may be renewed.
Eligibility Requirements: Eligible to apply are students entering or currently enrolled at the 24 private colleges and universities that are members of ACI. The program includes 5 categories of awards: 1) first-generation and minority scholarships, to support students who are the first in their family to attend college and encourage minority achievement and graduation; 2) college-to-work scholarships, to attract more students to specific fields of study and career paths; 3) basic needs scholarships, to address students' unmet financial needs; 4) emergency assistance scholarships, to direct critical financial support to students experiencing personal or family emergencies; and 5) academic merit scholarships, to reward the best and the brightest students. **Additional Information:** Members of ACI are Augustana College, Aurora University, Concordia University, Dominican University, Elmhurst College, Eureka College, Greenville College, Illinois College, Illinois Wesleyan University, Knox College, Lake Forest College, Lewis University, McKendree College, Millikin University, Monmouth College, North Central College, North Park University, Olivet Nazarene University, Principia College, Quincy University, Rockford College, Saint Xavier University, Trinity Christian College, and University of St. Francis. This program includes the following named scholarships: the A. Montgomery Ward Scholarship, the Betty A.

DeVries Memorial Fund, the Carole B. Whitcomb Endowed Scholarship, the Fifth Third Bank Scholarship Award, the Grover Hermann Foundation Scholarship, HSBC Scholars, the James S. Copley Foundation Scholarship, MB Financial Bank Scholarship, the McGraw Foundation Emergency Award, the Michelle and Peter Willmott Fund for Minority Leadership, the Motorola Scholarship, the Motorola Minority Scholarship, the Nick Amatangelo Scholarship, the Paul Hucko Memorial Scholarship, the Pepper Family Scholarship, the Polk Brothers Minority Scholarship, the UPS Scholarship, the Vulcan Materials Scholarship, and the Ward Scholarship.

305 ■ ASSOCIATED FOOD DEALERS OF MICHIGAN

Attn: AFD Foundation
30415 West Thirteen Mile Road
Farmington Hills, MI 48334
Tel: (248)671-9600
Free: 800-666-6233
Fax: (248)671-9610
E-mail: info@afdom.org
Web Site: http://www.afdom.org
To provide financial assistance to high school seniors and currently-enrolled college students who are employed or whose parents are employed by a company that belongs to the Associated Food Dealers of Michigan (AFD).
Title of Award: Associated Food Dealers of Michigan Academic Scholarships **Area, Field, or Subject:** General studies/Field of study not specified **Level of Education for which Award is Granted:** Undergraduate **Number Awarded:** At least 10 scholarships are awarded each year to AFD member company employees and their children and 3 to AFD member customers and their children. However, only 1 scholarship will be awarded per AFD-member company. **Funds Available:** The stipend is $1,500. **Duration:** 1 year; may be renewed 1 additional year.
Eligibility Requirements: This program is open to high school seniors as well as college freshmen, sophomores, and juniors. Applicants must 1) have been employed by an AFD member company for at least 6 months; 2) be the child of a full- or part-time employee who has worked for an AFD member company for at least 1 year; or 3) be an AFD member customer or child. Selection is based on academic performance, leadership, and participation in school and community activities; college grades are considered if the applicant is already enrolled in college. **Deadline for Receipt:** March of each year. **Additional Information:** This program is administered by Scholarship Program Administrators, Inc., 1201 Eighth Avenue South, P.O. Box 23737, Nashville, TN 27202-3737, (615) 320-3149, Fax: (615) 320-3151, E-mail: info@spaprog.com. Recipients must attend college on a full-time basis.

306 ■ ASSOCIATED FOOD DEALERS OF MICHIGAN

Attn: AFD Foundation
30415 West Thirteen Mile Road
Farmington Hills, MI 48334
Tel: (248)671-9600
Free: 800-666-6233
Fax: (248)671-9610
E-mail: info@afdom.org
Web Site: http://www.afdom.org
To provide financial assistance to minority high school seniors and currently-enrolled college students in Michigan.
Title of Award: Associated Food Dealers of Michigan Minority Scholarships **Area, Field, or Subject:** General studies/Field of study not specified **Level of Education for which Award is Granted:** Undergraduate **Number Awarded:** At least 10 each year. **Funds Available:** The stipend is $1,500. **Duration:** 1 year; may be renewed 1 additional year.
Eligibility Requirements: This program is open to high school seniors as well as college freshmen, sophomores, and juniors. Applicants must be members of at least 1 of the following minority groups: African American, Hispanic, Asian, Native American, or Arab/Chaldean. Preferential consideration is given to applicants with an AFD membership affiliation, although membership is not required. Selection is based on academic performance, leadership, and participation in school and community activities. **Deadline for Receipt:** March of each year. **Additional Information:** This program is administered by Scholarship Program Administrators, Inc., 1201 Eighth Avenue South, P.O. Box 23737, Nashville, TN 27202-3737, (615) 320-3149 ext. 106, (800) 310-4053, Fax: (615) 523-7100, E-mail: Lmarlow@spaprog.com. Recipients must attend college on a full-time basis.

307 ■ ASSOCIATED GENERAL CONTRACTORS OF ILLINOIS

Attn: Education Foundation
3219 Executive Park Drive
Springfield, IL 62703
Tel: (217)789-2650
Fax: (217)789-1048
E-mail: sdokey@agcil.org
Web Site: http://www.agcil.org/education1.htm
To provide financial assistance to children of employees of member firms of the Associated General Contractors of Illinois (AGCI) who plan to attend college to prepare for a career in the construction industry.
Title of Award: Associated General Contractors of Illinois Scholarships **Area, Field, or Subject:** Construction **Level of Education for which Award is Granted:** Undergraduate **Number Awarded:** 1 or more each year. **Funds Available:** A stipend is awarded (amount not specified). **Duration:** 1 year.
Eligibility Requirements: This program is open to high school seniors and graduates whose parent has been employed by an AGCI member firm for at least 2 years. Applicants must be majoring or planning to major in a program that is compatible with a career in the construction industry. They must have a GPA of 2.5 or higher. Along with their application, they must submit an essay explaining how their chosen field will apply to work in the construction industry, their goals, where they plan to attend school, and why they chose to apply for this scholarship. **Deadline for Receipt:** February of each year.

308 ■ ASSOCIATED GENERAL CONTRACTORS OF VERMONT

Attn: Director of Workforce Development
148 State Street
P.O. Box 750
Montpelier, VT 05601
Tel: (802)223-2374
Fax: (802)223-1809
E-mail: info@agcvt.org
Web Site: http://www.agcvt.org/workforce/scholarships.cfm
To provide financial assistance to Vermont residents who are interested in studying a field related to construction.
Title of Award: Associated General Contractors of Vermont Scholarships **Area, Field, or Subject:** Construction **Level of Education for which Award is Granted:** Undergraduate **Number Awarded:** 2 each year. **Funds Available:** The stipend is $1,000 and must be used within 1 year after being awarded. **Duration:** 1 year.
Eligibility Requirements: This scholarship is available to residents of Vermont who are high school seniors, high school graduates, or GED recipients and interested in pursuing an academic, vocational, technical, or advanced training program in a field related to construction. Applicants must be able to demonstrate financial need. Selection is based on a letter of recommendation, required essays, and financial need. **Deadline for Receipt:** April of each year. **Additional Information:** This program was established in 2002.

309 ■ ASSOCIATES OF VIETNAM VETERANS OF AMERICA

Attn: Scholarship Program
8605 Cameron Street, Suite 400
Silver Spring, MD 20910
800-VVA-1316
Web Site: http://www.avva.org/better_chance.htm
To provide financial assistance for college to members of Vietnam Veterans of American (VVA) and Associates of Vietnam Veterans of America (AVVA), their families, and the families of Vietnam veterans killed or missing in action.
Title of Award: Better Chance Scholarship **Area, Field, or Subject:** General studies/Field of study not specified **Level of Education for which Award is Granted:** Undergraduate **Number Awarded:** 3 each year: 1 at $1,000 and 2 at $500. **Funds Available:** Stipends are $1,000 or $500. **Duration:** 1 year.
Eligibility Requirements: This program is open to members of VVA and AVVA; their spouses, children, and grandchildren; and the spouses, children, and grandchildren of a Vietnam veteran killed in action (KIA) or missing in action (MIA). Especially encouraged to apply are average students who are not eligible for academic scholarships but who can demonstrate financial need. Applicants must submit essays on their long-term goals, work experience, organizations or activities, and community service. **Deadline for Receipt:** May of each year. **Additional Information:** This program was established in 1998.

310 ■ ASSOCIATION OF ALASKA SCHOOL BOARDS

1111 West Ninth Street
Juneau, AK 99801
Tel: (907)586-1083
Fax: (907)586-2995
E-mail: aasb@aasb.org
Web Site: http://www.aasb.org/JNMS.html
To provide financial assistance for college to high school seniors in Alaska.
Title of Award: June Nelson Memorial Scholarship **Area, Field, or Subject:** General studies/Field of study not specified **Level of Education for which Award is Granted:** Undergraduate **Number Awarded:** 8 each year. **Funds Available:** The stipend is $1,000, including $500 paid at high school graduation and $500 paid after the recipient completes 1 semester of college with a GPA of 2.5 or higher. **Duration:** 1 year; nonrenewable.
Eligibility Requirements: This program is open to seniors graduating from high schools in Alaska who have been accepted as a full-time student by a business, trade, or collegiate institution. Applicants must submit an essay, up to 750 words, on a topic that changes annually but relates to education; recently, the topic was, "Describe the ways specific Developmental Assets have contributed to your personal growth as a member of your community." Selection is based on the essay, high school transcripts, SAT or ACT scores, and 2 letters of recommendation; financial need is not considered. **Deadline for Receipt:** March of each year. **Additional Information:** This program began in 1992

311 ■ ASSOCIATION OF BLIND CITIZENS

P.O. Box 246
Holbrook, MA 02343
Tel: (781)961-1023
Fax: (781)961-0004
E-mail: scholarship@blindcitizens.org
Web Site: http://www.blindcitizens.org/abc_scholarship.htm
To provide financial assistance for college to individuals who are blind or visually impaired.
Title of Award: Association of Blind Citizens Scholarships **Area, Field, or Subject:** General studies/Field of study not specified **Level of Education for which Award is Granted:** Undergraduate **Number Awarded:** 15 each year: 1 at $3,000 (the Reggie Johnson Memorial Scholarship), 3 at $2,000, and 11 at $1,000. **Funds Available:** Stipends are $3,000, $2,000, or $1,000. Funds may be used to pay for tuition, living expenses, or related expenses resulting from vision impairment. **Duration:** 1 year.
Eligibility Requirements: Eligible to apply for this support are high school seniors, high school graduates, and currently-enrolled college students who are blind or visually impaired. They must be interested in working on a college degree. To apply, students must submit an autobiography, indicating how the scholarship award would help them achieve their goal of attending college or a recognized vocational program; a high school or college transcript; a certificate of legal blindness or a letter from their ophthalmologist; and 2 letters of reference. The highest ranked applicant receives the Reggie Johnson Memorial Scholarship. **Deadline for Receipt:** April of each year.

312 ■ ASSOCIATION OF FORMER INTELLIGENCE OFFICERS

Attn: Scholarships Committee
6723 Whittier Avenue, Suite 303A
McLean, VA 22101-4533
Tel: (703)790-0320
Fax: (703)991-1278
E-mail: afio@afio.com
Web Site: http://www.afio.com/sections/academic/scholarship.html
To provide financial assistance for continuing educational or professional development to current and former members of the U.S. Special Forces.
Title of Award: Front Line Forces Scholarship **Area, Field, or Subject:** General studies/Field of study not specified **Level of Education for which Award is Granted:** Graduate, Professional, Undergraduate **Number Awarded:** 1 each year. **Funds Available:** The stipend is $1,500 per year. **Duration:** 1 year.
Eligibility Requirements: This program is open to active and recently inactivated members of the U.S. Special Forces (e.g., Green Berets,

Delta, SEAL, Rangers). Applicants must be interested in a program of educational or professional advancement or transition. They must submit a cover letter that describes relevant prior experience and future plans to which the grant would be applied. **Deadline for Receipt:** August of each year.

313 ■ ASSOCIATION OF FORMER INTELLIGENCE OFFICERS

Attn: Scholarships Committee
6723 Whittier Avenue, Suite 303A
McLean, VA 22101-4533
Tel: (703)790-0320
Fax: (703)991-1278
E-mail: afio@afio.com
Web Site: http://www.afio.com/sections/academic/scholarship.html
To provide financial assistance to undergraduate and graduate students who have a career interest in intelligence and national security.
Title of Award: Harold and Maria Ransburg American Patriot Scholarships **Area, Field, or Subject:** General studies/Field of study not specified; Intelligence service **Level of Education for which Award is Granted:** Graduate, Undergraduate **Number Awarded:** Several each year. **Funds Available:** Stipends range from $1,500 to $3,000. **Duration:** 1 year.
Eligibility Requirements: This program is open to undergraduates who have completed their first or second year of study and graduate students who apply in their senior undergraduate year or first graduate year. Applicants must share the sponsor's educational mission on behalf of "national security, patriotism, and loyalty to the constitution." Along with their application, undergraduates must submit a 1-page book review on the subject of intelligence and national security. Graduate students must submit a dissertation or thesis proposal. Selection is based on merit, character, estimated future potential, background, and relevance of their studies to the full spectrum of national security interests and career ambitions. **Deadline for Receipt:** August of each year.

314 ■ ASSOCIATION OF GRADUATES

Attn: Vice President of Services
3116 Academy Drive, Suite 100
USAF Academy, CO 80840-4475
Tel: (719)472-0300
Fax: (719)333-4194
E-mail: gds@aog-usafa.org
Web Site: http://www.usafa.org/pages/MemberService/Scholarship.htm
To provide financial assistance for undergraduate education to children of Association of Graduates (AOG) members.
Title of Award: Association of Graduates Dependent Scholarships **Area, Field, or Subject:** General studies/Field of study not specified **Level of Education for which Award is Granted:** Undergraduate **Number Awarded:** Varies each year. **Funds Available:** The stipend is $1,000 per year. Funds are paid directly to the recipient. **Duration:** 1 year; recipients may reapply and be awarded 3 additional scholarships.
Eligibility Requirements: This program is open to children of graduates of the U.S. Air Force Academy who either are paid-in-full life members or have maintained annual membership for at least the 5 consecutive years immediately preceding submission of the application package. Applicants must be either the graduate's natural child or legally adopted child (although they need not be financially dependent upon the graduate or his/her surviving spouse). They must be working or planning to work full time on an undergraduate degree. Along with their application, they must submit an essay of 400 to 600 words in their educational goals and an essay of 200 to 400 words on the importance of this scholarship to the continuance of their education. Selection is based on overall demonstrated merit, although financial need may also receive some consideration. **Deadline for Receipt:** February of each year.

315 ■ ASSOCIATION OF INDEPENDENT COLLEGES AND UNIVERSITIES OF PENNSYLVANIA

101 North Front Street
Harrisburg, PA 17101-1405
Tel: (717)232-8649
Fax: (717)233-8574
E-mail: info@aicup.org
Web Site: http://www.aicup.org

To provide financial assistance to students at member institutions of the Association of Independent Colleges and Universities of Pennsylvania (AICUP) who have demonstrated outstanding commitment to community service.
Title of Award: Commonwealth "Good Citizen" Scholarships **Area, Field, or Subject:** General studies/Field of study not specified **Level of Education for which Award is Granted:** Four Year College **Number Awarded:** Varies each year; recently, 6 of these scholarships were awarded. **Funds Available:** The stipend is $1,000. **Duration:** 1 year.
Eligibility Requirements: This program is open to full-time undergraduate students at AICUP colleges and universities. Applicants must have shown an extraordinary commitment to community service and have demonstrated creativity in shaping their volunteer activities. As part of their application, they must submit a 2-page essay on their volunteer/extracurricular activities on and off campus, how those activities relate to their major, their career and academic goals after graduation, and how they will remain involved in their community after graduation. Selection is based on the extent of their volunteer and community service activities (30%), leadership activities and taking initiative (30%), evidence of commitment to community service (30%), and additional material, such as reference letters (10%). There is no minimum GPA requirement; grades are considered only in the event of a tie. Applications must be submitted to the financial aid office at the AICUP college or university that the student attends. **Deadline for Receipt:** April of each year. **Additional Information:** The AICUP includes 83 private colleges and universities in Pennsylvania. For a list of those institutions, contact AICUP.

316 ■ ASSOCIATION OF INDEPENDENT FUNERAL DIRECTORS OF FLORIDA

Attn: Scholarship Committee
217 South Adams Street
Tallahassee, FL 32301
Tel: (850)222-0198
Fax: (850)425-5268
Web Site: http://www.ifdf.org
To provide financial assistance to mortuary science students who are interested in entering the funeral service profession in Florida.
Title of Award: Lamar Danielson Scholarship **Area, Field, or Subject:** Mortuary science **Level of Education for which Award is Granted:** Undergraduate **Number Awarded:** 1 or more each year. **Funds Available:** A stipend is awarded (amount not specified). Funds are to be applied to tuition. **Duration:** Support is provided for the fourth and fifth quarter of study.
Eligibility Requirements: This program is open to full-time students at accredited colleges and departments of mortuary science who have expressed the intent to enter funeral service with an independently-owned firm in Florida after graduation. Applicants must be in the third quarter of study and have an overall scholastic average of 85% or higher for the first 2 quarters of study. They must be recommended and endorsed by the owner/manager of a funeral home that is a member of the Independent Funeral Directors of Florida. Preference is given to applicants who have funeral home employment experience. Financial need is considered in the selection process. **Deadline for Receipt:** March or September of each year.

317 ■ ASSOCIATION OF INDIANS IN AMERICA-NEW JERSEY CHAPTER

c/o Deepa Mehrotra
192 Midland Avenue
Glen Ridge, NJ 07028
Tel: (973)748-5310
E-mail: ravim2@verizon.net
Web Site: http://www.aianj.org
To provide financial assistance for college to high school seniors in New Jersey who are of Asian Indian ancestry.
Title of Award: AIA-NJ Scholarships **Area, Field, or Subject:** General studies/Field of study not specified **Level of Education for which Award is Granted:** Undergraduate **Number Awarded:** 3 each year. **Funds Available:** The stipend is $1,000. **Duration:** 1 year.
Eligibility Requirements: This program is open to seniors graduating from high schools in New Jersey who are of Asian Indian ancestry or origin. Applicants must have 1) a GPA of 3.5 or higher or class standing in the top 10% of their class; 2) an excellent SAT or ACT score; and 3) a

record of active participation in at least 2 non-academic extracurricular activities, such as varsity sports, social service, volunteer work, or cultural activities. **Deadline for Receipt:** February of each year.

318 ■ ASSOCIATION FOR IRON & STEEL TECHNOLOGY-GLOBE-TROTTERS CHAPTER

c/o Greg Bott
P.O. Box 3869
Beaumont, TX 77704
Web Site: http://www.aist.org/conf/globetrottersscholarship.htm
To provide financial assistance for college or graduate school to children of members of the Globe-Trotters and the Association for Iron & Steel Technology (AIST).
Title of Award: Globe-Trotters Scholarships **Area, Field, or Subject:** General studies/Field of study not specified **Level of Education for which Award is Granted:** Graduate, Undergraduate **Number Awarded:** 1 or more each year. **Funds Available:** A stipend is awarded (amount not specified). **Duration:** 1 year.
Eligibility Requirements: This program is open to children of members of Globe-Trotters who are also members of AIST. Applicants must be enrolled as an undergraduate or graduate student at an accredited college or university. Along with their application, they must submit a 300-word paper on why they have selected their field of study. Selection is based on the paper, academic and extracurricular activities, and a short memo on how the scholarship will be used. Financial need is not considered. **Deadline for Receipt:** April of each year. **Additional Information:** The AIST was formed in 2004 by the merger of the Iron and Steel Society (ISS) and the Association of Iron and Steel Engineers (AISE). The Globe-Trotters began in 1937 as part of the Southwestern Section of the American Institute of Mining, Metalurgical, and Petroleum Engineers (AIME), but it currently operates as a chapter of the AIST without a geographic focus.

319 ■ ASSOCIATION FOR IRON & STEEL TECHNOLOGY-MIDWEST CHAPTER

c/o Michael Heaney, Education Chair
Mittal Steel USA-East Chicago
3001 Dickey Road
East Chicago, IN 46312
Tel: (219)391-2026
Web Site: http://www.aist.org/chapters/midwest_scholarship.htm
To provide financial assistance to dependents of members of the Midwest Chapter of the Association for Iron & Steel Technology (AIST) who plan to study a field other than engineering in college.
Title of Award: Midwest Chapter AIST Non-Engineering Scholarship **Area, Field, or Subject:** General studies/Field of study not specified **Level of Education for which Award is Granted:** Undergraduate **Number Awarded:** 2 each year. **Funds Available:** The stipend is $1,000. **Duration:** 1 year.
Eligibility Requirements: This program is open to dependents of the AIST Midwest Chapter who are graduating high school seniors or currently enrolled in the first, second, or third year at an accredited college or university. Applicants must be studying or planning to study a field other than engineering on a full-time basis. Along with their application, they must submit a letter of recommendation, a current transcript, and a 1- to 2-page essay describing their objectives for college and career. Selection is based on merit. **Deadline for Receipt:** May of each year. **Additional Information:** The AIST was formed in 2004 by the merger of the Iron and Steel Society (ISS) and the Association of Iron and Steel Engineers (AISE). The Midwest Chapter replaced the former AISE Chicago Section in northern Illinois and northwestern Indiana and also includes the states of Wisconsin, Minnesota, Iowa, Nebraska, South Dakota, and North Dakota.

320 ■ ASSOCIATION FOR IRON & STEEL TECHNOLOGY-MIDWEST CHAPTER

c/o Michael Heaney, Education Chair
Mittal Steel USA-East Chicago
3001 Dickey Road
East Chicago, IN 46312
Tel: (219)391-2026
Web Site: http://www.aist.org/chapters/midwest_scholarship.htm
To provide financial assistance to dependents of members of the Midwest Chapter of the Association for Iron & Steel Technology (AIST) who plan to study any field in college.
Title of Award: Western States AIST Scholarship **Area, Field, or Subject:** General studies/Field of study not specified **Level of Education for which Award is Granted:** Undergraduate **Number Awarded:** 1 each year. **Funds Available:** The stipend is $2,500. **Duration:** 1 year.
Eligibility Requirements: This program is open to dependents of the AIST Midwest Chapter who are graduating high school seniors or currently enrolled in the first, second, or third year at an accredited college or university. Applicants must be studying or planning to study any field on a full-time basis. Along with their application, they must submit a letter of recommendation, a current transcript, and a 1- to 2-page essay describing their objectives for college and career. Selection is based on merit. **Deadline for Receipt:** May of each year. **Additional Information:** The AIST was formed in 2004 by the merger of the Iron and Steel Society (ISS) and the Association of Iron and Steel Engineers (AISE). The Midwest Chapter replaced the former AISE Chicago Section in northern Illinois and northwestern Indiana and also includes the states of Wisconsin, Minnesota, Iowa, Nebraska, South Dakota, and North Dakota.

321 ■ ASSOCIATION OF THE UNITED STATES ARMY

Attn: Strickland Memorial Scholarship Fund
2425 Wilson Boulevard
Arlington, VA 22201
Tel: (703)841-4300
Free: 800-336-4570
E-mail: jspencer@ausa.org
Web Site: http://www.ausa.org
To recognize and reward, with funding for additional education, Army noncommissioned officers who demonstrate outstanding leadership.
Title of Award: Larry Strickland Leadership Award and Scholarship **Area, Field, or Subject:** General studies/Field of study not specified **Level of Education for which Award is Granted:** Undergraduate **Number Awarded:** 1 each year. **Funds Available:** The award consists of a plaque and $1,500 to assist in covering educational costs that Army tuition assistance does not pay, such as instructional fees, laboratory fees, and books. **Duration:** The award is presented annually.
Eligibility Requirements: This award is presented to a noncommissioned officer who best exemplifies "the Army's vision and influences others in shaping future leaders." Candidates must also be interested in obtaining additional education. **Additional Information:** This award was established in 2003 to honor SGM Larry L. Strickland, who was killed in the Pentagon on September 11, 2001.

322 ■ ASSOCIATION OF THE UNITED STATES ARMY-GEORGE WASHINGTON CHAPTER

c/o Robbi Perna, Vice President, Scholarship Program
43593 Jackson Hole Circle
Leesburg, VA 20176-3960
Tel: (703)443-1283
E-mail: robbi.perna@adelphia.net
Web Site: http://www.gwcausa.org/Scholarship/scholarship.asp
To provide financial assistance for undergraduate or graduate study to members of the George Washington Chapter of the Association of the United States Army (AUSA) and their families.
Title of Award: George Washington Chapter Scholarships **Area, Field, or Subject:** General studies/Field of study not specified **Level of Education for which Award is Granted:** Graduate, Undergraduate **Number Awarded:** Varies each year. Recently, 12 of these scholarships were awarded: 1 at $1,000, 7 at $850, 3 at $775, and 1 at $725. **Funds Available:** Stipends range from $725 to $1,000. **Duration:** 1 year.
Eligibility Requirements: This program is open to active members of the AUSA George Washington Chapter (which serves the Washington, D.C. area) and the families of active members. Applicants must have a GPA of 2.5 or higher and be working on an undergraduate or advanced degree. Along with their application, they must submit a letter describing any family circumstances they believe are relevant and explaining why they deserve the scholarship. Members must also submit a favorable recommendation from their supervisor. Membership in AUSA is open to Army personnel (including Reserves and National Guard) who are either active or retired, ROTC cadets, and civilian employees of the Army. **Deadline for Receipt:** April of each year.

323 ■ ATHLETES OF GOOD NEWS
Attn: SportQuest All-American Program
6425 N.W. Cache Road, Suites 217 and 218
P.O. Box 6272
Lawton, OK 73506
Tel: (580)536-9524
Fax: (580)536-7495
E-mail: allamerican@aogn.org
Web Site: http://www.aogn.org
To provide financial assistance for college to outstanding female Christian high school athletes.
Title of Award: SportQuest All-American Scholarships for Females **Area, Field, or Subject:** General studies/Field of study not specified **Level of Education for which Award is Granted:** Undergraduate **Number Awarded:** 2 each year: 1 winner and 1 runner-up. **Funds Available:** The award is a $1,000 scholarship for the winner and a $500 scholarships for the runner-up. **Duration:** 1 year.
Eligibility Requirements: This program is open to female high school sophomores, juniors, and seniors who believe in the Lord Jesus Christ as their personal Lord and Savior and attend a church regularly. Nominees must be 1 of the top 3 Christian athletes in their school and have an overall GPA of 3.0 or higher. They must be able to demonstrate an active Christian influence in school and community. Selection is based on athletics, academics, and Christian influence. **Deadline for Receipt:** November of each year.

324 ■ ATHLETES OF GOOD NEWS
Attn: SportQuest All-American Program
6425 N.W. Cache Road, Suites 217 and 218
P.O. Box 6272
Lawton, OK 73506
Tel: (580)536-9524
Fax: (580)536-7495
E-mail: allamerican@aogn.org
Web Site: http://www.aogn.org
To provide financial assistance for college to outstanding male Christian high school athletes.
Title of Award: SportQuest All-American Scholarships for Males **Area, Field, or Subject:** General studies/Field of study not specified **Level of Education for which Award is Granted:** Undergraduate **Number Awarded:** 2 each year: 1 winner and 1 runner-up. **Funds Available:** The award is a $1,000 scholarship for the winner and a $500 scholarships for the runner-up. **Duration:** 1 year.
Eligibility Requirements: This program is open to male high school sophomores, juniors, and seniors who believe in the Lord Jesus Christ as their personal Lord and Savior and attend a church regularly. Nominees must be 1 of the top 3 Christian athletes in their school and have an overall GPA of 3.0 or higher. They must be able to demonstrate an active Christian influence in school and community. Selection is based on athletics, academics, and Christian influence. **Deadline for Receipt:** November of each year.

325 ■ AUTISM SOCIETY OF AMERICA
Attn: Awards and Scholarships
7910 Woodmont Avenue, Suite 300
Bethesda, MD 20814-3015
Tel: (301)657-0881
Free: 800-3-AUTISM
Fax: (301)657-0869
E-mail: info@autism-society.org
Web Site: http://www.autism-society.org
To provide financial assistance for college to high school seniors, high school graduates, and college students with autism.
Title of Award: Eden Services Charles H. Hoens, Jr. Scholars Program **Area, Field, or Subject:** General studies/Field of study not specified **Level of Education for which Award is Granted:** Undergraduate **Number Awarded:** 1 each year. **Funds Available:** The stipend is $1,000. **Duration:** 1 year.
Eligibility Requirements: This program is open to high school seniors or graduates who have been accepted to or are already enrolled in an accredited postsecondary school (college, trade school, etc.) and who have autism. Applicants must submit 3 copies of 1) documentation of their status as an individual with autism; 2) secondary school transcripts; 3)

documentation of acceptance into an accredited postsecondary educational or vocational program of study; 4) 2 letters of recommendation; and 5) a 500-word statement outlining their qualifications and proposed plan of study. A telephone interview may be required. **Deadline for Receipt:** February of each year. **Additional Information:** This program was formerly known as the Ann M. Martin Scholarship.

326 ■ AVIATION BOATSWAIN'S MATES ASSOCIATION
P.O. Box 1106
Lakehurst, NJ 08733
E-mail: Scholarship@abma-usn.org
Web Site: http://www.abma-usn.org/scholarship.htm
To provide financial assistance for college to the dependents of paid-up members of the Aviation Boatswains Mates Association (ABMA).
Title of Award: Isabella M. Gillen Memorial Scholarship **Area, Field, or Subject:** General studies/Field of study not specified **Level of Education for which Award is Granted:** Undergraduate **Number Awarded:** Varies each year. **Funds Available:** The stipend is $2,500 per year. **Duration:** 1 year; may be renewed.
Eligibility Requirements: Applicants must be dependents whose sponsor has been an active, dues-paying member of the ABMA for at least 2 years. They must prepare a statement describing their vocational or professional goals and relating how their past, present, and future activities make the accomplishment of those goals probable. Other submissions include transcripts, SAT or ACT scores, letters of recommendation, and copies of achievement in scholarship, leadership, athletics, dramatics, community service, or other activities. Selection is based on financial need, character, leadership, and academic achievement. **Deadline for Receipt:** May of each year. **Additional Information:** This program was established in 1976. Membership in ABMA is open to all U.S. Navy personnel (active, retired, discharged, or separated) who hold or held the rating of aviation boatswains mate. Information is also available from the Scholarship Chair Lanny Vines, 144 CR 1515, Alba, TX 75410.

327 ■ AXA FOUNDATION
c/o AXA Advisors, LLC
1290 Avenue of the Americas
New York, NY 10104
877-222-2144
Web Site: http://www.axaonline.com
To provide financial assistance for college to high school seniors who live and attend school in a community served by AXA Advisors, LLC.
Title of Award: AXA Achievement Community Scholarships **Area, Field, or Subject:** General studies/Field of study not specified **Level of Education for which Award is Granted:** Undergraduate **Number Awarded:** Up to 800 each year. Each of the 80 AXA Advisors branch office may award up to 10 of these scholarships each year. **Funds Available:** The stipend is $2,000. **Duration:** 1 year.
Eligibility Requirements: This program is open to graduating high school seniors who live in a community in the United States or Puerto Rico served by a branch office of AXA Advisors. Interested students may obtain an application from their local office. Selection is based on ambition and drive; determination to set and reach goals; respect for self, family, and community; and ability to succeed in college. **Deadline for Receipt:** February of each year. **Additional Information:** Selection of recipients is made by Scholarship Management Services of Scholarship America, One Scholarship Way, P.O. Box 297, St. Peter, MN 56082, (507) 931-1682, (800) 537-4180, Fax: (507) 931-9168, E-mail: axaachievement@scholarshipamerica.org

328 ■ BAPTIST FOUNDATION OF ALABAMA
Attn: Office of Administration
430 South Court Street
P.O. Box 4773
Montgomery, AL 36103-4773
Tel: (334)834-9586
Fax: (334)834-9597
E-mail: scholarship@tbfa.og
Web Site: http://tbfa.org/admin/scholarship_application.html
To provide financial assistance for college to members of Baptist churches in Alabama.
Title of Award: Baptist Foundation of Alabama Scholarships **Area, Field, or Subject:** General studies/Field of study not specified **Level of Educa-

tion for which Award is Granted: Undergraduate Number Awarded: 1 or more each year. Funds Available: A stipend is awarded (amount not specified). Duration: 1 year.

Eligibility Requirements: This program is open to full-time students who are affiliated with a Baptist church in Alabama. Applicants must have a GPA of 2.0 or higher. Deadline for Receipt: March of each year.

329 ■ GEORGE BARTOL MEMORIAL SCHOLARSHIP FUND

c/o Heather M. Bartol
4863 Riverton Drive
Orlando, FL 32817
Tel: (407)382-5982
E-mail: livebait3@aol.com
To provide financial assistance for college to children of brain cancer patients.

Title of Award: George Bartol Memorial Scholarships Area, Field, or Subject: General studies/Field of study not specified Level of Education for which Award is Granted: Undergraduate Number Awarded: 1 or more each year. Funds Available: The stipend is $1,000 per semester ($3,000 per year, including summer semester). Students at schools on the quarter system may receive $750 per quarter ($3,000 per year, including summer quarter). Funds are paid directly to the financial aid office at the school the recipient is attending. Duration: 1 semester or quarter; may be renewed if the recipient maintains a GPA of 2.5 or higher.

Eligibility Requirements: This program is open to full-time students at accredited 2-year and 4-year colleges and universities who have a GPA of 2.5 or higher. Applicants must have lost a biological mother or father to a form of brain cancer or have a biological mother or father who has been diagnosed with brain cancer. They must be between 18 and 23 years of age. Along with their application, they must submit 5 essays on the following topics: 1) their parent who has lost their battle to brain cancer or who is currently battling brain cancer; 2) how the scholarship will affect them and their family; 3) how cancer has impacted their life; 4) their biggest adjustment since their parent's battle with brain cancer began; and 5) what they have learned from this experience and how they might help others as a result. Selection is based on the essays, grades, letters of recommendation, and financial need. Children of Vietnam veterans who have not been awarded VA Chapter 35 benefits are strongly encouraged to apply. Deadline for Receipt: September of each year. Additional Information: This program was established in 2004. Information is also available from Kari Bartol, (407) 718-7601, or Brandy Bartol, (850) 926-1999.

330 ■ ALEXANDER GRAHAM BELL ASSOCIATION FOR THE DEAF

Attn: Financial Aid Coordinator
3417 Volta Place, N.W.
Washington, DC 20007-2778
Tel: (202)337-5220
Fax: (202)337-8314
E-mail: financialaid@agbell.org
Web Site: http://www.agbell.org/
DesktopDefault.aspx?p=College_Scholarship_Awards
To provide financial assistance to undergraduate and graduate students with moderate to profound hearing loss.

Title of Award: Lucille B. Abt Scholarships Area, Field, or Subject: General studies/Field of study not specified Level of Education for which Award is Granted: Graduate, Undergraduate Number Awarded: 10 each year. Funds Available: The stipend is $5,000 per year. Duration: 1 year; may be renewed 1 additional year.

Eligibility Requirements: This program is open to undergraduate and graduate students who have been diagnosed with a moderate to profound hearing loss prior to acquiring spoken language (hearing loss averages 60dB or greater in the better ear in the speech frequencies of 500, 1000, and 2000 Hz). Applicants must be committed to using spoken language and lipreading as their preferred mode of communication. They must be accepted or enrolled at a mainstream college or university as a full-time student. Along with their application, they must submit a 1-page essay discussing their career goals and how spoken communication is helping

them to reach those goals as a person with a hearing loss. Financial need is considered in the selection process. Deadline for Receipt: April of each year.

331 ■ ALEXANDER GRAHAM BELL ASSOCIATION FOR THE DEAF

Attn: Financial Aid Coordinator
3417 Volta Place, N.W.
Washington, DC 20007-2778
Tel: (202)337-5220
Fax: (202)337-8314
E-mail: financialaid@agbell.org
Web Site: http://www.agbell.org/
DesktopDefault.aspx?p=College_Scholarship_Awards
To provide financial assistance to undergraduate students with moderate to profound hearing loss.

Title of Award: Bennion Family Scholarship Area, Field, or Subject: General studies/Field of study not specified Level of Education for which Award is Granted: Undergraduate Number Awarded: 1 each year. Funds Available: The stipend is $2,000 per year. Duration: 1 year; may be renewed 1 additional year.

Eligibility Requirements: This program is open to undergraduate students who have been diagnosed with a moderate to profound hearing loss prior to acquiring spoken language (hearing loss averages 60dB or greater in the better ear in the speech frequencies of 500, 1000, and 2000 Hz). Applicants must be committed to using spoken language as their primary mode of communication. They must be accepted or enrolled at a mainstream college or university as a full-time student. Along with their application, they must submit a 1-page essay discussing their career goals and how spoken communication is helping them to reach those goals as a person with a hearing loss. Financial need is considered in the selection process. Deadline for Receipt: April of each year.

332 ■ ALEXANDER GRAHAM BELL ASSOCIATION FOR THE DEAF

Attn: Financial Aid Coordinator
3417 Volta Place, N.W.
Washington, DC 20007-2778
Tel: (202)337-5220
Fax: (202)337-8314
E-mail: financialaid@agbell.org
Web Site: http://www.agbell.org/
DesktopDefault.aspx?p=College_Scholarship_Awards
To provide financial assistance to undergraduate and graduate students with moderate to profound hearing loss.

Title of Award: Federation of Jewish Women's Organization Scholarship Area, Field, or Subject: General studies/Field of study not specified Level of Education for which Award is Granted: Graduate, Undergraduate Number Awarded: 1 each year. Funds Available: The stipend is $2,000 per year. Duration: 1 year; may be renewed 1 additional year.

Eligibility Requirements: This program is open to undergraduate and graduate students who have been diagnosed with a moderate to profound hearing loss prior to acquiring spoken language (hearing loss averages 60dB or greater in the better ear in the speech frequencies of 500, 1000, and 2000 Hz). Applicants must be committed to using spoken language as their primary mode of communication. They must be accepted or enrolled at a mainstream college or university as a full-time student. Along with their application, they must submit a 1-page essay discussing their career goals and how spoken communication is helping them to reach those goals as a person with a hearing loss. Financial need is considered in the selection process. Deadline for Receipt: April of each year.

333 ■ ALEXANDER GRAHAM BELL ASSOCIATION FOR THE DEAF

Attn: Financial Aid Coordinator
3417 Volta Place, N.W.
Washington, DC 20007-2778
Tel: (202)337-5220
Fax: (202)337-8314
E-mail: financialaid@agbell.org
Web Site: http://www.agbell.org/
DesktopDefault.aspx?p=College_Scholarship_Awards
To provide financial assistance to undergraduate and graduate students who are members of the Alexander Graham Bell Association for the Deaf (AG Bell) and their children.

Title of Award: Herbert P. Feibelman, Jr. Scholarship Area, Field, or Subject: General studies/Field of study not specified Level of Education for which **Award is Granted:** Graduate, Undergraduate **Number Awarded:** 1 each year. **Funds Available:** The stipend is $2,500 per year. **Duration:** 1 year; may be renewed 1 additional year.

Eligibility Requirements: This program is open to undergraduate and graduate students who have been diagnosed with a moderate to profound hearing loss prior to acquiring spoken language (hearing loss averages 60dB or greater in the better ear in the speech frequencies of 500, 1000, and 2000 Hz). Applicants must be committed to using spoken language as their primary mode of communication. They must be accepted or enrolled at a mainstream college or university as a full-time student. Along with their application, they must submit a 1-page essay discussing their career goals and how spoken communication is helping them to reach those goals as a person with a hearing loss. Financial need is considered in the selection process. This scholarship is reserved for students who are members of AG Bell or whose parents are members. **Deadline for Receipt:** April of each year.

334 ■ ALEXANDER GRAHAM BELL ASSOCIATION FOR THE DEAF

Attn: Financial Aid Coordinator
3417 Volta Place, N.W.
Washington, DC 20007-2778
Tel: (202)337-5220
Fax: (202)337-8314
E-mail: financialaid@agbell.org
Web Site: http://www.agbell.org/
DesktopDefault.aspx?p=College_Scholarship_Awards
To provide financial assistance to undergraduate and graduate students who have moderate to profound hearing loss and attend school in the Washington, D.C. area.

Title of Award: Elsie M. Bell Grosvenor Scholarship Awards **Area, Field, or Subject:** General studies/Field of study not specified **Level of Education for which Award is Granted:** Graduate, Undergraduate **Number Awarded:** 1 each year. **Funds Available:** The stipend is $2,000 per year. **Duration:** 1 year; may be renewed 1 additional year.

Eligibility Requirements: This program is open to undergraduate and graduate students who have been diagnosed with a moderate to profound hearing loss prior to acquiring spoken language (hearing loss averages 60dB or greater in the better ear in the speech frequencies of 500, 1000, and 2000 Hz). Applicants must be committed to using spoken language as their primary mode of communication. They must be accepted or enrolled at a mainstream college or university in the Washington, D.C. area as a full-time student. Along with their application, they must submit a 1-page essay discussing their career goals and how spoken communication is helping them to reach those goals as a person with a hearing loss. Financial need is considered in the selection process. **Deadline for Receipt:** April of each year.

335 ■ ALEXANDER GRAHAM BELL ASSOCIATION FOR THE DEAF

Attn: Financial Aid Coordinator
3417 Volta Place, N.W.
Washington, DC 20007-2778
Tel: (202)337-5220
Fax: (202)337-8314
E-mail: financialaid@agbell.org
Web Site: http://www.agbell.org/
DesktopDefault.aspx?p=College_Scholarship_Awards
To provide financial assistance to undergraduate and graduate students with moderate to profound hearing loss.

Title of Award: Walter W. and Thelma C. Hissey College Scholarships **Area, Field, or Subject:** General studies/Field of study not specified **Level of Education for which Award is Granted:** Graduate, Undergraduate **Number Awarded:** 2 each year. **Funds Available:** The stipend is $5,000 per year. **Duration:** 1 year; may be renewed 1 additional year.

Eligibility Requirements: This program is open to undergraduate and graduate students who have been diagnosed with a moderate to profound hearing loss prior to acquiring spoken language (hearing loss averages 60dB or greater in the better ear in the speech frequencies of 500, 1000, and 2000 Hz). Applicants must be committed to using spoken language as their primary mode of communication. They must be accepted or enrolled at a mainstream college or university as a full-time student. Along with their application, they must submit a 1-page essay discussing their career goals and how spoken communication is helping them to reach those goals as a person with a hearing loss. Financial need is considered

in the selection process. **Deadline for Receipt:** April of each year.

336 ■ ALEXANDER GRAHAM BELL ASSOCIATION FOR THE DEAF

Attn: Financial Aid Coordinator
3417 Volta Place, N.W.
Washington, DC 20007-2778
Tel: (202)337-5220
Fax: (202)337-8314
E-mail: financialaid@agbell.org
Web Site: http://www.agbell.org/
DesktopDefault.aspx?p=College_Scholarship_Awards
To provide financial assistance to undergraduate and graduate students with moderate to profound hearing loss.

Title of Award: Allie Raney Hunt Scholarship **Area, Field, or Subject:** General studies/Field of study not specified **Level of Education for which Award is Granted:** Graduate, Undergraduate **Number Awarded:** 1 each year. **Funds Available:** The stipend is $2,000 per year. **Duration:** 1 year; may be renewed 1 additional year.

Eligibility Requirements: This program is open to undergraduate and graduate students who have been diagnosed with a moderate to profound hearing loss prior to acquiring spoken language (hearing loss averages 60dB or greater in the better ear in the speech frequencies of 500, 1000, and 2000 Hz). Applicants must be committed to using spoken language as their primary mode of communication. They must be accepted or enrolled at a mainstream college or university as a full-time student. Along with their application, they must submit a 1-page essay discussing their career goals and how spoken communication is helping them to reach those goals as a person with a hearing loss. Financial need is considered in the selection process. **Deadline for Receipt:** April of each year.

337 ■ ALEXANDER GRAHAM BELL ASSOCIATION FOR THE DEAF

Attn: Financial Aid Coordinator
3417 Volta Place, N.W.
Washington, DC 20007-2778
Tel: (202)337-5220
Fax: (202)337-8314
E-mail: financialaid@agbell.org
Web Site: http://www.agbell.org/
DesktopDefault.aspx?p=College_Scholarship_Awards
To provide financial assistance to undergraduate and graduate students who are deaf.

Title of Award: Ladies' Auxiliary National Rural Letter Carriers Scholarship **Area, Field, or Subject:** General studies/Field of study not specified **Level of Education for which Award is Granted:** Graduate, Undergraduate **Number Awarded:** 1 each year. **Funds Available:** The stipend is $2,000 per year. **Duration:** 1 year; may be renewed 1 additional year.

Eligibility Requirements: This program is open to undergraduate and graduate students who have been diagnosed with a moderate to profound hearing loss prior to acquiring spoken language (hearing loss averages 60dB or greater in the better ear in the speech frequencies of 500, 1000, and 2000 Hz). Applicants must be committed to using spoken language as their primary mode of communication. They must be accepted or enrolled at a mainstream college or university as a full-time student. Along with their application, they must submit a 1-page essay discussing their career goals and how spoken communication is helping them to reach those goals as a person with a hearing loss. Financial need is considered in the selection process. This scholarship is reserved for students who are deaf. **Deadline for Receipt:** April of each year.

338 ■ ALEXANDER GRAHAM BELL ASSOCIATION FOR THE DEAF

Attn: Financial Aid Coordinator
3417 Volta Place, N.W.
Washington, DC 20007-2778
Tel: (202)337-5220
Fax: (202)337-8314
E-mail: financialaid@agbell.org
Web Site: http://www.agbell.org/
DesktopDefault.aspx?p=College_Scholarship_Awards
To provide financial assistance to undergraduate students who are oral deaf.

Title of Award: Sam Levy Scholarship Fund **Area, Field, or Subject:** General studies/Field of study not specified **Level of Education for which Award is Granted:** Undergraduate **Number Awarded:** 1 each year. **Funds Available:** The stipend is $2,000 per year. **Duration:** 1 year; may be renewed 1 additional year.

Eligibility Requirements: This program is open to undergraduate students who have been diagnosed with a moderate to profound hearing loss prior to acquiring spoken language (hearing loss averages 60dB or greater in the better ear in the speech frequencies of 500, 1000, and 2000 Hz). Applicants must be committed to using spoken language as their primary mode of communication. They must be accepted or enrolled at a mainstream college or university as a full-time student. Along with their application, they must submit a 1-page essay discussing their career goals and how spoken communication is helping them to reach those goals as a person with a hearing loss. Financial need is considered in the selection process. **Deadline for Receipt:** April of each year.

339 ■ ALEXANDER GRAHAM BELL ASSOCIATION FOR THE DEAF

Attn: Financial Aid Coordinator
3417 Volta Place, N.W.
Washington, DC 20007-2778
Tel: (202)337-5220
Fax: (202)337-8314
E-mail: financialaid@agbell.org
Web Site: http://www.agbell.org/
DesktopDefault.aspx?p=College_Scholarship_Awards
To provide financial assistance to undergraduate and graduate students who are oral deaf.
Title of Award: Volta Scholarship Fund **Area, Field, or Subject:** General studies/Field of study not specified **Level of Education for which Award is Granted:** Graduate, Undergraduate **Number Awarded:** 1 each year. **Funds Available:** The stipend is $2,000 per year. **Duration:** 1 year; may be renewed 1 additional year.
Eligibility Requirements: This program is open to undergraduate and graduate students who have been diagnosed with a moderate to profound hearing loss prior to acquiring spoken language (hearing loss averages 60dB or greater in the better ear in the speech frequencies of 500, 1000, and 2000 Hz). Applicants must be committed to using spoken language as their primary mode of communication. They must be accepted or enrolled at a mainstream college or university as a full-time student. Along with their application, they must submit a 1-page essay discussing their career goals and how spoken communication is helping them to reach those goals as a person with a hearing loss. Financial need is considered in the selection process. This scholarship is reserved for students who are oral deaf. **Deadline for Receipt:** April of each year.

340 ■ ALEXANDER GRAHAM BELL ASSOCIATION FOR THE DEAF

Attn: Financial Aid Coordinator
3417 Volta Place, N.W.
Washington, DC 20007-2778
Tel: (202)337-5220
Fax: (202)337-8314
E-mail: financialaid@agbell.org
Web Site: http://www.agbell.org
To provide financial assistance to undergraduate and graduate students who are members of the Alexander Graham Bell Association for the Deaf (AG Bell).
Title of Award: www.agbell.org/DesktopDefault.aspx?p=College_Scholarship_Awards **Area, Field, or Subject:** General studies/Field of study not specified **Level of Education for which Award is Granted:** Graduate, Undergraduate **Number Awarded:** 2 each year. **Funds Available:** The stipend is $1,000 per year. **Duration:** 1 year; may be renewed 1 additional year.
Eligibility Requirements: This program is open to undergraduate and graduate students who have been diagnosed with a moderate to profound hearing loss prior to acquiring spoken language (hearing loss averages 60dB or greater in the better ear in the speech frequencies of 500, 1000, and 2000 Hz). Applicants must be committed to using spoken language as their primary mode of communication. They must be accepted or enrolled at a mainstream college or university as a full-time student. Along with their application, they must submit a 1-page essay discussing their career goals and how spoken communication is helping them to reach those goals as a person with a hearing loss. Financial need is considered in the selection process. This scholarship is reserved for students who are

members of AG Bell and its Deaf and Hard of Hearing Section (DHHS). **Deadline for Receipt:** April of each year.

341 ■ BIG 33 SCHOLARSHIP FOUNDATION

Attn: Scholarship Committee
511 Bridge Street
P.O. Box 213
New Cumberland, PA 17070
Tel: (717)774-3303; 877-PABIG-33
Fax: (717)774-1749
E-mail: info@big33.org
Web Site: http://www.big33.org/scholarships/default.ashx
To provide financial assistance for college to graduating high school seniors in Ohio and Pennsylvania.
Title of Award: Big 33 Academic Scholarships **Area, Field, or Subject:** General studies/Field of study not specified **Level of Education for which Award is Granted:** Undergraduate **Number Awarded:** Varies each year; recently, 111 of these scholarships were awarded: 3 at $4,000, 1 at $1,500, 60 at $1,000, 3 at $600, 42 at $500, and 2 at $250 **Funds Available:** Stipends range up to $4,000, but most are $1,000. **Duration:** 1 year; nonrenewable.
Eligibility Requirements: This program is open to seniors graduating from public and accredited private high schools in Ohio and Pennsylvania. Applications are available from high school guidance counselors. Selection is based on special talents, leadership, obstacles overcome, academic achievement (at least a 2.0 GPA), community service, unique endeavors, financial need, and a 1-page essay on why the applicant deserves the scholarship. **Deadline for Receipt:** February of each year. **Additional Information:** Funds for this program are raised by the foundation through its sponsorship of an annual high school All-Star football game.

342 ■ BLACK WOMEN IN SISTERHOOD FOR ACTION

Attn: Chair of Scholarship Committee
P.O. Box 1592
Washington, DC 20013
Tel: (202)543-6013
Fax: (202)543-5719
E-mail: info@bisa-hq.org
Web Site: http://www.bisa-hq.org/scholarships/index.htm
To provide financial assistance for college to disadvantaged Black women.
Title of Award: BISA Scholarship Assistance Program **Area, Field, or Subject:** General studies/Field of study not specified **Level of Education for which Award is Granted:** Undergraduate **Number Awarded:** 40 to 50 each year. **Funds Available:** The stipend is $1,000 per year. Support is also provided for books and transportation. **Duration:** 4 years.
Eligibility Requirements: This program is open to Black women graduating from inner-city high schools and planning to attend a college or university, especially a designated Historically Black College or University (HBCU). Applicants must submit a transcript, SAT or ACT scores, documentation of financial need, and a 1-page self-portrait highlighting where they expect to be in their career development in 10 years. Selection is based on academic achievement, leadership potential, financial need, honors, and potential for academic growth and leadership development. **Deadline for Receipt:** February of each year. **Additional Information:** Black Women in Sisterhood for Action (BISA) was established in 1980. In 1995, it established partnership relationships with the following HBCUs: Bishop State Community College (Mobile, Alabama), Philander Smith College (Little Rock, Arkansas), Delaware State University (Dover, Delaware), Bethune-Cookman College (Daytona Beach, Florida), Chicago State University (Chicago, Illinois), Grambling State University (Grambling, Louisiana), Morgan State University (Maryland), Tougaloo College (Tougaloo, Mississippi), Medgar Evers College (New York), Bennett College (Greensboro, North Carolina), Lincoln University (Lincoln, Pennsylvania), Fisk University (Nashville, Tennessee), Texas Southern University (Houston, Texas), and Hampton University (Hampton, Virginia). Students who attend those schools also receive mentoring, counseling for

themselves and their parents, networking among distinguished Black women, and monthly contacts by a BISA member.

343 ■ BLACKFEET NATION
Attn: Higher Education Program
P.O. Box 850
Browning, MT 59417
Tel: (406)338-7539
Fax: (406)338-7530
E-mail: bhep@3rivers.net
Web Site: http://www.blackfeetnation.com
To provide financial assistance for vocational training to members of the Blackfeet and other tribes.
Title of Award: Blackfeet Adult Vocational Training Grants **Area, Field, or Subject:** General studies/Field of study not specified **Level of Education for which Award is Granted:** Vocational/Occupational **Number Awarded:** Varies each year. **Funds Available:** The amount awarded varies, depending upon the recipient's educational requirements and financial needs. The maximum for an unmarried student with no dependents is $3,200 per year; for a student with 3 or more dependents; the maximum stipend is $3,800 per year. Funds are sent to the school's financial aid officer. **Duration:** Up to 24 months (36 months for registered nursing students) of full-time training.
Eligibility Requirements: This program is open to enrolled members of a federally-recognized tribe between 18 and 35 years of age in need of training to obtain reasonable and satisfactory employment. Applicants must be willing to accept full-time employment as soon as possible after completion of training. Along with their application they must submit high school or GED transcripts, college transcripts (if they have ever attended college), a copy of the admission letter from the school they plan to attend, a financial needs analysis, a Certificate of Degree of Indian Blood, a copy of marriage license (if a spouse is claimed as financially dependent), a copy of birth certificates for any family members claimed as financially dependent, and military discharge papers (if applicable). Grants are awarded according to the following priorities: 1) Blackfeet Tribal members residing on or near the Blackfeet Reservation; 2) Blackfeet Tribal members residing off the Blackfeet Reservation; 3) members of other federally-recognized tribes (as funding permits); and 4) second training grant applicants (as funding permits). **Deadline for Receipt:** February of each year.

344 ■ BLACKFEET NATION
Attn: Higher Education Program
P.O. Box 850
Browning, MT 59417
Tel: (406)338-7539
Fax: (406)338-7530
E-mail: bhep@3rivers.net
Web Site: http://www.blackfeetnation.com
To provide financial assistance for undergraduate education to members of the Blackfeet Tribe.
Title of Award: Blackfeet Higher Education Program **Area, Field, or Subject:** General studies/Field of study not specified **Level of Education for which Award is Granted:** Undergraduate **Number Awarded:** Varies each year. **Funds Available:** The amount awarded varies, depending upon the recipient's educational requirements and financial needs. The maximum for an unmarried student with no dependents is $3,200 per year; for a student with 3 or more dependents; the maximum stipend is $3,800 per year. Funds are sent to the school's financial aid officer. **Duration:** 1 year; may be renewed up to a total of 10 semesters or 15 quarters.
Eligibility Requirements: Applicants must be enrolled members of the Blackfeet Tribe and be enrolled or accepted for enrollment as an undergraduate in an academically recognized college or university. They must submit a 1-page letter describing their career goals and academic plans, high school or GED transcripts, college transcripts (if they have previously attended college), a copy of the admission letter from the college or university they plan to attend, a financial needs analysis, and a Certificate of Degree of Indian Blood. Scholarships are awarded according to the following priorities: 1) renewal of grants to students currently funded who are in good academic and financial aid standing and submit the application packet on time; 2) college seniors not currently funded who can graduate within the current academic year; 3) 2-year degree graduates who apply within 1 year of earning their associate degree; 4)

high school seniors who apply within 1 year of earning their high school diploma; 5) applicants previously funded who are in good academic and financial aid standing and submit the application packet in a timely manner; and 6) candidates who submit late applications (supported only if funding permits). **Deadline for Receipt:** February of each year; March of each year for summer term. **Additional Information:** Recipients must enroll as full-time students and earn no less than 12 credit hours per term with a GPA of 2.0 or higher as freshmen, 13 credits and 2.2 as sophomores, 14 credits and 2.4 as juniors, and 15 credits and 2.6 as seniors. Students who attend private schools or institutions outside of Montana must pay the difference in tuition, unless no comparable program exists in Montana public institutions.

345 ■ BLACKS IN GOVERNMENT-NATIONAL INSTITUTES OF HEALTH CHAPTER
Attn: Scholarship Program
P.O. Box 31253
Bethesda, MD 20824-1253
Tel: (301)402-3336
Web Site: http://www.bignet.org/regional/nih
To provide financial assistance for college to high school seniors in the greater Washington, D.C. area.
Title of Award: Blacks in Government National Institutes of Health Chapter Scholarship **Area, Field, or Subject:** General studies/Field of study not specified **Level of Education for which Award is Granted:** Undergraduate **Number Awarded:** 1 or more each year. **Funds Available:** A stipend is awarded (amount not specified). **Duration:** 1 year.
Eligibility Requirements: This program is open to college-bound high school seniors who reside within 50 miles of Washington, D.C. Applicants must have a GPA of 2.0 or higher. Along with their application, they must submit an essay of 350 to 500 words on 1 of the following topics: 1) their chosen major and the reason for selecting it; 2) the person who has inspired them the most to attend college; or 3) why attending college is important to them. Preference is given to children of members of Blacks in Government. **Deadline for Receipt:** March of each year.

346 ■ BOIS FORTE RESERVATION TRIBAL COUNCIL
Attn: Education Director
5344 Lake Shore Drive
P.O. Box 16
Nett Lake, MN 55772
Tel: (218)757-3261
Free: 800-221-8129
Fax: (218)757-3312
E-mail: bmason@educ.boisforte.gov
Web Site: http://www.boisforte.com
To provide financial assistance for undergraduate or graduate study to enrolled members of the Bois Forte Band of Chippewa Indians.
Title of Award: Bois Forte Scholarship Program **Area, Field, or Subject:** General studies/Field of study not specified **Level of Education for which Award is Granted:** Master's, Undergraduate **Number Awarded:** Varies each year. **Funds Available:** The maximum amount awarded is $5,000 per year for undergraduates or $6,250 per year for graduate students. **Duration:** 1 year; may be renewed for a total of 10 semesters of full-time enrollment or part-time equivalent provided they maintain a GPA of 2.0 or higher.
Eligibility Requirements: Eligible to apply for this assistance are enrolled members of the Bois Forte Band of Chippewa Indians. Applicants must have been accepted at an institution of higher education and had their financial need determined by that institution based on the Free Application for Federal Student Aid (FAFSA). Minnesota residents must apply to the Indian Scholarship Assistance Program of the Minnesota Indian Scholarship Program. Applicants wishing to attend school outside of Minnesota must complete an out-of-state application form. Applicants must also apply for financial assistance from all other available sources, including but not limited to public and private grants and scholarships. They must not be in default of any tribal, federal, or state student education loan or in noncompliance with child support payments. Applicants are interviewed. Financial assistance is awarded on a first-come, first-served basis. **Deadline for Receipt:** Applications may be submitted any time after January 1 but should be received no later than 8 weeks prior to the first day of school. **Additional Information:** Students may receive financial assistance for summer school.

347 ■ BOY SCOUTS OF AMERICA

Attn: National Eagle Scout Association
1325 West Walnut Hill Lane
P.O. Box 152079
Irving, TX 75015-2079
Tel: (972)580-2431
Web Site: http://www.nesa.org/scholarships/index.html
To provide financial assistance for college to Eagle Scouts.
Title of Award: Mabel and Lawrence S. Cooke Scholarship **Area, Field, or Subject:** General studies/Field of study not specified **Level of Education for which Award is Granted:** Four Year College **Number Awarded:** 5 each year: 1 at $12,000 per year and 4 at $5,000 per year. **Funds Available:** Stipends are either $12,000 or $5,000 per year. **Duration:** 4 years, as long as the recipient remains in the upper third of his class. **Eligibility Requirements:** This program is open to Eagle Scouts who are graduating high school seniors planning to enroll as a full-time student at an accredited 4-year college or university. They must have an SAT score of at least 1090 and/or an ACT score of 26. Selection is based on financial need, scholastic accomplishment, involvement in Scouting, and school and community activities. **Deadline for Receipt:** February of each year.

348 ■ BOY SCOUTS OF AMERICA

Attn: National Eagle Scout Association
1325 West Walnut Hill Lane
P.O. Box 152079
Irving, TX 75015-2079
Tel: (972)580-2431
Web Site: http://www.nesa.org/scholarships/index.html
To provide financial assistance for college to Eagle Scouts.
Title of Award: Elks National Foundation Eagle Scout Scholarships **Area, Field, or Subject:** General studies/Field of study not specified **Level of Education for which Award is Granted:** Undergraduate **Number Awarded:** 8 each year: 4 (1 in each region) at $2,000 per year and 4 (1 in each region) at $1,000 per year. **Funds Available:** Stipends are $2,000 or $1,000 per year. **Duration:** 4 years. **Eligibility Requirements:** Eagle Scouts who are graduating high school seniors are eligible to apply for these scholarships. They must have an SAT score of at least 1090 and/or an ACT score of 26. Selection is based on financial need, scholastic accomplishment, involvement in Scouting, and school and community activities. **Deadline for Receipt:** February of each year. **Additional Information:** These scholarships are provided by the Elks National Foundation.

349 ■ BOY SCOUTS OF AMERICA

Attn: National Eagle Scout Association
1325 West Walnut Hill Lane
P.O. Box 152079
Irving, TX 75015-2079
Tel: (972)580-2431
Web Site: http://www.nesa.org/scholarships/index.html
To provide financial assistance for college to Eagle Scouts.
Title of Award: Hall/McElwain Merit Scholarships **Area, Field, or Subject:** General studies/Field of study not specified **Level of Education for which Award is Granted:** Undergraduate **Number Awarded:** 72 each year: 18 in each region. **Funds Available:** The stipend is $1,000. Awards may be used only for tuition, room, board, and books. **Duration:** 1 year; nonrenewable. **Eligibility Requirements:** This program is open to Eagle Scouts who are graduating high school seniors or currently-enrolled undergraduate students. Applicants must be able to demonstrate leadership ability in Scouting and a strong record of participation in activities outside of Scouting. Financial need is not considered. **Deadline for Receipt:** February of each year.

350 ■ BOY SCOUTS OF AMERICA

Attn: National Eagle Scout Association
1325 West Walnut Hill Lane
P.O. Box 152079
Irving, TX 75015-2079
Tel: (972)580-2431
Web Site: http://www.nesa.org/scholarships/index.html
To provide financial assistance for college to Eagle Scouts.
Title of Award: National Eagle Scout Association Scholarships **Area, Field, or Subject:** General studies/Field of study not specified **Level of**

Education for which Award is Granted: Four Year College **Number Awarded:** 12 each year: 3 in each region. **Funds Available:** The stipend is $3,000. Awards may be used only for tuition, room, board, and books. **Duration:** 1 year; nonrenewable. **Eligibility Requirements:** This program is open to Eagle Scouts who are graduating high school seniors planning to enroll as a full-time student at an accredited 4-year college or university. They must have an SAT score of at least 1090 and/or an ACT score of 26. Selection is based on financial need, scholastic accomplishment, involvement in Scouting, and school and community activities. **Deadline for Receipt:** February of each year.

351 ■ BP PRODUCTS NORTH AMERICA

c/o Charitable Management Systems, Inc.
700 West Fifth Avenue
Mail Code: 1003
Naperville, IL 60563
To provide financial assistance for college to high school seniors in the Washington, D.C. metropolitan area.
Title of Award: BP Community Scholarship Program **Area, Field, or Subject:** General studies/Field of study not specified **Level of Education for which Award is Granted:** Undergraduate **Number Awarded:** 1 or more each year. **Funds Available:** The stipend is $1,000. **Duration:** 1 year; nonrenewable. **Eligibility Requirements:** This program is open to seniors graduating from high schools in Washington, D.C., Montgomery and Prince George's counties, Maryland, and Fairfax and Prince William counties, Virginia. Applicants must have a GPA of 2.0 or higher and be able to demonstrate financial need. They must be planning to enroll full time in an accredited college or university in the United States. Along with their application, they must submit an essay on a topic that changes annually; recently, they were invited to write on the importance of education in a free society. Selection is based on the essay, academic performance, extracurricular activities, work experience, individual goals, and financial need. **Deadline for Receipt:** April of each year. **Additional Information:** This program is supported by participating BP station owners and operators in the area.

352 ■ BRISTOL BAY NATIVE CORPORATION

Attn: BBNC Education Foundation
800 Cordova Street, Suite 200
Anchorage, AK 99501-6299
Tel: (907)278-3602
Free: 800-426-3602
Fax: (907)276-3925
E-mail: pelagiol@bbnc.net
Web Site: http://www.bbnc.net
To provide financial assistance for college to shareholders of Bristol Bay Native Corporation (BBNC).
Title of Award: Bristol Bay Native Corporation Education Foundation Higher Education Scholarships **Area, Field, or Subject:** General studies/Field of study not specified **Level of Education for which Award is Granted:** Undergraduate **Number Awarded:** Varies each year. Recently, 100 of these scholarships were awarded. **Funds Available:** Stipends may be as high as $10,000 per year, but recently they ranged from $250 to $3,250 per year. **Duration:** 1 year. **Eligibility Requirements:** This program is open to BBNC shareholders who have a high school diploma or equivalent and are enrolled or planning to enroll in an accredited college or university as a full-time student. Applicants must have a GPA of 2.0 or higher and be able to demonstrate financial need. Along with their application, they must submit an essay on their career goals and desire to succeed in their chosen field of study. Selection is based on the essay (35%), cumulative GPA (40%), financial need (20%), and letters of recommendation (5%). **Deadline for Receipt:** April of each year.

353 ■ BRISTOL BAY NATIVE CORPORATION

Attn: BBNC Education Foundation
800 Cordova Street, Suite 200
Anchorage, AK 99501-6299
Tel: (907)278-3602
Free: 800-426-3602
Fax: (907)276-3925
E-mail: pelagiol@bbnc.net
Web Site: http://www.bbnc.net

To provide financial assistance to shareholders of Bristol Bay Native Corporation (BBNC) who are currently majoring in business or accounting in college.

Title of Award: H. Noble Dick Scholarship **Area, Field, or Subject:** Accounting; Business administration **Level of Education for which Award is Granted:** Four Year College **Funds Available:** The stipend is $1,000 per year. **Duration:** 1 year.

Eligibility Requirements: This program is open to BBNC shareholders who are enrolled full time as a college junior or senior majoring in accounting or business management. Applicants must have a GPA of 2.5 or higher and be able to demonstrate financial need. Along with their application, they must submit an essay on their career goals and desire to succeed in their chosen field of study. Selection is based on the essay (35%), cumulative GPA (40%), financial need (20%), and letters of recommendation (5%). **Deadline for Receipt:** April of each year.

354 ■ BRISTOL BAY NATIVE CORPORATION

Attn: BBNC Education Foundation
800 Cordova Street, Suite 200
Anchorage, AK 99501-6299
Tel: (907)278-3602
Free: 800-426-3602
Fax: (907)276-3925
E-mail: pelagiol@bbnc.net
Web Site: http://www.bbnc.net

To provide financial assistance for college or graduate school to descendants of shareholders of Bristol Bay Native Corporation (BBNC) and other Alaska Natives.

Title of Award: First Alaskans Institute/BBNC EF Scholarships **Area, Field, or Subject:** General studies/Field of study not specified **Level of Education for which Award is Granted:** Graduate, Undergraduate **Number Awarded:** A limited number of these scholarships are awarded each year. **Funds Available:** A stipend is awarded (amount not specified). **Duration:** 1 year.

Eligibility Requirements: This program is open to 1) BBNC shareholders, and 2) lineal descendants of Alaska Native enrollees and shareholders. Applicants must have a high school diploma or equivalent (GED) and be enrolled or planning to enroll in an accredited college, university, graduate program, or vocational/technical school. They must have a GPA of 2.0 or higher and be able to demonstrate financial need. Along with their application, they must submit an essay on their career goals and desire to succeed in their chosen field of study. Applicants who are not BBNC shareholders must also submit a birth certificate as proof of relationship to the enrollee or shareholder. Selection is based on the essay (35%), cumulative GPA (40%), financial need (20%), and letters of recommendation (5%). **Deadline for Receipt:** April of each year. **Additional Information:** This program was established in 2001 by the First Alaskans Institute.

355 ■ SUSAN THOMPSON BUFFETT FOUNDATION

Attn: Scholarship Office
222 Kiewit Plaza
Omaha, NE 68131
Tel: (402)943-1383
Fax: (402)943-1380
E-mail: scholarships@stbfoundation.org
Web Site: http://www.BuffettScholarships.org

To provide financial assistance to entering or currently-enrolled students at public colleges and universities in Nebraska.

Title of Award: Susan Thompson Buffett Foundation Scholarship Program **Area, Field, or Subject:** General studies/Field of study not specified **Level of Education for which Award is Granted:** Undergraduate **Funds Available:** The maximum stipend is $2,800 per semester. Funds are sent directly to the recipient's school and must be used to pay tuition and fees; they may not be used to pay for books or other expenses. **Duration:** Up to 5 years for a 4-year college, or up to 3 years for a 2-year school. Students on scholarship may not drop out for a period of time and be reinstated as a scholarship recipient; they must reapply along with first-time students.

Eligibility Requirements: This program is open to U.S. citizens who are Nebraska residents. Applicants must be entering or currently enrolled in a state public college, university, community college, or trade school in Nebraska. They must be in financial need, be the only family member

presently receiving a grant from the foundation, have at least a 2.5 GPA, and have applied for federal financial aid. Selection is based on academic performance and financial need. Preference is given to minority students, students with special needs, and married or nonmarried students with dependents. **Deadline for Receipt:** April of each year. **Additional Information:** Students on a 12-month program or the quarter system may use the scholarship for summer tuition; students on the semester system may not use funds for summer school. Students who are not working must enroll in at least 12 credit hours; students who are working must enroll in at least 9 credit hours.

356 ■ BUREAU OF INDIAN AFFAIRS

Attn: Office of Indian Education Programs
1849 C Street, N.W.
MS 3512-MIB
Washington, DC 20240-0001
Tel: (202)208-6123
Fax: (202)208-3312
Web Site: http://www.oiep.bia.edu

To provide financial assistance to undergraduate students who belong to or are affiliated with federally-recognized Indian tribes.

Title of Award: Bureau of Indian Affairs Higher Education Grant Program **Area, Field, or Subject:** General studies/Field of study not specified **Level of Education for which Award is Granted:** Undergraduate **Number Awarded:** Approximately 9,500 students receive assistance through this program annually. **Funds Available:** Individual awards depend on the financial need of the recipient; they range from $300 to $5,000 and average $2,800 per year. Recently, a total of $20,290,000 was available for this program. **Duration:** 1 year; may be renewed for up to 4 additional years.

Eligibility Requirements: This program is open to 1) members of American Indian tribes who are eligible for the special programs and services provided through the Bureau of Indian Affairs (BIA) because of their status as Indians, and 2) individuals who are at least one-quarter degree Indian blood descendants of those members. Applicants must be 1) enrolled or planning to enroll at an accredited college or university in a course of study leading to an associate of arts or bachelor's degree and 2) able to demonstrate financial need. Most tribes administer the grant program directly for their members, but other tribal members may contact the BIA Office of Indian Education Programs to learn the name and address of the nearest Education Line Officer who can provide an application and assistance in completing it. **Deadline for Receipt:** June of each year for fall term; October of each year for spring term; April of each year for summer school. **Additional Information:** Funds may be used for either part-time or full-time study. This program was authorized by the Snyder Act of 1921.

357 ■ BUREAU OF MAINE VETERANS' SERVICES

117 State House Station
Augusta, ME 04333-0117
Tel: (207)626-4464
Free: 800-345-0116
Fax: (207)626-4471
E-mail: mvs@me.ngb.army.mil
Web Site: http://www.mainebvs.org/benefits.htm

To provide financial assistance for undergraduate or graduate education to dependents of disabled and other Maine veterans.

Title of Award: Maine Veterans Dependents Educational Benefits **Area, Field, or Subject:** General studies/Field of study not specified **Level of Education for which Award is Granted:** Graduate, Undergraduate **Number Awarded:** Varies each year. **Funds Available:** Recipients are entitled to free tuition at institutions of higher education supported by the state of Maine. **Duration:** Benefits extend for a maximum of 8 semesters. Recipients have 6 consecutive academic years to complete their education.

Eligibility Requirements: Applicants for these benefits must be children (high school seniors or graduates under 25 years of age), non-divorced spouses, or unremarried widow(er)s of veterans who meet 1 or more of the following requirements: 1) living and determined to have a total permanent disability resulting from a service-connected cause; 2) killed in action; 3) died from a service-connected disability; 4) died while totally and permanently disabled due to a service-connected disability but whose death was not related to the service-connected disability; or 5) a member of the armed forces on active duty who has been listed for more than 90 days as missing in action, captured, forcibly detained, or interned in the line of duty by a foreign government or power. The veteran parent must have been a resident of Maine at the time of entry into service or a resident of Maine for 5 years preceding application for these benefits. Children may be seeking no higher than a bachelor's degree. Spouses, widows, and widowers may work on an advanced degree if they already have a bachelor's degree at the time of enrollment into this program. **Additional Information:** College preparatory schooling and correspondence courses do not qualify under this program.

358 ■ BUREAU FOR VETERANS AFFAIRS

Fort Indiantown Gap
Annville, PA 17003-5002
Tel: (717)865-8910
Free: 800-54
Fax: (717)865-8589
E-mail: jdavison@state.pa.us
Web Site: http://sites.state.pa.us/PA_Exec/Military_Affairs/va/benefits.htm
To provide financial assistance for college to the children of disabled or deceased Pennsylvania veterans.
Title of Award: Pennsylvania Educational Gratuity for Veterans' Dependents **Area, Field, or Subject:** General studies/Field of study not specified **Level of Education for which Award is Granted:** Undergraduate **Number Awarded:** Varies each year. **Funds Available:** The stipend is $500 per semester ($1,000 per year). The money is paid directly to the recipient's school and is to be applied to the costs of tuition, board, room, books, supplies, and/or matriculation fees. **Duration:** The allowance is paid for up to 4 academic years or for the duration of the course of study, whichever is less.
Eligibility Requirements: Children of honorably-discharged veterans who are rated totally and permanently disabled as a result of wartime service or who have died of such a disability are eligible if they are between 16 and 23 years of age, have lived in Pennsylvania for at least 5 years immediately preceding the date of application, can demonstrate financial need, and have been accepted or are currently enrolled in a Pennsylvania state or state-aided secondary or postsecondary educational institution.

359 ■ BUSINESS AND PROFESSIONAL WOMEN OF VIRGINIA

Attn: Virginia BPW Foundation
P.O. Box 4842
McLean, VA 22103-4842
Web Site: http://www.bpwva.org/Foundation.shtml
To provide financial assistance to girls and women pursuing postsecondary job-oriented career education (in business, trade, or industrial occupations) in Virginia.
Title of Award: Karen B. Lewis Career Education Scholarship **Area, Field, or Subject:** General studies/Field of study not specified **Level of Education for which Award is Granted:** Vocational/Occupational **Number Awarded:** At least 1 is awarded each year. **Funds Available:** Stipends range from $100 to $1,000 per year; funds may be used for tuition, fees, books, transportation, living expenses, and dependent care. **Duration:** Funds must be used within 12 months. Prior recipients may reapply, but they are not given priority.
Eligibility Requirements: This program is open to women who are at least 18 years of age; are U.S. citizens and Virginia residents; have been accepted into an accredited training program in Virginia; have a definite plan to use their education in a business, trade, or industrial occupation; and are able to demonstrate financial need. They may not be pursuing education leading to a bachelor's or higher degree. **Deadline for Receipt:** March of each year.

360 ■ BUSINESS PROFESSIONALS OF AMERICA

5454 Cleveland Avenue
Columbus, OH 43231-4021
Tel: (614)895-7277
Free: 800-334-2007
Fax: (614)895-1165
Web Site: http://www.bpa.org
To provide financial assistance for college to members of the Business Professionals of America (BPA).
Title of Award: BPA "Who's Who Among American High School Students" Scholarship **Area, Field, or Subject:** Business administration **Level of**

Education for which Award is Granted: Undergraduate **Number Awarded:** 1 each year. **Funds Available:** The stipend is $2,000. **Duration:** 1 year.
Eligibility Requirements: This program is open to high school seniors who are BPA members with a GPA of 3.0 or higher. Applicants must have held a chapter, state, or national BPA office and received the Ambassador Torch Award. Along with their application, they must submit 1) a 1-page resume of activities involving both BPA and other school and community activities; 2) letters of recommendation from their chapter advisor and 2 other individuals; 3) a high school transcript; and 4) a 1-page essay on where they see themselves professionally in 10 years. Selection is based on academic success and involvement within BPA. **Deadline for Receipt:** March of each year. **Additional Information:** These awards are funded by the ECI Scholarship Foundation of Educational Communications Inc., publisher of *Who's Who Among American High School Students*.

361 ■ CALIFORNIA ALARM ASSOCIATION

3401 Pacific Avenue, Suite 1C
Marina del Rey, CA 90292-7800
Tel: (310)305-1277
Free: 800-437-7658
Fax: (310)305-2077
E-mail: info@CAAonline.org
Web Site: http://www.CAAonline.org
To provide financial assistance for college to the children of active-duty law enforcement and fire service personnel in California.
Title of Award: CAA Youth Scholarship **Area, Field, or Subject:** General studies/Field of study not specified **Level of Education for which Award is Granted:** Undergraduate **Number Awarded:** 1 each year. **Funds Available:** The stipend is $1,500. **Duration:** 1 year; nonrenewable.
Eligibility Requirements: Applicants must be between the ages of 15 and 20; be a graduating high school senior in California; be accepted at an accredited college or university; and have a father, mother, or legal guardian who is a full-time active employee (not on disability) of the police or sheriff's department or a paid employee or volunteer of a fire department in California. Applicants must submit a high school transcript, proof of acceptance to a college or university, and proof of parent's occupation. Selection is based on class rank (25 points), class average (25 points), SAT scores (20 points), essay on "How Your Father, Mother or Guardian Helps Us Secure Our Community" (15 points), and extracurricular activities (15 points). Financial need is not considered in the selection process. First, regional winners (northern and southern California) are selected; from them a state winner is selected and that winner is entered in the national competition of the National Burglar & Fire Alarm Association. **Deadline for Receipt:** March of each year.

362 ■ CALIFORNIA ASSOCIATION FOR POSTSECONDARY EDUCATION AND DISABILITY

Attn: Executive Assistant
71423 Biskra Road
Rancho Mirage, CA 92270
Tel: (760)346-8206
Fax: (760)340-5275
E-mail: caped2000@aol.com
Web Site: http://www.caped.net/scholarship.html
To provide financial assistance to undergraduate and graduate students in California who have a disability and can demonstrate academic achievement and involvement in community and campus activities.
Title of Award: CAPED General Excellence Scholarship **Area, Field, or Subject:** General studies/Field of study not specified **Level of Education for which Award is Granted:** Graduate, Undergraduate **Number Awarded:** 1 each year. **Funds Available:** The stipend is $1,500. **Duration:** 1 year.
Eligibility Requirements: This program is open to students at public and private colleges and universities in California who have a disability. Undergraduates must have completed at least 6 semester credits and have a GPA of 2.5 or higher. Graduate students must have completed at least 3 semester units and have a GPA of 3.0 or higher. Applicants must submit a 1-page personal letter that demonstrates writing skills; progress toward meeting educational and vocational goals; how they accommodate their disability; involvement in community activities; and any other personal factor that might strengthen their application. They must also submit a letter of recommendation from a faculty member, verification of

disability, official transcripts, proof of current enrollment, and documentation of financial need. This award is presented to the applicant who demonstrates the highest level of academic achievement and involvement in community and campus life. **Deadline for Receipt:** August of each year. **Additional Information:** Information is also available from Janet Shapiro, Disabled Student Programs and Services, Santa Barbara City College, 721 Cliff Drive, Santa Barbara, CA 93109, (805) 965-0581, ext. 2365, E-mail: shapiro@sbcc.net.

363 ■ CALIFORNIA ASSOCIATION FOR POSTSECONDARY EDUCATION AND DISABILITY

Attn: Executive Assistant
71423 Biskra Road
Rancho Mirage, CA 92270
Tel: (760)346-8206
Fax: (760)340-5275
E-mail: caped2000@aol.com
Web Site: http://www.caped.net/scholarship.html
To provide financial assistance to undergraduate and graduate students in California who have a disability.
Title of Award: Steve Fasteau Past Presidents' Scholarship **Area, Field, or Subject:** General studies/Field of study not specified **Level of Education for which Award is Granted:** Graduate, Undergraduate **Number Awarded:** 1 each year. **Funds Available:** The stipend is $1,000. **Duration:** 1 year.
Eligibility Requirements: This program is open to students at public and private colleges and universities in California who have a disability. Undergraduates must have completed at least 6 semester credits and have a GPA of 2.5 or higher. Graduate students must have completed at least 3 semester units and have a GPA of 3.0 or higher. Applicants must submit a 1-page personal letter that demonstrates writing skills; progress toward meeting educational and vocational goals; how they accommodate their disability; involvement in community activities; and any other personal factor that might strengthen their application. They must also submit a letter of recommendation from a faculty person, verification of disability, official transcripts, proof of current enrollment, and documentation of financial need. **Deadline for Receipt:** August of each year. **Additional Information:** Information is also available from Janet Shapiro, Disabled Student Programs and Services, Santa Barbara City College, 721 Cliff Drive, Santa Barbara, CA 93109, (805) 965-0581, ext. 2365, E-mail: shapiro@sbcc.net.

364 ■ CALIFORNIA ASSOCIATION FOR POSTSECONDARY EDUCATION AND DISABILITY

Attn: Executive Assistant
71423 Biskra Road
Rancho Mirage, CA 92270
Tel: (760)346-8206
Fax: (760)340-5275
E-mail: caped2000@aol.com
Web Site: http://www.caped.net/scholarship.html
To provide financial assistance to 4-year college and universities students in California who have a disability.
Title of Award: Cindy Kolb Memorial Scholarship **Area, Field, or Subject:** General studies/Field of study not specified **Level of Education for which Award is Granted:** Four Year College **Number Awarded:** 1 each year. **Funds Available:** The stipend is $1,000. **Duration:** 1 year.
Eligibility Requirements: This program is open to students at 4-year colleges and universities in California who have a disability. Applicants must have completed at least 6 semester credits with a GPA of 2.5 or higher. They must submit a 1-page personal letter that demonstrates writing skills; progress toward meeting educational and vocational goals; how they accommodate their disability; involvement in community activities; and any other personal factor that might strengthen their application. They must also submit a letter of recommendation from a faculty member, verification of disability, official transcripts, proof of current enrollment, and documentation of financial need. **Deadline for Receipt:** August of each year. **Additional Information:** Information is also available from Janet

Shapiro, Disabled Student Programs and Services, Santa Barbara City College, 721 Cliff Drive, Santa Barbara, CA 93109, (805) 965-0581, ext. 2365, E-mail: shapiro@sbcc.net.

365 ■ CALIFORNIA ASSOCIATION FOR POSTSECONDARY EDUCATION AND DISABILITY

Attn: Executive Assistant
71423 Biskra Road
Rancho Mirage, CA 92270
Tel: (760)346-8206
Fax: (760)340-5275
E-mail: caped2000@aol.com
Web Site: http://www.caped.net/scholarship.html
To provide financial assistance to undergraduate and graduate students in California who have a disability.
Title of Award: William May Memorial Scholarship **Area, Field, or Subject:** General studies/Field of study not specified **Level of Education for which Award is Granted:** Graduate, Undergraduate **Number Awarded:** 1 each year. **Funds Available:** The stipend is $1,000. **Duration:** 1 year.
Eligibility Requirements: This program is open to students at public and private colleges and universities in California who have a disability. Undergraduates must have completed at least 6 semester credits and have a GPA of 2.5 or higher. Graduate students must have completed at least 3 semester units and have a GPA of 3.0 or higher. Applicants must submit a 1-page personal letter that demonstrates writing skills; progress toward meeting educational and vocational goals; how they accommodate their disability; involvement in community activities; and any other personal factor that might strengthen their application. They must also submit a letter of recommendation from a faculty person, verification of disability, official transcripts, proof of current enrollment, and documentation of financial need. **Deadline for Receipt:** August of each year. **Additional Information:** Information is also available from Janet Shapiro, Disabled Student Programs and Services, Santa Barbara City College, 721 Cliff Drive, Santa Barbara, CA 93109, (805) 965-0581, ext. 2365, E-mail: shapiro@sbcc.net.

366 ■ CALIFORNIA ASSOCIATION FOR POSTSECONDARY EDUCATION AND DISABILITY

Attn: Executive Assistant
71423 Biskra Road
Rancho Mirage, CA 92270
Tel: (760)346-8206
Fax: (760)340-5275
E-mail: caped2000@aol.com
Web Site: http://www.caped.net/scholarship.html
To provide financial assistance to community college students in California who have a disability.
Title of Award: Lynn M. Smith Memorial Scholarship **Area, Field, or Subject:** General studies/Field of study not specified **Level of Education for which Award is Granted:** Two Year College **Number Awarded:** 1 each year. **Funds Available:** The stipend is $1,000. **Duration:** 1 year.
Eligibility Requirements: This program is open to students at community colleges in California who have a disability. Applicants must be preparing for a vocational career and have completed at least 6 semester credits with a GPA of 2.5 or higher. They must submit a 1-page personal letter that demonstrates writing skills; progress toward meeting educational and vocational goals; how they accommodate their disability; involvement in community activities; and any other personal factor that might strengthen their application. They must also submit a letter of recommendation from a faculty member, verification of disability, official transcripts, proof of current enrollment, and documentation of financial need. **Deadline for Receipt:** August of each year. **Additional Information:** Information is also available from Janet Shapiro, Disabled Student Programs and Services, Santa Barbara City College, 721 Cliff Drive, Santa Barbara, CA 93109, (805) 965-0581, ext. 2365, E-mail: shapiro@sbcc.net.

367 ■ CALIFORNIA ASSOCIATION FOR POSTSECONDARY EDUCATION AND DISABILITY

Attn: Executive Assistant
71423 Biskra Road
Rancho Mirage, CA 92270

Tel: (760)346-8206
Fax: (760)340-5275
E-mail: caped2000@aol.com
Web Site: http://www.caped.net/scholarship.html
To provide financial assistance to undergraduate and graduate students in California who have a learning disability.
Title of Award: Susan Bunch Memorial Scholarship **Area, Field, or Subject:** General studies/Field of study not specified **Level of Education for which Award is Granted:** Graduate, Undergraduate **Number Awarded:** 1 each year. **Funds Available:** The stipend is $1,000. **Duration:** 1 year.
Eligibility Requirements: This program is open to students at public and private colleges and universities in California who have a learning disability. Undergraduates must have completed at least 6 semester credits and have a GPA of 2.5 or higher. Graduate students must have completed at least 3 semester units and have a GPA of 3.0 or higher. Applicants must submit a 1-page personal letter that demonstrates writing skills; progress toward meeting educational and vocational goals; how they accommodate their disability; involvement in community activities; and any other personal factor that might strengthen their application. They must also submit a letter of recommendation from a faculty member, verification of disability, official transcripts, proof of current enrollment, and documentation of financial need. **Deadline for Receipt:** August of each year. **Additional Information:** Information is also available from Janet Shapiro, Disabled Student Programs and Services, Santa Barbara City College, 721 Cliff Drive, Santa Barbara, CA 93109, (805) 965-0581, ext. 2365, E-mail: shapiro@sbcc.net.

368 ■ CALIFORNIA ASSOCIATION FOR POSTSECONDARY EDUCATION AND DISABILITY

Attn: Executive Assistant
71423 Biskra Road
Rancho Mirage, CA 92270
Tel: (760)346-8206
Fax: (760)340-5275
E-mail: caped2000@aol.com
Web Site: http://www.caped.net/scholarship.html
To provide financial assistance to blind and visually impaired undergraduate and graduate students in California.
Title of Award: Walter Young Memorial Scholarship **Area, Field, or Subject:** General studies/Field of study not specified **Level of Education for which Award is Granted:** Graduate, Undergraduate **Number Awarded:** 1 each year. **Funds Available:** The stipend is $1,000. **Duration:** 1 year.
Eligibility Requirements: This program is open to blind and visually impaired students at public and private colleges and universities in California. Undergraduates must have completed at least 6 semester credits and have a GPA of 2.5 or higher. Graduate students must have completed at least 3 semester units and have a GPA of 3.0 or higher. Applicants must submit a 1-page personal letter that demonstrates writing skills; progress toward meeting educational and vocational goals; how they accommodate their disability; involvement in community activities; and any other factor that might strengthen their application. They must also submit a letter of recommendation from a faculty member, verification of disability, official transcripts, proof of current enrollment, and documentation of financial need. **Deadline for Receipt:** August of each year. **Additional Information:** Information is also available from Janet Shapiro, Disabled Student Programs and Services, Santa Barbara City College, 721 Cliff Drive, Santa Barbara, CA 93109, (805) 965-0581, ext. 2365, E-mail: shapiro@sbcc.net.

369 ■ CALIFORNIA ASSOCIATION OF WINEGRAPE GROWERS

Attn: California Wine Grape Growers Foundation
601 University Avenue, Suite 135
Sacramento, CA 95825
Tel: (916)924-5370
Free: 800-241-1800
Fax: (916)924-5374
E-mail: info@cawg.org
Web Site: http://www.cawg.org/cwggf/scholar.htm
To provide financial assistance for college to high school seniors in California whose parent(s) work in the grape wine vineyards.
Title of Award: California Wine Grape Growers Foundation Scholarships **Area, Field, or Subject:** General studies/Field of study not specified

Level of Education for which Award is Granted: Undergraduate **Number Awarded:** 6 each year: 2 at 4-year universities and 4 at community colleges. **Funds Available:** The stipend is $1,000 per year at a 4-year university or $500 per year at a community college. **Duration:** 4 years at branches of the University of California or California State University system; 2 years at community colleges.
Eligibility Requirements: This program is open to high school seniors in California who plan to attend a branch of the University of California, a branch of the California State University system, or a community college in the state. Applicants must have a parent or legal guardian who was employed as a vineyard worker by a winegrape grower during either or both of the 2 preceding seasons. Applications are available in either English or Spanish. Along with their application, they must submit a high school transcript, a copy of their SAT or ACT scores (if they are planning to attend a 4-year university), a letter of recommendation from a school official, an endorsement from a member of the California Association of Winegrape Growers (CAWG), and a 2-page essay on themselves and their career goals. Selection is based on financial need, demonstrated academic ability, community involvement and leadership and/or work history, and determination to succeed. **Deadline for Receipt:** March of each year. **Additional Information:** Recipients must enroll in 12 college units each semester while receiving scholarship money.

370 ■ CALIFORNIA CORRECTIONAL PEACE OFFICERS ASSOCIATION

755 Riverpoint Drive, Suite 200
West Sacramento, CA 95605-1634
Tel: (916)372-6060
Web Site: http://www.ccpoanet.org
To provide financial assistance to the members and the families of members of the California Correctional Peace Officers Association (CCPOA).
Title of Award: CCPOA/Joe Harper Scholarship **Area, Field, or Subject:** General studies/Field of study not specified **Level of Education for which Award is Granted:** Undergraduate **Number Awarded:** Varies each year. **Funds Available:** Each year, the association distributes more than $100,000 in scholarship funds. **Duration:** 1 year; may be renewed, if the recipient maintains at least a 3.5 GPA in college.
Eligibility Requirements: This program is open to the members of the CCPOA and the immediate family or active, retired, or deceased members. Both high school seniors and current college students are eligible. Applicants must have at least a 3.0 GPA. Along with their application, they must submit an essay (750 words or less) on this topic: "My goals, present and future, and why I deserve this scholarship." Selection is based on academic record, school activities, financial need, and community service. **Deadline for Receipt:** April of each year.

371 ■ CALIFORNIA COUNCIL OF THE BLIND

578 B Street
Hayward, CA 94541
Tel: (510)537-7877
Free: 800-221-6359
Fax: (510)537-7830
E-mail: ccotb@earthlink.net
Web Site: http://www.ccbnet.org/scholar.htm
To provide financial assistance for undergraduate or graduate study to blind people in California.
Title of Award: California Council of the Blind Scholarships **Area, Field, or Subject:** General studies/Field of study not specified **Level of Education for which Award is Granted:** Graduate, Undergraduate **Number Awarded:** Varies each year. **Funds Available:** The amount of the assistance depends on the availability of funds and the needs of the applicant. **Duration:** 1 year; may be renewed. For graduate students, support is limited to 2 years of work for a master's degree or 3 years for a Ph.D.
Eligibility Requirements: Applicants must be legally blind residents of California who are enrolled or planning to enroll full time at an accredited college or university at either the undergraduate or graduate level. The

school may be in any state. Selection is based on academic achievement and financial need. **Deadline for Receipt:** June of each year.

372 ■ CALIFORNIA DEPARTMENT OF VETERANS AFFAIRS

Attn: Division of Veterans Services
1227 O Street, Room 101
Sacramento, CA 95814
Tel: (916)503-8397
Free: 800-952-LOAN
Fax: (916)653-2563
E-mail: ruckergl@cdva.ca.gov
Web Site: http://www.cdva.ca.gov/service/feewaiver.asp
To provide financial assistance for college to the children of disabled or deceased veterans in California.
Title of Award: California Fee Waiver Program for Children of Veterans **Area, Field, or Subject:** General studies/Field of study not specified **Level of Education for which Award is Granted:** Undergraduate **Number Awarded:** Varies each year. **Funds Available:** This program provides for waiver of registration fees to students attending any publicly-supported community or state college or university in California. **Duration:** 1 year; may be renewed.
Eligibility Requirements: Eligible for this program are the children of veterans who 1) died of a service-connected disability; 2) had a service-connected disability at the time of death; or 3) currently have a service-connected disability of any level of severity. Applicants must plan to attend a community college in California, branch of the California State University system, or campus of the University of California. Their income, including the value of support received from parents, cannot exceed the national poverty level. California veteran status is not required for this program. Dependents in college who are eligible to receive federal education benefits from the U.S. Department of Veterans Affairs are not eligible for these fee waivers.

373 ■ CALIFORNIA DEPARTMENT OF VETERANS AFFAIRS

Attn: Division of Veterans Services
1227 O Street, Room 101
Sacramento, CA 95814
Tel: (916)503-8397
Free: 800-952-LOAN
Fax: (916)653-2563
E-mail: ruckergl@cdva.ca.gov
Web Site: http://www.cdva.ca.gov/service/feewaiver.asp
To provide financial assistance for college to dependents of disabled and deceased members of the California National Guard.
Title of Award: California Fee Waiver Program for Dependents of Deceased or Disabled National Guard Members **Area, Field, or Subject:** General studies/Field of study not specified **Level of Education for which Award is Granted:** Undergraduate **Number Awarded:** Varies each year. **Funds Available:** Full-time college students receive a waiver of tuition and registration fees at any publicly-supported community or state college or university in California. **Duration:** 1 year; may be renewed.
Eligibility Requirements: Eligible for this program are spouses, children, and unmarried widow(er)s of members of the California National Guard who, in the line of duty and in the active service of the state, were killed, died of a disability, or became permanently disabled. Applicants must be attending or planning to attend a community college, branch of the California State University system, or campus of the University of California.

374 ■ CALIFORNIA DEPARTMENT OF VETERANS AFFAIRS

Attn: Division of Veterans Services
1227 O Street, Room 101
Sacramento, CA 95814
Tel: (916)503-8397
Free: 800-952-LOAN
Fax: (916)653-2563
E-mail: ruckergl@cdva.ca.gov
Web Site: http://www.cdva.ca.gov/service/feewaiver.asp
To provide financial assistance for college to dependents of disabled and other California veterans.
Title of Award: California Fee Waiver Program for Dependents of Totally Disabled Veterans **Area, Field, or Subject:** General studies/Field of study

not specified **Level of Education for which Award is Granted:** Undergraduate **Number Awarded:** Varies each year. **Funds Available:** Full-time college students receive a waiver of tuition and registration fees at any publicly-supported community or state college or university in California. **Duration:** Children of eligible veterans may receive postsecondary benefits until the needed training is completed or until the dependent reaches 27 years of age (extended to 30 if the dependent serves in the armed forces). Widow(er)s and spouses are limited to a maximum of 48 months' full-time training or the equivalent in part-time training.
Eligibility Requirements: Eligible for this program are spouses (including registered domestic partners), children, and unremarried widow(er)s of veterans who are currently totally service-connected disabled (or are being compensated for a service-connected disability at a rate of 100%) or who died of a service-connected cause or disability. The veteran parent must have served during a qualifying war period and must have been discharged or released from military service under honorable conditions. The child cannot be over 27 years of age (extended to 30 if the student was in the military); there are no age limitations for spouses or surviving spouses. This program does not have an income limit. Dependents in college are not eligible if they are qualified to receive educational benefits from the U.S. Department of Veterans Affairs. Applicants must be attending or planning to attend a community college, branch of the California State University system, or campus of the University of California.

375 ■ CALIFORNIA DEPARTMENT OF VETERANS AFFAIRS

Attn: Division of Veterans Services
1227 O Street, Room 101
Sacramento, CA 95814
Tel: (916)503-8397
Free: 800-952-LOAN
Fax: (916)653-2563
E-mail: ruckergl@cdva.ca.gov
Web Site: http://www.cdva.ca.gov/service/feewaiver.asp
To provide financial assistance for college to veterans in California who received the Medal of Honor and their children.
Title of Award: California Fee Waiver Program for Recipients of the Medal of Honor and Their Children **Area, Field, or Subject:** General studies/Field of study not specified **Level of Education for which Award is Granted:** Undergraduate **Number Awarded:** Varies each year. **Funds Available:** Full-time college students receive a waiver of tuition and registration fees at any publicly-supported community or state college or university in California. **Duration:** 1 year; may be renewed.
Eligibility Requirements: This program is open to recipients of the Medal of Honor and their children who are residents of California. Applicants must be attending or planning to attend a community college, branch of the California State University system, or campus of the University of California.

376 ■ CALIFORNIA FUNERAL DIRECTORS ASSOCIATION

Attn: Scholarship Director
One Capitol Mall
Sacramento, CA 95814
Tel: (916)325-2361
Free: 800-255-2332
Fax: (916)444-7462
E-mail: cfda@amgroup.us
Web Site: http://www.cafda.org
To provide financial assistance to California residents who are interested in attending a mortuary college in the state.
Title of Award: California Funeral Directors Association Scholarship **Area, Field, or Subject:** Mortuary science **Level of Education for which Award is Granted:** Undergraduate **Number Awarded:** 2 each year: 1 for a student in southern California and 1 for a student in northern California. **Funds Available:** The stipend is $1,000. Funds are paid to the recipient's school. **Duration:** 1 year.
Eligibility Requirements: Applicants must be attending or planning to attend a mortuary college in California. Selection is based on academic record, work experience, a 500-word essay on why the applicant is

interested in a career in funeral service in California, and financial need. **Deadline for Receipt:** April of each year.

377 ■ CALIFORNIA GOVERNOR'S COMMITTEE ON EMPLOYMENT OF PEOPLE WITH DISABILITIES

Attn: Employment Development Department
800 Capitol Mall, MIC 41
Sacramento, CA 95814
Tel: (916)654-8055
Free: 800-695-0350
Fax: (916)654-9821
E-mail: rnagle@edd.ca.gov
Web Site: http://www.disabilityemployment.org/yp_hal_con.htm
To provide financial assistance to disabled high school seniors in California who have participated in athletics.
Title of Award: Hal Connolly Scholar-Athlete Award **Area, Field, or Subject:** General studies/Field of study not specified **Level of Education for which Award is Granted:** Undergraduate **Number Awarded:** Up to 6 each year: 3 are set aside for females and 3 for males. **Funds Available:** The stipend is $1,000, contingent upon the winners' acceptance at an accredited California college or university. Funds may be used for tuition, books, supplies, and other educational expenses. Exceptions are granted to students who choose to attend schools out of state primarily to accommodate their disability. **Duration:** Awards are granted annually.
Eligibility Requirements: Applicants must be high school seniors with disabilities, no more than 19 years of age on January 1 of the year of application, who have competed in California high school athletics at a varsity or equivalent level and possess academic and athletic records that demonstrate qualities of leadership and accomplishment. They must have completed high school with a GPA of 2.8 or better and plan to attend an accredited college or university in California, but they do not have to intend to participate formally in collegiate athletic activities. Selection is based on cumulative GPA (15%), cumulative GPA as it relates to the nature of the student's disability (15%), athletic accomplishments as they relate to the student's disability (30%), an essay on "How Sports Participation Has Affected My Life at School and in the Community As a Person with a Disability" (25%), and overall personal achievement (15%). The top finalists may be interviewed before selections are made. Male and female students compete separately. **Deadline for Receipt:** January of each year.

378 ■ CALIFORNIA-HAWAII ELKS ASSOCIATION

Attn: Scholarship Committee
5450 East Lamona Avenue
Fresno, CA 93727-2224
Tel: (559)255-4531
Fax: (559)456-2659
Web Site: http://www.chea-elks.org/vocationalgrant.html
To provide financial assistance for vocational school to residents of California and Hawaii.
Title of Award: California-Hawaii Elks Association Vocational Grants **Area, Field, or Subject:** General studies/Field of study not specified **Level of Education for which Award is Granted:** Vocational/Occupational **Number Awarded:** 58 each year: 55 to residents of California and 3 to residents of Hawaii. **Funds Available:** The stipend is $1,000 per year. Funds may be used for tuition and fees, room and board (if living on campus), and books and supplies. They may not be used for general living expenses or child care costs. **Duration:** 1 year; may be renewed for 1 additional year.
Eligibility Requirements: This program is open to residents of California or Hawaii who are high school seniors or older. Applicants must be enrolled or planning to enroll in a vocational/technical program of 2 years or less that leads to a terminal associate degree, diploma, or certificate, but less than a bachelor's degree. Students planning to transfer to a 4-year school to work on a bachelor's degree are not eligible. Selection is based on motivation, financial need, aptitude toward chosen vocation, grades, and completeness and neatness of the application brochure. Applications are available from an Elks Lodge in California or Hawaii; they must be endorsed by the lodge. U.S. citizenship is required. **Deadline for**

Receipt: Applications may be submitted at any time. **Additional Information:** Recipients must enroll in at least 12 semester credit hours each term.

379 ■ CALIFORNIA-HAWAII ELKS ASSOCIATION

Attn: Scholarship Committee
5450 East Lamona Avenue
Fresno, CA 93727-2224
Tel: (559)255-4531
Fax: (559)456-2659
Web Site: http://www.chea-elks.org/uspsd.html
To provide financial assistance for college to residents of California and Hawaii with disabilities.
Title of Award: California-Hawaii Elks Major Project Undergraduate Scholarship Program for Students with Disabilities **Area, Field, or Subject:** General studies/Field of study not specified **Level of Education for which Award is Granted:** Undergraduate **Number Awarded:** 20 to 30 each year. **Funds Available:** The annual stipend is $1,000 for community colleges and vocational schools or $2,000 per year for 4-year colleges or universities. **Duration:** 1 year; may be renewed for up to 3 additional years.
Eligibility Requirements: This program is open to residents of California or Hawaii who have a physical impairment, neurological impairment, visual impairment, hearing impairment, and/or speech/language disorder. Applicants must be a senior in high school, be a high school graduate, or have passed the GED test. U.S. citizenship is required. Selection is based on financial need, GPA, severity of disability, seriousness of purpose, and depth of character. Applications are available from an Elks Lodge in California or Hawaii; students must first request an interview with the lodge's scholarship chairman or Exalted Ruler. **Deadline for Receipt:** March of each year.

380 ■ CALIFORNIA INTERSCHOLASTIC FEDERATION

Attn: State Office
333 Hegenberger Road, Suite 511
Oakland, CA 94621
Tel: (510)639-4445
Fax: (510)639-4449
E-mail: info@cifstate.org
Web Site: http://www.cifstate.org
To provide financial assistance to college-bound high school seniors in California who have participated in athletics.
Title of Award: CIF Scholar-Athlete of the Year **Area, Field, or Subject:** General studies/Field of study not specified **Level of Education for which Award is Granted:** Undergraduate **Number Awarded:** 2 each year: 1 for a female and 1 for a male. **Funds Available:** The stipend is $2,000. **Duration:** 1 year; nonrenewable.
Eligibility Requirements: This program is open to high school seniors in California who have an unweighted cumulative GPA of 3.7 or higher and have demonstrated superior athletic ability in at least 2 years of varsity play within California. Students must submit an application to their principal or counselor and an essay, up to 500 words, on how they display character in their athletic and academic efforts. They may include examples of meaningful behavior in their high school experience, lessons learned about the importance of character in their life, and opportunities that coaches, cheerleaders, athletes, and fans have to promote character in interscholastic athletics. Based on those essays, school officials nominate students for these scholarships. Males and females are judged separately. **Deadline for Receipt:** Students must submit their application and essay to their counselor or principal by mid-February of each year. School officials forward the packets to the state office by the end of March.

381 ■ CALIFORNIA JAPANESE AMERICAN ALUMNI ASSOCIATION

Attn: Ron Yamada
P.O. Box 15235
San Francisco, CA 94115-0235
Tel: (650)802-0939
E-mail: scholarships@cjaaa.org
Web Site: http://www.cjaaa.org/scholarship.html
To provide financial assistance to undergraduate or graduate students of Japanese American descent who are currently enrolled at 1 of the 9 University of California campuses.

Title of Award: CJAAA Scholarship Program **Area, Field, or Subject:** General studies/Field of study not specified **Level of Education for which Award is Granted:** Graduate, Undergraduate **Number Awarded:** 5 to 15 each year. **Funds Available:** Stipends range from $1,000 to $3,000. The Moriaki "Mo" Noguchi Memorial Scholarship of $3,000 is given to the top overall candidate. The George Kondo Award is at least $1,000 and is awarded to the applicant with the best community service record. The Yori Wada Award is $2,000 and is awarded to the applicant with the most outstanding record of public service. The stipend for a student accepted to the University of California Education Abroad Program ranges from $2,500 to $5,000. **Duration:** 1 year; nonrenewable. **Eligibility Requirements:** This program is open to continuing or returning undergraduate or graduate students of Japanese American descent who are attending 1 of the 9 University of California campuses. They must be American citizens and may be studying in any field or discipline. A GPA of 3.0 or higher is strongly recommended but not required. Applicants interested in participating in the University of California Education Abroad Program in Japan must have a GPA of 3.5 or higher. Selection is based on academic excellence, commitment to community and social concerns, personal attributes, and financial need (in that order). **Deadline for Receipt:** April of each year.

382 ■ CALIFORNIA LIBRARIANS BLACK CAUCUS-GREATER LOS ANGELES CHAPTER

Attn: Scholarship Award
P.O. Box 2906
Los Angeles, CA 90078-2906
E-mail: scholarship@clbc.org
Web Site: http://www.clbc.org/scholar.html
To provide financial assistance to African Americans in California who are interested in becoming librarians or library paraprofessionals.
Title of Award: Louise Jane Moses/Agnes Davis Memorial Scholarship **Area, Field, or Subject:** Library and archival sciences **Level of Education for which Award is Granted:** Master's, Undergraduate **Number Awarded:** Varies each year. Recently, 3 of these scholarships were awarded: 1 at $500, 1 at $750, and 1 at $1,000. **Funds Available:** Stipends range from $500 to $1,000. **Duration:** 1 year.
Eligibility Requirements: This program is open to African American residents of California who are working on a degree from an accredited library/information science program or an accredited library/information science paraprofessional program in the state. Selection is based on demonstrated financial need, scholastic achievement, and commitment to the goals of encouraging and supporting African American library professionals and improving library service to the African American community. Interviews are required. **Deadline for Receipt:** December of each year. **Additional Information:** Information is also available from Stephanie Brasley, University of California at Los Angeles, College Library, P.O. Box 951450, Los Angeles, CA 90095-1450, (310) 825-6726, Fax: (310) 206-9312, E-mail: sbrasley@library.ucla.edu.

383 ■ CALIFORNIA SCHOOL EMPLOYEES ASSOCIATION

Attn: Scholarship Committee
2045 Lundy Avenue
San Jose, CA 95131
Tel: (408)473-1000
Free: 800-632-2128
Fax: (408)954-0948
Web Site: http://www.csea.com
To provide financial assistance for college to dependents of members of the California School Employees Association (CSEA).
Title of Award: California School Employees Association Dependent Scholarships **Area, Field, or Subject:** General studies/Field of study not specified **Level of Education for which Award is Granted:** Undergraduate **Number Awarded:** Varies each year; recently, 30 scholarships were awarded to high school seniors, 1 to a community college student, and 3 to college/vocational school students. **Funds Available:** The stipend is $1,000. **Duration:** 1 year.
Eligibility Requirements: This program is open to dependents of members who are graduating high school seniors or students enrolled in a college, university, community college, or vocational school. Selection is based on academic achievement, character, leadership, and extracurricular activities within the community; financial need is also considered for some scholarships. **Deadline for Receipt:** March of each year.

384 ■ CALIFORNIA SCHOOL EMPLOYEES ASSOCIATION

Attn: Scholarship Committee
2045 Lundy Avenue
San Jose, CA 95131
Tel: (408)473-1000
Free: 800-632-2128
Fax: (408)954-0948
Web Site: http://www.csea.com
To provide financial assistance for college to members of the California School Employees Association (CSEA).
Title of Award: California School Employees Association Member Grants **Area, Field, or Subject:** General studies/Field of study not specified **Level of Education for which Award is Granted:** Undergraduate **Number Awarded:** 1 or more each year. **Funds Available:** The stipend is $1,000. **Duration:** 1 year.
Eligibility Requirements: This program is open to members who are attending college on a part-time or full-time basis. Selection is based on financial need, goals and objectives, citizenship, and CSEA activities. **Deadline for Receipt:** October of each year.

385 ■ CALIFORNIA STATE FAIR

Attn: Friends of the Fair Scholarship Program
1600 Exposition Boulevard
P.O. Box 15649
Sacramento, CA 95852
Tel: (916)274-5969
E-mail: wross@calexpo.com
Web Site: http://www.bigfun.org
To provide financial assistance to California residents of Asian Pacific Islander heritage who plan to attend a 4-year college or university in the state.
Title of Award: Asian Pacific Islander University Scholarship of the California State Fair **Area, Field, or Subject:** General studies/Field of study not specified **Level of Education for which Award is Granted:** Four Year College **Number Awarded:** 1 each year. **Funds Available:** The stipend is $1,000. **Duration:** 1 year.
Eligibility Requirements: This program is open to Asian Pacific Islanders who are currently enrolled in a high school or community college in California. Applicants must be planning to attend a 4-year college or university in the state in the following fall. They must have a GPA of 3.0 or higher. Along with their application, they must submit a 2-page statement on their Asian Pacific Islander background, community involvement, career goals, and desire to give back to their community. Selection is based on personal commitment, goals established for their chosen field, leadership potential, and civic accomplishments. **Deadline for Receipt:** March of each year. **Additional Information:** The Friends of the Fair Scholarship Program was established in 1993.

386 ■ CALIFORNIA STATE FAIR

Attn: Friends of the Fair Scholarship Program
1600 Exposition Boulevard
P.O. Box 15649
Sacramento, CA 95852
Tel: (916)274-5969
E-mail: wross@calexpo.com
Web Site: http://www.bigfun.org
To provide financial assistance for college to high school seniors in California who rank in the top 10% of their class.
Title of Award: California State Fair Academic Achievers Scholarships **Area, Field, or Subject:** General studies/Field of study not specified **Level of Education for which Award is Granted:** Undergraduate **Number Awarded:** 2 each year: 1 at $2,500 and 1 at $1,000. **Funds Available:** Stipends are $2,500 or $1,000. **Duration:** 1 year.
Eligibility Requirements: This program is open to seniors graduating from high schools in California who rank in the top 10% of their class for academic performance. Applicants must be planning to attend an accredited college or university in the state. Along with their application, they must submit a 500-word essay on why it is important to know where our food comes from. Selection is based on personal commitment, goals established for their chosen field, leadership potential, and civic accomplishments. **Deadline for Receipt:** March of each year. **Additional Information:** The Friends of the Fair Scholarship Program was established in 1993.

387 ■ CALIFORNIA STATE FAIR

Attn: Friends of the Fair Scholarship Program
1600 Exposition Boulevard
P.O. Box 15649
Sacramento, CA 95852
Tel: (916)274-5969
E-mail: wross@calexpo.com
Web Site: http://www.bigfun.org
To provide financial assistance to residents of California who are studying culinary cooking.
Title of Award: California State Fair Culinary Cooking Scholarships **Area, Field, or Subject:** Culinary arts **Level of Education for which Award is Granted:** Two Year College, Vocational/Occupational **Number Awarded:** 2 each year: 1 at $1,000 and 1 at $500. **Funds Available:** Stipends are $1,000 or $500. **Duration:** 1 year.
Eligibility Requirements: This program is open to residents of California currently enrolled at culinary arts vocational trade schools and community colleges in the state. Applicants must be enrolled in a culinary cooking program. They must have a GPA of 3.0 or higher. Along with their application, they must submit a 2-page essay on why they are pursuing their desired career and life goals. Selection is based on personal commitment, goals established for their chosen field, leadership potential, and civic accomplishments. **Deadline for Receipt:** March of each year. **Additional Information:** The Friends of the Fair Scholarship Program was established in 1993.

388 ■ CALIFORNIA STATE FAIR

Attn: Friends of the Fair Scholarship Program
1600 Exposition Boulevard
P.O. Box 15649
Sacramento, CA 95852
Tel: (916)274-5969
E-mail: wross@calexpo.com
Web Site: http://www.bigfun.org
To provide financial assistance to African American residents of California who plan to attend a 4-year college or university in the state.
Title of Award: California State Fair Scholarships for African American University Students **Area, Field, or Subject:** General studies/Field of study not specified **Level of Education for which Award is Granted:** Four Year College **Number Awarded:** 2 each year: 1 at $1,000 and 1 at $500. **Funds Available:** Stipends are $1,000 or $500. **Duration:** 1 year.
Eligibility Requirements: This program is open to African Americans who are currently enrolled in a high school or community college in California. Applicants must be planning to attend a 4-year college or university in the state in the following fall. They must have a GPA of 3.0 or higher. Along with their application, they must submit a 2-page essay on "The Keys to Economic Development in the African American Community." Selection is based on personal commitment, goals established for their chosen field, leadership potential, and civic accomplishments. **Deadline for Receipt:** March of each year. **Additional Information:** The Friends of the Fair Scholarship Program was established in 1993.

389 ■ CALIFORNIA STATE FAIR

Attn: Friends of the Fair Scholarship Program
1600 Exposition Boulevard
P.O. Box 15649
Sacramento, CA 95852
Tel: (916)274-5969
E-mail: wross@calexpo.com
Web Site: http://www.bigfun.org
To provide financial assistance to residents of California who are working on an undergraduate or graduate degree in viticulture or enology.
Title of Award: California State Fair Viticulture/Enology Scholarships **Area, Field, or Subject:** Enology; Viticulture **Level of Education for which Award is Granted:** Graduate, Undergraduate **Number Awarded:** 2 each year: 1 at $1,500 and 1 at $500. **Funds Available:** Stipends are $1,500 or $500. **Duration:** 1 year.
Eligibility Requirements: This program is open to residents of California currently working on an undergraduate or graduate degree at a college or university in the state. Applicants must be studying or majoring in viticulture or enology. They must have a GPA of 3.0 or higher. Along with their application, they must submit a 2-page essay on why they are pursuing their desired career and life goals. Selection is based on personal

commitment, goals established for their chosen field, leadership potential, and civic accomplishments. **Deadline for Receipt:** March of each year. **Additional Information:** The Friends of the Fair Scholarship Program was established in 1993.

390 ■ CALIFORNIA STATE FIREFIGHTERS' ASSOCIATION

Attn: Ladies Auxiliary
2701 K Street, Suite 201
Sacramento, CA 95816
800-451-2732
Fax: (916)446-9889
E-mail: crainey@csfa.net
Web Site: http://www.csfa.net/ladiesaux_scholarship.asp
To provide financial assistance for college to the children of members of the California State Firefighters' Association (CSFA) or its Ladies Auxiliary.
Title of Award: California State Firefighters' Association Ladies Auxiliary Scholarships **Area, Field, or Subject:** General studies/Field of study not specified **Level of Education for which Award is Granted:** Undergraduate **Number Awarded:** 1 or more each year. **Funds Available:** A stipend is awarded (amount not specified); students at 2-year institutions receive half as much as students at 4-year colleges and universities. **Duration:** 1 year.
Eligibility Requirements: This program is open to graduating high school seniors or high school graduates whose parent has been a member of CSFA for 3 consecutive years or a member of the Ladies Auxiliary for at least 1 year. Applicants must be attending or planning to attend an accredited trade school or 2-year or 4-year college or university in the United States. Entering students must apply within 5 years of graduation from high school. Continuing students must apply within 10 years of graduation from high school. Along with their application, they must submit a brief statement on their educational, vocational, and professional goals. Financial need is not considered in the selection process. **Deadline for Receipt:** February of each year. **Additional Information:** This program was established in 1949. Information is also available from Karen Frederick, Scholarship Chair, 10680 Devonshire Circle, Penn Valley, CA 95946, (530) 432-1739, E-mail: ktwo@jps.net.

391 ■ CALIFORNIA STATE UNIVERSITY

Office of the Chancellor
Attn: Lori Redfearn, Vice President
401 Golden Shore, Sixth Floor
Long Beach, CA 90802-4210
Tel: (562)951-4815
E-mail: lredfearn@calstate.edu
Web Site: http://www.calstate.edu/foundation/scholarship.shtml
To provide financial assistance to students at campuses of the California State University (CSU) system who demonstrate financial need and outstanding achievement.
Title of Award: William Randolph Hearst/CSU Trustees' Award for Outstanding Achievement **Area, Field, or Subject:** General studies/Field of study not specified **Level of Education for which Award is Granted:** Four Year College **Number Awarded:** 1 each year. **Funds Available:** The stipend is $3,000 per year. **Duration:** 1 year.
Eligibility Requirements: This program is open to students enrolled at campuses of the CSU system. Applicants must be able to demonstrate financial need and outstanding merit, including (but not limited to) superior academic performance, community service, personal hardship, and personal achievements. **Additional Information:** This program is supported by an endowment from the William Randolph Hearst Foundation and individual contributions from the CSU Board of Trustees.

392 ■ CALIFORNIA STATE UNIVERSITY

Office of the Chancellor
Attn: Lori Redfearn, Vice President
401 Golden Shore, Sixth Floor
Long Beach, CA 90802-4210
Tel: (562)951-4815
E-mail: lredfearn@calstate.edu
Web Site: http://www.calstate.edu/foundation/scholarship.shtml
To provide financial assistance to undergraduate and graduate students with visual impairments at campuses of the California State University (CSU) system.
Title of Award: Dale M. Schoettler Scholarship for Visually Impaired Students **Area, Field, or Subject:** General studies/Field of study not

specified **Level of Education for which Award is Granted:** Four Year College, Master's **Number Awarded:** 15 each year. **Funds Available:** The stipend is $5,000 per year. **Duration:** 1 year.

Eligibility Requirements: This program is open to undergraduate and graduate students enrolled at CSU campuses who have been declared visually impaired. Applicants must have a cumulative GPA of 2.8 or higher.

393 ■ CALIFORNIA STUDENT AID COMMISSION

Attn: Specialized Programs
10811 International Drive
P.O. Box 419029
Rancho Cordova, CA 95741-9029
Tel: (916)526-8276; 888-CA-GRANT
Fax: (916)526-7977
E-mail: specialized@csac.ca.gov
Web Site: http://www.csac.ca.gov
To provide financial assistance for college to the dependents of California law enforcement officers who have been totally disabled or killed in the line of duty.

Title of Award: California Law Enforcement Personnel Dependents Grant Program **Area, Field, or Subject:** General studies/Field of study not specified **Level of Education for which Award is Granted:** Undergraduate **Number Awarded:** Varies each year; recently, 14 students received $86,670 in assistance from this program. **Funds Available:** Stipends range from $100 to $11,259 per year, depending on the need of the recipient. **Duration:** 1 academic year; may be renewed for up to 5 additional years at 4-year colleges and universities or up to 3 additional years at community colleges.

Eligibility Requirements: This program is open to the natural children, adopted children, and spouses of a California peace officer (Highway Patrol, marshal, sheriff, police officer), employee of the Department of Corrections or Youth Authority, or fire fighter. The parent or spouse must have died or become totally disabled as the result of an accident or injury caused by external violence or physical force incurred in the performance of duty. Applicants must be enrolled for at least 6 units at an accredited California postsecondary institution and able to demonstrate financial need. **Deadline for Receipt:** Applications may be submitted at any time. **Additional Information:** If the student receives other scholarships or grants, the award may be adjusted or withdrawn, depending upon financial need. Acceptance of work-study, loans, or employment will generally not affect the amount of money offered through this program.

394 ■ CALIFORNIA TABLE GRAPE COMMISSION

Attn: Scholarship Committee
392 West Fallbrook, Suite 101
Fresno, CA 93711-6150
Tel: (559)447-8350
Free: 800-813-8478
Fax: (559)447-9184
E-mail: info@freshcaliforniagrapes.com
Web Site: http://www.freshcaliforniagrapes.com/en-US/Teachers/Scholarships.htm
To provide financial assistance to the children of California table grape field workers who are interested in attending a branch of the California State University system.

Title of Award: California Table Grape Workers' Scholarship Program **Area, Field, or Subject:** General studies/Field of study not specified **Level of Education for which Award is Granted:** Four Year College **Number Awarded:** 3 each year. **Funds Available:** The stipend is $4,000 per year. **Duration:** 4 years, provided the recipient maintains a GPA of 2.0 or higher.

Eligibility Requirements: This program is open to high school graduates or seniors graduating in June. They, or their parents, must have worked in either of the 2 previous California table grape harvests. Farmers and their families, raisin and wine grape workers, students currently enrolled in college, permanent staff and members of the California Table Grape Commission and their families, and commission suppliers are not eligible. All applicants must intend to attend a 4-year college or university in California. Selection is based on academic performance, financial need, obstacles overcome, leadership ability and/or community service, and ability to succeed. **Deadline for Receipt:** March of each year. **Additional Information:** Recipients must attend a branch of the California State University on a full-time basis.

395 ■ CALIFORNIANS FOR DISABILITY RIGHTS

Attn: CDR Foundation
909 12th Street, Suite 200
Sacramento, CA 95814
Tel: (916)447-2237
Free: 800-838-9237
E-mail: cdr@disabilityrights-cdr.org
Web Site: http://www.disabilityrights-cdr.org
To provide financial assistance for college to students with disabilities in California.

Title of Award: Californians for Disability Rights Scholarship **Area, Field, or Subject:** General studies/Field of study not specified **Level of Education for which Award is Granted:** Graduate, Undergraduate **Number Awarded:** 3 each year. **Funds Available:** The stipend is $1,000 for first place, $700 for second place, and $300 for third place. **Duration:** 1 year.

Eligibility Requirements: This program is open to persons with a verified physical, mental, or learning disability that substantially limits 1 or more major life activities. Applicants must be admitted to or enrolled at an accredited state university, community college, private college, or university in California. Along with their application, they must submit a 3-page essay of their disability advocacy and leadership skills, including how their student advocacy will improve the awareness and participation of Californians with disabilities in society. **Deadline for Receipt:** January of each year. **Additional Information:** Information is also available from Lesley Robinson, Scholarship Committee, 5567 Peacock Lane, Riverside, CA 92505.

396 ■ CALISTA CORPORATION

Attn: Calista Scholarship Fund
301 Calista Court, Suite A
Anchorage, AK 99518-3028
Tel: (907)279-5516
Free: 800-277-5516
Fax: (907)272-5060
E-mail: calista@calistacorp.com
Web Site: http://www.calistacorp.com
To provide financial assistance to Alaska Natives with ties to the Calista region who are interested in working on an undergraduate or graduate degree.

Title of Award: Calista Scholarship Fund **Area, Field, or Subject:** General studies/Field of study not specified **Level of Education for which Award is Granted:** Graduate, Undergraduate **Number Awarded:** Varies each year; recently, 79 of these scholarships were awarded. **Funds Available:** The amount awarded depends upon the recipient's GPA. Recipients with a GPA of 2.0 to 2.49 are awarded $500 per semester, recipients with a GPA of 2.5 to 2.99 are awarded $750 per semester, and recipients with a GPA of 3.0 or higher are awarded $1,000 per semester. The funds are paid in 2 equal installments; the second semester check is not issued until grades from the previous semester's work are received. **Duration:** 1 year; recipients may reapply.

Eligibility Requirements: This program is open to Alaska Native shareholders and lineal descendants of Alaska Native shareholders with ties to the Calista region. Applicants must be at least a high school graduate or have earned a GED and be in good academic standing with a GPA of 2.0 or higher. Along with their application, they must submit an essay (at least 1 page) on their educational and career goals. Financial need is considered in the selection process. **Deadline for Receipt:** June of each year. **Additional Information:** In past years, this program has included several named scholarships that may be offered again if funds are available. Those include the Buster Vanderpool Scholarship Award for students majoring in aviation, transportation, or business development; the David K. Nicolai Scholarship Award for students majoring in human services, health sciences, or social sciences; the Edward Hoffman Scholarship Award for students majoring in political science, public administration, public communications, or rural development-related fields; the Fred Notti Scholarship Award, for students majoring in rural economic development or aviation technology; the Gladys Jung Scholarship Award for students majoring in education, linguistics, or Alaska Native Language-related studies; the Henry Roberts Scholarship Award for students majoring in communications, computer technology, telecommunications, or data processing-related fields; the Herman Neck Scholarship Award for students majoring in business administration, management, accounting, marketing, economics, or finance-related fields; the

Jimmy Hoffman Scholarship Awards for students majoring in aviation, transportation, architecture, or an engineering-related field; the Nora Guinn Scholarship Award for students majoring in justice or law-related fields; the Phillip Guy Scholarship Award for students majoring in fields related to public administration or education; the Raymond C. Christiansen Scholarship Award for students majoring in natural sciences, fisheries, ecology, biology, or geology-related fields; and the William Tyson Scholarship Award for students majoring in religion, anthropology, archaeology, psychology, or counseling (including social work). This program was established in 1994.

397 ■ CANCER SURVIVORS' FUND
P.O. Box 792
Missouri City, TX 77459
Tel: (281)437-7142
Fax: (281)437-9568
E-mail: info@cancersurvivorsfund.org
Web Site: http://www.cancersurvivorsfund.org
To provide financial assistance for undergraduate study to residents of Texas who have had cancer.
Title of Award: Ronald G. Bliss Outstanding Achievement Award **Area, Field, or Subject:** General studies/Field of study not specified **Level of Education for which Award is Granted:** Undergraduate **Number Awarded:** 1 each year. **Funds Available:** The stipend is $10,000 per year. **Duration:** Up to 4 years.
Eligibility Requirements: This program is open to Texas residents who are enrolled as undergraduates at an accredited college or university. Applicants must be a cancer survivor or currently diagnosed with cancer; they do not have to be receiving treatment to qualify. They must be able to demonstrate a well-developed team spirit, strong people skills, emotional and spiritual intelligence, and a dedication to volunteerism. They must have maintained a GPA of 3.5 or higher for at least 2 consecutive semesters. **Deadline for Receipt:** January of each year. **Additional Information:** Recipients must agree to do volunteer work to use their cancer experience to help other young cancer patients and survivors cope with a life-threatening or life-altering event.

398 ■ CANCER SURVIVORS' FUND
P.O. Box 792
Missouri City, TX 77459
Tel: (281)437-7142
Fax: (281)437-9568
E-mail: info@cancersurvivorsfund.org
Web Site: http://www.cancersurvivorsfund.org
To provide financial assistance for undergraduate or graduate study to residents of Texas who have had cancer.
Title of Award: Cancer Survivors' Scholarship **Area, Field, or Subject:** General studies/Field of study not specified **Level of Education for which Award is Granted:** Graduate, Undergraduate **Number Awarded:** Varies each year; recently, 11 of these scholarships were awarded. **Funds Available:** A stipend is awarded (amount not specified). **Duration:** 1 year.
Eligibility Requirements: This program is open to Texas residents who are enrolled in or accepted for enrollment in an accredited undergraduate or graduate school. Applicants must be a cancer survivor or currently diagnosed with cancer; they do not have to be receiving treatment to qualify. They must submit an essay, from 500 to 1,200 words in length, on how their experience with cancer has impacted their life values and career goals. Selection is based on the applicant's personal hardship and financial need. **Deadline for Receipt:** January of each year for fall semester; July of each year for spring semester. **Additional Information:** Recipients must agree to do volunteer work to use their cancer experience to help other young cancer patients and survivors cope with a life-threatening or life-altering event.

399 ■ CAP CHARITABLE FOUNDATION
Attn: Ron Brown Scholar Program
1160 Pepsi Place, Suite 206
Charlottesville, VA 22901
Tel: (434)964-1588
Fax: (434)964-1589
E-mail: franh@ronbrown.org
Web Site: http://www.ronbrown.org
To provide financial assistance for college to African American high school seniors.
Title of Award: Ron Brown Scholar Program **Area, Field, or Subject:** General studies/Field of study not specified **Level of Education for which Award is Granted:** Undergraduate **Number Awarded:** At least 10 each year. **Funds Available:** The stipend is $10,000 per year. Funds may be used to cover tuition, fees, books, room, board, and other college-related expenses. Payment is made directly to the recipient's school. **Duration:** 4 years.
Eligibility Requirements: This program is open to academically-talented African American high school seniors who have demonstrated social commitment and leadership potential. They must be interested in working on a college degree on a full-time basis. U.S. citizenship or permanent resident status is required. Finalists are invited to participate in a weekend selection process in Washington, D.C.; their expenses are reimbursed. Final selection is based on academic promise, leadership ability, communication skills, school and community involvement, and financial need. **Deadline for Receipt:** January of each year. **Additional Information:** Established in 1996, this program honors a former Secretary of Commerce who served during the Clinton administration. During college, recipients are required to pursue 1 or more summer internships devoted to community service (e.g., in education, health, government, politics) and 1 pre-professional internship.

400 ■ CAREER TRANSITION FOR DANCERS
c/o The Caroline & Theodore Newhouse Center for Dancers
165 West 46th Street, Suite 701
New York, NY 10036-2501
Tel: (212)764-0172
Fax: (212)764-0343
E-mail: info@careertransition.org
Web Site: http://www.careertransition.org/progsscholarmain.html
To provide financial assistance to current and former professional dancers interested in acquiring an academic degree or a new skill.
Title of Award: Caroline H. Newhouse Scholarship Fund **Area, Field, or Subject:** General studies/Field of study not specified **Level of Education for which Award is Granted:** Professional, Undergraduate **Number Awarded:** Varies each year; recently, a total of $300,000 was available for this program. **Funds Available:** Recipients are entitled to grants totaling $2,500 over their lifetime. Funds may be used for tuition, fees, books, and materials at schools, institutes, and specialized certificate programs. **Duration:** Funding may extend over a period of years, as long as the total awarded does not exceed $2,000.
Eligibility Requirements: This program is open to current and former professional dancers who can demonstrate paid employment as a dancer under union jurisdiction for at least 100 weeks over a period of 7 years or more and earnings of at least $8,000 per year from dance employment in the 7 best years of their performing career; the performing years need not be consecutive current. Applicants must be at least 27 years of age, although that age requirement may be lowered depending on their age at the start of a professional performing dance career or because of a debilitating injury or illness. They must be interested in obtaining funding for 1) tuition for an academic degree; 2) retraining for the acquisition of a new skill; or 3) seed money to begin a business enterprise. **Deadline for Receipt:** January, March, May, July, September, or November of each year. **Additional Information:** Since this program was established in 1985, it has awarded more than 2,400 grants totaling more than $2 million. It is sponsored by the American Federation of Television and Radio Artists, the American Guild of Musical Artists, the Screen Actors Guild, the American Guild of Variety Artists, and other performing arts organizations. Information is also available from the Los Angeles office, 5757 Wilshire Boulevard, Suite 902, Los Angeles, CA 90036-3635, (323) 549-6660, Fax: (323) 549-6810, E-mail: info-la@careertransition.org.

401 ■ CAREMARK RX, INC.
Attn: Heather Post
211 Commerce Street, Suite 800
Nashville, TN 37201
(866)792-2731
Web Site: http://www.caremark.com
To provide financial assistance for college or graduate school to students with clinical hemophilia.
Title of Award: Eric Delson Memorial Scholarship **Area, Field, or Subject:** General studies/Field of study not specified **Level of Education**

for which Award is Granted: Graduate, Undergraduate **Number Awarded:** 4 each year: 3 at $2,500 per year and 1 at $1,500 per year. **Funds Available:** The stipend is $2,500 or $1,500. Funds are paid in 2 equal installments directly to the recipient. **Duration:** 1 year; may be renewed for up to 3 additional years, provided the recipient maintains a 3.0 GPA.

Eligibility Requirements: Students diagnosed with clinical hemophilia are eligible to apply for this program if they are 1) high school seniors, high school graduates, college students, or graduate students currently enrolled or planning to enroll in an accredited 2-year or 4-year college, university, vocational/technical school, or graduate school; or 2) students entering grades 7-12 at a private secondary school in the United States. This program is not open to students with related blood disorders (e.g., von Willebrand Disease). Selection is based on academic record, potential to succeed, leadership, participation in school and community activities, honors, work experience, statement of educational and career goals, recommendations, and unusual personal or family circumstances. **Deadline for Receipt:** June of each year.

402 ■ CARL'S JR.

Attn: Cheryl Beamer
6307 Carpinteria Avenue, Suite A
Carpinteria, CA 93013
Tel: (805)745-7663
Free: 800-422-4141
E-mail: cbeamer@ckr.com
Web Site: http://www.carlsjr.com

To provide financial assistance to students in designated states who can demonstrate that they have been "A Star" in their community.

Title of Award: La Estrella Latina de Carl's Jr. Scholarship Program **Area, Field, or Subject:** General studies/Field of study not specified **Level of Education for which Award is Granted:** Undergraduate **Number Awarded:** 60 each year. **Funds Available:** The stipend is $1,000. **Duration:** 1 year; nonrenewable.

Eligibility Requirements: This program is open to seniors graduating from high schools in Arizona, California, Nevada, New Mexico, and Texas. Applicants must be high school seniors or graduates younger than 21 years of age and planning to enroll for the first time as a full-time undergraduate student at an accredited 2-year or 4-year college, university, or vocational school. Along with their application, they must submit an essay describing how they have been "A Star" in their community. Selection is based on academic record, school and community leadership and participation, work experience, future goals, financial need, and other family circumstances. **Deadline for Receipt:** January of each year. **Additional Information:** This program began in 1999. Applications are available at participating Carl's Jr. restaurants. The program is administered by Scholarship Management Services of Scholarship America, One Scholarship Way, P.O. Box 297, St. Peter, MN 56082, (507) 931-1682, (800) 537-4180, Fax: (507) 931-9168, E-mail: smsinfo@csfa.org.

403 ■ ROY J. CARVER CHARITABLE TRUST

202 Iowa Avenue
Muscatine, IA 52761-3733
Tel: (563)263-4010
Fax: (563)263-1547
E-mail: info@carvertrust.org
Web Site: http://www.carvertrust.org

To provide financial assistance for college to students in Iowa who have overcome significant obstacles to attend college.

Title of Award: Carver Scholars Program **Area, Field, or Subject:** General studies/Field of study not specified **Level of Education for which Award is Granted:** Four Year College **Number Awarded:** Varies each year; since the program's establishment, it has awarded more than 1,300 scholarships worth more than $10 million. **Funds Available:** Stipends generally average $5,200 at public universities or $7,600 at private colleges in Iowa. **Duration:** 1 year; may be renewed 1 additional year.

Eligibility Requirements: This program is open to students attending the 3 public universities in Iowa, the 24 participating private 4-year colleges and universities in the state, or a community college in Iowa and planning to transfer to 1 of those 4-year institutions. Applicants must be sophomores seeking support for their junior year. They must present

evidence of unusual social and/or other barriers to attending college full time; examples include, but are not limited to, students who 1) are from 1-parent families; 2) are attending college while working full time; 3) have social, mental, or physical disabilities; and 4) have families to support. They must have graduated from a high school in Iowa or have been residents of the state for at least 5 consecutive years immediately prior to applying, be full-time students, have at least a 2.8 GPA, be U.S. citizens, and submit a financial profile indicating insufficient personal, family, and institutional resources to pay full-time college tuition. A particular goal of the program is to assist students "who fall between the cracks of other financial aid programs." Applications must be submitted to the financial aid office at the Iowa college or university the applicant attends. **Deadline for Receipt:** March of each year. **Additional Information:** This program was established in 1988.

404 ■ CENTER FOR EDUCATION SOLUTIONS

P.O. Box 208
San Francisco, CA 94104-0208
Tel: (925)934-7304
E-mail: scholarship@cesresources.org
Web Site: http://www.cesresources.org/charnon.html

To provide financial assistance to undergraduate students who demonstrate a commitment to their community.

Title of Award: A. Patrick Charnon Scholarship **Area, Field, or Subject:** General studies/Field of study not specified **Level of Education for which Award is Granted:** Four Year College **Number Awarded:** 1 each year. **Funds Available:** The stipend is $1,500 per year. **Duration:** 1 year; may be renewed up to 3 additional years.

Eligibility Requirements: Applicants must be admitted or enrolled in a full-time undergraduate program of study at an accredited 4-year college or university. They must demonstrate dedication and commitment to their communities. Along with their application, they must submit a 2- to 4-page essay on how community service experiences have shaped their lives and how they will use their college education to build communities in a manner consistent with values of compassion, tolerance, generosity, and respect. The selection committee looks for candidates whose values reflect the goals of the program and who have demonstrated their commitments to those values by their actions. **Deadline for Receipt:** March of each year. **Additional Information:** This program was established in 1995.

405 ■ THE CENTER FOR REINTEGRATION, INC.

Attn: Lilly Secretariat
310 Busse Highway
PMB 327
Park Ridge, IL 60068-3251
800-809-8202
E-mail: lillyscholarships@reintegration.com
Web Site: http://www.reintegration.com/resources/scholarships/scholarship.asp

To provide financial assistance to undergraduate and graduate students diagnosed with schizophrenia.

Title of Award: Lilly Moving Lives Forward Reintegration Scholarships **Area, Field, or Subject:** General studies/Field of study not specified **Level of Education for which Award is Granted:** Graduate, Undergraduate **Number Awarded:** Varies each year; recently, 50 of these scholarships (including renewals) were awarded. **Funds Available:** The amount awarded varies, depending upon the specific needs of the recipient. Funds may be used to pay for tuition and related expenses, such as textbooks and laboratory fees. **Duration:** 1 year; may be renewed.

Eligibility Requirements: This program is open to U.S. citizens diagnosed with bipolar disorder, schizophrenia, schizophreniform disorder, or schizoaffective disorder. Applicants must be receiving medical treatment for the disease and be actively involved in rehabilitative or reintegrative efforts. They must be interested in pursuing postsecondary education, including trade or vocational school programs, high school equivalency programs, associate degrees, bachelor's degrees, and graduate programs. Along with their application, they must submit an essay on their career goal and their rationale for choosing that goal, how this course of study will help them achieve their career goal, obstacles they have faced in life and how they have overcome them, steps they have taken to prepare for pursuit of this education, rationale for the specific school chosen, and their plans to continue treatment while pursuing an education. Selection is based on the quality of the essay, academic success, 3 references, thoughtfulness and appropriateness of academic and vocational/career goals, rehabilitation involvement, success in dealing with the disease, recent volunteer and/or vocational experience, and completion of application requirements. **Deadline for Receipt:** January of each year. **Additional Information:** This program, established in 1998, is funded by Eli Lilly and Company.

406 ■ CENTER FOR SCHOLARSHIP ADMINISTRATION, INC.

Attn: Scholarship Programs
P.O. Box 1465
Taylors, SC 29687-1465
Tel: (864)268-3363
Fax: (864)268-7160
E-mail: cfsainc@bellsouth.net
Web Site: http://www.scholarshipprograms.org/cscholarships.php
To provide financial assistance for college to residents of South Carolina who have a competitive or recreational interest in golf.
Title of Award: South Carolina Junior Golf Foundation Scholarship Program **Area, Field, or Subject:** General studies/Field of study not specified **Level of Education for which Award is Granted:** Undergraduate **Number Awarded:** 1 or more each year. **Funds Available:** The stipend is $2,500 per year. Funds are sent directly to the college, university, or technical college to be used for educational expenses, including tuition, fees, books, room, and board. **Duration:** 1 year; may be renewed up to 3 additional years or until completion of a bachelor's degree, whichever is earlier, provided the recipient maintains a GPA of 2.75 or higher and enrolled at a college or university in South Carolina.
Eligibility Requirements: This program is open to residents of South Carolina who are seniors in high school or already attending college in the state. Applicants must have a GPA of 2.75 or higher and a competitive or recreational interest in golf. Along with their application, they must submit a 1-page essay describing themselves, including their strengths and their most important achievements in school and community. Selection is based on academic merit (SAT/ACT scores, rank in class, and GPA), potential to succeed in their chosen education field, and financial need. **Deadline for Receipt:** February of each year. **Additional Information:** This program is administered by The Center for Scholarship Administration on behalf of the South Carolina Junior Golf Foundation.

407 ■ CENTRAL COUNCIL, TLINGIT AND HAIDA INDIAN TRIBES OF ALASKA

Attn: Higher Education Services
3239 Hospital Drive
Juneau, AK 99801
Tel: (907)463-7375
Free: 800-344-1432
Fax: (907)463-7173
Web Site: http://www.hied.org
To provide financial assistance for undergraduate and graduate studies to enrolled Tlingit or Haida tribal members.
Title of Award: Juanita Corwin Scholarships **Area, Field, or Subject:** General studies/Field of study not specified **Level of Education for which Award is Granted:** Graduate, Undergraduate **Number Awarded:** 3 each year: 1 to a graduating high school senior, 1 to a current undergraduate student, and 1 to a current graduate student. **Funds Available:** The stipend is $1,000. **Duration:** 1 year.
Eligibility Requirements: This program is open to both undergraduate and graduate students. Applicants must be Tlingit or Haida tribal members, regardless of service area, community affiliation, origination, residence, tribal compact, or signatory status. They must have a GPA of 3.0 or higher and be attending (or planning to attend) school on a full-time basis. Selection is based on financial need, a statement of personal goals, and a list of academic, professional, and/or personal activities. **Deadline for Receipt:** September of each year.

408 ■ CENTRAL COUNCIL, TLINGIT AND HAIDA INDIAN TRIBES OF ALASKA

Attn: Employment and Training Division
3239 Hospital Drive
Juneau, AK 99801
Tel: (907)463-7134
Free: 800-344-1432
Fax: (907)463-7173

Web Site: http://www.hied.org
To provide financial assistance for vocational training to enrolled Tlingit or Haida tribal members.
Title of Award: Tlingit and Haida Indian Tribes of Alaska Adult Vocational Training Program **Area, Field, or Subject:** General studies/Field of study not specified **Level of Education for which Award is Granted:** Undergraduate **Number Awarded:** Varies each year. **Funds Available:** The amount of the assistance depends on the need of the recipient. **Duration:** Up to 24 months (or 36 months for R.N. training).
Eligibility Requirements: This program is open to enrolled Tlingit or Haida tribal members who have resided in the service delivery area of southeast Alaska for at least 30 days. Applicants must be at least 18 years of age, have their high school diploma or GED, and be actively seeking employment and/or enrolled in a training program. Financial need must be demonstrated. **Deadline for Receipt:** May of each year.

409 ■ CENTRAL COUNCIL, TLINGIT AND HAIDA INDIAN TRIBES OF ALASKA

Attn: Higher Education Services
3239 Hospital Drive
Juneau, AK 99801
Tel: (907)463-7375
Free: 800-344-1432
Fax: (907)463-7173
Web Site: http://www.hied.org
To provide financial assistance for undergraduate and graduate studies to enrolled Tlingit or Haida tribal members.
Title of Award: Tlingit and Haida Indian Tribes of Alaska College Student Assistance Program **Area, Field, or Subject:** General studies/Field of study not specified **Level of Education for which Award is Granted:** Graduate, Undergraduate **Number Awarded:** Varies each year. **Funds Available:** This assistance is intended to be supplemental. Funds are to be used solely for tuition, required fees, textbooks, supplies, and miscellaneous educational expenses. No part of the award may be used to repay tuition from previous terms, educational or personal loans, or previously incurred debts. **Duration:** 1 year; may be renewed. Undergraduate recipients must maintain a GPA of 2.0 or higher; graduate students must maintain a GPA of 3.0 or higher. All recipients must be full-time students.
Eligibility Requirements: This program is open to both undergraduate and graduate students. Applicants must be Tlingit or Haida tribal members with a GPA of 2.0 or higher. Scholarship applications are given priority based on the following point system: 20 points for students residing in the following service areas of the Central Council: Craig, Juneau, Haines, Pelican, Saxman, Skagway, Tenakee, or Wrangell; 15 points for graduation from a high school within the service areas listed above; and 5 points if the applicant or the applicant's parents/guardians belong to a southeast Alaska IRA council, village, or regional corporation within the service areas listed above. Enrollment or corporation identification numbers must be supplied on the application form. In addition to this program, students are expected to apply for institution-sponsored financial aid, as well as funding from state and local community organizations or Native corporations. Financial need is considered in the selection process. **Deadline for Receipt:** May of each year. **Additional Information:** Faxed applications are permitted. With the exception of distance education or independent learning courses, this program does not fund part-time attendance, vocational training, student conferences, seminars, developmental courses (i.e., professional skill involvement), or any professional licensing examinations.

410 ■ CENTRAL INTELLIGENCE AGENCY

Attn: Recruitment Center
P.O. Box 4090
Reston, VA 20195
800-368-3886
Web Site: http://www.cia.gov/employment/jobs/students_scholar.html
To provide scholarship/loans and work experience to high school seniors and college sophomores, especially minorities and people with disabilities, who are interested in working for the Central Intelligence Agency (CIA) after graduation from college.
Title of Award: Central Intelligence Agency Undergraduate Scholarship Program **Area, Field, or Subject:** General studies/Field of study not specified **Level of Education for which Award is Granted:** Four Year College **Number Awarded:** Varies each year. **Funds Available:** Scholars

are provided a salary and up to $18,000 per year for tuition, fees, books, and supplies. They must agree to continue employment with the CIA after college graduation for a period 1.5 times the length of their college support. **Duration:** 1 year; may be renewed if the student maintains a GPA of 3.0 or higher and full-time enrollment in a 4- or 5-year college program. **Eligibility Requirements:** This program is open to U.S. citizens who are either high school seniors or college sophomores. Seniors must be at least 18 years of age by April of the year they apply and have minimum scores of 1000 on the SAT or 21 on the ACT. College sophomores must have a GPA of 3.0 or higher. All applicants must be able to demonstrate financial need (household income of $70,000 or less for a family of 4 or $80,000 or less for a family of 5 or more) and be able to meet the same employment standards as permanent employees of the CIA. This program was developed, in part, to assist minority and disabled students, but it is open to all students who meet the requirements. **Deadline for Receipt:** October of each year. **Additional Information:** Scholars work each summer at a CIA facility. In addition to a salary, they receive the cost of transportation between school and the Washington, D.C. area and a housing allowance.

411 ■ CHAIRSCHOLARS FOUNDATION, INC.

16101 Carencia Lane
Odessa, FL 33556-3278
Tel: (813)920-2737
E-mail: info@chairscholars.org
Web Site: http://www.chairscholars.org
To provide financial assistance for college to physically challenged students.
Title of Award: ChairScholars Foundation National Scholarships **Area, Field, or Subject:** General studies/Field of study not specified **Level of Education for which Award is Granted:** Undergraduate **Number Awarded:** 10 each year. **Funds Available:** Stipends are $5,000 or $3,000 per year. Funds are to be used for tuition and school expenses. **Duration:** Up to 4 years for high school seniors; up to 3 years for college freshmen. **Eligibility Requirements:** This program is open to high school seniors and college freshmen who are physically challenged, although they are not required to be in a wheelchair. Applicants should be able to demonstrate financial need, have a record of satisfactory academic performance (at least a "B+" average), and show some form of community service or social contribution in the past. Along with their application, they must submit an essay of 300 to 500 words on how they became physically challenged, how their situation has affected them and their family, and their goals and aspirations for the future. Graduate students and all students over 21 years of age are not eligible. **Deadline for Receipt:** February of each year.

412 ■ THE CHARTER FUND

Attn: Jeanette Montoya
370 17th Street, Suite 5300
Denver, CO 80202
Tel: (303)572-1727
Fax: (303)628-3839
To provide financial assistance for college to financially needy high school seniors in Colorado.
Title of Award: The Charter Fund Scholarships **Area, Field, or Subject:** General studies/Field of study not specified **Level of Education for which Award is Granted:** Undergraduate **Number Awarded:** Approximately 90 each year. **Funds Available:** Stipends range from $100 to $2,500. **Duration:** 1 year; nonrenewable.
Eligibility Requirements: This program is open to seniors graduating from high schools in Colorado who have worked during summer breaks. Applicants must be U.S. citizens or permanent residents planning to enter an accredited institution in the following fall. Selection is based on academic performance, aptitude, potential for achievement, and financial need. **Deadline for Receipt:** May of each year.

413 ■ CHELA FINANCIAL USA, INC.

388 Market Street, 12th Floor
San Francisco, CA 94111
Tel: (415)283-2800; (866)34-CHELA
Fax: (415)283-2888
E-mail: scholarships@chelafin.org
Web Site: http://www.chelastudentloans.org

To provide financial assistance for college to high school seniors and college students in California.
Title of Award: California Higher Education Scholarships **Area, Field, or Subject:** General studies/Field of study not specified **Level of Education for which Award is Granted:** Undergraduate **Number Awarded:** 10 each year. **Funds Available:** The stipend is $5,000. **Duration:** 1 year. **Eligibility Requirements:** This program is open to high school seniors and current college students who are residents of California and/or enrolled in a college or university in the state. Applicants must have a GPA of 2.0 or higher and a valid E-mail address. They must be enrolled at least half time. **Deadline for Receipt:** June of each year.

414 ■ CHEROKEE NATION

Attn: Office of Higher Education
17675 South Muskogee Avenue
P.O. Box 948
Tahlequah, OK 74465
Tel: (918)456-0671
Free: 800-256-0671
Fax: (918)458-6195
E-mail: highereducation@cherokee.org
Web Site: http://www.cherokee.org/Services/Education.asp
To provide financial assistance to undergraduate students who belong to the Cherokee Nation and qualify for federal Pell grants.
Title of Award: Cherokee Nation Pell Scholarships **Area, Field, or Subject:** General studies/Field of study not specified **Level of Education for which Award is Granted:** Undergraduate **Number Awarded:** Varies each year; nearly 1,600 students receive support from all Cherokee Nation Undergraduate Scholarship programs. **Funds Available:** Varies; the available funds are divided equally among all eligible students who complete the application process. **Duration:** Up to 8 semesters.
Eligibility Requirements: This program is open to members of the Cherokee Nation, regardless of their permanent residence. Applicants who qualify for federal Pell grant funding are eligible for this additional assistance through the U.S. Bureau of Indian Affairs (BIA). **Deadline for Receipt:** June of each year.

415 ■ CHEROKEE NATION

Attn: Office of Higher Education
17675 South Muskogee Avenue
P.O. Box 948
Tahlequah, OK 74465
Tel: (918)456-0671
Free: 800-256-0671
Fax: (918)458-6195
E-mail: highereducation@cherokee.org
Web Site: http://www.cherokee.org/Services/Education.asp
To provide financial assistance to undergraduate students who belong to the Cherokee Nation and do not qualify for federal Pell grants.
Title of Award: Cherokee Nation Scholarship Program **Area, Field, or Subject:** General studies/Field of study not specified **Level of Education for which Award is Granted:** Undergraduate **Number Awarded:** Varies each year; nearly 1,600 students receive support from all Cherokee Nation Undergraduate Scholarship programs. **Funds Available:** A stipend is awarded (amount not specified). **Duration:** Up to 8 semesters.
Eligibility Requirements: This program is open to members of the Cherokee Nation who are residents of Oklahoma and do not qualify for Pell Grant funding. In the selection process, applicants are ranked according to the following criteria: first, continuing students in the program; second, geographic location (students whose permanent residence is within the Cherokee nation area, defined as those counties within and contiguous to the Cherokee Nation boundaries, are given preference over residents of other Oklahoma counties); third, academic level (seniors, juniors, sophomores, freshmen, in that order); and fourth, academic performance (based on GPA and ACT/SAT score) and financial need. **Deadline for Receipt:** June of each year.

416 ■ CHI OMEGA FRATERNITY

Attn: Chi Omega Foundation
3395 Players Club Parkway
Memphis, TN 38125
Tel: (901)748-8600
Fax: (901)748-8686

E-mail: foundation@chiomega.com
Web Site: http://www.chiomega.com/chiomega/foundation/scholarship.asp
To provide financial assistance to women who are members of Chi Omega Fraternity entering their senior year of college.
Title of Award: Elizabeth Carmichael Orman Memorial Scholarship **Area, Field, or Subject:** General studies/Field of study not specified **Level of Education for which Award is Granted:** Undergraduate **Number Awarded:** Approximately 4 each year. **Funds Available:** A stipend is awarded (amount not specified). **Duration:** 1 year.
Eligibility Requirements: This program is open to women who are members of Chi Omega Fraternity enrolled in their junior year. Applicants must submit an essay, up to 200 words in length, on 1) why they want or need this scholarship, and 2) why they feel they are particularly qualified for a scholarship designed to honor Elizabeth Carmichael Orman. Selection is based on the essay; academic achievement; aptitude; contributions and service to Chi Omega, the university, and the community; professional and personal goals; and financial need. **Deadline for Receipt:** March of each year. **Additional Information:** This program was established in 1980.

417 ■ CHICAGO URBAN LEAGUE

Attn: Education Department
4510 South Michigan Avenue
Chicago, IL 60653-3898
Tel: (773)451-3565
Fax: (773)285-7772
E-mail: info@cul-chicago.org
Web Site: http://www.cul-chicago.org
To provide financial assistance to Illinois residents of color interested in full-time study at a 4-year college or university.
Title of Award: Anheuser-Busch Foundation Scholarships **Area, Field, or Subject:** General studies/Field of study not specified **Level of Education for which Award is Granted:** Four Year College **Number Awarded:** Varies each year. **Funds Available:** The stipend is $2,500 per year. **Duration:** 4 years.
Eligibility Requirements: This program is open to minority residents of Illinois who will be full-time freshmen at a 4-year college or university. Applicants must have a GPA of 2.5 or higher and be able to demonstrate financial need. An interview is required. **Deadline for Receipt:** May of each year. **Additional Information:** This program is supported by the Anheuser-Busch Foundation, which makes the final decision on selection of recipients.

418 ■ CHICAGO URBAN LEAGUE

Attn: Education Department
4510 South Michigan Avenue
Chicago, IL 60653-3898
Tel: (773)451-3565
Fax: (773)285-7772
E-mail: info@cul-chicago.org
Web Site: http://www.cul-chicago.org
To provide financial assistance to Illinois residents who are women of color interested in full-time study at a 4-year college or university.
Title of Award: Avon Grant Scholarships **Area, Field, or Subject:** General studies/Field of study not specified **Level of Education for which Award is Granted:** Four Year College **Number Awarded:** 2 each year. **Funds Available:** The stipend is $1,000 per year. **Duration:** 1 year.
Eligibility Requirements: This program is open to minority women residents of Illinois who will be full-time freshmen at a 4-year college or university. Applicants must have a GPA of 2.5 or higher, be a head of household, and be able to demonstrate financial need. An interview is required. **Deadline for Receipt:** May of each year.

419 ■ CHICAGO URBAN LEAGUE

Attn: Education Department
4510 South Michigan Avenue
Chicago, IL 60653-3898
Tel: (773)451-3565
Fax: (773)285-7772
E-mail: info@cul-chicago.org
Web Site: http://www.cul-chicago.org

To provide financial assistance to Illinois residents of color enrolled at a 4-year college or university.
Title of Award: Dr. Scholl Foundation Scholarships **Area, Field, or Subject:** General studies/Field of study not specified **Level of Education for which Award is Granted:** Four Year College **Number Awarded:** Varies each year. **Funds Available:** The stipend is $2,000 per year. **Duration:** 1 year.
Eligibility Requirements: This program is open to Illinois residents of color who are full-time undergraduate students at a 4-year college or university with at least a 2.5 GPA. Applicants may be majoring in any field. They must be able to demonstrate financial need. **Deadline for Receipt:** May of each year. **Additional Information:** This program is offered as part of the Chicago Urban League's Whitney M. Young, Jr. Memorial Scholarship Fund, established in 1970. It is sponsored by the Dr. Scholl Foundation.

420 ■ CHICKASAW FOUNDATION

P.O. Box 1726
Ada, OK 74821-1726
Tel: (580)421-9030
Fax: (580)421-9031
Web Site: http://www.cflink.org
To provide financial assistance to members of the Chickasaw Nation who are interested in working on an undergraduate degree.
Title of Award: Frederick L. Hill-The Hill Group Scholarship **Area, Field, or Subject:** General studies/Field of study not specified **Level of Education for which Award is Granted:** Undergraduate **Number Awarded:** 2 each year. **Funds Available:** The stipend is $1,250 per year. **Duration:** 1 year.
Eligibility Requirements: This program is open to Chickasaw students who are currently enrolled at an accredited institution of higher education as a full-time undergraduate student. Applicants may be majoring in any field, but they must have a GPA of 2.0 or higher. Along with their application, they must submit high school or college transcripts, 2 letters of recommendation, a copy of their Certificate of Degree of Indian Blood, a copy of their Chickasaw Nation citizenship card, and a 1-page essay on their long-term goals and plans for achieving them. Financial need is not considered in the selection process. **Deadline for Receipt:** May of each year.

421 ■ CHICKASAW NATION

Attn: Division of Education
124 East 14th
Ada, OK 74820
Tel: (580)421-7711
Fax: (580)436-3733
E-mail: education.services@Chickasaw.net
Web Site: http://www.Chickasaw.net
To provide financial assistance to members of the Chickasaw Nation who are working on an undergraduate or graduate degree.
Title of Award: Chickasaw Nation General Scholarships **Area, Field, or Subject:** General studies/Field of study not specified **Level of Education for which Award is Granted:** Graduate, Undergraduate **Number Awarded:** Varies each year. **Funds Available:** Stipends depend on the level of academic study, the number of units the recipient is taking, and their GPA. The range is from $150 per semester (for part-time freshmen and sophomores with a GPA of 3.0 to 3.49) to $550 per semester (for full-time graduate students with a GPA of 4.0) **Duration:** 1 semester; recipients may reapply.
Eligibility Requirements: This program is open to members of the Chickasaw Nation who are working full or part time on an undergraduate, graduate, or doctoral degree at an accredited college or university and have a GPA of 3.0 or higher. Applicants must submit a copy of their Chickasaw Nation citizenship card, high school and/or college transcripts, documentation of financial need, proof of their ACT/SAT scores, and a 2- to 3-page essay on why they should be awarded the scholarship, the purpose and goals they plan on achieving, and why their proposed discipline will benefit the tribe. **Deadline for Receipt:** January of each

year for spring semester; May of each year for summer semester; August of each year for fall semester for continuing students; March of each year for high school seniors.

422 ■ CHICKASAW NATION

Attn: Division of Education
124 East 14th
Ada, OK 74820
Tel: (580)421-7711
Fax: (580)436-3733
E-mail: education.services@Chickasaw.net
Web Site: http://www.Chickasaw.net
To provide financial assistance to needy members of the Chickasaw Nation who are working on an undergraduate or graduate degree.
Title of Award: Chickasaw Nation Higher Education Grants **Area, Field, or Subject:** General studies/Field of study not specified **Level of Education for which Award is Granted:** Graduate, Undergraduate **Number Awarded:** Varies each year. **Funds Available:** Maximum stipends are $1,000 per semester for full-time undergraduates, $30 per credit hour for part-time undergraduates, $1,000 per semester for full-time graduate students, $50 per credit hour for part-time graduate students, or $100 per hour for doctoral candidates. **Duration:** 1 year; recipients may reapply.
Eligibility Requirements: This program is open to members of the Chickasaw Nation who are working full or part time on an undergraduate, graduate, or doctoral degree at an accredited college or university and have a GPA of 2.0 or higher. Applicants must submit a copy of their Chickasaw Nation citizenship card, high school and/or college transcripts, documentation of financial need, proof of their ACT/SAT scores, and a 2- to 3-page essay on why they should be awarded the scholarship, the purpose and goals they plan on achieving, and why their proposed discipline will benefit the tribe. **Deadline for Receipt:** January of each year for spring semester; May of each year for summer semester; August of each year for fall semester for continuing students; March of each year for high school seniors.

423 ■ CHICKASAW NATION

Attn: Division of Education
124 East 14th
Ada, OK 74820
Tel: (580)421-7711
Fax: (580)436-3733
E-mail: education.services@Chickasaw.net
Web Site: http://www.Chickasaw.net
To provide financial assistance for college to graduating high school seniors who are members of the Chickasaw Nation.
Title of Award: Millennium Scholarship Program of the Chickasaw Nation **Area, Field, or Subject:** General studies/Field of study not specified **Level of Education for which Award is Granted:** Undergraduate **Number Awarded:** Up to 50 each year. **Funds Available:** The stipend is $1,000. **Duration:** 1 year; nonrenewable.
Eligibility Requirements: This program is open to members of the Chickasaw Nation who are graduating from high school with a GPA of 2.0 or higher. Applicants must submit a copy of their Chickasaw Nation citizenship card, high school and/or college transcripts, documentation of financial need, proof of their ACT/SAT scores, and a 2- to 3-page essay on why they should be awarded the scholarship, the purpose and goals they plan on achieving, and why their proposed discipline will benefit the tribe. **Deadline for Receipt:** March of each year.

424 ■ CHILDREN OF BREAST CANCER FOUNDATION

P.O. Box 4032
Chattanooga, TN 37405
Web Site: http://www.childrenofbreastcancer.org/scholarships.html
To provide financial assistance for college to children of mothers who have had breast cancer.
Title of Award: Children of Breast Cancer Scholarships **Area, Field, or Subject:** General studies/Field of study not specified **Level of Education for which Award is Granted:** Undergraduate **Number Awarded:** Varies each year. Recently, 22 of these scholarships were awarded: 18 at $3,000 and 4 at $1,500. **Funds Available:** Stipends are either $3,000 or $1,500. **Duration:** 1 year; may be renewed up to 3 additional years.
Eligibility Requirements: This program is open to students who have lost a mother either to breast cancer or to complications resulting from breast cancer, or who have a mother who has survived breast cancer. Applicants must have been accepted as a full-time student an accredited 2- or 4-year college or university. Along with their application, they must submit 3 essays on their choice of selected topics. Selection is based on those essays, grades, and financial need. **Deadline for Receipt:** February of each year. **Additional Information:** These scholarships were first awarded in 2002. Information is also available from Laurie Richardson, 3070 Stage Run, Hixson, TN 37343, and from the Community Foundation of Greater Chattanooga, 1270 Market Street, Chattanooga, TN 37402, (423) 265-0586, E-mail: info@cfgc.org.

425 ■ CHILDREN OF INJURED WORKERS, INC.

4983 Brittonfield Parkway
East Syracuse, NY 13057
Tel: (315)449-4306
Fax: (315)449-4358
E-mail: info@kidschanceny.org
Web Site: http://www.kidschanceny.org
To provide financial assistance for college to residents of New York whose parent was seriously injured or killed in a workplace accident.
Title of Award: Children of Injured Workers Scholarships **Area, Field, or Subject:** General studies/Field of study not specified **Level of Education for which Award is Granted:** Undergraduate **Number Awarded:** Varies each year. **Funds Available:** A stipend is awarded (amount not specified). **Duration:** 1 year; recipients may reapply.
Eligibility Requirements: This program is open to New York residents attending or planning to attend a college or technical school. Applicants must be the child of a worker who suffered injury or death in an accident that is either established or accepted under the Workers' Compensation Law of the state of New York. The injury or death must have had a demonstrable impact on the financial ability of the child to attend college.

426 ■ CHILDREN OF LESBIANS AND GAYS EVERYWHERE

Attn: Scholarship Committee
3543 18th Street, No. 1
San Francisco, CA 94110
Tel: (415)861-KIDS
E-mail: colage@colage.org
Web Site: http://www.colage.org/programs/academic/leedubin.htm
To provide financial assistance for college to children of lesbian, gay, bisexual, and transgender (LGBT) parents.
Title of Award: Lee Dubin Scholarship Fund **Area, Field, or Subject:** General studies/Field of study not specified **Level of Education for which Award is Granted:** Undergraduate **Number Awarded:** 3 to 5 each year. **Funds Available:** The stipend is $1,000 per year. **Duration:** 1 year; may be renewed.
Eligibility Requirements: This program is open to undergraduate students who have a GPA of 2.0 or higher and 1 or more LGBT parent. Applicants must be able to demonstrate ability in and commitment to affecting change in the LGBT community. As part of the application process, they must submit a 500- to 1,000-word essay on why support from this fund is important and meaningful to them; their community service, extracurricular activities, honors, or other special events that will help the committee see their strengths; how their experience as a child of LGBT parents has impacted their sense of civic responsibility; an event that dealt with social and/or political differences and their response to that situation; and how they think their reaction was impacted by their experience with their parents. Special consideration is given to applicants with demonstrated financial need. **Deadline for Receipt:** April of each year. **Additional Information:** This program began in 1994.

427 ■ CHINESE AMERICAN CITIZENS ALLIANCE

Attn: Scholarship Foundation
763 Yale Street
Los Angeles, CA 90012
Tel: (213)628-6368
Web Site: http://www.cacanational.org/foundation-scholar.html
To provide financial assistance to Chinese American undergraduate students at colleges and universities in California.
Title of Award: Chinese American Citizens Alliance Foundation Scholarships **Area, Field, or Subject:** General studies/Field of study not specified **Level of Education for which Award is Granted:** Four Year College **Number Awarded:** 6 each year. **Funds Available:** The stipend is $1,000. **Duration:** 1 year.

Eligibility Requirements: This program is open to students of Chinese descent who have completed the sophomore year at a college or university in California. Applicants must provide information on their volunteer work, accomplishments and honors received in college, organizational membership and offices held, previous scholarship awards, career plans, and how they will benefit from the scholarship. Financial need is not considered. Applicants must be available for an in-person interview in Los Angeles. **Deadline for Receipt:** June of each year. **Additional Information:** This program consists of the following named scholarships: the Yoke Quong Jung Memorial Scholarship, the Huan Lin Cheng Memorial Scholarship, the Y.C. Hong Memorial Scholarship, the Collin and Susan Lai Scholarship, the Julian and Eleanor Sue Scholarship, and the Robert and Edith Jung Scholarship.

428 ■ CHINESE AMERICAN CITIZENS ALLIANCE

Attn: Scholarship Foundation
763 Yale Street
Los Angeles, CA 90012
Tel: (213)628-6368
Web Site: http://www.cacanational.org/foundation-scholar.html
To provide financial assistance to Chinese American undergraduate students.
Title of Award: Walter U. Lum Undergraduate Scholarships **Area, Field, or Subject:** General studies/Field of study not specified **Level of Education for which Award is Granted:** Four Year College **Number Awarded:** 4 each year: 2 at $1,000 and 2 at $500. **Funds Available:** Stipends are $1,000 or $500. **Duration:** 1 year; nonrenewable.
Eligibility Requirements: This program is open to students of Chinese descent who have completed the sophomore year of college. Preference is given to U.S. citizens. Applicants must submit a copy of their college transcripts; copies of their and their parents' latest income tax returns; copies of successful applications for financial aid; an essay (up to 500 words) that describes their community activities, career goals, and personal outlook; and 2 reference letters. Selection is based on academic achievement, campus and community extracurricular activities, career goals and personal outlook, quality of the essay, and financial need. **Deadline for Receipt:** Applications are due from the lodges in early May of each year. **Additional Information:** Students must submit their applications and supporting information to their local lodge of the Chinese American Citizens Alliance; applications directly submitted by students are not accepted.

429 ■ CHINESE AMERICAN MEDICAL SOCIETY-MID-ATLANTIC CHAPTER

c/o Richard Change, Scholarship Committee Chair
12522 Stratford Garden Drive
Silver Spring, MD 20904
Tel: (301)424-0136
E-mail: orthochang62@hotmail.com
To provide financial assistance for college to high school students of Chinese descent in the greater Washington, D.C. metropolitan area.
Title of Award: Mid-Atlantic Chapter Awards **Area, Field, or Subject:** General studies/Field of study not specified **Level of Education for which Award is Granted:** Undergraduate **Number Awarded:** Varies each year. **Funds Available:** A stipend is awarded (amount not specified). **Duration:** 1 year.
Eligibility Requirements: This program is open to juniors and seniors at high schools in Washington, D.C., northern Virginia, and southern Maryland who are of Chinese descent. Applicants must submit an updated transcript, scores on national tests (e.g., PSAT, SAT), and a list of honors, extracurricular activities, and awards. They must also submit a 2-page essay on either of these topics: 1) how cultural stereotypes of Asian youth have affected them or influenced their development to the present, or 2) the relevance of their Asian heritage. **Deadline for Receipt:** December of each year.

430 ■ CHRISTERMON FOUNDATION

Attn: Beverage Industry Scholarship Program
9 Orchard Road, Suite 100
Lake Forest, CA 92630
Tel: (949)837-5291
Fax: (949)837-9481
E-mail: information@cfsc.occoxmail.com

Web Site: http://www.christermon.com/scholarship
To provide financial assistance to students transferring from a California community college to a 4-year institution who have a parent or grandparent working in the California beverage industry.
Title of Award: Beverage Industry Scholarship Program **Area, Field, or Subject:** General studies/Field of study not specified **Level of Education for which Award is Granted:** Four Year College **Number Awarded:** Varies each year; recently, 47 of these scholarships were awarded. **Funds Available:** Stipends range from $1,500 to $5,000. **Duration:** 1 year; nonrenewable.
Eligibility Requirements: This program is open to residents of California who may be either high school seniors or community college students as long as they are planning to attend an accredited 4-year college or university in the United States in the following fall term. Students currently enrolled in a 4-year institution or just entering a 2-year college are ineligible. Applicants must be the children, grandchildren, or legal guardians of persons who hold full-time employment with, or who are the proprietor of, a company holding a valid California liquor, beer, or wine license (including restaurants, hotels, retail and wholesale grocery establishments, airlines, breweries, wineries, and distributors). Student employment with an establishment holding a California liquor license and/or eligibility established through a family relationship other than parent, grandparent, or legal guardian does not qualify. Applicants must be planning to enroll full time and have a GPA of 3.0 or higher. **Deadline for Receipt:** January of each year. **Additional Information:** Since this program was established in 1987, it has awarded $2.9 million in college scholarships to 1,000 students.

431 ■ CHRISTIAN CONNECTOR, INC.

Attn: Thom Seagren
518 28 Road, Suite B102
Grand Junction, CO 81501
Tel: (970)256-1610
Free: 800-667-0600
Web Site: http://www.christianconnector.com
To provide financial assistance to high school seniors and transfer students interested in attending a Christ-centered Christian college or Bible college.
Title of Award: Christian Connector Undergraduate Scholarship **Area, Field, or Subject:** General studies/Field of study not specified **Level of Education for which Award is Granted:** Undergraduate **Number Awarded:** 1 each year. **Funds Available:** The award is $1,000. Funds are sent directly to the winner's school. **Duration:** The competition is held annually.
Eligibility Requirements: This competition is open to students planning to enroll for the first time at a Christ-centered Christian college or Bible college. Schools that are members of the CCCU, NACCAP, or AABC automatically qualify. Students currently enrolled at a Christian college or Bible college are not eligible. Applicants enter the competition by registering online with the sponsoring organization, indicating if they wish to receive information from Christian colleges and universities, Bible colleges, short term missions opportunities, Christian music/concerts/festivals, Christian teen publications, or Christian teen events and conferences. The recipient of the scholarship is selected in a random drawing. **Deadline for Receipt:** May of each year.

432 ■ CHUGACH ALASKA CORPORATION

Attn: Chugach Heritage Foundation
560 East 34th Avenue, Suite 104
Anchorage, AK 99503
Tel: (907)261-0339
Free: 800-858-2768
Fax: (907)563-8402
E-mail: jborer@chugach-ak.com
Web Site: http://www.chugachheritage.com/scholarshipmain.html
To provide financial assistance to Alaska Native students who are attending college to prepare for a career working for the Alyeska Pipeline Service Company or its subcontractors.
Title of Award: Chugach Alyeska Match Scholarships **Area, Field, or Subject:** General studies/Field of study not specified **Level of Education for which Award is Granted:** Undergraduate **Number Awarded:** Varies each year. **Funds Available:** The maximum stipend is $3,000 per semester. **Duration:** 1 year; may be renewed for total funding of up to $5,000.

Eligibility Requirements: This program is open to Alaska Natives who live anywhere in the United States. Applicants must be enrolled full time in an accredited college, university, or vocational program and working on a degree that can support a job position on the Alyeska Pipeline. They must have a GPA of 2.0 or higher and be able to demonstrate financial need. Along with their application, they must submit a 500-word personal statement that includes their personal history, accomplishments, and career goals; how their degree program fits with their educational and career plans; why they should receive this scholarship; and how it relates to work with the Alyeska Pipeline Service Company or its subcontractors. **Deadline for Receipt:** February of each year. **Additional Information:** After graduation, recipients must apply for a job with the Alyeska Pipeline Service Company or a subcontractor.

433 ■ CHUGACH ALASKA CORPORATION

Attn: Chugach Heritage Foundation
560 East 34th Avenue, Suite 104
Anchorage, AK 99503
Tel: (907)261-0339
Free: 800-858-2768
Fax: (907)563-8402
E-mail: kkomakkuk@chugach-ak.com
Web Site: http://www.chugachheritage.com/scholarshipmain.html
To provide financial assistance to undergraduate and graduate students who are shareholders or descendants of shareholders of the Chugach Alaska Corporation.
Title of Award: Chugach Heritage Foundation Scholarships **Area, Field, or Subject:** General studies/Field of study not specified **Level of Education for which Award is Granted:** Graduate, Undergraduate **Number Awarded:** Varies each year. **Funds Available:** The stipend is $2,000 per year for full-time students, $750 per semester for students taking 9 units, or $500 per semester for students taking 6 credits. Funds are to be used for tuition, registration fees, books, and campus-related room and/or meal plans. **Duration:** 1 year; may be renewed if the recipient maintains a GPA of 2.0 or higher.
Eligibility Requirements: This program is open to shareholders and descendants of shareholders of the Chugach Alaska Corporation who are enrolled or planning to enroll in an accredited college, university, or vocational program as an undergraduate or graduate student. Applicants must have a GPA of 2.0 or higher and be able to demonstrate financial need. Along with their application, they must submit a 500-word personal statement that includes their personal history, accomplishments, and career goals and how their degree program fits with their educational and career plans. **Deadline for Receipt:** May of each year for the academic year or fall semester; November of each year for spring semester.

434 ■ CHUGACHMIUT

Attn: Education and Training Coordinator
4201 Tudor Centre Drive, Suite 210
Anchorage, AK 99508
Tel: (907)562-4155
Free: 800-478-4155
Fax: (907)563-2891
E-mail: Tim@chugachmiut.org
Web Site: http://www.chugachmiut.org
To provide financial assistance for college to members of the Chugach Alaska Corporation.
Title of Award: Chugachmiut Higher Education Grants **Area, Field, or Subject:** General studies/Field of study not specified **Level of Education for which Award is Granted:** Undergraduate **Number Awarded:** Varies each year. **Funds Available:** The stipend depends on the need of the recipient. **Duration:** 1 year; may be renewed if the recipient maintains of GPA of 2.0 or higher.
Eligibility Requirements: This program is open to Chugach Alaska Corporation shareholders and their descendants who are enrolled or planning to enroll at an accredited college or university. Applicants must submit proof of native ancestry, transcripts, documentation of financial need, and an essay on their educational and career goals. Priority is given to students who are residents of the Chugach region and plan to return to work in the region or Alaska. **Deadline for Receipt:** June of each year for the academic year or fall semester; November of each year for the spring semester. **Additional Information:** Chugachmiut is a tribal consortium of 7 native communities in the Chugach region of Alaska.

435 ■ CHUGACHMIUT

Attn: Education and Training Coordinator
4201 Tudor Centre Drive, Suite 210
Anchorage, AK 99508
Tel: (907)562-4155
Free: 800-478-4155
Fax: (907)563-2891
E-mail: Tim@chugachmiut.org
Web Site: http://www.chugachmiut.org
To provide financial assistance for vocational training to Native Alaskans and American Indians living in the Chugach region of Alaska.
Title of Award: Chugachmiut Vocational Training Grants **Area, Field, or Subject:** General studies/Field of study not specified **Level of Education for which Award is Granted:** Undergraduate **Number Awarded:** Varies each year. **Funds Available:** The stipend depends on the need of the recipient. **Duration:** Until completion of the program, provided the recipient maintains regular attendance and satisfactory progress in all classes.
Eligibility Requirements: This program is open to Native Alaskans and American Indians who are residing in the Chugach region of Alaska. Applicants must be interested in an accredited program of career training, technical training, or certification that will lead to employment. They must submit documentation of financial need and a statement describing their career goals and how the proposed training will help them accomplish those goals. Priority is given to applicants who plan to work in the region. **Deadline for Receipt:** Applications may be submitted at any time, but they must be received at least 2 weeks before the start of the training program. **Additional Information:** Chugachmiut is a tribal consortium of 7 native communities in the Chugach region of Alaska.

436 ■ CIVITAN INTERNATIONAL FOUNDATION

Attn: Scholarship Administrator
P.O. Box 130744
Birmingham, AL 35213-0744
Tel: (205)591-8910
Fax: (205)592-6307
E-mail: civitan@civitan.org
Web Site: http://www.civitaninternational.com
To provide financial assistance for undergraduate or graduate study to Civitan members and families of members.
Title of Award: Dr. Courtney Shropshire Scholarship Program **Area, Field, or Subject:** General studies/Field of study not specified **Level of Education for which Award is Granted:** Graduate, Undergraduate **Number Awarded:** Varies each year. **Funds Available:** This stipend is $1,000. Funds are paid directly to the institution of the recipient's choice and may be used only for tuition, room, books, laboratory fees, and academic supplies. **Duration:** 1 year.
Eligibility Requirements: Applicants must be a Civitan (or a Civitan's immediate family member) and must have been a Civitan for at least 2 years and/or must be or have been a Junior Civitan for no less than 2 years. They must be enrolled in a degree or certificate program at an accredited community college, vocational school, 4-year college or university, or graduate school and be sponsored by a Civitan club in the United States or Canada. Full-time enrollment is required for undergraduates. Selection is based on Civitan club involvement, academic record, professional objectives, and financial need. **Deadline for Receipt:** January of each year.

437 ■ COAGULIFE

Attn: Scholarship Selection Committee
10800 Lyndale Avenue, Suite 112
Bloomington, MN 55420
Tel: (952)886-9200; (866)858-9200
Fax: 800-867-7145
E-mail: info@coagulife.com
Web Site: http://coagulife.com/4a-scholarships.html
To provide financial assistance for college to residents of designated states who have an inherited bleeding disorder.
Title of Award: CoaguLife 5 State Scholarship **Area, Field, or Subject:** General studies/Field of study not specified **Level of Education for which Award is Granted:** Undergraduate **Number Awarded:** 2 each year. **Funds Available:** The maximum stipend is $5,000 per year. Awards may not exceed the total yearly cost of tuition, books, fees, room, and board. Funds are paid directly to the institution. **Duration:** 1 year; may be renewed as long as the recipient maintains a GPA of 3.0 or higher.

Eligibility Requirements: This program is open to residents of Iowa, Minnesota, North Dakota, South Dakota, or Wisconsin who are college-bound graduating high school seniors or students already enrolled full time at an accredited college, university, or trade school. Applicants must have hemophilia, von Willebrand disease, or a similar inherited bleeding disorder. Along with their application, they must submit an essay on 1 of 3 assigned topics. Selection is based on the essay, GPA, difficulty of course work, letters of recommendation, community service, and a statement regarding personal, academic, and career goals. **Deadline for Receipt:** July of each year for spring semester; December of each year for fall semester. **Additional Information:** Recipients must perform at least 10 hours of community service per year for a hemophilia advocacy organization such as the Hemophilia Foundation of Minnesota and the Dakotas, the National Hemophilia Foundation, the Hemophilia Federation of America, or hemophilia summer camp programs.

438 ■ COAGULIFE

Attn: Scholarship Selection Committee
10800 Lyndale Avenue, Suite 112
Bloomington, MN 55420
Tel: (952)886-9200; (866)858-9200
Fax: 800-867-7145
E-mail: info@coagulife.com
Web Site: http://coagulife.com/4a-scholarships.html
To provide financial assistance for college to students who have an inherited bleeding disorder.
Title of Award: CoaguLife National Education Scholarship **Area, Field, or Subject:** General studies/Field of study not specified **Level of Education for which Award is Granted:** Undergraduate **Number Awarded:** 2 each year. **Funds Available:** The maximum stipend is $2,500 per year. Awards may not exceed the total yearly cost of tuition, books, fees, room, and board. Funds are paid directly to the institution. **Duration:** 1 year; may be renewed as long as the recipient maintains a GPA of 3.0 or higher.
Eligibility Requirements: This program is open to college-bound graduating high school seniors or students already enrolled full time at an accredited college, university, or trade school. Applicants must have hemophilia, von Willebrand disease, or a similar inherited bleeding disorder. Along with their application, they must submit an essay on 1 of 3 assigned topics. Selection is based on the essay, GPA, difficulty of course work, letters of recommendation, community service, and a statement regarding personal, academic, and career goals. **Deadline for Receipt:** July of each year for spring semester; December of each year for fall semester. **Additional Information:** Recipients must perform at least 10 hours of community service per year for a hemophilia advocacy organization such as the National Hemophilia Foundation (NHF), the Hemophilia Federation of America (HFA), local chapters of NHF or HFA, or hemophilia summer camp programs.

439 ■ COAST GUARD FOUNDATION

Commandant (G-WKW-2)
Attn: Foundation Scholarships
2100 Second Street, S.W., Room 6320
Washington, DC 20593-0001
Tel: (202)267-6728
Free: 800-872-4957
E-mail: ywright@comdt.uscg.mil
Web Site: http://www.uscg.mil
To provide financial assistance for college to the dependent children of Coast Guard enlisted personnel.
Title of Award: Coast Guard Foundation Scholarship Fund **Area, Field, or Subject:** General studies/Field of study not specified **Level of Education for which Award is Granted:** Undergraduate **Number Awarded:** 10 each year. **Funds Available:** Stipends range from $2,500 to $5,000 per year. **Duration:** 1 year; may be renewed up to 3 additional years.
Eligibility Requirements: This program is open to the dependent children of enlisted members of the U.S. Coast Guard on active duty, retired, or deceased and of enlisted personnel in the Coast Guard Reserve currently on extended active duty 180 days or more. Applicants must be attending or planning to attend a college, university, or vocational school as a full-time undergraduate student. Along with their application, they must submit their SAT or ACT scores, a letter of recommendation, transcripts, and a financial information statement. **Deadline for Receipt:** March of each year.

440 ■ COAST GUARD FOUNDATION

Commandant (G-WKW-2)
Attn: Foundation Scholarships
2100 Second Street, S.W., Room 6320
Washington, DC 20593-0001
Tel: (202)267-6728
Free: 800-872-4957
E-mail: ywright@comdt.uscg.mil
Web Site: http://www.uscg.mil
To provide financial assistance for college to the dependent children of Coast Guard enlisted personnel.
Title of Award: Arnold Sobel Endowment Fund Scholarships **Area, Field, or Subject:** General studies/Field of study not specified **Level of Education for which Award is Granted:** Undergraduate **Number Awarded:** 4 each year. **Funds Available:** The stipend is $5,000 per year. **Duration:** 1 year; may be renewed up to 3 additional years.
Eligibility Requirements: This program is open to the dependent children of enlisted members of the U.S. Coast Guard on active duty, retired, or deceased and of enlisted personnel in the Coast Guard Reserve currently on extended active duty 180 days or more. Applicants must be attending or planning to attend a college, university, or vocational school as a full-time undergraduate student. Along with their application, they must submit their SAT or ACT scores, a letter of recommendation, transcripts, and a financial information statement. **Deadline for Receipt:** March of each year.

441 ■ COAST GUARD MUTUAL ASSISTANCE

4200 Wilson Boulevard, Suite 610
Arlington, VA 22203-1804
Tel: (202)493-6624
Free: 800-881-2462
Fax: (202)493-6686
Web Site: http://www.cgmahq.org
To provide loans to the members of Coast Guard Mutual Assistance (CGMA) and their spouses and dependent children who require assistance for vocational or technical training.
Title of Award: Vocational and Technical Training Student Loan Program **Area, Field, or Subject:** General studies/Field of study not specified **Level of Education for which Award is Granted:** Vocational/Occupational **Number Awarded:** Varies each year. **Funds Available:** The maximum loan is $1,500.
Eligibility Requirements: This program is open to members of the organization, their spouses, and dependent children. Applicants should be seeking assistance to help pay the costs of non-college courses that provide the technical knowledge and skills needed for entry into a specific career field. Financial need must be demonstrated. **Deadline for Receipt:** Requests must be submitted within 30 days after the course begins. **Additional Information:** CGMA membership is open to active-duty and retired members of the U.S. Coast Guard, civilian employees of the U.S. Coast Guard, U.S. Coast Guard Reserve members, U.S. Coast Guard Auxiliary members, Public Health Service officers serving with the U.S. Coast Guard, and family members of all of those.

442 ■ COASTAL BEND COMMUNITY FOUNDATION

Attn: Edie Hamilton
600 Leopard Street, Suite 1716
Corpus Christi, TX 78473
Tel: (361)882-9745
Fax: (361)882-2865
E-mail: eh@cbcfoundation.org
Web Site: http://www.cbcfoundation.org/page27486.cfm
To provide financial assistance for college to members of the Texas Youth Rodeo Association.
Title of Award: Laura Woodman Memorial Scholarship **Area, Field, or Subject:** General studies/Field of study not specified **Level of Education for which Award is Granted:** Undergraduate **Number Awarded:** 1 each year. **Funds Available:** The stipend is $1,000. **Duration:** 1 year; may be renewed if the recipient maintains a GPA of 2.5 or higher.
Eligibility Requirements: This program is open to high school seniors who are members of the Texas Youth Rodeo Association. Applicants must be planning to enroll full time in a college or university in the continental United States. **Additional Information:** Information is also available from Linda Rangeley, (361) 854-1015.

443 ■ COASTAL COMMUNITY FOUNDATION OF SOUTH CAROLINA
Attn: Donor Services Associate
90 Mary Street
Charleston, SC 29403
Tel: (843)723-3635
Fax: (843)577-3671
E-mail: info@ccfgives.org
Web Site: http://www.ccfgives.org
To provide financial assistance for college to high school seniors from coastal South Carolina.
Title of Award: Santee Club Fund **Area, Field, or Subject:** General studies/Field of study not specified **Level of Education for which Award is Granted:** Undergraduate **Number Awarded:** 1 or 2 each year; a total of $2,000 is available for this program. **Funds Available:** The stipend ranges up to $2,000. **Duration:** 1 year; may be renewed up to 3 additional years.
Eligibility Requirements: This program is open to high school seniors who live in the area between McClellanville, South Carolina and the South Santee River. Applicants must submit a 2-page personal statement about their short- and long-term goals, a transcript, and up to 3 letters of recommendation. Selection is based on character, academic record, and financial need. **Deadline for Receipt:** March of each year. **Additional Information:** This program was established in 2001 by members of the Santee Club, a hunting preserve north of McClellanville.

444 ■ COCA-COLA SCHOLARS FOUNDATION, INC.
P.O. Box 442
Atlanta, GA 30301-0442
800-306-COKE
Fax: (404)733-5439
E-mail: questions@coca-colascholars.org
Web Site: http://www.coca-colascholars.org
To provide financial assistance for college to meritorious students.
Title of Award: Coca-Cola Scholarships **Area, Field, or Subject:** General studies/Field of study not specified **Level of Education for which Award is Granted:** Undergraduate **Number Awarded:** 250 each year: 50 National Scholars and 200 Regional Scholars. **Funds Available:** The stipend is $5,000 per year (for National Scholars) or $1,000 per year (for Regional Scholars). **Duration:** All scholarships are for 4 years.
Eligibility Requirements: This program is open to high school and home-school seniors who are planning to attend an accredited U.S. college or university. Applicants must have a GPA of 3.0 or higher at the end of their junior year in high school. They must be a U.S. citizen, national, permanent resident, refugee, asylee, Cuban-Haitian entrant, or humanitarian parolee. The program selects students who are leaders involved in school and the community; have special talents, skills, and interests; are socially aware; take advantage of opportunities; are persistent and overcome barriers; show character and commitment to high ideals; excel academically; express their thoughts clearly, originally, and creatively; and volunteer their time. **Deadline for Receipt:** October of each year; between 1,500 and 2,000 semifinalists are chosen and they submit an additional application, including detailed biographical data, an essay, secondary school report, and recommendations, by the end of January. **Additional Information:** This program was established by Coca-Cola bottlers to celebrate the 1986 Coca-Cola Centennial. Applications are available only from school guidance counselors.

445 ■ COCA-COLA SCHOLARS FOUNDATION, INC.
P.O. Box 1615
Atlanta, GA 30301-1615
800-306-COKE
Fax: (404)733-5439
E-mail: questions@coca-colascholars.org
Web Site: http://www.coca-colascholars.org
To provide financial assistance to students at 2-year colleges.
Title of Award: Coca-Cola Two-Year College Scholarships **Area, Field, or Subject:** General studies/Field of study not specified **Level of Education for which Award is Granted:** Undergraduate **Number Awarded:** 400 each year. **Funds Available:** The stipend is $1,000. **Duration:** 1 year; nonrenewable.
Eligibility Requirements: This program is open to U.S. citizens and permanent residents who are nominated by the 2-year degree-granting institution they are attending. Applicants must have a GPA of 2.5 or higher

and be able to document at least 100 hours of community service they have performed in the past 12 months. They must be planning to enroll in at least 2 courses during the next term. Selection is based on merit. **Deadline for Receipt:** May of each year. **Additional Information:** This program was established in 2000 through a grant from the Joseph B. Whitehead Foundation

446 ■ COCHLEAR AMERICAS
Attn: Scholarships
400 Inverness Parkway, Suite 400
Englewood, CO 80112
Tel: (303)790-9010
Free: 800-458-4999
E-mail: Recipients@Cochlear.com
Web Site: http://www.cochlearamericas.com
To provide financial assistance for college to students who have received a cochlear implant.
Title of Award: Graeme Clark Scholarship **Area, Field, or Subject:** General studies/Field of study not specified **Level of Education for which Award is Granted:** Undergraduate **Number Awarded:** Varies each year; recently, 3 of these scholarships were awarded. **Funds Available:** The stipend is $3,000 per year. **Duration:** 1 year; may be renewed up to 3 additional years.
Eligibility Requirements: This program is open to graduating high school seniors, current university students, and mature aged students who have been accepted into a university course. Applicants must have received a Cochlear Nucleus implant. Along with their application, they must submit a 1,000-word personal statement on their academic aspiration and other interests, including why they chose their proposed area of study, their post-graduation aspirations, their definition of success, and why they wish to receive this scholarship. Selection is based on academic achievement and demonstrated commitment to the ideals of leadership and humanity. **Deadline for Receipt:** June **Additional Information:** This program was established in 2002.

447 ■ CODA INTERNATIONAL
P.O. Box 30715
Santa Barbara, CA 93130-0715
E-mail: coda@coda-international.org
Web Site: http://coda-international.org/scholar.html
To provide financial assistance for college to the children of deaf parents.
Title of Award: Millie Brother Scholarship **Area, Field, or Subject:** General studies/Field of study not specified **Level of Education for which Award is Granted:** Undergraduate **Number Awarded:** 2 each year. **Funds Available:** The stipend is $3,000. **Duration:** 1 year.
Eligibility Requirements: This program is open to the hearing children of deaf parents who are high school seniors or graduates. Applicants must submit a 2-page essay on their experience as the child of deaf parents, how it has shaped them as individuals, and their future career aspirations; essays are judged on organization, content, creativity, and sense of purpose. In addition to the essay, selection is based on a high school transcript and 2 letters of recommendation. **Deadline for Receipt:** May of each year. **Additional Information:** Winning essays are published in the *CODA Connection,* the newsletter of Children of Deaf Adults (CODA) International. Information is also available from Dr. Robert Hoffmeister, Scholarship Committee Chair, Boston University, Programs in Deaf Studies, 605 Commonwealth Avenue, Boston, MA 02215, (617) 353-3205, TTY: (617) 353-3205, E-mail: rhoff@bu.edu.

448 ■ COLLEGE ASSISTANCE MIGRANT PROGRAM
Attn: Alumni Association
202 Sixth Avenue
Lewiston, ID 83501
Tel: (208)792-2101
Fax: (208)792-2550
E-mail: ggalindo@campaa.org
Web Site: http://
To provide financial assistance for college to high school seniors from migrant or seasonal farmworker families.
Title of Award: CAMP Scholarships **Area, Field, or Subject:** General studies/Field of study not specified **Level of Education for which Award is Granted:** Four Year College **Number Awarded:** Approximately 2,400 each year. **Funds Available:** The stipends depend on the need of the recipients and the school they attend. **Duration:** 1 year.

Eligibility Requirements: This program is open to migrant and seasonal farmworkers and their families working in agricultural activities directly related to the production of crops, dairy products, poultry, or livestock; the cultivation or harvesting of trees; or fish farms. Applicants may verify eligibility in 1 of 3 ways: 1) participation during high school or eligibility to participate in a Title 1 Migrant Education Program; 2) participation or eligibility to participate in the Workforce Investment Act (WIA); or 3) verification that they or their parents have spent at least 75 days during the past 24 months as a migrant and/or seasonal (not year-round) farmworker as their primary employment. They must also plan to enroll as a freshman at a 4-year college or university that participates in the College Assistance Migrant Program (CAMP) of the U.S. Department of Education to complete a bachelor's degree, be a U.S. citizen or permanent resident, and be able to document financial need. **Deadline for Receipt:** February of each year. **Additional Information:** Currently, 45 colleges and universities participate in the CAMP program, including schools in Arkansas, California, Colorado, Florida, Georgia, Idaho, Kansas, Michigan, Mississippi, Missouri, New Mexico, New York, Ohio, Oregon, Pennsylvania, Puerto Rico, Texas, Washington, and Wisconsin.

449 ■ COLLEGE BOUND, INC.

Attn: Program Coordinator
128 M Street, N.W., Suite 220
Washington, DC 20001
Tel: (202)842-0858; 888-265-0858
Fax: (202)842-1926
E-mail: scholarship@collegebound.org
Web Site: http://www.collegebound.org/alumni.asp
To provide financial assistance for college to high school seniors in the greater Washington, D.C. area who have participated in the College Bound program.
Title of Award: College Bound Scholarship Program **Area, Field, or Subject:** General studies/Field of study not specified **Level of Education for which Award is Granted:** Undergraduate **Number Awarded:** Varies each year. **Funds Available:** The stipend is $1,500 per year; $750 is paid each semester. **Duration:** 4 years, provided the recipient maintains a college GPA of 2.0 or higher. All funds must be used within 6 years of high school graduation.
Eligibility Requirements: This program is open to seniors graduating from charter and public high schools in the greater Washington, D.C. area who have a GPA of 2.0 or higher. Applicants must have attended at least 1 College Bound financial literacy workshop while in high school and have participated in College Night, Alumni Night, Career Night, Hands on DC, and End of the Year Celebration each year. Selection is based on academic performance, community service, participation in extracurricular activities, commitment to College Bound, and financial need.

450 ■ COLLEGEBOUND NETWORK

Attn: Student of the Year Contest
1200 South Avenue, Suite 202
Staten Island, NY 10314
Tel: (718)761-4800
Fax: (718)761-3300
E-mail: information@collegebound.net
Web Site: http://www.collegebound.net/soy/soy.html
To recognize and reward, with college scholarships, high school students who submit essays on a topic related to college.
Title of Award: CollegeBound Student of the Year Scholarships **Area, Field, or Subject:** General studies/Field of study not specified **Level of Education for which Award is Granted:** Undergraduate **Number Awarded:** 2 each year. **Funds Available:** The prize includes a $5,000 scholarship and other gifts. **Duration:** This competition is held annually.
Eligibility Requirements: This competition is open to juniors and seniors at high schools in the United States. Applicants must submit an essay of 300 to 500 words on a topic that changes annually but relates to their anticipated college experiences. Recently, they were invited to write the chapter on "My College Years" for their autobiography. Finalists are interviewed by telephone. **Deadline for Receipt:** May of each year. **Ad-**

ditional Information: Support for the scholarship is provided by Chela Educational Financing. Winners are announced in *College Bound Magazine.*

451 ■ COLORADO COMMISSION ON HIGHER EDUCATION

1380 Lawrence Street, Suite 1200
Denver, CO 80204
Tel: (303)866-2723
Fax: (303)866-4266
E-mail: cche@state.co.us
Web Site: http://www.state.co.us/cche/finaid/gos/index.html
To provide financial assistance to Colorado residents who have significant financial need and are planning to enter a college or university in the state as a first-time freshman.
Title of Award: Colorado College Opportunity Fund **Area, Field, or Subject:** General studies/Field of study not specified **Level of Education for which Award is Granted:** Undergraduate **Number Awarded:** Varies each year. **Funds Available:** The stipend varies annually, but does not exceed the student's total in-state tuition. At private colleges and universities in the state, the stipend is 50% of the annually set amount. Funds are paid directly to the recipient's institution. **Duration:** 1 year; may be renewed for a total of 145 undergraduate credit hours.
Eligibility Requirements: This program is open to residents of Colorado who are enrolled or planning to enroll at an eligible college or university in the state. Applicants must be able to demonstrate financial need. **Additional Information:** This program was established in 2005.

452 ■ COLORADO COMMISSION ON HIGHER EDUCATION

1380 Lawrence Street, Suite 1200
Denver, CO 80204
Tel: (303)866-2723
Fax: (303)866-4266
E-mail: cche@state.co.us
Web Site: http://www.state.co.us/cche/finaid/students/stateaid/types.html
To provide financial assistance for college to the dependents of disabled or deceased Colorado National Guardsmen, law enforcement officers, and fire fighters.
Title of Award: Colorado Dependents Tuition Assistance Program **Area, Field, or Subject:** General studies/Field of study not specified **Level of Education for which Award is Granted:** Undergraduate **Number Awarded:** Varies each year. **Funds Available:** Eligible students receive free tuition at Colorado public institutions of higher education. If the recipient wishes to attend a private college, university, or proprietary school, the award is limited to the amount of tuition at a comparable state-supported institution. Students who do not live at home also receive the actual cost of room and board charged for on-campus housing or, if no space is available at on-campus dormitories, a supplemental grant of $1,000 per semester to assist with living expenses. **Duration:** Up to 8 academic semesters or 12 academic quarters, provided the recipient maintains a GPA of 2.5 or higher.
Eligibility Requirements: Eligible for the program are dependents of Colorado law enforcement officers, fire fighters, and National Guardsmen disabled or killed in the line of duty, as well as dependents of prisoners of war or service personnel listed as missing in action. Students must be Colorado residents enrolled at a school participating in the program. Only dependents of disabled personnel must demonstrate financial need. **Additional Information:** Recipients must attend accredited postsecondary institutions in Colorado.

453 ■ COLORADO COMMISSION ON HIGHER EDUCATION

1380 Lawrence Street, Suite 1200
Denver, CO 80204
Tel: (303)866-2723
Fax: (303)866-4266
E-mail: cche@state.co.us
Web Site: http://www.state.co.us/cche/finaid/gos/index.html
To provide financial assistance to Colorado residents who have significant financial need and are planning to enter a college or university in the state as a first-time freshman.
Title of Award: Colorado Governor's Opportunity Scholarship **Area, Field, or Subject:** General studies/Field of study not specified **Level of Education for which Award is Granted:** Undergraduate **Number Awarded:** More than 250 each year. **Funds Available:** The amount of

assistance varies, to a maximum of $10,700 per year. **Duration:** 1 year; may be renewed up to 4 additional years if the recipient continues to meet financial need requirements, remains enrolled full time, and demonstrates satisfactory academic progress.

Eligibility Requirements: This program is open to residents of Colorado who are entering an eligible college or university in the state as a full-time freshman with no previous postsecondary experience after high school graduation. Applicants must come from a family with an adjusted gross income less than $29,767 (plus $6,031 for each family member in excess of 3) and an estimated family contribution (EFC) of zero. Students may nominate themselves or they may be nominated by a teacher, counselor, parent, or someone else who knows them well. U.S. citizenship or permanent resident status is required. **Deadline for Receipt:** Each participating institution sets its own deadlines. **Additional Information:** This program was established in 1999.

454 ■ COLORADO COMMISSION ON HIGHER EDUCATION

1380 Lawrence Street, Suite 1200
Denver, CO 80204
Tel: (303)866-2723
Fax: (303)866-4266
E-mail: cche@state.co.us
Web Site: http://www.state.co.us/cche/finaid/students/stateaid/types.html
To provide financial assistance for undergraduate education to residents of Colorado who can demonstrate financial need.

Title of Award: Colorado Leveraging Educational Assistance Partnership (CLEAP) **Area, Field, or Subject:** General studies/Field of study not specified **Level of Education for which Award is Granted:** Undergraduate **Number Awarded:** Varies each year. **Funds Available:** The amount of assistance varies, to a maximum of $5,000 per year. **Duration:** 1 year; renewable.

Eligibility Requirements: Eligible for the program are residents of Colorado who are enrolled or accepted for enrollment in eligible postsecondary institutions in Colorado. Selection is based on financial need. **Deadline for Receipt:** Each participating institution sets its own deadlines. **Additional Information:** Applications are available either from the Colorado Commission on Higher Education or from the financial aid office of eligible Colorado institutions. This program was formerly known as the Colorado Student Incentive Grant (CSIG) Program.

455 ■ COLORADO COMMISSION ON HIGHER EDUCATION

1380 Lawrence Street, Suite 1200
Denver, CO 80204
Tel: (303)866-2723
Fax: (303)866-4266
E-mail: cche@state.co.us
Web Site: http://www.state.co.us/cche/finaid/students/stateaid/types.html
To provide financial assistance for undergraduate education to residents of Colorado who can demonstrate financial need.

Title of Award: Colorado Student Grants **Area, Field, or Subject:** General studies/Field of study not specified **Level of Education for which Award is Granted:** Undergraduate **Number Awarded:** Varies each year. **Funds Available:** The amount of assistance varies. Students in level 1 receive from $1,500 to the maximum amount of unmet need, up to $5,000; students in level 2 receive up to $2,500 or the maximum amount of unmet need, whichever is less; students in level 3 receive up to $500. **Duration:** 1 year; renewable.

Eligibility Requirements: Eligible for the program are residents of Colorado who are enrolled or accepted for enrollment in participating postsecondary institutions in Colorado. Selection is based on financial need, as indicated by the student's expected family contribution (EFC) and the amount required for a federal Pell Grant. Students whose EFC is between zero and 150% of that required for a Pell Grant are in level 1, students whose EFC is between 150 and 200% of that required for the minimum Pell Grant are in level 2, and all other students who demonstrate financial need are in level 3. **Deadline for Receipt:** Each participating institution sets its own deadlines. **Additional Information:** Applications are available either from the Colorado Commission on Higher Education or from the financial aid office of eligible Colorado institutions.

456 ■ COLORADO COMMISSION ON HIGHER EDUCATION

1380 Lawrence Street, Suite 1200
Denver, CO 80204
Tel: (303)866-2723
Fax: (303)866-4266
E-mail: cche@state.co.us
Web Site: http://www.state.co.us/cche/finaid/students/stateaid/types.html
To provide financial assistance for college to residents of Colorado with special skills.

Title of Award: Colorado Undergraduate Merit Scholarship Program **Area, Field, or Subject:** General studies/Field of study not specified **Level of Education for which Award is Granted:** Undergraduate **Number Awarded:** Varies each year. **Funds Available:** The amount of assistance varies, up to the actual cost of tuition and fees. **Duration:** 1 year; renewable if the recipient maintains a GPA of 3.0 or higher.

Eligibility Requirements: Eligible for the program are residents of Colorado (as well as a limited number of nonresidents) who are enrolled or accepted for enrollment at public, private, and proprietary schools of higher education in Colorado. High school seniors must demonstrate academic achievement on the basis of GPA or class rank, standardized test scores, or a competitive process or portfolio review. Transfer students must demonstrate academic excellence by transferring into the institution with a cumulative college GPA of 3.0 or higher. **Deadline for Receipt:** Each participating institution sets its own deadlines. **Additional Information:** Applications are available either from Colorado Commission on Higher Education or from the financial aid office of eligible Colorado institutions.

457 ■ COLORADO COUNCIL ON HIGH SCHOOL/COLLEGE RELATIONS

Attn: Scholarship Committee
600 17th Street, Suite 2210 South
Denver, CO 80202
Tel: (970)264-2231
E-mail: mthompson@pagosa.k12.co.us
Web Site: http://www.coloradocouncil.org
To provide financial assistance for college to high school seniors in Colorado who have been involved in community service activities.

Title of Award: Colorado Council Volunteerism/Community Service Scholarships **Area, Field, or Subject:** General studies/Field of study not specified **Level of Education for which Award is Granted:** Undergraduate **Number Awarded:** 8 each year: 1 in each of the sponsor's districts. **Funds Available:** The stipend is $1,000. **Duration:** 1 year.

Eligibility Requirements: This program is open to high school seniors who have been Colorado residents for at least their final 2 years of high school. Applicants must have a GPA of 2.5 or higher and acceptance at a college or university that is a member of the Colorado Council on High School/College Relations as a full-time student. They must submit a 500-word essay on a significant experience or achievement that has special meaning to them in their involvement in a volunteer role. Selection is based on volunteerism and community service, extracurricular activities, and dedication to serving others. U.S. citizenship or permanent resident status is required. **Deadline for Receipt:** February of each year.

458 ■ COLORADO EDUCATIONAL SERVICES AND DEVELOPMENT ASSOCIATION

P.O. Box 40214
Denver, CO 80204
Web Site: http://www.cesda.org
To provide financial assistance for college to high school seniors in Colorado who are first-generation college students and/or members of underrepresented ethnic or racial minorities.

Title of Award: Gilbert Martinez Diversity Scholarships **Area, Field, or Subject:** General studies/Field of study not specified **Level of Education for which Award is Granted:** Undergraduate **Number Awarded:** 6 each year. **Funds Available:** The stipend is $1,000. **Duration:** 1 year; nonrenewable.

Eligibility Requirements: This program is open to seniors graduating from high schools in Colorado who are 1) the first member of their family to attend college; 2) members of an underrepresented ethnic or racial minority (African American, Asian-Pacific Islander, American Indian, Hispanic/Chicano/Latino; and/or 1) able to demonstrate financial need. Applicants must have a GPA of 2.8 or higher and be planning to enroll at a 2- or 4-year college or university in Colorado. U.S. citizenship or permanent resident status is required. Selection is based on leadership and community service (particularly within minority communities), past academic performance, personal and professional accomplishments, personal attributes, special abilities, academic goals, and financial need. **Deadline for Receipt:** February of each year. **Additional Information:** Information is also available from Marianna Bagge, Scholarship Committee, P.O. Box 621146, Littleton, CO 80162, (303) 225-8576, (800) 888-2787, ext. 8576.

459 ■ COLORADO FEDERATION OF BUSINESS AND PROFESSIONAL WOMEN

Attn: Colorado BPW Education Foundation
P.O. Box 1189
Boulder, CO 80306
Tel: (303)443-2573
Fax: (303)564-0397
E-mail: cbpwf@earthnet.net
Web Site: http://www.cbpwef.org
To provide financial assistance for college to mature women residing in Colorado.
Title of Award: Colorado BPW Education Foundation Scholarships **Area, Field, or Subject:** General studies/Field of study not specified **Level of Education for which Award is Granted:** Undergraduate **Number Awarded:** Varies each year; recently, 30 of these scholarships, worth $18,050, were awarded. **Funds Available:** Stipends range from $250 to $1,000. Funds are to be used for tuition, fees, or books. **Duration:** 1 semester; recipients may reapply.
Eligibility Requirements: This program is open to women 25 years of age and older who are enrolled in an accredited Colorado college or university. Applicants must be U.S. citizens who have resided in Colorado for at least 12 months. Along with their application, they must submit a copy of their most recent high school or college transcript, proof of Colorado residency and U.S. citizenship, a statement of their educational and career goals, 2 letters of recommendation, and documentation of financial need. **Deadline for Receipt:** March or September of each year.

460 ■ COLORADO STATE GRANGE LEADERSHIP AND SCHOLARSHIP FOUNDATION

Attn: Scholarship Foundation Secretary
7275 South Lima Street
Centennial, CO 80112-3850
Tel: (303)708-0606
Fax: (303)708-0411
E-mail: cograngé@na800.net
Web Site: http://www.coloradograngé.org
To provide financial assistance for college to Colorado Grange members or their children.
Title of Award: Colorado State Grange Scholarships **Area, Field, or Subject:** General studies/Field of study not specified **Level of Education for which Award is Granted:** Undergraduate **Number Awarded:** Varies each year. **Funds Available:** The amount awarded is determined annually by the foundation board. Funds are paid, in 2 equal installments, to either the recipient's school or to the recipient in the name of the school. **Duration:** 1 year.
Eligibility Requirements: This program is open to initiated or associate Colorado Grange members with at least 1 year's membership and their children or grandchildren. They may be high school seniors or currently-enrolled college students. Supportive members and their relatives are not eligible. Selection is based on scholastic achievement, Grange involvement, activities, personality, character, and promise of success. **Deadline for Receipt:** March of each year. **Additional Information:** Recipients must attend a college or university in Colorado on a full-time basis.

461 ■ COMMUNICATION DISORDERS FOUNDATION OF VIRGINIA

c/o Janet W. Stack
University of Virginia
Communication Disorders Program
2205 Fontaine Avenue, Suite 202
Charlottesville, VA 22903
Tel: (434)924-4625
Fax: (434)924-3352
E-mail: jws8n@virginia.edu
Web Site: http://www.cdf-virginia.org/hs_scholarship.htm
To provide financial assistance for college to high school seniors in Virginia who have a hearing impairment.
Title of Award: Communication Disorders Foundation of Virginia High School Award **Area, Field, or Subject:** General studies/Field of study not

specified **Level of Education for which Award is Granted:** Undergraduate **Number Awarded:** 1 each year. **Funds Available:** The stipend ranges between $500 and $1,000. **Duration:** 1 year.
Eligibility Requirements: This program is open to seniors graduating from high schools in Virginia who have a hearing impairment. Applicants must have at least a "B" average and be planning to attend a college, university, vocational school, or other postsecondary institution. They must submit brief statements on why they are interested in studying their proposed program; what kind of work they want to do when they complete the program; the type and severity of hearing loss they have; the kind of hearing aid, prosthetic device, or assistive learning device they use; their primary means of communication; how their hearing loss has influenced their life, educational choices, or career choices; and what they would like to teach others about hearing loss. Financial need is not considered in the selection process. **Deadline for Receipt:** April of each year.

462 ■ COMMUNITIES FOUNDATION OF TEXAS

Attn: Scholarship Department
5500 Caruth Haven Lane
Dallas, TX 75225-8146
Tel: (214)750-4222
Fax: (214)750-4210
E-mail: grants@cftexas.org
Web Site: http://www.cftexas.org
To provide financial assistance to children of certain veterans.
Title of Award: Dr. Frank E. Elliott Scholarship **Area, Field, or Subject:** General studies/Field of study not specified **Level of Education for which Award is Granted:** Undergraduate **Number Awarded:** 1 or more each year. **Funds Available:** A stipend is awarded (amount not specified). **Duration:** 1 year; nonrenewable.
Eligibility Requirements: Eligible to apply for this scholarship are children of veterans of the U.S. Army 173rd Airborne Division. Applicants may live in any state. **Deadline for Receipt:** January of each year.

463 ■ COMMUNITY FOUNDATION FOR GREATER ATLANTA, INC.

50 Hurt Plaza, Suite 449
Atlanta, GA 30303
Tel: (404)688-5525
Fax: (404)688-3060
E-mail: vweekes@atlcf.org
Web Site: http://www.atlcf.org/GrantsScholarships/Scholarships/NancyPennLyons.aspx
To provide financial assistance to seniors at high schools in Georgia planning to attend a "prestigious" or out-of-state university.
Title of Award: Nancy Penn Lyons Scholarship Fund **Area, Field, or Subject:** General studies/Field of study not specified **Level of Education for which Award is Granted:** Four Year College **Number Awarded:** Varies each year; recently, 5 of these scholarships were awarded. **Funds Available:** Stipends range up to $5,000 per year. **Duration:** 1 year; recipients may reapply.
Eligibility Requirements: This program is open to seniors graduating from high schools in Georgia who have been residents of the state for at least 1 year. Applicants must have a cumulative high school GPA of 3.0 or higher and a combined SAT score of 1000 or higher or an ACT composite score of 22 or higher. They must be able to demonstrate financial need and commitment to community service. The program is limited to students attending selective private and/or out-of-state universities. **Deadline for Receipt:** April of each year.

464 ■ COMMUNITY FOUNDATION FOR GREATER ATLANTA, INC.

50 Hurt Plaza, Suite 449
Atlanta, GA 30303
Tel: (404)688-5525
Fax: (404)688-3060
E-mail: vweekes@atlcf.org
Web Site: http://www.atlcf.org/GrantsScholarships/Scholarships/Pattillo.aspx
To provide financial assistance to undergraduate students, especially employees of Pattillo Construction Company and their dependents.
Title of Award: Pattillo Scholarship Fund **Area, Field, or Subject:** General studies/Field of study not specified **Level of Education for which Award is Granted:** Undergraduate **Number Awarded:** Varies each year; recently, 27 of these scholarships were awarded. **Funds Avail-**

able: Stipends range up to $3,500 per year. **Duration:** 1 year; recipients may reapply if they maintain a GPA of 2.0 or higher.

Eligibility Requirements: This program is open to students working on an undergraduate degree who have a GPA of 2.0 or higher. Preference is given to employees of Pattillo Construction Company and its affiliates who have worked full time for at least 3 years; their dependents are also given preference. **Deadline for Receipt:** March of each year.

465 ■ COMMUNITY FOUNDATION FOR GREATER NEW HAVEN

70 Audubon Street
New Haven, CT 06510-9755
Tel: (203)777-2386
Fax: (203)777-6584
E-mail: contactus@cfgnh.org
Web Site: http://www.cfgnh.org
To provide financial assistance for college to residents of Connecticut who demonstrate outstanding innovation and creativity.

Title of Award: Milton Fisher Scholarship for Innovation and Creativity **Area, Field, or Subject:** General studies/Field of study not specified **Level of Education for which Award is Granted:** Undergraduate **Number Awarded:** 4 to 6 each year. **Funds Available:** Stipends range from $1,000 to $5,000, depending on the need of the recipient. **Duration:** 1 year; nonrenewable.

Eligibility Requirements: This program is open to Connecticut residents who are high school juniors or seniors, recent high school graduates entering college for the first time, or first-year college students. Students attending or planning to attend a Connecticut college, university, vocational school, or technical school are also eligible. Applicants must submit a 400-word essay on their plans and goals, including what they hope to accomplish, how their goals build on what they have already accomplished, and special circumstances or obstacles in their lives. They must also submit a transcript, although academic achievement is not a major consideration. Selection is based primarily on innovation and creativity, as illustrated by another essay, up to 800 words in length, on whether they have solved a scientific, artistic, or technical problem in a new and unusual way; whether they have come up with a distinctive solution to a problem faced by their school, community, or family; and if they have created a group or organization that serves an important need. Financial need is not considered in the selection process, but it is used to determine the amount of the stipend. **Deadline for Receipt:** April of each year. **Additional Information:** Funding for this program is provided by the Renee B. Fisher Foundation.

466 ■ COMMUNITY FOUNDATION FOR GREATER NEW HAVEN

70 Audubon Street
New Haven, CT 06510-9755
Tel: (203)777-2386
Fax: (203)777-6584
E-mail: contactus@cfgnh.org
Web Site: http://www.cfgnh.org
To provide financial assistance for college to male high school seniors in Connecticut who have served as a caddie at a Connecticut State Golf Association club.

Title of Award: Bob Pryde Scholarship **Area, Field, or Subject:** General studies/Field of study not specified **Level of Education for which Award is Granted:** Four Year College **Funds Available:** A stipend is awarded (amount not specified). **Duration:** 1 year.

Eligibility Requirements: High school senior boys in Connecticut who have served for at least 2 years as a caddie at a club that is affiliated with the Connecticut State Golf Association are eligible to apply for this support. Applicants must require financial assistance to attend an accredited 4-year college. **Additional Information:** Funding for this program is provided by the Connecticut State Golf Association.

467 ■ COMMUNITY FOUNDATION OF LOUISVILLE

Attn: Director of Grants
Waterfront Plaza, Suite 1110
325 West Main Street
Louisville, KY 40202-4251
Tel: (502)585-4649
Fax: (502)587-7484
E-mail: info@cflouisville.org
Web Site: http://www.cflouisville.org

To provide financial assistance to students enrolled in a certified paramedic training program.

Title of Award: Brian Jenneman Memorial Scholarship **Area, Field, or Subject:** Emergency and disaster services **Level of Education for which Award is Granted:** Undergraduate **Number Awarded:** 4 each year. **Funds Available:** The stipend is $1,500. Funds are paid directly to the training institution. **Duration:** 1 year.

Eligibility Requirements: This program is open to residents of any state who are 18 years of age or older and enrolled in a certified paramedic training program offered by an educational institution, fire department, city, county, or other municipality. Applicants must submit essays on how they became interested in being a paramedic, where they plan to serve when they complete their training program, and why they are deserving of this scholarship. Financial need is not considered in the selection process. **Deadline for Receipt:** July of each year. **Additional Information:** This program was established in 2001.

468 ■ COMMUNITY FOUNDATION OF MIDDLE TENNESSEE

Attn: Scholarship Committee
3833 Cleghorn Avenue, Suite 400
Nashville, TN 37215-2519
Tel: (615)321-4939; 888-540-5200
Fax: (615)327-2746
E-mail: mail@cfmt.org
Web Site: http://www.cfmt.org/scholarship_info.htm
To provide financial assistance to women from Tennessee or Texas preparing for a career in the ministry.

Title of Award: B.J. Dean Scholarship **Area, Field, or Subject:** Religion **Level of Education for which Award is Granted:** Undergraduate **Number Awarded:** 1 or more each year. **Funds Available:** Stipends range from $500 to $2,500 per year. Funds are paid to the recipient's school and must be used for tuition, fees, books, supplies, room, board, or miscellaneous expenses. **Duration:** 1 year; recipients may reapply.

Eligibility Requirements: This program is open to women from Tennessee or Texas interested in entering the ministry; students enrolled at Yale Divinity School are also eligible. Applicants must be preparing for full-time ministry but not necessarily seeking ordination. There are no denominational restrictions. Interested students must submit a completed application, their high school and/or college transcript, and 2 letters of recommendation. Selection is based on academic record, standardized test scores, extracurricular activities, work experience, community involvement, recommendations, and financial need. **Deadline for Receipt:** March of each year. **Additional Information:** Recipients may attend seminary anywhere in the United States. They must enroll on a full-time basis. This fund was established in 1995.

469 ■ COMMUNITY FOUNDATION OF MIDDLE TENNESSEE

Attn: Scholarship Committee
3833 Cleghorn Avenue, Suite 400
Nashville, TN 37215-2519
Tel: (615)321-4939; 888-540-5200
Fax: (615)327-2746
E-mail: mail@cfmt.org
Web Site: http://www.cfmt.org/scholarship_info.htm
To provide financial assistance to residents of Tennessee preparing for a career as a certified public accountant.

Title of Award: Michael B. Kruse Scholarship **Area, Field, or Subject:** Accounting **Level of Education for which Award is Granted:** Four Year College, Master's **Number Awarded:** 1 or more each year. **Funds Available:** Stipends range from $500 to $2,500 per year. Funds are paid to the recipient's school and must be used for tuition, fees, books, supplies, room, board, or miscellaneous expenses. **Duration:** 1 year; recipients may reapply.

Eligibility Requirements: This program is open to rising juniors, seniors, and graduate students majoring in accounting with a goal of becoming a certified public accountant. Applicants must be residents of Tennessee attending an accredited college or university in the state with a GPA of 3.2 or higher. Special consideration is given to married students. Interested students must submit a completed application, their high school and/or college transcript, and 2 letters of recommendation. Selection is based on academic record, standardized test scores, extracurricular activities, work experience, community involvement, recommendations, and financial need. **Deadline for Receipt:** March of each year. **Additional Informa-**

tion: This program was established in 2003 by Kruse and Associates.

470 ■ COMMUNITY FOUNDATION OF MIDDLE TENNESSEE

Attn: Scholarship Committee
3833 Cleghorn Avenue, Suite 400
Nashville, TN 37215-2519
Tel: (615)321-4939; 888-540-5200
Fax: (615)327-2746
E-mail: mail@cfmt.org
Web Site: http://www.cfmt.org/scholarship_info.htm
To provide financial assistance for college to residents of middle Tennessee who are pregnant or parenting teens.
Title of Award: Heloise Werthan Kuhn Scholarship **Area, Field, or Subject:** General studies/Field of study not specified **Level of Education for which Award is Granted:** Undergraduate **Number Awarded:** 1 or more each year. **Funds Available:** Stipends range from $500 to $2,500 per year. Funds are paid to the recipient's school and must be used for tuition, fees, books, supplies, room, board, or miscellaneous expenses. **Duration:** 1 year; recipients may reapply.
Eligibility Requirements: This program is open to residents of middle Tennessee who are pregnant or parenting teens. Applicants must be attending or planning to attend an accredited college, university, junior college, technical school, or job training program to increase their job skills and become more employable. They must submit a completed application, their high school and/or college transcript, and 2 letters of recommendation. Selection is based on academic record, standardized test scores, extracurricular activities, work experience, community involvement, recommendations, and financial need. **Deadline for Receipt:** March of each year. **Additional Information:** This program was established in 2000.

471 ■ COMMUNITY FOUNDATION OF NEW JERSEY

Attn: Scholarship Services
Knox Hill Road
P.O. Box 338
Morristown, NJ 07963-0338
Tel: (973)267-5533
Free: 800-659-5533
Fax: (973)267-2903
E-mail: fkrueger@cfnj.org
Web Site: http://www.cfnj.org
To provide financial assistance for college to residents of New Jersey, New York, and Pennsylvania, especially those from immigrant families.
Title of Award: Bego Fund Scholarships **Area, Field, or Subject:** General studies/Field of study not specified **Level of Education for which Award is Granted:** Undergraduate **Number Awarded:** 1 each year: 1 high school senior and 1 college student. **Funds Available:** The stipend is $1,000 per year for high school seniors or $4,000 per year for college students. **Duration:** 1 year; recipients may reapply if they maintain a GPA of at least 3.0.
Eligibility Requirements: This program is open to residents of New Jersey, New York, and Pennsylvania who are either graduating high school seniors or current college students. Preference is given to students who are from immigrant families and are either U.S. residents, naturalized citizens, or first generation U.S. citizens. Applicants must submit a copy of official school transcripts; a resume outlining work experience, activities, and achievements; a 1-page statement of career goals and the reasons for those goals; and 1 character reference. **Deadline for Receipt:** May of each year. **Additional Information:** Information is also available from Santiago J. Fernandez, The Bego Fund, 1744 Arrowbrook Drive, Martinsville, NJ 08836, E-mail: santbego@optonline.net

472 ■ COMMUNITY FOUNDATION OF NEW JERSEY

Attn: Scholarship Services
Knox Hill Road
P.O. Box 338
Morristown, NJ 07963-0338
Tel: (973)267-5533
Free: 800-659-5533
Fax: (973)267-2903
E-mail: fkrueger@cfnj.org
Web Site: http://www.cfnj.org

To provide financial assistance for college to African American high school seniors in New Jersey.
Title of Award: Clanseer and Anna Johnson Scholarships **Area, Field, or Subject:** General studies/Field of study not specified **Level of Education for which Award is Granted:** Undergraduate **Number Awarded:** 4 each year. **Funds Available:** The stipend is $1,750 per year. Funds are made payable jointly to the recipients and their educational institution. **Duration:** 4 years, provided the recipient maintains a GPA of 2.5 or higher.
Eligibility Requirements: This program is open to African American seniors graduating from high schools in New Jersey who have been accepted to attend an educational institution in the United States. Applicants must have earned a grade of "A" or "B" in classes related to the sciences or mathematics and have maintained above average grades in all course work. They must have been born in the United States. Selection is based primarily on financial need, but academic performance, extracurricular activities, and work experience are also considered. **Deadline for Receipt:** April of each year. **Additional Information:** Recipients must agree to donate at least 10 hours of community service per week within New Jersey for 1 year following graduation.

473 ■ COMMUNITY FOUNDATION OF NEW JERSEY

Attn: Donor Services
Knox Hill Road
P.O. Box 338
Morristown, NJ 07963-0338
Tel: (973)267-5533
Fax: (973)267-2903
E-mail: Cangeleri@cfnj.org
Web Site: http://www.cfnj.org
To provide financial assistance for college to African American residents of New Jersey.
Title of Award: Clanseer and Anna Johnson Scholarships **Area, Field, or Subject:** General studies/Field of study not specified **Level of Education for which Award is Granted:** Undergraduate **Number Awarded:** 6 each year. **Funds Available:** The stipend is $2,500 per year. Funds are paid jointly to the recipient and the educational institution. **Duration:** 4 years, provided the recipient maintains a GPA of 2.5 or higher.
Eligibility Requirements: This program is open to African American seniors graduating from high schools in New Jersey who have been admitted to an accredited institution in the United States. Applicants must have maintained an average of "A" or "B" on subjects relating to the sciences or mathematics and an above average GPA overall. Selection is based on academic performance, extracurricular activities, work experience, and financial need. **Deadline for Receipt:** April of each year. **Additional Information:** This program was established in 2001. Recipients must agree to donate at least 10 hours of community service per week in New Jersey for 1 year following graduation.

474 ■ COMMUNITY FOUNDATION OF NEW JERSEY

Attn: Scholarship Services
Knox Hill Road
P.O. Box 338
Morristown, NJ 07963-0338
Tel: (973)267-5533
Free: 800-659-5533
Fax: (973)267-2903
E-mail: fkrueger@cfnj.org
Web Site: http://www.cfnj.org
To provide financial assistance for college to women who demonstrate outstanding scholarship, character, personality, and leadership qualities.
Title of Award: Dominique Lisa Pandolfo Scholarship **Area, Field, or Subject:** General studies/Field of study not specified **Level of Education for which Award is Granted:** Undergraduate **Number Awarded:** 1 each year. **Funds Available:** The stipend is $1,000 per year. Funds are made payable jointly to the recipient and her educational institution. **Duration:** 4 years, provided the recipient maintains a GPA of 2.8 or higher.
Eligibility Requirements: This program is open to graduating female high school seniors who have already been accepted at a postsecondary educational institution. Applicants may not necessary be the top student in their class, but they must have shown outstanding potential, merit, and/or improvement. Selection is based primarily on financial need, but academic performance, extracurricular activities, and work experience are also considered. **Deadline for Receipt:** April of each year. **Additional**

Information: This program was established after September 11, 2001 to honor a student who was killed in the attack on the World Trade Center.

475 ■ COMMUNITY FOUNDATION OF NEW JERSEY

Attn: Scholarship Services
Knox Hill Road
P.O. Box 338
Morristown, NJ 07963-0338
Tel: (973)267-5533
Free: 800-659-5533
Fax: (973)267-2903
E-mail: fkrueger@cfnj.org
Web Site: http://www.cfnj.org
To provide financial assistance for college to high school seniors in New Jersey who qualify as "deserving and disadvantaged."
Title of Award: Albert J. Speak Scholarships **Area, Field, or Subject:** General studies/Field of study not specified **Level of Education for which Award is Granted:** Undergraduate **Number Awarded:** 5 each year. **Funds Available:** The stipend is $1,000 per year. Funds are made payable jointly to the recipients and their educational institution. **Duration:** 4 years.
Eligibility Requirements: This program is open to seniors graduating from high schools in New Jersey who have been accepted to attend an educational institution in the United States. Applicants must qualify as "deserving and disadvantaged." Selection is based primarily on financial need, but academic performance, extracurricular activities, and work experience are also considered. **Deadline for Receipt:** April of each year.

476 ■ COMMUNITY FOUNDATION OF NEW JERSEY

Attn: Donor Services
Knox Hill Road
P.O. Box 338
Morristown, NJ 07963-0338
Tel: (973)267-5533
Fax: (973)267-2903
E-mail: Cangeleri@cfnj.org
Web Site: http://www.cfnj.org
To provide financial assistance for college to residents of New Jersey.
Title of Award: Alfred J. Speak Scholarships **Area, Field, or Subject:** General studies/Field of study not specified **Level of Education for which Award is Granted:** Undergraduate **Number Awarded:** 5 each year. **Funds Available:** The stipend is $1,000 per year. Funds are paid jointly to the recipient and the educational institution. **Duration:** 4 years, provided the recipient maintains a GPA of 2.5 or higher.
Eligibility Requirements: This program is open to seniors graduating from high schools in New Jersey who have been admitted to an accredited institution in the United States. Selection is based on academic performance, extracurricular activities, work experience, and financial need. **Deadline for Receipt:** May of each year.

477 ■ COMMUNITY FOUNDATION OF WESTERN MASSACHUSETTS

Attn: Education Office
1500 Main Street, Suite 1800
P.O. Box 15769
Springfield, MA 01115
Tel: (413)732-2858
Fax: (413)733-8565
E-mail: scholar@communityfoundation.org
Web Site: http://www.communityfoundation.org
To provide loans for college to students in Massachusetts.
Title of Award: James W. Colgan Loan Fund **Area, Field, or Subject:** General studies/Field of study not specified **Level of Education for which Award is Granted:** Undergraduate **Number Awarded:** Varies each year; recently, 186 of these loans, totaling $550,000, were awarded. **Funds Available:** Loans range from $2,000 to $4,000 per year. Repayment begins 3 months after graduation. No interest is charged if repaid within the guidelines of the trustee; the interest on any payment that is more than 30 days past due is 7%. **Duration:** 1 year; may be renewed for up to 3 additional years.
Eligibility Requirements: This program is open to high school and other secondary school graduates who have been a resident of Massachusetts for at least 5 years. Applicants must submit a copy of their Student Aid Report showing their expected family contribution and family adjusted

gross income, their most recent academic transcript, and a letter of reference (first-time applicants only). **Deadline for Receipt:** March of each year. **Additional Information:** The trustee for this loan program is Fleet Bank of Massachusetts, c/o Trust Department, P.O. Box 9006, Springfield, MA 01102-9006, (413) 787-8570, Fax: (413) 787-8553.

478 ■ CONFERENCE OF MINORITY TRANSPORTATION OFFICIALS

Attn: National Scholarship Program
818 18th Street, N.W., Suite 850
Washington, DC 20006
Tel: (202)530-0551
Fax: (202)530-0617
Web Site: http://www.comto.org/scholarship.htm
To provide financial assistance for college or graduate school to members of the Conference of Minority Transportation Officials (COMTO).
Title of Award: Thomas G. Neusom Scholarships **Area, Field, or Subject:** Transportation **Level of Education for which Award is Granted:** Graduate, Undergraduate **Number Awarded:** 2 each year. **Funds Available:** The stipend is $5,500. Funds are paid directly to the recipient's college or university. **Duration:** 1 year.
Eligibility Requirements: This program is open to undergraduate and graduate students who have been members of COMTO for at least 1 year. Applicants must be working on a degree in a field related to transportation with a GPA of 2.5 or higher. Along with their application, they must submit a cover letter with a 500-word statement of career goals. Financial need is not considered in the selection process. U.S. citizenship is required. **Deadline for Receipt:** April of each year. **Additional Information:** COMTO was established in 1971 to promote, strengthen, and expand the roles of minorities in all aspects of transportation. Recipients are expected to attend the COMTO National Scholarship Luncheon.

479 ■ CONFERENCE OF MINORITY TRANSPORTATION OFFICIALS

Attn: National Scholarship Program
818 18th Street, N.W., Suite 850
Washington, DC 20006
Tel: (202)530-0551
Fax: (202)530-0617
Web Site: http://www.comto.org/scholarship.htm
To provide financial assistance for college to children of members of the Conference of Minority Transportation Officials (COMTO) and to other students working on a bachelor's or master's degree in transportation.
Title of Award: Rosa L. Parks Scholarships **Area, Field, or Subject:** Transportation **Level of Education for which Award is Granted:** Master's, Undergraduate **Number Awarded:** 2 each year. **Funds Available:** The stipend is $4,500. Funds are paid directly to the recipient's college or university. **Duration:** 1 year.
Eligibility Requirements: This program is open to 1) college-bound high school seniors whose parent has been a COMTO member for at least 1 year; 2) undergraduates who have completed at least 60 semester credit hours in a transportation discipline; and 3) students working on a master's degree in transportation who have completed at least 15 credits. Applicants must have a GPA of 3.0 or higher. Along with their application, they must submit a cover letter with a 500-word statement of career goals. Financial need is not considered in the selection process. U.S. citizenship is required. **Deadline for Receipt:** April of each year. **Additional Information:** COMTO was established in 1971 to promote, strengthen, and expand the roles of minorities in all aspects of transportation. Recipients are expected to attend the COMTO National Scholarship Luncheon.

480 ■ CONFERENCE OF MINORITY TRANSPORTATION OFFICIALS

Attn: National Scholarship Program
818 18th Street, N.W., Suite 850
Washington, DC 20006
Tel: (202)530-0551
Fax: (202)530-0617
Web Site: http://www.comto.org/scholarship.htm
To provide financial assistance to undergraduate and graduate minority students working on a degree in a field related to transportation.
Title of Award: Trailblazer Scholarships **Area, Field, or Subject:** Transportation **Level of Education for which Award is Granted:** Graduate, Undergraduate **Number Awarded:** 2 each year. **Funds Available:** The stipend is $2,500. Funds are paid directly to the recipient's college or university. **Duration:** 1 year.

Eligibility Requirements: This program is open to undergraduate and graduate students who are working on a degree in a field related to transportation with a GPA of 2.5 or higher. Along with their application, they must submit a cover letter with a 500-word statement of career goals. Financial need is not considered in the selection process. U.S. citizenship is required. **Deadline for Receipt:** April of each year. **Additional Information:** The Conference of Minority Transportation Officials (COMTO) was established in 1971 to promote, strengthen, and expand the roles of minorities in all aspects of transportation. Recipients are expected to attend the COMTO National Scholarship Luncheon.

481 ■ CONFERENCE OF MINORITY TRANSPORTATION OFFICIALS

Attn: National Scholarship Program
818 18th Street, N.W., Suite 850
Washington, DC 20006
Tel: (202)530-0551
Fax: (202)530-0617
Web Site: http://www.comto.org/scholarship.htm
To provide financial assistance for college or graduate school to members of the Conference of Minority Transportation Officials (COMTO).
Title of Award: Carmen E. Turner Scholarships **Area, Field, or Subject:** Transportation **Level of Education for which Award is Granted:** Graduate, Undergraduate **Number Awarded:** 2 each year. **Funds Available:** The stipend is $3,500. Funds are paid directly to the recipient's college or university. **Duration:** 1 year.
Eligibility Requirements: This program is open to undergraduate and graduate students who have been members of COMTO for at least 1 year. Applicants must be working on a degree in a field related to transportation with a GPA of 2.5 or higher. Along with their application, they must submit a cover letter with a 500-word statement of career goals. Financial need is not considered in the selection process. U.S. citizenship is required. **Deadline for Receipt:** April of each year. **Additional Information:** COMTO was established in 1971 to promote, strengthen, and expand the roles of minorities in all aspects of transportation. Recipients are expected to attend the COMTO National Scholarship Luncheon.

482 ■ CONGRESSIONAL BLACK CAUCUS FOUNDATION, INC.

Attn: Director, Educational Programs
1720 Massachusetts Avenue, N.W.
Washington, DC 20036
Tel: (202)263-2836
Free: 800-784-2577
Fax: (202)775-0773
E-mail: spouses@cbcfinc.org
Web Site: http://www.cbcfinc.org
To provide financial assistance to minority and other undergraduate and graduate students who reside in a Congressional district represented by an African American.
Title of Award: Congressional Black Caucus Spouses Education Scholarship **Area, Field, or Subject:** General studies/Field of study not specified **Level of Education for which Award is Granted:** Graduate, Undergraduate **Number Awarded:** Varies each year. **Funds Available:** A stipend is awarded (amount not specified). **Duration:** 1 year.
Eligibility Requirements: This program is open to 1) minority and other graduating high school seniors planning to attend an accredited institution of higher education and 2) currently-enrolled full-time undergraduate, graduate, and doctoral students in good academic standing with a GPA of 2.5 or higher. Applicants must reside or attend school in a Congressional district represented by a member of the Congressional Black Caucus. Along with their application, they must submit a 500-word personal statement on 1) the field of study they intend to pursue and why they have chosen that field; 2) their interests, involvement in school activities, community and public service, hobbies, special talents, sports, and other highlight areas; and 3) any other experiences, skills, or qualifications they feel should be considered. They must also be able to document financial need. **Deadline for Receipt:** April of each year. **Additional Information:** The program was established in 1988.

483 ■ CONGRESSIONAL HISPANIC CAUCUS INSTITUTE, INC.

911 Second Street, N.E.
Washington, DC 20002
Tel: (202)543-1771
Free: 800-EXCEL-DC

Fax: (202)546-2143
E-mail: chci@chci.org
Web Site: http://www.chciyouth.org
To provide financial assistance for college or graduate school to students of Hispanic descent.
Title of Award: Congressional Hispanic Caucus Institute Scholarship Awards **Area, Field, or Subject:** General studies/Field of study not specified **Level of Education for which Award is Granted:** Graduate, Undergraduate **Number Awarded:** Varies each year. Recently, 63 of these scholarships were awarded: 5 to community college students, 40 to undergraduates, and 18 to graduate students. **Funds Available:** The stipend is $2,500 at 4-year and graduate institutions or $1,000 at 2-year community colleges. **Duration:** 1 year.
Eligibility Requirements: This program is open to U.S. citizens and permanent residents who are Hispanic as defined by the U.S. Census Bureau (individuals of Mexican, Puerto Rican, Cuban, Central and South American, and other Spanish and Latin American descent). Applicants must be attending or planning to attend an accredited community college, 4-year university, or professional or graduate program as a full-time student. They must submit evidence of financial need, consistent active participation in public and/or community service activities, good writing skills, and 1-page essays on 1) how effective the public education system has been in addressing the needs of the Latino community and what policy recommendations they suggest to improve the system; and 2) the field of study they plan to pursue and how the Latino community will benefit. **Deadline for Receipt:** April of each year.

484 ■ CONGRESSIONAL MEDAL OF HONOR SOCIETY

40 Patriots Point Road
Mt. Pleasant, SC 29464
Tel: (843)884-8862
Fax: (843)884-1471
E-mail: medalhq@earthlink.net
Web Site: http://www.cmohs.org
To provide financial assistance to dependents of Congressional Medal of Honor winners who are interested in pursuing postsecondary education.
Title of Award: Congressional Medal of Honor Society Scholarships **Area, Field, or Subject:** General studies/Field of study not specified **Level of Education for which Award is Granted:** Undergraduate **Number Awarded:** Varies; approximately 15 each year. **Funds Available:** The stipend is $2,000 per year. **Duration:** 1 year; may be renewed for up to 3 additional years.
Eligibility Requirements: Sons and daughters of Congressional Medal of Honor recipients are eligible to apply if they are high school seniors or graduates and have been accepted by an accredited college or university. **Deadline for Receipt:** August or December of each year.

485 ■ CONNECTICUT ARMY NATIONAL GUARD

Attn: Education Service Officer
360 Broad Street
Hartford, CT 06105-3795
Tel: (860)524-4816
Web Site: http://www.ct.ngb.army.mil/armyguard/join/tuition.asp
To provide financial assistance for college to members of the Connecticut National Guard.
Title of Award: Connecticut National Guard Tuition Waiver **Area, Field, or Subject:** General studies/Field of study not specified **Level of Education for which Award is Granted:** Undergraduate **Number Awarded:** Varies each year. **Funds Available:** The program provides a full waiver of tuition at state colleges or universities in Connecticut. **Duration:** 1 year; may be renewed.
Eligibility Requirements: This program is open to active members of the Connecticut Army or Air National Guard who are interested in working on an undergraduate degree at any branch of the University of Connecticut, any of the 4 state universities, or any of the 13 community/technical colleges in Connecticut. Applicants must have been residents of the state and a satisfactory Guard participant for at least 12 months.

486 ■ CONNECTICUT ASSOCIATION OF LATINOS IN HIGHER EDUCATION, INC.

950 Main Street, Suite 1104
Hartford, CT 06103-1207
Tel: (860)906-5234

E-mail: ca-CALAHE@ccc.commnet.edu
Web Site: http://www.calahe.org
To provide financial assistance for college to Latino residents of Connecticut.

Title of Award: Connecticut Association of Latinos in Higher Education Scholarships **Area, Field, or Subject:** General studies/Field of study not specified **Level of Education for which Award is Granted:** Undergraduate **Number Awarded:** Varies each year; recently, 7 of these scholarships were awarded. **Funds Available:** A stipend is awarded (amount not specified). **Duration:** 1 year.

Eligibility Requirements: This program is open to graduating high school seniors and current college students who have been residents of Connecticut during the preceding 12 months. Applicants must come from a Latino background and have a GPA of 3.0 or higher. U.S. citizenship or permanent resident status is required. Selection is based on academic achievement, financial need, community service, and an essay on "How do you feel education is going to impact your ability to continue assisting others to pursue an education?" **Deadline for Receipt:** April of each year. **Additional Information:** Further information on this program is available from Dr. Wilson Luna, Gateway Community College, Dean of Student Services, 60 Sargent Drive, New Haven, CT 06511, (203) 285-2210, Fax: (203) 285-2142, E-mail: wluna@gwcc.commnet.edu, and from the Hartford Foundation for Public Giving, 85 Gillett Street, Hartford, CT 06105, (860) 548-1888, Fax: (860) 524-8346, E-mail: hfpg2@hfpg.org. The program includes the John Soto Scholarship, the Marta Vallin Memorial Scholarship, and the Thomas M. Blake Memorial Scholarship (limited to students from the Hartford Public Schools).

487 ■ CONNECTICUT ASSOCIATION OF PROFESSIONAL FINANCIAL AID ADMINISTRATORS

c/o Bryan Lewis, Financial Aid Services
Capital Community College
950 Main Street
Hartford, CT 06103
Tel: (860)906-5098
Free: 800-894-6126
E-mail: blewis@ccc.commnet.edu
Web Site: http://www.capfaa.org
To provide financial assistance to undergraduate and graduate students at colleges and universities that are members of the Connecticut Association of Professional Financial Aid Administrators (CAPFAA).

Title of Award: CAPFAA Scholarships **Area, Field, or Subject:** General studies/Field of study not specified **Level of Education for which Award is Granted:** Graduate, Undergraduate **Number Awarded:** 10 each year. **Funds Available:** The stipend is $1,000. Funds are sent directly to the school. **Duration:** 1 year; nonrenewable.

Eligibility Requirements: This program is open to students enrolled full time in a CAPFAA-member postsecondary institution in a degree program or a program of at least 900 clock hours, 24 semester hours, or 36 quarter hours. Applicants must have completed at least 1 academic term or at least half of a clock hour or non-term based program. They must have a federal expected family contribution of $5,000 or less, an undergraduate GPA of 3.0 or higher or a graduate GPA of 3.5 or higher, and a record of community service or volunteer activities in the past 12 months. International students are not eligible. **Deadline for Receipt:** March of each year.

488 ■ CONNECTICUT ASSOCIATION OF SCHOOLS

Attn: Executive Director
30 Realty Drive
Cheshire, CT 06410
Tel: (203)250-1111
Fax: (203)250-1345
E-mail: msavage@casciac.org
Web Site: http://www.casciac.org
To provide financial assistance for college to "well-rounded" high school seniors in Connecticut.

Title of Award: Connecticut Dunkin' Donuts Franchisee Scholarship Program **Area, Field, or Subject:** General studies/Field of study not specified **Level of Education for which Award is Granted:** Undergraduate **Number Awarded:** 100 each year. **Funds Available:** The stipend is $1,000. **Duration:** 1 year.

Eligibility Requirements: This program is open to seniors graduating from high schools in Connecticut who plan to enroll at least half time in a baccalaureate degree program at an accredited college or university, an associate degree program at an accredited junior or community college, or a certificate program at an approved vocational or technical institute. Applicants must be able to demonstrate qualities of a "well-rounded" student: academic excellence (GPA of 3.0 or higher), leadership, and involvement in school and community activities. **Deadline for Receipt:** April of each year. **Additional Information:** This program was established in 2004.

489 ■ CONNECTICUT COMMISSION ON CULTURE AND TOURISM

Attn: Tourism Division
505 Hudson Street, Second Floor
Hartford, CT 06106
Tel: (860)270-8089
Fax: (860)270-8077
E-mail: joyce.fredericks@po.state.ct.us
Web Site: http://www.tourism.state.ct.us/tourism.asp
To provide financial assistance to undergraduate and graduate students from Connecticut who are preparing for a career in the tourism industry.

Title of Award: Walter Schoenknecht Tourism and Travel Scholarship **Area, Field, or Subject:** Travel and tourism **Level of Education for which Award is Granted:** Master's, Undergraduate **Number Awarded:** 1 each year. **Funds Available:** The stipend is $1,000. **Duration:** 1 year.

Eligibility Requirements: This program is open to residents of Connecticut who are high school seniors, high school graduates who have not yet enrolled in college, or enrolled undergraduate or graduate students at an accredited college or university. Applicants must be preparing for a career in the tourism industry. Along with their application, they must submit an essay on a topic about tourism as it relates to Connecticut, 2 letters of recommendation, a current transcript, a personal letter of intent explaining how this scholarship will help them to achieve their academic goals, and a personal resume. Selection is based on personal achievement and demonstrated interest in the tourism industry. **Deadline for Receipt:** September of each year.

490 ■ CONNECTICUT DAUGHTERS OF THE AMERICAN REVOLUTION

c/o Lynn Stewart, State Scholarship Chair
215 Loomis Street
North Granby, CT 06060
Fax: (860)653-4203
Web Site: http://www.ctdar.org
To provide financial assistance for college to high school seniors in Connecticut.

Title of Award: Connecticut State DAR Scholarships **Area, Field, or Subject:** General studies/Field of study not specified **Level of Education for which Award is Granted:** Undergraduate **Number Awarded:** 4 each year. **Funds Available:** The stipend is $1,000. **Duration:** 1 year; nonrenewable.

Eligibility Requirements: This program is open to seniors graduating from high schools in Connecticut in the top 25% of their class. They must be sponsored by their local chapter of the Daughters of the American Revolution. Selection is based on scholastic achievement, leadership, and financial need. **Deadline for Receipt:** January of each year.

491 ■ CONNECTICUT DEPARTMENT OF HIGHER EDUCATION

Attn: Office of Student Financial Aid
61 Woodland Street
Hartford, CT 06105-2326
Tel: (860)947-1855
Fax: (860)947-1313
E-mail: csp@ctdhe.org
Web Site: http://www.ctdhe.org/SFA/sfa.htm
To provide financial assistance for undergraduate education to high school seniors or graduates in Connecticut.

Title of Award: Capitol Scholarship Program **Area, Field, or Subject:** General studies/Field of study not specified **Level of Education for which Award is Granted:** Undergraduate **Number Awarded:** Varies each year. **Funds Available:** Stipends range from $1,500 to $2,000 at Connecticut 4-year degree and 2-year proprietary colleges or from $500 to $700 at Connecticut 2-year public colleges. Students attending out-of-state colleges receive grants of $500 per year. **Duration:** 1 year.

Eligibility Requirements: Applicants must be residents of Connecticut, U.S. citizens or nationals, and high school seniors or graduates. They must be in the top 20% of their graduating class or have SAT scores of 1200 or higher, and they must be planning to attend a college in Connecticut or in a state that has a reciprocity agreement with Connecticut. Financial need must be demonstrated. **Deadline for Receipt:** February of each year. **Additional Information:** These awards were formerly known as the Connecticut Scholastic Achievement Grants. The states that have reciprocity agreements with Connecticut are Maine, Massachusetts, New Hampshire, Pennsylvania, Rhode Island, Vermont, and the District of Columbia. Applications must be submitted through high school guidance offices.

492 ■ CONNECTICUT DEPARTMENT OF HIGHER EDUCATION

Attn: Office of Student Financial Aid
61 Woodland Street
Hartford, CT 06105-2326
Tel: (860)947-1855
Fax: (860)947-1311
E-mail: sfa@ctdhe.org
Web Site: http://www.ctdhe.org/SFA/sfa.htm
To provide financial assistance to Connecticut residents attending public colleges in the state.
Title of Award: Connecticut Aid for Public College Students **Area, Field, or Subject:** General studies/Field of study not specified **Level of Education for which Award is Granted:** Undergraduate **Number Awarded:** Varies each year. **Funds Available:** Awards up to the amount of unmet financial need are provided. **Duration:** 1 year.
Eligibility Requirements: Applicants must be residents of Connecticut who are attending a public college in the state. Selection is based on financial need. **Additional Information:** Applications are submitted through college financial aid offices.

493 ■ CONNECTICUT DEPARTMENT OF HIGHER EDUCATION

Attn: Office of Student Financial Aid
61 Woodland Street
Hartford, CT 06105-2326
Tel: (860)947-1855
Fax: (860)947-1311
E-mail: sfa@ctdhe.org
Web Site: http://www.ctdhe.org/SFA/sfa.htm
To provide financial assistance for undergraduate education to students attending independent colleges in Connecticut.
Title of Award: Connecticut Independent College Student Grants **Area, Field, or Subject:** General studies/Field of study not specified **Level of Education for which Award is Granted:** Undergraduate **Number Awarded:** Varies each year. **Funds Available:** Grants up to $8,500 per year are provided. **Duration:** 1 year.
Eligibility Requirements: Applicants must be residents of Connecticut who are attending an independent college in the state. Selection is based on financial need. **Additional Information:** Applications are submitted through college financial aid offices.

494 ■ CONNECTICUT DEPARTMENT OF HIGHER EDUCATION

Attn: Education and Employment Information Center
61 Woodland Street
Hartford, CT 06105-2326
Tel: (860)947-1810
Free: 800-842-0229
Fax: (860)947-1310
Web Site: http://www.ctdhe.org/eeic/SeniorCitizens.htm
To provide financial assistance for college to senior citizens in Connecticut.
Title of Award: Connecticut Senior Citizen Tuition Waiver **Area, Field, or Subject:** General studies/Field of study not specified **Level of Education for which Award is Granted:** Graduate, Undergraduate **Number Awarded:** Varies each year; recently, more than 3,000 seniors were taking classes and using these waivers. **Funds Available:** At the University of Connecticut branches, tuition for credit-bearing undergraduate and graduate degree-granting programs is waived; university and activity fees are not waived. At the campuses of Connecticut State University, tuition is waived for all courses (credit, non-credit, and summer extension fund) as long as the recipients are enrolled in a degree-granting program or space is available at the end of a regular registration period. At the 12 Community-Technical colleges, tuition is waived in all general fund

programs provided space exists; waivers do not apply to extension fund courses (generally summer school and non-credit, continuing education offerings). **Duration:** Up to 4 years.
Eligibility Requirements: This program is open to residents of Connecticut who are 62 years of age and older. Applicants must be planning to enroll at a campus of the University of Connecticut, a branch of Connecticut State University, or 1 of the 12 Community-Technical colleges. **Additional Information:** This is an entitlement program; applications are available at the respective college financial aid offices.

495 ■ CONNECTICUT DEPARTMENT OF HIGHER EDUCATION

Attn: Office of Student Financial Aid
61 Woodland Street
Hartford, CT 06105-2326
Tel: (860)947-1855
Fax: (860)947-1311
E-mail: sfa@ctdhe.org
Web Site: http://www.ctdhe.org/SFA/sfa.htm
To provide financial assistance for undergraduate education to students from any state attending public colleges in Connecticut.
Title of Award: Connecticut Tuition Set Aside Aid **Area, Field, or Subject:** General studies/Field of study not specified **Level of Education for which Award is Granted:** Undergraduate **Number Awarded:** Varies each year. **Funds Available:** Awards up to the amount of unmet financial need are provided. **Duration:** 1 year.
Eligibility Requirements: Applicants may be residents of any state but must be attending a public college in Connecticut. Selection is based on financial need. **Additional Information:** Applications are submitted through college financial aid offices.

496 ■ CONNECTICUT DEPARTMENT OF HIGHER EDUCATION

Attn: Education and Employment Information Center
61 Woodland Street
Hartford, CT 06105-2326
Tel: (860)947-1816
Free: 800-842-0229
Fax: (860)947-1310
E-mail: veterans@ctdhe.org
Web Site: http://www.ctdhe.org/vet/default.htm
To provide financial assistance for college to certain Connecticut veterans.
Title of Award: Connecticut Tuition Waiver for Veterans **Area, Field, or Subject:** General studies/Field of study not specified **Level of Education for which Award is Granted:** Undergraduate **Number Awarded:** Varies each year. **Funds Available:** The program provides a waiver of 100% of tuition for general fund courses at a Connecticut public college or university, 50% of tuition for extension and summer courses at Connecticut State University, and 50% of part-time fees at *OnlineCSU*. **Duration:** Up to 4 years.
Eligibility Requirements: Eligible are honorably-discharged Connecticut veterans who served at least 90 days in World War II, the Korean hostilities, Vietnam, Operations Desert Shield and Desert Storm, Somalia, or Bosnia, or who served in a combat or combat-support role in the peacekeeping mission in Lebanon, the Grenada invasion, Operation Earnest Will, or the Panama invasion. **Additional Information:** This is an entitlement program; applications are available at the respective college financial aid offices.

497 ■ CONNECTICUT DEPARTMENT OF HIGHER EDUCATION

Attn: Office of Student Financial Aid
61 Woodland Street
Hartford, CT 06105-2326
Tel: (860)947-1853
Fax: (860)947-1311
E-mail: gearup@ctdhe.org
Web Site: http://www.ctdhe.org/OEO/gearup.htm
To provide financial assistance for college to seniors at selected high schools in Connecticut who participated in a pre-college program.
Title of Award: GEAR UP Connecticut College Scholarship Program **Area, Field, or Subject:** General studies/Field of study not specified **Level of Education for which Award is Granted:** Undergraduate **Number Awarded:** Varies each year. **Funds Available:** Stipends range from $200 to $4,000. These scholarships are considered "last dollar" or gap-filling grants and are awarded to students only after they have been

formally accepted into the college or university of their choice and have received a financial aid package. **Duration:** 1 year; may be renewed if the recipient maintains full-time enrollment, Pell eligibility, and satisfactory academic progress.

Eligibility Requirements: This program is open to residents of Connecticut under 22 years of age who are U.S. citizens planning to enter an accredited college or university as a freshman. Applicants must have participated in ConnCAP, a pre-college program administered by the Connecticut Department of Higher Education at 24 schools in Bridgeport, Hartford, and New Haven. They must receive a Pell grant from the U.S. Department of Education. **Deadline for Receipt:** June of each year. **Additional Information:** GEAR UP stands for Gaining Early Awareness and Readiness for Undergraduate Programs. Funding for this program is provided by the Connecticut Department of Higher Education (CTDHE) and the U.S. Department of Education. For a list of the selected high schools, contact CTDHE.

498 ■ CONNECTICUT FUNERAL DIRECTORS ASSOCIATION

350 Silas Deane Highway, Suite 202
Wethersfield, CT 06109
Tel: (860)721-0234
Free: 800-919-CFDA
Fax: (860)257-3617
E-mail: connfda@aol.com
Web Site: http://www.ctfda.org
To provide financial assistance to residents of Connecticut who are working on a degree in mortuary science.

Title of Award: Connecticut Funeral Directors Association Mortuary Science Scholarship **Area, Field, or Subject:** Mortuary science **Level of Education for which Award is Granted:** Undergraduate **Number Awarded:** Up to 2 each year. **Funds Available:** The stipend is $1,000. **Duration:** 1 year.

Eligibility Requirements: This program is open to residents of Connecticut who are enrolled in an accredited mortuary science school. Applicants must be planning to complete their education and serve the public in their chosen profession in Connecticut. Along with their application, they must submit an essay describing the process they used and the experiences they underwent in their decision to enter the funeral service profession. Selection is based on the essay and academic record; financial need is not considered. **Deadline for Receipt:** October of each year.

499 ■ CONNECTICUT HIGHER EDUCATION SUPPLEMENTAL LOAN AUTHORITY

342 North Main Street, Suite 202
West Hartford, CT 06117
Tel: (860)236-1400
Free: 800-252-FELP
Fax: (860)236-0910
E-mail: chesla1@chesla.org
Web Site: http://www.chesla.org
To provide loans to undergraduate or graduate students in Connecticut.

Title of Award: Connecticut Family Education Loan Program **Area, Field, or Subject:** General studies/Field of study not specified **Level of Education for which Award is Granted:** Graduate, Undergraduate **Number Awarded:** Varies each year. **Funds Available:** Students may borrow from $2,000 up to the full cost of education, less other financial aid, to a cumulative total of $125,000. While the students remain in school and for a 6-month grace period after leaving, they pay only interest on the loan. Graduate and professional students may capitalize the interest while in school. The current interest rate is 5.5%. **Duration:** Until completion of a degree. Following completion of college, loans must be repaid over 140 months. The minimum payment is $4.58 per $1,000 borrowed during the in-school and 6-month grace period, and $9.69 per $1,000 borrowed during the 140-month repayment term.

Eligibility Requirements: These loans are available to students enrolled at least half time in a Connecticut nonprofit college or university and Connecticut residents enrolled at least half-time at a nonprofit college anywhere in the United States. Students must have a co-applicant (not necessarily a parent); together, the student and co-applicant must be credit worthy, have monthly installment payments amounting to 40% or less of monthly gross income, and have a minimum $20,000 gross annual income (there is no maximum income requirement). **Deadline for**

Receipt: Applications may be submitted at any time.

500 ■ CONNECTICUT JUNIOR SOCCER ASSOCIATION

Attn: Scholarship Committee
11 Executive Drive
Farmington, CT 06032
Tel: (860)676-1161
Fax: (860)676-1162
E-mail: cjsacup@bysa.org
Web Site: http://www.cjsa.net
To provide financial assistance for college to high school seniors in Connecticut who have been involved in soccer.

Title of Award: Connecticut Junior Soccer Association Scholarships **Area, Field, or Subject:** General studies/Field of study not specified **Level of Education for which Award is Granted:** Undergraduate **Number Awarded:** 4 each year. **Funds Available:** The stipend is $1,000. **Duration:** 1 year.

Eligibility Requirements: This program is open to seniors graduating from high schools in Connecticut who have played soccer with a club affiliated with the Connecticut Junior Soccer Association. Applicants must have a "C+" average or higher and plans to attend a school of higher education. Along with their application, they must submit a 250-word essay on "What Soccer Means to Me." **Deadline for Receipt:** March of each year.

501 ■ CONNECTICUT NATIONAL GUARD FOUNDATION, INC.

Attn: Scholarship Committee
360 Broad Street
Hartford, CT 06105-3795
Tel: (860)241-1550
Fax: (860)293-2929
E-mail: scholarship.committee@ctngfoundation.org
Web Site: http://www.ctngfoundation.org/Scholarship.asp
To provide financial assistance for college to members of the Connecticut National Guard and their families.

Title of Award: Connecticut National Guard Foundation Scholarships **Area, Field, or Subject:** General studies/Field of study not specified **Level of Education for which Award is Granted:** Undergraduate **Number Awarded:** 3 each year. **Funds Available:** The stipend is $1,500. **Duration:** 1 year.

Eligibility Requirements: This program is open to members of the Connecticut Army National Guard and Organized Militia, their children, and their spouses. Applicants must be enrolled or planning to enroll in an accredited college degree or technical program. Along with their application, they must submit a letter of recommendation, list of extracurricular activities, high school or college transcripts, and a 200-word statement on their educational and future goals. Selection is based on achievement and citizenship. **Deadline for Receipt:** April of each year.

502 ■ CONNECTICUT NATIONAL GUARD FOUNDATION, INC.

Attn: Scholarship Committee
360 Broad Street
Hartford, CT 06105-3795
Tel: (860)241-1550
Fax: (860)293-2929
E-mail: scholarship.committee@ctngfoundation.org
Web Site: http://www.ctngfoundation.org/Scholarship.asp
To provide financial assistance for college to children of members of the Connecticut Army National Guard.

Title of Award: SGT Felix Delgreco Jr. Scholarship **Area, Field, or Subject:** General studies/Field of study not specified **Level of Education for which Award is Granted:** Undergraduate **Number Awarded:** 1 each year. **Funds Available:** The stipend is $2,500. **Duration:** 1 year.

Eligibility Requirements: This program is open to children of members of the Connecticut Army National Guard who are enrolled or planning to enroll in an accredited college degree or technical program. Applicants must submit a letter of recommendation, list of extracurricular activities, high school or college transcripts, and a 200-word statement on their educational and future goals. Selection is based on achievement and citizenship. **Deadline for Receipt:** April of each year.

503 ■ CONNECTICUT STATE GOLF ASSOCIATION

Attn: Scholarship Committee
35 Cold Spring Road, Suite 212
Rocky Hill, CT 06067

Tel: (860)257-4171
Fax: (860)257-8355
E-mail: ctstategolf@asga.org
Web Site: http://www.csgalinks.org/widdyneale.htm
To provide financial assistance for college to high school seniors who have worked at a golf club that is a member of the Connecticut State Golf Association (CSGA).
Title of Award: William (Widdy) Neale Scholarships **Area, Field, or Subject:** General studies/Field of study not specified **Level of Education for which Award is Granted:** Undergraduate **Number Awarded:** 10 to 13 each year. **Funds Available:** Stipends range from $1,000 to $2,000. **Duration:** 1 year; may be renewed up to 3 additional years provided the recipient maintains satisfactory academic standing and continues to demonstrate financial need.
Eligibility Requirements: This program is open to seniors graduating from high schools in Connecticut who have worked at a CSGA member golf club for 1 full golf season in the pro shop, with the maintenance crew, or in the clubhouse, locker room, or dining room. Applicants must be recommended by the CSGA club representative, golf professional, course superintendent, or other official; each club may recommend only 1 student. Selection is based on grades, character, citizenship, community service, and financial need. **Deadline for Receipt:** May of each year. **Additional Information:** Information is also available from Herbert Emanuelson, Scholarship Chairman, 1575 Boston Post Road, Building B, P.O. Box 364, Guilford, CT 06437, Fax: (203) 453-8584.

504 ■ CONNECTICUT STUDENT LOAN FOUNDATION

Attn: Manager, Scholarships and Special Programs
525 Brook Street
P.O. Box 1009
Rocky Hill, CT 06067
Tel: (860)257-4001
Free: 800-237-9721
Fax: (860)563-3247
E-mail: vjmscholarship@mail.cslf.org
Web Site: http://www.cslf.com/students/VJM/index.htm
To provide financial assistance in the form of a contribution toward payment of a student loan to residents of Connecticut.
Title of Award: Vincent J. Maiocco Scholarship **Area, Field, or Subject:** General studies/Field of study not specified **Level of Education for which Award is Granted:** Four Year College **Number Awarded:** 1 or more each year. **Funds Available:** A stipend is awarded (amount not specified). Funds are paid directly to the recipient's lender to be applied to the outstanding principal balance of the existing Stafford Loan guaranteed by CSLF. **Duration:** 1 year.
Eligibility Requirements: This program is open to Connecticut residents who have completed the first year of undergraduate study at a 4-year college or university in the United States. Applicants must have received a Stafford Loan guaranteed by the Connecticut Student Loan Foundation (CSLF). Along with their application, they must submit a brief essay that describes school activities in which they have been actively involved (particularly positions of leadership), activities they are actively engaged in outside of school, why they find those rewarding, and any additional information that demonstrates financial need and/or the importance of this scholarship to them. U.S. citizenship is required. **Deadline for Receipt:** May of each year.

505 ■ CONSORTIUM OF INFORMATION AND TELECOMMUNICATIONS EXECUTIVES, INC.

c/o Diane C. Lewis, Scholarship Committee Chair
6000 Hadley Road
South Plainfield, NJ 07080
Tel: (908)412-6421
Web Site: http://www.forcite.org
To provide financial assistance for college to African American high school seniors in selected states.
Title of Award: CITE Scholarships **Area, Field, or Subject:** General studies/Field of study not specified **Level of Education for which Award is Granted:** Undergraduate **Number Awarded:** 12 each year: 1 to a student in each of the chapter areas. **Funds Available:** The stipend is $2,000. **Duration:** 1 year; nonrenewable.
Eligibility Requirements: This program is open to African American high school seniors who have been accepted by an accredited college or

university. Applicants must have a GPA of 3.0 or higher and be able to document financial need. They must submit their application to a chapter of the Consortium of Information and Telecommunications Executives (CITE), currently located in California, Florida, Indiana, Maryland, Metropolitan Washington, New England, New Jersey, New York, Pennsylvania and Delaware, Texas, Virginia, and West Virginia. Employees of Verizon Communications or an affiliated subsidiary and their family members are ineligible. **Deadline for Receipt:** May of each year. **Additional Information:** CITE is an organization of African American employees of Verizon, founded in 1984 after the dissolution of the former Bell systems. Recipients must attend the CITE annual conference. Travel, conference, lodging, and other expenses are paid by CITE.

506 ■ CONSORTIUM OF INFORMATION AND TELECOMMUNICATIONS EXECUTIVES-MARYLAND CHAPTER

P.O. Box 1286
Baltimore, MD 21203
Tel: (410)393-2337
Web Site: http://www.cite-md.org
To provide financial assistance for college to African American high school seniors in Maryland.
Title of Award: Elizabeth Knight Scholarship Awards **Area, Field, or Subject:** General studies/Field of study not specified **Level of Education for which Award is Granted:** Undergraduate **Number Awarded:** 5 each year. **Funds Available:** The stipend is $2,000. **Duration:** 1 year.
Eligibility Requirements: This program is open to African American seniors graduating from high schools in Maryland with a GPA of 3.0 or higher. Applicants must have been accepted by an accredited college or university and be able to document financial need. Employees and immediate family members of employees of the Verizon Corporation or an affiliated subsidiary are ineligible. **Deadline for Receipt:** March of each year. **Additional Information:** The Consortium of Information and Telecommunications Executives (CITE) is an organization of African American employees of Verizon, founded in 1984 after the dissolution of the former Bell systems.

507 ■ CONSORTIUM OF INFORMATION AND TELECOMMUNICATIONS EXECUTIVES-VIRGINIA CHAPTER

c/o Ralph Throckmorton, Scholarship Committee
P.O. Box 7294
Richmond, VA 23221
Tel: (804)772-4620
E-mail: ralph.throckmorton@verizon.com
Web Site: http://www.citeva.org/cite/programs.do
To provide financial assistance for college to African American high school seniors in Virginia.
Title of Award: Virginia CITE Scholarships **Area, Field, or Subject:** General studies/Field of study not specified **Level of Education for which Award is Granted:** Undergraduate **Number Awarded:** Varies each year, including 1 for a Verizon employee or family member. **Funds Available:** The stipend is $1,000. **Duration:** 1 year.
Eligibility Requirements: This program is open to African American seniors graduating from high schools in Virginia with a GPA of 2.5 or higher. Applicants must have been accepted by an accredited college or university. Their family income must be $50,000 per year or less if both parents are employed or $40,000 or less if only 1 parent is employed. Employees and immediate family members of employees of the Verizon Corporation or an affiliated subsidiary are ineligible to receive most awards, although 1 scholarship is reserved for Verizon employees and their families. **Deadline for Receipt:** April of each year. **Additional Information:** The Consortium of Information and Telecommunications Executives (CITE) is an organization of African American employees of Verizon, founded in 1984 after the dissolution of the former Bell systems.

508 ■ CONSTRUCTMYFUTURE.COM

111 East Wisconsin Avenue, Suite 1000
Milwaukee, WI 53202
Tel: (414)272-0943; (866)AEM-0442
Fax: (414)272-1170
E-mail: nhallada@aem.org
Web Site: http://www.constructmyfuture.com/stu-scholarships.html
To provide financial assistance for college to students who are interested in preparing for a career in the construction industry.

Title of Award: ConstructMyFuture.com Scholarships **Area, Field, or Subject:** Construction **Level of Education for which Award is Granted:** Undergraduate **Number Awarded:** 3 each year. **Funds Available:** The stipend is $1,000. **Duration:** 1 year; nonrenewable.

Eligibility Requirements: This program is open to 1) graduating high school seniors; 2) students currently enrolled in a postsecondary educational institution; and 3) workers currently employed in the construction industry. Applicants must be interested in 1) entering or continuing in a college program to prepare for a career in the construction industry; or 2) purchasing tools for use in a construction industry job. Along with their application, they must submit a 1,000-word essay on their interest in the construction industry, their educational goals, and any other information such as specialized hobbies, skills, rewards, or achievements they wish to share. Selection is based on current and past involvement in the construction field; financial need is not considered. **Deadline for Receipt:** February of each year.

509 ■ CONTINENTAL MISS TEEN AMERICA SCHOLARSHIP PROGRAM, INC.

Attn: CEO/President
P.O. Box 3250
New Haven, CT 06515-0173
Tel: (203)387-1377
Fax: (203)387-2076
Web Site: http://www.missteenamerica.com

To recognize and reward, with college scholarships and other prizes, teen-aged women who participate in a talent and beauty competition.

Title of Award: Miss Teen America **Area, Field, or Subject:** General studies/Field of study not specified **Level of Education for which Award is Granted:** Undergraduate **Number Awarded:** 5 winners receive national scholarships each year. **Funds Available:** Cash scholarships, for use at an accredited college or university, are $5,000 for Miss Teen America, $2,500 for the first alternate, $2,000 for the second alternate, $1,500 for the third alternate, and $1,000 for the fourth alternate. All winners, including those at the state level, receive scholarships for use at Nova Southeastern University and many other prizes and awards. **Duration:** The competition is held annually.

Eligibility Requirements: This competition is open to women between 14 and 18 years of age who have never been to college, been married, or given birth to a child. Applicants must first apply for state or metropolitan area competitions by submitting a 1-page essay on why they want to represent their state. At the national level, winners participate in basis of talent, modeling, and photogenic competitions. Selection is based on their application, including the essay, volunteer community service, academic achievement, and extracurricular activities (20%); verbal expression in an interview (15%); formal expression during the presentation (10%); talent (15%); modeling (10%); verbal presentation in a commercial or public service announcement on their state (10%); physical fitness (10%); and facial beauty and overall cover model look (10%). **Additional Information:** All participants are required to pay a total sponsorship fee of $925 and to buy a full-page ad in the national program book for $400.

510 ■ COOK INLET REGION, INC.

Attn: CIRI Foundation
2600 Cordova Street, Suite 206
Anchorage, AK 99503
Tel: (907)263-5582
Free: 800-764-3382
Fax: (907)263-5588
E-mail: tcf@ciri.com
Web Site: http://www.thecirifoundation.org/scholarship.html

To provide financial assistance for employment skills upgrades to Alaska Natives who are original enrollees to the Cook Inlet Region, Inc. (CIRI) and their lineal descendants.

Title of Award: Career Upgrade Grants **Area, Field, or Subject:** General studies/Field of study not specified **Level of Education for which Award is Granted:** Undergraduate **Number Awarded:** Varies each year; recently, 17 of these grants were awarded. **Funds Available:** The maximum stipend is $3,000 per calendar year. **Duration:** 1 quarter; recipients may reapply.

Eligibility Requirements: This program is open to Alaska Native enrollees to CIRI under the Alaska Native Claims Settlement Act (ANCSA) of 1971 and their lineal descendants. Applicants should have a high school diploma or GED, have a GPA of 2.5 or higher, be preparing to enter or reenter or upgrade in the job market upon completion of training, and be able to demonstrate the availability of employment. They must be accepted or enrolled part time in a course of study that directly contributes toward potential employment or employment upgrade. Alaska residency is not required. Selection is based on academic achievement, rigor of course work or degree program, quality of a statement of purpose, student financial contribution, financial need, grade level, previous work performance, education and community activities, letters of recommendation, seriousness of purpose, and practicality of educational and professional goals. **Deadline for Receipt:** March, June, September, or November of each year. **Additional Information:** Only part-time study is supported. Total course credits may not exceed 11 credit hours per application.

511 ■ COOK INLET REGION, INC.

Attn: CIRI Foundation
2600 Cordova Street, Suite 206
Anchorage, AK 99503
Tel: (907)263-5582
Free: 800-764-3382
Fax: (907)263-5588
E-mail: tcf@ciri.com
Web Site: http://www.thecirifoundation.org/scholarship.html

To provide financial assistance for undergraduate or graduate studies to Alaska Natives who are original enrollees to Cook Inlet Region, Inc. (CIRI) and their lineal descendants.

Title of Award: CIRI Foundation Achievement Scholarships **Area, Field, or Subject:** General studies/Field of study not specified **Level of Education for which Award is Granted:** Graduate, Undergraduate **Number Awarded:** Varies each year; recently, 12 of these scholarships were awarded. **Funds Available:** The stipend is $7,000 per year. **Duration:** 1 year (2 semesters).

Eligibility Requirements: This program is open to Alaska Native enrollees to CIRI under the Alaska Native Claims Settlement Act (ANCSA) of 1971 and their lineal descendants. There are no Alaska residency requirements or age limitations. Applicants must be accepted or enrolled full time in a 2-year, 4-year, or graduate degree program. They must have a GPA of 3.0 or higher. Selection is based on academic achievement, rigor of course work or degree program, quality of a statement of purpose, student financial contribution, financial need, grade level, previous work performance, education and community activities, letters of recommendation, seriousness of purpose, and practicality of educational and professional goals. **Deadline for Receipt:** May of each year. **Additional Information:** Recipients must attend school on a full-time basis.

512 ■ COOK INLET REGION, INC.

Attn: CIRI Foundation
2600 Cordova Street, Suite 206
Anchorage, AK 99503
Tel: (907)263-5582
Free: 800-764-3382
Fax: (907)263-5588
E-mail: tcf@ciri.com
Web Site: http://www.thecirifoundation.org/scholarship.html

To provide financial assistance for undergraduate or graduate studies to Alaska Natives who are original enrollees to Cook Inlet Region, Inc. (CIRI) and their lineal descendants.

Title of Award: CIRI Foundation Excellence Scholarships **Area, Field, or Subject:** General studies/Field of study not specified **Level of Education for which Award is Granted:** Four Year College, Graduate **Number Awarded:** Varies each year; recently, 12 of these scholarships were awarded. **Funds Available:** The stipend is $9,000 per year. **Duration:** 1 year (2 semesters).

Eligibility Requirements: This program is open to Alaska Native enrollees to CIRI under the Alaska Native Claims Settlement Act (ANCSA) of 1971 and their lineal descendants. There are no Alaska residency requirements or age limitations. Applicants must be accepted or enrolled full time in a 4-year undergraduate or a graduate degree program. They must have a GPA of 3.5 or higher. Selection is based on academic achievement, rigor of course work or degree program, quality of a statement of purpose, student financial contribution, financial need, grade level, previous work performance, education and community activities, letters of recommendation, seriousness of purpose, and practicality of educational and professional goals. **Deadline for Receipt:** May of each year. **Additional Information:** Recipients must attend school on a full-time basis.

513 ■ COOK INLET REGION, INC.

Attn: CIRI Foundation
2600 Cordova Street, Suite 206
Anchorage, AK 99503
Tel: (907)263-5582
Free: 800-764-3382
Fax: (907)263-5588
E-mail: tcf@ciri.com
Web Site: http://www.thecirifoundation.org/scholarship.html
To provide financial assistance for undergraduate or graduate studies to Alaska Natives who are original enrollees to Cook Inlet Region, Inc. (CIRI) and their lineal descendants.
Title of Award: CIRI Foundation Semester Scholarships **Area, Field, or Subject:** General studies/Field of study not specified **Level of Education for which Award is Granted:** Graduate, Undergraduate **Number Awarded:** Varies each year; recently, 202 of these scholarships were awarded. **Funds Available:** The stipend is $2,000 per semester. **Duration:** 1 semester; recipients may reapply.
Eligibility Requirements: This program is open to Alaska Native enrollees to CIRI under the Alaska Native Claims Settlement Act (ANCSA) of 1971 and their lineal descendants. There are no Alaska residency requirements or age limitations. Applicants must be accepted or enrolled full time in a 2-year, 4-year, or graduate degree program. They must have a GPA of 2.5 or higher. Selection is based on academic achievement, rigor of course work or degree program, quality of a statement of purpose, student financial contribution, financial need, grade level, previous work performance, education and community activities, letters of recommendation, seriousness of purpose, and practicality of educational and professional goals. **Deadline for Receipt:** May or November of each year. **Additional Information:** Recipients must attend school on a full-time basis.

514 ■ COOK INLET REGION, INC.

Attn: CIRI Foundation
2600 Cordova Street, Suite 206
Anchorage, AK 99503
Tel: (907)263-5582
Free: 800-764-3382
Fax: (907)263-5588
E-mail: tcf@ciri.com
Web Site: http://www.thecirifoundation.org/scholarship.html
To provide financial assistance for professional preparation after high school to Alaska Natives who are original enrollees to the Cook Inlet Region, Inc. (CIRI) and their lineal descendants.
Title of Award: CIRI Foundation Vocational Training Grants **Area, Field, or Subject:** General studies/Field of study not specified **Level of Education for which Award is Granted:** Vocational/Occupational **Number Awarded:** Varies each year; recently, 12 of these grants were awarded. **Funds Available:** The maximum stipend is $3,000 per calendar year. **Duration:** 1 quarter; recipients may reapply.
Eligibility Requirements: This program is open to Alaska Native enrollees to CIRI under the Alaska Native Claims Settlement Act (ANCSA) of 1971 and their lineal descendants. Applicants should have a high school diploma or GED, have a GPA of 2.5 or higher, and be able to document the availability of employment upon completion of the training. They must be accepted or enrolled part or full time in a technical skills certificate or degree program, such as (but not limited to) craft/trade, automotive technology, office occupations, and computer technology. Alaska residency is not required. Selection is based on academic achievement, rigor of course work or degree program, quality of a statement of purpose, student financial contribution, financial need, grade level, previous work performance, education and community activities, letters of recommendation, seriousness of purpose, and practicality of educational and professional goals. **Deadline for Receipt:** March, June, September, or November of each year.

515 ■ COOK INLET REGION, INC.

Attn: CIRI Foundation
2600 Cordova Street, Suite 206
Anchorage, AK 99503

Tel: (907)263-5582
Free: 800-764-3382
Fax: (907)263-5588
E-mail: tcf@ciri.com
Web Site: http://www.thecirifoundation.org/scholarship.html
To provide financial assistance for undergraduate or graduate studies to Alaska Natives who are original enrollees to Cook Inlet Region, Inc. (CIRI) and their lineal descendants.
Title of Award: Howard Keck/Westmin Endowment Scholarship Fund **Area, Field, or Subject:** General studies/Field of study not specified **Level of Education for which Award is Granted:** Graduate, Undergraduate **Number Awarded:** Varies each year; recently, 3 of these scholarships (1 at $7,000 per year and 2 at $2,000 per semester) were awarded. **Funds Available:** The stipend is $9,000 per year, $7,000 per year, or $2,000 per semester, depending on GPA. **Duration:** 1 year (2 semesters).
Eligibility Requirements: This program is open to Alaska Native enrollees to CIRI under the Alaska Native Claims Settlement Act (ANCSA) of 1971 and their lineal descendants. There are no Alaska residency requirements or age limitations. Applicants must be accepted or enrolled full time in a 2-year undergraduate, 4-year undergraduate, or graduate degree program. They may be studying in any field but must have a GPA of 2.5 or higher. Selection is based on academic achievement, rigor of course work or degree program, quality of a statement of purpose, student financial contribution, financial need, grade level, previous work performance, education and community activities, letters of recommendation, seriousness of purpose, and practicality of educational and professional goals. **Deadline for Receipt:** May of each year. **Additional Information:** This fund was established in 1986. Recipients must attend school on a full-time basis.

516 ■ COOK INLET REGION, INC.

Attn: CIRI Foundation
2600 Cordova Street, Suite 206
Anchorage, AK 99503
Tel: (907)263-5582
Free: 800-764-3382
Fax: (907)263-5588
E-mail: tcf@ciri.com
Web Site: http://www.thecirifoundation.org/scholarship.html
To provide financial assistance for undergraduate or graduate studies to Alaska Natives who are original enrollees of the Kenai Natives Association (KNA) and their lineal descendants.
Title of Award: Kenai Natives Association Scholarship and Grant Fund **Area, Field, or Subject:** General studies/Field of study not specified **Level of Education for which Award is Granted:** Graduate, Undergraduate **Number Awarded:** Varies each year. **Funds Available:** The stipend is $1,000 per semester. **Duration:** 1 semester; recipients must reapply each semester.
Eligibility Requirements: This program is open to Alaska Native enrollees of KNA under the Alaska Native Claims Settlement Act (ANCSA) of 1971 and their lineal descendants. There are no Alaska residency requirements or age limitations. Applicants must be accepted or enrolled full time in a 2-year, 4-year, or graduate degree program or technical skills training program. They must have a GPA of 2.5 or higher. Selection is based on academic achievement, rigor of course work or degree program, quality of a statement of purpose, student financial contribution, financial need, grade level, previous work performance, education and community activities, letters of recommendation, seriousness of purpose, and practicality of educational and professional goals. **Deadline for Receipt:** Applications for scholarships (for academic study) must be submitted by May or November of each year. Applications for grants (for vocational or technical programs) are due by March, June, September, or November of each year. **Additional Information:** This program was established in 1989. Funds are provided by the KNA and the Tanaina Corporation with matching funds from the CIRI Foundation. Recipients must attend school on a full-time basis.

517 ■ COOK INLET REGION, INC.

Attn: CIRI Foundation
2600 Cordova Street, Suite 206
Anchorage, AK 99503
Tel: (907)263-5582

Free: 800-764-3382

Fax: (907)263-5588

E-mail: tcf@ciri.com

Web Site: http://www.thecirifoundation.org/scholarship.html

To provide financial assistance for professional preparation after high school to Alaska Natives who are original enrollees or descendants of the Ninilchik Native Association.

Title of Award: Ninilchik Native Association Scholarship and Vocational Grant **Area, Field, or Subject:** General studies/Field of study not specified **Level of Education for which Award is Granted:** Undergraduate **Number Awarded:** Varies each year; recently, 3 of these scholarships were awarded. **Funds Available:** The stipend is $1,000 per semester for the general scholarship or up to $2,000 per year for the vocational technical grant. Funds are to be used for tuition, university fees, books, required class supplies, and campus housing and meal plans for students who must live away from their permanent home to attend college. Checks are sent directly to the recipient's school. **Duration:** 1 semester for the general scholarship and 1 calendar year for the vocational technical grant; recipients may reapply.

Eligibility Requirements: This program is open to 1) Alaska Native enrollees of the Ninilchik Native Association under the Alaska Native Claims Settlement Act (ANCSA) of 1971 and 2) their lineal descendants. Proof of eligibility must be submitted. There is no residency requirement. Applicants for the scholarships must be accepted or enrolled full time in an accredited or otherwise approved postsecondary college or university; applicants for the grants may be enrolled either part or full time in a technical skills certificate or degree program such as (but not limited to) craft/trade, automotive technology, office occupations, and computer technology. All applicants should have a GPA of 2.5 or higher. Selection is based on academic achievement, rigor of course work or degree program, quality of a statement of purpose, student financial contribution, financial need, grade level, previous work performance, education and community activities, letters of recommendation, seriousness of purpose, and practicality of educational and professional goals. **Deadline for Receipt:** May or November of each year. **Additional Information:** This program was established in 1987. Recipients must attend school on a full-time basis.

518 ■ COOK INLET REGION, INC.

Attn: CIRI Foundation

2600 Cordova Street, Suite 206

Anchorage, AK 99503

Tel: (907)263-5582

Free: 800-764-3382

Fax: (907)263-5588

E-mail: tcf@ciri.com

Web Site: http://www.thecirifoundation.org/scholarship.html

To provide financial assistance for undergraduate study to Alaska Natives and their lineal descendants.

Title of Award: Howard Rock Foundation Undergraduate Scholarship Program **Area, Field, or Subject:** General studies/Field of study not specified **Level of Education for which Award is Granted:** Four Year College **Funds Available:** The stipend is $2,500 per year. Funds are to be used for tuition, university fees, books, course-required supplies, and (for students who must live away from their permanent home in order to attend college) room and board. Checks are made payable to the student and the university and are sent directly to the student's university. **Duration:** 1 year.

Eligibility Requirements: This program is open to Alaska Natives who are original enrollees or lineal descendants of a regional or village corporation under the Alaska Native Claims Settlement Act (ANCSA) of 1971 or a member of a tribal organization or other Native organization. The corporation or other Native organization with which the applicant is affiliated must be a current member of Alaska Village Initiatives, Inc. Applicants must have a GPA of 2.5 or higher and must be able to demonstrate financial need. They must be accepted or enrolled full time in a 4-year undergraduate program. Preference is given to third- and fourth-year students. **Deadline for Receipt:** March of each year. **Additional Information:** This program, established in 1986, is funded by Alaska Vil-

lage Initiatives, Inc. The CIRI Foundation assumed its administration in 1999. Recipients must attend school on a full-time basis.

519 ■ COOK INLET REGION, INC.

Attn: CIRI Foundation

2600 Cordova Street, Suite 206

Anchorage, AK 99503

Tel: (907)263-5582

Free: 800-764-3382

Fax: (907)263-5588

E-mail: tcf@ciri.com

Web Site: http://www.thecirifoundation.org/scholarship.html

To provide financial assistance for undergraduate or graduate studies to Alaska Natives who are original enrollees of the Salamatof Native Association, Inc. (SNAI) and their spouses and lineal descendants.

Title of Award: Salamatof Native Association, Inc. Scholarship Program **Area, Field, or Subject:** General studies/Field of study not specified **Level of Education for which Award is Granted:** Graduate, Undergraduate **Number Awarded:** 2 each year. **Funds Available:** The stipend is $2,000 per semester. Funds are to be used for tuition, required fees, books, campus-related room and board, and other direct school-related costs. **Duration:** 1 year; recipients must reapply each year.

Eligibility Requirements: This program is open to Alaska Native enrollees to SNAI under the Alaska Native Claims Settlement Act (ANCSA) of 1971 and their spouses and lineal descendants. There are no Alaska residency requirements or age limitations. Applicants must be accepted or enrolled full time in a 2-year, 4-year undergraduate, or graduate degree program. They must have a GPA of 2.5 or higher. Selection is based on academic achievement, rigor of course work or degree program, quality of a statement of purpose, student financial contribution, financial need, grade level, previous work performance, education and community activities, letters of recommendation, seriousness of purpose, and practicality of educational and professional goals. **Deadline for Receipt:** May of each year. **Additional Information:** This program was established in 1992 by the Salamatof Native Association, Inc. which provides funds matched by the CIRI Foundation. Recipients must attend school on a full-time basis.

520 ■ COOK INLET REGION, INC.

Attn: CIRI Foundation

2600 Cordova Street, Suite 206

Anchorage, AK 99503

Tel: (907)263-5582

Free: 800-764-3382

Fax: (907)263-5588

E-mail: tcf@ciri.com

Web Site: http://www.thecirifoundation.org/scholarship.html

To provide financial assistance for professional preparation after high school to Alaska Natives who are original enrollees of the Tyonek Native Corporation (TNC) and their lineal descendants.

Title of Award: Tyonek Native Corporation Scholarship and Grant Program **Area, Field, or Subject:** General studies/Field of study not specified **Level of Education for which Award is Granted:** Undergraduate **Number Awarded:** Varies each year; recently, 4 academic scholarships and 1 vocational training grant were awarded. **Funds Available:** The stipend is $1,000 per semester for academic scholarships or $1,500 per year for vocational training grants. **Duration:** 1 semester; recipients must reapply each semester.

Eligibility Requirements: This program is open to Alaska Native enrollees to TNC under the Alaska Native Claims Settlement Act (ANCSA) of 1971 and their lineal descendants as well as tribal members of the Native Village of Tyonek. Applicants must be accepted or enrolled full time in an accredited or otherwise approved postsecondary college, university, or technical skills education program. They must have a GPA of 2.0 or higher. Selection is based on academic achievement, rigor of course work or degree program, quality of a statement of purpose, student financial contribution, financial need, grade level, previous work performance, education and community activities, letters of recommendation, seriousness of purpose, and practicality of educational and professional goals. **Deadline for Receipt:** Applications for scholarships (for academic study) must be submitted by May or November of each year. Applications for grants (for vocational or technical programs) are due by March, June, September, or November of each year. **Additional Information:** This program was established in 1989. Funds are provided equally by the TNC and the CIRI Foundation. Recipients must attend school on a full-time basis.

521 ■ COOK INLET TRIBAL COUNCIL, INC.
Attn: Tribal Scholarships and Grants Program
2600 Cordova Street, Suite 206
Anchorage, AK 99503
Tel: (907)265-5904; 877-985-5900
Fax: (907)561-3755
E-mail: scholarships@citci.com
Web Site: http://www.thecirifoundation.org/scholarship.html
To provide financial assistance to Alaska Native shareholders of the Cook Inlet Region, Inc. (CIRI) and their descendants who are working on an undergraduate or graduate degree.
Title of Award: Cook Inlet Tribal Council Tribal Higher Education Program **Area, Field, or Subject:** General studies/Field of study not specified **Level of Education for which Award is Granted:** Graduate, Undergraduate **Number Awarded:** Varies each year, depending on the availability of funds. **Funds Available:** This program provides supplementary matching financial aid. Awards are intended to be applied to tuition, fees, course-required books and supplies, and on-campus housing and meal plans only. Total funding over a lifetime educational career is limited to $15,000. **Duration:** 1 year; may be renewed up to 4 additional years if the recipient maintains a GPA of 2.0 or higher.
Eligibility Requirements: This program is open to Alaska Native shareholders of CIRI and their descendants, regardless of residence, who are enrolled or planning to enroll full time at an accredited college, university, or vocational training facility. Applicants must be working on a certificate, associate, bachelor's, or graduate degree. Along with their application they must submit a letter of reference, a 200-word statement of purpose, their Certificate of Degree of Indian Blood (CDIB), a letter of acceptance from the school, transcripts, their Student Aid Report, a budget forecast, and (for males) documentation of Selective Service registration. Awards are presented on a first-come, first-served basis as long as funds are available. **Deadline for Receipt:** June or each year for fall, November of each year for spring. **Additional Information:** Students whose CDIB gives their village as Tyonek, Kenai, Ninilchik, Knik, or Salamatof must apply directly to their village organization.

522 ■ COOK INLET TRIBAL COUNCIL, INC.
Attn: Tribal Scholarships and Grants Program
2600 Cordova Street, Suite 206
Anchorage, AK 99503
Tel: (907)265-5904; 877-985-5900
Fax: (907)561-3755
E-mail: scholarships@citci.com
Web Site: http://www.thecirifoundation.org/scholarship.html
To provide financial assistance for vocational training to Native Americans who reside in the Cook Inlet Region of Alaska.
Title of Award: Cook Inlet Tribal Council Tribal Training Grant Program **Area, Field, or Subject:** General studies/Field of study not specified **Level of Education for which Award is Granted:** Undergraduate **Number Awarded:** Varies each year, depending on the availability of funds. **Funds Available:** The grant is $500. **Duration:** Each recipient is eligible for only 2 grants in a lifetime.
Eligibility Requirements: This program is open to Alaska Natives, American Indians, and Native Hawaiians residing within the Cook Inlet Region. Applicants must be enrolled or planning to enroll in a program of short-term certification or vocational training for job enhancement and/or employability. Along with their application they must submit a verification of residency, their Certificate of Degree of Indian Blood (CDIB) or proof of tribal enrollment, proof of income, a budget forecast, and (for males) documentation of Selective Service registration. Awards are presented on a first-come, first-served basis as long as funds are available. First-time applicants receive higher priority than repeat applicants. **Deadline for Receipt:** Applications may be submitted at any time.

523 ■ JACK KENT COOKE FOUNDATION
44115 Woodridge Parkway, Suite 200
Lansdowne, VA 20176-5199
Tel: (703)723-8000
Free: 800-846-9025

Fax: (703)723-8030
E-mail: jkc@jackkentcookefoundation.org
Web Site: http://www.jackkentcookefoundation.org
To provide financial assistance for college to family members of those directly affected by the events of September 11, 2001.
Title of Award: Jack Kent Cooke Foundation September 11 Scholarships **Area, Field, or Subject:** General studies/Field of study not specified **Level of Education for which Award is Granted:** Undergraduate **Number Awarded:** A total of $1 million was set aside for this program. Grants are awarded on a first-come, first-served basis until all funds have been disbursed. **Funds Available:** Grants up to $15,000 per semester are available to help cover tuition, required fees, books, room, board, and other educational costs. **Duration:** 1 semester. Recipients must reapply each school term.
Eligibility Requirements: This program is open to 1) dependents and spouses of people killed aboard United Airlines Flight 93, American Airlines Flight 77, American Airlines Flight 11, or United Airlines Flight 175; 2) dependents or spouses of people killed, missing, or permanently disabled at the Pentagon or World Trade Center on September 11, 2001; and 3) dependents and spouses of persons killed in the anthrax attacks of September and October of 2001. Applicants must be working on an undergraduate degree at a 2-year, 4-year, technical, or trade school in the United States. Along with their application, they must submit documentation of financial need and (if appropriate) verification of the disability of a parent or spouse. **Deadline for Receipt:** June of each year. **Additional Information:** This program was first offered in 2002. Recipients must attend school on a full-time basis.

524 ■ JACK KENT COOKE FOUNDATION
44115 Woodridge Parkway, Suite 200
Lansdowne, VA 20176-5199
Tel: (703)723-8000
Free: 800-498-6478
Fax: (703)723-8030
E-mail: jkc@jackkentcookefoundation.org
Web Site: http://www.jackkentcookefoundation.org
To provide financial assistance to students at 2-year colleges planning to transfer to a 4-year college or university in the United States or abroad.
Title of Award: Jack Kent Cooke Undergraduate Transfer Scholarships **Area, Field, or Subject:** General studies/Field of study not specified **Level of Education for which Award is Granted:** Four Year College **Number Awarded:** Approximately 25 each year. **Funds Available:** Stipends up to $30,000 per year are provided. Funds are paid directly to the institution. **Duration:** 1 year; may be renewed until completion of an undergraduate degree, as long as the fellow continues to meet the eligibility requirements.
Eligibility Requirements: This program is open to students who are currently enrolled as sophomores at accredited U.S. community or 2-year colleges (or who graduated from such a college within the past 5 years). Candidates must be interested in transferring to a full-time baccalaureate program at an accredited college or university in the United States or abroad. They must be nominated by their college and have a GPA of 3.5 or higher. Selection is based on academic ability and achievement, critical thinking ability, financial need, will to succeed, leadership and public service, and appreciation for and participation in the arts and humanities. appreciation for and participation in the arts and humanities. **Deadline for Receipt:** Campus faculty representatives must submit applications by January of each year. **Additional Information:** This program was first offered in 2002. Information is also available from the Jack Kent Cooke Undergraduate Transfer Scholarship Program, 301 ACT Drive, P.O. Box 4030, Iowa City, IA 52243, E-mail: jkc-u@act.org.

525 ■ COOPERATIVE BAPTIST FELLOWSHIP OF FLORIDA
Attn: Education Ministry Committee
P.O. Box 2556
Lakeland, FL 33806-2556
Tel: (863)682-6802
Fax: 888-241-CBFF
E-mail: office@floridacbf.org
Web Site: http://www.floridacbf.org/fl
To provide financial assistance for college to members of the Cooperative Baptist Fellowship (CBF) of Florida.
Title of Award: Cooperative Baptist Fellowship of Florida Scholarships **Area, Field, or Subject:** General studies/Field of study not specified;

Religion **Level of Education for which Award is Granted:** Undergraduate **Number Awarded:** 1 or more each year. **Funds Available:** A stipend is awarded (amount not specified). **Duration:** 1 year.

Eligibility Requirements: This program is open to CBF members in Florida, including both clergy and laity. Applicants must be proposing to participate in an official educational endeavor that will enhance their ministry. The activity may be overtly religious or secular as long as the recipient will use the education to enhance a ministry within the Baptist community of faith. Applications are accompanied by 2 brochures, entitled "You Grew Up In a Baptist Church but Do You Still Belong?" and "The Southern Baptist Convention & the Cooperative Baptist FellowshipWhy It Matters Where You Serve the Lord." Applicants must submit their reaction to those brochures. They must also demonstrate financial need. **Deadline for Receipt:** April of each year.

526 ■ COORS HISPANIC EMPLOYEE NETWORK

Attn: Grace Valdez
P.O. Box 1454
Golden, CO 80401
Tel: (303)277-5258
Fax: (303)277-5568
To provide financial assistance for college to high school seniors in Colorado who are of Hispanic descent.

Title of Award: CHEN Scholarship **Area, Field, or Subject:** General studies/Field of study not specified **Level of Education for which Award is Granted:** Undergraduate **Number Awarded:** 10 each year. **Funds Available:** The stipend is $1,000 per year. **Duration:** 1 year.

Eligibility Requirements: Applicants must be U.S. citizens, be Colorado residents, be of Hispanic heritage, be high school seniors, have a GPA of 2.5 or higher, and be planning to attend college after graduation. Selection is based on academic record, financial need, and educational plans. To apply, students must submit a signed application, a personal statement, a transcript, and 2 letters of recommendation. **Deadline for Receipt:** February of each year. **Additional Information:** This program was established in 1991.

527 ■ CORNHUSKER STATE GAMES

Trabert Hall
2202 South 11th Street
P.O. Box 82411
Lincoln, NE 68501
Tel: (402)471-2544
Free: 800-30-GAMES
Fax: (402)471-9712
E-mail: csg@cornhuskerstategames.com
Web Site: http://www.cornhuskerstategames.com
To provide financial assistance for college to athletes who participate in the Cornhusker State Games in Nebraska.

Title of Award: Gallup Organization/Cornhusker State Games Scholarship Program **Area, Field, or Subject:** General studies/Field of study not specified **Level of Education for which Award is Granted:** Undergraduate **Number Awarded:** 5 each year. **Funds Available:** The stipend is $1,000. **Duration:** 1 year.

Eligibility Requirements: This program is open to athletes who participate in the summer Cornhusker State Games. All residents of Nebraska are eligible to participate in the games if they have resided in Nebraska for at least 30 days prior to the competition and have amateur status in the sport in which they compete. High school athletes must abide by the rules of the Nebraska School Activities Association. College athletes must abide by national collegiate rules. Participants who are high school graduates (including members of the current graduating class) are eligible for these scholarships. Selection is based on academic honors (15 points), athletic achievements (15 points), other activities (10 points), and an essay of 200 words or less in which they outline their educational objectives (20 points), career goals (20 points), and what this scholarship means to them (20 points). **Deadline for Receipt:** June of each year. **Additional Information:** These scholarships are sponsored by The Gallup Organization. Recipients must attend a postsecondary educational institution in Nebraska.

528 ■ COUNCIL OF CITIZENS WITH LOW VISION INTERNATIONAL

c/o Pat Beattie, President
906 North Chambliss Street
Alexandria, VA 22312-3005

Tel: (703)578-6513
Free: 800-733-2258
Fax: (703)671-9053
E-mail: pbeattie@nib.org
Web Site: http://www.cclvi.org/scholarship.html
To provide financial assistance to undergraduate and graduate students with low vision.

Title of Award: Fred Scheigert Scholarships **Area, Field, or Subject:** General studies/Field of study not specified **Level of Education for which Award is Granted:** Graduate, Undergraduate **Number Awarded:** 2 each year. **Funds Available:** The stipend is $1,000. **Duration:** 1 year.

Eligibility Requirements: Applicants must be certified by an ophthalmologist as having low vision (acuity of 20/70 or worse in the better seeing eye with best correction or side vision with a maximum diameter of no greater than 30 degrees). They may be part-time or full-time entering freshmen, undergraduates, or graduate students. A cumulative GPA of at least 3.0 is required. **Deadline for Receipt:** April of each year. **Additional Information:** Information is also available from Imogene Johnson, 5311 "B" Street, Little Rock, AR 72205-3509.

529 ■ COURAGE CENTER

Attn: Vocational Services
3915 Golden Valley Road
Minneapolis, MN 55422
Tel: (763)520-0553; 888-8-INTAKE
Fax: (763)520-0392
E-mail: suep@courage.org
Web Site: http://www.courage.org
To provide financial assistance for college to Minnesota residents who have a disability.

Title of Award: Courage Center Scholarship for People with Disabilities **Area, Field, or Subject:** General studies/Field of study not specified **Level of Education for which Award is Granted:** Undergraduate **Number Awarded:** 1 or more each year. **Funds Available:** The stipend is $1,000. **Duration:** 1 year.

Eligibility Requirements: This program is open to U.S. citizens who are residents of Minnesota or have received Courage Center services. Applicants must have a sensory impairment or physical disability and a desire to gain technical expertise beyond high school. Along with their application, they must submit a concise essay that reflects their educational aspirations, career goals, and how a scholarship will help meet their needs. Selection is based on that essay, employment history, honors and awards, leadership experience, and financial need. Graduation ranking is not considered. **Deadline for Receipt:** May of each year.

530 ■ CYSTIC FIBROSIS FOUNDATION

Attn: President
6931 Arlington Road, Suite 200
Bethesda, MD 20814
Tel: (301)951-4422
Free: 800-FIGHT
Fax: (301)951-6378
Web Site: http://www.cysticfibrosis.com
To provide financial assistance to graduate students who have cystic fibrosis (CF).

Title of Award: Willard Bernbaum Scholarship **Area, Field, or Subject:** General studies/Field of study not specified **Level of Education for which Award is Granted:** Four Year College, Graduate **Number Awarded:** 1 or more each year. **Funds Available:** The stipend is $1,000. **Duration:** 1 year.

Eligibility Requirements: This program is open to graduate students who have CF. Applicants must submit a 1-page letter describing their educational program and financial need.

531 ■ CYSTIC FIBROSIS SCHOLARSHIP FOUNDATION

2814 Grant Street
Evanston, IL 60201
Tel: (847)328-0127
Fax: (847)328-0127
E-mail: MKBCFSF@aol.com
Web Site: http://www.cfscholarship.org
To provide financial assistance to undergraduate students who have cystic fibrosis.

Title of Award: Cystic Fibrosis Scholarships **Area, Field, or Subject:** General studies/Field of study not specified **Level of Education for**

which **Award is Granted:** Four Year College **Number Awarded:** Varies each year; recently, 49 of these scholarships were awarded. **Funds Available:** The stipend is $1,000. Funds are sent directly to the student's institution to be used for tuition, books, room, and board. **Duration:** 1 year; recipients may reapply.

Eligibility Requirements: This program is open to students enrolled or planning to enroll in college (either a 2-year or a 4-year program) or vocational school. Applicants must have cystic fibrosis. Selection is based on academic achievement, leadership, and financial need. **Deadline for Receipt:** March of each year. **Additional Information:** These scholarships were first awarded for 2002.

532 ■ CZECH CULTURAL CENTER

Attn: Scholarship Coordinator
4920 San Jacinto Street
Houston, TX 77004
Tel: (713)528-2060
Fax: (713)528-2017
E-mail: czech@czechcenter.org
Web Site: http://www.czechcenter.org
To provide financial assistance for college to students of Czech descent.

Title of Award: Mary Karele Milligan Scholarship **Area, Field, or Subject:** General studies/Field of study not specified **Level of Education for which Award is Granted:** Four Year College **Number Awarded:** 3 each year. **Funds Available:** The stipend is $1,000. **Duration:** 1 year.

Eligibility Requirements: This program is open to full-time undergraduate students currently enrolled at a 4-year college or university. Applicants must be born of Czech parentage (at least 1 parent), be able to identify and communicate with the Czech community, be U.S. citizens, and be able to demonstrate financial need. **Deadline for Receipt:** February of each year.

533 ■ DALLAS STARS FOUNDATION

2601 Avenue of the Stars
Frisco, TX 75034
Tel: (214)387-5526
Fax: (214)387-5610
E-mail: starscommunity@dallasstars.com
Web Site: http://www.dallasstars.com/community/education-scholarship.jsp
To provide financial assistance for college to high school seniors in Texas who have been active in athletics.

Title of Award: Bob Gainey Honorary Scholarship **Area, Field, or Subject:** General studies/Field of study not specified **Level of Education for which Award is Granted:** Undergraduate **Number Awarded:** 1 each year. **Funds Available:** The stipend is $1,250 per year. Funds are paid directly to the recipient's institution. **Duration:** 4 years, provided the recipient maintains full-time enrollment and a GPA of 3.0 or higher.

Eligibility Requirements: This program is open to seniors graduating from high schools in Texas who have been an active member of 1 or more of their school's athletic teams. Applicants must be planning to attend an accredited U.S. 2- or 4-year college or university as a full-time student. They must have a GPA of 3.0 or higher and an SAT score of 1000 or higher or an ACT score of 24 or higher. Along with their application, they must submit an essay, up to 500 words in length, on the qualities that distinguish them from other applicants and explaining their career plans and goals. Selection is based on academic achievement, community and extracurricular involvement, and financial need. U.S. citizenship is required. **Deadline for Receipt:** March of each year. **Additional Information:** The Dallas Stars, a National Hockey League team, established this program in 2004.

534 ■ DANISH SISTERHOOD OF AMERICA

Attn: Lizette Burtis, Scholarship Chair
3020 Santa Juanita Court
Santa Rosa, CA 95405-8219
Tel: (707)539-1884
E-mail: lburtis@sbcglobal.net
Web Site: http://www.danishsisterhood.org/rschol.asp
To provide financial assistance for educational purposes in the United States or Denmark to members or relatives of members of the Danish Sisterhood of America.

Title of Award: Betty Hansen National Scholarships **Area, Field, or Subject:** General studies/Field of study not specified **Level of Education**

for which **Award is Granted:** Four Year College, Graduate **Number Awarded:** Up to 8 each year. **Funds Available:** The stipend is $1,000. **Duration:** 1 year; nonrenewable.

Eligibility Requirements: This program is open to members or the family of members of the sisterhood who are interested in attending an accredited 4-year college or university as a full-time undergraduate or graduate student. Members must have belonged to the sisterhood for at least 1 year. Selection is based on academic excellence (at least a 2.5 GPA). Upon written request, the scholarship may be used for study in Denmark. **Deadline for Receipt:** February of each year.

535 ■ DATATEL SCHOLARS FOUNDATION

4375 Fair Lakes Court
Fairfax, VA 22033
Tel: (703)968-9000
Free: 800-486-4332
Fax: (703)968-4573
E-mail: scholars@datatel.com
Web Site: http://www.datatel.com
To provide financial assistance to graduating high school seniors, continuing college students, and graduate students who will be studying at a Datatel client school and are veterans, veterans' dependents, or refugees from southeast Asia.

Title of Award: Angelfire Scholarship **Area, Field, or Subject:** General studies/Field of study not specified **Level of Education for which Award is Granted:** Graduate, Undergraduate **Number Awarded:** Varies each year. Recently, 10 of these scholarships were awarded: 7 at $2,400, 2 at $1,600, and 1 at $1,000. **Funds Available:** Stipends are $2,400, $1,600, or $1,000, depending upon the cost of undergraduate tuition at the participating institution. Funds are paid directly to the institution. **Duration:** 1 year.

Eligibility Requirements: This program is open to 1) veterans who served in the Asian theater (Vietnam, Cambodia, or Laos) between 1964 and 1975; 2) their spouses and children; 3) refugees from Vietnam, Cambodia, or Laos; and 4) veterans who served in Operation Desert Storm, Operation Enduring Freedom, and/or Operation Iraqi Freedom. Applicants must attend a Datatel client college or university during the upcoming school year. They must first apply to their institution, which selects 2 semifinalists and forwards their applications to the sponsor. Along with they application, they must include a 1,000-word personal statement that discusses how the conflict has affected them personally, summarizes how the conflict has impacted their educational goals, and describes how being awarded this scholarship will help them achieve their goals. Selection is based on the quality of the personal statement (40%), academic merit (30%), achievements and civic involvement (20%), and 2 letters of recommendation (10%). **Deadline for Receipt:** Students must submit online applications to their institution or organization by January of each year. **Additional Information:** Datatel, Inc. produces advanced information technology solutions for higher education. It has more than 470 client sites in the United States and Canada. This scholarship was created to commemorate those who lost their lives in Vietnam or Iraq and is named after a memorial administered by the Disabled American Veterans Association in Angelfire, New Mexico.

536 ■ DATATEL SCHOLARS FOUNDATION

4375 Fair Lakes Court
Fairfax, VA 22033
Tel: (703)968-9000
Free: 800-486-4332
Fax: (703)968-4573
E-mail: scholars@datatel.com
Web Site: http://www.datatel.com
To provide financial assistance to undergraduate and graduate students returning to school who will be studying at a Datatel client institution.

Title of Award: Datatel Scholars Foundation Returning Student Scholarships **Area, Field, or Subject:** General studies/Field of study not specified **Level of Education for which Award is Granted:** Graduate, Undergraduate **Number Awarded:** 50 each year. **Funds Available:** The stipend is $1,500. Funds are paid directly to the institution. **Duration:** 1 year.

Eligibility Requirements: This program is open to undergraduate and graduate students who are returning to school after an absence of 5 years or longer. Applicants must attend a Datatel client college or university during the upcoming school year. They must first apply to their institution, which selects 1 semifinalist and forwards the application to the sponsor. Along with their application, they must include a 1,000-word personal statement that discusses the impact of being a returning student, the challenges of combining life interests (such as work and family) along with school, and the importance of receiving this scholarship to help achieve a dream. Selection is based on the quality of the personal statement (40%), academic merit (30%), achievements and civic involvement (20%), and 2 letters of recommendation (10%). **Deadline for Receipt:** Students must submit online applications to their institution or organization by January of each year. **Additional Information:** Datatel, Inc. produces advanced information technology solutions for higher education. It has more than 470 client sites in the United States and Canada.

537 ■ DATATEL SCHOLARS FOUNDATION

4375 Fair Lakes Court
Fairfax, VA 22033
Tel: (703)968-9000
Free: 800-486-4332
Fax: (703)968-4573
E-mail: scholars@datatel.com
Web Site: http://www.datatel.com
To provide financial assistance to graduating high school seniors, continuing college students, or graduate students who will be studying at a Datatel client school.
Title of Award: Datatel Scholars Foundation Scholarships **Area, Field, or Subject:** General studies/Field of study not specified **Level of Education for which Award is Granted:** Graduate, Undergraduate **Number Awarded:** Varies each year; recently, 225 of these scholarships (totaling $375,000) were awarded. **Funds Available:** Stipends are $2,400, $1,600, or $1,000, depending upon the cost of undergraduate tuition at the participating institution. Funds are paid directly to the institution. **Duration:** 1 year.
Eligibility Requirements: This program is open to undergraduate and graduate students who will attend a Datatel client college or university during the upcoming school year. Applicants must first apply to their institution, which selects 2 semifinalists and forwards their application to the sponsor. Along with their application, they must include a 1,000-word personal statement that summarizes their educational goals and objectives, where they have been as an individual, and where they hope their education will take them. Selection is based on the quality of the personal statement (40%), academic merit (30%), achievements and civic involvement (20%), and 2 letters of recommendation (10%). **Deadline for Receipt:** Students must submit online applications to their institution or organization by January of each year. **Additional Information:** Datatel, Inc. produces advanced information technology solutions for higher education. It has more than 470 client sites in the United States and Canada.

538 ■ DATATRAC INFORMATION SYSTEMS, INC.

Attn: Scholarship Committee
14120 Newbrook Drive, Suite 200
Chantilly, VA 20151
Tel: (703)817-9700
Fax: (703)817-9791
E-mail: b.blakney@datatrac-dc.com
Web Site: http://www.datatrac-dc.com
To provide financial assistance for college to high school seniors in the Washington, D.C. metropolitan area who plan to attend a 2-year college or trade school.
Title of Award: Folsom Scholarships **Area, Field, or Subject:** General studies/Field of study not specified **Level of Education for which Award is Granted:** Two Year College, Vocational/Occupational **Number Awarded:** 2 each year. **Funds Available:** The stipend is $5,000. **Duration:** 1 year.
Eligibility Requirements: This program is open to seniors graduating from high schools in the Washington, D.C. metropolitan area. Residents of Maryland and Virginia must be planning to attend a 2-year accredited institution, certification or licensure program, or trade school in their state of residency; residents of Washington D.C. may attend a similar institution in the area. Students planning to attend a 4-year college or university are not eligible. Applicants must submit brief essays on their financial need and their personal goals. **Deadline for Receipt:** April of each year.

539 ■ DAUGHTERS OF THE AMERICAN REVOLUTION-COLORADO STATE SOCIETY

c/o Marilyn Fishburn, State Scholarship Chair
1546 West 28th Street
Loveland, CO 80538
E-mail: admin@coloradodar.org
Web Site: http://www.coloradodar.org/scholarships.htm
To provide financial assistance to adults in Colorado who are interested in returning to college after an interruption.
Title of Award: Colorado State Society Adult Education Scholarship **Area, Field, or Subject:** General studies/Field of study not specified **Level of Education for which Award is Granted:** Undergraduate **Number Awarded:** 1 each year. **Funds Available:** The maximum stipend is $1,000. Funds are paid directly to the student's school. **Duration:** 1 year; nonrenewable.
Eligibility Requirements: Eligible to apply are Colorado residents who are interested in returning to college after an interruption; high school seniors are not eligible to apply. Applicants must be American citizens and accepted at an accredited Colorado college or university. They must submit a completed application, a statement of career interest and goals (up to 500 words), 2 character references, college transcripts, a letter of sponsorship from the Daughters of the American Revolution's Colorado chapter, and a list of scholastic achievements, extracurricular activities, honors, and other significant accomplishments. Selection is based on financial need and academic record. **Deadline for Receipt:** January of each year.

540 ■ DAUGHTERS OF THE AMERICAN REVOLUTION-NEW YORK STATE ORGANIZATION

c/o Layla Voll
311 West 21st Street
New York, NY 10011
E-mail: Layla_Voll@hotmail.com
Web Site: http://www.nydar.org/education/whitman.html
To provide financial assistance for college to Native American women in New York.
Title of Award: Olive Whitman Memorial Scholarship **Area, Field, or Subject:** General studies/Field of study not specified **Level of Education for which Award is Granted:** Four Year College **Number Awarded:** 1 each year. **Funds Available:** The stipend is $2,000. **Duration:** 1 year.
Eligibility Requirements: This program is open to women who are at least 50% Native American and graduating seniors at high schools in New York. Applicants must be planning to attend an accredited 4-year college or university in the state. **Deadline for Receipt:** January of each year.

541 ■ DAUGHTERS OF THE CINCINNATI

Attn: Scholarship Administrator
122 East 58th Street
New York, NY 10022
Tel: (212)319-6915
Web Site: http://fdncenter.org/grantmaker/cincinnati
To provide financial assistance for college to high school seniors who are the daughters of active-duty, deceased, or retired military officers.
Title of Award: Daughters of the Cincinnati Scholarship Program **Area, Field, or Subject:** General studies/Field of study not specified **Level of Education for which Award is Granted:** Undergraduate **Number Awarded:** Approximately 12 each year. **Funds Available:** Scholarship amounts vary but generally range from $1,000 to $3,000 per year. Funds are paid directly to the college of the student's choice. **Duration:** Scholarships are awarded annually and may be renewed up to 3 additional years while recipients are studying at an accredited college and are in good standing.
Eligibility Requirements: This program is open to high school seniors who are the daughters of career commissioned officers of the regular Army, Navy, Air Force, Coast Guard, or Marine Corps on active duty, deceased, or retired. Applicants must submit an official school transcript, SAT or ACT scores, a letter of recommendation, and documentation of financial need. **Deadline for Receipt:** March of each year. **Additional**

Information: Scholarships are tenable at the college of the recipient's choice. This program was originally established in 1906.

542 ■ DAUGHTERS OF PENELOPE

Attn: Daughters of Penelope Foundation, Inc.
1909 Q Street, N.W., Suite 500
Washington, DC 20009-1007
Tel: (202)234-9741
Fax: (202)483-6983
E-mail: daughters@ahepa.org
Web Site: http://www.ahepa.org/dop/foundation.html
To provide financial assistance for college to women of Greek descent.
Title of Award: Daughters of Penelope Past Grand President's Scholarship **Area, Field, or Subject:** General studies/Field of study not specified **Level of Education for which Award is Granted:** Undergraduate **Number Awarded:** 1 each year. **Funds Available:** The stipend is $1,500 per year. **Duration:** 1 year; nonrenewable.
Eligibility Requirements: This program is open to women who have been members of the Daughters of Penelope or the Maids of Athena for at least 2 years, or whose parents or grandparents have been members of the Daughters of Penelope or the Order of Ahepa for at least 2 years. Applicants must be 1) high school seniors or recent high school graduates applying to a college, university, or accredited technical school, or 2) current undergraduates at the college level. They must have taken the SAT or ACT (or Canadian, Greek, or Cypriot equivalent) and must write an essay (in English) about their educational and vocational goals. Selection is based on academic merit and financial need. **Deadline for Receipt:** May of each year. **Additional Information:** Information is also available from Helen Santire, National Scholarship Chair, P.O. Box 19709, Houston, TX 77242-9709, (713) 468-6531, E-mail: helensantire@duchesne.org.

543 ■ DAUGHTERS OF PENELOPE

Attn: Daughters of Penelope Foundation, Inc.
1909 Q Street, N.W., Suite 500
Washington, DC 20009-1007
Tel: (202)234-9741
Fax: (202)483-6983
E-mail: daughters@ahepa.org
Web Site: http://www.ahepa.org/dop/foundation.html
To provide financial assistance for college to women of Greek descent.
Title of Award: Daughters of Penelope Undergraduate Scholarships **Area, Field, or Subject:** General studies/Field of study not specified **Level of Education for which Award is Granted:** Undergraduate **Number Awarded:** Varies each year. Recently, 13 of these scholarships were awarded: 2 at $1,500 and 11 at $1,000. **Funds Available:** Stipends are $1,500 or $1,000 per year. **Duration:** 1 year; nonrenewable.
Eligibility Requirements: This program is open to women who have been members of the Daughters of Penelope or the Maids of Athena for at least 2 years, or whose parents or grandparents have been members of the Daughters of Penelope or the Order of Ahepa for at least 2 years. Applicants must be 1) high school seniors or recent high school graduates applying to a college, university, or accredited technical school, or 2) current undergraduates at the college level. They must have taken the SAT or ACT (or Canadian, Greek, or Cypriot equivalent) and must write an essay (in English) about their educational and vocational goals. Selection is based on academic merit only. **Deadline for Receipt:** May of each year. **Additional Information:** This program includes the following endowed awards: the Daughters of Penelope Past Grand Presidents' Memorial Scholarship, the Kottis Family Scholarship, the Mary M. Verges Scholarship, the Joanne V. Hologgitas, Ph.D. Scholarship, the Eos No. 1 Mother Lodge Chapter Scholarship, and the Paula J. Alexander Memorial Scholarship. Information is also available from Helen Santire, National Scholarship Chair, P.O. Box 19709, Houston, TX 77242-9709, (713) 468-6531, E-mail: helensantire@duchesne.org.

544 ■ DAUGHTERS OF PENELOPE

Attn: Daughters of Penelope Foundation, Inc.
1909 Q Street, N.W., Suite 500
Washington, DC 20009-1007
Tel: (202)234-9741
Fax: (202)483-6983
E-mail: daughters@ahepa.org
Web Site: http://www.ahepa.org/dop/foundation.html
To provide financial assistance for college to women of Greek descent.
Title of Award: Alexandra Apostolides Sonenfeld Scholarship **Area, Field, or Subject:** General studies/Field of study not specified **Level of Education for which Award is Granted:** Undergraduate **Number Awarded:** 1 each year. **Funds Available:** The stipend is $1,500 per year. **Duration:** 1 year; nonrenewable.
Eligibility Requirements: This program is open to women who have been members of the Daughters or Penelope or the Maids of Athena for at least 2 years, or whose parents or grandparents have been members of the Daughters of Penelope or the Order of Ahepa for at least 2 years. Applicants must be 1) high school seniors or recent high school graduates applying to a college, university, or accredited technical school, or 2) current undergraduates at the college level. They must have taken the SAT or ACT (or Canadian, Greek, or Cypriot equivalent) and must write an essay (in English) about their educational and vocational goals. Selection is based on academic merit and financial need. **Deadline for Receipt:** May of each year. **Additional Information:** Information is also available from Helen Santire, National Scholarship Chair, P.O. Box 19709, Houston, TX 77242-9709, (713) 468-6531, E-mail: helensantire@duchesne.org.

545 ■ DAUGHTERS OF PENELOPE-DISTRICT 2

c/o Bessie Adams
5155 Isla Key Boulevard, Number 206
St. Petersburg, FL 33715
Web Site: http://www.ahepad2.org/scholarships/daughtersScholarship.htm
To provide financial assistance for college or graduate school to women who are residents of Florida or the Bahamas and members of organizations affiliated with the American Hellenic Educational Progressive Association (AHEPA).
Title of Award: Daughters of Penelope Citrus District 2 Scholarships **Area, Field, or Subject:** General studies/Field of study not specified **Level of Education for which Award is Granted:** Graduate, Undergraduate **Number Awarded:** 2 each year. **Funds Available:** A stipend is awarded (amount not specified). **Duration:** 1 year; may be renewed.
Eligibility Requirements: This program is open to women who are residents of Citrus District 2 (Florida and the Bahamas) and high school seniors, undergraduates, or graduate students with a high school or college GPA of 3.0 or higher. Applicants must have been a member of the Maids of Athena for at least 2 years or have an immediate family member who has belonged to the Daughters of Penelope or Order of Ahepa for at least 2 years. They must submit a personal essay of 200 to 500 words to give the selection committee a sense of their goals and personal effort. Selection is based on merit. **Deadline for Receipt:** May of each year. **Additional Information:** This program includes the Past District Governors/Julie P. Microutsicos Scholarship.

546 ■ DECA

1908 Association Drive
Reston, VA 20191-1594
Tel: (703)860-5000
Fax: (703)860-4013
E-mail: decainc@aol.com
Web Site: http://www.deca.org/student.html
To provide financial assistance for college to DECA members who are also members of the National Technical Honors Society (NTHS) and interested in attending a career or technical school.
Title of Award: National Technical Honor Society Scholarships **Area, Field, or Subject:** General studies/Field of study not specified **Level of Education for which Award is Granted:** Vocational/Occupational **Number Awarded:** 2 each year. **Funds Available:** The stipend is $1,000. **Duration:** 1 year.
Eligibility Requirements: This program is open to high school seniors who are members of both DECA and NTHS. Applicants must be interested in continuing with career and technical education after graduating from high school. Along with their application, they must submit a 1-page essay on what technical education means to them and how being a member of DECA and NTHS has contributed to their school performance and future career plans. Selection is based on academic achievement, skill development, leadership, honesty, responsibility, good character, and involvement in DECA. **Deadline for Receipt:** March of each year. **Additional Information:** This program is sponsored by the NTHS.

547 ■ DEFENSE COMMISSARY AGENCY

Attn: SSP
1300 E Avenue
Fort Lee, VA 23801-1800
Tel: (804)734-8134
Fax: (804)734-8248
E-mail: info@militaryscholar.org
Web Site: http://www.militaryscholar.org
To provide financial assistance for college to the children of veterans and military personnel.

Title of Award: Scholarships for Military Children **Area, Field, or Subject:** General studies/Field of study not specified **Level of Education for which Award is Granted:** Undergraduate **Number Awarded:** 1 scholarship is allocated for each of the commissaries worldwide operated by the Defense Commissary Agency (DeCA). **Funds Available:** The stipend is $1,500. **Duration:** 1 year; recipients must reapply.

Eligibility Requirements: This program is open to sons and daughters of U.S. military ID card holders, including active duty, retirees, Guard/Reserves and survivors of deceased members, who are enrolled or accepted for enrollment at a college or university. The eligibility of applicants, including survivors of deceased members, is based on the DoD ID Card Directive, which provides for eligibility up to 21 years of age or 23 if still enrolled as a full-time student. Applicants must have a GPA of 3.0 or higher and write a short essay on "What Being a Military Dependent Means to Me." Selection is based on merit. **Deadline for Receipt:** February of each year. **Additional Information:** This program, established in 2001, is supported by the Fisher House Foundation. Recipients must enroll as a full-time undergraduate student.

548 ■ DEGREE OF HONOR FOUNDATION

400 Robert Street North, Suite 1600
St. Paul, MN 55101-2029
Tel: (651)228-7600
Free: 800-947-5812
Fax: (651)224-7446
Web Site: http://www.degreeofhonor.com/pages/Scholar.html
To provide financial assistance to high school senior members of Degree of Honor who wish to attend college.

Title of Award: Degree of Honor Higher Education Scholarships **Area, Field, or Subject:** General studies/Field of study not specified **Level of Education for which Award is Granted:** Undergraduate **Number Awarded:** Varies each year; recently, 13 students received these scholarships, including 3 who received Teens with a Heart Scholarships. **Funds Available:** The stipend is $1,000. Recipients of Teens With a Heart Scholarships are awarded an additional $500 scholarship.

Eligibility Requirements: This program is open to graduating high school seniors who have been insured with Degree of Honor for at least 2 years and have a GPA of 2.75 or higher. Additional funding is provided to students who have also completed the Fraternal Heart (or "Teens With a Heart") Program. Applicants must submit an affirmation of their acceptance of Christian beliefs and other Degree of Honor principles; information on their Degree of Honor and other community service activities; a statement of what they enjoy most about their volunteer involvement; a list of hobbies, talents, or interests; an essay on their anticipated areas of study and career goals; and a description of their leadership qualities and positions held. **Deadline for Receipt:** March of each year. **Additional Information:** This program began in 1959. Degree of Honor is a fraternal insurance society licensed to operate in 23 states: Arkansas, Arizona, California, Colorado, Illinois, Indiana, Iowa, Michigan, Minnesota, Missouri, Montana, Nebraska, North Dakota, Ohio, Oklahoma, Oregon, Pennsylvania, South Dakota, Tennessee, Texas, Washington, West Virginia, and Wisconsin.

549 ■ DELAWARE HIGHER EDUCATION COMMISSION

Carvel State Office Building
820 North French Street
Wilmington, DE 19801
Tel: (302)577-3240
Free: 800-292-7935
Fax: (302)577-6765
E-mail: dhec@doe.k12.de.us
Web Site: http://www.doe.state.de.us/high-ed/agenda.htm
To provide financial assistance for undergraduate education to women in Delaware.

Title of Award: Agenda for Delaware Women Trailblazer Scholarships **Area, Field, or Subject:** General studies/Field of study not specified **Level of Education for which Award is Granted:** Undergraduate **Number Awarded:** 1 or more each year. **Funds Available:** The stipend is $2,500 per year. **Duration:** 1 year; may be renewed.

Eligibility Requirements: This program is open to women who are Delaware residents planning to enroll in a public or private nonprofit college in Delaware as an undergraduate student in the coming year. Applicants must have a cumulative GPA of 2.5 or higher. Selection is based on financial need (50%) and community and school activities, vision, participation, and leadership (50%). **Deadline for Receipt:** April of each year.

550 ■ DELAWARE HIGHER EDUCATION COMMISSION

Carvel State Office Building
820 North French Street
Wilmington, DE 19801
Tel: (302)577-3240
Free: 800-292-7935
Fax: (302)577-6765
E-mail: dhec@doe.k12.de.us
Web Site: http://www.doe.state.de.us/high-ed/vets.htm
To provide financial assistance for undergraduate education to dependents of deceased Delaware veterans and state police officers and members of the armed forces declared prisoners of war or missing in action.

Title of Award: Delaware Educational Benefits for Children of Deceased Veterans and Others **Area, Field, or Subject:** General studies/Field of study not specified **Level of Education for which Award is Granted:** Undergraduate **Number Awarded:** Varies each year. **Funds Available:** Eligible students receive full tuition at any state-supported institution in Delaware or, if the desired educational program is not available at a state-supported school, at any private institution in Delaware. If the desired educational program is not offered at either a public or private institution in Delaware, this program pays the full cost of tuition at the out-of-state school the recipient attends. Students who wish to attend a private or out-of-state school even though their program is offered at a Delaware public institution receive the equivalent of the average tuition and fees at the state school, currently set at $525 per year. **Duration:** 1 year; may be renewed for 3 additional years.

Eligibility Requirements: Applicants for this assistance must have been Delaware residents for 3 years and be the children, between 16 and 24 years of age, of members of the armed forces who were Delaware residents when they entered the services and who 1) were killed while on active duty; 2) died from disease, wounds, injuries, or disabilities suffered as a result of active service; or 3) have been declared prisoners of war or missing in action. Also eligible are children of Delaware State Police Officers who were killed in the line of duty or died as a result of disease, wounds, or disabilities incurred in the pursuit of official duties. Financial need must be demonstrated. U.S. citizenship or permanent resident status is required. **Deadline for Receipt:** Applications may be submitted at any time but at least 4 weeks before the beginning of classes.

551 ■ DELAWARE HIGHER EDUCATION COMMISSION

Carvel State Office Building
820 North French Street
Wilmington, DE 19801
Tel: (302)577-3240
Free: 800-292-7935
Fax: (302)577-6765
E-mail: dhec@doe.k12.de.us
Web Site: http://www.doe.state.de.us/high-ed/workforce.htm
To provide financial assistance for part-time education to Delaware working adults with financial need.

Title of Award: Delaware Governor's Workforce Development Grants **Area, Field, or Subject:** General studies/Field of study not specified **Level of Education for which Award is Granted:** Undergraduate **Number Awarded:** Varies each year. **Funds Available:** Awards up to $2,000 per year are available. **Duration:** 1 year; renewable.

Eligibility Requirements: This program is open to residents of Delaware and individuals employed in Delaware who are 18 years of age and older.

Applicants must be 1) employed on a part-time basis only by 1 or more employers; 2) employed by a small business (with 100 or fewer employees); 3) employed temporarily or by a temporary staffing agency; or 4) self-employed. Employers must contribute to the Blue Collar Training Fund Program. Applicants must be able to demonstrate financial need and part-time enrollment in a participating Delaware college or training program. Full-time students and students who receive any other federal or state educational grants are not eligible. **Deadline for Receipt:** Applications may be submitted at any time, but they must be received by the end of the drop/add date at the participating college. **Additional Information:** Current income limitations are $32,417 per year for a family of 1, rising to $91,260 for a family of 8.

552 ■ DELAWARE HIGHER EDUCATION COMMISSION

Carvel State Office Building
820 North French Street
Wilmington, DE 19801
Tel: (302)577-3240
Free: 800-292-7935
Fax: (302)577-6765
E-mail: dhec@doe.k12.de.us
Web Site: http://www.doe.state.de.us/high-ed/crosscountry.htm
To provide financial assistance for college to high school seniors in Delaware who participate in cross country racing.
Title of Award: Delaware Open Cross Country Championship Scholarships **Area, Field, or Subject:** General studies/Field of study not specified **Level of Education for which Award is Granted:** Undergraduate **Number Awarded:** 2 each year: 1 is set aside for a female and 1 for a male. **Funds Available:** The stipend is $1,000 per year. **Duration:** 1 year; nonrenewable.
Eligibility Requirements: This program is open to seniors who are Delaware residents at high schools in the state that are members of the New Castle County Cross Country and Track Coaches Association (N5CTA) and have participated in cross country programs during their junior and senior years. Each member may nominate 1 male and 1 female student. Nominees must have a cumulative GPA of 2.5 or higher and be planning to enroll full time in a 2- or 4-year program of study at an accredited college or university. Preference is given to students selected as All State, All County, and/or All Catholic. Selection is based on financial need (50%), GPA (25%), SAT scores (15%), and leadership or community activities (10%). **Deadline for Receipt:** October of each year.

553 ■ DELAWARE HIGHER EDUCATION COMMISSION

Carvel State Office Building
820 North French Street
Wilmington, DE 19801
Tel: (302)577-3240
Free: 800-292-7935
Fax: (302)577-6765
E-mail: dhec@doe.k12.de.us
Web Site: http://www.doe.state.de.us/high-ed/scip.htm
To provide financial assistance for undergraduate or graduate study to Delaware residents with financial need.
Title of Award: Delaware Scholarship Incentive Program **Area, Field, or Subject:** General studies/Field of study not specified **Level of Education for which Award is Granted:** Graduate, Undergraduate **Number Awarded:** Approximately 1,500 each year. **Funds Available:** The amount awarded depends on the need of the recipient but does not exceed the cost of tuition, fees, and books. Currently, the maximum for undergraduates ranges from $700 to $2,200 per year, depending on GPA; the maximum for graduate students is $1,000 per year. **Duration:** 1 year; renewable.
Eligibility Requirements: This program is open to Delaware residents who are 1) enrolled full time in an undergraduate degree program at a Delaware or Pennsylvania college or university, or 2) enrolled full time in a graduate degree program at an accredited out-of-state institution or at a private institution in Delaware if their major is not offered at the University of Delaware or Delaware State University. All applicants must be able to

demonstrate financial need and have a GPA of 2.5 or higher. U.S. citizenship or permanent resident status is required. **Deadline for Receipt:** April of each year.

554 ■ DELAWARE HIGHER EDUCATION COMMISSION

Carvel State Office Building
820 North French Street
Wilmington, DE 19801
Tel: (302)577-3240
Free: 800-292-7935
Fax: (302)577-6765
E-mail: dhec@doe.k12.de.us
Web Site: http://www.doe.state.de.us/high-ed/diamond.htm
To provide financial assistance for college to Delaware high school seniors with outstanding academic records.
Title of Award: Diamond State Scholarships **Area, Field, or Subject:** General studies/Field of study not specified **Level of Education for which Award is Granted:** Undergraduate **Number Awarded:** Approximately 50 each year. **Funds Available:** Awards up to $1,250 per year are available. **Duration:** 1 year; may be renewed up to 3 additional years.
Eligibility Requirements: This program is open to graduating high school seniors who are Delaware residents with a combined score of 1800 on the SAT and who rank in the upper quarter of their class. Applicants must be planning to enroll in an accredited college or university on a full-time basis. U.S. citizenship or permanent resident status is required. **Deadline for Receipt:** March of each year.

555 ■ DELAWARE HIGHER EDUCATION COMMISSION

Carvel State Office Building
820 North French Street
Wilmington, DE 19801
Tel: (302)577-3240
Free: 800-292-7935
Fax: (302)577-6765
E-mail: dhec@doe.k12.de.us
Web Site: http://www.doe.state.de.us/high-ed/firststatemanufactured.htm
To provide financial assistance for college to Delaware residents who live in a manufactured home.
Title of Award: First State Manufactured Housing Association Scholarship **Area, Field, or Subject:** General studies/Field of study not specified **Level of Education for which Award is Granted:** Undergraduate **Number Awarded:** 1 or more each year. **Funds Available:** The maximum stipend is $4,000 per year. **Duration:** 1 year.
Eligibility Requirements: This program is open to Delaware residents who have lived in a manufactured home for at least 1 year. Applicants may be planning to pursue any type of accredited training, licensing, or certification program or any accredited degree program. Selection is based on academic record, an essay, recommendations, and financial need. **Deadline for Receipt:** March of each year.

556 ■ DELAWARE HIGHER EDUCATION COMMISSION

Carvel State Office Building
820 North French Street
Wilmington, DE 19801
Tel: (302)577-3240
Free: 800-292-7935
Fax: (302)577-6765
E-mail: dhec@doe.k12.de.us
Web Site: http://www.doe.state.de.us/high-ed/portofwilmington.htm
To provide financial assistance to high school seniors and college students in Delaware whose family includes an employee of a company at the Port of Wilmington.
Title of Award: Port of Wilmington Maritime Society Scholarship **Area, Field, or Subject:** General studies/Field of study not specified **Level of Education for which Award is Granted:** Undergraduate **Funds Available:** The stipend is $2,500. **Duration:** 1 year; recipients may reapply.
Eligibility Requirements: This program is open to high school seniors and continuing/returning college students whose parent, grandparent, or legal guardian is employed by a company at the Port of Wilmington that has contributed at least $500 to the program. Applicants must be enrolled or planning to enroll at an accredited 2-year or 4-year college or university. Along with their application, they must submit an essay on 1 of

the following topics: 1) an opinion that they had to defend and the importance of that challenge; 2) a personal experience, achievement, or risk and its significance in their life; or 3) a book that strongly influenced them. Selection is based on financial need, academic performance, community or school involvement, and leadership ability. **Deadline for Receipt:** April of each year. **Additional Information:** This program is sponsored by the Port of Wilmington, 1 Hausel Road, Wilmington, DE 19801-5852, (302) 472-PORT, Fax: (302) 472-7740.

557 ■ DELAWARE STATE FEDERATION OF WOMEN'S CLUBS

9 East Loockerman, Suite 314
Dover, DE 19901
E-mail: sharronshulder@dsfwc.org
Web Site: http://
To provide financial assistance for college to high school seniors in Delaware.
Title of Award: Delaware State Federation of Women's Clubs Scholarship **Area, Field, or Subject:** General studies/Field of study not specified **Level of Education for which Award is Granted:** Undergraduate **Number Awarded:** 1 or more each year. **Funds Available:** The maximum stipend is $1,500. **Duration:** 1 year.
Eligibility Requirements: This program is open to high school seniors in Delaware. Applicants must submit a 150-word statement on what they intend to study in college and why, an official high school transcript, recommendations from their school counselor and clergyman, and a letter of sponsorship from the Delaware State Federation of Women's Clubs (local president). Selection is based on career interests, extracurricular activities, work experience, academic record, and financial need. **Deadline for Receipt:** March of each year. **Additional Information:** Information is also available from Joan Wood, Custodian of Student Funds, 184 Hopewell Drive, Clayton, DE 19938, (302) 659-3044.

558 ■ DELAWARE STATE GOLF ASSOCIATION

Attn: DSGA Scholarship Fund, Inc.
7234 Lancaster Pike, Suite 302-B
Hockessin, DE 19707
Tel: (302)234-3365
Fax: (302)234-3359
E-mail: dsga@usga.org
Web Site: http://www.dsga.org/Scholarship.htm
To provide financial assistance for college to residents of Delaware who have been active in golf.
Title of Award: Delaware State Golf Association Scholarships **Area, Field, or Subject:** General studies/Field of study not specified **Level of Education for which Award is Granted:** Undergraduate **Number Awarded:** Varies each year. Recently, the association awarded 6 4-year scholarships (1 at $4,000, 1 at $2,500, 2 at $2,000, and 2 at $1,000) and 4 1-year scholarships (each at $1,000). **Funds Available:** Stipends range from $1,000 to $4,000 per year for 4 years or $1,000 for 1 year. **Duration:** 1 year or 4 years.
Eligibility Requirements: This program is open to high school seniors and current college students in Delaware who have been active in golf. Applicants must submit an essay on why they desire this scholarship (including career plans), 2 letters of reference, transcripts, information on financial need, a list of golf accomplishments, and a list of extracurricular activities. **Deadline for Receipt:** March of each year. **Additional Information:** Information is also available directly from the Delaware State Golf Association Scholarship Fund, 240 West Side Drive, Rehoboth Beach, DE 19971.

559 ■ MICHAEL & SUSAN DELL FOUNDATION

Attn: Scholarships
c/o Weber Shandwick
6555 Sierra Drive
Irving, TX 75039
Tel: (972)830-2526
E-mail: tdonalson@webershandwick.com
Web Site: http://www.dellscholars.org
To provide financial assistance for college to high school seniors who have participated in a college readiness program sponsored by the Michael & Susan Dell Foundation (MSDF).
Title of Award: Dell Scholars Program **Area, Field, or Subject:** General studies/Field of study not specified **Level of Education for which Award**

is Granted: Undergraduate **Number Awarded:** 160 each year. **Funds Available:** The stipend is $5,000 per year. Funds may be used for tuition, fees, books, and on-campus room and board. With approval of the sponsor, they may also be used for approved internships and study abroad programs. **Duration:** 4 years.
Eligibility Requirements: This program is open to graduating high school seniors who have participated in an MSDF approved college readiness program for at least 2 years. Applicants must have a GPA of 2.4 or higher and be able to demonstrate financial need. They must be planning to enroll at an accredited 2-year or 4-year college or university in the following fall to work on a bachelor's degree. Selection is based on individual determination to succeed, future goals and plans to achieve them, ability to communicate the hardships they have overcome or currently face, self-motivation in completing challenging course work, and financial need. U.S. citizenship or permanent resident status is required. **Deadline for Receipt:** January of each year. **Additional Information:** This program, established in 2004, is administered by ACT Recognition Program Services, 500 ACT Drive, P.O. Box 168, Iowa City, IA 52243-0168, (319) 341-2363.

560 ■ DELTA SIGMA THETA SORORITY, INC.-BOSTON ALUMNAE CHAPTER

Attn: Scholarship Committee
P.O. Box 51424
Boston, MA 02205
Web Site: http://www.geocities.com/bostonalumnaechapter/index.html
To provide financial assistance to high school seniors in Massachusetts interested in attending a 4-year college or university.
Title of Award: Boston Alumnae Chapter Scholarships **Area, Field, or Subject:** General studies/Field of study not specified **Level of Education for which Award is Granted:** Four Year College **Number Awarded:** 1 or more each year. **Funds Available:** A stipend is awarded (amount not specified). **Duration:** 1 year.
Eligibility Requirements: This program is open to seniors graduating from high schools in Massachusetts. Applicants must be planning to attend a 4-year college or university. They must be able to demonstrate academic achievement and commitment to community service. Along with their application, they must submit a 500-word essay on the following topic: "What skills do you think you will need to be competitive in the 21st century and why? What are you doing now to prepare yourself?" Financial need is not considered in the selection process. **Deadline for Receipt:** April of each year. **Additional Information:** The sponsor is the local alumnae chapter of a traditionally African American social sorority. Information is also available from Keitha B. Hassell, (617) 427-6417, or from Sandra Malloy-Blake, (617) 633-5004.

561 ■ DELTA SIGMA THETA SORORITY, INC.-MINNEAPOLIS/ST. PAUL ALUMNAE CHAPTER

Attn: Scholarship Chair
P.O. Box 580709
Minneapolis, MN 55458-0709
Tel: (612)259-1472
E-mail: info@dstmsp.org
Web Site: http://www.dstmsp.org/new/Scholarship.htm
To provide financial assistance for college to African American high school seniors from Minnesota.
Title of Award: Vernetta Wilson Memorial Scholarship **Area, Field, or Subject:** General studies/Field of study not specified **Level of Education for which Award is Granted:** Four Year College **Number Awarded:** 1 or more each year. **Funds Available:** Stipends range from $500 to $1,500. **Duration:** 1 year.
Eligibility Requirements: This program is open to African American residents of Minnesota who are high school graduating seniors. Applicants must have been accepted at a 4-year college or university as a full-time student. They must 1) have a GPA of 2.7 or higher; 2) be able to demonstrate financial need; 3) have actively volunteered in community service activities; and 4) be able to demonstrate leadership skills.

Deadline for Receipt: March of each year. **Additional Information:** Information is also available from Kimberly Purifoy, (763) 559-9844, E-mail: kpurifoy16@yahoo.com.

562 ▪ DELTA SIGMA THETA SORORITY, INC.-PROVIDENCE ALUMNAE CHAPTER

Attn: Financial Awards Review Committee
P.O. Box 40175
Providence, RI 02904-0175
Web Site: http://www.dstprovidencealumnae.com
To provide financial assistance for college to African American high school seniors from Rhode Island.
Title of Award: Providence Alumnae Chapter General Awards **Area, Field, or Subject:** General studies/Field of study not specified **Level of Education for which Award is Granted:** Undergraduate **Number Awarded:** 1 or more each year. **Funds Available:** A stipend is awarded (amount not specified). **Duration:** 1 year.
Eligibility Requirements: This program is open to college-bound African American seniors graduating from high schools in Rhode Island. Applicants must submit a current official transcript, letter of recommendation, documentation of financial need, and an essay describing their career goals, community service activities, educational accomplishments, and personal interests and talents. **Deadline for Receipt:** February of each year.

563 ▪ DELTA SIGMA THETA SORORITY, INC.-WASHINGTON DC ALUMNAE CHAPTER

Attn: Scholarship Committee
P.O. Box 90202
Washington, DC 20090-0202
Web Site: http://www.wdcac.org
To provide financial assistance for college to high school seniors in Washington, D.C.
Title of Award: Washington Alumnae Chapter Scholarships **Area, Field, or Subject:** General studies/Field of study not specified **Level of Education for which Award is Granted:** Undergraduate **Number Awarded:** 1 or more each year. **Funds Available:** A stipend is awarded (amount not specified). **Duration:** 1 year.
Eligibility Requirements: This program is open to seniors graduating from public and private high schools in Washington, D.C. Applicants must submit an official high school transcript, a copy of their SAT or ACT scores, documentation of financial need, 2 letters of recommendation, and a 1-page autobiographical essay including their academic and career goals, public service involvement, why the scholarship is important, and its expected benefit. **Deadline for Receipt:** March of each year. **Additional Information:** The sponsor is the local alumnae chapter of a traditionally African American social sorority. Information is also available from Norma Bullock, (301) 350-0684, E-mail: nbullock68@aol.com or from Phyllis Goodman, (202) 526-7057, E-mail: phylgoo@aol.com.

564 ▪ DELTA ZETA SORORITY

Attn: Foundation Coordinator
202 East Church Street
Oxford, OH 45056
Tel: (513)523-7597
E-mail: DZFoundation@dzshq.com
Web Site: http://www.deltazeta.org/pages/content/scholarships.html
To provide financial assistance for continued undergraduate study to members of Delta Zeta Sorority.
Title of Award: Lavonne Heghinian Scholarship **Area, Field, or Subject:** General studies/Field of study not specified **Level of Education for which Award is Granted:** Undergraduate **Number Awarded:** 1 each year. **Funds Available:** The stipend ranges from $900 to $1,100, depending on the availability of funds. **Duration:** 1 year; nonrenewable.
Eligibility Requirements: This program is open to members of the sorority who have a GPA of 3.0 or higher. Applicants must submit an official transcript, a statement of their career goals, information on their service to the sorority, documentation of campus activities and/or community involvement, and a list of academic honors. Financial need is also

considered in the selection process. Preference is given to applicants from southern California. **Deadline for Receipt:** February of each year.

565 ▪ DELTA ZETA SORORITY

Attn: Foundation Coordinator
202 East Church Street
Oxford, OH 45056
Tel: (513)523-7597
E-mail: DZFoundation@dzshq.com
Web Site: http://www.deltazeta.org/pages/content/scholarships.html
To provide financial assistance for continued undergraduate study to members of Delta Zeta Sorority.
Title of Award: Geneva Thornberg Undergraduate Scholarship **Area, Field, or Subject:** General studies/Field of study not specified **Level of Education for which Award is Granted:** Undergraduate **Number Awarded:** 1 each year. **Funds Available:** The stipend ranges from $900 to $1,100, depending on the availability of funds. **Duration:** 1 year; nonrenewable.
Eligibility Requirements: This program is open to members of the sorority who have a GPA of 3.0 or higher. Applicants must submit an official transcript, a statement of their career goals, information on their service to the sorority, documentation of campus activities and/or community involvement, and a list of academic honors. Financial need is also considered in the selection process. **Deadline for Receipt:** February of each year.

566 ▪ DENVER FOUNDATION

Attn: Scholarships and Special Projects
950 South Cherry Street, Suite 200
Denver, CO 80246
Tel: (303)300-1790
Fax: (303)300-6547
E-mail: kbellina@denverfoundation.org
Web Site: http://www.denverfoundation.org
To provide financial assistance to undergraduate and graduate students working on a degree in a transportation, logistics, or supply chain program.
Title of Award: Terry L. Priest Educational Scholarships **Area, Field, or Subject:** Logistics; Transportation **Level of Education for which Award is Granted:** Four Year College, Graduate **Number Awarded:** 1 or more each year. **Funds Available:** Stipend amounts vary each year. **Duration:** 1 year.
Eligibility Requirements: This program is open to undergraduate and graduate students in transportation, logistics, and supply chain programs at accredited 4-year colleges and universities. Applicants must have a cumulative GPA of 3.0 or higher and be able to demonstrate financial need. They must submit a 2-page personal statement on why they chose to work on a degree in their field, their short- and long-term career goals, and their involvement in the transportation/logistics/supply chain profession or the community in general through clubs, activities, or employment. **Deadline for Receipt:** March of each year.

567 ▪ DENVER FOUNDATION

Attn: Scholarships and Special Projects
950 South Cherry Street, Suite 200
Denver, CO 80246
Tel: (303)300-1790
Fax: (303)300-6547
E-mail: kbellina@denverfoundation.org
Web Site: http://www.denverfoundation.org
To provide financial assistance for college to high school seniors from Colorado who can demonstrate exceptional levels of achievement.
Title of Award: RBC Dain Rauscher Colorado Scholarships **Area, Field, or Subject:** General studies/Field of study not specified **Level of Education for which Award is Granted:** Undergraduate **Number Awarded:** 10 or more each year. **Funds Available:** Stipends are at least $3,000. **Duration:** 1 year.
Eligibility Requirements: This program is open to seniors graduating from high schools in Colorado who can demonstrate exceptional levels of achievement in such areas as arts, athletics, community service, leadership, or academics. Applicants must have a GPA of 3.75 or higher, a rank in the top 5% of their class, or an SAT score of 1200 or higher or an ACT score of 26. They must have received an acceptance letter from an ac-

credited college, university, or technical school. Selection is based on academic excellence, leadership in school and community, personal achievements, significant challenges that have been overcome, and financial need. A personal interview may be required. **Deadline for Receipt:** March of each year. **Additional Information:** This program is sponsored by the securities firm RBC Dain Rauscher.

568 ■ DEPARTMENT OF EDUCATION
Office of Special Education and Rehabilitative Services
Attn: Rehabilitation Services Administration
400 Maryland Avenue, S.W.,
Washington, DC 20202-2800
Tel: (202)245-7488
Web Site: http://www.ed.gov/about/offices/list/osers/rsa/index.html
To provide financial assistance to individuals with disabilities for undergraduate or graduate study pursued as part of their program of vocational rehabilitation.
Title of Award: State Vocational Rehabilitation Services Program **Area, Field, or Subject:** General studies/Field of study not specified **Level of Education for which Award is Granted:** Graduate, Undergraduate **Number Awarded:** Varies each year. Recently, more than 1.2 million people (of whom more than 80% have significant disabilities) were participating in this program. **Funds Available:** Funding for this program is provided by the federal government through grants to state vocational rehabilitation agencies. Grants under the basic support program currently total nearly $2.7 billion per year. States must supplement federal funding with matching funds of 21.3%. Persons who are accepted for vocational rehabilitation by the appropriate state agency receive financial assistance based on the cost of their education and other funds available to them, including their own or family contribution and other sources of financial aid. Allowable costs in most states include tuition, fees, books, supplies, room, board, transportation, personal expenses, child care, and expenses related to disability (special equipment, readers, attendants, interpreters, or notetakers). **Duration:** Assistance is provided until the disabled person achieves an educational level necessary for employment as provided in the IWRP.
Eligibility Requirements: To be eligible for vocational rehabilitation services, an individual must 1) have a physical or mental impairment that is a substantial impediment to employment; 2) be able to benefit in terms of employment from vocational rehabilitation services; and 3) require vocational rehabilitation services to prepare for, enter, engage in, or retain gainful employment. Priority is given to applicants with the most significant disabilities. Persons accepted for vocational rehabilitation develop an Individualized Written Rehabilitation Program (IWRP) in consultation with a counselor for the vocational rehabilitation agency in the state in which they live. The IWRP may include a program of postsecondary education if the disabled person and counselor agree that such a program will fulfill the goals of vocational rehabilitation. In most cases, the IWRP will provide for postsecondary education only to a level at which the disabled person will become employable, but that may include graduate education if the approved occupation requires an advanced degree as a minimum condition of entry. Students accepted to a program of postsecondary education as part of their IWRP must apply for all available federal, state, and private financial aid. **Additional Information:** You will need to contact your state vocational rehabilitation agency to apply for this program.

569 ■ DEPARTMENT OF MILITARY AFFAIRS
Attn: State Tuition Assistance Director
6848 South Revere Parkway
Englewood, CO 80112-6703
Tel: (303)677-8913
Fax: (303)677-8859
E-mail: allison.gard@dma.state.co.us
Web Site: http://www.coloradoguard.army.mil/webpages/state_tuition.htm
To provide financial assistance for college or graduate school to members of the Colorado National Guard.
Title of Award: Colorado National Guard State Tuition Assistance **Area, Field, or Subject:** General studies/Field of study not specified **Level of Education for which Award is Granted:** Master's, Undergraduate **Number Awarded:** Varies each year. **Funds Available:** This program provides payment of up to 100% of the in-state tuition at public institutions in Colorado. **Duration:** 1 semester; may be renewed as long as the recipient remains an active member of the Guard and maintains a GPA of 2.0 or higher. Assistance is limited to a total of 132 semester hours.

Eligibility Requirements: This program is open to members of the Colorado National Guard who have completed at least 6 months of military service and are currently in drilling status. Applicants must be enrolled or planning to enroll at a public institution of higher education in Colorado to work on an associate, bachelor's, or master's degree. **Deadline for Receipt:** April of each year for the summer term; June of each year for the fall semester; November of each year for the spring semester. **Additional Information:** Recipients must serve 1 year in the Guard for each semester or quarter of assistance received.

570 ■ DEPARTMENT OF MILITARY AFFAIRS
Delaware Army National Guard
Attn: JFHQ-DE-J1-ES
First Regiment Road
Wilmington, DE 19808-2191
Tel: (302)326-7044
Fax: (302)326-7029
E-mail: deborah.welch@de.ngb.army.mil
Web Site: http://www.delawarenationalguard.com/benefits/education.htm
To provide financial assistance for college to members of the Delaware National Guard.
Title of Award: Delaware National Guard Education Assistance Program **Area, Field, or Subject:** General studies/Field of study not specified **Level of Education for which Award is Granted:** Undergraduate **Number Awarded:** Varies each year. **Funds Available:** Participants receive reimbursement of 100% of the tuition at state-supported colleges and universities in Delaware. Students who attend a Delaware private college receive a benefit equal to the average tuition of Delaware postsecondary public institutions. If total funding appropriated by the legislature is insufficient for all qualified applicants, the available funds are distributed among recipients according to a maximum allowable fair percentage formula. Recipients must complete 6 years of satisfactory membership in the Delaware National Guard (before, during, and after participation in the program) or repay the funds received. **Duration:** 1 semester; may be renewed. Guard members are eligible for this assistance only for 10 years after the date on which they begin the first course for which reimbursement was granted.
Eligibility Requirements: This program is open to active members of the Delaware National Guard who are interested in working on an undergraduate degree at a school in Delaware. Applicants must have made satisfactory progress in their assigned military career field, may not have missed more than 6 periods of scheduled unit training assembly periods in the preceding 12 months, and must have avoided all adverse personnel actions. They must earn a grade of 2.0 or higher in all courses to qualify for tuition reimbursement. **Deadline for Receipt:** Applications must be submitted within 45 days of completion of the course(s).

571 ■ DEPARTMENT OF MILITARY AFFAIRS
Attn: Education Services Officer
82 Marine Street
St. Augustine, FL 32084-5039
Tel: (904)823-0350
Web Site: http://www.dma.state.fl.us
To provide financial assistance for college to members of the Florida National Guard.
Title of Award: Florida National Guard Educational Dollars for Duty (EDD) Program **Area, Field, or Subject:** General studies/Field of study not specified **Level of Education for which Award is Granted:** Undergraduate **Number Awarded:** Varies each year. **Funds Available:** The program provides for payment of 100% of tuition and fees. **Duration:** 1 year; may be renewed. Guard members may not participate in this program for more than 5 years following the date of eligibility.
Eligibility Requirements: This program is open to members of the Florida National Guard who have enlisted since June 30, 1997. Applicants must be attending or planning to attend a state college or university in Florida. Guard members who have a baccalaureate degree, have 15 years or more of total military service creditable towards retirement, or have not completed basic military training are not eligible.

572 ■ DEPARTMENT OF MILITARY AFFAIRS
Attn: Education Services Officer
82 Marine Street
St. Augustine, FL 32084-5039

Tel: (904)823-0350
Web Site: http://www.dma.state.fl.us
To provide financial assistance for college to members of the Florida National Guard.
Title of Award: Florida National Guard State Tuition Exemption Program (STEP) **Area, Field, or Subject:** General studies/Field of study not specified **Level of Education for which Award is Granted:** Undergraduate **Number Awarded:** Varies each year. **Funds Available:** The program provides for payment of 50% of tuition and fees. **Duration:** 1 year; may be renewed. Guard members may not participate in this program for more than 10 years following the date of enrollment.
Eligibility Requirements: This program is open to members of the Florida National Guard who enlisted prior to June 30, 1997. Applicants must be attending or planning to attend a state college or university in Florida. Guard members who have a baccalaureate degree, have 15 years or more of total military service creditable towards retirement, or have not completed basic military training are not eligible.

573 ■ DEPARTMENT OF MILITARY AFFAIRS

Attn: Education Services
Veterans Services Building
20 West 12th Street
St. Paul, MN 55155-2098
Tel: (651)282-4590
Free: 800-657-3848
Fax: (651)282-4694
E-mail: kevin.olson@mn.ngb.army.mil
Web Site: http://www.dma.state.mn.us/about/education/education.html
To provide financial assistance for college or graduate school to members of the Minnesota National Guard.
Title of Award: Minnesota National Guard Tuition and Textbook Reimbursement Grants **Area, Field, or Subject:** General studies/Field of study not specified **Level of Education for which Award is Granted:** Graduate, Undergraduate **Number Awarded:** Varies each year. **Funds Available:** This program provides reimbursement of a portion of tuition (and textbooks, depending on the school). The funds are sent directly to the individual soldier upon satisfactory completion of course work. The maximum reimbursement is $54 per quarter credit or $81 per semester credit at branches of the University of Minnesota, $37 per quarter credit or $55 per semester credit at state universities, $31 per quarter credit or $46 per semester credit at community and technical colleges, or $1.45 per clock hour for schools that report in clock hours.
Eligibility Requirements: Eligible for this program are members of the Minnesota Army or Air National Guard, regardless of rank, who are enrolled as undergraduate or graduate students at public colleges or universities in Minnesota (graduate students must be at rank O-3 or below). Reimbursement is provided only for undergraduate courses completed with a grade of "C" or better or for graduate courses completed with a grade of "B" or better.

574 ■ DEPARTMENT OF MILITARY AFFAIRS

Attn: Wisconsin Education Services Office
P.O. Box 8111
Madison, WI 53708-8111
Tel: (608)242-3157
Free: 800-362-7444
E-mail: education@wi.ngb.army.mil
Web Site: http://www.wisconsinguard.com
To provide financial assistance for college to members of the Wisconsin National Guard.
Title of Award: Wisconsin National Guard Tuition Grant **Area, Field, or Subject:** General studies/Field of study not specified **Level of Education for which Award is Granted:** Undergraduate **Number Awarded:** Varies each year. **Funds Available:** This program offers assistance based on the undergraduate tuition rate of the University of Wisconsin at Madison. It provides for reimbursement of up to $2,627.04 per semester for full-time study. **Duration:** 8 semesters of full-time study or 120 credits of part-time work.
Eligibility Requirements: Eligible to apply for these grants are enlisted members and warrant officers in good standing in the Wisconsin National Guard who wish to work on an undergraduate degree. Applicants must be attending or planning to attend an extension division or campus of the University of Wisconsin system, a public institution of higher education

under the Minnesota-Wisconsin student reciprocity agreement, a public institution of higher education under a statutorily approved interstate agreement, or an accredited institution of higher education located within Wisconsin.

575 ■ DEPARTMENT OF MILITARY AND VETERANS AFFAIRS

Attn: Office of Veterans Affairs
P.O. Box 5800
Fort Richardson, AK 99505-5800
Tel: (907)428-6016
Fax: (907)428-6019
E-mail: jerry_beale@ak-prepared.com
Web Site: http://www.ak-prepared.com/vetaffairs/state_benefits.htm
To provide financial assistance for college to dependents and spouses in Alaska of service members who died or were declared prisoners of war or missing in action.
Title of Award: Alaska Free Tuition for Spouses and Dependents of Armed Services Members **Area, Field, or Subject:** General studies/Field of study not specified **Level of Education for which Award is Granted:** Undergraduate **Number Awarded:** Varies each year. **Funds Available:** Those eligible may attend any state-supported educational institution in Alaska without payment of tuition or fees. **Duration:** 1 year; may be renewed.
Eligibility Requirements: Eligible for this benefit are the spouses and dependent children of Alaska residents who died in the line of duty, died of injuries sustained in the line of duty, or were listed by the Department of Defense as a prisoner of war or missing in action. Applicants must be in good standing at a state-supported educational institution in Alaska. **Additional Information:** Information is available from the financial aid office of state-supported universities in Alaska.

576 ■ DEPARTMENT OF MILITARY AND VETERANS AFFAIRS

Attn: State Education Officer
2500 South Washington Avenue
Lansing, MI 48913-5101
Tel: (517)483-5685
Free: 800-292-1386
Web Site: http://www.michigan.gov/dmva
To provide financial assistance to members of the Michigan National Guard who are enrolled at designated universities in the state.
Title of Award: Michigan National Guard College Grants and Scholarships **Area, Field, or Subject:** General studies/Field of study not specified **Level of Education for which Award is Granted:** Undergraduate **Number Awarded:** Varies each year. **Funds Available:** The amount of the grant varies at each participating institution. **Duration:** 1 semester; may be renewed for a total of 4 years.
Eligibility Requirements: This program is open to all members of the Michigan National Guard who are in good standing with their unit and have completed IADT. Applicants must be enrolled full time at 1 of the following institutions: Baker College, Cleary University, Davenport University, Eastern Michigan University, Ferris State University, Kalamazoo Valley Community College, Kirtland Community College, Lake Superior State University, Lansing Community College, Lawrence Tech University, Mid Michigan Community College, Northern Michigan University, Oakland University, Olivet College, Rochester College, Siena Heights University, Spring Arbor University, University of Detroit Mercy, Walsh College, or Western Michigan University. **Additional Information:** These grants are in addition to funds received through the Michigan National Guard State Education Reimbursement Program.

577 ■ DEPARTMENT OF MILITARY AND VETERANS AFFAIRS

Attn: State Education Officer
2500 South Washington Avenue
Lansing, MI 48913-5101
Tel: (517)483-5685
Free: 800-292-1386
Web Site: http://www.michguard.com/education
To reimburse members of the Michigan National Guard for a portion of their postsecondary educational expenses.
Title of Award: Michigan National Guard State Education Reimbursement Program **Area, Field, or Subject:** General studies/Field of study not specified **Level of Education for which Award is Granted:** Graduate, Professional, Undergraduate **Number Awarded:** Varies each year. **Funds**

Available: Eligible members are reimbursed up to a maximum of $2,000 per academic year. Funds are paid directly to the recipient. **Duration:** 1 semester; may be renewed for a total of 4 years.

Eligibility Requirements: This program is open to all members of the Michigan National Guard who are in good standing with their unit and have completed IADT. Applicants must be enrolled in a course of instruction that is part of a degree program (undergraduate, graduate, postgraduate, and certificate) offered by an accredited college, technical college, vocational/trade school, or university in Michigan. They must have a cumulative GPA of 2.0 or higher. **Additional Information:** This reimbursement is in addition to funds provided at specified Michigan universities through the Michigan National Guard College Grants and Scholarships.

578 ■ DEPARTMENT OF MILITARY AND VETERANS AFFAIRS

Attn: Michigan Veterans Trust Fund
2500 South Washington Avenue
Lansing, MI 48913-5101
Tel: (517)483-5469
E-mail: paocmn@michigan.gov
Web Site: http://www.michigan.gov/dmva
To provide financial assistance for college to the children of Michigan veterans who are totally disabled or deceased as a result of service-connected causes.

Title of Award: Michigan Veterans Trust Fund Tuition Grants **Area, Field, or Subject:** General studies/Field of study not specified **Level of Education for which Award is Granted:** Undergraduate **Number Awarded:** Varies each year. **Funds Available:** Recipients are exempt from payment of the first $2,800 per year of tuition or any other fee that takes the place of tuition. **Duration:** 1 year; may be renewed for up to 36 months if the recipient maintains full-time enrollment and a GPA of 2.25 or higher.

Eligibility Requirements: This program is open to children of Michigan veterans who are totally disabled as a result of wartime service, or died from service-connected conditions, or were killed in action, or are listed as missing in action. Applicants must be between 16 and 26 years of age and must have lived in Michigan at least 12 months prior to the date of application. They must be or plan to become a full-time undergraduate student at a public institution of higher education in Michigan.

579 ■ DEPARTMENT OF VETERANS AFFAIRS

810 Vermont Avenue, N.W.
Washington, DC 20420
Tel: (202)418-4343; 888-GI-BILL1
Web Site: http://www.gibill.va.gov
To provide financial assistance for college, graduate school, and other types of postsecondary schools to new enlistees in any of the armed forces after they have completed their service obligation.

Title of Award: Montgomery GI Bill (Active Duty) **Area, Field, or Subject:** General studies/Field of study not specified **Level of Education for which Award is Granted:** Graduate, Undergraduate **Number Awarded:** Varies each year. **Funds Available:** For veterans in categories 1, 3, and 4 who served on active duty for 3 years or more, the current monthly stipend for college or university work is $1,034 for full-time study, $775.50 for three-quarter time study, or $517 for half-time study, or $258.50 for quarter-time study or less; for apprenticeship and on-the-job training, the monthly stipend is $878.90 for the first 6 months, $672.10 for the second 6 months, and $465.30 for the remainder of the program. For enlistees whose initial active-duty obligation was less than 3 years, the current monthly stipend for college or university work is $840 for full-time study, $630 for three-quarter time study, $420 for half-time study, or $210 for quarter-time study or less; for apprenticeship and on-the-job training, the monthly stipend is $714 for the first 6 months, $546 for the second 6 months, and $378 for the remainder of the program. For veterans in category 2 with remaining eligibility, the current monthly stipend for institutional study full time is $1,222 for no dependents, $1,258 with 1 dependent, $1,289 with 2 dependents, and $16 for each additional dependent; for three-quarter time study, the monthly stipend is $917 for no dependents, $943.50 with 1 dependent, $967 with 2 dependents, and $12 for each additional dependent; for half-time study, the monthly stipend is $611 for no dependents, $629 with 1 dependent, $644.50 with 2 dependents and $8.50 for each additional dependent. For those veterans pursuing an apprenticeship or on-the-job training, the current monthly stipend for the first 6 months is $995.35 for no dependents, $1,009.38

with 1 dependent, $1,021.70 with 2 dependents, and $5.95 for each additional dependent; for the second 6 months, the current monthly stipend is $738.73 for no dependents, $749.78 with 1 dependent, $758.88 with 2 dependents, and $4.55 for each additional dependent; for the third 6 months, the current monthly stipend is $495.90 for no dependents, $503.78 with 1 dependent, $509.85 with 2 dependents, and $3.15 for each additional dependent; for the remainder of the training period, the current monthly stipend is $480.60 for no dependents, $488.03 with 1 dependent, $494.78 with 2 dependents, and $3.15 for each additional dependent. Other rates apply for less than half-time study, cooperative education, correspondence courses, and flight training. Veterans who qualify for the accelerated payment and whose entitlement does not cover 60% of tuition and fees receive an additional lump sum payment to make up the different between their entitlement and 60% of tuition and fees. **Duration:** 36 months; active-duty servicemembers must utilize the funds within 10 years of leaving the armed services; Reservists may draw on their funds while still serving.

Eligibility Requirements: This program is open to veterans who received an honorable discharge and have a high school diploma, a GED, or, in some cases, up to 12 hours of college credit. Applicants must also meet the requirements of 1 of the following categories: 1) entered active duty for the first time after June 30, 1985, had military pay reduced by $100 per month for the first 12 months, and continuously served for 3 years, or 2 years if that was original enlistment, or 2 years if they entered Selected Reserve within a year of leaving active duty and served 4 years (the 2 by 4 program); 2) entered active duty before January 1, 1977, had remaining entitlement under the Vietnam Era GI Bill on December 31, 1989, served at least 1 day between October 19, 1984 and June 30, 1985, and stayed on active duty through June 30, 1988 (or June 30, 1987 if they entered Selected Reserve within 1 year of leaving active duty and served 4 years; 3) on active duty on September 30, 1990 and separated involuntarily after February 2, 1991, involuntarily separated on or after November 30, 1993, or voluntarily separated under either the Voluntary Separation Incentive (VSI) or Special Separation Benefit (SSB) program, and before separation had military pay reduced by $1,200; or 4) on active duty on October 9, 1996, had money remaining in an account from the Veterans Educational Assistance Program (VEAP), elected MGIB by October 9, 1997, and paid $1,200. Certain National Guard servicemembers may also qualify under category 4 if they served on full-time active duty between July 1, 1985 and November 28, 1989, elected MGIB between October 9, 1996 and July 8, 1997, and paid $1,200. Following completion of their service obligation, participants may enroll in colleges or universities for associate, bachelor, or graduate degrees; in courses leading to a certificate or diploma from business, technical, or vocational schools; for apprenticeships or on-job training programs; in correspondence courses; in flight training; for preparatory courses necessary for admission to a college or graduate school; for licensing and certification tests approved for veterans; or in state-approved teacher certification programs. Veterans who wish to enroll in certain high-cost technology programs (life science, physical science, engineering, mathematics, engineering and science technology, computer specialties, and engineering, science, and computer management) may be eligible for an accelerated payment **Additional Information:** Further information is available from local armed forces recruiters. This is the basic VA education program, referred to as Chapter 30.

580 ■ DEPARTMENT OF VETERANS AFFAIRS

810 Vermont Avenue, N.W.
Washington, DC 20420
Tel: (202)418-4343; 888-GI-BILL1
Web Site: http://www.gibill.va.gov
To provide financial assistance for college or graduate school to members of the Reserves or National Guard.

Title of Award: Montgomery GI Bill (Selected Reserve) **Area, Field, or Subject:** General studies/Field of study not specified **Level of Education for which Award is Granted:** Graduate, Undergraduate **Number Awarded:** Varies each year. **Funds Available:** The current monthly rate is $297 for full-time study, $222.75 for three-quarter time study, $148.50 for half-time study, or $74.25 for less than half-time study. For apprenticeship and on-the-job training, the monthly stipend is $252.45 for the first 6 months, $193.05 for the second 6 months, and $133.65 for the remainder of the program. Other rates apply for cooperative education, correspondence courses, and flight training. **Duration:** Up to 36 months for full-time study, 48 months for three-quarter study, 72 months for half-time study, or 144 months for less than half-time study.

Eligibility Requirements: Eligible to apply are members of the Reserve elements of the Army, Navy, Air Force, Marine Corps, and Coast Guard, as well as the Army National Guard and the Air National Guard. To be eligible, a Reservist must 1) have a 6-year obligation to serve in the Selected Reserves signed after June 30, 1985 (or, if an officer, to agree to serve 6 years in addition to the original obligation); 2) complete Initial Active Duty for Training (IADT); 3) meet the requirements for a high school diploma or equivalent certificate before completing IADT; and 4) remain in good standing in a drilling Selected Reserve unit. Reservists who enlisted after June 30, 1985 can receive benefits for undergraduate degrees, graduate training, or technical courses leading to certificates at colleges and universities. Reservists whose 6-year commitment began after September 30, 1990 may also use these benefits for a certificate or diploma from business, technical, or vocational schools; cooperative training; apprenticeship or on-the-job training; correspondence courses; independent study programs; tutorial assistance; remedial, deficiency, or refresher training; flight training; or state-approved alternative teacher certification programs. **Deadline for Receipt:** Applications may be submitted at any time. **Additional Information:** This program is frequently referred to as Chapter 1606 (formerly Chapter 106). Reservists who are enrolled for three-quarter or full-time study are eligible to participate in the work-study program. The Department of Defense periodically offers "kickers" of additional benefits on behalf of individuals in critical military fields, as deemed necessary to encourage enlistment. Information on currently-available "kickers" is available from Reserve and National Guard recruiters. Benefits end 10 years from the date the Reservist became eligible for the program. The Department of Veterans Affairs (VA) may extend the 10-year period if the individual could not train because of a disability caused by Selected Reserve service. Certain individuals separated from the Selected Reserve due to downsizing of the military between October 1, 1991 and September 30, 1999 will also have the full 10 years to use their benefits.

581 ■ DEPARTMENT OF VETERANS AFFAIRS
810 Vermont Avenue, N.W.
Washington, DC 20420
Tel: (202)418-4343; 888-GI-BILL1
Web Site: http://www.gibill.va.gov
To supplement the tuition assistance provided by the military services to their members.

Title of Award: Montgomery GI Bill Tuition Assistance Top-Up **Area, Field, or Subject:** General studies/Field of study not specified **Level of Education for which Award is Granted:** Graduate, Undergraduate **Number Awarded:** Varies each year. **Funds Available:** This program pays the difference between what the military services pay for tuition assistance and the full amount of tuition and fees. **Duration:** Up to 36 months of payments are available.

Eligibility Requirements: This program is open to military personnel who have served at least 2 full years on active duty and are approved for tuition assistance by their military service. Applicants must be participating in the Montgomery GI Bill (MGIB) Active Duty program and be eligible for MGIB benefits. This assistance is available to service members whose military service does not pay 100% of tuition and fees. **Additional Information:** This program was established in 2000.

582 ■ DEPARTMENT OF VETERANS' AFFAIRS
State Office Building
301 Centennial Mall South, Sixth Floor
P.O. Box 95083
Lincoln, NE 68509-5083
Tel: (402)471-2458
Fax: (402)471-2491
E-mail: dparker@notes.state.ne.us
Web Site: http://www.vets.state.ne.us
To provide financial assistance for college to members of Nebraska units of the active Reserves.

Title of Award: Nebraska Tuition Credit for Active Reservists **Area, Field, or Subject:** General studies/Field of study not specified **Level of Education for which Award is Granted:** Undergraduate **Number Awarded:** Varies each year; no more than 200 new awards may be granted in a year. **Funds Available:** Reservists who meet the requirements may receive a credit for 50% of the tuition charges at any state-supported

university or college in Nebraska, including any technical community college. **Duration:** 1 year; may be renewed until receipt of the degree or completion of the course of study.

Eligibility Requirements: Nebraska residents who are enlisted members of a Nebraska-based unit of the active selected Reserve are eligible for this benefit. They must have at least 2 years remaining on their enlistment, have agreed to serve at least 3 years in the Reserves, not have completed the tenth year of total service in the U.S. armed forces (including active and Reserve time), and be working on a degree at a state-supported college or university or an equivalent level of study in a technical community college.

583 ■ DEPARTMENT OF VETERANS' AFFAIRS
State Office Building
301 Centennial Mall South, Sixth Floor
P.O. Box 95083
Lincoln, NE 68509-5083
Tel: (402)471-2458
Fax: (402)471-2491
E-mail: dparker@notes.state.ne.us
Web Site: http://www.vets.state.ne.us
To provide financial assistance for college to dependents of deceased and disabled veterans and military personnel in Nebraska.

Title of Award: Nebraska Waiver of Tuition for Veterans' Dependents **Area, Field, or Subject:** General studies/Field of study not specified **Level of Education for which Award is Granted:** Undergraduate **Number Awarded:** Varies each year; recently, 302 of these grants were awarded. **Funds Available:** Tuition is waived at public institutions in Nebraska. **Duration:** The waiver is valid for 1 degree, diploma, or certificate from a community college and 1 baccalaureate degree.

Eligibility Requirements: Eligible are spouses, widow(er)s, and children who are residents of Nebraska and whose parent, stepparent, or spouse was a member of the U.S. armed forces and 1) died of a service-connected disability; 2) died subsequent to discharge as a result of injury or illness sustained while in service; 3) is permanently and totally disabled as a result of military service; or 4) is classified as missing in action or as a prisoner of war during armed hostilities after August 4, 1964. Applicants must be attending or planning to attend a branch of the University of Nebraska, a state college, or a community college in Nebraska. **Additional Information:** Applications may be submitted through 1 of the recognized veterans' organizations or any county service officer.

584 ■ DEPARTMENT OF VETERANS AFFAIRS
1411 32nd Street South
P.O. Box 9003
Fargo, ND 58106-9003
Tel: (701)239-7165; (866)634-8387
Fax: (701)239-7166
Web Site: http://www.state.nd.us/veterans/benefits/waiver.html
To provide financial assistance for college to the spouses, widow(er)s, and children of disabled and other North Dakota veterans and military personnel.

Title of Award: North Dakota Educational Assistance for Dependents of Veterans **Area, Field, or Subject:** General studies/Field of study not specified **Level of Education for which Award is Granted:** Undergraduate **Number Awarded:** Varies each year. **Funds Available:** Eligible dependents receive free tuition and are exempt from fees at any state-supported institution of higher education, technical school, or vocational school in North Dakota. **Duration:** Up to 36 months or 8 academic semesters.

Eligibility Requirements: This program is open to the spouses, widow(er)s, and dependent children of veterans who are totally disabled as a result of service-connected causes, or who were killed in action, or who have died as a result of wounds or service-connected disabilities, or who were identified as prisoners of war or missing in action. Veteran parents must have been born in and lived in North Dakota until entrance into the armed forces (or must have resided in the state for at least 6 months prior to entrance into military service) and must have served during wartime.

585 ■ DEPARTMENT OF VETERANS AFFAIRS
810 Vermont Avenue, N.W.
Washington, DC 20420
Tel: (202)418-4343; 888-GI-BILL1

Web Site: http://www.gibill.va.gov

To provide financial assistance for undergraduate or graduate study to children and spouses of deceased and disabled veterans, MIAs, and POWs.

Title of Award: Survivors' and Dependents' Educational Assistance Program **Area, Field, or Subject:** General studies/Field of study not specified **Level of Education for which Award is Granted:** Graduate, Undergraduate **Number Awarded:** Varies each year. **Funds Available:** Monthly stipends from this program for study at an academic institution are $827 for full time, $621 for three-quarter time, or $413 for half-time. For farm cooperative work, the monthly stipends are $667 for full-time, $500 for three-quarter time, or $334 for half-time. For an apprenticeship or on-the-job training, the monthly stipend is $650 for the first 6 months, $507 for the second 6 months, $366 for the third 6 months, and $151 for the remainder of the program. **Duration:** Up to 45 months (or the equivalent in part-time training). Spouses must complete their training within 10 years of the date they are first found eligible.

Eligibility Requirements: Eligible for this assistance are spouses and children of 1) veterans who died or are permanently and totally disabled as the result of active service in the armed forces; 2) veterans who died from any cause while rated permanently and totally disabled from a service-connected disability; 3) servicemembers listed for more than 90 days as currently missing in action or captured in the line of duty by a hostile force; and 4) servicemembers listed for more than 90 days as presently detained or interned by a foreign government or power. Children must be between 18 and 26 years of age, although extensions may be granted. Spouses and children over 14 years of age with physical or mental disabilities are also eligible. **Deadline for Receipt:** Applications may be submitted at any time. **Additional Information:** Benefits may be used to work on associate, bachelor, or graduate degrees at colleges and universities, including independent study, cooperative training, and study abroad programs. Courses leading to a certificate or diploma from business, technical, or vocational schools may also be taken. Other eligible programs include apprenticeships, on-job training programs, farm cooperative courses, correspondence courses (for spouses only), secondary school programs (for recipients who are not high school graduates), tutorial assistance, remedial deficiency and refresher training, or work-study (for recipients who are enrolled at least three-quarter time). Eligible children who are handicapped by a physical or mental disability that prevents pursuit of an educational program may receive special restorative training that includes language retraining, lip reading, auditory training, Braille reading and writing, and similar programs. Eligible spouses and children over 14 years of age who are handicapped by a physical or mental disability that prevents pursuit of an educational program may receive specialized vocational training that includes specialized courses, alone or in combination with other courses, leading to a vocational objective that is suitable for the person and required by reason of physical or mental handicap. Ineligible courses include bartending or personality development courses; correspondence courses by dependent or surviving children; non-accredited independent study courses; any course given by radio; self-improvement courses, such as reading, speaking, woodworking, basic seamanship, and English as a second language; audited courses; any course that is avocational or recreational in character; courses not leading to an educational, professional, or vocational objective; courses taken and successfully completed previously; courses taken by a federal government employee and paid for under the Government Employees' Training Act; and courses taken while in receipt of benefits for the same program from the Office of Workers' Compensation Programs.

586 ■ DEPARTMENT OF VETERANS AFFAIRS

810 Vermont Avenue, N.W.
Washington, DC 20420
Tel: (202)418-4343; 888-GI-BILL1
Web Site: http://www.gibill.va.gov

To provide funding to veterans who, while on active duty, participate voluntarily in a plan for future education in which their savings are administered and augmented by the government.

Title of Award: Veterans Educational Assistance Program (VEAP) **Area, Field, or Subject:** General studies/Field of study not specified **Level of Education for which Award is Granted:** Graduate, Undergraduate **Number Awarded:** Varies each year. **Funds Available:** Participants contribute to the program, through monthly deductions from their military pay, from $25 to $100 monthly, up to a maximum of $2,700. They may also, while on active duty, make a lump sum contribution to the training fund. At the time the eligible participant elects to use the benefits to pursue an approved course of education or training, the Department of Veterans Affairs (VA) will match the contribution at the rate of $2 for every $1 made by the participant. **Duration:** Participants receive monthly payments for the number of months they contributed, or for 36 months, whichever is less. The amount of the payments is determined by dividing the number of months benefits will be paid into the participant's training fund total. Participants have 10 years from the date of last discharge or release from active duty within which to use these benefits.

Eligibility Requirements: Veterans who served and military service members currently serving are eligible if they 1) entered active duty between January 1, 1977 and June 30, 1985; 2) were released under conditions other than dishonorable or continue on active duty; 3) served for a continuous period of 181 days or more (or were discharged earlier for a service-connected disability); and 4) have satisfactorily contributed to the program. No individuals on active duty could enroll in this program after March 31, 1987. Veterans who enlisted for the first time after September 7, 1980 or entered active duty as an office or enlistee after October 16, 1981 must have completed 24 continuous months of active duty. **Deadline for Receipt:** Applications may be submitted at any time. **Additional Information:** A participant may leave this program at the end of any 12-consecutive-month period of participation and those who do so may have their contributions refunded. This is the basic VA educational program for veterans and military personnel who entered active duty from January 1, 1977 through June 30, 1985. Veterans and service members who began active duty prior to that period and those who have entered subsequently may qualify for the Montgomery GI Bill. An individual who contributed or could have contributed to VEAP before being involuntarily separated from active duty with an honorable discharge after December 4, 1991 may make an irrevocable election before such separation to receive Montgomery GI Bill benefits. Benefits are available for the pursuit of an associate, bachelor, or graduate degree at a college or university; a certificate or diploma from a business, technical, or vocational school; apprenticeship or on-job training programs; cooperative courses; correspondence school courses; tutorial assistance; remedial, refresher, and deficiency training; flight training; study abroad programs leading to a college degree; nontraditional training away from school; and work-study for students enrolled at least three-quarter time. Ineligible courses include bartending or personality development courses; farm cooperative courses; non-accredited independent study courses; any course given by radio; self-improvement courses such as reading, speaking, woodworking, basic seamanship, and English as a second language; audited courses; any course that is avocational or recreational in character; courses not leading to an educational, professional, or vocational objective; courses taken and successfully completed previously; courses taken by a federal government employee and paid for under the Government Employees' Training Act; courses paid for in whole or in part by the armed forces while on active duty; and courses taken while in receipt of benefits for the same program from the Office of Workers' Compensation Programs.

587 ■ DEPARTMENT OF VETERANS AFFAIRS

810 Vermont Avenue, N.W.
Washington, DC 20420
Tel: (202)418-4343
Free: 800-827-1000
Web Site: http://www.va.gov

To provide vocational rehabilitation to certain categories of veterans with disabilities.

Title of Award: Vocational Rehabilitation for Disabled Veterans **Area, Field, or Subject:** Employment; General studies/Field of study not specified **Level of Education for which Award is Granted:** Graduate, Undergraduate, Other **Number Awarded:** Varies each year. **Funds Available:** While in training and for 2 months after, eligible disabled veterans may receive subsistence allowances in addition to their disability compensation or retirement pay. For training at an institution of higher education or in an unpaid work experience program, the full-time monthly rate is $474.27 with no dependents, $588.30 with 1 dependent, $693.25 with 2 dependents, and $50.54 for each additional dependent; the three-quarter time monthly rate is $356.36 for no dependents, $441.86 with 1 dependent, $518.31 with 2 dependents, and $38.86 for each additional dependent; the half-time monthly rate is $238.45 for no dependents, $295.44 with 1 dependent, $347.27 with 2 dependents, and $25.93 for each additional dependent. For unpaid on-the-job training, the monthly rate is $474.27 for no dependents, $588.30 with 1 dependent, $693.25 with 2 dependents, and $50.54 for each additional dependent. For paid training, the monthly rate is based on the wage received, to a maximum of $414.67 for no dependents, $501.46 with 1 dependent, $577.92 with 2 dependents, and $37.59 for each additional dependent. The VA also pays the costs of tuition, books, fees, supplies, and equipment; it may also pay for special supportive services, such as tutorial assistance, prosthetic devices, lipreading training, and signing for the deaf. If during training or employment services the veteran's disabilities cause transportation expenses that would not be incurred by nondisabled persons, the VA will pay for at least a portion of those expenses. If the veteran encounters financial difficulty during training, the VA may provide an advance against future benefit payments. **Duration:** Up to 48 months of full-time training or its equivalent in part-time training. If a veteran with a serious disability receives services under an extended evaluation to improve training potential, the total of the extended evaluation and the training phases of the rehabilitation program may exceed 48 months. Usually, the veteran must complete a rehabilitation program within 12 years from the date of notification of entitlement to compensation by the VA. Following completion of the training portion of a rehabilitation program, a veteran may receive counseling and job search and adjustment services for 18 months.

Eligibility Requirements: This program is open to veterans who have a service-connected disability of at least 10% and a serious employment handicap or 20% and an employment handicap. They must have been discharged or released from military service under other than dishonorable conditions. The Department of Veterans Affairs (VA) must determine that they would benefit from a training program that would help them prepare for, find, and keep suitable employment. The program may be 1) institutional training at a certificate, 2-year college, 4-year college or university, or technical program; 2) unpaid on-the-job training in a federal, state, or local agency or a federally-recognized Indian tribal agency, training in a home, vocational course in a rehabilitation facility or sheltered workshop, independent instruction, or institutional non-farm cooperative; or 3) paid training through a farm cooperative, apprenticeship, on-the-job training, or on-the-job non-farm cooperative. **Deadline for Receipt:** Applications are accepted at any time. **Additional Information:** The program may also provide employment assistance, self-employment assistance, training in a rehabilitation facility, or college and other training. Veterans who are seriously disabled may receive services and assistance to improve their ability to live more independently in their community. After completion of the training phase, the VA will assist the veteran to find and have a suitable job.

588 ■ DISABLED AMERICAN VETERANS

Attn: National Service and Legislative Headquarters
807 Maine Avenue, S.W.
Washington, DC 20024
Tel: (202)554-3501
Web Site: http://www.dav.org/volunteers/jesse_brown_scholarship.html
To provide financial assistance to college students who demonstrate outstanding volunteer service to hospitalized disabled veterans.
Title of Award: Jesse Brown Memorial Youth Scholarship Program **Area, Field, or Subject:** General studies/Field of study not specified **Level of Education for which Award is Granted:** Undergraduate **Number Awarded:** Varies each year; since the establishment of the program, 63 scholarships worth $413,000 have been awarded. **Funds Available:** Stipends range up to $15,000. **Duration:** Funds must be used before the recipient's 25th birthday.
Eligibility Requirements: This program is open to students who are 21 years of age or younger and have volunteered at least 100 hours for the Department of Veterans Affairs Voluntary Service (VAVS) programs to assist disabled veterans. They may be attending an accredited college, university, community college, or vocational school. Nominations must be submitted by Chiefs of Voluntary Services at VA medical centers. Self-nominations are also accepted if the student includes a 750-word essay on what volunteering at a VA medical center means to them. **Deadline for Receipt:** February of each year. **Additional Information:** This program was established in 2000 as the DAV National Commander's Youth Volunteer Scholarships and given its current name in 2003.

589 ■ DISABLED AMERICAN VETERANS AUXILIARY

Attn: National Education Loan Fund Director
3725 Alexandria Pike
Cold Spring, KY 41076
Tel: (606)441-7300
Fax: (606)442-2095
Web Site: http://www.dav.org/dava/index.html
To provide loans for college to women who are members of the Disabled American Veterans Auxiliary or to their children or grandchildren.
Title of Award: Disabled American Veterans Auxiliary National Education Loan Fund **Area, Field, or Subject:** General studies/Field of study not specified **Level of Education for which Award is Granted:** Undergraduate **Number Awarded:** Varies; generally, 15 each year. **Funds Available:** A maximum of $2,000 per year is loaned, payable to the school. The loan is to be repaid within 7 years in installments of at least $100 per month. Repayment must begin upon graduation or leaving school. No interest is charged. **Duration:** The loan is renewable each year for up to 4 consecutive years, provided the student maintains full-time status and a GPA of 2.0 or higher.
Eligibility Requirements: This loan fund is open to women who are paid life members of the auxiliary and to their children and grandchildren. Applicants must be enrolled full time in a college, university, or vocational school. They must demonstrate academic achievement and financial need. **Deadline for Receipt:** February of each year.

590 ■ DISTILLED SPIRITS WHOLESALERS OF FLORIDA EDUCATIONAL SCHOLARSHIP FOUNDATION, INC.

213 South Monroe Street, Suite 800A
Tallahassee, FL 32301-1858
To provide financial assistance to upper-division students in Florida who are majoring in business.
Title of Award: Distilled Spirits Wholesalers of Florida Educational Scholarship **Area, Field, or Subject:** Business administration **Level of Education for which Award is Granted:** Four Year College **Funds Available:** Awards cover the cost of tuition at a public university in Florida. **Duration:** 1 year.
Eligibility Requirements: Eligible to apply are students who are residents of Florida, accepted at or attending a state university in Florida, and majoring in business. They must be full-time students, have completed at least their sophomore year in college, and be U.S. citizens. Selection is based on financial need, academic potential, good citizenship, and character. **Deadline for Receipt:** March of each year. **Additional Information:** Recipients may not also receive another award that is intended to be spent on tuition only.

591 ■ DISTINGUISHED FLYING CROSS SOCIETY

Attn: Scholarship Program
4442 Vandever Avenue
San Diego, CA 92120-3322
(866)DFC-MEDAL
Web Site: http://www.dfcsociety.org
To provide financial assistance for college to descendants of members of the Distinguished Flying Cross Society (DFCS).
Title of Award: Distinguished Flying Cross Society Scholarships **Area, Field, or Subject:** General studies/Field of study not specified **Level of Education for which Award is Granted:** Undergraduate **Number Awarded:** 4 each year. **Funds Available:** The stipend is $1,000. **Duration:** 1 year.
Eligibility Requirements: This program is open to descendants (including legally adopted children) of DFCS members. Applicants must be working on an undergraduate degree at an accredited institution of higher education. Along with their application, they must submit a list of memberships in school-related organizations, a list of elected leadership positions they have held, information on activities that demonstrate community involvement, transcripts (including SAT scores), and a 500-word essay on why they feel they deserve this scholarship. **Deadline for Receipt:** November of each year. **Additional Information:** Membership in the sponsoring organization, founded in 1994, is limited to members of the U.S. armed forces who have been awarded the Distinguished Flying Cross as a result of deeds accomplished during aerial flight.

592 ■ DISTRICT 45 LION'S CLUB

Attn: Youth Outreach
c/o Danielle Coulombe

18 Golf Course Road
Richford, VT 05476-9766
To provide financial assistance for college to high school seniors from Vermont who have an illness or disability.
Title of Award: District 45 Lion's Youth Outreach Award **Area, Field, or Subject:** General studies/Field of study not specified **Level of Education for which Award is Granted:** Undergraduate **Number Awarded:** 3 each year: 1 at $1,000 and 2 at $500. **Funds Available:** Stipends are $1,000 or $500. **Duration:** 1 year.
Eligibility Requirements: This program is open to seniors graduating from public high schools in Vermont who plan to attend college. Applicants must provide confirmation from a doctor or special education director of their illness or disability. Along with their application, they must submit an essay describing how they have overcome their disability or illness and their major accomplishments in life. Selection is based on the essay, academic achievement, community involvement, 2 letters of recommendation, and financial need. **Deadline for Receipt:** March of each year.

593 ■ DISTRICT OF COLUMBIA NATIONAL GUARD

Attn: Education Services Office
2001 East Capitol Street
Washington, DC 20003-1719
Tel: (202)685-9825
Fax: (202)685-9815
E-mail: joanne.thweatt@dc.ngb.army.mil
Web Site: http://dcng.ngb.army.mil
To provide financial assistance for college to current members of the District of Columbia National Guard.
Title of Award: District of Columbia National Guard Tuition Assistance **Area, Field, or Subject:** General studies/Field of study not specified **Level of Education for which Award is Granted:** Undergraduate **Number Awarded:** Varies each year. **Funds Available:** Payment is made to the institution for the member/employee, up to $1,000 per semester. Funds must be used to pay for tuition, fees, and/or books. **Duration:** 1 semester; recipients may reapply.
Eligibility Requirements: This program is open to active members of the District of Columbia Air/Army National Guard and civilian employees in good standing. Applicants must have a high school diploma or equivalency and currently be attending an accredited postsecondary education institution. First priority goes to those working on their first undergraduate degree. **Deadline for Receipt:** July of each year for the fall session, October of each year for the spring session, or April of each year for the summer session.

594 ■ DIVISION OF VETERANS AFFAIRS

Albemarle Building
325 North Salisbury Street, Suite 1065
Raleigh, NC 27603-5941
Tel: (919)733-3851
Fax: (919)733-2834
E-mail: Charlie.Smith@ncmail.net
Web Site: http://www.doa.state.nc.us/vets/va.htm
To provide financial assistance for college to the children of disabled and other classes of North Carolina veterans.
Title of Award: North Carolina Scholarships for Children of War Veterans **Area, Field, or Subject:** General studies/Field of study not specified **Level of Education for which Award is Granted:** Undergraduate **Number Awarded:** An unlimited number of awards are made under Classes I-A, I-B, and IV. Classes II and III are limited to 100 awards each year in each class. **Funds Available:** Students in Classes I-A, II, III, and IV receive $4,500 per academic year if they attend a private college or junior college; if attending a public postsecondary institution, they receive free tuition, a room allowance, a board allowance, and exemption from certain mandatory fees. Students in Class I-B receive $1,500 per academic year if they attend a private college or junior college; if attending a public postsecondary institution, they receive free tuition and exemption from certain mandatory fees. **Duration:** 4 academic years.
Eligibility Requirements: Eligible applicants come from 5 categories: Class I-A: the veteran parent died in wartime service or as a result of a service-connected condition incurred in wartime service; Class I-B: the veteran parent is rated by the U.S. Department of Veterans Affairs (VA) as 100% disabled as a result of wartime service and currently or at the time

of death drawing compensation for such disability; Class II: the veteran parent is rated by the VA as much as 20 but less than 100% disabled due to wartime service, or was awarded a Purple Heart medal for wounds received, and currently or at the time of death drawing compensation for such disability; Class III: the veteran parent is currently or was at the time of death receiving a VA pension for total and permanent disability, or the veteran parent is deceased but does not qualify under any other provisions, or the veteran parent served in a combat zone or waters adjacent to a combat zone and received a campaign badge or medal but does not qualify under any other provisions; Class IV: the veteran parent was a prisoner of war or missing in action. For all classes, the veteran parent must have been a legal resident of North Carolina at the time of entrance into the armed forces or the child must have been born in North Carolina and lived in the state continuously since birth. **Deadline for Receipt:** April of each year.

595 ■ DIVISION OF VETERANS' AFFAIRS

480 Metacom Avenue
Bristol, RI 02809-0689
Tel: (401)462-0324
Fax: (401)254-2320
E-mail: devangelista@dhs.ri.gov
Web Site: http://www.dhs.state.ri.us
To provide assistance to disabled veterans in Rhode Island who wish to pursue higher education at a public institution in the state.
Title of Award: Rhode Island Educational Benefits for Disabled American Veterans **Area, Field, or Subject:** General studies/Field of study not specified **Level of Education for which Award is Granted:** Undergraduate **Number Awarded:** Varies each year. **Funds Available:** Eligible veterans are entitled to take courses at any public institution of higher education in Rhode Island without the payment of tuition, exclusive of other fees and charges.
Eligibility Requirements: This program is open to permanent residents of Rhode Island who have been verified by the Department of Veterans Affairs (DVA) as having a disability of at least 10% resulting from military service.

596 ■ DIXIE BOYS BASEBALL, INC.

P.O. Box 1778
Marshall, TX 75671
Tel: (903)927-1845
Fax: (903)927-1846
E-mail: boys@dixie.org
Web Site: http://www.dixie.org
To provide financial assistance for college to high school senior males who have participated in a Dixie Boys or Dixie Majors franchised baseball program.
Title of Award: Dixie Boys Baseball Scholarships **Area, Field, or Subject:** General studies/Field of study not specified **Level of Education for which Award is Granted:** Undergraduate **Number Awarded:** 11 each year. **Funds Available:** The stipend is $1,500. **Duration:** 1 year.
Eligibility Requirements: This program is open to high school senior males who played baseball in a Dixie Boys (for boys 13 and 14 years of age) or Dixie Majors (for boys from 15 through 18 years of age) franchised program. Applicants must submit a 150-word essay on their career objectives, how college relates to those, and how they expect to contribute to society. While it is a basic requirement that the applicants have participated in the baseball program, ability is not a factor. Selection is based on high school grades and testing, school and community leadership, and financial need. **Deadline for Receipt:** March of each year. **Additional Information:** This program was established in 1984. Dixie Boys and Majors Baseball operates in Alabama, Arkansas, Florida, Georgia, Louisiana, Mississippi, North Carolina, South Carolina, Tennessee, Texas, and Virginia.

597 ■ DIXIE SOFTBALL, INC.

Attn: President
1101 Skelton Drive
Birmingham, AL 35224
Tel: (205)785-2255
Fax: (205)785-2258
E-mail: softball@dixie.org
Web Site: http://www.dixie.org

To provide financial assistance for college to high school senior women who have participated in the Dixie Softball program.
Title of Award: Dixie Softball Scholarships **Area, Field, or Subject:** General studies/Field of study not specified **Level of Education for which Award is Granted:** Undergraduate **Number Awarded:** 4 each year. **Funds Available:** The stipend is $1,500. **Duration:** 1 year.
Eligibility Requirements: This program is open to high school senior women who played in the Dixie Softball program for at least 2 seasons. Applicants must submit a transcript of grades, letter of recommendation from high school principal or other school official, verification from a Dixie Softball local official of the number of years the applicant participated in the program, and documentation of financial need. Ability as an athlete is not considered in the selection process. **Deadline for Receipt:** February of each year. **Additional Information:** This program, established in 1979, includes the following named scholarships: the Billy Adkins Memorial Scholarship, the Frank L. Baxter Scholarship, the R.T. Adams Scholarship, and the Tim Neely Scholarship. Information is also available from Doug Garrett, Scholarship Chair, 106 Woodlake Drive, Pineville, LA 71360, (318) 442-3606, E-mail: dayprodoug@cox-internet.com. Dixie Softball operates in Alabama, Arkansas, Florida, Georgia, Louisiana, Mississippi, North Carolina, South Carolina, Tennessee, Texas, and Virginia.

598 ■ DIXIE YOUTH BASEBALL, INC.

Attn: Scholarship Committee
P.O. Box 877
Marshall, TX 75671-0877
Tel: (903)927-2255
Fax: (903)927-1846
E-mail: dyb@dixie.org
Web Site: http://www.dixie.org
To provide financial assistance for college to high school senior males who have participated in a Dixie Youth Baseball franchised league.
Title of Award: Dixie Youth Baseball Scholarships **Area, Field, or Subject:** General studies/Field of study not specified **Level of Education for which Award is Granted:** Undergraduate **Number Awarded:** Varies each year; recently, 50 of these scholarships were awarded. **Funds Available:** The stipend is $2,000. **Duration:** 1 year.
Eligibility Requirements: This program is open to high school senior males who played in a Dixie Youth Baseball franchised league when they were 12 years of age or younger. Applicants must submit a transcript of grades, letter of recommendation from high school principal or other school official, verification from a Dixie Youth local official of participation in a franchised league, and documentation of financial need. Ability as an athlete is not considered in the selection process. **Deadline for Receipt:** February of each year. **Additional Information:** This program was established in 1961. Dixie Boys and Majors Baseball operates in Alabama, Arkansas, Florida, Georgia, Louisiana, Mississippi, North Carolina, South Carolina, Tennessee, Texas, and Virginia.

599 ■ DOLPHIN SCHOLARSHIP FOUNDATION

5040 Virginia Beach Boulevard, Suite 104-A
Virginia Beach, VA 23462
Tel: (757)671-3200
Fax: (757)671-3330
E-mail: dsf@exis.net
Web Site: http://www.dolphinscholarship.org
To provide financial assistance for college to the children of members or former members of the Submarine Service.
Title of Award: Dolphin Scholarship **Area, Field, or Subject:** General studies/Field of study not specified **Level of Education for which Award is Granted:** Four Year College **Number Awarded:** Approximately 30 each year. **Funds Available:** The stipend is $3,000 per year. **Duration:** 1 year; may be renewed for 3 additional years.
Eligibility Requirements: Eligible to apply for these scholarships are the unmarried children and stepchildren under 24 years of age of members or former members of the Submarine Service who 1) qualified in submarines and served in the submarine force for at least 8 years, 2) served in submarine support activities for at least 10 years, or 3) died on active duty in the submarine force regardless of time served. Applicants must be working or intending to work toward a bachelor's degree at an accredited 4-year college or university. Awards are based on scholastic proficiency, non-scholastic activities, character, all-around ability, and financial need.
Deadline for Receipt: March of each year. **Additional Information:**

Since this program was established in 1961, it has awarded more than $4.2 million to more that 750 students. In includes awards previously offered by U.S. Submarine Veterans of World War II. In 1991, that organization agreed to turn over its funds to the Dolphin Scholarship Foundation with the stipulation that it would award 3 scholarships each year, designated the U.S. Submarine Veterans of World War II Scholarship, the Wives of the U.S. Submarine Veterans of World War II Scholarship, and the Arnold Krippendorf Scholarship.

600 ■ DOYON, LIMITED

Attn: Doyon Foundation
1 Doyon Place, Suite 300
Fairbanks, AK 99701-2941
Tel: (907)459-2040; 888-478-4755
Fax: (907)459-2065
E-mail: foundation@doyon.com
Web Site: http://www.doyonfoundation.com/scholarships.html
To provide financial assistance to undergraduate and graduate students enrolled or descended from enrolled members of Doyon, Limited.
Title of Award: Doyon Foundation Competitive Scholarships **Area, Field, or Subject:** General studies/Field of study not specified **Level of Education for which Award is Granted:** Graduate, Undergraduate **Number Awarded:** Varies each year. Recently, 26 of these scholarships were awarded: 4 at $7,000, 6 at $5,000, 10 at $3,000, 1 at $2,500, 4 at $1,500, and 1 at $1,000. **Funds Available:** Stipends range from $1,000 to $7,000. **Duration:** 1 year. Undergraduate students may reapply if they maintain a GPA of 2.0 or higher; graduate or master's degree students may reapply if they maintain a GPA of 3.0 or higher; and specialist or doctoral students may reapply if they maintain a GPA of 3.25 or higher.
Eligibility Requirements: This program is open to undergraduate or graduate students who are enrolled or the descendants of enrolled members of Doyon, Limited. Enrollees are defined as stockholders enrolled to Doyon, Limited under the Alaska Native Claims Settlement Act. Descendants are defined as children of enrollees. Applicants must be accepted or enrolled at an accredited school on a full-time basis. They must submit a personal essay (describing educational and professional development goals, extracurricular activities, and community service activities) and 2 letters of recommendation. Selection is based on the essay (40 points), GPA (40 points), letters of recommendation (30 points), and personal impression (10 points). **Deadline for Receipt:** June of each year. **Additional Information:** This program includes the Rosemarie Maher Memorial Scholarship and the Morris Thompson Fellowship. Recipients must attend school on a full-time basis. Scholarship recipients of $5,000 or more are encouraged to complete at least 1 summer internship during their 4 years of study. Scholarship recipients of less than $5,000 are encouraged to do 1 of the following: serve on a local or regional board or commission, volunteer at least 20 hours, or give presentations on their field of study. A written report detailing the internship or service and lessons learned is required upon completion of the internship.

601 ■ EAR FOUNDATION

Attn: Minnie Pearl Scholarship Program
1817 Patterson Street
P.O. Box 330867
Nashville, TN 37203
Tel: (615)627-2724
Free: 800-545-HEAR
Fax: (615)627-2728
Web Site: http://www.earfoundation.org
To provide financial assistance to hearing impaired students who want to attend college.
Title of Award: Minnie Pearl Scholarship Program **Area, Field, or Subject:** General studies/Field of study not specified **Level of Education for which Award is Granted:** Undergraduate **Number Awarded:** Varies each year; recently, 6 of these scholarships were awarded. **Funds Available:** The stipend is $2,500 per year. **Duration:** 1 year; may be renewed up to 3 additional years if the recipient maintains a GPA of 3.0 or higher.
Eligibility Requirements: Applicants must be mainstreamed high school seniors with severe to profound bilateral hearing loss. Their primary means of communication may be manual or oral. They must have a GPA of 3.0 or higher; plan to attend a junior college, university, or technical school on a full-time basis; and be U.S. citizens. Along with their applica-

tion, they must submit brief essays on how they feel about mainstreaming, their goals after graduating from college, and why they are a good candidate for this scholarship. **Deadline for Receipt:** February of each year. **Additional Information:** This program was established in 1986.

602 ■ EASTER SEALS SOUTH CAROLINA

Attn: Scholarship Program
3020 Farrow Road
Columbia, SC 29203
Tel: (803)256-0735
Fax: (803)765-9765
Web Site: http://sc.easterseals.com
To provide financial assistance for college or graduate school to South Carolina students who have a disability.

Title of Award: Jim and Mary Pearce Scholarships **Area, Field, or Subject:** General studies/Field of study not specified **Level of Education for which Award is Granted:** Graduate, Undergraduate **Number Awarded:** 1 or more each year. **Funds Available:** The maximum stipend is $1,000. **Duration:** 1 year; may be renewed.
Eligibility Requirements: This program is open to South Carolina residents and students attending a college or university in the state who have a significant and medically certified mobility impairment. Applicants must be enrolled or planning to enroll in an undergraduate or graduate program. They must be able to demonstrate financial need. Preference is given to students carrying at least 9 credit hours and making satisfactory academic progress toward graduation. **Deadline for Receipt:** June of each year.

603 ■ EASTERN AMPUTEE GOLF ASSOCIATION

Attn: Bob Buck, Executive Director
2015 Amherst Drive
Bethlehem, PA 18015-5606
888-868-0992
Fax: (610)867-9295
E-mail: info@eaga.org
Web Site: http://www.eaga.org
To provide financial assistance for college to members of the Eastern Amputee Golf Association (EAGA) and their families.

Title of Award: EAGA Scholarship Award **Area, Field, or Subject:** General studies/Field of study not specified **Level of Education for which Award is Granted:** Undergraduate **Number Awarded:** 8 each year. **Funds Available:** The stipend is $1,000. **Duration:** 1 year; may be renewed if the recipient maintains a GPA of 2.0 or higher and continues to demonstrate financial need.
Eligibility Requirements: This program is open to students who are residents of and/or currently enrolled or accepted for enrollment at a college or university in designated eastern states (Connecticut, Delaware, District of Columbia, Maine, Maryland, Massachusetts, New Hampshire, New Jersey, New York, Pennsylvania, Rhode Island, Vermont, Virginia, or West Virginia). Applicants must be amputee members of the association (those who have experienced the loss of 1 or more extremities at a major joint due to amputation or birth defect) or members of their families. Financial need is considered in the selection process. **Deadline for Receipt:** June of each year. **Additional Information:** The EAGA was incorporated in 1987. It welcomes 2 types of members: amputee members and associate members (non-amputees who are interested in the organization and support its work but are not eligible for these scholarships). This program includes the following named scholarships: the Paul DesChamps Scholarship Award, the Tom Reed Scholarship, the Ray Froncillo Scholarship, the Howard Taylor Amputee-Pro Classic Scholarship, and the Northeastern Amputee Class Scholarship.

604 ■ ECI SCHOLARSHIP FOUNDATION

1701 Directors Boulevard, Suite 920
P.O. Box 149319
Austin, TX 78714-9319
Tel: (512)440-2300
Fax: (512)447-1687
Web Site: http://www.thenationaldeanslist.com/3scholarshipsgrants/scholarshipprogram.aspx
To provide financial assistance to college students who are listed in *The National Dean's List.*

Title of Award: National Dean's List Scholarships **Area, Field, or Subject:** General studies/Field of study not specified **Level of Education**

for which Award is Granted: Undergraduate **Number Awarded:** 50 each year. **Funds Available:** Scholarships are $1,000; payments are issued directly to the financial aid office at the institution the student attends. **Duration:** 1 year.
Eligibility Requirements: This program is open to college students who are U.S. citizens and 1) have a GPA of "B+" or better or 2) rank in the upper 10% of their class. Candidates must first be nominated by their dean, honor society advisor, or other college official to have their name appear in *The National Dean's List.* All students listed in that publication automatically receive an application for these scholarships in the mail. Selection is based on GPA, achievement test scores, leadership qualifications, work experience, evaluation of an essay, and some consideration for financial need. **Deadline for Receipt:** May of each year. **Additional Information:** The ECI Scholarship Foundation was established in 1968 by Educational Communications Inc., publisher of *The National Dean's List.*

605 ■ ECI SCHOLARSHIP FOUNDATION

1701 Directors Boulevard, Suite 920
P.O. Box 149319
Austin, TX 78714-9319
Tel: (512)440-2300
Fax: (512)447-1687
Web Site: http://www.ecisf.org/hs_main.aspx
To provide financial assistance to high school honor students who are listed in *Who's Who Among American High School Students.*

Title of Award: Who's Who Among American High School Students Scholarships **Area, Field, or Subject:** General studies/Field of study not specified **Level of Education for which Award is Granted:** Undergraduate **Number Awarded:** 127 each year: 1 at $6,000, 10 at $5,000, 20 at $2,500, and 96 at $1,000. **Funds Available:** Stipends are $6,000, $5,000, $2,500, or $1,000; payments are issued directly to the financial aid office at the institution the student attends. **Duration:** 1 year.
Eligibility Requirements: This program is open to high school students with a GPA of 3.0 or higher who are U.S. citizens and have been involved in school or community activities. Candidates must first be nominated by a school official, youth activity sponsor, or educational organization to have their name appear in *Who's Who Among American High School Students.* All students listed in that publication automatically receive an application for these scholarships in the mail. Selection is based on GPA, achievement test scores, leadership qualifications, work experience, evaluation of an essay, and some consideration for financial need. **Deadline for Receipt:** May of each year. **Additional Information:** The ECI Scholarship Foundation was established in 1968 by Educational Communications Inc., publisher of *Who's Who Among American High School Students.* Applications must be accompanied by a $3.50 processing fee.

606 ■ ROYAL A. AND MILDRED D. EDDY STUDENT LOAN TRUST FUND

c/o NBD Bank
Trust Department
8585 Broadway, Suite 396
Merrillville, IN 46410
Tel: (219)738-4180
To provide loans to undergraduate and graduate school students who need financial assistance to complete their education.

Title of Award: Royal A. and Mildred D. Eddy Student Loans **Area, Field, or Subject:** General studies/Field of study not specified **Level of Education for which Award is Granted:** Graduate, Undergraduate **Number Awarded:** Varies each year. **Funds Available:** Any amount, up to $4,000, may be loaned. The interest rate charged is 10%. **Duration:** Recipients must begin repaying on the loan within 2 years. No monthly payments (interest or principal) are required during the first 5 months after graduation; payments after that are on a monthly basis.
Eligibility Requirements: Eligible to apply for these loans are undergraduate or graduate school students who are U.S. citizens and have completed at least 2 years of work at an accredited college or university. Loans are granted without regard to race, sex, creed, residence, university major, age, or marital status, as long as a need for the loan exists and applicants are capable of repayment. However, it should be noted that the general policy is to only loan to students who will begin earning money and repaying the loan within 2 years. No collateral is required, but 2 co-signers are necessary (these can be the student's

parents). **Deadline for Receipt:** Applications may be submitted at any time.

607 ■ EDUCATION IS FREEDOM FOUNDATION

c/o 7-Eleven, Inc.
2711 North Haskell Avenue
Dallas, TX 75204
(866)EIF-EDUC
Web Site: http://www.educationisfreedom.com/Scholarships/scholarships.asp

To provide financial assistance to high school seniors who have financial need and would be unable to attend college without assistance.

Title of Award: Education is Freedom National Scholarship Program **Area, Field, or Subject:** General studies/Field of study not specified **Level of Education for which Award is Granted:** Undergraduate **Number Awarded:** Approximately 250 each year. **Funds Available:** The stipend is $2,000. Funds are paid to the student and institution for payment of tuition, fees, and books. **Duration:** 1 year; may be renewed up to 3 years as long as the recipient remains enrolled full time with a GPA of 3.0 or higher.

Eligibility Requirements: This program is open to high school seniors and graduates under 24 years of age who have resided in the United States for at least 1 year. Applicants must be planning to enroll for the first time in a full-time undergraduate course of study at an accredited 2- or 4-year college or university. They must be able to demonstrate a GPA of 3.0 to 3.5, activities and leadership, work history, and unmet financial need. **Deadline for Receipt:** January of each year. **Additional Information:** This foundation was established in 2002 by James W. Keyes, president and CEO of 7-Eleven, Inc. Additional support is provided by Western Union, Anheuser-Busch Companies, Inc., and other corporate sponsors.

608 ■ EDUCATIONAL RESEARCH CENTER OF AMERICA, INC.

Attn: Scholarship Committee
2020 Pennsylvania Avenue, N.W., Room 7799
Washington, DC 20006
Tel: (202)393-7799
E-mail: info@studentresearch.org
Web Site: http://www.studentresearch.org/public/application.html

To provide financial assistance for college to high school seniors who have provided outstanding service to their community

Title of Award: ERCA Community Contribution Scholarship **Area, Field, or Subject:** General studies/Field of study not specified **Level of Education for which Award is Granted:** Undergraduate **Number Awarded:** Between 25 and 100 each year. **Funds Available:** The stipend is $1,000. **Duration:** 1 year.

Eligibility Requirements: This program is open to college-bound high school seniors. Applicants must submit a description of an activity in which they have participated that demonstrates their commitment to their community. Selection is based on that description, honors or awards received, GPA, and a letter of reference. **Deadline for Receipt:** June of each year. **Additional Information:** A processing fee of $3.50 must accompany the application.

609 ■ EGBAR FOUNDATION

Attn: Karen Suclla
15922 Pacific Coast Highway
Huntington Beach, CA 92649
Tel: (562)795-6000
Free: 800-EGBAR-55
Fax: (562)592-1124
E-mail: ksuclla@simplegreen.com
Web Site: http://www.egbar.org

To provide financial assistance for college to high school students who serve as the ambassador for the EGBAR Foundation.

Title of Award: EGBAR Spirit Ambassador Scholarship Fund **Area, Field, or Subject:** General studies/Field of study not specified **Level of Education for which Award is Granted:** Undergraduate **Number Awarded:** 1 each year. **Funds Available:** After their year of service, ambassadors receive a college scholarship (amount not specified). **Duration:** The award is presented annually.

Eligibility Requirements: The EGBAR Foundation was established by Sunshine Makers, Inc., manufacturer of the cleaner Simple Green. It oper-

ates a program called the EGBAR Clean-Up Challenge to encourage elementary school children to run environmental clean-ups at beaches, parks, and schools. Every year it selects a high school student to serve as its ambassador. The student should embody the essence of the foundation's acronym, "Everything's Gonna Be All Right." Applicants should have shown that, in the face of adversity, whether illness, a family loss, or poverty, they strive for self-improvement and the betterment of the community as a whole. They should also have embraced an appreciation for the environment and its well being.

610 ■ ELKS NATIONAL FOUNDATION

Attn: Scholarship Department
2750 North Lake View Avenue
Chicago, IL 60614-1889
Tel: (773)755-4732
Fax: (773)755-4729
E-mail: scholarship@elks.org
Web Site: http://www.elks.org/enf/scholars/eefgrants.cfm

To provide emergency financial assistance to college students who are children of deceased or disabled members of B.P.O. Elks.

Title of Award: Elks National Foundation Emergency Educational Fund Grants **Area, Field, or Subject:** General studies/Field of study not specified **Level of Education for which Award is Granted:** Two Year College **Number Awarded:** Varies each year. **Funds Available:** The amount of the assistance depends on the need of the applicant but normally ranges up to $4,000 per year. **Duration:** 1 year; may be renewed up to 3 additional years.

Eligibility Requirements: This program is open to children of Elks who have died or are totally disabled. Applicants must be unmarried, under 23 years of age, able to demonstrate financial need, and attending a college or university in the United States as a full-time undergraduate student. The student's parent must have been a member in good standing at the time of death or, if disabled, have been a member in good standing before he or she became incapacitated and must continue to be an Elk in good standing when the application for assistance is submitted. Applications must give the B.P.O. Elks Lodge affiliation of the Elk parent. **Deadline for Receipt:** December of each year for new applications; October of each year for renewal applications.

611 ■ ELKS NATIONAL FOUNDATION

Attn: Scholarship Department
2750 North Lake View Avenue
Chicago, IL 60614-1889
Tel: (773)755-4732
Fax: (773)755-4729
E-mail: scholarship@elks.org
Web Site: http://www.elks.org/enf/scholars/mvs.cfm

To provide financial assistance to outstanding high school seniors who can demonstrate financial need and are interested in attending college.

Title of Award: Elks National Foundation "Most Valuable Student" Scholarship Award **Area, Field, or Subject:** General studies/Field of study not specified **Level of Education for which Award is Granted:** Four Year College **Number Awarded:** 500 each year: 2 first awards (1 male and 1 female), 2 second awards (1 male and 1 female), 2 third awards (1 male and 1 female), and 494 fourth awards (247 males and 247 females). **Funds Available:** First place is $15,000 per year; second place is $10,000 per year; third place is $5,000 per year; fourth place is $1,000 per year. More than $2.2 million is distributed through this program each year. **Duration:** 4 years.

Eligibility Requirements: This program is open to graduating high school students (or the equivalent) who are U.S. citizens and residents within the jurisdiction of the B.P.O. Elks of the U.S.A. Applicants must be planning to work on a 4-year degree on a full-time basis at a college or university within the United States. They must submit an official form furnished by the Elks National Foundation (no photocopies; these are available at local Elks Lodges. Applications must be filed with the scholarship chair, Exalted Ruler, or secretary of the Elks Lodge in whose jurisdiction the applicant resides. Applications are reviewed by Lodge and District scholarship committees and then judged by the scholarship committee of the State Elks Association for inclusion in the state's quota of entries in the national competition. On the national level, selection is based on financial need (200 points), leadership (350 points), and scholarship (450 points). Male and female students compete separately. **Deadline for**

Receipt: January of each year. **Additional Information:** In addition to this program, established in 1931, many Elks State Associations and/or Lodges also offer scholarships. Applications must be submitted to an Elks Lodge in your community.

612 ■ ELKS NATIONAL FOUNDATION

Attn: Scholarship Department
2750 North Lake View Avenue
Chicago, IL 60614-1889
Tel: (773)755-4732
Fax: (773)755-4729
E-mail: scholarship@elks.org
Web Site: http://www.elks.org/enf/Scholars/legacy.cfm
To provide financial assistance for college to the children of members of the B.P.O. Elks.

Title of Award: Legacy Awards for the Children of Elks **Area, Field, or Subject:** General studies/Field of study not specified **Level of Education for which Award is Granted:** Undergraduate **Number Awarded:** 500 each year. Each state and area is eligible to receive a number of awards based on its support of the Elks National Foundation. The actual number of awards a state receives is the lesser of its quota or 25% of the total applicants from that state. **Funds Available:** The stipends are $1,000 per year. **Duration:** 1 year; nonrenewable.

Eligibility Requirements: This program is open to graduating high school seniors who are the children, stepchildren, grandchildren, and legal wards of Elks and plan to attend a college or university in the United States (or in Guam, Panama, Puerto Rico, or the Philippines for residents of those countries or territories). The Elk parent must have been a member for at least 2 years and must be a paid-up member through the year following the date of application. Applications must be accompanied by SAT or ACT scores, a transcript of high school credits, a biographical questionnaire, and 2 letters of application. Eligible applicants compete against other eligible applicants from their state or area. Selection is based entirely on merit; financial need is not considered. **Deadline for Receipt:** January of each year. **Additional Information:** Applications must be submitted to an Elks lodge in your community.

613 ■ ENLISTED ASSOCIATION NATIONAL GUARD OF KANSAS

c/o 1SG John Ryan
P.O. Box 841
Topeka, KS 66601-0841
Tel: (785)242-5678
Fax: (785)242-3765
E-mail: eangks@earthlink.net
Web Site: http://hometown.aol.com/EANGKS
To provide financial assistance for college to members of the Enlisted Association National Guard of Kansas and their families.

Title of Award: Enlisted Association National Guard of Kansas Scholarships **Area, Field, or Subject:** General studies/Field of study not specified **Level of Education for which Award is Granted:** Undergraduate **Number Awarded:** Varies each year. **Funds Available:** Stipends are normally approximately $1,000. **Duration:** 1 year.

Eligibility Requirements: This program is open to members of the association and their families. **Deadline for Receipt:** May of each year. **Additional Information:** This program is supported, in part, by USAA Insurance Corporation.

614 ■ ENLISTED ASSOCIATION NATIONAL GUARD OF NEW JERSEY

Attn: Scholarship Committee
101 Eggert Crossing Road
Lawrenceville, NJ 08648-2805
Tel: (609)530-6977
Fax: (609)530-7100
Web Site: http://www.eang-nj.org/scholarships.html
To provide financial assistance for college to New Jersey National Guard members and their children.

Title of Award: CSM Vincent Baldassari Memorial Scholarship **Area, Field, or Subject:** General studies/Field of study not specified **Level of Education for which Award is Granted:** Undergraduate **Number Awarded:** Varies each year; recently, 5 of these scholarships were awarded. **Funds Available:** The stipend is $1,000. **Duration:** 1 year.

Eligibility Requirements: This program is open to 1) children of New Jersey National Guard members who are also members of the Enlisted

Association National Guard of New Jersey, and 2) drilling Guard members who are also members of the Association. Applicants must submit 1) information on their church, school, and community activities; 2) a list of honors they have received; 3) 2 letters of recommendation; and 4) a letter with specific facts about their desire to continue their education and specifying their career goals. Financial need is not considered in the selection process. **Deadline for Receipt:** April of each year.

615 ■ ENLISTED ASSOCIATION NATIONAL GUARD OF NEW JERSEY

Attn: Scholarship Committee
101 Eggert Crossing Road
Lawrenceville, NJ 08648-2805
Tel: (609)530-6977
Fax: (609)530-7100
Web Site: http://www.eang-nj.org/scholarships.html
To provide financial assistance for college to New Jersey National Guard members and their children.

Title of Award: EANGNJ USAA Scholarship **Area, Field, or Subject:** General studies/Field of study not specified **Level of Education for which Award is Granted:** Undergraduate **Number Awarded:** 1 each year. **Funds Available:** The stipend is $1,000. **Duration:** 1 year.

Eligibility Requirements: This program is open to drilling members of the New Jersey National Guard and their children. Membership in the Enlisted Association National Guard of New Jersey (EANGNJ) is not required. Applicants must submit 1) information on their church, school, and community activities; 2) a list of honors they have received; 3) 2 letters of recommendation; and 4) a letter with specific facts about their desire to continue their education and specifying their career goals. Financial need is not considered in the selection process. **Deadline for Receipt:** April of each year. **Additional Information:** This program is administered by EANGNJ and funded by USAA Insurance Corporation.

616 ■ ENLISTED ASSOCIATION OF THE NATIONAL GUARD OF TENNESSEE

Attn: Scholarship Committee
4332 Kenilwood Drive, Suite B
Nashville, TN 37204-4401
Tel: (615)781-2000
Fax: (615)833-9173
Web Site: http://www.eangtn.org/Scholarships.htm
To provide financial assistance for college to members of the Enlisted Association of the National Guard of Tennessee (EANGTN) and to their dependents.

Title of Award: EANGTN Scholarship Program **Area, Field, or Subject:** General studies/Field of study not specified **Level of Education for which Award is Granted:** Undergraduate **Number Awarded:** 6 each year. **Funds Available:** The stipend is $1,000. Funds are paid to the recipient's school once enrollment is confirmed. **Duration:** 1 year.

Eligibility Requirements: This program is open to students who are members of both the Tennessee National Guard and EANGTN or the dependent son, daughter, or spouse of a member in good standing. Applicants are required to submit letters of recommendation verifying their status and describing their general personal traits. They must have achieved above average academic standing in high school and/or college, have participated in extracurricular and civic activities, and be able to document financial need. **Additional Information:** In 1985, the National Guard Association of Tennessee (NGAT) agreed that the EANGTN would fund the scholarships of both associations. Additional funding is also provided by USAA Insurance Corporation.

617 ■ ENLISTED ASSOCIATION OF THE NATIONAL GUARD OF THE UNITED STATES

3133 Mount Vernon Avenue
Alexandria, VA 22305-2640
Tel: (703)519-3846
Free: 800-234-EANG
Fax: (703)519-3849
E-mail: eangus@eangus.org
Web Site: http://www.eangus.org
To provide financial assistance to National Guardmembers and their dependents who are members of the Enlisted Association of the National Guard of the United States (EANGUS).

Title of Award: CSM Virgil R. Williams Scholarship Program **Area, Field, or Subject:** General studies/Field of study not specified **Level of Education for which Award is Granted:** Undergraduate **Number Awarded:** 2 or more each year. **Funds Available:** The stipend is $2,000. **Duration:** 1 year; nonrenewable.

Eligibility Requirements: This program is open to high school seniors and currently-enrolled college students. They must be 1) National Guardmembers who belong to EANGUS; 2) unmarried sons and daughters of EANGUS members; 3) spouses of EANGUS members; or 4) unmarried spouses and unmarried dependent children of deceased EANGUS members who were in good standing at the time of their death. Honorary, associate, or corporate membership alone does not qualify. Graduate students are not eligible. Applicants must submit a copy of their school transcript, 3 letters of recommendation, a letter of academic reference (from their principal, dean, or counselor), a photocopy of the qualifying state and/or national membership card (parent's, spouse's or applicant's), and a statement indicating why they want to continue their education and why financial assistance is necessary. Application packets must be submitted to the state EANGUS association; acceptable packets are then sent to the national offices for judging. Selection is based on academic achievement, character, leadership, and financial need. **Deadline for Receipt:** Applications must first be verified by the state office and then submitted by June to the national office. **Additional Information:** Recipients must enroll full time.

618 ■ ENLISTED ASSOCIATION OF THE NATIONAL GUARD OF UTAH

Attn: SFC Dianne Reed
12953 Minuteman Drive
P.O. Box 1776
Draper, UT 84020-1776
Tel: (801)523-4493
Fax: (801)523-4659
E-mail: dianne.reed@us.army.mil
Web Site: http://www.eangut.org
To provide financial assistance for college to National Guardmembers who are active members of the Enlisted Association National Guard of Utah (EANGUT) and their families.

Title of Award: EANGUT Scholarship **Area, Field, or Subject:** General studies/Field of study not specified **Level of Education for which Award is Granted:** Undergraduate **Number Awarded:** 1 or more each year. **Funds Available:** The stipend is $1,000. **Duration:** 1 year.

Eligibility Requirements: This program is open to members of the National Guard and EANGUT, their spouses, and their dependents. Applicants must have a GPA of 2.5 or higher and be able to demonstrate financial need. Along with their application, they must submit statements on their educational goals and why they need a scholarship and 3 letters of recommendation. **Deadline for Receipt:** January of each year.

619 ■ ENLISTED ASSOCIATION OF THE NEW YORK NATIONAL GUARD, INC.

Attn: Education Awards Chair
330 Old Niskayuna Road
Latham, NY 12110-2224
Tel: (518)220-4116
E-mail: ken.secor@ny.ngb.army.mil
Web Site: http://www.eanyng.org/AwardsandScholarships.html
To provide financial assistance for college to members of the Enlisted Association of the New York National Guard (EANYNG) and their families.

Title of Award: Robert H. Connal Scholarship Education Awards **Area, Field, or Subject:** General studies/Field of study not specified **Level of Education for which Award is Granted:** Undergraduate **Number Awarded:** 7 each year: 1 statewide scholarship at $1,000 and 6 at $500 in each area of the state. **Funds Available:** Stipends are $1,000 or $500. **Duration:** 1 year.

Eligibility Requirements: This program is open to EANYNG members and their spouses, children, and grandchildren. Applicants must be a college-bound high school senior or a current undergraduate. The applicant or sponsor must have belonged to EANYNG for more than 1 year. Membership in EANYNG is limited to enlisted personnel in the New York Air or Army National Guard. **Additional Information:** Funding for this program is provided by the production of the association's yearly journal, members' dues, and a donation from USAA Insurance Corporation.

620 ■ EPILEPSY FOUNDATION OF THE CHESAPEAKE REGION

Attn: Elen Falk
8503 La Salle Road
Towson, MD 21286
Tel: (410)828-7700
Free: 800-492-2523
Fax: (410)828-7708
Web Site: http://www.epilepsy-foundation.org
To provide financial assistance for college or graduate school to residents of the Chesapeake region of Maryland, Washington, D.C., and northern Virginia who have epilepsy.

Title of Award: Ira Rosenzwog Scholarship **Area, Field, or Subject:** General studies/Field of study not specified **Level of Education for which Award is Granted:** Graduate, Undergraduate **Number Awarded:** 1 or more each year. **Funds Available:** Stipends range from $500 to $1,200. **Duration:** 1 year; may be renewed up to 3 additional years.

Eligibility Requirements: This program is open to residents of Maryland, Washington, D.C., and northern Virginia who can provide a letter from their physician confirming a diagnosis of epilepsy. Applicants must be attending or planning to attend a 2-year college, 4-year college or university, trade/technical school, or graduate school. Along with their application, they must submit an essay on how epilepsy has affected their life, what they hope to gain from their college experience, and why they would make a deserving recipient. Financial need is also considered in the selection process. **Deadline for Receipt:** April of each year.

621 ■ EPILEPSY FOUNDATION OF IDAHO

310 West Idaho Street
Boise, ID 83702
Tel: (208)344-4340
Free: 800-237-6676
E-mail: efid@epilepsyidaho.org
Web Site: http://www.epilepsyidaho.org/gile-scholar.htm
To provide financial assistance for college and the purchase of medical drugs to Idaho residents who have epilepsy.

Title of Award: Gregory W. Gile Memorial Scholarship **Area, Field, or Subject:** General studies/Field of study not specified **Level of Education for which Award is Granted:** Undergraduate **Number Awarded:** 1 each year. **Funds Available:** The stipend is $1,000. **Duration:** 1 year.

Eligibility Requirements: This program is open to residents of Idaho who have had at least 1 year of a medical diagnosis of epilepsy. Applicants must have graduated from a high school in Idaho, be entering or continuing in college, be a U.S. citizen or permanent resident, and agree to enroll in at least 12 credits per term. Preference is given to applicants planning to attend an Idaho institution. Selection is based on career goals, recommendations, how the applicant has faced the challenges due to epilepsy, and financial need. **Deadline for Receipt:** March of each year. **Additional Information:** This program was established in 1988. The Epilepsy Foundation of Idaho also provides Limited Emergency Financial Assistance for anti-epileptic drug purchases.

622 ■ EPILEPSY FOUNDATION OF KENTUCKIANA

501 East Broadway, Suite 110
Louisville, KY 40202-2041
Tel: (502)584-8817; (866)275-1078
Web Site: http://www.epilepsyfoundation.org/local/kentuckiana/scholarship.cfm
To provide financial assistance for college to high school seniors in Kentucky and southern Indiana who have epilepsy.

Title of Award: Shannon O'Daniel Memorial Scholarship **Area, Field, or Subject:** General studies/Field of study not specified **Level of Education for which Award is Granted:** Undergraduate **Number Awarded:** 1 each year. **Funds Available:** The stipend is $1,000. **Duration:** 1 year.

Eligibility Requirements: This program is open to college-bound high school seniors in Kentucky and southern Indiana who have epilepsy or another seizure disorder. Applicants must submit a description of their participation in extracurricular activities, 2 letters of recommendation, their current transcript, and an essay (up to 250 words) on something of direct personal importance to them as a person with epilepsy. Financial need is also considered in the selection process. **Deadline for Receipt:** April of each year. **Additional Information:** This program was established in 2001.

623 ■ EPILEPSY FOUNDATION OF MASSACHUSETTS & RHODE ISLAND

540 Gallivan Boulevard, Second Floor
Boston, MA 02124-5401
Tel: (617)506-6041; 888-576-9996
E-mail: info@efmri.org
Web Site: http://www.epilepsyfoundation.org/local/massri
To provide financial assistance for college or graduate school to people who have epilepsy and live in Massachusetts or Rhode Island.
Title of Award: Epilepsy Foundation of Massachusetts & Rhode Island Scholarships **Area, Field, or Subject:** General studies/Field of study not specified **Level of Education for which Award is Granted:** Graduate, Undergraduate **Number Awarded:** Varies each year; recently, 6 of these scholarships were awarded. **Funds Available:** The stipend is $1,000.
Duration: 1 year; may be renewed.
Eligibility Requirements: This program is open to residents of Massachusetts or Rhode Island who have been diagnosed with epilepsy (seizure disorder). Applicants must be accepted or enrolled in a postsecondary educational or vocational program as an undergraduate or graduate student. As part of the application process, students must include an essay (up to 220 words in length) on their academic and career goals and how having epilepsy has affected or influenced those goals and their work towards achieving them. **Deadline for Receipt:** June of each year. **Additional Information:** This program includes the following named scholarships: the James Lyons Scholarship, the Dr. George F. Howard III Scholarship, the Lorraine Glidden Scholarship, the Maureen Metzler Scholarship, and the Shannon McDermott Scholarship.

624 ■ EPILEPSY FOUNDATION OF NEW JERSEY

429 River View Plaza
Trenton, NJ 08611-3420
Tel: (609)392-4900
Free: 800-EFNJ-TIE
Fax: (609)392-5621
E-mail: efnj@efnj.com
Web Site: http://www.efnj.com/programs/scholarshipprogram.shtml
To provide financial assistance for college to high school seniors with epilepsy in New Jersey.
Title of Award: Epilepsy Foundation of New Jersey Scholarship Program **Area, Field, or Subject:** General studies/Field of study not specified **Level of Education for which Award is Granted:** Undergraduate **Number Awarded:** Up to 4 each year. **Funds Available:** The stipend is $1,000 per year. Funds are paid directly to the recipient. **Duration:** 1 year.
Eligibility Requirements: This program is open to high school seniors who are residents of New Jersey and have epilepsy. Applicants must submit a brief personal statement explaining their academic and career goals. Selection is based on financial need, academic record, extracurricular activities, and extent of disability. **Deadline for Receipt:** May of each year. **Additional Information:** Recipients may attend college in any state. Information is also available from the EFNJ Scholarship Program, Lions Head Office Park, 33 Beaverson Boulevard, Suite 8A, Brick, NJ 08723, (732) 262-8020, (800) 372-6510.

625 ■ EPILEPSY FOUNDATION OF VERMONT

P.O. Box 6292
Rutland, VT 05702
Tel: (802)775-1686
Free: 800-565-0972
E-mail: epilepsy@sover.net
Web Site: http://www.sover.net/~epilepsy/default.htm
To provide financial assistance for college to high school seniors in Vermont who have epilepsy.
Title of Award: James A. Girard Scholarship **Area, Field, or Subject:** General studies/Field of study not specified **Level of Education for which Award is Granted:** Undergraduate **Number Awarded:** 1 each year. **Funds Available:** The stipend is $1,000. **Duration:** 1 year.
Eligibility Requirements: This program is open to high school seniors in Vermont who have epilepsy. Applicants must be planning to go on to higher education after graduation.

626 ■ EPISCOPAL DIOCESE OF BETHLEHEM

Attn: Archdeacon Rich Cluett
333 Wyandotte Street
Bethlehem, PA 18015
Tel: (610)691-5655
Free: 800-358-5655
Web Site: http://www.diobeth.org/Ministries/gressle.html
To provide financial assistance to residents of Pennsylvania who are sons of Episcopal clergy and interested in working on a college degree.
Title of Award: Gressle Fund **Area, Field, or Subject:** General studies/Field of study not specified **Level of Education for which Award is Granted:** Undergraduate **Number Awarded:** Varies each year. **Funds Available:** Stipends up to $1,500, depending on need, are available. **Duration:** 1 year; may be renewed until the recipient reaches the age of 20.
Eligibility Requirements: Applicants must be 1) residents of 1 of the 5 dioceses of Pennsylvania; 2) sons of an Episcopal priest; 3) younger than 20 years of age; and 4) interested in working on a college degree. The clergy parent must live in the Commonwealth of Pennsylvania and must be canonically resident in 1 of its dioceses. Preference is given to sons of clergy in the diocese of Bethlehem; only when surplus funds are available can scholarships to awarded to sons of clergy in the other 4 Pennsylvania dioceses. **Deadline for Receipt:** May of each year.

627 ■ EPISCOPAL DIOCESE OF BETHLEHEM

Attn: Archdeacon Rich Cluett
333 Wyandotte Street
Bethlehem, PA 18015
Tel: (610)691-5655
Free: 800-358-5655
Web Site: http://www.diobeth.org/Ministries/shannon.html
To provide financial assistance to residents of Pennsylvania who are daughters of Episcopal clergy and interested in working on a college degree.
Title of Award: Shannon Fund **Area, Field, or Subject:** General studies/Field of study not specified **Level of Education for which Award is Granted:** Undergraduate **Number Awarded:** Varies each year. **Funds Available:** Stipends up to $1,500, depending on need, are available. **Duration:** 1 year; may be renewed until the recipient reaches the age of 20.
Eligibility Requirements: Applicants must be 1) residents of 1 of the 5 dioceses of Pennsylvania; 2) daughters of an Episcopal priest; 3) younger than 20 years of age; and 4) interested in working on a college degree. The clergy parent must live in the Commonwealth of Pennsylvania and must be canonically resident in 1 of its dioceses. Preference is given to daughters of clergy in the diocese of Bethlehem; only when surplus funds are available can scholarships to awarded to daughters of clergy in the other 4 Pennsylvania dioceses. **Deadline for Receipt:** May of each year.

628 ■ EQUALITYMAINE

1 Pleasant Street, Fourth Floor
P.O. Box 1951
Portland, ME 04104
Tel: (207)761-3732
Fax: (207)828-8620
E-mail: info@equalitymaine.org
Web Site: http://www.equalitymaine.org
To provide financial assistance for college to high school seniors in Maine who submit an essay on preventing discrimination based on sexual orientation.
Title of Award: Joel Abromson Memorial Scholarship **Area, Field, or Subject:** General studies/Field of study not specified **Level of Education for which Award is Granted:** Undergraduate **Number Awarded:** 2 each year. **Funds Available:** The stipend is $1,000. **Duration:** 1 year; nonrenewable.
Eligibility Requirements: This program is open to seniors graduating from high schools in Maine who are planning to attend a college or university. Applicants must submit an essay on "How can schools become safer for all students regardless of their sexual orientation and gender

expression?" **Deadline for Receipt:** April of each year. **Additional Information:** These scholarships were first awarded in 2002.

629 ■ TAYLOR J. ERTEL FOSTER CHILDREN FOUNDATION

2245 Heim Hill Road
Montoursville, PA 17754-9699
Tel: (570)433-3494
Fax: (570)326-1050
E-mail: aertel@regscan.com
Web Site: http://www.tjefoundation.org
To provide financial assistance for college or graduate school to residents of Pennsylvania who have been in foster care.
Title of Award: Taylor J. Ertel Scholarships **Area, Field, or Subject:** General studies/Field of study not specified **Level of Education for which Award is Granted:** Graduate, Undergraduate **Number Awarded:** 1 or more each year. **Funds Available:** The stipend is $2,000 per year. **Duration:** 1 year.
Eligibility Requirements: This program is open to Pennsylvania residents who have been placed in foster care by a child welfare agency. Applicants must be attending or planning to attend a vocational school, college, university, or graduate school in the state. Along with their application, they must submit information on their school activities, educational record, school awards and honors, community activities, employment record, and a budget. **Additional Information:** This program was established in 1993.

630 ■ BOOMER ESIASON FOUNDATION

c/o Jerry Cahill
417 Fifth Avenue, Second Floor
New York, NY 10016
Tel: (646)344-3765
Fax: (646)344-3757
E-mail: jcahill@esiason.org
Web Site: http://www.esiason.org
To provide financial assistance to undergraduate and graduate students who have cystic fibrosis (CF).
Title of Award: Boomer Esiason Foundation Scholarship Program **Area, Field, or Subject:** General studies/Field of study not specified **Level of Education for which Award is Granted:** Graduate, Undergraduate **Number Awarded:** 10 to 15 each year. **Funds Available:** Stipends range from $500 to $2,000. Funds are paid directly to the academic institution to assist in covering the cost of tuition and fees. **Duration:** 1 year; nonrenewable.
Eligibility Requirements: This program is open to CF patients who are working on an undergraduate or graduate degree. Applicants must submit a letter from a social worker describing their needs, a detailed breakdown of tuition costs from their academic institution, transcripts, and a 1-page essay on their post-graduation goals. Selection is based on academic ability, character, leadership potential, service to the community, and financial need. Finalists are interviewed by telephone. **Additional Information:** Recipients must be willing to participate in the sponsor's CF Ambassador Program by speaking once a year at a designated CF event to help education the general public about CF.

631 ■ EARL L. ESTWICK TRAILBLAZER MEMORIAL FUND

P.O. Box 9213
Paramus, NJ 07653-9213
Tel: (201)343-4554
Fax: (201)343-4554
E-mail: blazer6@verizon.net
Web Site: http://www.estwickscholarships.com
To provide undergraduate scholarships to college-bound high school seniors from New York and New Jersey who can prove financial need.
Title of Award: Earl L. Estwick, Sr. Trailblazer Memorial Scholarship **Area, Field, or Subject:** General studies/Field of study not specified **Level of Education for which Award is Granted:** Undergraduate **Number Awarded:** 1 or more each year. **Funds Available:** A stipend is awarded (amount not specified). **Duration:** 1 year or more.
Eligibility Requirements: High school seniors from New York and New Jersey are eligible to apply for these scholarships if they can prove financial need, have at least a "B+" GPA, have a minimum SAT score of 1050, and have served their community in some capacity. Many of the applicants are the first in their family to attend college. Some of the

scholarships are set aside for students who lost parents in the World Trade Center disaster on September 11, 2001. **Additional Information:** This scholarship was first awarded in 1996. Since then, more than 20 scholarships have been awarded.

632 ■ EXPLOSIVE ORDNANCE DISPOSAL MEMORIAL

Attn: EOD Administrator
P.O. Box 594
Niceville, FL 32588
Tel: (850)729-2401
Fax: (850)729-2401
E-mail: eod@cox.net
Web Site: http://www.eodmemorial.org/scholarship.html
To provide financial assistance for college to family members of technicians or military officers who have worked in explosive ordnance disposal.
Title of Award: Explosive Ordnance Disposal (EOD) Memorial Scholarships **Area, Field, or Subject:** General studies/Field of study not specified **Level of Education for which Award is Granted:** Undergraduate **Number Awarded:** Varies each year; recently, 45 of these scholarships were awarded. **Funds Available:** The stipend is currently $1,800 per year. Funds are paid directly to the academic institution for the student's tuition, books, fees, and on-campus housing. **Duration:** 1 year; may be renewed up to 3 additional years.
Eligibility Requirements: Applicants for this scholarship must be family members, enrolled in DEERS, of explosive ordnance disposal (EOD) technicians or officers in the Army, Navy, Air Force, or Marine Corps who are currently on active duty (includes activated Reserves), retired, or deceased. Awards are presented in the following priority: 1) family members of those whose names are on the EOD Memorial; 2) applicants who have never received an EOD scholarship; and 3) prior EOD scholarship recipients. Selection is based on academic merit, community involvement, and financial need. **Deadline for Receipt:** February of each year.

633 ■ FACTOR SUPPORT NETWORK PHARMACY

Attn: Scholarship Committee
900 Avenida Acaso, Suite A
Camarillo, CA 93012-8749
Tel: (805)388-9336; 877-FSN-4-YOU
Fax: (805)482-6324
E-mail: Scholarships@FactorSupport.com
Web Site: http://www.factorsupport.com/scholarships.htm
To provide financial assistance for college to men with hemophilia and their immediate families.
Title of Award: Mike Hylton and Ron Niederman Scholarships **Area, Field, or Subject:** General studies/Field of study not specified **Level of Education for which Award is Granted:** Undergraduate **Number Awarded:** 10 each year. **Funds Available:** The stipend is $1,000. Funds are paid directly to the recipient. **Duration:** 1 year.
Eligibility Requirements: This program is open to men with bleeding disorders and their immediate family members. Applicants must be entering or attending a college, university, juniors college, or vocational school. They must submit 3 short essays: 1) their career goals; 2) how hemophilia or von Willebrand disease has affected their life; and 3) how they are educating themselves, their family, and their community about hemophilia and/or von Willebrand disease. Selection is based on academic goals, volunteer work, school activities, other pertinent experience and achievements, and financial need. **Deadline for Receipt:** April of each year. **Additional Information:** This program was established in 1999.

634 ■ FACTOR SUPPORT NETWORK PHARMACY

Attn: Scholarship Committee
900 Avenida Acaso, Suite A
Camarillo, CA 93012-8749
Tel: (805)388-9336; 877-FSN-4-YOU
Fax: (805)482-6324
E-mail: Scholarships@FactorSupport.com
Web Site: http://www.factorsupport.com/scholarships.htm
To provide financial assistance to women with hemophilia.
Title of Award: Millie Gonzalez Memorial Scholarships **Area, Field, or Subject:** General studies/Field of study not specified **Level of Education for which Award is Granted:** Undergraduate **Number Awarded:** 5 each year. **Funds Available:** The stipend is $1,000. Funds are paid directly to the recipient. **Duration:** 1 year.

Eligibility Requirements: This program is open to women with bleeding disorders who are entering or attending a college, university, juniors college, or vocational school. Applicants must submit 3 short essays: 1) their career goals; 2) how hemophilia or von Willebrand disease has affected their life; and 3) how they are educating themselves, their family, and their community about hemophilia and/or von Willebrand disease. Selection is based on academic goals, volunteer work, school activities, other pertinent experience and achievements, and financial need. **Deadline for Receipt:** April of each year.

635 ■ LATREESE NICOLE FAGAN MEMORIAL SCHOLARSHIP FUND, INC.

Attn: Board of Directors
P.O. Box 19370
Detroit, MI 48219-0370
Tel: (313)531-9922
Fax: (313)531-9926
E-mail: info@latreesefagan.org
Web Site: http://www.latreesefagan.org
To provide financial assistance for college to residents of Michigan who have lupus.
Title of Award: Latreese Nicole Fagan Memorial Scholarship **Area, Field, or Subject:** General studies/Field of study not specified **Level of Education for which Award is Granted:** Undergraduate **Number Awarded:** 1 each year. **Funds Available:** The stipend is $1,000. Funds are paid directly to the recipient's institution to help cover tuition, books, fees, room, and board. **Duration:** 1 year; nonrenewable.
Eligibility Requirements: This program is open to residents of Michigan who are lupus patients with a board-certified physician approving the diagnosis. Applicants must be attending or planning to attend an accredited 2-year or 4-year college, university, or vocational school in Michigan. They must be between 17 and 25 years of age. Along with their application, they must submit an essay on their reasons for desiring a higher education. Selection is based on high school or college transcripts, participation in outside activities, and 3 letters of recommendation. U.S. citizenship is required. **Deadline for Receipt:** March of each year. **Additional Information:** Information is also available from the Lupus Alliance of Michigan and Indiana, 26507 Harper Avenue, St. Clair Shores, MI 48081, (800) 705-6677, Fax: (586) 775-8494, E-mail: info@milupus.org.

636 ■ FALCON FOUNDATION

3116 Academy Drive, Suite 200
USAF Academy, CO 80840-4400
Tel: (719)333-4096
Web Site: http://www.falconfoundation.org
To provide financial assistance to people who require additional training for possible admission to the U.S. Air Force Academy.
Title of Award: Falcon Foundation Scholarships **Area, Field, or Subject:** General studies/Field of study not specified **Level of Education for which Award is Granted:** Undergraduate **Number Awarded:** Varies each year; recently, 99 of these scholarships were awarded for study at 5 preparatory schools. **Funds Available:** Amounts of the scholarships depend on the availability of funds but are intended to provide a large portion of the cost of room, board, and tuition at a preparatory school or junior college selected by the foundation.
Eligibility Requirements: Eligible for these scholarships are individuals who potentially qualify for admission to the U.S. Air Force Academy by meeting the following requirements: U.S. citizens, high school seniors or graduates, good moral character, between 17 and 21 years of age on July 1 of the year of potential admission to the Academy, in good physical condition, unmarried, and with no dependent children. Selection is based on motivation to enter and graduate from the USAF Academy and then follow a career as an Air Force officer; scholastic achievements; qualities of maturity, truthfulness, courage, kindliness, unselfishness, fellowship, and devotion to duty; exhibition of moral force of character and leadership instincts, with an interest in others; and physical vigor, as shown by a fondness for, and participation and success in, sports. **Deadline for Receipt:** April of each year. **Additional Information:** Students who meet the basic requirements but may have academic deficiencies that might disqualify them from admission to the Academy may enroll in preparatory school training to correct the deficiencies. Completion of the preparatory school training does not guarantee admission to the Academy. The Falcon Foundation recognizes that these scholarships may provide the student

with additional education if the applicant fails to receive an appointment at the Academy.

637 ■ FAMILY, CAREER AND COMMUNITY LEADERS OF AMERICA

Attn: Youth/Program Assistant
1910 Association Drive
Reston, VA 20191-1584
Tel: (703)476-4900
Free: 800-234-4425
Fax: (703)860-2713
E-mail: natlhdqtrs@fcclainc.org
Web Site: http://www.fcclainc.org
To provide financial assistance for college to members of Family, Career and Community Leaders of America (FCCLA) who have served as president of their state association.
Title of Award: Raye Virginia Allen State President's Scholarship **Area, Field, or Subject:** General studies/Field of study not specified **Level of Education for which Award is Granted:** Undergraduate **Number Awarded:** 1 each year. **Funds Available:** The stipend is $2,000. The funds are paid directly to the recipient's college or university and are to be used to pay for tuition, room, or board. **Duration:** 1 year; nonrenewable.
Eligibility Requirements: This program is open to affiliated FCCLA members who have held or are holding the office of president of a state FCCLA association. State presidents who have been elected to a national office are not eligible. Applicants must be in their senior year in high school and have applied to a degree-granting institution leading to an associate's or bachelor's degree (in any field of study). Selection is based on leadership and involvement in FCCLA, academic excellence, and significant volunteer experience. **Deadline for Receipt:** February of each year. **Additional Information:** This program was established in 1987 and is named for the first Texas state president of the Future Homemakers of America, currently known as Family, Career and Community Leaders of America. If the recipient withdraws from college, unused funds must be returned to FCCLA.

638 ■ FAMILY, CAREER AND COMMUNITY LEADERS OF AMERICA

Attn: Youth/Program Assistant
1910 Association Drive
Reston, VA 20191-1584
Tel: (703)476-4900
Free: 800-234-4425
Fax: (703)860-2713
E-mail: natlhdqtrs@fcclainc.org
Web Site: http://www.fcclainc.org
To provide financial assistance for college to members of Family, Career and Community Leaders of America (FCCLA).
Title of Award: FCCLA Who's Who Among American High School Students Scholarships **Area, Field, or Subject:** General studies/Field of study not specified **Level of Education for which Award is Granted:** Undergraduate **Number Awarded:** 2 each year. **Funds Available:** The stipend is $1,000. The funds are paid directly to the recipient's college or university and are to be used to pay for tuition, room, or board. **Duration:** 1 year; nonrenewable.
Eligibility Requirements: This program is open to FCCLA members who are high school seniors planning to work on an associate or bachelor's degree. Applicants must have taken the ACT or SAT examination. Selection is based on leadership and involvement in FCCLA, other activities and awards, academic excellence, and significant volunteer experience. **Deadline for Receipt:** February of each year. **Additional Information:** These awards are funded by the ECI Scholarship Foundation of Educational Communications Inc., publisher of *Who's Who Among American High School Students*. If a recipient withdraws from college, unused funds must be returned to FCCLA.

639 ■ FAMILY CIRCLE CUP

c/o Family Circle Tennis Center
161 Seven Farms Drive
Charleston, SC 29492
Tel: (843)856-7900
Free: 800-677-2293
Web Site: http://www.familycirclecup.com
To provide financial assistance for college to female high school seniors in North Carolina, South Carolina, and Georgia.

Title of Award: L'Oreal/Family Circle Cup "Personal Best" Scholarship **Area, Field, or Subject:** General studies/Field of study not specified **Level of Education for which Award is Granted:** Undergraduate **Number Awarded:** 3 each year: 1 from each of the eligible states. **Funds Available:** The stipend is $2,500. **Duration:** 1 year.
Eligibility Requirements: This program is open to women graduating from high schools in North Carolina, South Carolina, and Georgia. Applicants must be planning to enroll full time at an accredited 2-year or 4-year college or university. They must have a GPA of 2.0 or higher and be able to demonstrate that they have made a difference in the lives of others through role modeling, community involvement and services, volunteer experiences, athletics, and extracurricular activities. **Deadline for Receipt:** February of each year. **Additional Information:** This program was established in 1998. Winners and their families are also invited to attend the Family Circle Cup tennis championship on Daniel Island in Charleston, South Carolina with hotel and travel expenses provided.

640 ■ ETHEL AND EMERY FAST SCHOLARSHIP FOUNDATION, INC.

12620 Rolling Road
Potomac, MD 20854
Tel: (301)762-1102
To provide financial assistance to qualified Native Americans enrolled as undergraduates or graduate students.
Title of Award: Ethel and Emery Fast Scholarship **Area, Field, or Subject:** General studies/Field of study not specified **Level of Education for which Award is Granted:** Undergraduate **Number Awarded:** Varies each year. **Funds Available:** A stipend is awarded (amount not specified). Funds are paid directly to the recipient's college or university and can only be used to pay for tuition, room, board, and fees. **Duration:** 1 year.
Eligibility Requirements: Applicants must 1) be Native Americans enrolled in a federally-recognized tribe, 2) have successfully completed 1 year of their undergraduate or graduate school program, 3) be enrolled in school full time, and 4) be able to demonstrate financial need. To apply, students must submit a completed application. documentation of Native American eligibility, an original transcript, a letter confirming enrollment, a federal income tax return, a statement of financial need, and a personal statement (up to 2 pages) describing educational and career goals. **Deadline for Receipt:** August of each year for the fall semester; December of each year for the spring semester.

641 ■ FIELD SCOVELL SCHOLARSHIP FOUNDATION

P.O. Box 569420
Dallas, TX 75356
Tel: (972)289-7012
E-mail: field@sbccottonbowl.com
Web Site: http://www.sbccottonbowl.com/ca_field_scovell.asp
To provide financial assistance for college to high school seniors in north Texas who have been involved in sports.
Title of Award: Field Scovell Scholarships **Area, Field, or Subject:** General studies/Field of study not specified **Level of Education for which Award is Granted:** Undergraduate **Number Awarded:** 10 each year. **Funds Available:** The stipend is $2,000 per year. **Duration:** 1 year; the E.E. "Buddy" Fogelson Scholarship is awarded to 1 of the recipients for study beyond the first year of college.
Eligibility Requirements: This program is open to seniors graduating from high schools in north Texas who have a connection to sports (e.g., team, band, cheerleader, fan). Applicants must have a "C" or equivalent class average and be planning to attend an institution of higher education within Texas, the Big 12 Conference, or the Southeastern Conference. Selection is based on leadership qualities, personal character, and financial need. **Deadline for Receipt:** February of each year. **Additional Information:** This program was established in 1991 to honor Field Scovell, the longtime team selection chairman for the Cotton Bowl football game. It includes the SBC Scholarship, supported by the SBC Foundation. The Big 12 Conference (whose members include University of Colorado, Iowa State University, University of Kansas, Kansas State University, University of Missouri, University of Nebraska, University of Oklahoma, Oklahoma State University, Baylor University, Texas A&M University, Texas Tech University, and University of Texas) and the Southeastern Conference (whose members include Auburn University, University of Alabama, University of Arkansas, University of Florida, University of Georgia, University of Kentucky, Louisiana State University, University of Mississippi, Mississippi State University, University of South Carolina, Vanderbilt University, and University of Tennessee) are associated with the SBC Cotton Bowl Classic.

642 ■ FIERI-STATEN ISLAND CHAPTER

Attn: Scholarship Committee
P.O. Box 60433
Staten Island, NY 10306
E-mail: amar504@aol.com
Web Site: http://www.fieri.org
To provide financial assistance for college to high school seniors of Italian descent who live in the tri-state area of New York, New Jersey, and Connecticut.
Title of Award: Honorable Mario J. Esposito Memorial Scholarship **Area, Field, or Subject:** General studies/Field of study not specified **Level of Education for which Award is Granted:** Undergraduate **Number Awarded:** 1 or more each year. **Funds Available:** A stipend is awarded (amount not specified). **Duration:** 1 year.
Eligibility Requirements: This program is open to Italian American seniors graduating from high schools in the tri-state area and planning to attend college. Applicants must submit an essay on the significance of Italian culture to them and within their life and why they believe they should be recognized as an outstanding Italian American student. Selection is based on that essay; academic achievement and merit; involvement in community, academic, or social activities; and a letter of recommendation. Applicants may also provide an essay on any financial hardships of their family if they consider those relevant. **Deadline for Receipt:** November of each year.

643 ■ FIESTA BOWL

Attn: Queen and Court Scholarship Program
120 South Ash Avenue
Tempe, AZ 85281
Tel: (480)736-4809
Fax: (480)736-4180
Web Site: http://www.tostitosfiestabowl.com
To provide financial assistance to women enrolled at colleges and universities in Arizona who are selected to preside over the annual Fiesta Bowl Festival.
Title of Award: Fiesta Bowl Queen and Court Scholarship Program **Area, Field, or Subject:** General studies/Field of study not specified **Level of Education for which Award is Granted:** Undergraduate **Number Awarded:** 1 each year. **Funds Available:** The stipend is $2,000. **Duration:** 1 year.
Eligibility Requirements: This program is open to women who are enrolled full time at an Arizona college or university. Applicants must be between 19 and 23 years of age and may not have been married or have had any children. They must submit an essay of 500 words or less on what they feel to be the essence of volunteerism, the role it plays in their community, and how they will incorporate their experiences into a potential role as a court member within the Fiesta Bowl community. Selection of the Fiesta Bowl Queen, who receives the scholarship, is based on the essay, academic achievement, poise, community involvement, and personality. **Deadline for Receipt:** September of each year. **Additional Information:** The queen also attends such community activities as the Tostitos Fiesta Bowl, the Fort McDowell Fiesta Bowl Parade, the Blue Cross Blue Shield of Arizona Fiesta Bowl National Band Championship, and the VIAD Corp Fiesta Bowl Ball. Those activities take place during weekends in November and December and the days from December 22 through January 2.

644 ■ FIFTH MARINE DIVISION ASSOCIATION SCHOLARSHIP FUND

c/o Marine Corps Scholarship Foundation
P.O. Box 3008
Princeton, NJ 08543-3008
Tel: (609)921-3534
Free: 800-292-7777
Fax: (609)452-2259
E-mail: mcsfnj@mcsf.org
Web Site: http://www.marine-scholars.org
To provide financial assistance for college to the children of veterans who served with the Fifth Marine Division.

Title of Award: Fifth Marine Division Association Scholarship **Area, Field, or Subject:** General studies/Field of study not specified **Level of Education for which Award is Granted:** Undergraduate **Number Awarded:** Varies each year; recently, 5 of these scholarships were awarded. **Funds Available:** Stipends range from $500 to $2,500 per year. **Duration:** 1 year; may be renewed for up to 3 additional years.

Eligibility Requirements: Applicants must be high school graduates or equivalent and enrolled in or eligible for entry into the chosen institution, which may be any accredited degree-granting college, university, or postsecondary trade, technical, business, or nursing school. The applicant's father must have served with the Fifth Marine Division in World War II or the Vietnam conflict and must have a current membership in the Fifth Marine Division Association. Evidence of financial need, ability appropriate to the proposed program of study, and proof of acceptance into a postsecondary institution must accompany the application. **Deadline for Receipt:** March of each year. **Additional Information:** Recipients may also accept scholarship aid from other sources.

645 ■ FINANCE AUTHORITY OF MAINE

Attn: Education Finance Programs
5 Community Drive
P.O. Box 949
Augusta, ME 04332-0949
Tel: (207)623-3263
Free: 800-228-3734
Fax: (207)623-0095
E-mail: info@famemaine.com
Web Site: http://www.famemaine.com
To provide financial assistance to Maine residents who are the first member of their family to attend college.

Title of Award: Iris Scholarship Fund **Area, Field, or Subject:** General studies/Field of study not specified **Level of Education for which Award is Granted:** Undergraduate **Number Awarded:** 1 or more each year. **Funds Available:** The stipend is $1,500 per year. **Duration:** 1 year; may be renewed.

Eligibility Requirements: This program is open to residents of Maine who are high school seniors or full- or part-time college students. Applicants must be first generation college-bound students (neither parent holds an associate degree or higher). They must submit 2 letters of recommendation, a 250-word essay on why they need the scholarship and how they plan to use their education, and documentation of financial need. **Deadline for Receipt:** April of each year.

646 ■ FINANCE AUTHORITY OF MAINE

Attn: Education Finance Programs
5 Community Drive
P.O. Box 949
Augusta, ME 04332-0949
Tel: (207)623-3263
Free: 800-228-3734
Fax: (207)623-0095
E-mail: info@famemaine.com
Web Site: http://www.famemaine.com/html/education/fameprogs.html
To provide financial assistance to Maine residents interested in working on a college degree.

Title of Award: Maine State Grant Program **Area, Field, or Subject:** General studies/Field of study not specified **Level of Education for which Award is Granted:** Undergraduate **Number Awarded:** Scholarships are presented to students who demonstrate the greatest financial need. The award process continues until all available funds have been exhausted. **Funds Available:** The maximum annual stipend is $1,250 at private schools in Maine, $1,000 at public schools in Maine, $500 at public schools outside of Maine, or $1,000 at private schools outside of Maine. **Duration:** 1 year; may be renewed up to 4 additional years if the recipient remains a Maine resident and maintains satisfactory academic progress.

Eligibility Requirements: Eligible to apply are residents of Maine who have lived in the state for at least 1 year, have graduated from an approved secondary school, can demonstrate financial need, and are enrolled as full-time or part-time students in an approved institution for their first undergraduate degree. Approved schools include all accredited 2- and 4-year colleges, universities, and nursing programs in Maine, as well as regionally accredited 2- and 4-year colleges in states that have a reciprocity agreement with Maine (Connecticut, Massachusetts, New Hampshire, Pennsylvania, Rhode Island, Vermont, and Washington, D.C.). **Deadline for Receipt:** April of each year. **Additional Information:** This program was formerly known as the Maine Student Incentive Scholarship Program.

647 ■ FINANCE AUTHORITY OF MAINE

Attn: Education Finance Programs
5 Community Drive
P.O. Box 949
Augusta, ME 04332-0949
Tel: (207)623-3263
Free: 800-228-3734
Fax: (207)623-0095
E-mail: info@famemaine.com
Web Site: http://www.famemaine.com/html/education/fameprogs.html
To provide financial assistance for college to children and spouses of deceased law enforcement officers, fire fighters, and emergency medical services personnel in Maine.

Title of Award: Maine Tuition Waiver Program for Children and Spouses of Fire Fighters, Law Enforcement Officers, and Emergency Medical Services Personnel Killed in the Line of Duty **Area, Field, or Subject:** General studies/Field of study not specified **Level of Education for which Award is Granted:** Undergraduate **Funds Available:** Eligible students receive waivers of tuition and fees. **Duration:** 1 year; may be renewed up to 3 additional years.

Eligibility Requirements: This program is open to children and spouses of fire fighters, law enforcement officers, and emergency medical services personnel who have been killed in the line of duty or died as a result of injuries received during the performance of their duties. Applicants must be enrolled in or accepted for enrollment in a branch of the University of Maine system, the Maine Community College System, or the Maine Maritime Academy.

648 ■ FINANCE AUTHORITY OF MAINE

Attn: Education Finance Programs
5 Community Drive
P.O. Box 949
Augusta, ME 04332-0949
Tel: (207)623-3263
Free: 800-228-3734
Fax: (207)623-0095
E-mail: info@famemaine.com
Web Site: http://www.famemaine.com/html/education/fameprogs.html
To provide financial assistance for college to foster children in Maine.

Title of Award: Maine Tuition Waiver Program for Foster Children Under the Custody of the Department of Human Services **Area, Field, or Subject:** General studies/Field of study not specified **Level of Education for which Award is Granted:** Undergraduate **Funds Available:** Eligible students receive waivers of tuition and fees. **Duration:** 1 year; may be renewed up to 3 additional years.

Eligibility Requirements: Applicants must have been foster children under the custody of the Maine Department of Human Services when they graduate from high school. They must be enrolled in or accepted for enrollment in a branch of the University of Maine system, the Maine Community College System, or the Maine Maritime Academy.

649 ■ FINANCE AUTHORITY OF MAINE

Attn: Education Finance Programs
5 Community Drive
P.O. Box 949
Augusta, ME 04332-0949
Tel: (207)623-3263
Free: 800-228-3734
Fax: (207)623-0095
E-mail: info@famemaine.com
Web Site: http://www.famemaine.com/html/education/fameprogs.html
To provide financial assistance to Maine residents who are interested in working on a college degree but do not qualify for a Maine State Grant.

Title of Award: NextGen Access Scholarship Program **Area, Field, or Subject:** General studies/Field of study not specified **Level of Education for which Award is Granted:** Undergraduate **Funds Available:** The maximum annual stipend is $1,000 at institutions in Maine or $500 at institutions outside of Maine. **Duration:** 1 year; may be renewed up to 4 additional years if the recipient remains a Maine resident and maintains satisfactory academic progress.

Eligibility Requirements: This program is open to residents of Maine who are enrolled in the first year of college or university. Applicants may not be eligible for a Maine State Grant and must have an estimated family contribution of $1,500 or less. They must be enrolled at an institution in Maine or in a state that has a reciprocity agreement with Maine (Connecticut, Massachusetts, New Hampshire, Pennsylvania, Rhode Island, Vermont, or Washington, D.C.). **Deadline for Receipt:** April of each year.

650 ■ FINANCE AUTHORITY OF MAINE
Attn: Education Finance Programs
5 Community Drive
P.O. Box 949
Augusta, ME 04332-0949
Tel: (207)623-3263
Free: 800-228-3734
Fax: (207)623-0095
E-mail: info@famemaine.com
Web Site: http://www.famemaine.com/html/education/fameprogs.html
To provide financial assistance for college to Maine residents who can demonstrate financial need.
Title of Award: NextGen Student Grant Program **Area, Field, or Subject:** General studies/Field of study not specified **Level of Education for which Award is Granted:** Undergraduate **Funds Available:** Stipends range from $400 to $1,000 per year, depending on the need of the recipient. **Duration:** 1 year; may be renewed up to 4 additional years if the recipient remains a Maine resident and maintains satisfactory academic progress.
Eligibility Requirements: This program is open to residents of Maine who are enrolled full time at a college or university in Maine, Connecticut, Massachusetts, New Hampshire, Pennsylvania, Vermont, or Washington, D.C. Selection is based primarily on financial need. **Deadline for Receipt:** April of each year.

651 ■ FINANCIAL SERVICE CENTERS OF FLORIDA
P.O. Box 14629
Tallahassee, FL 32317
Tel: (850)222-6000
Fax: (850)222-6002
E-mail: Corey@fscfl.com
Web Site: http://www.fscfl.com
To provide financial assistance for college to disadvantaged high school seniors in Florida.
Title of Award: Financial Service Centers of Florida Disadvantaged Scholarship **Area, Field, or Subject:** General studies/Field of study not specified **Level of Education for which Award is Granted:** Undergraduate **Number Awarded:** 10 each year. **Funds Available:** The stipend is $1,000. **Duration:** 1 year.
Eligibility Requirements: This program is open to seniors graduating from high schools in Florida who qualify as disadvantaged. Applicants must have been admitted to a Florida college or university as a full-time student. They must have a GPA of 2.5 or higher. **Deadline for Receipt:** June of each year. **Additional Information:** Funds are issued only if the recipient earns a GPA of 2.0 or higher during the first term in college and 2.5 or higher during the second term.

652 ■ FIRST CATHOLIC SLOVAK LADIES ASSOCIATION
Attn: Director of Fraternal Scholarship Aid
24950 Chagrin Boulevard
Cleveland, OH 44122-5634
Tel: (216)464-8015
Free: 800-464-4642
Fax: (216)464-9260
E-mail: info@fcsla.com
Web Site: http://www.fcsla.com/scholarship.shtml
To provide financial assistance to college students who are members of the First Catholic Slovak Ladies Association.
Title of Award: First Catholic Slovak Ladies Association College and Graduate Scholarships **Area, Field, or Subject:** General studies/Field of study not specified **Level of Education for which Award is Granted:** Graduate, Undergraduate **Number Awarded:** 127 each year: 55 for freshmen, 25 for sophomores, 15 for juniors, 15 for seniors, and 17 for full-time graduate students. **Funds Available:** The stipend is $1,250 for undergraduates or $1,750 for graduate students. **Duration:** 1 year;

recipients may receive only 1 college scholarship but they may later apply for a graduate scholarship.
Eligibility Requirements: This program is open to students at accredited colleges and universities in the United States or Canada. Applicants must have been beneficial members of the First Catholic Slovak Ladies Association for at least 3 years on a $1,000 legal reserve certificate, a $5,000 term certificate, or an annuity certificate. Along with their application, they must submit an autobiographical essay of approximately 500 words that includes a statement of their goals and objectives. Selection is based on academic standing (50%), financial need (20%), family membership in the association (15%), leadership (10%), and extenuating circumstances (5%). **Deadline for Receipt:** February of each year. **Additional Information:** This program includes 2 awards designated as Theresa Sajan Scholarships for Graduate Students.

653 ■ FIRST CAVALRY DIVISION ASSOCIATION
Attn: Foundation
302 North Main Street
Copperas Cove, TX 76522-1799
Tel: (254)547-6537
E-mail: firstcav@1cda.org
Web Site: http://www.1cda.org
To provide financial assistance for undergraduate education to descendants of Army and Air Force personnel who fought in the battle of Ia Drang in 1965.
Title of Award: Ia Drang Scholarship Program **Area, Field, or Subject:** General studies/Field of study not specified **Level of Education for which Award is Granted:** Undergraduate **Number Awarded:** Varies each year. Since the program was established, 38 of these scholarships have been awarded. **Funds Available:** The stipend is $1,000 per year. The checks are made out jointly to the student and the school and may be used for whatever the student needs, including tuition, books, and clothing. **Duration:** 1 year; may be renewed up to 3 additional years.
Eligibility Requirements: This program is open to the children and grandchildren of members of designated Army and Air Force units who actually fought in the battle of the Ia Drang valley from November 3 through 19, 1965. For a list of the qualifying units, contact the sponsor. Children and grandchildren of personnel who were assigned to a unit that fought in the battles but were themselves at other locations during the specified dates are not eligible. **Deadline for Receipt:** August of each year. **Additional Information:** This program was established in 1994. Requests for applications must be accompanied by a self-addressed stamped envelope.

654 ■ FIRST CAVALRY DIVISION ASSOCIATION
Attn: Foundation
302 North Main Street
Copperas Cove, TX 76522-1799
Tel: (254)547-6537
E-mail: firstcav@1cda.org
Web Site: http://www.1cda.org
To provide financial assistance for undergraduate education to soldiers currently or formerly assigned to the First Cavalry Division and their families.
Title of Award: First Cavalry Division Association Scholarships **Area, Field, or Subject:** General studies/Field of study not specified **Level of Education for which Award is Granted:** Undergraduate **Number Awarded:** Varies each year. Since the program was established, more than $659,000 has been awarded to more than 560 recipients. **Funds Available:** The stipend is $1,000 per year. The checks are made out jointly to the student and the school and may be used for whatever the student needs, including tuition, books, and clothing. **Duration:** 1 year; may be renewed up to 3 additional years.
Eligibility Requirements: This program is open to children of soldiers who died or have been declared totally and permanently disabled from injuries incurred while serving with the First Cavalry Division during any armed conflict; children of soldiers who died while serving in the First Cavalry Division during peacetime; and active-duty soldiers currently assigned or attached to the First Cavalry Division and their spouses and

children. **Deadline for Receipt:** August of each year. **Additional Information:** Requests for applications must be accompanied by a self-addressed stamped envelope.

655 ■ FIRST CEREBRAL PALSY OF NEW JERSEY

Attn: Scholarship Coordinator
7 Sanford Avenue
Belleville, NJ 07109-1221
Tel: (973)751-0200
Fax: (973)751-4635
E-mail: cpcenter@excite.com
Web Site: http://www.cerebralpalsycenter.org/cpnj/index.cfm
To provide financial assistance for college to students with permanent physical disabilities in New Jersey.
Title of Award: Louise C. Nacca Memorial Scholarship **Area, Field, or Subject:** General studies/Field of study not specified **Level of Education for which Award is Granted:** Graduate, Undergraduate **Number Awarded:** 1 or more each year. **Funds Available:** A stipend is awarded (amount not specified). **Duration:** 1 year.
Eligibility Requirements: This program is open to high school seniors, high school graduates, and currently-enrolled college students who reside in New Jersey and have a permanent physical disability (e.g., cerebral palsy, spina bifida, muscular dystrophy, paraplegia, quadriplegia, spastic cerebral palsy, polio). Applicants must be attending or planning to attend college or a graduate, professional, business, or technical school to prepare for a career, profession, or occupation. They may attend school in any state. **Deadline for Receipt:** January of each year.

656 ■ FIRST COMMAND FINANCIAL PLANNING

Attn: First Command Educational Foundation
1 FirstComm Plaza
P.O. Box 901091
Fort Worth, TX 76109-1091
Tel: (817)731-8621; 877-872-8289
Fax: (817)569-2970
E-mail: edufoundation@firstcommand.org
Web Site: http://www.firstcommand.org/fcef/scholarship/index.htm
To provide financial assistance for college to the children of active, retired, or deceased military personnel.
Title of Award: First Command Educational Foundation Scholarships **Area, Field, or Subject:** General studies/Field of study not specified **Level of Education for which Award is Granted:** Undergraduate **Number Awarded:** Varies each year; recently, 146 were awarded. **Funds Available:** Scholarships are available in the amounts of $3,000, $2,000, or $1,000. **Duration:** 1 year.
Eligibility Requirements: This program is currently open to all undergraduate students, although it was established to serve the sons and daughters of active, retired, or deceased military personnel (officer or enlisted) and to deserving ROTC cadets. Students must be nominated by an officers' spouses' club or a noncommissioned officers' spouses' club at participating U.S. military installations worldwide. They must apply through their local First Command representative or spouses' club at their installation. The foundation does not accept applications directly. Selection is based primarily on academic achievement and financial need. **Additional Information:** The sponsoring organization was formerly known as the USPA & IRA Educational Foundation, founded in 1983. Since its establishment, it has awarded scholarships worth more than $3.1 million. Effective in 2005, eligibility expanded to include all undergraduate students.

657 ■ FIRST DATA WESTERN UNION FOUNDATION

Attn: Scholarship Program
6200 South Quebec Street, Suite 370 AU
Greenwood Village, CO 80111
Tel: (303)967-6606
Fax: (303)967-6492
Web Site: http://www.firstdatawesternunion.org
To provide financial assistance to nontraditional students so they can realize their educational dreams.
Title of Award: First Data Western Union Foundation Scholarship **Area, Field, or Subject:** General studies/Field of study not specified **Level of Education for which Award is Granted:** Undergraduate **Funds Available:** Stipends range from $500 to $3,000. Funds must be used for

tuition, fees, or books and must be used within 1 year of the award date. **Duration:** Both 1-time and renewable scholarships (up to 4 years) are offered.
Eligibility Requirements: This program is open to nontraditional students, from high school seniors to currently-enrolled college students. Applicants must have a high school diploma or GED and have been accepted at an accredited postsecondary educational institution in the United States or Puerto Rico. They must have a GPA of 2.0 or higher. Selection is based on ability to accept and deal with personal challenges, commitment to learning and working hard, and financial need. Special consideration is given to applicants from Colorado, Florida, Maryland, New Jersey, New York, and Texas (where a majority of First Data employees live and work). **Deadline for Receipt:** March of each year.

658 ■ FIRST MARINE DIVISION ASSOCIATION

410 Pier View Way
Oceanside, CA 92054
Tel: (760)967-8561; 877-967-8561
Fax: (760)967-8567
E-mail: oldbreed@sbcglobal.net
Web Site: http://www.1stmarinedivisionassociation.org/scholarship-fund-page.html
To provide financial assistance for college to dependents of deceased or disabled veterans of the First Marine Division.
Title of Award: First Marine Division Association Scholarships **Area, Field, or Subject:** General studies/Field of study not specified **Level of Education for which Award is Granted:** Undergraduate **Number Awarded:** Varies each year. **Funds Available:** The stipend is $1,500 per year. **Duration:** 1 year; may be renewed up to 3 additional years.
Eligibility Requirements: This program is open to dependents of veterans who served in the First Marine Division or in a unit attached to that Division who are honorably discharged and are now either totally and permanently disabled or deceased from any cause. Applicants must be attending or planning to attend an accredited college, university, or trade school as a full-time undergraduate student. Graduate students and students still in high school or prep school are not eligible. **Additional Information:** Award winners who marry before completing the course or who drop out for non-scholastic reasons must submit a new application before benefits can be resumed.

659 ■ FLEET RESERVE ASSOCIATION

Attn: Scholarship Administrator
125 North West Street
Alexandria, VA 22314-2754
Tel: (703)683-1400
Free: 800-372-1924
Fax: (703)549-6610
E-mail: fra@fra.org
Web Site: http://www.fra.org/Content/fra/MyFRA/Scholarships/Scholarships.htm
To provide financial assistance for undergraduate or graduate education to children of members of the Fleet Reserve Association (FRA) who are current or former naval personnel.
Title of Award: Stanley A. Doran Memorial Scholarships **Area, Field, or Subject:** General studies/Field of study not specified **Level of Education for which Award is Granted:** Graduate, Undergraduate **Number Awarded:** 3 each year. **Funds Available:** The amount awarded varies, depending on the needs of the recipient and the funds available. **Duration:** 1 year; may be renewed.
Eligibility Requirements: Applicants for these scholarships must be the dependent children of members of the association in good standing as of April 1 of the year of the award or at the time of death. Selection is based on financial need, scholastic standing, character, and leadership qualities. **Deadline for Receipt:** April of each year. **Additional Information:** Membership in the FRA is restricted to active-duty, retired, and reserve members of the Navy, Marine Corps, and Coast Guard.

660 ■ FLEET RESERVE ASSOCIATION

Attn: Scholarship Administrator
125 North West Street
Alexandria, VA 22314-2754
Tel: (703)683-1400
Free: 800-372-1924

Fax: (703)549-6610
E-mail: fra@fra.org
Web Site: http://www.fra.org/Content/fra/MyFRA/Scholarships/
Scholarships.htm
To provide financial assistance for undergraduate or graduate education
to members of the Fleet Reserve Association (FRA), their spouses,
children, and grandchildren.
Title of Award: Fleet Reserve Association Scholarship **Area, Field, or
Subject:** General studies/Field of study not specified **Level of Education
for which Award is Granted:** Graduate, Undergraduate **Number
Awarded:** 6 each year. **Funds Available:** The stipend is $5,000 per year.
Duration: 1 year; may be renewed.
Eligibility Requirements: This program is open to members of the FRA
and their dependent children, grandchildren, and spouses. The children,
grandchildren, and spouses of deceased FRA members are also eligible.
Selection is based on financial need, scholastic standing, character, and
leadership qualities. **Deadline for Receipt:** April of each year. **Additional
Information:** Membership in the FRA is restricted to active-duty, retired,
and reserve members of the Navy, Marines, and Coast Guard.

661 ■ FLEET RESERVE ASSOCIATION

Attn: Scholarship Administrator
125 North West Street
Alexandria, VA 22314-2754
Tel: (703)683-1400
Free: 800-372-1924
Fax: (703)549-6610
E-mail: fra@fra.org
Web Site: http://www.fra.org/Content/fra/MyFRA/Scholarships/
Scholarships.htm
To provide financial assistance for undergraduate education to children of
members of the Fleet Reserve Association or its Ladies Auxiliary.
Title of Award: Oliver and Esther R. Howard Scholarship **Area, Field, or
Subject:** General studies/Field of study not specified **Level of Education
for which Award is Granted:** Undergraduate **Number Awarded:** 1 each
year. **Funds Available:** The amount awarded varies, depending upon the
needs of the recipient and the funds available. **Duration:** 1 year; may be
renewed.
Eligibility Requirements: Applicants for these scholarships must be
dependent children of members of the association or its ladies auxiliary (in
good standing as of April 1 of the year of the award), or of members in
good standing at the time of death. They must be interested in working on
an undergraduate degree. Awards alternate annually between female
dependents (in even-numbered years) and male dependents (in odd-
numbered years). Selection is based on financial need, scholastic standing, character, and leadership qualities. **Deadline for Receipt:** April of
each year. **Additional Information:** Membership in the Fleet Reserve Association is restricted to active-duty, retired, and reserve members of the
Navy, Marine Corps, and Coast Guard.

662 ■ FLEET RESERVE ASSOCIATION

Attn: Scholarship Administrator
125 North West Street
Alexandria, VA 22314-2754
Tel: (703)683-1400
Free: 800-372-1924
Fax: (703)549-6610
E-mail: fra@fra.org
Web Site: http://www.fra.org/Content/fra/MyFRA/Scholarships/
Scholarships.htm
To provide financial assistance for undergraduate or graduate education
to members of the Fleet Reserve Association (FRA) who are current or
former naval personnel and their spouses and children.
Title of Award: Schuyler S. Pyle Scholarship **Area, Field, or Subject:**
General studies/Field of study not specified **Level of Education for
which Award is Granted:** Graduate, Undergraduate **Number Awarded:**
1 each year. **Funds Available:** The stipend is $5,000 per year. **Duration:**
1 year; may be renewed.
Eligibility Requirements: Applicants for these scholarships must be
dependent children or spouses of members of the association in good
standing as of April 1 of the year of the award or at the time of death. FRA
members are also eligible. Selection is based on financial need, academic
standing, character, and leadership qualities. **Deadline for Receipt:** April

of each year. **Additional Information:** Membership in the FRA is
restricted to active-duty, retired, and reserve members of the Navy, Marine
Corps, and Coast Guard.

663 ■ FLEET RESERVE ASSOCIATION-PEARL HARBOR-HONOLULU BRANCH 46

891 Valkenburgh Street at Nimitz Highway
P.O. Box 6067
Honolulu, HI 96818-0067
Tel: (808)422-2121
Fax: (808)423-6707
E-mail: flagsb46@aloha.com
Web Site: http://
To provide financial assistance for college to the wives and children of
Fleet Reserve Association (Branch 46) members.
Title of Award: Pearl Harbor-Honolulu Branch 46 Scholarship **Area,
Field, or Subject:** General studies/Field of study not specified **Level of
Education for which Award is Granted:** Undergraduate **Number
Awarded:** 1 or more each year. **Funds Available:** The maximum stipend
is $1,500. **Duration:** 1 year.
Eligibility Requirements: Spouses, daughters, and sons of Fleet
Reserve Association Pearl Harbor-Honolulu Branch 46 members are
eligible to apply. Selection is based on scholastic merit, character, leader-
ship ability, and financial need. **Deadline for Receipt:** April of each year.
Additional Information: Membership in the Fleet Reserve Association is
restricted to active-duty, retired, and reserve members of the Navy, Marine
Corps, and Coast Guard.

664 ■ FLICKER OF HOPE FOUNDATION

Attn: Scholarship Committee
8624 Janet Lane
Vienna, VA 22180
Tel: (703)698-1626
Fax: (703)573-8161
E-mail: info@flickerofhope.org
Web Site: http://www.flickerofhope.org
To provide financial assistance for college to burn survivors.
Title of Award: Flicker of Hope Scholarships **Area, Field, or Subject:**
General studies/Field of study not specified **Level of Education for
which Award is Granted:** Undergraduate **Number Awarded:** Varies
each year; recently, 6 of these scholarships were awarded. **Funds Avail-
able:** A stipend is awarded (amount not specified). Funds are paid directly
to the postsecondary institution. **Duration:** 1 year.
Eligibility Requirements: This program is open to high school seniors
and graduates who are burn survivors and enrolled or planning to enroll in
college. Applicants must submit a 500-word essay describing the
circumstances of how they were burned, how that injury has affected their
life, and the benefits to be derived from their planned course of study.
Financial need is also considered in the selection process.

665 ■ FLORIDA ASSOCIATION OF POSTSECONDARY SCHOOLS AND COLLEGES

150 South Monroe Street, Suite 303
Tallahassee, FL 32301
Tel: (850)577-3139
Fax: (850)577-3133
E-mail: mail@fapsc.org
Web Site: http://www.fapsc.org
To provide financial assistance to Florida residents interested in attending
a career or vocational school in the state.
Title of Award: FAPSC Scholarship Program **Area, Field, or Subject:**
General studies/Field of study not specified **Level of Education for
which Award is Granted:** Vocational/Occupational **Number Awarded:**
More than 300 each year. **Funds Available:** Scholarships provide either
full payment of tuition or $3,500 as partial payment of tuition. **Duration:** 1
academic term.
Eligibility Requirements: This program is open to seniors graduating
from high schools in Florida and recipients of a GED credential during the
current year. Applicants must be interested in attending a participating
Florida career or vocational school. They must have a GPA of 2.0 or
higher. Along with their application, they must submit a 300-word essay
that explains why they have chosen this particular career, how this
program of study will help them obtain that career, and why they want to

attend this particular institution. **Deadline for Receipt:** February of each year.

666 ■ FLORIDA COUNCIL FOR THE BLIND

Attn: Division of Blind Services
1003 Naples Drive
Orlando, FL 32804
Tel: (407)423-6300
E-mail: education-leadership@fcb.org
Web Site: http://www.fcb.org
To provide financial assistance for college to blind residents of Florida.
Title of Award: Florida Council for the Blind Scholarship **Area, Field, or Subject:** General studies/Field of study not specified **Level of Education for which Award is Granted:** Undergraduate **Number Awarded:** Varies each year; recently, 2 of these scholarships were awarded. **Funds Available:** The stipend is $1,000. **Duration:** 1 year.
Eligibility Requirements: This program is open to blind residents of Florida who are attending or planning to attend a college or university in the state. Applicants must have a GPA of 3.0 or higher. **Deadline for Receipt:** February of each year.

667 ■ FLORIDA DEPARTMENT OF EDUCATION

Attn: Office of Student Financial Assistance
1940 North Monroe Street, Suite 70
Tallahassee, FL 32303-4759
Tel: (850)410-5200; 888-827-2004
Fax: (850)487-1809
E-mail: osfa@fldoe.org
Web Site: http://www.FloridaStudentFinancialAid.org
To provide financial assistance to high school seniors interested in attending traditionally Black colleges in Florida.
Title of Award: Mary McLeod Bethune Scholarships **Area, Field, or Subject:** General studies/Field of study not specified **Level of Education for which Award is Granted:** Undergraduate **Number Awarded:** Varies each year; recently, 180 awards were available through this program. **Funds Available:** The stipend is $3,000 per year. **Duration:** 1 year; may be renewed up to 3 additional years if the student maintains full-time enrollment and a GPA of 3.0 or higher and continues to demonstrate financial need.
Eligibility Requirements: Eligible are high school seniors who wish to attend Florida A&M University, Bethune-Cookman College, Edward Waters College, or Florida Memorial College for a minimum of 12 credit hours per term. Applicants must be Florida residents, have a GPA of 3.0 or higher, demonstrate financial need, have complied with the Selective Service System registration requirements, have participated in the college-level communication and computation skills testing (CLAST) program, and not be in default or owe repayment on any federal or state grant, scholarship, or loan program. Priority may be given to students with the lowest total family resources. **Deadline for Receipt:** Deadlines are established by the participating institutions.

668 ■ FLORIDA DEPARTMENT OF EDUCATION

Attn: Office of Student Financial Assistance
1940 North Monroe Street, Suite 70
Tallahassee, FL 32303-4759
Tel: (850)410-5200; 888-827-2004
Fax: (850)487-1809
E-mail: osfa@fldoe.org
Web Site: http://www.FloridaStudentFinancialAid.org
To provide financial assistance to students at private colleges and universities in Florida.
Title of Award: William L. Boyd, IV, Florida Resident Access Grants **Area, Field, or Subject:** General studies/Field of study not specified **Level of Education for which Award is Granted:** Undergraduate **Number Awarded:** Varies each year; recently, this program provided 23,425 awards. **Funds Available:** The amount of the award is specified by the state legislature annually; actual amounts depend on the number of applicants and availability of funds. **Duration:** Up to 9 semesters or 14 quarters, provided the student maintains full-time enrollment and a GPA of 2.0 or higher.
Eligibility Requirements: Applicants must be full-time undergraduate students who are attending an eligible private nonprofit college or university in Florida and who have been Florida residents for at least 1

year. Financial need is not considered in the selection process. **Additional Information:** Applications are available from the financial aid office at the college the recipient plans to attend.

669 ■ FLORIDA DEPARTMENT OF EDUCATION

Attn: Office of Student Financial Assistance
1940 North Monroe Street, Suite 70
Tallahassee, FL 32303-4759
Tel: (850)410-5200; 888-827-2004
Fax: (850)487-1809
E-mail: osfa@fldoe.org
Web Site: http://www.myfloridaeducation.com/brfuture
To provide financial assistance for college to outstanding high school seniors in Florida.
Title of Award: Florida Academic Scholars Award Program **Area, Field, or Subject:** General studies/Field of study not specified **Level of Education for which Award is Granted:** Undergraduate **Number Awarded:** Varies each year. **Funds Available:** The scholarships provide 100% of tuition and fees (including lab fees up to $300 per semester) at Florida public colleges and universities or an equivalent amount at private institutions. Students also receive a stipend of $300 for college-related expenses. **Duration:** Recipients may use this award 1) for up to 132 credit hours required to complete a standard undergraduate degree at their institution; 2) for up to 7 years from high school graduation (if initially funded within 3 years after high school graduation); or 3) until completion of their first baccalaureate degree program, whichever comes first. Renewal requires a GPA of 3.0 or higher.
Eligibility Requirements: Eligible are seniors in Florida public and private high schools who have been Florida residents for at least 1 year and will attend eligible Florida institutions of higher education. Applicants must have 1) earned a GPA of 3.5 or higher in a specified high school academic curriculum, 2) achieved scores of at least 1270 on the SAT or 28 on the ACT, and 3) completed at least 75 hours of community service. Also eligible are National Merit and Achievement scholars and finalists, National Hispanic Scholars, IB Diploma recipients, and home-schooled students and GED recipients who achieve the same minimum SAT or ACT scores. U.S. citizenship or permanent resident status is required. **Deadline for Receipt:** March of each year. **Additional Information:** These scholarships are offered as part of the Florida Bright Futures Scholarship Program, established in 1997 with funding from the lottery.

670 ■ FLORIDA DEPARTMENT OF EDUCATION

Attn: Office of Student Financial Assistance
1940 North Monroe Street, Suite 70
Tallahassee, FL 32303-4759
Tel: (850)410-5200; 888-827-2004
Fax: (850)487-1809
E-mail: osfa@fldoe.org
Web Site: http://www.myfloridaeducation.com/brfuture
To provide financial assistance for college to the top high school seniors in Florida.
Title of Award: Florida Academic Top Scholars Award Program **Area, Field, or Subject:** General studies/Field of study not specified **Level of Education for which Award is Granted:** Undergraduate **Number Awarded:** 67 each year: 1 in each Florida county. **Funds Available:** The Academic Top Scholars awardees receive an annual stipend of $1,500 in addition to their Academic Scholars Award. **Duration:** Recipients may use this award 1) for up to 132 credit hours required to complete a standard undergraduate degree at their institution; 2) for up to 7 years from high school graduation (if initially funded within 3 years after high school graduation); or 3) until completion of their first baccalaureate degree program, whichever comes first. Renewal requires a GPA of 3.0 or higher.
Eligibility Requirements: Eligible to receive a Florida Academic Scholars Award are seniors in Florida public and private high schools who have been Florida residents for at least 1 year and will attend eligible Florida institutions of higher education. They must have completed a specified curriculum while in high school. U.S. citizenship or permanent resident status is required. The Academic Top Scholars Award is presented to the student with the highest academic ranking in each county, based on GPA and SAT/ACT test scores. **Deadline for Receipt:** March of each year. **Additional Information:** These scholarships are offered as part of the Florida Bright Futures Scholarship Program, established in 1997 with funding from the lottery.

671 ■ FLORIDA DEPARTMENT OF EDUCATION

Attn: Office of Student Financial Assistance
1940 North Monroe Street, Suite 70
Tallahassee, FL 32303-4759
Tel: (850)410-5200; 888-827-2004
Fax: (850)487-1809
E-mail: osfa@fldoe.org
Web Site: http://www.FloridaStudentFinancialAid.org
To provide financial assistance to Florida residents enrolled at private colleges and universities in the state.
Title of Award: Florida Access to Better Learning and Education Grant Program **Area, Field, or Subject:** General studies/Field of study not specified **Level of Education for which Award is Granted:** Undergraduate **Number Awarded:** Varies each year. **Funds Available:** The stipend is specified each year by the Florida legislation, but it may not exceed the total charged for tuition and fees by the institution. **Duration:** Funds may be received for up to 9 semesters or 14 quarters or until receipt of a bachelor's degree, whichever comes first. Renewal requires that the student earn a GPA of 2.0 or higher each semester.
Eligibility Requirements: This program is open to students enrolled full time at eligible private Florida colleges and universities who have been residents of the state for at least 1 year. Applicants may not have previously received a bachelor's degree and may not be enrolled in a program of study leading to a degree in theology or divinity. **Deadline for Receipt:** Each participating institution sets its own deadline.

672 ■ FLORIDA DEPARTMENT OF EDUCATION

Attn: Office of Student Financial Assistance
1940 North Monroe Street, Suite 70
Tallahassee, FL 32303-4759
Tel: (850)410-5200; 888-827-2004
Fax: (850)487-1809
E-mail: osfa@fldoe.org
Web Site: http://www.myfloridaeducation.com/brfuture
To provide financial assistance for vocational education to outstanding high school seniors in Florida.
Title of Award: Florida Gold Seal Vocational Scholars Awards **Area, Field, or Subject:** General studies/Field of study not specified **Level of Education for which Award is Granted:** Vocational/Occupational **Number Awarded:** Varies each year. **Funds Available:** The scholarships cover 75% of tuition and mandatory fees (including lab fees up to $300 per semester) at public vocational/technical institutions in Florida, or an equivalent amount at private schools. **Duration:** Recipients may use this award 1) for up to 90 semester hours; 2) for up to 7 years from high school graduation (if initially funded within 3 years after high school graduation); or 3) until completion of their first baccalaureate degree program, whichever comes first. Renewal requires a GPA of 2.75 or higher.
Eligibility Requirements: This program is open to graduating high school seniors in Florida who plan to attend a vocational, technical, trade, or business school in the state. Applicants must have earned a GPA of 3.0 or higher in their required academic program and 3.5 or higher in their vocational classes in high school. They must also have achieved the following minimum scores: 1) on the CPT, 83 in reading, 83 in sentence skills, and 72 in algebra; 2) on the SAT, 440 in verbal and 440 in mathematics; or 3) on the ACT, 17 in English, 18 in reading, and 19 in mathematics. U.S. citizenship or permanent resident status is required.
Deadline for Receipt: March of each year. **Additional Information:** These scholarships are offered as part of the Florida Bright Futures Scholarship Program, established in 1997 with funding from the lottery.

673 ■ FLORIDA DEPARTMENT OF EDUCATION

Attn: Office of Student Financial Assistance
1940 North Monroe Street, Suite 70
Tallahassee, FL 32303-4759
Tel: (850)410-5200; 888-827-2004
Fax: (850)487-1809
E-mail: osfa@fldoe.org
Web Site: http://www.myfloridaeducation.com/brfuture
To provide financial assistance for college to outstanding high school seniors in Florida.
Title of Award: Florida Medallion Scholars Awards **Area, Field, or Subject:** General studies/Field of study not specified **Level of Education for which Award is Granted:** Undergraduate **Number Awarded:** Varies

each year. **Funds Available:** The scholarships cover 75% of tuition and mandatory fees (including lab fees up to $300 per semester) at public colleges and universities in Florida, or an equivalent amount at private schools. **Duration:** Recipients may use this award 1) for up to 132 semester hours; 2) for up to 7 years from high school graduation (if initially funded within 3 years after high school graduation); or 3) until completion of their first baccalaureate degree program, whichever comes first. Renewal requires a GPA of 2.75 or higher.
Eligibility Requirements: Eligible are seniors in Florida public and private high schools who have been Florida residents for at least 1 year and who plan to attend eligible Florida institutions of higher education. Applicants must have 1) earned a GPA of 3.0 or higher in a specified high school academic curriculum, and 2) achieved scores of at least 970 on the SAT or 20 on the ACT. Also eligible are National Medallion and Achievement scholars and finalists who complete 75 hours of community service, National Hispanic Scholars who complete 75 hours of community service, home-schooled students who achieve scores of at least 1070 on the SAT or 23 on the ACT, and GED recipients who achieve test scores of at least 970 on the SAT or 20 on the ACT and a GPA of 3.0 or higher. **Deadline for Receipt:** March of each year. **Additional Information:** These scholarships, formerly known as Florida Merit Scholars Awards, are offered as part of the Florida Bright Futures Scholarship Program, established in 1997 with funding from the lottery.

674 ■ FLORIDA DEPARTMENT OF EDUCATION

Attn: Office of Student Financial Assistance
1940 North Monroe Street, Suite 70
Tallahassee, FL 32303-4759
Tel: (850)410-5200; 888-827-2004
Fax: (850)487-1809
E-mail: osfa@fldoe.org
Web Site: http://www.FloridaStudentFinancialAid.org
To provide financial assistance for college to the children of Florida veterans who are disabled, deceased, or officially classified as prisoners of war (POW) or missing in action (MIA).
Title of Award: Florida Scholarships for Children of Deceased or Disabled Veterans **Area, Field, or Subject:** General studies/Field of study not specified **Level of Education for which Award is Granted:** Undergraduate **Number Awarded:** Varies each year; recently, this program provided 215 awards. **Funds Available:** Qualified students who attend a Florida public institution of higher education receive payment of tuition and fees. Students who attend an eligible nonpublic Florida institution of higher education receive an award equal to the amount they would be required to pay for the average tuition and fees at a public institution at the comparable level. **Duration:** 1 quarter or semester; may be renewed for up to 11 additional quarters or 7 additional semesters as long as the student maintains a GPA of 2.0 or higher and full-time enrollment.
Eligibility Requirements: This program is open to residents of Florida between 16 and 22 years of age who are the dependent children of veterans or servicemen who 1) died as a result of service-connected injuries, diseases, or disabilities sustained while on active duty during a period of war; 2) have a service-connected 100% total and permanent disability; or 3) was classified as POW or MIA during the Korean War or Vietnam era and has not returned alive or remains have not been found. The official military and residency status of the veteran parent must be verified by the Florida Department of Veterans' Affairs. **Deadline for Receipt:** March of each year.

675 ■ FLORIDA DEPARTMENT OF EDUCATION

Attn: Office of Student Financial Assistance
1940 North Monroe Street, Suite 70
Tallahassee, FL 32303-4759
Tel: (850)410-5200; 888-827-2004
Fax: (850)487-1809
E-mail: osfa@fldoe.org
Web Site: http://www.FloridaStudentFinancialAid.org
To provide financial assistance for undergraduate studies to needy Florida residents.
Title of Award: Florida Student Assistance Grants **Area, Field, or Subject:** General studies/Field of study not specified **Level of Education for which Award is Granted:** Undergraduate **Number Awarded:** Varies each year; recently, this program provided 40,040 awards. **Funds Available:** Stipends range from $200 to a maximum that varies each year but

recently was $1,592 per year. **Duration:** Grants may be received for up to 9 semesters or 14 quarters or until receipt of a bachelor's degree, whichever comes first. Renewal requires that the student earn a GPA of 2.0 or higher each semester.

Eligibility Requirements: This program is open to 1) full-time undergraduate students who are attending an eligible public or private Florida institution, and 2) part-time undergraduate students at Florida public institutions. Applicants must be U.S. citizens or eligible noncitizens. A minimum of 1 year of Florida residency is required. Financial need must be documented; applicants must submit the Free Application for Federal Student Aid (FAFSA) and demonstrate substantial financial need. Priority is given to students who rank in the top 20% of their high school class and plan to attend 1 of the 11 state universities. **Deadline for Receipt:** Each participating institution sets its own deadline. **Additional Information:** This program receives funding from Florida general revenues and the federal Leveraging Educational Assistance Partnership program.

676 ■ FLORIDA DEPARTMENT OF EDUCATION
Attn: Office of Student Financial Assistance
1940 North Monroe Street, Suite 70
Tallahassee, FL 32303-4759
Tel: (850)410-5200; 888-827-2004
Fax: (850)487-1809
E-mail: osfa@fldoe.org
Web Site: http://www.FloridaStudentFinancialAid.org
To provide financial assistance to Hispanic American high school seniors and graduate students in Florida.
Title of Award: Jose Marti Scholarship Challenge Grant Fund **Area, Field, or Subject:** General studies/Field of study not specified **Level of Education for which Award is Granted:** Graduate, Undergraduate **Number Awarded:** Varies each year; recently, this program presented 98 awards. **Funds Available:** The grant is $2,000 per academic year. Available funds are contingent upon matching contributions from private sources. **Duration:** 1 year; may be renewed if the student maintains full-time enrollment and a GPA of 3.0 or higher and continues to demonstrate financial need.
Eligibility Requirements: This program is open to Florida residents of Spanish culture who were born in, or whose natural parent was born in, Mexico, Spain, or a Hispanic country of the Caribbean, Central America, or South America. Applicants must be citizens or eligible noncitizens of the United States, be enrolled or planning to enroll as full-time undergraduate or graduate students at an eligible postsecondary school in Florida, be able to demonstrate financial need as determined by a nationally-recognized needs analysis service, and have earned a cumulative GPA of 3.0 or higher in high school or, if a graduate school applicant, in undergraduate course work. **Deadline for Receipt:** March of each year.

677 ■ FLORIDA DEPARTMENT OF EDUCATION
Attn: Office of Student Financial Assistance
1940 North Monroe Street, Suite 70
Tallahassee, FL 32303-4759
Tel: (850)410-5200; 888-827-2004
Fax: (850)487-1809
E-mail: osfa@fldoe.org
Web Site: http://www.FloridaStudentFinancialAid.org
To provide financial assistance for undergraduate education to needy minority students who wish to study in Florida.
Title of Award: Rosewood Family Scholarship Fund **Area, Field, or Subject:** General studies/Field of study not specified **Level of Education for which Award is Granted:** Undergraduate **Number Awarded:** 25 each year. **Funds Available:** Awards cover the actual costs of tuition and fees, up to $4,000 per year. **Duration:** 1 year; may be renewed up to 3 additional years provided the student maintains full-time enrollment and a GPA of 2.0 or higher.
Eligibility Requirements: This program is open to residents of any state who wish to attend state universities, public community colleges, or public postsecondary vocational/technical schools in Florida. Applicants must be a minority, defined as Black but not of Hispanic origin, Asian, Pacific Islander, Hispanic, American Indian, or Alaskan Native. Preference is given to descendants of African American Rosewood families (whose members were killed by a mob in January 1923). Other minority undergraduate students are considered if funds remain available after

awarding Rosewood descendants, but it is expected that all available scholarships will be awarded to descendants of Rosewood families. Financial need must be demonstrated. **Deadline for Receipt:** March of each year.

678 ■ FLORIDA HIGH SCHOOL ATHLETIC ASSOCIATION
1801 N.W. 80th Boulevard
Gainesville, FL 32606
Tel: (352)372-9551
Fax: (352)373-1528
Web Site: http://www.fhsaa.org
To provide financial assistance for college to student-athletes in Florida who have excelled in academics and athletics.
Title of Award: FHSAA Academic All-State Awards **Area, Field, or Subject:** General studies/Field of study not specified **Level of Education for which Award is Granted:** Undergraduate **Number Awarded:** 24 honorees (12 boys and 12 girls) are selected each year. From among those, 2 Scholar-Athletes of the Year (1 boy and 1 girl) are selected each year. **Funds Available:** Each honoree receives a $500 award. From among those honorees, the Scholar-Athletes of the Year receive an additional $2,500 scholarship. **Duration:** The awards are presented annually.
Eligibility Requirements: This program is open to college-bound seniors graduating from high schools in Florida. Candidates must have a cumulative unweighted GPA of 3.5 or higher and have earned a varsity letter in at least 2 different sports during each of their junior and senior years. Boys and girls are judged separately.

679 ■ FLORIDA HOTEL & MOTEL ASSOCIATION, INC.
Attn: Director of Education and Research
Hospitality Square
P.O. Box 1529
Tallahassee, FL 32302-1529
Tel: (850)224-2888
Free: 800-476-FHMA
Fax: (850)222-FHMA
E-mail: parker@fhma.net
Web Site: http://www.flahotel.com
To provide financial assistance to students in Florida interested in preparing for a career in the lodging industry.
Title of Award: Florida Hotel & Motel Association Scholarships **Area, Field, or Subject:** Hotel, institutional, and restaurant management **Level of Education for which Award is Granted:** Undergraduate **Number Awarded:** 5 each year. **Funds Available:** The stipend is $2,000. **Duration:** 1 year.
Eligibility Requirements: This program is open to residents of Florida who are graduating high school seniors or current 2-year and 4-year college students in the state. Applicants must be interested in preparing for a career in the lodging industry. They must have a GPA of 2.5 or higher. **Deadline for Receipt:** April of each year. **Additional Information:** This program was established in 1998.

680 ■ FLORIDA SAFETY COUNCIL
Attn: Scholarship Committee
427 North Primrose Drive
Orlando, FL 32803
Tel: (407)896-1894
Fax: (407)895-2650
Web Site: http://www.occsafety.com/occscholarship.asp
To provide financial assistance for college to children of employees of members of the Florida Safety Council.
Title of Award: Florida Safety Council Member Scholarships **Area, Field, or Subject:** General studies/Field of study not specified **Level of Education for which Award is Granted:** Undergraduate **Number Awarded:** 1 or more each year. **Funds Available:** The stipend is $1,000. **Duration:** 1 year.
Eligibility Requirements: This program is open to children of employees who have worked for a company, municipality, or organization that is an active member of the Florida Safety Council for at least 12 months. Applicants must be attending or planning to attend an accredited college or university as a full-time undergraduate student. Along with their application, they must submit a 300-word essay on why they believe they should be awarded this scholarship (e.g., career goals, financial need). **Deadline**

for **Receipt:** December of each year.

681 ■ FOND DU LAC RESERVATION
Attn: Scholarship Director
1720 Big Lake Road
Cloquet, MN 55720
Tel: (218)879-4593
Free: 800-365-1613
Fax: (218)878-7529
E-mail: scholarships@fdlrez.com
Web Site: http://www.fdlrez.com
To provide financial assistance for college or graduate school to Lake Superior Chippewa students.
Title of Award: Fond du Lac Scholarship Program **Area, Field, or Subject:** General studies/Field of study not specified **Level of Education for which Award is Granted:** Graduate, Undergraduate **Number Awarded:** Varies each year. **Funds Available:** Stipends range up to $3,000 per year, depending on need. **Duration:** 1 year; may be renewed for up to 4 additional years if the recipient maintains a GPA of 2.0 or higher.
Eligibility Requirements: This program is open to enrolled members of the Fond du Lac Band of Lake Superior Chippewa who are attending or planning to attend community college, university, vocational school, or graduate school in any state as a full- or part-time student. Applicants must be able to demonstrate financial need. Students planning to attend a Minnesota institution must also apply to the Minnesota Indian Scholarship Program. **Deadline for Receipt:** Priority consideration is given to applications received by mid-May of each year; after that date, awards are presented on a first-come, first-served basis.

682 ■ FORCE RECON ASSOCIATION
P.O. Box 783
Angels Camp, CA 95222
E-mail: commchief@forcerecon.com
Web Site: http://www.forcerecon.com
To provide financial assistance for college to members of the Force Recon Association and their dependents.
Title of Award: Force Recon Association Scholarships **Area, Field, or Subject:** General studies/Field of study not specified **Level of Education for which Award is Granted:** Undergraduate **Number Awarded:** 1 or more each year. **Funds Available:** A stipend is awarded (amount not specified). **Duration:** 1 year; may be renewed.
Eligibility Requirements: This program is open to members of the Force Recon Association and family members of a relative who served both in the U.S. Marine Corps and was or is assigned to a Force Reconnaissance Company. The relative must be either an active or deceased member of the Force Recon Association. Family members include wives and widows, sons and daughters (including adopted and stepchildren), grandchildren, and great-grandchildren. Applicants may be pursuing scholastic, vocational, or technical education. Along with their application, they must submit a personal statement on why they desire this scholarship, their proposed course of study, their progress in their current course of study, and their long-range career goals. Selection is based on academic achievement, letters of recommendation, demonstrated character, and the written statements. **Deadline for Receipt:** Applications must be received at least 2 weeks prior to the annual meeting of the Force Recon Association. **Additional Information:** Information is also available from the Scholarship Committee Chair, Dr. Wayne M. Lingenfelter, 2992 Calle Gaucho, San Clemente, CA 92673.

683 ■ FORWARD FACE
Attn: Scholarship Committee
317 East 34th Street, Suite 901A
New York, NY 10016
Tel: (212)684-5860
Fax: (212)684-5864
E-mail: camille@forwardface.org
Web Site: http://www.forwardface.org
To provide financial assistance for educational purposes to students with craniofacial conditions.
Title of Award: Forward Face Scholarships **Area, Field, or Subject:** General studies/Field of study not specified **Level of Education for which Award is Granted:** Undergraduate **Number Awarded:** Up to 3

each year. **Funds Available:** The scholarship is $1,000. Funds must be used for educational purposes. **Duration:** 1 year; nonrenewable.
Eligibility Requirements: This program is open to students who are 13 years of age or older and have a craniofacial condition. Applicants must write essays on how a particular teacher or faculty member has made a positive impact on them, the impact of their craniofacial condition on their educational experiences, the personal qualities and abilities that make them the best candidate for the scholarship, a description of themselves that enables the readers to get to know them as persons, and where they see themselves in 10 years. Selection is based on personal qualities, goals, and recommendations. Financial need is not a consideration. **Deadline for Receipt:** January of each year.

684 ■ FOUNDATION FOR AMATEUR RADIO, INC.
Attn: Scholarship Committee
P.O. Box 831
Riverdale, MD 20738
E-mail: aa3of@arrl.net
Web Site: http://www.amateurradio-far.org/scholarships.php
To provide funding to licensed radio amateurs who are interested in working on an undergraduate or graduate degree.
Title of Award: 10-10 International Net Scholarships **Area, Field, or Subject:** General studies/Field of study not specified **Level of Education for which Award is Granted:** Graduate, Undergraduate **Number Awarded:** 5 each year. **Funds Available:** The stipend is $1,000. **Duration:** 1 year.
Eligibility Requirements: Applicants must be radio amateurs who have HF privileges and are working on an associate, bachelor's, or graduate degree. There is no restriction on the course of study. Non-U.S. amateurs are also eligible. Applicants must provide a recommendation from a member of the 10-10 International Net or be a member of that organization. **Deadline for Receipt:** Requests for applications must be submitted by April of each year. **Additional Information:** This program is sponsored by 10-10 International Net, Inc. Information is also available from Larry Berger, Scholarship Manager, 9 Nancy Boulevard, Merrick, NY 11566, E-mail: wa2suh@aol.com. Recipients must attend an accredited school (university, college, or technical institute) on a full-time basis.

685 ■ FOUNDATION FOR AMATEUR RADIO, INC.
Attn: Scholarship Committee
P.O. Box 831
Riverdale, MD 20738
E-mail: aa3of@arrl.net
Web Site: http://www.amateurradio-far.org/scholarships.php
To provide funding to licensed radio amateurs from Maryland who are interested in working on a college degree.
Title of Award: Baltimore Amateur Radio Club Scholarships **Area, Field, or Subject:** General studies/Field of study not specified **Level of Education for which Award is Granted:** Undergraduate **Number Awarded:** 5 each year: 4 at $1,000 plus the Ernie Dobos Memorial Scholarship at $1,500. **Funds Available:** The stipends are $1,000 or $1,500. **Duration:** 1 year; may be renewed for up to 3 additional years (if the recipient is a first-year student).
Eligibility Requirements: Applicants must have an amateur radio license of any class and be residents of the state of Maryland. There is no restriction on the course of study. For 3 of the awards, preference is given to those who have successfully completed 1 year of college or have been previous winners of this award. Another award is reserved for an entering first-year student. The Ernie Dobos Memorial Scholarship gives preference to a resident of the city of Baltimore. **Deadline for Receipt:** Requests for applications must be submitted by April of each year. **Additional Information:** This program is sponsored by the Baltimore Amateur Radio Club, P.O. Box 120, Reisterstown, MD 21136, (410) 526-4263, E-mail: info2005@baltarc.com. Recipients must attend an accredited school (university, college, or technical institute) on a full-time basis.

686 ■ FOUNDATION FOR AMATEUR RADIO, INC.
Attn: Scholarship Committee
P.O. Box 831
Riverdale, MD 20738
E-mail: aa3of@arrl.net
Web Site: http://www.amateurradio-far.org/scholarships.php

To provide funding to licensed radio amateurs who are interested in going to college.

Title of Award: Rose Ellen Bills Memorial Scholarship **Area, Field, or Subject:** General studies/Field of study not specified **Level of Education for which Award is Granted:** Undergraduate **Number Awarded:** 2 each year. **Funds Available:** The stipend is $2,000. **Duration:** 1 year. **Eligibility Requirements:** There is no restriction on the course of study. Applicants must be U.S. residents and intend to work on a bachelor's degree. The minimum license requirement is general class. **Deadline for Receipt:** Requests for applications must be submitted by April of each year. **Additional Information:** Recipients must attend an accredited school (university, college, or technical institute) on a full-time basis.

687 ■ FOUNDATION FOR AMATEUR RADIO, INC.

Attn: Scholarship Committee
P.O. Box 831
Riverdale, MD 20738
E-mail: aa3of@arrl.net
Web Site: http://www.amateurradio-far.org/scholarships.php
To provide funding to members of the American Radio Relay League (ARRL) who are interested in attending college.

Title of Award: Richard G. Chichester Memorial Scholarship **Area, Field, or Subject:** General studies/Field of study not specified **Level of Education for which Award is Granted:** Undergraduate **Number Awarded:** 1 each year. **Funds Available:** The stipend is $1,000. **Duration:** 1 year. **Eligibility Requirements:** This program is open to students working on a bachelor's degree who have an amateur radio license of at least general class. Applicants must be members of the ARRL and recommended by an ARRL-affiliated club, although they do not need to be a member of the club. There is no restriction on the course of study. Preference is given to residents of Texas living in the metropolitan areas of Austin, Kerrville, or San Antonio. **Deadline for Receipt:** Requests for applications must be submitted by April of each year. **Additional Information:** Recipients must attend an accredited school (university, college, or technical institute) on a full-time basis.

688 ■ FOUNDATION FOR AMATEUR RADIO, INC.

Attn: Scholarship Committee
P.O. Box 831
Riverdale, MD 20738
E-mail: aa3of@arrl.net
Web Site: http://www.amateurradio-far.org/scholarships.php
To provide funding to licensed radio amateurs from Maryland who are interested in going to college.

Title of Award: Columbia Amateur Radio Association, Inc. Scholarship **Area, Field, or Subject:** General studies/Field of study not specified **Level of Education for which Award is Granted:** Undergraduate **Number Awarded:** 1 each year. **Funds Available:** The stipend is $1,000. **Duration:** 1 year. **Eligibility Requirements:** Applicants must be residents of Maryland, be working on a bachelor's degree, and have an amateur radio license of technician class or higher. There is no restriction on the course of study. **Deadline for Receipt:** Requests for applications must be submitted by April of each year. **Additional Information:** This program is sponsored by the Columbia Amateur Radio Association, Inc., P.O Box 911, Columbia, MD 21044-0911. Recipients must attend an accredited school (university, college, or technical institute) on a full-time basis.

689 ■ FOUNDATION FOR AMATEUR RADIO, INC.

Attn: Scholarship Committee
P.O. Box 831
Riverdale, MD 20738
E-mail: aa3of@arrl.net
Web Site: http://www.amateurradio-far.org/scholarships.php
To provide money to licensed radio amateurs, especially those from the Washington, D.C. area, who are interested in going to college.

Title of Award: FAR Silent Key Memorial Scholarships **Area, Field, or Subject:** General studies/Field of study not specified **Level of Education for which Award is Granted:** Undergraduate **Number Awarded:** 3 each year. **Funds Available:** The stipend is $2,500. **Duration:** 1 year. **Eligibility Requirements:** Applicants must be residents of the United States, be working on a bachelor's degree, and have an amateur radio license of technician class or higher (preference is given to holders of

higher license classes). There is no restriction on the course of study. Preference is given to residents of the District of Columbia, Maryland, and northern Virginia. **Deadline for Receipt:** Requests for applications must be submitted by April of each year. **Additional Information:** Recipients must attend an accredited school (university, college, or technical institute) on a full-time basis.

690 ■ FOUNDATION FOR AMATEUR RADIO, INC.

Attn: Scholarship Committee
P.O. Box 831
Riverdale, MD 20738
E-mail: aa3of@arrl.net
Web Site: http://www.amateurradio-far.org/scholarships.php
To provide funding to licensed radio amateurs in Maryland who are interested in going to college.

Title of Award: Frederick Amateur Radio Club Scholarship **Area, Field, or Subject:** General studies/Field of study not specified **Level of Education for which Award is Granted:** Undergraduate **Number Awarded:** 1 each year. **Funds Available:** The stipend is $1,000. **Duration:** 1 year. **Eligibility Requirements:** Applicants must be working on a bachelor's degree, hold an amateur radio license of any class, and reside within 150 miles of Frederick, Maryland. Preference is given to qualified applicants from Frederick County, Maryland. There is no restriction on the course of study. **Deadline for Receipt:** Requests for applications must be submitted by April of each year. **Additional Information:** This program is sponsored by the Frederick Amateur Radio Club, P.O. Box 1260, Frederick, MD 21701-0260. Recipients must attend an accredited school (university, college, or technical institute) on a full-time basis.

691 ■ FOUNDATION FOR AMATEUR RADIO, INC.

Attn: Scholarship Committee
P.O. Box 831
Riverdale, MD 20738
E-mail: aa3of@arrl.net
Web Site: http://www.amateurradio-far.org/scholarships.php
To provide funding to licensed radio amateurs in Maryland who are interested in attending college on the undergraduate or graduate school level.

Title of Award: Free State Amateur Radio Club Scholarship **Area, Field, or Subject:** General studies/Field of study not specified **Level of Education for which Award is Granted:** Graduate, Undergraduate **Number Awarded:** 1 each year. **Funds Available:** The stipend is $1,000. **Duration:** 1 year. **Eligibility Requirements:** Applicants must be U.S. citizens and residents of Maryland who have a valid FCC amateur license with HF privileges. They must be working on an associate, bachelor's, or graduate degree from a college or university in the United States. There is no restriction on the course of study. **Deadline for Receipt:** Requests for applications must be submitted by April of each year. **Additional Information:** Recipients must attend an accredited school (university, college, or technical institute) on a full-time basis.

692 ■ FOUNDATION FOR AMATEUR RADIO, INC.

Attn: Scholarship Committee
P.O. Box 831
Riverdale, MD 20738
E-mail: aa3of@arrl.net
Web Site: http://www.amateurradio-far.org/scholarships.php
To provide funding to licensed radio amateurs in Wisconsin who are interested in working on a graduate or undergraduate degree.

Title of Award: Ozaukee Radio Club Scholarship **Area, Field, or Subject:** General studies/Field of study not specified **Level of Education for which Award is Granted:** Graduate, Undergraduate **Number Awarded:** 1 each year. **Funds Available:** The stipend is $1,000. **Duration:** 1 year. **Eligibility Requirements:** Applicants must be residents of the state of Wisconsin and have a valid amateur radio license of any class. They must be working on a bachelor's or graduate degree. There is no restriction on the course of study. **Deadline for Receipt:** Requests for applications must be submitted by April of each year. **Additional Information:** This program is sponsored by the Ozaukee Radio Club, Inc., 9822 North Andover Court, Mequon, WI 53097. Recipients must attend an accredited school (university, college, or technical institute) on a full-time basis.

693 ■ FOUNDATION FOR AMATEUR RADIO, INC.

Attn: Scholarship Committee
P.O. Box 831
Riverdale, MD 20738
E-mail: aa3of@arrl.net
Web Site: http://www.amateurradio-far.org/scholarships.php
To provide funding for college or graduate school to licensed radio amateurs who are recommended by members of the Quarter Century Wireless Association (QWCA).
Title of Award: Quarter Century Wireless Association Scholarships **Area, Field, or Subject:** General studies/Field of study not specified **Level of Education for which Award is Granted:** Graduate, Undergraduate **Number Awarded:** 16 each year: 3 at $1,500 and 13 at $1,000. **Funds Available:** Stipends are $1,500 or $1,000. **Duration:** 1 year; nonrenewable.
Eligibility Requirements: This program is open to licensed radio amateurs who intend to work on an associate, bachelor's, or graduate degree. There is no restriction on the course of study or license class. Further, there is no residence area preference. Applicants must be recommended by a member of the association but may not themselves be members. **Deadline for Receipt:** Requests for applications must be submitted by April of each year. **Additional Information:** Recipients must attend an accredited school (university, college, or technical institute) on a full-time basis.

694 ■ FOUNDATION FOR AMATEUR RADIO, INC.

Attn: Scholarship Committee
P.O. Box 831
Riverdale, MD 20738
E-mail: aa3of@arrl.net
Web Site: http://www.amateurradio-far.org/scholarships.php
To provide funding to licensed radio amateurs in the Maryland area who are interested in working on a college degree.
Title of Award: Ernest L. Walker, WB3DVL, Memorial Scholarship **Area, Field, or Subject:** General studies/Field of study not specified **Level of Education for which Award is Granted:** Undergraduate **Number Awarded:** 1 each year. **Funds Available:** The stipend is $1,000. **Duration:** 1 year.
Eligibility Requirements: Applicants must be interested in working on a bachelor's degree, have an amateur radio license of any class, and reside within 150 miles of Baltimore, Maryland. Preference is given to Maryland residents. There is no restriction on the course of study. **Deadline for Receipt:** Requests for applications must be submitted by April of each year. **Additional Information:** This program is sponsored by the Baltimore Radio Amateur Television Society, P.O. Box 5915, Baltimore, MD 21282-5915. Recipients must attend an accredited school (university, college, or technical institute) on a full-time basis.

695 ■ FOUNDATION FOR AMATEUR RADIO, INC.

Attn: Scholarship Committee
P.O. Box 831
Riverdale, MD 20738
E-mail: aa3of@arrl.net
Web Site: http://www.amateurradio-far.org/scholarships.php
To provide funding to licensed radio amateurs in Wisconsin who are interested in working on an undergraduate or graduate degree.
Title of Award: WARAC Memorial Scholarships **Area, Field, or Subject:** General studies/Field of study not specified **Level of Education for which Award is Granted:** Graduate, Undergraduate **Number Awarded:** 2 each year. **Funds Available:** The stipend is $1,500. **Duration:** 1 year.
Eligibility Requirements: Applicants must have an amateur radio license of any class, be a resident of Wisconsin, and be working on an associate, bachelor's, or graduate degree. There is no restriction on course of study. **Deadline for Receipt:** Requests for applications must be submitted by April of each year. **Additional Information:** These scholarships, first awarded in 1988, are sponsored by the West Allis Radio Amateur Club, Inc. (WARAC), P.O. Box 1072, Milwaukee, WI 53201. Recipients must attend an accredited school (university, college, or technical institute) on a full-time basis.

696 ■ FOUNDATION FOR AMATEUR RADIO, INC.

Attn: Scholarship Committee
P.O. Box 831
Riverdale, MD 20738

E-mail: aa3of@arrl.net
Web Site: http://www.amateurradio-far.org/scholarships.php
To provide funding to licensed radio amateurs (especially women) who are interested in earning a bachelor's or graduate degree in the United States.
Title of Award: Young Ladies' Radio League Scholarship **Area, Field, or Subject:** General studies/Field of study not specified **Level of Education for which Award is Granted:** Graduate, Undergraduate **Number Awarded:** 2 each year. **Funds Available:** The stipend is $1,500. **Duration:** 1 year.
Eligibility Requirements: Applicants must have at least an FCC Technician Class or equivalent foreign authorization and intend to work on a bachelor's or graduate degree in the United States. There are no restrictions on the course of study or residency location. Preference is given to female applicants. **Deadline for Receipt:** Requests for applications must be submitted by April of each year. **Additional Information:** This program is sponsored by the Young Ladies' Radio League. It includes the following named scholarships: the Ethel Smith-K4LMB Memorial Scholarship and the Mary Lou Brown-NM7N Memorial Scholarship. Recipients must attend an accredited school (university, college, or technical institute) on a full-time basis.

697 ■ FOUNDATION FOR RURAL SERVICE

Attn: Selection Committee
4121 Wilson Boulevard, Tenth Floor
Arlington, VA 22203
Tel: (703)351-2026
Fax: (703)351-2027
Web Site: http://www.frs.org
To provide financial assistance for college to high school seniors who live in rural areas of the United States.
Title of Award: Foundation for Rural Service College Scholarship Program **Area, Field, or Subject:** General studies/Field of study not specified **Level of Education for which Award is Granted:** Undergraduate **Number Awarded:** 25 each year: 1 per geographic region of NTCA membership, 1 to a student sponsored by an NTCA associate member, and 14 distributed proportionally to the number of applications received per region. **Funds Available:** The stipend is $2,500 (of which $500 is provided by the sponsoring NTCA member cooperative). **Duration:** 1 year; nonrenewable.
Eligibility Requirements: This program is open to graduating high school seniors who receive local telecommunications service from a current member of the National Telecommunications Cooperative Association (NTCA) that serves as a sponsor; associate NTCA members (businesses that provide goods and services to the telecommunications industry) may also sponsor a student. Applicants must live in a rural area, as defined by the Office of Rural Health Policy of the U.S. Department of Health and Human Services. They must have a GPA of 2.0 or higher and have been accepted by an accredited 2-year or 4-year college, university, or vocational/technical school. Along with their application, they must submit transcripts and information on their work experience, school activities, community and volunteer activities, awards and honors, and special circumstances such as family financial need. The must also submit a 300-word essay on 1 of 3 assigned topics. Preference is given to applicants who express an interest in returning to a rural community after graduation. **Deadline for Receipt:** February of each year.

698 ■ FOURTH MARINE DIVISION ASSOCIATION OF WWII

c/o Marine Corps Scholarship Foundation
P.O. Box 3008
Princeton, NJ 08543-3008
Tel: (609)921-3534
Free: 800-292-7777
Fax: (609)452-2259
E-mail: mcsfnj@mcsf.org
Web Site: http://www.marine-scholars.org
To provide financial assistance for college to the grandchildren of veterans who served with the Fourth Marine Division during World War II.
Title of Award: Fourth Marine Division Association of WWII Scholarship **Area, Field, or Subject:** General studies/Field of study not specified **Level of Education for which Award is Granted:** Undergraduate **Number Awarded:** Varies each year. **Funds Available:** Stipends depend on the need of the recipient and the availability of funds. **Duration:** 1 year; may be renewed for up to 3 additional years.

Eligibility Requirements: This program is open to grandchildren of veterans who served with the Fourth Marine Division during World War II and are or were members of the Fourth Marine Division Association of World War II. Applicants must submit academic transcripts, a copy of their grandparent's honorable discharge, and a 300-word essay on topics that change periodically. Recently, they were invited to write on the topic, "What is the most valuable lesson you have learned and who was responsible for teaching it?" Only undergraduate study is supported. The family income of applicants must be less than $63,000 per year. **Deadline for Receipt:** March of each year.

699 ■ BLANCHE NAUGHER FOWLER CHARITABLE SCHOLARSHIP TRUST

c/o AmSouth Bank
Attn: Scholarship Trust
2330 University Boulevard
P.O. Box 2028
Tuscaloosa, AL 35403
Tel: (205)391-5720
Fax: (205)391-5598
To provide financial assistance to undergraduate or graduate students attending colleges or universities in Alabama.
Title of Award: Blanche Naugher Fowler Charitable Scholarship **Area, Field, or Subject:** General studies/Field of study not specified **Level of Education for which Award is Granted:** Four Year College, Graduate **Funds Available:** A stipend is awarded (amount not specified). **Duration:** 1 year; may be renewed until completion of an undergraduate, graduate, or professional degree.
Eligibility Requirements: Applications may be submitted by students attending or accepted at a public or private nonprofit college or university (at least a 4-year baccalaureate-level institution) located in Alabama. Applicants must submit an application form, a transcript, a letter of admission or other evidence of acceptance to or enrollment in a school located in Alabama, SAT or ACT test scores, 2 letters of recommendation, a 1-page statement of educational and career goals and aspirations, and a list of all honors, activities, interests, and employment experiences. Financial need is not required, but applicants who wish to be considered on the basis of financial need must also submit a completed College Scholarship Service Financial Aid Form (FAF) and current tax return. **Deadline for Receipt:** March of each year.

700 ■ FRATERNAL ORDER OF EAGLES

Attn: Eagles Memorial Foundation
4710 14th Street West
Bradenton, FL 34207
Tel: (941)758-5456
Fax: (941)758-4042
Web Site: http://www.foe.com
To provide financial assistance for college to the children of deceased members of the Fraternal Order of Eagles.
Title of Award: Eagles Memorial Foundation Educational Grants **Area, Field, or Subject:** General studies/Field of study not specified **Level of Education for which Award is Granted:** Undergraduate **Number Awarded:** Varies each year. **Funds Available:** Stipends up to $6,000 per school year are provided. Funds must be used for tuition, fees, books, and course-related supplies. Room and board expenses are not covered. **Duration:** 1 year; may be renewed for up to 4 additional years, provided the recipient maintains a GPA of 2.0 or higher and remains an unmarried dependent.
Eligibility Requirements: Applicants must be the minor (under 25 years of age) unmarried children of a deceased parent who was a member of the Fraternal Order of Eagles or its Ladies Auxiliary at the time of death; the member must have died from injuries or diseases incurred within the scope of their employment.

701 ■ FRATERNAL ORDER OF EAGLES

Attn: Eagles Memorial Foundation
4710 14th Street West
Bradenton, FL 34207
Tel: (941)758-5456
Fax: (941)758-4042
Web Site: http://www.foe.com

To provide financial assistance for college to the children of deceased members of the Fraternal Order of Eagles who died in action.
Title of Award: Eagles Memorial Foundation Educational Grants for Military and Other Service Personnel **Area, Field, or Subject:** General studies/Field of study not specified **Level of Education for which Award is Granted:** Undergraduate **Number Awarded:** Varies each year. **Funds Available:** Stipends up to $6,000 per school year are provided. Funds must be used for tuition, fees, books, and course-related supplies. Room and board expenses are not covered. **Duration:** 1 year; may be renewed for up to 4 additional years, provided the recipient maintains a GPA of 2.0 or higher and remains an unmarried dependent.
Eligibility Requirements: Applicants must be the minor (under 25 years of age) unmarried children of a deceased parent who was a member of the Fraternal Order of Eagles or its Ladies Auxiliary at the time of death; the member must have died from injuries or diseases incurred or aggravated in the line of duty while serving 1) in the armed forces of the United States or Canada; 2) as volunteer law enforcement officers in the United States; 3) as volunteer fire fighters; or 4) as volunteer emergency medical service officers.

702 ■ FREEDOM ALLIANCE

Attn: Scholarship Fund
22570 Markey Court, Suite 240
Dulles, VA 20166-6915
Tel: (703)444-7940
Free: 800-475-6620
Fax: (703)444-9893
Web Site: http://www.freedomalliance.org/scholarship.htm
To provide financial assistance for college to the children of deceased and disabled military personnel.
Title of Award: Freedom Alliance Scholarships **Area, Field, or Subject:** General studies/Field of study not specified **Level of Education for which Award is Granted:** Undergraduate **Number Awarded:** Varies each year; recently, 70 of these scholarships were awarded. **Funds Available:** A stipend is awarded (amount not specified). **Duration:** 1 year; may be renewed up to 3 additional years provided the recipient remains enrolled full time with a GPA of 2.0 or higher.
Eligibility Requirements: This program is open to high school seniors, high school graduates, and undergraduate students who are dependent children of military personnel (soldier, sailor, airman, Marine, or Guardsman). The military parent must have been killed or permanently disabled in the line of duty or be currently classified as a POW or MIA. For disabled parents, the disability must be permanent, service-connected, and rated at 100% by the U.S. Department of Veterans Affairs. Family income must be less than $75,000. Along with their application, they must submit a 500-word essay on what their parent's service means to them. **Deadline for Receipt:** June of each year.

703 ■ FUNERAL DIRECTORS ASSOCIATION OF KENTUCKY

P.O. Box 4779
Frankfort, KY 40604
Tel: (502)223-0622
Free: 800-866-3211
Fax: (502)223-0628
E-mail: info@fdaofky.com
Web Site: http://www.fdaofky.com
To provide financial assistance to mortuary science students in Kentucky.
Title of Award: Funeral Directors Association of Kentucky Scholarships **Area, Field, or Subject:** Mortuary science **Level of Education for which Award is Granted:** Undergraduate **Number Awarded:** 2 each year. **Funds Available:** The stipend is $1,500. **Duration:** 1 year.
Eligibility Requirements: This program is open to mortuary science students who have completed 1 year of an internship in Kentucky. Selection is based on financial need, academic performance, recommendations, and articulation of the applicant.

704 ■ FUNERAL SERVICE FOUNDATION

Attn: Executive Director
13625 Bishop's Drive
Brookfield, WI 53005
Tel: (262)789-1880; 877-402-5900
Web Site: http://www.funeralservicefoundation.org/scholarships/index.htm
To provide financial assistance to mortuary science students.

Title of Award: Joseph E. Hagan Memorial Scholarship **Area, Field, or Subject:** Mortuary science **Level of Education for which Award is Granted:** Undergraduate **Number Awarded:** 1 each year. **Funds Available:** The stipend is $1,000. **Duration:** 1 year; nonrenewable

Eligibility Requirements: This program is open to full-time students who are currently enrolled or accepted for enrolment in a program of mortuary science accredited by the American Board of Funeral Service Education. Selection is based primarily on an essay of 400 to 500 words on the importance of the funeral ceremony and its effect on those who are grieving. **Deadline for Receipt:** April of each year. **Additional Information:** This program was established in 2000.

705 ■ FUNERAL SERVICE FOUNDATION

Attn: Executive Director
13625 Bishop's Drive
Brookfield, WI 53005
Tel: (262)789-1880; 877-402-5900
Web Site: http://www.funeralservicefoundation.org/scholarships/index.htm
To provide financial assistance to mortuary science students.

Title of Award: Key Memories Scholarships **Area, Field, or Subject:** Mortuary science **Level of Education for which Award is Granted:** Undergraduate **Number Awarded:** 5 each year. **Funds Available:** The stipend is $1,000. **Duration:** 1 year.

Eligibility Requirements: This program is open to students who are currently enrolled or accepted for enrollment in an accredited program of mortuary science. Selection is based primarily on an essay of 500 words or more on the following topic: "With the trend in funeral preferences moving from traditional burial, describe how you, as a funeral director, would provide personalized service, regardless of the family's choice of final disposition." **Deadline for Receipt:** May of each year. **Additional Information:** This program operates jointly with Keystone Group Holdings, Inc., 400 North Ashley Drive, Suite 1900, Tampa, FL 33602, (813) 225-4650, (888) 788-7526, Fax: (813) 225-4655.

706 ■ MIKE GALLAGHER SHOW CHARITABLE FOUNDATION

Attn: Educational Assistance Fund
350 Fifth Avenue, Suite 1818
New York, NY 10118
Tel: (212)244-5311
E-mail: jhudson@gallaghersarmy.com
Web Site: http://www.gallaghersarmy.com
To provide financial assistance for college to the children of armed forces personnel killed in action while fighting the war on terror.

Title of Award: Gallagher's Army Educational Assistance Fund **Area, Field, or Subject:** General studies/Field of study not specified **Level of Education for which Award is Granted:** Undergraduate **Number Awarded:** 1 or more each year. **Funds Available:** A stipend is awarded (amount not specified). **Duration:** 1 year; may be renewed.

Eligibility Requirements: This program is open to the children of members of the U.S. armed forces who were killed in action while fighting the war on terror. Applicants must be U.S. citizens who are graduating from high school and entering an accredited college or university as a full-time student. They must submit a statement describing their educational goals and why they need assistance. **Additional Information:** This program, established in 2005, is supported by General Steel Corporation.

707 ■ GATEWAY HEMOPHILIA ASSOCIATION

11404 Gravois, Lower Level
St. Louis, MO 63126
Tel: (314)729-0233; (866)729-0233
Fax: (314)729-7033
E-mail: info@gatewayhemophilia.org
Web Site: http://www.gatewayhemophilia.org/events
To provide financial assistance for college or graduate school to members of the Gateway Hemophilia Association.

Title of Award: Gateway Hemophilia Association Scholarship Program **Area, Field, or Subject:** General studies/Field of study not specified **Level of Education for which Award is Granted:** Graduate, Undergraduate **Number Awarded:** 3 each year. **Funds Available:** The stipend is $1,000. **Duration:** 1 year.

Eligibility Requirements: This program is open to members of the association who also have a bleeding disorder. Applicants must be enrolled or planning to enroll at an accredited vocational/technical school, college, university, or graduate school. Selection is based on potential to succeed, academic achievement, leadership, participation in school and community activities, and unusual personal or family circumstances. **Deadline for Receipt:** April of each year. **Additional Information:** The Gateway Hemophilia Association is the Missouri affiliate of the National Hemophilia Association.

708 ■ GENERAL FEDERATION OF WOMEN'S CLUBS OF VERMONT

c/o Kathy Moaratty, Scholarship Chair
183 Power House Road
Canaan, VT 05903
Tel: (802)266-3031
E-mail: kathmoaratty@aol.com
To provide financial assistance for college to displaced homemakers in Vermont.

Title of Award: Barbara Jean Barker Memorial Scholarship for a Displaced Homemaker **Area, Field, or Subject:** General studies/Field of study not specified **Level of Education for which Award is Granted:** Undergraduate **Number Awarded:** 1 to 3 each year. **Funds Available:** The stipend ranges from $500 to $1,500. **Duration:** 1 year.

Eligibility Requirements: Applicants must be Vermont residents who have been homemakers (primarily) for at least 15 years and have lost their main means of support through death, divorce, separation, spouse's long-time illness, or spouse's long-time unemployment. Applicants must be interested in upgrading their skills so they can work outside the home. As part of the application process, they must submit a completed application form and a letter of recommendation (from a personal friend or their postsecondary school). Selection is based on the information provided in the application form and a personal interview (finalists only). **Deadline for Receipt:** March of each year.

709 ■ GENERAL MOTORS CORPORATION

Chevrolet Motor Division
Attn: GM Scholarship Administration Center
700 West Fifth Avenue
Mail Code 2001
Naperville, IL 60563
888-377-5233
E-mail: scholarshipinfo@gmsac.com
To provide financial assistance for college to African American high school seniors.

Title of Award: Chevrolet Excellence in Education Award for African American Students **Area, Field, or Subject:** General studies/Field of study not specified **Level of Education for which Award is Granted:** Undergraduate **Number Awarded:** Varies each year. **Funds Available:** The stipend is $1,000 per year. **Duration:** 1 year.

Eligibility Requirements: This program is open to African American students currently completing the senior year of high school with sufficient credits to graduate in the spring term with a GPA of 3.2 or higher. Applicants must be planning to enrolled in an accredited 2-year or 4-year college or university in the following fall. They must be able to demonstrate both academic excellence and community service (e.g., activities, volunteerism, work experience) and be a U.S. citizen or have eligibility to work in the United States. Along with their application, they must include a letter of recommendation from a high school teacher or administrator, official transcripts from their high school, and a personal statement (500 to 750 words) about how their high school experiences (academics, extracurricular activities, outside activities, work experience) have prepared them for college and why they should be considered for this scholarship. Selection is based on that statement, academic performance, leadership and participation in school and community activities, work experience, and career and educational aspirations. Financial need is not considered. **Deadline for Receipt:** April of each year. **Additional Information:** This program was established by the Chevrolet Motor Division of General Motors Corporation.

710 ■ GENERAL MOTORS CORPORATION

Chevrolet Motor Division
Attn: GM Scholarship Administration Center
700 West Fifth Avenue
Mail Code 2001
Naperville, IL 60563

888-377-5233
E-mail: scholarshipinfo@gmsac.com
To provide financial assistance for college to Hispanic American high school seniors.

Title of Award: Chevrolet Excellence in Education Award for Hispanic Students **Area, Field, or Subject:** General studies/Field of study not specified **Level of Education for which Award is Granted:** Undergraduate **Number Awarded:** Varies each year. **Funds Available:** The stipend is $1,000 per year. **Duration:** 1 year.

Eligibility Requirements: This program is open to Hispanic students currently completing the senior year of high school with sufficient credits to graduate in the spring term with a GPA of 3.2 or higher. Applicants must be planning to enrolled in an accredited 2-year or 4-year college or university in the following fall. They must be able to demonstrate both academic excellence and community service (e.g., activities, volunteerism, work experience) and be a U.S. citizen or have eligibility to work in the United States. Along with their application, they must include a letter of recommendation from a high school teacher or administrator, official transcripts from their high school, and a personal statement (500 to 750 words) about how their high school experiences (academics, extracurricular activities, outside activities, work experience) have prepared them for college and why they should be considered for this scholarship. Selection is based on that statement, academic performance, leadership and participation in school and community activities, work experience, and career and educational aspirations. Financial need is not considered. **Deadline for Receipt:** April of each year. **Additional Information:** This program was established by the Chevrolet Motor Division of General Motors Corporation.

711 ■ GENERAL MOTORS MINORITY DEALERS ASSOCIATION

29433 Southfield Road, Suite 210
Southfield, MI 48076
Tel: (248)552-9040; 888-377-5233
Fax: (248)552-9022
E-mail: scholarshipinfo@gmsac.com
Web Site: http://www.gmmda.org
To provide financial assistance for college to ethnic minority high school seniors and college students.

Title of Award: General Motors Minority Dealers Association Minority Scholarship Program **Area, Field, or Subject:** General studies/Field of study not specified **Level of Education for which Award is Granted:** Undergraduate **Number Awarded:** Varies each year; recently, 18 of these scholarships were awarded. **Funds Available:** The stipend is $2,500. **Duration:** 1 year.

Eligibility Requirements: This program is open to ethnic minority graduating high school seniors and current college students who are enrolled or planning to enroll full time at an accredited 2-year or 4-year college or university in the United States. Applicants must be U.S. citizens with a GPA of 3.0 or higher. Along with their application, they must submit a personal statement of 500 to 750 words explaining 1) how their school experiences, including academics, extracurricular activities, outside activities, and work experiences, are shaping their educational and career goals, and 2) why they should be considered for this scholarship. Selection is based on that statement, academic excellence, leadership and participation in school and community activities, work experience, education, and career aspirations. **Deadline for Receipt:** November of each year. **Additional Information:** This program began in 2004.

712 ■ GEOFFREY FOUNDATION

Ocean Avenue
P.O. Box 1112
Kennebunkport, ME 04046
Tel: (207)967-5798
To provide financial assistance to deaf students who attend school with hearing students and communicate using spoken language.

Title of Award: Geoffrey Foundation Scholarships **Area, Field, or Subject:** General studies/Field of study not specified **Level of Education for which Award is Granted:** Undergraduate **Number Awarded:** Varies each year. The foundation awards grants in excess of $30,000 each year to children and college students. **Funds Available:** The amount awarded varies, depending upon the needs of the recipient. **Duration:** 1 year or longer.

Eligibility Requirements: This program is open to U.S. citizens who are hearing impaired (severe to profound hearing loss greater than 80 dB)

and are utilizing an auditory-verbal approach to communication. Applicant must be currently enrolled or planning to attend a preschool, elementary school, junior high or high school, or college for hearing students on a full-time basis in the forthcoming year. They must submit a current audiogram plus 3 letters of recommendation. **Deadline for Receipt:** March of each year. **Additional Information:** The foundation is closely aligned with Auditory-Verbal International, Inc. and the Alexander Graham Bell Association for the Deaf. Funds are also available to support hearing research as well as programs, initiatives, or organizations of interest to the foundation. Applications may be requested only by mail.

713 ■ GEORGIA ASSOCIATION OF HOMES AND SERVICES FOR CHILDREN

Attn: Celebration of Excellence
34 Peachtree Street, N.W., Suite 1710
Atlanta, GA 30303
Tel: (404)572-6170
Fax: (404)572-6171
E-mail: cara@gahsc.org
Web Site: http://www.celebrationofexcellence.org
To provide financial assistance for college or graduate school to residents of Georgia who have been in foster care.

Title of Award: Celebration of Excellence Scholarship **Area, Field, or Subject:** General studies/Field of study not specified **Level of Education for which Award is Granted:** Graduate, Undergraduate **Number Awarded:** 1 or more each year. **Funds Available:** The stipend is $1,000 per year. **Duration:** 1 year; may be renewed for a total of 4 years of undergraduate and/or graduate study.

Eligibility Requirements: This program is open to Georgia residents who were in the custody of the Georgia Department of Family and Children Services or placed at a licensed private residential program at the time of their 18th birthday. Applicants must be attending or planning to attend an approved college, university, vocational program, or graduate school. They must submit an essay of 3 to 5 pages that discusses their educational and career goals, their extracurricular activities and community involvement, and why they think this scholarship will help them reach their goals. Selection is based on that essay, transcripts, SAT/ACT scores, 2 letters of reference, and financial need. **Deadline for Receipt:** April of each year.

714 ■ GEORGIA COUNCIL OF THE BLIND

c/o Debbie Williams, Scholarship Committee Chair
1477 Nebo Road
Dallas, GA 30157
E-mail: williamsdebk@wmconnect.com
Web Site: http://www.georgiacounciloftheblind.org/scholarship.aspx
To provide financial assistance for college or graduate school to students in Georgia who have visual impairments or parents with visual impairments.

Title of Award: Georgia Council of the Blind Scholarships **Area, Field, or Subject:** General studies/Field of study not specified **Level of Education for which Award is Granted:** Graduate, Undergraduate **Number Awarded:** 1 or more each year. **Funds Available:** Stipends up to $1,000 per year are available. **Duration:** 1 year; recipients may reapply.

Eligibility Requirements: This program is open to residents of Georgia who are either 1) visually impaired or legally blind or 2) the sighted children of parents who are visually impaired or legally blind. Applicants must be enrolled or accepted for enrollment at a vocational/technical school, a 2-year or 4-year college, or a master's or doctoral program. All fields of study are eligible. Selection is based on academic transcripts, 2 letters of recommendation, a 1-page typed statement of the applicant's educational goals, an audio cassette recording of the applicant reading the goals statement, extracurricular activities, and financial need. **Deadline for Receipt:** June of each year. **Additional Information:** This program began in 1988.

715 ■ GEORGIA ELECTRIC MEMBERSHIP CORPORATION

2100 East Exchange Place
Tucker, GA 30084
Tel: (770)270-6950
Free: 800-544-4362
Fax: (770)270-7335
Web Site: http://www.georgiaemc.com

To provide financial assistance for college to residents of areas served by Georgia Electric Membership Corporation (GEMC).

Title of Award: Walter Harrison Scholarship **Area, Field, or Subject:** General studies/Field of study not specified **Level of Education for which Award is Granted:** Undergraduate **Number Awarded:** 7 each year. **Funds Available:** The stipend is $1,000. **Duration:** 1 year.

Eligibility Requirements: This program is open to high school seniors and current undergraduates who are members or employees of 1 of the 36 regional affiliates of GEMC. Applicants must be attending or planning to attend a college or technical school in Georgia. Along with their application, they must submit a 2-page autobiographical sketch, high school or college transcripts, SAT scores, 2 letters of recommendation, and documentation of financial need. They must submit their application to their EMC; each EMC may submit 1 application for each $1,000 that it has contributed to the scholarship fund. **Deadline for Receipt:** January of each year. **Additional Information:** This program was established in 1985.

716 ■ GEORGIA GUARD INSURANCE TRUST

P.O. Box 889
Mableton, GA 30126
Tel: (770)739-9651
Free: 800-229-1053
Fax: (770)745-0673
Web Site: http://www.ngaga.org/scholarship.html

To provide assistance for business or vocational education to members of the Georgia National Guard and their spouses, children, and grandchildren.

Title of Award: National Guard of Georgia Scholarship Fund for Business and Vocational School **Area, Field, or Subject:** General studies/Field of study not specified **Level of Education for which Award is Granted:** Vocational/Occupational **Number Awarded:** Varies each year. **Funds Available:** The maximum stipend is $1,000 per year. **Duration:** Up to 2 years.

Eligibility Requirements: This program is open to policyholders with the Georgia Guard Insurance Trust who are members of the National Guard Association of Georgia (NGAGA) or the Enlisted Association of the National Guard of Georgia (EANGGA); spouses, children, and grandchildren of NGAGA and EANGGA members; and unmarried widow(er)s, children, and grandchildren of deceased NGAGA and EANGGA members. Applicants must meet program-specific admission standards and institutional requirements and complete all admission procedures for admission to a degree/diploma program in regular program status. **Deadline for Receipt:** April of each year.

717 ■ GEORGIA GUARD INSURANCE TRUST

P.O. Box 889
Mableton, GA 30126
Tel: (770)739-9651
Free: 800-229-1053
Fax: (770)745-0673
Web Site: http://www.ngaga.org/scholarship.html

To provide money for college to members of the Georgia National Guard and their spouses, children, and grandchildren.

Title of Award: National Guard of Georgia Scholarship Fund for College **Area, Field, or Subject:** General studies/Field of study not specified **Level of Education for which Award is Granted:** Undergraduate **Number Awarded:** Varies each year. **Funds Available:** The maximum stipend is $5,000 per year. **Duration:** Up to 5 years.

Eligibility Requirements: This program is open to policyholders with the Georgia Guard Insurance Trust who are members of the National Guard Association of Georgia (NGAGA) or the Enlisted Association of the National Guard of Georgia (EANGGA); spouses, children, and grandchildren of NGAGA and EANGGA members; and unmarried widow(er)s, children, and grandchildren of deceased NGAGA and EANGGA members. Applicants who are high school seniors must have a combined SAT score of at least 1000 or a GPA of 3.0 or higher. Applicants already enrolled in a college or university must have a cumulative GPA of 3.0 or higher.

Deadline for Receipt: April of each year. **Additional Information:** Full-time undergraduate enrollment is required.

718 ■ GEORGIA STUDENT FINANCE COMMISSION

Attn: Scholarships and Grants Division
2082 East Exchange Place, Suite 200
Tucker, GA 30084-5305
Tel: (770)724-9000
Free: 800-505-GSFC
Fax: (770)724-9089
E-mail: info@mail.gsfc.state.ga.us
Web Site: http://www.gsfc.org

To provide financial assistance to high school students in Georgia who are enrolled concurrently in college-level courses.

Title of Award: Accel Program **Area, Field, or Subject:** General studies/Field of study not specified **Level of Education for which Award is Granted:** Undergraduate **Number Awarded:** Varies each year. **Funds Available:** Accel Scholars who attend public colleges or universities receive full tuition and mandatory fees plus a book allowance of $300 per academic year. The stipend for Accel Scholarships at private colleges and universities is $125 per semester hour, or up to $3,000 per year; funds may be used only for tuition and mandatory fees. **Duration:** 1 year; may be renewed for 1 additional year.

Eligibility Requirements: This program is open to Georgia residents who are enrolled simultaneously as a junior or senior at an eligible public or private high school in the state and at an eligible Georgia public or private postsecondary institution. Applicants must be taking college degree-level courses in English language arts, mathematics, social studies, science, or foreign language. U.S. citizenship or permanent resident status is required. **Additional Information:** This program, established in 2004, is funded by the Georgia Lottery for Education.

719 ■ GEORGIA STUDENT FINANCE COMMISSION

Attn: Scholarships and Grants Division
2082 East Exchange Place, Suite 200
Tucker, GA 30084-5305
Tel: (770)724-9000
Free: 800-505-GSFC
Fax: (770)724-9089
E-mail: info@mail.gsfc.state.ga.us
Web Site: http://www.gsfc.org/gsfc/grants/dsp_ggov.cfm

To provide financial assistance for college to outstanding high school seniors in Georgia.

Title of Award: Georgia Governor's Scholarship **Area, Field, or Subject:** General studies/Field of study not specified **Level of Education for which Award is Granted:** Undergraduate **Number Awarded:** Varies each year; recently, 2,828 of these scholarships were awarded. **Funds Available:** The stipend is currently $804 per year. **Duration:** 1 year; may be renewed for up to 3 additional years if the recipient maintains a cumulative GPA of 3.0 or higher and full-time enrollment.

Eligibility Requirements: Eligible to apply are Georgia residents planning to attend accredited institutions of higher education in the state as full-time entering freshmen. They must be graduating from a Georgia high school as a STAR Student or valedictorian and be in compliance with the Georgia Drug-Free Postsecondary Education Act. U.S. citizenship or permanent resident status is required. **Additional Information:** Information about this program, which began in the 1985-86 school year, is also available from local high school counselors.

720 ■ GEORGIA STUDENT FINANCE COMMISSION

Attn: Scholarships and Grants Division
2082 East Exchange Place, Suite 200
Tucker, GA 30084-5305
Tel: (770)724-9000
Free: 800-505-GSFC
Fax: (770)724-9089
E-mail: info@mail.gsfc.state.ga.us
Web Site: http://www.gsfc.org/gsfc/grants/dsp_glepd.cfm

To provide financial assistance for college to children of disabled or deceased Georgia law enforcement officers, fire fighters, and prison guards.

Title of Award: Georgia Law Enforcement Personnel Dependents Grant **Area, Field, or Subject:** General studies/Field of study not specified

Level of Education for which Award is Granted: Undergraduate **Number Awarded:** Varies each year; recently, 20 of these grants were awarded. **Funds Available:** The grant is $2,000 per academic year, not to exceed $8,000 during an entire program of study. **Duration:** 1 year; may be renewed (if satisfactory progress is maintained) for up to 3 additional years.

Eligibility Requirements: Eligible to apply are dependent children of law enforcement officers, fire fighters, and prison guards in Georgia who have been permanently disabled or killed in the line of duty. Applicants must be enrolled as full-time undergraduate students in a Georgia private or public college, university, or technical institution. U.S. citizenship or permanent resident status and compliance with the Georgia Drug-Free Postsecondary Education Act are required. **Deadline for Receipt:** July of each year.

721 ■ GEORGIA STUDENT FINANCE COMMISSION

Attn: Scholarships and Grants Division
2082 East Exchange Place, Suite 200
Tucker, GA 30084-5305
Tel: (770)724-9000
Free: 800-505-GSFC
Fax: (770)724-9089
E-mail: info@mail.gsfc.state.ga.us
Web Site: http://www.gsfc.org/gsfc/grants/dsp_leap.cfm
To provide financial assistance for college to residents of Georgia who demonstrate financial need.

Title of Award: Georgia LEAP Grant Program **Area, Field, or Subject:** General studies/Field of study not specified **Level of Education for which Award is Granted:** Undergraduate **Number Awarded:** Varies each year; recently, 3,008 of these grants were awarded. **Funds Available:** The maximum grant is $2,000 per academic year. **Duration:** 1 year; may be renewed (if satisfactory progress is maintained) for up to 3 additional years.

Eligibility Requirements: This program is open to Georgia residents who are enrolled as regular undergraduate students in an eligible Georgia public or private college, university, or technical college. Applicants must be able to demonstrate substantial financial need and must be eligible for a federal Pell Grant. They must be at least a half-time student maintaining satisfactory academic progress. U.S. citizenship or permanent resident status and compliance with the Georgia Drug-Free Postsecondary Education Act are required. **Additional Information:** This program began in 2001.

722 ■ GEORGIA STUDENT FINANCE COMMISSION

Attn: Scholarships and Grants Division
2082 East Exchange Place, Suite 200
Tucker, GA 30084-5305
Tel: (770)724-9000
Free: 800-505-GSFC
Fax: (770)724-9089
E-mail: info@mail.gsfc.state.ga.us
Web Site: http://www.gsfc.org/gsfa/SCL/dsp_gngscel.cfm
To provide forgivable loans to members of the Georgia National Guard who are interested in working on an undergraduate degree.

Title of Award: Georgia National Guard Service Cancelable Educational Loans **Area, Field, or Subject:** General studies/Field of study not specified **Level of Education for which Award is Granted:** Undergraduate **Number Awarded:** Varies each year. **Funds Available:** The maximum loan is equal to the tuition charged by the University of Georgia; currently, that is $1,819 per semester. Loans may be cancelled by service in the Guard during the period in which the loan is applicable. If the borrower falls below half-time enrollment or otherwise become ineligible, the loan must be repaid with interest of 8%. **Duration:** 1 year; may be renewed up to 4 additional years provided the recipient maintains a GPA of 2.0 or higher.

Eligibility Requirements: This program is open to members of the Georgia National Guard who are interested in working on a bachelor's or associate degree at an eligible college, university, or technical/vocational school in the state. Applicants must maintain good military standing as a member of the Guard and satisfactory academic progress as determined by their school. They must be enrolled at least half time.

723 ■ GEORGIA STUDENT FINANCE COMMISSION

Attn: Scholarships and Grants Division
2082 East Exchange Place, Suite 200
Tucker, GA 30084-5305
Tel: (770)724-9000
Free: 800-505-GSFC
Fax: (770)724-9089
E-mail: info@mail.gsfc.state.ga.us
Web Site: http://www.gsfc.org/gsfc/grants/dsp_gps.cfm
To provide financial assistance for college to the children of Georgia public safety officers who have been permanently disabled or killed in the line of duty.

Title of Award: Georgia Public Safety Memorial Grant **Area, Field, or Subject:** General studies/Field of study not specified **Level of Education for which Award is Granted:** Undergraduate **Number Awarded:** Varies each year; recently, 18 of these grants were awarded. **Funds Available:** The award covers the cost of attendance at a public postsecondary school in Georgia, minus any other aid received. **Duration:** 1 year; may be renewed (if satisfactory progress is maintained) for up to 3 additional years.

Eligibility Requirements: This program is open to dependent children of Georgia law enforcement officers, fire fighters, EMT, correction officers, or prison guards who have been permanently disabled or killed in the line of duty. Applicants must be enrolled or accepted as full-time undergraduate students in a Georgia public college, university, or technical institution and be in compliance with the Georgia Drug-Free Postsecondary Education Act. U.S. citizenship or permanent resident status is required. **Deadline for Receipt:** July of each year. **Additional Information:** This program began in 1994.

724 ■ GEORGIA STUDENT FINANCE COMMISSION

Attn: Scholarships and Grants Division
2082 East Exchange Place, Suite 200
Tucker, GA 30084-5305
Tel: (770)724-9000
Free: 800-505-GSFC
Fax: (770)724-9089
E-mail: hope@mail.gsfc.state.ga.us
Web Site: http://www.gsfc.org/HOPE/index.cfm
To help outstanding students who are interested in earning a certificate or diploma at a public technical institute in Georgia.

Title of Award: HOPE Grants for Certificate and Diploma Programs **Area, Field, or Subject:** General studies/Field of study not specified **Level of Education for which Award is Granted:** Undergraduate **Number Awarded:** Varies each year. **Funds Available:** These grants pay tuition and mandatory fees at public technical institutes in Georgia, along with a book allowance of up to $300 per year. **Duration:** This assistance may be used for a total of 2 technical programs of study leading to a certificate or diploma.

Eligibility Requirements: This program is open to Georgia residents who are working on a certificate or diploma in a non-degree program of study at a public institution in the state. The certificate or degree program must be approved by the Georgia Department of Technical and Adult education or be a comparable program approved by the Board of Regents. Continuing education programs are not eligible. **Additional Information:** HOPE stands for Helping Outstanding Pupils Educationally. Full-time enrollment is not required.

725 ■ GEORGIA STUDENT FINANCE COMMISSION

Attn: Scholarships and Grants Division
2082 East Exchange Place, Suite 200
Tucker, GA 30084-5305
Tel: (770)724-9000
Free: 800-505-GSFC
Fax: (770)724-9089
E-mail: hope@mail.gsfc.state.ga.us
Web Site: http://www.gsfc.org/HOPE/index.cfm
To provide financial assistance to outstanding students who are attending or planning to attend a college or university in Georgia.

Title of Award: HOPE Scholarships for Degree-Seeking Students **Area, Field, or Subject:** General studies/Field of study not specified **Level of**

Education for which Award is Granted: Undergraduate **Number Awarded:** Varies each year. **Funds Available:** HOPE Scholars who attend public colleges or universities receive full tuition and mandatory fees plus a book allowance of $300 per academic year. The stipend for HOPE Scholarships at private colleges and universities is up to $3,000 per year; funds may be used only for tuition and mandatory fees. **Duration:** 1 year; may be renewed for up to 3 additional years if the recipient maintains a cumulative GPA of 3.0 or higher in college.

Eligibility Requirements: This program is open to Georgia residents who are attending or planning to attend a college or university within the state. Students who are applying as high school seniors must have earned at least a 3.0 cumulative GPA if they followed the college preparatory track in high school or a 3.2 cumulative GPA if they followed a technical/career track. The college preparatory diploma requires completion of 4 units of English, 4 units of mathematics, 3 units of social studies, 3 units of science, and 2 units of a foreign language. The technical/career diploma requires completion of 4 units of English, 3 units of mathematics, 3 units of social studies, and 3 units of science. Students who are applying for the first time as college students must have earned a GPA of 3.0 or higher in college regardless of their high school GPA. Students who complete home study requirements may receive a scholarship retroactively if they earn a GPA of 3.0 or higher in their first year of college. U.S. citizenship or permanent resident status is required. **Additional Information:** HOPE stands for Helping Outstanding Pupils Educationally. Full-time enrollment (at least 12 hours) is required.

726 ■ GIRL SCOUTS OF THE USA

Attn: Program, Membership, and Research
420 Fifth Avenue
New York, NY 10018-2798
Tel: (212)852-8000
Free: 800-GSUSA-4U
Web Site: http://www.girlscouts.org/program/gs_central/scholarships
To provide financial assistance for college to members of the Girl Scouts of America who have achieved its Gold Award.

Title of Award: Elks Gold Award Scholarships **Area, Field, or Subject:** General studies/Field of study not specified **Level of Education for which Award is Granted:** Undergraduate **Number Awarded:** 8 each year: 1 in each Girl Scout Service Area. **Funds Available:** The stipend is $1,500 per year. **Duration:** 4 years.

Eligibility Requirements: This program is open to Gold Award winners who are graduating high school seniors. Applicants must be planning to attend an accredited college or university. Selection is based on academics, activities, community involvement, leadership, and pursuit of individual interests. **Deadline for Receipt:** Each Girl Scout Council sets its own deadline, but each council must submit its top application to headquarters by the end of April of each year. **Additional Information:** Funding for this program is provided by the Elks National Foundation.

727 ■ GIRLS INCORPORATED

Attn: Scholarships and Awards
120 Wall Street, Third Floor
New York, NY 10005-3902
Tel: (212)509-2000
Free: 800-374-4475
Fax: (212)509-8708
E-mail: girlsincorporated@girls-inc.org
Web Site: http://www.girls-inc.org
To provide financial assistance for college to Girls Incorporated members.

Title of Award: Girls Incorporated National Scholars Program **Area, Field, or Subject:** General studies/Field of study not specified **Level of Education for which Award is Granted:** Undergraduate **Number Awarded:** Up to 20 each year: 7 to 10 at $15,000 and 10 at $2,500. **Funds Available:** The scholarships are either $15,000 or $2,500. Funds are held in escrow and paid directly to the recipient's college, professional school, or technical institute. **Duration:** Up to 5 years.

Eligibility Requirements: This program is open to members of Girls Incorporated affiliates who are currently in high school (in grades 11 or 12) and have been members of the association for at least 2 years. They must have a GPA of 2.8 or higher. Selection is based on extracurricular activities, goals and objectives, soundness of ideas, motivation, communication skills, and presentation. Financial need is not considered. Academic record is of secondary importance. **Additional Information:** This program

was established in 1992 and replaces the Reader's Digest Career Key Awards. Funds may not be used for education at a vocational or technical school.

728 ■ GOVERNMENT FINANCE OFFICERS ASSOCIATION OF SOUTH CAROLINA

Attn: Scholarship Committee
P.O. Box 280334
Columbia, SC 29228
Tel: (803)951-7371
Fax: (803)359-4892
E-mail: lslee@sc.rr.com
Web Site: http://www.gfoasc.com/scholarshp.html
To provide financial assistance to South Carolina residents who are majoring in accounting, finance, or business administration at a college in the state.

Title of Award: Willa S. Bellamy Scholarship **Area, Field, or Subject:** Accounting; Business administration; Finance **Level of Education for which Award is Granted:** Undergraduate **Number Awarded:** 1 each year. **Funds Available:** The stipend is $2,000. **Duration:** 1 year.

Eligibility Requirements: This program is open to residents of South Carolina who are currently enrolled as a rising sophomore, junior, or senior at a public college or university in the state. Applicants must be enrolled full time and have a GPA of 3.0 or higher and a major in finance, accounting, or business administration with a concentration in accounting or finance. Financial need is not considered in the selection process. **Deadline for Receipt:** April of each year.

729 ■ GOVERNOR'S COALITION FOR YOUTH WITH DISABILITIES

Attn: Karen Burgess
P.O. Box 2485
Hartford, CT 06146-2485
Tel: (860)263-6018
E-mail: karen.burgess@gcyd.org
Web Site: http://www.gcyd.org
To provide financial assistance for college to Connecticut residents who have a disability.

Title of Award: Governor's Coalition for Youth with Disabilities Scholarships **Area, Field, or Subject:** General studies/Field of study not specified **Level of Education for which Award is Granted:** Undergraduate **Number Awarded:** The number of national scholarships varies each year; 4 Connecticut State University scholarships (1 at each campus) and 12 community college scholarships (1 at each college) are awarded each year. Since the program began, 174 students with disabilities from 82 Connecticut towns have received support from this program. **Funds Available:** For students at colleges and universities nationwide, the stipend is $3,000. For students at Connecticut State Universities, the stipend is $500 per semester. For students at Connecticut community colleges, the stipend is up to $2,672 per year. **Duration:** 1 year. National scholarships are nonrenewable, Connecticut State University scholarships may be renewed for a total of 8 semesters, and Connecticut community college scholarships may be renewed for a total of 3 years.

Eligibility Requirements: This program is open to Connecticut residents with a disability who are graduating high school seniors. Applicants must be planning to attend 1) a college or university in Connecticut or any other state; 2) any of the 4 campuses of the Connecticut State University System; or 3) any of the 12 Connecticut community colleges. Applicants must submit letters of recommendation, transcripts, information on their high school activities and work experience, a statement on how they feel this scholarship will assist them in their career, and an essay of 1 to 2 pages describing their disability and how they have overcome the challenges it has presented. Applications must be submitted to high school counselors. **Deadline for Receipt:** January of each year. **Additional Information:** This program was established in 1994 with support from the governor of Connecticut and many business, labor, and individual donors in the state.

730 ■ GRAND PORTAGE TRIBAL COUNCIL

Attn: Education Director
P.O. Box 428
Grand Portage, MN 55605
Tel: (218)475-0121
Fax: (218)475-2284

E-mail: gpeduc@boreal.org
Web Site: http://www.grandportage.com/tribal.html
To provide financial assistance for undergraduate or graduate study to Minnesota Chippewa Tribe members.
Title of Award: Grand Portage Scholarship Program **Area, Field, or Subject:** General studies/Field of study not specified **Level of Education for which Award is Granted:** Graduate, Undergraduate **Number Awarded:** Varies each year. **Funds Available:** The amount of the award is based on the need of the recipient. **Duration:** 1 year; may be renewed for a total of 10 semesters or 15 quarters to complete a 4-year degree program if recipients maintain full-time enrollment and a GPA of 2.0 or higher. Adjustments are considered for part-time and/or graduate study.
Eligibility Requirements: Applicants must be an enrolled member of the Grand Portage Band of Chippewa or have a parent who is enrolled. They must be enrolled at or accepted for enrollment at an accredited training program or degree-granting college or university and have applied for all other forms of financial aid. Residents of states other than Minnesota are eligible only for college or university study, not for vocational training. **Deadline for Receipt:** At least 8 weeks before school starts.

731 ■ EARL G. GRAVES LTD.
Attn: College Financial Newsletter
130 Fifth Avenue, Tenth Floor
New York, NY 10011-4399
Tel: (212)242-8000
Web Site: http://www.blackenterprise.com
To provide financial assistance to college students who utilize the College Financial Newsletter of BlackEnterprise.com.
Title of Award: College Financial Newsletter Scholarship **Area, Field, or Subject:** General studies/Field of study not specified **Level of Education for which Award is Granted:** Undergraduate **Number Awarded:** 3 each year. **Funds Available:** The stipend is $1,000. **Duration:** 1 year.
Eligibility Requirements: This program is open to U.S. citizens and permanent residents who are enrolled full time in a recognized college or university within the United States. Applicants must register online to utilize the College Financial e-Newsletter. Selection is based on a random drawing. **Additional Information:** This program began in 2005.

732 ■ GREAT COMEBACKS AWARD PROGRAM
c/o ConvaTec Customer Interaction Center
P.O. Box 5254
Princeton, NJ 08543-5254
800-422-8811
E-mail: info@greatcomebacks.com
Web Site: http://www.greatcomebacks.com/us/awardprogram/index.html
To provide financial assistance to college students with an inflammatory bowel disease (IBD) or other related physical conditions.
Title of Award: Ina Brudnick Scholarship Award **Area, Field, or Subject:** General studies/Field of study not specified **Level of Education for which Award is Granted:** Undergraduate **Number Awarded:** 1 each year. **Funds Available:** The stipend is $2,500. **Duration:** 1 year.
Eligibility Requirements: This program is open to people under 24 years of age who have undergone an ostomy and/or have an IBD (Crohn's disease or ulcerative colitis). Applicants must be able to demonstrate financial need. Along with their application, they must submit statements on how their life has been changed or affected by IBD or their ostomy, who or what helped them most in getting through their physical and emotional struggle, what advice they would give to someone struggling with IBD and/or facing ostomy surgery, and their dreams of what they want to accomplish in the future. **Deadline for Receipt:** September of each year. **Additional Information:** This scholarship is provided by ConvaTec, a Bristol-Myers Squibb Company.

733 ■ GREAT LAKES HEMOPHILIA FOUNDATION
638 North 18th Street, Suite 108
P.O. Box 704
Milwaukee, WI 53201-0704
Tel: (414)257-0200; 888-797-GLHF
Fax: (414)257-1225
E-mail: info@glhf.org
Web Site: http://www.glhf.org/scholar.htm
To provide financial assistance for college to Wisconsin residents with a bleeding disorder and their families.

Title of Award: Great Lakes Hemophilia Foundation Education and Training Assistance Scholarships **Area, Field, or Subject:** General studies/Field of study not specified **Level of Education for which Award is Granted:** Undergraduate **Number Awarded:** Several each year. **Funds Available:** Stipends range from $500 to $2,000. **Duration:** 1 year.
Eligibility Requirements: This program is open to residents of Wisconsin who have a bleeding disorder and their parents, spouses, children, and siblings. Applicants must be attending or planning to attend college, vocational school, technical school, or a certification program. Adults who require retraining because they can no longer function in their chosen field as a result of health complications from bleeding disorders are also eligible. **Deadline for Receipt:** April of each year.

734 ■ GREATER BENEFICIAL UNION OF PITTSBURGH
Attn: GBU Foundation
4254 Clairton Boulevard
Pittsburgh, PA 15227-3394
Tel: (412)884-5100
Free: 800-765-4GBU
Fax: (412)884-9815
E-mail: info@gbu.org
Web Site: http://www.gbu.org/foundatn.htm
To provide financial assistance for college or graduate school to members and annuitants of the Greater Beneficial Union of Pittsburgh (GBU).
Title of Award: Greater Beneficial Union Scholarships **Area, Field, or Subject:** General studies/Field of study not specified **Level of Education for which Award is Granted:** Graduate, Undergraduate **Number Awarded:** A total of 38 scholarships are awarded each year, including 10 to high school seniors (1 of whom is designated to receive the Bert Waltenberger Memorial Scholarship), 7 to undergraduates in bachelor's degree programs, 7 to graduate students, 6 to students in 2-year programs, and 9 1-time grants. **Funds Available:** For high school seniors entering college, the stipend is $1,000 for the freshman year and $500 per year for the next 3 years. For the Bert Waltenberger Memorial Scholarship, the stipend is $1,500 for the freshman year and $750 per year for the next 3 years. Stipends are $500 per year for students enrolled in undergraduate programs leading to a bachelor's degree, students enrolled in 2-year programs, graduate students, and recipients of 1-year grants. **Duration:** Scholarships are for 4 years for high school seniors, 3 years for students enrolled in bachelor-degree programs, 2 years for students enrolled in 2-year programs and graduate students, or 1 year for other recipients.
Eligibility Requirements: This program is open to GBU members and annuitants who are high school seniors; undergraduates enrolled in a 4-year college or university or 2-year technical school, nursing school, or community college; or graduate students. Selection is based on academic record, activities, and club memberships. The Bert Waltenberger Memorial Scholarship is awarded to a high school senior applicant who demonstrates involvement in German-related programs and sports activities. **Deadline for Receipt:** January of each year. **Additional Information:** The Greater Beneficial Union was founded in 1892 by German immigrants to promote German cultural activities and events. As a fraternal benefit society, it is currently licensed to conduct business in the following states: California, Colorado, Florida, Illinois, Indiana, Michigan, Minnesota, Missouri, New Jersey, New York, Ohio, Pennsylvania, and Wisconsin. It established this scholarship program in 1962. The GBU life policy or annuity must continue in force during the tenure of the scholarship.

735 ■ GREATER WASHINGTON URBAN LEAGUE
Attn: Parent Center
2901 14th Street, N.W.
Washington, DC 20009
Tel: (202)265-8200
Fax: (202)387-7019
E-mail: epperson@gwulparentcenter.org
Web Site: http://www.gwulparentcenter.org
To provide financial assistance for college to graduating high school seniors in the service area of the Greater Washington Urban League (GWUL).
Title of Award: Anheuser-Busch Urban Scholarships **Area, Field, or Subject:** General studies/Field of study not specified **Level of Education for which Award is Granted:** Undergraduate **Number Awarded:** 2 each

year. **Funds Available:** The stipend is $2,500 per year. **Duration:** 4 years.
Eligibility Requirements: This program is open to graduating high school seniors who reside in the GWUL service area. Applicants must write a 500-word essay on the value of education, have completed 90% of their school district's community service requirement, and have a GPA of 2.5 or higher. Their family income must be less than $40,000 per year. **Deadline for Receipt:** January of each year. **Additional Information:** Applications are available from high school counselors, local libraries, or the GWUL office. This program is sponsored by Anheuser-Busch Companies, Inc.

736 ■ GREATER WASHINGTON URBAN LEAGUE
Attn: Parent Center
2901 14th Street, N.W.
Washington, DC 20009
Tel: (202)265-8200
Fax: (202)387-7019
E-mail: epperson@gwulparentcenter.org
Web Site: http://www.gwulparentcenter.org
To provide financial assistance for college to graduating high school seniors in the service area of the Greater Washington Urban League (GWUL).
Title of Award: Nationwide Insurance/Greater Washington Urban League Scholarships **Area, Field, or Subject:** General studies/Field of study not specified **Level of Education for which Award is Granted:** Undergraduate **Number Awarded:** 1 each year. **Funds Available:** The stipend is $1,300 per year. **Duration:** 4 years.
Eligibility Requirements: This program is open to graduating high school seniors who reside in the GWUL service area. Applicants must write an essay on a subject selected annually by the sponsors, have completed 90% of their school district's community service requirement, and have a GPA of 3.0 or higher. **Deadline for Receipt:** January of each year. **Additional Information:** This program, established in 2003, is sponsored by Nationwide Insurance.

737 ■ GREATER WASHINGTON URBAN LEAGUE
Attn: Parent Center
2901 14th Street, N.W.
Washington, DC 20009
Tel: (202)265-8200
Fax: (202)387-7019
E-mail: epperson@gwulparentcenter.org
Web Site: http://www.gwulparentcenter.org
To provide financial assistance for college to graduating high school seniors in the service area of the Greater Washington Urban League (GWUL).
Title of Award: Safeway/Greater Washington Urban League Scholarships **Area, Field, or Subject:** General studies/Field of study not specified **Level of Education for which Award is Granted:** Undergraduate **Number Awarded:** 6 each year. **Funds Available:** The stipend is $3,000. **Duration:** 1 year.
Eligibility Requirements: This program is open to graduating high school seniors who reside in the GWUL service area. Applicants must write an essay on a subject selected annually by the sponsors, have completed 90% of their school district's community service requirement, and have a GPA of 3.0 or higher. **Deadline for Receipt:** January of each year. **Additional Information:** Applications are available from high school counselors, local libraries, the GWUL office, or local stores of Safeway (which sponsors the program).

738 ■ TIM & TOM GULLIKSON FOUNDATION
Attn: Executive Director
175 North Main Street
Branford, CT 06405
888-GULLIKSON
Web Site: http://www.gullikson.com
To provide financial assistance for college to patients or survivors and/or children of patients or survivors of brain tumors.
Title of Award: Tim & Tom Gullikson Foundation College Scholarships **Area, Field, or Subject:** General studies/Field of study not specified **Level of Education for which Award is Granted:** Undergraduate **Number Awarded:** Varies each year; a maximum of $25,000 is available

for these scholarships each year. **Funds Available:** The maximum stipend is $5,000 per year. Funds are paid directly to the recipient's school and may be used for tuition, fees, books, room, and board. **Duration:** 1 year. Recipients may reapply up to 3 additional years; however, the total money awarded to each recipient cannot exceed $20,000.
Eligibility Requirements: This program is open to high school seniors, high school graduates, and currently-enrolled or returning college students. Applicants must be brain tumor patients/survivors and/or children of brain tumor patients or survivors. Special consideration is given to applicants who have a connection to the tennis community. Financial need is considered in the selection process. **Deadline for Receipt:** March of each year.

739 ■ GUY AND GLORIA MUTO MEMORIAL SCHOLARSHIP FOUNDATION, INC.
P.O. Box 60159
Sacramento, CA 95860
E-mail: ggmuto@aol.com
Web Site: http://www.ggmuto.org
To provide financial assistance for college to individuals (or their immediate families) who are working in the swimming pool and spa industry.
Title of Award: Guy and Gloria Muto Memorial Scholarship **Area, Field, or Subject:** General studies/Field of study not specified **Level of Education for which Award is Granted:** Undergraduate **Number Awarded:** Varies each year; recently, 6 of these scholarships were awarded. **Funds Available:** Stipends up to $1,000 are available. Award checks are made out jointly to the recipient and the recipient's school or agency and may only be used for the course of study, not travel, lodging, food, etc. **Duration:** 1 year.
Eligibility Requirements: This program is open to applicants engaged in any way in the swimming pool and spa industry (or their immediate family members). Immediate family is defined as husband, wife, or children under the age of 30. Applicants must be enrolled or planning to enroll in an academic course, certification program, trade or technical course, or other educational program. Along with their application, they must submit a statement on why they want to take this program or course of study and how they think it will help them in their business or professional life. Financial need is not considered in the selection process. **Deadline for Receipt:** March of each year. **Additional Information:** No written requests for applications will be accepted. Applications are available only through the web site.

740 ■ JOHN GYLES EDUCATION FUND
Attn: Secretary
165 Riverside Drive
P.O. Box 4808, Station A
Fredericton, NB, Canada E3B 5G4
Tel: (506)459-7460
Web Site: http://www.johngyleseducationcenter.com
To provide financial assistance for college to American and Canadian residents.
Title of Award: John Gyles Education Awards **Area, Field, or Subject:** General studies/Field of study not specified **Level of Education for which Award is Granted:** Undergraduate **Number Awarded:** Varies each year. **Funds Available:** Stipends up to $3,000 are provided. **Duration:** 1 year.
Eligibility Requirements: This program is open to full-time students who are citizens of the United States or Canada. Applicants must have a GPA of 2.7 or higher. Along with their application, they must submit an essay on their career plans, goals, and personal ambitions. Selection is based on academic ability, financial need, and other criteria. **Deadline for Receipt:** May or November of each year. **Additional Information:** This fund was established in 1990. Recipients may use the funds to study in any subject area. Applications must be accompanied by a $7 service fee.

741 ■ HANSCOM OFFICERS' WIVES' CLUB
Attn: Scholarship Chair
P.O. Box 557
Bedford, MA 01730
Tel: (781)275-1251
E-mail: scholarship@hanscomowd.org
Web Site: http://www.hanscomowc.org

To provide financial assistance for college to spouses and children of military personnel and veterans in New England.

Title of Award: Hanscom Officers' Wives' Club Scholarships **Area, Field, or Subject:** General studies/Field of study not specified **Level of Education for which Award is Granted:** Undergraduate **Number Awarded:** Varies each year; recently, 17 of these scholarships were awarded. **Funds Available:** Stipends range from $1,200 to $4,000. **Duration:** 1 year; nonrenewable.

Eligibility Requirements: This program is open to high school seniors and spouses living in New England who are dependents of active-duty, retired, or deceased military members of any branch of service. Also eligible are dependents of military recruiters working in the New York area and students living elsewhere but whose military sponsor is stationed at Hanscom Air Force Base. Applicants must demonstrate qualities of responsibility, leadership, scholastics, citizenship, and diversity of interest. They must have a valid military identification card and be working on or planning to work on a bachelor's or associate degree. Along with their application, they must submit a 2-page essay on their educational goals, how their educational experience will help prepare them to pursue future goals, and how they intend to apply their education to better their community. The Chief of Staff Award is presented to the highest-ranked high school applicant. The Carmen Schipper Memorial Award is presented to the highest-ranked spouse applicant. The Scott Corey Scholarship is awarded to another spouse applicant. **Deadline for Receipt:** March of each year. **Additional Information:** The Paul Revere Chapter of the Air Force Association sponsors the Chief of Staff Award. Other sponsors include the Armed Forces Communications and Electronics Association, Boeing Company, First Command Educational Foundation, Association of Old Crows, Air Force Sergeants Association, Company Grade Officer's Council, and Patriot Senior Noncommissioned Officer's Council.

742 ■ HAWAII ASSOCIATION OF THE BLIND

1255 Nuuanu Avenue, Number 1102
Honolulu, HI 96817
Tel: (808)521-6213
E-mail: toyamaj005@hawaii.rr.com
Web Site: http://www.acb.org/hawaii/scholarship.htm
To provide financial assistance for college to blind residents of Hawaii.

Title of Award: Hawaii Association of the Blind Scholarship **Area, Field, or Subject:** General studies/Field of study not specified **Level of Education for which Award is Granted:** Undergraduate **Number Awarded:** 1 or more each year. **Funds Available:** Stipends are at least $500 per semester ($1,000 per year). **Duration:** 1 year.

Eligibility Requirements: This program is open to Hawaii residents who meet the legal definition of blindness or visual impairment. Applicants must be members of the American Council of the Blind but may not be members of any other national organization for the blind. They must submit high school and/or college transcripts, 2 letters of reference, and a 2-page letter describing their educational goals. **Deadline for Receipt:** May of each year for fall semester; November of each year for spring semester. **Additional Information:** Information is also available from Don Thomson, Scholarship Chair, (808) 455-0367, E-mail: thomsond@hawaii. edu.

743 ■ HAWAI'I COMMUNITY FOUNDATION

Attn: Scholarship Department
1164 Bishop Street, Suite 800
Honolulu, HI 96813
Tel: (808)566-5570; 888-731-3863
Fax: (808)521-6286
E-mail: scholarships@hcf-hawaii.org
Web Site: http://www.hawaiicommunityfoundation.org/scholar/scholar.php
To provide financial assistance for college to Protestants who are ministers, the dependents of ministers in Hawaii, or students preparing for the ministry.

Title of Award: Juliette M. Atherton Scholarship **Area, Field, or Subject:** General studies/Field of study not specified; Religion **Level of Education for which Award is Granted:** Master's, Professional, Postdoctoral, Undergraduate **Number Awarded:** Varies each year; recently, 76 of these scholarships were awarded. **Funds Available:** The amounts of the awards depend on the availability of funds and the need of the recipient; recently, stipends averaged $1,691 per year. **Duration:** 1 year.

Eligibility Requirements: This program is open to 1) the dependent sons or daughters of ordained and active Protestant ministers in an established

denomination in Hawaii; 2) students planning to attend an accredited graduate school of theology with the goal of being ordained in an established Protestant denomination; 3) ordained Protestant ministers in an established denomination in Hawaii planning to work on an advanced degree related to their ministerial profession; or 4) ordained Protestant ministers in an established denomination in Hawaii planning to pursue education in a field related to ministry through course work, workshops, or seminars. Applicants must be residents of the state of Hawaii, able to demonstrate financial need, interested in attending an accredited 2- or 4-year college or university as full-time students, and able to demonstrate academic achievement (GPA of 2.7 or higher). **Deadline for Receipt:** February of each year. **Additional Information:** Recipients may attend school in Hawaii or on the mainland.

744 ■ HAWAI'I COMMUNITY FOUNDATION

Attn: Scholarship Department
1164 Bishop Street, Suite 800
Honolulu, HI 96813
Tel: (808)566-5570; 888-731-3863
Fax: (808)521-6286
E-mail: scholarships@hcf-hawaii.org
Web Site: http://www.hawaiicommunityfoundation.org/scholar/scholar.php
To provide financial assistance for college to disabled public employees in Hawaii or their dependents.

Title of Award: Troy Barboza Education Fund **Area, Field, or Subject:** General studies/Field of study not specified **Level of Education for which Award is Granted:** Professional, Undergraduate **Number Awarded:** 1 or more each year. **Funds Available:** The amount awarded varies, depending upon the needs of the recipient and the funds available. **Duration:** 1 year.

Eligibility Requirements: This program is open to 1) disabled public employees in Hawaii who were injured in the line of duty or 2) dependents or other immediate family members of public employees in Hawaii who were disabled or killed in the line of duty. The public employee must work or have worked in a job where lives are risked for the protection and safety of others. The injury must have left the employee incapacitated or incapable of continuing in his or her profession and must have occurred after October 22, 1977. Also eligible are private citizens who have performed a heroic act for the protection and welfare of others. **Deadline for Receipt:** February of each year.

745 ■ HAWAI'I COMMUNITY FOUNDATION

Attn: Scholarship Department
1164 Bishop Street, Suite 800
Honolulu, HI 96813
Tel: (808)566-5570; 888-731-3863
Fax: (808)521-6286
E-mail: scholarships@hcf-hawaii.org
Web Site: http://www.hawaiicommunityfoundation.org/scholar/scholar.php
To provide financial assistance for college to seniors at high schools in Hawaii.

Title of Award: Cayetano Foundation Scholarships **Area, Field, or Subject:** General studies/Field of study not specified **Level of Education for which Award is Granted:** Undergraduate **Number Awarded:** Varies each year; recently, 10 of these scholarships were awarded. **Funds Available:** The amounts of the awards depend on the availability of funds and the need of the recipient; recently, stipends averaged $2,000. **Duration:** 1 year.

Eligibility Requirements: This program is open to seniors at public and private high schools in Hawaii who plan to attend an accredited college or university as a full-time student. Applicants must be able to demonstrate academic achievement (GPA of 3.5 or higher), good moral character, and financial need. In addition to filling out the standard application form, they must write a short statement describing their participation in community service projects or activities and an essay asking them to imagine they are in their late 50s and reflecting on the major accomplishments of their adult life. Preference is given to applicants with the greatest financial need. **Deadline for Receipt:** February of each year. **Additional Information:** Recipients may attend college in Hawaii or on the mainland.

746 ■ HAWAI'I COMMUNITY FOUNDATION

Attn: Scholarship Department
1164 Bishop Street, Suite 800
Honolulu, HI 96813

Tel: (808)566-5570; 888-731-3863
Fax: (808)521-6286
E-mail: scholarships@hcf-hawaii.org
Web Site: http://www.hawaiicommunityfoundation.org/scholar/scholar.php
To provide financial assistance to Hawaii residents who are interested in studying at a college or university in that state.
Title of Award: Dolly Ching Scholarship Fund **Area, Field, or Subject:** General studies/Field of study not specified **Level of Education for which Award is Granted:** Undergraduate **Number Awarded:** Varies each year; recently, 2 of these scholarships were awarded. **Funds Available:** The amounts of the awards depend on the availability of funds and the need of the recipient; recently, stipends averaged $2,000. **Duration:** 1 year.
Eligibility Requirements: This program is open to seniors graduating from high schools on the island of Kaua'i who are planning to attend a branch of the University of Hawai'i system (including the community colleges) as a full-time undergraduate student. They must be able to demonstrate academic achievement (GPA of 3.0 or higher), good moral character, and financial need. In addition to filling out the standard application form, applicants must write a short statement indicating their reasons for attending college, their planned course of study, and their career goals. Preference is given to applicants with the greatest financial need and who demonstrate greatest community service. **Deadline for Receipt:** February of each year.

747 ■ HAWAI'I COMMUNITY FOUNDATION

Attn: Scholarship Department
1164 Bishop Street, Suite 800
Honolulu, HI 96813
Tel: (808)566-5570; 888-731-3863
Fax: (808)521-6286
E-mail: scholarships@hcf-hawaii.org
Web Site: http://www.hawaiicommunityfoundation.org/scholar/scholar.php
To provide financial assistance to Hawaii residents who are interested in preparing for a career in occupational therapy.
Title of Award: Laura N. Dowsett Fund Scholarships **Area, Field, or Subject:** Occupational therapy **Level of Education for which Award is Granted:** Four Year College, Graduate **Number Awarded:** Varies each year; recently, 2 of these scholarships were awarded. **Funds Available:** The amounts of the awards depend on the availability of funds and the need of the recipient; recently, stipends averaged $1,500. **Duration:** 1 year.
Eligibility Requirements: This program is open to Hawaii residents who are studying occupational therapy as full-time juniors, seniors, or graduate students. They must be able to demonstrate academic achievement (GPA of 2.7 or higher), good moral character, and financial need. In addition to filling out the standard application form, applicants must write a short statement indicating their reasons for attending college, their planned course of study, and their career goals. **Deadline for Receipt:** February of each year. **Additional Information:** Recipients may attend college in Hawaii or on the mainland.

748 ■ HAWAI'I COMMUNITY FOUNDATION

Attn: Scholarship Department
1164 Bishop Street, Suite 800
Honolulu, HI 96813
Tel: (808)566-5570; 888-731-3863
Fax: (808)521-6286
E-mail: scholarships@hcf-hawaii.org
Web Site: http://www.hawaiicommunityfoundation.org/scholar/scholar.php
To provide financial assistance to Hawaii residents who are interested in studying business at 1 of the campuses of the University of Hawai'i.
Title of Award: Oscar and Rosetta Fish Fund **Area, Field, or Subject:** Business administration **Level of Education for which Award is Granted:** Graduate, Undergraduate **Number Awarded:** Varies each year; recently, 30 of these scholarships were awarded. **Funds Available:** The amounts of the awards depend on the availability of funds and the need of the recipient; recently, stipends averaged $1,867. **Duration:** 1 year.
Eligibility Requirements: This program is open to Hawaii residents who are interested in studying business on the undergraduate or graduate school level at any campus of the University of Hawai'i except Manoa. Applicants must be able to demonstrate academic achievement (GPA of 2.7 or higher), good moral character, and financial need. In addition to

filling out the standard application form, applicants must write a short statement indicating their reasons for attending college, their planned course of study, and their career goals. **Deadline for Receipt:** February of each year. **Additional Information:** This program was established in 1999. Recipients must be full-time students.

749 ■ HAWAI'I COMMUNITY FOUNDATION

Attn: Scholarship Department
1164 Bishop Street, Suite 800
Honolulu, HI 96813
Tel: (808)566-5570; 888-731-3863
Fax: (808)521-6286
E-mail: scholarships@hcf-hawaii.org
Web Site: http://www.hawaiicommunityfoundation.org/scholar/scholar.php
To provide financial assistance to women tennis players in Hawaii who are just beginning college.
Title of Award: Jean Fitzgerald Scholarship **Area, Field, or Subject:** General studies/Field of study not specified **Level of Education for which Award is Granted:** Undergraduate **Number Awarded:** Varies each year; recently, 5 of these scholarships were awarded. **Funds Available:** The amounts of the awards depend on the availability of funds and the need of the recipient; recently, stipends averaged $2,000. **Duration:** 1 year.
Eligibility Requirements: This program is open to female Hawaiian residents who have been active members of the Hawai'i Pacific Tennis Association for at least 4 years and are entering their freshman year in college as full-time students. They must be able to demonstrate academic achievement (GPA of 2.7 or higher), good moral character, and financial need. In addition to filling out the standard application form, applicants must write a short statement indicating their reasons for attending college, their planned course of study, and their career goals. **Deadline for Receipt:** February of each year. **Additional Information:** Recipients may attend college in Hawaii or on the mainland.

750 ■ HAWAI'I COMMUNITY FOUNDATION

Attn: Scholarship Department
1164 Bishop Street, Suite 800
Honolulu, HI 96813
Tel: (808)566-5570; 888-731-3863
Fax: (808)521-6286
E-mail: scholarships@hcf-hawaii.org
Web Site: http://www.hawaiicommunityfoundation.org/scholar/scholar.php
To provide financial assistance to Hawaii residents who are interested in attending college or graduate school and have been in the foster care (or similar) system.
Title of Award: Victoria S. and Bradley L. Geist Foundation Scholarship **Area, Field, or Subject:** General studies/Field of study not specified **Level of Education for which Award is Granted:** Graduate, Undergraduate **Number Awarded:** Varies each year; recently, 54 of these scholarships were awarded. **Funds Available:** The amounts of the awards depend on the availability of funds and the need of the recipient; recently, stipends averaged $2,400. **Duration:** 1 year.
Eligibility Requirements: This program is open to Hawaii residents who are permanently separated from their parents and currently in (or formerly in) the foster care system. Applicants must be or planning to become full-time students at the undergraduate or graduate school level. They must be able to demonstrate academic achievement, good moral character, and financial need. In addition to filling out the standard application form, applicants must 1) write a short statement indicating their reasons for attending college, their planned course of study, and their career goals, and 2) supply a confirmation letter from their social worker, foster parent, hanai parent, or other appropriate individual. **Deadline for Receipt:** February of each year. **Additional Information:** Recipients may attend college in Hawaii or on the mainland.

751 ■ HAWAI'I COMMUNITY FOUNDATION

Attn: Scholarship Department
1164 Bishop Street, Suite 800
Honolulu, HI 96813
Tel: (808)566-5570; 888-731-3863
Fax: (808)521-6286
E-mail: scholarships@hcf-hawaii.org
Web Site: http://www.hawaiicommunityfoundation.org/scholar/scholar.php

To provide financial assistance to Hawaii residents who are interested in attending college or graduate school and have turned their lives around after facing social problems.

Title of Award: Ho'omaka Hou Scholarship **Area, Field, or Subject:** General studies/Field of study not specified **Level of Education for which Award is Granted:** Graduate, Undergraduate **Number Awarded:** Varies each year. **Funds Available:** The amounts of the awards depend on the availability of funds and the need of the recipient. **Duration:** 1 year. **Eligibility Requirements:** This program is open to Hawaii residents who have turned their lives around after facing social problems (e.g., substance abuse, domestic violence). Applicants must be or planning to become full-time students at the undergraduate or graduate school level. They must be able to demonstrate academic achievement (GPA of 2.7 or higher), good moral character, and financial need. **Deadline for Receipt:** February of each year. **Additional Information:** Recipients may attend college in Hawaii or on the mainland.

752 ■ HAWAI'I COMMUNITY FOUNDATION

Attn: Scholarship Department
1164 Bishop Street, Suite 800
Honolulu, HI 96813
Tel: (808)566-5570; 888-731-3863
Fax: (808)521-6286
E-mail: scholarships@hcf-hawaii.org
Web Site: http://www.hawaiicommunityfoundation.org/scholar/scholar.php
To provide financial assistance to residents of Hawaii's Big Island who are interested in attending college or graduate school on that island.

Title of Award: Arthur Jackman Memorial Scholarship **Area, Field, or Subject:** General studies/Field of study not specified **Level of Education for which Award is Granted:** Graduate, Undergraduate **Number Awarded:** Varies each year. **Funds Available:** The amounts of the awards depend on the availability of funds and the need of the recipient. **Duration:** 1 year. **Eligibility Requirements:** This program is open to residents of the island of Hawaii who are attending or planning to attend a college or vocational school on that island. Applicants must plan full-time study on the undergraduate (preferred) or graduate school level. They must be able to demonstrate academic achievement (GPA of 2.7 or higher), good moral character, and financial need. **Deadline for Receipt:** February of each year. **Additional Information:** This scholarship was first offered in 2002. Information is available from the foundation's Waimea Office, (808) 885-2174.

753 ■ HAWAI'I COMMUNITY FOUNDATION

Attn: Scholarship Department
1164 Bishop Street, Suite 800
Honolulu, HI 96813
Tel: (808)566-5570; 888-731-3863
Fax: (808)521-6286
E-mail: scholarships@hcf-hawaii.org
Web Site: http://www.hawaiicommunityfoundation.org/scholar/scholar.php
To provide financial assistance for college to residents of designated areas of Hawaii.

Title of Award: Tommy Lee Memorial Scholarship Fund **Area, Field, or Subject:** General studies/Field of study not specified **Level of Education for which Award is Granted:** Undergraduate **Number Awarded:** Varies each year; recently, 4 of these scholarships were awarded. **Funds Available:** The amounts of the awards depend on the availability of funds and the need of the recipient; recently, stipends averaged $1,000. **Duration:** 1 year. **Eligibility Requirements:** This program is open to high school seniors residing in the Waialua or Haleiwa areas who plan to attend an accredited college or university. Applicants must be able to demonstrate academic achievement (GPA of 2.7 or higher), good moral character, and financial need. In addition to filling out the standard application form, they must write a short statement indicating their reasons for attending college, their planned course of study, and their career goals. **Deadline for Receipt:**

February of each year. **Additional Information:** Recipients may attend college in Hawaii or on the mainland. This program was established in 1996.

754 ■ HAWAI'I COMMUNITY FOUNDATION

Attn: Scholarship Department
1164 Bishop Street, Suite 800
Honolulu, HI 96813
Tel: (808)566-5570; 888-731-3863
Fax: (808)521-6286
E-mail: scholarships@hcf-hawaii.org
Web Site: http://www.hawaiicommunityfoundation.org/scholar/scholar.php
To provide financial assistance to residents of Hawaii who are interested in preparing for a career in business administration.

Title of Award: George Mason Business Scholarship Fund **Area, Field, or Subject:** Business administration **Level of Education for which Award is Granted:** Undergraduate **Number Awarded:** Varies each year; recently, 1 of these scholarships was awarded. **Funds Available:** The amount of the award depends on the availability of funds and the need of the recipient; recently, stipends averaged $1,000. **Duration:** 1 year. **Eligibility Requirements:** This program is open to residents of Hawaii who are entering their senior year at a 4-year college or university in the state. Applicants must be majoring in business administration. They must be able to demonstrate academic achievement (GPA of 3.0 or higher), good moral character, and financial need. In addition to filling out the standard application form, they must write a short statement indicating why they have chosen business as an intended career and how they expect to make a difference in the business world. **Deadline for Receipt:** February of each year.

755 ■ HAWAI'I COMMUNITY FOUNDATION

Attn: Scholarship Department
1164 Bishop Street, Suite 800
Honolulu, HI 96813
Tel: (808)566-5570; 888-731-3863
Fax: (808)521-6286
E-mail: scholarships@hcf-hawaii.org
Web Site: http://www.hawaiicommunityfoundation.org/scholar/scholar.php
To provide financial assistance to residents of Hawaii's Big Island who are interested in attending college and returning to the Island.

Title of Award: John M. Ross Foundation Scholarships **Area, Field, or Subject:** General studies/Field of study not specified **Level of Education for which Award is Granted:** Undergraduate **Number Awarded:** Varies each year; recently, 12 of these scholarships were awarded. **Funds Available:** The amounts of the awards depend on the availability of funds and the need of the recipient; recently, stipends averaged $1,000. **Duration:** 1 year. **Eligibility Requirements:** This program is open to residents of Hawaii's Big Island; preference is given to those born on and with ancestors from this area who plan to remain or return to the Big Island. Applicants must plan full-time study on the undergraduate level. They must be able to demonstrate academic achievement (GPA of 2.7 or higher), good moral character, and financial need. In addition to filling out the standard application form, applicants must write a short statement indicating their reasons for attending college, their planned course of study, their career goals, and their intention to remain or return to the Big Island. **Deadline for Receipt:** February of each year. **Additional Information:** Recipients may attend college in Hawaii or on the mainland.

756 ■ HAWAI'I COMMUNITY FOUNDATION

Attn: Scholarship Department
1164 Bishop Street, Suite 800
Honolulu, HI 96813
Tel: (808)566-5570; 888-731-3863
Fax: (808)521-6286
E-mail: scholarships@hcf-hawaii.org
Web Site: http://www.hawaiicommunityfoundation.org/scholar/scholar.php
To provide financial assistance to Hawaii residents of Japanese ancestry who are interested in attending college.

Title of Award: Eizo and Toyo Sakumoto Trust Scholarships **Area, Field, or Subject:** General studies/Field of study not specified **Level of Education for which Award is Granted:** Graduate, Undergraduate **Number Awarded:** Varies each year; recently, 43 of these scholarships were awarded. **Funds Available:** The amounts of the awards depend on the availability of funds and the need of the recipient; recently, the stipend was $1,000. **Duration:** 1 year.

Eligibility Requirements: This program is open to Hawaii residents of Japanese ancestry who are enrolled in or planning to enroll in an accredited college or university in Hawaii. Applicants must be full-time undergraduate or graduate students and able to demonstrate academic achievement (GPA of 3.5 or higher), good moral character, and financial need. They must have been born in Hawaii. **Deadline for Receipt:** February of each year.

757 ■ HAWAI'I COMMUNITY FOUNDATION

Attn: Scholarship Department
1164 Bishop Street, Suite 800
Honolulu, HI 96813
Tel: (808)566-5570; 888-731-3863
Fax: (808)521-6286
E-mail: scholarships@hcf-hawaii.org
Web Site: http://www.hawaiicommunityfoundation.org/scholar/scholar.php
To provide financial assistance to Hawaii residents who are attending college in the state at schools other than the University of Hawai'i.
Title of Award: Toraji and Toki Yoshinaga Scholarship **Area, Field, or Subject:** General studies/Field of study not specified **Level of Education for which Award is Granted:** Undergraduate **Number Awarded:** Varies each year; recently, 2 of these scholarships were awarded. **Funds Available:** The amounts of the awards depend on the availability of funds and the need of the recipient; recently, stipends averaged $1,250. **Duration:** 1 year.
Eligibility Requirements: This program is open to Hawaii residents who are sophomores attending college at a school in the state that is not part of the University of Hawai'i system. Applicants must meet at least 3 of the following criteria: 1) born in Hawaii; 2) graduate of a Hawaii high school; 3) registered to vote in Hawaii; and 4) lived in Hawaii for 4 years. They must be able to demonstrate academic achievement (GPA of 2.7 or higher), good moral character, and financial need. In addition to filling out the standard application form, applicants must write a short statement indicating their reasons for attending college, their planned course of study, and their career goals. **Deadline for Receipt:** February of each year. **Additional Information:** This program was established in 1999. Recipients must be full-time students.

758 ■ HAWAII DEPARTMENT OF DEFENSE

Attn: Education Services Officer
3949 Diamond Head Road
Honolulu, HI 96816-4495
Tel: (808)733-4120
Fax: (808)735-9208
E-mail: michele.hall@hi.ngb.army.mil
Web Site: http://www.dod.state.hi.us/education/state_tuition.html
To provide tuition assistance to members of the Hawaii Army National Guard who are attending public colleges and universities in the state.
Title of Award: Hawaii National Guard State Tuition Assistance Program **Area, Field, or Subject:** General studies/Field of study not specified **Level of Education for which Award is Granted:** Undergraduate **Number Awarded:** Varies each year. **Funds Available:** Current stipends for full-time enrollment per semester are $756 at the University of Hawai'i at Manoa, $570 at the University of Hawai'i at Hilo, $475 at the University of Hawai'i-West Oahu, or $516 at all the community college campuses. For part-time enrollment, the rates per credit hour are $63 at Manoa, $48 at Hilo, $40 at West Oahu, or $43 at the community colleges. **Duration:** 1 semester; recipients may reapply.
Eligibility Requirements: This program is open to residents of Hawaii who are members of the Hawaii Army National Guard at the rank of enlisted, warrant officer, or company grade officer (O1 through O3). Applicants must be attending or planning to attend 1 of the following 2-year or 4-year campuses of the University of Hawai'i: University of Hawai'i at Manoa, University of Hawai'i at Hilo, University of Hawai'i-West Oahu, University of Hawai'i-Hawaii Community College, University of Hawai'i-Honolulu Community College, University of Hawai'i-Kapiolani Community College, University of Hawai'i-Kauai Community College, University of Hawai'i-Leeward Community College, University of Hawai'i-Maui Community College, and University of Hawai'i-Windward Community College. They may not 1) have earned a bachelor's or master's degree; 2) have

completed 90 or more semester hours at a community college without receiving an associate degree; or 3) have completed 150 or more semester hours at a 4-year college without receiving a bachelor's degree. First priority is given to first-term enlisted members who have less than 6 years of duty (active or reserve). Second priority is given to applicants who are enrolled in the Army OCS/ROTC/SMP program. All other applicants are considered as third priority.

759 ■ HAWAI'I HOTEL & LODGING ASSOCIATION

Attn: Hawaii Hotel Industry Foundation
2250 Kalakaua Avenue, Suite 404-4
Honolulu, HI 96815-2564
Tel: (808)923-0407
Fax: (808)924-3843
E-mail: hhla@hawaiihotels.org
Web Site: http://www.hawaiihotels.org
To provide financial assistance to Native Hawaiians who are upper-division students working on a degree in hotel management.
Title of Award: Clem Judd, Jr. Memorial Scholarship **Area, Field, or Subject:** Hotel, institutional, and restaurant management **Level of Education for which Award is Granted:** Four Year College **Number Awarded:** 1 each year. **Funds Available:** The stipend ranges from $2,000 to $2,500. **Duration:** 1 year.
Eligibility Requirements: This program is open to Hawaii residents who can provide proof of their Hawaiian ancestry through birth certificates of their parents or grandparents. Applicants must be a junior, senior, or fifth-year undergraduate at an accredited college or university (in any state) and majoring in hotel management. They must have a GPA of 2.8 or higher. Financial need is considered in the selection process. **Deadline for Receipt:** June of each year.

760 ■ HEALTHCARE FINANCIAL MANAGEMENT ASSOCIATION-NEW HAMPSHIRE/VERMONT CHAPTER

c/o Sperry Wilson Kelley
Sperry Small Business Services
220 Vermont Route 132
P.O. Box 237
South Strafford, VT 05070
Tel: (802)765-4556
E-mail: sperrysbs@aol.com
Web Site: http://www.nhvthfma.org
To provide financial assistance to relatives members of the New Hampshire/Vermont chapter of the Healthcare Financial Management Association (HFMA) who are interested in working on a degree in finance.
Title of Award: Christopher F. Weinheimer Scholarship Program **Area, Field, or Subject:** Finance **Level of Education for which Award is Granted:** Four Year College **Number Awarded:** 2 each year. **Funds Available:** The stipend is $1,000. Funds are paid directly to the school. **Duration:** 1 year.
Eligibility Requirements: This program is open to seniors graduating from high schools in New Hampshire and Vermont who are the immediate family of HFMA members. Applicants must have been accepted by an accredited college or university to work on a 4-year degree in finance. They must have a GPA of 3.0 or higher. Along with their application, they must submit a short essay describing their career goal and why they should a recipient of this scholarship. **Deadline for Receipt:** May of each year. **Additional Information:** Information is also available from Thomas Lenkowski, Scholarship Committee Chair, (802) 447-5011, E-mail: link@phin.org.

761 ■ HEALTHCARE FINANCIAL MANAGEMENT ASSOCIATION-VIRGINIA CHAPTER

c/o Herbert D. Harvey, Scholarship Committee Chair
Obici Health System
2800 Godwin Boulevard
Suffolk, VA 23435
Tel: (757)934-4642
E-mail: hharvey@obici.com
Web Site: http://www.vahfma.org
To provide financial assistance for college to high school seniors, especially descendants of members of the Healthcare Financial Management Association (HFMA), in Virginia.
Title of Award: Jay C. Ellis Memorial Scholarship **Area, Field, or Subject:** General studies/Field of study not specified **Level of Education**

for which Award is Granted: Undergraduate **Number Awarded:** 1 each year. **Funds Available:** The stipend is $1,000. Funds may be used for tuition only. **Duration:** 1 year.

Eligibility Requirements: This program is open to all high school seniors in Virginia, but preference is given to descendants of members of the Virginia chapter of HFMA. Applicants must submit an essay on what this scholarship means to them. Selection is based on the essay, academic achievement, extracurricular activities in school and the community, and financial need. **Deadline for Receipt:** April of each year.

762 ■ LINLY HEFLIN UNIT

c/o Mrs. Beff King, Scholarship Committee Co-Chair
13 Office Park Circle, Suite 8
Birmingham, AL 35223
Tel: (205)870-4192
To provide financial assistance to women attending colleges and universities in Alabama.

Title of Award: Linly Heflin Scholarship **Area, Field, or Subject:** General studies/Field of study not specified **Level of Education for which Award is Granted:** Four Year College **Number Awarded:** A limited number of these scholarships are awarded each year. **Funds Available:** The stipend is $2,500 per year. **Duration:** 1 year; may be renewed until completion of an undergraduate degree, provided the recipient continues to demonstrate financial need and maintains a GPA of 2.5 or higher.

Eligibility Requirements: This program is open to female residents of Alabama attending accredited 4-year colleges in the state. Applicants must have an ACT score of 22 or higher. U.S. citizenship is required. Selection is based on academic proficiency and financial need. **Deadline for Receipt:** January of each year.

763 ■ HELLENIC TIMES SCHOLARSHIP FUND

Attn: Nick Katsoris
823 Eleventh Avenue, Fifth Floor
New York, NY 10019-3535
Tel: (212)986-6881
Fax: (212)977-3662
E-mail: HTSFund@aol.com
Web Site: http://www.HTSFund.org
To provide financial assistance to undergraduate or graduate students of Greek descent.

Title of Award: Hellenic Times Scholarships **Area, Field, or Subject:** General studies/Field of study not specified **Level of Education for which Award is Granted:** Graduate, Undergraduate **Number Awarded:** Varies; approximately $100,000 is available for this program each year. **Funds Available:** The amount of the awards depends on the availability of funds and the number of recipients.

Eligibility Requirements: This program is open to undergraduate and graduate students of Greek descent who are between 17 and 25 years of age and enrolled in an accredited college or university. Students who are receiving other financial aid that exceeds 50% of their annual tuition are ineligible. Selection is based on need and merit. **Deadline for Receipt:** January of each year. **Additional Information:** This program began in 1990.

764 ■ HEMOPHILIA FEDERATION OF AMERICA

Attn: Scholarship Committee
1405 West Pinhook Road, Suite 101
Lafayette, LA 70503
Tel: (337)261-9787
Free: 800-230-9797
Fax: (337)261-1787
E-mail: info@hemophiliafed.org
Web Site: http://www.hemophiliafed.org/scholarships.php
To provide financial assistance for college to students who have a blood clotting disorder.

Title of Award: Hemophilia Federation of America Educational Scholarships **Area, Field, or Subject:** General studies/Field of study not specified **Level of Education for which Award is Granted:** Undergraduate **Number Awarded:** 4 each year. **Funds Available:** The stipend is $1,500 per year. **Duration:** 1 year; may be renewed.

Eligibility Requirements: This program is open to high school seniors and current college students who have a blood clotting disorder. Applicants must be attending or planning to attend an accredited 2-year or

4-year college, university, or trade school in the United States. Along with their application, they must submit a 1-page essay on their goals and aspirations and how the blood clotting community has played a part in their lives. Financial need is also considered in the selection process. **Deadline for Receipt:** March of each year.

765 ■ HEMOPHILIA FEDERATION OF AMERICA

Attn: Scholarship Committee
1405 West Pinhook Road, Suite 101
Lafayette, LA 70503
Tel: (337)261-9787
Free: 800-230-9797
Fax: (337)261-1787
E-mail: info@hemophiliafed.org
Web Site: http://www.hemophiliafed.org/scholarships.php
To provide financial assistance for college to parents of children with a blood clotting disorder.

Title of Award: Hemophilia Federation of America Parent Continuing Education Scholarships **Area, Field, or Subject:** General studies/Field of study not specified **Level of Education for which Award is Granted:** Undergraduate **Number Awarded:** 2 each year. **Funds Available:** The stipend is $1,500 per year. **Duration:** 1 year; may be renewed.

Eligibility Requirements: This program is open to parents of children who have a blood clotting disorder. Applicants must be attending or planning to attend an accredited 2-year or 4-year college, university, or trade school in the United States. Along with their application, they must submit a 1-page essay on their goals and aspirations and how the blood clotting community has played a part in their lives. Financial need is also considered in the selection process. **Deadline for Receipt:** March of each year.

766 ■ HEMOPHILIA FEDERATION OF AMERICA

Attn: Scholarship Committee
1405 West Pinhook Road, Suite 101
Lafayette, LA 70503
Tel: (337)261-9787
Free: 800-230-9797
Fax: (337)261-1787
E-mail: info@hemophiliafed.org
Web Site: http://www.hemophiliafed.org/scholarships.php
To provide financial assistance for college to siblings of people with a blood clotting disorder.

Title of Award: Hemophilia Federation of America Sibling Continuing Education Scholarships **Area, Field, or Subject:** General studies/Field of study not specified **Level of Education for which Award is Granted:** Undergraduate **Number Awarded:** 3 each year. **Funds Available:** The stipend is $1,500 per year. **Duration:** 1 year; may be renewed.

Eligibility Requirements: This program is open to siblings of people who have a blood clotting disorder. Applicants must be attending or planning to attend an accredited 2-year or 4-year college, university, or trade school in the United States. Along with their application, they must submit a 1-page essay on their goals and aspirations and how the blood clotting community has played a part in their lives. Financial need is also considered in the selection process. **Deadline for Receipt:** March of each year.

767 ■ HEMOPHILIA FOUNDATION OF GREATER FLORIDA

1320 North Orange Avenue, Suite 227
Winter Park, FL 32789
800-293-6527
E-mail: info@hemophiliaflorida.org
Web Site: http://www.hemophiliaflorida.org
To provide financial assistance for college to residents of Florida with bleeding disorders and to members of their families.

Title of Award: Calvin Dawson Memorial Scholarship **Area, Field, or Subject:** General studies/Field of study not specified **Level of Education for which Award is Granted:** Undergraduate **Number Awarded:** Varies each year; recently, 4 of these scholarships were awarded. **Funds Available:** Stipends range up to $1,000. **Duration:** 1 year.

Eligibility Requirements: This program is open to residents of Florida who have hemophilia or other related hereditary bleeding disorder. Spouses, parents, siblings, and other significant family members are also eligible. Applicants may be graduating high school seniors or students already enrolled at a college, technical or trade school, or other certification program. **Deadline for Receipt:** April of each year.

768 ■ HEMOPHILIA FOUNDATION OF MICHIGAN

Attn: Client Services Coordinator
1921 West Michigan Avenue
Ypsilanti, MI 48197
Tel: (734)544-0015
Free: 800-482-3041
Fax: (734)544-0095
E-mail: colleen@hfmich.org
Web Site: http://www.hfmich.org/support_scholarships.cfm
To provide financial assistance for college to Michigan residents with hemophilia and their families.
Title of Award: Hemophilia Foundation of Michigan Academic Scholarships **Area, Field, or Subject:** General studies/Field of study not specified **Level of Education for which Award is Granted:** Undergraduate **Number Awarded:** Varies each year. **Funds Available:** Stipends range from $500 to $1,500. **Duration:** 1 year.
Eligibility Requirements: High school seniors, high school graduates, and currently-enrolled college students are eligible to apply if they are Michigan residents and have hemophilia or another bleeding disorder. Family members of people with bleeding disorders and family members of people who have died from the complications of a bleeding disorder are also eligible. Applicants must submit a 300-word statement on their educational and career goals, the role that the bleeding disorder has played in influencing those goals, and how receiving the scholarship will help them to meet those goals. Selection is based on that statement, academic merit, employment status, reference letters, financial need, and the impact of bleeding disorder on educational activities. **Deadline for Receipt:** March of each year.

769 ■ HEMOPHILIA FOUNDATION OF MICHIGAN

c/o Cathy McAdam
22226 Doxtator
Dearborn, MI 48128
Tel: (313)563-0515
Fax: (313)563-1412
E-mail: mcmcadam@comcast.net
To provide financial assistance for college to students with a bleeding disorder or members of their families.
Title of Award: Bill McAdam Scholarship Fund **Area, Field, or Subject:** General studies/Field of study not specified **Level of Education for which Award is Granted:** Undergraduate **Number Awarded:** 1 each year. **Funds Available:** The stipend is $2,000. **Duration:** 1 year.
Eligibility Requirements: This program is open to 1) students with a hereditary bleeding disorder (hemophilia, von Willebrand, etc.) or 2) members of their families (spouse, partner, child, sibling). Applicants must be U.S. citizens and enrolled or planning to enroll at an accredited 2- or 4-year college, trade or technical school, or other certification program. Along with their application, they must submit 2 letters of recommendation and 3 essays: 1) their short- and long-term goals and who or what influenced the shaping of their goals; 2) why they should receive this scholarship; and 3) if they had 3 wishes, what those would be. **Deadline for Receipt:** May of each year.

770 ■ HEMOPHILIA OF GEORGIA

8800 Roswell Road, Suite 170
Atlanta, GA 30350
Tel: (770)518-8272
Fax: (770)518-3310
E-mail: mail@hog.org
Web Site: http://www.hog.org/programs/scholarships.asp
To provide financial assistance for college to residents of Georgia who have a bleeding disorder or have lost a parent because of the disorder.
Title of Award: John Youtsey Memorial Scholarship Fund **Area, Field, or Subject:** General studies/Field of study not specified **Level of Education for which Award is Granted:** Undergraduate **Funds Available:** A stipend is awarded (amount not specified). **Duration:** 1 year.
Eligibility Requirements: This program is open to permanent residents of Georgia who have hemophilia or related bleeding disorders and to children who have lost a parent to complications from a bleeding disorder. They may be graduating high school seniors or currently-enrolled college students. Selection is based on academic record, financial need, and

personal goals. **Additional Information:** Funds may be used for either a college or a vocational education.

771 ■ HEMOPHILIA HEALTH SERVICES

Attn: Scholarship Committee
6820 Charlotte Pike, Suite 100
Nashville, TN 37209-4234
Tel: (615)850-5175
Free: 800-800-6606
Fax: (615)352-2588
E-mail: scholarship@HemophiliaHealth.com
Web Site: http://www.HemophiliaHealth.com/consumers/products_services/scholarship.htm
To provide financial assistance for college or graduate school to people with hemophilia or other bleeding disorders.
Title of Award: Hemophilia Health Services Memorial Scholarships **Area, Field, or Subject:** General studies/Field of study not specified **Level of Education for which Award is Granted:** Graduate, Undergraduate **Number Awarded:** Several each year. **Funds Available:** The stipend is $1,500. Funds are issued payable to the recipient's school. **Duration:** 1 year; recipients may reapply.
Eligibility Requirements: This program is open to individuals with hemophilia (factor VIII or IX), von Willebrand Disease (type 1, 2, 2A, 2B, 2M, 2N, or 3), or other bleeding disorders. Applicants must be 1) high school seniors; 2) college freshmen, sophomores, or juniors; or 3) college seniors planning to attend graduate school or students already enrolled in graduate school. They must be attending or planning to attend an accredited nonprofit college, university, or vocational/technical school in the United States or Puerto Rico as a full-time student. Along with their application, they must submit an essay, up to 250 words, on the following topic: "What has been your own personal challenge in living with a bleeding disorder?" U.S. citizenship is required. Selection is based on academic achievement in relation to tested ability, involvement in extracurricular and community activities, and financial need. **Deadline for Receipt:** April of each year. **Additional Information:** This program, which started in 1995, includes the following named scholarships: the Cindy Beck Scholarship, the Osborn DeWitt Scholarship, the Tim Haas Scholarship, the Ricky Hobson Scholarship, the Michael Moses Scholarship, and the Jim Stineback Scholarship. It is administered by Scholarship Program Administrators, Inc., 1201 Eighth Avenue South, P.O. Box 23737, Nashville, TN 27202-3737, (615) 320-3149, Fax: (615) 320-3151, E-mail: info@spaprog.com. Recipients must enroll full time.

772 ■ HEMOPHILIA SOCIETY OF COLORADO

Attn: Scholarship Committee
655 Broadway, Suite 575
Denver, CO 80203-3468
Tel: (303)629-6990; 888-687-CLOT
Fax: (303)629-7035
E-mail: hsc@cohemo.org
Web Site: http://www.cohemo.org/scholarships.php
To provide financial assistance for college or graduate school to students from Colorado who have a bleeding disorder.
Title of Award: Mike Conley Memorial Scholarships **Area, Field, or Subject:** General studies/Field of study not specified **Level of Education for which Award is Granted:** Graduate, Undergraduate **Number Awarded:** 2 each year. **Funds Available:** The stipend is $1,000. Funds must be used for tuition, room, board, and related educational expenses. **Duration:** 1 year.
Eligibility Requirements: This program is open to residents of Colorado who have hemophilia or a related inherited bleeding disorder. Applicants must be enrolled or planning to enroll at a 2-year or 4-year college or university, vocational/technical school, or graduate school. Along with their application, they must submit an essay on why they think they should receive this scholarship and how it might affect their future goals. Selection is based on the essay, demonstrated scholastic ability and intellectual promise, letters of recommendation, community involvement (especially involvement with the hemophilia community), and financial need. Prefer-

ence is given to students at Metropolitan State College or the University of Colorado at Denver. **Deadline for Receipt:** April of each year.

773 ■ HEMOPHILIA SOCIETY OF COLORADO

Attn: Scholarship Committee
655 Broadway, Suite 575
Denver, CO 80203-3468
Tel: (303)629-6990; 888-687-CLOT
Fax: (303)629-7035
E-mail: hsc@cohemo.org
Web Site: http://www.cohemo.org/scholarships.php
To provide financial assistance for college to members of the Hemophilia Society of Colorado (HSC) and to members of their families.
Title of Award: Mark Reames Memorial Scholarships **Area, Field, or Subject:** General studies/Field of study not specified **Level of Education for which Award is Granted:** Graduate, Undergraduate **Number Awarded:** Several each year. **Funds Available:** The stipend is $1,000. Funds must be used for tuition, room, board, and related educational expenses. **Duration:** 1 year.
Eligibility Requirements: This program is open to HSC members who have hemophilia or a related inherited bleeding disorder and their immediate family members. Applicants must be enrolled or planning to enroll at a 2-year or 4-year college or university, vocational/technical school, or graduate school. Along with their application, they must submit an essay on how their varied interests, life experiences, and/or community involvement led to their current career goals. Selection is based on the essay, demonstrated scholastic ability and intellectual promise, letters of recommendation, community involvement (especially involvement with the hemophilia community), and financial need. **Deadline for Receipt:** April of each year.

774 ■ COLIN HIGGINS FOUNDATION

Attn: Youth Courage Awards
P.O. Box 29903
San Francisco, CA 94129-0903
Tel: (415)561-6323
Fax: (415)561-6401
E-mail: info@colinhiggins.org
Web Site: http://www.colinhiggins.org/courageawards/index.cfm
To recognize and reward young people who have shown courage in the face of adversity related to discrimination against members of the lesbian, gay, bisexual, transgender, and questioning (LGBTQ) communities.
Title of Award: Colin Higgins Foundation Youth Courage Awards **Area, Field, or Subject:** General studies/Field of study not specified **Level of Education for which Award is Granted:** Graduate, Undergraduate **Number Awarded:** 2 or 3 each year. **Funds Available:** The award is a $10,000 grant. **Duration:** The awards are presented annually.
Eligibility Requirements: Eligible to be nominated for these awards are young people under 24 years of age who are 1) LGBTQ youth who have "bravely stood up to hostility and intolerance based on their sexual orientation and triumphed over bigotry"; or 2) allies who are working to end homophobia and discrimination against LGBTQ communities. Letters of nomination must include 350-word essays describing why the nominee represents the ideals of this award. Self-nominations are not accepted. **Deadline for Receipt:** March of each year. **Additional Information:** This award program was established in 2000.

775 ■ HISPANIC ALLIANCE FOR CAREER ENHANCEMENT

Attn: College Programs
25 East Washington Street, Suite 1500
Chicago, IL 60602
Tel: (312)435-0498
Fax: (312)435-1494
E-mail: haceorg@hace-usa.org
Web Site: http://www.hace-usa.org/collegepage.htm
To provide financial assistance to Hispanic students working on an undergraduate degree.
Title of Award: HACE Scholarships **Area, Field, or Subject:** General studies/Field of study not specified **Level of Education for which Award is Granted:** Undergraduate **Number Awarded:** Varies each year; recently, 9 of these scholarships were awarded. **Funds Available:** The stipend is $1,000. **Duration:** 1 year; nonrenewable.
Eligibility Requirements: This program is open to U.S. citizens and permanent residents who are enrolled or planning to enroll in a college or

university in the United States (other than a partner institution of the sponsoring organization). Applicants must have a GPA of 2.5 or higher and at least 1 parent of Hispanic or Latino heritage. Along with their application, they must submit 300-word essays on 1) their autobiography, including their Hispanic background, where they grew up, and their immediate family; and 2) their career plans for the next 5 to 10 years. **Deadline for Receipt:** February of each year. **Additional Information:** The partner institutions are DePaul University, the University of Illinois at Chicago, the University of Texas at Austin, Rice University, the University of Houston, Texas A&M University, Columbia University, Cornell University, New York University, and Rutgers University.

776 ■ HISPANIC CHAMBER OF COMMERCE-WISCONSIN

Attn: Scholarship Committee
816 West National Avenue
Milwaukee, WI 53204
Tel: (414)643-6963
Fax: (414)643-6994
E-mail: eagosto@hccw.org
Web Site: http://www.hccw.org
To provide financial assistance to Hispanic students at colleges and universities in Wisconsin.
Title of Award: Phillip Arreola Returning Student Scholarships **Area, Field, or Subject:** General studies/Field of study not specified **Level of Education for which Award is Granted:** Undergraduate **Number Awarded:** Varies each year; recently, 2 of these scholarships were awarded. **Funds Available:** The stipend is $1,000. **Duration:** 1 year; nonrenewable.
Eligibility Requirements: This program is open to Hispanic students currently enrolled full time at a college or university in Wisconsin or who have experienced at least a 1-year lapse in their undergraduate education. Applicants must be residents of Wisconsin, have a high school diploma or GED, and be U.S. citizens or permanent residents. Selection is based on academic achievement, participation in school activities, involvement in community activities, and financial need. **Deadline for Receipt:** March of each year.

777 ■ HISPANIC CHAMBER OF COMMERCE-WISCONSIN

Attn: Scholarship Committee
816 West National Avenue
Milwaukee, WI 53204
Tel: (414)643-6963
Fax: (414)643-6994
E-mail: eagosto@hccw.org
Web Site: http://www.hccw.org
To provide financial assistance for college to Hispanic high school seniors in Wisconsin.
Title of Award: Phillip Arreola Scholarships **Area, Field, or Subject:** General studies/Field of study not specified **Level of Education for which Award is Granted:** Undergraduate **Number Awarded:** Varies each year; recently, 3 of these scholarships were awarded. **Funds Available:** The stipend is $2,500 per year. **Duration:** 4 years, provided the recipient remains enrolled full time with a GPA of 2.5 or higher.
Eligibility Requirements: This program is open to Hispanic students graduating from high school in Wisconsin and planning to attend an accredited college or university in the state. Applicants must be residents of Wisconsin; have a history of academic achievement, participation in school activities, and involvement in community activities; be able to demonstrate financial need; and be U.S. citizens or permanent residents. **Deadline for Receipt:** March of each year. **Additional Information:** Recipients are required to volunteer for 20 hours of community service work annually.

778 ■ HISPANIC HERITAGE AWARDS FOUNDATION

2600 Virginia Avenue, N.W., Suite 406
Washington, DC 20037
Tel: (202)861-9797; (866)665-2112
Fax: (202)861-9799
E-mail: contact@hispanicheritageawards.org
Web Site: http://www.hispanicheritageawards.org
To recognize and reward, with college scholarships, Hispanic high school seniors from selected metropolitan areas who have excelled in various areas of activity.

Title of Award: Hispanic Heritage Youth Awards **Area, Field, or Subject:** General studies/Field of study not specified **Level of Education for which Award is Granted:** Undergraduate **Number Awarded:** Recently, 144 regional winners were selected: a gold and a silver in each of the 6 categories from each of the 12 cities. From those, 6 national winners were chosen: 1 in each of the categories. **Funds Available:** In each category and each city, gold regional winners receive $3,000 and silver regional winners receive $2,000. Awards are in the form of educational grants that recipients may use for any aspect of their college career (tuition, books, room, and board). The gold regional winners then advance to a national competition. National winners receive an additional $5,000 educational grant, a state-of-the-art laptop computer, an all-expense paid trip to Miami for the winner and a parent to attend the award announcement event, and an all-expense paid trip to Washington, D.C. for the winner and a parent to attend the awards ceremony at the John F. Kennedy Center for the Performing Arts. **Duration:** The awards are presented annually.

Eligibility Requirements: This program is open to high school seniors who are U.S. citizens or permanent residents and of Hispanic heritage (at least 1 parent must be of able to trace family origins to Spain, Latin America, or the Spanish-speaking Caribbean). Awards were recently presented to students in 12 metropolitan regions: Chicago, Dallas, Houston, Los Angeles, Miami, New York City, Philadelphia, Phoenix, San Antonio, San Diego, northern California, and Washington, D.C. Applicants competed for awards in the following 6 categories: community service, engineering and mathematics, academic excellence, journalism, sports, or health care. They must have a GPA of 2.75 or higher. Along with their application, they must submit a personal essay that describes their personal qualities and strengths, dedication to community service and the impact it has had on their life, future career goals, areas of interest, and significance of heritage and/or family in their life. Selection criteria include, but are not limited to, the following: academic achievement, compelling essay responses, meritorious achievements in the applicant's chosen category, contribution to the community, overall character as a role model, and letters of recommendation. **Deadline for Receipt:** February of each year. **Additional Information:** This program began in 1998 with sponsorship by the Fannie Mae Foundation for 5 cities and 1 category. More sponsors have resulted in the additional categories as more cities have also been added. Recent sponsors have included Dr Pepper for community service, ExxonMobil for engineering and mathematics, Chase Manhattan Bank and MasterCard for academic excellence, NBC and Telemundo for journalism, Subway for sports, and GlaxoSmithKline for health care. Awardees must attend, at their own expense, a local awards ceremony for the region they have selected.

779 ■ HISPANIC METROPOLITAN CHAMBER

Attn: Scholarship Committee
P.O. Box 1837
Portland, OR 97207
Tel: (503)222-0280
Web Site: http://www.hmccoregon.com/Scholarships/scholarship.htm
To provide financial assistance for college and graduate school to Hispanic residents of Oregon and Clark County, Washington who are from a farmworker household.

Title of Award: CASA of Oregon Scholarship **Area, Field, or Subject:** General studies/Field of study not specified **Level of Education for which Award is Granted:** Graduate, Undergraduate **Number Awarded:** Varies each year; recently, 3 of these scholarships were awarded. **Funds Available:** The stipend is $2,500. **Duration:** 1 year; may be renewed.

Eligibility Requirements: This program is open to residents of Oregon and Clark County, Washington who are of Hispanic ancestry. Applicants must be from a farmworker family and be enrolled or planning to enroll in an accredited community college, 4-year university, or graduate school. Along with their application, they must submit 250-word essays on what being a Latino student means to them, their life as a member of a farmworker family and the obstacles they have had to overcome, why they should be selected to receive another scholarship from this sponsor (if they are applying for a renewal), and/or what they intend to do with their degree in 10 years (if they are a first-time applicant). If they wish to be

considered for a scholarship for low-income families, they may also submit documentation of financial need. **Deadline for Receipt:** February of each year.

780 ■ HISPANIC METROPOLITAN CHAMBER

Attn: Scholarship Committee
P.O. Box 1837
Portland, OR 97207
Tel: (503)222-0280
Web Site: http://www.hmccoregon.com/Scholarships/scholarship.htm
To provide financial assistance for college and graduate school to Hispanic residents of Oregon and Clark County, Washington.

Title of Award: Hispanic Metropolitan Chamber Scholarships **Area, Field, or Subject:** General studies/Field of study not specified **Level of Education for which Award is Granted:** Graduate, Undergraduate **Number Awarded:** Varies each year; recently, 45 of these scholarships were awarded. **Funds Available:** Stipends range from $1,000 to $5,000. **Duration:** 1 year; may be renewed.

Eligibility Requirements: This program is open to residents of Oregon and Clark County, Washington who are of Hispanic ancestry. Applicants must have a GPA of 2.75 or higher and be enrolled or planning to enroll in an accredited community college, 4-year university, or graduate school. Along with their application, they must submit 250-word essays on what being a Latino student means to them, why they should be selected to receive another scholarship from this sponsor (if they are applying for a renewal), and/or what they intend to do with their degree in 10 years (if they are a first-time applicant). If they wish to be considered for a scholarship for low-income families, they may also submit documentation of financial need. **Deadline for Receipt:** February of each year.

781 ■ HISPANIC SCHOLARSHIP FUND

Attn: Selection Committee
55 Second Street, Suite 1500
San Francisco, CA 94105
Tel: (415)808-2350; 877-HSF-INFO
Fax: (415)808-2302
E-mail: cctransfer@hsf.net
Web Site: http://www.hsf.net/scholarship/programs/cocalcola.php
To provide financial assistance to Hispanic American students who are attending selected community colleges and interested in transferring to a 4-year institution.

Title of Award: Coca-Cola Advancing to Universities Scholarship Program **Area, Field, or Subject:** General studies/Field of study not specified **Level of Education for which Award is Granted:** Four Year College **Number Awarded:** 1 or more each year. **Funds Available:** Stipends range from $1,000 to $2,000 per year. **Duration:** 1 year.

Eligibility Requirements: This program is open to U.S. citizens, permanent residents, and visitors with a passport stamped I-551. Applicants must be of Hispanic heritage and enrolled part time or full time at designated community colleges with a GPA of 3.0 or higher. They must be planning to transfer and enroll full time at an accredited 4-year college or university in the United States. Along with their application, they must submit 600-word essays on 1) how their Hispanic heritage, family upbringing, and/or role models have influenced their personal long-term goals; 2) how they contribute to their community and what they have learned from their experiences; and 3) an academic challenge they have faced and how they have overcome it. Selection is based on academic achievement, personal strengths, leadership, and financial need. **Deadline for Receipt:** January of each year. **Additional Information:** The designated community colleges include those in the Atlanta area (Atlanta Metropolitan College, Dalton College, Darton College, Gainesville College, Georgia Perimeter College); California (East Los Angeles College, Los Angeles City College, Los Angeles Mission College, Los Angeles Pierce College, Chabot College, Ohlone College, San Jose City College); Chicago (Harold Washington College, Richard J. Daley College, Wilbur Wright College); Florida (Broward Community College, Miami-Dade Community College, Daytona Beach Community College, Southern College, Valencia Community College, Hillsborough Community College, St. Petersburg Junior College); New York (Borough of Manhattan Community College, Bronx Community College, La Guardia Community College, Queensborough Community College); and Texas (El Paso Community College, El Centro College, Eastfield College, Richland College, Houston Community College). This program is sponsored by the Hispanic Scholarship Fund

(HSF) in partnership with the Coca-Cola Foundation.

782 ■ HISPANIC SCHOLARSHIP FUND

Attn: Selection Committee
55 Second Street, Suite 1500
San Francisco, CA 94105
Tel: (415)808-2350; 877-HSF-INFO
Fax: (415)808-2302
E-mail: college1@hsf.net
Web Site: http://www.hsf.net/scholarship/programs/college.php
To provide financial assistance for college or graduate school to Hispanic American students.

Title of Award: College Scholarship Program of the Hispanic Scholarship Fund **Area, Field, or Subject:** General studies/Field of study not specified **Level of Education for which Award is Granted:** Graduate, Undergraduate **Number Awarded:** More than 4,000 each year. **Funds Available:** Stipends normally range from $1,000 to $3,000 per year. **Duration:** 1 year; recipients may reapply.

Eligibility Requirements: This program is open to U.S. citizens, permanent residents, and visitors with a passport stamped I-551. Applicants must be of Hispanic heritage and enrolled full time in a degree-seeking program at an accredited community college, 4-year university, or graduate school in the United States, Puerto Rico, or the U.S. Virgin Islands. They must have completed at least 12 undergraduate units with a GPA of 3.0 or higher and have applied for federal financial aid. Along with their application, they must submit 600-word essays on 1) how their Hispanic heritage, family upbringing, and/or role models have influenced their personal long-term goals; 2) how they contribute to their community and what they have learned from their experiences; and 3) an academic challenge they have faced and how they have overcome it. Selection is based on academic achievement, personal strengths, leadership, and financial need. **Deadline for Receipt:** October of each year. **Additional Information:** Since this program began in 1975, more than $144 million has been awarded to more than 68,000 Hispanic students.

783 ■ HISPANIC SCHOLARSHIP FUND

Attn: Selection Committee
55 Second Street, Suite 1500
San Francisco, CA 94105
Tel: (415)808-2350; 877-HSF-INFO
Fax: (415)808-2302
E-mail: cctransfer@hsf.net
Web Site: http://www.hsf.net/scholarship/programs/cctransfer.php
To provide financial assistance to Hispanic American students who are attending a community college and interested in transferring to a 4-year institution.

Title of Award: Community College Transfer Program of the Hispanic Scholarship Fund **Area, Field, or Subject:** General studies/Field of study not specified **Level of Education for which Award is Granted:** Four Year College **Number Awarded:** At least 600 each year. **Funds Available:** Stipends range from $1,000 to $2,500 per year. **Duration:** 1 year; may reapply.

Eligibility Requirements: This program is open to U.S. citizens, permanent residents, and visitors with a passport stamped I-551. Applicants must be of Hispanic heritage and part-time or full-time community college students with a GPA of 3.0 or higher. They must be planning to transfer and enroll full time at an accredited 4-year college or university in the United States, Puerto Rico, or the U.S. Virgin Islands and have applied for federal financial aid. Along with their application, they must submit 600-word essays on 1) how their Hispanic heritage, family upbringing, and/or role models have influenced their personal long-term goals; 2) how they contribute to their community and what they have learned from their experiences; and 3) an academic challenge they have faced and how they have overcome it. Selection is based on academic achievement, personal strengths, leadership, and financial need. **Deadline for Receipt:** January of each year.

784 ■ HISPANIC SCHOLARSHIP FUND

Attn: Selection Committee
55 Second Street, Suite 1500
San Francisco, CA 94105
Tel: (415)808-2350; 877-HSF-INFO
Fax: (415)808-2302

E-mail: highschool@hsf.net
Web Site: http://www.hsf.net/scholarship/programs/hs.php
To provide financial assistance to Hispanic American high school seniors who are interested in attending college.

Title of Award: High School Scholarship Program of the Hispanic Scholarship Fund **Area, Field, or Subject:** General studies/Field of study not specified **Level of Education for which Award is Granted:** Undergraduate **Number Awarded:** Varies each year. **Funds Available:** Stipends range from $1,000 to $2,500 per year. **Duration:** 1 year.

Eligibility Requirements: This program is open to U.S. citizens, permanent residents, and visitors with a passport stamped I-551. Applicants must be high school seniors of Hispanic heritage and have applied for federal financial aid. They must have a GPA of 3.0 or higher and concrete plans to enroll full time at an accredited 2-year or 4-year college or university in the United States, Puerto Rico, or the U.S. Virgin Islands for the following fall. Along with their application, they must submit 600-word essays on 1) how their Hispanic heritage, family upbringing, and/or role models have influenced their personal long-term goals; 2) how they contribute to their community and what they have learned from their experiences; and 3) an academic challenge they have faced and how they have overcome it. Selection is based on academic achievement, personal strengths, leadership, and financial need. **Deadline for Receipt:** December of each year. **Additional Information:** Since this program began in 1975, more than $144 million has been awarded to more than 68,000 Hispanic students.

785 ■ DONG JI HOI SOCIETY

c/o Dianne Lim, Scholarship Chair
91-201 Kaana Place
Kapolei, HI 96707-1931
To provide financial assistance to Korean Americans in Hawaii who are interested in pursuing postsecondary education.

Title of Award: Dr. Syngman Rhee Scholarship **Area, Field, or Subject:** General studies/Field of study not specified **Level of Education for which Award is Granted:** Undergraduate **Number Awarded:** 10 to 16 each year. **Funds Available:** The stipend is $1,500 per year. **Duration:** Up to 4 years.

Eligibility Requirements: This program is open to graduating high school seniors in Hawaii who are at least 50% Korean ancestry. Applicants must be planning to attend a 4-year college or university. Selection is based on academic achievement, community service, extracurricular activities, and SAT scores. **Deadline for Receipt:** June of each year. **Additional Information:** Recipients may study in Hawaii or on the mainland. Requests for applications must be accompanied by a self-addressed stamped envelope.

786 ■ HOME BUILDERS ASSOCIATION OF ALABAMA

Attn: Alabama Home Builders Foundation
P.O. Box 241305
Montgomery, AL 36124
Tel: (334)834-3006
Free: 800-745-4222
E-mail: info@hbaa.org
Web Site: http://www.hbaa.org/careers/scholarships.php
To provide financial assistance for college to Alabama residents interested in preparing for a career in the home building industry.

Title of Award: Alabama Home Builders Scholarships **Area, Field, or Subject:** Construction **Level of Education for which Award is Granted:** Undergraduate **Number Awarded:** Varies each year. **Funds Available:** A stipend is awarded (amount not specified). **Duration:** 1 year.

Eligibility Requirements: This program is open to residents of Alabama enrolled in, or attending, a junior college, technical school, or university in the state. Applicants must be working on a certificate or degree in a construction-related field. They must be able to demonstrate financial need. **Deadline for Receipt:** March of each year.

787 ■ HONOLULU ALUMNAE PANHELLENIC ASSOCIATION

Attn: Scholarship and Recruitment Chair
P.O. Box 11962
Honolulu, HI 96828-0962
Tel: (808)284-1290
E-mail: sdilbeck@netscape.net
Web Site: http://www.greekhawaii.com/hawaiiaphscholarships.htm

To provide financial assistance to female college student from Hawaii who are members of a National Panhellenic Conference (NPC) sorority. **Title of Award:** Honolulu Alumnae Panhellenic Association Collegiate Scholarships **Area, Field, or Subject:** General studies/Field of study not specified **Level of Education for which Award is Granted:** Undergraduate **Number Awarded:** 1 or more each year. **Funds Available:** A stipend is awarded (amount not specified). **Duration:** 1 year. **Eligibility Requirements:** This program is open to women who are initiated and active members of an NPC-affiliated sorority at a college or university where they are working on an undergraduate degree. Their permanent home address or college address must be in Hawaii. Along with their application, they must submit 1) a brief essay stating why they would like the scholarship, their plans, and the part they feel sorority membership has played in their lives; 2) a list of all school, sorority, and community activities and offices; and 3) letters of recommendation from a professor, sorority officer, and another person in the community. Financial need is not considered in the selection process. **Deadline for Receipt:** February of each year.

788 ■ HONOLULU ALUMNAE PANHELLENIC ASSOCIATION

Attn: Scholarship and Recruitment Chair
P.O. Box 11962
Honolulu, HI 96828-0962
Tel: (808)284-1290
E-mail: sdilbeck@netscape.net
Web Site: http://www.greekhawaii.com/hawaiiaphscholarships.htm
To provide financial assistance to female high school seniors in Hawaii who are interested in going to a college with National Panhellenic Conference (NPC) sororities on campus. **Title of Award:** Honolulu Alumnae Panhellenic Association High School Scholarships **Area, Field, or Subject:** General studies/Field of study not specified **Level of Education for which Award is Granted:** Undergraduate **Number Awarded:** 1 or more each year. **Funds Available:** A stipend is awarded (amount not specified). **Duration:** 1 year. **Eligibility Requirements:** This program is open to females graduating from high schools in Hawaii. Applicants must be interested in attending 1 of the more than 500 colleges and universities with NPC sororities. Along with their application, they must submit 1) a brief essay stating why they would like the scholarship, what they hope to get out of their college experience, and the part they feel sorority membership could play in their college years; 2) SAT and/or ACT scores; 3) a list of all class and school offices, other offices and responsibilities, school and athletic activities, extracurricular and community activities, honors, and awards; and 4) letters of recommendation from their high school senior counselor and another person in the community. Financial need is also considered in the selection process, but the program gives priority to well-rounded students who have balanced scholastics with school and/or community activities. Interviews are included. **Deadline for Receipt:** February of each year.

789 ■ HOPI TRIBE

Attn: Office of Education
P.O. Box 123
Kykotsmovi, AZ 86039
Tel: (928)734-3533
Free: 800-762-9630
Fax: (928)734-9575
E-mail: IPolingyumptewa@hopi.nsn.us
Web Site: http://www.hopi.nsn.us/education_htgsp.asp
To provide financial assistance to needy students of Hopi ancestry who are working on an undergraduate, graduate, or postgraduate degree. **Title of Award:** BIA Higher Education Grants for Hopi Tribal Members **Area, Field, or Subject:** General studies/Field of study not specified **Level of Education for which Award is Granted:** Graduate, Professional, Undergraduate **Number Awarded:** Varies each year. **Funds Available:** The maximum grant is $2,500 per semester. **Duration:** 1 semester; may be renewed. **Eligibility Requirements:** This program is open to students who are working on an associate, baccalaureate, graduate, or postgraduate degree. Applicants must be enrolled members of the Hopi Tribe. They must be able to demonstrate financial need. Entering freshmen must have a high school GPA of 2.0 or higher or a minimum composite score of 45% on the GED exam. Continuing students must have a GPA of 2.0 or higher for all college work. **Deadline for Receipt:** July of each year for fall

semester; November of each year for spring semester; April of each year for summer session. **Additional Information:** This grant is awarded as a secondary source of financial aid to eligible students who are also receiving aid from the Bureau of Indian Affairs (BIA) Higher Education program. Recipients must attend school on a full-time basis.

790 ■ HOPI TRIBE

Attn: Office of Education
P.O. Box 123
Kykotsmovi, AZ 86039
Tel: (928)734-3542
Free: 800-762-9630
Fax: (928)734-9575
E-mail: IPolingyumptewa@hopi.nsn.us
Web Site: http://www.hopi.nsn.us/education_avtp.asp
To provide financial assistance to members of the Hopi Tribe who are interested in vocational training. **Title of Award:** Hopi Adult Vocational Training Program **Area, Field, or Subject:** General studies/Field of study not specified **Level of Education for which Award is Granted:** Undergraduate **Number Awarded:** Varies each year. **Funds Available:** A stipend is awarded (amount not specified). **Duration:** Support is provided until completion of the program. **Eligibility Requirements:** This program is open to enrolled members of the Hopi Tribe who are unskilled, unemployed, or underemployed. Applicants must be between 17 and 35 years of age and residing on or near the Hopi Reservation. They must be interested in full-time vocational training at an accredited private or public institution approved by the Hopi Tribe Adult Vocational Training Program to acquire marketable vocational skills.

791 ■ HOPI TRIBE

Attn: Office of Education
P.O. Box 123
Kykotsmovi, AZ 86039
Tel: (928)734-3533
Free: 800-762-9630
Fax: (928)734-9575
E-mail: IPolingyumptewa@hopi.nsn.us
Web Site: http://www.hopi.nsn.us/education_htgsp.asp
To provide financial assistance to academically outstanding students of Hopi ancestry who are working on an undergraduate, graduate, or postgraduate degree. **Title of Award:** Hopi Scholarship **Area, Field, or Subject:** General studies/Field of study not specified **Level of Education for which Award is Granted:** Graduate, Professional, Undergraduate **Number Awarded:** Varies each year. **Funds Available:** The stipend is $1,000 per semester. **Duration:** 1 semester; may be renewed. **Eligibility Requirements:** This program is open to students who are working on an associate, baccalaureate, graduate, or postgraduate degree. Applicants must be enrolled members of the Hopi Tribe. Entering freshmen must be in the top 10% of their graduating class or score at least 21 on the ACT or at least 930 on the SAT. Undergraduate students must have a GPA of 3.0 or higher. Graduate, postgraduate, and professional students must have a 3.2 cumulative GPA or higher for all graduate course work. Selection is based on academic merit. **Deadline for Receipt:** July of each year. **Additional Information:** Recipients must attend school on a full-time basis.

792 ■ HOPI TRIBE

Attn: Office of Education
P.O. Box 123
Kykotsmovi, AZ 86039
Tel: (928)734-3533
Free: 800-762-9630
Fax: (928)734-9575
E-mail: IPolingyumptewa@hopi.nsn.us
Web Site: http://www.hopi.nsn.us/education_htgsp.asp
To provide financial assistance to students of Hopi ancestry who are working on an undergraduate, graduate, or postgraduate degree. **Title of Award:** Hopi Tuition/Book Scholarship **Area, Field, or Subject:** General studies/Field of study not specified **Level of Education for which Award is Granted:** Graduate, Professional, Undergraduate **Number Awarded:** Varies each year. **Funds Available:** The scholarship covers the cost of tuition/fees and books. **Duration:** 1 year; may be renewed if the recipient maintains a cumulative GPA of 2.0 or higher.

Eligibility Requirements: This program is open to students who are working on an associate, baccalaureate, graduate, or postgraduate degree. Applicants must be an enrolled member of the Hopi Tribe. They must be pursuing a postsecondary degree for at least 1 of the following reasons: personal growth, career enhancement, career change, and/or continuing education. Both full- and part-time students may apply. Financial need is not required, but students must have applied for federal aid before applying for this award. **Deadline for Receipt:** July of each year for fall semester; November of each year for spring semester; April of each year for summer session.

793 ■ HOPI TRIBE

Attn: Office of Education
P.O. Box 123
Kykotsmovi, AZ 86039
Tel: (928)734-3533
Free: 800-762-9630
Fax: (928)734-9575
E-mail: IPolingyumptewa@hopi.nsn.us
Web Site: http://www.hopi.nsn.us/education_htgsp.asp
To provide financial assistance to needy students of Hopi ancestry who are working on an undergraduate, graduate, or postgraduate degree.
Title of Award: Supplemental Education Grants for Hopi Tribal Members **Area, Field, or Subject:** General studies/Field of study not specified **Level of Education for which Award is Granted:** Graduate, Professional, Undergraduate **Number Awarded:** Varies each year. **Funds Available:** The maximum grant is $1,500 per semester. **Duration:** 1 semester; may be renewed.
Eligibility Requirements: This program is open to students who are working on an associate, baccalaureate, graduate, or postgraduate degree. Applicants must be enrolled members of the Hopi Tribe. They must be able to demonstrate financial need. Entering freshmen must have a high school GPA of 2.0 or higher or a minimum composite score of 45% on the GED exam. Continuing students must have a GPA of 2.0 or higher for all college work. **Deadline for Receipt:** July of each year for fall semester; November of each year for spring semester; April of each year for summer session. **Additional Information:** This grant is awarded as a secondary source of financial aid to eligible students who are also receiving aid from the Bureau of Indian Affairs (BIA) Higher Education program. Recipients must attend school on a full-time basis.

794 ■ HUGUENOT SOCIETY OF AMERICA

Attn: Office of the Scholarship Committee
122 East 58th Street
New York, NY 10022
Tel: (212)755-0592
Web Site: http://www.huguenotsocietyofamerica.org/scholarships.html
To provide financial assistance for undergraduate education to the descendants of Huguenots.
Title of Award: Marie L. Rose Huguenot Scholarships **Area, Field, or Subject:** General studies/Field of study not specified **Level of Education for which Award is Granted:** Undergraduate **Number Awarded:** Varies each year. **Funds Available:** The award is $3,000 per year. **Duration:** 1 year.
Eligibility Requirements: Applicants must be able to submit proof of descent from a Huguenot who emigrated from France and either settled in what is now the United States or left France for other countries before 1787. The scholarships are available to students at 1 of 50 participating universities; for a list, contact the Huguenot Society. **Additional Information:** Applications are available only from financial aid offices at the participating universities and must be submitted to those offices. Applications sent directly to the Huguenot Society are not accepted.

795 ■ HUNA HERITAGE FOUNDATION

Attn: Education Programs
9309 Glacier Highway, Suite A-103
Juneau, AK 99801
Tel: (907)789-7514
Fax: (907)789-1896
E-mail: education@hunaheritage.org
Web Site: http://www.hunaheritage.org/education.shtml
To provide emergency supplemental funding for undergraduate or graduate studies to Huna Totem shareholders and their descendants.

Title of Award: Huna Heritage Foundation Emergency Education Assistance Program **Area, Field, or Subject:** General studies/Field of study not specified **Level of Education for which Award is Granted:** Graduate, Undergraduate **Number Awarded:** Varies each year; recently, 19 of these scholarships were awarded for the fall semester and 29 for the spring semester. **Funds Available:** This program provides emergency supplemental educational funding, to a maximum of $2,000 per year. Emergencies are defined to mean whatever costs other grant programs do not cover. **Duration:** 1 year; recipients may reapply.
Eligibility Requirements: This program is open to Huna Totem shareholders and descendants who have a high school diploma or GED certificate. Applicants must be accepted by or attending a college or university as a full-time undergraduate or graduate student. Internships, apprenticeships, and on-the-job training may also be funded. Students must have applied to other programs before they apply for this assistance. Proof of awards or denial by other programs must be supplied. **Deadline for Receipt:** October of each year for first or second quarter or fall semester; January of each year for third or fourth quarter or spring or summer semester.

796 ■ HUNA HERITAGE FOUNDATION

Attn: Education Programs
9309 Glacier Highway, Suite A-103
Juneau, AK 99801
Tel: (907)789-7514
Fax: (907)789-1896
E-mail: education@hunaheritage.org
Web Site: http://www.hunaheritage.org/education.shtml
To provide financial assistance to Huna Totem shareholders and their descendants who are interested in pursuing vocational education.
Title of Award: Huna Heritage Foundation Vocational Education Assistance Program **Area, Field, or Subject:** General studies/Field of study not specified **Level of Education for which Award is Granted:** Undergraduate **Number Awarded:** Varies each year; recently, 7 of these awards were presented. **Funds Available:** The amount of assistance depends on the nature of the program and the need of the recipient. **Duration:** 1 year. Recipients may be eligible for a second award only if they can demonstrate that they continue to be unemployed, underemployed, or unable to work in their primary occupation due to physical or other disability.
Eligibility Requirements: This program is open to Huna Totem shareholders or descendants (as defined in accordance with the Alaska Native Claim Settlement Act Amendments of 1987) who are at least 18 years of age (high school students are eligible at 17 years of age) and either unemployed or underemployed. They must be in need of training in order to be employable. Applicants who are underemployed must show how the lack of additional training would result in hardship. All applicants must be interested in pursuing vocational education or apprenticeships that 1) are approved by the National Accreditation Association, the Alaska Department of Education's Division of Vocational Education, or the U.S. Bureau of Apprenticeship Training; 2) are enrolled full time (at least 30 hours of study per week and include shop practices as an integral component); and 3) lead to employment at the completion of training. **Deadline for Receipt:** October of each year for first or second quarter or fall semester; January of each year for third or fourth quarter or spring or summer semester.

797 ■ ICE SKATING INSTITUTE OF AMERICA

Attn: ISIA Education Foundation
17120 North Dallas Parkway, Suite 140
Dallas, TX 75248-1187
Tel: (972)735-8800
Fax: (972)735-8815
E-mail: kchase@skateisi.com
Web Site: http://www.skateisi.com
To provide financial assistance to high school seniors and currently-enrolled undergraduates who are members of the Ice Skating Institute of America (ISI).
Title of Award: ISIA Education Foundation Scholarship **Area, Field, or Subject:** General studies/Field of study not specified **Level of Education for which Award is Granted:** Undergraduate **Number Awarded:** Varies each year; recently, 4 of these scholarships were awarded. **Funds Available:** The stipend is at least $4,000 per year. **Duration:** 1 year.

Eligibility Requirements: Applicants may be graduating high school seniors or currently-enrolled college students. They must have completed at least 3 years of high school with a GPA of 3.0 or higher, have been an individual member of ISI for at least 4 years, have participated in ISI group classes or ISI endorsed competitions within the last 2 years, and have completed 240 hours of verified service (of which 120 must be volunteered) with an ISI administrative member rink or skating school. Along with their application process, they must submit an official transcript, SAT/ACT scores, 2 evaluation forms, and a statement (up to 500 words) on "Why I should receive an ISIA Education Foundation Scholarship." Selection is based on community service, education awards and recognition, educational goals, and competitive ice skating experience. **Deadline for Receipt:** February of each year. **Additional Information:** Recipients must attend college on a full-time basis.

798 ■ IDAHO STATE BOARD OF EDUCATION

Len B. Jordan Office Building
650 West State Street, Room 307
P.O. Box 83720
Boise, ID 83720-0037
Tel: (208)332-1574
Fax: (208)334-2632
E-mail: board@osbe.state.id.us
Web Site: http://www.idahoboardofed.org/scholarships/freedom.asp
To provide financial assistance for college to dependent children of Idaho veterans who are listed as prisoners of war or missing in action.
Title of Award: Idaho Freedom Scholarships **Area, Field, or Subject:** General studies/Field of study not specified **Level of Education for which Award is Granted:** Undergraduate **Number Awarded:** Varies each year. **Funds Available:** Each scholarship provides a full waiver of tuition and fees at public institutions of higher education or public vocational schools within Idaho, an allowance of $500 per semester for books, and on-campus housing and subsistence. **Duration:** Benefits are available for a maximum of 36 months.
Eligibility Requirements: Eligible for these scholarships are dependent children of Idaho veterans who are listed as prisoners of war (POW) or missing in action (MIA) in southeast Asia (including Korea) or who become listed as POW or MIA in any area of armed conflict in which the United States is a party.

799 ■ IDAHO STATE BOARD OF EDUCATION

Len B. Jordan Office Building
650 West State Street, Room 307
P.O. Box 83720
Boise, ID 83720-0037
Tel: (208)332-1574
Fax: (208)334-2632
E-mail: board@osbe.state.id.us
Web Site: http://www.idahoboardofed.org/scholarships/challenge.asp
To provide financial assistance to outstanding high school seniors in Idaho who wish to attend a postsecondary institution in the state.
Title of Award: Idaho Governor's Challenge Academic Scholarship **Area, Field, or Subject:** General studies/Field of study not specified **Level of Education for which Award is Granted:** Undergraduate **Number Awarded:** 6 each year. **Funds Available:** The stipend is $3,000 per year. **Duration:** 1 year; may be renewed for up to 3 additional years.
Eligibility Requirements: This program is open to graduating high school seniors who are U.S. citizens, Idaho residents, and planning to enroll full time at an eligible postsecondary educational institution in the state. Applicants must have maintained a GPA of 2.8 or better, must take the ACT or SAT examinations, and must have demonstrated a commitment to public service. **Deadline for Receipt:** December of each year.

800 ■ IDAHO STATE BOARD OF EDUCATION

Len B. Jordan Office Building
650 West State Street, Room 307
P.O. Box 83720
Boise, ID 83720-0037
Tel: (208)332-1574
Fax: (208)334-2632
E-mail: board@osbe.state.id.us
Web Site: http://www.idahoboardofed.org/scholarships/challenge.asp

To provide financial assistance to outstanding high school seniors in Idaho who wish to attend a professional/technical school in the state.
Title of Award: Idaho Governor's Challenge Professional-Technical Scholarship **Area, Field, or Subject:** General studies/Field of study not specified **Level of Education for which Award is Granted:** Vocational/Occupational **Number Awarded:** 6 each year. **Funds Available:** The stipend is $3,000 per year. **Duration:** 1 year; may be renewed for up to 2 additional years.
Eligibility Requirements: This program is open to graduating high school seniors who are U.S. citizens, Idaho residents, and planning to enroll full time in a professional/technical program in the state. Applicants must have maintained a GPA of 2.8 or better and have demonstrated a commitment to public service. They must identify their proposed program; selection is based in part on their identified professional-technical program. **Deadline for Receipt:** December of each year.

801 ■ IDAHO STATE BOARD OF EDUCATION

Len B. Jordan Office Building
650 West State Street, Room 307
P.O. Box 83720
Boise, ID 83720-0037
Tel: (208)332-1574
Fax: (208)334-2632
E-mail: board@osbe.state.id.us
Web Site: http://www.idahoboardofed.org/scholarships/leap.asp
To provide financial assistance to students from any state attending a college or university in Idaho.
Title of Award: Idaho Leveraging Educational Assistance State Partnership Program **Area, Field, or Subject:** General studies/Field of study not specified **Level of Education for which Award is Granted:** Undergraduate **Number Awarded:** Varies each year; recently, approximately 1,800 students received these grants. **Funds Available:** Awards range up to $5,000 per year for full-time students.
Eligibility Requirements: This program is open to students from any state attending a designated public or private college or university within Idaho. Applicants must have financial need; they may be enrolled part time. **Additional Information:** For applications and information about deadlines, contact the financial aid office at the college you plan to attend. This program was formerly known as the Idaho State Student Incentive Grant.

802 ■ IDAHO STATE BOARD OF EDUCATION

Len B. Jordan Office Building
650 West State Street, Room 307
P.O. Box 83720
Boise, ID 83720-0037
Tel: (208)332-1574
Fax: (208)334-2632
E-mail: board@osbe.state.id.us
Web Site: http://www.idahoboardofed.org/scholarships/minority.asp
To provide financial assistance for college to disabled and other "at risk" high school seniors in Idaho.
Title of Award: Idaho Minority and "At Risk" Student Scholarship **Area, Field, or Subject:** General studies/Field of study not specified **Level of Education for which Award is Granted:** Undergraduate **Number Awarded:** Approximately 40 each year. **Funds Available:** The maximum stipend is $3,000 per year. **Duration:** 1 year; may be renewed for up to 3 additional years.
Eligibility Requirements: This program focuses on talented students who may be at risk of failing to meet their goals because of physical, economic, or cultural limitations. Applicants must be high school graduates, be Idaho residents, and meet at least 3 of the following 5 requirements: 1) have a disability; 2) be a member of an ethnic minority group historically underrepresented in higher education in Idaho; 3) have substantial financial need; 4) be a first-generation college student; 5) be a migrant farm worker or a dependent of a farm worker. **Additional Information:** This program was established in 1991 by the Idaho state legislature. Information is also available from high school counselors and financial aid offices of colleges and universities in Idaho. Recipients must

plan to attend or be attending 1 of 8 participating colleges and universities in the state on a full-time basis. For a list of those schools, write to the State of Idaho Board of Education.

803 ■ IDAHO STATE BOARD OF EDUCATION

Len B. Jordan Office Building
650 West State Street, Room 307
P.O. Box 83720
Boise, ID 83720-0037
Tel: (208)332-1574
Fax: (208)334-2632
E-mail: board@osbe.state.id.us
Web Site: http://www.idahoboardofed.org/scholarships/freedom.asp
To provide financial assistance for college to dependents of disabled or deceased Idaho public safety officers.

Title of Award: Idaho Public Safety Officer Dependent Scholarship **Area, Field, or Subject:** General studies/Field of study not specified **Level of Education for which Award is Granted:** Undergraduate **Number Awarded:** Varies each year; recently, 4 of these scholarships were awarded. **Funds Available:** Each scholarship provides a full waiver of tuition and fees at public institutions of higher education or public vocational schools within Idaho, an allowance of $500 per semester for books, and on-campus housing and a campus meal plan. **Duration:** Benefits are available for a maximum of 36 months.

Eligibility Requirements: Eligible for these scholarships are dependents of full-time Idaho public safety officers employed in the state who were killed or disabled in the line of duty.

804 ■ IDAHO STATE BOARD OF EDUCATION

Len B. Jordan Office Building
650 West State Street, Room 307
P.O. Box 83720
Boise, ID 83720-0037
Tel: (208)332-1574
Fax: (208)334-2632
E-mail: board@osbe.state.id.us
Web Site: http://www.idahoboardofed.org/scholarships/promisea.asp
To provide financial assistance for college or professional/technical school to outstanding high school seniors in Idaho.

Title of Award: Robert R. Lee Category A Promise Scholarship **Area, Field, or Subject:** General studies/Field of study not specified **Level of Education for which Award is Granted:** Undergraduate **Number Awarded:** Approximately 30 each year. Academic students receive 75% of the awards and professional/technical students receive 25%. **Funds Available:** The stipend is $3,000 per year. **Duration:** 1 year. Academic scholarships may be renewed for up to 3 additional years and professional/technical scholarships may be renewed for up to 2 additional years; renewal is granted only if the recipient remains enrolled full time with a rank in the top 50% of the students in the class and a GPA of 3.0 or higher.

Eligibility Requirements: This program is open to graduating high school seniors who are Idaho residents planning to enroll full time in academic or professional/technical programs in public or private institutions in the state. Academic applicants must also be in the top 10% of their class and have a cumulative GPA of 3.5 or higher and an ACT score of 28 or higher. Professional/technical applicants must have a cumulative GPA of 2.8 or higher and must take the COMPASS test (reading, writing, and algebra scores are required). U.S. citizenship is also required. **Deadline for Receipt:** December of each year. **Additional Information:** This program was formerly known as the State of Idaho Scholarship Program.

805 ■ ILLINOIS DEPARTMENT OF CHILDREN AND FAMILY SERVICES

Attn: Scholarship Coordinator
406 East Monroe Street
Springfield, IL 62701-1498
Tel: (217)785-2509
Fax: (217)524-3715
E-mail: JHamm@idcfs.state.il.us
Web Site: http://www.state.il.us/dcfs
To provide financial support for college to children under the care of the Illinois Department of Children and Family Services (DCFS).

Title of Award: Department of Children and Family Services Scholarship Program **Area, Field, or Subject:** General studies/Field of study not specified **Level of Education for which Award is Granted:** Undergraduate **Number Awarded:** 48 each year; of those, 4 are awarded to children of veterans. **Funds Available:** Scholarships provide waiver of all tuition and fees at designated universities plus a stipend equal to the standard board rate for youth of that age (recently, $444.85 per month). Funding is not provided for room, board, or dormitory fees. Children of veterans receive an additional stipend of $500. **Duration:** Up to 4 years or until students reach 21 years of age, provided they maintain full-time enrollment and a GPA of 2.0 or higher.

Eligibility Requirements: This program is open to high school seniors and students currently enrolled in college who are under guardianship of the Illinois DCFS or have left guardianship through adoption or private guardianship arrangements. Applicants must be attending or planning to attend a public institution in Illinois. Along with their application, they must submit a transcript of high school grades or a copy of their GED certificate, ACT or SAT test scores, and 3 letters of recommendation. Selection is based on scholastic record and aptitude, community and extracurricular activities, and interest in higher education. Some scholarships are reserved for the children of veterans. **Deadline for Receipt:** March of each year. **Additional Information:** Recipients may attend colleges or universities other than those designated and receive the stipend, but they are not eligible for any allowance for tuition and fees. The scholarships for children of veterans are supported by the American Legion.

806 ■ ILLINOIS DEPARTMENT OF VETERANS' AFFAIRS

833 South Spring Street
P.O. Box 19432
Springfield, IL 62794-9432
Tel: (217)782-6641
Free: 800-437-9824
Fax: (217)524-0344
E-mail: webmail@dva.state.il.us
Web Site: http://www.state.il.us/agency/dva
To provide financial assistance for college to the children of Illinois veterans (with preference given to the children of disabled or deceased veterans).

Title of Award: Illinois Honorary Scholarships **Area, Field, or Subject:** General studies/Field of study not specified **Level of Education for which Award is Granted:** Undergraduate **Number Awarded:** Each county in Illinois is entitled to award 1 scholarship. The Board of Trustees of the university may, from time to time, add to the number of honorary scholarships (when such additions will not create an unnecessary financial burden on the university). **Funds Available:** Students selected for this program receive free tuition at any branch of the University of Illinois. **Duration:** Up to 4 years.

Eligibility Requirements: Each county in the state is entitled to award an honorary scholarship to the child of a veteran of World War I, World War II, the Korean Conflict, or the Vietnam Conflict. Preference is given to children of disabled or deceased veterans.

807 ■ ILLINOIS DEPARTMENT OF VETERANS' AFFAIRS

833 South Spring Street
P.O. Box 19432
Springfield, IL 62794-9432
Tel: (217)782-6641
Free: 800-437-9824
Fax: (217)524-0344
E-mail: webmail@dva.state.il.us
Web Site: http://www.state.il.us/agency/dva
To provide financial assistance for 1) the undergraduate education of Illinois dependents of disabled or deceased veterans or those listed as prisoners of war or missing in action, and 2) the rehabilitation or education of disabled dependents of those veterans.

Title of Award: Illinois MIA/POW Scholarship **Area, Field, or Subject:** General studies/Field of study not specified **Level of Education for which Award is Granted:** Undergraduate **Number Awarded:** Varies each year. **Funds Available:** An eligible dependent is entitled to full payment of tuition and certain fees at any Illinois state-supported college, university, or community college. In lieu of that benefit, an eligible dependent who has a physical, mental, or developmental disability is entitled to receive a grant to be used to cover the cost of treating the disability at 1 or more appropriate therapeutic, rehabilitative, or educational facilities. For disabled dependents, the total benefit cannot exceed the cost equivalent of 4 calendar years of full-time enrollment, including summer terms, at the University of Illinois. **Duration:** This scholarship may be used for a period equivalent to 4 calendar years, including summer term. Dependents have 12 years from the initial term of study to complete the equivalent of 4 calendar years. Disabled dependents who elect to use the grant for rehabilitative purposes may do so as long as the total benefit does not exceed the cost equivalent of 4 calendar years of full-time enrollment at the University of Illinois.

Eligibility Requirements: This program is open to the spouses, natural children, legally adopted children, or stepchildren of a veteran or service member who 1) has been declared by the U.S. Department of Defense or the U.S. Department of Veterans Affairs to be permanently disabled from service-connected causes with 100% disability, deceased as the result of a service-connected disability, a prisoner of war, or missing in action, and 2) at the time of entering service was an Illinois resident or was an Illinois resident within 6 months of entering such service. Special support is available for dependents who are disabled. **Additional Information:** An eligible child must begin using the scholarship prior to his or her 26th birthday. An eligible spouse must begin using the scholarship prior to 10 years from the effective date of eligibility (e.g., prior to August 12, 1989 or 10 years from date of disability or death).

808 ■ ILLINOIS PORK PRODUCERS ASSOCIATION

6411 South Sixth Street Road
Springfield, IL 62712-6817
Tel: (217)529-3100
Fax: (217)529-1771
E-mail: info@ilpork.com
Web Site: http://www.ilpork.com/youth_page/scholarships.html
To provide financial assistance for college to Illinois residents who have been involved in the pork industry, especially those who are active in the Illinois Pork Producers Association (IPPA).

Title of Award: Illinois Pork Donor-Advised Fund Scholarships **Area, Field, or Subject:** General studies/Field of study not specified **Level of Education for which Award is Granted:** Undergraduate **Number Awarded:** 9 each year: 3 at each monetary level. **Funds Available:** Stipends are $1,250, $750, or $500. **Duration:** 1 year.

Eligibility Requirements: This program is open to Illinois residents who are enrolled or planning to enroll as an undergraduate student. Applicants must submit an essay (up to 3 pages) on a specific topic identifying the greatest challenge facing the Illinois pork industry. Selection is based on the essay (35 points), participation in the IPPA Ambassador Program (10 points), IPPA membership (15 points), activities (20 points), and grades (20 points). **Deadline for Receipt:** May of each year. **Additional Information:** This program was formerly limited to members of the IPPA and their families and called the IPPA Scholarships. Previous winners are only eligible to receive a scholarship of greater value.

809 ■ ILLINOIS STATE BOARD OF EDUCATION

100 North First Street
Springfield, IL 62777-0001
Tel: (217)782-4321; (866)262-6663
Fax: (217)524-4928
Web Site: http://www.isbe.net/gov-relations/html/scholarships.htm
To provide financial assistance for college to high school seniors in Illinois who are sponsored by members of the state legislature.

Title of Award: Illinois General Assembly Scholarships **Area, Field, or Subject:** General studies/Field of study not specified **Level of Education for which Award is Granted:** Undergraduate **Number Awarded:** Each state legislator awards 2 4-year scholarships or 1 4-year scholarship and 4 1-year scholarships. **Funds Available:** A stipend is awarded (amount not specified). **Duration:** Either 1 year or 4 years.

Eligibility Requirements: Illinois law provides for each state legislator, each year, to award a 4-year scholarship to the University of Illinois and a 4-year scholarship or 4 1-year scholarships to any other state-supported university. High school seniors in Illinois applying for these scholarships must be a resident within the legislative district of the awarding legislator and contact their state senator or state representative for information on the application process. **Additional Information:** If you do not know the name or phone number of your state legislator, contact your county clerk's

election office. The qualifying state-supported universities include: Chicago State University, Eastern Illinois University, Governors State University, Illinois State University, Northern Illinois University, Northeastern Illinois University, Southern Illinois University at Carbondale, Southern Illinois University at Edwardsville, University of Illinois, and Western Illinois University.

810 ■ ILLINOIS STUDENT ASSISTANCE COMMISSION

Attn: Scholarship and Grant Services
1755 Lake Cook Road
Deerfield, IL 60015-5209
Tel: (847)948-8550
Free: 800-899-ISAC
Fax: (847)831-8549
E-mail: collegezone@isac.org
Web Site: http://www.collegezone.com
To provide extra funding to holders of Illinois College Savings Bonds.

Title of Award: Illinois Bonus Incentive Grant **Area, Field, or Subject:** General studies/Field of study not specified **Level of Education for which Award is Granted:** Undergraduate **Number Awarded:** Varies each year. **Funds Available:** Grant amounts range from $40 to $440 per $5,000 of compound accreted value at maturity, depending on the maturity of the bond. Only 1 student may be designated for each bond redeemed, but the same student beneficiary may be named for up to 5 bonds with up to $25,000 of aggregate compound accreted value at maturity for each academic year. These funds are given directly to the student beneficiaries by the State of Illinois.

Eligibility Requirements: This program is open to holders of Illinois College Savings Bonds who are using the proceeds to pay for educational expenses at eligible Illinois colleges and universities. Bondholders must have continuously owned the bonds for at least 12 months preceding the date of maturity, use at least 70% of the proceeds to finance the student beneficiary's educational expenses, use the proceeds from the bonds in either the academic year in which the bonds were redeemed or the next year, and designate only 1 student beneficiary for each bond redeemed. The student beneficiary must be enrolled either half time or full time at an approved Illinois public or private 2- or 4-year college or university and not be enrolled in a program of religious studies. Financial need is not considered. **Deadline for Receipt:** May of each year. **Additional Information:** This program is dependent upon funding from the Illinois General Assembly.

811 ■ ILLINOIS STUDENT ASSISTANCE COMMISSION

Attn: Scholarship and Grant Services
1755 Lake Cook Road
Deerfield, IL 60015-5209
Tel: (847)948-8550
Free: 800-899-ISAC
Fax: (847)831-8549
E-mail: collegezone@isac.org
Web Site: http://www.collegezone.com
To provide financial assistance for college to the children or spouses of disabled or deceased Illinois correctional workers.

Title of Award: Illinois Grant Program for Dependents of Correctional Officers **Area, Field, or Subject:** General studies/Field of study not specified **Level of Education for which Award is Granted:** Undergraduate **Number Awarded:** Varies each year. **Funds Available:** The grants provide full payment of tuition and mandatory fees at approved public colleges in Illinois or an equivalent amount at private colleges. **Duration:** Up to 8 academic semesters or 12 academic quarters of study.

Eligibility Requirements: This program is open to the spouses and children of Illinois correctional officers who were at least 90% disabled or killed in the line of duty. Applicants must be enrolled on at least a half-time basis as an undergraduate at an approved Illinois public or private 2-year or 4-year college, university, or hospital school. They need not be Illinois residents at the time of application.

812 ■ ILLINOIS STUDENT ASSISTANCE COMMISSION

Attn: Scholarship and Grant Services
1755 Lake Cook Road
Deerfield, IL 60015-5209
Tel: (847)948-8550
Free: 800-899-ISAC

Fax: (847)831-8549
E-mail: collegezone@isac.org
Web Site: http://www.collegezone.com
To provide financial assistance for college or graduate school to the children or spouses of disabled or deceased Illinois police or fire officers.
Title of Award: Illinois Grant Program for Dependents of Police or Fire Officers **Area, Field, or Subject:** General studies/Field of study not specified **Level of Education for which Award is Granted:** Graduate, Undergraduate **Number Awarded:** Varies each year. **Funds Available:** The grants provide full payment of tuition and mandatory fees at approved public colleges in Illinois or an equivalent amount at private colleges. **Duration:** Up to 8 academic semesters or 12 academic quarters of study. **Eligibility Requirements:** This program is open to the spouses and children of Illinois police and fire officers who were at least 90% disabled or killed in the line of duty. Applicants must be enrolled on at least a half-time basis in either undergraduate or graduate study at an approved Illinois public or private 2-year or 4-year college, university, or hospital school. They need not be Illinois residents at the time of application.

813 ■ ILLINOIS STUDENT ASSISTANCE COMMISSION

Attn: Scholarship and Grant Services
1755 Lake Cook Road
Deerfield, IL 60015-5209
Tel: (847)948-8550
Free: 800-899-ISAC
Fax: (847)831-8549
E-mail: collegezone@isac.org
Web Site: http://www.collegezone.com
To provide financial assistance for college to outstanding students in Illinois.
Title of Award: Illinois Merit Recognition Scholarships **Area, Field, or Subject:** General studies/Field of study not specified **Level of Education for which Award is Granted:** Undergraduate **Number Awarded:** Varies each year. **Funds Available:** The stipend is $1,000. Funds may be used for payment of tuition, fees, and other educational expenses. **Duration:** 1 year; nonrenewable.
Eligibility Requirements: Eligible are Illinois high school seniors who either 1) rank in the top 5% of their class through the end of the sixth semester of high school, or 2) received a score in the top 5% of Illinois students on the ACT, SAT, or Prairie State Achievement Examination. U.S. citizenship or permanent resident status is required. Recipients must use the award within 1 year of high school graduation as at least a half-time student at an approved Illinois postsecondary institution or at 1 of the nation's 4 military service academies. Financial need is not considered in the selection process. **Deadline for Receipt:** June of the year following high school graduation. **Additional Information:** Information on this award is also available from high school counselors. The amount of funding available each year depends on action by the state legislature.

814 ■ ILLINOIS STUDENT ASSISTANCE COMMISSION

Attn: Scholarship and Grant Services
1755 Lake Cook Road
Deerfield, IL 60015-5209
Tel: (847)948-8550
Free: 800-899-ISAC
Fax: (847)831-8549
E-mail: collegezone@isac.org
Web Site: http://www.collegezone.com
To provide financial assistance to undergraduate students in Illinois.
Title of Award: Illinois Monetary Award Program **Area, Field, or Subject:** General studies/Field of study not specified **Level of Education for which Award is Granted:** Undergraduate **Number Awarded:** Varies each year. **Funds Available:** The actual dollar amount of the award depends on financial need and the cost of the recipient's schooling; in no case does the award exceed the actual cost of tuition and fees or $4,968 per year, whichever is less. The funds may be used only for tuition and mandatory fees; funds cannot be spent on books, travel, or housing. All awards are paid directly to the recipient's school. **Duration:** 1 year; may be renewed up to 4 additional years.
Eligibility Requirements: Applicants must be Illinois residents and U.S. citizens or eligible noncitizens. They must be able to demonstrate financial need, be enrolled at least half time as an undergraduate student at an approved Illinois institution of higher education, and not be in default

on any student loan. High school grades and test scores are not considered in the selection process. **Deadline for Receipt:** Funding for this program is limited. To increase your chances of receiving funding, apply as soon after the beginning of January as possible.

815 ■ ILLINOIS STUDENT ASSISTANCE COMMISSION

Attn: Scholarship and Grant Services
1755 Lake Cook Road
Deerfield, IL 60015-5209
Tel: (847)948-8550
Free: 800-899-ISAC
Fax: (847)831-8549
E-mail: collegezone@isac.org
Web Site: http://www.collegezone.com
To provide financial assistance for undergraduate or graduate education to members of the Illinois National Guard.
Title of Award: Illinois National Guard Grant Program **Area, Field, or Subject:** General studies/Field of study not specified **Level of Education for which Award is Granted:** Graduate, Undergraduate **Number Awarded:** Varies each year. **Funds Available:** Recipients are eligible for payment of tuition and some fees for either undergraduate or graduate study at an Illinois state-supported college or university. **Duration:** This assistance extends for 8 semesters or 12 quarters (or the equivalent in part-time study).
Eligibility Requirements: This program is open to members of the Illinois National Guard who are either currently active or have been active for at least 5 consecutive years, have been called to federal active duty for at least 6 months, and are within 12 months after their discharge date. Applicants must also: 1) be enlisted personnel or officers up to and including the rank of captain; 2) be enrolled at an Illinois public 2- or 4-year college or university; and 3) have served at least 1 full year in the Guard. **Deadline for Receipt:** September of each year for fall semester or quarter; February of each year for spring semester, winter quarter, or spring quarter; June of each year for summer term.

816 ■ ILLINOIS STUDENT ASSISTANCE COMMISSION

Attn: Scholarship and Grant Services
1755 Lake Cook Road
Deerfield, IL 60015-5209
Tel: (847)948-8550
Free: 800-899-ISAC
Fax: (847)831-8549
E-mail: collegezone@isac.org
Web Site: http://www.collegezone.com
To provide financial assistance for undergraduate and graduate education to Illinois veterans.
Title of Award: Illinois Veteran Grant Program **Area, Field, or Subject:** General studies/Field of study not specified **Level of Education for which Award is Granted:** Graduate, Undergraduate **Number Awarded:** Varies each year. **Funds Available:** This program pays all tuition and certain fees at all Illinois public colleges, universities, and community colleges. **Duration:** This scholarship may be used for the equivalent of up to 4 years of full-time enrollment, provided the recipient maintains the minimum GPA required by their college or university.
Eligibility Requirements: This program is open to Illinois residents who served in the U.S. armed forces (including members of the Reserves and the Illinois National Guard) for at least 1 year on active duty and have been honorably discharged. The 1-year service requirement does not apply to veterans who 1) served in a foreign country in a time of hostilities in that country, 2) were medically discharged for service-related reasons, or 3) were discharged prior to August 11, 1967. Applicants must have been Illinois residents for at least 6 months before entering service and they must have returned to Illinois within 6 months after separation from service. Current members of the Reserve Officer Training Corps are not eligible. **Deadline for Receipt:** Applications may be submitted at any time. **Additional Information:** This is an entitlement program; once eligibility has been established, no further applications are necessary.

817 ■ IMMUNE DEFICIENCY FOUNDATION

Attn: Scholarship/Medical Programs
40 West Chesapeake Avenue, Suite 308
Towson, MD 21204-4803
Tel: (410)321-6647

Free: 800-296-4433

Fax: (410)321-9165

E-mail: tb@primaryimmune.org

Web Site: http://www.primaryimmune.org/services/scholarship.htm

To provide financial assistance to undergraduates with a primary immune deficiency disease.

Title of Award: Immune Deficiency Foundation Scholarship **Area, Field, or Subject:** General studies/Field of study not specified **Level of Education for which Award is Granted:** Undergraduate **Number Awarded:** Varies each year. Recently, 43 of these scholarships were awarded. **Funds Available:** Stipends range from $750 to $2,000, depending on the recipient's financial need. **Duration:** 1 year; may be renewed.

Eligibility Requirements: This program is open to students entering or attending colleges, universities, and community colleges who have a primary immune deficiency disease. Applicants must submit an autobiographical statement, 2 letters of recommendation, a family financial statement, and a letter of verification from their immunologist. Financial need is the main factor considered in selecting the recipients and the size of the award. **Deadline for Receipt:** March of each year. **Additional Information:** This program, established in 1986, is administered by the Immune Deficiency Foundation (IDF) with funding from ZLB Behring, Baxter Healthcare Corporation, Talecris Biotherapeutics, NuFACTOR, Grifols, and Octapharma.

818 ■ INCIGHT COMPANY

Attn: Executive Director

733 S.W. Oak Street, Suite 200

Portland, OR 97205

Tel: (971)244-0305

Fax: (503)223-9488

E-mail: scholarship@incight.org

Web Site: http://www.incight.com/incight/edu1.html

To provide financial assistance for college to students who have a physical disability or impairment.

Title of Award: Incight Go-Getter Scholarship **Area, Field, or Subject:** General studies/Field of study not specified **Level of Education for which Award is Granted:** Undergraduate **Number Awarded:** 1 or more each year. **Funds Available:** A stipend is awarded (amount not specified). **Duration:** 1 year

Eligibility Requirements: This program is open to students who have a physical disability or impairment, including a learning disability or sight or hearing impairment. Applicants must have a GPA of 2.5 or higher and be entering or attending college as a full-time student. Along with their application, they must submit a 250-word essay on what they think of the word "handicrap," a term that the sponsoring organization feels is prevalent in the disabled and non-disabled communities and that it is trying to change. They must also submit another 250-word essay, either on the topic, "If you were a tree, how would you describe yourself," or on their choice of a quotation from Franklin D. Roosevelt or from Christopher Reeve. **Deadline for Receipt:** April of each year.

819 ■ INDEPENDENT BANKERS OF COLORADO

Attn: IBC Education Foundation

1580 Logan Street, Suite 510

Denver, CO 80203

Tel: (303)832-2000

Fax: (303)832-2040

Web Site: http://www.ibcbanks.org/education_forums/index.html

To provide financial assistance for college to high school seniors who are children of customers or employees of banks that are members of Independent Bankers of Colorado (IBC).

Title of Award: IBC Education Foundation Scholarships **Area, Field, or Subject:** General studies/Field of study not specified **Level of Education for which Award is Granted:** Undergraduate **Number Awarded:** 6 each year: 2 at $1,000 and 4 at $500. **Funds Available:** Stipends are $1,000 or $500. **Duration:** 1 year.

Eligibility Requirements: This program is open to high school seniors who are children of IBC member bank customers (with an account for at least 6 months) or employees. Applicants must be planning to enrolled at an institution of higher education in Colorado. They must have a GPA of

3.0 or higher. Selection is based primarily on an essay competition. **Deadline for Receipt:** March of each year.

820 ■ INDIA AMERICAN CULTURAL ASSOCIATION

1281 Cooper Lake Road, S.E.

Smyrna, GA 30082

Tel: (770)436-3719

Web Site: http://www.myiaca.org/scholarships.html

To provide financial assistance for college to high school seniors in Georgia whose parents or grandparents came from what is now India.

Title of Award: Darshan S. Bhatia Memorial Award **Area, Field, or Subject:** General studies/Field of study not specified **Level of Education for which Award is Granted:** Four Year College **Number Awarded:** 1 each year. **Funds Available:** The stipend is $1,250 per year. **Duration:** 4 years.

Eligibility Requirements: This program is open to high school seniors who 1) are living in Georgia and 2) whose parents or grandparents came from present day India. For the purposes of this program, citizens of Pakistan and Bangladesh are not included. Applicants must be planning to attend a 4-year college or university as a full-time student. Along with their application, they must submit official school transcript, resume, SAT score report, the best essay they submitted to a college to which they applied, and documentation of financial need. Selection is based primarily on financial need. **Deadline for Receipt:** May of each year. **Additional Information:** This program was established in 1993. Information is also available from the Indian American Scholarship Fund, 719 Vinings Estates Drive, Mableton, GA 30126, E-mail: manochaa@bellsouth.net. Membership in the India American Cultural Association (IACA) is not required to apply, but recipients must become members of the association.

821 ■ INDIA AMERICAN CULTURAL ASSOCIATION

1281 Cooper Lake Road, S.E.

Smyrna, GA 30082

Tel: (770)436-3719

Web Site: http://www.myiaca.org/scholarships.html

To provide financial assistance for college to high school seniors in Georgia whose parents or grandparents came from what is now India.

Title of Award: IASF Financial Aid Scholarships **Area, Field, or Subject:** General studies/Field of study not specified **Level of Education for which Award is Granted:** Undergraduate **Number Awarded:** Several each year. **Funds Available:** Stipends range from $500 to $1,250. **Duration:** 1 year; nonrenewable.

Eligibility Requirements: This program is open to high school seniors who 1) are living in Georgia and 2) whose parents or grandparents came from present day India. For the purposes of this program, citizens of Pakistan and Bangladesh are not included. Applicants must be planning to attend a 4-year college or university as a full-time student. Along with their application, they must submit official school transcript, resume, SAT score report, the best essay they submitted to a college to which they applied, and documentation of financial need. Selection is based primarily on financial need. **Deadline for Receipt:** May of each year. **Additional Information:** This program was established in 1993. Information is also available from the Indian American Scholarship Fund (IASF), 719 Vinings Estates Drive, Mableton, GA 30126, E-mail: manochaa@bellsouth.net. Membership in the India American Cultural Association (IACA) is not required to apply, but recipients must become members of the association.

822 ■ INDIA AMERICAN CULTURAL ASSOCIATION

1281 Cooper Lake Road, S.E.

Smyrna, GA 30082

Tel: (770)436-3719

Web Site: http://www.myiaca.org/scholarships.html

To provide financial assistance for college to high school seniors in Georgia whose parents or grandparents came from what is now India.

Title of Award: Indian American Scholarship Fund Merit Scholarships **Area, Field, or Subject:** General studies/Field of study not specified **Level of Education for which Award is Granted:** Four Year College **Number Awarded:** Several each year. **Funds Available:** Stipends range from $500 to $1,250. **Duration:** 1 year; nonrenewable.

Eligibility Requirements: This program is open to high school seniors who 1) are living in Georgia and 2) whose parents or grandparents came from present day India. For the purposes of this program, citizens of

Pakistan and Bangladesh are not included. Applicants must be planning to attend a 4-year college or university as a full-time student. Along with their application, they must submit official school transcript, resume, SAT score report, and the best essay they submitted to a college to which they applied. Financial need is not considered in the selection process. **Deadline for Receipt:** April of each year. **Additional Information:** This program was established in 1993. Information is also available from the Indian American Scholarship Fund (IASF), 719 Vinings Estates Drive, Mableton, GA 30126, E-mail: manochaa@bellsouth.net. Membership in the India American Cultural Association (IACA) is not required to apply, but recipients must become members of the association.

823 ■ INDIA AMERICAN CULTURAL ASSOCIATION

1281 Cooper Lake Road, S.E.
Smyrna, GA 30082
Tel: (770)436-3719
Web Site: http://www.myiaca.org/scholarships.html
To provide financial assistance for college to high school seniors in Georgia whose parents or grandparents came from what is now India.
Title of Award: Jasumati B. Patel Memorial Award **Area, Field, or Subject:** General studies/Field of study not specified **Level of Education for which Award is Granted:** Four Year College **Number Awarded:** 1 each year. **Funds Available:** The stipend is $1,000 per year. **Duration:** 4 years.
Eligibility Requirements: This program is open to high school seniors who 1) are living in Georgia and 2) whose parents or grandparents came from present day India. For the purposes of this program, citizens of Pakistan and Bangladesh are not included. Applicants must be planning to attend a 4-year college or university as a full-time student. Along with their application, they must submit official school transcript, resume, SAT score report, the best essay they submitted to a college to which they applied, and documentation of financial need. Selection is based on financial need and academic excellence. **Deadline for Receipt:** May of each year. **Additional Information:** This program was established in 1993. Information is also available from the Indian American Scholarship Fund, 719 Vinings Estates Drive, Mableton, GA 30126, E-mail: manochaa@bellsouth.net. Membership in the India American Cultural Association (IACA) is not required to apply, but recipients must become members of the association.

824 ■ INDIA AMERICAN CULTURAL ASSOCIATION

1281 Cooper Lake Road, S.E.
Smyrna, GA 30082
Tel: (770)436-3719
Web Site: http://www.myiaca.org/scholarships.html
To provide financial assistance for college to high school seniors in Georgia whose parents or grandparents came from what is now India.
Title of Award: P.V. Jagannatha Rao Memorial Award **Area, Field, or Subject:** General studies/Field of study not specified **Level of Education for which Award is Granted:** Four Year College **Number Awarded:** 1 each year. **Funds Available:** The stipend is $1,250 per year. **Duration:** 4 years.
Eligibility Requirements: This program is open to high school seniors who 1) are living in Georgia and 2) whose parents or grandparents came from present day India. For the purposes of this program, citizens of Pakistan and Bangladesh are not included. Applicants must be planning to attend a 4-year college or university as a full-time student. Along with their application, they must submit official school transcript, resume, SAT score report, the best essay they submitted to a college to which they applied, and documentation of financial need. Selection is based on financial need and demonstrated excellence and dedication in a particular endeavor. **Deadline for Receipt:** May of each year. **Additional Information:** This program was established in 1993. Information is also available from the Indian American Scholarship Fund, 719 Vinings Estates Drive, Mableton, GA 30126, E-mail: manochaa@bellsouth.net. Membership in the India American Cultural Association (IACA) is not required to apply, but recipients must become members of the association.

825 ■ INDIANA DEPARTMENT OF VETERANS' AFFAIRS

302 West Washington Street, Room E-120
Indianapolis, IN 46204-2738
Tel: (317)232-3910
Free: 800-400-4520
Fax: (317)232-7721
E-mail: jkiser@dva.state.in.us
Web Site: http://www.in.gov/veteran/sso/brochure/remission.html
To enable the children of disabled and other Indiana veterans to attend public colleges and universities in the state without payment of tuition.
Title of Award: Remission of Fees for Children of Indiana Veterans **Area, Field, or Subject:** General studies/Field of study not specified **Level of Education for which Award is Granted:** Graduate, Undergraduate **Number Awarded:** Varies each year. **Funds Available:** Qualified students receive remission of 100% of tuition and mandatory fees. **Duration:** Fees are remitted for up to 124 semester hours of education.
Eligibility Requirements: This program is open to natural and legally-adopted children of veterans who served on active duty in the U.S. armed forces during a period of wartime and have been residents of Indiana for at least 36 consecutive months during their lifetimes. The veteran must 1) be rated as 10% or greater service-connected disabled by the U.S. Department of Veterans Affairs or a military service; 2) have received a Purple Heart Medal; or 3) have been a resident of Indiana at the time of entry into the service and declared a prisoner of war (POW) or missing in action (MIA) after January 1, 1960. Students who were veteran-related pupils at the Indiana Soldiers' and Sailors' Children's Home are also eligible. Applicants must be attending or planning to attend a state-supported postsecondary college or university in Indiana as an undergraduate or graduate student. **Deadline for Receipt:** Requests for assistance may be submitted at any time.

826 ■ INTERNATIONAL ASSOCIATION OF CULINARY PROFESSIONALS FOUNDATION

Attn: Culinary Trust Scholarship Program
304 West Liberty Street, Suite 201
Louisville, KY 40202
Tel: (502)581-9786
Free: 800-928-4227
Fax: (502)589-3602
E-mail: tgribbins@hqtrs.com
Web Site: http://www.iacpfoundation.org/html/scholarships.html
To provide financial assistance to culinary professionals and students interested in pursuing additional training in the United States or abroad in the culinary arts.
Title of Award: Culinary Trust Scholarships **Area, Field, or Subject:** Culinary arts **Level of Education for which Award is Granted:** Master's, Professional, Undergraduate **Number Awarded:** Varies each year. **Funds Available:** Stipends range from $1,500 to $5,000. **Duration:** 1 year.
Eligibility Requirements: This program is open to 1) culinary professionals who have at least 2 years of food service experience (paid, volunteer, or a combination of both); and 2) students who have a GPA of 3.0 or higher. Applicants must submit 2 letters of recommendation and a 2-page essay on their educational and career goals and how they plan to achieve them. They may be from any country. Selection is based on merit, food service work experience, culinary goals and skills, and references. **Deadline for Receipt:** December of each year. **Additional Information:** This program includes a number of named scholarships that varies each year, many of them for specified culinary arts schools. Recently, support was available at L'Academie de Cuisine (Gaithersburg, Maryland), the Art Institute of New York City, the Institute of Culinary Education (New York, New York), the Singapore Cooking School and Spice Garden, Le Cordon Bleu London, Le Cordon Bleu Mexico, Le Cordon Bleu Paris, Le Cordon Bleu Sydney, Le Cordon Bleu Australia (Adelaide), Le Cordon Bleu Ottawa, New England Culinary Institute (Montpelier, Vermont), the French Culinary Institute (New York, New York), and the Culinary Institute of America at Greystone (St. Helena, California). Other scholarships included the Cuisinart Scholarship for students of any nationality at any accredited culinary school, the Charlie Trotter Culinary Education Foundation Scholarship for residents of Illinois, the Julia Child Endowment Fund Scholarship for independent study in France, and the Julia Child Fund at the Boston Foundation Scholarship for research, writing, or teaching in France. There is a $25 application fee.

827 ■ INTERNATIONAL ASSOCIATION OF MACHINISTS AND AEROSPACE WORKERS

Attn: IAM Scholarship Program
9000 Machinists Place, Room 117
Upper Marlboro, MD 20772-2687

Tel: (301)967-4500
Web Site: http://www.iamaw.org
To provide financial assistance for college to members and children of members of the International Association of Machinists and Aerospace Workers (IAM).
Title of Award: IAM Scholarship Competition **Area, Field, or Subject:** General studies/Field of study not specified **Level of Education for which Award is Granted:** Undergraduate **Number Awarded:** Varies each year, depending on the availability of funds; recently, 3 members and 13 children received scholarships. **Funds Available:** Awards to members are $2,000 per year. Awards to children attending college are $1,000 per year. Awards to children attending vocational/technical school are $2,000 per year. **Duration:** 1 year. For students in college, awards may be renewed up to 3 additional years or until completion of a bachelor's degree, whichever occurs first. For students in vocational/technical school, awards may be renewed 1 additional year or until certification, whichever occurs first.
Eligibility Requirements: This program is open to IAM members with 2 years of continuous good standing in the union in the United States or Canada, and their children, stepchildren, or legally adopted children. Members must be working in a company under contract with the IAM and expect to continue this work until entering school; they may be entering college as a freshman or some higher undergraduate level. Children of members must be graduating high school seniors; the qualifying parent must be living or must have died after the child entered high school. Scholarships are not available to applicants who do not intend to work without interruption for a bachelor's degree or a vocational/technical school certification, to members' children who are attending or have already attended college, to children of members on the payroll of the Grand Lodge, or to graduate students. Selection is based on grades, attitude toward study, personal references, available test scores, the opinion of counselors and teachers, and activities outside of school; for member applicants, weight also is given to participation in local lodge activities.
Deadline for Receipt: February of each year. **Additional Information:** This scholarship fund was established in 1960.

828 ■ INTERNATIONAL BROTHERHOOD OF BOILERMAKERS, IRON SHIP BUILDERS, BLACKSMITHS, FORGERS AND HELPERS

Attn: Scholarship Program
753 State Avenue, Suite 570
Kansas City, KS 66101
Tel: (913)371-2640
Fax: (913)281-8101
Web Site: http://www.boilermakers.org
To provide financial assistance for college to the dependents of members of the International Brotherhood of Boilermakers, Iron Ship Builders, Blacksmiths, Forgers and Helpers.
Title of Award: International Brotherhood of Boilermakers Scholarship Program **Area, Field, or Subject:** General studies/Field of study not specified **Level of Education for which Award is Granted:** Undergraduate **Number Awarded:** Varies each year. Recently, 37 of these scholarships were awarded: 1 at $5,000, 2 at $4,000, 2 at $3,000, 4 at $2,000, and 28 at $1,000 (including scholarships from the Canadian Federation of Labour and local lodges). **Funds Available:** The stipends range from $1,000 to $5,000; funds are paid directly to the financial aid office of the recipient's accredited college or university. **Duration:** 1 year.
Eligibility Requirements: This program is open to dependents of union members in good standing (including dependents of retired, disabled, or deceased members). Applicants must be high school seniors who will be entering their first year of a 2-year or 4-year program at a degree-granting, accredited college or university. They must submit ACT or SAT scores, high school transcripts, and a 300- to 500-word essay on a topic that changes annually (recently: "What should be the role of labor in local or national legislative issues that affect workers?"). Selection is based on academic achievement, performance on the essay, career goals, outside school activities, and extracurricular activities. **Deadline for Receipt:** March of each year. **Additional Information:** Applications are available only from local lodges of the union.

829 ■ INTERNATIONAL CINEMATOGRAPHERS GUILD

Attn: Scholarships
7755 Sunset Boulevard
Los Angeles, CA 90046

Tel: (323)876-0160
Fax: (323)876-6383
Web Site: http://www.cameraguild.com
To provide financial assistance for college or graduate school to children and grandchildren of members of the International Cinematographers Guild (ICG).
Title of Award: International Cinematographers Guild Scholarships **Area, Field, or Subject:** General studies/Field of study not specified **Level of Education for which Award is Granted:** Graduate, Undergraduate **Number Awarded:** 10 each year. **Funds Available:** The stipend is $1,500. **Duration:** 1 year.
Eligibility Requirements: This program is open to high school seniors and students in a postsecondary educational program who are the children or grandchildren of ICG members in good standing. Applicants must be attending or planning to attend, as a full-time student, an accredited college, university, graduate school, junior college, conservatory, or technical school. Along with their application, they must submit a 2-page essay on what they care about, their passion, and how those things relate to their academic, extracurricular, or employment life. They may also submit a second optional essay on other matters they want the selection committee to consider, such as their financial need or special circumstances. **Deadline for Receipt:** January of each year.

830 ■ INTERNATIONAL FACILITY MANAGEMENT ASSOCIATION

Attn: IFMA Foundation
1 East Greenway Plaza, Suite 1100
Houston, TX 77046
Tel: (713)623-4362
Fax: (713)623-6124
E-mail: foundation@ifmafoundation.org
Web Site: http://www.ifmafoundation.org
To provide financial assistance to undergraduate and graduate students working on a degree in facility management.
Title of Award: IFMA Foundation Scholarships **Area, Field, or Subject:** Management **Level of Education for which Award is Granted:** Four Year College, Graduate **Number Awarded:** Varies each year. Recently, 15 of these scholarships were awarded: 1 at $5,000, 4 at $3,000, 1 at $2,500, 1 at $1,500, and 8 at $1,000. Since the foundation was established, it has awarded 123 scholarships worth $230,000. **Funds Available:** Stipends range from $1,000 to $5,000. **Duration:** 1 year.
Eligibility Requirements: This program is open to students enrolled full time at an accredited 4-year college or university in an undergraduate or graduate program in facility management or a related field. Undergraduates must have completed at least 2 years of study and have a GPA of 3.0 or higher. Graduate students must have a GPA of 3.5 or higher. Applicants may not be currently employed full time in facility management. Selection is based on a letter of intent, resume, achievement, accomplishments, involvement, and faculty appraisals; financial need is not considered. **Additional Information:** The IFMA Foundation was established in 1990. Its programs include the following named awards: the Barbara Pryor Scholarship, the Doug Underwood Scholarship, the George Graves Scholarship, and the Lee Forrest Scholarship.

831 ■ INTERNATIONAL FEDERATION OF PROFESSIONAL AND TECHNICAL ENGINEERS

Attn: IFPTE Scholarships
8630 Fenton Street, Suite 400
Silver Spring, MD 20910
Tel: (301)565-9016
Fax: (301)565-0018
Web Site: http://www.ifpte.org/Member%20Tools/benefits_scholarshipspre.htm
To provide financial assistance for college to the children and grandchildren of members of the International Federation of Professional and Technical Engineers (IFPTE).
Title of Award: IFPTE Scholarships **Area, Field, or Subject:** General studies/Field of study not specified **Level of Education for which Award is Granted:** Undergraduate **Number Awarded:** 3 each year: 1 each to children or grandchildren of members employed in the private, public, and federal sectors. **Funds Available:** The stipend is $1,500. Funds must be used for tuition. **Duration:** 1 year.
Eligibility Requirements: This program is open to high school seniors whose parents or grandparents belong to IFPTE. Applicants must wish to

continue their education beyond high school (in accredited public or private colleges or universities, community colleges, or technical institutes). They must submit an official transcript, 3 letters of recommendation, an essay (at least 500 words) on "What Being a Member of a Union Family Has Meant to Me," and a completed application form. Evidence of standardized test scores is optional. Selection is based on the essay (40%), academic achievement (20%), and school and community activities (40%). **Deadline for Receipt:** March of each year.

832 ■ INTERNATIONAL METAL DECORATORS ASSOCIATION

Attn: Director
9616 Deereco Road
Timonium, MD 21093
Tel: (410)252-5205
Fax: (410)628-8079
Web Site: http://www.nmda.org
To provide financial assistance for college to members of the International Metal Decorators Association (IMDA) and their families.

Title of Award: IMDA Scholarship Program **Area, Field, or Subject:** General studies/Field of study not specified **Level of Education for which Award is Granted:** Undergraduate **Number Awarded:** 1 or more each year. **Funds Available:** A stipend is awarded (amount not specified). Funds are paid directly to the recipient's school. **Duration:** 1 year.

Eligibility Requirements: This program is open to IMDA members and their families. Applicants must be interested in attending college or an industry-related seminar to enhance their trade knowledge. **Deadline for Receipt:** March of each year.

833 ■ INTERNATIONAL ORDER OF THE GOLDEN RULE

Attn: Education Department
P.O. Box 28689
St. Louis, MO 63146-1189
Tel: (314)209-7412
Free: 800-637-8030
Fax: (314)209-1289
E-mail: education@ogr.org
Web Site: http://www.ogr.org/scholarships.php
To provide financial assistance to students majoring in mortuary science.

Title of Award: OGR Awards of Excellence Scholarships **Area, Field, or Subject:** Mortuary science **Level of Education for which Award is Granted:** Undergraduate **Number Awarded:** 3 each year. **Funds Available:** Stipends are $2,500, $1,500, or $500. **Duration:** 1 year.

Eligibility Requirements: This program is open to students majoring in mortuary science in their final semester of study. Applicants must have a GPA of 3.0 or higher and be able to demonstrate financial need. They must submit an essay of 150 words or less on what they hope to achieve during their funeral service career. **Deadline for Receipt:** September of each year.

834 ■ INTERNATIONAL PUBLISHING MANAGEMENT ASSOCIATION

Attn: Scholarship
1205 West College Street
Liberty, MO 64068
Tel: (816)781-1111
Fax: (816)781-2790
E-mail: ipmainfo@ipma.org
Web Site: http://www.ipma.org/brahney_award.html
To provide financial assistance to members of the International Publishing Management Association (IMPA) and their descendants who are interested in taking courses related to publishing in college.

Title of Award: James M. Brahney Scholarships **Area, Field, or Subject:** Publishing **Level of Education for which Award is Granted:** Undergraduate **Number Awarded:** 5 each year. **Funds Available:** The stipend is $1,000. **Duration:** 1 year.

Eligibility Requirements: This program is open to IPMA members and their children and grandchildren. Applicants must be attending or planning to attend a college, university, or technical school that offers courses applicable to in-house corporate publishing. Along with their application, they

must submit information on the program that they are proposing to study and their career plans. **Deadline for Receipt:** January of each year.

835 ■ INTERNATIONAL UNION OF BRICKLAYERS AND ALLIED CRAFTSWORKERS

Attn: Education Department
1776 Eye Street, N.W.
Washington, DC 20006
Tel: (202)783-3788; 888-880-8BAC
E-mail: askbac@bacweb.org
Web Site: http://www.bacweb.org
To provide financial assistance to children of members of the International Union of Bricklayers and Allied Craftsworkers (BAC) who wish to work on a college degree.

Title of Award: Harry C. Bates Scholarship Program **Area, Field, or Subject:** General studies/Field of study not specified **Level of Education for which Award is Granted:** Undergraduate **Number Awarded:** 4 each year: 2 to Americans and 2 to Canadians. **Funds Available:** The stipend for U.S. students is $2,000 per year; the stipends for Canadians are $C1,500 or $C1,200 per year. **Duration:** 4 years.

Eligibility Requirements: This competition is open to the children (natural or legally adopted) of members of the union. To compete, U.S. students must take the Preliminary Scholastic Assessment Test (PSAT/NMSQT) during their junior year in high school. Students will be notified in September of their senior year if their PSAT/NMSQT results qualify them as a semifinalist. Union members whose children qualify must report this information to the union. The union then sends the names of eligible candidates to the National Merit Scholarship Corporation (NMSC). The recipient in the scholarship competition is chosen by NMSC. Selection is based on high school academic record, test scores, leadership qualities, and significant accomplishments. Canadian students must submit a formal application to the Association of Universities and Colleges of Canada, which administers the program in Canada. **Deadline for Receipt:** February of each year. **Additional Information:** Information and applications for Canadians are available from the BAC Canadian Office, Attn: Joseph Bognar, 141 Laurier Avenue West, Unit A, Ottawa, Ontario K1P 5J3, Canada, (877) 276-7774.

836 ■ INTERNATIONAL UNION OF ELECTRONIC, ELECTRICAL, SALARIED, MACHINE, AND FURNITURE WORKERS

Attn: IUE-CWA International Scholarship Program
501 Third Street, N.W., Suite 975
Washington, DC 20001
Tel: (202)434-1417
Fax: (202)434-1250
E-mail: bgray@iue-cwa.org
Web Site: http://www.iue-cwa.org/skills.html
To provide financial assistance for undergraduate education to children and grandchildren of members and employees of the International Union of Electronic, Electrical, Salaried, Machine, and Furniture Workers (IUE)-Communications Workers of America (CWA).

Title of Award: James B. Carey Scholarships **Area, Field, or Subject:** General studies/Field of study not specified **Level of Education for which Award is Granted:** Undergraduate **Number Awarded:** 9 each year: 8 divided among the 6 union districts and 1 at large. **Funds Available:** The stipend is $1,000 per year. **Duration:** 1 year.

Eligibility Requirements: This program is open to children and grandchildren of IUE-CWA members and employees (including retired or deceased members or employees). Applicants must be accepted for admission or already enrolled as full-time students at an accredited college, university, nursing school, or technical school offering college credit classes. Along with their application, they must submit an academic transcript (including rank in class, GPA, and SAT/ACT scores); a short statement of interests and civic activities; an essay (300 to 500 words) describing their career goals and aspirations, highlighting their relationship with the union and the labor movement, and explaining why they are deserving of a union scholarship. They must also have demonstrated a commitment to equality of opportunity for all, a concern for improving the quality of life for all people, an interest in service to the community, good character, leadership ability, and a desire to improve and move ahead. **Deadline for Receipt:** March of each year.

837 ■ INTERNATIONAL UNION OF ELECTRONIC, ELECTRICAL, SALARIED, MACHINE, AND FURNITURE WORKERS

Attn: IUE-CWA International Scholarship Program
501 Third Street, N.W., Suite 975
Washington, DC 20001
Tel: (202)434-1417
Fax: (202)434-1250
E-mail: bgray@iue-cwa.org
Web Site: http://www.iue-cwa.org/skills.html
To provide financial assistance for undergraduate education to children and grandchildren of members and employees of the International Union of Electronic, Electrical, Salaried, Machine, and Furniture Workers (IUE)-Communications Workers of America (CWA).

Title of Award: Sal Ingrassia Scholarship **Area, Field, or Subject:** General studies/Field of study not specified **Level of Education for which Award is Granted:** Undergraduate **Number Awarded:** 1 each year. **Funds Available:** The stipend is $2,500 per year. **Duration:** 1 year. **Eligibility Requirements:** This program is open to children and grandchildren of IUE-CWA members and employees. Applicants must be accepted for admission or already enrolled as full-time students at an accredited college, university, nursing school, or technical school offering college credit classes. Along with their application, they must submit an academic transcript (including rank in class, GPA, and SAT/ACT scores); a short statement of interests and civic activities; an essay (300 to 500 words) describing their career goals and aspirations, highlighting their relationship with the union and the labor movement, and explaining why they are deserving of a union scholarship. They must also have demonstrated a commitment to equality of opportunity for all, a concern for improving the quality of life for all people, an interest in service to the community, good character, leadership ability, and a desire to improve and move ahead. **Deadline for Receipt:** March of each year.

838 ■ INTERNATIONAL UNION OF ELECTRONIC, ELECTRICAL, SALARIED, MACHINE, AND FURNITURE WORKERS

Attn: IUE-CWA International Scholarship Program
501 Third Street, N.W., Suite 975
Washington, DC 20001
Tel: (202)434-1417
Fax: (202)434-1250
E-mail: bgray@iue-cwa.org
Web Site: http://www.iue-cwa.org/skills.html
To provide financial assistance for undergraduate education to the children and grandchildren of officials of the International Union of Electronic, Electrical, Salaried, Machine, and Furniture Workers (IUE)-Communications Workers of America (CWA).

Title of Award: Paul Jennings Scholarship **Area, Field, or Subject:** General studies/Field of study not specified **Level of Education for which Award is Granted:** Undergraduate **Number Awarded:** 1 each year. **Funds Available:** The stipend is $3,000 per year. **Duration:** 1 year. **Eligibility Requirements:** This program is open to children and grandchildren of IUE-CWA members who are now or have been union elected officials. Applicants must be accepted for admission or already enrolled as full-time students at an accredited college, university, nursing school, or technical school offering college credit courses. Families of full-time international union officers or employees are not eligible to apply. Along with their application, they must submit an academic transcript (including rank in class, GPA, and SAT/ACT scores); a short statement of interests and civic activities; an essay (300 to 500 words) describing their career goals and aspirations, highlighting their relationship with the union and the labor movement, and explaining why they are deserving of a union scholarship. They must also have demonstrated a commitment to equality of opportunity for all, a concern for improving the quality of life for all people, interest in service to the community, good character, leadership ability, and a desire to improve and move ahead. **Deadline for Receipt:** March of each year.

839 ■ INTERNATIONAL UNION OF ELECTRONIC, ELECTRICAL, SALARIED, MACHINE, AND FURNITURE WORKERS

Attn: IUE-CWA International Scholarship Program
501 Third Street, N.W., Suite 975
Washington, DC 20001

Tel: (202)434-1417
Fax: (202)434-1250
E-mail: bgray@iue-cwa.org
Web Site: http://www.iue-cwa.org/skills.html
To provide financial assistance for undergraduate education to children of members of the Automotive Conference Board of the International Union of Electronic, Electrical, Salaried, Machine, and Furniture Workers (IUE)-Communications Workers of America (CWA).

Title of Award: Robert L. Livingston Scholarships **Area, Field, or Subject:** General studies/Field of study not specified **Level of Education for which Award is Granted:** Undergraduate **Number Awarded:** 2 each year. **Funds Available:** The stipend is $1,500 per year. **Duration:** 1 year. **Eligibility Requirements:** This program is open to children of IUE-CWA Automotive Conference Board members. Applicants must be accepted for admission or already enrolled as full-time students at an accredited college, university, nursing school, or technical school offering college credit classes. Along with their application, they must submit a short statement of interests and goals, including career objectives, civic commitment and activities, and extracurricular activities. They must also have demonstrated a commitment to equality of opportunity for all, a concern for improving the quality of life for all people, an interest in service to the community, good character, leadership ability, and a desire to improve and move ahead. **Deadline for Receipt:** March of each year.

840 ■ INTERNATIONAL UNION OF ELECTRONIC, ELECTRICAL, SALARIED, MACHINE, AND FURNITURE WORKERS

Attn: IUE-CWA International Scholarship Program
501 Third Street, N.W., Suite 975
Washington, DC 20001
Tel: (202)434-1417
Fax: (202)434-1250
E-mail: bgray@iue-cwa.org
Web Site: http://www.iue-cwa.org/skills.html
To provide financial assistance for undergraduate education to children and grandchildren of members and employees of the International Union of Electronic, Electrical, Salaried, Machine, and Furniture Workers (IUE)-Communications Workers of America (CWA).

Title of Award: Willie Rudd Scholarship **Area, Field, or Subject:** General studies/Field of study not specified **Level of Education for which Award is Granted:** Undergraduate **Number Awarded:** 1 each year. **Funds Available:** The stipend is $1,000 per year. **Duration:** 1 year. **Eligibility Requirements:** This program is open to children and grandchildren of IUE-CWA members and employees. Applicants must be accepted for admission or already enrolled as full-time students at an accredited college, university, nursing school, or technical school offering college credit classes. Along with their application, they must submit an academic transcript (including rank in class, GPA, and SAT/ACT scores); a short statement of interests and civic activities; an essay (300 to 500 words) describing their career goals and aspirations, highlighting their relationship with the union and the labor movement, and explaining why they are deserving of a union scholarship. They must also have demonstrated a commitment to equality of opportunity for all, a concern for improving the quality of life for all people, good character, leadership ability, and a desire to improve and move ahead. **Deadline for Receipt:** March of each year.

841 ■ INTERNATIONAL UNION OF ELECTRONIC, ELECTRICAL, SALARIED, MACHINE, AND FURNITURE WORKERS

Attn: IUE-CWA International Scholarship Program
501 Third Street, N.W., Suite 975
Washington, DC 20001
Tel: (202)434-1417
Fax: (202)434-1250
E-mail: bgray@iue-cwa.org
Web Site: http://www.iue-cwa.org/skills.html
To provide financial assistance for undergraduate education to children and grandchildren of members and employees of the International Union of Electronic, Electrical, Salaried, Machine, and Furniture Workers (IUE)-Communications Workers of America (CWA).

Title of Award: Bruce Van Ess Scholarship **Area, Field, or Subject:** General studies/Field of study not specified **Level of Education for which Award is Granted:** Undergraduate **Number Awarded:** 1 each year. **Funds Available:** The stipend is $2,500 per year. **Duration:** 1 year.

Eligibility Requirements: This program is open to children and grandchildren of IUE-CWA members and employees. Applicants must be accepted for admission or already enrolled as full-time students at an accredited college, university, nursing school, or technical school offering college credit classes. Along with their application, they must submit an academic transcript (including rank in class, GPA, and SAT/ACT scores); a short statement of interests and civic activities; an essay (300 to 500 words) describing their career goals and aspirations, highlighting their relationship with the union and the labor movement, and explaining why they are deserving of a union scholarship. They must also have demonstrated a commitment to equality of opportunity for all, a concern for improving the quality of life for all people, an interest in service to the community, good character, leadership ability, and a desire to improve and move ahead. **Deadline for Receipt:** March of each year.

842 ■ IOWA GIRLS' HIGH SCHOOL ATHLETIC UNION

Attn: Scholarships
2900 Grand Avenue
P.O. Box 10348
Des Moines, IA 50306-0348
Tel: (515)288-9741
Fax: (515)284-1969
E-mail: lisa@ighsau.org
Web Site: http://www.ighsau.org
To provide financial assistance to female high school seniors in Iowa who have participated in athletics and plan to attend college in the state.
Title of Award: E. Wayne Cooley Scholarship Award **Area, Field, or Subject:** General studies/Field of study not specified **Level of Education for which Award is Granted:** Undergraduate **Number Awarded:** 1 each year. **Funds Available:** The stipend is $3,750 per year. **Duration:** 4 years, provided the recipient maintains at least a 2.5 GPA while enrolled in college.
Eligibility Requirements: This program is open to females graduating from high schools in Iowa who have a GPA of 3.75 or higher. Applicants must 1) have earned a varsity letter in at least 2 different sports, 2) be a first team all-conference selection, and/or 3) have participated in a state tournament in at least 1 sport. They must be planning to attend a college or university in Iowa. Each high school in the state may nominate 1 student. Selection is based on academic achievements, athletic accomplishments, non-sports extracurricular activities, and community involvement. **Deadline for Receipt:** December of each year.

843 ■ IOWA GIRLS' HIGH SCHOOL ATHLETIC UNION

Attn: Scholarships
2900 Grand Avenue
P.O. Box 10348
Des Moines, IA 50306-0348
Tel: (515)288-9741
Fax: (515)284-1969
E-mail: lisa@ighsau.org
Web Site: http://www.ighsau.org
To provide financial assistance to female high school seniors in Iowa who have participated in athletics and plan to attend college in the state.
Title of Award: Robert Smiley Scholarship **Area, Field, or Subject:** General studies/Field of study not specified **Level of Education for which Award is Granted:** Undergraduate **Number Awarded:** 1 each year. **Funds Available:** The stipend is $1,000. **Duration:** 1 year.
Eligibility Requirements: This program is open to females graduating from high schools in Iowa who have lettered in 1 varsity sport sponsored by the Iowa Girls' High School Athletic Union (IGHSAU) each year of high school and have a GPA of 2.5 or higher. Applicants must be planning to attend a college or university in Iowa. Each high school in the state may nominate 1 student. Selection is based on academic achievements, athletic accomplishments, non-sports extracurricular activities, and community involvement. **Deadline for Receipt:** January of each year.

844 ■ IOWA NATIONAL GUARD

Attn: Education Services Office
7105 N.W. 70th Avenue
Johnston, IA 50131-1824
Tel: (515)252-4468
Free: 800-294-6607
Fax: (515)252-4656

E-mail: kingr@ia-arng.ngb.army.mil
Web Site: http://www.iowanationalguard.com/Education/
TuitionAssistance.htm
To provide financial assistance to members of the Iowa National Guard who wish to attend college.
Title of Award: Iowa National Guard Educational Assistance Program **Area, Field, or Subject:** General studies/Field of study not specified **Level of Education for which Award is Granted:** Undergraduate **Number Awarded:** Varies each year, depending on the availability of funds. Assistance is provided on a first-come, first-served basis. **Funds Available:** Awards provide payment of 100% of tuition, to a maximum of $2,701 per semester for full-time enrollment or $196 per semester hour for part-time enrollment. Funds may be used for any educational expense, including tuition, room, board, supplies, books, fees, and other associated costs. **Duration:** 1 year; may be renewed.
Eligibility Requirements: This program is open to residents of Iowa who are members of an Iowa Army or Air National Guard unit. Applicants must have satisfactorily completed Initial Active Duty for Training (IADT), have maintained satisfactory performance of duty (including attending a minimum 90% of scheduled drill dates and scheduled annual training in the preceding 12 months), have maintained satisfactory academic progress as determined by their academic institution, and not have completed their baccalaureate degree. They may be seeking to attend a state-supported university, community college, or participating private accredited institution of postsecondary education located in Iowa. **Deadline for Receipt:** All applications received by August of each year are funded; applications received in September or later are approved if funds are available. **Additional Information:** This program was established in 1999.

845 ■ IOWA SCOTTISH RITE MASONIC EDUCATIONAL FUND

Attn: Office of Secretary-Treasurer
316 East College Street
Iowa City, IA 52240
Tel: (319)338-8181
To provide loans to undergraduate and graduate students residing in or attending school in Iowa.
Title of Award: Iowa Scottish Rite Masonic Educational Loans **Area, Field, or Subject:** General studies/Field of study not specified **Level of Education for which Award is Granted:** Graduate, Undergraduate **Number Awarded:** Varies each year. **Funds Available:** Students may borrow up to $2,000 per year (lifetime maximum: $6,000). Principal payments need not be made until the recipient's education is completed or discontinued. The interest rate charged is 6% per year. Payments should be made semiannually. **Duration:** 1 year; recipients may reapply.
Eligibility Requirements: These loans are intended for Iowa residents attending colleges and universities in the state. In certain circumstances, however, they may also be available to residents attending out-of-state schools and out-of-state students attending a college or university in Iowa. Applicants must be able to document financial need and must be at least sophomores in college. They must have a GPA of 2.75 or higher if a college sophomore or 2.5 or higher if a junior, senior, or graduate student. A transcript must be submitted, along with 3 character references.

846 ■ IOWA SPORTS TURF MANAGER'S ASSOCIATION

c/o Iowa Turf Office
17017 U.S. Highway 69
Ames, IA 50010-9294
Tel: (515)232-8222
Free: 800-605-0420
Fax: (515)232-8228
Web Site: http://www.iowaturfgrass.org/istma/istmascholarships.htm
To provide financial assistance to students enrolled or planning to enroll in a turfgrass management program at a college or university in Iowa.
Title of Award: ISTMA Scholarships **Area, Field, or Subject:** Turfgrass management **Level of Education for which Award is Granted:** Undergraduate **Number Awarded:** 1 or more each year. **Funds Available:** A stipend is awarded (amount not specified). **Duration:** 1 year.
Eligibility Requirements: This program is open to 1) seniors at high schools in Iowa planning to enroll in turfgrass management or a related program at a university, college, area technical school, or community college in Iowa; and 2) students already enrolled in such a program. Applicants must submit answers to essay questions on what stimulated their

initial interest in the sports turf management profession, what they expect from a career as a sports turf manager, and their goals in the next 10 years. Selection is based on their answers to those essay questions, academic excellence and GPA, appropriateness of career preparation, potential to make an outstanding professional contribution, class rank, and reports from academic advisors and employers. Financial need is also considered. **Deadline for Receipt:** October of each year.

847 ■ JAPANESE AMERICAN CITIZENS LEAGUE-ARIZONA CHAPTER

c/o Michele Namba, Scholarship Committee Secretary
5414 West Glenn Drive
Glendale, AZ 85301
E-mail: webmaster@azjacl.org
Web Site: http://www.azjacl.org
To provide financial assistance to graduating high school seniors in Arizona who are of Japanese heritage.
Title of Award: Sara Hutchings Clardy Scholarship Awards **Area, Field, or Subject:** General studies/Field of study not specified **Level of Education for which Award is Granted:** Undergraduate **Number Awarded:** 4 each year. **Funds Available:** A stipend is awarded (amount not specified). **Duration:** 1 year.
Eligibility Requirements: This program is open to graduating high school seniors in Arizona who have a GPA of 3.0 or higher. Applicants or their parents must have been members of 1 of the following organizations for at least the preceding 3 years: Arizona Chapter of the Japanese American Citizens League (JACLA), the Phoenix Japanese Free Methodist Church, the Arizona Buddhist Church, a youth group of JACLA, a youth group of the Phoenix Free Methodist Church, or a youth group of the Arizona Buddhist Church. Financial need is not considered in the selection process. **Deadline for Receipt:** February of each year. **Additional Information:** Recipients must attend the association's scholarship awards banquet and accept the award in person; failure to do so results in forfeiture of the award. The sponsor also offers a number of other, similar scholarships, including the Herbert Jensen Scholarship and the Joe Allman Scholarship.

848 ■ JAYCEES OF WISCONSIN FOUNDATION, INC.

Attn: Scholarship Committee
P.O. Box 1547
Appleton, WI 54912
Tel: (920)386-2393
Web Site: http://www.jcwf.org/BertucciScholarship.htm
To provide financial assistance to students at Wisconsin postsecondary institutions who are working on a college degree after having been out of school for at least 2 years.
Title of Award: Denise Bertucci Memorial Scholarship **Area, Field, or Subject:** General studies/Field of study not specified **Level of Education for which Award is Granted:** Undergraduate **Number Awarded:** 1 or more each year. **Funds Available:** A stipend is awarded (amount not specified). **Duration:** 1 year.
Eligibility Requirements: This program is open to full-time students attending a Wisconsin postsecondary institution pursuing at least a 2-year undergraduate program. Applicants must be at least 21 years of age and have completed at least 2 semesters of school since returning after an absence of at least 2 years. They must have a GPA of 3.0 or higher. Along with their application, they must submit brief essays describing the activities in which they have participated within their community, identifying honors and other recognitions they have received, explaining why they decided to return to work on a degree after taking a break in their education, explaining how this education will help to prepare them to be a leader in their community, and describing any obstacles (financial or otherwise) that will affect their working on a degree. **Deadline for Receipt:** May of each year. **Additional Information:** Information is also available from Janet Byrne, (608) 762-5212, E-mail: jbyrne9@netscape.net.

849 ■ JAY'S WORLD CHILDHOOD CANCER FOUNDATION

c/o Napolitano
5 Knoll Lane
Glen Head, NY 11545
Tel: (516)671-7410
Web Site: http://www.jaysworld.org/html/scholarship.cfm

To provide financial assistance for college to residents of New York who have had childhood cancer.
Title of Award: Jay's World College Scholarship Program **Area, Field, or Subject:** General studies/Field of study not specified **Level of Education for which Award is Granted:** Undergraduate **Number Awarded:** 1 or more each year. **Funds Available:** A stipend is awarded (amount not specified). **Duration:** 1 year.
Eligibility Requirements: This program is open to New York residents who have been cured of cancer, are in remission, or are able to attend college while undergoing treatment for cancer. Applicants must submit a brief paper describing what it was like to be a child with cancer; how it affected their family, friends, and school life; and what the experience has taught them and how it can benefit their life. Financial need is considered in the selection process. **Deadline for Receipt:** April of each year. **Additional Information:** The sponsoring foundation was founded in 1997.

850 ■ JEWISH GUILD FOR THE BLIND

Attn: GuildScholar Program
15 West 65th Street
New York, NY 10023
Tel: (212)769-7801
Free: 800-284-4422
Fax: (212)769-6266
E-mail: guildscholar@jgb.org
Web Site: http://www.jgb.org
To provide financial assistance for college to blind high school seniors.
Title of Award: GuildScholar Program **Area, Field, or Subject:** General studies/Field of study not specified **Level of Education for which Award is Granted:** Undergraduate **Number Awarded:** Up to 15 each year. **Funds Available:** The stipend is approximately $15,000. **Duration:** 1 year.
Eligibility Requirements: The program is open to college-bound high school seniors who can document legal blindness. Applicants must submit copies of school transcripts and SAT/ACT scores, proof of U.S. citizenship, 3 letters of recommendation, a 500-word personal statement describing their educational and personal goals, and documentation of financial need (if they wish that to be considered in the selection process). **Additional Information:** This program was established in 2004.

851 ■ JEWISH WAR VETERANS OF THE U.S.A.

1811 R Street, N.W.
Washington, DC 20009-1659
Tel: (202)265-6280
Fax: (202)234-5662
E-mail: jwv@jwv.org
Web Site: http://www.jwv.org/program/s.html
To provide financial assistance for college to descendants of members of the Jewish War Veterans of the U.S.A.
Title of Award: Jewish War Veterans National Educational Grants **Area, Field, or Subject:** General studies/Field of study not specified **Level of Education for which Award is Granted:** Undergraduate **Number Awarded:** 3 each year. **Funds Available:** First prize is the $1,000 Bernard Rotberg Memorial Scholarship; second prize is the $750 Louis S. Silvey Grant; third prize is $500. **Duration:** 1 year; nonrenewable.
Eligibility Requirements: Eligible to apply are children, grandchildren, and great-grandchildren of members or of deceased members of Jewish War Veterans in good standing who have been accepted by an accredited 4-year college or university or a 3-year hospital school of nursing as a freshman. Applicants must be high school seniors in the upper 25% of their class. The selection process emphasizes extracurricular activities at school, in the Jewish community, and in the community at large. **Deadline for Receipt:** Applications must be submitted to the department commander by April of each year. **Additional Information:** Applications must be submitted through your Jewish War Veterans' department commander.

852 ■ DEXTER G. JOHNSON EDUCATIONAL AND BENEVOLENT TRUST

622 N.E. 19th Street
Oklahoma City, OK 73105-8006
Tel: (405)232-3340
Fax: (405)232-3340
To provide financial assistance for vocational training, audiological evaluations, corrective surgery, speech therapy, or medical devices to the children of residents of Oklahoma with disabilities.

Title of Award: Dexter G. Johnson Educational and Benevolent Trust Grants **Area, Field, or Subject:** General studies/Field of study not specified **Level of Education for which Award is Granted:** Undergraduate **Number Awarded:** Varies; approximately 10 each year. **Funds Available:** Grants range from $70 to $2,500.

Eligibility Requirements: Residents of Oklahoma with disabilities are eligible to apply for this program for their children if they need financial assistance for vocational training, audiological evaluations, corrective surgery, speech therapy, or orthopedic or hearing aid devices. **Deadline for Receipt:** Applications may be submitted at any time.

853 ■ JOLLY GREEN ASSOCIATION

Attn: Secretary
P.O. Box 965
O'Fallon, IL 62269
E-mail: bill6100@aol.com
Web Site: http://www.jollygreen.org/
jolly_green_memorial_scholarship.htm
To provide financial assistance for college to dependents of current and former members of the Air Force Combat Rescue or Support Forces.

Title of Award: Jolly Green Memorial Scholarship **Area, Field, or Subject:** General studies/Field of study not specified **Level of Education for which Award is Granted:** Undergraduate **Number Awarded:** 1 or more each year. **Funds Available:** A stipend is awarded (amount not specified). **Duration:** 1 year.

Eligibility Requirements: This program is open to high school seniors who are dependents of current or former uniformed members of the USAF Combat Rescue or Support Forces. Applicants must have taken the ACT or SAT examinations and be eligible for admission to the college or university of their choice. Selection is based on academic achievement (40%), scholastic or public service achievements (10%), and financial need (50%). **Deadline for Receipt:** April of each year.

854 ■ JUNIOR ACHIEVEMENT

Attn: Scholarships Coordinator
One Education Way
Colorado Springs, CO 80906-4477
Tel: (719)540-6255; 888-4JA-ALUM
Fax: (719)540-6175
E-mail: scholarships@ja.org
Web Site: http://www.ja.org/programs/programs_schol_joe.shtml
To provide financial assistance for college to high school seniors who have participated in the Junior Achievement (JA) program.

Title of Award: Joe Francomano Scholarship **Area, Field, or Subject:** General studies/Field of study not specified **Level of Education for which Award is Granted:** Four Year College **Number Awarded:** 1 each year. **Funds Available:** The stipend is $5,000 per year. **Duration:** 4 years.

Eligibility Requirements: This program is open to graduating high school seniors who have participated in the JA Company Program or JA Economics. Applicants must have a GPA of 3.0 or higher and be able to demonstrate financial need, achievement, leadership, and college and career potential. Along with their application, they must submit a 500-word essay on a topic that changes annually but relates to ethical issues in business. **Deadline for Receipt:** January of each year. **Additional Information:** This scholarship, first awarded in 1997, is sponsored by the Achievement Foundation, Inc. Recipients must attend a 4-year college or university.

855 ■ JUNIOR ACHIEVEMENT

Attn: Scholarships Coordinator
One Education Way
Colorado Springs, CO 80906-4477
Tel: (719)540-6255; 888-4JA-ALUM
Fax: (719)540-6175
E-mail: scholarships@ja.org
Web Site: http://studentcenter.ja.org/aspx/PayCollege/
NelnetScholarships.aspx
To provide financial assistance for college to high school seniors who have participated in the Junior Achievement (JA) program.

Title of Award: Nelnet Scholarships **Area, Field, or Subject:** General studies/Field of study not specified **Level of Education for which Award is Granted:** Undergraduate **Number Awarded:** 10 each year. **Funds Available:** The stipend is $1,000. **Duration:** 1 year.

Eligibility Requirements: This program is open to graduating high school seniors who have completed 2 JA programs. Applicants must have a GPA of 3.0 or higher and be able to demonstrate financial need, achievement, leadership, and college and career potential. Along with their application, they must submit a 500-word essay on the importance of professional integrity and excellence in today's job market. **Deadline for Receipt:** March of each year. **Additional Information:** This program is sponsored by Nelnet, Inc.

856 ■ JUNIOR ACHIEVEMENT

Attn: Scholarships Coordinator
One Education Way
Colorado Springs, CO 80906-4477
Tel: (719)540-6255; 888-4JA-ALUM
Fax: (719)540-6175
E-mail: scholarships@ja.org
Web Site: http://www.ja.org/programs/programs_schol_hugh.shtml
To provide financial assistance for college to high school seniors who have participated in the Junior Achievement (JA) program.

Title of Award: Hugh B. Sweeney Scholarship **Area, Field, or Subject:** General studies/Field of study not specified **Level of Education for which Award is Granted:** Undergraduate **Number Awarded:** 1 each year. **Funds Available:** The stipend is $5,000. **Duration:** 1 year; nonrenewable.

Eligibility Requirements: This program is open to graduating high school seniors who have participated in the JA Company Program or JA Economics. Applicants must have a GPA of 3.0 or higher and be able to demonstrate financial need, achievement, citizenship, creativity, leadership, and motivation. They must be planning to attend an accredited college, university, trade school, or community college. Preference is given to students who can demonstrate leadership in creating a community organization, project, or event, or solving a community problem in a unique and entrepreneurial way. Along with their application, they must submit a 500-word essay on a topic that changes annually but relates to their involvement in JA. **Deadline for Receipt:** January of each year. **Additional Information:** This scholarship, first awarded in 2002, is sponsored by the Achievement Foundation, Inc.

857 ■ KAISER PERMANENTE AFRICAN AMERICAN PROFESSIONAL ASSOCIATION

c/o Kaiser Permanente
Waterpark One
2500 Havana Street
Aurora, CO 80014
E-mail: P.J.Ballard@kp.org
To provide financial assistance to undergraduate and graduate students who identify with an ethnic minority group.

Title of Award: KPAAPA Scholarships **Area, Field, or Subject:** General studies/Field of study not specified **Level of Education for which Award is Granted:** Graduate, Undergraduate **Number Awarded:** 5 each year. **Funds Available:** The stipend is $1,000 per year. **Duration:** 1 year.

Eligibility Requirements: This program is open to new and continuing undergraduate and graduate students enrolled or planning to enroll full time at an accredited college or university. Applicants must have a GPA of 3.0 or higher, although students who have strong leadership skills and community service but a lower GPA are encouraged to apply. Along with their application, they must submit a 1-page essay on their personal philosophy how obtaining a college degree could benefit this country in building a stronger foundation in areas of youth issues, educational opportunities, and career potential. On their application, they must also indicate the ethnic minority group with which they identify and include a photograph. **Deadline for Receipt:** December of each year. **Additional Information:** The photograph and essay of recipients are published in the Black History Month Souvenir Journal of the Kaiser Permanente African American Professional Association (KPAAPA).

858 ■ EDITH KANAKA'OLE FOUNDATION

Attn: Higher Education Scholarship
1500 Kalaniana'ole Avenue
Hilo, HI 96720-4814
Tel: (808)961-5242
Fax: (808)961-4789

Web Site: http://www.edithkanakaolefoundation.org/scholarships/scholarships_index.htm

To provide financial assistance to Native Hawaiians who are attending or planning to attend a college or university on the island of Hawai'i.

Title of Award: Edith Kanaka'ole Foundation Higher Education Scholarship **Area, Field, or Subject:** General studies/Field of study not specified **Level of Education for which Award is Granted:** Graduate, Undergraduate **Number Awarded:** 1 each year. **Funds Available:** A stipend is awarded (amount not specified); funds are not intended to be the recipient's primary source of higher education funding. **Duration:** 1 year; may be renewed if the recipient maintains a GPA of 3.0 or higher.

Eligibility Requirements: This program is open to students who are of Native Hawaiian ancestry in whole or in part. Applicants must be attending or planning to attend a college or university on Hawai'i island as a full-time student. They must have a GPA of 2.5 or higher and agree to complete a "give back" program. Preference is given to 1) students in a discipline that has little or no Native Hawaiian representation, very low Hawaiian enrollment, and/or low exit degree completion; 2) lessees in the Department of Hawaiian Homes or a child of a lessee; 3) students born and raised in the districts of Ka'u, Kohala, Puna, or Hilo; 4) upper-division or advanced standing students; and 5) Hawaiian cultural practitioners.

859 ■ KANSAS ADJUTANT GENERAL'S DEPARTMENT

Attn: Chuck Bredahl
2800 S.W. Topeka Boulevard
Topeka, KS 66611-1287
Tel: (785)274-1001

To provide financial assistance to Army ROTC students in Kansas.

Title of Award: Kansas Army National Guard Scholarship **Area, Field, or Subject:** General studies/Field of study not specified **Level of Education for which Award is Granted:** Undergraduate **Number Awarded:** 40 each year. **Funds Available:** This program provides free tuition at the participating schools (where there are Army ROTC programs). Beginning with their fifth semester in the program, they also receive a stipend of $200 per month. Recipients must agree to become a commissioned officer and serve at least 8 years in the military after completing ROTC and graduating from college. That service includes at least 4 years in the Kansas Army National Guard, 2 years with a Reserve component unit, and 2 years in the Individual Ready Reserves (IRR). If they fail to graduate or fulfill the military service obligation, they must either repay all funds received or serve 4 years as an enlisted member of the Kansas Army National Guard. **Duration:** 4 years, or until the recipient completes the baccalaureate degree.

Eligibility Requirements: This program is open to non-scholarship Army ROTC students planning to enroll full time at a state university in Kansas. Applicants must be U.S. citizens and residents of Kansas eligible for in-state tuition. They must have an ACT score of 17 or higher, be able to meet medical and physical fitness requirements for military service, and be able to complete all requirements for a college degree and a commission while they are younger than 30 years of age. Selection is based on scholastic potential and achievement, participation in extracurricular activities, demonstrated leadership, interest in service with the Kansas Army National Guard, and an interview. **Deadline for Receipt:** January of each year.

860 ■ KANSAS BOARD OF REGENTS

Attn: Student Financial Aid
1000 S.W. Jackson Street, Suite 520
Topeka, KS 66612-1368
Tel: (785)296-3518
Fax: (785)296-0983
E-mail: dlindeman@ksbor.org
Web Site: http://www.kansasregents.com/financial_aid/awards.html

To provide need-based grants to Kansas residents who are attending college in the state.

Title of Award: Kansas Comprehensive Grants **Area, Field, or Subject:** General studies/Field of study not specified **Level of Education for which Award is Granted:** Undergraduate **Number Awarded:** Varies; generally, 7,000 or more each year. The funding level allows about 1 in 3 eligible students to be assisted. **Funds Available:** Stipends range from $200 to $3,000 per year at the private institutions and from $100 to $1,100 at the public institutions. **Duration:** 1 year; may be renewed as long as the recipient remains in academic "good standing" and is able to demonstrate financial need.

Eligibility Requirements: This program is open to residents of Kansas who are enrolled full time at 1) 18 private colleges and universities located in the state, 2) the 6 public universities, or 3) Washburn University. Financial need must be demonstrated. **Deadline for Receipt:** March of each year. **Additional Information:** There is a $10 application fee.

861 ■ KANSAS BOARD OF REGENTS

Attn: Student Financial Aid
1000 S.W. Jackson Street, Suite 520
Topeka, KS 66612-1368
Tel: (785)296-3518
Fax: (785)296-0983
E-mail: dlindeman@ksbor.org
Web Site: http://www.kansasregents.com/financial_aid/awards.html

To provide financial assistance for college to residents of Kansas whose parent died in the line of duty as a public safety officer.

Title of Award: Kansas Enrollment without Charge for Dependents of Deceased Public Safety Officers. **Area, Field, or Subject:** General studies/Field of study not specified **Level of Education for which Award is Granted:** Undergraduate **Number Awarded:** Varies each year. **Funds Available:** Qualifying students are permitted to enroll at an approved Kansas institution without payment of tuition or fees. They are responsible for other costs, such as books, room, and board. **Duration:** 1 year; may be renewed up to 8 semesters of full-time enrollment.

Eligibility Requirements: This program is open to residents of Kansas who are the dependent children of public safety officers (law enforcement officers, fire fighters, and emergency medical services attendants) who died as the result of injuries sustained in the line of duty. Applicants must be enrolled or planning to enroll full time at educational institutions in Kansas, including area vocational/technical schools and colleges, community colleges, regents universities, and Washburn University.

862 ■ KANSAS BOARD OF REGENTS

Attn: Student Financial Aid
1000 S.W. Jackson Street, Suite 520
Topeka, KS 66612-1368
Tel: (785)296-3518
Fax: (785)296-0983
E-mail: dlindeman@ksbor.org
Web Site: http://www.kansasregents.com/financial_aid/awards.html

To provide financial assistance for college to residents of Kansas who have been in foster care.

Title of Award: Kansas Enrollment without Charge for Foster Children Program **Area, Field, or Subject:** General studies/Field of study not specified **Level of Education for which Award is Granted:** Undergraduate **Number Awarded:** Varies each year. No institution is required to honor more than 5 waivers in any academic year. **Funds Available:** Qualifying students are permitted to enroll at an approved Kansas institution without payment of tuition or fees. They are responsible for other costs, such as books, room, and board. **Duration:** 1 year; may be renewed as long as the recipient remains enrolled as a full-time undergraduate and employed an average of at least 10 hours per week.

Eligibility Requirements: This program is open to residents of Kansas who were 1) foster care children in the custody of the Department of Social and Rehabilitation Services at age 18; 2) in foster care placement while graduating from high school or completing their GED requirements prior to their 18th birthday; or 3) adopted from foster care after 16 years of age. Applicants must be enrolled or planning to enroll full time at educational institutions in Kansas, including area vocational/technical schools and colleges, community colleges, regents universities, and Washburn University. Enrollment must begin within 2 years following graduation from high school or completion of GED requirements.

863 ■ KANSAS BOARD OF REGENTS

Attn: Student Financial Aid
1000 S.W. Jackson Street, Suite 520
Topeka, KS 66612-1368
Tel: (785)296-3518
Fax: (785)296-0983
E-mail: dlindeman@ksbor.org
Web Site: http://www.kansasregents.com/financial_aid/minority.html

To provide financial assistance to minority students who are interested in attending college in Kansas.

Title of Award: Kansas Ethnic Minority Scholarship Program **Area, Field, or Subject:** General studies/Field of study not specified **Level of Education for which Award is Granted:** Undergraduate **Number Awarded:** Approximately 200 each year. **Funds Available:** A stipend of up to $1,850 is provided, depending on financial need and availability of state funds. **Duration:** 1 year; may be renewed for up to 3 additional years (4 additional years for designated 5-year programs) if the recipient maintains a 2.0 cumulative GPA and has financial need.

Eligibility Requirements: Eligible to apply are Kansas residents who fall into 1 of these minority groups: American Indian, Alaskan Native, African American, Asian, Pacific Islander, or Hispanic. Applicants may be current college students (enrolled in community colleges, colleges, or universities in Kansas), but high school seniors graduating in the current year receive priority consideration. Minimum academic requirements include 1 of the following: 1) ACT score of 21 or higher or SAT score of 816 or higher; 2) cumulative GPA of 3.0 or higher; 3) high school rank in upper 33%; 4) completion of the Kansas Scholars Curriculum (4 years of English, 3 years of mathematics, 3 years of science, 3 years of social studies, and 2 years of foreign language); 5) selection by the National Merit Corporation in any category; or 6) selection by the College Board as a Hispanic Scholar. **Deadline for Receipt:** April of each year. **Additional Information:** There is a $10 application fee.

864 ■ KANSAS BOARD OF REGENTS

Attn: Student Financial Aid
1000 S.W. Jackson Street, Suite 520
Topeka, KS 66612-1368
Tel: (785)296-3518
Fax: (785)296-0983
E-mail: dlindeman@ksbor.org
Web Site: http://www.kansasregents.com/financial_aid/awards.html
To provide financial assistance to members of the Kansas National Guard who wish to take additional college courses.

Title of Award: Kansas National Guard Educational Assistance **Area, Field, or Subject:** General studies/Field of study not specified **Level of Education for which Award is Granted:** Undergraduate **Number Awarded:** Varies each year; recently, approximately 300 of these awards were granted each semester. **Funds Available:** The program reimburses up to 100% of tuition and fees at public and designated private institutions in Kansas. Current maximums are $2,388.25 for a 4-year university, $1,155 for a community college, or $2,570 for a technical school. **Duration:** 1 semester; may be renewed.

Eligibility Requirements: This program is open to members of the Kansas National Guard (Air or Army) who are interested in working on a vocational, associate, or bachelor's degree. Applicants must be newly enlisted or reenlisted Guard member with no more than 15 years of service. They must agree to complete their current service obligation plus 3 months of additional service for each semester of assistance received. **Deadline for Receipt:** September of each year for fall semester; February of each year for spring semester.

865 ■ KANSAS BOARD OF REGENTS

Attn: Student Financial Aid
1000 S.W. Jackson Street, Suite 520
Topeka, KS 66612-1368
Tel: (785)296-3518
Fax: (785)296-0983
E-mail: dlindeman@ksbor.org
Web Site: http://www.kansasregents.com/financial_aid/state.html
To provide need-based assistance to students who are in the top of their high school class in Kansas and planning to attend college.

Title of Award: Kansas State Scholarships **Area, Field, or Subject:** General studies/Field of study not specified **Level of Education for which Award is Granted:** Undergraduate **Number Awarded:** Varies; generally, at least 1,200 each year. Generally, between 20 and 40% of high school seniors who complete the Kansas Scholars Curriculum are designated as Kansas State Scholars. **Funds Available:** The stipend ranges up to $1,000 per year, depending upon the recipient's financial need. **Duration:** Up to 4 academic years (unless enrolled in a designated 5-year program) as long as the recipient maintains a 3.0 GPA and financial need.

Eligibility Requirements: This program is open to high school seniors in Kansas who are designated as State Scholars. Selection for this program is based on ACT Assessment scores (recently, the average score of designees was 29), completion of the Kansas Scholars Curriculum (4 years of English, 4 years of mathematics, 3 years of science, 3 years of social studies, 2 years of foreign language, and 1 year of computer technology), and academic record (recently, the average GPA of designees was 3.90). State Scholars who demonstrate financial need are eligible for these scholarships. **Deadline for Receipt:** April of each year. **Additional Information:** The school the recipient listed first in the school section of the Free Application for Federal Student Aid will be notified by the Board of Regents that the student has been funded. The award will be listed in the financial aid letter the school sends the recipient. There is a $10 application fee. Recipients must attend school in Kansas as a full-time student.

866 ■ KANSAS COMMISSION ON VETERANS' AFFAIRS

Jayhawk Towers
700 S.W. Jackson Street, Suite 701
Topeka, KS 66603-3150
Tel: (785)296-3976
Fax: (785)296-1462
E-mail: KVH007@ink.org
Web Site: http://www.kcva.org
To provide financial assistance for college to children of Kansas veterans who were prisoners of war or killed in Vietnam.

Title of Award: Kansas Educational Benefits for Dependents of POWs/KIAs/MIAs of the Vietnam War **Area, Field, or Subject:** General studies/Field of study not specified **Level of Education for which Award is Granted:** Undergraduate **Number Awarded:** Varies each year. **Funds Available:** Eligible dependents receive free tuition and fees at any Kansas state-supported college, university, community college, or area vocational school. **Duration:** Up to 12 semesters.

Eligibility Requirements: Applicants for these benefits may be residents of any state as long as their veteran parent was a legal resident of Kansas upon entering military service and, while serving in Vietnam after January 1, 1960, either died of service-connected causes or was declared by the Secretary of Defense to be a prisoner of war or missing in action.

867 ■ KANSAS FEDERATION OF BUSINESS & PROFESSIONAL WOMEN'S CLUBS, INC.

Attn: Kansas BPW Educational Foundation
c/o Diane Smith, Executive Secretary
10418 Haskins
Lenexa, KS 66215-2162
E-mail: desmith@fcbankonline.com
Web Site: http://www.bpwkansas.org/bpw_foundation.htm
To provide financial assistance to women in Kansas who are already in the workforce but are interested in pursuing additional education.

Title of Award: Mara Crawford Hall of Fame Scholarship **Area, Field, or Subject:** General studies/Field of study not specified **Level of Education for which Award is Granted:** Undergraduate **Number Awarded:** 1 or more each year. **Funds Available:** A stipend is awarded (amount not specified). **Duration:** 1 year.

Eligibility Requirements: This program is open to women residents of Kansas who graduated from high school more than 5 years previously and are already in the workforce. Applicants may be seeking a degree in any field of study and may be attending a 2-year, 4-year, vocational, or technological program. They must submit 1) documentation of financial need, and 2) a 3-page personal biography in which they express their career goals, the direction they want to take in the future, their proposed field of study, their reason for selecting that field, the institutions they plan to attend and why, their circumstances for reentering school (if a factor), and what makes them uniquely qualified for this scholarship. Applications must be submitted through a local unit of the sponsor. **Deadline for Receipt:** December of each year.

868 ■ KANSAS FEDERATION OF BUSINESS & PROFESSIONAL WOMEN'S CLUBS, INC.

Attn: Kansas BPW Educational Foundation
c/o Diane Smith, Executive Secretary
10418 Haskins
Lenexa, KS 66215-2162
E-mail: desmith@fcbankonline.com
Web Site: http://www.bpwkansas.org/bpw_foundation.htm

To provide financial assistance to residents of Kansas who are interested in broadening their education and/or increasing their earning abilities.
Title of Award: Kansas BPW Educational Foundation Career Development Scholarship **Area, Field, or Subject:** General studies/Field of study not specified **Level of Education for which Award is Granted:** Undergraduate **Number Awarded:** 1 or more each year. **Funds Available:** A stipend is awarded (amount not specified). **Duration:** 1 year.
Eligibility Requirements: This program is open to Kansas residents (men and women) who have a career and want to broaden their education and/or increase their earning abilities. Applicants must submit a 3-page personal biography in which they express their career goals, the direction they want to take in the future, their proposed field of study, their reason for selecting that field, the institutions they plan to attend and why, their circumstances for reentering school (if a factor), and what makes them uniquely qualified for this scholarship. They must also be able to document financial need. Applications must be submitted through a local unit of the sponsor. **Deadline for Receipt:** December of each year.

869 ■ KANSAS FEDERATION OF BUSINESS & PROFESSIONAL WOMEN'S CLUBS, INC.
Attn: Kansas BPW Educational Foundation
c/o Diane Smith, Executive Secretary
10418 Haskins
Lenexa, KS 66215-2162
E-mail: desmith@fcbankonline.com
Web Site: http://www.bpwkansas.org/bpw_foundation.htm
To provide financial assistance to residents of Kansas who are interested in working on a 1- or 2-year college degree or certificate.
Title of Award: Kansas BPW Educational Foundation Career Preparatory Scholarship **Area, Field, or Subject:** General studies/Field of study not specified **Level of Education for which Award is Granted:** Two Year College, Vocational/Occupational **Number Awarded:** 1 or more each year. **Funds Available:** A stipend is awarded (amount not specified). **Duration:** 1 year.
Eligibility Requirements: This program is open to Kansas residents (men and women) who are enrolled in either a 1or 2-year academic, career, vocational, or technical program that will qualify them for immediate employment or transfer to a 4-year undergraduate program. Applicants must submit a 3-page personal biography in which they express their career goals, the direction they want to take in the future, their proposed field of study, their reason for selecting that field, the institutions they plan to attend and why, their circumstances for reentering school (if a factor), and what makes them uniquely qualified for this scholarship. They must also be able to document financial need. Applications must be submitted through a local unit of the sponsor. **Deadline for Receipt:** December of each year.

870 ■ KANSAS FEDERATION OF BUSINESS & PROFESSIONAL WOMEN'S CLUBS, INC.
Attn: Kansas BPW Educational Foundation
c/o Diane Smith, Executive Secretary
10418 Haskins
Lenexa, KS 66215-2162
E-mail: desmith@fcbankonline.com
Web Site: http://www.bpwkansas.org/bpw_foundation.htm
To provide college loans to residents of Kansas who are attending an institution in the state.
Title of Award: Kansas BPW Educational Foundation Loans **Area, Field, or Subject:** General studies/Field of study not specified **Level of Education for which Award is Granted:** Undergraduate **Number Awarded:** Varies each year. **Funds Available:** The amount of the loan depends on the availability of funds and the need of the borrower. No interest is charged. Repayment of the loan must begin no later than 18 months after completing school and must be completed within 5 years. **Duration:** 1 year; renewable for a maximum of $800 in loans.
Eligibility Requirements: This program is open to residents of Kansas who are at least 18 years of age, high school graduates, and attending a school located in Kansas. Applicants must submit a 3-page personal biography in which they express their career goals, the direction they want to take in the future, their proposed field of study, their reason for selecting that field, the institutions they plan to attend and why, their circumstances for reentering school (if a factor), and what makes them uniquely qualified for this scholarship. They must also be able to document financial need.

Applications must be submitted through a local unit of the sponsor. **Deadline for Receipt:** December of each year.

871 ■ KANSAS FEDERATION OF BUSINESS & PROFESSIONAL WOMEN'S CLUBS, INC.
Attn: Kansas BPW Educational Foundation
c/o Diane Smith, Executive Secretary
10418 Haskins
Lenexa, KS 66215-2162
E-mail: desmith@fcbankonline.com
Web Site: http://www.bpwkansas.org/bpw_foundation.htm
To provide financial assistance for college to residents of Kansas.
Title of Award: Kansas BPW Educational Foundation Undergraduate Scholarship **Area, Field, or Subject:** General studies/Field of study not specified **Level of Education for which Award is Granted:** Four Year College **Number Awarded:** 1 or more each year. **Funds Available:** A stipend is awarded (amount not specified). **Duration:** 1 year.
Eligibility Requirements: This program is open to Kansas residents (men and women) who are college sophomores, juniors, or seniors enrolled in a 4-year academic program at an accredited college or university. Applicants must submit a 3-page personal biography in which they express their career goals, the direction they want to take in the future, their proposed field of study, their reason for selecting that field, the institutions they plan to attend and why, their circumstances for reentering school (if a factor), and what makes them uniquely qualified for this scholarship. They must also be able to document financial need. Applications must be submitted through a local unit of the sponsor. **Deadline for Receipt:** December of each year.

872 ■ KANSAS FEDERATION OF BUSINESS & PROFESSIONAL WOMEN'S CLUBS, INC.
Attn: Kansas BPW Educational Foundation
c/o Diane Smith, Executive Secretary
10418 Haskins
Lenexa, KS 66215-2162
E-mail: desmith@fcbankonline.com
Web Site: http://www.bpwkansas.org/bpw_foundation.htm
To provide financial assistance for college to residents of Kansas who can demonstrate a record of public and community service.
Title of Award: Carol Nigus Leadership Scholarship **Area, Field, or Subject:** General studies/Field of study not specified **Level of Education for which Award is Granted:** Undergraduate **Number Awarded:** 1 or more each year. **Funds Available:** A stipend is awarded (amount not specified). **Duration:** 1 year.
Eligibility Requirements: This program is open to Kansas residents (men and women) who are enrolled in a school of higher education in the state and have demonstrated an extensive record of public service and outstanding leadership potential. Applicants must submit 1) a written summary of their involvement in community affairs, and 2) a 3-page personal biography in which they express their career goals, the direction they want to take in the future, their proposed field of study, their reason for selecting that field, the institutions they plan to attend and why, their circumstances for reentering school (if a factor), and what makes them uniquely qualified for this scholarship. They must also be able to document financial need. Applications must be submitted through a local organization of the sponsor. **Deadline for Receipt:** December of each year.

873 ■ KANSAS FEDERATION OF BUSINESS & PROFESSIONAL WOMEN'S CLUBS, INC.
Attn: Kansas BPW Educational Foundation
c/o Diane Smith, Executive Secretary
10418 Haskins
Lenexa, KS 66215-2162
E-mail: desmith@fcbankonline.com
Web Site: http://www.bpwkansas.org/bpw_foundation.htm
To provide financial assistance for college to residents of Kansas who have participated in the Young Careerist Program of the Kansas BPW Educational Foundation.
Title of Award: Dr. Sharon Wiber Young Careerist Scholarship **Area, Field, or Subject:** General studies/Field of study not specified **Level of Education for which Award is Granted:** Undergraduate **Number Awarded:** 1 or more each year. **Funds Available:** A stipend is awarded (amount not specified). **Duration:** 1 year.

Eligibility Requirements: This program is open to Kansas residents (men and women) who have represented their local BPW organization in district, regional, or state Young Careerist competitions and are majoring in a subject that will increase their employable skills. Applicants must submit 1) proof of participation in the Young Careerist program, and 2) a 3-page personal biography in which they express their career goals, the direction they want to take in the future, their proposed field of study, their reason for selecting that field, the institutions they plan to attend and why, their circumstances for reentering school (if a factor), and what makes them uniquely qualified for this scholarship. They must also be able to document financial need. Applications must be submitted through a local unit of the sponsor. **Deadline for Receipt:** December of each year.

874 ■ KANSAS FUNERAL DIRECTORS AND EMBALMERS ASSOCIATION

Attn: KFDA Foundation
1200 South Kansas Avenue
P.O. Box 1904
Topeka, KS 66601-1904
Tel: (913)232-7789
Fax: (913)232-7791
E-mail: kfda@inlandnet.net
Web Site: http://www.ksfda.org/educareer.htm
To provide financial assistance to Kansas residents who are currently enrolled in a school of mortuary science.
Title of Award: Kansas Funeral Directors Association Foundation Scholarship **Area, Field, or Subject:** Mortuary science **Level of Education for which Award is Granted:** Undergraduate **Number Awarded:** 2 to 4 each year. **Funds Available:** Stipends range from $250 to $1,500. **Duration:** 1 year.
Eligibility Requirements: This program is open to Kansas residents who are currently attending a mortuary school. They must have at least 1 but not more than 2 semesters of schooling left and be registered with the Kansas State Board of Mortuary Arts. Selection is based on academic achievement, leadership qualities, financial need, and special abilities. Preference is given to applicants who intend to practice in Kansas. **Deadline for Receipt:** September of each year.

875 ■ KANSAS GOLF ASSOCIATION

Attn: Kansas Golf Foundation
3301 Clinton Parkway Court, Suite 4
Lawrence, KS 66047
Tel: (785)842-4833
Fax: (785)842-3831
E-mail: foundation@kansasgolf.org
Web Site: http://www.kansasgolf.org/KGF/Scholarships.htm
To provide financial assistance to college students from Kansas who are working on a degree in turfgrass management or preparing to become a golf course superintendent.
Title of Award: Richard J. Copple Memorial Scholarships **Area, Field, or Subject:** Turfgrass management **Level of Education for which Award is Granted:** Undergraduate **Number Awarded:** 2 each year. **Funds Available:** A stipend is awarded (amount not specified). **Duration:** 1 year.
Eligibility Requirements: This program is open to residents of Kansas who are working on a degree in turfgrass management or studying to become a golf course superintendent. Applicants must provide information on their high school and college experiences (including GPA, extracurricular activities, awards, and honors), career plans after graduation, and past involvement with golf (either as a player or work experience). **Deadline for Receipt:** September of each year. **Additional Information:** This program was established in 1994.

876 ■ KANSAS GOLF ASSOCIATION

Attn: Kansas Golf Foundation
3301 Clinton Parkway Court, Suite 4
Lawrence, KS 66047
Tel: (785)842-4833
Fax: (785)842-3831
E-mail: foundation@kansasgolf.org
Web Site: http://www.kansasgolf.org/KGF/Scholarships,htm
To provide financial assistance for college to high school seniors in Kansas who have been active in playing golf.
Title of Award: Kansas Junior Golf Scholarships **Area, Field, or Subject:** General studies/Field of study not specified **Level of Education for**

which Award is Granted: Four Year College **Number Awarded:** 5 each year. **Funds Available:** The stipend is $1,250. **Duration:** 1 year.
Eligibility Requirements: This program is open to seniors graduating from high schools in Kansas who are enrolling as a full-time student at an accredited 4-year college or university in the state. Applicants must have participated in each of the 2 previous seasons in high school golf or junior golf programs sponsored by Kansas organizations. They must submit a 2-page essay on why they deserve this scholarship, how they have benefited from the game of golf, and explaining their 5- and 10-year goals. Selection is based on the essay, academic record, leadership, letters of recommendation, financial need, and participation in golf (but not playing ability or performance). **Deadline for Receipt:** March of each year.

877 ■ KANSAS MASONIC FOUNDATION, INC.

320 S.W. Eighth Avenue
P.O. Box 1217
Topeka, KS 66601-1217
Tel: (785)357-7646
Fax: (785)357-7406
E-mail: info@kmfonline.org
Web Site: http://www.kmfonline.org/education.html
To provide educational loans to Kansas residents attending a college or university in the state.
Title of Award: Kansas Masonic Foundation Student Loan Program **Area, Field, or Subject:** General studies/Field of study not specified **Level of Education for which Award is Granted:** Graduate, Undergraduate **Number Awarded:** Varies each year; recently, a total of 181 students were receiving loans through this program. **Funds Available:** The amount of the loan depends on the need of the borrower. Repayment begins 1 year after completion of school and must be accomplished over a 4-year period with interest at 4%. **Duration:** Up to 4 years, provided the borrower remains enrolled full time with a GPA of 2.0 or higher.
Eligibility Requirements: This program is open to residents of Kansas who are attending to planning to attend an institution of higher education in the state. Applicants must be enrolled as a full-time undergraduate or graduate student. Along with their application, they must submit a cover letter on their educational and career plans, a recent official transcript, a photograph, and at least 1 letter of recommendation. **Deadline for Receipt:** March of each year. **Additional Information:** This program began in 1970.

878 ■ KANSAS MASONIC FOUNDATION, INC.

320 S.W. Eighth Avenue
P.O. Box 1217
Topeka, KS 66601-1217
Tel: (785)357-7646
Fax: (785)357-7406
E-mail: info@kmfonline.org
Web Site: http://www.kmfonline.org/education.html
To provide financial assistance to physically challenged Kansas residents attending a college or university in the state.
Title of Award: Cynthia Ruth Russell Memorial Grants **Area, Field, or Subject:** General studies/Field of study not specified **Level of Education for which Award is Granted:** Graduate, Undergraduate **Number Awarded:** 2 each year. **Funds Available:** A stipend is awarded (amount not specified). **Duration:** 1 year; recipients may reapply.
Eligibility Requirements: This program is open to residents of Kansas who are physically challenged. Applicants must be attending to planning to attend an institution of higher education in the state as a full-time undergraduate or graduate student. Along with their application, they must submit a cover letter on their educational and career plans, a recent official transcript, a photograph, and at least 1 letter of recommendation. **Deadline for Receipt:** March of each year.

879 ■ KANSAS-NEBRASKA CONVENTION OF SOUTHERN BAPTISTS

Attn: Kansas-Nebraska Southern Baptist Foundation
5410 S.W. Seventh Street
Topeka, KS 66606-2398
Tel: (785)273-4880
Free: 800-984-9092
Fax: (785)273-4992
E-mail: pdavis@kncsb.org

Web Site: http://kncsb.org

To provide financial assistance for college or seminary to Southern Baptists from Kansas and Nebraska.

Title of Award: Kansas-Nebraska Christian Higher Education Fund **Area, Field, or Subject:** General studies/Field of study not specified; Religion **Level of Education for which Award is Granted:** Master's, Undergraduate **Number Awarded:** 1 or more each year. **Funds Available:** A stipend is awarded (amount not specified). **Duration:** 1 year. Seminary students may reapply.

Eligibility Requirements: This program is open to members of churches in the Kansas-Nebraska Convention of Southern Baptists. Applicants must be entering their first year at a Southern Baptist college, university, or seminary. **Deadline for Receipt:** February of each year.

880 ■ KAWERAK, INC.

Attn: Education, Employment, and Training Division
P.O. Box 948
Nome, AK 99762
Tel: (907)443-4399
Free: 800-450-4341
Fax: (907)443-4454
E-mail: eet.intake@kawerak.org
Web Site: http://www.kawerak.org/servicedivisions/eet/hes/index.html

To provide financial assistance for college to Alaska Natives from the Bering Straits region.

Title of Award: Kawerak Higher Education Scholarships **Area, Field, or Subject:** General studies/Field of study not specified **Level of Education for which Award is Granted:** Undergraduate **Number Awarded:** Varies each year. **Funds Available:** The stipend depends on the need of the recipient. The program provides only supplemental funding; students must apply for additional resources. **Duration:** 1 year; may be renewed if the recipient remains enrolled full time with a GPA of 2.0 or higher.

Eligibility Requirements: This program is open to tribally enrolled members of native villages in the Bering Straits region of Alaska. Applicants must be enrolled or accepted for enrollment in a 2-year or 4-year degree program. They must submit verification of tribal membership, documentation of financial need, official transcripts, 2 letters of recommendation, and a letter of intent providing the name of the school they wish to attend, their class standing, major area of study, projected graduation date, and educational and personal goals. **Deadline for Receipt:** July of each year for fall semester or quarter; December of each year for spring semester or winter quarter; February of each year for spring quarter; April of each year for summer semester or quarter.

881 ■ KAWERAK, INC.

Attn: Education, Employment, and Training Division
P.O. Box 948
Nome, AK 99762
Tel: (907)443-4399
Free: 800-450-4341
Fax: (907)443-4454
E-mail: eet.intake@kawerak.org
Web Site: http://www.kawerak.org/servicedivisions/eet/hes/index.html

To provide financial assistance to Alaska Natives from the Bering Straits region who are interested in vocational training.

Title of Award: Kawerak Vocational Training Scholarships **Area, Field, or Subject:** General studies/Field of study not specified **Level of Education for which Award is Granted:** Vocational/Occupational **Number Awarded:** Varies each year. **Funds Available:** The stipend depends on the need of the recipient. Tribal members who no longer reside in the region may receive a grant up to $1,500. **Duration:** Funding is provided for a single training program. Recipients may reapply, but their applications receive a lower priority.

Eligibility Requirements: This program is open to tribally enrolled members of native villages in the Bering Straits region of Alaska. Applicants must be unemployed or underemployed and interested in obtaining vocational training to gain job skills for employment. They must have been accepted into an accredited vocational or trade school for training in an occupation that is in demand in the region. Along with their application, they must submit verification of tribal membership, documentation of financial need, official transcripts, 2 letters of recommendation, and a letter of intent providing the name of the school they wish to attend, their employment and personal goals, and where they wish to seek employ-

ment. **Deadline for Receipt:** Applications may be submitted at any time, but they must be received at least 2 weeks before the start of the training program.

882 ■ KENTUCKY COMMUNITY AND TECHNICAL COLLEGE SYSTEM

Attn: Financial Aid
300 North Main Street
Versailles, KY 40383
Tel: (859)256-3100; 877-528-2748
Web Site: http://www.kctcs.edu/student/financialaidscholarships/index.htm

To provide financial assistance to high school seniors in Kentucky who are interested in working on a technical diploma or degree at a participating institution within the Kentucky Community and Technical College System (KCTCS).

Title of Award: Governor's Kentucky Technical College Scholarships **Area, Field, or Subject:** General studies/Field of study not specified **Level of Education for which Award is Granted:** Vocational/Occupational **Number Awarded:** Varies each year; participating colleges generally award new scholarships to 2 high school seniors and 1 GED recipient each year. **Funds Available:** Stipends vary at each participating college, but are intended to provide full payment of tuition and required fees, books, supplies, tools, personal safety equipment, and uniforms. **Duration:** 1 year; may be renewed 1 additional year.

Eligibility Requirements: This program is open to Kentucky high school seniors and GED recipients who plan to work on a diploma or degree at a KCTCS technical college. Selection is based on academic achievement, character excellence, and career potential. **Deadline for Receipt:** Each college sets its own deadline. **Additional Information:** This program was established in 1993.

883 ■ KENTUCKY COMMUNITY AND TECHNICAL COLLEGE SYSTEM

Attn: Financial Aid
300 North Main Street
Versailles, KY 40383
Tel: (859)256-3100; 877-528-2748
Web Site: http://www.kctcs.edu/student/financialaidscholarships/index.htm

To provide financial assistance to sophomores attending a school within the Kentucky Community and Technical College System (KCTCS).

Title of Award: Martha C. Johnson Tuition Scholarships **Area, Field, or Subject:** General studies/Field of study not specified **Level of Education for which Award is Granted:** Two Year College, Vocational/Occupational **Number Awarded:** Varies each year. **Funds Available:** Stipends vary at each participating college but are intended to provide full payment of tuition and required fees. **Duration:** 1 year.

Eligibility Requirements: This program is open to KCTCS students entering their sophomore year with a GPA of 3.0 or higher. Applicants must have completed at least 30 hours of a pre-baccalaureate program for transfer to a 4-year college or university. They must be able to demonstrate financial need and outside community service and involvement. Along with their application, they must submit a 1-page essay on their career choice, personal values, and community service. Preference is given to women.

884 ■ KENTUCKY COMMUNITY AND TECHNICAL COLLEGE SYSTEM

Attn: Financial Aid
300 North Main Street
Versailles, KY 40383
Tel: (859)256-3100; 877-528-2748
Web Site: http://www.kctcs.edu/student/financialaidscholarships/index.htm

To provide financial assistance to outstanding students at participating institutions within the Kentucky Community and Technical College System (KCTCS).

Title of Award: KCTCS Commonwealth Scholarships **Area, Field, or Subject:** General studies/Field of study not specified **Level of Education for which Award is Granted:** Two Year College, Vocational/Occupational **Number Awarded:** Varies each year. **Funds Available:** Stipends vary at each participating college, but are intended to provide full payment of

tuition and required fees. **Duration:** 1 year; may be renewed 1 additional year.
Eligibility Requirements: This program is open to Kentucky residents who are 1) current-year valedictorians in their high school class, 2) valedictorians who graduated from high school during the previous academic year, and 3) salutatorian or the top 10% of the current high school graduating class. Applicants must be attending or planning to attend a participating KCTCS institution. They must be able to demonstrate unmet financial need. Most colleges require full-time enrollment. **Deadline for Receipt:** Each college sets its own deadline.

885 ■ KENTUCKY COMMUNITY AND TECHNICAL COLLEGE SYSTEM

Attn: Financial Aid
300 North Main Street
Versailles, KY 40383
Tel: (859)256-3100; 877-528-2748
Web Site: http://www.kctcs.edu/student/financialaidscholarships/index.htm
To provide financial assistance to students at participating institutions within the Kentucky Community and Technical College System (KCTCS).
Title of Award: KCTCS Presidential Scholarships **Area, Field, or Subject:** General studies/Field of study not specified **Level of Education for which Award is Granted:** Two Year College, Vocational/Occupational **Number Awarded:** Varies each year. **Funds Available:** Stipends vary at each participating college, but are intended to provide full payment of tuition and required fees. **Duration:** 1 year; may be renewed 1 additional year.
Eligibility Requirements: This program is open to students entering or attending participating KCTCS institutions. Each college establishes its own selection criteria, but most are based on academic excellence and financial need. **Deadline for Receipt:** Each college sets its own deadline. **Additional Information:** This program was established in 2000.

886 ■ KENTUCKY COMMUNITY AND TECHNICAL COLLEGE SYSTEM

Attn: Financial Aid
300 North Main Street
Versailles, KY 40383
Tel: (859)256-3100; 877-528-2748
Web Site: http://www.kctcs.edu/student/financialaidscholarships/index.htm
To provide financial assistance to single parents attending or planning to attend 1 of the schools within the Kentucky Community and Technical College System (KCTCS).
Title of Award: Kentucky Colonels Better Life Scholarships **Area, Field, or Subject:** General studies/Field of study not specified **Level of Education for which Award is Granted:** Two Year College, Vocational/Occupational **Number Awarded:** 16 each year: 1 in each of the KCTCS districts. **Funds Available:** The stipend is $2,500 per year. **Duration:** 1 year; may be renewed 1 additional year if the recipient maintains full-time enrollment and satisfactory academic progress.
Eligibility Requirements: This program is open to Kentucky residents who are single working parents with at least 1 child under 12 years of age. Applicants must be attending or planning to attend a KCTCS institution and able to demonstrate unmet financial need. Selection is based on demonstrated enthusiasm for learning and potential for academic success.

887 ■ KENTUCKY COMMUNITY AND TECHNICAL COLLEGE SYSTEM

Attn: Financial Aid
300 North Main Street
Versailles, KY 40383
Tel: (859)256-3100; 877-528-2748
Web Site: http://www.kctcs.edu/student/financialaidscholarships/index.htm
To provide financial assistance to African American students attending or planning to attend participating institutions within the Kentucky Community and Technical College System (KCTCS).
Title of Award: John T. Smith Scholarships **Area, Field, or Subject:** General studies/Field of study not specified **Level of Education for which Award is Granted:** Two Year College, Vocational/Occupational

Number Awarded: Varies each year. **Funds Available:** Stipends vary at each participating college, but are intended to provide full payment of tuition and required fees. **Duration:** 1 year; may be renewed 1 additional year.
Eligibility Requirements: This program is open to Kentucky residents who are African Americans attending or planning to attend a participating KCTCS institution. Applicants must be enrolled or planning to enroll in a transfer program to a 4-year institution. They must be able to demonstrate unmet financial need and a GPA of 2.5 or higher. Most colleges require full-time enrollment. **Deadline for Receipt:** Each college sets its own deadline.

888 ■ KENTUCKY DEPARTMENT OF VETERANS AFFAIRS

Attn: Division of Field Operations
545 South Third Street, Room 123
Louisville, KY 40202
Tel: (502)595-4447
Free: 800-928-4012
Fax: (502)595-4448
Web Site: http://www.kdva.net/tuitionwaiver.htm
To provide financial assistance for undergraduate or graduate education to the children or unremarried widow(er)s of deceased Kentucky veterans.
Title of Award: Exemption from Tuition Fees for Dependents of Kentucky Veterans **Area, Field, or Subject:** General studies/Field of study not specified **Level of Education for which Award is Granted:** Graduate, Undergraduate **Number Awarded:** Varies each year. **Funds Available:** Eligible dependents and survivors are exempt from tuition and matriculation fees at any state-supported institution of higher education in Kentucky. **Duration:** There are no age or time limits on the waiver.
Eligibility Requirements: This program is open to the children, stepchildren, adopted children, and unremarried widow(er)s of veterans who were residents of Kentucky when they entered military service or joined the Kentucky National Guard. The qualifying veteran must have been killed in action during a wartime period or died as a result of a service-connected disability incurred during a wartime period. Applicants must be attending or planning to attend a state-supported college or university in Kentucky to work on an undergraduate or graduate degree.

889 ■ KENTUCKY DEPARTMENT OF VETERANS AFFAIRS

Attn: Division of Field Operations
545 South Third Street, Room 123
Louisville, KY 40202
Tel: (502)595-4447
Free: 800-928-4012
Fax: (502)595-4448
Web Site: http://www.kdva.net/tuitionwaiver.htm
To provide financial assistance for college to the children, spouses, or unremarried widow(er)s of disabled or deceased Kentucky veterans.
Title of Award: Kentucky Veterans Tuition Waiver Program **Area, Field, or Subject:** General studies/Field of study not specified **Level of Education for which Award is Granted:** Undergraduate **Number Awarded:** Varies each year. **Funds Available:** Eligible dependents and survivors are exempt from tuition and matriculation fees at any state-supported institution of higher education in Kentucky. **Duration:** Tuition is waived until the recipient completes 36 months of training, receives a college degree, or (in the case of children of veterans) reaches 23 years of age, whichever comes first. Spouses and unremarried widow(er)s are not subject to the age limitation.
Eligibility Requirements: This program is open to the children, stepchildren, spouses, and unremarried widow(er)s of veterans who are residents of Kentucky (or were residents at the time of their death). The qualifying veteran must meet 1 of the following conditions: 1) died on active duty (regardless of wartime service); 2) died as a result of a service-connected disability (regardless of wartime service); 3) has a 100% service-connected disability; or 4) was a prisoner of war or declared missing in action. The military service may have been as a member of the U.S. armed forces, the Kentucky National Guard, or a Reserve component; service in the Guard or Reserves must have been on state active duty, active duty for training, inactive duty training, or active duty with the U.S. armed forces. Children of veterans must be under 23 years of age; no age limit applies to spouses or unremarried widow(er)s. All applicants must be attending or planning to attend a 2-year, 4-year, or vocational technical school operated and funded by the Kentucky Department of Education.

890 ■ KENTUCKY DEPARTMENT OF VETERANS AFFAIRS

Attn: Division of Field Operations
545 South Third Street, Room 123
Louisville, KY 40202
Tel: (502)595-4447
Free: 800-928-4012
Fax: (502)595-4448
Web Site: http://www.kdva.net/tuitionwaiver.htm
To provide financial assistance for college to the children of Kentucky veterans who have a disability related to their parent's military service.
Title of Award: Tuition Waiver for Disabled Children of Kentucky Veterans **Area, Field, or Subject:** General studies/Field of study not specified **Level of Education for which Award is Granted:** Undergraduate **Number Awarded:** Varies each year. **Funds Available:** Eligible children are exempt from payment of tuition at state-supported institutions of higher education in Kentucky. **Duration:** There are no age or time limits on the waiver.
Eligibility Requirements: This program is open to the children of veterans who have acquired a disability as a direct result of their parent's military service. The disability must have been designated by the U.S. Department of Veterans Affairs as compensable (currently defined as spina bifida). The veteran parent must 1) have served on active duty with the U.S. armed forces or in the National Guard or Reserve component on state active duty, active duty for training, or inactive duty training; and 2) be (or if deceased have been) a resident of Kentucky. Applicants must have been admitted to a state-supported university, college, or vocational training institute in Kentucky.

891 ■ KENTUCKY FEDERATION OF BUSINESS AND PROFESSIONAL WOMEN

Attn: BPW/KY Foundation
c/o Zayda Hurd Flanery, Chair
563 Red Lick Road
Berea, KY 40403
Tel: (606)287-4964
Fax: (606)287-4710
E-mail: zayda25@yahoo.com
Web Site: http://www.bpw-ky.org/ky_foundation.html
To provide funding to Kentucky residents interested in pursuing educational and personal development activities.
Title of Award: BPW/KY Foundation Grants **Area, Field, or Subject:** General studies/Field of study not specified **Level of Education for which Award is Granted:** Professional, Undergraduate **Number Awarded:** Varies each year. **Funds Available:** The amount of the grant depends on the nature of the activity to be funded. **Duration:** An individual may receive a grant only once every 24 months.
Eligibility Requirements: This program is open to residents of Kentucky (male and female) over 18 years of age. Applicants must be interested in pursuing 1 of the following activities: 1) job-related seminars, workshops, and other continuing education programs (not degree programs); 2) training programs that increase the number of public leadership positions; 3) research as it applies to labor market trends or issues facing Kentucky business and industry; 4) retraining for reentering the workforce, upgrading skills, or changing careers; 5) degree programs for nontraditional students (those not straight out of high school); or 6) literacy or GED programs. They must be currently in or planning a career in the Kentucky workforce. Selection is based on the availability of funds, the need of the applicant, and compliance with deadline, eligibility, and funding requirements. **Deadline for Receipt:** April or October of each year.

892 ■ KENTUCKY FIRE COMMISSION

Attn: Executive Director
300 North Main Street
Versailles, KY 40383
Tel: (859)256-3478
Free: 800-782-6823
Fax: (859)256-3125
E-mail: ronnie.day@kctcs.net
Web Site: http://www.kctcs.net/kyfirecommission
To provide financial assistance for college to the children and spouses of Kentucky police officers or fire fighters deceased or disabled in the line of duty.
Title of Award: Kentucky Deceased or Disabled Law Enforcement Officer and Fire Fighter Dependent Tuition Waiver **Area, Field, or Subject:**

General studies/Field of study not specified **Level of Education for which Award is Granted:** Undergraduate **Number Awarded:** Varies each year; all qualified applicants are entitled to this aid. **Funds Available:** Recipients are entitled to a waiver of tuition at state-supported universities, community colleges, and technical training institutions in Kentucky. **Duration:** 1 year; may be renewed up to a maximum total of 36 months.
Eligibility Requirements: This program is open to spouses, widow(er)s, and children of Kentucky residents who became a law enforcement officer, fire fighter, or volunteer fire fighter and who 1) was killed while in active service or training for active service; 2) died as a result of a service-connected disability; or 3) became permanently and totally disabled as a result of active service or training for active service. Children must be younger than 23 years of age; spouses and widow(er)s may be of any age.

893 ■ KENTUCKY HIGH SCHOOL ATHLETIC ASSOCIATION

2280 Executive Drive
Lexington, KY 40505
Tel: (859)299-5472
Fax: (859)293-5999
Web Site: http://www.khsaa.org
To provide financial assistance for college to student-athletes in Kentucky high schools.
Title of Award: National City/KHSAA Sweet 16 Scholarships **Area, Field, or Subject:** General studies/Field of study not specified **Level of Education for which Award is Granted:** Undergraduate **Number Awarded:** 32 each year: 1 female and 1 male in each of 16 regions in Kentucky. **Funds Available:** The stipend is $1,000. **Duration:** 1 year; nonrenewable.
Eligibility Requirements: This program is open to high school seniors in Kentucky who have participated in athletics or cheerleading. The awards are presented in conjunction with the state basketball tournament, but all student-athletes, not just basketball players, are eligible. Students must be nominated by a school representative. Letters of nomination must explain why the student is an exemplary leader and should receive the scholarship. Selection is based on academic achievement, leadership, citizenship, and sportsmanship. Men and women are judged separately. **Deadline for Receipt:** February of each year. **Additional Information:** This program is sponsored by National City Bank.

894 ■ KENTUCKY HIGH SCHOOL ATHLETIC ASSOCIATION

2280 Executive Drive
Lexington, KY 40505
Tel: (859)299-5472
Fax: (859)293-5999
Web Site: http://www.khsaa.org
To recognize and reward, with college scholarships, outstanding student-athletes (including cheerleaders) in Kentucky high schools.
Title of Award: Sportsmanship Recognition Program Scholarship **Area, Field, or Subject:** General studies/Field of study not specified **Level of Education for which Award is Granted:** Undergraduate **Number Awarded:** 2 each year: 1 for a female and 1 for a male. **Funds Available:** The stipend is $2,500. **Duration:** 1 year.
Eligibility Requirements: This program is open to high school seniors in Kentucky who have participated in athletics or cheerleading. Applicants must have at least a 2.5 GPA, 3 letters of recommendation from coaches and administrators illustrating the student's traits of good sportsmanship, demonstrated leadership within the school and the community, and a 2-page response to a case study developed for each competition. They must be planning to attend a college or university in Kentucky. A male and a female are recognized from each school in the state. They are chosen on the basis of these traits: playing the game by the rules; treating game officials and others with due respect, shaking hands with opponents, taking victory and defeat without undue emotionalism, controlling their tempers, being positive with officials and others who criticize them, cooperating with officials and others, being positive with opponents, letting student and adult audiences know that inappropriate behavior reflects poorly on the team, and serving as a role model for future student-athletes. These students are awarded a certificate and are entered into a regional competition. Males and females continue to compete separately. The regional winners are given a plaque and are considered for the Sportsmanship Recognition Program Scholarship. Selection is based on GPA, recommendations, leadership roles and honors, and the case study

essay. **Deadline for Receipt:** Applications must be submitted to the school's athletic director in March. **Additional Information:** This program, instituted in 1997, is currently sponsored by First Corbin Financial Corporation.

895 ■ KENTUCKY NATIONAL GUARD

Attn: Education Office
Boone National Guard Center
Frankfort, KY 40601-6168
Tel: (502)607-1039; 888-KY-GUARD
E-mail: Michelle.Kelley@ky.ngb.army.mil
To provide financial assistance for college or graduate school to members of the Kentucky National Guard.

Title of Award: Kentucky National Guard Tuition Award Program **Area, Field, or Subject:** General studies/Field of study not specified **Level of Education for which Award is Granted:** Graduate, Undergraduate **Number Awarded:** Varies each year. **Funds Available:** The program provides payment of full tuition and fees at any state-supported university, community college, or vocational or technical school in Kentucky. **Duration:** 1 semester; may be renewed.

Eligibility Requirements: This program is open to active enlisted members of the Kentucky National Guard who are interested in working on an undergraduate or graduate degree. Applicants must have maintained standards of satisfactory membership in the Guard, including passing the most recent physical fitness test, meeting the height-weight standard, meeting attendance standards, having no unsatisfactory performance or absence-without-leave records, and having no other restrictions on their personnel file. Preference is given to applicants working on their first undergraduate degree. **Deadline for Receipt:** March of each year for summer or fall terms; September of each year for spring term.

896 ■ KENTUCKY TURFGRASS COUNCIL

c/o David Williams, Executive Secretary
University of Kentucky
Plant and Soil Science Department
N-222 Agriculture Science Center North
Lexington, KY 40546-0091
Tel: (859)257-2715
Fax: (859)323-1952
E-mail: dwilliam@uky.edu
Web Site: http://www.uky.edu/Agriculture/ukturf/KTC2002/ktc_legacy_scholarship.htm
To provide financial assistance for college to children and grandchildren of members of the Kentucky Turfgrass Council (KTC).

Title of Award: Kentucky Turfgrass Council Legacy Scholarship **Area, Field, or Subject:** General studies/Field of study not specified **Level of Education for which Award is Granted:** Undergraduate **Number Awarded:** 1 each year. **Funds Available:** The stipend is $1,000. **Duration:** 1 year. Recipients are not eligible in the following year but they may reapply after a hiatus of 1 year.

Eligibility Requirements: This program is open to high school seniors and currently-enrolled college students who are enrolled or planning to enroll full time at an accredited institution of higher learning. A parent or grandparent of the applicant must have been a KTC member for 5 or more consecutive years. Applicants must submit transcripts from high school or colleges attended and a 500-word essay on their future goals and aspirations. Selection is based on academic achievement, extracurricular and community involvement, leadership, and outside employment. Financial need is not considered. **Deadline for Receipt:** October of each year. **Additional Information:** Information is also available from Gary Duvardo, Scholarship Committee Chair, P.O. Box 323, Bardstown, KY 40004, E-mail: garyd67@hotmail.com.

897 ■ PATRICK KERR SKATEBOARD SCHOLARSHIP FUND

P.O. Box 2054
Jenkintown, PA 19046
Fax: (215)663-5897
E-mail: info@skateboardscholarship.org
Web Site: http://www.skateboardscholarship.org
To provide financial assistance to college to high school seniors who are skateboarders.

Title of Award: Patrick Kerr Skateboard Scholarship **Area, Field, or Subject:** General studies/Field of study not specified **Level of Education**

for which Award is Granted: Undergraduate **Number Awarded:** 4 each year: 1 at $5,000 and 3 at $1,000. **Funds Available:** Stipends are $5,000 or $1,000. **Duration:** 1 year.

Eligibility Requirements: This program is open to graduating high school seniors who are skateboarders planning to enroll full time at an accredited 2-year or 4-year college or university. Applicants must have a GPA of 2.5 or higher and be able to demonstrate financial need. Along with their application, they must submit a 300-word essay on how skateboarding has been a positive influence in their life. Special consideration is given to applicants who have been actively promoting skateboarding in their community, but skateboarding skill is not considered in the selection process. U.S. citizenship is required. **Deadline for Receipt:** April of each year.

898 ■ KFC CORPORATION

Attn: KFC Colonel's Kids
P.O. Box 725489
Atlanta, GA 31139
(866)KFC-7240
E-mail: kfcscholars@act.org
Web Site: http://www.kfcscholars.org
To provide financial assistance to high school seniors who agree to work while attending college.

Title of Award: KFC Colonel's Scholars **Area, Field, or Subject:** General studies/Field of study not specified **Level of Education for which Award is Granted:** Four Year College **Number Awarded:** 50 each year. **Funds Available:** The stipend is $5,000 per year. **Duration:** 1 year; may be renewed up to 3 additional years provided the recipients remain enrolled full time with a GPA of 2.75 or higher. Beginning in the second year of the scholarship, they must also work an average of 10 hours per week in an approved position.

Eligibility Requirements: This program is open to graduating high school seniors planning to at public college or university in their home state to work on a bachelor's degree. They must have a GPA of 2.75 or higher and be able to demonstrate financial need. U.S. citizenship is required. **Deadline for Receipt:** March of each year. **Additional Information:** This program, established in 2006, is administered by ACT Recognition Program Services, 500 ACT Drive, P.O. Box 168, Iowa City, IA 52243-0168, (319) 341-2363.

899 ■ KIDS' CHANCE OF ARIZONA

P.O. Box 36753
Phoenix, AZ 85067-6753
Tel: (602)253-4360
Web Site: http://www.kidschance.org/Arizona/arizona.html
To provide financial assistance for college to Arizona residents whose parent was killed or permanently disabled in an employment-related accident.

Title of Award: Kids' Chance of Arizona Scholarships **Area, Field, or Subject:** General studies/Field of study not specified **Level of Education for which Award is Granted:** Undergraduate **Number Awarded:** Varies each year; since the program was established, it has awarded 54 scholarships worth $104,545. **Funds Available:** A stipend is awarded (amount not specified). **Duration:** 1 year; may be renewed.

Eligibility Requirements: This program is open to Arizona residents between 16 and 25 years of age whose parent was killed or disabled in an employment-related accident. Applicants must be attending or planning to attend a college, university, or trade school. They must submit high school transcripts, letters of recommendation, verification of school attendance, and a 1-page letter explaining their educational goals and need for financial assistance. **Additional Information:** This program was established in 1997. Information is also available from Cheryl Altman, scholarship vice president, (602) 541-9863.

900 ■ KIDS' CHANCE OF ARKANSAS, INC.

501 Woodlane, Suite 101
Little Rock, AR 72201-1024
(866)880-8444
E-mail: KidsChance@awcc.state.ar.us
Web Site: http://www.awcc.state.ar.us/kids_chance/kchance1.html
To provide financial assistance for college to Arkansas residents whose parent was killed or permanently disabled in an employment-related accident.

Title of Award: Kids' Chance of Arkansas Scholarships **Area, Field, or Subject:** General studies/Field of study not specified **Level of Education**

for which Award is Granted: Undergraduate Number Awarded: Varies each year; recently, 22 of these scholarships were awarded. Funds Available: The stipend depends on the financial need of the recipient. Duration: 1 year.

Eligibility Requirements: This program is open to children of workers who have been killed or become permanently and totally disabled from a compensable Arkansas Workers' Compensation injury or accident. Applicants must be between 16 and 22 years of age; be able to demonstrate academic achievement and aptitude; and be attending or planning to attend an accredited vocational/technical school, college, or university. The injury or death of their parent must have resulted in a decrease in family earnings that creates an obstacle to the continuation of their education. Deadline for Receipt: May of each year. Additional Information: This program was established in 2002.

901 ■ KIDS' CHANCE, INC.

P.O. Box 623
Valdosta, GA 31603
Tel: (229)244-0153
Fax: (229)245-0413
E-mail: kids300@bellsouth.net
Web Site: http://kidschance.org
To provide financial assistance for college to Georgia residents whose parent was killed or permanently disabled in an employment-related accident.

Title of Award: Kids' Chance Scholarships Area, Field, or Subject: General studies/Field of study not specified Level of Education for which Award is Granted: Undergraduate Number Awarded: Varies each year; recently, 60 students were receiving $176,076 in support through this program. Funds Available: The stipend depends on the financial need of the recipient, to a maximum of $5,333. Funds may be used for tuition, books, housing, meals, transportation, and/or as a supplement to the income of the family to compensate for money the student would earn by dropping out of school. Duration: 1 year; may be renewed if the recipient maintains satisfactory academic progress.

Eligibility Requirements: This program is open to Georgia residents between 16 and 25 years of age whose parent's on-the-job death or injury resulted in a substantial decline in family income. Applicants must be attending or planning to attend college or technical school. Additional Information: This program was established by the Workers' Compensation Section of the Georgia Bar in 1988. It has served as a model for comparable programs that currently operate in 26 other states.

902 ■ KIDS' CHANCE INC. OF MISSOURI

Attn: Scholarship Committee
P.O. Box 410384
St. Louis, MO 63141
Tel: (314)997-3390
Free: 800-484-5733
Fax: (314)432-5894
E-mail: susgrp@charter.net
Web Site: http://www.mokidschance.org
To provide financial assistance for college to Missouri residents whose parent was killed or permanently disabled in a work-related accident.

Title of Award: Kids' Chance of Missouri Scholarships Area, Field, or Subject: General studies/Field of study not specified Level of Education for which Award is Granted: Undergraduate Number Awarded: Varies each year. Funds Available: Stipends depend on the need of the recipient. Funds may be used to cover tuition, books, supplies, housing, meals, and other expenses not covered by other grants and/or scholarships. Duration: 1 year; may be renewed.

Eligibility Requirements: This program is open to Missouri residents whose parent sustained a serious injury or fatality in a Missouri work-related accident covered by workers' compensation. Applicants must be attending or planning to attend an accredited vocational school or college within the United States. They must be able to demonstrate financial need. Deadline for Receipt: April or October of each year. Additional Information: This program was established in 1996.

903 ■ KIDS' CHANCE OF INDIANA, INC.

Attn: Scholarship Committee
721 East Broadway
Fortville, IN 46040

Tel: (317)485-0043
Fax: (317)485-4299
E-mail: office@kidschancein.org
Web Site: http://www.kidschancein.org
To provide financial assistance for college or graduate school to Indiana residents whose parent was killed or permanently disabled in a work-related accident.

Title of Award: Kids' Chance of Indiana Scholarship Program Area, Field, or Subject: General studies/Field of study not specified Level of Education for which Award is Granted: Graduate, Undergraduate Number Awarded: Varies each year. Funds Available: Stipends range up to $6,000 per year. Funds may be used for tuition and fees, books, room and board, and utilities. Duration: 1 year; may be renewed.

Eligibility Requirements: This program is open to Indiana residents between 16 and 25 years of age who are the children of workers fatally or catastrophically injured as a result of a work-related accident or occupational disease. The death or injury must be compensable by the Workers' Compensation Board of the state of Indiana and must have resulted in a substantial decline in the family's income that is likely to impede the student's pursuit of his or her educational objectives. Applicants must be attending or planning to attend a trade/vocational school, junior/community college, 4-year college or university, or graduate school. Financial need is considered in the selection process. Additional Information: Recipients may attend a public or private educational institution in any state.

904 ■ KIDS' CHANCE OF IOWA

c/o Vern Vogel
P.O. Box 7673
Des Moines, IA 50322
Tel: (515)267-2848
E-mail: vvogel@hy-vee.com
Web Site: http://www.kidschanceiowa.org
To provide financial assistance for college to Iowa residents whose parent was killed or permanently disabled in an employment-related accident.

Title of Award: Kids' Chance of Iowa Scholarships Area, Field, or Subject: General studies/Field of study not specified Level of Education for which Award is Granted: Undergraduate Number Awarded: Varies each year. Funds Available: The stipend depends on the financial need of the recipient. Funding is intended to cover tuition and books, but it may also include housing and meals. Duration: 1 year; may be renewed if the recipient maintains acceptable grades.

Eligibility Requirements: This program is open to Iowa residents between 17 and 25 years of age who have had a parent permanently or catastrophically injured or killed in an employment-related accident. Applicants must be attending or planning to attend an accredited college or technical school. The parent's death or injury must have resulted in a substantial decline in the family income. Additional Information: This program was established in 1997. Information is also available from Patricia L. McCollom, Chair, 114 N.W. Fifth Street, P.O. Box 95, Ankeny, IA 50021, (515) 964-3868, Fax: (515) 965-1286, E-mail: IALCP@aol.com.

905 ■ KIDS' CHANCE OF LOUISIANA

c/o The Louisiana Bar Foundation
601 St. Charles Avenue, Third Floor
New Orleans, LA 70130
Tel: (504)561-1046
Fax: (504)566-1926
E-mail: kidschance@raisingthebar.org
Web Site: http://www.raisingthebar.org
To provide financial assistance for college to Louisiana residents whose parent was killed or permanently disabled in an employment-related accident.

Title of Award: Kids' Chance of Louisiana Scholarships Area, Field, or Subject: General studies/Field of study not specified Level of Education for which Award is Granted: Undergraduate Number Awarded: Varies each year. Funds Available: Stipends range from $500 to $3,000. Funds, paid directly to the school where the child is enrolled, may be used for tuition, books, fees, room, and general living expenses. Duration: 1 year; recipients may reapply as long as they maintain a "C" average or higher.

Eligibility Requirements: This program is open to Louisiana residents between 16 and 25 years of age who are the dependent of a worker killed or permanently and totally disabled in an accident that is compensable under a state or federal Workers' Compensation Act or law. Applicants must be attending or planning to attend an accredited Louisiana university; community, technical, or vocational college; or state-approved proprietary school. Financial need is considered in the selection process. **Deadline for Receipt:** February of each year. **Additional Information:** Kids' Chance was founded in 1988 by the Workers' Compensation Section of the Georgia Bar Association. The program in Louisiana is administered by the Louisiana Bar Foundation.

906 ■ KIDS' CHANCE OF MARYLAND, INC.

P.O. Box 20262
Baltimore, MD 21284
Tel: (410)832-4702
Fax: (410)832-4726
E-mail: info@kidschance-md.org
Web Site: http://www.kidschance-md.org
To provide financial assistance for college to Maryland residents whose parent was killed or permanently disabled in an employment-related accident.

Title of Award: Kids' Chance of Maryland Scholarships **Area, Field, or Subject:** General studies/Field of study not specified **Level of Education for which Award is Granted:** Undergraduate **Number Awarded:** Varies each year. **Funds Available:** Stipends depend on the need of the students. Funds are intended to cover tuition and books but may also including housing and meals. **Duration:** 1 year; recipients may reapply.

Eligibility Requirements: This program is open to Maryland residents between 16 and 25 years of age who had a parent permanently or catastrophically injured or killed in an employment-related accident compensable under the Maryland Workers' Compensation Act. Applicants must be attending or planning to attend college or technical school. Financial need is considered in the selection process.

907 ■ KIDS' CHANCE OF NORTH CAROLINA, INC.

c/o Martha Dealy, President
P.O. Box 470426
Charlotte, NC 28247-0426
Tel: (704)264-9111
Fax: (704)553-0241
E-mail: mdealy@cesinet.com
Web Site: http://www.kidschancenc.org
To provide financial assistance for college to North Carolina residents who parent was seriously injured or killed in a workplace accident.

Title of Award: Kids' Chance of North Carolina Scholarships **Area, Field, or Subject:** General studies/Field of study not specified **Level of Education for which Award is Granted:** Undergraduate **Number Awarded:** Varies each year. **Funds Available:** A stipend is awarded (amount not specified). Funds may be used for tuition, books, and meals. **Duration:** 1 year; may be renewed if the recipient maintains an acceptable academic level.

Eligibility Requirements: This program is open to residents of North Carolina between 16 and 25 years of age who are attending or planning to attend college or vocational school. Applicants must be children of employees who have been seriously injured or killed as a result of a workplace accident that is covered under the North Carolina Workers' Compensation Act. They must be able to demonstrate financial hardship caused by the death or serious injury of their parent. **Additional Information:** This program was established in 2004.

908 ■ KIDS' CHANCE OF PENNSYLVANIA

P.O. Box 543
Pottstown, PA 19464
Tel: (484)945-2104
Fax: (610)970-7520
E-mail: info@kidschanceofpa.org
Web Site: http://www.kidschanceofpa.org
To provide financial assistance for college to Pennsylvania residents whose parent was killed or permanently disabled in a work-related accident.

Title of Award: Kids' Chance of Pennsylvania Scholarships **Area, Field, or Subject:** General studies/Field of study not specified **Level of Education for which Award is Granted:** Undergraduate **Number Awarded:** Varies each year; recently, 35 students were receiving support through this program. **Funds Available:** Regardless of the state where the recipi-

ent attends school, the stipend may not exceed the annual cost of tuition and books at the most expensive public postsecondary educational institution in Pennsylvania. **Duration:** 1 year; may be renewed.

Eligibility Requirements: This program is open to Pennsylvania residents between 16 and 25 years of age who have been accepted by an accredited postsecondary educational institution anywhere in the United States. At least 1 parent must have been killed or seriously injured as a result of a work-related accident covered under the Pennsylvania Workers' Compensation Act. Financial need is considered in the selection process. **Deadline for Receipt:** April of each year.

909 ■ KIDS' CHANCE OF SOUTH CAROLINA

1135 Dixie Red Road
Leesville, SC 29070
Tel: (803)532-0608
Fax: (803)532-9892
Web Site: http://www.kidschancesc.org
To provide financial assistance for college or graduate school to South Carolina residents whose parent was killed or permanently disabled in a work-related accident.

Title of Award: Kids' Chance of South Carolina Scholarships **Area, Field, or Subject:** General studies/Field of study not specified **Level of Education for which Award is Granted:** Graduate, Undergraduate **Number Awarded:** Varies each year. **Funds Available:** Stipends range from $500 to $6,000 per year. Funds may be used for tuition and fees, books, room and board, and utilities. **Duration:** 1 year; may be renewed.

Eligibility Requirements: This program is open to South Carolina residents between 16 and 25 years of age who are the children of workers fatally or catastrophically injured as a result of a work-related accident or occupational disease. Applicants must be attending or planning to attend a trade school, vocational school, community or junior college, 4-year college or university, or graduate school. The work-related injury or occupational disease from which their parent suffers or died must be compensable by the Workers' Compensation Board of the state of South Carolina and must have resulted in a substantial decline in the family's income that is likely to interfere with the student's pursuit of his or her educational objectives. **Additional Information:** Recipients may attend school in any state.

910 ■ KIDS' CHANCE OF WASHINGTON

P.O. Box 185
Olympia, WA 98507-0185
800-572-5762
Fax: (360)943-2333
E-mail: debbie@wscff.org
Web Site: http://www.kidschancewa.com
To provide financial assistance for college to residents of Washington whose parent or spouse was killed or seriously disabled in a workplace accident.

Title of Award: Kids' Chance of Washington Scholarships **Area, Field, or Subject:** General studies/Field of study not specified **Level of Education for which Award is Granted:** Undergraduate **Number Awarded:** Varies each year. **Funds Available:** A stipend is awarded (amount not specified). Funds are paid directly to the student's school to be used for tuition, books, fees, room, and general living expenses. **Duration:** 1 year; may be renewed.

Eligibility Requirements: This program is open to Washington residents attending or planning to attend an accredited community college, university, college, or technical/vocational school. Applicants must be the child or spouse of a Washington worker permanently or catastrophically injured or deceased while on the job. Selection is based primarily on financial need. **Additional Information:** This program was established in 2001.

911 ■ PETER KIEWIT FOUNDATION

Attn: Legacy Scholarship Program
8805 Indian Hills Drive, Suite 225
Omaha, NE 68114
Tel: (402)344-7890
To provide financial assistance for college to high school seniors in Nebraska.

Title of Award: Peter Kiewit Foundation Legacy Scholarship Program **Area, Field, or Subject:** General studies/Field of study not specified

Level of Education for which Award is Granted: Undergraduate **Number Awarded:** 50 each year. **Funds Available:** The stipend is $7,500 per year. **Duration:** 1 year; may be renewed up to 3 additional years.

Eligibility Requirements: This program is open to seniors graduating from high schools in Nebraska who rank in the top 20% of their class. Applicants must be planning to attend a 4-year college or university in Nebraska. Along with their application, they must submit a 1-page essay on the single extracurricular activity that has meant the most to them and why. Selection is based on academic achievement and financial need. **Deadline for Receipt:** January of each year. **Additional Information:** This foundation began awarding scholarships in 1980, and has provided more than $41,800,000 in support to Nebraska students in that time. In 2004, it consolidated several programs into this Legacy Scholarship Program.

912 ■ KNIGHTS OF COLUMBUS

Attn: Director of Scholarship Aid
P.O. Box 1670
New Haven, CT 06507-0901
Tel: (203)752-4332
Fax: (203)772-2696
E-mail: info@kofc.org
Web Site: http://www.kofc.org/members/scholarships/index.cfm
To provide financial assistance to entering freshmen at Catholic colleges and universities.

Title of Award: Fourth Degree Pro Deo and Pro Patria Scholarship Program **Area, Field, or Subject:** General studies/Field of study not specified **Level of Education for which Award is Granted:** Undergraduate **Number Awarded:** 62 each year, of which 12 are to Catholic University of America and 50 are to other Catholic institutions. **Funds Available:** The stipend is $1,500 per year. **Duration:** 1 year; may be renewed up to 3 additional years upon evidence of satisfactory academic performance.

Eligibility Requirements: Eligible are students entering their freshman year in a program leading to a baccalaureate degree at a Catholic college or university in the United States; applicants must be members in good standing of the Columbian Squires or Knights of Columbus, or the son or daughter of a member, or the child of a deceased member who was in good standing at the time of death. Selection is based on secondary school record, class rank, and aptitude test scores. **Deadline for Receipt:** February of each year. **Additional Information:** Of the scholarships for Catholic University of America, preference on 2 is given to Columbian Squires; of the scholarships for other Catholic colleges, preference on 2 is given to Columbian Squires.

913 ■ KNIGHTS OF COLUMBUS

Attn: Director of Scholarship Aid
P.O. Box 1670
New Haven, CT 06507-0901
Tel: (203)752-4332
Fax: (203)772-2696
E-mail: info@kofc.org
Web Site: http://www.kofc.org/members/scholarships/index.cfm
To provide financial assistance to freshmen men entering Catholic colleges and universities.

Title of Award: Percy J. Johnson Scholarships **Area, Field, or Subject:** General studies/Field of study not specified **Level of Education for which Award is Granted:** Undergraduate **Number Awarded:** 1 or more each year, depending on the availability of funds. **Funds Available:** The stipend is $1,500 per year. **Duration:** 1 year; may be renewed up to 3 additional years upon evidence of satisfactory academic performance.

Eligibility Requirements: Eligible are male students entering their freshman year in a program leading to a bachelor's degree at a Catholic college or university in the United States; applicants must be members in good standing of the Columbian Squires or Knights of Columbus, or the son of a member, or the son of a deceased member who was in good standing at the time of death. Selection is based on secondary school

record, class rank, financial need, and aptitude test scores. **Deadline for Receipt:** February of each year. **Additional Information:** This program was established in 1990.

914 ■ KNIGHTS OF COLUMBUS

Attn: Student Loan Committee
P.O. Box 1670
New Haven, CT 06507-0901
Tel: (203)752-4224
Fax: (203)772-2696
E-mail: info@kofc.org
Web Site: http://www.kofc.org/members/scholarships/index.cfm
To make educational loans to members and relatives of the Knights of Columbus, members of the Catholic clergy, and members of Columbian Squires.

Title of Award: Knights of Columbus Student Loan Program **Area, Field, or Subject:** General studies/Field of study not specified **Level of Education for which Award is Granted:** Graduate, Professional, Undergraduate **Number Awarded:** Varies each year. **Funds Available:** The maximum loans are: first-year college students: $2,625 per academic year; second-year college students: $3,500 per academic year; third-year and fourth-year college students: $5,500 per academic year; graduate students: $8,500 per academic year. Funds are paid to the recipient's school. Any Federal Stafford Loans borrowed from other lenders or state guarantee agencies in addition to the Knights of Columbus loan may not exceed the federal maximums. The Stafford Loan program consists of both subsidized (for students with financial need) and unsubsidized loans (for students who do not qualify in whole or in part for a subsidized Stafford Loan). If the student qualifies for a subsidized loan, the government pays the interest that accrues on the loan during the time he or she is in school. If the loan is unsubsidized, the student is responsible for accrued interest. For a first-time borrower, the loan interest rate is variable and may change every July but will never exceed 9%. **Duration:** 1 year; may be renewed. All loans must be repaid within 10 years.

Eligibility Requirements: Applicants must be enrolled as at least a half-time student and must be a U.S. citizen or resident alien. They must be enrolled or accepted at a school that is recognized by the U.S. government under the Federal Stafford Loan program (this includes technical and vocational schools, community and junior colleges, colleges and universities, and major seminaries both within the United States and in other countries). Eligible students include members of the Knights of Columbus; wives and children of members; widows and children of deceased members; members of the Columbian Squires; and priests, brothers, sisters, seminarians, and postulants at the college, seminary, and postgraduate level (affiliation with the Knights of Columbus not required). **Additional Information:** The guarantee agency of the state of Connecticutthe Connecticut Student Loan Foundationhas agreed to insure loans for Knights of Columbus borrowers nationwide. All student loans are insured. This means that in the event of the death or disability of the student, the entire amount owed to the Knights of Columbus will be paid by the Connecticut Student Loan Foundation and will not be the liability of the borrower's family or estate.

915 ■ KNIGHTS OF COLUMBUS

Attn: Director of Scholarship Aid
P.O. Box 1670
New Haven, CT 06507-0901
Tel: (203)752-4332
Fax: (203)772-2696
E-mail: info@kofc.org
Web Site: http://www.kofc.org/members/scholarships/index.cfm
To provide financial assistance at Catholic colleges or universities to children of disabled or deceased veterans, law enforcement officers, or firemen who are/were also Knights of Columbus members.

Title of Award: Francis P. Matthews and John E. Swift Educational Trust Scholarships **Area, Field, or Subject:** General studies/Field of study not specified **Level of Education for which Award is Granted:** Four Year College **Number Awarded:** Varies each year. **Funds Available:** The amounts of the awards vary but are designed to cover tuition, room and board, books, and required fees at the Catholic college or university of the recipient's choice. **Duration:** 1 year; may be renewed up to 3 additional years.

Eligibility Requirements: This program is open children of members of the sponsoring organization who are high school seniors planning to attend a 4-year Catholic college or university. The parent must be 1) totally and permanently disabled or deceased as a result of military service during World War II, the Korean Conflict, the Vietnam War, or the Persian Gulf War; 2) a full-time law enforcement officer who became disabled or lost his life as a result of criminal violence; or 3) a fire fighter who became disabled or deceased in the line of duty. For the children of veterans, the death or disability must have occurred during a period of conflict or within 10 years of its official termination. **Deadline for Receipt:** April of each year.

916 ■ KNIGHTS OF COLUMBUS

Attn: Director of Scholarship Aid
P.O. Box 1670
New Haven, CT 06507-0901
Tel: (203)752-4332
Fax: (203)772-2696
E-mail: info@kofc.org
Web Site: http://www.kofc.org/members/scholarships/index.cfm
To provide financial assistance to entering freshmen at Catholic colleges and universities who have ties to the Knights of Columbus.
Title of Award: John W. McDevitt (Fourth Degree) Scholarships **Area, Field, or Subject:** General studies/Field of study not specified **Level of Education for which Award is Granted:** Undergraduate **Number Awarded:** Approximately 36 each year. **Funds Available:** The stipend is $1,500 per year. **Duration:** 1 year; may be renewed up to 3 additional years upon evidence of satisfactory academic performance.
Eligibility Requirements: Eligible are students entering their freshman year in a program leading to a baccalaureate degree at a Catholic college or university in the United States; applicants must be members in good standing of the Knights of Columbus, or the wife, widow, son, or daughter of a current member or of a deceased member who was in good standing at the time of death. Selection is based on secondary school record, class rank, and aptitude test scores. **Deadline for Receipt:** February of each year.

917 ■ KNIGHTS OF COLUMBUS-MARYLAND STATE COUNCIL

Attn: Scholarship Committee
6243 Gilston Park Road
Baltimore, MD 21228-2841
Tel: (410)521-6200
Fax: (410)521-0203
Web Site: http://www.kofc-md.org/pages/Committees/scholarship/scholar.htm
To provide financial assistance for college to members of the Knights of Columbus in Maryland and their families.
Title of Award: Father Amos Gaudette Memorial College Scholarship **Area, Field, or Subject:** General studies/Field of study not specified **Level of Education for which Award is Granted:** Four Year College **Number Awarded:** 2 each year. **Funds Available:** The stipend is $1,500 per year. **Duration:** Up to 4 years.
Eligibility Requirements: This program is open to members of the Knights of Columbus within Maryland and their children and wives. Applicants must be entering their first year at an accredited 4-year college or university. Selection is based on academic excellence, personal qualifications, and financial need, with primary emphasis placed on academic excellence. **Deadline for Receipt:** February of each year. **Additional Information:** Information is also available from Richard L. Sherbert, Scholarship Committee Chair, P.O. Box 518, Dunkirk, MD 20754, E-mail: rsherbert@erols.com.

918 ■ KNIGHTS OF COLUMBUS-MARYLAND STATE COUNCIL

Attn: Scholarship Committee
6243 Gilston Park Road
Baltimore, MD 21228-2841
Tel: (410)521-6200
Fax: (410)521-0203
Web Site: http://www.kofc-md.org/pages/Committees/scholarship/scholar.htm
To provide financial assistance for college to Catholic residents of Maryland.
Title of Award: Monsignor William F. Sauer College Scholarship **Area, Field, or Subject:** General studies/Field of study not specified **Level of**

Education for which Award is Granted: Four Year College **Number Awarded:** 2 each year. **Funds Available:** The stipend is $1,500 per year. **Duration:** Up to 4 years.
Eligibility Requirements: This program is open to high school seniors who are Catholics and residents of Maryland. Applicants must be entering their first year at an accredited 4-year college or university. Selection is based on academic excellence, personal qualifications, and financial need, with primary emphasis placed on financial need. **Deadline for Receipt:** February of each year. **Additional Information:** Information is also available from Richard L. Sherbert, Scholarship Committee Chair, P.O. Box 518, Dunkirk, MD 20754, E-mail: rsherbert@erols.com.

919 ■ KNIGHTS OF COLUMBUS-TEXAS STATE COUNCIL

Attn: Aid to Education Committee
6633 Highway 290 East, Suite 204
Austin, TX 78723-1157
Tel: (512)442-1492
Fax: (512)326-1492
E-mail: info@tkofc.org
Web Site: http://www.tkofc.org/AwardsEducation.cfm
To provide financial assistance for college to members of the Knights of Columbus in Texas and their families.
Title of Award: Texas State Council Educational Grants **Area, Field, or Subject:** General studies/Field of study not specified **Level of Education for which Award is Granted:** Undergraduate **Number Awarded:** 1 or more each year. **Funds Available:** The stipend is $1,000. **Duration:** 1 year.
Eligibility Requirements: This program is open to members of the Knights of Columbus in Texas and their wives, children, and grandchildren. Applicants must be attending or planning to attend a college, university, junior college, technical school, business school, or seminary. They must submit an essay, up to 250 words, on their personal reasons for applying and how the receipt of the grant will effect their decision to continue with their education. **Deadline for Receipt:** February of each year.

920 ■ KNIGHTS OF LITHUANIA

c/o John P. Baltrus, Scholarship Committee Chair
118 Vine Street
Jefferson Hills, PA 15025
Web Site: http://www.knightsoflithuania.com/ScholarshipCommittee.html
To provide financial assistance to undergraduate or graduate students of Lithuanian ancestry.
Title of Award: Knights of Lithuania Scholarship Program **Area, Field, or Subject:** General studies/Field of study not specified **Level of Education for which Award is Granted:** Graduate, Undergraduate **Number Awarded:** Varies each year. **Funds Available:** Stipends range up to $1,000 per year. Funds are generally paid in 2 equal installments. **Duration:** 1 year; nonrenewable.
Eligibility Requirements: Applicants must have been a member of the Knights of Lithuania for at least 2 years, be of Lithuanian ancestry, and be in financial need. There is no age limitation. Selection is based on recommendations, scholastic record, financial need, a personal interview, and organizational activity within the Knights of Lithuania. **Deadline for Receipt:** June of each year.

921 ■ SUSAN G. KOMEN BREAST CANCER FOUNDATION

Attn: Grants Department
5005 LBJ Freeway, Suite 250
Dallas, TX 75244
Tel: (972)855-1616; 888-300-5582
Fax: (972)855-1605
E-mail: ccombs@komen.org
Web Site: http://www.komen.org
To provide financial assistance for college to high school seniors who lost a parent to breast cancer.
Title of Award: Susan G. Komen Breast Cancer Foundation College Scholarship Awards **Area, Field, or Subject:** General studies/Field of study not specified **Level of Education for which Award is Granted:** Undergraduate **Number Awarded:** 5 each year. **Funds Available:** Stipends up to $10,000 per year are available. Funds may be used for tuition, books, fees, and on-campus room and board. **Duration:** 4 years, provided the recipient remains enrolled full time and makes reasonable progress toward completion of a baccalaureate degree.

Eligibility Requirements: This program is open to students who lost a parent to breast cancer and would otherwise find attending college to be a significant financial burden or impossible. Applicants must be sponsored by a local affiliate of the foundation in the area where they live. They must be high school seniors or young adults under 25 years of age, be U.S. citizens or permanent residents, have a college GPA of 2.8 or higher (if already attending college), and be attending or planning to attend a state-supported college or university in the state where they permanently reside. Along with their application, they must submit 2 essays of 500 words each on 1) how breast cancer has changed them, and 2) how their education will help them achieve their career objectives and personal goals. Financial need is also considered in the selection process. All eligible applicants are interviewed at the local level and finalists are invited to the foundation's headquarters in Dallas for final interviews. **Deadline for Receipt:** November of each year.

922 ■ KONIAG INCORPORATED

Attn: Koniag Education Foundation
6927 Old Seward Highway, Suite 103
Anchorage, AK 99518-2283
Tel: (907)562-9093; 888-562-9093
Fax: (907)562-9023
E-mail: kef@alaska.net
Web Site: http://www.koniageducation.org
To provide financial assistance for college to Alaska Natives of the Koniag region who have demonstrated leadership.
Title of Award: Glenn Godfrey Leadership Scholarship **Area, Field, or Subject:** General studies/Field of study not specified **Level of Education for which Award is Granted:** Four Year College **Number Awarded:** 1 each year. **Funds Available:** The stipend is $5,000. Funds are sent directly to the recipient's school and may be used for tuition, fees, books, and on-campus room and meals. **Duration:** 1 year; may be renewed up to 2 additional years provided the recipient maintains a GPA of 2.5 or higher and participates in school, community, or church activities.
Eligibility Requirements: This program is open to college sophomores, juniors, seniors who are 1) Alaska Natives enrolled under Section 5 of the Alaska Native Claims Settlement Act to the Koniag region, or 2) direct or legally adopted descendants of those original enrollees. Applicants must have a GPA of 2.5 or higher and be able to demonstrate leadership in school, community, athletics, church, or Native culture. Along with their application, they must submit a 400- to 500-word on what they expect to accomplish in the next 10 years, how the scholarship will help them achieve that goal, and how they plan to give back to the community. **Deadline for Receipt:** July of each year.

923 ■ KONIAG INCORPORATED

Attn: Koniag Education Foundation
6927 Old Seward Highway, Suite 103
Anchorage, AK 99518-2283
Tel: (907)562-9093; 888-562-9093
Fax: (907)562-9023
E-mail: kef@alaska.com
Web Site: http://www.koniageducation.org
To provide financial assistance for undergraduate or graduate school to Alaska Natives of the Koniag region.
Title of Award: Koniag Education Foundation Academic Achievement/ Graduate Scholarships **Area, Field, or Subject:** General studies/Field of study not specified **Level of Education for which Award is Granted:** Graduate, Undergraduate **Number Awarded:** Varies each year. **Funds Available:** Stipends range up to $2,500. Funds are sent directly to the recipient's school and may be used for tuition, books, supplies, room, board, and transportation. **Duration:** 1 year; may be renewed.
Eligibility Requirements: This program is open to high school seniors, high school and GED graduates, college students, and graduate students who are 1) Alaska Natives enrolled under Section 5 of the Alaska Native Claims Settlement Act to the Koniag region, and 2) direct or legally adopted descendants of those original enrollees. Applicants must supply proof of eligibility and documentation of financial need. They must have a GPA of 3.0 or higher and be enrolled or planning to enroll full time. Along with their application, they must submit 1) a 300- to 600-word letter that includes their personal and family history, their schooling or work history, and their educational and life goals; and 2) a 200- to 400-word essay on how their education may benefit the Alutiiq people. **Deadline for Receipt:**

March of each year for summer or continuation of regular term; May of each year for regular school year. **Additional Information:** The Koniag Education Foundation was established in 1993 by the directors of Koniag, Inc. The Koniag region covers Kodiak Island, many smaller islands, and a portion of the Alaska Peninsula.

924 ■ KONIAG INCORPORATED

Attn: Koniag Education Foundation
6927 Old Seward Highway, Suite 103
Anchorage, AK 99518-2283
Tel: (907)562-9093; 888-562-9093
Fax: (907)562-9023
E-mail: kef@alaska.net
Web Site: http://www.koniageducation.org
To provide financial assistance for college to Alaska Natives of the Koniag region.
Title of Award: Koniag Education Foundation College/University Basic Scholarships **Area, Field, or Subject:** General studies/Field of study not specified **Level of Education for which Award is Granted:** Undergraduate **Number Awarded:** Varies each year. **Funds Available:** Stipends range up to $1,000. Funds are sent directly to the recipient's school and may be used for tuition, books, supplies, room, board, and transportation. **Duration:** 1 year; may be renewed.
Eligibility Requirements: This program is open to high school seniors, high school and GED graduates, and college students who are 1) Alaska Natives enrolled under Section 5 of the Alaska Native Claims Settlement Act to the Koniag region, and 2) direct or legally adopted descendants of those original enrollees. Applicants must supply proof of eligibility and documentation of financial need. They must have a GPA of 2.0 or higher and be enrolled or planning to enroll full time. Along with their application, they must submit 1) a 300- to 600-word letter that includes their personal and family history, their schooling or work history, and their educational and life goals; and 2) a 200- to 400-word essay on how their education may benefit the Alutiiq people. **Deadline for Receipt:** March of each year for summer or continuation of regular term; May of each year for regular school year. **Additional Information:** The Koniag Education Foundation was established in 1993 by the directors of Koniag, Inc. The Koniag region covers Kodiak Island, many smaller islands, and a portion of the Alaska Peninsula.

925 ■ KONIAG INCORPORATED

Attn: Koniag Education Foundation
6927 Old Seward Highway, Suite 103
Anchorage, AK 99518-2283
Tel: (907)562-9093; 888-562-9093
Fax: (907)562-9023
E-mail: kef@alaska.net
Web Site: http://www.koniageducation.org
To provide financial assistance to Alaska Natives of the Koniag region who are interested in a program of vocational education.
Title of Award: Koniag Education Foundation Vocational Education Grants **Area, Field, or Subject:** General studies/Field of study not specified **Level of Education for which Award is Granted:** Vocational/ Occupational **Number Awarded:** Varies each year. **Funds Available:** Stipends range up to $2,500. Funds are sent directly to the recipient's school and may be used for tuition, books, supplies, room, board, and transportation. **Duration:** At least 6 weeks; may be renewed.
Eligibility Requirements: This program is open to high school seniors, high school graduates, and currently-enrolled vocational school students who are 1) Alaska Natives enrolled under Section 5 of the Alaska Native Claims Settlement Act to the Koniag region, and 2) direct or legally adopted descendants of those original enrollees. Applicants must have a GPA of 2.0 or higher and be enrolled or planning to enroll in a state-accredited or municipally-recognized vocational school. They must supply proof of eligibility; a demonstration of how the training will assist them in gaining employment, job security, and/or advancement; and documentation of financial need. Along with their application, they must submit 1) a 300- to 600-word letter that includes their personal and family history, their schooling or work history, and their educational and life goals; and 2) a 200- to 400-word essay on how their education may benefit the Alutiiq people. **Deadline for Receipt:** March of each year for summer or continuation of regular term; May of each year for regular school year. **Additional Information:** The Koniag Education Foundation was established in 1993

by the directors of Koniag, Inc. The Koniag region covers Kodiak Island, many smaller islands, and a portion of the Alaska Peninsula.

926 ■ KOREAN AMERICAN SCHOLARSHIP FOUNDATION
Eastern Region
1952 Gallows Road, Suite 340B
10301 Georgia Avenue, Suite 303
Vienna, VA 22182
Tel: (703)748-5935
Fax: (703)748-1874
E-mail: kasfdc@hotmail.com
Web Site: http://www.kasf.org/home/regional/eastern/eastern.html
To provide financial assistance to Korean American undergraduate and graduate students who attend school in the eastern states.
Title of Award: Eastern Region Korean American Scholarships **Area, Field, or Subject:** General studies/Field of study not specified **Level of Education for which Award is Granted:** Four Year College, Graduate **Number Awarded:** Varies each year. Recently, 65 of these scholarships were awarded: 1 at $5,000, 20 at $2,000, 3 at $1,500, 33 at $1,000, 2 at $500, and 6 at $350. **Funds Available:** Stipends range from $350 to $5,000. **Duration:** 1 year; renewable.
Eligibility Requirements: This program is open to Korean American students who are currently enrolled in a college or university in an eastern state as a full-time undergraduate or graduate student. Applicants may reside anywhere in the United States as long as they attend school in the eastern region: Delaware, District of Columbia, Kentucky, Maryland, North Carolina, Pennsylvania, Virginia, and West Virginia. Selection is based on academic achievement, school activities, community service, and financial need. **Deadline for Receipt:** May of each year.

927 ■ KOREAN AMERICAN SCHOLARSHIP FOUNDATION
Mideastern Region
c/o Chang S. Choi, Scholarship Committee Chair
6410 Lahser Road
Bloomfield Hills, MI 48301
Tel: (248)752-3180
Fax: (248)644-0507
E-mail: cschoi@comcast.net
Web Site: http://www.kasf.org/home/regional/mideastern/mideastern.html
To provide financial assistance to Korean American undergraduate and graduate students who attend school in Indiana, Michigan, or Ohio.
Title of Award: Mideastern Region Korean American Scholarships **Area, Field, or Subject:** General studies/Field of study not specified **Level of Education for which Award is Granted:** Four Year College, Graduate **Number Awarded:** Varies each year. Recently, the midwestern regional chapter (which then included the current mideastern regional chapter) awarded 69 of these scholarships. **Funds Available:** Stipends range from $1,000 to $2,000. **Duration:** 1 year; renewable.
Eligibility Requirements: This program is open to Korean American students who are currently enrolled in a college or university as full-time undergraduate or graduate students. Applicants may reside anywhere in the United States as long as they attend school in Indiana, Michigan, or Ohio. Selection is based on academic achievement, school activities, community service, and financial need. **Deadline for Receipt:** March of each year.

928 ■ KOREAN AMERICAN SCHOLARSHIP FOUNDATION
Midwestern Region
c/o Tony S. Hahm, Scholarship Committee Chair
P.O. Box 0416
Northbrook, IL 60065-0416
Tel: (847)797-1291
Fax: (847)797-1304
E-mail: tonyhahm@yahoo.com
Web Site: http://www.kasf.org/home/regional/midwestern/midwestern.html
To provide financial assistance to Korean American undergraduate and graduate students who attend school in the Midwest.
Title of Award: Midwestern Region Korean American Scholarships **Area, Field, or Subject:** General studies/Field of study not specified **Level of Education for which Award is Granted:** Four Year College, Graduate **Number Awarded:** Varies each year. Recently, the midwestern regional chapter (which then included the current mideastern regional chapter)

awarded 69 of these scholarships. **Funds Available:** Stipends range from $1,000 to $2,000. **Duration:** 1 year; renewable.
Eligibility Requirements: This program is open to Korean American students who are currently enrolled in a college or university in the midwestern states as full-time undergraduate or graduate students. Applicants may reside anywhere in the United States as long as they attend school in the midwest region: Illinois, Iowa, Kansas, Minnesota, Missouri, Nebraska, North Dakota, South Dakota, and Wisconsin. Selection is based on academic achievement, school activities, community service, and financial need. **Deadline for Receipt:** June of each year.

929 ■ KOREAN AMERICAN SCHOLARSHIP FOUNDATION
NorthEastern Region
c/o William Kim, Scholarship Committee Chair
51 West Overlook
Port Washington, NY 11050
Tel: (516)883-1142
Fax: (516)883-1964
E-mail: wkim@alson.com
Web Site: http://www.kasf.org/home/regional/northeastern/northeastern.html
To provide financial assistance to Korean American undergraduate and graduate students who attend school in the northeastern states.
Title of Award: NorthEastern Region Korean American Scholarships **Area, Field, or Subject:** General studies/Field of study not specified **Level of Education for which Award is Granted:** Four Year College, Graduate **Number Awarded:** Varies each year; recently, 60 of these scholarships were awarded **Funds Available:** Stipends range from $1,000 to $2,000. **Duration:** 1 year; renewable.
Eligibility Requirements: This program is open to Korean American students who are currently enrolled in a college or university in a northeastern state as a full-time undergraduate or graduate student. Applicants may reside anywhere in the United States as long as they attend school in the northeastern region: Connecticut, Maine, Massachusetts, New Hampshire, New Jersey, New York, Rhode Island, and Vermont. Selection is based on academic achievement, school activities, community service, and financial need. **Deadline for Receipt:** June of each year.

930 ■ KOREAN AMERICAN SCHOLARSHIP FOUNDATION
Southern Region
c/o Dr. Sam Sook Chung, Scholarship Committee Chair
2989 Preston Drive
Rex, GA 30273
Tel: (770)968-6768
E-mail: southern@kasf.org
Web Site: http://www.kasf.org/home/regional/southern/southern.html
To provide financial assistance to Korean American undergraduate and graduate students who attend school in the southern states.
Title of Award: Southern Region Korean American Scholarships **Area, Field, or Subject:** General studies/Field of study not specified **Level of Education for which Award is Granted:** Four Year College, Graduate **Number Awarded:** Varies each year. Recently, 39 of these scholarships, worth $42,700, were awarded. **Funds Available:** Stipends range from $1,000 to $2,000. **Duration:** 1 year; renewable.
Eligibility Requirements: This program is open to Korean American students who are currently enrolled in a college or university in the southern states as full-time undergraduate or graduate students. Applicants may reside anywhere in the United States as long as they attend school in the southern region: Alabama, Arkansas, Florida, Georgia, Louisiana, Mississippi, Oklahoma, South Carolina, Tennessee, and Texas. Selection is based on academic achievement, school activities, community service, and financial need. **Deadline for Receipt:** June of each year.

931 ■ KOREAN AMERICAN SCHOLARSHIP FOUNDATION
Western Region
Attn: Scholarship Committee
3435 Wilshire Boulevard, Suite 2450B
Los Angeles, CA 90010
Tel: (213)380-KASF
Fax: (213)380-KASF
E-mail: western@kasf.org

Web Site: http://www.kasf.org/home/regional/western/western.html
To provide financial assistance to Korean American undergraduate and graduate students attending college in the western states.
Title of Award: Western Region Korean American Scholarships **Area, Field, or Subject:** General studies/Field of study not specified **Level of Education for which Award is Granted:** Four Year College, Graduate **Number Awarded:** Varies each year. Recently, 60 of these scholarships were awarded. **Funds Available:** Stipends range from $1,000 to $2,000. **Duration:** 1 year; renewable.
Eligibility Requirements: This program is open to full-time Korean American students who have completed at least 1 year of study at a 4-year college, graduate school, or professional school. Applicants may be residents of any state as long as they attend school in the western region (Alaska, Arizona, California, Colorado, Hawaii, Idaho, Montana, Nevada, New Mexico, Oregon, Utah, Washington, or Wyoming). Selection is based on academic achievement, community service, school activities, and financial need. **Deadline for Receipt:** February of each year.

932 ■ KOREAN UNIVERSITY CLUB
c/o Martha C. Im
1608 Laukahi Street
Honolulu, HI 96821
To provide financial assistance to Korean Americans in Hawaii who are interested in working on a college degree.
Title of Award: Korean University Club Scholarship **Area, Field, or Subject:** General studies/Field of study not specified **Level of Education for which Award is Granted:** Undergraduate **Number Awarded:** 1 each year. **Funds Available:** The stipend is $1,400 per year. **Duration:** 4 years.
Eligibility Requirements: Applicants must be high school seniors/graduates, U.S. citizens, residents of Hawaii, and at least part Korean. They must be able to demonstrate financial need. **Deadline for Receipt:** March of each year. **Additional Information:** Recipients may attend either a 2-year college (if they plan to transfer to a 4-year college/university) or a 4-year college/university in Hawaii.

933 ■ KOREAN WAR VETERANS ASSOCIATION
Attn: Scholarship Coordinator
13730 Loumont Street
Whittier, CA 90601
To provide financial assistance for college to descendants of Army veterans who served in Korea during or prior to the war there.
Title of Award: Korean War Veterans Association Scholarships **Area, Field, or Subject:** General studies/Field of study not specified **Level of Education for which Award is Granted:** Undergraduate **Number Awarded:** Varies each year; recently, 4 of these scholarships were awarded. **Funds Available:** The stipend depends on the need of the recipient, to a maximum of $5,000 per year. **Duration:** 1 year; may be renewed up to 3 additional years or until completion of a bachelor's degree.
Eligibility Requirements: This program is open to the children, grandchildren, and great-grandchildren of veterans who served on active duty in the U.S. Army in Korea between August 15, 1945 and December 31, 1955. Applicants must be attending or planning to attend an accredited college or university. Selection is based on academic achievement (GPA of 2.75 or higher), extracurricular activities, and financial need. **Deadline for Receipt:** April of each year.

934 ■ KOSCIUSZKO FOUNDATION
Attn: Educational Programs
15 East 65th Street
New York, NY 10021-6595
Tel: (212)734-2130
Fax: (212)628-4552
E-mail: addy@thekf.org
Web Site: http://www.thekf.org/EDScholarships_US_MFPW.html
To provide financial assistance for college to students of Polish ancestry.
Title of Award: Massachusetts Federation of Polish Women's Clubs Scholarships **Area, Field, or Subject:** General studies/Field of study not specified **Level of Education for which Award is Granted:** Undergraduate **Number Awarded:** 1 or more each year. **Funds Available:** The stipend is $1,250. **Duration:** 1 year; nonrenewable.
Eligibility Requirements: These scholarships are available to students of Polish ancestry in the second, third, or fourth year of undergraduate study at an accredited college or university. Applicants must be U.S. citizens or permanent residents of Polish descent and have a GPA of 3.0 or higher. First preference is given to members or children or grandchildren of members of the Massachusetts Federation of Polish Women's Clubs. If no members or relatives apply, qualified residents of Massachusetts are considered. Selection is based on academic excellence; the applicant's academic achievements, interests, and motivation; the applicant's interest in Polish subjects or involvement in the Polish American community; and financial need. **Deadline for Receipt:** January of each year. **Additional Information:** This program is funded by the Massachusetts Federation of Polish Women's Clubs and administered by the Kosciuszko Foundation. There is a nonrefundable application fee of $25.

935 ■ KOSCIUSZKO FOUNDATION
Attn: Educational Programs
15 East 65th Street
New York, NY 10021-6595
Tel: (212)734-2130
Fax: (212)628-4552
E-mail: addy@thekf.org
Web Site: http://www.thekf.org/EDScholarships_US_PAC.html
To provide financial assistance for college or graduate school to members of the Polish American Club of North Jersey.
Title of Award: Polish American Club of North Jersey Scholarships **Area, Field, or Subject:** General studies/Field of study not specified **Level of Education for which Award is Granted:** Graduate, Undergraduate **Number Awarded:** Varies each year. **Funds Available:** The stipend is $1,000. **Duration:** 1 year; may be renewed.
Eligibility Requirements: This program is open to full-time students who are active members in good standing for at least 3 years or the children or grandchildren of active members in good standing for at least 3 years. Undergraduates are eligible, but the majority of scholarships are awarded to graduate students. Applicants must be U.S. citizens or permanent residents of Polish descent and have a GPA of 3.0 or higher. Selection is based on academic excellence; the applicant's academic achievements, interests, and motivation; the applicant's interest in Polish subjects or involvement in the Polish American community; and financial need. **Deadline for Receipt:** January of each year. **Additional Information:** This program is funded by the Polish American Club of North Jersey but administered by the Kosciuszko Foundation. There is a nonrefundable application fee of $25.

936 ■ JEFF KROSNOFF SCHOLARSHIP FUND
P.O. Box 8585
La Crescenta, CA 91224-0585
E-mail: badjefft@charter.net
Web Site: http://www.krosnoffscholarship.com/Scholarship.htm
To provide financial assistance for college to high school seniors in California who submit outstanding essays.
Title of Award: Jeff Krosnoff Scholarship **Area, Field, or Subject:** General studies/Field of study not specified **Level of Education for which Award is Granted:** Four Year College **Number Awarded:** 1 each year. **Funds Available:** The stipend is $10,000. **Duration:** 1 year.
Eligibility Requirements: This program is open to seniors graduating from high schools in California who plan to attend a 4-year college or university. Applicants must be able to demonstrate excellent academic credentials, a breadth of interests, a driving desire to succeed in their chosen endeavors, outstanding community citizenship, and the ability to share their experiences through the written word. They must have a GPA of 3.0 or higher. Selection is based on an essay on a topic that changes annually; recently, applicants were asked to select a song or poem that inspires them and to explain why. **Deadline for Receipt:** January of each year. **Additional Information:** This program was established in 1997.

937 ■ THE KUSKOKWIM CORPORATION
Attn: Kuskokwim Educational Foundation, Inc.
4300 B Street, Suite 207
Anchorage, AK 99503
Tel: (907)243-2944
Free: 800-478-2171
Fax: (907)243-2984
E-mail: dg@kuskokwim.com
Web Site: http://www.kuskokwim.com

To provide financial assistance for college or graduate school to Native people and their descendants from The Kuskokwim Corporation (TKC) region.

Title of Award: Kuskokwim Educational Foundation General Scholarships **Area, Field, or Subject:** General studies/Field of study not specified **Level of Education for which Award is Granted:** Graduate, Undergraduate **Number Awarded:** Varies each year; recently, 20 of these scholarships were awarded. **Funds Available:** Stipends range from $100 to $1,500 per year. Funds are sent to the recipient's school in 2 equal installments. **Duration:** 1 year; may be renewed if the recipient maintains full-time enrollment and a GPA of 2.0 or higher as an undergraduate, a GPA of 3.0 or higher as a graduate student, or satisfactory progress as a vocational student.

Eligibility Requirements: This program is open to Native people and their descendants from The Kuskokwim Corporation region in Alaska. Applicants may be high school seniors, high school graduates, currently-enrolled college students, college graduates, or graduate students. They must be interested in attending school on a full-time basis. Along with their application, they must submit a letter or essay describing their talents, special interests, accomplishments, educational objectives, reasons for selecting those objectives, and progress toward achieving those objectives; documentation of financial need; transcripts; and 2 letters of recommendation. **Deadline for Receipt:** June of each year for fall semester; November of each year for spring semester. **Additional Information:** Recipients may use the funds for college and university courses, vocational and continuing education, student exchange programs, and other educational opportunities approved by the board. The Corporation also sponsors other scholarships for eligible students who want to work on a degree in a health, business, or construction-related field.

938 ■ LA UNIDAD LATINA FOUNDATION, INC.

359 Prospect Avenue
Brooklyn, NY 11215
E-mail: foundation@launidadlatina.org
Web Site: http://foundation.launidadlatina.org
To provide financial assistance to Hispanic students who are working on a bachelor's or master's degree.

Title of Award: La Unidad Latina Scholarships **Area, Field, or Subject:** General studies/Field of study not specified **Level of Education for which Award is Granted:** Four Year College, Master's **Number Awarded:** Varies each year; recently, 24 of these scholarships (18 in fall, 6 in spring) were awarded. **Funds Available:** Stipends range from $250 to $1,000. **Duration:** 1 year.

Eligibility Requirements: This program is open to students of Hispanic background who have completed at least 1 semester of higher education. Applicants must be enrolled full time at an accredited 4-year college or university in the United States. Along with their application, they must submit brief essays on the courses in which they are enrolled in the current semester, their financial need, their academic plans and career goals, an instance in which someone has left an indelible mark in their life and why, their extracurricular activities, any honors or awards they have received, and their special interests or hobbies. **Deadline for Receipt:** February of each year for spring semester; October of each year for fall semester.

939 ■ JON C. LADDA MEMORIAL FOUNDATION

P.O. Box 55
Unionville, CT 06085
E-mail: info@jonladda.org
Web Site: http://www.jonladda.org
To provide financial assistance for college to children of deceased and disabled U.S. Naval Academy graduates and members of the Navy submarine service.

Title of Award: Jon C. Ladda Memorial Foundation Scholarship **Area, Field, or Subject:** General studies/Field of study not specified **Level of Education for which Award is Granted:** Four Year College **Number Awarded:** 1 or more each year. **Funds Available:** A stipend is awarded (amount not specified). Funds are disbursed directly to the recipient's institution. **Duration:** 1 year; may be renewed.

Eligibility Requirements: This program is open to children of U.S. Naval Academy graduates and members of the U.S. Navy submarine service. The parent must have died on active duty or been medically retired with a 100% disability. Applicants must be enrolled or accepted at a 4-year col-

lege or university, including any of the service academies. Along with their application, they must submit an essay on the topic, "When choosing a leader, what quality is most important to you and how does that reflect your values?" Selection is based on academic achievement, financial need, and merit. **Deadline for Receipt:** March of each year.

940 ■ LADIES AUXILIARY OF THE FLEET RESERVE ASSOCIATION

Attn: Scholarship Administrator
125 North West Street
Alexandria, VA 22314-2754
Tel: (703)683-1400
Free: 800-372-1924
Fax: (703)549-6610
E-mail: fra@fra.org
Web Site: http://www.fra.org/Content/fra/MyFRA/Scholarships/Scholarships.htm
To provide financial assistance for college to the children and grandchildren of naval personnel.

Title of Award: LA FRA National President's Scholarship **Area, Field, or Subject:** General studies/Field of study not specified **Level of Education for which Award is Granted:** Undergraduate **Number Awarded:** 1 each year. **Funds Available:** The stipend is $2,500. **Duration:** 1 year; may be renewed.

Eligibility Requirements: Eligible to apply for these scholarships are the children and grandchildren of Navy, Marine, Coast Guard, active Fleet Reserve, Fleet Marine Corps Reserve, and Coast Guard Reserve personnel on active duty, retired with pay, or deceased while on active duty or retired with pay. Selection is based on financial need, academic proficiency, and character. Preference is given to dependents of members of the Fleet Reserve Association and the Ladies Auxiliary of the Fleet Reserve Association, if other factors are equal. **Deadline for Receipt:** April of each year.

941 ■ LADIES AUXILIARY OF THE FLEET RESERVE ASSOCIATION

Attn: Scholarship Administrator
125 North West Street
Alexandria, VA 22314-2754
Tel: (703)683-1400
Free: 800-372-1924
Fax: (703)549-6610
E-mail: fra@fra.org
Web Site: http://www.fra.org/Content/fra/MyFRA/Scholarships/Scholarships.htm
To provide financial assistance for college to the daughters and granddaughters of naval personnel.

Title of Award: LA FRA Scholarship **Area, Field, or Subject:** General studies/Field of study not specified **Level of Education for which Award is Granted:** Undergraduate **Number Awarded:** 1 each year. **Funds Available:** The stipend is $2,500. **Duration:** 1 year; may be renewed.

Eligibility Requirements: Eligible to apply for these scholarships are the daughters and granddaughters of Navy, Marine, Coast Guard, active Fleet Reserve, Fleet Marine Corps Reserve, and Coast Guard Reserve personnel on active duty, retired with pay, or deceased while on active duty or retired with pay. Selection is based on financial need, academic proficiency, and character. Preference is given to dependents of members of the Fleet Reserve Association and the Ladies Auxiliary of the Fleet Reserve Association, if other factors are equal. **Deadline for Receipt:** April of each year.

942 ■ LADIES AUXILIARY OF THE FLEET RESERVE ASSOCIATION

Attn: Scholarship Administrator
125 North West Street
Alexandria, VA 22314-2754
Tel: (703)683-1400
Free: 800-372-1924
Fax: (703)549-6610
E-mail: fra@fra.org
Web Site: http://www.fra.org/Content/fra/MyFRA/Scholarships/Scholarships.htm
To provide financial assistance for college to the children and grandchildren of the Fleet Reserve Association (FRA) or its Ladies Auxiliary.

Title of Award: Allie Mae Oden Memorial Scholarship **Area, Field, or Subject:** General studies/Field of study not specified **Level of Education for which Award is Granted: Undergraduate **Number Awarded:** 1 each year. **Funds Available:** The stipend is $2,500. **Duration:** 1 year; may be renewed.

Eligibility Requirements: Eligible to apply for these scholarships are the children and grandchildren of members of the association or its ladies auxiliary. Selection is based on financial need, academic proficiency, and character. **Deadline for Receipt:** April of each year. **Additional Information:** Membership in the FRA is open to active-duty, retired, and reserve members of the Navy, Marine Corps, and Coast Guard.

943 ■ LADIES AUXILIARY OF THE FLEET RESERVE ASSOCIATION

Attn: Scholarship Administrator
125 North West Street
Alexandria, VA 22314-2754
Tel: (703)683-1400
Free: 800-372-1924
Fax: (703)549-6610
E-mail: fra@fra.org
Web Site: http://www.fra.org/Content/fra/MyFRA/Scholarships/Scholarships.htm
To provide financial assistance for college to the children and grandchildren of naval personnel or deceased members of the Fleet Reserve Association (FRA).

Title of Award: Sam Rose Memorial Scholarship **Area, Field, or Subject:** General studies/Field of study not specified **Level of Education for which Award is Granted:** Undergraduate **Number Awarded:** 1 each year. **Funds Available:** The stipend is $2,500. **Duration:** 1 year.

Eligibility Requirements: Children and grandchildren of deceased members of the association or those who were eligible to be members at the time of death are given preference for this scholarship, but children and grandchildren of active-duty and retired Navy, Marine, and Coast Guard personnel are also considered. Selection is based on financial need, academic proficiency, and character. **Deadline for Receipt:** April of each year.

944 ■ LADIES AUXILIARY TO THE VETERANS OF FOREIGN WARS

c/o National Headquarters
406 West 34th Street
Kansas City, MO 64111
Tel: (816)561-8655
Fax: (816)931-4753
E-mail: info@ladiesauxvfw.com
Web Site: http://www.ladiesauxvfw.com
To provide financial assistance for college to outstanding members of a Junior Girls Unit of the Ladies Auxiliary to the Veterans of Foreign Wars.

Title of Award: Junior Girls Scholarships **Area, Field, or Subject:** General studies/Field of study not specified **Level of Education for which Award is Granted:** Undergraduate **Number Awarded:** 2 each year. **Funds Available:** The first-place winner receives a $10,000 scholarship; the second-place winner receives a $5,000 scholarship. Funds are paid directly to the college of the recipient's choice. In addition, $100 is awarded to each Junior Girl who is selected as the department winner and entered in the national competition. **Duration:** 1 year.

Eligibility Requirements: Applicants must have been active members of a unit for 1 year, have held an office in the unit, and be between 13 and 16 years of age. Previous winners are not eligible, although former applicants who did not receive scholarships may reapply. Selection is based on participation in the Junior Girls Unit, community activities, school activities, and scholastic aptitude. **Deadline for Receipt:** March of each year. **Additional Information:** The first-place winner must attend the Ladies Auxiliary National Convention and participate in the American Academy of Achievement's Salute to Excellence.

945 ■ LATIN AMERICAN EDUCATIONAL FOUNDATION

Attn: Scholarship Selection Committee
924 West Colfax Avenue, Suite 103
Denver, CO 80204
Tel: (303)446-0541
Fax: (303)446-0526
E-mail: carmen@laef.org
Web Site: http://www.laef.org
To provide financial aid to Hispanic American undergraduate students in Colorado.

Title of Award: Latin American Educational Foundation Scholarships **Area, Field, or Subject:** General studies/Field of study not specified **Level of Education for which Award is Granted:** Undergraduate **Number Awarded:** Varies each year; recently, 221 of these scholarships were awarded. **Funds Available:** The amount of the award depends on the need of the recipient, ranging from $500 to $3,000. Scholarships may be used at Colorado colleges and universities or at out-of-state institutions. Most colleges and universities within Colorado participate in the Colorado Higher Education Partnership; member institutions provide additional funds to match the award granted by this foundation. **Duration:** 1 year; recipients may reapply.

Eligibility Requirements: This program is open to Colorado residents who are of Hispanic heritage and/or actively involved in the Hispanic community. Applicants must have been accepted at an accredited college, university, or vocational school and must have a cumulative GPA of 3.0 or higher. Along with their application, they must submit a 1-page essay on their interests and career goals, how they anticipate achieving their goals, and what has motivated them to pursue higher education. Selection is based on the essay, community involvement, academic achievement, letters of recommendation, an interview, and financial need. **Deadline for Receipt:** February of each year. **Additional Information:** This program was established in 1949. Sponsors include Hewlett Packard, American Family Insurance, CH2MHill, Coors Brewing Company, State Farm Insurance, Lucent Technologies, and Wells Fargo Bank. Recipients are required to perform 10 hours of community service during the academic year.

946 ■ LEAGUE OF UNITED LATIN AMERICAN CITIZENS

Attn: LULAC National Education Service Centers
2000 L Street, N.W., Suite 610
Washington, DC 20036
Tel: (202)835-9646
Fax: (202)835-9685
E-mail: scholarships@lnesc.org
Web Site: http://www.lnesc.org
To provide financial assistance to Hispanic American undergraduate and graduate students.

Title of Award: LULAC General Awards **Area, Field, or Subject:** General studies/Field of study not specified **Level of Education for which Award is Granted:** Graduate, Undergraduate **Number Awarded:** Varies; approximately 500 each year. **Funds Available:** The stipend ranges from $250 to $1,000 per year, depending on the need of the recipient. **Duration:** 1 year.

Eligibility Requirements: This program is open to Hispanic Americans who are U.S. citizens or permanent residents currently enrolled or planning to enroll at an accredited college or university as a graduate or undergraduate student. Although grades are considered in the selection process, emphasis is placed on the applicant's motivation, sincerity, and integrity, as revealed through a personal interview and in an essay. Need, community involvement, and leadership activities are also considered. Candidates must live near a participating local council of the League of United Latin American Citizens (LULAC) and must apply directly to that council. **Deadline for Receipt:** March of each year. **Additional Information:** This program represents an attempt to forge a partnership between the corporate world and the community. Under its fundsharing concept, LULAC's National Education Service Center gathers contributions nationally from corporations, while LULAC councils raise money locally. The total corporate donations are then apportioned back to the councils according to effort. Applications must be obtained directly from participating LULAC councils; for a list, send a self-addressed stamped envelope to the sponsor.

947 ■ LEAGUE OF UNITED LATIN AMERICAN CITIZENS

Attn: LULAC National Education Service Centers
2000 L Street, N.W., Suite 610
Washington, DC 20036
Tel: (202)835-9646
Fax: (202)835-9685
E-mail: scholarships@lnesc.org
Web Site: http://www.lnesc.org
To provide financial assistance to Hispanic American undergraduate and graduate students who are doing well in school.

Title of Award: LULAC Honors Awards **Area, Field, or Subject:** General studies/Field of study not specified **Level of Education for which Award**

is **Granted:** Graduate, Undergraduate **Number Awarded:** Varies each year. **Funds Available:** The stipend ranges from $250 to $1,000 per year, depending on the need of the recipient. **Duration:** 1 year.

Eligibility Requirements: This program is open to Hispanic Americans who are U.S. citizens or permanent residents currently enrolled or planning to enroll at an accredited college or university as a graduate or undergraduate student. Applicants who are already in college must have a GPA of 3.25 or higher. Entering freshmen must have ACT scores of 20 or higher or SAT scores of 840 or higher. In addition, applicants must demonstrate motivation, sincerity, and integrity through a personal interview and in an essay. Need, community involvement, and leadership activities are also considered. Candidates must live near a participating local council of the League of United Latin American Citizens (LULAC) and must apply directly to that council. **Deadline for Receipt:** March of each year. **Additional Information:** This program represents an attempt to forge a partnership between the corporate world and the community. Under its fundsharing concept, LULAC's National Education Service Center gathers contributions nationally from corporations, while LULAC councils raise money locally. The total corporate donations are then apportioned back to the councils according to effort. Applications must be obtained directly from participating LULAC councils; for a list, send a self-addressed stamped envelope to the sponsor.

948 ■ LEAGUE OF UNITED LATIN AMERICAN CITIZENS
Attn: LULAC National Education Service Centers
2000 L Street, N.W., Suite 610
Washington, DC 20036
Tel: (202)835-9646
Fax: (202)835-9685
E-mail: scholarships@lnesc.org
Web Site: http://www.lnesc.org
To provide financial assistance to academically outstanding Hispanic American undergraduate and graduate students.

Title of Award: LULAC National Scholastic Achievement Awards **Area, Field, or Subject:** General studies/Field of study not specified **Level of Education for which Award is Granted:** Graduate, Undergraduate **Number Awarded:** Varies each year. **Funds Available:** Stipends are at least $1,000 per year. **Duration:** 1 year.

Eligibility Requirements: This program is open to Hispanic Americans who are U.S. citizens or permanent residents currently enrolled or planning to enroll at an accredited college or university as a graduate or undergraduate student. Applicants who are already in college must have a GPA of 3.5 or higher. Entering freshmen must have ACT scores of 23 or higher or SAT scores of 970 or higher. In addition, applicants must demonstrate motivation, sincerity, and integrity through a personal interview and in an essay. Need, community involvement, and leadership activities are also considered. Candidates must live near a participating local council of the League of United Latin American Citizens (LULAC) and must apply directly to that council. **Deadline for Receipt:** March of each year. **Additional Information:** This program represents an attempt to forge a partnership between the corporate world and the community. Under its fundsharing concept, LULAC's National Education Service Center gathers contributions nationally from corporations, while LULAC councils raise money locally. The total corporate donations are then apportioned back to the councils according to effort. Applications must be obtained directly from participating LULAC councils; for a list, send a self-addressed stamped envelope to the sponsor.

949 ■ LIGHTHOUSE INTERNATIONAL
Attn: Career Incentive Awards Program
111 East 59th Street
New York, NY 10022-1202
Tel: (212)821-9428
Free: 800-829-0500
Fax: (212)821-9703
E-mail: kboyle@lighthouse.org
Web Site: http://www.lighthouse.org/events/scholarship_awards.htm
To provide financial assistance for college to legally blind high school seniors and graduates residing and attending school in selected eastern states.

Title of Award: College-Bound Award of Lighthouse International **Area, Field, or Subject:** General studies/Field of study not specified **Level of Education for which Award is Granted:** Undergraduate **Number**

Awarded: 1 each year. **Funds Available:** The stipend is $5,000. **Duration:** 1 year.

Eligibility Requirements: This program is open to high school seniors or recent high school graduates now planning to begin college who are blind or partially sighted and U.S. citizens. Applicants must be residents of Connecticut, Delaware, Florida, Georgia, Maine, Maryland, Massachusetts, New Hampshire, New Jersey, New York, North Carolina, Pennsylvania, Rhode Island, South Carolina, Vermont, Virginia, Washington, D.C., or West Virginia and planning to attend school in those states. They must submit a 500-word essay, describing their academic achievements and career goals. Financial need is not considered in the selection process. **Deadline for Receipt:** February of each year.

950 ■ LIGHTHOUSE INTERNATIONAL
Attn: Scholarship Awards
111 East 59th Street
New York, NY 10022-1202
Tel: (212)821-9428
Free: 800-829-0500
Fax: (212)821-9703
E-mail: kboyle@lighthouse.org
Web Site: http://www.lighthouse.org/events/scholarship_awards.htm
To provide financial assistance to legally blind students residing and attending school in designated eastern states who have experienced an interruption in their education.

Title of Award: Lighthouse Undergraduate Award for Returning Students **Area, Field, or Subject:** General studies/Field of study not specified **Level of Education for which Award is Granted:** Undergraduate **Number Awarded:** 1 each year. **Funds Available:** The stipend is $5,000. **Duration:** 1 year.

Eligibility Requirements: This program is open to blind and partially sighted U.S. citizens who are residents of Connecticut Delaware, Florida, Georgia, Maine, Maryland, Massachusetts, New Hampshire, New Jersey, New York, North Carolina, Pennsylvania, Rhode Island, South Carolina, Vermont, Virginia, Washington, D.C., or West Virginia. Applicants must be working on an undergraduate degree in those states after an absence of 10 years or more. They must submit a 500-word essay describing their academic achievements and career goals. Financial need is not considered in the selection process. **Deadline for Receipt:** February of each year.

951 ■ LIGHTHOUSE INTERNATIONAL
Attn: Scholarship Awards
111 East 59th Street
New York, NY 10022-1202
Tel: (212)821-9428
Free: 800-829-0500
Fax: (212)821-9703
E-mail: kboyle@lighthouse.org
Web Site: http://www.lighthouse.org/events/scholarship_awards.htm
To provide financial assistance to legally blind undergraduate students residing and attending school in designated eastern states.

Title of Award: Undergraduate Awards of Lighthouse International **Area, Field, or Subject:** General studies/Field of study not specified **Level of Education for which Award is Granted:** Undergraduate **Number Awarded:** 1 each year. **Funds Available:** The stipend is $5,000. **Duration:** 1 year.

Eligibility Requirements: This program is open to blind and partially sighted U.S. citizens who are residents of Connecticut Delaware, Florida, Georgia, Maine, Maryland, Massachusetts, New Hampshire, New Jersey, New York, North Carolina, Pennsylvania, Rhode Island, South Carolina, Vermont, Virginia, Washington, D.C., or West Virginia. Applicants must be attending college (at any level) in those states They must submit a 500-word essay describing their academic achievements and career goals. Financial need is not considered in the selection process. **Deadline for Receipt:** February of each year.

952 ■ FRANKLIN LINDSAY STUDENT AID FUND
Attn: Bank One, N.S., Trustee
P.O. Box 2266
Austin, TX 78780
Tel: (512)479-2634; (866)300-6222
Fax: (512)479-2656

E-mail: info@franklinlindsay.org
Web Site: http://www.franklinlindsay.org
To loan money to deserving students interested in attending college in Texas.
Title of Award: Franklin Lindsay Student Aid Fund Loans **Area, Field, or Subject:** General studies/Field of study not specified **Level of Education for which Award is Granted:** Graduate, Undergraduate **Number Awarded:** Varies each year. **Funds Available:** Up to $5,000 may be loaned per academic year (up to a lifetime maximum of $20,000). While the recipient is in college, no interest is charged. Within 4 months after graduation, interest of 4% is charged. Loans must be repaid within 7 years. **Duration:** 1 year; may be renewed.
Eligibility Requirements: This program is open to students at colleges and universities in Texas. Applicants must have completed 24 credit hours, have a GPA of 2.0 or higher (if an undergraduate) or 3.0 or higher (if a graduate student), and be a full-time student (12 hours for undergraduates or 9 hours for graduate students). U.S. citizenship is required. **Deadline for Receipt:** Applications may be submitted at any time. **Additional Information:** This program was established in 1957. Recipients must attend school in Texas.

953 ■ LOMA SOCIETY OF NEBRASKA

c/o Jon Boomgaarden, Scholarship Chair
Mutual of Omaha
2 - I/S Micro Server Services Team
Mutual of Omaha Plaza
Omaha, NE 68175
Tel: (402)351-8579
Fax: (402)351-5197
E-mail: jon.boomgaarden@mutualofomaha.com
Web Site: http://loma-ne.org
To provide financial assistance to upper-division and graduate students in Nebraska who are preparing for a career in business, especially in the insurance industry.
Title of Award: LOMA Society of Nebraska Scholarships **Area, Field, or Subject:** Actuarial science; Business administration; Insurance and insurance-related fields **Level of Education for which Award is Granted:** Four Year College, Graduate **Number Awarded:** Varies each year. **Funds Available:** A total of $4,000 is available for this program each year. Individual stipends depend on the number of recipients selected. **Duration:** 1 year.
Eligibility Requirements: This program is open to students enrolled full time as juniors, seniors, or graduate students at colleges and universities in Nebraska. Applicants must be preparing for a career in business; preference is given to students who have an interest in a career in an aspect of the insurance industry. They should have a record of academic success, but interest in a chosen field and the ability to express career ambitions are more important factors than high grades. Financial need is also considered in the selection process. Special consideration is given to children and relatives of people holding the LOMA (Life Office Management Association) designation. **Deadline for Receipt:** June of each year.

954 ■ LOUISIANA BAPTIST CONVENTION

Attn: Women's Missions and Ministry Division
1250 MacArthur Drive
P.O. Box 311
Alexandria, LA 71309-0311
Tel: (318)448-3402
Free: 800-622-6549
E-mail: jill.morrow@lbc.org
Web Site: http://www.lbc.org
To provide financial assistance for college or seminary to members of Southern Baptist churches in Louisiana.
Title of Award: Louisiana College Scholarships **Area, Field, or Subject:** General studies/Field of study not specified; Religion **Level of Education for which Award is Granted:** Master's, Undergraduate **Number Awarded:** Varies each year. **Funds Available:** A stipend is awarded (amount not specified). **Duration:** 1 year.
Eligibility Requirements: This program is open to members of churches affiliated with the Louisiana Baptist Convention. Applicants must be 1) men or women working on a bachelor's degree at Louisiana College (Pineville, Louisiana); 2) women working on a master's degree at a Southern Baptist seminary; or 3) mission pastors or Black mission pastors

attending a seminary to work on a Diploma of Christian Ministries or a master's degree. **Deadline for Receipt:** January of each year.

955 ■ LOUISIANA DEPARTMENT OF VETERANS AFFAIRS

1885 Wooddale Boulevard, Room 1013
P.O. Box 94095, Capitol Station
Baton Rouge, LA 70804-9095
Tel: (225)922-0500
Fax: (225)922-0511
E-mail: dperkins@vetaffairs.com
Web Site: http://www.vetaffairs.com
To provide financial assistance for college to children and surviving spouses of certain disabled or deceased Louisiana veterans.
Title of Award: Louisiana Veterans State Aid Program **Area, Field, or Subject:** General studies/Field of study not specified **Level of Education for which Award is Granted:** Undergraduate **Number Awarded:** Varies each year. **Funds Available:** Eligible persons accepted as full-time students at Louisiana state-supported colleges, universities, trade schools, or vocational/technical schools will be admitted free and are exempt from payment of all tuition, laboratory, athletic, medical, and other special fees. Free registration does not cover books, supplies, room and board, or fees assessed by the student body on themselves (such as yearbooks and weekly papers). **Duration:** Tuition, fee exemption, and possible payment of cash subsistence allowance are provided for a maximum of 4 school years to be completed in not more than 5 years from date of original entry.
Eligibility Requirements: Eligible under this program are children (between 16 and 25 years of age) of veterans who served during World War I, World War II, the Korean war, or the Vietnam conflict and either died or sustained a disability rated as 90% or more by the U.S. Department of Veterans Affairs. Deceased veterans must have resided in Louisiana for at least 12 months prior to entry into service. Living disabled veterans must have resided in Louisiana for at least 24 months prior to the child's admission into the program. Also eligible are surviving spouses (of any age) of veterans who had been residents of Louisiana for at least 1 year preceding entry into service and who died in war service in the line of duty or from an established wartime service-connected disability subsequently. **Deadline for Receipt:** Applications must be received no later than 3 months prior to the beginning of a semester. **Additional Information:** Attendance must be on a full-time basis. Surviving spouses must remain unmarried and must take advantage of the benefit within 10 years after eligibility is established.

956 ■ LOUISIANA HEMOPHILIA FOUNDATION

Attn: Scholarship Committee
3636 South Sherwood Forest Boulevard, Suite 450
Baton Rouge, LA 70816
Tel: (225)291-1675
Free: 800-749-1680
Fax: (225)291-1679
E-mail: lahemophilia@etigers.net
Web Site: http://www.louisianahemophilia.org/Scholarships.htm
To provide financial assistance for college to Louisiana residents who have hemophilia or von Willebrand disease.
Title of Award: Louisiana Hemophilia Foundation Scholarships **Area, Field, or Subject:** General studies/Field of study not specified **Level of Education for which Award is Granted:** Four Year College **Number Awarded:** 2 each semester. **Funds Available:** The stipend is $500 per semester. **Duration:** 1 semester. Recipients may reapply if they remain enrolled full time with a GPA of 2.5 or higher.
Eligibility Requirements: This program is open to residents of Louisiana who have hemophilia or von Willebrand disease. Applicants must be enrolled or planning to enroll at a 2- or 4-year Louisiana college, university, or trade school. Along with their application, they must submit a 250-word essay on why they should receive this scholarship. **Deadline for Receipt:** July of each year for fall semester; December of each year for spring semester.

957 ■ LOUISIANA HEMOPHILIA FOUNDATION

Attn: Scholarship Committee
3636 South Sherwood Forest Boulevard, Suite 450
Baton Rouge, LA 70816
Tel: (225)291-1675

Free: 800-749-1680
Fax: (225)291-1679
E-mail: lahemophilia@etigers.net
Web Site: http://www.louisianahemophilia.org/Scholarships.htm
To provide financial assistance for college to Louisiana residents who have hemophilia or von Willebrand disease.
Title of Award: Huey and Angelina Wilson Scholarships **Area, Field, or Subject:** General studies/Field of study not specified **Level of Education for which Award is Granted:** Four Year College **Number Awarded:** Up to 15 each semester. **Funds Available:** The stipend is $1,000 per semester. **Duration:** 1 semester. Recipients may reapply if they remain enrolled full time with a GPA of 2.5 or higher.
Eligibility Requirements: This program is open to residents of Louisiana who have hemophilia or von Willebrand disease. Applicants must be enrolled or planning to enroll at a 4-year Louisiana college or university as a full-time undergraduate student. They must qualify for the Louisiana Tuition Opportunity Program for Students (TOPS) or would have qualified had the program existed when they entered college. Along with their application, they must submit a 250-word essay on why they should receive this scholarship. **Deadline for Receipt:** July of each year for fall semester; December of each year for spring semester.

958 ■ LOUISIANA HIGH SCHOOL ATHLETIC ASSOCIATION

Attn: Commissioner
8075 Jefferson Highway
Baton Rouge, LA 70809-7675
Tel: (225)925-0100
Fax: (225)925-5901
E-mail: lhsaa@lhsaa.org
Web Site: http://www.lhsaa.org/scholarships.htm
To provide financial assistance to student-athletes in Louisiana who plan to attend college in the state.
Title of Award: Fuzzy Brown Memorial Scholarships **Area, Field, or Subject:** General studies/Field of study not specified **Level of Education for which Award is Granted:** Undergraduate **Number Awarded:** 2 each year. **Funds Available:** The stipend is $1,000. **Duration:** 1 year.
Eligibility Requirements: This program is open to student-athletes who are seniors graduating from high schools in Louisiana. Applicants must be planning to attend a college or university in the state. They must be nominated by their principal. **Deadline for Receipt:** April of each year.
Additional Information: This program honors James E. "Big Fuzzy" and Ellis A. "Little Fuzzy" Brown.

959 ■ LOUISIANA HIGH SCHOOL ATHLETIC ASSOCIATION

Attn: Commissioner
8075 Jefferson Highway
Baton Rouge, LA 70809-7675
Tel: (225)925-0100
Fax: (225)925-5901
E-mail: lhsaa@lhsaa.org
Web Site: http://www.lhsaa.org/scholarships.htm
To provide financial assistance for college to high school seniors in Louisiana who are children of members of the Louisiana High School Coaches Association (LHSCA).
Title of Award: LHSCA Scholarships **Area, Field, or Subject:** General studies/Field of study not specified **Level of Education for which Award is Granted:** Undergraduate **Number Awarded:** 4 each year. **Funds Available:** The stipend is $1,000. **Duration:** 1 year.
Eligibility Requirements: This program is open to seniors and graduates of high schools in Louisiana whose parent has been a member of the LHSCA for at least 5 years or, if deceased, was a member for the 5 years immediately prior to death. Applicants must be attending or planning to attend an accredited institution of higher education. **Deadline for Receipt:** April of each year.

960 ■ LOUISIANA NATIONAL GUARD

Attn: Education Services Office
Military Development (DMP-XD)
Jackson Barracks
New Orleans, LA 70146-0330
Tel: (504)278-8304
Free: 800-899-6355
E-mail: dmp-xd@la.ngb.army.mil

Web Site: http://www.la.ngb.army.mil/Guard/education/index.html
To provide financial assistance for college to members of the Louisiana National Guard.
Title of Award: Louisiana National Guard State Tuition Exemption Program **Area, Field, or Subject:** General studies/Field of study not specified **Level of Education for which Award is Granted:** Undergraduate **Number Awarded:** Varies each year. **Funds Available:** Recipients are exempt from all tuition charges at Louisiana state-funded colleges, universities, or community colleges. **Duration:** The exemption may be claimed for 5 separate academic years or until the receipt of a bachelor's degree, whichever occurs first.
Eligibility Requirements: This program is open to active drilling members of the Louisiana Army National Guard or Air National Guard. Guard members are ineligible if they have been disqualified by their unit commander for any adverse action, have already obtained a bachelor's degree, are placed on academic probation or suspension, test positive on a drug/alcohol test or declare themselves as a self-referral, are separated or transfer to the Inactive National Guard, or have 9 or more AWOLs. Applicants must have been accepted for admission or be enrolled in a Louisiana public institution of higher learning, either part time or full time.
Additional Information: The state legislature established this program in 1974.

961 ■ LOUISIANA NATIONAL GUARD ENLISTED ASSOCIATION

c/o CMSgt R.B. Guillory
3448 Louise Street
Harvey, LA 70058-5458
Tel: (504)367-8047
E-mail: bguill3331@aol.com
Web Site: http://www.la.ngb.army.mil/laea/scholar.html
To provide financial assistance for college to members of the Louisiana National Guard Enlisted Association (LANGEA) and their dependents.
Title of Award: Tony Lopez Scholarship Program **Area, Field, or Subject:** General studies/Field of study not specified **Level of Education for which Award is Granted:** Undergraduate **Number Awarded:** 3 each year. **Funds Available:** The stipend is $2,000. **Duration:** 1 year; nonrenewable.
Eligibility Requirements: This program is open to members of the association, their spouses and unmarried dependent children, and the unmarried spouses and unmarried dependent children of deceased members who were in good standing at the time of their death. The qualifying LANGEA members must have at least 1 year remaining on their enlistment following completion of the school year for which the application is submitted or have served 20 years of more in the Louisiana National Guard. Applicants must be enrolled or planning to enroll full time at an accredited college, university, trade school, or business school. Graduate students are not eligible. Selection is based on academic achievement, character, leadership, and financial need. **Deadline for Receipt:** January of each year.

962 ■ LOWRIDER MAGAZINE

Attn: Scholarship Fund
2400 East Katella Avenue, 11th Floor
Anaheim, CA 92806
Tel: (714)939-2400
Fax: (714)978-6390
Web Site: http://www.lowridermagazine.com
To provide financial assistance for college to Chicano/Latino students.
Title of Award: Lowrider Magazine Scholarship Fund **Area, Field, or Subject:** General studies/Field of study not specified **Level of Education for which Award is Granted:** Undergraduate **Number Awarded:** Varies each year. **Funds Available:** Stipends range from $100 to $1,000. **Duration:** 1 year.
Eligibility Requirements: Applicants must be of Latino descent, have a GPA of 3.0 or higher, and be currently enrolled as college sophomores, juniors, or seniors. They must submit an official transcript, 2 letters of recommendation, a 1-page essay outlining their financial situation, and a 2-page essay on 1 of 3 topics that change annually. Recently, the topics were 1) "What does calling yourself Chicano or Chicana mean to you?" 2) "How can you use your education/degree to help the Chicano community?" or 3) "Has Affirmative Action served a good purpose and should institutes of higher learning continue to use this policy?" **Deadline for Receipt:** May of each year. **Additional Information:** This program

started in 1990. No phone calls are accepted. Requests for applications must be accompanied by a self-addressed stamped envelope.

963 ■ LOYAL CHRISTIAN BENEFIT ASSOCIATION

Attn: Scholarship Committee
700 Peach Street
P.O. Box 13005
Erie, PA 16514-1305
Tel: (814)453-4331
Free: 800-234-5222
Fax: (814)453-3211
E-mail: zubaw@lcba.com
Web Site: http://www.lcba.com/benefits/scholarships/postsecondaryscholarship.htm
To provide financial assistance for college to students who are benefit members of the Loyal Christian Benefit Association (LCBA)
Title of Award: Loyal Christian Benefit Association Postsecondary School Scholarships **Area, Field, or Subject:** General studies/Field of study not specified **Level of Education for which Award is Granted:** Undergraduate **Number Awarded:** Varies each year, depending on the availability of funds; recently, 5 of these scholarships were awarded. **Funds Available:** The stipend is $2,500 per year. **Duration:** Up to 4 years.
Eligibility Requirements: This program is open to high school seniors and current undergraduate students who are the base insured (not covered under a rider) on an association life or annuity certificate issued no later than the application deadline. Applicants must have a GPA of 2.5 or higher. Selection is based on a random drawing. Students are given bonus entries for the drawing based on 1) their GPA (up to 4 bonus entries for a GPA up to 3.75); 2) years of continuous LCBA membership as a base insured (up to 5 bonus entries for each year of membership); and 3) acts of LCBA fraternal service as attested to by LCBA branch or national officers (up to 5 bonus entries for each act of service). **Deadline for Receipt:** April of each year. **Additional Information:** Recipients may attend any 2-year or 4-year college or university in the United States or Canada, except a U.S. military academy. Students attending a junior college must provide the name of the 4-year college they intend to attend and provide evidence that full credit will be given there for courses taken at the junior college. Any course of study may be chosen.

964 ■ LUSO-AMERICAN EDUCATION FOUNDATION

Attn: Administrative Director
7080 Donlon Way, Suite 202
P.O. Box 2967
Dublin, CA 94568
Tel: (925)828-3883
Fax: (925)828-3883
Web Site: http://www.luso-american.org/laef
To provide financial assistance for undergraduate study to members of the Luso-American Fraternal Federation.
Title of Award: Luso-American Fraternal Federation Youth Council Recognition Scholarship **Area, Field, or Subject:** General studies/Field of study not specified **Level of Education for which Award is Granted:** Four Year College **Number Awarded:** 1 each year. **Funds Available:** The stipend is $1,000 per year. **Duration:** 4 years.
Eligibility Requirements: This program is open to graduating high school seniors who are entering a 4-year college or university. Applicants must be current youth members of the federation, in good standing, who have not previously received a federation scholarship. Selection is based on promise of success in college, financial need, vocational promise, and sincerity of purpose. **Deadline for Receipt:** February of each year. **Additional Information:** This program is funded by the Luso-American Fraternal Federation and administered by the Luso-American Education Foundation. Membership in the Luso-American Fraternal Federation is limited to people who hold Luso-American Life Insurance policies or annuities.

965 ■ LUSO-AMERICAN EDUCATION FOUNDATION

Attn: Administrative Director
7080 Donlon Way, Suite 202
P.O. Box 2967
Dublin, CA 94568
Tel: (925)828-3883
Fax: (925)828-3883

Web Site: http://www.luso-american.org/laef
To provide financial assistance for undergraduate study to members of the Luso-American Fraternal Federation who excel in sports.
Title of Award: Antonio Mattos Memorial Scholarships **Area, Field, or Subject:** General studies/Field of study not specified **Level of Education for which Award is Granted:** Undergraduate **Number Awarded:** 1 each year. **Funds Available:** A stipend is provided (amount not specified). **Duration:** 1 year; renewable.
Eligibility Requirements: This program is open to members of the federation who are high school seniors with a GPA of 3.0 or higher. Applicants should have excelled in sports while achieving academic success. They must be residents of California younger than 21 years of age. **Deadline for Receipt:** February of each year.

966 ■ MAIDS OF ATHENA

1909 Q Street, N.W., Suite 500
Washington, DC 20009-1007
Tel: (202)232-6300
Fax: (202)232-2140
Web Site: http://www.ahepa.org
To provide financial assistance for undergraduate and graduate education to women of Greek descent.
Title of Award: Maids of Athena Scholarships **Area, Field, or Subject:** General studies/Field of study not specified **Level of Education for which Award is Granted:** Graduate, Undergraduate **Number Awarded:** 3 each year: 1 each to a graduating high school senior, undergraduate student, and graduate student. **Funds Available:** The stipend is $1,000. **Duration:** 1 year.
Eligibility Requirements: This program is open to women who are members of the Maids of Athena. Applicants may be a graduating high school senior, an undergraduate student, or a graduate student. Selection is based on academic merit, financial need, and participation in the organization. **Additional Information:** Membership in Maids of Athena is open to unmarried women between 14 and 24 years of age who are of Greek descent from either parent.

967 ■ MAINE BANKERS ASSOCIATION

Attn: Maine Higher Education Assistance Foundation
132 State Street
P.O. Box 735
Augusta, ME 04332-0735
Tel: (207)622-6131
Fax: (207)622-0314
Web Site: http://www.mainebankers.com/index.pl/heaf
To provide financial assistance to college students in Maine who are majoring in a field related to business.
Title of Award: Maine Higher Education Assistance Foundation Scholarships **Area, Field, or Subject:** Business administration **Level of Education for which Award is Granted:** Undergraduate **Number Awarded:** 13 each year. **Funds Available:** Stipends average $1,000. **Duration:** 1 year.
Eligibility Requirements: This program is open to students enrolled in the second, third, or fourth year at a designated college or university in Maine. Applicants have graduated from a high school in Maine, be majoring in a business-related subject, have good academic standing, and be able to demonstrate financial need. **Additional Information:** The Maine Higher Education Assistance Foundation (HEAF) was established in the 1950s to support a guarantee fund for student loans. It began offering these scholarships in 1990.

968 ■ MAINE BANKERS ASSOCIATION

Attn: Mayo ALS Scholarship Committee
132 State Street
P.O. Box 735
Augusta, ME 04332-0735
Tel: (207)622-6131
Fax: (207)622-0314
E-mail: joep@mainebankers.com
Web Site: http://www.mainebankers.com/index.pl/joemayo
To provide financial assistance to college students from Maine who have a relative with Amyotrophic Lateral Sclerosis.
Title of Award: Joseph W. Mayo ALS Scholarship **Area, Field, or Subject:** General studies/Field of study not specified **Level of Education for which Award is Granted:** Undergraduate **Number Awarded:** 1 or

more each year. **Funds Available:** Stipends range from $500 to $2,000. **Duration:** 1 year.

Eligibility Requirements: This program is open to students enrolled at a 2-year or 4-year college or university who graduated from a Maine high school or GED program. Applicants must be the child, stepchild, grandchild, spouse, or domestic partner of an ALS patient. Along with their application, they must submit essays on their educational plans and involvement with school or community service activities, including any associated with ALS programs. **Deadline for Receipt:** November of each year.

969 ■ MAINE COMMUNITY FOUNDATION

Attn: Program Director
245 Main Street
Ellsworth, ME 04605
Tel: (207)667-9735; 877-700-6800
Fax: (207)667-0447
E-mail: info@mainecf.org
Web Site: http://www.mainecf.org/html/scholarships/index.html
To provide financial assistance for undergraduate or graduate study to Vietnam veterans or the dependents of Vietnam or other veterans in Maine.

Title of Award: Lest We Forget POW/MIA/KIA Scholarship Fund **Area, Field, or Subject:** General studies/Field of study not specified **Level of Education for which Award is Granted:** Graduate, Undergraduate **Number Awarded:** 3 to 6 each year. **Funds Available:** The stipend is $1,000 per year. **Duration:** 1 year.

Eligibility Requirements: This program is open to residents of Maine who are Vietnam veterans or the descendants of veterans who served in the Vietnam Theater. As a second priority, children of veterans from other time periods are also considered. Graduating high school seniors, nontraditional students, undergraduates, and graduate students are eligible to apply. Selection is based on financial need, extracurricular activities, work experience, academic achievement, and a personal statement of career goals and how the applicant's educational plans relate to them. **Deadline for Receipt:** April of each year. **Additional Information:** This fund was transferred to the Maine Community Foundation in 1996. There is a $3 processing fee.

970 ■ MAINE COMMUNITY FOUNDATION

Attn: Program Director
245 Main Street
Ellsworth, ME 04605
Tel: (207)667-9735; 877-700-6800
Fax: (207)667-0447
E-mail: info@mainecf.org
Web Site: http://www.mainecf.org/html/scholarships/index.html
To provide financial assistance for college to children of members of the Maine National Guard who have been called to active duty.

Title of Award: Maine Sentinel Scholarship Fund **Area, Field, or Subject:** General studies/Field of study not specified **Level of Education for which Award is Granted:** Undergraduate **Number Awarded:** Varies each year. **Funds Available:** A stipend is awarded (amount not specified). **Duration:** 1 year.

Eligibility Requirements: This program is open to children of members of the Maine National Guard who have been called to active duty after September 11, 2001. Applicants must be attending or planning to attend a 2-year or 4-year college or university. Preference is given to students who can demonstrate financial need. **Deadline for Receipt:** April of each year. **Additional Information:** This program was established in 1985. There is a $3 processing fee.

971 ■ MAINE COMMUNITY FOUNDATION

Attn: Program Director
245 Main Street
Ellsworth, ME 04605
Tel: (207)667-9735; 877-700-6800
Fax: (207)667-0447
E-mail: info@mainecf.org
Web Site: http://www.mainecf.org/html/scholarships/index.html
To provide financial assistance for college or graduate school to Vietnam veterans or the dependents of Vietnam or other veterans in Maine.

Title of Award: Maine Vietnam Veterans Scholarship Fund **Area, Field, or Subject:** General studies/Field of study not specified **Level of Educa-**

tion for which **Award is Granted:** Graduate, Undergraduate **Number Awarded:** 3 to 6 each year. **Funds Available:** The stipend is $1,000 per year. **Duration:** 1 year.

Eligibility Requirements: This program is open to residents of Maine who are Vietnam veterans or the descendants of veterans who served in the Vietnam Theater. As a second priority, children of veterans from other time periods are also considered. Graduating high school seniors, nontraditional students, undergraduates, and graduate students are eligible to apply. Selection is based on financial need, extracurricular activities, work experience, academic achievement, and a personal statement of career goals and how the applicant's educational plans relate to them. **Deadline for Receipt:** April of each year. **Additional Information:** This program was established in 1985. There is a $3 processing fee.

972 ■ MAINE COMMUNITY FOUNDATION

Attn: Program Director
245 Main Street
Ellsworth, ME 04605
Tel: (207)667-9735; 877-700-6800
Fax: (207)667-0447
E-mail: info@mainecf.org
Web Site: http://www.mainecf.org/html/scholarships/index.html
To provide financial assistance for college to graduating high school seniors in specified areas of Maine.

Title of Award: Ted Rand Memorial Scholarship Fund **Area, Field, or Subject:** General studies/Field of study not specified **Level of Education for which Award is Granted:** Undergraduate **Number Awarded:** 1 or more each year. **Funds Available:** A stipend is paid (amount not specified). **Duration:** 1 year.

Eligibility Requirements: This program is open to graduating seniors from the Casco Bay Islands, including Peaks, Little Diamond, Long, Chebeague, and Cliff Islands. Preference is given to students graduating from Portland, Deering, Greely, and South Portland High Schools. Selection is based on civic responsibility, moral character, work ethic, participation in extracurricular or community activities, academic achievement, and financial need. **Deadline for Receipt:** April of each year.

973 ■ MAINE COMMUNITY FOUNDATION

Attn: Program Director
245 Main Street
Ellsworth, ME 04605
Tel: (207)667-9735; 877-700-6800
Fax: (207)667-0447
E-mail: info@mainecf.org
Web Site: http://www.mainecf.org/html/scholarships/index.html
To provide financial assistance for college to residents of specified areas of Maine.

Title of Award: Rice Scholarship Fund **Area, Field, or Subject:** General studies/Field of study not specified **Level of Education for which Award is Granted:** Undergraduate **Number Awarded:** 1 or more each year. **Funds Available:** A stipend is paid (amount not specified). **Duration:** 1 year.

Eligibility Requirements: Applicants must have resided during their formative years on 1 of the off-shore islands of Maine in the area from Seguin to Eastport. They must be attending an accredited college or vocational training school. Selection is based on community service and financial need. **Deadline for Receipt:** April of each year. **Additional Information:** This program was established in 1996.

974 ■ MAINE COMMUNITY FOUNDATION

Attn: Program Director
245 Main Street
Ellsworth, ME 04605
Tel: (207)667-9735; 877-700-6800
Fax: (207)667-0447
E-mail: info@mainecf.org
Web Site: http://www.mainecf.org/html/scholarships/index.html
To provide financial assistance for college to students and adults in specified areas of Maine who have an interest in athletics.

Title of Award: Marion and Irving Spurling Scholarship Fund **Area, Field, or Subject:** General studies/Field of study not specified **Level of Education for which Award is Granted:** Undergraduate **Number Awarded:** 1 or more each year. **Funds Available:** A stipend is paid (amount not specified). **Duration:** 1 year.

Eligibility Requirements: This program is open to students and adults from the Cranberry Isles; Frenchboro, Long Island; Swans Island; and Mt. Desert Island who are seeking vocational training or education. Priority is given to applicants from the outer islands who demonstrate the greatest financial need. **Deadline for Receipt:** May of each year. **Additional Information:** This program was established in 1984.

975 ■ MAINE DEMOLAY AND PINE TREE YOUTH FOUNDATION

c/o Anah Shriners
The Oasis of Bangor Maine
586 Main Street
P.O. Box 735
Bangor, ME 04402-0735
Tel: (207)942-2254; 888-225-2624
Fax: (207)942-1994
E-mail: pinetree@bangordemolay.org
Web Site: http://www.bangordemolay.org/pinetree.htm
To provide financial assistance for college to high school seniors in Maine.
Title of Award: Maine DeMolay and Pine Tree Youth Foundation Scholarships **Area, Field, or Subject:** General studies/Field of study not specified **Level of Education for which Award is Granted:** Undergraduate **Number Awarded:** Varies each year. Recently, 13 of these scholarships were awarded: 2 at $1,500 and 11 at $1,000. **Funds Available:** Stipends are $1,500 or $1,000. **Duration:** 1 year.
Eligibility Requirements: This program is open to high school seniors in Maine. Certain scholarships are limited to graduates of particular schools, but most are given based on an open competition. Scholarships are awarded without regard to race, religion, age, gender, national origin, or "Masonic Family" relationships. Applicants should submit their high school transcript, a summary of their honors and extracurricular activities, and a narrative describing themselves, their background, and their future plans. Financial need is considered in the selection process. **Deadline for Receipt:** March of each year. **Additional Information:** The 2 highest ranked applicants receive scholarships designated as the Guy Matthews Scholarship and the Raymond N. Atherton Memorial Scholarship.

976 ■ MAINE EMPLOYERS' MUTUAL INSURANCE COMPANY

Attn: MEMIC Education Fund
261 Commercial Street
P.O. Box 11409
Portland, ME 04104
Tel: (207)791-3300
Free: 800-660-1306
Fax: (207)791-3335
E-mail: mbourque@memic.com
Web Site: http://www.memic.com
To provide financial assistance for college or graduate school to Maine residents whose parent or spouse was killed or permanently disabled in a work-related accident.
Title of Award: Horizon Scholarships **Area, Field, or Subject:** General studies/Field of study not specified **Level of Education for which Award is Granted:** Graduate, Undergraduate **Number Awarded:** Varies each year; recently, 2 of these scholarships were awarded. **Funds Available:** Stipends range up to $5,000, depending on the need of the recipient. Funds are paid directly to the recipient's institution. **Duration:** 1 year; may be renewed.
Eligibility Requirements: This program is open to Maine residents who are the child or spouse of a worker killed or permanently disabled as the result of a work-related injury. The worker must have been insured through the sponsor at the time of the workplace injury. Applicants must be attending or planning to attend an accredited college or university as an undergraduate or graduate student. They must submit a personal statement of 500 words or less on their aspirations and how their educational plans relate to them. Selection is based on financial need, academic performance, community involvement, and other life experiences. **Deadline for Receipt:** April of each year. **Additional Information:** The Maine Employers' Mutual Insurance Company (MEMIC) was established in 1993 as the result of reforms in Maine's workers'

compensation laws. It is currently the largest workers' compensation insurance company in the state. It established this scholarship program in 2001.

977 ■ MAINE FEDERATION OF BUSINESS AND PROFESSIONAL WOMEN

Attn: Futurama Foundation
c/o Jeanne L. Hammond, President
RR 1, Box 1610
Albion, ME 04910-9719
Tel: (207)437-2325
E-mail: jlhammon@colby.edu
Web Site: http://www.bpwmaine.org/Scholarship.htm
To provide financial assistance to Maine women over 30 years of age who are continuing a program of higher education.
Title of Award: Futurama Foundation Career Advancement Scholarship **Area, Field, or Subject:** General studies/Field of study not specified **Level of Education for which Award is Granted:** Undergraduate **Number Awarded:** 1 or more each year. **Funds Available:** The stipend is $1,200. **Duration:** 1 year.
Eligibility Requirements: This program is open to women who are older than 30 years of age and residents of Maine. Applicants must be continuing in, or returning to, an accredited program of higher education or job-related training, either full or part time. They must be able to demonstrate financial need. **Deadline for Receipt:** March of each year. **Additional Information:** Information is also available from Nancy Wadman, Scholarship Chair, BPW Maine Futurama Foundation, 478 Surry Road, Ellsworth, ME 04605.

978 ■ MAINE FEDERATION OF BUSINESS AND PROFESSIONAL WOMEN

Attn: Futurama Foundation
c/o Jeanne L. Hammond, President
RR 1, Box 1610
Albion, ME 04910-9719
Tel: (207)437-2325
E-mail: jlhammon@colby.edu
Web Site: http://www.bpwmaine.org/Scholarship.htm
To provide financial assistance for college to female high school seniors in Maine.
Title of Award: Rachel E. Lemieux Youth Scholarship **Area, Field, or Subject:** General studies/Field of study not specified **Level of Education for which Award is Granted:** Undergraduate **Number Awarded:** 1 or more each year. **Funds Available:** The stipend is $1,200. **Duration:** 1 year.
Eligibility Requirements: This program is open to women who are seniors graduating from high schools in Maine. Applicants must be planning to attend an accredited college or university. They must be able to demonstrate financial need. **Deadline for Receipt:** March of each year. **Additional Information:** Information is also available from Nancy Wadman, Scholarship Chair, BPW Maine Futurama Foundation, 478 Surry Road, Ellsworth, ME 04605.

979 ■ MAINE FEDERATION OF BUSINESS AND PROFESSIONAL WOMEN

Attn: Futurama Foundation
c/o Jeanne L. Hammond, President
RR 1, Box 1610
Albion, ME 04910-9719
Tel: (207)437-2325
E-mail: jlhammon@colby.edu
Web Site: http://www.bpwmaine.org/Scholarship.htm
To provide financial assistance for college to women in Maine.
Title of Award: Maine BPW Continuing Education Scholarship **Area, Field, or Subject:** General studies/Field of study not specified **Level of Education for which Award is Granted:** Undergraduate **Number Awarded:** 1 or more each year. **Funds Available:** The stipend is $1,200. **Duration:** 1 year.
Eligibility Requirements: This program is open to women who are residents of Maine. Applicants must be continuing in an accredited program of higher education or job-related training, either full or part time. They must be able to demonstrate financial need. **Deadline for Receipt:** March of each year. **Additional Information:** Information is also available

from Nancy Wadman, Scholarship Chair, BPW Maine Futurama Foundation, 478 Surry Road, Ellsworth, ME 04605.

980 ■ MAINE FUNERAL DIRECTORS ASSOCIATION

Attn: Executive Director
38 Young Avenue
Brunswick, ME 04011
Tel: (207)729-9100
Free: 800-880-6332
E-mail: sallybelanger@aol.com
Web Site: http://www.mefda.org
To provide financial assistance to residents of Maine who are currently preparing for a career in funeral service.
Title of Award: Maine Funeral Directors Association Scholarship **Area, Field, or Subject:** Mortuary science **Level of Education for which Award is Granted:** Undergraduate **Number Awarded:** 1 or more each year. **Funds Available:** A stipend is awarded (amount not specified). **Duration:** 1 year.
Eligibility Requirements: This program is open to residents of Maine who are currently enrolled in the second semester at a school of mortuary science. Applicants must submit educational and personal references, official transcripts, and a statement of their career plans.

981 ■ MAINE INNKEEPERS ASSOCIATION

Attn: MEIA Education Foundation
304 US Route 1
Freeport, ME 04032
Tel: (207)865-6100
E-mail: info@maineinns.com
Web Site: http://www.maineinns.com
To provide financial assistance to Maine residents who wish to prepare for a career in the hospitality industry.
Title of Award: Maine Innkeepers Association Hospitality Scholarships **Area, Field, or Subject:** Culinary arts; Hotel, institutional, and restaurant management **Level of Education for which Award is Granted:** Undergraduate **Number Awarded:** Varies each year. Recently, 8 of these scholarships were awarded: 1 at $1,500, 2 at $1,000, and 5 at $500. **Funds Available:** Stipends range from $500 to $1,500. **Duration:** 1 year; recipients may reapply.
Eligibility Requirements: This program is open to Maine residents who wish take courses related to the hospitality industry. Applicants must be interested in preparing for a career in the hotel and motel industry and accepted at an accredited school that specializes in hotel administration or culinary sciences. They may be graduating high school seniors, the children of members of the association, or employees of association properties; they must have a GPA of at least 2.5. Selection is based on academic record, employment history, extracurricular activities, desire for a career in the hospitality industry, and financial need. **Deadline for Receipt:** April of each year.

982 ■ MAINE NATIONAL GUARD

Attn: Benefit Support Center
Camp Keyes
Augusta, ME 04333-0033
Tel: (207)626-4271
Free: 800-462-3101
Fax: (207)626-4509
Web Site: http://www.me.ngb.army.mil
To provide financial assistance for undergraduate or graduate study to members of the Maine National Guard.
Title of Award: Maine National Guard Education Assistance Program **Area, Field, or Subject:** General studies/Field of study not specified **Level of Education for which Award is Granted:** Graduate, Undergraduate **Number Awarded:** Varies each year. **Funds Available:** This program provides payment of up to 100% of tuition and fees at a Maine accredited public postsecondary institution. Recipients may also attend a private college or university in Maine, but the benefit is capped at the tuition rates at the University of Maine. **Duration:** 1 semester; may be renewed for a total of 150 credit hours, as long as the recipient maintains satisfactory participation in the Guard and an academic GPA of 2.0 or higher.
Eligibility Requirements: This program is open to active members of the Maine National Guard who are interested in working on an undergraduate

or graduate degree or certificate at a college or university within the state. Applicants must be Maine residents who have successfully completed basic training or received a commission. They may not have any unsatisfactory record of participation in the Guard. First priority is given to Guard members who do not have a baccalaureate degree and are working on a degree; second priority is given to members without a graduate degree who are working on a degree, teacher certification, principal certification, or superintendent certification; third priority is for all others. **Deadline for Receipt:** October of each year for college terms beginning from January through April; February of each year for college terms beginning from May through July; June of each year for college terms beginning in August or September.

983 ■ MAINE STATE GOLF ASSOCIATION

Attn: Scholarship Fund
374 U.S. Route One
Yarmouth, ME 04096
Tel: (207)846-3800
Fax: (207)846-4055
E-mail: msga@mesga.org
Web Site: http://www.mesga.org
To provide financial assistance for college to high school seniors and graduates in Maine who have participated in golf.
Title of Award: Maine State Golf Association Scholarship **Area, Field, or Subject:** General studies/Field of study not specified **Level of Education for which Award is Granted:** Undergraduate **Number Awarded:** 1 or more each year. **Funds Available:** The stipend is $1,100 per year. **Duration:** 1 year; may be renewed until completion of a baccalaureate degree provided the recipient maintains a satisfactory academic record.
Eligibility Requirements: This program is open to graduates and prospective graduates of accredited Maine secondary schools. Applicants must have shown an active interest in golf by participating as a player, serving as a caddie, and/or working at a golf shop or course. They must demonstrate outstanding character, integrity, and leadership by participation in extracurricular, civic, and/or community activities. Financial need is also considered. **Deadline for Receipt:** March of each year.

984 ■ MAINE STATE SOCIETY OF WASHINGTON, D.C.

c/o Hugh L. Dwelley
3508 Wilson Street
Fairfax, VA 22030
Web Site: http://www.mainestatesociety.org/MSSFoundation.htm
To provide financial assistance to students who are currently enrolled full time at a university or 4-year degree-granting, nonprofit institution of higher learning within Maine.
Title of Award: Maine State Society of Washington, D.C. Foundation Scholarship Program **Area, Field, or Subject:** General studies/Field of study not specified **Level of Education for which Award is Granted:** Four Year College **Number Awarded:** 3 each year. **Funds Available:** The stipend is at least $1,000. **Duration:** 1 year; nonrenewable.
Eligibility Requirements: This program is open to full-time students enrolled at a 4-year degree-granting, nonprofit institution of higher learning in Maine. High school seniors are not eligible to apply. Applicants must have been legal residents of Maine for at least 4 years (or have at least 1 parent who has been a resident of Maine for at least 4 years). They must be under 25 years of age, be enrolled in at least 14 semester hours or the equivalent, have at least a 3.0 GPA, be working on a baccalaureate degree, and write an essay (up to 500 words) with background information on their qualifications for this scholarship. **Deadline for Receipt:** March of each year.

985 ■ MAINELY CHARACTER

P.O. Box 11131
Portland, ME 04104
E-mail: info@mainelycharacter.org
Web Site: http://www.mainelycharacter.org
To provide financial assistance for college to Maine residents who demonstrate principles of character.
Title of Award: Mainely Character Scholarship **Area, Field, or Subject:** General studies/Field of study not specified **Level of Education for which Award is Granted:** Undergraduate **Number Awarded:** 1 or more each year. **Funds Available:** The stipend is $5,000. **Duration:** 1 year; nonrenewable.

Eligibility Requirements: This program is open to residents of Maine who are high school seniors or have received a high school diploma and are entering the first year of postsecondary education. Selection is based on character, determined by an assessment process that includes a written essay demonstrating the principles of courage, integrity, responsibility, and concern. A personal interview is also required. **Deadline for Receipt:** February of each year. **Additional Information:** This program was established in 2000.

986 ■ STEPHEN T. MARCHELLO SCHOLARSHIP FOUNDATION

1170 East Long Place
Centennial, CO 80122
Tel: (303)886-5018
E-mail: fmarchello@earthlink.net
Web Site: http://www.stmfoundation.org
To provide financial assistance for college to students from designated western states who have survived childhood cancer.
Title of Award: Stephen T. Marchello Scholarships **Area, Field, or Subject:** General studies/Field of study not specified **Level of Education for which Award is Granted:** Undergraduate **Number Awarded:** Varies each year. Recently, 4 of these scholarships were awarded: 2 at $4,000, 1 at $1,250, and 1 at $1,000. **Funds Available:** Stipends range up to $4,000 per year. **Duration:** 1 year; may be renewed.
Eligibility Requirements: This program is open to high school seniors who either live in or were treated for cancer in Arizona, California, Colorado, or Montana. Applicants must be working on or planning to work on an undergraduate degree. They must submit essays on 2 topics: 1) their academic and professional goals, why they have chosen to pursue those goals, and how this scholarship will help them obtain their goals; and 2) an event in world history that has made a significant positive effect and their reasons why they feel this was important. In addition to those 2 essays, selection is based on high school GPA; SAT or ACT scores; information provided by the doctor, clinic, or hospital where they were treated; and 2 letters of reference. **Deadline for Receipt:** March of each year. **Additional Information:** This foundation was established by the family of Stephen T. Marchello who died of cancer in 1999. It awarded its first scholarship in 2000.

987 ■ MARINE CORPS COUNTERINTELLIGENCE ASSOCIATION

c/o Samuel L. Moyer
3125 Palmdale Drive
Oldsmar, FL 34677
E-mail: scholarship@mccia.org
Web Site: http://www.mccia.org
To provide financial assistance for college to dependents of members of the Marine Corps Counterintelligence Association (MCCIA).
Title of Award: Marine Corps Counterintelligence Association Scholarships **Area, Field, or Subject:** General studies/Field of study not specified **Level of Education for which Award is Granted:** Undergraduate **Number Awarded:** Varies each year; recently, 5 of these scholarships, at $1,000 each, were awarded. **Funds Available:** Stipends are $1,000 or $500. Funds must be used to help pay for tuition, books, fees, and materials; they may not be used for personal or living expenses. **Duration:** 1 year; may be renewed up to 3 additional years (need not be consecutive).
Eligibility Requirements: This program is open to children, grandchildren, and spouses of 1) current MCCIA members; 2) deceased Marines who were MCCIA members at the time of death; and 3) counterintelligence Marines who lost his life in the line of duty (whether he was a member of MCCIA or not). Spouses of deceased Marines must also be MCCIA Auxiliary members. Applicants must be enrolled or planning to enroll as a full-time undergraduate student at an accredited college or university. Along with their application, they must submit a 1-page essay on a topic of their choice, letters of recommendation, SAT or ACT scores, transcripts, copies of awards and other honors, and evidence of acceptance at a college or university. Financial need is not considered. **Deadline for Receipt:** June of each year.

988 ■ MARINE CORPS INTELLIGENCE ASSOCIATION, INC.

Attn: Marine Corps Intelligence Educational Foundation
P.O. Box 1028
Quantico, VA 22134-1028
Web Site: http://mcia-inc.org/mcief.htm

To provide financial assistance for college to members of the Marine Corps Intelligence Association (MCIA) and their dependent children.
Title of Award: John J. Guenther Scholarship **Area, Field, or Subject:** General studies/Field of study not specified **Level of Education for which Award is Granted:** Four Year College **Number Awarded:** At least 1 each year. **Funds Available:** The stipend is $1,500. **Duration:** 1 year.
Eligibility Requirements: This program is open to current MCIA members, their dependent children, and their survivors. Applicants must be attending or planning to attend an accredited 4-year college or university as a full-time student. They must submit a 300-word essay on a risk that has led to a significant change in their personal or intellectual life, the most challenging obstacles they have had to overcome and what they learned from the experience, and where they envision themselves in 10 years. Selection is based on the essay, academic achievement, extracurricular activities, and work experience. Financial need is not considered. **Deadline for Receipt:** July of each year. **Additional Information:** Membership in the MCIA is open to Marine Corps intelligence personnel, including active duty, Reserve, and retired. Information is also available from John Carey, MCIA Scholarship Committee Chair, 15412 Silvan Glen Drive, Dumfries, VA 22025, E-mail: careyja@hqmc.usmc.mil.

989 ■ MARINE CORPS LEAGUE

Attn: National Executive Director
P.O. Box 3070
Merrifield, VA 22116-3070
Tel: (703)207-9588
Free: 800-MCL-1775
Fax: (703)207-0047
E-mail: mcl@mcleague.org
Web Site: http://www.mcleague.org
To provide college aid to students whose parents served in the Marines and to members of the Marine Corps League or Marine Corps League Auxiliary.
Title of Award: Marine Corps League Scholarships **Area, Field, or Subject:** General studies/Field of study not specified **Level of Education for which Award is Granted:** Undergraduate **Number Awarded:** Varies, depending upon the amount of funds available each year. **Funds Available:** The stipend varies. Funds are paid directly to the recipient. **Duration:** 1 year; may be renewed up to 3 additional years (all renewals must complete an application and attach a transcript from the college or university).
Eligibility Requirements: The scholarships are awarded to qualified applicants in the following order of preference: 1) sons and daughters of Marines who lost their lives in the line of duty; 2) children and grandchildren of active Marine Corps Leaguers and/or Auxiliary members; and 3) members of the Marine Corps League and/or Marine Corps League Auxiliary who are honorably discharged and in need of rehabilitation training not provided by government programs. Applicants must be seeking further education and training as a full-time student and be recommended by the commandant of an active chartered detachment of the Marine Corps League or the president of an active chartered unit of the Auxiliary. Financial need is not considered in the selection process. **Deadline for Receipt:** June of each year. **Additional Information:** Information is also available from the Marine Corps League Scholarship Committee, Vic Voltaggio, Chairman, 1049 Florian Way, Spring Hall, FL 34609-9021, (352) 683-8254, E-mail: reconvic@yahoo.com.

990 ■ MARINE CORPS SCHOLARSHIP FOUNDATION, INC.

P.O. Box 3008
Princeton, NJ 08543-3008
Tel: (609)921-3534
Free: 800-292-7777
Fax: (609)452-2259
E-mail: mcsfnj@marine-scholars.org
Web Site: http://www.marine-scholars.org
To provide financial assistance for college to the children of present or former members of the U.S. Marine Corps.
Title of Award: Marine Corps Scholarships **Area, Field, or Subject:** General studies/Field of study not specified **Level of Education for which Award is Granted:** Undergraduate **Number Awarded:** Varies each year; recently, 967 of these scholarships, with a total value of more than $1,750,000, were awarded. **Funds Available:** The stipends of most scholarships range from $500 to $2,500 per year, depending upon the

recipient's financial needs and educational requirements. The Toyota Scholars Program, established in 2004 by Toyota Motor Sales, U.S.A., Inc., provides stipends of $5,000 per year. Certain named scholarships (including the Dr. Jack C. Berger and Virginia Butts Berger Memorial Cornerstone Scholarship, the General and Mrs. Graves B. Erskine Memorial Cornerstone Scholarship, the Frederick L. Swindal Cornerstone Scholarship, the Davenport Family Foundation Cornerstone Scholarship, and the Ralph M. Parsons Foundation Cornerstone Scholarship) are for $10,000 per year. **Duration:** 1 year; may be renewed upon reapplication. **Eligibility Requirements:** This program is open to the children of 1) Marines on active duty or in the Reserves; 2) former Marines and Marine Reservists who have received an honorable discharge, received a medical discharge, or were killed while serving in the U.S. Marines; 3) active duty, Reserve, and former U.S. Navy Corpsmen who are serving or have served with the U.S. Marine Corps; and 4) U.S. Navy Corpsmen who have served with the U.S. Marine Corps and have received an honorable discharge, medical discharge, or who were killed while serving in the U.S. Navy. Applicants must be high school seniors, high school graduates, or current undergraduates in an accredited college, university, or postsecondary vocational/technical school. They must submit academic transcripts; a written statement of service from their parent's commanding officer or a copy of their parent's honorable discharge; and a 300-word essay on topics that change periodically. Recently, they were invited to write on the topic, "What is the most valuable lesson you have learned and who was responsible for teaching it?" The family income of applicants must be less than $63,000 per year. **Deadline for Receipt:** April of each year. **Additional Information:** Recipients may pursue only undergraduate study at accredited colleges, universities, or postsecondary technical institutions.

991 ■ THURGOOD MARSHALL SCHOLARSHIP FUND

90 William Street, Suite 1203
New York, NY 10038
Tel: (212)573-8888
Fax: (212)573-8497
E-mail: bcolbert@tmsf.org
Web Site: http://www.thurgoodmarshallfund.org
To provide financial assistance to African American high school seniors or graduates who are interested in working on a degree at colleges and universities that are members of the Thurgood Marshall Scholarship Fund (TMSF).
Title of Award: Thurgood Marshall Scholarships **Area, Field, or Subject:** General studies/Field of study not specified **Level of Education for which Award is Granted:** Undergraduate **Number Awarded:** Varies each year; recently, nearly 1,000 students were receiving support from this program. **Funds Available:** Stipends range up to $2,200 per semester, depending on the need of the recipient. Funds are awarded through the institution to be used for tuition, room, board, books, and fees. **Duration:** 1 year; may be renewed for up to 3 additional years if the recipient maintains a GPA of 3.0 or higher in college. **Eligibility Requirements:** This program is open to full-time students enrolled or accepted at 1 of 47 designated TMSF institutions, most of which are Historically Black Colleges and Universities or other schools with large African American enrollments. Applicants must be African Americans who are U.S. citizens, have a high school GPA of 3.0 or higher, have scored at least 1100 on the SAT or 25 on the ACT, are recommended by their high school as academically exceptional or outstanding in the creative and performing arts, and can demonstrate financial need. They must apply through the TMSF school they attend, and the institutions select the recipients. **Deadline for Receipt:** Deadline dates vary by school; check with the institution you plan to attend. **Additional Information:** This program was founded in 1987 by the Miller Brewing Company in cooperation with the American Association of State Colleges and Universities and the Office for the Advancement of Public Black Colleges of the National Association of State Universities and Land-Grant Colleges. Additional support is provided by the Bank of America Foundation, Dow Chemical Company, the Doug Banks Foundation, Ketchum Public Relations, Northwestern Mutual, Philip Morris Companies, Texaco, and the Tom Joyner Foundation The participating TMSF institutions are Alabama A&M University, Alabama State University, Albany State University, Alcorn State University, Bluefield State College, Bowie State University, Central State University (Ohio), Charles R. Drew University of Medicine (California), Cheyney University, Chicago State University, Coppin State

College, Delaware State University, Elizabeth City State University, Fayetteville State University, Florida A&M University, Fort Valley State University, Grambling State University, Harris-Stowe State College, Howard University, Jackson State University, Kentucky State University, Langston University, Lincoln University (Missouri), Lincoln University (Pennsylvania), Medgar Evers College (New York), Mississippi Valley State University, Morgan State University, Norfolk State University, North Carolina A&T State University, North Carolina Central University, Prairie View A&M University, Savannah State University, South Carolina State University, Southern University and A&M College, Southern University at New Orleans, Southern University at Shreveport, Tennessee State University, Texas Southern University, Tuskegee University, University of Arkansas at Pine Bluff, University of the District of Columbia, University of Maryland-Eastern Shore, University of the Virgin Islands, Virginia State University, West Virginia State College, Winston-Salem State University, and York College.

992 ■ MARYLAND HIGHER EDUCATION COMMISSION

Attn: Office of Student Financial Assistance
839 Bestgate Road, Suite 400
Annapolis, MD 21401-3013
Tel: (410)260-4563
Free: 800-974-1024
Fax: (410)974-5376
E-mail: osfamail@mhec.state.md.us
Web Site: http://www.mhec.state.md.us/financialAid/ProgramDescriptions/prog_conroy.asp
To provide financial assistance for college or graduate school to specified categories of veterans, public safety employees, and their children in Maryland.
Title of Award: Edward T. Conroy Memorial Scholarship Program **Area, Field, or Subject:** General studies/Field of study not specified **Level of Education for which Award is Granted:** Graduate, Undergraduate **Number Awarded:** Varies each year. **Funds Available:** The amount of the award is equal to tuition and fees at a Maryland postsecondary institution, to a maximum of $17,800 for children and spouses of the September 11 terrorist attacks or $8,550 for all other recipients. **Duration:** Up to 5 years of full-time study or 8 years of part-time study. **Eligibility Requirements:** This program is open to undergraduate and graduate students in the following categories: 1) children and unremarried surviving spouses of state or local public safety employees or volunteers who died in the line of duty; 2) children of armed forces members whose death or 100% disability was directly caused by military service; 3) POW/MIA veterans of the Vietnam Conflict and their children; 4) children and surviving spouses of victims of the September 11, 2001 terrorist attacks who died in the World Trade Center in New York City, the Pentagon in Virginia, or United Airlines Flight 93 in Pennsylvania; 5) veterans who have, as a direct result of military service, a disability of 25% or greater and have exhausted or are no longer eligible for federal veterans' educational benefits; and 6) state or local public safety officers or volunteers who were 100% disabled in the line of duty. The parent, veteran, POW, or public safety officer or volunteer must have been a resident of Maryland at the time of death or when declared disabled. Financial need is not considered. **Deadline for Receipt:** July of each year. **Additional Information:** Recipients must enroll at a 2-year or 4-year Maryland college or university as a full-time or part-time degree-seeking undergraduate or graduate student or attend a private career school.

993 ■ MARYLAND HIGHER EDUCATION COMMISSION

Attn: Office of Student Financial Assistance
839 Bestgate Road, Suite 400
Annapolis, MD 21401-3013
Tel: (410)260-4565
Free: 800-974-1024
Fax: (410)974-5376
E-mail: osfamail@mhec.state.md.us
Web Site: http://www.mhec.state.md.us/financialAid/ProgramDescriptions/prog_delegate.asp
To provide financial assistance to vocational, undergraduate, and graduate students in Maryland.
Title of Award: Maryland Delegate Scholarship Program **Area, Field, or Subject:** General studies/Field of study not specified **Level of Education**

for which Award is Granted: Graduate, Undergraduate **Number Awarded:** Varies each year. **Funds Available:** The minimum annual award is $200. The total amount of all state awards may not exceed the cost of attendance as determined by the school's financial aid office or $17,800, whichever is less. **Duration:** 1 year; may be renewed for up to 3 additional years if the recipient maintains satisfactory academic progress. **Eligibility Requirements:** This program is open to students enrolled or planning to enroll either part time or full time in a vocational, undergraduate, or graduate program in Maryland. Applicants and their parents must be Maryland residents. Awards are made by state delegates to students in their district. Financial need must be demonstrated if the Office of Student Financial Assistance makes the award for the delegate. **Deadline for Receipt:** February of each year. **Additional Information:** Recipients may attend an out-of-state institution if their major is not available at a Maryland school and if their delegate agrees. Students should contact all 3 delegates in their state legislative district for application instructions.

994 ■ MARYLAND HIGHER EDUCATION COMMISSION

Attn: Office of Student Financial Assistance
839 Bestgate Road, Suite 400
Annapolis, MD 21401-3013
Tel: (410)260-4565
Free: 800-974-1024
Fax: (410)974-5376
E-mail: osfamail@mhec.state.md.us
Web Site: http://www.mhec.state.md.us/financialAid/
ProgramDescriptions/prog_ea.asp
To provide financial assistance to undergraduate students in Maryland.
Title of Award: Maryland Educational Assistance Grants **Area, Field, or Subject:** General studies/Field of study not specified **Level of Education for which Award is Granted:** Undergraduate **Number Awarded:** Varies each year. **Funds Available:** The amount of the grant equals 35% of the financial need, ranging from $400 to $2,700 per year. The total amount of all state awards may not exceed the cost of attendance as determined by the school's financial aid office or $17,800, whichever is less. **Duration:** 1 year; recipients may reapply for up to 3 additional years if they maintain satisfactory academic progress and continue to demonstrate financial need.
Eligibility Requirements: This program is open to Maryland residents who are enrolled or planning to enroll full time as an undergraduate student at a Maryland 2- or 4-year college or university. Financial need must be documented. **Deadline for Receipt:** February of each year.

995 ■ MARYLAND HIGHER EDUCATION COMMISSION

Attn: Office of Student Financial Assistance
839 Bestgate Road, Suite 400
Annapolis, MD 21401-3013
Tel: (410)260-4555
Free: 800-974-1024
Fax: (410)974-5376
E-mail: osfamail@mhec.state.md.us
Web Site: http://www.mhec.state.md.us/financialAid/
ProgramDescriptions/prog_ga.asp
To provide financial assistance to needy undergraduate students in Maryland.
Title of Award: Maryland Guaranteed Access Grants **Area, Field, or Subject:** General studies/Field of study not specified **Level of Education for which Award is Granted:** Undergraduate **Number Awarded:** Varies each year. **Funds Available:** Awards equal 100% of financial need, ranging from $400 to $13,800 per year. The total amount of all state awards may not exceed the cost of attendance as determined by the school's financial aid office or $17,800, whichever is less. **Duration:** 1 year; recipients may reapply for up to 3 additional years if they maintain satisfactory academic progress and continue to demonstrate financial need.
Eligibility Requirements: This program is open to seniors graduating from high schools in Maryland and planning to enroll as full-time undergraduate students in a program leading to a degree, diploma, or certificate at a 2- or 4-year college or university in the state. Applicants must have a high school GPA of 2.5 or higher and be able to demonstrate financial need. Currently, the maximum allowable total income is $12,103 for a family of 1, rising to $41,041 for a family of 8 plus $4,134 for each additional family member. **Deadline for Receipt:** February of each year.

996 ■ MARYLAND HIGHER EDUCATION COMMISSION

Attn: Office of Student Financial Assistance
839 Bestgate Road, Suite 400
Annapolis, MD 21401-3013
Tel: (410)260-4565
Free: 800-974-1024
Fax: (410)974-5376
E-mail: osfamail@mhec.state.md.us
Web Site: http://www.mhec.state.md.us/financialAid/
ProgramDescriptions/prog_ptgrant.asp
To provide financial assistance to students in Maryland who are attending college on a part-time basis.
Title of Award: Maryland Part-Time Grants **Area, Field, or Subject:** General studies/Field of study not specified **Level of Education for which Award is Granted:** Undergraduate **Number Awarded:** Varies each year. **Funds Available:** Grants range from $200 to $1,000 per year. **Duration:** 1 year; may be renewed for up to 7 additional years.
Eligibility Requirements: This program is open to students at Maryland colleges who are enrolled for at least 6 but no more than 11 credits each semester. Applicants must be able to demonstrate financial need. Both they and their parents must be Maryland residents. **Deadline for Receipt:** February of each year. **Additional Information:** Applications are available at the financial aid office of each college or university in Maryland.

997 ■ MARYLAND HIGHER EDUCATION COMMISSION

Attn: Office of Student Financial Assistance
839 Bestgate Road, Suite 400
Annapolis, MD 21401-3013
Tel: (410)260-4565
Free: 800-974-1024
Fax: (410)974-5376
E-mail: osfamail@mhec.state.md.us
Web Site: http://www.mhec.state.md.us/financialAid/
ProgramDescriptions/prog_senatorial.asp
To provide financial assistance to vocational, undergraduate, and graduate students in Maryland.
Title of Award: Maryland Senatorial Scholarships **Area, Field, or Subject:** General studies/Field of study not specified **Level of Education for which Award is Granted:** Graduate, Undergraduate **Number Awarded:** Varies each year. **Funds Available:** Stipends range from $200 to $2,000 per year, depending on the need of the recipient. The total amount of all state awards may not exceed the cost of attendance as determined by the school's financial aid office or $17,800, whichever is less. **Duration:** 1 year; may be renewed for up to 3 additional years of full-time study or 7 additional years of part-time study, provided the recipient maintains satisfactory academic progress.
Eligibility Requirements: This program is open to students enrolled either part time or full time in a vocational, undergraduate, or graduate program in Maryland. Applicants and their parents must be Maryland residents and able to demonstrate financial need. Awards are made by state senators to students in their districts. Some senators ask the Office of Student Financial Assistance to make awards for them; those awards are made on the basis of financial need. **Deadline for Receipt:** February of each year. **Additional Information:** Recipients may attend an out-of-state institution if their major is not available at a Maryland school and if their senator agrees.

998 ■ MARYLAND HIGHER EDUCATION COMMISSION

Attn: Office of Student Financial Assistance
839 Bestgate Road, Suite 400
Annapolis, MD 21401-3013
Tel: (410)260-4565
Free: 800-974-1024
Fax: (410)974-5376
E-mail: osfamail@mhec.state.md.us
Web Site: http://www.mhec.state.md.us/financialAid/
ProgramDescriptions/prog_fostercare.asp
To provide financial assistance for college to residents of Maryland who have lived in foster care.
Title of Award: Maryland Tuition Waiver for Foster Care Recipients **Area, Field, or Subject:** General studies/Field of study not specified **Level of Education for which Award is Granted:** Undergraduate **Number Awarded:** Varies each year. **Funds Available:** Recipients are exempt from paying tuition and mandatory fees at public colleges and universities

in Maryland. **Duration:** 1 year; may be renewed for an additional 4 years or until completion of a bachelor's degree, whichever comes first, provided the recipient maintains satisfactory academic progress.

Eligibility Requirements: This program is open to Maryland residents under 21 years of age who either 1) resided in a foster care home in the state at the time they graduated from high school or completed a GED examination, or 2) resided in a foster care home in the state on their 14th birthday and were then adopted. Applicants must be planning to enroll as a degree candidate at a public 2-year or 4-year higher educational institution in Maryland. **Deadline for Receipt:** February of each year.

999 ■ MARYLAND NATIONAL GUARD

Attn: Education Services Office
Fifth Regiment Armory
29th Division Street, Room D24
Baltimore, MD 21201-2288
Tel: (410)576-1499
Free: 800-492-2526
Fax: (410)576-6082
E-mail: mdng_education@md.ngb.army.mil
Web Site: http://www.marylandguard.com
To provide tuition reimbursement to members of the Maryland National Guard.

Title of Award: Maryland National Guard State Tuition Assistance **Area, Field, or Subject:** General studies/Field of study not specified **Level of Education for which Award is Granted:** Undergraduate **Number Awarded:** Varies each year. **Funds Available:** Eligible Guard members receive an amount equal to 50% of their college/university tuition and related course fees. **Duration:** 1 semester; recipients may reapply.

Eligibility Requirements: This program is open to members of the Maryland National Guard in grades E-1 through O-4 who have at least 24 months of service remaining in the Guard from the start of the course date. Applicants must be attending or planning to attend a state-supported college or university in Maryland to work on an undergraduate degree. **Additional Information:** Individuals must apply for reimbursement within 45 days after their course is completed. They must have earned at least a grade of "C" in the course to qualify for reimbursement.

1000 ■ MARYLAND NATIONAL GUARD

Attn: Education Services Office
Fifth Regiment Armory
29th Division Street, Room D24
Baltimore, MD 21201-2288
Tel: (410)576-1499
Free: 800-492-2526
Fax: (410)576-6082
E-mail: mdng_education@md.ngb.army.mil
Web Site: http://www.marylandguard.com
To waive tuition for members of the Maryland National Guard at colleges and universities in the state.

Title of Award: Maryland National Guard State Tuition Waiver **Area, Field, or Subject:** General studies/Field of study not specified **Level of Education for which Award is Granted:** Graduate, Undergraduate **Number Awarded:** Varies each year. **Funds Available:** The amount of the waiver ranges from 25% to 50%. **Duration:** 1 semester; recipients may reapply.

Eligibility Requirements: All state-supported colleges and universities in Maryland have developed a tuition waiver program for members of the National Guard who are taking graduate or university courses. **Additional Information:** Some schools also limit the number of credits for which a Guard member can receive waivers during any semester.

1001 ■ MARYLAND STATE DEPARTMENT OF EDUCATION

Attn: AIMMS
200 West Baltimore Street
Baltimore, MD 21201
Tel: (410)887-2446
Web Site: http://www.msde.state.md.us/minority/WhatsNew/WHATSNEW.html
To provide financial assistance for college to Maryland high school seniors who have demonstrated leadership in addressing diversity.

Title of Award: AIMMS Excellence Scholarships **Area, Field, or Subject:** General studies/Field of study not specified **Level of Education for which Award is Granted:** Undergraduate **Number Awarded:** 11 each

year: 1 at $1,000 and 10 at $500. **Funds Available:** Stipends are $1,000 or $500. **Duration:** 1 year.

Eligibility Requirements: This program is open to seniors in high schools in Maryland who plan to attend a community college, university, college, or technical/vocational school. Applicants must have a GPA of 3.0 or higher. They must submit an essay about their leadership in 1 or more of the following areas: 1) academic, school, or community support for diverse students; 2) promotion of positive intergroup relations and understanding; or 3) performance of services to increase success among diverse groups of students. Diverse groups include race/ethnicity, gender, age, disability, or poverty. Selection is based on academic success and contributions to better understanding and appreciation among diverse groups. **Deadline for Receipt:** July of each year. **Additional Information:** This program began in 1999. The scholarship for $1,000 is designated the Barbara Dezmon Scholarship.

1002 ■ MARYLAND STATE FUNERAL DIRECTORS ASSOCIATION

Attn: Memorial Scholarship
311 Crain Highway, S.E.
P.O. Box 10
Glen Burnie, MD 21061
Tel: (410)553-9106; 888-459-9693
Fax: (410)553-9107
E-mail: msfda@msfda.net
Web Site: http://www.msfda.net/scholarship.php
To provide financial assistance to Maryland residents who are interested in preparing for a career in funeral service.

Title of Award: Daniel T. Mulheran Memorial Scholarship **Area, Field, or Subject:** Mortuary science **Level of Education for which Award is Granted:** Professional, Undergraduate **Number Awarded:** 1 each year. **Funds Available:** The stipend is $1,000. **Duration:** 1 year.

Eligibility Requirements: This program is open to Maryland residents who have completed at least two-thirds of their educational requirements in an accredited mortuary science program or have graduated within the past 6 months. Applicants must have an overall GPA of 2.5 or higher and may not have earned a grade of "D" in any mortuary science class. They must be eligible for licensure in Maryland. Along with their application, they must submit 2 essays of approximately 500 words on 1) the process they used and the experiences they underwent in their decision to enter the funeral service profession, and 2) themselves. Selection is based on academic record and the essays; financial need is not considered. **Deadline for Receipt:** September of each year.

1003 ■ MASSACHUSETTS COMMUNITY COLLEGES

Attn: Executive Office
Old South Building
294 Washington Street, Suite 301
Boston, MA 02108
Tel: (617)542-2911
E-mail: mherbert@mcceo.mass.edu
Web Site: http://www.masscc.org/student_tuition.asp
To provide reduced tuition at community colleges in Massachusetts to students who meet financial need requirements.

Title of Award: Massachusetts Community Colleges Access Grant Program **Area, Field, or Subject:** General studies/Field of study not specified **Level of Education for which Award is Granted:** Two Year College **Number Awarded:** Varies each year. **Funds Available:** Students who qualify for full assistance receive payment of the full cost of tuition and fees. **Duration:** 1 year; may be renewed.

Eligibility Requirements: This program is open to students at community colleges in Massachusetts who are working on an associate degree. Applicants must have a household income of $36,000 or less to qualify for full assistance. Students with a household income greater than $36,000 may also qualify for partial assistance.

1004 ■ MASSACHUSETTS NATIONAL GUARD

Attn: Education Services Office
50 Maple Street
Milford, MA 01757-3604
888-301-3103
Fax: (508)233-6781
E-mail: education@ma.ngb.army.mil
Web Site: http://www.mass.gov/guard/education/index.htm

To provide financial assistance for undergraduate or graduate study to members of the Massachusetts National Guard.

Title of Award: Massachusetts National Guard Educational Assistance Program **Area, Field, or Subject:** General studies/Field of study not specified **Level of Education for which Award is Granted:** Graduate, Undergraduate **Number Awarded:** Varies each year. **Funds Available:** Eligible Guard members are exempt from any tuition payments at colleges or universities operated by the Commonwealth of Massachusetts and funded by the Massachusetts Board of Higher Education. **Duration:** Up to a total of 130 semester hours.

Eligibility Requirements: This program is open to actively participating members of the Army or Air National Guard in Massachusetts. Applicants must have less than 9 AWOLs (Absence Without Leave) at all times and must not ETS (Expiration of Term of Service) during the period enrolled. They must be accepted for admission or enrolled at 1 of 28 Massachusetts public colleges, universities, or community colleges and working on an associate, bachelor's, master's, or doctoral degree. The institution must have a vacancy after all tuition-paying students and all students who are enrolled under any scholarship or tuition waiver provisions have enrolled. **Additional Information:** Recipients may enroll either part or full time in a Massachusetts state-supported institution. This program, commonly referred to as the 100% Tuition Waiver Program, is funded through the Massachusetts Board of Higher Education.

1005 ■ MASSACHUSETTS OFFICE OF STUDENT FINANCIAL ASSISTANCE

454 Broadway, Suite 200
Revere, MA 02151
Tel: (617)727-9420
Fax: (617)727-0667
E-mail: osfa@osfa.mass.edu
Web Site: http://www.osfa.mass.edu

To provide financial assistance for college to Massachusetts residents who earn high scores on the MCAS tests.

Title of Award: John and Abigail Adams Scholarship Program **Area, Field, or Subject:** General studies/Field of study not specified **Level of Education for which Award is Granted:** Undergraduate **Number Awarded:** Varies each year. **Funds Available:** Recipients of these scholarships are eligible for an award of a non-need-based tuition waiver for state-supported undergraduate courses in Massachusetts. **Duration:** Up to 4 academic years, provided the student maintains a college GPA of 3.0 or higher.

Eligibility Requirements: This program is open to permanent Massachusetts residents who are U.S. citizens or permanent residents. Applicants must score "Advanced" in either the mathematics or the English language section of the grade 10 MCAS and score either "Advanced" or "Proficient" in the other of those 2 sections. They must also have a combined MCAS score on those assessments that ranks in the top 25% in their school district and be planning to enroll full time at a Massachusetts public college or university.

1006 ■ MASSACHUSETTS OFFICE OF STUDENT FINANCIAL ASSISTANCE

454 Broadway, Suite 200
Revere, MA 02151
Tel: (617)727-9420
Fax: (617)727-0667
E-mail: osfa@osfa.mass.edu
Web Site: http://www.osfa.mass.edu

To provide financial assistance for college to Massachusetts residents who are the spouse or child of a victim of the terrorism that occurred on September 11, 2001.

Title of Award: Commonwealth September 11, 2001 Tragedy Tuition Waiver Program **Area, Field, or Subject:** General studies/Field of study not specified **Level of Education for which Award is Granted:** Undergraduate **Number Awarded:** Varies each year. **Funds Available:** Eligible students are exempt from any tuition payments for an undergraduate degree or certificate program at public colleges or universities in Massachusetts. **Duration:** Up to 4 academic years, for a total of 130 semester hours.

Eligibility Requirements: This program is open to the spouses and children of residents of Massachusetts who died or are missing and presumed dead as a result of the acts of terrorism that occurred on September 11, 2001. Applicants must be enrolled or planning to enroll at a public higher education institution in Massachusetts.

1007 ■ MASSACHUSETTS OFFICE OF STUDENT FINANCIAL ASSISTANCE

454 Broadway, Suite 200
Revere, MA 02151
Tel: (617)727-9420
Fax: (617)727-0667
E-mail: osfa@osfa.mass.edu
Web Site: http://www.osfa.mass.edu

To provide financial assistance for college to Massachusetts residents who are attending accredited independent institutions.

Title of Award: Gilbert Matching Student Grant Program **Area, Field, or Subject:** General studies/Field of study not specified **Level of Education for which Award is Granted:** Undergraduate **Number Awarded:** Varies each year. **Funds Available:** Awards range from $200 to $2,500 per year, depending on the need of the recipient. **Duration:** 1 year; may be renewed.

Eligibility Requirements: Applicants for these scholarships must have been permanent legal residents of Massachusetts for at least 1 year and be working full time on an associate or bachelor's degree at an independent, regionally accredited college or university in Massachusetts. U.S. citizenship or permanent resident status is required. Selection is based on financial need. **Deadline for Receipt:** Deadlines are established by the school the student attends.

1008 ■ MASSACHUSETTS OFFICE OF STUDENT FINANCIAL ASSISTANCE

454 Broadway, Suite 200
Revere, MA 02151
Tel: (617)727-9420
Fax: (617)727-0667
E-mail: osfa@osfa.mass.edu
Web Site: http://www.osfa.mass.edu

To provide financial assistance for college to Massachusetts residents who overcome major adversities.

Title of Award: Christian A. Herter Memorial Scholarship **Area, Field, or Subject:** General studies/Field of study not specified **Level of Education for which Award is Granted:** Undergraduate **Number Awarded:** 25 each year. **Funds Available:** Awards cover up to 50% of the student's unmet financial need, to a maximum of $15,000 per year. **Duration:** 4 years.

Eligibility Requirements: Applicants for these scholarships must have been permanent legal residents of Massachusetts for at least 1 year, must be attending a secondary school in the 10th or 11th grade, must have a cumulative GPA of 2.5 or higher, and must be planning to work full time on an undergraduate degree at an accredited institution in the United States. They must be able to demonstrate 1) difficult personal circumstances in their lives (e.g., physical or mental abuse, catastrophic illness) or other personal obstacles or hardships of a societal, geographic, mental, or physical nature; 2) high financial need; and 3) strong academic promise to continue their education beyond high school at a college or university. **Deadline for Receipt:** April of each year. **Additional Information:** This program was established in 1972.

1009 ■ MASSACHUSETTS OFFICE OF STUDENT FINANCIAL ASSISTANCE

454 Broadway, Suite 200
Revere, MA 02151
Tel: (617)727-9420
Fax: (617)727-0667
E-mail: osfa@osfa.mass.edu
Web Site: http://www.osfa.mass.edu

To provide financial assistance for college to Massachusetts residents who earn a Stanley Z. Koplik Certificate of Mastery while in high school.

Title of Award: Stanley Z. Koplik Certificate of Mastery Tuition Waiver Program **Area, Field, or Subject:** General studies/Field of study not specified **Level of Education for which Award is Granted:** Undergraduate **Number Awarded:** Varies each year. **Funds Available:** Recipients of Koplik Certificates are eligible for an award of a non-need-based tuition waiver for state-supported undergraduate courses in Massachusetts. **Duration:** Up to 4 academic years, provided the student maintains a college GPA of 3.3 or higher.

Eligibility Requirements: This program is open to permanent Massachusetts residents who are U.S. citizens or permanent residents. In order to become a candidate for the Stanley Z. Koplik Certificate of Mastery, students must score "Advanced" on at least 1 grade 10 MCAS test subject and score "Proficient" on the remaining sections of the grade 10 MCAS. Once they become candidates, they must then fulfill additional requirements through 1 of the following combinations covering both arts/humanities and mathematics/science: 2 AP exams; 2 SAT II exams; 1 SAT II exam and 1 AP exam; 1 SAT II exam and 1 other achievement; or 1 AP exam and 1 other achievement. They must score at least 3 on any AP exam; if there are SAT II and AP exams in the same subject area, they must receive a score on the SAT II exam determined by the Department of Education to be comparable to a score of 3 on the AP exam. In subject areas where they are no corresponding AP exams, a student must achieve an SAT II score designated by the Department of Education.

1010 ■ MASSACHUSETTS OFFICE OF STUDENT FINANCIAL ASSISTANCE
454 Broadway, Suite 200
Revere, MA 02151
Tel: (617)727-9420
Fax: (617)727-0667
E-mail: osfa@osfa.mass.edu
Web Site: http://www.osfa.mass.edu
To waive tuition at Massachusetts public colleges and universities for members of the armed forces.
Title of Award: Massachusetts Armed Forces Tuition Waiver Program **Area, Field, or Subject:** General studies/Field of study not specified **Level of Education for which Award is Granted:** Undergraduate **Number Awarded:** Varies each year. **Funds Available:** Eligible military personnel are exempt from any tuition payments toward an undergraduate degree or certificate program at public colleges or universities in Massachusetts. **Duration:** Up to 4 academic years, for a total of 130 semester hours.
Eligibility Requirements: Applicants for these scholarships must have been permanent legal residents of Massachusetts for at least 1 year and stationed in Massachusetts as members of the Army, Navy, Marine Corps, Air Force, or Coast Guard. They may not be in default on any federal student loan. They must enroll in at least 3 undergraduate credits per semester. **Additional Information:** Recipients may enroll either part or full time in a Massachusetts publicly-supported institution.

1011 ■ MASSACHUSETTS OFFICE OF STUDENT FINANCIAL ASSISTANCE
454 Broadway, Suite 200
Revere, MA 02151
Tel: (617)727-9420
Fax: (617)727-0667
E-mail: osfa@osfa.mass.edu
Web Site: http://www.osfa.mass.edu
To provide financial assistance to Massachusetts residents who are attending state-supported colleges and universities.
Title of Award: Massachusetts Cash Grant Program **Area, Field, or Subject:** General studies/Field of study not specified **Level of Education for which Award is Granted:** Undergraduate **Number Awarded:** Varies each year. **Funds Available:** These awards provide assistance in meeting institutionally-held charges, such as mandatory fees and non-state-supported tuition. The amount of the award depends on the need of the recipient. **Duration:** 1 year; may be renewed.
Eligibility Requirements: Applicants for these scholarships must have been permanent legal residents of Massachusetts for at least 1 year and must be an undergraduate at a state-supported college or university. U.S. citizenship or permanent resident status is required. Financial need must be demonstrated. **Deadline for Receipt:** Deadlines are established by the financial aid office of each participating Massachusetts institution. **Additional Information:** This program complements the Need-Based Tuition Waiver Program.

1012 ■ MASSACHUSETTS OFFICE OF STUDENT FINANCIAL ASSISTANCE
454 Broadway, Suite 200
Revere, MA 02151
Tel: (617)727-9420

Fax: (617)727-0667
E-mail: osfa@osfa.mass.edu
Web Site: http://www.osfa.mass.edu
To provide financial assistance for college to students adopted through the Massachusetts Department of Social Services (DSS).
Title of Award: Massachusetts DSS Adopted Children Tuition Waiver **Area, Field, or Subject:** General studies/Field of study not specified **Level of Education for which Award is Granted:** Undergraduate **Number Awarded:** Varies each year. **Funds Available:** All tuition for state-supported courses is waived. **Duration:** Up to 4 academic years.
Eligibility Requirements: This program is open to students 24 years of age or younger who were adopted through DSS by state employees or eligible Massachusetts residents, regardless of the date of adoption. Applicants must be U.S. citizens or permanent residents attending or planning to attend a Massachusetts public institution of higher education as an undergraduate student. **Additional Information:** This waiver does not apply to graduate courses, courses in the M.D. program at the University of Massachusetts Medical Center, or non-state supported courses and/or programs.

1013 ■ MASSACHUSETTS OFFICE OF STUDENT FINANCIAL ASSISTANCE
454 Broadway, Suite 200
Revere, MA 02151
Tel: (617)727-9420
Fax: (617)727-0667
E-mail: osfa@osfa.mass.edu
Web Site: http://www.osfa.mass.edu
To provide financial assistance for college to foster children in the custody of the Massachusetts Department of Social Services (DSS).
Title of Award: Massachusetts DSS Tuition Waiver for Foster Care Children **Area, Field, or Subject:** General studies/Field of study not specified **Level of Education for which Award is Granted:** Undergraduate **Number Awarded:** Varies each year. **Funds Available:** All tuition for state-supported courses is waived. **Duration:** Up to 4 academic years.
Eligibility Requirements: This program is open to students 24 years of age or younger who have been in the custody of the DSS for at least 12 consecutive months. Applicants may not have been adopted or returned home. They must be U.S. citizens or permanent residents attending or planning to attend a college or university in Massachusetts as a full-time undergraduate student. **Additional Information:** This waiver does not apply to graduate courses, courses in the M.D. program at the University of Massachusetts Medical Center, or non-state supported courses and/or programs. The sponsor also offers a $6,000 Foster Child Grant for students 24 years of age or younger who are current of former foster children placed in the custody of the DSS through a care and protection petition. Those students may attend college in any state.

1014 ■ MASSACHUSETTS OFFICE OF STUDENT FINANCIAL ASSISTANCE
454 Broadway, Suite 200
Revere, MA 02151
Tel: (617)727-9420
Fax: (617)727-0667
E-mail: osfa@osfa.mass.edu
Web Site: http://www.osfa.mass.edu
To provide financial assistance to Massachusetts students who transfer from a community college to a public 4-year institution in the state.
Title of Award: Massachusetts Joint Admissions Tuition Advantage Program **Area, Field, or Subject:** General studies/Field of study not specified **Level of Education for which Award is Granted:** Four Year College **Number Awarded:** Varies each year. **Funds Available:** Eligible students receive a waiver of tuition equal to 33% of the resident tuition rate at the college or university they attend. **Duration:** Up to 2 academic years, if the recipient maintains a cumulative GPA of 3.0 or higher.
Eligibility Requirements: This program is open to students who completed an associate degree at a public community college in Massachusetts within the prior calendar year as a participant in a Joint Admis-

sions Program. Applicants must have earned a GPA of 3.0 or higher and be transferring to a state college or participating university.

1015 ■ MASSACHUSETTS OFFICE OF STUDENT FINANCIAL ASSISTANCE

454 Broadway, Suite 200
Revere, MA 02151
Tel: (617)727-9420
Fax: (617)727-0667
E-mail: osfa@osfa.mass.edu
Web Site: http://www.osfa.mass.edu

To provide financial assistance for college to Massachusetts residents who are Native Americans.

Title of Award: Massachusetts Native American Tuition Waiver Program **Area, Field, or Subject:** General studies/Field of study not specified **Level of Education for which Award is Granted:** Undergraduate **Number Awarded:** Varies each year. **Funds Available:** Eligible students are exempt from any tuition payments for an undergraduate degree or certificate program at public colleges or universities in Massachusetts. **Duration:** Up to 4 academic years, for a total of 130 semester hours.

Eligibility Requirements: Applicants for these scholarships must have been permanent legal residents of Massachusetts for at least 1 year and certified by the Bureau of Indian Affairs as Native Americans. They may not be in default on any federal student loan. **Additional Information:** Recipients may enroll either part or full time in a Massachusetts publicly-supported institution.

1016 ■ MASSACHUSETTS OFFICE OF STUDENT FINANCIAL ASSISTANCE

454 Broadway, Suite 200
Revere, MA 02151
Tel: (617)727-9420
Fax: (617)727-0667
E-mail: osfa@osfa.mass.edu
Web Site: http://www.osfa.mass.edu

To provide financial assistance for college to Massachusetts residents who demonstrate financial need.

Title of Award: Massachusetts Need Based Tuition Waiver Program **Area, Field, or Subject:** General studies/Field of study not specified **Level of Education for which Award is Granted:** Undergraduate **Number Awarded:** Varies each year. **Funds Available:** Eligible students are exempt from any tuition payments for an undergraduate degree or certificate program at public colleges or universities in Massachusetts. These awards, in combination with other resources in the student's financial aid package, may not exceed the student's demonstrated financial need. **Duration:** Up to 4 academic years, for a total of 130 semester hours.

Eligibility Requirements: Applicants for this program must have been permanent legal residents of Massachusetts for at least 1 year, be U.S. citizens or permanent residents, be in compliance with Selective Service registration, not be in default on any federal student loan, be enrolled for at least 3 undergraduate units in an eligible program at a Massachusetts institution of higher learning, and be able to document financial need. **Additional Information:** Recipients may enroll either part or full time in a Massachusetts publicly-supported institution. This program was established in 1981.

1017 ■ MASSACHUSETTS OFFICE OF STUDENT FINANCIAL ASSISTANCE

454 Broadway, Suite 200
Revere, MA 02151
Tel: (617)727-9420
Fax: (617)727-0667
E-mail: osfa@osfa.mass.edu
Web Site: http://www.osfa.mass.edu

To provide financial assistance for college to Massachusetts residents.

Title of Award: Massachusetts No Interest Loan Program **Area, Field, or Subject:** General studies/Field of study not specified **Level of Education for which Award is Granted:** Undergraduate **Number Awarded:** Varies each year. **Funds Available:** Loans from $1,000 to $4,000 per year are available, depending on the student's financial need. The maximum lifetime borrowing limit is $20,000. The minimum monthly repayment is $50. Borrowers are granted a 6-month grace period beginning at gradua-

tion, withdrawal, or dropping below at least half-time attendance; after the grace period, they have 10 years to repay the loan. **Duration:** 1 year; may be renewed up to 4 additional years.

Eligibility Requirements: Applicants for these loans must have been permanent legal residents of Massachusetts for at least 1 year and attending a regionally accredited participating postsecondary educational institution in Massachusetts as full-time students in a certificate, associate, or bachelor's degree program. **Deadline for Receipt:** Deadlines are established by the school the student attends. **Additional Information:** Borrowers may defer repayment of the loan while enrolled at least half-time in an eligible undergraduate or graduate program; during service in the military, Peace Corps, ACTION Program, or VISTA Program; as an active-duty member of the National Oceanic and Atmospheric Administrative Corps; while holding office in the commissioned corps of the U.S. Public Health Service; because of temporary total disability, including spousal or dependent care; if unemployed; or because of other hardship due to extenuating circumstances.

1018 ■ MASSACHUSETTS OFFICE OF STUDENT FINANCIAL ASSISTANCE

454 Broadway, Suite 200
Revere, MA 02151
Tel: (617)727-9420
Fax: (617)727-0667
E-mail: osfa@osfa.mass.edu
Web Site: http://www.osfa.mass.edu

To provide financial assistance to Massachusetts residents who are attending colleges and universities on a part-time basis.

Title of Award: Massachusetts Part-Time Grant Program **Area, Field, or Subject:** General studies/Field of study not specified **Level of Education for which Award is Granted:** Undergraduate **Number Awarded:** Varies each year. **Funds Available:** Awards range from $200 to a maximum that depends on the type of institution the student attends. **Duration:** 1 year; may be renewed.

Eligibility Requirements: Applicants for these scholarships must have been permanent legal residents of Massachusetts for at least 1 year and must be a part-time undergraduate at a public, private, independent, for profit, or nonprofit institution in Massachusetts. U.S. citizenship or permanent resident status is required. Financial need must be demonstrated. **Deadline for Receipt:** Deadlines are established by the financial aid office of each participating Massachusetts institution.

1019 ■ MASSACHUSETTS OFFICE OF STUDENT FINANCIAL ASSISTANCE

454 Broadway, Suite 200
Revere, MA 02151
Tel: (617)727-9420
Fax: (617)727-0667
E-mail: osfa@osfa.mass.edu
Web Site: http://www.osfa.mass.edu

To provide financial assistance for college to children or widow(er)s of deceased public service officers and others in Massachusetts.

Title of Award: Massachusetts Public Service Grant Program **Area, Field, or Subject:** General studies/Field of study not specified **Level of Education for which Award is Granted:** Undergraduate **Number Awarded:** Varies each year. **Funds Available:** Scholarships provide up to the cost of tuition at a state-supported college or university in Massachusetts; if the recipient attends a private Massachusetts college or university, the scholarship is equivalent to tuition at a public institution, up to $2,500. **Duration:** 1 year; renewable.

Eligibility Requirements: Only Massachusetts residents are eligible. They must be 1) the children or spouses of fire fighters, police officers, or corrections officers who were killed or died from injuries incurred in the line of duty; 2) children of prisoners of war or military service personnel missing in action in southeast Asia whose wartime service was credited to Massachusetts and whose service was between February 1, 1955 and the termination of the Vietnam campaign; or 3) children of veterans whose service was credited to Massachusetts and who were killed in action or died as a result of their service. **Deadline for Receipt:** April of each year.

1020 ■ MASSACHUSETTS OFFICE OF STUDENT FINANCIAL ASSISTANCE

454 Broadway, Suite 200
Revere, MA 02151

Tel: (617)727-9420

Fax: (617)727-0667

E-mail: osfa@osfa.mass.edu

Web Site: http://www.osfa.mass.edu

To provide financial assistance for college to Massachusetts residents who are clients of specified state disability agencies.

Title of Award: Massachusetts Rehabilitation Commission or Commission for the Blind Tuition Waiver Program **Area, Field, or Subject:** General studies/Field of study not specified **Level of Education for which Award is Granted:** Undergraduate **Number Awarded:** Varies each year. **Funds Available:** Eligible clients are exempt from any tuition payments for an undergraduate degree or certificate program at public colleges or universities in Massachusetts. **Duration:** Up to 4 academic years, for a total of 130 semester hours.

Eligibility Requirements: Applicants for these scholarships must be certified as clients by the Massachusetts Rehabilitation Commission or Commission for the Blind. They must have been permanent residents of Massachusetts for at least 1 year, must be U.S. citizens or permanent residents, and may not be in default on any federal student loan. **Additional Information:** Recipients may enroll either part or full time in a Massachusetts publicly-supported institution.

1021 ■ MASSACHUSETTS OFFICE OF STUDENT FINANCIAL ASSISTANCE

454 Broadway, Suite 200

Revere, MA 02151

Tel: (617)727-9420

Fax: (617)727-0667

E-mail: osfa@osfa.mass.edu

Web Site: http://www.osfa.mass.edu

To provide financial assistance for college to Massachusetts residents who have been designated as valedictorians at their high school.

Title of Award: Massachusetts Valedictorian Tuition Waiver Program **Area, Field, or Subject:** General studies/Field of study not specified **Level of Education for which Award is Granted:** Undergraduate **Number Awarded:** Varies each year. **Funds Available:** Eligible students are exempt from any tuition payments for an undergraduate degree or certificate program at public colleges or universities in Massachusetts. **Duration:** Up to 4 academic years, for a total of 130 semester hours.

Eligibility Requirements: This program is open to seniors designated by a public or private high school in Massachusetts as a valedictorian. Applicants must have been permanent legal residents of Massachusetts for at least 1 year and be planning to enroll at a public higher education institution in the state. They must be in compliance with Selective Service registration and may not be in default on any federal student loan.

1022 ■ MASSACHUSETTS OFFICE OF STUDENT FINANCIAL ASSISTANCE

454 Broadway, Suite 200

Revere, MA 02151

Tel: (617)727-9420

Fax: (617)727-0667

E-mail: osfa@osfa.mass.edu

Web Site: http://www.osfa.mass.edu

To provide financial assistance for college to Massachusetts residents who are veterans.

Title of Award: Massachusetts Veterans Tuition Waiver Program **Area, Field, or Subject:** General studies/Field of study not specified **Level of Education for which Award is Granted:** Undergraduate **Number Awarded:** Varies each year. **Funds Available:** Eligible veterans are exempt from any tuition payments for an undergraduate degree or certificate program at public colleges or universities in Massachusetts. **Duration:** Up to 4 academic years, for a total of 130 semester hours.

Eligibility Requirements: Applicants for these scholarships must have been permanent legal residents of Massachusetts for at least 1 year and veterans who served actively during the Spanish-American War, World War I, World War II, Korea, Vietnam, the Lebanese peace keeping force, the Grenada rescue mission, the Panamanian intervention force, the Persian Gulf, or Operation Restore Hope in Somalia. They may not be in

default on any federal student loan. **Additional Information:** Recipients may enroll either part or full time in a Massachusetts publicly-supported institution.

1023 ■ MASSACHUSETTS OFFICE OF STUDENT FINANCIAL ASSISTANCE

454 Broadway, Suite 200

Revere, MA 02151

Tel: (617)727-9420

Fax: (617)727-0667

E-mail: osfa@osfa.mass.edu

Web Site: http://www.osfa.mass.edu

To provide financial assistance for college to Massachusetts residents who are attending approved schools in designated states.

Title of Award: MASSGrant Program **Area, Field, or Subject:** General studies/Field of study not specified **Level of Education for which Award is Granted:** Undergraduate **Number Awarded:** Varies each year. **Funds Available:** Awards range from $300 to $2,300 per year. **Duration:** 1 year; may be renewed for up to 4 additional years.

Eligibility Requirements: This program is open to students enrolled in a certificate, associate, or bachelor's degree program. Applicants must have been permanent legal residents of Massachusetts for at least 1 year and attending state-approved postsecondary schools (public, private, independent, for profit, or nonprofit) as full-time undergraduate students in Connecticut, Maine, Massachusetts, New Hampshire, Pennsylvania, Rhode Island, Vermont, or Washington, D.C. U.S. citizenship or permanent resident status is required. Selection is based on financial need, with an expected family contribution between zero and $3,850. **Deadline for Receipt:** April of each year.

1024 ■ MASSACHUSETTS OFFICE OF STUDENT FINANCIAL ASSISTANCE

454 Broadway, Suite 200

Revere, MA 02151

Tel: (617)727-9420

Fax: (617)727-0667

E-mail: osfa@osfa.mass.edu

Web Site: http://www.osfa.mass.edu

To provide financial assistance for college to Massachusetts residents who participate in the Massachusetts Educational Financing Authority (MEFA) Prepaid Tuition Program.

Title of Award: MEFA-Prepaid Tuition Program Waiver **Area, Field, or Subject:** General studies/Field of study not specified **Level of Education for which Award is Granted:** Undergraduate **Number Awarded:** Varies each year. **Funds Available:** If the tuition charged by the participating public institution exceeds the amount received as a tuition credit pursuant to the student's participation in Prepaid Tuition Program, the institution may waive the difference. **Duration:** Up to 4 academic years.

Eligibility Requirements: This program is open to students who are the owner or a qualifying beneficiary of a MEFA Prepaid Tuition Program. Applicants must be admitted to a Massachusetts public institution of higher education that participates in the MEFA Prepaid Tuition Program. **Additional Information:** Information on the Prepaid Tuition Program is available from MEFA at (617) 261-9760.

1025 ■ MASSACHUSETTS OFFICE OF STUDENT FINANCIAL ASSISTANCE

454 Broadway, Suite 200

Revere, MA 02151

Tel: (617)727-9420

Fax: (617)727-0667

E-mail: osfa@osfa.mass.edu

Web Site: http://www.osfa.mass.edu

To provide financial assistance to Massachusetts students who attend 1 of the state colleges in Massachusetts.

Title of Award: Paul Tsongas Scholarship Program **Area, Field, or Subject:** General studies/Field of study not specified **Level of Education for which Award is Granted:** Undergraduate **Number Awarded:** 45 each year; 5 at each state college in Massachusetts. **Funds Available:** Eligible students receive a waiver of tuition and mandatory fees. **Duration:** Up to 4 academic years, if the recipient maintains a GPA of 3.3 or higher in college.

Eligibility Requirements: This program is open to residents of Massachusetts who have graduated from high school within 3 years and are attending or planning to attend a state college in Massachusetts. Applicants must be U.S. citizens or permanent residents and have a GPA of 3.75 or higher and SAT score of 1200 or higher.

1026 ■ MAYS MISSION FOR THE HANDICAPPED, INC.

Attn: Scholarship Program
604 Colonial Drive
Heber Springs, AR 72545
Tel: (501)362-7526
Fax: (501)362-7529
E-mail: info@maysmission.org
Web Site: http://www.maysmission.org/schol.html
To provide financial assistance to college students with significant physical and/or mental disabilities.
Title of Award: Mays Mission Scholarships **Area, Field, or Subject:** General studies/Field of study not specified **Level of Education for which Award is Granted:** Four Year College **Number Awarded:** 7 scholars are supported at a time. **Funds Available:** A stipend is awarded (amount not specified). **Duration:** 1 year; may be renewed provided the recipient remains enrolled full time with a GPA of 2.3 or higher.
Eligibility Requirements: This program is open to U.S. residents with significant physical and/or mental disabilities. Applicants must be working on a baccalaureate degree at a 4-year college or university. They must have a score of 18 or higher on the ACT or equivalent on the SAT. Along with their application, they must submit a short biography that includes their goals, aspirations, and accomplishments along with a brief description of how they have overcome their disability. **Deadline for Receipt:** June of each year for fall semester; October of each year for spring semester.

1027 ■ MBNA EDUCATION FOUNDATION

c/o MBNA Corporation, National Headquarters
1100 North King Street
Wilmington, DE 19884-0722
Tel: (302)432-4800
Free: 800-205-8877
Web Site: http://www.mbna.com/about/foundation/scholarsde2.html
To provide financial assistance for college to graduating high school seniors in Delaware.
Title of Award: MBNA Delaware Scholars Program **Area, Field, or Subject:** General studies/Field of study not specified **Level of Education for which Award is Granted:** Four Year College **Number Awarded:** Varies each year. **Funds Available:** Stipends range up to $7,500 per year, depending on the financial need of the recipient. Funds are paid to the financial aid office of the student's chosen college or university. **Duration:** 1 year; may be renewed for up to 3 additional years provided the recipient remains enrolled full time, maintains a GPA of 2.5 or higher at the end of the freshman year and 3.0 for the following years; and makes satisfactory progress toward a degree.
Eligibility Requirements: This program is open to seniors graduating from high schools in Delaware. Applicants must be interested in attending a 4-year college or university in the state as a full-time student. They must be U.S. citizens or legal residents, be able to demonstrate financial need, have at least a 2.5 GPA, and be actively applying for other sources of financial aid (such as federal and state grants). Selection is based on academic record, standardized test scores, financial need, recommendations, extracurricular activities, leadership qualities, work records, and an interview. **Deadline for Receipt:** December of each year. **Additional Information:** Recipients are also provided with a mentor program and an offer of full-time summer employment. Information is also available from Scholarship Management Services of Scholarship America, One Scholarship Way, P.O. Box 297, St. Peter, MN 56082, (507) 931-1682, (800) 537-4180, Fax: (507) 931-9168, E-mail: smsinfo@csfa.org.

1028 ■ MBNA EDUCATION FOUNDATION

c/o MBNA Corporation, National Headquarters
1100 North King Street
Wilmington, DE 19884-0722
Tel: (302)432-4800
Free: 800-205-8877
Web Site: http://www.mbna.com/about/foundation/scholarshbcu.html
To provide financial assistance to graduating high school seniors in Delaware who are interested in attending a Historically Black College and University (HBCU).

Title of Award: MBNA Foundation HBCU Scholarship Program **Area, Field, or Subject:** General studies/Field of study not specified **Level of Education for which Award is Granted:** Four Year College **Number Awarded:** Varies each year. **Funds Available:** Stipends range up to $7,500 per year, depending on the financial need of the recipient. Funds are paid to the financial aid office of the student's chosen HBCU. **Duration:** 1 year; may be renewed for up to 3 additional years provided the recipient remains enrolled full time, maintains a GPA of 2.5 or higher at the end of the freshman year and 3.0 for the following years; and makes satisfactory progress toward a degree.
Eligibility Requirements: This program is open to seniors graduating from high schools in Delaware. Applicants must be interested in attending a 4-year HBCU in the United States as a full-time student. They must be U.S. citizens or legal residents, be able to demonstrate financial need, have at least a 2.5 GPA, and be actively applying for other sources of financial aid (such as federal and state grants). Selection is based on academic record, standardized test scores, financial need, recommendations, extracurricular activities, leadership qualities, work records, and an interview. **Deadline for Receipt:** December of each year. **Additional Information:** Recipients are also provided with a mentor program and an offer of full-time summer employment. Information is also available from Scholarship Management Services of Scholarship America, One Scholarship Way, P.O. Box 297, St. Peter, MN 56082, (507) 931-1682, (800) 537-4180, Fax: (507) 931-9168, E-mail: smsinfo@csfa.org.

1029 ■ RONALD MCDONALD HOUSE CHARITIES

Attn: National Scholarship Program
One Kroc Drive
Oak Brook, IL 60523
Tel: (630)623-7048
Fax: (630)623-7488
Web Site: http://www.rmhc.org/rmhc/index/programs/rmhc_scholarship_program.html
To provide financial assistance for college to high school seniors in specified geographic areas.
Title of Award: RMHC National Scholarship Program **Area, Field, or Subject:** General studies/Field of study not specified **Level of Education for which Award is Granted:** Undergraduate **Number Awarded:** Varies each year; since the program began, it has awarded more than $19 million in scholarships. **Funds Available:** Most awards are $1,000 per year. Funds are paid directly to the recipient's school. **Duration:** 1 year; nonrenewable.
Eligibility Requirements: This program is open to high school seniors in designated McDonald's market areas. Applicants must be planning to attend a 2-year or 4-year college or university on a full-time basis. Along with their application, they must submit a personal statement, up to 2 pages in length, on their community involvement, career goals, and desire to contribute to their community; information about unique, personal, or financial circumstances may be added. Selection is based on that statement, high school transcripts, a letter of recommendation, and financial need. **Deadline for Receipt:** January of each year. **Additional Information:** This program, sponsored by Ronald McDonald House Charities (RMHC), began in 1985 as the HACER (Hispanic American Commitment to Education Resources) Scholarship Program, limited to Hispanic students. In 2001, RMHC added the ASIA (Asian Students Increasing Achievement) and African American Future Achievers Scholarships programs. In 2005, it altered the program to make it available to students of all ethnic backgrounds. Applications are available from high school counselors and local McDonald's restaurants in participating market areas. Some of those market areas are extensive, extending over whole regions and including locations in more than 1 state. The market areas that were participating in the program recently were the following: Albuquerque, New Mexico; Atlanta, Georgia (including Cleburne County in Alabama and Clay County in North Carolina); Augusta, Georgia (including portions of South Carolina); Austin, Texas; Billings, Montana (including Sheridan County in Wyoming); Bismarck, North Dakota; Chattanooga, Tennessee (including portions of Georgia and Jackson County in Alabama); Chicago, Illinois (including northwestern Indiana); Colorado Springs, Colorado; Corpus Christi, Texas; Dallas/Fort Worth, Texas; Denver, Colorado (including portions of Kansas, Nebraska, and Wyoming); Des Moines, Iowa; El Paso, Texas (covering El Paso County in Texas and Dona Ana County in New Mexico); Fargo, North Dakota (including portions of Minnesota and Roberts County in South Dakota);

Fresno/Madera, California; Greenville/Spartanburg/Asheville, North Carolina (including portions of South Carolina and Georgia); Harlingen, Texas; Hartford, Connecticut (including western Massachusetts); Houston, Texas; La Crosse/Eau Claire, Wisconsin (including Goodhue County in Minnesota); Las Vegas, Nevada; Los Angeles, California; Lubbock/Midland/Odessa, Texas; Miami, Florida; Milwaukee, Wisconsin; New York/New Jersey (including Fairfield County, Connecticut); Norfolk, Virginia (including portions of North Carolina); Oklahoma City, Oklahoma; Orlando, Florida; Philadelphia, Pennsylvania (including portions of Delaware and New Jersey); Phoenix, Arizona; Raleigh, North Carolina (including portions of South Carolina); Reno, Nevada (including Placerville, California); Richmond, Virginia; Sacramento, California; Salt Lake City, Utah (including adjoining areas in Nevada); San Antonio, Texas: San Francisco, California; Seattle, Washington; Sioux City, Iowa (including portions of Nebraska and South Dakota); Tallahassee, Florida (including portions of Georgia); Tampa Bay, Florida; Temple/Waco, Texas; and Washington (including portions of Maryland, Virginia, and West Virginia). The program is administered by Scholarship Program Administrators, Inc. P.O. Box 22376, Nashville, TN 37202.

1030 ■ MELMAC EDUCATION FOUNDATION

188 Whitten Road
Augusta, ME 04330
Tel: (207)622-3066; (866)622-3066
Fax: (207)622-3053
E-mail: info@MELMACFoundation.org
Web Site: http://www.melmacfoundation.org/grants/principal/default.aspx
To provide financial assistance for college to high school seniors in Maine who demonstrate significant financial need.

Title of Award: Richard W. Tyler Principals Scholarship Program **Area, Field, or Subject:** General studies/Field of study not specified **Level of Education for which Award is Granted:** Undergraduate **Number Awarded:** 1 at each participating high school in Maine. **Funds Available:** The stipend is $1,000. **Duration:** Awards are presented when the recipient enters the third semester of college.

Eligibility Requirements: This program is open to seniors graduating from high schools in Maine who have been accepted to college. Candidates must face significant challenges and obstacles in the pursuit of higher education and be able to demonstrate exceptional financial need. They must also make a difference in the lives of others and that of their community; be a solid school citizen; have made a positive contribution to the school environment and/or extracurricular activities; exhibit a commitment to public service; have the potential to make a difference in the world, and demonstrate satisfactory academic progress in college. The principal of each high school in Maine may nominate 1 student for this scholarship. **Additional Information:** These scholarships were first awarded in 2001.

1031 ■ MIAMI NATION

Attn: Education Committee
202 South Eight Tribes Trail
P.O. Box 1326
Miami, OK 74355
Tel: (918)542-1445
Fax: (918)542-7260
E-mail: edu@miamination.com
Web Site: http://www.miamination.com/Miamination/scholarships.htm
To provide financial assistance for college to high school seniors who are enrolled members of the Miami Tribe of Oklahoma.

Title of Award: Myaamia Scholarship **Area, Field, or Subject:** General studies/Field of study not specified **Level of Education for which Award is Granted:** Undergraduate **Number Awarded:** Only 10 students may be receiving this scholarship at any given time. **Funds Available:** The stipend is $1,000 per semester. **Duration:** 1 semester; may be renewed up to 7 additional semesters if the recipient remains enrolled full time with a college GPA of 3.0 or higher.

Eligibility Requirements: This program is open to graduating high school seniors who are enrolled members of the Miami Tribe of Oklahoma. Applicants must have a GPA of 3.0 or higher and be planning to attend a college or university as a full-time student. Along with their application, they must submit a high school transcript or equivalent (GED), 3 letters of recommendation, documentation of financial need, and a 1-page essay with the title, "Tell Us About Yourself." **Deadline for**

Receipt: April of each year. **Additional Information:** A similar scholarship is also available for enrolled tribal members who are currently in college ($1,500 per year).

1032 ■ MICHIGAN COMMISSION ON LAW ENFORCEMENT STANDARDS

Attn: Michigan Department of State Police
7426 North Canal Road
Lansing, MI 48913
Tel: (517)322-6627
E-mail: email@mcoles.org
Web Site: http://www.michigan.gov/msp
To provide financial assistance for college to children and spouses of deceased Michigan police officers and fire fighters.

Title of Award: Michigan Police Officer and Fire Fighters Survivor Tuition **Area, Field, or Subject:** General studies/Field of study not specified **Level of Education for which Award is Granted:** Undergraduate **Number Awarded:** Varies each year. **Funds Available:** This program provides waiver of tuition at Michigan public colleges, universities, and community colleges. **Duration:** Until completion of 124 credit hours or 9 semesters of study.

Eligibility Requirements: This program is open to children and spouses of Michigan police officers (including sheriffs, deputy sheriffs, police officers of any city or other local jurisdiction, or officer of the state police) or fire fighter (including a member, volunteer or paid, of a fire department or other organization who was directly involved in fire suppression) killed in the line of duty. Children must have younger than 21 at the time of death of the police officer or fire fighter and must apply for this assistance before the age of 21. Applicants must have been residents of Michigan for 12 consecutive months prior to applying. Their family income must be less than 400% of the federal poverty level. **Deadline for Receipt:** April of each year. **Additional Information:** This program was established in 1996.

1033 ■ MICHIGAN FUNERAL DIRECTORS ASSOCIATION

Attn: Michigan Mortuary Science Foundation
2420 Science Parkway
Okemos, MI 48864
Tel: (517)349-9565
Free: 800-937-6332
Fax: (517)349-9819
E-mail: info@mfda.org
Web Site: http://www.mfda.org
To provide financial assistance to Michigan residents who are interested in preparing for a career in mortuary science.

Title of Award: Michigan Mortuary Science Foundation Scholarship **Area, Field, or Subject:** Mortuary science **Level of Education for which Award is Granted:** Undergraduate **Number Awarded:** 3 each year. **Funds Available:** The stipends are $2,500, $1,500, or $750. Funds may be used to pay for tuition, books, supplies, room and board, and other educational expenses. **Duration:** 1 year.

Eligibility Requirements: Applicants must be either a resident of Michigan or a full-time mortuary science student at Wayne State University (in Detroit, Michigan). They must be attending school on a full-time basis and must submit the following material as part of the application process: a cover letter, an essay (between 1,000 and 2,500 words) on a topic that changes annually, and a letter of recommendation from the mortuary science school the applicant is attending. Selection is based on the essay, the recommendation of the mortuary college, and financial need.

1034 ■ MICHIGAN HIGH SCHOOL ATHLETIC ASSOCIATION

1661 Ramblewood Drive
East Lansing, MI 48823-7392
Tel: (517)332-5046
Fax: (517)332-4071
Web Site: http://www.mhsaa.com/recognition/sahome.htm
To provide financial assistance for college to seniors who have participated in athletics at high schools that are members of the Michigan High School Athletic Association (MHSAA).

Title of Award: MHSAA Scholar-Athlete Awards **Area, Field, or Subject:** General studies/Field of study not specified **Level of Education for which Award is Granted:** Undergraduate **Number Awarded:** 28 each year: 1 for each of the eligible sports (14 for girls and 14 for boys). **Funds**

Available: The stipend is $1,000. **Duration:** 1 year; nonrenewable.

Eligibility Requirements: This program is open to seniors graduating from high schools that are members of the MHSAA. Applicants must be planning to attend an accredited college, university, or trade school and have a GPA of 3.5 or higher. They must have won a varsity letter in 1 of the following 28 sports in which post-season tournaments are sponsored by MHSAA: baseball, boys' and girls' basketball, boys' and girls' bowling, girls' competitive cheer, boys' and girls' cross country, football, boys' and girls' golf, girls' gymnastics, ice hockey, boys' and girls' lacrosse, boys' and girls' soccer, softball, boys' and girls' skiing, boys' and girls' swimming and diving, boys' and girls' tennis, boys' and girls' track and field, girls' volleyball, and wrestling. Along with their application, they must submit 2 essays of 150 words each on how they have benefited from participating in high school sports and how they have benefited from participating in other out-of-classroom activities, and a 500-word essay on the importance of sportsmanship in educational athletics. Selection is based on the essays, involvement in other school-sponsored activities, involvement in activities outside of school, and 2 letters of support. **Deadline for Receipt:** Students must submit applications to their school by November of each year. Each schools may nominate 1 student in each sport. **Additional Information:** This program is sponsored by Farm Bureau Insurance.

1035 ■ MICHIGAN STATE TROOPERS ASSISTANCE FUND

c/o Scholarship Committee
1715 Abbey Road, Suite B
East Lansing, MI 48823
To provide financial assistance for college to high school seniors in Michigan.

Title of Award: Michigan State Troopers Assistance Fund Scholarship Program **Area, Field, or Subject:** General studies/Field of study not specified **Level of Education for which Award is Granted:** Undergraduate **Number Awarded:** 20 each year. **Funds Available:** The stipend is $1,000. **Duration:** 1 year.

Eligibility Requirements: This program is open to seniors graduating from high schools in Michigan to plan to attend an accredited college or vocational school. Applicants must submit an essay describing the community events in which they have participated and how the experience has affected them. Selection is based on GPA, extracurricular and leadership service activities, and financial need. **Deadline for Receipt:** March of each year.

1036 ■ MICHIGAN STATE YOUTH SOCCER ASSOCIATION

9401 General Drive, Suite 120
Plymouth, MI 48170
Tel: (734)459-6220
Fax: (734)459-6242
Web Site: http://www.msysa.net/programs/scholarship.html
To provide financial assistance for college to high school seniors in Michigan who have played soccer.

Title of Award: Michigan State Youth Soccer Association College Scholarships **Area, Field, or Subject:** General studies/Field of study not specified **Level of Education for which Award is Granted:** Undergraduate **Number Awarded:** 5 each year. **Funds Available:** The stipend is $1,000. **Duration:** 1 year.

Eligibility Requirements: This program is open to high school seniors who have played on an affiliate team of the Michigan State Youth Soccer Association for at least 6 seasons (3 years). Applicants must have a GPA of 2.75 or higher and be planning to attend an accredited college, university, or community college. Along with their application, they must submit 1) an official high school transcript, including ACT and/or SAT scores; 2) a 1-page personal biography that includes their athletic achievements, honorary or special interest organizations, community involvement, high school major, course of study they plan to pursue, awards or scholarships they have received, and a description of any way they have given back to soccer; and 3) an essay about how they feel soccer has helped them as an individual. **Deadline for Receipt:** February of each year. **Additional Information:** Recipients are not required to play college soccer.

1037 ■ MIDWEST DAIRY ASSOCIATION-IOWA DIVISION

Attn: Industry Relations Manager
101 N.E. Trilein Drive
Ankeny, IA 50021

Tel: (515)964-0696
Fax: (515)964-5498
E-mail: info@midwestdairy.com
Web Site: http://www.midwestdairy.com
To provide financial assistance for college to family members of dairy farmers in Iowa.

Title of Award: Iowa Division Scholarships **Area, Field, or Subject:** General studies/Field of study not specified **Level of Education for which Award is Granted:** Undergraduate **Number Awarded:** 11 each year: 3 at $1,000 and 8 at $500. **Funds Available:** Stipends are $1,000 or $500. **Duration:** 1 year; recipients may reapply.

Eligibility Requirements: This program is open to producers who fund Midwest Dairy Association, their spouses, and their children. The producer must have an active dairy operation and must reside in Iowa. Applicants must be attending or planning to attend an accredited college or university as a full-time student, but there are no restrictions on the length of the program or major. Along with their application, they must submit an essay that includes their career aspirations, special dairy projects or other accomplishments, involvement in the dairy industry and/or participation in their family farm, and any special circumstances related to financial need. Selection is based on that essay (25 points), school leadership activities and events (20 points), other leadership activities and work experience (20 points), academic performance (20 points), and 2 to 3 references (15 points). **Deadline for Receipt:** February of each year.

1038 ■ MIDWESTERN HIGHER EDUCATION COMMISSION

Attn: Midwest Student Exchange Program
1300 South Second Street, Suite 130
Minneapolis, MN 55454-1079
Tel: (612)626-8288
Fax: (612)626-8290
E-mail: mhec@mhec.org
Web Site: http://www.mhec.org/msep/index.htm
To provide a tuition discount to undergraduate and graduate students from selected midwestern states who are attending schools affiliated with the Midwest Student Exchange Program.

Title of Award: Midwest Student Exchange Program **Area, Field, or Subject:** General studies/Field of study not specified **Level of Education for which Award is Granted:** Graduate, Undergraduate **Number Awarded:** Varies each year. **Funds Available:** Participants in this program pay no more than 150% of the regular resident tuition, plus any required fees, at public colleges and universities in the state where are enrolled. Students attending designated independent colleges and universities participating in the program receive at least a 10% reduction in their tuition. Savings typically range from $500 to $3,000. **Duration:** Students receive these benefits as long as they are enrolled in the program to which they were originally admitted and are making satisfactory progress towards a degree.

Eligibility Requirements: The Midwest Student Exchange Program is an interstate initiative established to increase interstate educational opportunities for students in the member states. The Tuition Discount Program includes the 6 participating states of Kansas, Michigan, Minnesota, Missouri, Nebraska and North Dakota. Residents of these states may enroll in programs in the other participating states, but only at the level at which their home state admits students. All of the enrollment and eligibility decisions for the program are made by the institution. **Additional Information:** Extension of the tuition privileges to students already enrolled is at the discretion of the institution.

1039 ■ MILITARY BENEFIT ASSOCIATION

Attn: Member Services Department
P.O. Box 221110
Chantilly, VA 20153-1110
Tel: (703)968-6200
Free: 800-336-0100
Web Site: http://www.militarybenefit.org/mbascholarships.htm
To provide financial assistance for college to children of members of the Military Benefit Association (MBA).

Title of Award: Military Benefit Association Scholarships **Area, Field, or Subject:** General studies/Field of study not specified **Level of Education for which Award is Granted:** Undergraduate **Number Awarded:** 5 each year. **Funds Available:** The stipend is $2,000. **Duration:** 1 year.

Eligibility Requirements: This program is open to dependent children of MBA members who are enrolled or planning to enroll as a full-time undergraduate student at an accredited 2- or 4-year college, university, or vocational/technical school. Applicants must have a GPA of 2.5 or higher. Race, color, creed, religion, gender, disability, and national origin are not considered in the selection process. **Deadline for Receipt:** February of each year. **Additional Information:** The MBA is an organization of military personnel and civilian employees of the U.S. government and their spouses.

1040 ■ MILITARY DEPARTMENT OF ARKANSAS
Office of the Adjutant General
Attn: Education Services Officer
Camp Robinson
North Little Rock, AR 72199-9600
Tel: (501)212-4021
E-mail: Education@ar.ngb.army.mil
Web Site: http://www.arguard.org/Education/index.htm
To provide financial assistance for college to members of the Arkansas National Guard.

Title of Award: Arkansas National Guard Tuition Assistance Program **Area, Field, or Subject:** General studies/Field of study not specified **Level of Education for which Award is Granted:** Undergraduate **Number Awarded:** Varies; a total of $500,000 is available for this program each year. **Funds Available:** The stipend is $1,000 per semester for full-time enrollment; part-time enrollment is prorated. **Duration:** 1 semester; may be renewed if the recipient maintains a GPA of 2.0 or higher.

Eligibility Requirements: This program is open to members of the Arkansas National Guard who enlist or reenlist for a period of at least 3 years. Applicants must be enrolled or accepted for enrollment in an undergraduate program at an accredited school in Arkansas. **Deadline for Receipt:** August of each year for fall semester; December of each year for spring semester.

1041 ■ MILITARY OFFICERS ASSOCIATION OF AMERICA
Attn: Educational Assistance Program
201 North Washington Street
Alexandria, VA 22314-2539
Tel: (703)549-2311
Free: 800-234-MOAA
E-mail: edassist@moaa.org
Web Site: http://www.moaa.org
To provide financial assistance for undergraduate education to children of members of the uniformed services who have died.

Title of Award: American Patriot Scholarships **Area, Field, or Subject:** General studies/Field of study not specified **Level of Education for which Award is Granted:** Undergraduate **Number Awarded:** Varies each year, depending on the availability of funds. **Funds Available:** The stipend is $2,500 per year. **Duration:** 1 year.

Eligibility Requirements: This program is open to children under 24 years of age of active, Reserve, and National Guard uniformed service personnel (Army, Navy, Air Force, Marines, Coast Guard, Public Health Service, or National Oceanographic and Atmospheric Administration) whose parent has died on active service. Applicants must be working on an undergraduate degree. **Deadline for Receipt:** February of each year. **Additional Information:** The MOAA was formerly named The Retired Officers Association (TROA). It established this program in 2002 in response to the tragic events of September 11, 2001.

1042 ■ MILITARY OFFICERS ASSOCIATION OF AMERICA
Attn: Educational Assistance Program
201 North Washington Street
Alexandria, VA 22314-2539
Tel: (703)549-2311
Free: 800-234-MOAA
E-mail: edassist@moaa.org
Web Site: http://www.moaa.org
To provide financial assistance for undergraduate education to dependents of active-duty military officers and enlisted personnel.

Title of Award: MOAA Base/Post Scholarships **Area, Field, or Subject:** General studies/Field of study not specified **Level of Education for which Award is Granted:** Undergraduate **Number Awarded:** 50 each year. **Funds Available:** The stipend is $1,000 per year. **Duration:** 1 year.

Eligibility Requirements: This program is open to dependent children under 24 years of age of active-duty (including drilling Reserves and National Guard) officers and enlisted military personnel. Applicants are not required to be related to a member of the Military Officers Association of America (MOAA) and do not need to meet a minimum GPA requirement. Selection is based on a random drawing. **Deadline for Receipt:** February of each year. **Additional Information:** The MOAA was formerly named The Retired Officers Association (TROA).

1043 ■ MILITARY OFFICERS ASSOCIATION OF AMERICA
Attn: Educational Assistance Program
201 North Washington Street
Alexandria, VA 22314-2539
Tel: (703)549-2311
Free: 800-234-MOAA
E-mail: edassist@moaa.org
Web Site: http://www.moaa.org
To provide loans for undergraduate education to dependent children of members of Military Officers Association of America (MOAA).

Title of Award: MOAA Educational Assistance Program **Area, Field, or Subject:** General studies/Field of study not specified **Level of Education for which Award is Granted:** Undergraduate **Number Awarded:** Varies each year; recently, 1,500 students received loans through this program, including about 400 first-time recipients. **Funds Available:** Loans up to $4,000 per year are available. Repayment at an agreed rate begins 3 to 4 months after graduation or after leaving college, but no interest is charged. **Duration:** 1 year; may be renewed for 4 additional years as long as the recipient remains enrolled full time.

Eligibility Requirements: This program is open to never married dependent children of active, Reserve, National Guard, and retired uniformed service personnel (Army, Navy, Air Force, Marines, Coast Guard, Public Health Service, or National Oceanographic and Atmospheric Administration). Applicants must be under the age of 24. Parents who are officers eligible for membership in the association must be members. Unmarried dependent children of enlisted personnel are also eligible to apply. Selection is based on scholastic ability (GPA of 3.0 or higher), participation, character, leadership, and financial need. **Deadline for Receipt:** February of each year. **Additional Information:** The MOAA was formerly named The Retired Officers Association (TROA). No loans are made for graduate study.

1044 ■ MILITARY OFFICERS ASSOCIATION OF AMERICA
Attn: Educational Assistance Program
201 North Washington Street
Alexandria, VA 22314-2539
Tel: (703)549-2311
Free: 800-234-MOAA
E-mail: edassist@moaa.org
Web Site: http://www.moaa.org
To provide financial assistance to dependent children of members of Military Officers Association of America (MOAA) who are rising seniors in college.

Title of Award: MOAA Special Grants **Area, Field, or Subject:** General studies/Field of study not specified **Level of Education for which Award is Granted:** Four Year College **Number Awarded:** Varies each year. **Funds Available:** The stipend is $5,000 per year. **Duration:** 1 year.

Eligibility Requirements: This program is open to never married dependent children under 24 years of age of active, Reserve, National Guard, and retired uniformed service personnel (Army, Navy, Air Force, Marines, Coast Guard, Public Health Service, or National Oceanographic and Atmospheric Administration). Parents who are officers eligible for membership in the association must be members. Applicants must be entering their senior year of college. Unmarried dependent children of enlisted personnel are also eligible to apply. Applicants for the MOAA Educational Assistance Program loans are automatically considered for these scholarships; no separate application is necessary. Selection is based on scholastic ability (GPA of 3.0 or higher), participation, character, leadership, and financial need. **Deadline for Receipt:** February of each year. **Additional Information:** The MOAA was formerly named The Retired Officers Association (TROA).

1045 ■ MILITARY OFFICERS ASSOCIATION OF AMERICA

Attn: Educational Assistance Program
201 North Washington Street
Alexandria, VA 22314-2539
Tel: (703)549-2311
Free: 800-234-MOAA
E-mail: edassist@moaa.org
Web Site: http://www.moaa.org
To provide financial support for undergraduate education to dependent children of auxiliary members of Military Officers Association of America (MOAA).
Title of Award: General John Paul Ratay Educational Fund Grants **Area, Field, or Subject:** General studies/Field of study not specified **Level of Education for which Award is Granted:** Undergraduate **Number Awarded:** Varies each year. **Funds Available:** The stipend is $4,000 per year. **Duration:** 1 year; may be renewed for up to 4 additional years if the recipient remains enrolled full time.
Eligibility Requirements: This program is open to children of surviving spouses of deceased retired military officers. Applicants must be younger than 24 years of age and have never been married. Applicants for the MOAA Educational Assistance Program loans are automatically considered for these scholarships; no separate application is necessary. Selection is based on scholastic ability (GPA of 3.0 or higher), participation, character, leadership, and financial need. **Deadline for Receipt:** February of each year. **Additional Information:** The MOAA was formerly named The Retired Officers Association (TROA). No grants are made for graduate study.

1046 ■ MILITARY OFFICERS ASSOCIATION OF AMERICA-ALOHA CHAPTER

Attn: Tak Yoshihara, Scholarship Committee Chair
P.O. Box 19267
Honolulu, HI 96817-8267
Tel: (808)488-7013
E-mail: Takyosh@aol.com
Web Site: http://www.aloha-moaa.org
To provide financial assistance for college to residents of Hawaii who have a connection to the military.
Title of Award: Aloha Chapter Scholarships **Area, Field, or Subject:** General studies/Field of study not specified **Level of Education for which Award is Granted:** Undergraduate **Number Awarded:** 4 each year. **Funds Available:** The stipend is $1,000. **Duration:** 1 year.
Eligibility Requirements: This program is open to residents of Hawaii who are members of the uniformed services, their spouses and children, members of Military Officers Association of America (MOAA), or their spouses, children, and grandchildren. Applicants must be attending or planning to attend a college or university. Selection is based on scholastic ability, personal qualities, and financial need. **Deadline for Receipt:** March of each year. **Additional Information:** This program began in 2004.

1047 ■ MILITARY OFFICERS ASSOCIATION OF AMERICA-ARIZONA CHAPTER

Attn: Daniel Conway, President
14435 North 66th Place
Scottsdale, AZ 85254
Tel: (480)368-1427
E-mail: arizconway@msn.com
Web Site: http://www.azchaptermoaa.org/awards_scholarship/awards_&_scholarships.htm
To provide financial assistance for college to high school seniors in Arizona who have participated in the Junior ROTC program.
Title of Award: Arizona Chapter MOAA Educational Scholarships **Area, Field, or Subject:** General studies/Field of study not specified **Level of Education for which Award is Granted:** Undergraduate **Number Awarded:** Varies each year; recently, 5 of these scholarships were awarded. **Funds Available:** The stipend is $1,000. **Duration:** 1 year.
Eligibility Requirements: This program is open to seniors at high schools in Arizona who have participated in the JROTC program. Applicants must rank in the upper half of their class and be able to

demonstrate qualities of leadership, moral character, and concern for their fellow man through service to others.

1048 ■ MILITARY OFFICERS' BENEVOLENT CORPORATION

1010 American Eagle Boulevard
P.O. Box 301
Sun City Center, FL 33573
Tel: (813)634-4675
Fax: (813)633-2412
E-mail: office@mobc-online.org
Web Site: http://www.mobc-online.org
To provide financial assistance for college to children and grandchildren of retired and deceased officers who served in the military or designated public service agencies.
Title of Award: Military Officers' Benevolent Corporation Scholarships **Area, Field, or Subject:** General studies/Field of study not specified **Level of Education for which Award is Granted:** Undergraduate **Number Awarded:** 9 each year: 2 at $2,000 per year, 4 at $1,500 per year, and 3 at $500 per year. **Funds Available:** Stipends are $2,000, $1,500, or $500 per year. **Duration:** 4 years, provided the recipient maintains a GPA of 3.0 or higher.
Eligibility Requirements: This program is open to graduating high school seniors who have a GPA of 3.0 and a minimum score of 21 on the ACT or equivalent score on the SAT. Applicants must have a parent, guardian, or grandparent who is 1) a retired active-duty, National Guard, or Reserve officer or former officer of the U.S. Army, Navy, Marine Corps, Air Force, Coast Guard, Public Health Service, or National Oceanic and Atmospheric Administration, at the rank of O-1 through O-10, WO-1 through WO-5, or E-7 through E-9; 2) an officer who died while on active duty in service to the country; 3) a recipient of the Purple Heart, regardless of pay grade or length of service; 4) a World War II combat veteran of the Merchant Marine; 5) a federal employee at the grade of GS-7 or higher; 6) a Foreign Service Officer at the grade of FSO-8 or lower; or 7) an honorably discharged or retired foreign military officer of an allied nation meeting the service and disability retirement criteria of the respective country and living in the United States. Applicants must have been accepted to an accredited program at a college or university. Selection is based on leadership (40%), scholarship (30%), and financial need (30%). **Deadline for Receipt:** February of each year. **Additional Information:** This foundation was established in 1992.

1049 ■ MILITARY ORDER OF THE PURPLE HEART

Attn: Scholarships
5413-B Backlick Road
Springfield, VA 22151-3960
Tel: (703)642-5360
Fax: (703)642-2054
E-mail: info@purpleheart.org
Web Site: http://www.purpleheart.org/scholar.html
To provide financial assistance for college or graduate school to spouses and children of members of the Military Order of the Purple Heart.
Title of Award: Military Order of the Purple Heart Scholarship Program **Area, Field, or Subject:** General studies/Field of study not specified **Level of Education for which Award is Granted:** Graduate, Undergraduate **Number Awarded:** Varies each year; recently, 28 of these scholarships were awarded. **Funds Available:** The stipend is $1,750 per year. **Duration:** 1 year; may be renewed up to 3 additional years.
Eligibility Requirements: This program is open to children (natural, step-, and adopted), grandchildren, great-grandchildren and spouses of veterans who are members in good standing of the order or who received the Purple Heart. Applicants must be U.S. citizens, graduating seniors or graduates of an accredited high school, enrolled or accepted for enrollment in a full-time program of study in a college, trade school, or graduate school with a GPA of 3.5 or higher. Selection is based on merit; financial need is not considered in the selection process. **Deadline for Receipt:** March of each year.

1050 ■ PATSY TAKEMOTO MINK EDUCATION FOUNDATION FOR LOW-INCOME WOMEN AND CHILDREN

Attn: Gwendolyn Mink
P.O. Box 1599
Northampton, MA 01061-1599
E-mail: admin@ptmfoundation.net

Web Site: http://www.ptmfoundation.net

To provide financial assistance for college or graduate school to low-income women.

Title of Award: Patsy Takemoto Mink Education Foundation Education Support Award **Area, Field, or Subject:** General studies/Field of study not specified **Level of Education for which Award is Granted:** Graduate, Undergraduate **Number Awarded:** 7 each year. **Funds Available:** The stipend is $2,000. **Duration:** 1 year.

Eligibility Requirements: This program is open to women who are at least 18 years of age and are from a low-income family (less than $14,000 annually for a family of 1, rising to $30,000 annually for a family of 4). Applicants must be 1) enrolled in a skills training, ESL, or GED program; or 2) working on an associate, bachelor's, master's, professional, or doctoral degree. Along with their application, they must submit brief essays on what this award will help them accomplish, the program in which they are or will be enrolled, how they decided on that educational pursuit, their educational goals, their educational experience, and their personal and educational history. **Deadline for Receipt:** June of each year. **Additional Information:** This foundation was established in 2003.

1051 ■ MINNESOTA ASSOCIATION OF TOWNSHIPS

Attn: Scholarship Program
P.O. Box 267
St. Michael, MN 55376
Tel: (763)497-2330
Free: 800-228-0296
Fax: (763)497-3361
E-mail: info@mntownships.org
Web Site: http://www.mntownships.org

To provide financial assistance to college-bound high school juniors in Minnesota.

Title of Award: Minnesota Association of Townships Scholarship Program **Area, Field, or Subject:** General studies/Field of study not specified **Level of Education for which Award is Granted:** Undergraduate **Number Awarded:** 2 each year. **Funds Available:** The stipend is $1,000. **Duration:** 1 year.

Eligibility Requirements: This program is open to students currently enrolled as juniors at public, private, and parochial high schools and home study programs in Minnesota. Applicants must be planning to attend a college, university, or vocational school following graduation from high school. They must submit an essay, from 450 to 500 words, on a topic that changes annually but relates to the township form of government in Minnesota, its place and purpose in local government, and the involvement of citizens in grassroots government. Along with their application and essay, they must submit a current high school transcript and a letter of recommendation from a high school teacher or counselor. **Deadline for Receipt:** April of each year.

1052 ■ MINNESOTA BENEFIT ASSOCIATION

Attn: Scholarship Committee
6701 Upper Afton Road
Woodbury, MN 55125
Tel: (651)735-9874
Free: 800-360-6117
Fax: (651)739-3260
E-mail: mail@minnesotabenefitassociation.com
Web Site: http://www.minnesotabenefitassociation.com/scholarship.htm

To provide financial assistance for college to public employees and elected officials in Minnesota and their family members.

Title of Award: Minnesota Benefit Association Scholarships **Area, Field, or Subject:** General studies/Field of study not specified **Level of Education for which Award is Granted:** Undergraduate **Number Awarded:** 4 each year. **Funds Available:** The stipend is $1,000. **Duration:** 1 year.

Eligibility Requirements: This program is open to high school seniors and current college students who are Minnesota public employees, elected officials, or members of their families. Applicants must submit an essay, of 300 to 500 words, on a topic that changes annually but relates to matters of interest to public employees in Minnesota. Selection is based

on that essay, academic achievement, vocational goals, employment history, community involvement, and financial need. **Deadline for Receipt:** January of each year.

1053 ■ MINNESOTA DEPARTMENT OF EDUCATION

Attn: Manager, Minnesota Indian Education
1500 Highway 36 West
Roseville, MN 55113-4266
Tel: (651)582-8200
Free: 800-657-3927
Web Site: http://education.state.mn.us/html/intro_indian_scholar.htm

To provide financial assistance to Native Americans in Minnesota who are interested in working on an undergraduate or graduate degree.

Title of Award: Ethel Curry Scholarships **Area, Field, or Subject:** General studies/Field of study not specified **Level of Education for which Award is Granted:** Four Year College, Graduate **Number Awarded:** Varies each year; recently, 12 of these scholarships were awarded. **Funds Available:** The stipend is $3,000 per year for undergraduates or $6,000 per year for graduate students. **Duration:** Up to 4 years.

Eligibility Requirements: This program is open to Indians who are enrolled in a Minnesota-based tribe or community. Applicants must be attending an accredited postsecondary institution in Minnesota as a junior, senior, or graduate student. They must have a GPA of 3.0 or higher. Selection is based on merit. **Deadline for Receipt:** April of each year.

1054 ■ MINNESOTA DEPARTMENT OF EDUCATION

Attn: Manager, Minnesota Indian Education
1500 Highway 36 West
Roseville, MN 55113-4266
Tel: (651)582-8846
Free: 800-657-3927
E-mail: cfl.indianeducation@state.mn.us
Web Site: http://education.state.mn.us/mde/Academic_Excellence/Indian_Education/index.htm

To provide financial assistance to Native Americans in Minnesota who are interested in working on an undergraduate or graduate degree.

Title of Award: Minnesota Indian Scholarship Program **Area, Field, or Subject:** General studies/Field of study not specified **Level of Education for which Award is Granted:** Graduate, Undergraduate **Number Awarded:** Approximately 700 each year. **Funds Available:** The stipend depends on need, to a maximum of $3,300 per year for undergraduates or $6,600 per year for graduate students. Awards are paid directly to the student's school or college. **Duration:** 1 year; renewable for an additional 4 years.

Eligibility Requirements: Applicants must be at least one-fourth degree Indian ancestry; members of a recognized Indian tribe; at least high school graduates (or approved equivalent); accepted by an accredited college, university, or vocational school in Minnesota; and residents of Minnesota for at least 1 year. Undergraduates must be attending college full time; graduate students may be either full or part time. **Deadline for Receipt:** June of each year. **Additional Information:** Recipients must maintain a GPA of 2.0 or higher, earn 12 credits per quarter, and send official grade transcripts to the office for review after each quarter or semester. They must attend a school in Minnesota.

1055 ■ MINNESOTA DEPARTMENT OF HUMAN SERVICES

Attn: Social Services Program Consultant
444 Lafayette Road, Third Floor South
St. Paul, MN 55155-3832
Tel: (651)296-4471
E-mail: claire.d.hill@state.mn.us
Web Site: http://www.dhs.state.mn.us

To provide financial assistance for college to Minnesota residents who have been foster children.

Title of Award: Minnesota Education and Training Vouchers for Former Youth in Care **Area, Field, or Subject:** General studies/Field of study not specified **Level of Education for which Award is Granted:** Undergraduate **Number Awarded:** Varies each year; recently, a total of 42 students had received support through this program. **Funds Available:** Stipends depend on the need of the recipient, to a maximum of $5,000 per year. **Duration:** 1 year; may be renewed provided the recipient maintains a GPA of 2.0 or higher.

Eligibility Requirements: This program is open to Minnesota residents who experienced a county approved out-of-home placement after the age of 14, are currently under state guardianship, or were adopted at age 16 or older. Applicants must have been accepted into an accredited postsecondary program that they began or will begin when they are between 18 and 21 years of age. They must attach a copy of their Free Application for Federal Student Aid (FAFSA), apply for other sources of financial aid, and submit 2 letters of recommendation. **Deadline for Receipt:** May of each year. **Additional Information:** This program was established in 2003 in accordance with the federal Chafee Foster Care Independence Act.

1056 ■ MINNESOTA DEPARTMENT OF VETERANS AFFAIRS

Veterans Service Building
20 West 12th Street, Room 206C
St. Paul, MN 55155-2006
Tel: (651)297-4141
Fax: (651)296-3954
E-mail: paula.plum@mdva.state.mn.us
Web Site: http://www.mdva.state.mn.us
To provide financial assistance for college to the dependents of deceased Minnesota veterans.
Title of Award: Minnesota Educational Assistance for War Orphans **Area, Field, or Subject:** General studies/Field of study not specified **Level of Education for which Award is Granted:** Undergraduate **Number Awarded:** Varies each year. **Funds Available:** Students who attend technical and community colleges and state universities are granted free tuition until they have earned a bachelor's or equivalent degree (this does not apply to private institutions or the University of Minnesota). All eligible students may also receive up to $750 in any 1 calendar year to be used for tuition, fees, board, room, books, and supplies at the University of Minnesota, state universities, community colleges, vocational/technical institutions, or any other accredited college of higher learning, nursing school, trade school, or business school within Minnesota. **Duration:** 1 year; may be renewed.
Eligibility Requirements: To be eligible for this assistance, applicants must have been residents of Minnesota for 2 years prior to application. They must be the children of veterans who were Minnesota residents prior to entry on active duty and who died on active duty or as a result of service-connected injuries or diseases.

1057 ■ MINNESOTA HIGHER EDUCATION SERVICES OFFICE

1450 Energy Park Drive, Suite 350
St. Paul, MN 55108-5227
Tel: (651)642-0567
Free: 800-657-3866
Fax: (651)642-0675
E-mail: info@heso.state.mn.us
Web Site: http://www.mheso.state.mn.us
To provide financial assistance for child care to students in Minnesota who are not receiving Minnesota Family Investment Program (MFIP) benefits.
Title of Award: Minnesota Child Care Grant Program **Area, Field, or Subject:** General studies/Field of study not specified **Level of Education for which Award is Granted:** Undergraduate **Number Awarded:** Varies each year. Recently, a total of $1.1 million was provided for this program. **Funds Available:** The amount of the assistance depends on the income of applicant and spouse, number of day care hours necessary to cover education and work obligations, the student's enrollment status, and number of eligible children in applicant's family. The maximum available is $2,200 per eligible child per academic year. **Duration:** 1 year; may be renewed as long as the recipient remains enrolled on at least a half-time basis in an undergraduate program.
Eligibility Requirements: Minnesota residents who are working on an undergraduate degree or vocational certificate in the state and who have children age 12 and under (14 and under if disabled) may receive this assistance to help pay child care expenses. Recipients must demonstrate financial need but must not be receiving MFIP benefits. U.S. citizenship or permanent resident status is required. **Additional Information:** Assistance may cover up to 40 hours per week per eligible child.

1058 ■ MINNESOTA HIGHER EDUCATION SERVICES OFFICE

1450 Energy Park Drive, Suite 350
St. Paul, MN 55108-5227

Tel: (651)642-0567
Free: 800-657-3866
Fax: (651)642-0675
E-mail: info@heso.state.mn.us
Web Site: http://www.mheso.state.mn.us
To provide financial assistance for college to survivors of deceased Minnesota public safety officers.
Title of Award: Minnesota Public Safety Officers' Survivor Grant **Area, Field, or Subject:** General studies/Field of study not specified **Level of Education for which Award is Granted:** Undergraduate **Number Awarded:** Varies each year; recently, a total of $40,000 was available for this program. **Funds Available:** Scholarships cover tuition and fees at state-supported institutions or provide an equivalent amount at private colleges and universities. Recently, awards averaged $3,230. **Duration:** 1 year; may be renewed for a maximum of 8 semesters or 12 quarters.
Eligibility Requirements: Eligible for this support are dependent children (under 23 years of age) and surviving spouses of public safety officers killed in the line of duty on or after January 1, 1973. Applicants must be Minnesota residents who are enrolled at least half time in an undergraduate degree or certificate program at a Minnesota public postsecondary institution or at a private, residential, 2- or 4-year, liberal arts, degree-granting college or university in Minnesota.

1059 ■ MINNESOTA HIGHER EDUCATION SERVICES OFFICE

1450 Energy Park Drive, Suite 350
St. Paul, MN 55108-5227
Tel: (651)642-0567
Free: 800-657-3866
Fax: (651)642-0675
E-mail: info@heso.state.mn.us
Web Site: http://www.mheso.state.mn.us
To provide financial assistance to undergraduate students in Minnesota who demonstrate financial need.
Title of Award: Minnesota State Grant Program **Area, Field, or Subject:** General studies/Field of study not specified **Level of Education for which Award is Granted:** Undergraduate **Number Awarded:** Varies each year; recently, approximately 72,000 undergraduate students received $133.6 million in support through this program. **Funds Available:** Applicants are required to contribute at least 46% of their cost of attendance (tuition and fees plus allowances for room and board, books and supplies, and miscellaneous expenses) from savings, earnings, loans, or other assistance from school or private sources. The other 54% is to be contributed by parents (for dependent students) or by independent students, along with a federal Pell Grant and these State Grants. The average State Grant is approximately $1,860; the minimum award is $100 per year and the maximum ranges from $4,802 at a public technical college to $7,662 at a private 4-year college. **Duration:** Assistance continues until the student has completed a baccalaureate degree or full-time enrollment of 8 semesters or 12 quarters, whichever comes first.
Eligibility Requirements: Minnesota residents who are enrolled for at least 3 credits as undergraduate students at 1 of 128 eligible schools in Minnesota may apply for these grants. They must be 1) an independent student who has resided in Minnesota for purposes other than postsecondary education for at least 12 months; 2) a dependent student whose parent or legal guardian resides in Minnesota; 3) a student who graduated from a Minnesota high school, if the student was a resident of Minnesota during high school; or 4) a student who, after residing in Minnesota for a minimum of 1 year, earned a high school equivalency certificate in Minnesota. Students in default on a student loan or more than 30 days behind for child support owed to a public agency are not eligible. **Deadline for Receipt:** June of each year. **Additional Information:** Students may continue to receive assistance even if they enroll for as few as 3 credits, but their cost of attendance is prorated accordingly.

1060 ■ MINNESOTA HIGHER EDUCATION SERVICES OFFICE

1450 Energy Park Drive, Suite 350
St. Paul, MN 55108-5227
Tel: (651)642-0567
Free: 800-657-3866
Fax: (651)642-0675
E-mail: info@heso.state.mn.us
Web Site: http://www.mheso.state.mn.us
To provide loans for college or graduate school to Minnesota residents.

Title of Award: Minnesota Student Educational Loan Fund **Area, Field, or Subject:** General studies/Field of study not specified **Level of Education for which Award is Granted:** Graduate, Undergraduate **Number Awarded:** Varies each year; recently, approximately $107 million was issued in loans through this program. **Funds Available:** Undergraduates may borrow up to $4,500 per year for the first 2 years and $6,000 per year thereafter, to a maximum of $25,000. Graduate students may borrow up to $9,000 per year, but their total loan from this program, including undergraduate and graduate debt, may not exceed $40,000. Borrowers must pay interest while in school and for up to 3 years after graduating or leaving school; the interest rate, adjusted quarterly, was recently 6.1%. They must then begin repaying the loan principal as well as interest, and complete repayment within 10 years from the termination of study or 15 years from the date of the first loan disbursement. **Duration:** 1 year; may be renewed.
Eligibility Requirements: This program is open to 1) Minnesota residents who are enrolled at least half time in a certificate, associate, baccalaureate, or graduate program at an eligible school in Minnesota, another state, or a Canadian province that has signed an operating agreement with the Higher Education Services Office; and 2) residents of other states attending an eligible school in Minnesota who are enrolled at least half time in a certificate, associate, baccalaureate, or graduate degree program. Applicants must not be delinquent or in default on any student loan and must have a credit-worthy cosigner. **Additional Information:** Recently, 151 institutions in Minnesota and 183 in Canada and other states had agreed to participate in this program.

1061 ■ MINNESOTA HIGHER EDUCATION SERVICES OFFICE

1450 Energy Park Drive, Suite 350
St. Paul, MN 55108-5227
Tel: (651)642-0567
Free: 800-657-3866
Fax: (651)642-0675
E-mail: info@heso.state.mn.us
Web Site: http://www.mheso.state.mn.us
To provide financial assistance for college to the dependents of Minnesota veterans and military personnel listed as POWs or MIAs.
Title of Award: Minnesota Veterans' Dependents Assistance Program **Area, Field, or Subject:** General studies/Field of study not specified **Level of Education for which Award is Granted:** Undergraduate **Number Awarded:** Varies each year. **Funds Available:** Students who attend private postsecondary institutions receive up to $250 per year for tuition and fees. Students who attend a Minnesota public postsecondary institution are exempt from tuition charges. **Duration:** Assistance continues until the student completes a bachelor's degree or receives a certificate of completion.
Eligibility Requirements: Eligible for this assistance are 1) spouses of a prisoner of war or person missing in action, or 2) children born before or during the period of time the parent served as a POW or was declared MIA, or 3) children legally adopted or in the legal custody of a parent prior to and during the time the parent served as a POW or was declared to be MIA. Veteran parents must have been residents of Minnesota at the time of entry into service or at the time declared to be a POW or MIA, which must have occurred after August 1, 1958.

1062 ■ MINNESOTA STATE HIGH SCHOOL LEAGUE

2100 Freeway Boulevard
Brooklyn Center, MN 55430-1735
Tel: (763)560-2262
Web Site: http://www.mshsl.org
To provide financial assistance for college to high school seniors in Minnesota who excel in the Triple "A" activities: academics, arts, and athletics.
Title of Award: Minnesota State High School League Triple "A" Awards **Area, Field, or Subject:** General studies/Field of study not specified **Level of Education for which Award is Granted:** Undergraduate **Number Awarded:** 4 each year: a female and a male from each of the 2 classes of schools. **Funds Available:** The stipend is $1,000 per year. **Duration:** 4 years.
Eligibility Requirements: This program is open to college-bound seniors graduating from high schools in Minnesota. Each school may nominate 2 students, a female and a male. Selection of state winners is based on academic performance; involvement in athletic programs sponsored by

the Minnesota State High School League (badminton, baseball, basketball, cross country running, football, golf, gymnastics, hockey, lacrosse, skiing, soccer, softball, swimming and diving, synchronized swimming, tennis, track, volleyball, wrestling, and adapted soccer, bowling, floor hockey, and softball); involvement in League-sponsored fine arts activities (state, section, sub-section, school, or community-sponsored activities in instrumental or vocal music, drama, debate, or speech); and involvement in other school and community activities. Nominees must have a GPA of 3.0 or higher and be in compliance with the League's Student Code of Conduct. Students from Class A and Class AA schools are judged separately, as are females and males. **Deadline for Receipt:** January of each year.

1063 ■ MINNESOTA STATE UNIVERSITY STUDENT ASSOCIATION

Attn: Scholarship
108 Como Avenue
St. Paul, MN 55103-1820
Tel: (651)224-1518
Fax: (651)224-9753
E-mail: nsj@msusa.net
Web Site: http://www.msusa.net/nellie_stjo.html
To provide financial assistance to racial minority union members and their families who are interested in working on an undergraduate or graduate degree at a Minnesota state college or university.
Title of Award: Nellie Stone Johnson Scholarship **Area, Field, or Subject:** General studies/Field of study not specified **Level of Education for which Award is Granted:** Master's, Undergraduate **Number Awarded:** 1 or more each year. If multiple awards are made, at least 1 recipient must be female. **Funds Available:** Stipends range from $500 to $2,000. **Duration:** 1 year; may be renewed up to 3 additional years for student working on a bachelor's degree, 1 additional year for students working on a master's degree, or 1 additional year for students in a community or technical college program.
Eligibility Requirements: This program is open to students in 2-year, undergraduate, and graduate programs at a Minnesota state university, community college, or consolidated campus. Applicants must be a minority (Asian, American Indian, Alaska Native, Black/African American, Hispanic/Latino, Native Hawaiian, or Pacific Islander) union member or the child, grandchild, or spouse of a minority union member. They must submit a 2-page statement about their background, educational goals, career goals, and other activities that may impact the cause of human or civil rights. Awards may be reserved for women. Preference is given to Minnesota residents. A personal or telephone interview may be required. **Deadline for Receipt:** March of each year.

1064 ■ MINNESOTA TIMBERWOLVES

Attn: FastBreak Foundation
600 First Avenue North
Minneapolis, MN 55403-1416
Tel: (612)673-1200
Web Site: http://www.nba.com/timberwolves/community/education.html
To provide financial assistance for college to high school seniors in Minnesota, North Dakota, and South Dakota.
Title of Award: Timberwolves and Lynx/American Family Insurance Scholarships **Area, Field, or Subject:** General studies/Field of study not specified **Level of Education for which Award is Granted:** Undergraduate **Number Awarded:** 5 each year. **Funds Available:** The stipend is $2,000. **Duration:** 1 year.
Eligibility Requirements: This program is open to seniors graduating from high schools in Minnesota, North Dakota, and South Dakota who plan to attend a college or university in the following fall. Applicants must 1) have a GPA of 3.0 or higher; 2) have an ACT of 19 or higher or an SAT or 850 or higher; 3) participate in extracurricular activities; and 4) complete 45 hours of community service, outside of school, during the course of a school year. Along with their application, they must submit an essay of 500 words or less that describes who they are, how they view themselves, and any other information they want the selection committee to consider. Financial need is not required. **Deadline for Receipt:** February of each year. **Additional Information:** This program is jointly

sponsored by the FastBreak Foundation of the Minnesota Timberwolves and Lynx (professional basketball teams) and American Family Insurance.

1065 ■ MINNESOTA WOMEN'S GOLF ASSOCIATION

Attn: MWGA Charitable Foundation
6550 York Avenue South, Suite 211
Edina, MN 55435-2333
Tel: (952)345-3961
Fax: (952)927-9642
E-mail: paula@mngolf.org
Web Site: http://www.mwga-online.org
To provide financial assistance for college to female high school seniors in Minnesota who are interested in golf.
Title of Award: Minnesota Women's Golf Association Scholarship **Area, Field, or Subject:** General studies/Field of study not specified **Level of Education for which Award is Granted:** Four Year College **Number Awarded:** Varies each year; recently, 3 of these scholarships were awarded. **Funds Available:** The stipend is $2,000 per year. **Duration:** 1 year; may be renewed up to 3 additional years.
Eligibility Requirements: This program is open to women who are graduating seniors at high schools in Minnesota planning to attend a 4-year college or university. Applicants must have an interest or involvement in the sport of golf, although skill or excellence in the game is not considered in the selection process. They must have a GPA of 3.0 or higher and be able to demonstrate financial need. **Deadline for Receipt:** March of each year.

1066 ■ MISS CHEERLEADER OF AMERICA

Attn: Program Director
P.O. Box 667
Taylor, MI 48180
Tel: (734)946-1200
Fax: (734)946-1204
E-mail: misscheerleaderofamerica@yahoo.com
Web Site: http://www.misscheerleaderofamerica.com
To recognize and reward, with college scholarships, women who are high school cheerleaders.
Title of Award: Miss Cheerleader of America Scholarships **Area, Field, or Subject:** General studies/Field of study not specified **Level of Education for which Award is Granted:** Undergraduate **Number Awarded:** Varies each year; normally, 3 prizes are awarded in each state in which a pageant is held. **Funds Available:** Prizes are generally scholarships of $1,000 for first place, $750 for second, and $500 for third. **Duration:** The competition is held annually.
Eligibility Requirements: This program is open to female high school cheerleaders in grades 9 through 12. Girls who are interested apply to participate in a pageant in their home state. Based on their applications, finalists are invited to their state pageant where they participate in an evening gown demonstration and an interview. The program is not a beauty, bathing suit, cheer skill, or talent competition. Judges attempt to select "the all-American girl, who normally would not even think about being in a pageant."

1067 ■ MISS UNIVERSE ORGANIZATION

1370 Avenue of the Americas, 16th Floor
New York, NY 10019
Tel: (212)373-4999
Fax: (212)315-5378
E-mail: MissUPR@missuniverse.com
Web Site: http://www.missteenusa.com
To recognize and reward beautiful and talented women between 15 and 19 years of age in the United States.
Title of Award: Miss Teen USA **Area, Field, or Subject:** General studies/Field of study not specified **Level of Education for which Award is Granted:** Undergraduate **Number Awarded:** 1 national winner each year.
Funds Available: Miss Teen USA receives cash and prizes worth more than $150,000. Recently, that included a $45,000 scholarship to the School for Film and Television, a Preciosa trophy worth $3,500, a crystal chandelier from Preciosa worth $5,000, a $2,500 pre-paid VISA BUXX card, a $2,000 cash prize and complimentary UV-Free Tanning for the year of her reign from Mystic Tan, a pearl tiara worth $12,000 from Mikimoto, a fashion footwear wardrobe from Nina Footwear, a swimwear wardrobe from Pink Sands Swim, a 5-day/4 night trip for 2 anywhere

American Airlines flies in the continental United States or Caribbean, a pajama wardrobe by Jamatex worth $500, a 1-year salary, a luxury apartment while in New York City, a personal appearance wardrobe, a modeling portfolio, and other services and training. Other prizes included $3,000 for first runner-up, $2,000 for second runner-up, $1,000 for third and fourth runners-up, and $500 for semifinalists. In addition, the delegate selected by the television audience as Miss Photogenic and the delegate selected by her peers as Miss Congeniality each received $1,000 cash prizes and a commemorative Preciosa crystal trophy worth $3,500. **Duration:** The national pageant is held annually, usually at the end of the summer.
Eligibility Requirements: Some cities and all states have preliminary pageants. The winner of the city pageant goes on to compete in the state pageant for her home city. A delegate may also enter a state pageant without having won a city title. One delegate from each of the 50 states and the District of Columbia is selected to compete in the pageant. Participants must be between 15 and 19 years of age. They must never have been married or pregnant. Selection is based on beauty, intelligence, and ability to handle an interview. **Deadline for Receipt:** June of each year. **Additional Information:** The competition began in 1983.

1068 ■ MISS UNIVERSE ORGANIZATION

1370 Avenue of the Americas, 16th Floor
New York, NY 10019
Tel: (212)373-4999
Fax: (212)315-5378
E-mail: MissUPR@missuniverse.com
Web Site: http://www.missusa.com
To identify and reward the most beautiful women selected in a competition among women from each state.
Title of Award: Miss USA **Area, Field, or Subject:** General studies/Field of study not specified **Level of Education for which Award is Granted:** Undergraduate, Other **Number Awarded:** 1 each year. **Funds Available:** Miss USA receives cash and prizes worth more than $225,000. Recently, that included a scholarship valued $45,000 from The School for Film and Television, a Preciosa trophy worth $3,500, a crystal chandelier from Preciosa worth $5,000, a pearl tiara worth $12,000 from Mikimoto, a fashion footwear wardrobe from Steve Madden, a swimwear wardrobe from Endless Sun Apparel, a 5-day/4 night trip for 2 anywhere American Airlines flies in the continental United States or Caribbean, a 1-year salary, a luxury apartment while in New York City, a personal appearance wardrobe from Tadashi Fashions, a modeling portfolio, and other services and training. Other prizes included $3,000 for first runner-up, $2,000 for second runner-up, $1,000 for third and fourth runners-up, and $500 for semifinalists. In addition, the delegate selected by the television audience as Miss Photogenic and the delegate selected by her peers as Miss Congeniality each received $1,000 cash prizes and a commemorative Preciosa crystal trophy worth $3,500. **Duration:** The national pageant is held annually, in February or March.
Eligibility Requirements: This program is open to women between 18 and 27 years of age who have never been married or pregnant. Entrants are first selected in state competitions, and then 51 women (1 from each state and the District of Columbia) compete in the Miss USA Pageant. Selection of the winner is based on interviews by pageant judges (on successes, talents, goals, and ambitions), a swimsuit competition (with swimsuit styles provided by the pageant), and an evening gown competition (with gowns chosen by the competitors). The Photogenic Award is presented to the delegate voted on and selected by the television audience, and the Congeniality Award is presented to the delegate selected by her sister delegates as the most charismatic and inspirational. **Deadline for Receipt:** January of each year. **Additional Information:** This pageant began in 1952. Miss USA competes for additional prizes in the Miss Universe Pageant.

1069 ■ MISSISSIPPI BAR FOUNDATION

Attn: Administrative Law Section
643 North State Street
P.O. Box 2168
Jackson, MS 39225-2168
Tel: (601)948-5234
Fax: (601)355-8635
E-mail: acook@msbar.org
Web Site: http://www.msbar.org/kidchance.php

To provide financial assistance for college to Mississippi residents whose parent was killed or disabled on the job.

Title of Award: Kids' Chance of Mississippi Scholarship Fund **Area, Field, or Subject:** General studies/Field of study not specified **Level of Education for which Award is Granted:** Undergraduate **Number Awarded:** Varies each year. **Funds Available:** A stipend is awarded (amount not specified). **Duration:** 1 year; may be renewed.

Eligibility Requirements: This program is open to Mississippi residents between 17 and 23 years of age who have had a parent killed or permanently and totally disabled in an accident that is compensable under the Mississippi Workers' Compensation Act. Applicants must demonstrate substantial financial need. **Deadline for Receipt:** April of each year.

1070 ■ MISSISSIPPI COUNCIL OF THE BLIND

P.O. Box 31112
Jackson, MS 39286
Tel: (601)982-1718; 888-346-5622
E-mail: mcb@netdoor.com
Web Site: http://www.acb.org/mcb

To provide funding for college to legally blind residents of Mississippi and their children.

Title of Award: James Doyle Case Memorial Scholarships **Area, Field, or Subject:** General studies/Field of study not specified **Level of Education for which Award is Granted:** Graduate, Undergraduate **Number Awarded:** 2 each year. **Funds Available:** The stipend is $2,500 per year. **Duration:** 1 year.

Eligibility Requirements: This program is open to residents of Mississippi who are legally blind or the children of at least 1 legally blind parent. Applicants must be enrolled or accepted for enrollment in an undergraduate or graduate program and carrying or planning to carry at least 12 academic hours. Selection is based on a transcript from the last school or college attended, college entrance examination score, 2 letters of recommendation, and a 300-word biographical essay on the applicant's educational and employment goals. Membership in the sponsoring organization is not required. **Deadline for Receipt:** February of each year. **Additional Information:** Information is also available from Rebecca Floyd, President, 131 Red Fox Lane, Madison, MS 39110, (601) 981-8207.

1071 ■ MISSISSIPPI MILITARY DEPARTMENT

Attn: Education Services Office
JFH-MS-J1-ED
1410 Riverside Drive
P.O. Box 5027
Jackson, MS 39296-5027
Tel: (601)313-6248
Fax: (601)313-6151
E-mail: penny.boggan@ms.ngb.army.mil
Web Site: http://www.ngms.state.ms.us/edu

To provide payment of tuition for members of the Mississippi National Guard.

Title of Award: Mississippi National Guard State Educational Assistance Program **Area, Field, or Subject:** General studies/Field of study not specified **Level of Education for which Award is Granted:** Undergraduate **Number Awarded:** Varies each year. **Funds Available:** Stipends cover the actual cost of tuition, to a maximum of $1,000 per semester ($2,000 per year) at a 4-year college or university or $500 per semester at a 2-year college. **Duration:** 1 year; may be renewed until the Guard member earns a bachelor's degree, as long as the member maintains a minimum GPA of 2.0. The full benefit must be utilized within a 10-year period.

Eligibility Requirements: Applicants must be members of the Mississippi Army or Air National Guard (cadets, officer candidates, warrant officers, or commissioned officers below the rank of major); residents of Mississippi; registered to vote in Mississippi; and enrolled or accepted for enrollment at a state-accredited college or university (public or private) in Mississippi. **Deadline for Receipt:** Applications must be submitted not later than 2 weeks after the start date of the semester.

1072 ■ MISSISSIPPI NATIONAL GUARD NONCOMMISSIONED OFFICERS ASSOCIATION

Attn: SFC James Dettor
P.O. Box 699
Brandon, MS 39043

Tel: (601)824-0304
Free: 800-205-5797
Fax: (601)313-6335
E-mail: james.dettor@ms.ngb.army.mil
Web Site: http://

To provide financial assistance for college to dependents of members of the Mississippi National Guard Noncommissioned Officers Association.

Title of Award: Mississippi National Guard Noncommissioned Officers Association Scholarships **Area, Field, or Subject:** General studies/Field of study not specified **Level of Education for which Award is Granted:** Undergraduate **Number Awarded:** Varies each year. **Funds Available:** The stipend depends on the availability of funds. **Duration:** 1 year.

Eligibility Requirements: This program is open to the unmarried dependent children and spouses of annual, enlisted, retired, and life members of the association. Applicants must be high school seniors or undergraduate students with at least 1 full semester remaining before graduation. They must be attending or planning to attend an accredited university, college, community college, vo-tech, business, or trade school. Along with their application, they must submit a letter explaining why they wish to continue their education, and why they need financial assistance. **Deadline for Receipt:** January of each year. **Additional Information:** Information is also available from the Scholarship Chair, P.O. Box 7, Columbus, MS 39703.

1073 ■ MISSISSIPPI OFFICE OF STUDENT FINANCIAL AID

3825 Ridgewood Road
Jackson, MS 39211-6453
Tel: (601)432-6997
Free: 800-327-2980
Fax: (601)432-6527
E-mail: sfa@ihl.state.ms.us
Web Site: http://www.ihl.state.ms.us/financialaid/mesg.html

To provide financial assistance for college to residents of Mississippi who have exceptional academic records.

Title of Award: Mississippi Eminent Scholars Grants **Area, Field, or Subject:** General studies/Field of study not specified **Level of Education for which Award is Granted:** Undergraduate **Number Awarded:** Varies each year. **Funds Available:** The stipend is $2,500 per year, not to exceed tuition and required fees. **Duration:** 1 year; may be renewed for up to 4 additional years or completion of an undergraduate degree, as long as the recipient maintains continuous full-time enrollment and a cumulative GPA of 3.5 or higher.

Eligibility Requirements: This program is open to seniors graduating from high schools in Mississippi, home-schooled students in the state with less than 12 college hours, and college students who graduated from high school or completed a home school program within the past 3 years and have completed 12 or more college hours. Applicants must have been residents of Mississippi for at least 1 year prior to enrolling in college and have a high school GPA of 3.5 or higher and a score of 29 or higher on the ACT or 1280 or higher on the SAT; if they qualified as a semifinalist or finalist in the National Merit Scholarship Competition or the National Achievement Scholarship Competition, they are not required to have the minimum ACT score. They must be enrolled or planning to enroll as a full-time student at an approved college or university in the state. **Deadline for Receipt:** September of each year. **Additional Information:** This program was established in 1995. Further information is available from the student financial aid office at approved colleges and universities.

1074 ■ MISSISSIPPI OFFICE OF STUDENT FINANCIAL AID

3825 Ridgewood Road
Jackson, MS 39211-6453
Tel: (601)432-6997
Free: 800-327-2980
Fax: (601)432-6527
E-mail: sfa@ihl.state.ms.us
Web Site: http://www.ihl.state.ms.us/financialaid/help.html

To provide financial assistance for college to residents of Mississippi who demonstrate financial need.

Title of Award: Mississippi Higher Education Legislative Plan for Needy Students **Area, Field, or Subject:** General studies/Field of study not specified **Level of Education for which Award is Granted:** Undergraduate **Number Awarded:** Varies each year, depending on the availability of funds; awards are granted on a first-come, first-served basis. **Funds**

Available: Students in this program receive a full waiver of tuition at eligible Mississippi public institutions of higher learning or eligible Mississippi public community/junior colleges. Students attending private institutions receive an award amount equal to the award of a student attending the nearest comparable public institution. **Duration:** 1 year; may be renewed up to 4 additional years provided the recipient continues to meet all program requirement and maintains a GPA of 2.5 or higher.

Eligibility Requirements: Applicants must have been residents of Mississippi for at least 2 years and have graduated from high school within the immediate past 2 years. They must be enrolled or planning to enroll full time at a college or university in the state. High school seniors entering their freshman year in college must have a cumulative high school GPA of 2.5 or higher and have completed specific high school core curriculum requirements. College freshmen entering their sophomore year must have achieved a cumulative GPA of 2.5 or higher on all college course work previously completed. All applicants must have scored 20 or higher on the ACT and be able to demonstrate financial need with an average family adjusted gross income of $36,500 or less over the prior 2 years (rising by $5,000 for each sibling in the family under 21 years of age). **Deadline for Receipt:** March of each year.

1075 ■ MISSISSIPPI OFFICE OF STUDENT FINANCIAL AID
3825 Ridgewood Road
Jackson, MS 39211-6453
Tel: (601)432-6997
Free: 800-327-2980
Fax: (601)432-6527
E-mail: sfa@ihl.state.ms.us
Web Site: http://www.ihl.state.ms.us/financialaid/law.html
To provide financial assistance for college to the spouses and children of disabled or deceased Mississippi law enforcement officers and fire fighters.
Title of Award: Mississippi Law Enforcement Officers and Firemen Scholarship Program **Area, Field, or Subject:** General studies/Field of study not specified **Level of Education for which Award is Granted:** Undergraduate **Number Awarded:** Varies each year. **Funds Available:** Students in this program receive full payment of tuition fees, the average cost of campus housing, required fees, and applicable course fees at state-supported colleges and universities in Mississippi. Funds may not be used to pay for books, food, school supplies, materials, dues, or fees for extracurricular activities. **Duration:** Up to 8 semesters.
Eligibility Requirements: This program is open to children and spouses of full-time law enforcement officers and fire fighters who became permanently and totally disabled or who died in the line of duty and were Mississippi residents at the time of death or injury. Applicants must be high school seniors or graduates interested in attending a state-supported postsecondary institution in Mississippi on a full-time basis. Children may be natural, adopted, or stepchildren up to 23 years of age; spouses may be of any age. **Deadline for Receipt:** Applications may be submitted at any time.

1076 ■ MISSISSIPPI OFFICE OF STUDENT FINANCIAL AID
3825 Ridgewood Road
Jackson, MS 39211-6453
Tel: (601)432-6997
Free: 800-327-2980
Fax: (601)432-6527
E-mail: sfa@ihl.state.ms.us
Web Site: http://www.ihl.state.ms.us/financialaid/leap.html
To provide financial assistance for college to Mississippi residents who demonstrate significant financial need.
Title of Award: Mississippi Leveraging Educational Assistance Partnership Program **Area, Field, or Subject:** General studies/Field of study not specified **Level of Education for which Award is Granted:** Undergraduate **Number Awarded:** Varies each year. **Funds Available:** The amount of assistance varies. **Duration:** 1 year; may be renewed for up to 3 additional years.
Eligibility Requirements: Applicants must be current legal Mississippi residents who are enrolled or accepted for enrollment as full-time undergraduate students at a nonprofit college or university in Mississippi and who demonstrate substantial financial need. U.S. citizenship or permanent resident status is required. **Deadline for Receipt:** Each participating college and university establishes its own deadline date for

applications. **Additional Information:** Participating colleges and universities in Mississippi select the recipients of these grants through their regular financial aid award process. Further information is available from the student financial aid office at educational institutions in the state. This program was formerly known as the Mississippi State Student Incentive Grant Program.

1077 ■ MISSISSIPPI OFFICE OF STUDENT FINANCIAL AID
3825 Ridgewood Road
Jackson, MS 39211-6453
Tel: (601)432-6997
Free: 800-327-2980
Fax: (601)432-6527
E-mail: sfa@ihl.state.ms.us
Web Site: http://www.ihl.state.ms.us/financialaid/mtag.html
To provide financial assistance for college to Mississippi residents who demonstrate significant financial need.
Title of Award: Mississippi Resident Tuition Assistance Grants **Area, Field, or Subject:** General studies/Field of study not specified **Level of Education for which Award is Granted:** Undergraduate **Number Awarded:** Varies each year. **Funds Available:** Awards depend on the availability of funds and the need of the recipient; the maximum award for a freshman or sophomore is $500 per year; the maximum award for a junior or senior is $1,000 per year. **Duration:** 1 year; may be renewed for up to 4 additional years or completion of an undergraduate degree, as long as the recipient maintains continuous full-time enrollment and a GPA of 2.5 or higher.
Eligibility Requirements: Applicants must have been legal Mississippi residents for at least 1 year and be receiving less than the full federal Pell Grant for college. High school seniors must have a GPA of 2.5 or higher and either an ACT score of 15 or higher or an SAT score of 720 or higher. Home-schooled students must submit a transcript showing the course work corresponding to that of a high school graduate for grades 9-12 and either an ACT score of 15 or higher or an SAT score of 720 or higher. Students already enrolled in college must have a cumulative GPA of 2.5 or higher. All applicants must be attending or planning to attend a 2-year or 4-year public or private accredited college or university in Mississippi. **Deadline for Receipt:** September of each year. **Additional Information:** Further information is available from the student financial aid offices at educational institutions in Mississippi.

1078 ■ MISSISSIPPI OFFICE OF STUDENT FINANCIAL AID
3825 Ridgewood Road
Jackson, MS 39211-6453
Tel: (601)432-6997
Free: 800-327-2980
Fax: (601)432-6527
E-mail: sfa@ihl.state.ms.us
Web Site: http://www.ihl.state.ms.us/financialaid/nissan.html
To provide financial assistance for college to high school seniors in Mississippi who plan to attend a public college in the state.
Title of Award: Nissan Mississippi Scholarships **Area, Field, or Subject:** General studies/Field of study not specified **Level of Education for which Award is Granted:** Undergraduate **Number Awarded:** 1 or more each year. **Funds Available:** Students in this program receive full payment of tuition and required fees plus an allowance for books. **Duration:** 1 year; may be renewed 1 additional year for students at 2-year public colleges (followed by up to 3 years of support if the recipient transfers to a 4-year college or university) or up to 4 additional years for students at 4-year public colleges and universities. Renewal requires that the recipient reapplies each year; maintains a GPA of 2.5 or higher; displays leadership skills through participation in community service, extracurricular, or other activities; demonstrates full-time enrollment and satisfactory academic progress toward completion of a degree; maintains Mississippi residency; and maintains good standing at the college or university.
Eligibility Requirements: This program is open to residents of Mississippi who are graduating seniors at high schools in the state. Applicants must have been accepted for enrollment at a public 2-year or 4-year college or university in the state. They must have a GPA of 2.0 or higher after 7 semesters of high school and minimum scores of 20 on the ACT or 940 on the SAT. Along with their application, they must submit a 200-word essay on the topic, "How do my plans for the future and my college major support the automotive industry in Mississippi?" Selection is based on the

essay (5%); academic achievement (50%); 2 letters of nomination (5%); extracurricular activities, work, leadership, and community involvement (20%); and demonstrated financial need (20%). **Deadline for Receipt:** February of each year. **Additional Information:** This program is supported by Nissan North America, Inc.

1079 ■ MISSISSIPPI STATE VETERANS AFFAIRS BOARD
3460 Highway 80 East
P.O. Box 5947
Pearl, MS 39288-5947
Tel: (601)576-4850
Fax: (601)576-4868
E-mail: grice@vab.state.ms.us
Web Site: http://www.vab.state.ms.us
To provide financial assistance for college to the children of Mississippi residents who are POWs or MIAs.
Title of Award: Mississippi Educational Assistance for MIA/POW Dependents **Area, Field, or Subject:** General studies/Field of study not specified **Level of Education for which Award is Granted:** Undergraduate **Number Awarded:** Varies each year. **Funds Available:** This assistance covers all costs of college attendance. **Duration:** Up to 8 semesters.
Eligibility Requirements: This entitlement program is open to the children of members of the armed services whose official home of record and residence is in Mississippi and who are officially reported as being either a prisoner of a foreign government or missing in action. Applicants must be attending or planning to attend a state-supported college or university in Mississippi.

1080 ■ MISSOURI ASSOCIATION OF FAIRS & FESTIVALS
Attn: Executive Director
941 East Rodney
Cape Girardeau, MO 63701
Tel: (573)334-9250
Fax: (573)270-0898
Web Site: http://www.mofairsfest.org/scholarships.htm
To provide financial assistance for college to high school seniors in Missouri who have participated in county fairs or festivals.
Title of Award: Missouri STAATS Company Scholarship **Area, Field, or Subject:** General studies/Field of study not specified **Level of Education for which Award is Granted:** Undergraduate **Number Awarded:** 1 each year. **Funds Available:** The stipend is $1,000. **Duration:** 1 year.
Eligibility Requirements: This program is open to seniors graduating from high schools in Missouri with a GPA of 2.5 or higher. Applicants must be planning to enroll full time at a 2- or 4-year college or university. They must be able to demonstrate past support of school, community, and the fair and festival environment. Along with their application, they must submit a letter of recommendation from their high school guidance counselor and the sponsoring Missouri Association of Fairs & Festivals (MAFF) member fair board. Financial need is also considered in the selection process. **Deadline for Receipt:** December of each year. **Additional Information:** This scholarship, sponsored by STAATS Custom Awards, was first awarded in 2006. Information is also available from Elizabeth Schlueter, P.O. Box 317, Troy, MO 63379.

1081 ■ MISSOURI BUSINESS AND PROFESSIONAL WOMEN'S FOUNDATION, INC.
P.O. Box 338
Carthage, MO 64836-0338
Web Site: http://www.bpwmo.org/scholarship.htm
To provide financial assistance for college to women in Missouri.
Title of Award: Missouri General BPW Scholarships **Area, Field, or Subject:** General studies/Field of study not specified **Level of Education for which Award is Granted:** Undergraduate **Number Awarded:** Varies each year; recently, 3 of these scholarships were awarded. **Funds Available:** A stipend is awarded (amount not specified). **Duration:** 1 year.
Eligibility Requirements: This program is open to women in Missouri who have been accepted into an accredited program or course of study to upgrade their skills and/or complete education for career advancement. Along with their application, they must submit brief statements on the following: their achievements and/or specific recognitions in their field of endeavor; professional and/or civic affiliations; present and long-range career goals; how they plan to participate in and contribute to their com-

munity upon completion of their program of study; why they feel they would make a good recipient; and any special circumstances that may have influenced their ability to continue or complete their education. They must also demonstrate financial need and U.S. citizenship. **Deadline for Receipt:** January of each year. **Additional Information:** Information is also available from Pat Henderson, Scholarship Committee Chair, P.O. Box 296, Hillsboro, MO 63050, (636) 789-2119.

1082 ■ MISSOURI BUSINESS AND PROFESSIONAL WOMEN'S FOUNDATION, INC.
P.O. Box 338
Carthage, MO 64836-0338
Web Site: http://www.bpwmo.org/scholarship.htm
To provide financial assistance for college to members of the Missouri Federation of Business and Professional Women (BPW Missouri).
Title of Award: Phyllis Sanders Scholarship **Area, Field, or Subject:** General studies/Field of study not specified **Level of Education for which Award is Granted:** Undergraduate **Number Awarded:** Varies each year; recently, 2 of these scholarships were awarded. **Funds Available:** A stipend is awarded (amount not specified). **Duration:** 1 year.
Eligibility Requirements: This program is open to BPW Missouri members who have been accepted into an accredited program or course of study to upgrade their skills and/or complete education for career advancement. Along with their application, they must submit brief statements on the following: their achievements and/or specific recognitions in their field of endeavor; professional and/or civic affiliations; present and long-range career goals; how they plan to participate in and contribute to their community upon completion of their program of study; why they feel they would make a good recipient; and any special circumstances that may have influenced their ability to continue or complete their education. They must also demonstrate financial need and U.S. citizenship. **Deadline for Receipt:** January of each year. **Additional Information:** Information is also available from Pat Henderson, Scholarship Committee Chair, P.O. Box 296, Hillsboro, MO 63050, (636) 789-2119.

1083 ■ MISSOURI COUNCIL OF THE BLIND
5453 Chippewa Street
St. Louis, MO 63109-1635
Tel: (314)832-7172
Free: 800-342-5632
Fax: (314)832-7796
E-mail: moblind@mindspring.com
Web Site: http://www.acb.org/missouri
To provide financial assistance for college to blind students in Missouri.
Title of Award: Missouri Council of the Blind Scholarships **Area, Field, or Subject:** General studies/Field of study not specified **Level of Education for which Award is Granted:** Graduate, Undergraduate **Number Awarded:** Varies each year; recently, 14 of these scholarships were awarded. **Funds Available:** The stipend is $1,200. **Duration:** 1 year; may be renewed if the recipient maintains a GPA of 2.0 or higher.
Eligibility Requirements: This program is open to Missouri residents who are high school or college graduates, legally blind, and in good academic standing. Applicants must be working on or planning to work on an undergraduate or graduate degree. They should have a specific goal in mind and that goal should be realistically within reach. Applications are received through the Missouri Division of Family Services/Rehabilitation Services for the Blind. **Deadline for Receipt:** April of each year. **Additional Information:** Information is also available from Phyllis Lovett, Scholarship Chair, 3925 South Jefferson, Number 45, Springfield, MO 65807, (417) 883-7408, E-mail: phyllisbww@sbcglobal.net.

1084 ■ MISSOURI DEPARTMENT OF HIGHER EDUCATION
Attn: Student Financial Assistance
3515 Amazonas Drive
Jefferson City, MO 65109-5717
Tel: (573)526-7958
Free: 800-473-6757
Fax: (573)751-6635
E-mail: info@dhe.mo.gov
Web Site: http://www.dhe.mo.gov/hsstudentsrossbarnett.shtml
To provide financial assistance for college to students in Missouri who are employed while attending school part time.
Title of Award: Marguerite Ross Barnett Memorial Scholarship **Area, Field, or Subject:** General studies/Field of study not specified **Level of

Education for which Award is Granted: Undergraduate **Number Awarded:** Varies each year; recently, 239 of these scholarships were awarded. **Funds Available:** The maximum annual award is the least of 1) the actual tuition charged at the school the recipient is attending part time; 2) the amount of tuition charged to a Missouri undergraduate resident enrolled part time in the same class level at the University of Missouri; or 3) the recipient's demonstrated financial need. **Duration:** 1 semester; may be renewed until the recipient has obtained a baccalaureate degree or has completed 150 semester credit hours, whichever comes first.
Eligibility Requirements: This program is open to residents of Missouri who are enrolled at least half time but less than full time at participating Missouri postsecondary institutions. Applicants must be able to demonstrate financial need and must be employed at least 20 hours per week. Students working on a degree or certificate in theology or divinity are not eligible. U.S. citizenship or permanent resident status is required. **Deadline for Receipt:** March of each year. **Additional Information:** Awards are not available for summer study.

1085 ■ MISSOURI DEPARTMENT OF HIGHER EDUCATION
Attn: Student Financial Assistance
3515 Amazonas Drive
Jefferson City, MO 65109-5717
Tel: (573)526-7958
Free: 800-473-6757
Fax: (573)751-6635
E-mail: info@dhe.mo.gov
Web Site: http://www.dhe.mo.gov/hsstudentscharlesgallagher.shtml
To provide financial assistance to college students in Missouri who demonstrate financial need.
Title of Award: Charles Gallagher Student Financial Assistance Program **Area, Field, or Subject:** General studies/Field of study not specified **Level of Education for which Award is Granted:** Undergraduate **Number Awarded:** Varies each year; recently, 12,704 students received support through this program. **Funds Available:** The annual award is the lesser of 1) the unmet financial need (after counting any federal Pell Grant the student receives); 2) half of the school's prior year tuition and fees; or 3) $1,500. **Duration:** 1 year; may be renewed.
Eligibility Requirements: This program is open to residents of Missouri who are full-time students working on their first baccalaureate degree at a participating postsecondary school in the state. Applicants must be able to demonstrate financial need. Students working on a degree or certificate in theology or divinity are not eligible. U.S. citizenship or permanent resident status is required. **Deadline for Receipt:** March of each year. **Additional Information:** Currently, 84 postsecondary schools in Missouri are approved to participate in this program; applications and further information are available at the financial aid office of those schools.

1086 ■ MISSOURI DEPARTMENT OF HIGHER EDUCATION
Attn: Student Financial Assistance
3515 Amazonas Drive
Jefferson City, MO 65109-5717
Tel: (573)526-7958
Free: 800-473-6757
Fax: (573)751-6635
E-mail: info@dhe.mo.gov
Web Site: http://www.dhe.mo.gov/hsstudentscollegeguaranteeplus.shtml
To provide financial assistance for college to full-time students in Missouri who have financial need and who participate in a federal TRIO program or who graduated from a high school GEAR UP program.
Title of Award: Missouri College Guarantee PLUS Program **Area, Field, or Subject:** General studies/Field of study not specified **Level of Education for which Award is Granted:** Undergraduate **Number Awarded:** Varies each year. **Funds Available:** The maximum annual award is based on the tuition cost at the University of Missouri. **Duration:** 1 year; may be renewed.
Eligibility Requirements: This program is open to residents of Missouri who are attending or planning to attend participating Missouri postsecondary institutions as full-time undergraduate students. Applicants must have a high school GPA of 2.5 or higher and a score of 20 or higher on the ACT or 950 or higher on the SAT. They must be able to demonstrate financial need and participation in high school extracurricular activities. This program is limited to students who 1) participate in a federal TRIO program (e.g., Upward Bound), or 2) graduated from a high school GEAR

UP (Gaining Early Awareness and Readiness for Undergraduate Programs) activity. Students working on a degree or certificate in theology or divinity are not eligible. U.S. citizenship or permanent resident status is required. **Deadline for Receipt:** March of each year.

1087 ■ MISSOURI DEPARTMENT OF HIGHER EDUCATION
Attn: Student Financial Assistance
3515 Amazonas Drive
Jefferson City, MO 65109-5717
Tel: (573)526-7958
Free: 800-473-6757
Fax: (573)751-6635
E-mail: info@dhe.mo.gov
Web Site: http://www.dhe.mo.gov/hsstudentscollegeguarantee.shtml
To provide financial assistance for college to full-time students in Missouri who have financial need.
Title of Award: Missouri College Guarantee Program **Area, Field, or Subject:** General studies/Field of study not specified **Level of Education for which Award is Granted:** Undergraduate **Number Awarded:** Varies each year; recently, 4,006 students received support through this program. **Funds Available:** The maximum annual award is based on the tuition cost at the University of Missouri. **Duration:** 1 year; may be renewed.
Eligibility Requirements: This program is open to residents of Missouri who are attending or planning to attend participating Missouri postsecondary institutions as full-time undergraduate students. Applicants must have a high school GPA of 2.5 or higher and a score of 20 or higher on the ACT or 950 or higher on the SAT. They must be able to demonstrate financial need. Students working on a degree or certificate in theology or divinity are not eligible. U.S. citizenship or permanent resident status is required. **Deadline for Receipt:** March of each year. **Additional Information:** This program was established in 1999.

1088 ■ MISSOURI DEPARTMENT OF HIGHER EDUCATION
Attn: Student Financial Assistance
3515 Amazonas Drive
Jefferson City, MO 65109-5717
Tel: (573)526-7958
Free: 800-473-6757
Fax: (573)751-6635
E-mail: info@dhe.mo.gov
Web Site: http://www.dhe.mo.gov/hsstudentsbrightflight.shtml
To provide financial assistance for college to outstanding high school seniors in Missouri.
Title of Award: Missouri Higher Education Academic "Bright Flight" Scholarship Program **Area, Field, or Subject:** General studies/Field of study not specified **Level of Education for which Award is Granted:** Undergraduate **Number Awarded:** Varies each year; recently, 8,262 of these scholarships were awarded. **Funds Available:** The stipend is $2,000 per year. **Duration:** 1 year; may be renewed for up to 4 additional years or until completion of a baccalaureate degree, if the recipient maintains full-time status and satisfactory academic progress.
Eligibility Requirements: This program is open to high school seniors in Missouri who score in the top 3% of all Missouri students taking the SAT or ACT. Applicants must be planning to attend a participating college or university in Missouri full time. Students working on a degree or certificate in theology or divinity are not eligible. U.S. citizenship or permanent resident status is required. **Deadline for Receipt:** July of each year. **Additional Information:** Awards are not available for summer study.

1089 ■ MISSOURI DEPARTMENT OF HIGHER EDUCATION
Attn: Student Financial Assistance
3515 Amazonas Drive
Jefferson City, MO 65109-5717
Tel: (573)526-7958
Free: 800-473-6757
Fax: (573)751-6635
E-mail: info@dhe.mo.gov
Web Site: http://www.dhe.mo.gov/hsstudentspublicservice.shtml
To provide financial assistance for college to spouses and children of disabled and deceased Missouri public employees and public safety officers.
Title of Award: Missouri Public Officer or Employee's Child Survivor Grant Program **Area, Field, or Subject:** General studies/Field of study

not specified **Level of Education for which Award is Granted:** Undergraduate **Number Awarded:** Varies each year. **Funds Available:** The maximum annual grant is the lesser of 1) the actual tuition charged at the school where the recipient is enrolled, or 2) the amount of tuition charged to a Missouri undergraduate resident enrolled full time in the same class level and in the same academic major as an applicant at the University of Missouri at Columbia. **Duration:** 1 year; may be renewed.

Eligibility Requirements: This program is open to dependent children and spouses of 1) Missouri Department of Transportation employees who were killed or permanently disabled while engaged in the construction or maintenance of highways, roads, and bridges; and 2) Missouri public safety officers who were killed or permanently disabled in the line of duty. Applicants must be Missouri residents enrolled or accepted for enrollment as a full-time undergraduate student at a participating Missouri college or university; children must be younger than 24 years of age. Students working on a degree or certificate in theology or divinity are not eligible. U.S. citizenship or permanent resident status is required. **Deadline for Receipt:** There is no application deadline, but early submission of the completed application is encouraged.

1090 ■ MISSOURI DEPARTMENT OF HIGHER EDUCATION

Attn: Student Financial Assistance
3515 Amazonas Drive
Jefferson City, MO 65109-5717
Tel: (573)526-7958
Free: 800-473-6757
Fax: (573)751-6635
E-mail: info@dhe.mo.gov
Web Site: http://www.dhe.mo.gov/hsstudentsvietnamvet.shtml
To provide financial assistance for college to survivors of certain deceased Missouri Vietnam veterans.

Title of Award: Missouri Vietnam Veterans Survivor Grant Program **Area, Field, or Subject:** General studies/Field of study not specified **Level of Education for which Award is Granted:** Undergraduate **Number Awarded:** Varies each year. **Funds Available:** The maximum annual grant is the lesser of 1) the actual tuition charged at the school where the recipient is enrolled, or 2) the amount of tuition charged to a Missouri undergraduate resident enrolled full time in the same class level and in the same academic major as an applicant at the Missouri public 4-year regional institutions. **Duration:** 1 semester; may be renewed until the recipient has obtained a baccalaureate degree or has completed 150 semester credit hours, whichever comes first.

Eligibility Requirements: This program is open to surviving spouses and children of veterans who served in the military in Vietnam or the war zone in southeast Asia, who were residents of Missouri when first entering military service and at the time of death, whose death was attributed to or caused by exposure to toxic chemicals during the Vietnam conflict, and who served in the Vietnam theater between 1961 and 1972. Applicants must be Missouri residents enrolled in a program leading to a certificate, associate degree, or baccalaureate degree at an approved postsecondary institution in the state. Students working on a degree or certificate in theology or divinity are not eligible. U.S. citizenship or permanent resident status is required. **Additional Information:** Awards are not available for summer study.

1091 ■ MONTANA FUNERAL DIRECTORS ASSOCIATION

P.O. Box 4267
Helena, MT 59604-4267
Tel: (406)449-7244
Fax: (406)443-0979
E-mail: mfda@sy-key.com
To provide financial assistance to Montana residents who are interested in studying mortuary science.

Title of Award: Montana Funeral Directors Association Scholarships **Area, Field, or Subject:** Mortuary science **Level of Education for which Award is Granted:** Undergraduate **Number Awarded:** Up to 2 each year. **Funds Available:** The stipend is $1,000. **Duration:** 1 year.

Eligibility Requirements: This program is open to Montana residents who are beginning or working on a degree in mortuary science. The sole requirement is that the applicant be willing to return to Montana and work in the funeral service profession. In addition, the following information will strengthen an application (but is not required): a GPA of 3.0 or higher, support of a funeral home that belongs to the sponsoring association,

submission of a transcript of mortuary school grades, and 2 letters of recommendation. Financial need is not considered in the selection process. **Deadline for Receipt:** May of each year.

1092 ■ MONTANA GUARANTEED STUDENT LOAN PROGRAM

2500 Broadway
P.O. Box 203101
Helena, MT 59620-3101
Tel: (406)444-0638
Free: 800-537-7508
Fax: (406)444-1869
E-mail: scholar@mgslp.state.mt.us
Web Site: http://www.mgslp.state.mt.us
To provide financial assistance for undergraduate education to athletes attending universities in Montana.

Title of Award: Montana Athletic Fee Waiver **Area, Field, or Subject:** General studies/Field of study not specified **Level of Education for which Award is Granted:** Undergraduate **Number Awarded:** Varies each year, to the maximum authorized by the National Collegiate Athletic Association, National Association of Intercollegiate Athletics, or appropriate affiliated conferences for officially sanctioned or recognized intercollegiate sports. **Funds Available:** Students eligible for this benefit are entitled to attend any unit of the Montana University System without payment of undergraduate registration, incidental, or out-of-state fees. **Duration:** Undergraduate students are eligible for continued fee waiver as long as they maintain reasonable academic progress as full-time students.

Eligibility Requirements: Athletes selected by the staff of branches of the Montana University System are eligible for these fee waivers.

1093 ■ MONTANA GUARANTEED STUDENT LOAN PROGRAM

2500 Broadway
P.O. Box 203101
Helena, MT 59620-3101
Tel: (406)444-0638
Free: 800-537-7508
Fax: (406)444-1869
E-mail: scholar@mgslp.state.mt.us
Web Site: http://www.mgslp.state.mt.us
To provide financial assistance to outstanding community college students in Montana planning to transfer to a university in the state.

Title of Award: Montana Community College Honor Scholarships **Area, Field, or Subject:** General studies/Field of study not specified **Level of Education for which Award is Granted:** Four Year College **Number Awarded:** 1 scholarship is awarded to a member of each community college graduating class. **Funds Available:** Students eligible for this benefit are entitled to attend any unit of the Montana University System without payment of undergraduate registration or incidental fees. **Duration:** The waiver is valid through the completion of the first academic year of enrollment.

Eligibility Requirements: Eligible for this benefit are residents of Montana who are graduating from a community college in the state and planning to transfer to a branch of the Montana University System. Their college must verify that they are the highest ranking member of their class desiring to attend a Montana University System unit. **Additional Information:** The scholarship must be utilized within 9 months after receiving an associate degree from the community college.

1094 ■ MONTANA GUARANTEED STUDENT LOAN PROGRAM

2500 Broadway
P.O. Box 203101
Helena, MT 59620-3101
Tel: (406)444-0638
Free: 800-537-7508
Fax: (406)444-1869
E-mail: scholar@mgslp.state.mt.us
Web Site: http://www.mgslp.state.mt.us
To provide financial assistance for undergraduate education to residents of custodial facilities in Montana.

Title of Award: Montana Custodial Student Fee Waiver **Area, Field, or Subject:** General studies/Field of study not specified **Level of Education for which Award is Granted:** Undergraduate **Number Awarded:** Varies each year. **Funds Available:** Students eligible for this benefit are entitled to attend any unit of the Montana University System without payment of undergraduate registration or incidental fees. **Duration:** Undergraduate students are eligible for continued fee waiver as long as they maintain reasonable academic progress as full-time students.

Eligibility Requirements: Eligible for this benefit are residents of Montana who attend the Riverside Correctional Facility at Boulder, the Pine Hills Youth Correctional Facility at Miles City, or similar facilities or private charitable institutions. Applicants must be recommended by the Department of Corrections or the administration of the private institutions. Financial need is considered.

1095 ■ MONTANA GUARANTEED STUDENT LOAN PROGRAM

2500 Broadway
P.O. Box 203101
Helena, MT 59620-3101
Tel: (406)444-0638
Free: 800-537-7508
Fax: (406)444-1869
E-mail: scholar@mgslp.state.mt.us
Web Site: http://www.mgslp.state.mt.us
To provide financial assistance for college to dependents of veterans and military personnel declared missing in action or prisoners of war in southeast Asia.

Title of Award: Montana Dependents of Prisoners of War Fee Waiver **Area, Field, or Subject:** General studies/Field of study not specified **Level of Education for which Award is Granted:** Undergraduate **Number Awarded:** Varies each year. **Funds Available:** Students eligible for this benefit are entitled to attend any unit of the Montana University System without payment of undergraduate registration or incidental fees. **Duration:** Undergraduate students are eligible for continued fee waivers as long as they maintain reasonable academic progress as full-time students.

Eligibility Requirements: To be eligible for this fee waiver, students must be the spouses or children of residents of Montana who, while serving in southeast Asia after January 1, 1961 either in the armed forces or as a civilian, have been declared missing in action or prisoner of war. Financial need is considered.

1096 ■ MONTANA GUARANTEED STUDENT LOAN PROGRAM

2500 Broadway
P.O. Box 203101
Helena, MT 59620-3101
Tel: (406)444-0638
Free: 800-537-7508
Fax: (406)444-1869
E-mail: scholar@mgslp.state.mt.us
Web Site: http://www.mgslp.state.mt.us
To provide financial assistance for college to juniors at high schools in Montana that are participating in the Gaining Early Awareness and Readiness for Undergraduate Programs (GEAR UP) federal program.

Title of Award: Montana GEAR UP Achievement Grants **Area, Field, or Subject:** General studies/Field of study not specified **Level of Education for which Award is Granted:** Undergraduate **Number Awarded:** Varies each year; recently, 77 students received these grants. **Funds Available:** The stipend is $1,000. **Duration:** 1 year.

Eligibility Requirements: This program is open to high school juniors who have been enrolled in the college preparatory curriculum for at least 2 years at a Montana high school that is participating in the GEAR UP program. Applicants must have a cumulative GPA of 2.0 or higher at the end of the fourth semester of high school and upon high school graduation. They must enroll in a Montana postsecondary institution within 18 months of high school graduation. **Additional Information:** For a list of the 23 GEAR UP high schools in the state, contact the Montana Guaranteed Student Loan Program.

1097 ■ MONTANA GUARANTEED STUDENT LOAN PROGRAM

2500 Broadway
P.O. Box 203101
Helena, MT 59620-3101
Tel: (406)444-0638
Free: 800-537-7508
Fax: (406)444-1869
E-mail: scholar@mgslp.state.mt.us
Web Site: http://www.mgslp.state.mt.us

To provide financial assistance for undergraduate education to National Merit Scholarship semifinalists in Montana.

Title of Award: Montana Honor Scholarships for National Merit Scholarship Semifinalists **Area, Field, or Subject:** General studies/Field of study not specified **Level of Education for which Award is Granted:** Undergraduate **Number Awarded:** Varies each year. **Funds Available:** Students eligible for this benefit are entitled to attend any unit of the Montana University System without payment of undergraduate registration or incidental fees. **Duration:** The waiver is valid through the completion of the first academic year of enrollment.

Eligibility Requirements: Eligible for this benefit are residents of Montana who are National Merit Scholarship semifinalists. Students must enroll at a campus of the Montana University System or community college in the state within 9 months of high school graduation. **Additional Information:** The scholarship must be utilized within 9 months after high school graduation.

1098 ■ MONTANA GUARANTEED STUDENT LOAN PROGRAM

2500 Broadway
P.O. Box 203101
Helena, MT 59620-3101
Tel: (406)444-0638
Free: 800-537-7508
Fax: (406)444-1869
E-mail: scholar@mgslp.state.mt.us
Web Site: http://www.mgslp.state.mt.us
To provide financial assistance for undergraduate education to selected Montana veterans.

Title of Award: Montana Honorably Discharged Veteran Fee Waiver **Area, Field, or Subject:** General studies/Field of study not specified **Level of Education for which Award is Granted:** Graduate, Undergraduate **Number Awarded:** Varies each year. **Funds Available:** Students eligible for this benefit are entitled to attend any unit of the Montana University System without payment of undergraduate registration or incidental fees. **Duration:** Undergraduate students are eligible for continued fee waiver as long as they maintain reasonable academic progress as full-time students.

Eligibility Requirements: This program is open to honorably-discharged veterans who served with the U.S. armed forces in any war and who are residents of Montana. Only veterans who at some time qualified for U.S. Department of Veterans Affairs (VA) educational benefits, but who are no longer eligible, are entitled to this waiver. Veterans who served in the armed forces subsequent to the conflict in Vietnam and are working on their initial undergraduate degree are also eligible if they received an Armed Forces Expeditionary Medal for service in Lebanon, Grenada, or Panama; or served in a combat theater in the Persian Gulf between August 2, 1990 and April 11, 1991 and received the Southwest Asia Service Medal; or were awarded the Kosovo Campaign Medal. Veterans who served in World War II, Korea, or Vietnam are eligible to work on undergraduate or graduate degrees; other veterans are eligible only to work on their first undergraduate degree. Financial need is considered in the selection process.

1099 ■ MONTANA GUARANTEED STUDENT LOAN PROGRAM

2500 Broadway
P.O. Box 203101
Helena, MT 59620-3101
Tel: (406)444-6570
Free: 800-537-7508
Fax: (406)444-1869
E-mail: scholar@mgslp.state.mt.us
Web Site: http://www.mgslp.state.mt.us
To provide financial assistance to Montana Indian students interested in attending college or graduate school in the state.

Title of Award: Montana Indian Student Fee Waiver **Area, Field, or Subject:** General studies/Field of study not specified **Level of Education for which Award is Granted:** Graduate, Undergraduate **Number Awarded:** Varies; more than $1 million in waivers are approved each year. **Funds Available:** Students eligible for this benefit are entitled to attend any unit of the Montana University System without payment of undergraduate or graduate registration or incidental fees. **Duration:** Students are eligible for continued fee waiver as long as they maintain reasonable academic progress and full-time status (12 or more credits for undergraduates, 9 or more credits for graduate students).

Eligibility Requirements: Eligible to apply are Native American students (one-quarter Indian blood or more) who have been residents of Montana for at least 1 year prior to application, have graduated from an accredited high school or federal Indian school, and can demonstrate financial need.

1100 ■ MONTANA GUARANTEED STUDENT LOAN PROGRAM

2500 Broadway
P.O. Box 203101
Helena, MT 59620-3101
Tel: (406)444-0638
Free: 800-537-7508
Fax: (406)444-1869
E-mail: scholar@mgslp.state.mt.us
Web Site: http://www.mgslp.state.mt.us
To provide financial assistance for undergraduate education in Montana to dependents of victims of the September 11, 2001 terrorist action.

Title of Award: Montana September 11, 2001 Victims Fee Waiver **Area, Field, or Subject:** General studies/Field of study not specified **Level of Education for which Award is Granted:** Undergraduate **Number Awarded:** Varies each year. **Funds Available:** Students eligible for this benefit are entitled to attend any unit of the Montana University System without payment of undergraduate registration, incidental fees, or out-of-state fees. **Duration:** Undergraduate students are eligible for continued fee waiver as long as they maintain reasonable academic progress as full-time students.

Eligibility Requirements: This program is open to persons whose spouse, parent, or legal guardian was a victim of the September 11, 2001 terrorist actions at the New York World Trade Center, the Pentagon, or the Pennsylvania airplane crash. The term "victim" includes a person killed as a direct result of physical injuries suffered on or about September 11 directly related to the terrorist actions and includes rescuers, relief workers, or fire and policy personnel. It does not include any individuals identified by federal law enforcement personnel as likely perpetrators of the terrorist activities. Applicants must be enrolled in a program leading to their initial associate or baccalaureate degree at a unit of the Montana University System.

1101 ■ MONTANA GUARANTEED STUDENT LOAN PROGRAM

2500 Broadway
P.O. Box 203101
Helena, MT 59620-3101
Tel: (406)444-0638
Free: 800-537-7508
Fax: (406)444-1869
E-mail: scholar@mgslp.state.mt.us
Web Site: http://www.mgslp.state.mt.us
To provide financial assistance to Montana residents who are attending college in the state and are working to support themselves.

Title of Award: Montana Tuition Assistance Program Baker Grants **Area, Field, or Subject:** General studies/Field of study not specified **Level of Education for which Award is Granted:** Undergraduate **Number Awarded:** Varies each year. Recently, a total of $1.5 million was available for this program. **Funds Available:** The grant is intended to offset any federal Pell Grant dollars the student may have lost due to earned wages. Recently, grants ranged from $100 to $1,000. **Duration:** 1 year.

Eligibility Requirements: This program is open to residents of Montana who are attending units of the Montana University System, community colleges, Indian colleges, or designated private institutions in the state full time. Applicants must be working and have at least $2,575 in earned income during the prior calendar year. (That amount is based on the minimum wage multiplied by 500 hours; if the minimum wage is increased, the amount a student must earn is increased accordingly.) They must be making satisfactory academic progress toward their first undergraduate degree and have an expected family contribution from the results of their Free Application for Federal Student Aid (FAFSA) of $6,500 or less. **Additional Information:** This program is named in honor of Dr. Jeffery D. Baker who served as Commissioner of Higher Education from 1993 to 1996.

1102 ■ MONTANA GUARANTEED STUDENT LOAN PROGRAM

2500 Broadway
P.O. Box 203101
Helena, MT 59620-3101

Tel: (406)444-0638
Free: 800-537-7508
Fax: (406)444-1869
E-mail: scholar@mgslp.state.mt.us
Web Site: http://www.mgslp.state.mt.us
To provide financial assistance for undergraduate education to outstanding high school students in Montana.

Title of Award: Montana University System Honor Scholarships **Area, Field, or Subject:** General studies/Field of study not specified **Level of Education for which Award is Granted:** Undergraduate **Number Awarded:** Varies each year. **Funds Available:** Students eligible for this benefit are entitled to attend any unit of the Montana University System or any community college in the state without payment of tuition or registration fees. **Duration:** 1 year; may be renewed for up to 3 additional years if the recipient maintains full-time enrollment and a GPA of 3.4 or higher.

Eligibility Requirements: This program is open to residents of Montana who are graduating from high school and planning to attend a branch of the Montana University System or a community college in the state. Applicants must have been enrolled in an accredited high school for at least 2 of the 3 years prior to graduation, meet the college preparatory requirements, rank in the top quarter of their class, and have a GPA of 3.5 or higher. **Additional Information:** The scholarship must be utilized within 9 months after high school graduation.

1103 ■ MONTANA GUARANTEED STUDENT LOAN PROGRAM

2500 Broadway
P.O. Box 203101
Helena, MT 59620-3101
Tel: (406)444-0638
Free: 800-537-7508
Fax: (406)444-1869
E-mail: scholar@mgslp.state.mt.us
Web Site: http://www.mgslp.state.mt.us
To provide financial assistance for undergraduate education to the children of Montana veterans who died in the line of duty or as a result of service-connected disabilities.

Title of Award: Montana War Orphans Fee Waiver **Area, Field, or Subject:** General studies/Field of study not specified **Level of Education for which Award is Granted:** Undergraduate **Number Awarded:** Varies each year. **Funds Available:** Students eligible for this benefit are entitled to attend any unit of the Montana University System without payment of undergraduate registration or incidental fees. **Duration:** Undergraduate students are eligible for continued fee waiver as long as they maintain reasonable academic progress as full-time students.

Eligibility Requirements: This program is open to children of members of the U.S. armed forces who served on active duty during World War II, the Korean Conflict, or the Vietnam Conflict; were legal residents of Montana at the time of entry into service; and were killed in action or died as a result of injury, disease, or other disability while in the service. Applicants must be no older than 25 years of age. Financial need is considered in the selection process.

1104 ■ MONTANA GUARANTEED STUDENT LOAN PROGRAM

2500 Broadway
P.O. Box 203101
Helena, MT 59620-3101
Tel: (406)444-0638
Free: 800-537-7508
Fax: (406)444-1869
E-mail: scholar@mgslp.state.mt.us
Web Site: http://www.mgslp.state.mt.us
To provide financial assistance for college to dependents of deceased fire fighters or peace officers in Montana.

Title of Award: Surviving Dependents of Montana Fire Fighters/Peace Officers Waiver **Area, Field, or Subject:** General studies/Field of study not specified **Level of Education for which Award is Granted:** Undergraduate **Number Awarded:** Varies each year. **Funds Available:** Students eligible for this benefit are entitled to attend any unit of the Montana University System without payment of undergraduate registration or incidental fees. **Duration:** Undergraduate students are eligible for continued fee waiver as long as they maintain reasonable academic progress as full-time students.

Eligibility Requirements: Eligible for this benefit are residents of Montana who are surviving spouses or children of Montana fire fighters or peace officers killed in the course and scope of employment. Financial need is considered. **Additional Information:** The waiver does not apply if the recipient is eligible for educational benefits from any governmental or private program that provides comparable benefits.

1105 ■ MONTANA GUARANTEED STUDENT LOAN PROGRAM

2500 Broadway
P.O. Box 203101
Helena, MT 59620-3101
Tel: (406)444-0638
Free: 800-537-7508
Fax: (406)444-1869
E-mail: scholar@mgslp.state.mt.us
Web Site: http://www.mgslp.state.mt.us
To provide financial assistance for undergraduate study to dependents of deceased National Guard members in Montana.

Title of Award: Surviving Dependents of Montana National Guard Member Waiver **Area, Field, or Subject:** General studies/Field of study not specified **Level of Education for which Award is Granted:** Undergraduate **Number Awarded:** Varies each year. **Funds Available:** Students eligible for this benefit are entitled to attend any unit of the Montana University System without payment of undergraduate registration or incidental fees. **Duration:** Undergraduate students are eligible for continued fee waiver as long as they maintain reasonable academic progress as full-time students.

Eligibility Requirements: Eligible for this benefit are residents of Montana who are surviving spouses or children of Montana National Guard members killed as a result of injury, disease, or other disability incurred in the line of duty while serving on state active duty. Financial need is considered. **Additional Information:** The waiver does not apply if the recipient is eligible for educational benefits from any governmental or private program that provides comparable benefits.

1106 ■ MONTANA STATE ELKS ASSOCIATION

c/o Ted Byers
P.O. Box 1018
Great Falls, MT 59401
Tel: (406)727-1288
Web Site: http://www.elksmt.com
To provide financial assistance to second-year students at Montana colleges and universities.

Title of Award: Sara E. Jenne Scholarship **Area, Field, or Subject:** General studies/Field of study not specified **Level of Education for which Award is Granted:** Undergraduate **Number Awarded:** 1 or more each year. **Funds Available:** A stipend is awarded (amount not specified). **Duration:** 1 year.

Eligibility Requirements: This program is open to students who have completed their first year of education at a Montana university, college, vocational school, or community college with at least a 2.0 GPA. Selection is based primarily on financial need, effort, activities, and community involvement (and less on academic achievement). **Additional Information:** This program was established in 1977.

1107 ■ MONUMENTAL RIFLE AND PISTOL CLUB, INC.

c/o Joe Schwartz, Scholarship Committee Chair
P.O. Box 494
New Windsor, MD 21776
Tel: (410)465-6360
E-mail: joe@qis.net
Web Site: http://www.monumental.org/Scholarshippressrelease.htm
To provide financial assistance for college to high school juniors and seniors in Maryland who submit an outstanding essay on citizenship.

Title of Award: Dave Ward Memorial Scholarship **Area, Field, or Subject:** General studies/Field of study not specified **Level of Education for which Award is Granted:** Undergraduate **Number Awarded:** 1 each year. **Funds Available:** The stipend is $1,000. **Duration:** 1 year.

Eligibility Requirements: This program is open to juniors and seniors at high schools in Maryland who plan to continue on to college. Selection is based primarily on an essay on "What Citizenship Means to Me." Finalists are invited to attend a meeting of the sponsoring organization to present their essay to its members. **Deadline for Receipt:** June of each year.

1108 ■ MOOSE INTERNATIONAL, INC.

Attn: R. Robert Dale Scholarship Program
155 South International Drive
Mooseheart, IL 60539
Tel: (630)966-2200
Fax: (630)859-6626
Web Site: http://www.mooseintl.org
To provide financial assistance for college to children of members of Moose International.

Title of Award: R. Robert Dale Scholarships **Area, Field, or Subject:** General studies/Field of study not specified **Level of Education for which Award is Granted:** Undergraduate **Number Awarded:** 48 each year. **Funds Available:** The stipend is $1,000. Winners may use the funds for tuition, books, and fees at an accredited college or trade school after graduation from high school. **Duration:** 1 year.

Eligibility Requirements: This program is open to high school juniors whose mother, father, or legal guardian is a member of Moose International. Applicants must have a GPA of 2.5 or higher. Recipients are selected in a random drawing from among qualifying applicants. **Deadline for Receipt:** July of each year.

1109 ■ MORONGO BAND OF MISSION INDIANS

Attn: Tribal Administration
11581 Potrero Road
Banning, CA 92220
Tel: (951)849-4697
E-mail: jdelatore@naqcom.com
Web Site: http://www.morongonation.org/scholarship.asp
To provide financial assistance for college or graduate school to California Indians.

Title of Award: Rodney T. Mathews Memorial Scholarship for California Indians **Area, Field, or Subject:** General studies/Field of study not specified **Level of Education for which Award is Granted:** Graduate, Undergraduate **Number Awarded:** 3 each year. **Funds Available:** The maximum stipend is $10,000 per year. Funds are paid directly to the recipient's school for tuition, housing, textbooks, and required fees. **Duration:** 1 year; may be renewed 1 additional year.

Eligibility Requirements: This program is open to California Indians (must provide documentation of Native identity) who have been actively involved in the Native American community. Applicants must submit documentation of financial need, an academic letter of recommendation, and a letter of recommendation from the American Indian community. They must be enrolled full time at an accredited college or university. Undergraduates must have a GPA of 2.75 or higher; graduate students must have a GPA of 3.5 or higher. Along with their application, they must submit 1) a 2-page personal statement on their academic, career, and personal goals; any extenuating circumstances they wish to have considered; how they view their Native American heritage and its importance to them; how they plan to "give back" to Native Americans after graduation; and their on-going active involvement in the Native American community both on and off campus; and 2) a 2-page essay, either on what they feel are the most critical issues facing tribal communities today and how they see themselves working in relationship to those issues, or on where they see Native people in the 21st century in terms of survival, governance, and cultural preservation, and what role they see themselves playing in that future. **Deadline for Receipt:** March of each year. **Additional Information:** Recipients are required to complete 60 hours of service with a designated California Indian community agency: California Indian Museum and Cultural Center, Indian Health Care Services, National Indian Justice Center, California Indian Legal Services, California Indian Professors Association, California Indian Culture and Awareness Conference, or California Democratic Party Native American Caucus.

1110 ■ MORRIS SCHOLARSHIP FUND

Attn: Scholarship Selection Committee
525 S.W. Fifth Street, Suite A
Des Moines, IA 50309-4501
Tel: (515)282-8192
Fax: (515)282-9117

E-mail: morris@assoc-mgmt.com

Web Site: http://www.morrisscholarship.org

To provide financial assistance for college to African American high school seniors in Iowa.

Title of Award: Fred Johnson Youth Scholarship **Area, Field, or Subject:** General studies/Field of study not specified **Level of Education for which Award is Granted:** Undergraduate **Number Awarded:** 1 or more each year. **Funds Available:** A stipend is awarded (amount not specified). **Duration:** 1 year.

Eligibility Requirements: This program is open to African American seniors graduating from high schools in Iowa. Applicants must be planning to attend a college or university. **Deadline for Receipt:** January of each year.

1111 ■ P. BUCKLEY MOSS SOCIETY

20 Stoneridge Drive, Suite 102

Waynesboro, VA 22980

Tel: (540)943-5678

Fax: (540)949-8408

E-mail: society@mosssociety.org

Web Site: http://www.mosssociety.org

To provide financial assistance for college to high school seniors with language-related learning disabilities.

Title of Award: Anne and Matt Harbison Scholarship **Area, Field, or Subject:** General studies/Field of study not specified **Level of Education for which Award is Granted:** Undergraduate **Number Awarded:** 1 each year. **Funds Available:** The stipend is $1,000. Funds are paid to the recipient's college or university. **Duration:** 1 year; may be renewed for up to 3 additional years.

Eligibility Requirements: Eligible to be nominated for this scholarship are high school seniors with language-related learning disabilities. Nominations may be submitted by society members only. The nomination packet must include verification of a language-related learning disability from a counselor or case manager, a high school transcript, 2 letters of recommendation, and 4 essays by the nominees (on themselves; their learning disability and its effect on their lives; their extracurricular, community, work, and church accomplishments; and their plans for next year). **Deadline for Receipt:** March of each year.

1112 ■ MOUNTAIN VIEW ELECTRIC ASSOCIATION, INC.

Attn: Scholarships

1655 Fifth Street

P.O. Box 1600

Limon, CO 80828

Tel: (719)775-2861

Free: 800-388-9881

Web Site: http://www.mvea.coop

To provide financial assistance to entering freshmen at colleges and universities in Colorado whose families receive electric service from the Mountain View Electric Association (MVEA).

Title of Award: E.A. "Mick" Geesen Memorial Scholarship **Area, Field, or Subject:** General studies/Field of study not specified **Level of Education for which Award is Granted:** Undergraduate **Number Awarded:** 1 each year. **Funds Available:** The stipend is $1,000. Funds are paid jointly to students and their schools. **Duration:** 1 year.

Eligibility Requirements: This program is open to students entering accredited colleges, universities, and junior or community colleges in Colorado on a full-time basis. Applicants must have a cumulative GPA of 3.5 or higher and scores on their ACT of at least 22 or combined SAT of at least 1000. Their parents or legal guardians must be currently receiving electric service from MVEA. Along with their application, they must submit a 1-page letter commenting on their goals, financial need, work experience, and any other information that would be helpful in determining their need. **Deadline for Receipt:** January of each year.

1113 ■ MR. COLLEGIATE AFRICAN AMERICAN SCHOLARSHIP PAGEANT

P.O. Box 841595

Houston, TX 77284-1595

Tel: (713)927-6947; 888-313-7431

E-mail: mrcollegiate@iwon.com

To recognize and reward, with college scholarships, outstanding African American men who participate in a pageant.

Title of Award: Mr. Collegiate African American Scholarship Program **Area, Field, or Subject:** General studies/Field of study not specified **Level of Education for which Award is Granted:** Four Year College **Number Awarded:** 3 each year. **Funds Available:** The winner receives a $2,000 scholarship and $1,500 in prizes, including a $500 wardrobe allowance. The first runner-up receives a $1,200 scholarship and $300 in prizes. The second runner-up receives a $750 scholarship and $300 in prizes. **Duration:** The pageant is held annually.

Eligibility Requirements: This competition is open to African American men between 18 and 30 years of age attending 4-year colleges and universities. Applicants must be interested in participating in a pageant where they are judged on a personal and private interview (20%), platform expression (25%), talent (35%), evening wear (10%), and on-stage interview (10%). **Deadline for Receipt:** February of each year. **Additional Information:** This program was established in 1990. The pageant is held in Houston, Texas. Contestants must pay a $495 fee.

1114 ■ RYAN MULLALY SECOND CHANCE FUND

26 Meadow Lane

Pennington, NJ 08534

Tel: (609)737-1800

E-mail: The2dChanceFund@aol.com

Web Site: http://www.ryans2dchancefund.org

To provide financial assistance for college to students who have cancer.

Title of Award: Ryan Mullaly Second Chance Scholarships **Area, Field, or Subject:** General studies/Field of study not specified **Level of Education for which Award is Granted:** Undergraduate **Number Awarded:** Up to 15 each year. **Funds Available:** The stipend is $1,000. **Duration:** 1 year; nonrenewable.

Eligibility Requirements: This program is open to U.S. citizens and permanent residents who were diagnosed with cancer or a recurrence of cancer between age 13 and graduation from high school. Applicants must have a treatment history that includes chemotherapy and/or radiation and must be able to demonstrate that their high school years were substantially impacted by treatment and/or side effects of treatment. They must be 22 years of age or younger and currently 1) working on an associate or bachelor's degree at an accredited 2-year or 4-year college or university, or 2) enrolled in an accredited postsecondary vocational or trade program that will culminate in certification. Priority is given to students still undergoing treatment, those with permanent effects from treatment, and those at the beginning of their postsecondary education. **Deadline for Receipt:** May of each year. **Additional Information:** This program was established in 2003.

1115 ■ MULTIPLE SCLEROSIS HELPING HANDS

Attn: Financial Assistance Scholarship Fund

9792 Edmonds Way, Suite 229

Edmonds, WA 98020

Tel: (425)712-1804

Fax: (425)672-1411

E-mail: info@mshelp.org

Web Site: http://www.mshelp.org

To provide financial assistance for college to residents of Washington who have multiple sclerosis.

Title of Award: Multiple Sclerosis Helping Hands Financial Assistance Scholarships **Area, Field, or Subject:** General studies/Field of study not specified **Level of Education for which Award is Granted:** Undergraduate **Number Awarded:** 1 or more each year. **Funds Available:** A stipend is awarded (amount not specified). **Duration:** 1 year.

Eligibility Requirements: This program is open to Washington residents who have a medical diagnosis of multiple sclerosis. Applicants must be able to document financial need and a record of rejection by other agencies (e.g., Medicaid, DSHS, insurance companies). **Deadline for Receipt:** Applications may be submitted at any time. **Additional Information:** This program began in 2006.

1116 ■ MUSCOGEE (CREEK) NATION OF OKLAHOMA

Attn: Higher Education Program

P.O. Box 580

Okmulgee, OK 74447

Tel: (918)756-8700

Free: 800-482-1979

E-mail: cdavis@muscogeenation-nsn.gov

Web Site: http://www.muscogeenation-nsn.gov/humandeve/
hum_higheredu/hum_highereduc.htm
To provide educational grants to aid needy Creek undergraduate
students.
Title of Award: Creek Nation Higher Education Undergraduate Grant
Program **Area, Field, or Subject:** General studies/Field of study not
specified **Level of Education for which Award is Granted:** Undergraduate **Number Awarded:** Varies each year. **Funds Available:** The amount
awarded varies, up to a maximum of $2,000 per year. The exact amount
depends upon the financial needs of the recipient. Full-time students may
use these funds to pay for tuition and fees, books and supplies, room and
board, transportation, and personal expenses (including medical and child
care). Part-time students (less than 12 credits) may use their funds for
tuition, fees, and books, not to exceed the in-state cost at a 2- or 4-year
college or university. **Duration:** 1 year; may be renewed for a maximum of
10 semesters of funding as long as the recipient enrolls in at least 15
hours per term and maintains a GPA of 2.0 or higher.
Eligibility Requirements: This program is open to Creek students of any
degree of Indian blood who are attending or planning to attend an accredited institution of higher learning. Applicants must be eligible to
receive Pell Grants. They must submit copies of their Certificate of Degree
of Indian Blood (CDIB) and tribal enrollment card. **Deadline for Receipt:**
May of each year. **Additional Information:** The Muscogee (Creek) Nation of Oklahoma administers the Higher Education Program. This
program expends funds appropriated by Congress for the education of
Indian students and administered by the Bureau of Indian Affairs.
Recipients who withdraw from school are suspended until they have
financed themselves for 1 full semester and passed 12 credit hours with a
GPA of 2.0 or higher.

1117 ■ MUSCOGEE (CREEK) NATION OF OKLAHOMA
Attn: Higher Education Program
P.O. Box 580
Okmulgee, OK 74447
Tel: (918)756-8700
Free: 800-482-1979
E-mail: cdavis@muscogeenation-nsn.gov
Web Site: http://www.muscogeenation-nsn.gov/humandeve/
hum_higeredu/hum_highereduc.htm
To provide financial assistance to enrolled citizens of the Muscogee
(Creek) Nation attending an accredited college or university.
Title of Award: Creek Nation Tribal Funds Grant Program **Area, Field, or
Subject:** General studies/Field of study not specified **Level of Education
for which Award is Granted:** Undergraduate **Number Awarded:** Varies
each year. **Funds Available:** The maximum stipend is $500 per semester
for full-time students (12 credit hours or more per semester) or $250 per
semester for part-time students (less than 12 hours). Support may not
exceed $1,000 per year. The award may be used to supplement other
financial aid sources. **Duration:** 1 year; may be renewed up to 3 additional years (as long as the recipient maintains at least a 2.5 GPA).
Eligibility Requirements: This program is open to enrolled citizens of the
Muscogee (Creek) Nation (with no minimum blood quantum required) who
are enrolled or planning to enroll in an accredited college or university.
Applicants must submit copies of their Certificate of Degree of Indian
Blood (CDIB) and tribal enrollment card. Financial need is not required.
Deadline for Receipt: May of each year. **Additional Information:**
Recipients who withdraw from school or earn less than a 1.5 GPA are
suspended until they have financed themselves for 1 full semester and
passed 12 credit hours with a GPA of 2.0 or higher.

1118 ■ MUSCOGEE (CREEK) NATION OF OKLAHOMA
Attn: Higher Education Program
P.O. Box 580
Okmulgee, OK 74447
Tel: (918)756-8700
Free: 800-482-1979
E-mail: cdavis@muscogeenation-nsn.gov
Web Site: http://www.muscogeenation-nsn.gov/humandeve/
hum_higeredu/hum_highereduc.htm
To provide financial assistance to enrolled citizens of the Muscogee
(Creek) Nation who have an excellent academic record and are attending
an accredited college or university.
Title of Award: Creek Nation Tribal Incentive Grant Program **Area, Field,
or Subject:** General studies/Field of study not specified **Level of Educa-

tion for which Award is Granted:** Undergraduate **Number Awarded:**
Varies each year. **Funds Available:** The maximum award is $1,000 per
academic year. **Duration:** 1 semester; may be renewed for up to 9 additional semesters.
Eligibility Requirements: This program is open to enrolled citizens of the
Muscogee (Creek) Nation (with no minimum blood quantum required) who
are enrolled or planning to enroll in an accredited college or university.
Applicants must have a GPA of 3.0 or higher. They must submit copies of
their Certificate of Degree of Indian Blood (CDIB) and tribal enrollment
card. **Deadline for Receipt:** June of each year. **Additional Information:**
Recipients who withdraw from school are suspended until they have
financed themselves for 1 full semester and passed 12 credit hours with
an acceptable GPA.

1119 ■ NANA REGIONAL CORPORATION
Attn: Robert Aqqaluk Newlin, Sr. Memorial Trust
P.O. Box 509
Kotzebue, AK 99752
Tel: (907)442-1607; (866)442-1607
Fax: (907)442-2289
E-mail: toni.bergan@nana.com
Web Site: http://www.aqqaluktrust.com/scholar.html
To provide financial assistance for college to Alaska Natives who are as-
sociated with the Northwest Alaska Native Association (NANA) Regional
Corporation.
Title of Award: NANA Regional Corporation Scholarship Fund **Area,
Field, or Subject:** General studies/Field of study not specified **Level of
Education for which Award is Granted:** Undergraduate **Number
Awarded:** Varies each year, depending upon the availability of funds and
qualified applicants. **Funds Available:** Stipends are $750 per semester
for full-time students or $350 per semester for part-time students. Funds
must be used for tuition, fees, books, course-related supplies, room,
board, and similar expenses. **Duration:** 1 semester; recipients may reapply by providing a letter updating their educational and career goals,
explaining how they are moving toward their goals, and reporting how the
previous funds were spend.
Eligibility Requirements: This program is open to NANA shareholders,
descendants of NANA shareholders, and dependents of NANA shareholders and their descendants. Applicants must have a GED or high school
diploma with a cumulative GPA of 2.0 or higher and be enrolled or accepted for enrollment at an accredited or authorized college, university, or
vocational technical skills program for which a certificate of completion is
issued at the conclusion of studies. Along with their application, they must
submit a statement that explains how they intend to use their education to
enhance Inupiaq values and culture, summarizes their accomplishments,
and describes their educational and career goals. **Deadline for Receipt:**
College and university students must apply by July of each year for fall
semester, January of each year for spring semester, or May of each year
for summer school. Vocational/technical students must apply at least 30
days before the start of training.

1120 ■ ELIZABETH NASH FOUNDATION
P.O. Box 1260
Los Gatos, CA 95031-1260
E-mail: scholarships@elizabethnashfoundation.org
Web Site: http://www.elizabethnashfoundation.org/
scholarshipprogram.html
To provide financial assistance for college or graduate school to individu-
als with cystic fibrosis (CF).
Title of Award: Elizabeth Nash Foundation Scholarship Program **Area,
Field, or Subject:** General studies/Field of study not specified **Level of
Education for which Award is Granted:** Graduate, Undergraduate
Number Awarded: 1 or more each year. **Funds Available:** Stipends
range from $500 to $2,000. Funds are paid directly to the academic
institution to be applied to tuition and fees. **Duration:** 1 year; recipients
may reapply.
Eligibility Requirements: This program is open to undergraduate and
graduate students who have CF. Applicants must be able to demonstrate
clear academic goals and a commitment to participate in activities outside
the class room. Selection is based on academic record, character,
demonstrated leadership, service to the community, and financial need.
Deadline for Receipt: September of each year. **Additional Information:**
This program was established in 2005. Recipients must agree to support

the program by speaking at a local event or writing an article for publication by the foundation.

1121 ■ NATIONAL 4TH INFANTRY (IVY) DIVISION ASSOCIATION
c/o Alexander Cooker, Scholarship Administrator
78 North Dupont Road
Carneys Point, NJ 08069
Tel: (609)299-4406
E-mail: alexcooker@aol.com
Web Site: http://www.4thinfantry.org
To provide financial assistance for college to members of the National 4th Infantry (IVY) Division Association and their families.
Title of Award: National 4th Infantry (IVY) Division Association Scholarship **Area, Field, or Subject:** General studies/Field of study not specified **Level of Education for which Award is Granted:** Undergraduate **Number Awarded:** 3 each year. **Funds Available:** The stipend is $1,000. **Duration:** 1 year; may be renewed.
Eligibility Requirements: This program is open to association members in good standing and all blood relatives of active association members in good standing. Recipients are chosen by lottery. **Additional Information:** The trust fund from which these scholarships are awarded was created by the officers and enlisted men of the 4th Infantry Division as a living memorial to the men of the division who died in Vietnam. Originally, it was only open to children of members of the division who died in the line of duty while serving in Vietnam between August 1, 1966 and December 31, 1977. When all those eligible had completed college, it adopted its current requirements.

1122 ■ NATIONAL ALLIANCE FOR SCHOLASTIC ACHIEVEMENT
Attn: Selection Committee
10820 Beverly Boulevard A5
PMB 600
Whittier, CA 90601-2576
Web Site: http://www.eee.org/bus/nasa
To provide financial assistance for college to high school seniors who demonstrate outstanding academic achievement.
Title of Award: National Alliance for Scholastic Achievement Scholarships **Area, Field, or Subject:** General studies/Field of study not specified **Level of Education for which Award is Granted:** Four Year College **Number Awarded:** 5 each year. **Funds Available:** The top award is $3,750 per year, second award is $2,500 per year, third award is $1,250 per year, fourth award is $750 per year, and fifth award is $500 per year. Funds are paid directly to the recipient's institution of choice. **Duration:** 1 year; may be renewed up to 3 additional years.
Eligibility Requirements: This program is open to high school seniors who have been accepted or anticipate being accepted at a 4-year academic institution. Applicants must have a GPA of 2.75 or higher and have taken the SAT or ACT test. Along with their application, they must submit a 500-word essay on an experience during their high school career that taught them something of great importance and how that will impact or shape their future learning. Financial need, race, and gender are not considered in the selection process. Generally, GPAs are 3.9 to 4.0 for the top award, 3.7 to 4.0 for the second award, 3.5 to 3.9 for third, 2.8 to 3.7 for fourth, and 2.75 to 3.5 for fifth. U.S. citizenship or permanent resident status is required. **Deadline for Receipt:** March of each year. **Additional Information:** Requests for an application must be accompanied by a self-addressed stamped envelope and an application fee of $15.

1123 ■ NATIONAL AMATEUR BASEBALL FEDERATION, INC.
Attn: Executive Director
P.O. Box 705
Bowie, MD 20718
Tel: (301)464-5460
Fax: (301)352-0214
E-mail: NABF1914@aol.com
Web Site: http://www.nabf.com/membership/scholarships.htm
To provide financial assistance for college to students who have participated in National Amateur Baseball Federation (NABF) events.
Title of Award: National Amateur Baseball Federation Scholarship Program **Area, Field, or Subject:** General studies/Field of study not specified **Level of Education for which Award is Granted:** Undergraduate **Number Awarded:** Varies each year; recently, 10 of these scholarships were awarded. **Funds Available:** A stipend is awarded (amount not specified). **Duration:** 1 year.

Eligibility Requirements: To be eligible for this support, students must be entering or enrolled at an accredited college or university and have participated in NABF events. Applicants must be sponsored by an NABF-member association. Selection is based on academic record and financial need. **Additional Information:** The National Amateur Baseball Federation was established in 1914 and is the oldest continually operated national baseball organization in the country. The scholarship program was established in 1984 and designated the Ronald and Irene McMinn Scholarship Fund. In 2000, the Germaine and Edward "Red" Carrington Scholarship Fund was added.

1124 ■ NATIONAL AMPUTEE GOLF ASSOCIATION
Attn: Scholarship Grant Program
11 Walnut Hill Road
Amherst, NH 03031
Tel: (603)672-6444
Free: 800-633-NAGA
Fax: (603)672-2987
E-mail: info@nagagolf.org
Web Site: http://www.nagagolf.org/scholarship1.shtml
To provide financial assistance for college to members of the National Amputee Golf Association and their dependents.
Title of Award: National Amputee Golf Association Scholarship **Area, Field, or Subject:** General studies/Field of study not specified **Level of Education for which Award is Granted:** Undergraduate **Number Awarded:** 1 or more each year. **Funds Available:** The stipend for a 4-year bachelor's degree program is $2,000 per year. The stipend for a 2-year technical or associate degree is $1,000 per year. **Duration:** Up to 4 years, provided the recipient maintains at least half-time enrollment and a GPA of 2.0 or higher and continues to demonstrate financial need.
Eligibility Requirements: This program is open to amputee members in good standing in the association and their dependents. Applicants must submit information on their scholastic background (GPA in high school and college, courses of study); type of amputation and cause (if applicable), a cover letter describing their plans for the future; and documentation of financial need. They need not be competitive golfers. Selection is based on academic record, financial need, involvement in extracurricular or community activities, and area of study. **Deadline for Receipt:** July of each year.

1125 ■ NATIONAL ASSOCIATION OF ASIAN AMERICAN PROFESSIONALS-BOSTON CHAPTER
Attn: Scholarship Committee
P.O. Box 381435
Cambridge, MA 02238-1435
Tel: (781)937-7072
E-mail: naaap@naaapboston.org
Web Site: http://www.naaapboston.org/pages/_cmt/scholarship.jsp
To provide financial assistance for college to Asian American high school seniors from Massachusetts.
Title of Award: Boston Chapter Significant Achievement and Future Leadership Awards **Area, Field, or Subject:** General studies/Field of study not specified **Level of Education for which Award is Granted:** Undergraduate **Number Awarded:** 1 or more each year. **Funds Available:** The stipend is at least $1,000. **Duration:** 1 year.
Eligibility Requirements: This program is open to seniors of Asian heritage who attend high school in Massachusetts. Applicants must submit official high school transcripts that include standardized test scores and 2 letters of recommendation. They must also submit essays of 500 words each on themselves and on how they think being an Asian American has shaped their perspective and will shape their contributions to society in the future. Selection is based on the essays, academic achievement, community service, and extracurricular activities. Personal interviews are required. U.S. citizenship or permanent resident status is required. **Deadline for Receipt:** February of each year. **Additional Information:** Information is also available from May Yu, Scholarship co-chair, E-mail: myu@mba2006.hbs.edu.

1126 ■ NATIONAL ASSOCIATION OF COLORED WOMEN'S CLUBS
5808 16th Street, N.W.
Washington, DC 20011-2898
Tel: (202)726-2044
Fax: (202)726-0023

To provide financial assistance to Black American college students who are interested in pursuing postsecondary education.

Title of Award: Hallie Q. Brown Scholarship Fund **Area, Field, or Subject:** General studies/Field of study not specified **Level of Education for which Award is Granted:** Undergraduate **Number Awarded:** Approximately 20 every other year. **Funds Available:** The amount awarded varies, according to financial need, but does not exceed $1,000 per year. **Duration:** The award is presented biennially, in even-numbered years. **Eligibility Requirements:** Black students who are U.S. citizens and can demonstrate financial need are eligible if they have completed at least 1 semester of postsecondary education with a minimum GPA of 2.0. Candidates must be nominated by a member of the National Association of Colored Women's Clubs; students may not apply directly. **Deadline for Receipt:** April of even-numbered years. **Additional Information:** In the past, recipients were to attend 1 of the United Negro College Fund universities or colleges; now, recipients may enroll in any accredited postsecondary institution of their choice.

1127 ■ NATIONAL ASSOCIATION FOR THE EDUCATION OF HOMELESS CHILDREN AND YOUTH

Attn: LeTendre Education Fund
4701 Connecticut Avenue, N.W., Suite 402
Washington, DC 20008
Tel: (202)364-7392
Fax: (202)318-7523
E-mail: bduffield@naehcy.org
Web Site: http://www.naehcy.org/about_letendre.html

To provide financial assistance for college to high school students and recent graduates who are currently or formerly homeless.

Title of Award: LeTendre Education Fund Scholarships **Area, Field, or Subject:** General studies/Field of study not specified **Level of Education for which Award is Granted:** Undergraduate **Number Awarded:** At least 2 each year. **Funds Available:** The stipend is $1,000. Funds must be used for tuition, application fees, books, preparation courses, visits to prospective colleges, or other educationally-related expenses. **Duration:** 1 year; nonrenewable.

Eligibility Requirements: This program is open to high school juniors, seniors, and recent graduates/GED recipients (under 20 years of age) who are homeless or who have been homeless during their school attendance. This includes students who live in shelters, cars, campgrounds, or other places "not meant for human habitation." Also eligible are students who are living with friends or relatives temporarily because they lack permanent housing. Applicants must be high school seniors, students enrolled in GED or other alternative education programs, or students who recently obtained their diploma or GED certificate. They must submit an essay of at least 500 words about the impact of homelessness on their lives and their desire to attend college. Selection is based on demonstrated commitment to education during the experience of homelessness, academic achievement, discussion of how the scholarship would be used to help advance the desire to attend college, statement of goals, use of language, and organization of essay. **Deadline for Receipt:** September of each year. **Additional Information:** This fund was established in 1998 by the National Coalition for the Homeless.

1128 ■ NATIONAL ASSOCIATION OF MASTER APPRAISERS

303 West Cypress Street
P.O. Box 12617
San Antonio, TX 78212-0617
800-229-NAMA
Fax: (210)225-8450
Web Site: http://www.masterappraisers.org

To provide financial assistance to students who want to prepare for a career in real estate appraising.

Title of Award: NAMA Scholarship Program **Area, Field, or Subject:** Real estate **Level of Education for which Award is Granted:** Professional, Undergraduate **Number Awarded:** Varies each year. **Funds Available:** Scholarship awards pay for tuition and books for courses approved by the sponsor. **Duration:** 1 year.

Eligibility Requirements: This program is open to high school seniors and current undergraduates who either 1) are nominated by a state chapter of the National Association of Master Appraisers (NAMA); or 2) live in a state where there is no NAMA state chapter and apply directly to the national office. Applicants must be able to demonstrate an interest in the profession of appraising through an essay explaining their career ambitions, completion of real estate educational programs, and/or work experience. They must have a GPA of 2.5 or higher and be able to document financial need. If they have not attended school in the last 5 years, work history may be used to qualify the applicant (rather than academic record). Preference is given to applicants with at least 2 years of work experience related to real estate. **Deadline for Receipt:** July of each year.

1129 ■ NATIONAL ASSOCIATION OF RAILWAY BUSINESS WOMEN

c/o Lynn Sisto, National Publication Chair
78 West Street
Mechanicville, NY 12118
E-mail: narbwinfo@narbw.org
Web Site: http://www.narbw.org

To provide financial assistance for college to members of the National Association of Railway Business Women (NARBW) and their families.

Title of Award: National Association of Railway Business Women Scholarships **Area, Field, or Subject:** General studies/Field of study not specified **Level of Education for which Award is Granted:** Professional, Undergraduate **Number Awarded:** Varies each year. Recently, 9 of these scholarships were awarded: 2 at $1,500 and 7 at $1,000. **Funds Available:** Stipends are $1,500 or $1,000. **Duration:** 1 year; recipients may reapply.

Eligibility Requirements: This program is open to NARBW members, their dependents, and other family members (including grandchildren, nieces, and nephews). Applicants may be high school seniors or currently-enrolled college students. Selection is based on scholastic ability (20 points), ambition and potential (45 points), and financial need (35 points). **Additional Information:** This organization was formed in 1941 and today has more than 900 members in 26 chapters nationwide. The scholarship program was established in 1977. The highest scoring applicant receives the Kathryn Whelan Memorial Scholarship.

1130 ■ NATIONAL ASSOCIATION FOR THE SELF-EMPLOYED

P.O. Box 612067
DFW Airport
Dallas, TX 75261-2067
800-232-NASE
Fax: 800-551-4446
Web Site: http://www.nase.org

To provide financial assistance to high school seniors interested in studying entrepreneurship in college.

Title of Award: Future Entrepreneur of the Year Award **Area, Field, or Subject:** Business administration **Level of Education for which Award is Granted:** Undergraduate **Number Awarded:** 1 each year. **Funds Available:** The stipend is $12,000 for the first year and $4,000 for each subsequent year. **Duration:** 1 year; may be renewed up to 3 additional years.

Eligibility Requirements: This program is open to high school seniors who demonstrate leadership, academic excellence, ingenuity, and entrepreneurial spirit. Applicants must be interested in a college program that stresses the philosophy of entrepreneurship rather than a specific field of study. **Deadline for Receipt:** April of each year.

1131 ■ NATIONAL ASSOCIATION FOR THE SELF-EMPLOYED

P.O. Box 612067
DFW Airport
Dallas, TX 75261-2067
800-232-NASE
Fax: 800-551-4446
Web Site: http://www.nase.org

To provide financial assistance for college to dependents of members of the National Association for the Self-Employed (NASE).

Title of Award: NASE Scholarship Program **Area, Field, or Subject:** General studies/Field of study not specified **Level of Education for which Award is Granted:** Undergraduate **Number Awarded:** 22 each year. **Funds Available:** The stipend is $4,000. **Duration:** 1 year.

Eligibility Requirements: This program is open to dependents of members of NASE who are between 16 and 24 years of age. Applicants must be interested in working on an undergraduate degree at an accredited college or university. Selection is based on leadership abilities, academic performance, school and community participation, business experience, career and educational background, recommendations from teachers, and financial need. **Deadline for Receipt:** May of each year. **Additional Information:** This program was established in 1988 so NASE could provide children of the self-employed and micro-business owners with scholarship opportunities similar to those for students whose parents work in large corporations.

1132 ■ NATIONAL ASSOCIATION OF VOCATIONAL EDUCATION SPECIAL NEEDS PERSONNEL
c/o Marjorie Eckman, Awards Chair
719 Gulf Lab Road
Cheswick, PA 15024
Tel: (412)323-3970
E-mail: ME50@aol.com
Web Site: http://www.specialpopulations.org
To provide financial assistance to vocational/technical students who are members of a special population.
Title of Award: NAVESNP/Piney Mountain Press Student Award **Area, Field, or Subject:** General studies/Field of study not specified **Level of Education for which Award is Granted:** Vocational/Occupational **Number Awarded:** 1 each year. **Funds Available:** The stipend is $1,000. **Duration:** 1 year.
Eligibility Requirements: This program is open to vocational/technical students who are members of a special population, defined to include those who are academically or economically disadvantaged, limited English proficient, nontraditional, disabled, pregnant teenagers, single/teen parents, or foster children. Applicants must submit brief essays on the vocational program they plan to study or are currently studying, why they chose that vocational program, their professional and career goals, the challenges they have had to overcome to reach their educational goal, what they did to overcome those challenges successfully, how any special services they have received helped them, and how this award will help them in their vocational program. Selection is based on their choice of a realistic career goal, financial need, unusual circumstances, and letters of reference. **Deadline for Receipt:** October of each year. **Additional Information:** Piney Mountain Press supports half the stipend.

1133 ■ NATIONAL ASSOCIATION OF WOMEN IN CONSTRUCTION
Attn: NAWIC Founders' Scholarship Foundation
327 South Adams
Fort Worth, TX 76104-1081
Tel: (817)877-5551
Free: 800-552-3506
Fax: (817)877-0324
E-mail: nawic@nawic.org
Web Site: http://www.nawic.org/nfsf.htm
To provide financial assistance to students pursuing training in a construction-related crafts program.
Title of Award: Construction Trades Scholarship Competition **Area, Field, or Subject:** Construction **Level of Education for which Award is Granted:** Vocational/Occupational **Number Awarded:** Varies; a total of $25,000 is available in scholarships each year. **Funds Available:** Stipends range from $1,000 to $2,000 per year. **Duration:** 1 year; may be renewed if the recipient provide evidence of continued need, continued interest in construction, and continued enrollment and good standing in a construction-related field.
Eligibility Requirements: This program is open to students who are currently enrolled or enrolling in a construction-related craft training program that is approved by the Bureau of Apprenticeship Training or their home state's postsecondary education commission. Applicants must be obtaining training in a construction-related craft or trade at an institution in the United States or Canada. Along with their application, they must submit brief essays on 1) their ultimate goal in the construction industry; 2) their most important extracurricular activity, their most important contribution to it, and what their participation has meant to them as an individual; and 3) why they are interested in a construction industry career and what event or series of events has led them to this decision. Selection is based on the applicant's interest in construction, extracurricular activities, employment experience, and financial need. Semifinalists may be interviewed. **Deadline for Receipt:** March of each year. **Additional Information:** Information is also available from Marcia Rackley, NAWIC Founders' Scholarship Foundation Administrator, P.O. Box 410079, Kansas City, MO 64141, E-mail: mrackley@capitalelectric.com.

1134 ■ NATIONAL ATHLETIC TRAINERS' ASSOCIATION
Attn: Research and Education Foundation
2952 Stemmons Freeway, Suite 200
Dallas, TX 75247-6103
Tel: (214)637-6282
Free: 800-TRY-NATA
Fax: (214)637-2206
E-mail: barbaran@nata.org
Web Site: http://www.natafoundation.org/scholarship.html
To provide financial aid to undergraduate student members of the National Athletic Trainers' Association (NATA).
Title of Award: NATA Undergraduate Scholarships **Area, Field, or Subject:** Athletics **Level of Education for which Award is Granted:** Four Year College **Number Awarded:** Varies each year; recently, 30 of these scholarships were awarded. **Funds Available:** The stipend is $2,000 per year. **Duration:** 1 year.
Eligibility Requirements: This program is open to members of the association who are sponsored by an NATA certified athletic trainer, have a GPA of 3.2 or higher, and intend to pursue athletic training as a profession. Applicants must apply during their junior year or immediately prior to their final undergraduate year. They must submit a statement on their athletic training background, experience, philosophy, and goals. Selection is based on that essay; participation in their school's athletic training program, academic major, institution, intercollegiate athletics, and American higher education; and participation in campus activities other than academic and athletic training. Financial need is not considered. **Deadline for Receipt:** February of each year.

1135 ■ NATIONAL CENTER FOR AMERICAN INDIAN ENTERPRISE DEVELOPMENT
Attn: Scholarship Committee
953 East Juanita Avenue
Mesa, AZ 85204
Tel: (480)545-1298
Fax: (480)545-4208
E-mail: events@ncaied.org
Web Site: http://www.ncaied.org/fundraising
To provide financial assistance to American Indian upper-division and graduate students working on a business degree.
Title of Award: American Indian Fellowship in Business Scholarship **Area, Field, or Subject:** Business administration **Level of Education for which Award is Granted:** Four Year College, Graduate **Number Awarded:** Up to 5 each year. **Funds Available:** A stipend is awarded (amount not specified). **Duration:** 1 year.
Eligibility Requirements: This program is open to American Indians who are currently enrolled full time in college at the upper-division or graduate school level and working on a business degree. Applicants must submit a letter on their reasons for pursuing higher education and their plans following completing of their degree. Selection is based on grades (30%), an essay on their community involvement (30%), an essay on personal challenges they have faced (25%), an essay on their paid or volunteer business experience (10%), and the quality of those essays (10%). **Deadline for Receipt:** August of each year.

1136 ■ NATIONAL CENTER FOR LEARNING DISABILITIES
Attn: Scholarship
381 Park Avenue South, Suite 1401
New York, NY 10016-8806
Tel: (212)545-7510
Fax: (212)545-9665
E-mail: AFScholarship@ncld.org
Web Site: http://www.ld.org/awards/afscholarinfo.cfm
To provide financial assistance for college to high school seniors with learning disabilities.
Title of Award: Anne Ford Scholarship **Area, Field, or Subject:** General studies/Field of study not specified **Level of Education for which Award is Granted:** Undergraduate **Number Awarded:** 1 each year. **Funds Available:** The stipend is $2,500 per year. **Duration:** 4 years, provided the recipients submit annual reports (written or in video format) detailing their progress in school and describing their insights about their personal growth.
Eligibility Requirements: This program is open to high school seniors with learning disabilities who plan to work on a university degree. Ap-

plicants must have a GPA of 3.0 or higher and be able to demonstrate financial need. Along with their application, they must submit an essay (750 to 1,000 words in length) describing their frustrations and triumphs in dealing with their specific learning disability; their essay should also include the characteristics they possess that make them an ideal candidate for this scholarship and should make specific mention of how they believe a college education will enhance their lives. If they prefer, they may submit a video or audio tape (up to 15 minutes in length) with accompanying script or outline that presents the same information as the essay. Other required submissions include high school transcripts, 3 letters of recommendation, a financial statement, standardized test (SAT, ACT) scores, and current documentation of a learning disability that includes evaluation reports, I.E.P., and/or 504 plan. U.S. citizenship is required. **Deadline for Receipt:** December of each year. **Additional Information:** This program was established in 2002.

1137 ■ NATIONAL CHIEF PETTY OFFICERS' ASSOCIATION

c/o Marjorie Hays, Treasurer
1014 Ronald Drive
Corpus Christi, TX 78412-3548
Web Site: http://www.goatlocker.org/ncpoa/scholarship.htm
To provide financial assistance for college to descendants of members of the National Chief Petty Officers' Association (NCPOA).
Title of Award: National Chief Petty Officers' Association Scholarships **Area, Field, or Subject:** General studies/Field of study not specified **Level of Education for which Award is Granted:** Undergraduate **Number Awarded:** 2 each year. **Funds Available:** The stipend is $1,000. **Duration:** 1 year.
Eligibility Requirements: This program is open to children and grandchildren of members of the NCPOA. Applicants must be attending or planning to attend an accredited college or university. **Additional Information:** Membership in the NCPOA is limited to men and women who served as Chief Petty Officers in the U.S. Navy, U.S. Coast Guard, or their Reserve components for at least 30 days.

1138 ■ NATIONAL CONFERENCE OF CPA PRACTITIONERS, INC.

Attn: Scholarship Committee
50 Jericho Turnpike, Suite 106
Jericho, NY 11753
Tel: (516)333-8282; 888-488-5400
Fax: (516)333-4099
E-mail: office@nccpap.org
Web Site: http://www.nccpap.org
To provide financial assistance to high school seniors planning to attend college to prepare for a career as a certified public accountant (C.P.A.).
Title of Award: NCCPAP Scholarships for Graduating High School Seniors **Area, Field, or Subject:** Accounting **Level of Education for which Award is Granted:** Undergraduate **Number Awarded:** Varies each year; recently, 16 of these scholarships were awarded. **Funds Available:** The stipend is $1,000. **Duration:** 1 year.
Eligibility Requirements: This program is open to seniors graduating from high school with a GPA of 3.3 or higher. Applicants must be planning to attend a 2-year or 4-year college or university as a full-time student to prepare for a career as a C.P.A. Along with their application, they must submit a 200-word essay that explains why they desire to prepare for a career as a C.P.A. Financial need is not considered in the selection process. **Deadline for Receipt:** April of each year. **Additional Information:** This program, established in 2003, is offered jointly by the National Conference for CPA Practitioners (NCCPAP) and the American Institute of Certified Public Accountants (AICPA).

1139 ■ NATIONAL COUNCIL OF JEWISH WOMEN-NEW YORK SECTION

820 Second Avenue
New York, NY 10017-4504
Tel: (212)687-5030
Fax: (212)687-5032
E-mail: info@ncjwny.org
Web Site: http://www.ncjwny.org/services_scholarships.htm
To provide financial assistance for college to physically challenged residents of New York City, New Jersey, and Connecticut.
Title of Award: Jackson-Stricks Scholarship Fund **Area, Field, or Subject:** General studies/Field of study not specified **Level of Education for which Award is Granted:** Undergraduate **Number Awarded:** 1 or

more each year. **Funds Available:** A stipend is awarded (amount not specified). **Duration:** 1 year.
Eligibility Requirements: This program is open to residents of Connecticut, New Jersey, and New York City who are physically challenged. Applicants must be interested in engaging in academic study or vocational training that leads to independent living. Along with their application, they must submit a short essay on why they are applying for this scholarship and how it relates to their educational and life goals. **Deadline for Receipt:** April of each year.

1140 ■ NATIONAL DEFENSE TRANSPORTATION ASSOCIATION

Attn: Forum and Professional Development Committee
50 South Pickett Street, Suite 220
Alexandria, VA 22304-7296
Tel: (703)751-5011
Fax: (703)823-8761
E-mail: info@ndtahq.com
Web Site: http://www.ndtahq.com/scholarships.htm
To provide financial assistance to college students who are members or dependents of members of the National Defense Transportation Association (NDTA) and are majoring in transportation.
Title of Award: NDTA Academic Scholarship Program A **Area, Field, or Subject:** Logistics; Transportation **Level of Education for which Award is Granted:** Undergraduate **Number Awarded:** 1 or more each year. **Funds Available:** A stipend is awarded (amount not specified). **Duration:** 1 year; may be renewed.
Eligibility Requirements: This program is open to NDTA members and dependents of members who have satisfactorily completed 45 semester hours of work at a regionally accredited college or university. Applicants must be majoring in transportation, physical distribution, logistics, or a combination of those. They must 1) provide college transcripts; 2) attach a listing of academic and other honors and awards received, extracurricular activities, and work experiences; 3) identify the courses in transportation, physical distribution, or logistics that they plan to incorporate into their degree program; and 4) submit a 300- to 500-word statement outlining their career goals and methods of attaining those goals, indicating why they should be awarded the scholarship. Financial need is not considered in the selection process. **Deadline for Receipt:** April of each year.

1141 ■ NATIONAL DEFENSE TRANSPORTATION ASSOCIATION

Attn: Forum and Professional Development Committee
50 South Pickett Street, Suite 220
Alexandria, VA 22304-7296
Tel: (703)751-5011
Fax: (703)823-8761
E-mail: info@ndtahq.com
Web Site: http://www.ndtahq.com/scholarships.htm
To provide financial assistance to high school seniors who are members or dependents of members of the National Defense Transportation Association (NDTA) and planning to study a transportation-related field in college.
Title of Award: NDTA Academic Scholarship Program B **Area, Field, or Subject:** General studies/Field of study not specified; Logistics; Transportation **Level of Education for which Award is Granted:** Undergraduate **Number Awarded:** 1 or more each year. **Funds Available:** A stipend is awarded (amount not specified). **Duration:** 1 year; may be renewed.
Eligibility Requirements: This program is open to NDTA members and dependents of members who have satisfactorily completed 3 1/2 years of academic work at an accredited high school. Applicants may be planning to major in any field, but preference is given to those planning to work on a degree in transportation, logistics, or a related field. They must 1) provide high school transcripts, including SAT or ACT scores, 2) attach a listing of academic and other honors and awards received, extracurricular activities, and work experiences; and 3) submit a 300- to 500-word statement outlining their career goals and methods of attaining those goals, indicating why they should be awarded the scholarship. Financial need is not considered in the selection process. **Deadline for Receipt:** April of each year.

1142 ■ NATIONAL FARMERS UNION

Attn: Director of Education
11900 East Cornell Avenue
Aurora, CO 80014

Tel: (303)337-5500
Free: 800-347-1961
Fax: (303)368-1390
E-mail: jennifer.luitjens@nfu.org
Web Site: http://www.nfu.org
To provide financial assistance for college to high school seniors who are members of the National Farmers Union.

Title of Award: Hubert K. Seymour Scholarship **Area, Field, or Subject:** General studies/Field of study not specified **Level of Education for which Award is Granted:** Undergraduate **Number Awarded:** 1 each year. **Funds Available:** The stipend is $2,000. Funds may be used for tuition and books. **Duration:** 1 year.

Eligibility Requirements: This program is open to graduating high school seniors who are planning to continue their education in a 2-year or 4-year accredited college or university. Applicants must be members of the National Farmers Union. They may be planning to major in any field. Along with their application, they must submit an essay on the significance of rural values in America on their life. Selection is based on the essay, academic record, and school and community activities. A telephone interview is also required. **Deadline for Receipt:** February of each year.

1143 ■ NATIONAL FEDERATION OF THE BLIND

c/o Peggy Elliott, Scholarship Committee Chair
805 Fifth Avenue
Grinnell, IA 50112
Tel: (641)236-3366
Web Site: http://www.nfb.org/sch_intro.htm
To provide financial assistance to female blind students interested in working on an undergraduate or graduate degree.

Title of Award: Hermione Grant Calhoun Scholarships **Area, Field, or Subject:** General studies/Field of study not specified; Visual impairment **Level of Education for which Award is Granted:** Graduate, Undergraduate **Number Awarded:** 1 each year. **Funds Available:** The stipend is $3,000. **Duration:** 1 year; recipients may resubmit applications up to 2 additional years.

Eligibility Requirements: This program is open to legally blind women students who are working on or planning to work full time on an undergraduate or graduate degree. Selection is based on academic excellence, service to the community, and financial need. **Deadline for Receipt:** March of each year. **Additional Information:** Scholarships are awarded at the federation convention in July. Recipients attend the convention at federation expense; that funding is in addition to the scholarship grant.

1144 ■ NATIONAL FEDERATION OF THE BLIND

c/o Peggy Elliott, Scholarship Committee Chair
805 Fifth Avenue
Grinnell, IA 50112
Tel: (641)236-3366
Web Site: http://www.nfb.org/sch_intro.htm
To provide financial assistance to undergraduate and graduate blind students.

Title of Award: Jennica Ferguson Memorial Scholarship **Area, Field, or Subject:** General studies/Field of study not specified **Level of Education for which Award is Granted:** Graduate, Undergraduate **Number Awarded:** 1 each year. **Funds Available:** The stipend is $5,000. **Duration:** 1 year; recipients may resubmit applications up to 2 additional years.

Eligibility Requirements: This program is open to legally blind students who are working on or planning to work full time on an undergraduate or graduate degree. Selection is based on academic excellence, service to the community, and financial need. **Deadline for Receipt:** March of each year. **Additional Information:** Scholarships are awarded at the federation convention in July. Recipients attend the convention at federation expense; that funding is in addition to the scholarship grant.

1145 ■ NATIONAL FEDERATION OF THE BLIND

c/o Peggy Elliott, Scholarship Committee Chair
805 Fifth Avenue
Grinnell, IA 50112
Tel: (641)236-3366
Web Site: http://www.nfb.org/sch_intro.htm
To provide financial assistance to undergraduate and graduate blind students.

Title of Award: Kenneth Jernigan Scholarship **Area, Field, or Subject:** General studies/Field of study not specified **Level of Education for which Award is Granted:** Graduate, Undergraduate **Number Awarded:** 1 each year. **Funds Available:** The stipend is $12,000. **Duration:** 1 year; recipients may resubmit applications up to 2 additional years.

Eligibility Requirements: This program is open to legally blind students who are working on or planning to work full time on an undergraduate or graduate degree. Selection is based on academic excellence, service to the community, and financial need. **Deadline for Receipt:** March of each year. **Additional Information:** Scholarships are awarded at the federation convention in July. Recipients attend the convention at federation expense; that funding is in addition to the scholarship grant. This scholarship is given by the American Action Fund for Blind Children and Adults, a nonprofit organization that assists blind people.

1146 ■ NATIONAL FEDERATION OF THE BLIND

c/o Peggy Elliott, Scholarship Committee Chair
805 Fifth Avenue
Grinnell, IA 50112
Tel: (641)236-3366
Web Site: http://www.nfb.org/sch_intro.htm
To provide financial assistance to undergraduate and graduate blind students.

Title of Award: Kuchler-Killian Memorial Scholarship **Area, Field, or Subject:** General studies/Field of study not specified **Level of Education for which Award is Granted:** Graduate, Undergraduate **Number Awarded:** 1 each year. **Funds Available:** The stipend is $3,000. **Duration:** 1 year; recipients may resubmit applications up to 2 additional years.

Eligibility Requirements: This program is open to legally blind students who are working on or planning to work full time on an undergraduate or graduate degree. Selection is based on academic excellence, service to the community, and financial need. **Deadline for Receipt:** March of each year. **Additional Information:** Scholarships are awarded at the federation convention in July. Recipients attend the convention at federation expense; that funding is in addition to the scholarship grant.

1147 ■ NATIONAL FEDERATION OF THE BLIND

c/o Peggy Elliott, Scholarship Committee Chair
805 Fifth Avenue
Grinnell, IA 50112
Tel: (641)236-3366
Web Site: http://www.nfb.org/sch_intro.htm
To provide financial assistance to legally blind students working on an undergraduate or graduate degree.

Title of Award: Hank LeBonne Scholarship **Area, Field, or Subject:** General studies/Field of study not specified **Level of Education for which Award is Granted:** Graduate, Undergraduate **Number Awarded:** 1 each year. **Funds Available:** The stipend is $5,000. **Duration:** 1 year; recipients may resubmit applications up to 2 additional years.

Eligibility Requirements: This program is open to legally blind students who are working on or planning to work full time on an undergraduate or graduate degree. Selection is based on academic excellence, service to the community, and financial need. **Deadline for Receipt:** March of each year. **Additional Information:** Scholarships are awarded at the federation convention in July. Recipients attend the convention at federation expense; that funding is in addition to the scholarship grant.

1148 ■ NATIONAL FEDERATION OF THE BLIND

c/o Peggy Elliott, Scholarship Committee Chair
805 Fifth Avenue
Grinnell, IA 50112
Tel: (641)236-3366
Web Site: http://www.nfb.org/sch_intro.htm
To provide financial assistance for college or graduate school to blind students.

Title of Award: National Federation of the Blind Scholarships **Area, Field, or Subject:** General studies/Field of study not specified **Level of Education for which Award is Granted:** Graduate, Undergraduate **Number Awarded:** 17 each year: 2 at $7,000 and 15 at $3,000. **Funds Available:** Stipends are $7,000 or $3,000. **Duration:** 1 year; recipients may resubmit applications up to 2 additional years.

Eligibility Requirements: This program is open to legally blind students who are working on or planning to work on an undergraduate or graduate degree. In general, full-time enrollment is required, although 1 scholarship may be awarded to a part-time student who is working full time. Selection is based on academic excellence, service to the community, and financial need. **Deadline for Receipt:** March of each year. **Additional Information:** Scholarships are awarded at the federation convention in July. Recipients attend the convention at federation expense; that funding is in addition to the scholarship grant.

1149 ■ NATIONAL FEDERATION OF THE BLIND
c/o Peggy Elliott, Scholarship Committee Chair
805 Fifth Avenue
Grinnell, IA 50112
Tel: (641)236-3366
Web Site: http://www.nfb.org/sch_intro.htm
To provide financial assistance to blind undergraduate or graduate students.
Title of Award: Charles and Melva T. Owen Memorial Scholarships **Area, Field, or Subject:** General studies/Field of study not specified **Level of Education for which Award is Granted:** Graduate, Undergraduate **Number Awarded:** 2 each year: 1 at $10,000 and 1 at $3,000. **Funds Available:** Stipends are $10,000 or $3,000. **Duration:** 1 year; recipients may resubmit applications up to 2 additional years.
Eligibility Requirements: This program is open to legally blind students who are working on or planning to work full time on an undergraduate or graduate degree. Scholarships, however, will not be awarded for the study of religion or solely to further general or cultural education; the academic program should be directed towards attaining financial independence. Selection is based on academic excellence, service to the community, and financial need. **Deadline for Receipt:** March of each year. **Additional Information:** Scholarships are awarded at the federation convention in July. Recipients attend the convention at federation expense; that funding is in addition to the scholarship grant.

1150 ■ NATIONAL FEDERATION OF THE BLIND
c/o Peggy Elliott, Scholarship Committee Chair
805 Fifth Avenue
Grinnell, IA 50112
Tel: (641)236-3366
Web Site: http://www.nfb.org/sch_intro.htm
To provide financial assistance to blind undergraduate and graduate students.
Title of Award: E.U. Parker Scholarship **Area, Field, or Subject:** General studies/Field of study not specified **Level of Education for which Award is Granted:** Graduate, Undergraduate **Number Awarded:** 1 each year. **Funds Available:** The stipend is $3,000. **Duration:** 1 year; recipients may resubmit applications up to 2 additional years.
Eligibility Requirements: This program is open to legally blind students who are working on or planning to work full time on an undergraduate or graduate degree. Selection is based on academic excellence, service to the community, and financial need. **Deadline for Receipt:** March of each year. **Additional Information:** Scholarships are awarded at the federation convention in July. Recipients attend the convention at federation expense; that funding is in addition to the scholarship grant.

1151 ■ NATIONAL FEDERATION OF THE BLIND OF COLORADO
c/o Colorado Center for the Blind
2233 West Shepperd Avenue
Littleton, CO 80120-2038
Tel: (303)778-1130
Free: 800-401-4NFB
Fax: (303)778-1598
Web Site: http://www.nfbco.org/scholarships.htm
To provide financial assistance for college to visually impaired students in Colorado.
Title of Award: National Federation of the Blind of Colorado Scholarship **Area, Field, or Subject:** General studies/Field of study not specified **Level of Education for which Award is Granted:** Undergraduate **Number Awarded:** Varies each year. **Funds Available:** The stipend depends on the need of the recipient and the availability of funds. **Duration:** 1 year.
Eligibility Requirements: This program is open to legally blind residents of Colorado who are working on or planning to work on a full-time college course of study in the state. At least 1 scholarship is reserved for an ap-

plicant who is employed full time and attending or planning to attend a part-time course of study that will result in a new degree and broader opportunities in present or future work. Selection is based on academic excellence, service to the community, and financial need. **Deadline for Receipt:** August of each year. **Additional Information:** Information is also available from Kevan Worley, Chair, Scholarship Committee, 18121-C East Hampden Avenue, PMB 196, Aurora, CO 80013, (303) 306-7122, E-mail: kevanworley@blindmerchants.org.

1152 ■ NATIONAL FEDERATION OF THE BLIND OF CONNECTICUT
580 Burnside Avenue, Suite 1
East Hartford, CT 06108
Tel: (860)289-1971
E-mail: info@nfbct.org
Web Site: http://www.nfbct.org/html/schinfo.htm
To provide financial assistance to blind students pursuing a full-time college education in Connecticut.
Title of Award: C. Rodney Demarest Memorial Scholarship **Area, Field, or Subject:** General studies/Field of study not specified **Level of Education for which Award is Granted:** Undergraduate **Number Awarded:** 1 each year. **Funds Available:** The stipend is $3,000. **Duration:** 1 year.
Eligibility Requirements: Applicants must be legally blind and either residents of or full-time college students in Connecticut. Along with their application, they must submit a letter on their career goals and how the scholarship might help them achieve those. Selection is based on academic excellence, extracurricular activities, service to the community, and financial need. **Deadline for Receipt:** September of each year.

1153 ■ NATIONAL FEDERATION OF THE BLIND OF CONNECTICUT
580 Burnside Avenue, Suite 1
East Hartford, CT 06108
Tel: (860)289-1971
E-mail: info@nfbct.org
Web Site: http://www.nfbct.org/html/schinfo.htm
To provide financial assistance to blind students pursuing a full-time college education in Connecticut.
Title of Award: Mary Main Memorial Scholarship **Area, Field, or Subject:** General studies/Field of study not specified **Level of Education for which Award is Granted:** Undergraduate **Number Awarded:** 1 each year. **Funds Available:** The stipend is $2,000. **Duration:** 1 year.
Eligibility Requirements: Applicants must be legally blind and either residents of or full-time college students in Connecticut. Along with their application, they must submit a letter on their career goals and how the scholarship might help them achieve those. Selection is based on academic excellence, extracurricular activities, service to the community, and financial need. **Deadline for Receipt:** September of each year.

1154 ■ NATIONAL FEDERATION OF THE BLIND OF CONNECTICUT
580 Burnside Avenue, Suite 1
East Hartford, CT 06108
Tel: (860)289-1971
E-mail: info@nfbct.org
Web Site: http://www.nfbct.org/html/schinfo.htm
To provide financial assistance to blind students pursuing a full-time college education in Connecticut.
Title of Award: Howard E. May Memorial Scholarship **Area, Field, or Subject:** General studies/Field of study not specified **Level of Education for which Award is Granted:** Undergraduate **Number Awarded:** 1 each year. **Funds Available:** The stipend is $5,000. **Duration:** 1 year.
Eligibility Requirements: Applicants must be legally blind and either residents of or full-time college students in Connecticut. Along with their application, they must submit a letter on their career goals and how the scholarship might help them achieve those. Selection is based on academic excellence, extracurricular activities, service to the community, and financial need. **Deadline for Receipt:** September of each year.

1155 ■ NATIONAL FEDERATION OF THE BLIND OF CONNECTICUT
580 Burnside Avenue, Suite 1
East Hartford, CT 06108
Tel: (860)289-1971
E-mail: info@nfbct.org
Web Site: http://www.nfbct.org/html/schinfo.htm

To provide financial assistance to blind students pursuing a full-time college education in Connecticut.
Title of Award: Jonathan May Memorial Scholarships **Area, Field, or Subject:** General studies/Field of study not specified **Level of Education for which Award is Granted:** Undergraduate **Number Awarded:** 1 each year. **Funds Available:** The stipend is $3,000. **Duration:** 1 year.
Eligibility Requirements: Applicants must be legally blind and either residents of or full-time college students in Connecticut. Along with their application, they must submit a letter on their career goals and how the scholarship might help them achieve those. Selection is based on academic excellence, extracurricular activities, service to the community, and financial need. **Deadline for Receipt:** September of each year.

1156 ■ NATIONAL FEDERATION OF THE BLIND OF CONNECTICUT

580 Burnside Avenue, Suite 1
East Hartford, CT 06108
Tel: (860)289-1971
E-mail: info@nfbct.org
Web Site: http://www.nfbct.org/html/coccomo.htm
To provide financial assistance to blind people in Connecticut interested in a program of training, employment, independent living, or technological advancement.
Title of Award: NFBCT-Coccomo Quarterly Grants **Area, Field, or Subject:** General studies/Field of study not specified **Level of Education for which Award is Granted:** Undergraduate, Other **Number Awarded:** Varies each year. **Funds Available:** Grants depend on the nature of the request. **Duration:** These are 1-time grants. Recipients are eligible for a second grant 2 years after receiving the first grant.
Eligibility Requirements: This assistance is available to residents of Connecticut who meet the state's definition of legal blindness. Applicants must be seeking support for activities in the areas of training, employment, independent living, or technological advancement. A wide range of requests are considered, including a talking watch, a computer system, a note taker such as a Braille Note or Braille Lite, payment assistance for postsecondary part-time course work, or even a new suit for the sake of maximizing impressions on job interviews. Along with their application, they must submit a statement about themselves, their goals, and how the requested product or service will enhance their daily life and/or career aspirations. **Deadline for Receipt:** February, May, August, or November of each year.

1157 ■ NATIONAL FEDERATION OF THE BLIND OF FLORIDA

c/o Kathy Davis, President
121 Deer Lake Circle
Ormond Beach, FL 32174
Tel: (386)677-6886; 888-282-5972
E-mail: president@nfbflorida.org
Web Site: http://www.nfbflorida.org
To provide financial assistance for college to legally blind residents of Florida.
Title of Award: National Federation of the Blind of Florida Scholarships **Area, Field, or Subject:** General studies/Field of study not specified **Level of Education for which Award is Granted:** Undergraduate **Number Awarded:** Varies each year. **Funds Available:** The stipend is $1,000 per year. **Duration:** 1 year.
Eligibility Requirements: This program is open to high school seniors and college students who are legally blind, are Florida residents, are enrolled or planning to enroll in college, and have a GPA of 2.7 or higher. To apply, students must fill out an application form and send a copy of their current college transcript. Financial need is not considered in the selection process. **Deadline for Receipt:** April of each year. **Additional Information:** Winners are provided with ground transportation, registration, room, and board at the state federation's annual conference.

1158 ■ NATIONAL FEDERATION OF THE BLIND OF IDAHO

1301 South Capitol Boulevard, Suite C
Boise, ID 83706-2926
Tel: (208)343-1377
Web Site: http://www.nfbidaho.org/education/scholorship.htm
To provide financial assistance for college to blind residents of Idaho.
Title of Award: National Federation of the Blind of Idaho Scholarships **Area, Field, or Subject:** General studies/Field of study not specified **Level of Education for which Award is Granted:** Undergraduate

Number Awarded: 3 each year: 1 at $1,000 and 2 at $500. **Funds Available:** Stipends are either $1,000 or $500. **Duration:** 1 year.
Eligibility Requirements: This program is open to blind residents of Idaho who are enrolled or planning to enroll in college. Selection is based on academic achievement, community service, and financial need. **Additional Information:** Information is also available from Paula Achter, President, 9008 West Lorinda Drive, Boise, ID 83704, (208) 377-9825, E-mail: pbachter@msn.net.

1159 ■ NATIONAL FEDERATION OF THE BLIND OF KANSAS

c/o Susan L. Stanzel, President
11905 Mohawk Lane
Leawood, KS 66209-1038
Tel: (913)339-9341
E-mail: susan.stanzel@kc.rr.com
Web Site: http://www.nfbks.org/state/nfb-sklr.shtml
To provide financial assistance for college to blind residents of Kansas.
Title of Award: Kenneth Tiede Memorial Scholarships **Area, Field, or Subject:** General studies/Field of study not specified **Level of Education for which Award is Granted:** Undergraduate **Number Awarded:** Up to 3 each year. **Funds Available:** A stipend is awarded (amount not specified). **Duration:** 1 year.
Eligibility Requirements: This program is open to residents of Kansas who are legally blind. Applicants must be attending or planning to attend a technical school or a college or university. They must be able to attend the state convention of the National Federation of the Blind of Kansas. Selection is based on academic excellence, community service, and financial need. **Deadline for Receipt:** March of each year. **Additional Information:** Information is also available from Carol C. Clark, Recording Secretary, E-mail: circa1944@aol.com.

1160 ■ NATIONAL FEDERATION OF THE BLIND OF KENTUCKY

c/o Mrs. Cathy Jackson, President
210 Cambridge Drive
Louisville, KY 40214-2809
Tel: (502)366-2317
E-mail: cathyj@iglou.com
Web Site: http://www.nfbky.org/scholarship.htm
To provide financial assistance for college to blind residents of Kentucky.
Title of Award: Emerson Foulke Memorial Scholarship **Area, Field, or Subject:** General studies/Field of study not specified **Level of Education for which Award is Granted:** Undergraduate **Number Awarded:** 1 each year. **Funds Available:** The stipend is $1,000. **Duration:** 1 year.
Eligibility Requirements: This program is open to blind residents of Kentucky who are attending or planning to attend a college or university. Applicants must submit a letter, up to 2 pages in length, describing how the scholarship will help them achieve their career goals; how they are involved in their community, organizations, and other activities; any honors, awards, or special recognition they have received; and how they would like to be involved in the National Federation of the Blind of Kentucky. **Deadline for Receipt:** July of each year. **Additional Information:** Information is also available from Lora J. Felty, Scholarship Chair, E-mail: lorajf@aol.com.

1161 ■ NATIONAL FEDERATION OF THE BLIND OF KENTUCKY

c/o Mrs. Cathy Jackson, President
210 Cambridge Drive
Louisville, KY 40214-2809
Tel: (502)366-2317
E-mail: cathyj@iglou.com
Web Site: http://www.nfbky.org/scholarship.htm
To provide financial assistance for college to blind residents of Kentucky.
Title of Award: Betty Niceley Memorial Scholarship **Area, Field, or Subject:** General studies/Field of study not specified **Level of Education for which Award is Granted:** Undergraduate **Number Awarded:** 1 each year. **Funds Available:** The stipend is $1,000. **Duration:** 1 year.
Eligibility Requirements: This program is open to blind residents of Kentucky who are attending or planning to attend a college or university. Applicants must submit a letter, up to 2 pages in length, describing how the scholarship will help them achieve their career goals; how they are involved in their community, organizations, and other activities; any honors, awards, or special recognition they have received; and how they would like to be involved in the National Federation of the Blind of

Kentucky. **Deadline for Receipt:** July of each year. **Additional Information:** Information is also available from Lora J. Felty, Scholarship Chair, E-mail: lorajf@aol.com.

1162 ■ NATIONAL FEDERATION OF THE BLIND OF MARYLAND

c/o Sharon Maneki, President
9013 Nelson Way
Columbia, MD 21045-5148
Tel: (410)715-9596
Fax: (410)715-9597
E-mail: nfbmd@earthlink.net
To provide financial assistance for college to blind students from Maryland.
Title of Award: John T. McCraw Scholarship **Area, Field, or Subject:** General studies/Field of study not specified **Level of Education for which Award is Granted:** Undergraduate **Number Awarded:** 2 each year: 1 at $1,800 and 1 at $1,200. **Funds Available:** The stipend is either $1,800 or $1,200. **Duration:** 1 year; recipients may reapply.
Eligibility Requirements: This program is open to legally blind students who are residents of Maryland or pursuing postsecondary (university, 2- or 4-year college, vocational/technical school) studies in the state. Applicants must submit a completed application form, 2 letters of recommendation, a current transcript, and a statement that summarizes their honors, goals, and plans. Financial need is not considered in the selection process. **Deadline for Receipt:** May of each year. **Additional Information:** A special scholarship may be awarded to former McCraw Scholarship recipients. To apply for this special scholarship, former recipients must still meet all of the requirements for the scholarship program and submit a new application. Recipients must attend school on a full-time basis. They must attend the sponsor's annual convention; financial assistance to attend the convention may be provided if the recipient needs and requests it (this is in addition to the scholarship grant).

1163 ■ NATIONAL FEDERATION OF THE BLIND OF MINNESOTA

c/o Joyce Scanlan
1022 East 22nd Street
Minneapolis, MN 55404
Tel: (612)872-9363
E-mail: joyce.scanlan@earthlink.net
Web Site: http://members.tcq.net/nfbmn
To provide financial assistance for college to blind residents of Minnesota.
Title of Award: National Federation of the Blind of Minnesota Scholarship **Area, Field, or Subject:** General studies/Field of study not specified **Level of Education for which Award is Granted:** Undergraduate **Number Awarded:** 1 each year. **Funds Available:** The stipend is $1,000. **Duration:** 1 year.
Eligibility Requirements: This program is open to residents of Minnesota who are blind or visually impaired. Applicants must be attending or planning to attend a college, university, or technical school. Along with their application, they must submit a personal letter, official transcript, and 2 letters of recommendation. **Deadline for Receipt:** June of each year. **Additional Information:** Information is also available from Sheila Koenig, E-mail: shekoenig@msn.com.

1164 ■ NATIONAL FEDERATION OF THE BLIND OF MISSOURI

c/o Gary Wunder, President
3910 Tropical Lane
Columbia, MO 65202-6205
Tel: (573)874-1774; 888-604-1774
E-mail: info@nfbmo.org
Web Site: http://www.nfbmo.org
To provide financial assistance for college to blind students in Missouri.
Title of Award: John and Rhoda Dower Scholarship **Area, Field, or Subject:** General studies/Field of study not specified **Level of Education for which Award is Granted:** Graduate, Undergraduate **Number Awarded:** Up to 3 each year. **Funds Available:** The maximum stipend is $1,000. **Duration:** 1 year.
Eligibility Requirements: This program is open to legally blind residents of Missouri who are working or planning to work on an undergraduate or graduate degree. **Deadline for Receipt:** February of each year. **Additional Information:** Additional information is also available from the Chair of the Achievement Awards Committee: Sheila Koenig, 634 South National, Apartment 303, Springfield, MO 65804, (417) 869-1078.

1165 ■ NATIONAL FEDERATION OF THE BLIND OF NEBRASKA

1033 O Street, Suite 24B
Lincoln, NE 68508-3621
Tel: (402)477-7711; (866)BLIND-IS
E-mail: nfbn@inetnebr.com
Web Site: http://nfbn.inebraska.com/student/scholarships.shtml
To provide financial assistance for college to blind residents of Nebraska.
Title of Award: National Federation of the Blind of Nebraska Scholarship **Area, Field, or Subject:** General studies/Field of study not specified **Level of Education for which Award is Granted:** Undergraduate **Number Awarded:** 5 each year: 1 first-place winner and 4 other finalists **Funds Available:** The stipend is $1,000 for first place; cash stipends are paid to other finalists. **Duration:** 1 year.
Eligibility Requirements: This program is open to residents of Nebraska who are blind and attending or planning to attend a postsecondary institution. Applicants must submit a letter that describes their educational plans, vocational goals, and awards. Their letter should also explain how they deal with situations involving their blindness and how the scholarship will help them. **Deadline for Receipt:** September of each year. **Additional Information:** Further information is also available from Shane Buresh, Scholarship Chair, 6210 Walker Avenue, Lincoln, NE 68507, (402) 465-5468, E-mail: sburesh@neb.rr.com. The second-place award is sponsored by the Nebraska Association of Blind Students.

1166 ■ NATIONAL FEDERATION OF THE BLIND OF NEW MEXICO

c/o Arthur Schreiber, President
1331 Park Avenue, N.W., Suite 1504
Albuquerque, NM 87102
Tel: (505)243-6165
E-mail: arturo70@aol.com
Web Site: http://www.nfbnm.org
To provide financial assistance to blind students in New Mexico who are interested in attending college.
Title of Award: National Federation of the Blind of New Mexico Scholarship Program **Area, Field, or Subject:** General studies/Field of study not specified **Level of Education for which Award is Granted:** Undergraduate **Number Awarded:** At least 3 each year. **Funds Available:** Stipends up to $1,000 are available. **Duration:** 1 year.
Eligibility Requirements: This program is open to blind students in New Mexico who are high school seniors or currently enrolled full time in college. Applicants must submit a copy of their transcript, a 250-word essay on how this scholarship will benefit them (including comments on their philosophy of blindness), and 3 letters of recommendation (including at least 1 from a member of the National Federation of the Blind). Priority is given to applicants attending school in New Mexico, but consideration is given to individuals who plan to go outside the state. **Deadline for Receipt:** April of each year. **Additional Information:** Information is also available from James L. Salas, P.O. Box 36032, Albuquerque, NM 87176-6032, (505) 841-8844.

1167 ■ NATIONAL FEDERATION OF THE BLIND OF OHIO

c/o Barbara Pierce, President
237 Oak Street
Oberlin, OH 44074-1517
Tel: (440)775-2216
Free: 800-396-NFBO
E-mail: bbpierce@pobox.com
Web Site: http://www.nfbohio.org/scholarship.html
To provide financial assistance for undergraduate or graduate studies to Ohio residents who are legally blind.
Title of Award: National Federation of the Blind of Ohio Scholarships **Area, Field, or Subject:** General studies/Field of study not specified **Level of Education for which Award is Granted:** Graduate, Undergraduate **Number Awarded:** 2 each year: 1 at $1,500 and 1 at $1,000. **Funds Available:** The stipend is $1,500 or $1,000. **Duration:** 1 year.
Eligibility Requirements: Eligible to apply for this support are high school seniors, currently-enrolled college students, and graduate students who reside in Ohio and are legally blind. They must attend or be preparing to attend an accredited institution of higher education on a full-time basis. Selection is based on academic excellence, community service, and financial need. **Deadline for Receipt:** May of each year. **Additional Information:** Information is also available from Dr. J. Webster Smith, Chair, Scholarship Committee, 2 Canterbury Street, Athens, OH 45701,

(740) 593-4838, E-mail: jsmith1@ohiou.edu. The $1,500 scholarship is named the Jennica Ferguson Memorial Scholarship.

1168 ■ NATIONAL FEDERATION OF THE BLIND OF OREGON
Attn: Scholarship Committee
5005 Main Street
Springfield, OR 97478-6065
Tel: (541)726-6924
Free: 800-422-7093
Fax: (541)726-5527
E-mail: nfb_or/msn.com
Web Site: http://www.nfb-or.org/scholarships.htm
To provide financial assistance for college or graduate school to blind residents of Oregon.
Title of Award: National Federation of the Blind of Oregon Scholarships **Area, Field, or Subject:** General studies/Field of study not specified **Level of Education for which Award is Granted:** Graduate, Undergraduate **Number Awarded:** 3 each year: 1 at $1,500 and 2 at $1,000. **Funds Available:** Stipends are either $1,500 or $1,000. **Duration:** 1 year. **Eligibility Requirements:** This program is open to blind residents of Oregon who are working on or planning to work on an undergraduate or graduate degree at a college or university in the state. Applicants must be enrolled full time or enrolled part time and working full time. Selection is based on academic and professional promise as well as potential for leadership in the National Federation of the Blind of Oregon. **Deadline for Receipt:** May of each year. **Additional Information:** Information is also available from the Scholarship Committee, Chair, (503) 963-1973, E-mail: mmebrock@spiritone.com.

1169 ■ NATIONAL FEDERATION OF THE BLIND OF TEXAS
c/o Tommy Craig, President
6909 Rufus Drive
Austin, TX 78752-3123
Tel: (512)323-5444
E-mail: tommy.craig@nfb-texas.org
Web Site: http://www.nfb-texas.org/scholarships.html
To provide financial assistance for college to blind residents of Texas.
Title of Award: National Federation of the Blind of Texas Scholarships **Area, Field, or Subject:** General studies/Field of study not specified **Level of Education for which Award is Granted:** Undergraduate **Number Awarded:** Varies each year. **Funds Available:** Stipends range from $1,000 to $2,000. **Duration:** 1 year. **Eligibility Requirements:** This program is open to blind residents of Texas who are enrolled or planning to enroll in a college or university. Applicants must submit proof of legal blindness, a current transcript, a 2-page personal letter, and 2 letters of recommendation. Selection is based on merit and financial need. **Deadline for Receipt:** June of each year. **Additional Information:** Information is also available from Elizabeth Campbell, Scholarship Chair, (817) 738-0350, E-mail: scholarship@nfb-texas.org.

1170 ■ NATIONAL FEDERATION OF THE BLIND OF UTAH
Attn: Scholarship Committee
132 West Penman Lane
Bountiful, UT 84010-7634
Tel: (801)292-3000
E-mail: president@nfbutah.org
Web Site: http://www.nfbutah.org/utabs/scholarships.html
To provide financial assistance for college or graduate school to blind residents of Utah.
Title of Award: National Federation of the Blind of Utah Scholarships **Area, Field, or Subject:** General studies/Field of study not specified **Level of Education for which Award is Granted:** Graduate, Undergraduate **Number Awarded:** 3 to 5 each year. **Funds Available:** Stipends range from $500 to $1,500. **Duration:** 1 year. **Eligibility Requirements:** This program is open to blind residents of Utah who are working on or planning to work on an undergraduate or graduate degree. Selection is based on academic excellence, community service, and financial need. **Deadline for Receipt:** April of each year.

1171 ■ NATIONAL FEDERATION OF THE BLIND OF WASHINGTON
Attn: Scholarship Committee
P.O. Box 2516
Seattle, WA 98111
Tel: (425)823-6380
E-mail: info@nfbw.org
Web Site: http://www.nfbw.org
To provide financial assistance for undergraduate or graduate study to blind students in Washington.
Title of Award: Hazel ten Broek Merit Scholarship **Area, Field, or Subject:** General studies/Field of study not specified **Level of Education for which Award is Granted:** Graduate, Undergraduate **Number Awarded:** 1 each year. **Funds Available:** The stipend is $2,000. **Duration:** 1 year. **Eligibility Requirements:** This program is open to legally blind residents of Washington state who are working on or planning to work on a full-time college or graduate degree. Applicants must submit a letter describing themselves (hobbies, interests, school activities, and future goals), high school and/or college transcripts, and 3 letters of reference. **Deadline for Receipt:** August of each year. **Additional Information:** Information is also available from Rita Szantay, 1420 Fifth Avenue, Suite 2200, Seattle, WA 98101, (206) 224-7242 (days) or (206) 352-7320 (evenings and weekends). This scholarship was first awarded in 1996. Winners must attend the state convention of the National Federation of the Blind of Washington to accept the award; convention expenses are covered.

1172 ■ NATIONAL FEDERATION OF THE BLIND OF WASHINGTON
Attn: Scholarship Committee
P.O. Box 2516
Seattle, WA 98111
Tel: (425)823-6380
E-mail: info@nfbw.org
Web Site: http://www.nfbw.org
To provide financial assistance for undergraduate or graduate study to blind students in Washington.
Title of Award: Beverly Prows Memorial Scholarship **Area, Field, or Subject:** General studies/Field of study not specified **Level of Education for which Award is Granted:** Graduate, Undergraduate **Number Awarded:** 1 each year. **Funds Available:** The stipend is $3,000. **Duration:** 1 year. **Eligibility Requirements:** This program is open to legally blind residents of Washington state who are working on or planning to work on a full-time college or graduate degree. Applicants must submit a letter describing themselves (hobbies, interests, school activities, and future goals), high school and/or college transcripts, and 3 letters of reference. **Deadline for Receipt:** August of each year. **Additional Information:** Information is also available from Rita Szantay, 1420 Fifth Avenue, Suite 2200, Seattle, WA 98101, (206) 224-7242 (days) or (206) 352-7320 (evenings and weekends). This scholarship was first awarded in 1991. Winners must attend the state convention of the National Federation of the Blind of Washington to accept the award; convention expenses are covered.

1173 ■ NATIONAL FEDERATION OF INDEPENDENT BUSINESS
Attn: NFIB Education Foundation
1020 F Street, N.W., Suite 200
Washington, DC 20004
Tel: (202)554-9000
Free: 800-NFIB-NOW
E-mail: aaron.taylor@nfib.org
Web Site: http://www.nfib.com/YoungEntrepreneurFoundation.html
To provide financial assistance for college to high school seniors who are interested in private enterprise and entrepreneurship.
Title of Award: NFIB Free Enterprise Scholars Program **Area, Field, or Subject:** Business administration; General studies/Field of study not specified **Level of Education for which Award is Granted:** Undergraduate **Number Awarded:** Varies each year; recently, a total of 221 of these scholarships were awarded. **Funds Available:** The highest-ranked applicant receives $10,000 and 4 other finalists receive $5,000. Other stipends are $1,000. **Duration:** 1 year; nonrenewable. **Eligibility Requirements:** This program is open to graduating high school seniors who plan to enter their freshman year at an accredited 2-year college, 4-year college or university, or vocational/technical institute. Students must be nominated by a member of the National Federation of Independent Business (NFIB). Nominees must meet or exceed academic standards, using standardized test scores (ACT/SAT), class rank, and GPA as indicators. They must answer a short, personal question defining their entrepreneurial efforts and compose another essay

of 500 words or less about the importance of free enterprise. Selection is based on those essays, involvement in extracurricular and/or community activities, and special recognition or honors. **Deadline for Receipt:** March of each year. **Additional Information:** These scholarships were first awarded in 2003.

1174 ■ NATIONAL FEDERATION OF MUSIC CLUBS

1336 North Delaware Street
Indianapolis, IN 46202-2481
Tel: (317)638-4003
Fax: (317)638-0503
E-mail: info@nfmc-music.org
Web Site: http://www.nfmc-music.org/Competitions/Annual%20Student/annual_student.htm

To provide financial assistance to members of the National Federation of Music Clubs (NFMC) who are majoring in music therapy.

Title of Award: Dorothy Dann Bullock Music Therapy Award **Area, Field, or Subject:** Music therapy **Level of Education for which Award is Granted:** Undergraduate **Number Awarded:** 1 each year. **Funds Available:** The award is $1,000; funds must be used for further study. **Duration:** The award is presented annually.

Eligibility Requirements: Eligible to enter are music therapy majors (college sophomores, juniors, and seniors) in accredited schools offering music therapy degrees approved by the National Association of Music Therapists. Student membership in the federation, and U.S. citizenship are required. Applicants must demonstrate musical talent, skills, and training, especially pianistic ability in accompanying and sight reading; ability to direct; pleasant singing voice; emotional stability; self-reliance; patience; tact; leadership; intelligence; good health; ability to work with groups; and dedication to music therapy as a career. **Deadline for Receipt:** February of each year. **Additional Information:** Further information on this award is also available from Lorraine Peery Long, 814 Nebraska Avenue, Kansas City, KS 66101-2112; information on all federation scholarships and awards is available from Chair, Competitions and Awards Board, Dr. George R. Keck, 421 Cherry Street, Arkadelphia, AR 71923-5116, E-mail: keckg@obu.edu.

1175 ■ NATIONAL FFA ORGANIZATION

Attn: Scholarship Office
6060 FFA Drive
P.O. Box 68960
Indianapolis, IN 46268-0960
Tel: (317)802-4321
Fax: (317)802-5321
E-mail: scholarships@ffa.org
Web Site: http://www.ffa.org

To provide financial assistance for college to FFA members from designated states.

Title of Award: American Family Insurance Scholarships **Area, Field, or Subject:** General studies/Field of study not specified **Level of Education for which Award is Granted:** Four Year College **Number Awarded:** 3 each year: 1 for each of the qualifying states. **Funds Available:** The stipend is $1,000 per year. Funds are paid directly to the recipient. **Duration:** 1 year; nonrenewable.

Eligibility Requirements: This program is open to members who are graduating high school seniors planning to enroll full time in college. Applicants must be residents of Wisconsin, Missouri, or Minnesota who are planning to work on a 4-year college degree with any major at an accredited institution. Selection is based on academic achievement (10 points for GPA, 10 points for SAT or ACT score, 10 points for class rank), leadership in FFA activities (30 points), leadership in community activities (10 points), and participation in the Supervised Agricultural Experience (SAE) program (30 points). U.S. citizenship is required. **Deadline for Receipt:** February of each year. **Additional Information:** Funding for these scholarships is provided by American Family Insurance.

1176 ■ NATIONAL FFA ORGANIZATION

Attn: Scholarship Office
6060 FFA Drive
P.O. Box 68960
Indianapolis, IN 46268-0960
Tel: (317)802-4321
Fax: (317)802-5321

E-mail: scholarships@ffa.org
Web Site: http://www.ffa.org

To provide financial assistance for college to FFA members from specified states.

Title of Award: Anderson Foundation Scholarships **Area, Field, or Subject:** General studies/Field of study not specified **Level of Education for which Award is Granted:** Four Year College **Number Awarded:** 2 each year. **Funds Available:** The stipend is $1,250. Funds are paid directly to the recipient. **Duration:** 1 year; nonrenewable.

Eligibility Requirements: This program is open to members who are graduating high school seniors from Illinois, Indiana, Michigan, Ohio, or Pennsylvania and planning to enroll full time at a 4-year college or university. Applicants must have work-related experience in agriculture, but they may major in any field. Selection is based on academic achievement (10 points for GPA, 10 points for SAT or ACT score, 10 points for class rank), leadership in FFA activities (30 points), leadership in community activities (10 points), and participation in the Supervised Agricultural Experience (SAE) program (30 points). U.S. citizenship is required. **Deadline for Receipt:** February of each year. **Additional Information:** Funding for this scholarship is provided by the Anderson Foundation.

1177 ■ NATIONAL FFA ORGANIZATION

Attn: Scholarship Office
6060 FFA Drive
P.O. Box 68960
Indianapolis, IN 46268-0960
Tel: (317)802-4321
Fax: (317)802-5321
E-mail: scholarships@ffa.org
Web Site: http://www.ffa.org

To provide financial assistance to FFA members from Vermont interested in working on a degree in production dairy.

Title of Award: Bourdeau and Bushey Scholarship **Area, Field, or Subject:** Dairy science **Level of Education for which Award is Granted:** Undergraduate **Number Awarded:** 1 each year. **Funds Available:** The stipend is $1,000 per year. Funds are paid directly to the recipient. **Duration:** 1 year; nonrenewable.

Eligibility Requirements: This program is open to members from Vermont who are graduating high school seniors planning to enroll or college students currently enrolled full time. Applicants must be planning to work on a degree in production dairy. More than 50% of their family income must come from dairy production. Selection is based on academic achievement (10 points for GPA, 10 points for SAT or ACT score, 10 points for class rank), leadership in FFA activities (30 points), leadership in community activities (10 points), and participation in the Supervised Agricultural Experience (SAE) program (30 points). Financial need is also considered. U.S. citizenship is required. **Deadline for Receipt:** February of each year. **Additional Information:** Funding for these scholarships is provided by Bourdeau Bros Inc., Bourdeau and Bushey Inc., and Feed Commodities International Inc.

1178 ■ NATIONAL FFA ORGANIZATION

Attn: Scholarship Office
6060 FFA Drive
P.O. Box 68960
Indianapolis, IN 46268-0960
Tel: (317)802-4321
Fax: (317)802-5321
E-mail: scholarships@ffa.org
Web Site: http://www.ffa.org

To provide financial assistance for college to high school seniors who live near a facility of Cargill, Inc.

Title of Award: Cargill Community Scholarship Program **Area, Field, or Subject:** General studies/Field of study not specified **Level of Education for which Award is Granted:** Undergraduate **Number Awarded:** 350 each year. **Funds Available:** The stipend is $1,000. Funds are paid directly to the recipient. Each recipient's high school is eligible for a $200 library grant. **Duration:** 1 year; nonrenewable.

Eligibility Requirements: This program is open to graduating high school seniors who live near a Cargill facility and have their application signed by a local Cargill manager. Applicants must be planning to work full time on a 2-year or 4-year degree in any major at an accredited college or university in the United States. They must submit information on their work experience with an explanation of how it relates to their future goals; FFA members must include their Supervised Agricultural Experience (SAE) activities and 4-H members must include their projects. Other selection criteria include leadership activities and academic achievement. **Deadline for Receipt:** February of each year. **Additional Information:** Funding for this program is provided by Cargill, Inc. Information on the location of Cargill facilities is available at (888) 476-9332, E-mail: cargill@ffa.org.

1179 ■ NATIONAL FFA ORGANIZATION

Attn: Scholarship Office
6060 FFA Drive
P.O. Box 68960
Indianapolis, IN 46268-0960
Tel: (317)802-4321
Fax: (317)802-5321
E-mail: scholarships@ffa.org
Web Site: http://www.ffa.org
To provide financial assistance for college to FFA members from Indiana, Michigan, and Ohio.
Title of Award: Carter Lumber Scholarships **Area, Field, or Subject:** General studies/Field of study not specified **Level of Education for which Award is Granted:** Undergraduate **Number Awarded:** 3 each year: 1 to a student from each of the 3 states. **Funds Available:** The stipend is $2,000. Funds are paid directly to the recipient. **Duration:** 1 year; nonrenewable.
Eligibility Requirements: This program is open to members who are graduating high school seniors planning to enroll full time in college. Applicants must be residents of Indiana, Michigan, or Ohio planning to work on a 2-year or 4-year college degree in any major at a college or university in their state. They must have a GPA of 3.0 or higher. Selection is based on academic achievement (10 points for GPA, 10 points for SAT or ACT score, 10 points for class rank), leadership in FFA activities (30 points), leadership in community activities (10 points), and participation in the Supervised Agricultural Experience (SAE) program (30 points). U.S. citizenship is required. **Deadline for Receipt:** February of each year. **Additional Information:** Funding for these scholarships is provided by Carter Lumber Company of Kent, Ohio.

1180 ■ NATIONAL FFA ORGANIZATION

Attn: Scholarship Office
6060 FFA Drive
P.O. Box 68960
Indianapolis, IN 46268-0960
Tel: (317)802-4321
Fax: (317)802-5321
E-mail: scholarships@ffa.org
Web Site: http://www.ffa.org
To provide financial assistance for college to current FFA members.
Title of Award: Chevrolet Scholarships **Area, Field, or Subject:** General studies/Field of study not specified **Level of Education for which Award is Granted:** Undergraduate **Number Awarded:** 40 each year. **Funds Available:** The stipend is $2,500. Funds are paid directly to the recipient. **Duration:** 1 year; nonrenewable.
Eligibility Requirements: This program is open to members who are graduating high school seniors planning to enroll full time in college. Applicants must 1) have recruitment and leadership skills that have contributed to their local FFA chapter; 2) show participation in a Supervised Agricultural Experience (SAE) program; and 3) be recommended by their local FFA advisor. They may be working on a 2-or 4-year degree in any major. Selection is based on academic achievement (10 points for GPA, 10 points for SAT or ACT score, 10 points for class rank), leadership in FFA activities (30 points), leadership in community activities (10 points), and participation in the SAE program (30 points). U.S. citizenship is required. **Deadline for Receipt:** February of each year. **Additional Information:** Funding for these scholarships is provided by the Chevrolet division of General Motors.

1181 ■ NATIONAL FFA ORGANIZATION

Attn: Scholarship Office
6060 FFA Drive
P.O. Box 68960
Indianapolis, IN 46268-0960

Tel: (317)802-4321
Fax: (317)802-5321
E-mail: scholarships@ffa.org
Web Site: http://www.ffa.org
To provide financial assistance for college to members of FFA.
Title of Award: Dodge Trucks Scholarships **Area, Field, or Subject:** General studies/Field of study not specified **Level of Education for which Award is Granted:** Undergraduate **Number Awarded:** 50 each year. **Funds Available:** The stipend is $1,000 per year. Funds are paid directly to the recipient. **Duration:** 1 year; nonrenewable.
Eligibility Requirements: This program is open to members who are graduating high school seniors planning to enroll full time in college. Applicants must be interested in working on a degree at an accredited 2- or 4-year college, university, or vocational/technical school. They may be majoring in any field. Farm Bureau membership is also required. Selection is based on academic achievement (10 points for GPA, 10 points for SAT or ACT score, 10 points for class rank), leadership in FFA activities (30 points), leadership in community activities (10 points), and participation in the Supervised Agricultural Experience (SAE) program (30 points). Financial need is also considered, and applicants must complete the parent financial analysis section. U.S. citizenship is required. **Deadline for Receipt:** February of each year. **Additional Information:** Funding for these scholarships is provided by the Dodge Trucks Division of DaimlerChrysler Corporation.

1182 ■ NATIONAL FFA ORGANIZATION

Attn: Scholarship Office
6060 FFA Drive
P.O. Box 68960
Indianapolis, IN 46268-0960
Tel: (317)802-4321
Fax: (317)802-5321
E-mail: scholarships@ffa.org
Web Site: http://www.ffa.org
To provide financial assistance to male FFA members interested in attending a university with a chapter of FarmHouse Fraternity.
Title of Award: FarmHouse Fraternity Scholarship **Area, Field, or Subject:** General studies/Field of study not specified **Level of Education for which Award is Granted:** Four Year College **Number Awarded:** 1 each year. **Funds Available:** The stipend is $1,000 per year. Funds are paid directly to the recipient. **Duration:** 1 year; nonrenewable.
Eligibility Requirements: This program is open to members who are male graduating high school seniors planning to enroll full time at a 4-year university with a FarmHouse Fraternity chapter. Applicants may major in any area. Selection is based on academic achievement (10 points for GPA, 10 points for SAT or ACT score, 10 points for class rank), leadership in FFA activities (30 points), leadership in community activities (10 points), and participation in the Supervised Agricultural Experience (SAE) program (30 points). U.S. citizenship is required. **Deadline for Receipt:** February of each year. **Additional Information:** Funding for this scholarship is provided by FarmHouse Fraternity.

1183 ■ NATIONAL FFA ORGANIZATION

Attn: Scholarship Office
6060 FFA Drive
P.O. Box 68960
Indianapolis, IN 46268-0960
Tel: (317)802-4321
Fax: (317)802-5321
E-mail: scholarships@ffa.org
Web Site: http://www.ffa.org
To provide financial assistance to FFA members who are interested in working on a 2-year or 4-year college degree in any field.
Title of Award: Ford Truck Scholarship Program **Area, Field, or Subject:** General studies/Field of study not specified **Level of Education for which Award is Granted:** Undergraduate **Number Awarded:** Approximately 705 each year: approximately 700 on behalf of participating Ford Truck dealerships and 5 on a nationwide basis. **Funds Available:** The stipend is $1,000. Funds are paid directly to the recipient. **Duration:** 1 year; nonrenewable.
Eligibility Requirements: This program is open to members who are graduating high school seniors planning to enroll or students currently enrolled full time at an accredited 2- or 4-year college, university, or

vocational/technical school. Applicants may be majoring in any field. They must visit a Ford Truck dealership and obtain a signature on the scholarship application. Selection is based on academic achievement (10 points for GPA, 10 points for SAT or ACT score, 10 points for class rank), leadership in FFA activities (30 points), leadership in community activities (10 points), and participation in the Supervised Agricultural Experience (SAE) program (30 points). U.S. citizenship is required. **Deadline for Receipt:** February of each year. **Additional Information:** Funding for these scholarships is provided by the Ford Truck Division of the Ford Motor Company. This program began in 1998.

1184 ■ NATIONAL FFA ORGANIZATION

Attn: Scholarship Office
6060 FFA Drive
P.O. Box 68960
Indianapolis, IN 46268-0960
Tel: (317)802-4321
Fax: (317)802-5321
E-mail: scholarships@ffa.org
Web Site: http://www.ffa.org
To provide financial assistance for college to female FFA members from Kentucky, Georgia, or Tennessee.
Title of Award: Cheryl Hennesy Scholarship **Area, Field, or Subject:** General studies/Field of study not specified **Level of Education for which Award is Granted:** Undergraduate **Number Awarded:** 1 or more each year. **Funds Available:** The stipend is $1,250 per year. **Duration:** 1 year; may be renewed up to 3 additional years if the recipient maintains a GPA of 2.0 or higher.
Eligibility Requirements: This program is open to female members who are graduating high school seniors planning to enroll full time in college. Applicants must be residents of Kentucky, Georgia, or Tennessee interested in working on a 2- or 4-year degree in any area of study. They must demonstrate financial need and personal motivation. Selection is based on academic achievement (10 points for GPA, 10 points for SAT or ACT score, 10 points for class rank), leadership in FFA activities (30 points), leadership in community activities (10 points), and participation in the Supervised Agricultural Experience (SAE) program (30 points). U.S. citizenship is required. **Deadline for Receipt:** February of each year.

1185 ■ NATIONAL FFA ORGANIZATION

Attn: Scholarship Office
6060 FFA Drive
P.O. Box 68960
Indianapolis, IN 46268-0960
Tel: (317)802-4321
Fax: (317)802-5321
E-mail: scholarships@ffa.org
Web Site: http://www.ffa.org
To provide financial assistance for college to FFA members from designated states.
Title of Award: Hy-Vee Scholarship **Area, Field, or Subject:** General studies/Field of study not specified **Level of Education for which Award is Granted:** Undergraduate **Number Awarded:** 1 each year. **Funds Available:** The stipend is $1,000. Funds are paid directly to the recipient. **Duration:** 1 year; nonrenewable.
Eligibility Requirements: This program is open to members who are either graduating high school seniors planning to enroll full time or college students already enrolled on a full-time basis. Applicants must be residents of or planning to attend school in Illinois, Iowa, Kansas, Minnesota, Missouri, Nebraska, or South Dakota. They must be planning to work on a 2-year or 4-year degree in any field. Selection is based on academic achievement (10 points for GPA, 10 points for SAT or ACT score, 10 points for class rank), leadership in FFA activities (30 points), leadership in community activities (10 points), and participation in the Supervised Agricultural Experience (SAE) program (30 points). U.S. citizenship is required. **Deadline for Receipt:** February of each year. **Additional Information:** Funding for this scholarship is provided by Hy-Vee Inc.

1186 ■ NATIONAL FFA ORGANIZATION

Attn: Scholarship Office
6060 FFA Drive
P.O. Box 68960
Indianapolis, IN 46268-0960

Tel: (317)802-4321
Fax: (317)802-5321
E-mail: scholarships@ffa.org
Web Site: http://www.ffa.org
To provide financial assistance to FFA members interested in studying dairy science in college.
Title of Award: KenAG Scholarship **Area, Field, or Subject:** Dairy science **Level of Education for which Award is Granted:** Four Year College **Number Awarded:** 1 each year. **Funds Available:** The stipend is $1,000 per year. Funds are paid directly to the recipient. **Duration:** 1 year; nonrenewable.
Eligibility Requirements: This program is open to members who are graduating high school seniors planning to enroll full time in college. Applicants must be interested in working on a 4-year degree in dairy science. Selection is based on academic achievement (10 points for GPA, 10 points for SAT or ACT score, 10 points for class rank), leadership in FFA activities (30 points), leadership in community activities (10 points), and participation in the Supervised Agricultural Experience (SAE) program (30 points). U.S. citizenship is required. **Deadline for Receipt:** February of each year.

1187 ■ NATIONAL FFA ORGANIZATION

Attn: Scholarship Office
6060 FFA Drive
P.O. Box 68960
Indianapolis, IN 46268-0960
Tel: (317)802-4321
Fax: (317)802-5321
E-mail: scholarships@ffa.org
Web Site: http://www.ffa.org
To provide financial assistance for college to FFA members in Wisconsin.
Title of Award: Kikkoman Foods Scholarship **Area, Field, or Subject:** General studies/Field of study not specified **Level of Education for which Award is Granted:** Four Year College **Number Awarded:** 1 each year. **Funds Available:** The stipend is $1,000. Funds are paid directly to the recipient. **Duration:** 1 year; nonrenewable.
Eligibility Requirements: This program is open to members who are graduating high school seniors planning to enroll full time in college and major in any subject. Applicants must be Wisconsin residents interested in attending a 4-year college or university in the state. Selection is based on academic achievement (10 points for GPA, 10 points for SAT or ACT score, 10 points for class rank), leadership in FFA activities (30 points), leadership in community activities (10 points), and participation in the Supervised Agricultural Experience (SAE) program (30 points). U.S. citizenship is required. **Deadline for Receipt:** February of each year. **Additional Information:** Funding for this scholarship is provided by Kikkoman Corporation.

1188 ■ NATIONAL FFA ORGANIZATION

Attn: Scholarship Office
6060 FFA Drive
P.O. Box 68960
Indianapolis, IN 46268-0960
Tel: (317)802-4321
Fax: (317)802-5321
E-mail: scholarships@ffa.org
Web Site: http://www.ffa.org
To provide financial assistance for college to FFA members.
Title of Award: National Honor Roll Scholarship **Area, Field, or Subject:** General studies/Field of study not specified **Level of Education for which Award is Granted:** Undergraduate **Number Awarded:** 1 each year. **Funds Available:** The stipend is $1,000. Funds are paid directly to the recipient. **Duration:** 1 year; nonrenewable.
Eligibility Requirements: This program is open to members who are graduating high school seniors planning to enroll full time in college. Applicants must have a GPA of 3.0 or higher and be interested in working on a degree in any field. Selection is based on academic achievement (10 points for GPA, 10 points for SAT or ACT score, 10 points for class rank), leadership in FFA activities (30 points), leadership in community activities (10 points), and participation in the Supervised Agricultural Experience (SAE) program (30 points). U.S. citizenship is required. **Deadline for Receipt:** February of each year. **Additional Information:** Funding for these scholarships is provided by National Honor Roll.

1189 ■ NATIONAL FFA ORGANIZATION

Attn: Scholarship Office
6060 FFA Drive
P.O. Box 68960
Indianapolis, IN 46268-0960
Tel: (317)802-4321
Fax: (317)802-5321
E-mail: scholarships@ffa.org
Web Site: http://www.ffa.org
To provide financial assistance to FFA members from selected states who are interested in working on a 4-year degree in dairy science.
Title of Award: Prairie Farms Dairy Scholarships **Area, Field, or Subject:** Dairy science **Level of Education for which Award is Granted:** Four Year College **Number Awarded:** 1 each year. **Funds Available:** The stipend is $1,000. Funds are paid directly to the recipient. **Duration:** 1 year; nonrenewable.
Eligibility Requirements: This program is open to members who are graduating high school seniors planning to enroll and college students currently enrolled full time. Applicants must be residents of Illinois, Indiana, Iowa, Michigan, Missouri, or Ohio and interested in working on a 4-year degree in dairy science. Selection is based on academic achievement (10 points for GPA, 10 points for SAT or ACT score, 10 points for class rank), leadership in FFA activities (30 points), leadership in community activities (10 points), and participation in the Supervised Agricultural Experience (SAE) program (30 points). U.S. citizenship is required. **Deadline for Receipt:** February of each year. **Additional Information:** Funding for these scholarships is provided by Prairie Farms Dairy, Inc. of Carlinville, Illinois.

1190 ■ NATIONAL FFA ORGANIZATION

Attn: Scholarship Office
6060 FFA Drive
P.O. Box 68960
Indianapolis, IN 46268-0960
Tel: (317)802-4321
Fax: (317)802-5321
E-mail: scholarships@ffa.org
Web Site: http://www.ffa.org
To provide financial assistance to FFA members from inner-city schools who are interested in working on a college degree.
Title of Award: Who's Who Among American High School Students Scholarships **Area, Field, or Subject:** General studies/Field of study not specified **Level of Education for which Award is Granted:** Undergraduate **Number Awarded:** 1 each year. **Funds Available:** The stipend is $1,500. Funds are paid directly to the recipient. **Duration:** 1 year; nonrenewable.
Eligibility Requirements: This program is open to members who are graduating high school seniors planning to enroll full time in college. Applicants must be interested in working on a degree with any major at a 2-year or 4-year institution and currently attending an inner-city school. Selection is based on academic achievement (10 points for GPA, 10 points for SAT or ACT score, 10 points for class rank), leadership in FFA activities (30 points), leadership in community activities (10 points), and participation in the Supervised Agricultural Experience (SAE) program (30 points). Financial need is also considered. U.S. citizenship is required. **Deadline for Receipt:** February of each year. **Additional Information:** This program is funded by the ECI Scholarship Foundation of Educational Communications Inc., publisher of *Who's Who Among American High School Students.*

1191 ■ NATIONAL FLUID MILK PROCESSOR PROMOTION BOARD

Attn: Scholar Athlete Milk Mustache of the Year (SAMMY)
1250 H Street, N.W., Suite 950
Washington, DC 20005
Tel: (202)737-0153
Free: 800-WHY-MILK
Web Site: http://www.whymilk.com
To provide financial assistance for college to outstanding high school scholar-athletes.
Title of Award: SAMMY Awards **Area, Field, or Subject:** General studies/Field of study not specified **Level of Education for which Award is Granted:** Undergraduate **Number Awarded:** 25 each year (1 from each of 25 geographic districts). **Funds Available:** College scholarships of $7,500 each are awarded. In addition, each winner plus 2 guests are

invited to attend the winners' ceremony at Disney World in Orlando, Florida. **Duration:** The awards are presented annually.
Eligibility Requirements: This program is open to residents of the 48 contiguous United States and the District of Columbia who are currently high school seniors and who participate in a high school or club sport. The country is divided into 25 geographic regions, and 3 finalists are selected from each region. From those, 1 winner from each region is chosen. Selection is based on academic achievement (35%), athletic excellence (35%), leadership (15%), citizenship/community service (10%), and a 75-word essay on how drinking milk is part of their life and training regimen (5%). **Deadline for Receipt:** March of each year. **Additional Information:** This program, which began in 1998, is sponsored by the National Fluid Milk Processor Promotion Board, Dairy Management Inc., and USA Today, Information is also available from Weber Shandwick Worldwide, Attn: Adena Miller, (312) 988-2295.

1192 ■ NATIONAL FOSTER PARENT ASSOCIATION

Attn: Scholarship Committee
7512 Stanich Avenue, Suite 6
Gig Harbor, WA 98335
Tel: (253)853-4000
Free: 800-557-5238
Fax: (253)853-4001
E-mail: info@nfpainc.org
Web Site: http://www.nfpainc.org/awards/youthScholarships.cfm
To assist students whose families are members of the National Foster Parent Association (NFPA) and who are interested in attending college or vocational school.
Title of Award: National Foster Parent Association Youth Scholarship Program **Area, Field, or Subject:** General studies/Field of study not specified **Level of Education for which Award is Granted:** Undergraduate **Number Awarded:** 5 each year: 3 to foster children and 2 to birth or adoptive children of foster parent NFPA members. **Funds Available:** The stipend is $1,000. **Duration:** 1 year.
Eligibility Requirements: This program is open to students who are in foster care at the time of application; are entering the first year of college or its equivalent (including vocational school, job training, correspondence studies, or GED work); and reside with an association member family. Adopted children and birth children of foster parents are also eligible. Students entering a college or university must be high school seniors (regardless of age); students entering vocational or equivalent training must be at least 17 years of age, whether in or out of school. All applicants must submit a statement (300 to 500 words) on why they want to further their education and why they should be considered for this scholarship. Financial need is considered in the selection process. **Deadline for Receipt:** March of each year. **Additional Information:** These scholarships were formerly named in memory of Benjamin Eaton who, in 1636 at the age of 7, became the nation's first recorded foster child. The program includes 1 scholarship designated the Gordon Evans Scholarship.

1193 ■ NATIONAL FOUNDATION FOR ECTODERMAL DYSPLASIAS

410 East Main Street
P.O. Box 114
Mascoutah, IL 62258-0114
Tel: (618)566-2020
Fax: (618)566-4718
E-mail: info@nfed.org
Web Site: http://www.nfed.org/College.htm
To provide financial assistance for college to students with ectodermal dysplasia.
Title of Award: NFED Memorial Scholarship Program **Area, Field, or Subject:** General studies/Field of study not specified **Level of Education for which Award is Granted:** Undergraduate **Number Awarded:** Varies each year; recently, 17 of these scholarships, with a total value of $24,000, were awarded. **Funds Available:** A stipend is awarded; the exact amount depends upon the needs of the recipient. Funds are sent to the recipient's school. **Duration:** 1 year.
Eligibility Requirements: This program is open to individuals who are affected by ectodermal dysplasia and are attending or planning to attend a college, university, trade school, or junior college. Selection is based on demonstrated academic ability, a written essay (topic changes annually), extracurricular activities, community involvement, employment, and financial need. **Deadline for Receipt:** April of each year. **Additional**

Information: This program, established in 1995, includes the following named scholarships: the Ethelyn Draser Boyd Scholarship and the Louis J. and June E. Kay Scholarship.

1194 ■ NATIONAL FRATERNAL SOCIETY OF THE DEAF

1118 South Sixth Street
Springfield, IL 62703
Tel: (217)789-7429
Fax: (217)789-7489
E-mail: thefrat@nfsd.com
Web Site: http://www.nfsd.com/scholarships.htm
To provide financial assistance for college to members of the National Fraternal Society of the Deaf.

Title of Award: National Fraternal Society of the Deaf Scholarships **Area, Field, or Subject:** General studies/Field of study not specified **Level of Education for which Award is Granted:** Undergraduate **Number Awarded:** 10 each year. **Funds Available:** The stipend is $1,000. **Duration:** 1 year; may be renewed 1 additional year.
Eligibility Requirements: This program is open to deaf, hard of hearing, or hearing persons who are enrolled in or accepted as a full-time student at a postsecondary educational institution. Applicants must have been members of the society for at least 1 year prior to application. **Deadline for Receipt:** June of each year. **Additional Information:** These scholarships have been awarded since 1973.

1195 ■ NATIONAL GUARD ASSOCIATION OF ARIZONA

5640 East McDowell Road
Phoenix, AZ 85008
Tel: (602)275-8307
Fax: (602)275-9254
E-mail: ngaofaz@aol.com
Web Site: http://www.ngaaz.org
To provide financial assistance for college to members of the Arizona National Guard.

Title of Award: Arizona National Guard Scholarship **Area, Field, or Subject:** General studies/Field of study not specified **Level of Education for which Award is Granted:** Undergraduate **Number Awarded:** Varies each year. **Funds Available:** The program provides up to $500 per semester ($1,000 per year) to cover tuition at any state college or university in Arizona. **Duration:** Up to 4 years, as long as the recipient maintains a GPA of 3.0 or higher.
Eligibility Requirements: This program is open to active members of the Arizona National Guard who are enrolled for at least 12 hours in an undergraduate degree program. Selection is based on current GPA, academic honors or awards, military decorations and awards, unit involvement, community involvement as a National Guard representative, and potential for future contribution to the National Guard. **Deadline for Receipt:** March of each year.

1196 ■ NATIONAL GUARD ASSOCIATION OF ARKANSAS, INC.

Attn: Scholarship Program
P.O. Box 663
North Little Rock, AR 72115-0663
Tel: (501)758-6422
Free: 800-522-1617
Fax: (501)758-2097
E-mail: dsears@ngaa.org
Web Site: http://www.ngaa.org
To provide financial assistance for college to students who are enrolled in the state-sponsored life insurance program of the National Guard Association of Arkansas (NGAA).

Title of Award: NGAA/EAANG Scholarship Program **Area, Field, or Subject:** General studies/Field of study not specified **Level of Education for which Award is Granted:** Undergraduate **Number Awarded:** 30 each year. **Funds Available:** The stipend is $500 per year. **Duration:** 1 year; may be renewed.
Eligibility Requirements: This program is open to current, retired, and former members of the Arkansas National Guard and to their dependents. The Guard member must also be enrolled in the association's life insurance program and must be a member of NGAA or the Enlisted Association of the Arkansas National Guard (EAANG). Dependents of deceased members of NGAA/EAANG may apply if the deceased member had coverage under the NGAA group life insurance program. Students may be

enrolled in or planning to enroll in an accredited vocational school, technical school, community college, or university in any state as either a full-time or part-time student. Selection is based on leadership potential; involvement in civic, community, school, and military activities; community, school, and military achievements; academic excellence; and financial need. **Deadline for Receipt:** February of each year. **Additional Information:** This program is jointly sponsored by the NGAA and the EAANG.

1197 ■ NATIONAL GUARD ASSOCIATION OF CALIFORNIA

Attn: Executive Director
3336 Bradshaw Road, Suite 230
Sacramento, CA 95827-2615
Tel: (916)362-3411
Free: 800-647-0018
Fax: (916)362-3707
E-mail: jmlubey@ngac.org
Web Site: http://www.ngac.org/scholarships.htm
To provide financial assistance for college or graduate school to members of the National Guard Association of California.

Title of Award: National Guard Association of California Scholarships **Area, Field, or Subject:** General studies/Field of study not specified **Level of Education for which Award is Granted:** Graduate, Undergraduate **Number Awarded:** Varies each year; recently, 19 of these scholarships were awarded. **Funds Available:** The amount of the award depends on the availability of funds. **Duration:** 1 year; recipients are ineligible for 2 successive awards.
Eligibility Requirements: This program is open to members of the association who are also currently serving in the California National Guard. Applicants must be attending or planning to attend a college, university, graduate school, business school, or trade school in California. They may have no record of AWOL or unsatisfactory performance for the previous year or since enlistment. Selection is based on academic merit and financial need. **Deadline for Receipt:** Applications may be submitted at any time, but recipients are selected in October and April of each year.

1198 ■ NATIONAL GUARD ASSOCIATION OF COLORADO

Attn: NGACO Educational Foundation
6848 South Revere Parkway, Suite 2-234
Centennial, CO 80112-6709
Tel: (720)250-1565
Fax: (303)250-1569
E-mail: ngaco@ngaco.org
Web Site: http://www.ngaco.org/scholarship/apply.shtml
To provide financial assistance for undergraduate and graduate studies to members of the National Guard Association of Colorado (NGACO), Colorado National Guard, and their families.

Title of Award: NGACO Scholarship Program **Area, Field, or Subject:** General studies/Field of study not specified **Level of Education for which Award is Granted:** Graduate, Undergraduate **Number Awarded:** 11 each year: 4 at $1,000 to members of the NGACO, 2 at $750 to dependents of members of the NGACO, 2 at $500 to current enlisted members of the Colorado National Guard, 2 at $500 to current officer members of the Colorado National Guard, and 1 at $1,000 to a Colorado National Guard member working on a graduate degree. **Funds Available:** Stipends are $1,000, $750, or $500 per year. **Duration:** 1 year; may be renewed.
Eligibility Requirements: This program is open to 1) current members of the Colorado National Guard and the NGACO; 2) dependent unmarried children of current members of the Colorado National Guard and the NGACO; 3) spouses of current members of the Colorado National Guard and the NGACO; and 4) unremarried spouses and unmarried dependent children of deceased members of the Colorado National Guard and the NGACO. Applicants must be enrolled or planning to enroll full or part time at a college, university, trade school, business school, or graduate school. They must submit a transcript of high school and (if applicable) college grades, an essay on why they want to continue their education and why financial assistance is required, 3 letters of recommendation, and 1 letter of academic reference. **Deadline for Receipt:** February of each year. **Additional Information:** Members of the Colorado National Guard must

perform at least 1 year of service following the completion of the school year for which the scholarship was received.

1199 ■ NATIONAL GUARD ASSOCIATION OF ILLINOIS

Attn: Executive Vice President
P.O. Box 8220
Melrose Park, IL 60161-8220
Tel: (708)343-1945
Fax: (708)343-1989
E-mail: exvpil@ngai.com
Web Site: http://www.ngai.com/service.html
To provide financial assistance for college to dependents of members of the National Guard Association of Illinois (NGAI).
Title of Award: Prairie Minuteman Scholarship **Area, Field, or Subject:** General studies/Field of study not specified **Level of Education for which Award is Granted:** Undergraduate **Number Awarded:** 3 each year: 1 to an Illinois Army National Guard dependent, 1 to an Illinois Air National Guard dependent, and 1 (sponsored by USAA Insurance Corporation) to an enlisted Illinois National Guard dependent. **Funds Available:** The stipend is $1,000. **Duration:** 1 year.
Eligibility Requirements: This program is open to dependents (children and spouses) of NGAI members in good standing. Applicants may be high school seniors, high school graduates, or currently-enrolled college students. They must submit a completed application form, official transcripts, 2 letters of recommendation, a verified copy of their ACT/SAT scores, and a 250-word essay on their scholastic and professional goals and aspirations. Financial need is considered in the selection process. **Deadline for Receipt:** Applications must be submitted at least 45 days prior to the sponsor's annual conference. The conference is usually in late April, so applications are due in mid-March.

1200 ■ NATIONAL GUARD ASSOCIATION OF INDIANA

Attn: Educational Grant Committee
2002 South Holt Road, Building 9
Indianapolis, IN 46241-4839
Tel: (317)247-3196
Free: 800-219-2173
Fax: (317)247-3575
E-mail: director@ngai.net
Web Site: http://www.ngai.net/benefits.htm
To provide financial assistance for college to members of the National Guard Association of Indiana (NGAI) and their dependents.
Title of Award: National Guard Association of Indiana Educational Grants **Area, Field, or Subject:** General studies/Field of study not specified **Level of Education for which Award is Granted:** Undergraduate **Number Awarded:** A limited number are awarded each year. **Funds Available:** The stipend is $1,000. **Duration:** 1 year; recipients may reapply.
Eligibility Requirements: This program is open to NGAI members who are currently serving in the Indiana National Guard and their dependents. Children and widow(er)s of former Guard members killed or permanently disabled while on duty with the Indiana National Guard are also eligible. Applicants must submit 2 letters of recommendation, a copy of high school or college transcripts, SAT or ACT scores (if taken), a letter of acceptance from a college or university (if not currently attending college), and an essay on the educational program they intend to pursue and the goals they wish to attain. Selection is based on academic achievement, commitment and desire to achieve, extracurricular activities, accomplishments, goals, and financial need. **Deadline for Receipt:** February of each year.

1201 ■ NATIONAL GUARD ASSOCIATION OF MARYLAND

Attn: Scholarship Committee
P.O. Box 1040
Bel Air, MD 21014-7040
Tel: (410)557-2606
Free: 800-844-1394
Fax: (410)893-7529
E-mail: executivedirector@ngam.net
Web Site: http://www.ngam.net/NGAM-BenefitsScholarships.htm
To provide financial assistance for college to current and former members of the Maryland National Guard and their dependents.
Title of Award: National Guard Association of Maryland Scholarships **Area, Field, or Subject:** General studies/Field of study not specified

Level of Education for which Award is Granted: Undergraduate **Number Awarded:** 1 or more each year. **Funds Available:** Stipends are $1,000 or $500. Funds may be used for tuition, fees, and books. **Duration:** 1 year; recipients may reapply.
Eligibility Requirements: This program is open to active and retired members of the Maryland National Guard and their spouses, sons, and daughters. Applicants must be enrolled or planning to enroll in an accredited college, university, or vocational technical school on either a part-time or full-time basis. They must submit a resume in which they outline their academic background, activities in which they have participated, and honors they have received; 3 letters of recommendation; the name of the college; and information on financial need. **Deadline for Receipt:** March of each year.

1202 ■ NATIONAL GUARD ASSOCIATION OF MASSACHUSETTS

Attn: Scholarship Committee
50 Maple Street
Milford, MA 01757
Tel: (508)735-6544
Web Site: http://www.ngama.org
To provide financial assistance for college to members of the Massachusetts National Guard and their dependents.
Title of Award: NGAMA Scholarships **Area, Field, or Subject:** General studies/Field of study not specified **Level of Education for which Award is Granted:** Undergraduate **Number Awarded:** 5 each year: 2 to members of the Massachusetts National Guard, 2 to dependents of NGAMA members, and 1 to a dependent of a Massachusetts National Guard member. **Funds Available:** The stipend is $1,000. **Duration:** 1 year.
Eligibility Requirements: This program is open to 1) current members of the Massachusetts National Guard; 2) children and spouses of current members of the National Guard Association of Massachusetts (NGAMA); and 3) children and spouses of current members of the Massachusetts National Guard. Applicants must be enrolled in or planning to enroll in an accredited college or technical program. Along with their application, they must submit a letter of recommendation, a list of extracurricular activities and other significant accomplishments, high school or college transcripts, and an essay on the role of the National Guard in homeland defense. **Deadline for Receipt:** March of each year.

1203 ■ NATIONAL GUARD ASSOCIATION OF MICHIGAN

Attn: Scholarships
300 Elvin Court
Lansing, MI 48913-5103
Tel: (517)484-1644
Free: 800-477-1644
Fax: (517)484-1680
E-mail: ngam@voyager.net
Web Site: http://www.ngam.org/edgrant.htm
To provide financial assistance for college to members of the National Guard Association of Michigan.
Title of Award: National Guard Association of Michigan Education Grants **Area, Field, or Subject:** General studies/Field of study not specified **Level of Education for which Award is Granted:** Undergraduate **Number Awarded:** Varies each year. **Funds Available:** The stipend is $500 per semester. **Duration:** 1 semester; may be renewed.
Eligibility Requirements: This program is open to members of the association who are also current members of the Michigan National Guard. Applicants may be enlisted members of any rank, warrant officers through CW3, or commissioned officers through the rank of captain. **Deadline for Receipt:** June of each year for the fall term/semester; November of each year for the winter term/semester.

1204 ■ NATIONAL GUARD ASSOCIATION OF NEW JERSEY

Attn: Scholarship Committee
101 Eggert Crossing Road
Lawrenceville, NJ 08648-2805
Tel: (609)562-0222
Fax: (609)562-0229
E-mail: dutko@njdmava.state.nj.us
Web Site: http://www.nganj.org
To provide financial assistance for college or graduate school to New Jersey National Guard members or their dependents.

Title of Award: National Guard Association of New Jersey Scholarship Program **Area, Field, or Subject:** General studies/Field of study not specified **Level of Education for which Award is Granted:** Graduate, Undergraduate **Number Awarded:** Varies each year; recently, 10 of these scholarships were awarded. **Funds Available:** Stipends up to $1,000 are available. **Duration:** 1 year.
Eligibility Requirements: This program is open to active members of the New Jersey National Guard; the spouses, children, legal wards, and grandchildren of active members; and the children, legal wards, and grandchildren of retired (with at least 20 years of service) or deceased members. Applicants may be high school seniors or graduates entering college; students currently enrolled in college, business school, or trade school; or graduate students. Selection is based on civic and academic activities; offices, honors, awards, and special recognitions; and high school and/or college transcripts. **Deadline for Receipt:** March of each year.

1205 ■ NATIONAL GUARD ASSOCIATION OF OKLAHOMA

Attn: Scholarship Foundation
3535 Military Circle
Oklahoma City, OK 73111
Tel: (405)424-1231
Fax: (405)424-1235
E-mail: ngaok@sbcglobal.net
Web Site: http://www.ngaok.org/Scholarship.htm
To provide financial assistance for college to members of the National Guard Association of Oklahoma (NGAOK) and their dependents.
Title of Award: Oklahoma National Guard Association Scholarships **Area, Field, or Subject:** General studies/Field of study not specified **Level of Education for which Award is Granted:** Undergraduate **Number Awarded:** 1 or more each year. **Funds Available:** A stipend is awarded (amount not specified). **Duration:** 1 year.
Eligibility Requirements: This program is open to NGAOK members and their dependents. Applicants must submit a brief statement of their goals and career objectives. Selection is based on that statement, community service, extracurricular activities, awards and recognition, work experience, and financial need. **Deadline for Receipt:** January of each year.

1206 ■ NATIONAL GUARD ASSOCIATION OF RHODE ISLAND

Attn: Jessica Perry
645 New London Avenue
Cranston, RI 02920
Tel: (401)228-6586
Fax: (401)541-9182
E-mail: jessica.perry@ri.ngb.army.mil
Web Site: http://www.ngari.org
To provide financial assistance for college to current and former members of the Rhode Island National Guard and their families.
Title of Award: National Guard Association of Rhode Island Scholarships **Area, Field, or Subject:** General studies/Field of study not specified **Level of Education for which Award is Granted:** Undergraduate **Number Awarded:** Varies each year. **Funds Available:** The stipend depends on the availability of funds. **Duration:** 1 year; nonrenewable.
Eligibility Requirements: This program is open to active and retired members of the Rhode Island National Guard and their immediate family members. Applicants must be high school seniors, high school graduates, or undergraduate students. They must be attending or accepted at an accredited college, university, or vocational/technical school. As part of their application, they must explain their needs, goals, and other information that may help the selection committee. **Deadline for Receipt:** May of each year. **Additional Information:** Enlisted Rhode Island National Guard personnel are automatically associate members of the National Guard Association of Rhode Island.

1207 ■ NATIONAL GUARD ASSOCIATION OF SOUTH CAROLINA

Attn: Scholarship Foundation
2001 Assembly Street, Suite 204
Columbia, SC 29201
Tel: (803)254-8456
Free: 800-822-3235
Fax: (803)254-3869
E-mail: nginco@ngasc.org
Web Site: http://www.ngasc.org

To provide financial assistance for college or graduate school to current and former South Carolina National Guard members and their dependents.
Title of Award: National Guard Association of South Carolina Scholarships **Area, Field, or Subject:** General studies/Field of study not specified **Level of Education for which Award is Granted:** Graduate, Undergraduate **Number Awarded:** Varies each year. Recently, 58 of these scholarships were awarded: 1 at $1,500 and 57 at $1,000. **Funds Available:** Stipends are $1,500 or $1,000. **Duration:** 1 year.
Eligibility Requirements: This program is open to 1) current, retired, and deceased members of the South Carolina National Guard; 2) their dependents; and 3) members of the National Guard Association of South Carolina. Applicants must be attending or interested in attending a college or university in South Carolina. Several of the scholarships include additional restrictions on school or academic major **Deadline for Receipt:** January of each year. **Additional Information:** Among the named scholarships included in this program are the BG (Ret) C. Norwood Gayle Memorial Scholarship Award, the CMSgt Jim Burgess Scholarship Award, the Mrs. Kaye Helgeson Memorial Scholarship Award, the BG (Ret) Jerald R. Helgeson Scholarship Award, the LTC (Ret) Glenny J. (Jeff) Matthews Memorial Scholarship Awards, the LTC (Ret) Jerome N. McLeod Memorial Scholarship Award, the BG (Ret) and Mrs. Louis C. Addison Scholarship Award, the LTC (Ret) and Mrs. M. Bond Thomas Honorary Scholarship, the MSG Michael S. Cash Memorial Scholarship Awards, the LT COL and Mrs. Thad Myers Scholarship Award, the USAA Enlisted Scholarship Awards (sponsored by the USAA Insurance Corporation), the South Carolina Army National Guard Federal Credit Union Award, and the McEntire Federal Credit Union Scholarship Award.

1208 ■ NATIONAL GUARD ASSOCIATION OF TENNESSEE

Attn: Scholarship Committee
4332 Kenilwood Drive
Nashville, TN 37204-4401
Tel: (615)833-9100; 888-642-8448
Fax: (615)833-9173
E-mail: don@ngatn.org
Web Site: http://www.ngatn.org
To provide financial assistance for college to members or dependents of members of the National Guard Association of Tennessee (NGAT).
Title of Award: National Guard Association of Tennessee Scholarship Program **Area, Field, or Subject:** General studies/Field of study not specified **Level of Education for which Award is Granted:** Undergraduate **Number Awarded:** 6 each year: 1 to an active National Guard member; 2 to current association members or their dependents; 2 to active National Guard members or their dependents; and 1 to current Guard members who participated in Operation Desert Storm or dependents of a former member of an Operation Desert Storm unit. **Funds Available:** The stipends are $1,500. **Duration:** 1 year.
Eligibility Requirements: This program is open to active Tennessee National Guard members and to active annual or life members of the NGAT. If no active Guard or association member qualifies, the scholarships may be awarded to the child of a Guard or association member, including life members who have retired or are deceased. All applicants must be high school seniors or graduates who meet entrance or continuation requirements at a Tennessee college or university. Selection is based on leadership in school and civic activities, motivation for continued higher education, academic achievement in high school and/or college, and financial need. **Deadline for Receipt:** June of each year.

1209 ■ NATIONAL GUARD ASSOCIATION OF TEXAS

Attn: Education Committee
3706 Crawford
P.O. Box 10045
Austin, TX 78766-1045
Tel: (512)454-7300
Free: 800-252-NGAT
Fax: (512)467-6803
E-mail: dpyeatt@ngat.org
Web Site: http://www.ngat.org/programs/edfound.htm
To provide financial assistance for college or graduate school to members and dependents of members of the National Guard Association of Texas.
Title of Award: National Guard Association of Texas Scholarship Program **Area, Field, or Subject:** General studies/Field of study not specified

Level of Education for which Award is Granted: Graduate, Undergraduate **Number Awarded:** At least 9 each year: 4 to high school seniors (1 at $1,000, 1 at $750, and 2 at $500), 3 to undergraduate students (1 at $1,000, 1 at $750, and 1 at $500), 1 at $500 to a graduate student, and 1 or more at $500 to any academic level. Traditionally, 5 additional scholarships are awarded annually: 2 by the Chief Masters Sergeants, 2 by the Command Sergeants Major, and 1 by the Warrant Officers Association. **Funds Available:** Stipends are $1,000, $750, or $500 per year. **Duration:** 1 year (nonrenewable).
Eligibility Requirements: This program is open to annual and life members of the association and their spouses and children (associate members and their dependents are not eligible). Applicants must be high school seniors, undergraduate students, or graduate students, either enrolled or planning to enroll in an institution of higher education. Selection is based on scholarship, citizenship, and leadership. **Deadline for Receipt:** January of each year.

1210 ■ NATIONAL GUARD OFFICERS ASSOCIATION OF FLORIDA
Attn: Scholarship Committee
P.O. Box 3446
St. Augustine, FL 32085-3446
Tel: (904)823-0628
Fax: (904)829-2068
E-mail: mary.paul@fl.ngb.army.mil
Web Site: http://www.floridaguard.org/ngoa/scholarships.html
To provide financial assistance for college to members of the Florida National Guard and their families who are also members of either the National Guard Officers Association of Florida (NGOA-FL) or the Enlisted National Guard Association of Florida (ENGAF).
Title of Award: NGOA and ENGA of Florida Scholarship Program **Area, Field, or Subject:** General studies/Field of study not specified **Level of Education for which Award is Granted:** Undergraduate **Number Awarded:** 15 each year. **Funds Available:** Scholarships are $1,000 for full-time students or $500 for part-time students; funds are paid directly to the recipient's institution. **Duration:** 1 year; may be renewed.
Eligibility Requirements: This program is open to active members of the Florida National Guard (enlisted, officer, and warrant officer), their spouses, and children, but preference is given to Guard members. Applicants must be residents of Florida attending a college, university, or vocational/technical school in the state. They must also be a member, spouse of a member, or child of a member of their respective association. Selection is based on academic achievement, civic and moral leadership, character, and financial need. **Deadline for Receipt:** May of each year. **Additional Information:** This program is jointly sponsored by the respective associations.

1211 ■ NATIONAL HEAD START ASSOCIATION
Attn: Scholarships and Awards
1651 Prince Street
Alexandria, VA 22314
Tel: (703)739-0875
Fax: (703)739-0878
E-mail: satkinson@nhsa.org
Web Site: http://www.nhsa.org/program/program_scholarship.htm
To provide financial assistance for college to students who were in the Head Start program.
Title of Award: Phyllis J. Jones Memorial Scholarships for Head Start Graduates **Area, Field, or Subject:** General studies/Field of study not specified **Level of Education for which Award is Granted:** Undergraduate **Number Awarded:** 2 each year. **Funds Available:** The stipend is $1,500. **Duration:** 1 year.
Eligibility Requirements: This program is open to former Head Start students who are enrolled or planning to enroll at a 4-year college or university, 2-year community college, or vocational/technical school. Applicants must submit a 200-word statement on their goals and aspirations for furthering their education and the role Head Start has played in their education. Selection is based on that statement (40 points), financial need (30 points), letters of reference or recommendation (20 points), and completeness of information (10 points). Students submit their applications to their local program, which forwards 2 to the state association. Each state association forwards 2 applications to the regional association, which selects 2 for nomination to the national headquarters. **Deadline for Receipt:** Regional associations must submit applications to national

headquarters by December of each year. **Additional Information:** This program was established in 1990.

1212 ■ NATIONAL HEAD START ASSOCIATION
Attn: Scholarships and Awards
1651 Prince Street
Alexandria, VA 22314
Tel: (703)739-0875
Fax: (703)739-0878
E-mail: satkinson@nhsa.org
Web Site: http://www.nhsa.org/program/program_scholarship.htm
To provide financial assistance for college to Head Start parents.
Title of Award: Ann Phipps Memorial Scholarships **Area, Field, or Subject:** General studies/Field of study not specified **Level of Education for which Award is Granted:** Undergraduate **Number Awarded:** 2 each year. **Funds Available:** The stipend is $1,500. **Duration:** 1 year.
Eligibility Requirements: This program is open to Head Start parents who are enrolled or planning to enroll at a 4-year college or university, 2-year community college, or vocational/technical school. Applicants must submit a 200-word statement on their personal goals. Selection is based on that statement (40 points), Head Start involvement and community contribution (30 points), letters of reference or recommendation (20 points), and completeness of information (10 points). Parents submit their applications to their local program, which forwards 1 to the state association. Each state association forwards 2 applications to the regional association, which selects 2 for nomination to the national headquarters. **Deadline for Receipt:** Regional associations must submit applications to national headquarters by December of each year. **Additional Information:** These scholarships were first awarded in 1979.

1213 ■ NATIONAL HEAD START ASSOCIATION
Attn: Scholarships and Awards
1651 Prince Street
Alexandria, VA 22314
Tel: (703)739-0875
Fax: (703)739-0878
E-mail: satkinson@nhsa.org
Web Site: http://www.nhsa.org/program/program_scholarship.htm
To provide financial assistance for college to hearing-impaired students who were in the Head Start program.
Title of Award: Curtis Pride Scholarship for the Hearing Impaired **Area, Field, or Subject:** General studies/Field of study not specified **Level of Education for which Award is Granted:** Undergraduate **Number Awarded:** 1 each year. **Funds Available:** The stipend is $1,000. **Duration:** 1 year.
Eligibility Requirements: This program is open to former Head Start students who have a hearing impairment. Applicants must be enrolled or planning to enroll at a 4-year college or university, 2-year community college, or vocational/technical school. They must submit a 200-word statement on their goals and aspirations for furthering their education and the role Head Start has played in their education. Selection is based on that statement (40 points), financial need (30 points), letters of reference or recommendation (20 points), and completeness of information (10 points). Students submit their applications to their local program, which forwards 1 to the state association. Each state association forwards 1 application to the regional association, which selects 1 for nomination to the national headquarters. **Deadline for Receipt:** Regional associations must submit applications to national headquarters by December of each year.

1214 ■ NATIONAL HEMOPHILIA FOUNDATION
Attn: Department of Finance, Administration & MIS
116 West 32nd Street, 11th Floor
New York, NY 10001-3212
Tel: (212)328-3700
Free: 800-42-HANDI
Fax: (212)328-3777
E-mail: info@hemophilia.org
Web Site: http://www.hemophilia.org
To provide financial assistance for college to students with hemophilia.
Title of Award: Kevin Child Scholarship **Area, Field, or Subject:** General studies/Field of study not specified **Level of Education for which Award is Granted:** Four Year College **Number Awarded:** 1 each year. **Funds Available:** The stipend is $1,000. **Duration:** 1 year.

Eligibility Requirements: This program is open to high school seniors entering their first year of undergraduate study as well as those currently enrolled in college. Applicants must have hemophilia or another bleeding disorder. Selection is based on academic performance, participation in school and community activities, and an essay on their occupational objectives and goals in life. **Deadline for Receipt:** June of each year. **Additional Information:** The program was established by the Child family after the death of 21-year old Kevin in 1989. Information is also available from Mary Child Smoot, (203) 968-2776, E-mail: Smooter@aol.com.

1215 ■ NATIONAL HEMOPHILIA FOUNDATION

Attn: Department of Finance, Administration & MIS
116 West 32nd Street, 11th Floor
New York, NY 10001-3212
Tel: (212)328-3700
Free: 800-42-HANDI
Fax: (212)328-3777
E-mail: info@hemophilia.org
Web Site: http://www.hemophilia.org
To provide financial assistance for college or graduate school to women who have a bleeding disorder.
Title of Award: Project Red Flag Academic Scholarship for Women with Bleeding Disorders **Area, Field, or Subject:** General studies/Field of study not specified **Level of Education for which Award is Granted:** Four Year College, Graduate **Number Awarded:** 2 each year. **Funds Available:** The stipend is $2,500. **Duration:** 1 year.
Eligibility Requirements: This program is open to women who are entering or already enrolled in an undergraduate or graduate program at a university, college, or accredited vocational school. Applicants must have von Willebrand disease, hemophilia or other clotting factor deficiency, or carrier status. Along with their application, they must submit a 250-word essay that describes their educational and future career plans, including how they intend to use their education to enhance the bleeding disorders community. Financial need is not considered in the selection process. **Deadline for Receipt:** May of each year. **Additional Information:** The program was established in 2005.

1216 ■ NATIONAL HOOK-UP OF BLACK WOMEN, INC.

Attn: Scholarship Committee
1809 East 71st Street, Suite 205
Chicago, IL 60649
Tel: (773)667-7061
Fax: (773)667-7064
E-mail: nhbwdir@aol.com
Web Site: http://www.nhbwinc.com
To provide financial assistance to African American high school and college students who are interested in earning an undergraduate degree.
Title of Award: Arnita Young Boswell Scholarship **Area, Field, or Subject:** General studies/Field of study not specified **Level of Education for which Award is Granted:** Undergraduate **Number Awarded:** 5 each year. **Funds Available:** The stipend is $1,000. Funds are paid directly to the college or university of the recipient's choice. **Duration:** 1 year.
Eligibility Requirements: This program is open to African American high school seniors or currently-enrolled college students. They must be attending or preparing to attend an accredited school and have a GPA of 2.75 or higher. They must demonstrate written communication skills by preparing an essay of 300 to 500 words on a topic that changes annually; recently, the topic was "Electing a U.S. President: Should the Electoral College Process Remain a Component of the Election Procedure?" Selection is based on academic record, financial need, community service, concern for the African American family, and a desire to complete a college degree. **Deadline for Receipt:** February of each year.

1217 ■ NATIONAL HOUSING ENDOWMENT

1201 15th Street, N.W.
Washington, DC 20005
Tel: (202)266-8483
Free: 800-368-5242
Fax: (202)266-8177
E-mail: nhe@nahb.com
Web Site: http://www.nationalhousingendowment.com/Scholarships.htm
To provide financial assistance to undergraduate and graduate students interested in preparing for a career in the residential construction industry.

Title of Award: Lee S. Evans Scholarships **Area, Field, or Subject:** Construction **Level of Education for which Award is Granted:** Graduate, Undergraduate **Number Awarded:** Varies each year; recently, 12 of these scholarships were awarded. **Funds Available:** Stipends range from $2,000 to $5,000. Funds are made payable to the recipient and sent to the recipient's school. **Duration:** 1 year; may be renewed.
Eligibility Requirements: This program is open to full-time undergraduate and graduate students who have at least 1 full academic year of course work remaining and are able to demonstrate an interest in obtaining employment in the residential construction industry upon graduation. Preference is given to students who are current members (or will be members in the upcoming semester) of a student chapter of the National Association of Home Builders and to students enrolled in a 4-year program emphasizing construction management. Applicants must submit an essay on an issue faced by the housing industry and their recommendations for resolving it. Selection is based on financial need, career goals, academic achievement, employment history, extracurricular activities, and letters of recommendation. **Deadline for Receipt:** November of each year. **Additional Information:** The National Housing Endowment is the philanthropic arm of the National Association of Home Builders. This scholarship was established in 1990.

1218 ■ NATIONAL HOUSING ENDOWMENT

1201 15th Street, N.W.
Washington, DC 20005
Tel: (202)266-8483
Free: 800-368-5242
Fax: (202)266-8177
E-mail: nhe@nahb.com
Web Site: http://www.nationalhousingendowment.com/Scholarships.htm
To provide financial assistance to undergraduate and graduate students interested in preparing for a career in the housing construction industry.
Title of Award: Herman J. Smith Scholarships **Area, Field, or Subject:** Construction; Finance **Level of Education for which Award is Granted:** Graduate, Undergraduate **Number Awarded:** Varies each year; recently, 18 of these scholarships were awarded. **Funds Available:** The stipend is $2,000. Funds are made payable to the recipient and sent to the recipient's school. **Duration:** 1 year; may be renewed if the recipient continues to demonstrate academic progress and financial need.
Eligibility Requirements: This program is open to full-time undergraduate and graduate students who have at least 1 full academic year of course work remaining and are able to demonstrate an interest in obtaining employment in the construction industry, mortgage finance, or a construction-related field upon graduation. Preference is given to 1) applicants who are residents of Texas or attending an institution in Texas; 2) students who are current members (or will be members in the upcoming semester) of a student chapter of the National Association of Home Builders; and 3) junior and seniors. Applicants must submit an essay on their previous experience (vocational and academic) and their aspirations and potential as a professional in the construction industry. Selection is based on financial need, career goals, academic achievement, employment history, extracurricular activities, and letters of recommendation. Finalists are interviewed by the board of directors of the Builder's Association of Fort Worth and Tarrant County Education Foundation. **Deadline for Receipt:** April of each year. **Additional Information:** The National Housing Endowment is the philanthropic arm of the National Association of Home Builders.

1219 ■ NATIONAL HUGUENOT SOCIETY

Attn: Executive Director
9033 Lyndale Avenue South, Suite 108
Bloomington, MN 55420-3535
Tel: (952)885-9776
E-mail: scholarship@huguenot.netnation.com
Web Site: http://huguenot.netnation.com/general/scholarship.htm
To provide financial assistance for college or graduate school to members of the National Huguenot Society.
Title of Award: National Huguenot Society Scholarships **Area, Field, or Subject:** General studies/Field of study not specified **Level of Education for which Award is Granted:** Four Year College, Graduate **Number Awarded:** 1 each year. **Funds Available:** The stipend is $5,000. **Duration:** 1 year; nonrenewable.
Eligibility Requirements: This program is open to students at accredited colleges, universities, and graduate schools who have completed at least

2 years of college with a GPA of 3.0 or higher. Applicants must be a regular member of the National Huguenot Society which requires that they 1) be at least 18 years of age; 2) adhere to the Huguenot principles of faith and liberty; 3) be a member of the Protestant faith; and 4) be lineally descended from a Huguenot who either emigrated from France to North America or another country between 1520 and 1787 or remained in France. Their program of study must have included at least 2 semesters of history, including a history of religion. Along with their application, they may submit a short statement on their scholastic achievements and goals and how a scholarship would be advantageous to them. Financial need is not considered in the selection process. **Additional Information:** Information is also available from Richard Dana Smith, Sr., Huguenot Scholarship Awards, 647 Brintons Bridge Road, West Chester, PA 19382.

1220 ■ NATIONAL INDEPENDENT AUTOMOBILE DEALERS ASSOCIATION

Attn: Selection Committee
2521 Brown Boulevard, Suite 100
Arlington, TX 76006-5203
Tel: (817)640-3838
Free: 800-682-3837
Fax: (817)649-5866
E-mail: rachel@niada.com
Web Site: http://www.niada.com
To provide financial assistance for college to children of members of the National Independent Automobile Dealers Association (NIADA).
Title of Award: National Independent Automobile Dealers Association Scholarship **Area, Field, or Subject:** General studies/Field of study not specified **Level of Education for which Award is Granted:** Undergraduate **Number Awarded:** 4 each year: 1 in each region. **Funds Available:** The stipend is $2,500. **Duration:** 1 year.
Eligibility Requirements: This program is open to high school seniors who are the children or grandchildren of association members in good standing. Applicants must have excellent high school records and must demonstrate an aptitude for college work. Financial need is not considered in the selection process. **Deadline for Receipt:** January of each year.

1221 ■ NATIONAL INSTITUTES OF HEALTH BLACK SCIENTISTS ASSOCIATION

Attn: Scholarship Committee
P.O. Box 2262
Kensington, MD 20891-2262
Web Site: http://bsa.od.nih.gov
To provide financial assistance to underrepresented minority high school seniors from Washington, D.C. who plan to study science in college.
Title of Award: Cheryl Torrence-Campbell Scholarships **Area, Field, or Subject:** Science **Level of Education for which Award is Granted:** Undergraduate **Number Awarded:** 2 each year. **Funds Available:** The stipend is $1,000. **Duration:** 1 year.
Eligibility Requirements: This program is open to seniors graduating from public and private high schools in the District of Columbia who are members of ethnic or racial groups underrepresented in the field of biomedical research. Applicants must have been accepted into an accredited college or university to major in the sciences. They must submit a 1-page essay on why they have chosen to major in science in college. Preference is given to students who are financially disadvantaged. **Deadline for Receipt:** May of each year.

1222 ■ NATIONAL KIDNEY FOUNDATION OF ARKANSAS

No. 1 Lile Court, Suite 201
P.O. Box 453
Little Rock, AR 72203
Tel: (501)664-4343
Free: 800-254-2277
Fax: (501)664-7145
E-mail: hpowell@kidneyar.org
Web Site: http://www.kidneyar.org
To provide financial assistance for college to kidney patients in Arkansas.
Title of Award: National Kidney Foundation of Arkansas Academic Awards **Area, Field, or Subject:** General studies/Field of study not specified **Level of Education for which Award is Granted:** Undergraduate **Number Awarded:** Varies each year. **Funds Available:** A stipend is awarded (amount not specified). **Duration:** 1 year.

Eligibility Requirements: This program is open to residents of Arkansas who are on dialysis or are kidney transplant recipients. Applicants must be attending or planning to attend a postsecondary school. Selection is based primarily on financial need.

1223 ■ NATIONAL KIDNEY FOUNDATION OF INDIANA, INC.

Attn: Program Coordinator
911 East 86th Street, Suite 100
Indianapolis, IN 46204-1840
Tel: (317)722-5640
Free: 800-382-9971
Fax: (317)722-5650
E-mail: nkfi@myvine.com
Web Site: http://www.kidneyindiana.org
To provide financial assistance to kidney patients in Indiana who are interested in pursuing higher education in an academic or monitored occupational setting.
Title of Award: Larry Smock Scholarship **Area, Field, or Subject:** General studies/Field of study not specified **Level of Education for which Award is Granted:** Undergraduate **Number Awarded:** Several each year. **Funds Available:** The amount awarded depends upon the needs of the recipient. Funds are paid directly to the recipient's school. **Duration:** 1 year; may be renewed.
Eligibility Requirements: Eligible to apply for this award are Indiana residents who have at least a high school diploma or its equivalent and who have received a kidney transplant or are on dialysis. Applicants must be interested in attending college, trade school, or vocational school to work on an academic or occupational degree. Finalists are interviewed. Letters of reference (not from the applicant's family) are required. Financial need is considered in the selection process. **Deadline for Receipt:** February of each year. **Additional Information:** This fund was established in 1992.

1224 ■ NATIONAL KIDNEY FOUNDATION OF MAINE

Attn: Scholarship Committee
630 Congress Street
P.O. Box 1134
Portland, ME 04104
Tel: (207)772-7270
Free: 800-639-7220
Fax: (207)772-4202
E-mail: info@kidneyme.org
Web Site: http://www.kidneyme.org
To provide financial assistance for college to kidney patients and their families in Maine.
Title of Award: National Kidney Foundation of Maine Scholarships **Area, Field, or Subject:** General studies/Field of study not specified **Level of Education for which Award is Granted:** Undergraduate **Number Awarded:** Varies each year; recently, 4 of these scholarships were awarded. **Funds Available:** A stipend is awarded (amount not specified). **Duration:** 1 year.
Eligibility Requirements: This program is open to residents of Maine who are kidney patients (dialysis patients, kidney transplant recipients, or newly diagnosed patients who are in early intervention programs) or immediately family members of patients. Applicants must be attending or planning to attend an accredited college or university. Along with their application, they must submit documentation of financial need and brief essays on their educational goals and how kidney disease has impacted their life. **Deadline for Receipt:** May of each year.

1225 ■ NATIONAL LATINA ALLIANCE

633 West Fifth Street, Suite 1150
Los Angeles, CA 90071
Tel: (323)980-7992
E-mail: info@nationallatinaalliance.org
Web Site: http://www.nationallatinaalliance.org/ScholProg.htm
To provide financial assistance for college or other career education to Latinas.
Title of Award: National Latina Alliance Scholarships **Area, Field, or Subject:** General studies/Field of study not specified **Level of Education for which Award is Granted:** Undergraduate **Number Awarded:** Varies each year; recently, 17 of these scholarships were awarded. **Funds Available:** Stipends range from $500 to $1,000, depending on the need of the recipient. **Duration:** 1 year.

Eligibility Requirements: This program is open to Latinas who are 1) graduating high school seniors; 2) currently enrolled in a college or university; 3) returning to school after an absence of at least 2 years; or 4) preparing for a non-traditional career (e.g., chef, artist, entrepreneur, nurse). Applicants must have a GPA of 2.5 or higher and be able to document financial need. They must submit a 1-page essay on the question, "As a Latina, what do you think is important for the success of the community?" Reentry applicants must also provide a 1-page essay discussing their reason for withdrawing from school. Non-traditional career students must provide documentation regarding their career. **Deadline for Receipt:** March of each year. **Additional Information:** Information is also available from Gloria Michel, Education Committee Chair, c/o Guerra & Associates, 1100 South Flower Street, Suite 2100, Los Angeles, CA 90015.

1226 ■ NATIONAL MILITARY FAMILY ASSOCIATION, INC.

Attn: Spouse Scholarship Program
2500 North Van Dorn Street, Suite 102
Alexandria, VA 22302-1601
Tel: (703)931-NMFA
Free: 800-260-0218
Fax: (703)931-4600
E-mail: families@nmfa.org
Web Site: http://www.nmfa.org
To provide financial assistance for college or graduate school to spouses of active and retired uniformed services personnel.
Title of Award: Joanne Holbrook Patton Military Spouse Scholarship Program **Area, Field, or Subject:** General studies/Field of study not specified **Level of Education for which Award is Granted:** Graduate, Undergraduate **Number Awarded:** Varies each year; recently, 25 of these scholarships were awarded. **Funds Available:** The stipend is $1,000. Funds are paid directly to the educational institution to be used for tuition, fees, books, and school room and board. **Duration:** 1 year; recipients may reapply.
Eligibility Requirements: This program is open to the spouses of uniformed services personnel (active, retired, Reserve, Guard, or survivor). Applicants must be attending or planning to attend an accredited postsecondary institution to work on a professional certificate or undergraduate or graduate degree. Selection is based on an essay question, community involvement, and academic achievement. **Deadline for Receipt:** March of each year. **Additional Information:** This program began in 2004. It is currently sponsored by General Dynamics. Applications must be submitted online.

1227 ■ NATIONAL MULTIPLE SCLEROSIS SOCIETY

Attn: Scholarship Fund
700 Broadway, Suite 810
Denver, CO 80203
Tel: (303)813-6664
Free: 800-FIGHT-MS
Fax: (212)986-7981
E-mail: Katherine.Swank@nmss.org
Web Site: http://www.nationalmssociety.org/Research-otherawards.asp
To provide financial assistance for college to students who have Multiple Sclerosis (MS) or are the children of people with MS.
Title of Award: National MS Society Scholarship Program **Area, Field, or Subject:** General studies/Field of study not specified **Level of Education for which Award is Granted:** Undergraduate **Number Awarded:** Varies each year; recently, 88 of these scholarships, worth $207,000, were awarded. **Funds Available:** Stipends range from $1,000 to $3,000. **Duration:** 1 year; nonrenewable.
Eligibility Requirements: This program is open to 1) high school seniors who have MS and will be attending an accredited postsecondary school for the first time; 2) high school seniors who are the children of people with MS and will be attending an accredited postsecondary school for the first time; and 3) high school (or GED) graduates of any age who have MS and will be attending an accredited postsecondary school for the first time. Applicants must be U.S. citizens or permanent residents who plan to enroll in an undergraduate course of study at an accredited 2- or 4-year college, university, or vocational/technical school in the United States to work on a degree, license, or certificate. Selection is based on academic record, leadership and participation in school or community activities; work experience, a statement of educational and career goals, an outside

appraisal, unusual personal or family circumstances, an essay on the impact of MS on their life, and financial need. **Deadline for Receipt:** February of each year. **Additional Information:** This program is managed by Scholarship America, One Scholarship Way, P.O. Box 297, St. Peter, MN 56082, (507) 931-1682, (800) 537-4180, ext 471, Fax: (507) 931-9168, E-mail: smsinfo@csfa.org.

1228 ■ NATIONAL NAVAL OFFICERS ASSOCIATION-WASHINGTON, D.C. CHAPTER

Attn: Scholarship Program
2701 Park Center Drive, B704
Alexandria, VA 22302
E-mail: williams.stephen@hq.navy.mil
Web Site: http://www.dcnnoa.org
To provide financial assistance to minority high school seniors from the Washington, D.C. area.
Title of Award: Ester Boone Memorial Scholarships **Area, Field, or Subject:** General studies/Field of study not specified **Level of Education for which Award is Granted:** Undergraduate **Number Awarded:** 4 each year. **Funds Available:** The stipend is $1,000 per year. **Duration:** 1 year.
Eligibility Requirements: This program is open to minority seniors at high schools in the Washington, D.C. metropolitan area who plan to enroll full time at an accredited 2-year or 4-year college or university. Applicants must have a GPA of 2.5 or higher. Selection is based on academic achievement, community involvement, and financial need. **Deadline for Receipt:** April of each year. **Additional Information:** Recipients are not required to join or affiliate with the military in any way.

1229 ■ NATIONAL NAVAL OFFICERS ASSOCIATION-WASHINGTON, D.C. CHAPTER

Attn: Scholarship Program
2701 Park Center Drive, B704
Alexandria, VA 22302
E-mail: williams.stephen@hq.navy.mil
Web Site: http://www.dcnnoa.org
To provide financial assistance to minority high school seniors from the Washington, D.C. area.
Title of Award: Capstone Corporation Scholarship Award **Area, Field, or Subject:** General studies/Field of study not specified **Level of Education for which Award is Granted:** Undergraduate **Number Awarded:** 1 each year. **Funds Available:** The stipend is $1,000 per year. **Duration:** 1 year.
Eligibility Requirements: This program is open to minority seniors at high schools in the Washington, D.C. metropolitan area who plan to enroll full time at an accredited 2-year or 4-year college or university. Applicants must have a GPA of 3.0 or higher. U.S. citizenship or permanent resident status is required. Selection is based on academic achievement, community involvement, and financial need. **Deadline for Receipt:** April of each year. **Additional Information:** Recipients are not required to join or affiliate with the military in any way. This program is supported by Capstone Corporation, a minority-owned business incorporated in 1986 by former active-duty Navy officers.

1230 ■ NATIONAL NAVAL OFFICERS ASSOCIATION-WASHINGTON, D.C. CHAPTER

Attn: Scholarship Program
2701 Park Center Drive, B704
Alexandria, VA 22302
E-mail: williams.stephen@hq.navy.mil
Web Site: http://www.dcnnoa.org
To provide financial assistance for college to African American high school seniors from the Washington, D.C. area.
Title of Award: Vice Admiral Samuel L. Gravely, Jr. Memorial Scholarship **Area, Field, or Subject:** General studies/Field of study not specified **Level of Education for which Award is Granted:** Undergraduate **Number Awarded:** 1 each year. **Funds Available:** The stipend is $1,000 per year. **Duration:** 1 year; nonrenewable.
Eligibility Requirements: This program is open to African American seniors at high schools in the Washington, D.C. metropolitan area who plan to enroll full time at an accredited 2-year or 4-year college or university. Applicants must have a GPA of 2.5 or higher and be U.S. citizens or permanent residents. Selection is based on academic achievement, community involvement, and financial need. **Deadline for Receipt:** April of each year.

1231 ■ NATIONAL NAVAL OFFICERS ASSOCIATION-WASHINGTON, D.C. CHAPTER

Attn: Scholarship Program
2701 Park Center Drive, B704
Alexandria, VA 22302
E-mail: williams.stephen@hq.navy.mil
Web Site: http://www.dcnnoa.org
To provide financial assistance to minority high school seniors from the Washington, D.C. area.
Title of Award: Madison/Davis Scholarship Award **Area, Field, or Subject:** General studies/Field of study not specified **Level of Education for which Award is Granted:** Undergraduate **Number Awarded:** 1 each year. **Funds Available:** The stipend is $1,000 per year. **Duration:** 1 year.
Eligibility Requirements: This program is open to minority seniors at high schools in the Washington, D.C. metropolitan area who plan to enroll full time at an accredited 2-year or 4-year college or university. Applicants must have a GPA of 3.0 or higher. Selection is based on academic achievement, community involvement, and financial need. **Deadline for Receipt:** April of each year. **Additional Information:** Recipients are not required to join or affiliate with the military in any way.

1232 ■ NATIONAL NAVAL OFFICERS ASSOCIATION-WASHINGTON, D.C. CHAPTER

Attn: Scholarship Program
2701 Park Center Drive, B704
Alexandria, VA 22302
E-mail: williams.stephen@hq.navy.mil
Web Site: http://www.dcnnoa.org
To provide financial assistance for college to minority high school seniors from the Washington, D.C. area who have participated in Navy or Marine Corps Junior ROTC.
Title of Award: Navy/Marine Corps JROTC Scholarship **Area, Field, or Subject:** General studies/Field of study not specified **Level of Education for which Award is Granted:** Undergraduate **Number Awarded:** 1 each year. **Funds Available:** The stipend is $1,000 per year. **Duration:** 1 year; nonrenewable.
Eligibility Requirements: This program is open to minority seniors at high schools in the Washington, D.C. metropolitan area who have participated in Navy or Marine Corps JROTC. Applicants must be planning to enroll full time at an accredited 2-year or 4-year college or university. They must have a GPA of 2.5 or higher and be U.S. citizens or permanent residents. Selection is based on academic achievement, community involvement, and financial need. **Deadline for Receipt:** April of each year.

1233 ■ NATIONAL ORGANIZATION FOR WOMEN-NEW YORK STATE, INC.

Attn: NOW-NYS Foundation, Inc.
800 Main Street, Suite 3B
Niagara Falls, NY 14301
Tel: (716)285-5598
Fax: (716)285-5602
E-mail: nownys@nownys.com
Web Site: http://www.nownys.org/sgs.html
To provide financial assistance to undergraduate and graduate students in New York.
Title of Award: Shirley U. Graber Scholarship **Area, Field, or Subject:** General studies/Field of study not specified **Level of Education for which Award is Granted:** Graduate, Undergraduate **Number Awarded:** Varies each year. **Funds Available:** Stipends range from $200 to $2,000. **Duration:** 1 year.
Eligibility Requirements: This program is open to students in New York enrolled at a 2-year or 4-year college or university, graduate school, law school, or other professional graduate program. Applicants must have completed at least 1 course in women's studies. At least 1 award is reserved for a student attending Brooklyn College. Financial need is considered in the selection process. **Deadline for Receipt:** Applications are accepted on a rolling basis, but they should be submitted from 8 months to 1 year in advance of the semester for which funding is requested.

1234 ■ NATIONAL PANHELLENIC CONFERENCE

Attn: NPC Foundation
8777 Purdue Road, Suite 117
Indianapolis, IN 46268

Tel: (317)872-3185
Fax: (317)872-3192
E-mail: npccentral@npcwomen.org
Web Site: http://www.npcwomen.org/foundation/f_scholarships.php
To provide financial assistance to undergraduate women who are members of Greek-letter societies.
Title of Award: NPC Foundation Regional Scholarships **Area, Field, or Subject:** General studies/Field of study not specified **Level of Education for which Award is Granted:** Undergraduate **Number Awarded:** 5 each year. **Funds Available:** The stipend is $1,000. **Duration:** 1 year.
Eligibility Requirements: This program is open to Greek-affiliated women at colleges and universities in the United States. Applicants must provide information on their university committees, activities, and honors received; Panhellenic offices, committees, and honors received; chapter offices, committees, and honors received; and financial need. Scholarships are presented to students in each of 4 regions of the country. **Deadline for Receipt:** January of each year. **Additional Information:** This program includes the Mid-American Greek Council Association Scholarship the Northeast Greek Leadership Association Scholarship the Southeastern Panhellenic Conference Scholarship the Western Regional Greek Association Scholarship, awarded respectively in the 4 regions. In addition, the Alpha Phi/Betty Mullins Jones Scholarship is awarded to the highest-ranked applicant from all regions.

1235 ■ NATIONAL PKU NEWS

6869 Woodlawn Avenue, N.E., Suite 116
Seattle, WA 98115-5469
Tel: (206)525-8140
Fax: (206)525-5023
E-mail: schuett@pkunews.org
Web Site: http://www.pkunews.org
To provide financial assistance for college to students with phenylketonuria (PKU).
Title of Award: Robert Guthrie PKU Scholarship **Area, Field, or Subject:** General studies/Field of study not specified **Level of Education for which Award is Granted:** Undergraduate **Number Awarded:** Varies each year; recently, 2 of these scholarships were awarded. **Funds Available:** Stipends vary but recently have been $2,000. **Duration:** 1 year.
Eligibility Requirements: This program is open to college-age people with PKU who are on the required diet. Applicants must be accepted to an accredited college or technical school before the scholarship is awarded, but they may apply before acceptance is confirmed. Residents of all countries are eligible to apply. Selection is based on academic achievement and financial need. **Deadline for Receipt:** October of each year.

1236 ■ NATIONAL SCHOOL BOARDS ASSOCIATION

Attn: National Caucus of Hispanic School Board Members
1680 Duke Street
Alexandria, VA 22314-3493
Tel: (703)838-6157
Fax: (703)683-7590
E-mail: info@nsba.org
Web Site: http://www.nsba.org/caucus
To provide financial assistance for college to Hispanic high school seniors.
Title of Award: National Caucus of Hispanic School Board Members Scholarships **Area, Field, or Subject:** General studies/Field of study not specified **Level of Education for which Award is Granted:** Four Year College **Number Awarded:** 5 each year. **Funds Available:** The stipend is $1,000. **Duration:** 1 year.
Eligibility Requirements: This program is open to high school seniors of Hispanic origin who have been accepted to an accredited 4-year college or university. Applicants must have a GPA of 3.0 or higher and be able to demonstrate financial need. Along with their application, they must submit an autobiographical statement that includes a paragraph about their financial need. **Deadline for Receipt:** March of each year. **Additional Information:** This program was established in 1999. Funding is provided by Washington Mutual Bank and the Philip Morris Corporation.

1237 ■ NATIONAL TONGAN AMERICAN SOCIETY

2480 South Main Street, Suite 108
Salt Lake City, UT 84115
Tel: (801)467-8712
E-mail: ntas@planet-tonga.com

Web Site: http://www.planet-tonga.com/NTAS/scholarship.htm
To provide financial assistance to undergraduate students of Tongan background who live in Utah.

Title of Award: Tu'ipelehake Leadership Scholarship **Area, Field, or Subject:** General studies/Field of study not specified **Level of Education for which Award is Granted:** Undergraduate **Number Awarded:** 1 or more each year. **Funds Available:** The stipend is $1,000. **Duration:** 1 year.

Eligibility Requirements: This program is open to residents of Utah who are of Tongan background and enrolled or planning to enroll as a full-time undergraduate or graduate student. Applicants must have a cumulative GPA of 3.0 or higher. They must be able to demonstrate financial need, leadership abilities, community service, extracurricular activities, and motivation to succeed in school. **Deadline for Receipt:** January of each year.

1238 ■ NATIVE DAUGHTERS OF THE GOLDEN WEST

543 Baker Street
San Francisco, CA 94117-1405
Tel: (415)563-9091
Free: 800-994-NDGW
Fax: (415)563-5230
E-mail: ndgwgpo@mindspring.com
Web Site: http://www.ndgw.org/edu.htm
To provide financial assistance for college to members of the Native Daughters of the Golden West in California and their families.

Title of Award: Native Daughters of the Golden West Scholarship Program **Area, Field, or Subject:** General studies/Field of study not specified **Level of Education for which Award is Granted:** Undergraduate **Number Awarded:** Varies each year; recently, 4 of these scholarships were awarded. **Funds Available:** A stipend is awarded (amount not specified). **Duration:** 1 year; may be renewed if the recipient maintains a GPA of 3.0 or higher.

Eligibility Requirements: This program is open to members and their children who are attending or planning to attend an accredited university, college, or vocational school in California. Applicants must have been born in the state. **Deadline for Receipt:** April of each year. **Additional Information:** Information is also available from Pat Riley, Education and Scholarship Chair, 527 29th Avenue, San Mateo, CA 94403. This program includes the Annie L. Adair Scholarship and the Sue J. Irwin Scholarship. Requests for applications must be accompanied by a self-addressed envelope.

1239 ■ NAVAL ACADEMY WOMEN'S CLUB

Attn: Scholarship Committee
P.O. Box 826
Annapolis, MD 21404-0826
Tel: (410)266-7306
E-mail: MaryadaJR@aol.com
Web Site: http://www.usna.edu/WomensClub/nawcscholarship.html
To provide financial assistance for college to the family members of armed forces personnel or others associated with the U.S. Naval Academy.

Title of Award: Naval Academy Women's Club Scholarship **Area, Field, or Subject:** General studies/Field of study not specified **Level of Education for which Award is Granted:** Undergraduate **Number Awarded:** 1 or more each year. **Funds Available:** A stipend is awarded (amount not specified). **Duration:** 1 year; may be renewed for 3 additional years.

Eligibility Requirements: Eligible to apply for these scholarships are 1) dependents under 23 years of age of active-duty, retired, or deceased armed services personnel (Navy, Marine, Air Force, Army, Coast Guard) who are or have been stationed under permanent orders at the United States Naval Academy complex; 2) dependent under 23 years of age of civilian staff or faculty members who are presently employed, retired, or deceased after employment at the Naval Academy complex for at least 3 consecutive years; 3) children under 23 years of age of current board members of the Naval Academy Women's Club (NAWC); and 4) current regular and board members of the NAWC for at least 1 year. Applicants must be in their senior year at (or have graduated from) an accredited high school and must be applying to or attending as a full-time student an accredited 2-year or 4-year college or university, visual or performing arts school, or vocational/technical school. Along with their application, they must submit an essay of 500 to 1,000 words on a topic that changes annually; recently, applicants were invited to identify 4 virtues for themselves

and explain what they are and why. Financial need is not considered in the selection process. **Deadline for Receipt:** March of each year.

1240 ■ NAVAL ENLISTED RESERVE ASSOCIATION

Attn: National Headquarters
6703 Farragut Avenue
Falls Church, VA 22042-2189
Tel: (703)534-1329
Free: 800-776-9020
Fax: (703)534-3617
E-mail: members@nera.org
Web Site: http://www.nera.org
To provide financial assistance for college to enlisted members of the sea service Reserves and their families.

Title of Award: Naval Enlisted Reserve Association Scholarships **Area, Field, or Subject:** General studies/Field of study not specified **Level of Education for which Award is Granted:** Undergraduate **Number Awarded:** 4 each year. **Funds Available:** The stipend is $2,500. **Duration:** 1 year.

Eligibility Requirements: This program is open to drilling Reservists of the Navy, Marines, and Coast Guard who are in a satisfactory participation status, including Training and Administration of Reserves (TAR) personnel, Canvasser Recruiters (CANREC), and U.S. Navy personnel assigned to a Naval Reserve Activity (NRA). Their dependents and grandchildren are also eligible. Applicants must be enrolled in an accredited college or university. They must submit proof of enrollment, a copy of their military identification card, and a 1-page essay on "What a strong Naval Reserve means to me." **Deadline for Receipt:** April of each year. **Additional Information:** This program is funded in part by USAA Insurance Corporation. Information is also available from Bill Norris, Scholarship Chair, P.O. Box 9193, Mobile, AL 36691-0193, (251) 473-6242, E-mail: btcmnorris@aol.com.

1241 ■ NAVAL ENLISTED RESERVE ASSOCIATION

Attn: National Headquarters
6703 Farragut Avenue
Falls Church, VA 22042-2189
Tel: (703)534-1329
Free: 800-776-9020
Fax: (703)534-3617
E-mail: members@nera.org
Web Site: http://www.nera.org
To provide financial assistance for college to children and grandchildren of members of the Naval Enlisted Reserve Association (NERA).

Title of Award: NERA Dependent Scholarship **Area, Field, or Subject:** General studies/Field of study not specified **Level of Education for which Award is Granted:** Undergraduate **Number Awarded:** 1 each year. **Funds Available:** The stipend is $2,500. **Duration:** 1 year.

Eligibility Requirements: This program is open to children and grandchildren of association members who are graduating seniors or currently enrolled in college and have a GPA of 2.8 or higher. Applicants must submit proof of enrollment in or acceptance to an accredited college or university, a copy of their military identification card, and a 1-page essay on "What a strong Naval Reserve means to me." **Deadline for Receipt:** May of each year.

1242 ■ NAVAL ENLISTED RESERVE ASSOCIATION

Attn: National Headquarters
6703 Farragut Avenue
Falls Church, VA 22042-2189
Tel: (703)534-1329
Free: 800-776-9020
Fax: (703)534-3617
E-mail: members@nera.org
Web Site: http://www.nera.org
To provide financial assistance for college to sea service enlisted Reservists who are also members of the Naval Enlisted Reserve Association (NERA).

Title of Award: NERA Member Scholarship **Area, Field, or Subject:** General studies/Field of study not specified **Level of Education for which Award is Granted:** Four Year College **Number Awarded:** 2 each year: 1 at $3,000 and 1 at $2,500. **Funds Available:** Stipends are $3,000 or $2,500. **Duration:** 1 year.

Eligibility Requirements: This program is open to drilling Reservists of the Coast Guard, Navy, and Marines who are members of the association. Applicants must be attending an accredited college or university offering a 4-year program leading to a bachelor's degree. They must submit proof of enrollment, a copy of their military identification card, and a 1-page essay on "What a strong Naval Reserve means to me." **Deadline for Receipt:** April of each year. **Additional Information:** Information is also available from Bill Norris, Scholarship Chair, P.O. Box 9193, Mobile, AL 36691-0193, (251) 473-6242, E-mail: btcmnorris@aol.com.

1243 ■ NAVAL HELICOPTER ASSOCIATION

Attn: Scholarship Fund
P.O. Box 180578
Coronado, CA 92178-0578
Tel: (619)435-7139
Fax: (619)435-7354
E-mail: nhascholars@hotmail.com
Web Site: http://www.navalhelicopterassn.org/scholar/scholar.htm
To provide financial assistance for full-time undergraduate study to students in the United States.
Title of Award: Naval Helicopter Association Undergraduate Scholarships **Area, Field, or Subject:** General studies/Field of study not specified **Level of Education for which Award is Granted:** Undergraduate **Number Awarded:** 7 each year: 2 at $3,000 (the named scholarships) and 5 at $1,500. **Funds Available:** Stipends are $3,000 or $1,500 per year. **Duration:** 1 year; may be renewed if the recipient maintains at least a 2.75 GPA.
Eligibility Requirements: This program is open to U.S. citizens, regardless of race, religion, age, or gender, who are seniors in high school or currently enrolled in or accepted at an accredited college or university in the United States in an undergraduate program. Selection is based on academic proficiency, scholastic achievements and awards, extracurricular activities, employment history, letters of recommendation, and a personal statement on educational plans and future goals. **Deadline for Receipt:** November of each year. **Additional Information:** This program includes the Sikorsky Scholarship (sponsored by Sikorsky Aircraft Corporation) and DPA's Thousand Points of Light Award (sponsored by D.P. Associates Inc. and L3 Communications). Recipients must enroll full time.

1244 ■ NAVAL OFFICERS' WIVES' CLUB OF WASHINGTON, D.C.

Attn: Celia Jacoby Scholarship Chair
3214 Juniper Lane
Falls Church, VA 22044
E-mail: jacoby@sec.gov
To provide financial assistance for college to the children of naval personnel and veterans in Naval District Washington.
Title of Award: Naval Officers' Wives' Club of Washington, D.C. Scholarship Program **Area, Field, or Subject:** General studies/Field of study not specified **Level of Education for which Award is Granted:** Undergraduate **Number Awarded:** Varies each year: several at $2,000 and 2 at $1,000. **Funds Available:** Stipends are $2,000 or $1,000. Funds may be used only for tuition. **Duration:** 1 year; nonrenewable.
Eligibility Requirements: This program is open to dependent children of U.S. Navy service members who are 1) residing and on active duty serving in a command within the boundaries of Naval District Washington; 2) residing, are retired, and had served in a command in Naval District Washington; or 3) deceased and had served in a command in Naval District Washington. Applicants must be high school seniors at an accredited high school in Naval District Washington, U.S. citizens, and planning to attend an accredited 2- or 4-year undergraduate college or university, visual or performing arts school, or vocational/technical school as a full-time student. Along with their application, they must submit essays that describe 1) any personal accomplishment or challenges they have met in their high school years (e.g., Navy moves, physical handicaps, or learning disabilities); 2) how being a Navy dependent has affected their life; and 3) their personal ambitions and goals. Selection is based on academic achievement, involvement in extracurricular activities, and community service. **Deadline for Receipt:** March of each year. **Additional Information:** Naval District Washington covers the District of Columbia; the Maryland counties of Calvert, Charles, Montgomery, Prince George's, and St. Mary's; and the Virginia counties of Arlington, Fairfax, Fauquier, King George, Loudoun, Prince William, and Stafford (plus the

independent cities within their boundaries). The $1,000 scholarships are sponsored by the First Command Educational Foundation of First Command Financial Services, Inc.

1245 ■ NAVAL SEA CADET CORPS

Attn: Executive Director
2300 Wilson Boulevard
Arlington, VA 22201-3308
Tel: (703)243-6910
Fax: (703)243-3985
Web Site: http://www.seacadets.org
To provide financial assistance to Naval Sea Cadet Corps cadets and former cadets who are interested in continuing their education at an accredited 4-year college/university.
Title of Award: Lewis A. Kingsley Foundation Scholarship Fund **Area, Field, or Subject:** General studies/Field of study not specified **Level of Education for which Award is Granted:** Four Year College **Number Awarded:** 5 each year. **Funds Available:** The stipend is $1,000. **Duration:** 1 year.
Eligibility Requirements: This program is open to cadets and former cadets who are interested in continuing their education at an accredited 4-year college or university. They must have been a member of the corps for at least 2 years, have attained a minimum rating of NSCC E-3, be recommended by their commanding officer or other official, have earned at least a 3.0 GPA, and have been accepted by an accredited college or university. Applicants may submit financial need statements. All other factors being equal, these statements may be considered in determining award recipients. Applicants who have received full scholarships from other sources (e.g., ROTC) will be considered for this award only if there are no other qualified applicants. **Deadline for Receipt:** May of each year. **Additional Information:** Cadets are also eligible to apply for scholarships sponsored by the Navy League of the United States.

1246 ■ NAVAL SEA CADET CORPS

Attn: Executive Director
2300 Wilson Boulevard
Arlington, VA 22201-3308
Tel: (703)243-6910
Fax: (703)243-3985
Web Site: http://www.seacadets.org
To provide financial assistance to Naval Sea Cadet Corps cadets and former cadets who are interested in continuing their education at an accredited 4-year college/university.
Title of Award: NLUS Stockholm Scholarship Fund **Area, Field, or Subject:** General studies/Field of study not specified **Level of Education for which Award is Granted:** Four Year College **Number Awarded:** 1 every 4 years. **Funds Available:** The stipend is $2,000 per year. **Duration:** Up to 4 years.
Eligibility Requirements: This program is open to cadets and former cadets who are interested in continuing their education at an accredited 4-year college or university. They must have been a member of the corps for at least 2 years, have a minimum rating of NSCC E-3, be recommended by their commanding officer or other official, have earned at least a 3.0 GPA, and have been accepted by an accredited college or university. Applicants may submit financial need statements. All other factors being equal, these statements may be considered in determining award recipients. Applicants who have received full scholarships from other sources (e.g., ROTC) will be considered for this award only if there are no other qualified applicants. **Deadline for Receipt:** May of the competition year. **Additional Information:** This program was established by the Navy League of the United States (NLUS) through a bequest by Carl G. Stockholm, a past national president, to provide financial assistance to a selected cadet. This assistance is provided for up to 4 years and, during that time, no other Stockholm Scholarships are awarded; there can be only 1 designated "Stockholm Scholar" at any 1 time.

1247 ■ NAVAL SEA CADET CORPS

Attn: Executive Director
2300 Wilson Boulevard
Arlington, VA 22201-3308
Tel: (703)243-6910
Fax: (703)243-3985
Web Site: http://www.seacadets.org

To provide financial assistance to Naval Sea Cadet Corps cadets and former cadets who are interested in continuing their education at an accredited 4-year college/university.

Title of Award: NSCC Board of Directors Scholarship Fund **Area, Field, or Subject:** General studies/Field of study not specified **Level of Education for which Award is Granted:** Four Year College **Number Awarded:** 1 each year. **Funds Available:** The stipend is $1,500. **Duration:** 1 year.

Eligibility Requirements: This program is open to cadets and former cadets who are interested in continuing their education at an accredited 4-year college or university. They must have been a member of the corps for at least 2 years, have a minimum rating of NSCC E-3, be recommended by their commanding officer or other official, have earned at least a 3.0 GPA, and have been accepted by an accredited college or university. Applicants may submit financial need statements. All other factors being equal, these statements may be considered in determining award recipients. Applicants who have received full scholarships from other sources (e.g., ROTC) will be considered for this award only if there are no other qualified applicants. **Deadline for Receipt:** May of each year. **Additional Information:** Cadets are also eligible to apply for scholarships sponsored by the Navy League of the United States.

1248 ■ NAVAL SEA CADET CORPS

Attn: Executive Director
2300 Wilson Boulevard
Arlington, VA 22201-3308
Tel: (703)243-6910
Fax: (703)243-3985
Web Site: http://www.seacadets.org

To provide financial assistance to Naval Sea Cadet Corps cadets and former cadets who are interested in continuing their education at an accredited 4-year college/university.

Title of Award: NSCC Named Scholarship Program **Area, Field, or Subject:** General studies/Field of study not specified **Level of Education for which Award is Granted:** Four Year College **Number Awarded:** Varies each year. **Funds Available:** Stipends depend on the availability of funds; recently, they ranged up to $2,000. **Duration:** 1 year.

Eligibility Requirements: This program is open to cadets and former cadets who are interested in continuing their education at an accredited 4-year college or university. They must have been a member of the corps for at least 2 years, have a minimum rating of NSCC E-3, be recommended by their commanding officer or other official, have earned at least a 3.0 GPA, and have been accepted by an accredited college or university. Applicants may submit financial need statements. All other factors being equal, these statements may be considered in determining award recipients. Applicants who have received full scholarships from other sources (e.g., ROTC) will be considered for this award only if there are no other qualified applicants. **Deadline for Receipt:** May of each year. **Additional Information:** Cadets are also eligible to apply for scholarships sponsored by the Navy League of the United States.

1249 ■ NAVAL SEA CADET CORPS

Attn: Executive Director
2300 Wilson Boulevard
Arlington, VA 22201-3308
Tel: (703)243-6910
Fax: (703)243-3985
Web Site: http://www.seacadets.org

To provide financial assistance to Naval Sea Cadet Corps cadets and former cadets who are interested in continuing their education at an accredited 4-year college/university.

Title of Award: NSCC Scholarship Fund **Area, Field, or Subject:** General studies/Field of study not specified **Level of Education for which Award is Granted:** Four Year College **Number Awarded:** 2 each year. **Funds Available:** The stipend is $1,000. **Duration:** 1 year.

Eligibility Requirements: This program is open to cadets and former cadets who are interested in continuing their education at an accredited 4-year college or university. They must have been a member of the corps for at least 2 years, have a minimum rating of NSCC E-3, be recommended by their commanding officer or other official, have earned at least a 3.0 GPA, and have been accepted by an accredited college or university. Applicants may submit financial need statements. All other factors being equal, these statements may be considered in determining award recipients. Applicants who have received full scholarships from

other sources (e.g., ROTC) will be considered for this award only if there are no other qualified applicants. **Deadline for Receipt:** May of each year. **Additional Information:** Cadets are also eligible to apply for scholarships sponsored by the Navy League of the United States.

1250 ■ NAVAL SPECIAL WARFARE FOUNDATION

Attn: Scholarship Committee
P.O. Box 5965
Virginia Beach, VA 23471
Tel: (757)363-7490
Fax: (757)363-7491
E-mail: info@nswfoundation.org
Web Site: http://www.nswfoundation.org

To provide financial assistance for college to Navy personnel serving on active duty in the SEALS and their families.

Title of Award: Agron SEAL Scholarship **Area, Field, or Subject:** General studies/Field of study not specified **Level of Education for which Award is Granted:** Undergraduate **Number Awarded:** 1 each year. **Funds Available:** The stipend is $1,000 per year. **Duration:** Up to 4 years, provided the recipient maintains a GPA of 3.2 or higher.

Eligibility Requirements: This program is open to active-duty SEALs, their current spouses, and immediate children. Applicants must be high school seniors or current college students working on or planning to work on an associate or bachelor's degree. Selection is based on academic merit, extracurricular and community activities, and contributions made within the SEAL community. **Deadline for Receipt:** March of each year.

1251 ■ NAVAL SPECIAL WARFARE FOUNDATION

Attn: Scholarship Committee
P.O. Box 5965
Virginia Beach, VA 23471
Tel: (757)363-7490
Fax: (757)363-7491
E-mail: info@nswfoundation.org
Web Site: http://www.nswfoundation.org

To provide financial assistance for college to dependents of military personnel serving on active duty in Naval Special Warfare (NSW) commands.

Title of Award: Naval Special Warfare Scholarships for Spouses and Children **Area, Field, or Subject:** General studies/Field of study not specified **Level of Education for which Award is Granted:** Undergraduate **Number Awarded:** 1 or more each year. **Funds Available:** A stipend is awarded (amount not specified). **Duration:** 1 year; may be renewed.

Eligibility Requirements: This program is open to the dependent spouses and children of active-duty SEALs or Special Warfare Combatant crewmen (SWCC) and other active-duty military personnel serving in NSW commands. Family members of a SEAL or SWCC who died in service to the country are also eligible. Applicants must be entering or continuing in college with the goal of working on an associate or bachelor's degree. Selection is based on merit and academic potential, judged by scholastic achievement and a written essay. **Deadline for Receipt:** March of each year.

1252 ■ NAVAL SPECIAL WARFARE FOUNDATION

Attn: Scholarship Committee
P.O. Box 5965
Virginia Beach, VA 23471
Tel: (757)363-7490
Fax: (757)363-7491
E-mail: info@nswfoundation.org
Web Site: http://www.nswfoundation.org

To provide financial assistance for college to children of members of the UDT-SEAL Association.

Title of Award: Had Richards UDT-SEAL Memorial Scholarship **Area, Field, or Subject:** General studies/Field of study not specified **Level of Education for which Award is Granted:** Undergraduate **Number Awarded:** 1 each year. **Funds Available:** The stipend is $1,000. **Duration:** 1 year; may be renewed.

Eligibility Requirements: This program is open to children of members who are single, under 22 years of age, and a dependent of a sponsoring member of the association. Sponsors must be serving or have served in the armed forces and the Naval Special Warfare Community, been an association member for the last 4 consecutive years, and paid their dues for the current year. Applicants may be high school seniors, high school graduates, or undergraduate students; preference is given to high school seniors. Selection is based on a written essay, academic achievement, and extracurricular involvement. **Deadline for Receipt:** March of each year. **Additional Information:** Membership in the association is open to all officers and enlisted personnel of the armed forces (active, retired, discharged, or separated) who have served with a Navy Combat Demolition Unit (NCDU), Underwater Demolition Team (UDT), or SEAL Team.

1253 ■ NAVAL SPECIAL WARFARE FOUNDATION

Attn: Scholarship Committee
P.O. Box 5965
Virginia Beach, VA 23471
Tel: (757)363-7490
Fax: (757)363-7491
E-mail: info@nswfoundation.org
Web Site: http://www.nswfoundation.org
To provide financial assistance for college to children of members of the UDT-SEAL Association.
Title of Award: UDT-SEAL Scholarship **Area, Field, or Subject:** General studies/Field of study not specified **Level of Education for which Award is Granted:** Undergraduate **Number Awarded:** 1 or more each year. **Funds Available:** A stipend is awarded (amount not specified). **Duration:** 1 year; may be renewed.
Eligibility Requirements: This program is open to children of members who are single, under 22 years of age, and a dependent of a sponsoring member of the association. Sponsors must be serving or have served in the armed forces and the Naval Special Warfare Community, have been an association member for the last 4 consecutive years, and have paid their dues for the current year. Applicants may be high school seniors, high school graduates, or undergraduate students; preference is given to high school seniors. Along with their application, they must submit an essay, up to 2 pages in length, on a topic that changes annually; recently, the topic involved homeland security in the wake of the September 11 attacks on the World Trade Center and the Pentagon, and its relationship to personal freedoms guaranteed by the Constitution. Selection is based on the essay, academic achievement, and extracurricular activities. **Deadline for Receipt:** March of each year. **Additional Information:** Membership in the association is open to all officers and enlisted personnel of the armed forces (active, retired, discharged, or separated) who have served with a Navy Combat Demolition Unit (NCDU), Underwater Demolition Team (UDT), or SEAL Team.

1254 ■ NAVY COUNSELOR ASSOCIATION

Attn: National Headquarters
P.O. Box 15023
Norfolk, VA 23511-0023
Web Site: http://www.usnca.org/scholarships.htm
To provide financial assistance for college to the dependent children of members of the Navy Counselor Association (NCA).
Title of Award: Navy Counselor Association Educational Scholarship Fund **Area, Field, or Subject:** General studies/Field of study not specified **Level of Education for which Award is Granted:** Undergraduate **Number Awarded:** Varies each year. Recently, 3 of these scholarships were awarded: 1 at $2,500, 1 at $2,000, and 1 at $1,500. **Funds Available:** Stipends are $2,500, $2,000, or $1,500. **Duration:** 1 year; may be renewed 1 additional year.
Eligibility Requirements: This program is open to the dependent children of active-duty, retired, and deceased NCA members. Applicants must be between 17 and 23 years of age with proof of enrollment, acceptance, or certified intention to attend an accredited college, university, or vocational/technical school. Along with their application they must submit a 500-word essay on their educational and post-educational goals, and how those goals will benefit them and the community. Selection is based on the essay, academics, civic involvement, extracurricular activities, and goals. **Deadline for Receipt:** April of each year. **Additional Information:** This scholarship is offered by the NCA with funds

established from membership dues. More information on this program can also be obtained from the NCA at the parent's current duty station (or last duty station, if deceased).

1255 ■ NAVY LEAGUE OF THE UNITED STATES

Attn: Scholarships
2300 Wilson Boulevard
Arlington, VA 22201-3308
Tel: (703)528-1775
Free: 800-356-5760
Fax: (703)528-2333
E-mail: cjarvis@navyleague.org
Web Site: http://www.navyleague.org/scholarship
To provide financial assistance for college to spouses and dependent children of naval personnel in Alaska.
Title of Award: Alaska Sea Services Scholarships **Area, Field, or Subject:** General studies/Field of study not specified **Level of Education for which Award is Granted:** Four Year College **Number Awarded:** Up to 4 each year. **Funds Available:** The stipend is $1,000 per year; funds are paid directly to the academic institution for tuition, books, and fees. **Duration:** 1 year; may be renewed 1 additional year.
Eligibility Requirements: This program is open to the spouses and dependent children of active duty, inactive duty, and retired (with or without pay) members of the regular and Reserve Navy, Marine Corps, or Coast Guard who are residents of Alaska. Applicants must be enrolled or planning to enroll full time at an accredited 4-year college or university to work on an undergraduate degree. Selection is based on academic proficiency, character, leadership ability, community involvement, and financial need. **Deadline for Receipt:** February of each year.

1256 ■ NAVY LEAGUE OF THE UNITED STATES

Attn: Scholarships
2300 Wilson Boulevard
Arlington, VA 22201-3308
Tel: (703)528-1775
Free: 800-356-5760
Fax: (703)528-2333
E-mail: cjarvis@navyleague.org
Web Site: http://www.navyleague.org/scholarship
To provide financial assistance for college to dependent children of sea service personnel, especially Native Americans.
Title of Award: Jewell Hilton Bonner Scholarship **Area, Field, or Subject:** General studies/Field of study not specified **Level of Education for which Award is Granted:** Undergraduate **Number Awarded:** 1 each year. **Funds Available:** The stipend is $2,500 per year. **Duration:** 4 years, provided the recipient maintains a GPA of 3.0 or higher.
Eligibility Requirements: This program is open to U.S. citizens who are 1) dependents or direct descendants of an active, Reserve, retired, or honorably discharged member of the U.S. sea service (including the Navy, Marine Corps, Coast Guard, or Merchant Marines), or 2) currently an active member of the Naval Sea Cadet Corps. Applicants must be entering their freshman year of college. Along with their application, they must submit transcripts, 2 letters of recommendation, SAT/ACT scores, documentation of financial need, proof of qualifying sea service duty, and a 1-page personal statement on why they should be considered for this scholarship. Preference is given to applicants of Native American heritage. **Deadline for Receipt:** February of each year.

1257 ■ NAVY LEAGUE OF THE UNITED STATES

Attn: Scholarships
2300 Wilson Boulevard
Arlington, VA 22201-3308
Tel: (703)528-1775
Free: 800-356-5760
Fax: (703)528-2333
E-mail: cjarvis@navyleague.org
Web Site: http://www.navyleague.org/scholarship
To provide financial assistance for college to dependent children of sea service personnel.
Title of Award: Navy League Foundation Scholarships **Area, Field, or Subject:** General studies/Field of study not specified **Level of Education for which Award is Granted:** Undergraduate **Number Awarded:** Approximately 5 each year. **Funds Available:** The stipend is $2,500 per year. **Duration:** 4 years, provided the recipient maintains a GPA of 3.0 or higher.

Eligibility Requirements: This program is open to U.S. citizens who are 1) dependents or direct descendants of an active, Reserve, retired, or honorably discharged member of the U.S. sea service (including the Navy, Marine Corps, Coast Guard, or Merchant Marines), or 2) currently an active member of the Naval Sea Cadet Corps. Applicants must be entering their freshman year of college. Along with their application, they must submit transcripts, 2 letters of recommendation, SAT/ACT scores, documentation of financial need, proof of qualifying sea service duty, and a 1-page personal statement on why they should be considered for this scholarship. **Deadline for Receipt:** February of each year. **Additional Information:** This program includes the following named awards: the John G. Brokaw Scholarship, the Jack and Eileen Anderson Scholarship, the Anne E. Clark Foundation Scholarship, the Harold E. Wirth Scholarship, the Albert Levinson Scholarship, the CAPT Earnest G. "Scotty" and Renee Campbell, USN (Ret.) Scholarship, the CAPT Winifred Quick Collins, USN (Ret.) Scholarship, the John "Jack" Schiff Scholarship, and the Wesley C. Cameron Scholarship. Requests for applications must be accompanied by a stamped self-addressed envelope.

1258 ■ NAVY LEAGUE OF THE UNITED STATES

Attn: Scholarships
2300 Wilson Boulevard
Arlington, VA 22201-3308
Tel: (703)528-1775
Free: 800-356-5760
Fax: (703)528-2333
E-mail: cjarvis@navyleague.org
Web Site: http://www.navyleague.org/scholarship
To provide financial assistance for college to dependent children of sea service personnel or veterans who were attached to U.S. Naval Facility commands in the Philippines during specified times.
Title of Award: Subic Bay-Cubi Point Scholarship **Area, Field, or Subject:** General studies/Field of study not specified **Level of Education for which Award is Granted:** Undergraduate **Number Awarded:** 1 each year. **Funds Available:** The stipend is $2,500 per year. **Duration:** 4 years, provided the recipient maintains a GPA of 3.0 or higher.
Eligibility Requirements: This program is open to U.S. citizens who are 1) dependents or direct descendants of an active, Reserve, retired, or honorably discharged member of the U.S. sea service (including the Navy, Marine Corps, Coast Guard, or Merchant Marines), or 2) currently an active member of the Naval Sea Cadet Corps. Applicants must be entering their freshman year of college. Along with their application, they must submit transcripts, 2 letters of recommendation, SAT/ACT scores, documentation of financial need, proof of qualifying sea service duty, and a 1-page personal statement on why they should be considered for this scholarship. Preference is given to dependents of sea service personnel who were permanently attached to the U.S. Naval Facility commands at Subic Bay, Cubi Point, or San Miguel in the Philippines between January 1980 and December 1992. There is no citizenship restriction for this scholarship. **Deadline for Receipt:** February of each year.

1259 ■ NAVY LEAGUE OF THE UNITED STATES

Attn: Scholarships
2300 Wilson Boulevard
Arlington, VA 22201-3308
Tel: (703)528-1775
Free: 800-356-5760
Fax: (703)528-2333
E-mail: cjarvis@navyleague.org
Web Site: http://www.navyleague.org/scholarship
To provide financial assistance for college to dependent children of sea service personnel and veterans, especially those who reside in the San Diego, California area.
Title of Award: RADM William A. Sullivan, USN (Ret.) Scholarship **Area, Field, or Subject:** General studies/Field of study not specified **Level of Education for which Award is Granted:** Undergraduate **Number Awarded:** 1 each year. **Funds Available:** The stipend is $2,500 per year. **Duration:** 4 years, provided the recipient maintains a GPA of 3.0 or higher.
Eligibility Requirements: This program is open to U.S. citizens who are 1) dependents or direct descendants of an active, Reserve, retired, or honorably discharged member of the U.S. sea service (including the Navy, Marine Corps, Coast Guard, or Merchant Marines), or 2) currently

an active member of the Naval Sea Cadet Corps. Applicants must be entering their freshman year of college. Along with their application, they must submit transcripts, 2 letters of recommendation, SAT/ACT scores, documentation of financial need, proof of qualifying sea service duty, and a 1-page personal statement on why they should be considered for this scholarship. Preference is given to applicants who reside in or near the San Diego, California area. **Deadline for Receipt:** February of each year.

1260 ■ NAVY LEAGUE OF THE UNITED STATES

Attn: Scholarships
2300 Wilson Boulevard
Arlington, VA 22201-3308
Tel: (703)528-1775
Free: 800-356-5760
Fax: (703)528-2333
E-mail: cjarvis@navyleague.org
Web Site: http://www.navyleague.org/scholarship
To provide financial assistance for college to dependent children of sea service personnel or veterans, especially those who served on the *USS Mahan.*
Title of Award: USS Mahan Scholarship **Area, Field, or Subject:** General studies/Field of study not specified **Level of Education for which Award is Granted:** Undergraduate **Number Awarded:** 1 each year. **Funds Available:** The stipend is $2,500 per year. **Duration:** 4 years, provided the recipient maintains a GPA of 3.0 or higher.
Eligibility Requirements: This program is open to U.S. citizens who are 1) dependents or direct descendants of an active, Reserve, retired, or honorably discharged member of the U.S. sea service (including the Navy, Marine Corps, Coast Guard, or Merchant Marines), or 2) currently an active member of the Naval Sea Cadet Corps. Applicants must be entering their freshman year of college. Along with their application, they must submit transcripts, 2 letters of recommendation, SAT/ACT scores, documentation of financial need, proof of qualifying sea service duty, and a 1-page personal statement on why they should be considered for this scholarship. Preference is given to direct descendants of sea service personnel who served on the *USS Mahan* and to the dependents of sea service personnel who are now serving. **Deadline for Receipt:** February of each year.

1261 ■ NAVY-MARINE CORPS RELIEF SOCIETY

Attn: Education Division
875 North Randolph Street, Suite 225
Arlington, VA 22203-1977
Tel: (703)696-4960
Fax: (703)696-0144
E-mail: education@hq.nmcrs.org
Web Site: http://www.nmcrs.org/child-dec.html
To provide financial assistance for college to the children of Navy or Marine Corps personnel who died as a result of disabilities or length of service.
Title of Award: Assistance for Surviving Children of Naval Personnel Deceased after Retirement (CDR) **Area, Field, or Subject:** General studies/Field of study not specified **Level of Education for which Award is Granted:** Undergraduate **Number Awarded:** Varies each year. **Funds Available:** Grants up to $4,000 per year are available.
Eligibility Requirements: Eligible for this assistance are the unmarried, dependent children, stepchildren, or legally adopted children under the age of 23 of members of the Navy or Marine Corps who died after retirement due to disability or length of service. **Deadline for Receipt:** February of each year. **Additional Information:** This program is limited to undergraduate studies and vocational training.

1262 ■ NAVY-MARINE CORPS RELIEF SOCIETY

Attn: Education Division
875 North Randolph Street, Suite 225
Arlington, VA 22203-1977
Tel: (703)696-4960
Fax: (703)696-0144
E-mail: education@hq.nmcrs.org
Web Site: http://www.nmcrs.org/child-dec.html
To provide financial assistance for college to the children of deceased Navy or Marine Corps personnel.
Title of Award: Assistance for Surviving Children of Naval Personnel Deceased While on Active Duty (CDAD) **Area, Field, or Subject:** General

studies/Field of study not specified **Level of Education for which Award is Granted:** Undergraduate **Number Awarded:** Varies each year. **Funds Available:** Grants up to $4,000 per year are available.

Eligibility Requirements: Eligible for this assistance are the unmarried, dependent children, stepchildren, or legally adopted children under the age of 23 of members of the Navy or Marine Corps who died while on active duty. Applicants must possess a current valid dependents' Uniformed Services Identification and Privilege Card. **Deadline for Receipt:** February of each year. **Additional Information:** This program is limited to undergraduate studies and vocational training.

1263 ■ NAVY-MARINE CORPS RELIEF SOCIETY

Attn: Education Division
875 North Randolph Street, Suite 225
Arlington, VA 22203-1977
Tel: (703)696-4960
Fax: (703)696-0144
E-mail: education@hq.nmcrs.org
Web Site: http://www.nmcrs.org/boorda.html
To provide supplemental assistance to Navy or Marine Corps personnel selected for or enrolled in enlisted commissioning programs.
Title of Award: Admiral Mike Boorda Scholarship Program **Area, Field, or Subject:** General studies/Field of study not specified **Level of Education for which Award is Granted:** Undergraduate **Number Awarded:** Varies each year. **Funds Available:** Grants up to $2,000 per year are available, depending on need.

Eligibility Requirements: Eligible for this assistance are active-duty members of the Navy or Marine Corps selected for or enrolled in the Marine Enlisted Commissioning Education Program (MECEP) or the Navy's Medical Enlisted Commissioning Program (MECP). Midshipmen who have been released from active duty for immediate assignment to the Naval Reserve Officers' Training Corps (NROTC) are also eligible. Participants in the Navy's Seaman to Admiral-21 program are not eligible. **Deadline for Receipt:** April of each year. **Additional Information:** This program is limited to undergraduate studies.

1264 ■ NAVY-MARINE CORPS RELIEF SOCIETY

Attn: Education Division
875 North Randolph Street, Suite 225
Arlington, VA 22203-1977
Tel: (703)696-4960
Fax: (703)696-0144
E-mail: education@hq.nmcrs.org
Web Site: http://www.nmcrs.org/tap-gi.html
To loan supplemental funds to Navy or Marine Corps members attending college.
Title of Award: GI Bill Bridge Loans **Area, Field, or Subject:** General studies/Field of study not specified **Level of Education for which Award is Granted:** Undergraduate **Number Awarded:** Varies each year. **Funds Available:** Loans are available to allow enrollment under the GI Bill if education benefits from the VA are not received in time to permit enrollment.

Eligibility Requirements: Eligible for this assistance are active-duty members of the Navy or Marine Corps attending college utilizing any of the educational GI Bill programs of the U.S. Department of Veterans Affairs (VA). Applications must be submitted to a field office of the Navy-Marine Corps Relief Society. **Deadline for Receipt:** Applications may be submitted at any time.

1265 ■ NAVY-MARINE CORPS RELIEF SOCIETY

Attn: Education Division
875 North Randolph Street, Suite 225
Arlington, VA 22203-1977
Tel: (703)696-4960
Fax: (703)696-0144
E-mail: education@hq.nmcrs.org
Web Site: http://www.nmcrs.org/child-dec.html
To provide financial assistance for college to the children and spouses of deceased military personnel who died at the Pentagon on September 11, 2001.
Title of Award: Pentagon Assistance Fund **Area, Field, or Subject:** General studies/Field of study not specified **Level of Education for which Award is Granted:** Undergraduate **Number Awarded:** Varies

each year. **Funds Available:** The amount of assistance varies; funds may be used for any purpose, including tuition, fees, books, room, or board at a college or university offering a 2-year or 4-year course of study or at a vocational training school. **Duration:** Up to 4 years.

Eligibility Requirements: Eligible for this assistance are the children and spouses of deceased military personnel who died at the Pentagon as a result of the terrorist attack of September 11, 2001. The families of Marines whose aircraft crashed in Pakistan and Afghanistan in mid-January 2002 are also eligible. **Deadline for Receipt:** Applications may be submitted at any time.

1266 ■ NAVY-MARINE CORPS RELIEF SOCIETY

Attn: Education Division
875 North Randolph Street, Suite 225
Arlington, VA 22203-1977
Tel: (703)696-4960
Fax: (703)696-0144
E-mail: education@hq.nmcrs.org
Web Site: http://www.nmcrs.org/tap-gi.html
To provide supplemental assistance loans to naval personnel working on a college degree with the Navy Department's Tuition Assistance Program (TAP).
Title of Award: TAP Bridge Loans **Area, Field, or Subject:** General studies/Field of study not specified **Level of Education for which Award is Granted:** Undergraduate **Number Awarded:** Varies each year. **Funds Available:** Loans are provided to cover all or a portion of the servicemember's share of the cost of tuition.

Eligibility Requirements: Eligible for this assistance are active-duty members of the Navy or Marine Corps who are taking college classes and utilizing the Navy TAP program. Applications must be submitted to a field office of the Navy-Marine Corps Relief Society. **Deadline for Receipt:** Applications may be submitted at any time.

1267 ■ NAVY-MARINE CORPS RELIEF SOCIETY

Attn: Education Division
875 North Randolph Street, Suite 225
Arlington, VA 22203-1977
Tel: (703)696-4960
Fax: (703)696-0144
E-mail: education@hq.nmcrs.org
Web Site: http://www.nmcrs.org/travers.html
To provide interest-free loans for college to the dependents Navy and Marine Corps personnel.
Title of Award: Vice Admiral E.P. Travers Loan Program **Area, Field, or Subject:** General studies/Field of study not specified **Level of Education for which Award is Granted:** Undergraduate **Number Awarded:** Varies each year. **Funds Available:** The loan amount is determined on the basis of need, from $500 to $3,000 per academic year. No interest is charged on the money borrowed. The loan must be repaid within 24 months by allotment of pay, at a monthly rate of at least $50.

Eligibility Requirements: This program is open to the dependent children of active-duty and retired Navy and Marine Corps personnel and the spouses of active-duty Navy and Marine Corps personnel. Applicants must have a GPA of 2.0 or higher and be able to demonstrate financial need. They must be enrolled or planning to enroll as a full-time undergraduate student at an accredited college, university, or vocational/technical school. **Deadline for Receipt:** February of each year.

1268 ■ NAVY-MARINE CORPS RELIEF SOCIETY

Attn: Education Division
875 North Randolph Street, Suite 225
Arlington, VA 22203-1977
Tel: (703)696-4960
Fax: (703)696-0144
E-mail: education@hq.nmcrs.org
Web Site: http://www.nmcrs.org/travers.html
To provide financial assistance for college to the dependents of Navy and Marine Corps personnel.
Title of Award: Vice Admiral E.P. Travers Scholarship **Area, Field, or Subject:** General studies/Field of study not specified **Level of Education for which Award is Granted:** Undergraduate **Number Awarded:** Up to 500 each year. **Funds Available:** The stipend is $2,000 per year. **Duration:** 1 year; may be renewed up to 3 additional years as long as the

recipient maintains a GPA of 2.0 or higher and the parent remains on active duty in the Navy or Marines.

Eligibility Requirements: This program is open to the dependent children of active-duty and retired Navy and Marine Corps personnel and the spouses of active-duty Navy and Marine Corps personnel. Applicants must have a cumulative GPA of 2.0 or higher and must demonstrate financial need. They must be enrolled or planning to enroll as a full-time undergraduate student at an accredited college, university, or vocational/technical school. **Deadline for Receipt:** February of each year.

1269 ■ NAVY-MARINE CORPS RELIEF SOCIETY

Attn: Education Division
875 North Randolph Street, Suite 225
Arlington, VA 22203-1977
Tel: (703)696-4960
Fax: (703)696-0144
E-mail: education@hq.nmcrs.org
Web Site: http://www.nmcrs.org/child-dec.html
To provide financial assistance for college to the children of deceased crewmembers of the *USS Cole*.

Title of Award: USS Cole Memorial Scholarship Fund **Area, Field, or Subject:** General studies/Field of study not specified **Level of Education for which Award is Granted:** Undergraduate **Number Awarded:** Varies each year. **Funds Available:** The amount of assistance varies; funds may be used for any purpose, including tuition, fees, books, room, or board at a college or university offering a 2-year or 4-year course of study or at a vocational training school. **Duration:** Up to 4 years.

Eligibility Requirements: Eligible for this assistance are the children of crewmembers of the *USS Cole* who died as a result of the terrorist attack on the ship on October 12, 2000. **Deadline for Receipt:** Applications may be submitted at any time.

1270 ■ NAVY-MARINE CORPS RELIEF SOCIETY

Attn: Education Division
875 North Randolph Street, Suite 225
Arlington, VA 22203-1977
Tel: (703)696-4960
Fax: (703)696-0144
E-mail: education@hq.nmcrs.org
Web Site: http://www.nmcrs.org/child-dec.html
To provide financial assistance for college to the spouses and children of deceased crewmembers of the *USS Stark* (FFG 31).

Title of Award: USS Stark Memorial Scholarship Fund **Area, Field, or Subject:** General studies/Field of study not specified **Level of Education for which Award is Granted:** Undergraduate **Number Awarded:** Varies each year. **Funds Available:** The amount of assistance varies; funds may be used for any purpose, including tuition, fees, books, room, or board at a college or university offering a 2-year or 4-year course of study or at a vocational training school. **Duration:** Up to 4 years.

Eligibility Requirements: Eligible for this assistance are the spouses and children of crewmembers of the *USS Stark* (FFG 31) who died as a result of the missile attack on the ship in the Persian Gulf on May 17, 1987. **Deadline for Receipt:** February of each year.

1271 ■ NAVY-MARINE CORPS RELIEF SOCIETY

Attn: Education Division
875 North Randolph Street, Suite 225
Arlington, VA 22203-1977
Tel: (703)696-4960
Fax: (703)696-0144
E-mail: education@hq.nmcrs.org
Web Site: http://www.nmcrs.org/spec-prgm.html
To provide financial assistance for college to children of current or former crewmembers of the *USS Tennessee*.

Title of Award: USS Tennessee Scholarship Fund **Area, Field, or Subject:** General studies/Field of study not specified **Level of Education for which Award is Granted:** Undergraduate **Number Awarded:** Varies each year. **Funds Available:** The stipend is $2,000 per year; funds may be used for any purpose, including tuition, fees, books, room, or board at a college or university offering a 2-year or 4-year course of study or at a vocational training school. **Duration:** 1 year; renewable.

Eligibility Requirements: This program is open to the dependent children of active-duty and retired personnel currently or previously as-

signed to duty aboard the *USS Tennessee* (SSBN 734). Applicants must be enrolled or planning to enroll as an undergraduate student. Selection is based on financial need. **Deadline for Receipt:** February of each year.

1272 ■ NAVY SUPPLY CORPS FOUNDATION

c/o Jack Evans
1425 Prince Avenue
Athens, GA 30606-2205
Tel: (706)354-4111
Fax: (706)354-0334
E-mail: foundation@usnscf.com
Web Site: http://www.usnscf.com/scholarship.html
To provide financial assistance for college to high school seniors willing to serve in the Navy Supply Corps.

Title of Award: Chief of Supply Corps Officer Development Scholarships **Area, Field, or Subject:** General studies/Field of study not specified **Level of Education for which Award is Granted:** Undergraduate **Number Awarded:** 2 each year. **Funds Available:** The stipend is $10,000 per year. **Duration:** 4 years, provided the recipient maintains a GPA of 3.0 or higher.

Eligibility Requirements: This program is open to high school seniors who agree to serve on active duty as a Navy Supply Corps officer upon graduation from college. Applicants must be have a high school GPA of 3.0 or higher and be physically able to serve in the Supply Corps. They must be planning to attend a 2-year or 4-year college or university as a full-time student. Selection is based on the applicant's willingness and suitability to serve as an officer in the Supply Corps. **Deadline for Receipt:** April of each year.

1273 ■ NAVY SUPPLY CORPS FOUNDATION

c/o Jack Evans
1425 Prince Avenue
Athens, GA 30606-2205
Tel: (706)354-4111
Fax: (706)354-0334
E-mail: foundation@usnscf.com
Web Site: http://www.usnscf.com/scholarship.html
To provide financial assistance for college to the dependents of Navy Supply Corps personnel who are blind or disabled.

Title of Award: Navy Supply Corps Foundation NIB/NISH Scholarships **Area, Field, or Subject:** General studies/Field of study not specified **Level of Education for which Award is Granted:** Undergraduate **Number Awarded:** 1 or more each year. **Funds Available:** A stipend is awarded (amount not specified). **Duration:** 1 year; may be renewed if the recipient maintains a GPA of 2.5 or higher.

Eligibility Requirements: This program is open to dependents of a Navy Supply Corps officer, warrant officer, or enlisted personnel on active duty, with prior service in the Supply Corps, in Reserve status, retired with pay, or deceased. Enlisted ratings that apply are AK (Aviation Storekeeper), SK (Storekeeper), MS (Mess Specialist), DK (Disbursing Clerk), SH (Ship Serviceman), LI (Lithographer), and PC (Postal Clerk). Applicants must be attending or planning to attend a 2-year or 4-year accredited college on a full-time basis and have a GPA of 2.5 or higher in high school and/or college. They must be able to document blindness or severe disability. Selection is based on character, leadership, academic performance, and financial need. **Deadline for Receipt:** April of each year. **Additional Information:** This program was established in 2005 with support from the National Institute for the Blind (NIB) and NISH (formerly the National Industries for the Severely Handicapped).

1274 ■ NAVY SUPPLY CORPS FOUNDATION

c/o Jack Evans
1425 Prince Avenue
Athens, GA 30606-2205
Tel: (706)354-4111
Fax: (706)354-0334
E-mail: foundation@usnscf.com
Web Site: http://www.usnscf.com/scholarship.html
To provide financial assistance for college to the dependents of Navy Supply Corps personnel.

Title of Award: Navy Supply Corps Foundation Scholarships **Area, Field, or Subject:** General studies/Field of study not specified **Level of Education for which Award is Granted:** Undergraduate **Number Awarded:**

Varies each year; recently, the foundation awarded 78 scholarships with a value of $190,000. **Funds Available:** A stipend is awarded (amount not specified). **Duration:** 1 year; may be renewed if the recipient maintains a GPA of 2.5 or higher.
Eligibility Requirements: This program is open to dependents of a Navy Supply Corps officer, warrant officer, or enlisted personnel on active duty, with prior service in the Supply Corps, in Reserve status, retired with pay, or deceased. Enlisted ratings that apply are AK (Aviation Storekeeper), SK (Storekeeper), MS (Mess Specialist), DK (Disbursing Clerk), SH (Ship Serviceman), LI (Lithographer), and PC (Postal Clerk). Applicants must be attending or planning to attend a 2-year or 4-year accredited college on a full-time basis and have a GPA of 2.5 or higher in high school and/or college. Selection is based on character, leadership, academic performance, and financial need. **Deadline for Receipt:** April of each year.

1275 ■ NAVY WIVES CLUB OF AMERICA
P.O. Box 54022
Millington, TN 38053-6022
(866)511-NWCA
E-mail: nwca@navywivesclubsofamerica.org
Web Site: http://www.navywivesclubsofamerica.org/nwc/scholarships.htm
To provide financial assistance for college to the adult children of members of the Navy Wives Club of America (NWCA).
Title of Award: Judith Haupt Member's Child Scholarship **Area, Field, or Subject:** General studies/Field of study not specified **Level of Education for which Award is Granted:** Undergraduate **Number Awarded:** 1 or more each year. **Funds Available:** A stipend is provided (amount not specified). **Duration:** 1 year.
Eligibility Requirements: This program is open to children of NWCA members who no longer carry a military ID card because they have reached adult status. Applicants must be attending or planning to attend an accredited college or university. Financial need is considered in the selection process. **Deadline for Receipt:** May of each year. **Additional Information:** Information is also available from Denise Johnson, NWCA National President, 534 Madrona Street, Chula Vista, CA 91910, E-mail: president@navywivesclubofamerica.org. Membership in the NWCA is open to spouses of enlisted personnel serving in the Navy, Marine Corps, Coast Guard, and the active Reserve units of those services; spouses of enlisted personnel who have been honorable discharged, retired, or transferred to the Fleet Reserve on completion of duty; and widows of enlisted personnel in those services.

1276 ■ NAVY WIVES CLUB OF AMERICA
P.O. Box 54022
Millington, TN 38053-6022
(866)511-NWCA
E-mail: nwca@navywivesclubsofamerica.org
Web Site: http://www.navywivesclubsofamerica.org/nwc/scholarships.htm
To provide financial assistance for undergraduate or graduate study to spouses of naval personnel.
Title of Award: Navy/Marine Corps/Coast Guard Enlisted Dependent Spouse Scholarship **Area, Field, or Subject:** General studies/Field of study not specified **Level of Education for which Award is Granted:** Graduate, Undergraduate **Number Awarded:** 1 or more each year. **Funds Available:** The stipends range from $500 to $1,000 each year (depending upon the donations from chapters of the Navy Wives Club of America). **Duration:** 1 year.
Eligibility Requirements: This program is open to the spouses of active-duty Navy, Marine Corps, or Coast Guard members who can demonstrate financial need. Applicants must be 1) a high school graduate or senior planning to attend college full time next year; 2) currently enrolled in an undergraduate program and planning to continue as a full-time undergraduate; 3) a college graduate or senior planning to be a full-time graduate student next year; and 4) a high school graduate or GED recipient planning to attend vocational or business school next year. **Deadline for Receipt:** May of each year. **Additional Information:** Information is also available from NWCA National Vice President, Winnie Rednour, 39743 Clements Way, Murrieta, GA 92563-4021, E-mail: vice-president@navywivesclubofamerica.org.

1277 ■ NAVY WIVES CLUB OF AMERICA
P.O. Box 54022
Millington, TN 38053-6022

(866)511-NWCA
E-mail: nwca@navywivesclubsofamerica.org
Web Site: http://www.navywivesclubsofamerica.org/nwc/scholarships.htm
To provide financial assistance for undergraduate or graduate study to members of the Navy Wives' Club of America (NWCA).
Title of Award: Mary Paolozzi Member's Scholarship **Area, Field, or Subject:** General studies/Field of study not specified **Level of Education for which Award is Granted:** Graduate, Undergraduate **Number Awarded:** 1 or more each year. **Funds Available:** Stipends range from $500 to $1,000 each year (depending upon the donations from the NWCA chapters). **Duration:** 1 year.
Eligibility Requirements: This program is open to NWCA members who can demonstrate financial need. Applicants must be 1) a high school graduate or senior planning to attend college full time next year; 2) currently enrolled in an undergraduate program and planning to continue as a full-time undergraduate; 3) a college graduate or senior planning to be a full-time graduate student next year; and 4) a high school graduate or GED recipient planning to attend vocational or business school next year. **Deadline for Receipt:** May of each year. **Additional Information:** Information is also available from Denise Johnson, NWCA National President, 534 Madrona Street, Chula Vista, CA 91910, E-mail: president@navywivesclubofamerica.org. Membership in the NWCA is open to spouses of enlisted personnel serving in the Navy, Marine Corps, Coast Guard, and the active Reserve units of those services; spouses of enlisted personnel who have been honorable discharged, retired, or transferred to the Fleet Reserve on completion of duty; and widows of enlisted personnel in those services.

1278 ■ NEBRASKA AMATEUR SOFTBALL ASSOCIATION
Attn: Foundation
4103 Osborne Drive East
Hastings, NE 68901
Tel: (402)462-7100
Fax: (402)461-3297
E-mail: info@nebraskasoftball.org
Web Site: http://nebraskasoftball.org
To provide financial assistance for college to Nebraska residents who have worked as an official for a sports organization and their families.
Title of Award: Pat Schartz Memorial Scholarship **Area, Field, or Subject:** General studies/Field of study not specified **Level of Education for which Award is Granted:** Undergraduate **Number Awarded:** 1 each year. **Funds Available:** The stipend is $1,000. **Duration:** 1 year; nonrenewable.
Eligibility Requirements: This program is open to residents of Nebraska who have been a registered official or family member of a baseball, softball, or football official. Applicants must be high school seniors and enrolled or planning to enroll as a full-time student at a college or university in Nebraska. They must have a GPA of 3.0 or higher. Along with their application, they must submit a statement on how officiating or being a family member of an official has been part of their life lessons and why they should be considered for this scholarship. Selection is based on academic ability, officiating activities, personal qualities, community activities, higher education potential, and financial need. **Deadline for Receipt:** November of each year.

1279 ■ NEBRASKA ELKS ASSOCIATION
c/o Melvin Nespor, Scholarship Committee
P.O. Box 14
Endicott, NE 68350
E-mail: mnespor@beatricene.com
To provide financial assistance to high school seniors in Nebraska who plan to attend a vocational school in the state.
Title of Award: Nebraska Elks Association Vocational Scholarship Grants **Area, Field, or Subject:** General studies/Field of study not specified **Level of Education for which Award is Granted:** Vocational/Occupational **Number Awarded:** 6 each year. **Funds Available:** Stipends depend on the need of the recipient, to a maximum of $1,000. **Duration:** 1 year.
Eligibility Requirements: This program is open to seniors graduating from high schools in Nebraska. Applicants must be planning to attend a 2-year or less vocational/technical program for an associate degree, diploma, or certificate. Selection is based on motivation (general worthiness, desire); aptitude toward chosen vocation; grades and test scores;

completeness, neatness, and accuracy in following instructions when filling out the application; and financial need. Each Nebraska Elks Lodge can submit 1 application. **Deadline for Receipt:** January of each year.

1280 ■ NEBRASKA FUNERAL DIRECTORS ASSOCIATION

Attn: Laughlin Trust Committee
201 North Eighth Street, Suite 400
P.O. Box 83313
Lincoln, NE 68501-3313
Tel: (402)423-8900
Fax: (402)476-6547
E-mail: nefda@assocoffice.net
Web Site: http://www.nefda.org/careers
To provide financial assistance to residents of Nebraska who are interested in preparing for a career in mortuary science.
Title of Award: Wallace S. and Wilma K. Laughlin Foundation Trust Scholarships **Area, Field, or Subject:** Mortuary science **Level of Education for which Award is Granted:** Undergraduate **Number Awarded:** Varies, depending upon the funds available. **Funds Available:** Stipends are at least $1,000 per year. Funds are paid directly to the recipient's school. **Duration:** 1 year.
Eligibility Requirements: This program is open to residents of Nebraska who are graduates of a high school in the state and have met the pre-mortuary academic requirements set by the state prior to entering a mortuary science college. Students planning to attend a 1-year course of study must apply prior to entering an accredited mortuary school. Students planning a 4-year course of study must apply prior to entering the third year of study. Applicants must be recommended by a member of the Nebraska Funeral Directors Association. Interviews are required. Financial need is not considered in the selection process. **Deadline for Receipt:** June of each year.

1281 ■ NEBRASKA SPACE GRANT CONSORTIUM

c/o University of Nebraska at Omaha
Allwine Hall 422
6001 Dodge Street
Omaha, NE 68182-0589
Tel: (402)554-3772
Free: 800-858-8648
Fax: (402)554-3781
E-mail: nasa@unomaha.edu
Web Site: http://www.unomaha.edu/~nasa/Scholarships%20Internships/
columbia.php
To provide financial assistance to undergraduate students majoring in science at institutions that are members of the Nebraska Space Grant Consortium.
Title of Award: Columbia Memorial Scholarship **Area, Field, or Subject:** Science **Level of Education for which Award is Granted:** Graduate, Undergraduate **Funds Available:** A stipend is awarded (amount not specified). **Duration:** 1 year.
Eligibility Requirements: This program is open to undergraduate and graduate students at schools that are members of the Nebraska Space Grant Consortium. Applicants must submit an essay that describes their scientific research track, past or ongoing research, their career goals, and how the scientific research track they are pursuing will be helpful in such a career. This program is sponsored by the U.S. National Aeronautics and Space Administration (NASA), which strongly encourages women, minorities, and students with disabilities to apply. U.S. citizenship is required. **Deadline for Receipt:** April of each year. **Additional Information:** This program was established in 2003 to honor the Columbia astronauts, especially Creighton University graduate Lt. Col. Michael Anderson. The following schools are members of the Nebraska Space Grant Consortium: University of Nebraska at Omaha, University of Nebraska at Lincoln, University of Nebraska at Kearney, University of Nebraska Medical Center, Creighton University, Western Nebraska Community College, Chadron State College, College of St. Mary, Metropolitan Community College, Grace University, Hastings College, Little Priest Tribal College, and Nebraska Indian Community College.

1282 ■ NEBRASKA SPACE GRANT CONSORTIUM

c/o University of Nebraska at Omaha
Allwine Hall 422
6001 Dodge Street
Omaha, NE 68182-0406

Tel: (402)554-3772
Free: 800-858-8648
Fax: (402)554-3781
E-mail: nasa@unomaha.edu
Web Site: http://nasa.unomaha.edu/Funding/funding.php
To provide financial assistance to undergraduate and graduate students at member institutions of the Nebraska Space Grant Consortium.
Title of Award: Nebraska Space Grant Statewide Scholarship Competition **Area, Field, or Subject:** General studies/Field of study not specified **Level of Education for which Award is Granted:** Graduate, Undergraduate **Number Awarded:** At least 2 students from each institution are supported each year. **Funds Available:** A stipend is awarded (amount not specified). **Duration:** 1 year.
Eligibility Requirements: This program is open to undergraduate and graduate students at schools that are members of the Nebraska Space Grant Consortium. Students in all academic disciplines are eligible. This program is sponsored by the U.S. National Aeronautics and Space Administration (NASA), which strongly encourages women, minorities, and students with disabilities to apply. U.S. citizenship is required. Financial need is not considered in the selection process. **Deadline for Receipt:** April of each year. **Additional Information:** The following schools are members of the Nebraska Space Grant Consortium: University of Nebraska at Omaha, University of Nebraska at Lincoln, University of Nebraska at Kearney, University of Nebraska Medical Center, Creighton University, Western Nebraska Community College, Chadron State College, College of St. Mary, Metropolitan Community College, Grace University, Hastings College, Little Priest Tribal College, and Nebraska Indian Community College.

1283 ■ NEBRASKA STATE HISTORICAL SOCIETY FOUNDATION

Attn: Executive Director
Kinman-Oldfield Suite 1010
128 North 13th Street
Lincoln, NE 68508-1565
Tel: (402)435-3535; 888-515-3535
Fax: (402)435-3986
E-mail: nshsf@alltel.net
Web Site: http://www.nebraskahistory.org/foundatn/index.htm
To provide financial assistance for college to high school seniors in Nebraska.
Title of Award: Nebraskans of World War II Scholarships **Area, Field, or Subject:** General studies/Field of study not specified **Level of Education for which Award is Granted:** Undergraduate **Number Awarded:** 5 each year. **Funds Available:** The stipend is $1,000. **Duration:** 1 year; nonrenewable.
Eligibility Requirements: This program is open to seniors graduating from high schools in Nebraska with a GPA of 3.5 or higher. Applicants must be planning to attend a 4-year college or university as a full-time student. Along with their application, they must submit a 1- to 2-page essay on the significance of the history of World War II to them and their community. **Deadline for Receipt:** January of each year. **Additional Information:** This program was established in 2000 to honor Nebraskans who died during World War II, particularly Edward J. Clough and Adrian B. DePutron, both of Lincoln.

1284 ■ NEVADA NATIONAL GUARD

Attn: Education Officer
2460 Fairview Drive
Carson City, NV 89701-6807
Tel: (775)887-7326
Fax: (775)887-7279
E-mail: Renae.Greenlee@nv.ngb.army.mil
Web Site: http://www.nv.ngb.army.mil
To provide financial assistance for college or graduate school to Nevada National Guard members.
Title of Award: Nevada National Guard State 100% Tuition Waiver Program **Area, Field, or Subject:** General studies/Field of study not specified **Level of Education for which Award is Granted:** Graduate, Undergraduate **Number Awarded:** Varies each year. **Funds Available:** This program provides a waiver of 100% of tuition at state-supported community colleges, colleges, or universities in Nevada. **Duration:** 1 year; may be renewed.
Eligibility Requirements: This program is open to active members of the Nevada National Guard who are interested in attending a community col-

lege, 4-year college, or university in the state. Applicants must be residents of Nevada. Independent study, correspondence courses, and study at the William S. Boyd School of Law, the University of Nevada School of Medicine, and the UNLV School of Dental Medicine are not eligible. **Deadline for Receipt:** Applications must be received at least 3 weeks prior to the start of the semester. **Additional Information:** This program was established on a pilot basis in 2003 and became permanent in 2005. Recipients must attain a GPA of at least 2.0 or refund all tuition received.

1285 ■ NEW ENGLAND BOARD OF HIGHER EDUCATION
45 Temple Place
Boston, MA 02111
Tel: (617)357-9620
Fax: (617)338-1577
E-mail: tuitionbreak@nebhe.org
Web Site: http://www.nebhe.org
To enable students in New England to attend a college or graduate school within the region at reduced tuition when their area of study is not offered at their own state's public institutions.
Title of Award: New England Regional Student Program **Area, Field, or Subject:** General studies/Field of study not specified **Level of Education for which Award is Granted:** Graduate, Undergraduate **Number Awarded:** Varies each year; recently, more than 8,050 New England students took advantage of this program. **Funds Available:** With this program, students accepted at a public college or university in New England (but outside their own state) generally pay 150% of the in-state tuition for residents of the state. The average tuition saving is approximately $5,000. **Duration:** Up to 4 years.
Eligibility Requirements: This program is open to residents of the 6 New England states: Connecticut, Maine, Massachusetts, New Hampshire, Rhode Island, and Vermont. Students may apply for this support when their chosen field of study is not offered at any of the public institutions within their own state. Contact the New England Board of Higher Education for a catalog of degree programs and states that qualify for this program. Undergraduate program eligibility is based on entire degree programs only, not on concentrations or options within degree programs. Some highly specialized graduate programs might be available even if they are not listed in the catalog. Eligibility is not based on financial need.
Additional Information: In addition to reduced tuition, participants in this program also receive admission preference among out-of-state applicants. Because this is a tuition-reduction program, not a financial assistance program, participants are still eligible to apply for financial aid from other sources. Students must apply for this program when they apply to their chosen out-of-state public college or university.

1286 ■ NEW ENGLAND EMPLOYEE BENEFITS COUNCIL
440 Totten Pond Road
Waltham, MA 02451
Tel: (781)684-8700
Fax: (781)684-9200
E-mail: info@neebc.org
Web Site: http://www.neebc.org/scholar/scholar.html
To provide financial assistance to residents and students in the New England states who are working on an undergraduate or graduate degree in a field related to employee benefits.
Title of Award: NEEBC Scholarship Program **Area, Field, or Subject:** Actuarial science; Employment; Insurance and insurance-related fields; Personnel administration/human resources **Level of Education for which Award is Granted:** Graduate, Undergraduate **Number Awarded:** 1 or more each year. **Funds Available:** The stipend is $5,000 per year. **Duration:** 1 year; may be renewed up to 3 additional years or until completion of a degree.
Eligibility Requirements: This program is open to full-time undergraduate and graduate students who are residents of New England or enrolled in a college in the region. Applicants must be interested in preparing for a career in such areas as health care program design; pension fund design, implementation, or administration; retirement strategies; ERISA and legal aspects of employee benefits; health risk management; multiemployer plans; workers compensation; employee benefits communications; actuarial and underwriting analysis; work/life programs; or institutional investing of retirement savings. Along with their application, they must submit an essay (up to 500 words) describing why they are interested in

entering the employee benefits field and what careers within the field are of interest to them and why. Selection is based on 1) study, activities, and goals related to employee benefits; 2) school and community activities; 3) work experience; and 4) academic performance and potential. **Deadline for Receipt:** March of each year.

1287 ■ NEW HAMPSHIRE CHARITABLE FOUNDATION
37 Pleasant Street
Concord, NH 03301-4005
Tel: (603)225-6641
Free: 800-464-6641
Fax: (603)225-1700
E-mail: info@nhcf.org
Web Site: http://www.nhcf.org
To provide financial assistance for college to graduating high school seniors in New Hampshire.
Title of Award: Bank of New Hampshire LEAP Scholarships **Area, Field, or Subject:** General studies/Field of study not specified **Level of Education for which Award is Granted:** Undergraduate **Number Awarded:** 9 each year. **Funds Available:** The stipend is $2,500 per year. **Duration:** 1 year.
Eligibility Requirements: This program is open to seniors at high schools in New Hampshire who will be enrolling full time in a postsecondary institution. Selection is based on financial need, academic achievement, involvement in school activities, community volunteer activity, and work experience. **Deadline for Receipt:** March of each year. **Additional Information:** This program is offered by Bank of New Hampshire as part of its Local Educational Advancement Programs (LEAP). Recipients are also offered 3-month paid internships with the bank during the summer after their first year of postsecondary education. Further information is available from the bank at (800) 922-5705.

1288 ■ NEW HAMPSHIRE CHARITABLE FOUNDATION
37 Pleasant Street
Concord, NH 03301-4005
Tel: (603)225-6641
Free: 800-464-6641
Fax: (603)225-1700
E-mail: info@nhcf.org
Web Site: http://www.nhcf.org
To provide financial assistance to New Hampshire residents preparing for a vocational or technical career.
Title of Award: Career Aid for Technical Students Program **Area, Field, or Subject:** General studies/Field of study not specified **Level of Education for which Award is Granted:** Two Year College, Vocational/Occupational **Number Awarded:** Varies each year. **Funds Available:** Stipends range from $100 to $2,500, depending on the need of the recipient. A total of $200,000 is distributed annually. **Duration:** 1 year.
Eligibility Requirements: This program is open to residents of New Hampshire entering a 2-year or 3-year degree program or a shorter-term technical degree training program that leads to an associate degree, a trade license, or certification. Applicants must be dependent students younger than 24 years of age and planning to enroll at least half time at a community college, vocational school, trade school, or other short-term training program. They must be able to demonstrate financial need. Although academic excellence is not considered in the selection process, applicants should be able to demonstrate reasonable achievement and a commitment to their chosen field of study. **Deadline for Receipt:** June of each year.

1289 ■ NEW HAMPSHIRE CHARITABLE FOUNDATION
37 Pleasant Street
Concord, NH 03301-4005
Tel: (603)225-6641
Free: 800-464-6641
Fax: (603)225-1700
E-mail: info@nhcf.org
Web Site: http://www.nhcf.org
To provide financial assistance for college to residents of seacoast New Hampshire communities.
Title of Award: Billy Cheverie Memorial Scholarship Fund **Area, Field, or Subject:** General studies/Field of study not specified **Level of Education for which Award is Granted:** Undergraduate **Number Awarded:** 1 or

more each year. **Funds Available:** The stipend is $1,000. **Duration:** 1 year.

Eligibility Requirements: This program is open to seniors graduating from Portsmouth, York, Winnacunnet high schools and Traip Academy in New Hampshire. Students from New Hampshire seacoast communities who attend St. Thomas High School, Philips Exeter Academy, or Berwick Academy are also eligible. Financial need must be demonstrated. Preference is given to students who have participated in athletics. Applicants should also demonstrate a commitment to leadership, community service, and academic effort. **Deadline for Receipt:** March of each year.

1290 ■ NEW HAMPSHIRE CHARITABLE FOUNDATION

37 Pleasant Street
Concord, NH 03301-4005
Tel: (603)225-6641
Free: 800-464-6641
Fax: (603)225-1700
E-mail: info@nhcf.org
Web Site: http://www.nhcf.org
To provide financial assistance for college to minority and other students from New Hampshire.

Title of Award: Monsignor Philip Kenney Scholarship Fund **Area, Field, or Subject:** General studies/Field of study not specified **Level of Education for which Award is Granted:** Undergraduate **Number Awarded:** Varies; in addition to the 1 scholarship for a minority student from Merrimack County, a total of $10,000 is available each year. **Funds Available:** The scholarship designated for a minority student from Merrimack has a stipend of $1,000. Other stipends vary. **Duration:** 1 year; recipients may reapply.

Eligibility Requirements: This program is open to New Hampshire students who are economically disadvantaged, with a preference for Hispanics and other minorities who are enrolled in undergraduate study. Nontraditional students, both full and part time, are encouraged to apply. At least 1 scholarship is designated for a minority student from Merrimack County. **Deadline for Receipt:** April of each year.

1291 ■ NEW HAMPSHIRE CHARITABLE FOUNDATION

37 Pleasant Street
Concord, NH 03301-4005
Tel: (603)225-6641
Free: 800-464-6641
Fax: (603)225-1700
E-mail: info@nhcf.org
Web Site: http://www.nhcf.org
To provide financial assistance to New Hampshire residents preparing for a vocational or technical career.

Title of Award: Manchester Regional Community Foundation Medallion Fund **Area, Field, or Subject:** General studies/Field of study not specified **Level of Education for which Award is Granted:** Two Year College, Vocational/Occupational **Number Awarded:** Varies each year. **Funds Available:** Stipends are provided (amount not specified). **Duration:** 1 year.

Eligibility Requirements: This program is open to residents of New Hampshire of any age who are enrolling in an accredited vocational or technical program that does not lead to a 4-year baccalaureate degree. Applicants must be planning to attend a community college, vocational school, trade school, apprenticeship, or other short-term training program. They must be able to demonstrate financial need. Applicants should be able to demonstrate competence and a commitment to their chosen field of study. Preference is given to applicants 1) whose fields are in the traditional manufacturing trade sector (e.g., plumbing, electrical, constructing, machining); 2) who have a clear vision for how their education will help them achieve or improve their employment goals; 3) who have had little or no other educational or training opportunities; and 4) who have made a commitment to their educational program both financially and otherwise. **Deadline for Receipt:** Applications may be submitted at any time.

1292 ■ NEW HAMPSHIRE CHARITABLE FOUNDATION

37 Pleasant Street
Concord, NH 03301-4005
Tel: (603)225-6641
Free: 800-464-6641

Fax: (603)225-1700
E-mail: info@nhcf.org
Web Site: http://www.nhcf.org
To provide funding for undergraduate study to adults in New Hampshire who are returning to school.

Title of Award: New Hampshire Charitable Foundation Adult Student Aid Program **Area, Field, or Subject:** General studies/Field of study not specified **Level of Education for which Award is Granted:** Undergraduate **Number Awarded:** Varies each year. **Funds Available:** The maximum award is $500 each term ($1,000 per year). Most awards are in the form of grants, although no-interest or low-interest loans are also available. **Duration:** 1 academic term; may be renewed up to 2 additional terms.

Eligibility Requirements: This program is open to New Hampshire residents who are 24 years of age or older. Applicants should 1) have had little or no education beyond high school, and 2) be now returning to school to upgrade skills for employment or career advancement, to qualify for a degree program, or to make a career change. They must demonstrate that they have secured all available financial aid and still have a remaining unmet need. Preference for funding is given in the following order: 1) students who have previously received funding through this program and have successfully completed prior work; 2) students with the least amount of higher education or training; and 3) single parents. Only undergraduate students are eligible. **Deadline for Receipt:** May, August, or December of each year. **Additional Information:** A $15 application fee is required.

1293 ■ NEW HAMPSHIRE CHARITABLE FOUNDATION

37 Pleasant Street
Concord, NH 03301-4005
Tel: (603)225-6641
Free: 800-464-6641
Fax: (603)225-1700
E-mail: info@nhcf.org
Web Site: http://www.nhcf.org
To provide scholarships or loans for undergraduate or graduate study to New Hampshire residents.

Title of Award: New Hampshire Charitable Foundation Statewide Student Aid Program **Area, Field, or Subject:** General studies/Field of study not specified **Level of Education for which Award is Granted:** Four Year College, Graduate **Number Awarded:** Varies each year; recently, a total of $3 million was awarded. **Funds Available:** Awards range from $500 to $2,500 and average $1,800. Most are made in the form of grants (recently, 82% of all awards) or no-interest or low-interest loans (recently 18% of all awards). **Duration:** 1 year; approximately one third of the awards are renewable.

Eligibility Requirements: This program is open to New Hampshire residents who are graduating high school seniors or undergraduate students between 17 and 23 years of age or graduate students of any age. Applicants must be enrolled in or planning to enroll in an accredited 2- or 4-year college, university, or vocational school on at least a half-time basis. The school may be in New Hampshire or another state. Selection is based on financial need, academic merit, community service, school activities, and work experience. Priority is given to students with the fewest financial resources and to vocational/technical school students. **Deadline for Receipt:** April of each year. **Additional Information:** Through this program, students submit a single application for more than 250 different scholarship and loan funds. Many of the funds have additional requirements, including field of study; residency in region, county, city, or town; graduation from designated high schools; and special attributes (of Belgian descent, employee of designated firms, customer of Granite State Telephone Company, disabled, suffering from a life-threatening or serious chronic illness, of Lithuanian descent, dependent of a New Hampshire police officer, dependent of a New Hampshire Episcopal minister, of Polish descent, former Sea Cadet or Naval Junior ROTC, or employed in the tourism industry). The Citizens' Scholarship Foundation of America reviews all applications; recipients are selected by the New Hampshire Charitable Foundation. A $20 application fee is required.

1294 ■ NEW HAMPSHIRE POSTSECONDARY EDUCATION COMMISSION

3 Barrell Court, Suite 300
Concord, NH 03301-8543

Tel: (603)271-2555
Fax: (603)271-2696
E-mail: pedes@pec.state.nh.us
Web Site: http://www.state.nh.us/postsecondary/finnhip.html
To provide financial assistance to New Hampshire residents who are interested in attending college in New England.

Title of Award: New Hampshire Incentive Program **Area, Field, or Subject:** General studies/Field of study not specified **Level of Education for which Award is Granted:** Undergraduate **Number Awarded:** Varies; recently, 2,586 were granted. **Funds Available:** The stipends range from $125 to $1,000 per year. **Duration:** 1 year.

Eligibility Requirements: Residents of New Hampshire are eligible to apply for this program if they are U.S. citizens or permanent residents, are accepted at or enrolled part or full time in an eligible postsecondary institution in 1 of the 6 New England states, and can demonstrate both academic ability and financial need. Upperclassmen must have a GPA of 2.0 or higher. **Deadline for Receipt:** April of each year. **Additional Information:** The only application for this program is the Free Application for Federal Student Aid (FAFSA).

1295 ■ NEW HAMPSHIRE POSTSECONDARY EDUCATION COMMISSION

3 Barrell Court, Suite 300
Concord, NH 03301-8543
Tel: (603)271-2555
Fax: (603)271-2696
E-mail: pedes@pec.state.nh.us
Web Site: http://www.state.nh.us/postsecondary/finligp.html
To provide financial assistance to New Hampshire residents who are attending college in the state and can demonstrate financial need.

Title of Award: New Hampshire Leveraged Incentive Grant Program **Area, Field, or Subject:** General studies/Field of study not specified **Level of Education for which Award is Granted:** Undergraduate **Number Awarded:** Varies each year. **Funds Available:** The stipend depends on the need of the recipient, as determined by the institution. **Duration:** 1 year; may be renewed.

Eligibility Requirements: This program is open to residents of New Hampshire who are currently enrolled as sophomores, juniors, or seniors at accredited colleges and universities in the state. Selection is based on financial need (as determined by federal formulas) and academic merit (as determined by the institution). **Additional Information:** Information is available at the financial aid office of New Hampshire institutions.

1296 ■ NEW HAMPSHIRE POSTSECONDARY EDUCATION COMMISSION

3 Barrell Court, Suite 300
Concord, NH 03301-8543
Tel: (603)271-2555
Fax: (603)271-2696
E-mail: pedes@pec.state.nh.us
Web Site: http://www.state.nh.us/postsecondary/finsfoov.html
To provide financial assistance for college to the children of New Hampshire veterans who died of service-connected disabilities.

Title of Award: New Hampshire Scholarships for Orphans of Veterans **Area, Field, or Subject:** General studies/Field of study not specified **Level of Education for which Award is Granted:** Undergraduate **Number Awarded:** Varies each year. **Funds Available:** The stipend is $1,000 per year, to be used for the payment of room, board, books, and supplies. **Duration:** 1 year; may be renewed for up to 3 additional years.

Eligibility Requirements: This program is open to New Hampshire residents between 16 and 25 years of age whose parent(s) died as a result of a service-related disability incurred during World War I, World War II, the Korean Conflict, or the southeast Asian Conflict. These parents must have been residents of New Hampshire at the time of death. Applicants must be enrolled as full-time undergraduate students at a public college or university in New Hampshire.

1297 ■ NEW JERSEY ASSOCIATION OF REALTORS

Attn: Educational Foundation
295 Pierson Avenue
P.O. Box 2098
Edison, NJ 08818
Tel: (732)494-5616

Fax: (732)494-4723
E-mail: info@njar.com
Web Site: http://www.njar.com/edfoundpublic.shtml
To provide financial assistance to members and relatives of members of the New Jersey Association of Realtors (NJAR) who are interested in a career in real estate.

Title of Award: New Jersey Association of Realtors Educational Foundation Scholarships **Area, Field, or Subject:** Real estate **Level of Education for which Award is Granted:** Four Year College, Graduate **Number Awarded:** Varies each year. Recently, 22 of these scholarships were awarded: 2 (named the Nancy F. Reynolds Memorial Awards) at $2,000 each, 8 at $1,500 each, and 12 at $1,250 each. **Funds Available:** Stipends range from $1,250 to $2,000. **Duration:** 1 year.

Eligibility Requirements: This program is open to high school seniors planning to attend a 4-year college or university, undergraduate students currently enrolled at 4-year colleges and universities, and graduate students in New Jersey who are interested in preparing for a career in real estate. Applicants must be NJAR members or relatives of members. U.S. citizenship or permanent resident status is required. Selection is based on academic achievements; sincerity of purpose in real estate endeavors; contribution to family, school, and community; and financial need. **Deadline for Receipt:** April of each year.

1298 ■ NEW JERSEY CHRONIC FATIGUE SYNDROME ASSOCIATION, INC.

P.O. Box 477
Florham Park, NJ 07932
Tel: (609)219-0662
Web Site: http://njcfsa.org
To provide financial assistance for college to high school seniors in New Jersey who have Chronic Fatigue Syndrome (CFS).

Title of Award: New Jersey Chronic Fatigue Syndrome Association Scholarship **Area, Field, or Subject:** General studies/Field of study not specified **Level of Education for which Award is Granted:** Undergraduate **Number Awarded:** 1 each year. **Funds Available:** The stipend is $1,000. **Duration:** 1 year.

Eligibility Requirements: This program is open to college-bound seniors graduating from high schools in New Jersey. Applicants must have been diagnosed with CFS. They must have a GPA of 2.0 or higher. Along with their application, they must submit a 350-word essay on what they see as their goal for higher education or career direction and how having CFS has influenced their choice. **Deadline for Receipt:** April of each year. **Additional Information:** Information is also available from Betty McConnell, Scholarship Committee, P.O. Box 328, Port Republic, NJ 08241, (609) 748-3559, E-mail: ElizabethMcConn@cs.com.

1299 ■ NEW JERSEY COALITION ON WOMEN AND DISABILITIES

c/o Dorothy McDowell, President
67 Bay View Drive
Brick, NJ 08723-7449
Tel: (732)255-2733
E-mail: DorMcD@aol.com
To provide financial assistance for college to women with disabilities in New Jersey.

Title of Award: New Jersey Coalition on Women and Disabilities Scholarship **Area, Field, or Subject:** General studies/Field of study not specified **Level of Education for which Award is Granted:** Undergraduate **Number Awarded:** Up to 5 each year. **Funds Available:** The stipend is $1,000. **Duration:** 1 year.

Eligibility Requirements: This program is open to women with a diagnosed disability who is attending an accredited New Jersey college, university, or vocational/technical school. Applicants must submit proof of current enrollment in good standing. **Additional Information:** This program was established in 1999.

1300 ■ NEW JERSEY COMMISSION ON HIGHER EDUCATION

Attn: Educational Opportunity Fund
20 West State Street, Seventh Floor
P.O. Box 542
Trenton, NJ 08625-0542
Tel: (609)984-2709
Fax: (609)292-7225
E-mail: nj_che@che.state.nj.us

Web Site: http://www.nj.gov/highereducation/eligible.htm
To provide financial assistance for undergraduate or graduate study in New Jersey to students from disadvantaged backgrounds.
Title of Award: New Jersey Educational Opportunity Fund Grants **Area, Field, or Subject:** General studies/Field of study not specified **Level of Education for which Award is Granted:** Graduate, Undergraduate **Funds Available:** Undergraduate grants range from $200 to $2,400 and graduate grants from $200 to $4,250, depending on college costs and financial need. **Duration:** 1 year; renewable annually (based on satisfactory academic progress and continued eligibility).
Eligibility Requirements: This program is open to students from economically and educationally disadvantaged backgrounds who have been legal residents of New Jersey for at least 12 consecutive months. Applicants must be from families with annual incomes below specified limits, ranging from $18,620 for a household size of 1 to $63,140 for a household size of 8. They must be attending or accepted for attendance as full-time undergraduate or graduate students at institutions of higher education in New Jersey. To apply, students must fill out the Free Application for Federal Student Aid. Some colleges may also require students to complete the College Scholarship Service's (CSS) Financial Aid Form to apply for institutional aid. **Deadline for Receipt:** September of each year.
Additional Information: This is a campus-based program; each college or university has its own specific criteria for admission and program participation; students should contact the Educational Opportunity Fund (EOF) director at their institution for specific admissions information and requirements for participating in the program. Participants are also eligible for supportive services, such as counseling, tutoring, and developmental course work.

1301 ■ NEW JERSEY DEPARTMENT OF MILITARY AND VETERANS AFFAIRS

Attn: New Jersey Army National Guard Education Center
3650 Saylors Pond Road
Fort Dix, NJ 08640-7600
Tel: (609)562-0654; 888-859-0352
Fax: (609)562-0201
Web Site: http://www.state.nj.us/military/education/NJNGTP.htm
To provide financial assistance for college or graduate school to New Jersey National Guard members and the surviving spouses and children of deceased members.
Title of Award: New Jersey National Guard Tuition Program **Area, Field, or Subject:** General studies/Field of study not specified **Level of Education for which Award is Granted:** Graduate, Undergraduate **Number Awarded:** Varies each year. **Funds Available:** Tuition for up to 15 credits per semester is waived for full-time recipients in state-supported colleges or community colleges in New Jersey. **Duration:** 1 semester; may be renewed.
Eligibility Requirements: This program is open to active members of the New Jersey National Guard who have completed Initial Active Duty for Training (IADT). Applicants must be New Jersey residents who have been accepted into a program of undergraduate or graduate study at any of 31 public institutions of higher education in the state. The surviving spouses and children of deceased members of the Guard who had completed IADT and were killed in the performance of their duties while a member of the Guard are also eligible if the school has classroom space available.

1302 ■ NEW JERSEY DEPARTMENT OF MILITARY AND VETERANS AFFAIRS

Attn: Division of Veterans Programs
101 Eggert Crossing Road
P.O. Box 340
Trenton, NJ 08625-0340
Tel: (609)530-7045
Free: 800-624-0508
Fax: (609)530-7075
Web Site: http://www.state.nj.us/military/veterans/programs.html
To provide financial assistance for college to the children of New Jersey military personnel reported as missing in action or prisoners of war during the southeast Asian conflict.
Title of Award: New Jersey POW/MIA Tuition Benefit Program **Area, Field, or Subject:** General studies/Field of study not specified **Level of Education for which Award is Granted:** Undergraduate **Number Awarded:** Varies each year. **Funds Available:** This program entitles

recipients to full undergraduate tuition at any public or independent postsecondary educational institution in New Jersey. **Duration:** Assistance continues until completion of a bachelor's degree.
Eligibility Requirements: Eligible to apply for this assistance are New Jersey residents attending or accepted at a New Jersey public or independent postsecondary institution whose parents were military service personnel officially declared prisoners of war or missing in action after January 1, 1960. **Deadline for Receipt:** February of each year for the spring term and September for the fall and spring terms.

1303 ■ NEW JERSEY FUNERAL DIRECTORS ASSOCIATION

Attn: New Jersey Funeral Service Education Corporation
P.O. Box L
Manasquan, NJ 08736
Tel: (732)974-9444
Fax: (732)974-8144
E-mail: njsfda@njsfda.org
Web Site: http://www.njsfda.org/education/edu_3scholar.shtml
To provide financial assistance to New Jersey residents who are currently enrolled in a mortuary science program.
Title of Award: New Jersey Funeral Service Education Corporation Scholarships **Area, Field, or Subject:** Mortuary science **Level of Education for which Award is Granted:** Undergraduate **Number Awarded:** 4 each year. **Funds Available:** The stipend is $2,000. **Duration:** 1 year.
Eligibility Requirements: This program is open to New Jersey residents who are currently enrolled in a mortuary science program and planning to enter the field of funeral service in the state after graduation. Applicants must have a college GPA of 2.5 or higher. They must submit an essay on either 1) why they have chosen funeral service as a career, or 2) what they feel they can contribute to funeral service. A personal interview is required. Selection is based on the essay, academic record, commitment to funeral service as a career, and (to a lesser extent) financial need. **Deadline for Receipt:** June of each year.

1304 ■ NEW JERSEY SCHOOL COUNSELOR ASSOCIATION, INC.

c/o Marcy Rosner, Scholarship Chair
Elizabeth Haddon Elementary School
501 Redman Avenue
Haddonfield, NJ 08033
Tel: (856)234-8884
E-mail: trosner1@comcast.net
Web Site: http://www.njsca.org
To provide financial assistance for college to high school seniors in New Jersey who submit outstanding essays on their school counselor.
Title of Award: New Jersey School Counselor Association Scholarships **Area, Field, or Subject:** General studies/Field of study not specified **Level of Education for which Award is Granted:** Undergraduate **Number Awarded:** 3 each year. **Funds Available:** The stipend is $1,000. **Duration:** 1 year.
Eligibility Requirements: This program is open to college-bound seniors graduating from high schools in New Jersey. Applicants must submit an essay of 300 to 500 words on how a school counselor has influenced their life in a positive way. The counselor must be a member of the New Jersey School Counselor Association. Along with the essay and the application, students must submit, through their counselor, copies of their high school transcript, high school profile, and letter of acceptance to a postsecondary institution. Financial need is not considered in the selection process. **Deadline for Receipt:** April of each year.

1305 ■ NEW JERSEY STATE ELKS

Attn: Handicapped Children's Committee
665 Rahway Avenue
P.O. Box 1596
Woodbridge, NJ 07095-1596
Tel: (732)326-1300
E-mail: info@njelks.org
Web Site: http://www.njelks.org
To provide financial assistance for college to high school seniors in New Jersey who have a disability.
Title of Award: New Jersey State Elks Handicapped Children's Scholarship **Area, Field, or Subject:** General studies/Field of study not specified **Level of Education for which Award is Granted:** Undergraduate **Number Awarded:** 2 each year: 1 to a boy and 1 to a girl. **Funds Avail-

able: The stipend is $2,500 per year. Funds are paid directly to the recipient's college or university. **Duration:** 4 years.

Eligibility Requirements: This program is open to seniors graduating from high schools in New Jersey who have a disability. Selection is based on academic standing, general worthiness, and financial need. Boys and girls are judged separately. **Deadline for Receipt:** April of each year.

1306 ■ NEW JERSEY STATE GOLF ASSOCIATION

Attn: Education Director
1000 Broad Street
Bloomfield, NJ 07003
Tel: (973)338-8334
Fax: (973)338-5525
E-mail: Caddiescholarship@njsga.org
Web Site: http://www.njsga.org
To provide financial assistance for college to students who have caddied at a New Jersey State Golf Association (NJSGA) member club.
Title of Award: New Jersey State Golf Association Caddie Scholarship **Area, Field, or Subject:** General studies/Field of study not specified **Level of Education for which Award is Granted:** Undergraduate **Number Awarded:** Approximately 20 each year. **Funds Available:** Stipends range from $1,200 to $2,500 per year. **Duration:** 1 year; may be renewed up to 3 additional years if the recipient continues to meet program eligibility requirements.
Eligibility Requirements: This program is open to students who have caddied at an association club for at least 1 year and are enrolled or planning to enroll as a full-time undergraduate student. Applicants must have their golf club's golf professional or caddie master attest to their eligibility as a caddie at the club, include a copy of their parent's income tax forms, and submit a copy of their transcript. Children of members of private golf clubs are not eligible. Selection is based on scholastic achievement, SAT scores, qualities of character and leadership, length and quality of service as a caddie, and financial need. **Deadline for Receipt:** April of each year.
Additional Information: A full tuition, fee, room, board, and book allowance scholarship is offered to the most deserving applicant who plants to attend Rutgers, the State University of New Jersey. Applications for that scholarship must be submitted by February of each year. This program began in 1947. Information is also available from the New Jersey Golf Caddie Scholarship Program, P.O. Box 6947, Freehold, NJ 07728-4015, (732) 780-4822, E-mail: j.o.petersen@att.net.

1307 ■ NEW JERSEY UTILITIES ASSOCIATION

50 West State Street, Suite 1117
Trenton, NJ 08608
Tel: (609)392-1000
Fax: (609)396-4231
Web Site: http://www.njua.org
To provide financial assistance for college 1) to employees who work for New Jersey Utilities Association member companies and 2) to their families.
Title of Award: James R. Leva Scholarship Program **Area, Field, or Subject:** General studies/Field of study not specified **Level of Education for which Award is Granted:** Undergraduate **Funds Available:** The stipend is $3,000 per year. Funds are sent directly to the recipient's school and are intended to cover expenses not paid by an employer tuition aid/educational assistance program. **Duration:** 1 year.
Eligibility Requirements: Applicants must be 1) regular, full-time employees of a member company or 2) the spouse or dependent children of member utilities' employees. Employee applicants must meet eligibility criteria for any tuition aid program the member company might have or, if none exists, must have at least 6 months of company service. All applicants must enroll or be enrolled in an approved course of study at an accredited junior college, college, or university. Selection is based on past academic performance and future potential, school and community participation, work experience, career and educational aspirations, financial need, unusual personal or family circumstances, and recommendations. **Deadline for Receipt:** April of each year.

1308 ■ NEW MEXICO DEPARTMENT OF VETERANS' SERVICES

P.O. Box 2324
Santa Fe, NM 87504-2324
Tel: (505)827-6300; (866)433-VETS
Fax: (505)827-6372

E-mail: nmdvs@state.nm.us
Web Site: http://www.state.nm.us/veterans/scholarship.html
To provide financial assistance for college or graduate school to the children of deceased military and state police personnel in New Mexico.
Title of Award: New Mexico Children of Deceased Military and State Police Personnel Scholarships **Area, Field, or Subject:** General studies/Field of study not specified **Level of Education for which Award is Granted:** Master's, Undergraduate **Funds Available:** The scholarships provide payment of matriculation fees, board, room, books, and supplies at state-supported institutions of higher education in New Mexico. **Duration:** 1 year; may be renewed.
Eligibility Requirements: This program is open to the children of 1) military personnel killed in action or as a result of such action during a period of armed conflict; 2) members of the New Mexico National Guard killed while on active duty; and 3) New Mexico State Police killed on active duty. Applicants must be between the ages of 16 and 26 and enrolled in a state-supported school in New Mexico. Children of deceased veterans must be nominated by the New Mexico Veterans' Service Commission; children of National Guard members must be nominated by the adjutant general of the state; children of state police must be nominated by the New Mexico State Police Board. Selection is based on merit and financial need.

1309 ■ NEW MEXICO DEPARTMENT OF VETERANS' SERVICES

P.O. Box 2324
Santa Fe, NM 87504-2324
Tel: (505)827-6300; (866)433-VETS
Fax: (505)827-6372
E-mail: nmdvs@state.nm.us
Web Site: http://www.state.nm.us/veterans/scholarship.html
To provide financial assistance for undergraduate and graduate education to Vietnam veterans in New Mexico.
Title of Award: New Mexico Vietnam Veterans Scholarships **Area, Field, or Subject:** General studies/Field of study not specified **Level of Education for which Award is Granted:** Graduate, Undergraduate **Funds Available:** The scholarships pay tuition, fees, and books at any postsecondary institution in New Mexico, up to $1,520 for tuition and fees and $500 for books. **Duration:** 1 year.
Eligibility Requirements: This program is open to Vietnam veterans who have been residents of New Mexico for at least 10 years. Applicants must have been honorably discharged and have been awarded the Vietnam Service Medal or the Vietnam Campaign Medal. They must be planning to attend a state-supported college, university, or community college in New Mexico to work on an undergraduate or graduate degree.

1310 ■ NEW MEXICO ELKS ASSOCIATION

Attn: Charitable and Benevolent Trust Commission
c/o Jim Larrabbee, Scholarship Committee
302 Ciniza Court
Gallup, NM 87301
Fax: (505)863-3821
E-mail: JimLarrabee@cnetco.com
Web Site: http://www.nmelks.org
To provide financial assistance for college to high school seniors in New Mexico.
Title of Award: New Mexico Elks Association Charitable and Benevolent Trust Scholarships **Area, Field, or Subject:** General studies/Field of study not specified **Level of Education for which Award is Granted:** Undergraduate **Number Awarded:** 14 each year: 1 at $2,000 per year for 4 years to the top female applicant, 1 at $2,000 per year for 4 years to the top male applicant, 6 at $2,000 for 1 year, and 6 at $1,000 for 1 year. **Funds Available:** Stipends are either $2,000 or $1,000 per year. **Duration:** 1 or 4 years.
Eligibility Requirements: Applicants must be seniors graduating from a high school in New Mexico. They must have exhibited outstanding scholastic and leadership ability, including extracurricular and civic activities. High school class rank, GPA, and standardized test scores must be validated by a school official. An endorsement from the local Elks Lodge is required. Financial need is also considered in the selection process. Some awards are designated for females and some for males. **Deadline for Receipt:** March of each year. **Additional Information:** Recipients may attend any level of academic institution and may major in any field. This program includes the following named awards: the Charles Mahr

Memorial Scholarship, the Evelyn Boney Memorial Scholarships, the Howard Medlin Memorial Scholarship, and the Robert E. Boney Memorial Scholarship.

1311 ■ NEW MEXICO ELKS ASSOCIATION

Attn: Charitable and Benevolent Trust Commission
c/o Jim Larrabbee, Scholarship Committee
302 Ciniza Court
Gallup, NM 87301
Fax: (505)863-3821
E-mail: JimLarrabee@cnetco.com
Web Site: http://www.nmelks.org
To provide financial assistance for vocational or trade school to high school seniors in New Mexico.

Title of Award: Aubrey Warren Memorial Scholarship **Area, Field, or Subject:** General studies/Field of study not specified **Level of Education for which Award is Granted:** Vocational/Occupational **Number Awarded:** 1 or more each year. **Funds Available:** A stipend is awarded, generally either $1,000 or $2,000. **Duration:** 1 year.

Eligibility Requirements: Applicants must be seniors graduating from a high school in New Mexico and interested in attending a vocational program or technical/trade school after graduation They must have exhibited outstanding scholastic and leadership ability, including extracurricular and civic activities. High school class rank, GPA, and standardized test scores must be validated by a school official. An endorsement from the local Elks Lodge is required. Financial need is also considered in the selection process. **Deadline for Receipt:** March of each year. **Additional Information:** Recipients must attend a vocational program or technical/trade school.

1312 ■ NEW MEXICO LAND TITLE ASSOCIATION

500 Marquette, N.W., Suite 1480
Albuquerque, NM 87102
Tel: (505)883-2683; 888-65-NMLTA
Fax: (505)872-3759
E-mail: director.nmlta.org
Web Site: http://www.nmlta.org
To provide financial assistance for college to students in New Mexico.

Title of Award: "Chili" Currier Scholarship Fund **Area, Field, or Subject:** General studies/Field of study not specified **Level of Education for which Award is Granted:** Undergraduate **Number Awarded:** Varies each year. **Funds Available:** Initially, each scholarship is $200 per semester for part-time students and $500 for full-time students. Recipients who reapply and have maintained at least a 3.0 GPA are awarded an additional $100 per semester after completion of every third semester, up to a maximum of $700 per semester. Funds must be used for tuition and/or books. **Duration:** 1 semester; may be renewed.

Eligibility Requirements: This program is open to U.S. citizens who are current New Mexico residents, have graduated from a New Mexico high school (or received a GED through a New Mexico Department of Education approved program), and are attending a postsecondary institution of higher education in the state. Applicants must be enrolled for a minimum of 6 hours if they have a full-time job, for a minimum of 9 hours if they have a part-time job, or for a minimum of 12 hours (full-time student) if they are not employed. Financial need and academic achievement must be demonstrated. All applicants must be recommended by an individual within the title industry and an individual from their own community.

1313 ■ NEW MEXICO NATIONAL GUARD

Attn: Education Services Officer
47 Bataan Boulevard
Santa Fe, NM 87508
Tel: (505)474-1243
E-mail: EducationNM@nm.ngb.army.mil
Web Site: http://www.nm.ngb.army.mil/education/educate.htm
To provide financial assistance to members of the New Mexico National Guard who are working on an undergraduate degree.

Title of Award: New Mexico National Guard Tuition Scholarship Program **Area, Field, or Subject:** General studies/Field of study not specified **Level of Education for which Award is Granted:** Undergraduate **Number Awarded:** Varies each year, depending on the availability of funds. **Funds Available:** This program provides payment of 100% of the cost of tuition, including instructional fees in lieu of tuition and laboratory shop fees that are specifically required.

Eligibility Requirements: This program is open to members of the New Mexico National Guard who are working on their first degree at the undergraduate or vocational school level. Applicants must be attending a state-supported school in New Mexico. **Deadline for Receipt:** June of each year.

1314 ■ NEW YORK LOTTERY

Attn: LOT Scholarship
One Broadway Center
P.O. Box 7540
Schenectady, NY 12301-7540
Tel: (518)388-3415
Fax: (518)366-3423
E-mail: lotscholar@lottery.state.ny.us
Web Site: http://www.nylottery.org/lot
To provide financial assistance for college to seniors graduating from high schools in New York State.

Title of Award: New York State Leaders of Tomorrow Scholarships **Area, Field, or Subject:** General studies/Field of study not specified **Level of Education for which Award is Granted:** Undergraduate **Number Awarded:** 1 from each high school in New York State. **Funds Available:** The stipend is $1,000 per year. **Duration:** Up to 4 years, provided the recipient remains enrolled full time at an accredited New York State institution with a GPA of 3.0 or higher. The college program must be completed within 5 years of high school graduation.

Eligibility Requirements: The principal of every public and non-public high school in New York State is entitled to nominate 2 graduating seniors for this program. For each high school, 1 nominee is selected. Nominees must have at least a 3.0 GPA, leadership skills, U.S. citizenship, and experience in extracurricular and community activities. They must plan to attend a New York State accredited college, university, trade school, or community college as a full-time student. **Deadline for Receipt:** March of each year.

1315 ■ NEW YORK STATE DIVISION OF MILITARY AND NAVAL AFFAIRS

Attn: Education Services Officer
New York State Office Building
330 Old Niskayuna Road
Latham, NY 12110-2224
Tel: (518)786-4937
Fax: (518)786-4409
E-mail: education@ny.ngb.army.mil
Web Site: http://www.dmna.state.ny.us/education/Htm/tuition_waiver.htm
To provide financial assistance for college to members of the New York State Military Forces.

Title of Award: New York Recruitment Incentive and Retention Program **Area, Field, or Subject:** General studies/Field of study not specified **Level of Education for which Award is Granted:** Undergraduate **Number Awarded:** Varies each year. **Funds Available:** The program pays for the cost of tuition (up to $4,350 or the maximum cost of the State University of New York undergraduate tuition) for credit bearing courses, or courses that are required as a prerequisite within the declared degree program. **Duration:** Up to 8 semesters of full-time study, or the equivalent of 4 academic years, are supported; if the undergraduate program normally requires 5 academic years of full-time study, then this program will support 10 semesters of full-time study or the equivalent of 5 academic years. For part-time (from 6 to 11 semester hours per semester) study, the program provides up to 16 semesters of support.

Eligibility Requirements: This program is open to members of the New York Army National Guard, New York Air National Guard, and New York Naval Militia in good military and academic standing. Applicants must have been enrolled in a degree program for a minimum of 6 credit hours per semester, have been legal residents of New York state for at least 186 days prior to using the program for the first time and 186 days per year (excluding periods of active federal service), and be enrolled in their first baccalaureate degree program. They must have completed Initial Active Duty for Training (IADT), naval enlisted code (NEC) training, or a commissioning program. **Deadline for Receipt:** August of each year for fall semester; December of each year for spring semester. **Additional Information:** This program became effective in 1997.

1316 ■ NEW YORK STATE HIGHER EDUCATION SERVICES CORPORATION

Attn: Student Information
99 Washington Avenue
Albany, NY 12255
Tel: (518)473-1574; 888-NYS-HESC
Fax: (518)473-3749
E-mail: webmail@hesc.com
Web Site: http://www.hesc.com
To provide financial assistance for college in New York to disabled veterans and the family members of deceased or disabled veterans.
Title of Award: New York State Military Service Recognition Scholarships **Area, Field, or Subject:** General studies/Field of study not specified **Level of Education for which Award is Granted:** Undergraduate **Number Awarded:** Varies each year. **Funds Available:** At public colleges and universities, this program provides payment of actual tuition and mandatory educational fees; actual room and board charged to students living on campus or an allowance for room and board for commuter students; and allowances for books, supplies, and transportation. At private institutions, the award is equal to the amount charged at the State University of New York (SUNY) for 4-year tuition and average mandatory fees (or the student's actual tuition and fees, whichever is less) plus allowances for room, board, books, supplies, and transportation. **Duration:** This program is available for 4 years of full-time undergraduate study (or 5 years in an approved 5-year bachelor's degree program).
Eligibility Requirements: This program is open to New York residents who served in the armed forces of the United States or state organized militia at any time on or after August 2, 1990 and became severely and permanently disabled as a result of injury or illness suffered or incurred in a combat theater or combat zone or during military training operations in preparation for duty in a combat theater or combat zone of operations. Also eligible are the children, spouses, or financial dependents of members of the armed forces of the United States or state organized militia who at any time after August 2, 1990 1) died, became severely and permanently disabled as a result of injury or illness suffered or incurred, or are classified as missing in action in a combat theater or combat zone of operations, 2) died as a result of injuries incurred in those designated areas, or 3) died or became severely and permanently disabled as a result of injury or illness suffered or incurred during military training operations in preparation for duty in a combat theater or combat zone of operations. Applicants must be attending or accepted at an approved program of study as full-time undergraduates at a public college or university or private institution in New York. Residents of the state who were enrolled as an undergraduate at a college or university outside the state as of September 11, 2001 are eligible for scholarship payment at that school. **Deadline for Receipt:** April of each year.

1317 ■ NEW YORK STATE HIGHER EDUCATION SERVICES CORPORATION

Attn: Student Information
99 Washington Avenue
Albany, NY 12255
Tel: (518)473-1574; 888-NYS-HESC
Fax: (518)473-3749
E-mail: webmail@hesc.com
Web Site: http://www.hesc.com
To provide financial assistance to high school seniors in New York who have a record of academic excellence and plan to attend a college or university in the state.
Title of Award: New York State Scholarships for Academic Excellence **Area, Field, or Subject:** General studies/Field of study not specified **Level of Education for which Award is Granted:** Undergraduate **Number Awarded:** 8,000 each year: 2,000 at $1,500 and 6,000 at $500. **Funds Available:** Stipends are $1,500 or $500. Recipients can accept other non-loan student aid, but the total of that assistance and this scholarship cannot exceed the cost of attendance. **Duration:** This program is available for 4 years of full-time undergraduate study (or 5 years in an approved 5-year bachelor's degree program).
Eligibility Requirements: This program is open to seniors graduating from high schools in New York who plan to enroll in an approved

undergraduate program in the state. Selection is based on student grades in certain Regents examinations. The top graduating scholar at each registered high school in New York receives 1 of these awards, and the others are distributed to other outstanding high school graduates in the same ratio of total students graduating from each high school in the state as compared to the total number of students who graduated during the prior school year. **Deadline for Receipt:** April of each year.

1318 ■ NEW YORK STATE HIGHER EDUCATION SERVICES CORPORATION

Attn: Student Information
99 Washington Avenue
Albany, NY 12255
Tel: (518)473-1574; 888-NYS-HESC
Fax: (518)473-3749
E-mail: webmail@hesc.com
Web Site: http://www.hesc.com
To provide financial assistance to undergraduates in New York who are relatives of people killed or severely and permanently disabled as a result of the terrorist attacks on September 11, 2001.
Title of Award: New York State World Trade Center Memorial Scholarships **Area, Field, or Subject:** General studies/Field of study not specified **Level of Education for which Award is Granted:** Undergraduate **Number Awarded:** Varies each year. **Funds Available:** At public colleges and universities, this program provides payment of actual tuition and mandatory educational fees; actual room and board charged to students living on campus or an allowance for room and board for commuter students; and allowances for books, supplies, and transportation. At private institutions, the award is equal to the amount charged at the State University of New York (SUNY) for 4-year tuition and average mandatory fees (or the student's actual tuition and fees, whichever is less) plus allowances for room, board, books, supplies, and transportation. **Duration:** This program is available for 4 years of full-time undergraduate study (or 5 years in an approved 5-year bachelor's degree program).
Eligibility Requirements: This program is open to the children, spouses, and financial dependents of deceased or severely and permanently disabled victims of the September 11, 2001 terrorist attacks or the subsequent rescue and recovery operations. Applicants must be attending or accepted at an approved program of study as full-time undergraduates at a public college or university or private institution in New York. They are not required to be New York residents or U.S. citizens. New York residents who were enrolled as an undergraduate at a college or university outside the state as of September 11, 2001 are eligible for scholarship payment at that school. **Deadline for Receipt:** April of each year.

1319 ■ NEW YORK STATE HIGHER EDUCATION SERVICES CORPORATION

Attn: Student Information
99 Washington Avenue
Albany, NY 12255
Tel: (518)473-1574; 888-NYS-HESC
Fax: (518)473-3749
E-mail: webmail@hesc.com
Web Site: http://www.hesc.com
To provide tuition assistance to eligible veterans enrolled in an undergraduate or graduate program in New York.
Title of Award: New York Vietnam Tuition Award (VTA) Program **Area, Field, or Subject:** General studies/Field of study not specified **Level of Education for which Award is Granted:** Graduate, Undergraduate **Number Awarded:** Varies each year. **Funds Available:** Awards are $1,000 per semester for full-time study or $500 for part-time study, but in no case can the award exceed the amount charged for tuition. Total lifetime awards for undergraduate and graduate study under this program cannot exceed $10,000. **Duration:** For full-time undergraduate study, up to 8 semesters, or up to 10 semesters for a program requiring 5 years for completion; for full-time graduate study, up to 6 semesters; for full-time vocational programs, up to 4 semesters; for part-time undergraduate study, up to 16 semesters, or up to 20 semesters for a 5-year program; for part-time graduate study, up to 12 semesters; for part-time vocational programs, up to 8 semesters.
Eligibility Requirements: This program is open to veterans who served in the U.S. armed forces in 1) Indochina between December 22, 1961 and May 7, 1975; 2) in the Persian Gulf on or after August 2, 1990; or 3) in

Afghanistan on or after September 11, 2001. Applicants must have been discharged from the service under other than dishonorable conditions, must be a New York resident, must be enrolled full or part time at an undergraduate or graduate degree-granting institution in New York State or in an approved vocational training program in the state, and must apply for a New York Tuition Assistance Program (TAP) award if a full-time student (12 or more credits) or a Pell Grant if a part-time student (at least 3 but less than 12 credits). **Deadline for Receipt:** April of each year. **Additional Information:** If a TAP award is also received, the combined academic year award cannot exceed tuition costs. If it does, the TAP award will be reduced accordingly.

1320 ■ NEW YORK STATE SOCIETY OF PROFESSIONAL ENGINEERS

c/o Kelly K. Norris, Executive Director
RPI Technology Park
385 Jordan Road
Troy, NY 12180-7620
Tel: (518)283-7490
Fax: (518)283-7495
E-mail: kknorris@nysspe.org
Web Site: http://www.nysspe.org
To provide financial assistance for college to the children of members of the New York State Society of Professional Engineers (NYSSPE).
Title of Award: NYSSPE Past Officers' Scholarship **Area, Field, or Subject:** General studies/Field of study not specified **Level of Education for which Award is Granted:** Undergraduate **Number Awarded:** 1 each year. **Funds Available:** The stipend is $2,000. **Duration:** 1 year.
Eligibility Requirements: Eligible to apply for this scholarship are high school seniors in New York whose parent is a member of NYSSPE. Selection is based solely on academic merit. **Deadline for Receipt:** December of each year.

1321 ■ NEWSPAPER PURCHASING MANAGEMENT ASSOCIATION

c/o Gerry Wiest, NPMA Scholarship Director
The Patriot-News
812 Market Street
Harrisburg, PA 17101
Tel: (717)255-8270
E-mail: gwiest@pnco.com
Web Site: http://www.npma.net/scholarship.php
To provide financial assistance for college to high school seniors whose parents work for an organization affiliated with the Newspaper Purchasing Management Association (NPMA).
Title of Award: Richard N. Miller Scholarship **Area, Field, or Subject:** General studies/Field of study not specified **Level of Education for which Award is Granted:** Undergraduate **Number Awarded:** 2 each year. **Funds Available:** The first-place winner receives $1,000 and the runner-up receives $500. **Duration:** 1 year.
Eligibility Requirements: This program is open to high school seniors who will enroll in an accredited college or university within 16 months of graduation. The applicant must be the child, stepchild, or legally adopted child of a full-time employee of an organization affiliated with NPMA. An NPMA-member organization is defined as an individual newspaper, a corporate newspaper supply group, or the corporate headquarters of a newspaper group that holds an individual membership. Selection is based on GPA, standardized test scores, participation in high school activities, participating in community activities, and recommendations from high school officials. Financial need is not considered in the selection process. **Deadline for Receipt:** February of each year. **Additional Information:** This program was established in 1988.

1322 ■ NISEI STUDENT RELOCATION COMMEMORATIVE FUND, INC.

19 Scenic Drive
Portland, CT 06480
E-mail: info@nsrcfund.org
Web Site: http://www.nsrcfund.org
To provide financial assistance for college to high school seniors in a designated area who are southeast Asian refugees.
Title of Award: NSRCF Scholarships **Area, Field, or Subject:** General studies/Field of study not specified **Level of Education for which Award is Granted:** Undergraduate **Number Awarded:** Varies each year;

recently, this program awarded 12 scholarships to students in the Oregon/Clark County, Washington area and 24 scholarships to students in Michigan. **Funds Available:** Recently, stipends ranged from $500 to $1,000. **Duration:** 1 year.
Eligibility Requirements: Each year, this program operates in a different city or state. Within the selected area, graduating high school seniors are eligible to apply if they are southeast Asian refugees of Cambodian, Hmong, Laotian, or Vietnamese ancestry. Applicants must have a high school GPA of 2.5 or higher and be planning to attend an accredited 2-year or 4-year college or university. Selection is based on academic record, references, extracurricular activities, work experience, financial need, and a personal essay on educational and career goals. Finalists may be interviewed. **Deadline for Receipt:** March of each year. **Additional Information:** The 2006 program is scheduled for the Phoenix/Tempe area of Arizona.

1323 ■ NON COMMISSIONED OFFICERS ASSOCIATION OF THE UNITED STATES OF AMERICA

Attn: Scholarship Administrator
10635 IH 35 North
P.O. Box 33610
San Antonio, TX 78265-3610
Tel: (210)653-6161
Free: 800-662-2620
E-mail: membsvc@ncoausa.org
Web Site: http://www.ncoausa.org
To provide financial assistance for college to spouses and children of members of the Non Commissioned Officers Association.
Title of Award: Non Commissioned Officers Association Scholarship Fund **Area, Field, or Subject:** General studies/Field of study not specified **Level of Education for which Award is Granted:** Undergraduate **Number Awarded:** 15 each year: 9 scholarships to children of members, 4 scholarships to spouses of members, and 2 special awards. **Funds Available:** The scholarship stipend is $900 and the special awards are $1,000; funds are paid directly to the designated school to be used for the recipient's room and board, tuition, library fees, textbooks, and related instructional material. **Duration:** 1 year; may be renewed if the student maintains a GPA of 3.0 or higher and carries at least 15 hours.
Eligibility Requirements: This program is open to spouses and children (under 25 years of age) of members of the association. Children must submit 2 letters of recommendation from teachers, a personal recommendation from an adult who is not a relative, a handwritten autobiography, a certified transcript of high school or college grades, ACT or SAT scores, and a composition on Americanism. Spouses must submit a copy of their high school diploma or GED equivalent; a certified transcript of all college courses completed (if any); a certificate of completion for any other courses or training; a brief biographical background statement; and a letter of intent that includes a description of their proposed course of study for a degree, plans for completion of a degree, and a paragraph on "What a College Degree Means to Me." Financial need is not normally considered in the selection process and no applicant will be rejected because of a lack of need, but in some cases of extreme need it may be used as a factor. Each year, 2 special awards are presented: the Mary Barraco Scholarship to the student submitting the best essay on Americanism, and the William T. Green Scholarship to the student with the best high school academic record. **Deadline for Receipt:** March of each year. **Additional Information:** Spouses who receive a grant must apply for membership in 1 of the NCOA membership categories (regular, associate, veteran, or auxiliary).

1324 ■ NORTH CAROLINA 4-H DEVELOPMENT FUND

c/o North Carolina State University
Department of 4-H Youth Development
202 Ricks Hall
P.O. Box 7606
Raleigh, NC 27695-7606
Tel: (919)515-8486
Fax: (919)515-7812
Web Site: http://www.nc4h.org
To provide financial assistance for college to high school seniors in North Carolina who are members of 4-H.
Title of Award: L.R. Harrill 4-H Support Scholarships **Area, Field, or Subject:** General studies/Field of study not specified **Level of Education**

for which Award is Granted: Undergraduate Number Awarded: 2 each year. Funds Available: The stipend is $1,000 per year. Duration: 1 year; may be renewed for up to 3 additional years if the recipient maintains a GPA of 3.0 or higher.

Eligibility Requirements: This program is open to 4-H members who are graduating from high schools in North Carolina. Applicants must be planning to attend a college or university in the state. Selection is based on accomplishments in 4-H (50%), academic achievement as indicated by GPA and class rank (25%), and aptitude for college as indicated by grades and SAT or ACT scores (25%). Deadline for Receipt: January of each year.

1325 ■ NORTH CAROLINA 4-H DEVELOPMENT FUND

c/o North Carolina State University
Department of 4-H Youth Development
202 Ricks Hall
P.O. Box 7606
Raleigh, NC 27695-7606
Tel: (919)515-8486
Fax: (919)515-7812
Web Site: http://www.nc4h.org

To provide financial assistance for college to high school seniors in North Carolina who have been active in the 4-H horse program.

Title of Award: North Carolina 4-H Horse Scholarships Area, Field, or Subject: General studies/Field of study not specified Level of Education for which Award is Granted: Undergraduate Number Awarded: 2 each year. Funds Available: The stipend is $1,000 per year. Funds are issued only after the recipient has completed 1 semester or quarter of college with a GPA of 2.5 or higher. Duration: 1 year.

Eligibility Requirements: This program is open to seniors graduating from high schools in North Carolina who have been active in the 4-H horse program. Applicants must be planning to attend a college or university in the state. Along with their application, they must submit an essay on "How 4-H has prepared me for the challenges of the future." Selection is based on accomplishments in 4-H (50%), academic achievement as indicated by GPA and class rank (25%), and aptitude for college as indicated by grades and SAT or ACT scores (25%). Deadline for Receipt: January of each year.

1326 ■ NORTH CAROLINA 4-H DEVELOPMENT FUND

c/o North Carolina State University
Department of 4-H Youth Development
202 Ricks Hall
P.O. Box 7606
Raleigh, NC 27695-7606
Tel: (919)515-8486
Fax: (919)515-7812
Web Site: http://www.nc4h.org

To provide financial assistance for college study in any field to high school seniors in North Carolina who are members of 4-H.

Title of Award: Dr. Clarence Poe 4-H Scholarships Area, Field, or Subject: General studies/Field of study not specified Level of Education for which Award is Granted: Undergraduate Number Awarded: 2 each year. Funds Available: The stipend is $1,000 per year. Duration: 1 year. Eligibility Requirements: This program is open to 4-H members who are graduating from high schools in North Carolina. Applicants must be planning to attend a college or university in the state. Selection is based on accomplishments in 4-H (50%), academic achievement as indicated by GPA and class rank (25%), and aptitude for college as indicated by grades and SAT or ACT scores (25%). Deadline for Receipt: January of each year.

1327 ■ NORTH CAROLINA BAR ASSOCIATION

Attn: Young Lawyers Division Scholarship Committee
8000 Weston Parkway
P.O. Box 3688
Cary, NC 27519-3688
Tel: (919)677-0561
Free: 800-662-7407
Fax: (919)677-0761
E-mail: jtfount@mail.ncbar.org
Web Site: http://www.ncbar.org

To provide financial assistance for college or graduate school to the children of disabled or deceased law enforcement officers in North Carolina.

Title of Award: North Carolina Bar Association Scholarships Area, Field, or Subject: General studies/Field of study not specified Level of Education for which Award is Granted: Graduate, Undergraduate Number Awarded: Varies each year; recently, 4 new and 14 renewal scholarships were awarded. Funds Available: The stipend is $2,000 per academic year. Duration: Up to 4 years.

Eligibility Requirements: This program is open to the natural or adopted children of North Carolina law enforcement officers who were permanently disabled or killed in the line of duty. Applicants must be younger than 27 years of age and enrolled in or accepted at an accredited institution of higher learning (including community colleges, trade schools, colleges, universities, and graduate programs) in North Carolina. Selection is based on academic performance and financial need. Deadline for Receipt: March of each year.

1328 ■ NORTH CAROLINA CHILD SUPPORT COUNCIL

Attn: Scholarships
P.O. Box 20421
Raleigh, NC 27619-0421
Web Site: http://www.nccscouncil.org/scholarship.htm

To provide financial assistance for college to high school seniors who have a connection to the North Carolina Child Support Council (NCCSC).

Title of Award: Bob McGuire Memorial Scholarship Area, Field, or Subject: General studies/Field of study not specified Level of Education for which Award is Granted: Undergraduate Number Awarded: 3 each year; 1 in each of 3 regions in the state. Funds Available: The stipend is $1,000. Funds are paid directly to the recipient's school. Duration: 1 year; nonrenewable.

Eligibility Requirements: This program is open to graduating high school seniors who are residents of North Carolina planning to attend a college, university, or technical institute in the state. At least 1 parent must be a member of the NCCSC or a client of the child support program (either through IVD services or AOC Clerk of Court services). Applicants must have maintained an overall "C" average or above during their high school career. Financial need is not considered in the selection process. Deadline for Receipt: April of each year. Additional Information: Information is also available from Lorraine Jackson, Supervisor, Duplin County Child Support, P.O. Box 969, Kenansville, NC 28349, (910) 296-2200.

1329 ■ NORTH CAROLINA COMMUNITY COLLEGE SYSTEM

Attn: Student Development Services
200 West Jones Street
5016 Mail Service Center
Raleigh, NC 27699-5016
Tel: (919)807-7104
Fax: (919)807-7164
E-mail: whitehurstk@ncccs.cc.nc.us
Web Site: http://www.ncccs.cc.nc.us

To provide financial assistance to students attending community colleges in North Carolina.

Title of Award: North Carolina Community College Grant Program Area, Field, or Subject: General studies/Field of study not specified Level of Education for which Award is Granted: Two Year College Number Awarded: Approximately 10,000 each year. Funds Available: Stipends depend on the recipient's enrollment status and financial need. Stipends range from $250 to $1,900 per year for full-time students, from $188 to $1,425 per year for three-quarter-time students, or from $125 to $950 per year for half-time students. Duration: 1 year; may be renewed.

Eligibility Requirements: This program is open to North Carolina residents enrolled at least half time at 1 of the 58 institutions in North Carolina's community college system. Applicants must be able to demonstrate financial need. Students who already have a bachelor's degree are ineligible. Additional Information: This program was established in 1999 as a replacement for the North Carolina Community College Scholarship Program. It is jointly administered by the North Carolina State Education Assistance Authority, the North Carolina Community College System, College Foundation of North Carolina, and financial aid administrators at the community college. There are no special application forms for the scholarships. Students apply to their local community college, not to the system office. Each eligible school selects its own recipients from applicants meeting the above criteria.

1330 ■ NORTH CAROLINA COMMUNITY COLLEGE SYSTEM

Attn: Student Development Services
200 West Jones Street
5016 Mail Service Center
Raleigh, NC 27699-5016
Tel: (919)807-7104
Fax: (919)807-7164
E-mail: whitehurstk@ncccs.cc.nc.us
Web Site: http://www.ncccs.cc.nc.us
To provide financial assistance to students attending community colleges in North Carolina and majoring in selected fields.
Title of Award: North Carolina Community College Targeted Financial Assistance Program **Area, Field, or Subject:** General studies/Field of study not specified **Level of Education for which Award is Granted:** Two Year College **Number Awarded:** Varies each year; recently, $500,000 was available for this program. **Funds Available:** Stipends depend on the recipient's enrollment status and financial need. **Duration:** 1 year; may be renewed.
Eligibility Requirements: This program is open to North Carolina residents enrolled at least half time at 1 of the 58 institutions in North Carolina's community college system. Applicants must be able to demonstrate financial need. They must be majoring in a low-enrollment program that prepares students for high demand occupations. Students who already have a bachelor's degree are ineligible. **Additional Information:** This program was established in 2001 as a supplement to the North Carolina Community College Grant and Loan Program. It is jointly administered by the North Carolina State Education Assistance Authority, the North Carolina Community College System, College Foundation of North Carolina, and financial aid administrators at the community college. There are no special application forms for the scholarships. Students apply to their local community college, not to the system office. Each eligible school selects its own recipients from applicants meeting the above criteria.

1331 ■ NORTH CAROLINA COMMUNITY COLLEGE SYSTEM

Attn: Student Development Services
200 West Jones Street
5016 Mail Service Center
Raleigh, NC 27699-5016
Tel: (919)807-7106
Fax: (919)807-7164
E-mail: littlep@ncccs.cc.nc.us
Web Site: http://www.ncccs.cc.nc.us
To provide financial assistance at North Carolina community colleges to students who completed their GED certification or high school credential while committed to a Youth Development Center (YDC).
Title of Award: Youth Development Centers Scholarships **Area, Field, or Subject:** General studies/Field of study not specified **Level of Education for which Award is Granted:** Two Year College **Number Awarded:** Varies each year. **Funds Available:** Stipends are $2,000 per year ($1,000 per semester) for full-time students in curriculum programs or up to $500 per semester for registration fees, textbook costs, and course supplies for students in occupational extension courses and/or human resources development programs. **Duration:** 1 year.
Eligibility Requirements: This program is open to students enrolled in North Carolina community colleges who completed their GED certification or high school credential while committed to a YDC of the North Carolina Department of Juvenile Justice and Delinquency Prevention (DJJDP). Applicants must be enrolled in either 1) a curriculum program or 2) an occupational extension program and/or human resources development program.

1332 ■ NORTH CAROLINA COUNCIL OF THE BLIND

c/o Pat Yelton, Office Manager
7326 Eliza Lane
Mebane, NC 27302
800-344-7113
Fax: (336)562-2625
E-mail: nccb@netpath.net
Web Site: http://www.nccouncioftheblind.org/scholar.html

To provide financial assistance for college to blind and visually impaired North Carolina residents.
Title of Award: North Carolina Council of the Blind Scholarship **Area, Field, or Subject:** General studies/Field of study not specified **Level of Education for which Award is Granted:** Undergraduate **Number Awarded:** 3 each year. **Funds Available:** The stipend is $1,500. **Duration:** 1 year.
Eligibility Requirements: Eligible to apply are blind and visually impaired high school seniors, college students, and vocational school students in North Carolina. Applicants must complete an application form and submit 2 character reference letters, a transcript of courses completed, and a brief biographical statement. Financial need is considered in the selection process. **Deadline for Receipt:** April of each year. **Additional Information:** This program includes the Lisa Mizelle Scholarship, the Marie Boring Scholarship, and the Theodore Bryant Scholarship. Information is also available from Catherleen Thomas, 308 South Peartree Lane, Raleigh, NC 27610.

1333 ■ NORTH CAROLINA FRATERNAL ORDER OF POLICE

Attn: NCFOB Foundation, Inc.
1500 Walnut Street
Cary, NC 27511-5927
Tel: (919)461-4939
E-mail: ncfop@aol.com
Web Site: http://www.ncfop.com/foundation.htm
To provide financial assistance for college to families of disabled or deceased law enforcement officers in North Carolina.
Title of Award: NCFOP Foundation Scholarships **Area, Field, or Subject:** General studies/Field of study not specified **Level of Education for which Award is Granted:** Undergraduate **Number Awarded:** Varies each year; recently, 3 of these scholarships were awarded. **Funds Available:** A stipend is awarded (amount not specified). **Duration:** 1 year.
Eligibility Requirements: This program is open to North Carolina residents who are enrolled in an appropriate postsecondary institution, including colleges and vocational schools. Applicants must be the child or spouse of a North Carolina law enforcement officer killed or disabled in the line of duty. **Additional Information:** Information is also available from Terry Mangum, Secretary, NCFOP Foundation, Inc., P.O. Box 72484, Durham, NC 27722-2484.

1334 ■ NORTH CAROLINA LIONS FOUNDATION

Camp Dogwood Drive
P.O. Box 39
Sherrills Ford, NC 28673
Tel: (828)478-2135
Free: 800-662-7401
Fax: (828)478-4419
E-mail: nclions@nclf.org
Web Site: http://www.nclf.org/Edgrant.htm
To provide financial assistance for college to sighted children of blind or visually impaired parents in North Carolina.
Title of Award: William L. Woolard Educational Grant Program **Area, Field, or Subject:** General studies/Field of study not specified **Level of Education for which Award is Granted:** Undergraduate **Number Awarded:** 1 or more each year. **Funds Available:** The stipend is $1,500. Funds are paid directly to the college, community college, or trade/technical school selected by the recipient. **Duration:** 1 year; may be renewed up to 4 additional years provided the recipient maintains full-time enrollment and a GPA of 2.0 or higher.
Eligibility Requirements: This program is open to residents of North Carolina who are sighted children of blind or visually impaired parents. Applicants must be working on or planning to work on an undergraduate degree or certificate. Family income may not exceed $40,000 for families with 1 dependent child, increasing by $10,000 for each additional dependent child. Selection is based on the financial need of the family and the academic record and character of the applicant. **Deadline for Receipt:** March of each year.

1335 ■ NORTH CAROLINA NATIONAL GUARD

Attn: JFHQ-NC-J1-ESO
4105 Reedy Creek Road
Raleigh, NC 27607-6410
Tel: (919)664-6272

Free: 800-621-4136
Fax: (919)664-6520
E-mail: zaire.mcrae@nc.ngb.army.mil
Web Site: http://www.nc.ngb.army.mil/education/taps.asp
To provide financial assistance for college or graduate school to members of the North Carolina National Guard.
Title of Award: North Carolina National Guard Tuition Assistance Program **Area, Field, or Subject:** General studies/Field of study not specified **Level of Education for which Award is Granted:** Graduate, Undergraduate **Number Awarded:** Varies each year. **Funds Available:** The maximum stipend is $2,000 per year, up to a lifetime maximum of $8,000. **Duration:** 1 year; may be renewed.
Eligibility Requirements: Applicants must be active members of the North Carolina National Guard (officer, warrant officer, or enlisted) with at least 2 years of enlistment remaining after the end of the academic period for which tuition assistance is provided. Applicants must be enrolled in an eligible business or trade school, private institution, or public college/university in North Carolina. They may be working on a vocational, undergraduate, graduate, or doctoral degree.

1336 ■ NORTH CAROLINA SOCIETY OF HISPANIC PROFESSION-ALS

P.O. Box 1557
Apex, NC 27502-3557
Tel: (919)654-4516
Fax: (919)654-4524
E-mail: mailbox@theNCSHP.org
Web Site: http://www.theNCSHP.org/NCHCF/NCHCF.htm
To provide financial assistance for college to Hispanic students from North Carolina.
Title of Award: North Carolina Hispanic College Fund **Area, Field, or Subject:** General studies/Field of study not specified **Level of Education for which Award is Granted:** Undergraduate **Number Awarded:** Varies each year. **Funds Available:** Stipends range from $500 to $2,500. Funds are paid directly to the college or university. Scholarships under $1,000 are paid in the fall semester. For scholarships over $1,000, half is paid in the fall and half in the spring. Funds are designated for tuition, room, and board. **Duration:** 1 year; may be renewed up to 3 additional years.
Eligibility Requirements: This program is open to seniors and recent graduates from North Carolina high schools who are of Hispanic/Latino background. Applicants must be enrolled or planning to enroll at a community college or a 2- or 4-year college or university and be committed to public service and community development. They must have a high school GPA of 2.5 or higher. Along with their application, they must submit a 500-word essay on their Hispanic parentage and family background, personal and academic achievements, academic plans and career goals, and past and current efforts (as well as future plans) towards making a difference in their community. Semi-finalists are asked to have a personal interview. Preference is given to full-time students (although part-time students are encouraged to apply) and to foreign-born applicants and the native-born children of foreign-born parents. Previous involvement in a club or community organization is encouraged. Financial need is not considered in the selection process. **Deadline for Receipt:** January of each year.

1337 ■ NORTH CAROLINA STATE EDUCATION ASSISTANCE AUTHORITY

Attn: Scholarship and Grant Services
10 T.W. Alexander Drive
P.O. Box 14103
Research Triangle Park, NC 27709-4103
Tel: (919)549-8614
Free: 800-700-1775
Fax: (919)549-8481
E-mail: information@ncseaa.edu
Web Site: http://www.ncseaa.edu
To provide financial assistance to high school seniors planning to attend 1 of the branches of the University of North Carolina.
Title of Award: Jagannathan Scholarships **Area, Field, or Subject:** General studies/Field of study not specified **Level of Education for which Award is Granted:** Four Year College **Number Awarded:** Varies each year; recently, a total of 14 students received $46,077 in scholarships through this program. **Funds Available:** Awards cannot exceed

demonstrated financial need, to a maximum of $3,500 per year. **Duration:** 1 year; may be renewed up to 3 additional years if the recipient continues to demonstrate financial need and maintains satisfactory academic progress.
Eligibility Requirements: This program is open to high school seniors in North Carolina who are planning to attend any of the constituent institutions of the University of North Carolina as a full-time student. Special consideration is given to applicants whose parents are employees of TIEPET, Universal Fibers, and related companies. Selection is based on academic achievement (as measured by class rank, cumulative GPA, and SAT scores), leadership, and financial need. **Deadline for Receipt:** February of each year. **Additional Information:** This program was established by industrialist N.S. Jagannathan and began in the 1996-97 academic year.

1338 ■ NORTH CAROLINA STATE EDUCATION ASSISTANCE AUTHORITY

Attn: Scholarship and Grant Services
10 Alexander Drive
P.O. Box 14103
Research Triangle Park, NC 27709-4103
Tel: (919)549-8614
Free: 800-700-1775
Fax: (919)549-8481
E-mail: information@ncseaa.edu
Web Site: http://www.ncseaa.edu
To provide financial assistance to residents of North Carolina who are attending or planning to attend a public university in the state.
Title of Award: James Lee Love Scholarships **Area, Field, or Subject:** General studies/Field of study not specified **Level of Education for which Award is Granted:** Four Year College **Number Awarded:** 16 each year: 1 at each constituent institution of the University of North Carolina system. **Funds Available:** The stipend depends on the availability of funds; recently, a total of $41,600 was awarded through this program. **Duration:** 1 year; nonrenewable.
Eligibility Requirements: This program is open to residents of North Carolina who are entering or attending a public university in the state. Applicants must be enrolled or planning to enroll full time and able to demonstrate financial need. Current high school seniors must rank in the top 25% of their graduating class; current university students must have a GPA of 3.0 or higher. **Deadline for Receipt:** February of each year.

1339 ■ NORTH CAROLINA STATE EDUCATION ASSISTANCE AUTHORITY

Attn: Scholarship and Grant Services
10 T.W. Alexander Drive
P.O. Box 14103
Research Triangle Park, NC 27709-4103
Tel: (919)549-8614
Free: 800-700-1775
Fax: (919)549-8481
E-mail: information@ncseaa.edu
Web Site: http://www.ncseaa.edu
To provide financial assistance to students enrolled in private colleges in North Carolina.
Title of Award: North Carolina Legislative Tuition Grants **Area, Field, or Subject:** General studies/Field of study not specified **Level of Education for which Award is Granted:** Undergraduate **Number Awarded:** Varies each year; recently, a total of 30,732 students were receiving $47,980,273 through this program. **Funds Available:** The stipend is $1,800 per year. Funds are paid to the institution on behalf of the recipient. **Duration:** 1 year; may be renewed.
Eligibility Requirements: This program is open to North Carolina residents attending a legislatively-designated private college in the state on a full-time basis. Financial need is not considered in the selection process. Students of theology, divinity, religious education, or any other course of study designed primarily for career preparation in a religious vocation are not eligible. **Additional Information:** This program was established in 1975.

1340 ■ NORTH CAROLINA STATE EDUCATION ASSISTANCE AUTHORITY

Attn: Scholarship and Grant Services
10 T.W. Alexander Drive

P.O. Box 14103
Research Triangle Park, NC 27709-4103
Tel: (919)549-8614
Free: 800-700-1775
Fax: (919)549-8481
E-mail: information@ncseaa.edu
Web Site: http://www.ncseaa.edu

To provide financial assistance for education at private colleges and universities to students in North Carolina with financial need.

Title of Award: North Carolina State Contractual Scholarship Fund Program **Area, Field, or Subject:** General studies/Field of study not specified **Level of Education for which Award is Granted:** Undergraduate **Number Awarded:** Varies each year; recently, a total of 13,415 students were receiving $33,793,025 through this program. **Funds Available:** Stipends range up to $1,100 per year, depending on the need of the recipient and the availability of funds. **Duration:** 1 year.

Eligibility Requirements: Eligible for this program are North Carolina residents who are enrolled as full-time or part-time undergraduate students at approved North Carolina private colleges and universities. Students enrolled in a program of study in theology, divinity, religious education, or any other program of study designed primarily for career preparation in a religious vocation are not eligible. **Additional Information:** Recipients are selected by the financial aid offices of the eligible private institutions in North Carolina. This program was established in 1971.

1341 ■ NORTH CAROLINA STATE EDUCATION ASSISTANCE AUTHORITY

Attn: Scholarship and Grant Services
10 Alexander Drive
P.O. Box 14103
Research Triangle Park, NC 27709-4103
Tel: (919)549-8614
Free: 800-700-1775
Fax: (919)549-8481
E-mail: information@ncseaa.edu
Web Site: http://www.ncseaa.edu

To provide financial assistance to students at University of North Carolina (UNC) constituent institutions whose enrollment contributes to the diversity of the undergraduate population.

Title of Award: University of North Carolina Campus Scholarships-Part I **Area, Field, or Subject:** General studies/Field of study not specified **Level of Education for which Award is Granted:** Four Year College **Number Awarded:** Varies each year; recently, a total of 3,076 UNC Campus Scholarships, with a total value of $5,648,874, were awarded. **Funds Available:** The amount of the award depends upon the financial need of the recipient and the availability of funds. **Duration:** 1 year; may be renewed.

Eligibility Requirements: This program is open to undergraduate students who are enrolled or planning to enroll full time at 1 of the 16 UNC institutions. Applicants must have graduated in the top 40% of their high school class, have a weighted GPA of 3.0 or higher, have an SAT score higher than the SAT score of the previous freshman class, and have a record of positive involvement in extracurricular activities. They must be able to demonstrate "exceptional financial need." Their enrollment must "contribute to the intellectual experiences and diversity of the undergraduate population." **Deadline for Receipt:** Deadline dates vary; check with the appropriate constituent institution. **Additional Information:** This program was established in 2003 as a replacement for the former North Carolina Minority Presence Grants, North Carolina Freshmen Scholars Program, North Carolina Incentive Scholarship Program, and the North Carolina Legislative College Opportunity Program. Students must submit applications to the constituent institution's financial aid office rather than directly to the North Carolina State Education Assistance Authority.

1342 ■ NORTH CAROLINA STATE EDUCATION ASSISTANCE AUTHORITY

Attn: Scholarship and Grant Services
10 Alexander Drive
P.O. Box 14103
Research Triangle Park, NC 27709-4103
Tel: (919)549-8614
Free: 800-700-1775

Fax: (919)549-8481
E-mail: information@ncseaa.edu
Web Site: http://www.ncseaa.edu

To provide financial assistance to Native American residents of North Carolina interested in working on an undergraduate degree at a public institution in the state.

Title of Award: University of North Carolina Campus Scholarships-Part II **Area, Field, or Subject:** General studies/Field of study not specified **Level of Education for which Award is Granted:** Four Year College **Number Awarded:** Varies each year; recently, a total of 3,076 UNC Campus Scholarships, with a total value of $5,648,874, were awarded. **Funds Available:** The maximum stipend is $3,000 per year. **Duration:** 1 year; may be renewed if the student maintains financial need and satisfactory academic progress.

Eligibility Requirements: This program is open to residents of North Carolina who maintain cultural and political identification as a Native American through membership in an Indian tribe recognized by the United States or by the state of North Carolina, or through tribal affiliation or community recognition. Incoming freshmen must rank in the top half of their graduating class at a North Carolina high school; incoming transfers must have completed an associate degree and must have earned a GPA of 2.5 or higher at the 2-year college, or they must have a certificate in a program that articulates directly with an academic program at a constituent university and must have earned a GPA of 2.0 or higher at the college. Applicants must be admitted or enrolled in a regular undergraduate degree-granting program at 1 of the 16 constituent institutions of the University of North Carolina (UNC). They must be able to demonstrate financial need. **Deadline for Receipt:** Deadline dates vary; check with the participating school. **Additional Information:** This program was established in 2003 as a replacement for the former North Carolina Incentive Scholarship and Grant Program for Native Americans.

1343 ■ NORTH CAROLINA STATE EDUCATION ASSISTANCE AUTHORITY

Attn: Scholarship and Grant Services
10 T.W. Alexander Drive
P.O. Box 14103
Research Triangle Park, NC 27709-4103
Tel: (919)549-8614
Free: 800-700-1775
Fax: (919)549-8481
E-mail: information@ncseaa.edu
Web Site: http://www.ncseaa.edu

To provide financial assistance to students enrolled at 1 of the branches of the University of North Carolina.

Title of Award: University of North Carolina System Need-Based Grants **Area, Field, or Subject:** General studies/Field of study not specified **Level of Education for which Award is Granted:** Four Year College **Number Awarded:** Varies each year. Recently, 26,630 students were receiving $28,785,533 in support through this program **Funds Available:** Stipends depend on the need of the recipient and the availability of funds, to a maximum of $3,000 per year. **Duration:** 1 year.

Eligibility Requirements: This program is open to residents of North Carolina enrolled for at least 6 credit hours at any of the constituent institutions of the University of North Carolina. Applicants must be able to demonstrate financial need, based on data from the Free Application for Federal Student Aid (FAFSA). **Additional Information:** The constituent institutions are Appalachian State University, East Carolina University, Elizabeth City State University, Fayetteville State University, North Carolina A&T State University, North Carolina Central University, North Carolina School of the Arts, North Carolina State University, University of North Carolina at Asheville, University of North Carolina at Chapel Hill, University of North Carolina at Charlotte, University of North Carolina at Greensboro, University of North Carolina at Pembroke, University of North Carolina at Wilmington, Western Carolina University, and Winston-Salem State University.

1344 ■ NORTH DAKOTA ASSOCIATION OF THE BLIND

c/o Carol Schmitt, Scholarship Committee Chair
1412 Fifth Street S.W.
Minot, ND 58701
Tel: (701)838-3063
Web Site: http://www.ndab.org/Scholarship.html

To provide financial assistance for college or graduate school to blind students in North Dakota.
Title of Award: North Dakota Association of the Blind Scholarships **Area, Field, or Subject:** General studies/Field of study not specified **Level of Education for which Award is Granted:** Graduate, Undergraduate **Number Awarded:** 3 each year: 1 at $1,000 and 2 at $500. **Funds Available:** Stipends are $1,000 or $500. **Duration:** 1 year.
Eligibility Requirements: This program is open to North Dakota residents who are legally blind and attending an institution of higher education in the state. Applicants must be full-time students with a class standing of a sophomore through a graduate student and a GPA of 2.5 or higher. They must submit 2 letters of recommendation, transcripts, a family financial aid statement, and an essay that describes their vocational interests, how the scholarship will help them, their goals and aspirations, and what they have done to deal with situations involving their blindness. Selection is based on academic excellence, financial need, and service to the community. **Deadline for Receipt:** March of each year. **Additional Information:** This program was established in 1990.

1345 ■ NORTH DAKOTA COUNCIL ON ABUSED WOMEN'S SERVICES

418 East Rosser, Suite 320
Bismarck, ND 58501-4046
Tel: (701)255-6240; 888-255-6240
Fax: (701)255-1904
Web Site: http://www.ndcaws.org/projects/scholarship/scholarship.asp
To provide financial assistance to women in North Dakota who are interested in attending a college or university in the state.
Title of Award: North Dakota Women's Opportunity Scholarship Fund **Area, Field, or Subject:** General studies/Field of study not specified **Level of Education for which Award is Granted:** Undergraduate **Number Awarded:** Varies each year. **Funds Available:** A stipend is awarded (amount not specified). **Duration:** 1 year; may be renewed.
Eligibility Requirements: This program is open to women residents of North Dakota who plan to enroll as a full-time student at a college, university, or certification program in the state. Applicants must be able to demonstrate income lower than established financial guidelines (currently less than $11,638 for a single person, rising to $39,463 for a family of 8). Along with their application, they must submit an essay of 500 to 1,000 words on their motivation for attending college and their plans for the future. Priority is given to 1) first-time students and current students in special circumstances that may prevent them from completing a pending degree or program; and 2) applicants who may not be eligible for sources of funding normally available to low-income applicants. **Deadline for Receipt:** June of each year.

1346 ■ NORTH DAKOTA NATIONAL GUARD

Attn: Education Services Office
P.O. Box 5511
Bismarck, ND 58506-5511
Tel: (701)333-3008
E-mail: ndtuitionast@nd.ngb.army.mil
Web Site: http://www.guard.bismarck.nd.us/benefits/default.asp?ID=298
To provide financial assistance for college to members of the North Dakota National Guard.
Title of Award: North Dakota National Guard Tuition Assistance Program **Area, Field, or Subject:** General studies/Field of study not specified **Level of Education for which Award is Granted:** Undergraduate **Number Awarded:** Varies each year. **Funds Available:** Members of the North Dakota Air National Guard receive reimbursement of 100% of their basic tuition costs, up to rates at the University of North Dakota; the school reimburses 25% of the tuition cost and the Guard reimburses the difference. Members of the North Dakota Army National Guard receive reimbursement of 25% of their basic tuition costs, up to rates at the University of North Dakota, from their school and up to $1,000 per semester from the Guard. Both the school and the Guard portion are paid after grades are posted; that may take 4 to 6 weeks before benefits are paid or credited. **Duration:** Benefits are available for up to 130 credit hours or the completion of an undergraduate degree.
Eligibility Requirements: Applicants must be members of the North Dakota National Guard and attending a participating undergraduate school: all North Dakota higher education public institutions, Jamestown College, University of Mary in Bismarck, and Trinity Bible College. They

must earn a grade of "C" or higher in each course for which reimbursement is requested. Full-time AGR personnel do not qualify for this program. This is an entitlement program, provided all requirements are met. **Deadline for Receipt:** Applications should be submitted at least 30 days before the semester begins.

1347 ■ NORTH DAKOTA UNIVERSITY SYSTEM

Attn: Director of Financial Aid
State Capitol, Tenth Floor
600 East Boulevard Avenue, Department 215
Bismarck, ND 58505-0230
Tel: (701)328-4114
Fax: (701)328-2961
E-mail: peggy_wipf@ndus.nodak.edu
Web Site: http://www.ndus.nodak.edu
To waive tuition and fees for survivors of deceased fire fighters and peace officers at public institutions in North Dakota.
Title of Award: North Dakota Fee Waiver for Survivors of Deceased Fire Fighters and Peace Officers **Area, Field, or Subject:** General studies/ Field of study not specified **Level of Education for which Award is Granted:** Undergraduate **Number Awarded:** Varies each year. **Funds Available:** Qualified students are entitled to a waiver of all tuition and fees (except fees charged to retire outstanding bonds). **Duration:** 1 academic year; renewable.
Eligibility Requirements: Eligible for this benefit are residents of North Dakota who are the survivors of fire fighters and peace officers who died as a direct result of injuries received in the performance of official duties. Applicants must be attending or planning to attend a public college or university in North Dakota.

1348 ■ NORTH DAKOTA UNIVERSITY SYSTEM

Attn: North Dakota Indian Scholarship Program
919 South Seventh Street, Suite 603
Bismarck, ND 58504
Tel: (701)328-9661
Fax: (701)328-9662
E-mail: rhonda_schauer@ndus.nodak.edu
Web Site: http://www.ndus.nodak.edu/students/financial-aid/details.asp?id=111
To provide financial assistance to Native American students in North Dakota colleges and universities.
Title of Award: North Dakota Indian Scholarship Program **Area, Field, or Subject:** General studies/Field of study not specified **Level of Education for which Award is Granted:** Undergraduate **Number Awarded:** Varies; approximately 150 to 175 each year. **Funds Available:** The amount of the stipend varies from $500 to $2,000 depending on scholastic ability, funds available, total number of applicants, and financial need. The award is divided into semester or quarter payments. The money is to be used to pay registration, health fees, board, room, books, and other necessary items handled by the institution. Any remaining balance may be used to cover the student's personal expenses. **Duration:** 1 academic year; renewable up to 3 additional years, if the recipient maintains a 2.0 GPA and continues to be in financial need.
Eligibility Requirements: Applicants must have at least one-quarter degree Indian blood, be residents of North Dakota or enrolled members of a tribe resident in North Dakota, and be accepted as full-time undergraduate students by an institution of higher learning or vocational education in North Dakota. Students must have at least a 2.0 GPA, although priority in funding is given to those with a GPA of 3.5 or higher. Participants in internships, student teaching, teaching assistance, or cooperative education programs are eligible only if participation in that program is required for the degree and only if tuition must be paid for the credits earned. **Deadline for Receipt:** July of each year.

1349 ■ NORTH DAKOTA UNIVERSITY SYSTEM

Attn: Director of Financial Aid
State Capitol, Tenth Floor
600 East Boulevard Avenue, Department 215
Bismarck, ND 58505-0230
Tel: (701)328-4114
Fax: (701)328-2961
E-mail: peggy_wipf@ndus.nodak.edu
Web Site: http://www.ndus.nodak.edu

To waive tuition and fees for members of the National Guard at public institutions in North Dakota.

Title of Award: North Dakota National Guard Fee Waiver **Area, Field, or Subject:** General studies/Field of study not specified **Level of Education for which Award is Granted:** Undergraduate **Number Awarded:** Varies each year. **Funds Available:** Qualified members are entitled to a waiver of all tuition and fees (except fees charged to retire outstanding bonds). **Duration:** 1 academic year; renewable.

Eligibility Requirements: Eligible for this benefit are members of the North Dakota National Guard who meet the limitations and rules established by the Guard. Applicants must be attending or planning to attend a public college or university in North Dakota.

1350 ■ NORTH DAKOTA UNIVERSITY SYSTEM

Attn: Director of Financial Aid
State Capitol, Tenth Floor
600 East Boulevard Avenue, Department 215
Bismarck, ND 58505-0230
Tel: (701)328-4114
Fax: (701)328-2961
E-mail: peggy_wipf@ndus.nodak.edu
Web Site: http://www.ndus.nodak.edu

To provide financial assistance to outstanding high school seniors in North Dakota who are interested in attending college in the state.

Title of Award: North Dakota Scholars Program **Area, Field, or Subject:** General studies/Field of study not specified **Level of Education for which Award is Granted:** Undergraduate **Number Awarded:** 25 to 30 each year. **Funds Available:** Students who attend a public or tribal college receive full payment of tuition. Students who attend a private institution in North Dakota receive a stipend equivalent to tuition at North Dakota State University or the University of North Dakota. **Duration:** 1 academic year; renewable up to 3 additional years, if the recipient maintains a cumulative GPA of 3.5 or higher.

Eligibility Requirements: This program is open to seniors at high schools in North Dakota who took the ACT test in their junior year and scored in the upper 5th percentile of all North Dakota ACT test takers. Applicants must be interested in attending a college or university in North Dakota.

1351 ■ NORTH DAKOTA UNIVERSITY SYSTEM

Attn: Director of Financial Aid
State Capitol, Tenth Floor
600 East Boulevard Avenue, Department 215
Bismarck, ND 58505-0230
Tel: (701)328-4114
Fax: (701)328-2961
E-mail: peggy_wipf@ndus.nodak.edu
Web Site: http://www.ndus.nodak.edu

To waive tuition and fees for dependents of deceased or other veterans at public institutions in North Dakota.

Title of Award: North Dakota Veterans Dependents Fee Waiver **Area, Field, or Subject:** General studies/Field of study not specified **Level of Education for which Award is Granted:** Undergraduate **Number Awarded:** Varies each year. **Funds Available:** Qualified students are entitled to a waiver of all tuition and fees (except fees charged to retire outstanding bonds) at public institutions in North Dakota. **Duration:** 1 academic year; renewable.

Eligibility Requirements: Eligible for this benefit are the dependents of veterans who were North Dakota residents when they entered the armed forces and died of service-related causes, were killed in action, were prisoners of war, or were declared missing in action. Applicants must be attending or planning to attend a public college or university in North Dakota.

1352 ■ NORTHERN CHEYENNE

Attn: Tribal Education Department
P.O. Box 307
Lame Deer, MT 59043
Tel: (406)477-6567
Free: 800-353-8183
Fax: (406)477-8150
E-mail: norma@rangeweb.net
Web Site: http://www.ncheyenne.net/nctribaled/index.htm

To provide financial assistance to Northern Cheyenne tribal members who are interested in vocational training.

Title of Award: Northern Cheyenne Adult Vocational Training Program **Area, Field, or Subject:** General studies/Field of study not specified **Level of Education for which Award is Granted:** Vocational/Occupational **Number Awarded:** Varies each year. **Funds Available:** Funding under this program is supplemental to any other income. Grants are intended to cover living expenses, tuition, books, supplies related directly to the course, and child care. Transportation costs to training sites off the reservation are provided for the student and eligible family members. Medical coverage is provided by the Northern Cheyenne Indian Health Service for the duration of the training period. **Duration:** Up to 24 months for vocational training; up to 36 months for nursing training.

Eligibility Requirements: Applicants must be enrolled members of the Northern Cheyenne tribe, be between the ages of 18 and 40, be high school graduates or have obtained a high school equivalency before applying, and be enrolled or accepted in a Bureau of Indian Affairs-approved school. Northern Cheyennes are not required to reside on the Northern Cheyenne Reservation; other eligible Indian members may qualify for this assistance if they reside on the Northern Cheyenne Reservation. The applicant must intend to enroll in a full-time trade or vocational program that can be completed in 3 to 24 months and that will prepare the student for employment. Selection is based on academic achievement, educational goals, need for financial support, choice of school, and plans after graduation. Awards are made according to the following priorities: 1) renewal of grants to continuing students in good standing; 2) new applicants who are enrolled Northern Cheyenne residing on or near the Northern Cheyenne Indian Reservation; 3) enrolled Northern Cheyenne new applicants who reside outside the service area of the reservation; 4) other Indian enrolled tribal members residing on the Northern Cheyenne Indian Reservation; and 5) individuals requesting retraining. **Deadline for Receipt:** February of each year for fall quarter/semester; September of each year for winter quarter/spring semester/spring quarter; March of each year for summer school. **Additional Information:** Individuals can request support for retraining, provided they can supply a physician's statement explaining why they cannot continue in their present occupation. Recipients must complete at least 12 units each semester or quarter with a GPA of 2.0 or higher. Recipients who voluntarily discontinue training without prior approval from the tribe or because of poor attendance or academic performance are not eligible for continued financial assistance.

1353 ■ NORTHERN CHEYENNE

Attn: Tribal Education Department
P.O. Box 307
Lame Deer, MT 59043
Tel: (406)477-6567
Free: 800-353-8183
Fax: (406)477-8150
E-mail: norma@rangeweb.net
Web Site: http://www.ncheyenne.net/nctribaled/index.htm

To provide financial assistance for college or graduate school to Northern Cheyenne tribal members.

Title of Award: Northern Cheyenne Higher Education Scholarship Program **Area, Field, or Subject:** General studies/Field of study not specified **Level of Education for which Award is Granted:** Graduate, Undergraduate **Number Awarded:** Approximately 80 each year. **Funds Available:** The stipend depends on the need of the recipient, to a maximum of $6,000 per year. These awards are intended to supplement other available sources of funding. The scholarship must be used for tuition, subsistence, required fees, and textbooks. **Duration:** 1 year; may be renewed if the recipient maintains a GPA of 2.0 or higher and completes at least 14 quarter or 16 semester units as a freshman and sophomore and at least 16 quarter or 18 semester units as a junior or senior.

Eligibility Requirements: This program is open to enrolled Northern Cheyenne tribal members who have been accepted to a degree program at an accredited college or university. The priority order for awards is 1) continuing and former college students in good standing; 2) graduating high school seniors in good standing or first-time adult college applicants not previously funded; 3) students or other individuals who have previously failed to meet the requirements of the scholarship program; and 4) graduate students (if funds are still available). All applicants must be able to demonstrate financial need. **Deadline for Receipt:** February of each year for fall quarter/semester; September of each year for winter quarter/spring semester/spring quarter; March of each year for summer school. **Additional Information:** Recipients who reside in Montana are expected to attend a postsecondary institution in the state. They must pay the difference in cost between Montana public postsecondary schools and private or out-of-state schools, if they elect to attend either of those. An exception is made if no comparable course of study exists in a Montana public institution. Eligible Northern Cheyenne Indians residing out of state are subject to the same regulation; however, they may enroll in a Montana institution of higher learning if there is no comparable course of study at a public institution in their home state.

1354 ■ NORTHERN NEW YORK COMMUNITY FOUNDATION, INC.

120 Washington Street, Suite 400
Watertown, NY 13601
Tel: (315)782-7110
Fax: (315)782-0047
E-mail: info@nnycf.org
Web Site: http://www.nnycf.org

To provide financial assistance for college to members of the 10th Mountain Division who have been awarded the Purple Heart while the division was stationed at Fort Drum, New York and their dependents. who are majoring in nursing or a related health field.
Title of Award: Rotary Purple Heart Scholarships **Area, Field, or Subject:** General studies/Field of study not specified **Level of Education for which Award is Granted:** Undergraduate **Number Awarded:** 3 each year. **Funds Available:** The stipend is $1,000. **Duration:** 1 year.
Eligibility Requirements: This program is open to members of the 10th Mountain Division and their dependents. Applicants must have been awarded the Purple Heart while the division was stationed at Fort Drum, New York. They must be high school seniors applying for the freshmen year, college sophomores for the junior year (at least a 3.0 GPA is required for them), and nontraditional students for any year in college. High school juniors who will graduate early because they are in an advanced placement program may also apply. Interviews are required. Selection is based on academic achievement, personal data, and financial need. **Deadline for Receipt:** Applications may be submitted at any time. **Additional Information:** These scholarships were first awarded in 2005.

1355 ■ NUFACTOR

Attn: Scholarship Administrator
41093 Country Center Drive, Suite B
Temecula, CA 92591
Tel: (951)296-2516
Free: 800-323-6832
Fax: (951)296-2565
E-mail: info@kelleycom.com
Web Site: http://www.nufactor.com/web_pages/edostie_scholarship.html

To provide financial assistance for college to students with hemophilia or members of their families.
Title of Award: Eric Dostie Memorial College Scholarship **Area, Field, or Subject:** General studies/Field of study not specified **Level of Education for which Award is Granted:** Undergraduate **Number Awarded:** 10 each year. **Funds Available:** The stipend is $1,000. **Duration:** 1 year.
Eligibility Requirements: This program is open to 1) students with hemophilia or a related bleeding disorder or 2) members of their families. Applicants must be U.S. citizens and enrolled or planning to enroll full time in an accredited 2- or 4-year college program. They must have a GPA of 2.5 or higher. Along with their application, they must submit a 400-word essay that explains what motivates them to pursue a higher education, what subjects they plan to study, what major forces or obstacles in their life has led to that path of study, what they plan to do with their education after school, and how that may be of benefit to humankind. Financial need is also considered in the selection process. **Deadline for Receipt:** February of each year.

1356 ■ OAHU COUNCIL OF FILIPINO CATHOLIC CLUBS

Attn: Josie Rayray, Information and Education Committee
47-464 Poomau Street
Kaneohe, HI 96744
Tel: (808)266-9893

To provide financial assistance for high school, college, or seminary to descendants of members of the Oahu Council of Filipino Catholic Clubs.

Title of Award: Oahu Council of Filipino Catholic Clubs Scholarship Program **Area, Field, or Subject:** General studies/Field of study not specified; Religion **Level of Education for which Award is Granted:** Master's, Undergraduate **Number Awarded:** Several each year. **Funds Available:** A stipend is awarded (amount not specified). **Duration:** 1 year.
Eligibility Requirements: This program is open to high school, college, and seminary students from Hawaii whose parents or grandparents have been members of the organization for at least 1 year. Applicants must be 1) Filipino Catholics attending Catholic colleges or high schools or non-Catholic colleges, or 2) Filipino students attending a seminary or convent. They must have a GPA of 3.0 or higher and be able to demonstrate financial need. Along with their application, they must submit an essay about their significant experiences, accomplishments, future goals, and service to school, church, and community. An interview is required. **Deadline for Receipt:** July of each year.

1357 ■ HUGH O'BRIAN YOUTH LEADERSHIP

Attn: Director of Constituency Services
10880 Wilshire Boulevard, Suite 410
Los Angeles, CA 90024
Tel: (310)474-4370
Fax: (310)475-5426
E-mail: hoby@hoby.org
Web Site: http://www.hoby.org

To provide financial assistance for college to students who have performed community service activities as part of participation in the Hugh O'Brian Youth (HOBY) Leadership for Service activities.
Title of Award: Leadership for Service Scholarships **Area, Field, or Subject:** General studies/Field of study not specified **Level of Education for which Award is Granted:** Undergraduate **Number Awarded:** 2 each year. **Funds Available:** The stipend is $1,000. **Duration:** 1 year.
Eligibility Requirements: All students in grade 10 in public and private high schools in the United States and certain foreign countries are eligible to apply to participate in the HOBY program. Students who complete at least 100 hours of community service as part of the Leadership for Service program are eligible to apply for these scholarships. **Additional Information:** This program is funded by the ECI Scholarship Foundation of Educational Communications Inc., publisher of *Who's Who Among American High School Students.*

1358 ■ OFFICE OF THE ADJUTANT GENERAL

Attn: Education Assistance Office
2302 Militia Drive
Jefferson City, MO 65101-1203
Tel: (573)638-9637; 888-526-6664
Fax: (573)638-9620
E-mail: information@mo.ngb.army.mil
Web Site: http://www.moguard.com/StateEdAsst/edu.htm

To provide financial assistance for college to members of the Missouri National Guard.
Title of Award: Missouri National Guard State-Sponsored Educational Assistance Program **Area, Field, or Subject:** General studies/Field of study not specified **Level of Education for which Award is Granted:** Undergraduate **Number Awarded:** Varies each year, depending on the availability of funds. **Funds Available:** Personnel who entered the Missouri National Guard prior to April 1, 2001 and have less than 10 total years of military service receive 100% tuition funding. Personnel who became members of the Missouri National Guard after April 1, 2001 receive 50% tuition funding. Awards may not exceed the tuition rate charged at the University of Missouri. **Duration:** Support is provided for 10 semesters, or 150 credit hours, or completion of a bachelor's degree, whichever comes first. Recipients must maintain a GPA of 2.5 or higher.
Eligibility Requirements: This program is open to members of the Missouri National Guard who are participating satisfactorily in required training. Applicants must be enrolled or accepted for enrollment as a full-time or part-time undergraduate at an approved public or private institution of higher learning. If they have already completed some college courses, they must have earned a GPA of 2.5 or higher. As currently structured, priority is given to personnel in the following order: 1) officers who do not have a bachelor's degree, regardless of their length of service; 2) non prior service enlistees accessed to fill a valid unit vacancy; 3) prior service transfers access to fill a valid unit vacancy; and 4) prior service beyond first term with less than 10 years total military service. **Deadline for**

Receipt: September of each year for fall semester; January of each year for spring semester.

1359 ■ OFFICE OF THE ADJUTANT GENERAL

Attn: Nebraska National Guard
1300 Military Road
Lincoln, NE 68508-1090
Tel: (402)309-7143
E-mail: cindy.york@ne.ngb.army.mil
Web Site: http://www.neguard.com
To provide an opportunity for enlisted members of the Nebraska National Guard to pursue additional education.

Title of Award: Nebraska National Guard Tuition Assistance Program **Area, Field, or Subject:** General studies/Field of study not specified **Level of Education for which Award is Granted:** Undergraduate **Number Awarded:** Up to 1,200 each year. **Funds Available:** Students at state-supported institutions are exempted from payment of 75% of the tuition charges at their schools. Students at independent, nonprofit, accredited colleges and universities in Nebraska receive a credit equal to the amount they would receive if they attended the University of Nebraska at Lincoln. All funds are paid directly to the school. **Duration:** 1 year; may be renewed.

Eligibility Requirements: Eligible for this benefit are members of the Nebraska National Guard who are enrolled in a Nebraska university, college, or community college. Commissioned and warrant officers and enlisted personnel who already have a baccalaureate degree are not eligible. Guard members must apply for this assistance within 10 years of the date of initial enlistment. The credit is not available for graduate study or noncredit courses. Priority is given to Guard members who have previously received these benefits. **Deadline for Receipt:** June of each year for academic terms beginning between July and September; September of each year for academic terms beginning between October and December; December of each year for academic terms beginning between January and March; March of each year for academic terms beginning between April and June. **Additional Information:** Any member of the Nebraska National Guard who receives this assistance must agree to serve in the Guard for 3 years after completion of the courses for which assistance was given.

1360 ■ OFFICE OF THE ADJUTANT GENERAL

Attn: State Scholarship Committee
State Military Reservation
4 Pembroke Road
Concord, NH 03301-5652
Tel: (603)227-1550
Fax: (603)225-1257
E-mail: education@nharmyguard.com
Web Site: http://www.nharmyguard.com/members/educationBenefits/index.htm
To provide financial assistance for college or graduate school to members of the New Hampshire National Guard.

Title of Award: New Hampshire National Guard Tuition Waiver Program **Area, Field, or Subject:** General studies/Field of study not specified **Level of Education for which Award is Granted:** Graduate, Undergraduate **Number Awarded:** Varies each year, depending on availability of space. **Funds Available:** A portion of tuition is waived for Guard members who attend on a space-available basis. The amount of the waiver depends on other assistance the student is receiving. **Duration:** 1 year; may be renewed.

Eligibility Requirements: This program is open to active members of the New Hampshire National Guard who have completed advanced individual training or commissioning and have at least a 90% attendance rate at annual training and drill assemblies. Applicants may be working on any type of academic degree at designated institutions in New Hampshire. They must apply for financial aid from their school, for the New Hampshire National Guard Scholarship Program, and for federal tuition assistance. **Additional Information:** This program began in 1996. The designated institutions are the University of New Hampshire, Keene State College, Plymouth State College, The College for Lifelong Learning, and all New Hampshire community technical colleges.

1361 ■ OFFICE OF THE ADJUTANT GENERAL

789 Vermont National Guard Road
Colchester, VT 05446-3099

Tel: (802)338-3450
Web Site: http://www.vtguard.com
To provide financial assistance for college to the children and spouses of deceased members of the armed services in Vermont.

Title of Award: Vermont Armed Services Scholarships **Area, Field, or Subject:** General studies/Field of study not specified **Level of Education for which Award is Granted:** Undergraduate **Number Awarded:** Varies each year. **Funds Available:** Full tuition, in excess of any funds the student receives as a federal Pell Grant, is paid at Vermont public institutions. **Duration:** 1 year; may be renewed until completion of 130 academic credits.

Eligibility Requirements: This program is open to the children and spouses of 1) members of the Vermont National Guard who have been killed since 1955 or who since January 1, 2001 have died while on active or inactive duty; 2) members in good standing of the active Reserve forces of the United States who since January 1, 2001 have died while on active or inactive duty and who were Vermont residents at the time of death; and 3) members of the active armed forces of the United States who since January 1, 2001 have died while on active duty and who, at the time of death, were Vermont residents, nonresident members of the Vermont National Guard mobilized to active duty, or nonresident active Reserve force members of a Vermont-based Reserve unit mobilized to active duty. Applicants must be residents of Vermont and attending or planning to attend a Vermont public university, college, or technical institute.

1362 ■ OFFICE OF THE ADJUTANT GENERAL

Attn: Education Office
1703 Coonskin Drive
Charleston, WV 25311-1085
Tel: (304)561-6306; (866)986-4326
Fax: (304)561-6377
Web Site: http://www.wv.ngb.army.mil
To provide financial assistance for undergraduate studies to members of the National Guard in West Virginia.

Title of Award: West Virginia National Guard Educational Encouragement Program **Area, Field, or Subject:** General studies/Field of study not specified **Level of Education for which Award is Granted:** Undergraduate **Number Awarded:** Varies each year. **Funds Available:** If the recipient attends a publicly-supported school in West Virginia, 100% of the tuition and fees are covered. Recipients attending private schools in the state are awarded a sum not to exceed the highest amounts paid for tuition/fees at state institutions. **Duration:** 1 academic year; may be renewed.

Eligibility Requirements: This program is open to active members of the West Virginia National Guard who are residents of West Virginia and interested in working on an undergraduate degree at a public or private college in the state. Recipients must maintain satisfactory participation (90% attendance) in the Guard. Persons who have received a baccalaureate degree or its equivalent, or a trade school certification, are deemed to have completed undergraduate study and are not eligible to participate in this program.

1363 ■ OFFICE OF THE GOVERNOR

Attn: Press Office
206 the Capitol
Tallahassee, FL 32399
Tel: (850)488-5394
Fax: (850)413-0909
E-mail: blackhistoryessay@myflorida.com
Web Site: http://www.floridablackhistory.com
To recognize and reward, with college scholarships, students in Florida who submit outstanding essays on a topic related to Black History Month.

Title of Award: Florida Governor's Black History Month Essay Contest **Area, Field, or Subject:** General studies/Field of study not specified **Level of Education for which Award is Granted:** Four Year College **Number Awarded:** 3 each year: 1 in each of the grade categories. **Funds Available:** Winners receive full payment of tuition at the Florida state college or university of their choice. **Duration:** The competition is held annually. Winners receive payment of tuition for 4 years.

Eligibility Requirements: This competition is open to all Florida students in 3 categories: elementary (grades K-5), middle (grades 6-8), and high school (grades 9-12). Applicants must submit an essay, up to 500 words in length, on a topic that changes annually but relates to Black History. A recent topic was "What Impact Has an African American Athlete from Florida Had on My Life?" **Deadline for Receipt:** January of each year. **Additional Information:** This competition was first held in 2003.

1364 ■ OHIO BOARD OF REGENTS

Attn: State Grants and Scholarships
57 East Main Street, Fourth Floor
P.O. Box 182452
Columbus, OH 43218-2452
Tel: (614)466-7420; 888-833-1133
Fax: (614)752-5903
E-mail: bmetheney@regents.state.oh.us
Web Site: http://www.regents.state.oh.us/sgs/OAS.htm
To provide financial assistance for college to outstanding high school seniors in Ohio.

Title of Award: Ohio Academic Scholarship Program **Area, Field, or Subject:** General studies/Field of study not specified **Level of Education for which Award is Granted:** Undergraduate **Number Awarded:** 1 for each public, private, or vocational high school in Ohio; additional awards are then granted until a total of 1,000 have been presented. **Funds Available:** The stipend is $2,205 per year. **Duration:** Up to 8 semesters or 12 quarters.

Eligibility Requirements: This program is open to seniors graduating from high schools in Ohio. Applicants must be planning to enroll for full-time undergraduate study at a college or university in Ohio. Selection is based on ACT scores and high school grades. Each high school in the state identifies the top 5 applicants and submits those 5 applications to the Ohio Board of Regents. The top candidate receives an award and the remaining applicants are placed in a statewide pool and chosen on a competitive basis until all the awards have been presented. **Deadline for Receipt:** February of each year. **Additional Information:** This program was established in 1978.

1365 ■ OHIO BOARD OF REGENTS

Attn: State Grants and Scholarships
57 East Main Street, Fourth Floor
P.O. Box 182452
Columbus, OH 43218-2452
Tel: (614)466-7420; 888-833-1133
Fax: (614)752-5903
E-mail: bmetheney@regents.state.oh.us
Web Site: http://www.regents.state.oh.us/sgs/oig.htm
To provide financial assistance for college to students from Ohio.

Title of Award: Ohio Instructional Grant Program **Area, Field, or Subject:** General studies/Field of study not specified **Level of Education for which Award is Granted:** Undergraduate **Number Awarded:** Varies, depending upon the funds available. Recently, approximately 83,000 students received these grants. **Funds Available:** Awards are based on the need of the recipient and range from $174 to $5,466 per year. They may not exceed tuition costs. **Duration:** 1 year; may be renewed up to 3 additional years.

Eligibility Requirements: To be eligible for these scholarships, students must be Ohio residents and U.S. citizens who are attending or planning to attend eligible colleges and universities in Ohio or Pennsylvania as full-time undergraduate students. Financial need (family income of $39,000 per year or less) must be demonstrated. **Deadline for Receipt:** September of each year. **Additional Information:** This program was established in 1970.

1366 ■ OHIO BOARD OF REGENTS

Attn: State Grants and Scholarships
57 East Main Street, Fourth Floor
P.O. Box 182452
Columbus, OH 43218-2452
Tel: (614)466-7420; 888-833-1133
Fax: (614)752-5903
E-mail: bmetheney@regents.state.oh.us
Web Site: http://www.regents.state.oh.us/sgs/parttimegrant.htm
To provide financial assistance for part-time undergraduate education to students in Ohio.

Title of Award: Ohio Part-time Student Instructional Grant Program **Area, Field, or Subject:** General studies/Field of study not specified **Level of

Education for which Award is Granted:** Undergraduate **Number Awarded:** Varies each year; recently, 28,349 students received these grants. **Funds Available:** Participating schools determine the amount of each award, based on guidelines set by the Board of Regents and the need of the recipient. Grants may not exceed the actual cost of attendance. **Duration:** 1 year; may be renewed up to 3 additional years.

Eligibility Requirements: To be eligible for these scholarships, students must be Ohio residents who are attending or planning to attend public, private, and proprietary colleges and universities in Ohio and take fewer than 12 credit hours per term. Financial need must be demonstrated. Special consideration is given to single heads of household and displaced homemakers. Participating schools select the recipients. **Deadline for Receipt:** Each participating college or university sets its own deadline. **Additional Information:** This program was established in 1993.

1367 ■ OHIO BOARD OF REGENTS

Attn: State Grants and Scholarships
57 East Main Street, Fourth Floor
P.O. Box 182452
Columbus, OH 43218-2452
Tel: (614)466-7420; 888-833-1133
Fax: (614)752-5903
E-mail: bmetheney@regents.state.oh.us
Web Site: http://www.regents.state.oh.us/sgs/ohiosafetyofficers.htm
To provide financial assistance for the undergraduate education of children of Ohio peace officers and fire fighters killed in the line of duty.

Title of Award: Ohio Safety Officers College Memorial Fund **Area, Field, or Subject:** General studies/Field of study not specified **Level of Education for which Award is Granted:** Undergraduate **Number Awarded:** Varies each year; recently, 54 students received benefits from this program. **Funds Available:** At Ohio public colleges and universities, the program provides full payment of tuition. At Ohio private colleges and universities, the stipend is equivalent to the average amounts paid to students attending public institutions, currently $3,990 per year. **Duration:** 1 year; may be renewed up to 3 additional years.

Eligibility Requirements: This program is open to Ohio residents whose parent or spouse was a peace officer, fire fighter, or other safety officer killed in the line of duty anywhere in the United States. Applicants must be interested in attending a participating Ohio college or university. **Deadline for Receipt:** Application deadlines are established by each participating college and university. **Additional Information:** Eligible institutions are Ohio state-assisted colleges and universities and Ohio institutions approved by the Board of Regents. This program was established in 1980.

1368 ■ OHIO BOARD OF REGENTS

Attn: State Grants and Scholarships
57 East Main Street, Fourth Floor
P.O. Box 182452
Columbus, OH 43218-2452
Tel: (614)466-7420; 888-833-1133
Fax: (614)752-5903
E-mail: bmetheney@regents.state.oh.us
Web Site: http://www.regents.state.oh.us/sgs/warorphans.htm
To provide financial assistance for college to the children of deceased or disabled Ohio veterans.

Title of Award: Ohio War Orphans Scholarship **Area, Field, or Subject:** General studies/Field of study not specified **Level of Education for which Award is Granted:** Undergraduate **Number Awarded:** Varies, depending upon the funds available. If sufficient funds are available, all eligible applicants are given a scholarship. Recently, 861 students received benefits from this program. **Funds Available:** At Ohio public colleges and universities, the program provides full payment of tuition. At Ohio private colleges and universities, the stipend is equivalent to the average amount paid to students attending public institutions, currently $4,710 per year. **Duration:** 1 year; may be renewed up to 4 additional years.

Eligibility Requirements: To be eligible for these scholarships, students must be between 16 and 21 years of age at the time of application; must have been residents of Ohio for the past year or, if the parent was not a resident of Ohio at the time of enlistment, for the year immediately preceding application and any other 4 of the last 10 years; and must be enrolled for full-time undergraduate study at an eligible Ohio college or university. At least 1 parent must have been a member of the U.S. armed forces, including the organized Reserves and Ohio National Guard, for a period of 90 days or more (or discharged because of a disability incurred after less than 90 days of service) who served during World War I, World War II, the Korean Conflict, the Vietnam era, or the Persian Gulf War, and who, as a result of that service, either was killed or became at least 60% service-connected disabled. Also eligible are children of veterans who have a permanent and total non-service connected disability and are receiving disability benefits from the U.S. Department of Veterans Affairs. Children of veteran parents who served in the organized Reserves or Ohio National Guard are also eligible if the parent was killed or became permanently and totally disabled while at a scheduled training assembly (of any duration or length) or active duty for training, pursuant to bona fide orders issued by a competent authority. **Deadline for Receipt:** June of each year. **Additional Information:** Eligible institutions are Ohio state-assisted colleges and universities and Ohio institutions approved by the Board of Regents. This program was established in 1957.

1369 ■ OHIO NATIONAL GUARD ENLISTED ASSOCIATION

1266 West Third Avenue
Columbus, OH 43212
Tel: (740)574-5932
Free: 800-642-6642
Fax: (614)486-2216
E-mail: ongea@juno.com
Web Site: http://www.ongea.org
To provide financial assistance for college to members of the Ohio National Guard Enlisted Association (ONGEA) and children of members of the ONGEA Auxiliary.
Title of Award: ONGEA Scholarship Program **Area, Field, or Subject:** General studies/Field of study not specified **Level of Education for which Award is Granted:** Undergraduate **Number Awarded:** 5 to 10 each year, depending upon the availability of funds. **Funds Available:** Stipends are $1,000 or $500. After verification of enrollment is provided, checks are sent to the recipient and made out to the recipient's school. **Duration:** 1 year; nonrenewable.
Eligibility Requirements: The following persons are eligible to apply: sons and daughters of ONGEA Auxiliary members (spouse must have at least 1 year remaining on his/her enlistment following the completion of the school year for which the application is submitted); unmarried dependent sons and daughters of deceased ONGEA and ONGEA Auxiliary members who were in good standing the time of their death; and single ONGEA members. Spouses of ONGEA members must also be a member of the ONGEA Auxiliary in order for a dependent to be considered for this award (unless the ONGEA member is a single parent). Applicants must be enrolling as full-time undergraduate students at a college, university, trade school, or business school. Graduate students are not eligible. All applications must be accompanied by a transcript of high school and (if appropriate) college credits, a letter from the applicant describing educational goals and financial need, 3 letters of recommendation, and a copy of the current membership cards of both parents or current membership card of the single parent. Selection is based on academic record, character, leadership, and financial need. **Deadline for Receipt:** April of each year. **Additional Information:** This program is sponsored jointly by ONGEA, the ONGEA Auxiliary, USAA Insurance Corporation, and the First Cleveland Cavalry Association. Information is also available from the ONGEA Scholarship Chair, Nancy McDowell, 817 Franklin Avenue, Wheelersburg, OH 45694.

1370 ■ OKLAHOMA BUSINESS AND PROFESSIONAL WOMEN

Attn: OK/BPW State Foundation
P.O. Box 160
Maud, OK 74854-0160
Tel: (405)374-2866
Fax: (405)374-2316
E-mail: askkathy@okbpw.org
Web Site: http://www.okbpw.org/found.htm
To provide financial assistance for college to women, especially nontraditional students, in Oklahoma.
Title of Award: Oklahoma BPW Foundation Scholarships **Area, Field, or Subject:** General studies/Field of study not specified **Level of Education for which Award is Granted:** Undergraduate **Number Awarded:** Varies each year. Recently, 8 of these scholarships were awarded: 3 at $1,000, 3 at $750, and 2 at $500. **Funds Available:** Stipends are $1,000, $750, or $500. **Duration:** 1 year.

Eligibility Requirements: This program is open to women who are attending a college, university, or technical school in Oklahoma. Special consideration is given to nontraditional students. Selection is based on financial need, a description of career plans and goals, academics, and employment and volunteer record. **Additional Information:** This program includes the following named scholarships: the Jewell Russell Mann Scholarship, the Dorothy Dickerson Scholarship, the Ann Garrison/Delores Schofield Scholarship, and the Dr. Ann Marie Benson Scholarship.

1371 ■ OKLAHOMA FUNERAL DIRECTORS ASSOCIATION

Attn: Scholarship Committee
6801 North Broadway, Suite 106
Oklahoma City, OK 73116
Tel: (405)843-0730
Fax: (405)843-5404
To provide financial assistance to Oklahoma residents who are interested in attending a mortuary college.
Title of Award: J. Paul Norwood Memorial Scholarship **Area, Field, or Subject:** Mortuary science **Level of Education for which Award is Granted:** Undergraduate **Funds Available:** The maximum stipend is $1,500. Funds are sent to the recipient's school and must be used only for tuition and books. **Duration:** 1 year; may be renewed if the recipient continues to do satisfactory work.
Eligibility Requirements: This program is open to high school seniors in Oklahoma who have a GPS of 2.0 or higher. Applicants must be recommended by a member of the sponsoring organization, meet the educational requirements of the Oklahoma State Board of Embalmers and Funeral Directors, and possess the following personal characteristics: an acute mind, a pleasing personality, good character, ambition, and leadership abilities. They must "have abstained from participation in activities which created behavior incidents." Financial need is also considered in the selection process. **Additional Information:** Recipients must work at a funeral home in Oklahoma for 2 years following graduation. If they fail to complete that obligation, they must repay all funds received plus 10% interest.

1372 ■ OKLAHOMA STATE REGENTS FOR HIGHER EDUCATION

Attn: Director of Scholarship and Grant Programs
655 Research Parkway, Suite 200
P.O. Box 108850
Oklahoma City, OK 73101-8850
Tel: (405)225-9239
Free: 800-858-1840
Fax: (405)225-9230
E-mail: studentinfo@osrhe.edu
Web Site: http://www.okhighered.org/student-center/financial-aid/heartland.shtml
To provide financial assistance for college to families of victims of the bombing of the Oklahoma City federal building.
Title of Award: Heartland Scholarship Program **Area, Field, or Subject:** General studies/Field of study not specified **Level of Education for which Award is Granted:** Undergraduate **Number Awarded:** This is an entitlement program, open only to qualified individuals. **Funds Available:** Annual awards are $5,500 for students attending a comprehensive university, $4,000 for students attending a 4-year regional university, or $3,500 for students attending a 2-year college. **Duration:** Up to 5 years of undergraduate study.
Eligibility Requirements: This program is open to dependent children of individuals killed in the April 19, 1995 bombing of the Alfred P. Murrah Federal Building in Oklahoma City, or surviving dependent children who were injured in the federal building daycare center. Applicants may attend accredited institutions of higher education in Oklahoma or outside the state.

1373 ■ OKLAHOMA STATE REGENTS FOR HIGHER EDUCATION

Attn: Director of Scholarship and Grant Programs
655 Research Parkway, Suite 200
P.O. Box 108850
Oklahoma City, OK 73101-8850
Tel: (405)225-9239
Free: 800-858-1840
Fax: (405)225-9230

E-mail: ohlapinfo@osrhe.edu

Web Site: http://www.okpromise.org

To provide financial assistance to Oklahoma residents who complete a specified high school curriculum.

Title of Award: Oklahoma Higher Learning Access Program **Area, Field, or Subject:** General studies/Field of study not specified **Level of Education for which Award is Granted:** Undergraduate **Number Awarded:** Varies each year. **Funds Available:** Students enrolled at an institution in the Oklahoma State System of Higher Education receive resident tuition, paid to the institution on their behalf. Students enrolled at an accredited private institution have tuition paid at an amount equivalent to the resident tuition at a comparable institution of the state system. Students enrolled in eligible vocational/technical programs have their tuition paid. No provision is made for other educational expenses, such as books, supplies, room, board, or other special fees. **Duration:** Up to 5 years or until completion of a bachelor's degree, whichever occurs first. The award must be taken up within 3 years of high school graduation.

Eligibility Requirements: Applicants for this program sign up during their 8th, 9th, or 10th grade year at an Oklahoma high school. If they complete a specified high school curriculum and demonstrate a commitment to academic success, they receive assistance when they attend college. Applicants must 1) demonstrate financial need (currently defined as a family income less than $50,000); 2) achieve a GPA of 2.5 or higher both cumulatively and in the required curriculum; 3) fulfill an agreement to attend school, do homework regularly, refrain from substance abuse and criminal or delinquent acts, and have school work and records reviewed by mentors; and 4) be admitted as a regular entering freshman at an Oklahoma college, university, or area vocational technical school. **Deadline for Receipt:** Applications must be submitted by June following completion of the student's 8th, 9th, or 10th grade year. **Additional Information:** The required curriculum consists of 17 units: 4 of English, 2 of laboratory science, 3 of mathematics, 3 of history and citizenship skills (including 1 of U.S. history and 2 from the subjects of history, government, economics, civics, and/or non-Western culture), 2 of a foreign language or computer technology, 1 of fine arts (music, art, drama) or speech, and 2 additional units from any of those subjects.

1374 ■ OKLAHOMA STATE REGENTS FOR HIGHER EDUCATION

Attn: Director of Scholarship and Grant Programs

655 Research Parkway, Suite 200

P.O. Box 108850

Oklahoma City, OK 73101-8850

Tel: (405)225-9239

Free: 800-858-1840

Fax: (405)225-9230

E-mail: studentinfo@osrhe.edu

Web Site: http://www.okhighered.org/student-center/financial-aid/dhs.shtml

To provide financial assistance for college to residents in Oklahoma who have been in a foster care program of the Department of Human Services (DHS).

Title of Award: Oklahoma Independent Living Act Tuition Waivers **Area, Field, or Subject:** General studies/Field of study not specified **Level of Education for which Award is Granted:** Undergraduate **Number Awarded:** Varies each year. **Funds Available:** Under this program, all resident tuition fees are waived. **Duration:** 1 year; may be renewed until the student reaches 26 years of age or completes a baccalaureate degree or program certificate, whichever comes first.

Eligibility Requirements: This program is open to residents of Oklahoma who graduated within the previous 3 years from an accredited high school in the state or from a high school bordering Oklahoma as approved by the State Board of Education, or who have completed the GED requirements. Applicants must be younger than 21 years of age and have been in DHS custody for at least 9 months between 16 and 18 years of age. They must currently be enrolled at an Oklahoma public college or university or in certain programs at technology centers. **Additional Information:** The Oklahoma State Legislature established this program in 2000.

1375 ■ OKLAHOMA STATE REGENTS FOR HIGHER EDUCATION

Attn: Director of Scholarship and Grant Programs

655 Research Parkway, Suite 200

P.O. Box 108850

Oklahoma City, OK 73101-8850

Tel: (405)225-9239

Free: 800-858-1840

Fax: (405)225-9230

E-mail: studentinfo@osrhe.edu

Web Site: http://www.okhighered.org/student-center/financial-aid/natl-guard.shtml

To provide financial assistance for college to members of the Oklahoma National Guard.

Title of Award: Oklahoma National Guard Tuition Waiver Program **Area, Field, or Subject:** General studies/Field of study not specified **Level of Education for which Award is Granted:** Undergraduate **Number Awarded:** Varies each year. **Funds Available:** Under this program, all tuition is waived. **Duration:** 1 year; may be renewed as long as the Guard member remains in good standing both in the unit and in the college or university, to a maximum of 6 years from the date of first application.

Eligibility Requirements: This program is open to current members in good standing of the Oklahoma National Guard who do not have any other baccalaureate or graduate degree. Applicants must be attending or planning to attend a state-supported college or university in Oklahoma to work on an associate or baccalaureate degree. They must have submitted a plan for completion of their degree to the Guard. Courses leading to a certification, continuing education courses, and career technology courses that are not counted towards a degree at another institution are not covered. **Additional Information:** Information is also available from the Oklahoma Military Department, Attn: Educational Service Office, 3501 Military Circle, Oklahoma City, OK 73111, (405) 425-8300, (800) 362-4534, Fax: (405) 425-8674, E-mail: okguard@keytech.com, Web site: www.okguard.com.

1376 ■ OKLAHOMA STATE REGENTS FOR HIGHER EDUCATION

Attn: Director of Scholarship and Grant Programs

655 Research Parkway, Suite 200

P.O. Box 108850

Oklahoma City, OK 73101-8850

Tel: (405)225-9239

Free: 800-858-1840

Fax: (405)225-9230

E-mail: aharris@osrhe.edu

Web Site: http://www.okhighered.org/academic-scholars

To provide financial assistance to outstanding high school seniors and recent graduates who wish to attend a college or university in Oklahoma.

Title of Award: Oklahoma State Regents Academic Scholars Program **Area, Field, or Subject:** General studies/Field of study not specified **Level of Education for which Award is Granted:** Undergraduate **Number Awarded:** Varies each year; recently, 620 entering freshmen received this support (including 382 "automatic qualifiers" and 238 institutional nominees). A total of 2,078 students were enrolled in the program. **Funds Available:** The program provides funding for tuition, fees, room and board, and textbooks. The exact amount of funding awarded varies each year; for "automatic qualifiers" (the first 4 ways to qualify), it is currently $5,500 per year for students at the 3 comprehensive universities, $4,000 per year for students at other 4-year public or private colleges or universities in Oklahoma, or $3,500 per year for students at Oklahoma 2-year colleges. For institutional nominees, the current rate is $2,800 per year at the 3 comprehensive universities, $2,000 per year at other 4-year institutions, or $1,800 at 2-year colleges. Students who enroll at public universities and colleges are also eligible for a tuition waiver. **Duration:** Up to 4 years of undergraduate study, as long as the recipient remains a full-time student with a GPA of 3.25 or higher.

Eligibility Requirements: This program is open to high school seniors who have 5 ways to qualify: 1) residents of Oklahoma whose ACT or SAT score is at least at the 99.5 percentile level and whose GPA and/or class rank are considered exceptional; 2) residents of any state designated as a National Merit Scholar; 3) residents of any state designated as a National Merit Scholar Finalist; 4) residents of any state designated as a Presidential Scholar; or 5) institutional nominees, from Oklahoma's comprehensive universities (University of Oklahoma, University of Tulsa, Oklahoma State University) who have either an ACT of at least 32 (or SAT equivalent) or a GPA of 3.9 or higher and a ranking in the top 2% of their class, from Oklahoma's regional universities who have either an ACT of at least 30 (or SAT equivalent) or a GPA of 3.8 or higher and a ranking in the top 4% of their class, or from Oklahoma's 2-year colleges who have either an ACT of at least 29 (or SAT equivalent) or a GPA of 3.7 or higher and a ranking in the top 5% of their class. **Deadline for Receipt:** September of each year. **Additional Information:** Recipients may enroll in either public or private schools. This program was established in 1988. Recipients must attend a school in Oklahoma.

1377 ■ OKLAHOMA STATE REGENTS FOR HIGHER EDUCATION

655 Research Parkway, Suite 200
P.O. Box 108850
Oklahoma City, OK 73101-8850
Tel: (405)225-9456; 877-662-6231
Fax: (405)225-9476
E-mail: otaginfo@otag.org
Web Site: http://www.okhighered.org/student-center/financial-aid/otag.shtml

To provide financial assistance for college to Oklahoma residents who demonstrate financial need.

Title of Award: Oklahoma Tuition Aid Grant Program **Area, Field, or Subject:** General studies/Field of study not specified **Level of Education for which Award is Granted:** Undergraduate **Number Awarded:** Varies each year. **Funds Available:** At public colleges, universities, and technology centers, the annual stipend is $1,000 or 75% of enrollment costs, whichever is less. At private colleges and universities, the annual stipend is $1,300 or 75% of enrollment costs, whichever is less. **Duration:** 1 year; renewable.

Eligibility Requirements: This program is open to residents of Oklahoma who are attending or planning to attend public or private institutions in Oklahoma. To apply, they must complete the Free Application for Federal Student Aid and demonstrate financial need. **Deadline for Receipt:** Applications are accepted through June of each year, but students should apply as early after the beginning of January as possible and by the end of April for best consideration. **Additional Information:** This program is supported by state funds and by federal funds from the Leveraging Educational Assistance Partnership (LEAP) Program.

1378 ■ OKLAHOMA STATE REGENTS FOR HIGHER EDUCATION

Attn: Director of Scholarship and Grant Programs
655 Research Parkway, Suite 200
P.O. Box 108850
Oklahoma City, OK 73101-8850
Tel: (405)225-9456; 877-662-6231
Fax: (405)225-9230
E-mail: studentinfo@osrhe.edu
Web Site: http://www.okhighered.org/student-center/financial-aid/oteg.shtml

To provide financial assistance to Oklahoma residents who meet financial need requirements and are entering college as first-time freshmen.

Title of Award: Oklahoma Tuition Equalization Grant Program **Area, Field, or Subject:** General studies/Field of study not specified **Level of Education for which Award is Granted:** Undergraduate **Number Awarded:** Varies each year. **Funds Available:** The stipend is $2,000 per year. **Duration:** 1 year.

Eligibility Requirements: This program is open to residents of Oklahoma entering a nonprofit private or independent institution of higher education in the state as a full-time undergraduate for the first time. Applicants must have a family income of $50,000 or less.

1379 ■ OKLAHOMA STATE REGENTS FOR HIGHER EDUCATION

Attn: Director of Scholarship and Grant Programs
655 Research Parkway, Suite 200
P.O. Box 108850
Oklahoma City, OK 73101-8850
Tel: (405)225-9239
Free: 800-858-1840
Fax: (405)225-9230
E-mail: studentinfo@osrhe.edu
Web Site: http://www.okhighered.org

To provide financial assistance for college to the children of deceased Oklahoma peace officers and fire fighters.

Title of Award: Oklahoma Tuition Waiver for Dependents of Peace Officers and Fire Fighters **Area, Field, or Subject:** General studies/Field of study not specified **Level of Education for which Award is Granted:** Undergraduate **Number Awarded:** Varies each year. **Funds Available:** Eligible applicants are entitled to receive free tuition at any Oklahoma

state-supported postsecondary educational, technical, or vocational school. **Duration:** Assistance continues for 5 years or until receipt of a bachelor's degree, whichever occurs first.

Eligibility Requirements: Applicants for this assistance must be children of Oklahoma peace officers or fire fighters who lost their lives in the line of duty. Selection is based on financial need, academic aptitude and achievement, student activity participation, academic level, and academic discipline or field of study.

1380 ■ OKLAHOMA STATE REGENTS FOR HIGHER EDUCATION

Attn: Director of Scholarship and Grant Programs
655 Research Parkway, Suite 200
P.O. Box 108850
Oklahoma City, OK 73101-8850
Tel: (405)225-9239
Free: 800-858-1840
Fax: (405)225-9230
E-mail: studentinfo@osrhe.edu
Web Site: http://www.okhighered.org

To provide financial assistance for college to Oklahoma residents (or their dependents) who were declared prisoners of war or missing in action.

Title of Award: Oklahoma Tuition Waiver for Prisoners of War, Persons Missing in Action, and Dependents **Area, Field, or Subject:** General studies/Field of study not specified **Level of Education for which Award is Granted:** Undergraduate **Number Awarded:** Varies each year. **Funds Available:** Eligible applicants are entitled to receive free tuition at any Oklahoma state-supported postsecondary educational, technical, or vocational school. **Duration:** Assistance continues for 5 years or until receipt of a bachelor's degree, whichever occurs first.

Eligibility Requirements: Applicants for this assistance must be veterans who were declared prisoners of war or missing in action after January 1, 1960 and were residents of Oklahoma at the time of entrance into the armed forces or when declared POW/MIA. Dependent children of those veterans are also eligible as long as they are under 24 years of age. Selection is based on financial need, academic aptitude and achievement, student activity participation, academic level, and academic discipline or field of study **Additional Information:** This assistance is not available to persons eligible to receive federal benefits.

1381 ■ OKLAHOMA STATE REGENTS FOR HIGHER EDUCATION

Attn: Director of Scholarship and Grant Programs
655 Research Parkway, Suite 200
P.O. Box 108850
Oklahoma City, OK 73101-8850
Tel: (405)225-9239
Free: 800-858-1840
Fax: (405)225-9230
E-mail: studentinfo@osrhe.edu
Web Site: http://www.okhighered.org/student-center/financial-aid/rubs.shtml

To provide financial assistance to Oklahoma residents who are attending designated publicly-supported regional universities in the state.

Title of Award: Regional University Baccalaureate Scholarship Program **Area, Field, or Subject:** General studies/Field of study not specified **Level of Education for which Award is Granted:** Undergraduate **Number Awarded:** Up to 165 each year: 15 at each of the 11 participating regional universities. **Funds Available:** The stipend is $3,000 per year. Awardees also receive a resident tuition waiver from the institution. **Duration:** Up to 4 years if the recipient maintains a cumulative GPA of 3.25 or higher and full-time enrollment.

Eligibility Requirements: This program is open to residents of Oklahoma who are attending 1 of 11 designated regional public institutions in the state and working on an undergraduate degree. Applicants must 1) be designated a National Merit Semifinalist or Commended Student, or 2) have an ACT score of at least 30 and have an exceptional GPA and class ranking as determined by the collegiate institution. Selection is based on academic promise. **Additional Information:** Applicants apply through the financial aid office of the university. The participating regional universities are the University of Central Oklahoma, East Central University, Northeastern State University, Northwestern Oklahoma State University, Southeastern Oklahoma State University, Southwestern Oklahoma State University, Cameron University, Langston University, Rogers State University, Oklahoma Panhandle State University, and the University of Science and Arts of Oklahoma.

1382 ■ ONEIDA NATION OF WISCONSIN
Attn: Higher Education Office
Norbert Hill Center, Room 1175
N7210 Seminary Road
P.O. Box 365
Oneida, WI 54155-0365
Tel: (920)869-4033
Free: 800-236-2214
Fax: (920)869-4039
E-mail: cvanden2@oneidanation.org
Web Site: http://www.oneidanation.org
To provide financial assistance for undergraduate or graduate study to members of the Oneida Tribe of Wisconsin.
Title of Award: Oneida Tribe Higher Education Grant Program **Area, Field, or Subject:** General studies/Field of study not specified **Level of Education for which Award is Granted:** Graduate, Undergraduate **Number Awarded:** Varies each year, depending upon the funds available. **Funds Available:** Stipends range up to $20,000 per year, depending on the need of the recipient. **Duration:** The total length of eligibility is 6 terms for vocation/technical students, 10 terms for undergraduate students, 6 terms for graduate students, and 10 terms for doctoral students. To be eligible for renewal, vocational/technical students and undergraduates must maintain a GPA of 2.0 or higher and graduate and doctoral students must maintain a GPA of 3.0 or higher.
Eligibility Requirements: This program is open to enrolled members of the Oneida Tribe of Wisconsin who have a high school diploma, HSED diploma, or GED. Applicants must be working on or planning to work on a vocational/technical, undergraduate, graduate, or doctoral degree. They must be able to demonstrate financial need. **Deadline for Receipt:** Applications must be submitted by April of each year for the fall term, by September of each year for the spring term, or by April of each year for the summer term.

1383 ■ ORANGE COUNTY COMMUNITY FOUNDATION
Attn: Administrative Assistant
30 Corporate Park, Suite 410
Irvine, CA 92606
Tel: (949)553-4202
Fax: (949)553-4211
E-mail: rho@oc-cf.org
Web Site: http://www.oc-cf.org
To provide financial assistance for college to leukemia patients and the children of non-surviving leukemia patients.
Title of Award: Michael A. Hunter Memorial Scholarship **Area, Field, or Subject:** General studies/Field of study not specified **Level of Education for which Award is Granted:** Undergraduate **Number Awarded:** 2 each year. **Funds Available:** The stipend is $5,000. **Duration:** 1 year.
Eligibility Requirements: This program is open to graduating high school seniors, community college students, and 4-year university students nationwide. Applicants must be leukemia patients and/or the children of non-surviving leukemia patients who are enrolled or planning to enroll full time. They must have a GPA of 3.0 or higher and be able to document financial need. Along with their application, they must submit an essay (up to 600 words) on how leukemia has affected their life, including the type of leukemia, date of diagnosis, and current status. **Deadline for Receipt:** March of each year.

1384 ■ ORDER SONS OF ITALY IN AMERICA
Attn: Sons of Italy Foundation
219 E Street, N.E.
Washington, DC 20002
Tel: (202)547-5106
Fax: (202)546-8168
E-mail: scholarships@osia.org
Web Site: http://www.osia.org/public/scholarships/grants.asp
To provide financial assistance to undergraduate and graduate students of Italian descent.
Title of Award: Sons of Italy National Leadership Grant Competition **Area, Field, or Subject:** General studies/Field of study not specified **Level of Education for which Award is Granted:** Four Year College, Graduate **Number Awarded:** Varies each year; recently, 14 of these awards were presented. **Funds Available:** Stipends range from $4,000 to $25,000. **Duration:** 1 year; nonrenewable.

Eligibility Requirements: Eligible are U.S. citizens of Italian descent who are enrolled as full-time students in an undergraduate or graduate program at an accredited 4-year college or university. Both high school seniors and students already enrolled in college are eligible for the undergraduate awards. Applications must be accompanied by essays, from 500 to 750 words in length, on the principal contribution of Italian Americans to the development of U.S. culture and society. These merit-based awards are presented to students who have demonstrated exceptional leadership qualities and distinguished scholastic abilities. **Deadline for Receipt:** February of each year. **Additional Information:** Applications must be accompanied by a $25 processing fee.

1385 ■ OREGON NATIONAL GUARD ASSOCIATION
Attn: Scholarship Committee
1776 Militia Way S.E.
Salem, OR 97309-5008
Tel: (503)584-3030
Fax: (503)584-3052
E-mail: ornga@mil.state.or.us
Web Site: http://www.mil.state.or.us/ornga/index.html
To provide financial assistance for college to members of the Oregon National Guard, the Oregon National Guard Association (ORNGA), and their children and spouses.
Title of Award: Oregon National Guard Association Scholarships **Area, Field, or Subject:** General studies/Field of study not specified **Level of Education for which Award is Granted:** Undergraduate **Number Awarded:** 1 or more each year. **Funds Available:** A stipend is awarded (amount not specified). Funds are paid directly to the school of the recipient's choice. **Duration:** 1 year.
Eligibility Requirements: This program is open to active members of the Oregon Army and Air National Guard, life members of the ORNGA, and their children and spouses. Applicants must be high school seniors, graduates, or GED recipients. The parent, spouse, or applicant must have an ETS date beyond the end of the academic year for which the scholarship is used. Selection is based on participation in school and civic activities, motivation for continued higher education, and academic achievement in high school and/or college. **Deadline for Receipt:** February of each year. **Additional Information:** Support is provided for undergraduate study only.

1386 ■ OREGON STUDENT ASSISTANCE COMMISSION
Attn: Grants and Scholarships Division
1500 Valley River Drive, Suite 100
Eugene, OR 97401-2146
Tel: (541)687-7395
Free: 800-452-8807
Fax: (541)687-7419
E-mail: awardinfo@mercury.osac.state.or.us
Web Site: http://www.osac.state.or.us
To provide financial assistance for college to women in Oregon who are interested in golf.
Title of Award: Dorothy Campbell Memorial Scholarship **Area, Field, or Subject:** General studies/Field of study not specified **Level of Education for which Award is Granted:** Four Year College **Number Awarded:** Varies each year; recently, 2 of these scholarships were awarded. **Funds Available:** The stipend is at least $1,500. **Duration:** 1 year; may be renewed up to 3 additional years.
Eligibility Requirements: This program is open to residents of Oregon who are U.S. citizens or permanent residents. Applicants must be female high school seniors or graduates with a cumulative GPA of 2.75 or higher and a strong continuing interest in golf. They must be or planning to become full-time students at an Oregon 4-year college. Along with their application, they must submit a 1-page essay on the contribution that golf has made to their development. Financial need must be demonstrated. **Deadline for Receipt:** February of each year. **Additional Information:** This program is administered by the Oregon Student Assistance Commission (OSAC) with funds provided by the Oregon Community Foundation, 1221 S.W. Yamhill, Suite 100, Portland, OR 97205, (503) 227-6846, Fax: (503) 274-7771.

1387 ■ OREGON STUDENT ASSISTANCE COMMISSION
Attn: Grants and Scholarships Division
1500 Valley River Drive, Suite 100
Eugene, OR 97401-2146

Tel: (541)687-7395

Free: 800-452-8807

Fax: (541)687-7419

E-mail: awardinfo@mercury.osac.state.or.us

Web Site: http://www.osac.state.or.us

To provide financial assistance for college to residents of Oregon who are or were in foster care or related programs.

Title of Award: Children, Adult, and Family Services Scholarship **Area, Field, or Subject:** General studies/Field of study not specified **Level of Education for which Award is Granted:** Undergraduate **Number Awarded:** Varies each year. **Funds Available:** Stipends range from $500 to $5,000. **Duration:** 1 year.

Eligibility Requirements: This program is open to residents of Oregon who are either 1) graduating high school seniors currently in foster care or participating in the Independent Living Program (ILP); and 2) GED recipients and continuing college students formerly in foster care. Applicants must be attending or planning to attend a public college or university in Oregon. **Deadline for Receipt:** February of each year. **Additional Information:** Information on this scholarship is also available from Children, Adult, and Family Services.

1388 ■ OREGON STUDENT ASSISTANCE COMMISSION

Attn: Grants and Scholarships Division

1500 Valley River Drive, Suite 100

Eugene, OR 97401-2146

Tel: (541)687-7395

Free: 800-452-8807

Fax: (541)687-7419

E-mail: awardinfo@mercury.osac.state.or.us

Web Site: http://www.osac.state.or.us

To provide financial assistance for college to children and grandchildren of solid waste company members in Oregon.

Title of Award: Roger W. Emmons Memorial Scholarship **Area, Field, or Subject:** General studies/Field of study not specified **Level of Education for which Award is Granted:** Undergraduate **Number Awarded:** Varies each year; recently, 3 of these scholarships were awarded. **Funds Available:** The stipend is at least $1,000. **Duration:** 1 year; may be renewed.

Eligibility Requirements: This program is open to seniors graduating from high schools in Oregon who are planning to attend college. Applicants must be children or grandchildren of solid waste company members, or children or grandchildren of employees (for at least 3 years) of members of Oregon Refuse and Recycling Association. **Deadline for Receipt:** February of each year. **Additional Information:** This program is administered by the Oregon Student Assistance Commission (OSAC) with funds provided by the Oregon Community Foundation, 1221 S.W. Yamhill, Suite 100, Portland, OR 97205, (503) 227-6846, Fax: (503) 274-7771.

1389 ■ OREGON STUDENT ASSISTANCE COMMISSION

Attn: Ford Family Foundation Scholarship Office

1700 Valley River Drive, Suite 400

Eugene, OR 97401

Tel: (541)485-6211; 877-864-2872

E-mail: fordscholarships@tfff.org

Web Site: http://www.osac.state.or.us/ford_opportunity.html

To provide financial assistance to Oregon residents who are single parents working on a college degree.

Title of Award: Ford Opportunity Program Scholarship **Area, Field, or Subject:** General studies/Field of study not specified **Level of Education for which Award is Granted:** Four Year College **Number Awarded:** 50 each year. **Funds Available:** This program provides up to 90% of a recipient's unmet financial need; recently, stipends averaged $11,261. **Duration:** 1 year; may be renewed for up to 3 additional years.

Eligibility Requirements: This program is open to residents of Oregon who are U.S. citizens or permanent residents. Applicants must be single heads of household with custody of a dependent child or children. They must have a cumulative high school or college GPA of 3.0 or higher or a GED score of 2650 or higher, and they must be planning to earn a 4-year degree at an Oregon college. Selection is based on community service, work ethic, personal initiative, and financial need. **Deadline for Receipt:**

February of each year. **Additional Information:** This program, funded by the Ford Family Foundation, began in 1996.

1390 ■ OREGON STUDENT ASSISTANCE COMMISSION

Attn: Ford Family Foundation Scholarship Office

1700 Valley River Drive, Suite 400

Eugene, OR 97401

Tel: (541)485-6211; 877-864-2872

E-mail: fordscholarships@tfff.org

Web Site: http://www.osac.state.or.us/ford_restart.html

To provide financial assistance to residents of Oregon and northern California who wish to return to college to earn a degree.

Title of Award: Ford ReStart Program Scholarship **Area, Field, or Subject:** General studies/Field of study not specified **Level of Education for which Award is Granted:** Undergraduate **Number Awarded:** 30 each year. **Funds Available:** This program provides up to 90% of a recipient's unmet financial need; recently, stipends averaged $7,781. **Duration:** 1 year; may be renewed for up to 3 additional years.

Eligibility Requirements: This program is open to residents of Oregon and Siskiyou County, California who are 25 years of age or older, have a high school diploma or GED, and wish to pursue a technical school, community college, or 4-year degree in the state. Holders of existing baccalaureate degrees are not eligible. There are no minimum high school or college GPA requirements. Preference is given to applicants with less than 1 year of college experience. Students from Oregon must attend a college or university in the state; students from Siskiyou County, California must attend a college or university in California. Selection is based on community service, work ethic, personal initiative, and financial need. **Deadline for Receipt:** February of each year. **Additional Information:** This program, funded by the Ford Family Foundation, began in 2001.

1391 ■ OREGON STUDENT ASSISTANCE COMMISSION

Attn: Ford Family Foundation Scholarship Office

1700 Valley River Drive, Suite 400

Eugene, OR 97401

Tel: (541)485-6211; 877-864-2872

E-mail: fordscholarships@tfff.org

Web Site: http://www.osac.state.or.us/ford_scholars.html

To provide financial assistance to residents of Oregon and Siskiyou County, California who are seeking a college degree.

Title of Award: Ford Scholars Program **Area, Field, or Subject:** General studies/Field of study not specified **Level of Education for which Award is Granted:** Four Year College **Number Awarded:** 100 each year from Oregon plus others from Siskiyou County, California. **Funds Available:** This program provides up to 90% of a recipient's unmet financial need; recently, stipends averaged $5,836. **Duration:** 1 year; may be renewed for up to 3 additional years.

Eligibility Requirements: This program is open to U.S. citizens and permanent residents who are residents of Oregon or of Siskiyou County, California. Applicants must be 1) graduating high school seniors; 2) high school graduates who have not yet been full-time undergraduates; or 3) students who have completed 2 years at a community college and are entering their junior year at a 4-year college. They must have a cumulative high school or college GPA of 3.0 or higher or a GED score of 2650 or higher, and they must be planning to complete a 4-year degree. Students from Oregon must attend a college or university in the state; students from Siskiyou County, California must attend a college or university in California. Selection is based on community service, work ethic, personal initiative, and financial need. **Deadline for Receipt:** February of each year. **Additional Information:** This program, funded by the Ford Family Foundation, began in 1994.

1392 ■ OREGON STUDENT ASSISTANCE COMMISSION

Attn: Grants and Scholarships Division

1500 Valley River Drive, Suite 100

Eugene, OR 97401-2146

Tel: (541)687-7395

Free: 800-452-8807

Fax: (541)687-7419

E-mail: awardinfo@mercury.osac.state.or.us

Web Site: http://www.osac.state.or.us

To provide financial assistance for college to graduating high school seniors in Oregon.

Title of Award: Benjamin Franklin/Edith Green Scholarship **Area, Field, or Subject:** General studies/Field of study not specified **Level of Education for which Award is Granted:** Four Year College **Number Awarded:** Varies each year; recently, 14 of these scholarships were awarded. **Funds Available:** Stipends are at least $1,000. **Duration:** 1 year; nonrenewable.

Eligibility Requirements: This program is open to seniors graduating from high schools in Oregon. Applicants must be planning to attend a 4-year college or university in the state. **Deadline for Receipt:** February of each year. **Additional Information:** This program is administered by the Oregon Student Assistance Commission (OSAC) with funds provided by the Oregon Community Foundation, 1221 S.W. Yamhill, Suite 100, Portland, OR 97205, (503) 227-6846, Fax: (503) 274-7771.

1393 ■ OREGON STUDENT ASSISTANCE COMMISSION

Attn: Grants and Scholarships Division
1500 Valley River Drive, Suite 100
Eugene, OR 97401-2146
Tel: (541)687-7395
Free: 800-452-8807
Fax: (541)687-7419
E-mail: awardinfo@mercury.osac.state.or.us
Web Site: http://www.osac.state.or.us
To provide financial assistance for college to children of employees of specified state agencies in Oregon.

Title of Award: Glen Jackson Scholars Program **Area, Field, or Subject:** General studies/Field of study not specified **Level of Education for which Award is Granted:** Undergraduate **Number Awarded:** Varies each year; recently, 2 of these scholarships were awarded. **Funds Available:** The stipend is at least $2,500. **Duration:** 1 year; may be renewed.

Eligibility Requirements: This program is open to seniors graduating from Oregon high schools. Applicants must be the dependents of employees or retirees of the Oregon Department of Transportation or the Parks and Recreation Department. The qualifying parent must have been employed by the department for at least 3 years. Along with their application, students must submit 2 essays (1 page each) on "How do you plan to finance your college education?" and "If you could have a personal meeting with the governor of Oregon, what would you talk about and why?" **Deadline for Receipt:** February of each year. **Additional Information:** This program is administered by the Oregon Student Assistance Commission (OSAC) with funds provided by the Oregon Community Foundation, 1221 S.W. Yamhill, Suite 100, Portland, OR 97205, (503) 227-6846, Fax: (503) 274-7771.

1394 ■ OREGON STUDENT ASSISTANCE COMMISSION

Attn: Grants and Scholarships Division
1500 Valley River Drive, Suite 100
Eugene, OR 97401-2146
Tel: (541)687-7395
Free: 800-452-8807
Fax: (541)687-7419
E-mail: awardinfo@mercury.osac.state.or.us
Web Site: http://www.osac.state.or.us
To provide financial assistance for college to residents of Oregon who are visually impaired.

Title of Award: Harry Ludwig Memorial Scholarship **Area, Field, or Subject:** General studies/Field of study not specified **Level of Education for which Award is Granted:** Graduate, Undergraduate **Number Awarded:** Varies each year; recently, 7 of these scholarships were awarded. **Funds Available:** Stipend amounts vary; recently, they were at least $1,643. **Duration:** 1 year.

Eligibility Requirements: This program is open to residents of Oregon who are visually impaired (have residual acuity of 20/70 or less in the better eye with correction, or their visual field is restricted to 20 degrees or less in the better eye). Applicants must be enrolled or planning to enroll as full-time undergraduate or graduate students at a college or university in Oregon. **Deadline for Receipt:** February of each year. **Additional Information:** This program is administered by the Oregon Student Assistance Commission (OSAC) with funds provided by the Oregon Com-

munity Foundation, 1221 S.W. Yamhill, Suite 100, Portland, OR 97205, (503) 227-6846, Fax: (503) 274-7771.

1395 ■ OREGON STUDENT ASSISTANCE COMMISSION

Attn: Grants and Scholarships Division
1500 Valley River Drive, Suite 100
Eugene, OR 97401-2146
Tel: (541)687-7395
Free: 800-452-8807
Fax: (541)687-7419
E-mail: awardinfo@mercury.osac.state.or.us
Web Site: http://www.osac.state.or.us
To provide financial assistance for college to dependents of members of the Multnoham County Deputy Sheriffs Association in Oregon.

Title of Award: Multnomah County Deputy Sheriffs Association Dependents Scholarship **Area, Field, or Subject:** General studies/Field of study not specified **Level of Education for which Award is Granted:** Undergraduate **Number Awarded:** 1 or more each year. **Funds Available:** A stipend is awarded (amount not specified). **Duration:** 1 year.

Eligibility Requirements: This program is open to the natural, adopted, or stepchildren of active or deceased members of the association. Applicants must be attending or planning to attend a college or university. **Deadline for Receipt:** February of each year.

1396 ■ OREGON STUDENT ASSISTANCE COMMISSION

Attn: Grants and Scholarships Division
1500 Valley River Drive, Suite 100
Eugene, OR 97401-2146
Tel: (541)687-7395
Free: 800-452-8807
Fax: (541)687-7419
E-mail: awardinfo@mercury.osac.state.or.us
Web Site: http://www.osac.state.or.us
To provide financial assistance for college to graduating high school seniors in Oregon who submit an essay on a labor-related topic.

Title of Award: Oregon AFL-CIO Scholarships **Area, Field, or Subject:** General studies/Field of study not specified **Level of Education for which Award is Granted:** Undergraduate **Number Awarded:** 4 each year. **Funds Available:** The stipends are $3,000, $1,200, $1,000, or $850. **Duration:** 1 year; nonrenewable.

Eligibility Requirements: This program is open to seniors graduating from high schools in Oregon who submit an essay of 500 words or less on either 1) their own experience as an employee and why it leads them to believe that workers do (or do not) need a union on the job; or 2) why many people who work full time cannot provide a decent standard of living for their families and what they believe should be done about it. Selection is based on the essay, financial need, GPA, and an interview by a panel of individuals with expertise in labor history and labor affairs. Preference is given to applicants from union families. **Deadline for Receipt:** February of each year. **Additional Information:** The award can be used at an accredited college or university in the United States, at any public community college in Oregon, or at any established trade school. The $3,000 and $1,000 scholarships are designated the May Darling Scholarships, the $1,200 scholarship is designated the Asa T. Williams Scholarship, and the $850 scholarship is designated the Northwest Labor Press Scholarship. This program is sponsored by the Oregon AFL-CIO, 2110 State Street, Salem, OR 97301, (503) 585-6320, Fax: (503) 585-1668.

1397 ■ OREGON STUDENT ASSISTANCE COMMISSION

Attn: Grants and Scholarships Division
1500 Valley River Drive, Suite 100
Eugene, OR 97401-2146
Tel: (541)687-7394
Free: 800-452-8807
Fax: (541)687-7414
E-mail: awardinfo@mercury.osac.state.or.us
Web Site: http://www.osac.state.or.us/chafeeetv.html
To provide financial assistance for college to Oregon residents who are or have been in foster care.

Title of Award: Oregon Chafee Education and Training Scholarships **Area, Field, or Subject:** General studies/Field of study not specified **Level of Education for which Award is Granted:** Undergraduate **Number Awarded:** 1 or more each year. **Funds Available:** The stipend is $5,000. **Duration:** 1 year; may be renewed until recipient reaches 23 years of age.

Eligibility Requirements: This program is open to residents of Oregon who either currently are in foster care or have been in foster care for at least 180 days after their 14th birthday. Foster care placement must have been with Oregon's Department of Human Services or 1 of the 9 federally-recognized tribes in the state. Applicants must be younger than 21 years of age. Along with their application, they must submit essays of 250 to 350 words on 1) their most significant challenge or accomplishment and its value to their life, and 2) their long-range goals and why they need to achieve them. **Deadline for Receipt:** February of each year. **Additional Information:** Information is also available from the Department of Human Services, Attn: Children, Adults, and Families, Independent Living Program, 500 Sumner Street N.E., E76, Salem, OR 97301.

1398 ■ OREGON STUDENT ASSISTANCE COMMISSION

Attn: Grants and Scholarships Division
1500 Valley River Drive, Suite 100
Eugene, OR 97401-2130
Tel: (541)687-7466
Free: 800-452-8807
Fax: (541)687-7419
E-mail: awardinfo@mercury.osac.state.or.us
Web Site: http://www.ossc.state.or.us/grants.html
To provide financial assistance for college to the children of disabled or deceased Oregon peace officers.
Title of Award: Oregon Deceased or Disabled Public Safety Officer Grant Program **Area, Field, or Subject:** General studies/Field of study not specified **Level of Education for which Award is Granted:** Graduate, Undergraduate **Number Awarded:** Varies each year. **Funds Available:** At a public 2- or 4-year college or university, the amount of the award is equal to the cost of tuition and fees. At an eligible private college, the award amount is equal to the cost of tuition and fees at the University of Oregon. **Duration:** 1 year; may be renewed for up to 3 additional years of undergraduate study, if the student maintains satisfactory academic progress and demonstrates continued financial need. Children of deceased public safety officers may receive support for 12 quarters of graduate study.
Eligibility Requirements: This program is open to the natural, adopted, or stepchildren of Oregon public safety officers (fire fighters, state fire marshal, chief deputy fire marshal, deputy state fire marshals, police chiefs, police officers, sheriffs, deputy sheriffs, county adult parole and probation officers, correction officers, and investigators of the Criminal Justice Division of the Department of Justice) who, in the line of duty, were killed or disabled. Applicants must be enrolled or planning to enroll as a full-time undergraduate student at a public or private college or university in Oregon. Children of deceased officers are also eligible for graduate study. Financial need must be demonstrated.

1399 ■ OREGON STUDENT ASSISTANCE COMMISSION

Attn: Grants and Scholarships Division
1500 Valley River Drive, Suite 100
Eugene, OR 97401-2146
Tel: (541)687-7395
Free: 800-452-8807
Fax: (541)687-7419
E-mail: awardinfo@mercury.osac.state.or.us
Web Site: http://www.osac.state.or.us
To provide financial assistance for undergraduate or graduate education to the children and spouses of disabled or deceased workers in Oregon.
Title of Award: Oregon Occupational Safety and Health Division Workers Memorial Scholarships **Area, Field, or Subject:** General studies/Field of study not specified **Level of Education for which Award is Granted:** Graduate, Undergraduate **Number Awarded:** 1 or more each year. **Funds Available:** Stipend amounts vary; recently, they were at least $4,786 **Duration:** 1 year.
Eligibility Requirements: This program is open to residents of Oregon who are U.S. citizens or permanent residents. Applicants must be high school seniors or graduates who 1) are dependents or spouses of an Oregon worker who has suffered permanent total disability on the job; or 2) are receiving, or have received, fatality benefits as dependents or spouses of a worker fatally injured in Oregon. Selection is based on financial need and an essay of up to 500 words on "How has the injury or death of your parent or spouse affected or influenced your decision to further your education?" **Deadline for Receipt:** February of each year.

1400 ■ OREGON STUDENT ASSISTANCE COMMISSION

1500 Valley River Drive, Suite 100
Eugene, OR 97401-2130
Tel: (541)687-7400
Free: 800-452-8807
Fax: (541)687-7419
E-mail: awardinfo@mercury.osac.state.or.us
Web Site: http://www.ossc.state.or.us/ong_2.html
To provide financial assistance for college to residents of Oregon who have financial need.
Title of Award: Oregon Opportunity Grants **Area, Field, or Subject:** General studies/Field of study not specified **Level of Education for which Award is Granted:** Undergraduate **Number Awarded:** Varies each year; recently, more than 30,000 of these grants were awarded. **Funds Available:** Awards depend on the need of the recipient. At public schools, the maximum annual award is $1,323 at a community college, $1,587 at an institution within the Oregon University system, or $2,121 at Oregon Health and Sciences University. Specific award amounts are established for each eligible private college or university within Oregon, ranging from $2,410 at Mount Angel Seminary to $4,432 at Reed College. Contact the sponsor for the amount of the supplemental awards available at other private institutions. **Duration:** 1 year; may be renewed for up to 3 additional years, if the student maintains satisfactory academic progress and demonstrates continued financial need.
Eligibility Requirements: This program is open to residents of Oregon who are attending or planning to attend a nonprofit college or university in Oregon as a full-time student. Applicants must have an annual family income below specified levels; for dependent students, the maximum family income ranges from $20,960 for a household size of 2 to $43,460 for a household size of 9; for independent students, the maximum family income ranges from $8,740 for a household size of 1 to $38,660 for a household size of 8. Students who are working on a degree in theology, divinity, or religious education are not eligible. **Additional Information:** This program was formerly known as Oregon Need Grants.

1401 ■ OREGON STUDENT ASSISTANCE COMMISSION

Attn: Grants and Scholarships Division
1500 Valley River Drive, Suite 100
Eugene, OR 97401-2146
Tel: (541)687-7395
Free: 800-452-8807
Fax: (541)687-7419
E-mail: awardinfo@mercury.osac.state.or.us
Web Site: http://www.osac.state.or.us
To provide financial assistance for college or graduate school to ex-prisoners of war and their descendants.
Title of Award: Peter Connacher Memorial Trust Fund **Area, Field, or Subject:** General studies/Field of study not specified **Level of Education for which Award is Granted:** Graduate, Undergraduate **Number Awarded:** Varies each year; recently, 4 of these scholarships were awarded. **Funds Available:** The stipend amount varies; recently, it was at least $1,150. **Duration:** 1 year; may be renewed for up to 3 additional years for undergraduate students or 2 additional years for graduate students. Renewal is dependent on evidence of continued financial need and satisfactory academic progress.
Eligibility Requirements: Applicants must be American citizens who 1) were military or civilian prisoners of war or 2) are the descendants of ex-prisoners of war. They may be undergraduate or graduate students. A copy of the ex-prisoner of war's discharge papers from the U.S. armed forces must accompany the application. In addition, written proof of POW status must be submitted, along with a statement of the relationship between the applicant and the ex-prisoner of war (father, grandfather, etc.). Selection is based on academic record and financial need. Preference is given to Oregon residents or their dependents. **Deadline for Receipt:** February of each year. **Additional Information:** This program is administered by the Oregon Student Assistance Commission (OSAC) with funds provided by the Oregon Community Foundation, 1221 S.W. Yamhill, Suite 100, Portland, OR 97205, (503) 227-6846, Fax: (503) 274-7771.

Funds are also provided by the Columbia River Chapter of the American Ex-prisoners of War, Inc. Recipients must attend college on a full-time basis.

1402 ■ OREGON STUDENT ASSISTANCE COMMISSION
Attn: Grants and Scholarships Division
1500 Valley River Drive, Suite 100
Eugene, OR 97401-2146
Tel: (541)687-7395
Free: 800-452-8807
Fax: (541)687-7419
E-mail: awardinfo@mercury.osac.state.or.us
Web Site: http://www.osac.state.or.us
To provide financial assistance to college students who graduated from a high school in Oregon.
Title of Award: Portland Women's Club Scholarship **Area, Field, or Subject:** General studies/Field of study not specified **Level of Education for which Award is Granted:** Undergraduate **Number Awarded:** Varies each year; recently, 5 of these scholarships were awarded. **Funds Available:** The stipend is at least $1,500 per year. **Duration:** 1 year; may be renewed if the recipient shows satisfactory academic progress and continued financial need.
Eligibility Requirements: This program is open to graduates of high schools in Oregon who had a cumulative high school GPA of 3.0 or higher. Preference is given to women. **Deadline for Receipt:** February of each year.

1403 ■ OREGON STUDENT ASSISTANCE COMMISSION
Attn: Grants and Scholarships Division
1500 Valley River Drive, Suite 100
Eugene, OR 97401-2146
Tel: (541)687-7395
Free: 800-452-8807
Fax: (541)687-7419
E-mail: awardinfo@mercury.osac.state.or.us
Web Site: http://www.osac.state.or.us
To provide financial assistance for college to dependents of members of Professional Land Surveyors of Oregon (PLSO).
Title of Award: Professional Land Surveyors of Oregon Dependents Scholarship **Area, Field, or Subject:** General studies/Field of study not specified **Level of Education for which Award is Granted:** Undergraduate **Number Awarded:** 1 or more each year. **Funds Available:** A stipend is awarded (amount not specified). **Duration:** 1 year.
Eligibility Requirements: This program is open to dependents of PLSO members who are enrolled or planning to enroll at a college or university in Oregon. Applicants must be preparing for a career in a field other than land surveying. Along with their application, they must submit a brief essay on what led them to prepare for a career outside the field of land surveying. **Deadline for Receipt:** February of each year. **Additional Information:** This program is administered by the Oregon Student Assistance Commission (OSAC) with funds provided by the Oregon Community Foundation, 1221 S.W. Yamhill, Suite 100, Portland, OR 97205, (503) 227-6846, Fax: (503) 274-7771.

1404 ■ OREGON STUDENT ASSISTANCE COMMISSION
Attn: Grants and Scholarships Division
1500 Valley River Drive, Suite 100
Eugene, OR 97401-2146
Tel: (541)687-7395
Free: 800-452-8807
Fax: (541)687-7419
E-mail: awardinfo@mercury.osac.state.or.us
Web Site: http://www.osac.state.or.us
To provide financial assistance to students in Oregon interested in a career in land surveying.
Title of Award: Professional Land Surveyors of Oregon Scholarship **Area, Field, or Subject:** Cartography/Surveying **Level of Education for which Award is Granted:** Undergraduate **Number Awarded:** Varies each year; recently, 5 of these scholarships were awarded. **Funds Available:** The stipend is at least $1,600 per year. **Duration:** 1 year.
Eligibility Requirements: This program is open to students at colleges and universities in Oregon. Applicants must be enrolled in a program leading to a career as a land surveyor, including community college applicants

who intend to transfer to eligible 4-year schools or complete a degree in land surveying at the community college level. They must intend to take the Fundamentals of Land Surveying (FLS) examination. Along with their application, they must submit a brief essay on what led them to prepare for a land surveying career and what surveying means to them. **Deadline for Receipt:** February of each year. **Additional Information:** This program is administered by the Oregon Student Assistance Commission (OSAC) with funds provided by the Oregon Community Foundation, 1221 S.W. Yamhill, Suite 100, Portland, OR 97205, (503) 227-6846, Fax: (503) 274-7771.

1405 ■ OREGON STUDENT ASSISTANCE COMMISSION
Attn: Grants and Scholarships Division
1500 Valley River Drive, Suite 100
Eugene, OR 97401-2146
Tel: (541)687-7395
Free: 800-452-8807
Fax: (541)687-7419
E-mail: awardinfo@mercury.osac.state.or.us
Web Site: http://www.osac.state.or.us
To provide financial assistance for college to children of elected state officials in Oregon.
Title of Award: Friends of Bill Rutherford Scholarship **Area, Field, or Subject:** General studies/Field of study not specified **Level of Education for which Award is Granted:** Undergraduate **Number Awarded:** 1 or more each year. **Funds Available:** A stipend is awarded (amount not specified). **Duration:** 1 year.
Eligibility Requirements: This program is open to graduates of Oregon high schools (including home schooled graduates and GED recipients) attending or planning to attend college. Applicants must be dependent children of individuals holding statewide elected office (Governor, Secretary of State, Treasurer, Commissioner of Labor, Superintendent of Public Instruction, or Attorney General) or currently serving in the Oregon State Legislature. **Deadline for Receipt:** February of each year. **Additional Information:** This program is administered by the Oregon Student Assistance Commission (OSAC) with funds provided by the Oregon Community Foundation, 1221 S.W. Yamhill, Suite 100, Portland, OR 97205, (503) 227-6846, Fax: (503) 274-7771.

1406 ■ OREGON STUDENT ASSISTANCE COMMISSION
Attn: Grants and Scholarships Division
1500 Valley River Drive, Suite 100
Eugene, OR 97401-2146
Tel: (541)687-7395
Free: 800-452-8807
Fax: (541)687-7419
E-mail: awardinfo@mercury.osac.state.or.us
Web Site: http://www.osac.state.or.us
To provide financial assistance for college to residents of Oregon.
Title of Award: Ben Selling Scholarship **Area, Field, or Subject:** General studies/Field of study not specified **Level of Education for which Award is Granted:** Undergraduate **Number Awarded:** Varies each year; recently, 25 of these scholarships were awarded. **Funds Available:** Stipends are least $1,000. **Duration:** 1 year.
Eligibility Requirements: This program is open to residents of Oregon who are entering their sophomore or higher years in college. Applicants must have a cumulative GPA of 3.5 or higher. **Deadline for Receipt:** February of each year.

1407 ■ ORGANIZATION OF CHINESE AMERICANS, INC.
1001 Connecticut Avenue, N.W., Suite 601
Washington, DC 20036
Tel: (202)223-5500
Fax: (202)296-0540
E-mail: oca@ocanatl.org
Web Site: http://www.ocanatl.org
To provide financial assistance to Asian Pacific American women entering their first year at a 2-year or 4-year college.
Title of Award: OCA/Avon Scholarships **Area, Field, or Subject:** General studies/Field of study not specified **Level of Education for which Award is Granted:** Undergraduate **Number Awarded:** 15 each year. **Funds Available:** The stipend is $2,000. **Duration:** 1 year.
Eligibility Requirements: This program is open to Asian Pacific American women (including east Asian Americans, Filipino Americans,

Pacific Islander Americans, south Asian Americans, and southeast Asian Americans) who are entering their first year of college. Applicants must be U.S. citizens or permanent residents who have earned a GPA of 3.0 or higher in high school. Selection is based on academic achievement, community service, and financial need. **Deadline for Receipt:** April of each year. **Additional Information:** This program, established in 1995, is administered by the Organization of Chinese Americans (OCA), Inc. and funded by the Avon Foundation. Recipients must write a paper by the end of their freshman year describing their college experience as an Asian Pacific American woman.

1408 ■ ORGANIZATION OF CHINESE AMERICANS, INC.

1001 Connecticut Avenue, N.W., Suite 601
Washington, DC 20036
Tel: (202)223-5500
Fax: (202)296-0540
E-mail: oca@ocanatl.org
Web Site: http://www.ocanatl.org
To provide financial assistance for college to Asian Pacific Americans who are entering their first year of college and can demonstrate academic merit.
Title of Award: OCA/AXA Achievement Scholarships **Area, Field, or Subject:** General studies/Field of study not specified **Level of Education for which Award is Granted:** Undergraduate **Number Awarded:** 6 each year. **Funds Available:** The stipend is $2,000. **Duration:** 1 year.
Eligibility Requirements: This program is open to Asian Pacific American students entering their first year of college, university, or community college in the following fall. Applicants must be able to demonstrate academic achievement, leadership ability, and community service. They must have a cumulative GPA of 3.0 or higher and be a U.S. citizen or permanent resident. **Deadline for Receipt:** April of each year. **Additional Information:** This program, established in 2004, is funded by the AXA Foundation and administered by the Organization of Chinese Americans (OCA). Asian Pacific Americans are defined to include east Asian Americans, Filipino Americans, Pacific Islander Americans, south Asian Americans, and southeast Asian Americans.

1409 ■ ORGANIZATION OF CHINESE AMERICANS, INC.

1001 Connecticut Avenue, N.W., Suite 601
Washington, DC 20036
Tel: (202)223-5500
Fax: (202)296-0540
E-mail: oca@ocanatl.org
Web Site: http://www.ocanatl.org
To provide financial assistance for college to Asian Pacific Americans who are entering their first year of college and can demonstrate financial need.
Title of Award: OCA/SYSCO Scholarships **Area, Field, or Subject:** General studies/Field of study not specified **Level of Education for which Award is Granted:** Undergraduate **Number Awarded:** 6 each year. **Funds Available:** The stipend is $2,000. **Duration:** 1 year.
Eligibility Requirements: This program is open to Asian Pacific American students entering their first year of college, university, or community college in the following fall. Applicants must be able to demonstrate financial need, have a cumulative GPA of 3.0 or higher, and be a U.S. citizen or permanent resident. **Deadline for Receipt:** April of each year. **Additional Information:** This program, established in 2004, is funded by SYSCO Corporation and administered by the Organization of Chinese Americans (OCA). Asian Pacific Americans are defined to include east Asian Americans, Filipino Americans, Pacific Islander Americans, south Asian Americans, and southeast Asian Americans.

1410 ■ ORGANIZATION OF CHINESE AMERICANS, INC.

1001 Connecticut Avenue, N.W., Suite 601
Washington, DC 20036
Tel: (202)223-5500
Fax: (202)296-0540
E-mail: oca@ocanatl.org
Web Site: http://www.ocanatl.org
To provide financial assistance for college to Asian Pacific Americans who are entering their first year of college and have significant financial need.
Title of Award: OCA/Verizon Scholarships **Area, Field, or Subject:** General studies/Field of study not specified **Level of Education for which Award is Granted:** Undergraduate **Number Awarded:** 25 each year. **Funds Available:** The stipend is $2,000. **Duration:** 1 year.

Eligibility Requirements: This program is open to Asian Pacific American students entering their first year of college, university, or community college in the following fall. Applicants must be able to demonstrate significant financial need, have a cumulative GPA of 3.0 or higher, and be a U.S. citizen or permanent resident. **Deadline for Receipt:** April of each year. **Additional Information:** This program, established in 2002, is funded by the Verizon Foundation and administered by the Organization of Chinese Americans (OCA). Asian Pacific Americans are defined to include east Asian Americans, Filipino Americans, Pacific Islander Americans, south Asian Americans, and southeast Asian Americans.

1411 ■ ORGANIZATION OF CHINESE AMERICANS, INC.

1001 Connecticut Avenue, N.W., Suite 601
Washington, DC 20036
Tel: (202)223-5500
Fax: (202)296-0540
E-mail: oca@ocanatl.org
Web Site: http://www.ocanatl.org
To provide financial assistance for college to Asian Pacific Americans who are the first person in their family to attend an institution of higher education.
Title of Award: UPS Gold Mountain Scholarship **Area, Field, or Subject:** General studies/Field of study not specified **Level of Education for which Award is Granted:** Undergraduate **Number Awarded:** 12 each year. **Funds Available:** The stipend is $2,000. **Duration:** 1 year.
Eligibility Requirements: This program is open to Asian Pacific American students entering their first year of college in the following fall. Applicants must be the first person in their immediate family to attend college, have a cumulative GPA of 3.0 or higher, be in financial need, and be a U.S. citizen or permanent resident. **Deadline for Receipt:** April of each year. **Additional Information:** This program is funded by the UPS Foundation and administered by the Organization of Chinese Americans (OCA). Asian Pacific Americans are defined to include east Asian Americans, Filipino Americans, Pacific Islander Americans, south Asian Americans, and southeast Asian Americans.

1412 ■ ORPHAN FOUNDATION OF AMERICA

Attn: Director of Student Services
Tall Oaks Village Center
12020-D North Shore Drive
Reston, VA 20190-4977
Tel: (571)203-0270
Free: 800-950-4673
Fax: (571)203-0273
E-mail: scholarships@orphan.org
Web Site: http://www.orphan.org
To recognize and reward minority male students who have been in foster care and are completing a vocational or undergraduate degree.
Title of Award: Casey Family Scholarships for Male Students of Color **Area, Field, or Subject:** General studies/Field of study not specified **Level of Education for which Award is Granted:** Undergraduate **Number Awarded:** Awards are presented until funds are exhausted. **Funds Available:** Awards range up to $5,000. **Duration:** These are 1-time awards.
Eligibility Requirements: This program is open to male minority students enrolled in their final year of a vocational program or their senior year of an undergraduate program. Applicants must have aged out of the U.S. foster care system. Along with their application, they must submit 1) verification of their foster care status; 2) documentation of their total outstanding federal loan amount; 3) documentation from their school regarding any outstanding tuition balance they currently owe; and 4) a 5-paragraph essay explaining the single most important thing their postsecondary education has taught them and how they will take that lesson and apply it to their professional and personal life to help ensure their future success. Selection is based on financial need and merit, as commendation for ambition and tenacity in pursuing a higher education. **Additional Information:** This program was established in 2004 by Casey Family Programs.

1413 ■ ORPHAN FOUNDATION OF AMERICA

Attn: Executive Director
Tall Oaks Village Center
12020-D North Shore Drive
Reston, VA 20190-4977

Tel: (571)203-0270
Free: 800-950-4673
Fax: (571)203-0273
E-mail: eileenm@orphan.org
Web Site: http://www.orphan.org
To provide financial assistance for college to students who have been in foster care.

Title of Award: Chafee Education and Training Vouchers Program **Area, Field, or Subject:** General studies/Field of study not specified **Level of Education for which Award is Granted:** Undergraduate **Number Awarded:** Varies; approximately $42 million is available nation-wide to this program each year. **Funds Available:** Stipends range up to $5,000. **Duration:** 1 year; may be renewed up to 3 additional years.
Eligibility Requirements: This program is open to U.S. citizens and permanent residents who are in foster care or were in foster care as a teenager. Applicants must have aged out of the foster care system at age 18 or were adopted from foster care with adoption finalization after their 16th birthday. They must have been accepted to or be enrolled in a degree, certificate, or other program at a college, university, technical school, or vocational school and be able to show progress toward that degree or certificate. Other eligibility requirements vary from state to state.
Additional Information: This program was established by Congress in 2002 and assigned to the U.S. Department of Health and Human Services. Funds are provided to states, each of which has designated an agency to administer the program in that state. The Orphan Foundation of America (OFA) administers the program in Alabama, Arkansas, Colorado, Indiana, North Carolina, and Ohio. For the name and address of the administrative agency in other states, check with OFA or consult its special web site, www.statevoucher.org.

1414 ■ ORPHAN FOUNDATION OF AMERICA

Attn: Director of Student Services
Tall Oaks Village Center
12020-D North Shore Drive
Reston, VA 20190-4977
Tel: (571)203-0270
Free: 800-950-4673
Fax: (571)203-0273
E-mail: scholarships@orphan.org
Web Site: http://www.orphan.org
To provide financial assistance for college to students currently or previously in foster care.

Title of Award: Hildegard Lash Merit Scholarship **Area, Field, or Subject:** General studies/Field of study not specified **Level of Education for which Award is Granted:** Four Year College **Number Awarded:** 1 each year. **Funds Available:** The stipend is $5,000. Half the funds are paid at the beginning of the first semester and the other half at the beginning of the second semester if the recipient maintains a full-time course load and a GPA of 3.2 or higher. **Duration:** 1 year; nonrenewable.
Eligibility Requirements: This program is open to students who are entering their sophomore, junior, or senior year as a full-time student at a 4-year college or university. Applicants must have been in foster care or a ward of the court for at least 1 year at the time of their 18th birthday and currently be under 25 years of age. They must submit a 2- to 3-page essay on their goals for school, career, and personal fulfillment. Selection is based on the essay, 2 letters of recommendation, academic record, extracurricular involvement, and other personal achievements. Finalists are interviewed by telephone. **Deadline for Receipt:** Applicants must first register online by the end of March of each year. **Additional Information:** This program was established in 1997 with funds from the Hildegard Lash Foundation. Mrs. Lash had died penniless in 1987 as a victim of financial abuse by a trusted fiduciary. When the foundation recovered the embezzled funds, it established this program.

1415 ■ ORPHAN FOUNDATION OF AMERICA

Attn: Director of Student Services
Tall Oaks Village Center
12020-D North Shore Drive
Reston, VA 20190-4977
Tel: (571)203-0270
Free: 800-950-4673
Fax: (571)203-0273
E-mail: scholarships@orphan.org

Web Site: http://www.orphan.org
To provide financial assistance for college to students currently or previously in foster care.

Title of Award: Orphan Foundation of America Scholarships **Area, Field, or Subject:** General studies/Field of study not specified **Level of Education for which Award is Granted:** Undergraduate **Number Awarded:** Varies each year. Recently, Casey Family Programs alone supported 122 new and 150 renewal scholarships. **Funds Available:** Stipends range up to $10,000 per year. Recently, the average was more than $4,000. **Duration:** 1 year; may be renewed if the recipient maintains a GPA of 2.0 or higher and financial need.
Eligibility Requirements: This program is open to students who are currently enrolled in or have applied to college or a postsecondary training program. Applicants must have been in foster care or a ward of the court for at least 1 year at the time of their 18th birthday and currently be under 25 years of age. They must submit a 2- to 3-page essay on their goals for school, career, and personal fulfillment. Selection is based on the essay, 2 letters of recommendation, transcripts, and financial need. **Deadline for Receipt:** Applicants must first register online by the end of March of each year. **Additional Information:** As part of this program, Casey Family Programs added its support in 2001.

1416 ■ OSAGE SCHOLARSHIP FUND

c/o Roman Catholic Diocese of Tulsa
P.O. Box 690240
Tulsa, OK 74169-0240
Tel: (918)294-1904
Fax: (918)294-0920
E-mail: sarah.jameson@dioceseoftulsa.org
Web Site: http://www.osagetribe.com
To provide financial assistance to Osage Indians who are Roman Catholics attending college or graduate school.

Title of Award: Mae Lasley/Osage Scholarships **Area, Field, or Subject:** General studies/Field of study not specified **Level of Education for which Award is Granted:** Graduate, Undergraduate **Number Awarded:** Normally, 10 each year: 2 for students attending St. Gregory's University in Shawnee, Oklahoma as freshmen and 8 for any college or university. **Funds Available:** The stipend is $1,000 per year. **Duration:** 1 year; may be renewed if the recipient maintains full-time enrollment and a GPA of 2.5 or higher as an undergraduate or 3.0 or higher as a graduate student.
Eligibility Requirements: This program is open to Roman Catholics who are attending or planning to attend a college or university as an undergraduate or graduate student. Applicants must be Osage Indians on the rolls in Pawhuska, Oklahoma and have of copy of their Certificate of Degree of Indian Blood or Osage Tribal membership card. Selection is based on academic ability and financial need. **Deadline for Receipt:** April of each year.

1417 ■ PACIFIC FLEET SUBMARINE MEMORIAL ASSOCIATION

c/o USS Bowfin Submarine Museum and Park
11 Arizona Memorial Drive
Honolulu, HI 96818
Tel: (808)423-1341
Fax: (808)422-5201
E-mail: info@bowfin.org
Web Site: http://www.bowfin.org
To provide financial assistance for college to the children of submarine force personnel who live in Hawaii.

Title of Award: Bowfin Memorial Academic Scholarships **Area, Field, or Subject:** General studies/Field of study not specified **Level of Education for which Award is Granted:** Undergraduate **Number Awarded:** Varies each year; recently, 11 of these scholarships were awarded. **Funds Available:** Stipends range from $500 to $2,500 per year. **Duration:** 1 year; may be renewed upon annual reapplication.
Eligibility Requirements: This program is open to the children of submarine force personnel (active duty, retired, or deceased) who are under 23 years of age. Applicants may attend school anywhere in the United States, but their submarine sponsor or surviving parent must live in Hawaii. Selection is based on scholastic proficiency, financial need, extracurricular activities, and demonstrated potential. **Deadline for Receipt:** February of each year. **Additional Information:** This program was established in 1985 to honor the 3,505 submariners and 52 submarines lost during World War II.

1418 ■ PACIFIC FLEET SUBMARINE MEMORIAL ASSOCIATION

c/o USS Bowfin Submarine Museum and Park
11 Arizona Memorial Drive
Honolulu, HI 96818
Tel: (808)423-1341
Fax: (808)422-5201
E-mail: info@bowfin.org
Web Site: http://www.bowfin.org
To provide financial assistance for continuing education to former or current Submarine Force personnel who live in Hawaii or their spouses.
Title of Award: Bowfin Memorial Continuing Education Scholarships **Area, Field, or Subject:** General studies/Field of study not specified **Level of Education for which Award is Granted:** Undergraduate **Number Awarded:** Varies each year; recently, 14 of these scholarships were awarded. **Funds Available:** Stipends range from $500 to $2,500 per year. **Duration:** 1 year; may be renewed upon annual reapplication.
Eligibility Requirements: This program is open to active-duty and retired submarine force personnel, their spouses, and the spouses of deceased submarine force personnel. Applicants must be entering college, returning to college, or training for entry into the work force. They must live in Hawaii and attend school in Hawaii. Selection is based on academic performance, community involvement, motivation, goals, and financial need. **Deadline for Receipt:** February of each year. **Additional Information:** This program was established in 1985 to honor the 3,505 submariners and 52 submarines lost during World War II.

1419 ■ PACIFIC GAS AND ELECTRIC COMPANY

Asian Employees Association
Attn: Scholarship Committee
77 Beale Street, Mailcode B1E
San Francisco, CA 94105-1814
E-mail: AEAscholarship@pge.com
Web Site: http://www.pge.com/scholarships
To provide financial assistance to graduating high school seniors in Pacific Gas and Electric Company's (PG&E) service area.
Title of Award: Asian Employees Association Scholarships **Area, Field, or Subject:** General studies/Field of study not specified **Level of Education for which Award is Granted:** Undergraduate **Number Awarded:** At least 10 each year. **Funds Available:** The stipend is $1,000. **Duration:** 1 year.
Eligibility Requirements: This program is open to college-bound high school seniors who reside in PG&E's service area. Applicants must have a GPA of 3.5 or higher and a record of active involvement in community organizations, academic or vocational activities, and student organizations. Along with their application, they must submit an essay, up to 2 pages in length, on 1 of the following topics: 1) "Describe any special financial hardships, physical challenges, or any other circumstance that you have encountered. How has your future outlook on life changed as a result of this difficulty?"; or 2) "Many of us are shaped by events, people, or situations which we have encountered. In your community, what is the single most important influence in your life? How did it affect you and what have you learned from it?" Financial need is also considered in the selection process. Students of all ethnicities are eligible. **Deadline for Receipt:** February of each year. **Additional Information:** These scholarships have been presented annually since 1984.

1420 ■ PACIFIC GAS AND ELECTRIC COMPANY

Black Employees Association
Attn: Belinda Bates, Scholarship Director
P.O. Box 192873
San Francisco, CA 94119
Tel: (415)973-6626
E-mail: BDB9@pge.com
Web Site: http://www.pge.com/scholarships
To provide financial assistance for college to high school seniors who live in the service area of Pacific Gas and Electric Company (PG&E).
Title of Award: Black Employees Association Scholarships **Area, Field, or Subject:** General studies/Field of study not specified **Level of Education for which Award is Granted:** Undergraduate **Number Awarded:** 5 or more each year. **Funds Available:** Stipends range from $250 to $2,500 per year. **Duration:** 1 year.
Eligibility Requirements: This program is open to residents of the PG&E service area who are either graduating high school seniors or currently enrolled in a college, university, or vocational school with a GPA of 2.5 or higher. Applicants must submit an official school transcript, 2 letters of recommendation, and a 500-word essay on a topic that changes annually. Financial need is considered in the selection process. **Deadline for Receipt:** May of each year.

1421 ■ PACIFIC GAS AND ELECTRIC COMPANY

Filipino Employees Association
Attn: Zenaida Arcayena
Mailcode B16A
P.O. Box 770000
San Francisco, CA 94177-0001
Tel: (415)973-0557
E-mail: zpa1@pge.com
Web Site: http://www.pge.com/scholarships
To provide financial assistance to graduating high school seniors in Pacific Gas and Electric Company's (PG&E) service area who can demonstrate Filipino community involvement.
Title of Award: Filipino Employees Association Scholarships **Area, Field, or Subject:** General studies/Field of study not specified **Level of Education for which Award is Granted:** Undergraduate **Number Awarded:** 8 each year. **Funds Available:** The stipend is $1,000. **Duration:** 1 year.
Eligibility Requirements: This program is open to college-bound high school seniors who reside in PG&E's service area. Applicants must have a GPA of 3.25 or higher and a record of active participation as a leader in school and the Filipino community. They must submit an essay of 300 to 400 words on a topic that changes annually; recently, the topic was "How Can California Improve Its National Test Results by Enhancing Its Educational System?" **Deadline for Receipt:** May of each year.

1422 ■ PADGETT BUSINESS SERVICES FOUNDATION

Attn: Scholarship Program
160 Hawthorne Park
Athens, GA 30606
Tel: (706)548-1040
Free: 800-723-4388
Fax: 800-548-1040
E-mail: scholarship@smallbizpros.com
Web Site: http://www.smallbizpros.com/newsite/scholar.htm
To provide financial assistance for college to high school seniors whose parents own and operate a small business.
Title of Award: Padgett Business Services Scholarship Program **Area, Field, or Subject:** General studies/Field of study not specified **Level of Education for which Award is Granted:** Undergraduate **Number Awarded:** The number of regional scholarships varies; 2 national scholarships and 1 international scholarship are awarded each year. Approximately $50,000 is awarded by this program each year. **Funds Available:** Regional scholarships are $500; the national scholarships are an additional $1,000; the international scholarship is an additional $2,000. **Duration:** 1 year.
Eligibility Requirements: Applicants must be 1) the dependent of a small business owner who employs fewer than 20 individuals, owns at least 10% of the stock or capital in the business, and is active in the day-to-day operations; and 2) a graduating high school senior planning to attend an accredited postsecondary institution. They may reside in the United States or Canada. Applications must be obtained from a local Padgett Business Service office (the phone number and address will be in the local telephone directory). Applicants must submit a completed questionnaire and write a 100-word essay describing their education and career plans. Students first compete for regional scholarships. Each regional winner in Canada is eligible for the Canada National Scholarship and each regional winner in the United States is eligible for the U.S. National Scholarship. The national scholarship winners are eligible for the international scholarship. **Deadline for Receipt:** February of each year. **Additional Information:** This program began in 1990. Since then, more than $600,000 has been awarded.

1423 ■ PAGE EDUCATION FOUNDATION

P.O. Box 581254
Minneapolis, MN 55458-1254
E-mail: info@page-ed.org
Web Site: http://www.page-ed.org
To provide funding for college to students of color in Minnesota.

Title of Award: Page Education Foundation Grants **Area, Field, or Subject:** General studies/Field of study not specified **Level of Education for which Award is Granted:** Undergraduate **Number Awarded:** Varies each year; recently, 570 Page Scholars were enrolled, of whom 61% were African American, 27% Asian American, 11% Chicano/Latino, and 1% American Indian. **Funds Available:** Stipends range from $900 to $2,500 per year. **Duration:** 1 year; may be renewed up to 3 additional years. **Eligibility Requirements:** This program is open to students of color who are graduating from high school in Minnesota and planning to attend a postsecondary school in the state. Applicants must submit an essay of 400 to 500 words that deals with why they believe education is important, their plans for the future, and the service-to-children project they would like to complete in the coming school year. Selection is based on the essay, 3 letters of recommendation, and financial need. **Deadline for Receipt:** April of each year. **Additional Information:** This program was founded in 1988 by Alan Page, a former football player for the Minnesota Vikings. While attending college, the Page Scholars fulfill a service-to-children contract that brings them into contact with K-8 grade school students of color.

1424 ■ PALOMINO HORSE BREEDERS OF AMERICA

Attn: Youth Scholarship and Educational Fund
15253 East Skelly Drive
Tulsa, OK 74116-2637
Tel: (918)438-1234
Fax: (918)438-1232
E-mail: yellahrses@aol.com
Web Site: http://www.palominohba.com/Youth%20Scholarship/phba_youth_scholarship_program.htm
To provide financial assistance for college to youth members of the Palomino Horse Breeders of America (PHBA-Y).
Title of Award: Palomino Horse Breeders of America Youth Scholarship and Educational Fund **Area, Field, or Subject:** General studies/Field of study not specified **Level of Education for which Award is Granted:** Undergraduate **Number Awarded:** Varies each year. **Funds Available:** The amount of the stipend varies each year. **Duration:** 1 year; may be renewed if the recipient maintains a GPA of 2.5 or higher.
Eligibility Requirements: This program is open to 1) high school seniors who have been a member in good standing of the PHBA-Y during the previous 2 years and either rank in the upper 20% of their high school graduating class or achieved a rank above the 80th percentile on a national college entrance examination; and 2) full-time students who have completed at least 1 semester of college and are younger than 21 years of age. Applicants must provide information on their career goals, academic achievements, extracurricular activities, hobbies, PHBA-Y activities and experiences, awards and honors, and 4-H or FFA projects and achievements. They must also submit a letter on why they desire to continue their education and their personal qualities that qualify them to receive a scholarship. Financial need is not considered in the selection process. **Deadline for Receipt:** January of each year.

1425 ■ PAN AMERICAN ROUND TABLE OF TEXAS

c/o Dorothy Schatzman, Scholarship Chair
555 Lombardy Avenue
El Paso, TX 79922-1739
Web Site: http://www.partt.org/scholarship.html
To provide financial assistance to women students from Pan American countries who are interested in studying in Texas.
Title of Award: Florence Terry Griswold Scholarship I **Area, Field, or Subject:** General studies/Field of study not specified **Level of Education for which Award is Granted:** Graduate, Undergraduate **Number Awarded:** 1 each year. **Funds Available:** The stipend is $2,500. **Duration:** 1 year.
Eligibility Requirements: This program is open to women who are citizens of 1 of the 31 Pan American countries (other than the United States) and interested in studying in a degree program at a Texas state-supported college or university. Preference is given to applicants who plan to return to their home country and put their training to use there after

completion of studies in Texas. There are no restrictions on academic field. **Deadline for Receipt:** January of each year.

1426 ■ PANCRETAN ASSOCIATION OF AMERICA

Attn: General Secretary
8530 Sharon Drive
White Lake, MI 48386-3472
Fax: (248)698-8573
E-mail: erasmia@aol.com
Web Site: http://www.pancretan.org
To provide financial assistance for college or graduate school to members of the Pancretan Association of America (PAA) or affiliated organizations.
Title of Award: Venizelion Scholarship Program **Area, Field, or Subject:** General studies/Field of study not specified **Level of Education for which Award is Granted:** Graduate, Undergraduate **Number Awarded:** 1 or more each year. **Funds Available:** A stipend is awarded (amount not specified). **Duration:** 1 year.
Eligibility Requirements: Applicants must be a member in good standing, and must have been a member for at least 2 years, of a duly recognized chapter of PAA, or a chapter of Pancretan Youth of America (PYA), or a PAA member at large. They must have a GPA of 3.0 or higher and be attending, or planning to attend, a college or university as a full-time undergraduate or graduate student. **Deadline for Receipt:** December of each year. **Additional Information:** Information is also available from Kostas Tsiskakis, PAA Scholarship Committee Chair, 26834 McLaughlin Boulevard, Bonita Springs, FL 34134-3845, E-mail: ktsiskos@aol.com. This program includes the Ioanna Ahladiotis Memorial Scholarship, established to honor a victim of the September 11, 2001 attack on the World Trade Center.

1427 ■ PAPA JOHN'S INTERNATIONAL, INC.

Attn: Scholarship Program
2002 Papa John's Boulevard
Louisville, KY 40299
Tel: (502)261-7272
Free: 800-865-9373
E-mail: info@papajohnsscholars.com
Web Site: http://www.papajohnsscholars.com
To provide financial assistance for college to high school seniors at selected U.S. high schools.
Title of Award: Papa John's Scholarships **Area, Field, or Subject:** General studies/Field of study not specified **Level of Education for which Award is Granted:** Undergraduate **Number Awarded:** Varies each year; recently, 1,185 of these scholarships were awarded. **Funds Available:** The stipend is $1,000. **Duration:** 1 year.
Eligibility Requirements: This program is open to graduating high school seniors who have a GPA of 2.5 or higher. Applicants must attend a high school located near a participating Papa John's restaurant. Selection is based on creative ability, community involvement, academic achievement, quality of character, demonstrated leadership, obstacles overcome, life goals and interests, athletic achievement, and meaningful obstacles overcome. **Additional Information:** This program, which began in 1996, is funded by participating Papa John's restaurants and administered by Scholarly Pursuits, Inc., 4005 Briar Ridge Road, LaGrange, KY 40031.

1428 ■ PAPER, ALLIED-INDUSTRIAL, CHEMICAL AND ENERGY WORKERS INTERNATIONAL UNION

Attn: Scholarship Coordinator
3340 Perimeter Hill Drive
P.O. Box 1475
Nashville, TN 37202
Tel: (615)834-8590
Fax: (615)834-7741
E-mail: debitay@isdn.net
Web Site: http://
To provide financial assistance for college to children of members of the Paper, Allied-Industrial, Chemical and Energy Workers (PACE) International Union
Title of Award: PACE International Union Scholarship Awards Program **Area, Field, or Subject:** General studies/Field of study not specified **Level of Education for which Award is Granted:** Undergraduate **Number Awarded:** 20 each year. **Funds Available:** The stipend is $1,000; funds are paid directly to the college or university designated by the recipient. **Duration:** 1 year.

Eligibility Requirements: Applicants must be 1) high school seniors planning to attend a college or university and 2) children of active members in good standing with the union. Selection is based on academic achievement, character, financial need, leadership, patriotism, seriousness of purpose, and service to others. **Deadline for Receipt:** March of each year. **Additional Information:** PACE was formed in 1999 as a result of the merger of the United Paperworkers International Union and the Oil, Chemical and Atomic Workers International Union.

1429 ■ PAPER, ALLIED-INDUSTRIAL, CHEMICAL AND ENERGY WORKERS INTERNATIONAL UNION

Attn: Scholarship Coordinator
3340 Perimeter Hill Drive
P.O. Box 1475
Nashville, TN 37202
Tel: (615)834-8590
Fax: (615)834-7741
E-mail: debitay@isdn.net
Web Site: http://
To provide financial assistance for college to members of the Paper, Allied-Industrial, Chemical and Energy Workers (PACE) International Union.
Title of Award: Nicholas C. Vrataric Scholarship Awards Program **Area, Field, or Subject:** General studies/Field of study not specified **Level of Education for which Award is Granted:** Undergraduate **Number Awarded:** 2 each year. **Funds Available:** The stipend is $1,000. **Duration:** 1 year.
Eligibility Requirements: This program is open to members of the union who are currently enrolled in a program to further their education. Applicants must submit a 500-word essay on the history of their local. Selection is based on a random drawing. **Deadline for Receipt:** March of each year. **Additional Information:** PACE was formed in 1999 as a result of the merger of the United Paperworkers International Union and the Oil, Chemical and Atomic Workers International Union.

1430 ■ PARALYZED VETERANS OF AMERICA

Attn: Education and Training Foundation
801 18th Street, N.W.
Washington, DC 20006-3517
Tel: (202)416-7651
Fax: (202)416-7641
E-mail: foundations@pva.org
Web Site: http://www.pva.org/member/scholar.htm
To provide financial assistance for college to members of the Paralyzed Veterans of America (PVA) and their families.
Title of Award: PVA Educational Scholarship Program **Area, Field, or Subject:** General studies/Field of study not specified **Level of Education for which Award is Granted:** Undergraduate **Number Awarded:** Varies each year; recently 14 full-time and 3 part-time students received these scholarships. Since this program was established, it has awarded more than $280,000 in scholarships. **Funds Available:** Stipends are $1,000 for full-time students or $500 for part-time students. **Duration:** 1 year.
Eligibility Requirements: This program is open to PVA members and their families. Applicants must be attending or planning to attend a postsecondary institution. **Deadline for Receipt:** August of each year. **Additional Information:** This program was established in 1986.

1431 ■ PARENTS, FAMILIES AND FRIENDS OF LESBIANS AND GAYS

Attn: National Scholarships Program
1726 M Street, N.W., Suite 400
Washington, DC 20036
Tel: (202)467-8180
Fax: (202)467-8194
E-mail: schools@pflag.org
Web Site: http://www.pflag.org
To provide financial assistance for college to high school seniors and recent graduates who have a connection to Parents, Families and Friends of Lesbians and Gays (PFLAG).
Title of Award: Palmer B. Carson-PFLAG General Scholarships **Area, Field, or Subject:** General studies/Field of study not specified **Level of Education for which Award is Granted:** Undergraduate **Number Awarded:** 13 each year. **Funds Available:** The stipend is $1,000. **Duration:** 1 year; nonrenewable.

Eligibility Requirements: This program is open to high school seniors and prior-year graduates who have not attended college. Applicants must have applied to an accredited high education institution to work on 1) an associate degree leading to transfer to complete a bachelor's degree, or 2) a bachelor's degree at a 4-year college or university. They must self-identify either as a gay, lesbian, bisexual, or transgender (GLBT) person or as a supporter of GLBT people. Along with their application, they must submit a high school transcript showing a GPA of 3.0 or higher, 2 letters of recommendation, and a 2-page essay discussing either their life as an LGBT student or how they have been involved with and supported the LGBT community. Financial need is also considered in the selection process. **Deadline for Receipt:** February of each year. **Additional Information:** This scholarship was first offered in 2004.

1432 ■ PARENTS, FAMILIES AND FRIENDS OF LESBIANS AND GAYS

Attn: National Scholarships Program
1726 M Street, N.W., Suite 400
Washington, DC 20036
Tel: (202)467-8180
Fax: (202)467-8194
E-mail: schools@pflag.org
Web Site: http://www.pflag.org
To provide financial assistance for college to high school seniors and recent graduates who have a connection to Parents, Families and Friends of Lesbians and Gays (PFLAG).
Title of Award: Palmer B. Carson-PFLAG Scholarship for LGBT Advocacy **Area, Field, or Subject:** General studies/Field of study not specified **Level of Education for which Award is Granted:** Undergraduate **Number Awarded:** 1 each year. **Funds Available:** The stipend is $2,500. **Duration:** 1 year; nonrenewable.
Eligibility Requirements: This program is open to high school seniors and prior-year graduates who have not attended college. Applicants must have applied to an accredited high education institution to work on 1) an associate degree leading to transfer to complete a bachelor's degree, or 2) a bachelor's degree at a 4-year college or university. They must self-identify either as a gay, lesbian, bisexual, or transgender (GLBT) person or as a supporter of GLBT people. Along with their application, they must submit a high school transcript showing a GPA of 3.0 or higher, 2 letters of recommendation, and a 2-page essay discussing either their life as an LGBT student or how they have been involved with and supported the LGBT community. Financial need is also considered in the selection process. This scholarship is presented to the applicant who demonstrates outstanding LGBT advocacy. **Deadline for Receipt:** February of each year. **Additional Information:** This scholarship was first offered in 2004.

1433 ■ PARENTS, FAMILIES AND FRIENDS OF LESBIANS AND GAYS

Attn: National Scholarships Program
1726 M Street, N.W., Suite 400
Washington, DC 20036
Tel: (202)467-8180
Fax: (202)467-8194
E-mail: schools@pflag.org
Web Site: http://www.pflag.org
To provide financial assistance for college to high school seniors and recent graduates who have a connection to Parents, Families and Friends of Lesbians and Gays (PFLAG).
Title of Award: Jeanne Mannford Scholarship for LGBT Leadership **Area, Field, or Subject:** General studies/Field of study not specified **Level of Education for which Award is Granted:** Undergraduate **Number Awarded:** 1 each year. **Funds Available:** The stipend is $2,500. **Duration:** 1 year; nonrenewable.
Eligibility Requirements: This program is open to high school seniors and prior-year graduates who have not attended college. Applicants must have applied to an accredited high education institution to work on 1) an associate degree leading to transfer to complete a bachelor's degree, or 2) a bachelor's degree at a 4-year college or university. They must self-identify either as a gay, lesbian, bisexual, or transgender (GLBT) person or as a supporter of GLBT people. Along with their application, they must submit a high school transcript showing a GPA of 3.0 or higher, 2 letters of recommendation, and a 2-page essay discussing either their life as an LGBT student or how they have been involved with and supported the

LGBT community. Financial need is also considered in the selection process. This scholarship is presented to the applicant who demonstrates outstanding leadership in the LGBT community. **Deadline for Receipt:** February of each year. **Additional Information:** This scholarship was first offered in 2004.

1434 ■ PARENTS, FAMILIES AND FRIENDS OF LESBIANS AND GAYS

Attn: National Scholarships Program
1726 M Street, N.W., Suite 400
Washington, DC 20036
Tel: (202)467-8180
Fax: (202)467-8194
E-mail: schools@pflag.org
Web Site: http://www.pflag.org
To provide financial assistance for college to high school seniors and recent graduates who have a connection to Parents, Families and Friends of Lesbians and Gays (PFLAG).
Title of Award: PFLAG National Donor Scholarships **Area, Field, or Subject:** General studies/Field of study not specified **Level of Education for which Award is Granted:** Undergraduate **Number Awarded:** 2 each year: 1 at 2,500 and 1 at $1,000. **Funds Available:** Stipends are $2,500 or $1,000. **Duration:** 1 year; nonrenewable.
Eligibility Requirements: This program is open to high school seniors and prior-year graduates who have not attended college. Applicants must have applied to an accredited high education institution to work on 1) an associate degree leading to transfer to complete a bachelor's degree, or 2) a bachelor's degree at a 4-year college or university. They must self-identify either as a gay, lesbian, bisexual, or transgender (GLBT) person or as a supporter of GLBT people. Along with their application, they must submit a high school transcript showing a GPA of 3.0 or higher, 2 letters of recommendation, and a 2-page essay discussing either their life as an LGBT student or how they have been involved with and supported the LGBT community. Financial need is also considered in the selection process. **Deadline for Receipt:** February of each year. **Additional Information:** This scholarship was first offered in 2004.

1435 ■ PARENTS, FAMILIES AND FRIENDS OF LESBIANS AND GAYS

Attn: National Scholarships Program
1726 M Street, N.W., Suite 400
Washington, DC 20036
Tel: (202)467-8180
Fax: (202)467-8194
E-mail: schools@pflag.org
Web Site: http://www.pflag.org
To provide financial assistance for college to high school seniors and recent graduates who have a connection to Parents, Families and Friends of Lesbians and Gays (PFLAG).
Title of Award: Sakia Gunn Scholarship for LGBT Community Involvement **Area, Field, or Subject:** General studies/Field of study not specified **Level of Education for which Award is Granted:** Undergraduate **Number Awarded:** 1 each year. **Funds Available:** The stipend is $2,500. **Duration:** 1 year; nonrenewable.
Eligibility Requirements: This program is open to high school seniors and prior-year graduates who have not attended college. Applicants must have applied to an accredited high education institution to work on 1) an associate degree leading to transfer to complete a bachelor's degree, or 2) a bachelor's degree at a 4-year college or university. They must self-identify either as a gay, lesbian, bisexual, or transgender (GLBT) person or as a supporter of GLBT people. Along with their application, they must submit a high school transcript showing a GPA of 3.0 or higher, 2 letters of recommendation, and a 2-page essay discussing either their life as an LGBT student or how they have been involved with and supported the LGBT community. Financial need is also considered in the selection process. This scholarship is presented to the applicant who demonstrates outstanding LGBT involvement. **Deadline for Receipt:** February of each year. **Additional Information:** This scholarship was first offered in 2004.

1436 ■ PARENTS, FAMILIES AND FRIENDS OF LESBIANS AND GAYS

Attn: National Scholarships Program
1726 M Street, N.W., Suite 400
Washington, DC 20036

Tel: (202)467-8180
Fax: (202)467-8194
E-mail: schools@pflag.org
Web Site: http://www.pflag.org
To provide financial assistance for college to high school seniors and recent graduates who have a connection to Parents, Families and Friends of Lesbians and Gays (PFLAG).
Title of Award: Esera Tualolo Scholarship for Athletic Achievement **Area, Field, or Subject:** General studies/Field of study not specified **Level of Education for which Award is Granted:** Undergraduate **Number Awarded:** 1 each year. **Funds Available:** The stipend is $2,500. **Duration:** 1 year; nonrenewable.
Eligibility Requirements: This program is open to high school seniors and prior-year graduates who have not attended college. Applicants must have applied to an accredited high education institution to work on 1) an associate degree leading to transfer to complete a bachelor's degree, or 2) a bachelor's degree at a 4-year college or university. They must self-identify either as a gay, lesbian, bisexual, or transgender (GLBT) person or as a supporter of GLBT people. Along with their application, they must submit a high school transcript showing a GPA of 3.0 or higher, 2 letters of recommendation, and a 2-page essay discussing either their life as an LGBT student or how they have been involved with and supported the LGBT community. Financial need is also considered in the selection process. This scholarship is presented to the applicant who demonstrates outstanding athletic achievement. **Deadline for Receipt:** February of each year. **Additional Information:** This scholarship was first offered in 2004.

1437 ■ PATIENT ADVOCATE FOUNDATION

Attn: Vice President of Special Programs
700 Thimble Shoals Boulevard, Suite 200
Newport News, VA 23606
800-532-5274
Fax: (757)873-8999
E-mail: help@patientadvocate.org
Web Site: http://www.patientadvocate.org
To provide financial assistance for college or graduate school to students seeking to initiate or complete a course of study that has been interrupted or delayed by a diagnosis of cancer or other life threatening disease.
Title of Award: Patient Advocate Foundation Scholarships for Survivors **Area, Field, or Subject:** General studies/Field of study not specified **Level of Education for which Award is Granted:** Graduate, Undergraduate **Number Awarded:** Varies each year; recently, 10 of these scholarships were awarded. **Funds Available:** The stipend is $2,000. Funds are paid directly to the college or university to help cover tuition and other fee costs. The cost of books is not included. **Duration:** 1 year; recipients may reapply.
Eligibility Requirements: This program is open to students working full time on a 2-year, 4-year, or advanced degree with a GPA of 3.0 or higher. The college or graduate education of applicants must have been interrupted or delayed by a diagnosis of cancer or other life threatening, chronic, or debilitating disease. They must be able to demonstrate that their course of study will make them immediately employable after graduation. Along with their application, they must submit a 1,000-word essay on why they have chosen to further their education, how the illness has affected their family and their decision to continue their education, and how they feel they can help others by earning their degree. Financial need is also considered in the selection process. **Deadline for Receipt:** April of each year. **Additional Information:** This program includes the Cheryl Grimmel Award and the Monica Bailes Award. Support has come from a variety of sources, including Pfizer, Inc., AstraZeneca Pharmaceuticals, Aventis Pharmaceuticals, GlaxoSmithKline, and Novartis Oncology. Students must complete 20 hours of community service during each year they receive support.

1438 ■ PEARL HARBOR SURVIVORS ASSOCIATION

c/o Bob Kerr, Chair, Scholarship Committee
2634 Bonnybrook Drive, S.W.
Atlanta, GA 30311-5516
Tel: (404)344-3260
E-mail: kerr2634@aol.com
Web Site: http://www.pearlharborsurvivorsonline.org

To provide financial assistance for college to descendants of members of the Pearl Harbor Survivors Association (PHSA).

Title of Award: Pearl Harbor Survivors Association Scholarships **Area, Field, or Subject:** General studies/Field of study not specified **Level of Education for which Award is Granted:** Undergraduate **Number Awarded:** 4 each year: 2 to university and college students and 2 to technical and trade school students. **Funds Available:** The stipend is $1,500 per year for students in a college or university or $1,000 per year for students in a technical or trade school. **Duration:** 1 year.

Eligibility Requirements: This program is open to the direct, adopted, and step-descendants of PHSA members or deceased members who are U.S. citizens and either high school seniors or currently enrolled in college. Along with their application, they must submit an essay of 250 words or less on their future goals and how higher education will help attain those goals, and an essay of up to 500 words on a topic that changes annually. **Deadline for Receipt:** July of each year.

1439 ■ PEDIATRIC BRAIN TUMOR FOUNDATION OF THE UNITED STATES

Attn: National Family Support Program Coordinator
302 Ridgefield Court
Asheville, NC 28806
Tel: (828)665-6891
Free: 800-253-6530
Fax: (828)665-6894
E-mail: familysupport@pbtfus.org
Web Site: http://www.pbtfus.org/famsvcs/fam_sprt.htm
To provide financial assistance for college to brain tumor survivors.

Title of Award: Pediatric Brain Tumor Foundation Scholarship Program **Area, Field, or Subject:** General studies/Field of study not specified **Level of Education for which Award is Granted:** Undergraduate **Number Awarded:** Varies each year; recently, 55 of these scholarships were awarded. **Funds Available:** The stipend is $2,500 per year. **Duration:** 2 years.

Eligibility Requirements: This program is open to high school seniors who have been diagnosed with a childhood brain or spinal cord tumor. Applicants must be enrolled or planning to enroll at a technical school, vocational school, junior college, or 4-year college or university. They must submit an essay, proof of brain tumor diagnosis, GPA, intent to register for college, high school transcripts, and recommendations **Deadline for Receipt:** May or November of each year.

1440 ■ WILLIAM PENN ASSOCIATION

Attn: Scholarship Foundation, Inc.
709 Brighton Road
Pittsburgh, PA 15233-1821
Tel: (412)231-2979
Free: 800-848-PENN
Fax: (412)231-8535
E-mail: mail@williampennassociation.org
Web Site: http://www.williampennassociation.org
To provide financial assistance for college to members of the William Penn Association.

Title of Award: William Penn Association Scholarships **Area, Field, or Subject:** General studies/Field of study not specified **Level of Education for which Award is Granted:** Undergraduate **Number Awarded:** Varies each year. **Funds Available:** A stipend is awarded (amount not specified). **Duration:** 2 years or 4 years; renewal requires the recipient to maintain a GPA of 2.5 or higher.

Eligibility Requirements: This program is open to full-time undergraduate students who have been an individual life benefit member of the William Penn Association for 4 years; their parent or grandparent must have been a life benefit member for at least 3 years (4 years effective in 2006). Applicants must be attending or planning to attend an accredited college, university, or school or nursing as a full-time student. Along with their application, they must submit a high school transcript and their latest SAT/ACT scores. **Deadline for Receipt:** May of each year. **Additional**

Information: The William Penn Association is the largest Hungarian fraternal society in the United States.

1441 ■ PENNSYLVANIA FEDERATION OF BUSINESS AND PROFESSIONAL WOMEN'S CLUBS, INC.

Attn: Education and Service Funds Chair
2111 Old Barn Road
East Greenville, PA 18041
E-mail: buschandnancy@yahoo.com
Web Site: http://www.bpwpa.org
To provide financial assistance for continuing education to women in Pennsylvania.

Title of Award: Pennsylvania Business and Professional Women Scholarship **Area, Field, or Subject:** General studies/Field of study not specified **Level of Education for which Award is Granted:** Undergraduate **Number Awarded:** Varies each year. **Funds Available:** A stipend is awarded (amount not specified).

Eligibility Requirements: This program is open to women in Pennsylvania who have been accepted into an accredited educational institution. Applicants must be able to demonstrate financial need. They must submit an essay that discusses their specific short-term career goals, how the proposed training will help them to accomplish those goals, and how those apply to their long-range career goals. The essay should include a summary of the following topics: self, educational goals, and issues that are important to working women in today's world. **Deadline for Receipt:** June of each year for programs beginning in September; October of each year for programs beginning in January.

1442 ■ PENNSYLVANIA HIGHER EDUCATION ASSISTANCE AGENCY

Attn: Development and Regional Services
1200 North Seventh Street
P.O. Box 2455
Harrisburg, PA 17105-2455
Tel: (717)720-2800
Free: 800-831-0797
E-mail: paetg@pheaa.org
Web Site: http://www.pheaa.org/specialprograms/index.shtml
To provide financial assistance for college to residents of Pennsylvania who have been in foster care.

Title of Award: Pennsylvania Chafee Education and Training Grant Program **Area, Field, or Subject:** General studies/Field of study not specified **Level of Education for which Award is Granted:** Undergraduate **Number Awarded:** Varies each year. **Funds Available:** The maximum stipend is $5,000 per year. Awards may not exceed the actual cost of attendance, minus other financial aid the student receives. **Duration:** 1 year; may be renewed if the recipient remains enrolled at least half time and makes satisfactory academic progress.

Eligibility Requirements: This program is open to residents of Pennsylvania who are eligible for services under the state's Chafee Foster Care Independence Program, were adopted from foster care after their 16th birthday, or were participating in this program on their 21st birthday (until they turn 23 years of age). Applicants must be enrolled in an approved college or career school on at least a half time basis. **Deadline for Receipt:** April of each year. **Additional Information:** This program is administered by the Pennsylvania Higher Education Assistance Agency (PHEAA) on behalf of the Pennsylvania Department of Public Welfare.

1443 ■ PENNSYLVANIA HIGHER EDUCATION ASSISTANCE AGENCY

Attn: State Grant and Special Programs Division
1200 North Seventh Street
Harrisburg, PA 17102-1444
Tel: (717)720-2800
Free: 800-692-7392
E-mail: info@pheaa.org
Web Site: http://www.pheaa.org/specialprograms/index.shtml
To provide financial assistance for college to the children of POWs/MIAs from Pennsylvania.

Title of Award: Pennsylvania Grants for Children of Soldiers Declared POW/MIA **Area, Field, or Subject:** General studies/Field of study not specified **Level of Education for which Award is Granted:** Undergradu-

ate **Number Awarded:** Varies each year. **Funds Available:** The amount of the award depends on the financial need of the recipient, up to a maximum of $3,500 at a Pennsylvania school or $800 at a school outside of Pennsylvania that is approved for participation in the program. **Duration:** 1 year; may be renewed for 3 additional years.
Eligibility Requirements: This program is open to dependent children of members or former members of the U.S. armed services who served on active duty after January 31, 1955, who are or have been prisoners of war or are or have been listed as missing in action, and who were residents of Pennsylvania for at least 12 months preceding service on active duty. Eligible children must be enrolled in a program of at least 1 year in duration on at least a half-time basis at an approved school and must demonstrate financial need. **Deadline for Receipt:** March of each year.
Additional Information: With certain exceptions, recipients may attend any accredited college in the United States. Excluded from coverage are 2-year public colleges located outside Pennsylvania and schools in states bordering on Pennsylvania that do not allow their state grant recipients to attend Pennsylvania schools (i.e., New York, Maryland, and New Jersey).

1444 ■ PENNSYLVANIA HIGHER EDUCATION ASSISTANCE AGENCY

Attn: State Grant and Special Programs Division
1200 North Seventh Street
Harrisburg, PA 17102-1444
Tel: (717)720-2800
Free: 800-692-7392
E-mail: info@pheaa.org
Web Site: http://www.pheaa.org/specialprograms/index.shtml
To provide financial assistance for college to Pennsylvania veterans.
Title of Award: Pennsylvania Grants for Veterans **Area, Field, or Subject:** General studies/Field of study not specified **Level of Education for which Award is Granted:** Undergraduate **Number Awarded:** Varies each year. **Funds Available:** The amount of the award depends on the financial need of the recipient, up to a maximum of $3,300 at a Pennsylvania school or $800 at a school outside of Pennsylvania that is approved for participation in the program. **Duration:** 1 year; may be renewed for 3 additional years.
Eligibility Requirements: This program is open to veterans who served on active duty with the U.S. armed services (or were a cadet or midshipman at a service academy); were released or discharged under conditions other than dishonorable, bad conduct, uncharacterized, or other than honorable; have resided in Pennsylvania for at least 12 months immediately preceding the date of application; graduated from high school; and are enrolled on at least a half-time basis in an approved program of study that is at least 2 academic years in length. First priority is given to veterans who have separated from active duty after January 1 of the current year. All veterans are considered without regard to the financial status of their parents. **Deadline for Receipt:** April of each year for renewal applicants and any nonrenewals who will enroll in a baccalaureate degree program; July of each year for nonrenewals who will enroll in a 2-year or 3-year terminal program. **Additional Information:** With certain exceptions, recipients may attend any accredited college in the United States. Excluded from coverage are 2-year public colleges located outside Pennsylvania and schools in states bordering on Pennsylvania that do not allow their state grant recipients to attend Pennsylvania schools (i.e., New York, Maryland, and New Jersey).

1445 ■ PENNSYLVANIA HIGHER EDUCATION ASSISTANCE AGENCY

Attn: State Grant and Special Programs Division
1200 North Seventh Street
Harrisburg, PA 17102-1444
Tel: (717)720-2800
Free: 800-692-7392
E-mail: info@pheaa.org
Web Site: http://www.pheaa.org/specialprograms/index.shtml
To provide financial assistance for college to the children of Pennsylvania public service personnel who died in the line of service.
Title of Award: Pennsylvania Postsecondary Educational Gratuity Program **Area, Field, or Subject:** General studies/Field of study not specified **Level of Education for which Award is Granted:** Undergraduate **Number Awarded:** Varies each year. **Funds Available:** Grants cover tuition, fees, room, and board charged by the institution, less awarded scholarships and federal and state grants. **Duration:** Up to 5 years.
Eligibility Requirements: This program is open to residents of Pennsylvania who are the children of 1) Pennsylvania police officers, fire fighters, rescue and ambulance squad members, corrections facility employees, or National Guard members who died in the line of duty after January 1, 1976; or 2) Pennsylvania sheriffs, deputy sheriffs, National Guard members, and certain other individuals on federal or state active military duty who died after September 11, 2001 as a direct result of performing their official duties. Applicants must be 25 years of age or younger and enrolled or accepted at a Pennsylvania community college, state-owned institution, or state-related institution as a full-time student working on an associate or baccalaureate degree. They must have already applied for other scholarships, including state and federal grants and financial aid from the postsecondary institution to which they are applying. **Deadline for Receipt:** March of each year. **Additional Information:** This program began in the 1998-99 winter/spring term to cover service personnel who died after January 1, 1976. It was amended in 2004 to cover additional service personnel who died after September 11, 2001.

1446 ■ PENNSYLVANIA HIGHER EDUCATION ASSISTANCE AGENCY

Attn: State Grant and Special Programs Division
1200 North Seventh Street
Harrisburg, PA 17102-1444
Tel: (717)720-2800
Free: 800-692-7392
E-mail: info@pheaa.org
Web Site: http://www.pheaa.org/stategrants/index.shtml
To provide financial assistance for college to students in Pennsylvania who have financial need.
Title of Award: Pennsylvania State Grants **Area, Field, or Subject:** General studies/Field of study not specified **Level of Education for which Award is Granted:** Undergraduate **Number Awarded:** Varies each year. **Funds Available:** Grants depend on financial need and the type of school attended. Recently, annual grants ranged from $2,750 to $3,300 at 4-year private schools, from $1,000 to $3,250 at state system schools, from $1,700 to $3,300 at state-related schools, from $1,650 to $3,300 at junior colleges, from $300 to $1,050 at community colleges, from $1,150 to $3,200 at nursing school, and from $1,600 to $3,300 at business, trade, and technical schools. **Duration:** 1 year; may be renewed for 3 additional years.
Eligibility Requirements: This program is open to seniors graduating from high schools in Pennsylvania who plan to attend a postsecondary school in Pennsylvania on at least a half-time basis. Applicants may also attend accredited colleges in other states, except those states that border Pennsylvania and do not allow their grant recipients to attend Pennsylvania schools (i.e., Maryland, New Jersey, and New York). Their family income may not exceed $69,000. **Deadline for Receipt:** April of each year for renewal applicants, new applicants who plan to enroll in a baccalaureate degree program, and students in college transfer programs at 2-year public or junior colleges; July of each year for first-time applicants for business, trade, or technical schools, hospital schools of nursing, or 2-year terminal programs at community, junior, or 4-year colleges.

1447 ■ PENNSYLVANIA HIGHER EDUCATION ASSISTANCE AGENCY

Attn: State Grant and Special Programs Division
1200 North Seventh Street
Harrisburg, PA 17102-1444
Tel: (717)720-2800
Free: 800-692-7392
E-mail: info@pheaa.org
Web Site: http://www.pheaa.org/specialprograms/index.shtml
To provide financial assistance for college to students in Pennsylvania who qualify for a federal Robert C. Byrd Honors Scholarship but did not receive that scholarship.
Title of Award: PHEAA Academic Excellence Scholarship Award Program **Area, Field, or Subject:** General studies/Field of study not specified **Level of Education for which Award is Granted:** Undergraduate **Number Awarded:** Varies each year. **Funds Available:** The stipend is $1,500 per year. **Duration:** 1 year; may be renewed if the recipient remains enrolled full time and makes satisfactory academic progress.
Eligibility Requirements: This program is open to seniors graduating from high schools in Pennsylvania who plan to attend a postsecondary

school in Pennsylvania on a full-time basis. Applicants must have applied and qualified for a Robert C. Byrd Honors Scholarship and also be a Pennsylvania State Grant recipient for at least 1 term during their freshman year. Eligibility for the Byrd Scholarship requires that applicants be U.S. citizens, nationals, or permanent residents; rank in the top 5% of their graduating class (or in the top 3 if their class has 60 students or less); have a GPA of 3.5 or higher; and have a combined mathematics and critical reading SAT score of 1150 or higher, an ACT score of 25 or higher, or a GED score of 3550 or above. If they qualify for the Byrd Scholarship but fail to receive it, they are automatically eligible for this scholarship from the Pennsylvania Higher Education Assistance Agency (PHEAA). **Deadline for Receipt:** April of each year.

1448 ■ PENNSYLVANIA NATIONAL GUARD
Department of Military and Veterans Affairs
Fort Indiantown Gap
Annville, PA 17003-5002
Tel: (717)861-8949
Free: 800-PA-GRD-PA
Web Site: http://www.paguard.com/html/free_tuition_eap.html
To provide scholarship/loans for college or graduate school to Pennsylvania National Guard members.
Title of Award: Pennsylvania National Guard Educational Assistance Program **Area, Field, or Subject:** General studies/Field of study not specified **Level of Education for which Award is Granted:** Master's, Undergraduate **Number Awarded:** Varies each year; recently, 1,789 members of the Pennsylvania National Guard were enrolled in this program. **Funds Available:** Full-time students receive payment of 100% of tuition at a state-owned university (recently, $4,810 per year). Part-time students receive one half of the tuition actually charged or one third of the full-time tuition charged to a Pennsylvania resident at a state-owned university (recently, $1,603 per year), whichever is less. Recipients who fail to fulfill the service obligation must repay all funds received within 10 years, including interest at 7%. **Duration:** Up to 5 years.
Eligibility Requirements: This program is open to active members of the Pennsylvania National Guard who are Pennsylvania residents and serving as enlisted personnel, warrant officers, or commissioned officers of any grade. Applicants must accept an obligation to serve in the Pennsylvania National Guard for a period of 6 years from the date of entry into the program. Students who do not possess a baccalaureate degree must be enrolled full or part time in an approved program of education at an approved institution of higher learning in Pennsylvania. Master's degree students are supported on a part-time basis only. Guard members receiving an ROTC scholarship of any type are not eligible. **Deadline for Receipt:** June of each year for fall semester; October of each year for spring semester; May of each year for summer school. **Additional Information:** This program, first offered in 1997, is jointly administered by the Pennsylvania Department of Military and Veterans Affairs and the Pennsylvania Higher Education Assistance Agency. Support for summer and graduate school is available only if funding permits.

1449 ■ PENNSYLVANIA NATIONAL GUARD ASSOCIATIONS
Attn: Executive Director
MP-PA, Building 7-10
Fort Indiantown Gap
Annville, PA 17003-5002
Tel: (717)861-2888
Free: 800-997-8885
Fax: (717)861-5560
E-mail: admin@pngas.net
Web Site: http://www.pngas.net/pngsf1.htm
To provide financial assistance for undergraduate education to Pennsylvania National Guard members and the children of disabled or deceased members.
Title of Award: Pennsylvania National Guard Scholarship Fund **Area, Field, or Subject:** General studies/Field of study not specified **Level of Education for which Award is Granted:** Undergraduate **Number Awarded:** 17 each year: 2 at $1,000, 1 at $500, and 14 at $400. **Funds Available:** Stipends are $1,000, $500, or $400. **Duration:** 1 year.
Eligibility Requirements: This program is open to active members of the Pennsylvania Army or Air National Guard. Children of members of the Guard who died or were permanently disabled while on Guard duty are also eligible. Applicants must be entering their first year of higher educa-

tion as a full-time student or presently attending a college or vocational school as a full-time student. As part of the selection process, they must submit an essay that outlines their military and civilian plans for the future. Other selection criteria include academic achievement, leadership abilities, and contributions to citizenship. Graduate students are not eligible. **Deadline for Receipt:** June of each year. **Additional Information:** The sponsoring organization includes the National Guard Association of Pennsylvania and the Pennsylvania National Guard Enlisted Association. This program began in 1977. The $500 scholarship is sponsored by the USAA Insurance Corporation.

1450 ■ PENOBSCOT NATION
Attn: Department of Education and Career Services
6 River Road
Indian Island, ME 04468
Tel: (207)827-1649
Fax: (207)827-2088
E-mail: pinedu@penobscotnation.org
Web Site: http://www.penobscotnation.org/Education/education.htm
To provide financial assistance to members of the Penobscot Nation who are working on 2-year degrees or training programs.
Title of Award: Penobscot Nation Adult Vocational Training **Area, Field, or Subject:** General studies/Field of study not specified **Level of Education for which Award is Granted:** Two Year College, Vocational/Occupational **Number Awarded:** Varies each year. **Funds Available:** The amount awarded varies, depending upon the needs of the recipient. **Duration:** 1 year or more.
Eligibility Requirements: This program is open to students who are members of the Penobscot Nation and are enrolled full time in an associate degree, diploma, or certificate training program. Awards are granted on the basis of financial need (as determined by the institution the student is attending). **Deadline for Receipt:** June of each year. **Additional Information:** Funding for this program is provided to the Penobscot Nation through the Bureau of Indian Affairs.

1451 ■ PENOBSCOT NATION
Attn: Department of Education and Career Services
6 River Road
Indian Island, ME 04468
Tel: (207)827-1649
Fax: (207)827-2088
E-mail: pinedu@penobscotnation.org
Web Site: http://www.penobscotnation.org/Education/education.htm
To provide financial assistance to members of the Penobscot Nation who are or will be working on a 4-year degree.
Title of Award: Penobscot Nation Higher Education Grant Program **Area, Field, or Subject:** General studies/Field of study not specified **Level of Education for which Award is Granted:** Four Year College **Number Awarded:** Varies each year. **Funds Available:** The amount awarded varies, depending upon the needs of the recipient. Funds may be used to pay for tuition, fees, room, board, books, or living expenses. **Duration:** 1 year or more.
Eligibility Requirements: This program is open to students who are members of the Penobscot Nation and are enrolled (or going to be enrolled) full time in a 4-year degree program. Awards are granted on the basis of financial need as determined by the institution the student is attending. **Deadline for Receipt:** June of each year. **Additional Information:** Funding for this program is provided to the Penobscot Nation through the Bureau of Indian Affairs.

1452 ■ P.E.O. SISTERHOOD
Attn: Executive Office
3700 Grand Avenue
Des Moines, IA 50312-2899
Tel: (515)255-3153
Fax: (515)255-3820
Web Site: http://www.peointernational.org
To offer low-interest loans to women interested in pursuing educational activities beyond high school.
Title of Award: P.E.O. Educational Loan Fund **Area, Field, or Subject:** General studies/Field of study not specified **Level of Education for which Award is Granted:** Graduate, Undergraduate **Number Awarded:** Varies each year; recently, nearly $9 million was available for loans.

Funds Available: The amount of the loan varies, depending upon the needs of the recipient, to a maximum of $9,000. The loan must be repaid within 6 years at an interest rate of 2%. **Duration:** 1 year; renewable. **Eligibility Requirements:** Women from the United States or Canada who are interested in working on a college degree are eligible to apply. They must be sponsored by a local P.E.O. chapter and within 2 years of completing their educational goals. **Deadline for Receipt:** Applications may be submitted at any time. **Additional Information:** This program began in 1907; it is the oldest project of the international chapter of the Women's Philanthropic Educational Organization (P.E.O.).

1453 ■ P.E.O. SISTERHOOD

Attn: Executive Office
3700 Grand Avenue
Des Moines, IA 50312-2899
Tel: (515)255-3153
Fax: (515)255-3820
Web Site: http://www.peointernational.org
To provide financial assistance to mature women interested in resuming or continuing their education.
Title of Award: P.E.O. Program for Continuing Education **Area, Field, or Subject:** General studies/Field of study not specified **Level of Education for which Award is Granted:** Undergraduate **Number Awarded:** Varies each year; recently, 1,467 of these grants were awarded, including 365 for the full amount of $1,500. **Funds Available:** The maximum award is $1,500. **Duration:** 1 year; nonrenewable. **Eligibility Requirements:** This program is open to mature women who are citizens of the United States or Canada and have experienced an interruption in their education that has lasted at least 24 consecutive months during their adult life. Applicants are frequently single parents who must acquire marketable skills to support their families. They must be within 2 years of completing an academic or technical course of study. Applicants must be sponsored by a local P.E.O. chapter. Students enrolled in a doctoral degree program are not eligible. **Deadline for Receipt:** Applications may be submitted at any time. **Additional Information:** This program was established in 1973 by the Women's Philanthropic Educational Organization (P.E.O.).

1454 ■ PFIZER INC.

c/o Eden Communications Group
515 Valley Street, Suite 200
Maplewood, NJ 07040
Tel: (973)275-6518
Free: 800-AWARD-PF
Fax: (973)275-9792
E-mail: info@epilepsy-scholarship.com
Web Site: http://www.epilepsy-scholarship.com
To provide financial assistance for undergraduate or graduate study to individuals with epilepsy.
Title of Award: Pfizer Epilepsy Scholarship Award **Area, Field, or Subject:** General studies/Field of study not specified **Level of Education for which Award is Granted:** Graduate, Undergraduate **Number Awarded:** 25 each year. **Funds Available:** The stipend is $3,000. **Duration:** 1 year; nonrenewable. **Eligibility Requirements:** Applicants must be under a physician's care for epilepsy (and taking prescribed medication) and must submit an application with 2 letters of recommendation (1 from the physician) and verification of academic status. They must be high school seniors entering college in the fall; college freshmen, sophomores, or juniors continuing in the fall; or college seniors planning to enter graduate school in the fall. Along with their application, they must submit a 250-word essay on something of direct personal importance to them as a person with epilepsy. Selection is based on demonstrated achievement in academic and extracurricular activities; financial need is not considered. **Deadline for Receipt:** February of each year.

1455 ■ PHI ETA SIGMA

c/o John F. Sagabiel
Western Kentucky University
525 Grise Hall
1 Big Red Way
Bowling Green, KY 42101
Tel: (270)745-6540

Fax: (270)745-3893
E-mail: Phi.Eta.Sigma@WKU.edu
Web Site: http://www.phietasigma.org/scholarships.htm
To provide financial assistance for college to members of Phi Eta Sigma Honor Society.
Title of Award: Phi Eta Sigma Honor Society Distinguished Member Undergraduate Scholarships **Area, Field, or Subject:** General studies/Field of study not specified **Level of Education for which Award is Granted:** Undergraduate **Number Awarded:** Varies each year; recently, 31 of these scholarships were awarded. **Funds Available:** The stipend is $2,000. **Duration:** 1 year. **Eligibility Requirements:** This program is open to members of the honor society who are enrolled full time in a college or university. Membership in the society requires a GPA of 3.5 or higher. Selection is based on academic record, participation in Phi Eta Sigma chapter activities, creative ability, potential for success in their chosen field, and 3 letters of recommendation. **Deadline for Receipt:** February of each year. **Additional Information:** Many local chapters also award scholarships.

1456 ■ PHI ETA SIGMA

c/o John F. Sagabiel
Western Kentucky University
525 Grise Hall
1 Big Red Way
Bowling Green, KY 42101
Tel: (270)745-6540
Fax: (270)745-3893
E-mail: Phi.Eta.Sigma@WKU.edu
Web Site: http://www.phietasigma.org/scholarships.htm
To provide financial assistance for college to members of Phi Eta Sigma Honor Society.
Title of Award: Phi Eta Sigma Honor Society Undergraduate Scholarships **Area, Field, or Subject:** General studies/Field of study not specified **Level of Education for which Award is Granted:** Undergraduate **Number Awarded:** Varies each year; recently, 72 of these scholarships were awarded. **Funds Available:** The stipend is $1,000. **Duration:** 1 year. **Eligibility Requirements:** This program is open to members of the honor society who are enrolled full time in a college or university. Membership in the society requires a GPA of 3.5 or higher. Selection is based on academic record, participation in Phi Eta Sigma chapter activities, creative ability, potential for success in their chosen field, and 3 letters of recommendation. **Deadline for Receipt:** February of each year. **Additional Information:** Many local chapters also award scholarships.

1457 ■ PHILIPPIANS FOUNDATION

P.O. Box 157
Hickory, NC 28603
Tel: (828)328-3529
Fax: (828)396-4689
To provide financial assistance for college to North Carolina residents whose parents are stricken with Amyotrophic Lateral Sclerosis (ALS).
Title of Award: Philippians Foundation Scholarships **Area, Field, or Subject:** General studies/Field of study not specified **Level of Education for which Award is Granted:** Undergraduate **Number Awarded:** 1 each year. **Funds Available:** The stipend is $1,000 per year. **Duration:** Up to 4 years. **Eligibility Requirements:** This program is open to students who have been a resident of North Carolina for at least 1 year and who are the dependent of a parent or legal guardian stricken with ALS. Applicants must be enrolling at an accredited college, university, or nursing school. **Deadline for Receipt:** September of each year.

1458 ■ STEPHEN PHILLIPS MEMORIAL SCHOLARSHIP FUND

34 Chestnut Street
Salem, MA 01970
Tel: (978)744-2111
Fax: (978)744-0456
E-mail: info@spscholars.org
Web Site: http://www.Phillips-scholarship.org
To provide financial assistance for college to residents of the New England and mid-Atlantic states.
Title of Award: Stephen Phillips Memorial Scholarship **Area, Field, or Subject:** General studies/Field of study not specified **Level of Education**

for which **Award is Granted:** Undergraduate **Number Awarded:** Varies each year; recently, 175 new and 416 renewal scholarships were awarded. **Funds Available:** Stipends generally range from $3,000 to $10,000 per year. Funds are paid in 2 equal installments to the recipient's school and must be used to pay for tuition and fees. **Duration:** 1 year; may be renewed for up to 3 additional years, provided the recipient maintains a GPA of 2.5 or higher.

Eligibility Requirements: This program is open to residents of the New England and mid-Atlantic states (Connecticut, Delaware, District of Columbia, Maine, Maryland, Massachusetts, New Hampshire, New Jersey, New York, Pennsylvania, Rhode Island, Vermont, Virginia, or West Virginia) who are entering or returning college students. Preference is given to graduating high school seniors. Applicants must have a GPA of 3.0 or higher, be enrolled in a demanding course of study, demonstrate skilled writing ability, have at least 1100 on their SATs (or 22 on their ACTs), and rank in the top 20% of their graduating high school class. In addition, they should demonstrate a desire to make a meaningful contribution to society; be involved in a balance of community, school, and work activities; be able to demonstrate integrity, resolution, self-discipline, and judgment; and have substantial unmet financial need. **Deadline for Receipt:** April of each year.

1459 ■ PINNACOL FOUNDATION

Attn: Elizabeth Starkey
7501 East Lowry Boulevard
Denver, CO 80230
Tel: (303)361-4775
Free: 800-873-7248
Fax: (303)361-5775
Web Site: http://www.pinnacol.com/foundation
To provide financial assistance for college to Colorado residents whose parent was killed or permanently disabled in a work-related accident.
Title of Award: Pinnacol Foundation Scholarship Program **Area, Field, or Subject:** General studies/Field of study not specified **Level of Education for which Award is Granted:** Undergraduate **Number Awarded:** Varies each year; recently, 31 of these scholarships were awarded. **Funds Available:** The stipend depends on the need of the recipient. **Duration:** 1 year; may be renewed.
Eligibility Requirements: This program is open to the natural, adopted, step, or fully dependent children of workers killed or permanently injured in a compensable work-related accident during the course and scope of employment with a Colorado-based employer and entitled to receive benefits under the Colorado Workers' Compensation Act. Applicants must be between 16 and 24 years of age and attending or planning to attend a college or technical school. Selection is based on academic achievement and aptitude, community service, and financial need. **Deadline for Receipt:** March of each year. **Additional Information:** Pinnacol Assurance, a workers' compensation insurance carrier, established this program in 2001. Students are eligible regardless of the insurance carrier for their parent's accident.

1460 ■ PKU ORGANIZATION OF ILLINOIS

P.O. Box 102
Palatine, IL 60078-0102
Tel: (630)415-2219
Fax: (208)978-8963
E-mail: info@pkuil.org
Web Site: http://www.pkuil.org
To provide financial assistance for college to Illinois residents who have been diagnosed with phenylketonuria (PKU).
Title of Award: Andrew Craig Memorial Scholarship **Area, Field, or Subject:** General studies/Field of study not specified **Level of Education for which Award is Granted:** Undergraduate **Number Awarded:** 2 each year. **Funds Available:** The stipend is $1,000 per year. **Duration:** 1 year; recipients may reapply but not in successive years.
Eligibility Requirements: This program is open to residents of Illinois who have been diagnosed with either classic or variant PKU. Applicants must be 17 years of age or older and either 1) entering college or vocational school, or 2) returning to school for a degree. Along with their application, they must submit a short essay about themselves, their experiences with PKU, and their future aspirations. **Deadline for Receipt:** August of each year. **Additional Information:** This program was established in 1997. Information is also available from Peter Neill, (630)

922-9330, E-mail: pneill@odysseytel.com.

1461 ■ POINT FOUNDATION

P.O. Box 11210
Chicago, IL 60611
(866)33-POINT
Fax: (866)39-POINT
E-mail: info@thepointfoundation.org
Web Site: http://www.thepointfoundation.org
To provide financial assistance for college or graduate school to students who have been involved in the lesbian, gay, bisexual, or transgender (LGBT) community.
Title of Award: Point Foundation Scholarships **Area, Field, or Subject:** General studies/Field of study not specified **Level of Education for which Award is Granted:** Graduate, Undergraduate **Number Awarded:** Varies each year; recently, 20 of these scholarships were awarded. **Funds Available:** Stipends range from $5,000 to $28,000 per year. **Duration:** 1 year; may be renewed if the recipient maintains a GPA of 3.5 or higher.
Eligibility Requirements: This program is open to citizens of any country who are attending or planning to attend a college or university in the United States to work on an undergraduate or graduate degree. Applicants are not required to be LGBT, but they should have a history of leadership in the LGBT community and plan to be a LGBT leader in the future. Selection is based on academic accomplishment; financial, emotional, and social need; extracurricular activities; personal circumstances; and goals. **Deadline for Receipt:** February of each year. **Additional Information:** This program began in 2001. It includes the following named scholarships the Merle Aronson Scholarship, the Carlos Enrique Cisneros Scholarship (for students at American University in Washington, D.C.), the Walter M. Decker Scholarship, the Bryan L. Knapp Scholarship (for students from the New York City area at Cornell University in Ithaca, New York) the Elsie De Wolfe Scholarship, and the mtvU Scholarship (for students at universities participating in the mtvU program).

1462 ■ POLISH NATIONAL ALLIANCE

Attn: Education Department
6100 North Cicero Avenue
Chicago, IL 60646-4386
Tel: (773)286-0500
Free: 800-621-3723
E-mail: mary.srodon@pna-znp.org
Web Site: http://www.pna-znp.org/content/educationaldept/scholarships.htm
To provide financial assistance for college to members of the Polish National Alliance (PNA).
Title of Award: Polish National Alliance Scholarships **Area, Field, or Subject:** General studies/Field of study not specified **Level of Education for which Award is Granted:** Four Year College **Number Awarded:** Varies each year; a total of $250,000 is available for scholarships each year. **Funds Available:** Stipends range from $500 to $1,500. Funds are paid directly to the recipient's college. **Duration:** 1 year.
Eligibility Requirements: This program is open to full-time college sophomores, juniors, and seniors (incoming freshmen are not eligible to apply) who have been beneficial premium paying members of PNA for at least 3 years; also eligible are students who have been members of PNA for only 2 years but whose parents have been members for at least 5 years. Applicants who joined PNA after January 1, 1999 must have a premium paying permanent plan of insurance that excludes modified life paid up at 65 and annuities. Applicants who joined after January 1, 2002 must have a premium paying permanent plan such as universal life, ordinary life, executive life paid up at 90, life paid up at 65, 20 pay life, or single premium whole life. Selection is based on academic record, educational goals, involvement in fraternal and youth activities of the PNA, family PNA membership, and participation in church, community, and college activities. **Deadline for Receipt:** April of each year. **Additional Information:** Recipients may study only at U.S. colleges or universities.

1463 ■ POLISH ROMAN CATHOLIC UNION OF AMERICA

Attn: Education Fund Scholarship Program
984 North Milwaukee Avenue
Chicago, IL 60622-4101

Tel: (773)782-2600
Free: 800-772-8632
Fax: (773)278-4595
E-mail: info@prcua.org
Web Site: http://www.prcua.org/benefits/educationfundscholarship.htm
To provide financial assistance to undergraduate and graduate students of Polish heritage.

Title of Award: Stanley W. Marion Fund **Area, Field, or Subject:** General studies/Field of study not specified **Level of Education for which Award is Granted:** Graduate, Undergraduate **Number Awarded:** 1 or more each year. **Funds Available:** A stipend is awarded (amount not specified). Funds are paid directly to the institution. **Duration:** 1 year.
Eligibility Requirements: This program is open to students enrolled full time as sophomores, juniors, and seniors in an undergraduate program or full or part time as a graduate or professional school students. Selection is based on academic achievement, Polonia involvement, and community service. **Deadline for Receipt:** May of each year.

1464 ■ POLISH ROMAN CATHOLIC UNION OF AMERICA

Attn: Secretary-Treasurer
984 North Milwaukee Avenue
Chicago, IL 60622-4101
Tel: (773)782-2600
Free: 800-772-8632
Fax: (773)278-4595
E-mail: info@prcua.org
Web Site: http://www.prcua.org/benefits/educationalloan.htm
To provide loans for college to members of the Polish Roman Catholic Union of American (PRCUA).

Title of Award: Polish Roman Catholic Union of America Educational Loans **Area, Field, or Subject:** General studies/Field of study not specified **Level of Education for which Award is Granted:** Undergraduate **Number Awarded:** Varies each year. **Funds Available:** The maximum loan is $1,000 per year. Funds may be used only for tuition and are issued jointly to the student and the school. No interest is charged while the student remains in school, but repayment must begin within 6 months of graduating or leaving school with interest at 5%. **Duration:** 1 year; may be renewed up to 3 additional years.
Eligibility Requirements: This program is open to active PRCUA members who have held at least $5,000 in permanent life insurance for at least 1 year. Applicants must be attending or planning to attend an accredited college or university as a full-time student.

1465 ■ POLISH ROMAN CATHOLIC UNION OF AMERICA

Attn: President
984 North Milwaukee Avenue
Chicago, IL 60622-4101
Tel: (773)782-2600
Free: 800-772-8632
Fax: (773)278-4595
E-mail: info@prcua.org
Web Site: http://www.prcua.org/benefits/scholarship.htm
To provide financial assistance for college or graduate school to members of the Polish Roman Catholic Union of American (PRCUA).
Title of Award: Polish Roman Catholic Union of America Student Scholarships **Area, Field, or Subject:** General studies/Field of study not specified **Level of Education for which Award is Granted:** Graduate, Undergraduate **Number Awarded:** Varies each year. **Funds Available:** A stipend is awarded (amount not specified). Funds are paid directly to the institution. **Duration:** 1 year; may be renewed up to 3 additional years.
Eligibility Requirements: This program is open to active PRCUA members who have held at least $5,000 in permanent life insurance for at least 5 years. Applicants must be enrolled as a full-time sophomore, junior, or senior in an undergraduate program or as a graduate or professional student. They must have a GPA of 2.5 or higher. Along with their application, they must submit a 500-word essay on "How I can use my degree to benefit my Polish heritage." Selection is based on that essay and statements on their career goals and how they plan to achieve those goals, educational and other accomplishments, educational organizations

to which they belong, and extracurricular activities. U.S. citizenship or permanent resident status is required. **Deadline for Receipt:** June of each year.

1466 ■ POP WARNER LITTLE SCHOLARS, INC.

Attn: Director of Scholastics
586 Middletown Boulevard, Suite C-100
Langhorne, PA 19047-1829
Tel: (215)752-2691
Fax: (215)752-2879
E-mail: scholastics@popwarner.com
Web Site: http://www.popwarner.com/scholastics/pop.asp
To provide financial assistance for college to Pop Warner football players or cheerleaders.

Title of Award: Pop Warner Little Scholars Scholastic Awards **Area, Field, or Subject:** General studies/Field of study not specified **Level of Education for which Award is Granted:** Undergraduate **Number Awarded:** Varies each year. Recently, 67 of these scholarships were awarded: 2 at $5,000, 2 at $2,500, 1 at $1,250, 31 at $1,000, 1 at $750, 1 at $625 and 29 at $500. **Funds Available:** Stipends range from $500 to $5,000. The funds are held in escrow until the recipient enters college; at that time, the sponsor sends the scholarship amount directly to the chosen institution. **Duration:** The stipends are awarded annually.
Eligibility Requirements: This program is open to Pop Warner players or cheerleaders who are currently in the fifth through eighth grades (or above). Applicants need a 96% average or better to be considered and should have been involved in school-affiliated organizations and/or academic clubs. Selection is based on school marks, other academic accomplishments, and club involvements. The top 35 players and 25 cheerleaders in each of 4 grade categories (fifth through eighth grades or above) are named to the "Pop Warner First Team of All-American Scholars." The Senior First Team of All-American Scholars (those in the eighth grade or above) are considered for this scholarship. **Deadline for Receipt:** Regional associations submit nominations in January of each year.

1467 ■ POSSIBLE WOMAN ENTERPRISES

Attn: Possible Woman Foundation International
2968 Four Oaks Drive
Atlanta, GA 30360
Tel: (770)863-1515; 888-663-4767
Fax: (770)863-1090
E-mail: denise@possiblewomanfoundation.org
Web Site: http://www.possiblewomanfoundation.org/Home.htm
To provide financial assistance for college or graduate school to women of all ages.

Title of Award: Possible Woman Foundation International Scholarship **Area, Field, or Subject:** General studies/Field of study not specified **Level of Education for which Award is Granted:** Graduate, Undergraduate **Number Awarded:** 1 each year. **Funds Available:** The stipend ranges from $3,000 to $3,500. **Duration:** 1 year; nonrenewable.
Eligibility Requirements: This program is open to women who are changing careers and/or seeking advancement in their current career or worklife; stay at home mothers looking to enhance their skills; volunteers supporting society through giving to organizations in the community; and young women in the early stages of achieving their educational aspirations. Applicants may be of any age and at any level of education (high school graduate, some college, 4-year college graduate, graduate school, doctoral). Along with their application, they must submit a 2-page essay on the topic, "How Having the Opportunity for Beginning or Continuing My Academic Education Will Positively Impact My Life." Selection is based on the essay, career and life goals, leadership and participation in community activities, honors and awards received, and financial need. **Deadline for Receipt:** March of each year.

1468 ■ PROFESSIONAL BOWLERS ASSOCIATION

Attn: Billy Welu Bowling Scholarship
719 Second Avenue, Suite 701
Seattle, WA 98104
Tel: (206)332-9688
Fax: (206)654-6030
Web Site: http://www.pba.com/corporate/scholarships.asp

To provide financial assistance to college students who are active bowlers.

Title of Award: Billy Welu Scholarship **Area, Field, or Subject:** General studies/Field of study not specified **Level of Education for which Award is Granted:** Undergraduate **Number Awarded:** 1 each year. **Funds Available:** The stipend is $1,000. **Duration:** 1 year.

Eligibility Requirements: This program is open to currently-enrolled college students who compete in the sport of bowling. Applicants must submit a 500-word essay describing how the scholarship will positively affect their bowling, academic, and personal goals. They must have a GPA of 2.5 or higher. Financial need is not considered in the selection process. **Deadline for Receipt:** May of each year.

1469 ■ PUEBLO OF ISLETA

Attn: Higher Education Program
P.O. Box 1270
Isleta, NM 87022
Tel: (505)869-2680
Fax: (505)869-7690
Web Site: http://

To provide financial assistance for undergraduate or graduate study to members of the Pueblo of Isleta.

Title of Award: Pueblo of Isleta Higher Education Program **Area, Field, or Subject:** General studies/Field of study not specified **Level of Education for which Award is Granted:** Graduate, Undergraduate **Number Awarded:** Varies each year. **Funds Available:** The stipend depends on the need of the recipient. **Duration:** 1 year; may be renewed if the recipient maintains a GPA of 2.5 or higher.

Eligibility Requirements: This program is open to undergraduate and graduate students who can document tribal membership in the Pueblo of Isleta or at least one-quarter Isleta blood. Applicants must have a GPA of 2.5 or higher and be able to demonstrate financial need They must have applied for federal aid by submitting a Free Application for Federal Student Aid (FAFSA). **Deadline for Receipt:** June of each year for the academic year; October of each year for the spring semester or winter quarter; March of each year for summer term.

1470 ■ PUEBLO OF JEMEZ

Attn: Higher Education Center
P.O. Box 60
Jemez Pueblo, NM 87024
Tel: (505)834-9102; 888-834-3936
Fax: (505)834-7900
E-mail: scholarships@jemezpueblo.org
Web Site: http://www.jemezpueblo.org/education/highered/scholar/tribal.html

To provide financial assistance to Jemez Pueblo students who are interested in earning a college degree.

Title of Award: Pueblo of Jemez Scholarship Program **Area, Field, or Subject:** General studies/Field of study not specified **Level of Education for which Award is Granted:** Undergraduate **Number Awarded:** Varies each year. **Funds Available:** The stipend depends on the need of the recipient. **Duration:** 1 semester; may be renewed if the recipient remains enrolled full time with a GPA of 2.0 or higher.

Eligibility Requirements: This program is open to Jemez Pueblo students working on or planning to work on an associate or bachelor's degree at an accredited institution of higher education as a full-time student. Applicants must be at least one quarter Jemez and recognized under the Jemez Pueblo census office (a Certificate of Degree of Indian Blood must be provided). They must submit 2 letters of recommendation, a copy of their letter of acceptance from the institution they are or are planning to attend, and an official transcript from the high school or college they last attended. It is required that all students fill out the Free Application for Federal Student Aid (FAFSA) and apply for aid from the college they plan to attend. **Deadline for Receipt:** April of each year for fall semester; October of each year for spring semester.

1471 ■ PUEBLO OF LAGUNA

Attn: Laguna Acoma Vocational Rehabilitation Project
P.O. Box 550
New Laguna, NM 87038
Tel: (505)552-0619
Fax: (505)552-0623

E-mail: grpotter@hotmail.com
Web Site: http://www.ldoe.org/vocrehab.htm

To provide vocational rehabilitation to American Indian adults with disabilities who reside on the Laguna and Acoma reservations in New Mexico.

Title of Award: Laguna Acoma Vocational Rehabilitation **Area, Field, or Subject:** General studies/Field of study not specified **Level of Education for which Award is Granted:** Vocational/Occupational **Number Awarded:** Varies each year. **Funds Available:** This program provides services based on individual need and interest, availability of jobs, and selection of career goals. **Duration:** Services are provided until the participant obtains employment.

Eligibility Requirements: This program is open to residents of the Laguna and Acoma reservations who either apply directly or are referred by an agency, family member, or community member. Applicants must have a physical or mental impairment that is a barrier to employment and require services in order to prepare for, enter, or obtain employment. They must submit a Certificate of Degree of Indian Blood and (if they are receiving Supplemental Security Income) the SSI letter indicating eligibility for monthly support. **Deadline for Receipt:** Applications may be submitted at any time.

1472 ■ PUEBLO OF LAGUNA

Attn: Higher Education Program
P.O. Box 207
Laguna, NM 87026
Tel: (505)552-7182
Fax: (505)552-7235
E-mail: m.conant@lagunaed.net
Web Site: http://www.ldoe.org/highered.htm

To provide financial assistance for college or graduate school to regular members of the Pueblo of Laguna.

Title of Award: Pueblo of Laguna Higher Education Program **Area, Field, or Subject:** General studies/Field of study not specified **Level of Education for which Award is Granted:** Graduate, Undergraduate **Number Awarded:** Varies each year. **Funds Available:** Undergraduate stipends are intended to cover unmet financial need, to a maximum of $8,000 per year. Most awards range from $2,000 to $5,000 per academic year. Limited funding is available for graduate students. **Duration:** 1 year; may be renewed for a maximum of 5 academic years if the recipient maintains full-time enrollment and a GPA of 2.0 or higher.

Eligibility Requirements: This program is open to regular enrolled members of the Pueblo of Laguna. Applicants must have a high school diploma or GED certificate and be working on a bachelor's, graduate, or transferable associate degree. They must have been accepted by an accredited college or university in the United States as a full-time student. Along with their application, they must submit documentation of financial need, a 1-page personal statement on their purpose for working on a degree in their chosen field of study and their career or professional goals, high school and/or college transcripts, ACT scores, and verification of tribal membership or Indian blood. Vocational students, part-time students, and "naturalized" Laguna tribal members are not eligible. **Deadline for Receipt:** May of each year for the fall term or academic year; September of each year for the winter/spring term.

1473 ■ PUEBLO OF ZUNI

Attn: Education and Career Development Center
P.O. Box 339
Zuni, NM 87327
Tel: (505)782-7178
Fax: (505)782-7223
E-mail: zunihe@hotmail.com
Web Site: http://www.ashiwi.org/highered/higheredmain.html

To provide financial assistance for college or graduate school to members of the Pueblo of Zuni.

Title of Award: Zuni Higher Education Scholarships **Area, Field, or Subject:** General studies/Field of study not specified **Level of Education for which Award is Granted:** Graduate, Undergraduate **Number Awarded:** Varies each year. **Funds Available:** The amount awarded depends on the need of the recipient, up to $5,000 per year. **Duration:** 1 year; may be renewed if the recipient maintains a GPA of 2.0 or higher.

Eligibility Requirements: This program is open to enrolled members of the Pueblo of Zuni who are high school seniors or graduates. Applicants must have earned a GPA of 2.0 or higher and be interested in working on an associate, bachelor's, or graduate degree as a full-time student. They must have also applied for a federal Pell Grant. **Deadline for Receipt:** April of each year for the summer session; June of each year for the fall term; October of each year for the spring term.

1474 ■ PUERTO RICO NATIONAL GUARD

Attn: Education Services Officer
P.O. Box 9023786
San Juan, PR 00902-3786
Tel: (787)721-3131
Fax: (787)723-6360
E-mail: ortegaj@pr.ngb.army.mil
To provide financial assistance for college or graduate school to National Guard members in Puerto Rico and their families.
Title of Award: Puerto Rico National Guard Tuition Assistance Fund **Area, Field, or Subject:** General studies/Field of study not specified **Level of Education for which Award is Granted:** Graduate, Undergraduate **Number Awarded:** Varies each year. **Funds Available:** For Guard members, the program pays $50 per credit to a maximum of $900 per year for undergraduate or vocational study, $75 per credit to a maximum of $1,350 per year for graduate study, or a maximum of $1,000 per year for study for an M.D. degree. For spouses, the program pays $75 per credit to a maximum of $1,350 per semester for graduate study. For spouses and children, the program pays $50 per credit to a maximum of $900 per semester for undergraduate or vocational study ($1,800 per year). **Duration:** 1 year; may be renewed. Guard members are limited to 18 credits of study per year; spouses and children are limited to 18 credits per semester.
Eligibility Requirements: This program is open to 1) active members of the Puerto Rico National Guard who are interested in preparing for a career on the undergraduate or graduate level (up to the Ph.D. degree); 2) spouses of members interested in working on an undergraduate or graduate degree (up to a master's degree); and 3) children of members interested in undergraduate or vocational study. Guard members may not receive support at the same time as a spouse and/or child.

1475 ■ DAWN RAMOS PRODUCTIONS

607 South Loving Avenue
Sherman, TX 75090-6743
Tel: (903)891-9761
E-mail: info@misslatina.com
Web Site: http://www.misslatina.com
To recognize and reward young Latina women who compete in a national beauty pageant.
Title of Award: Ms. Latina USA **Area, Field, or Subject:** General studies/Field of study not specified **Level of Education for which Award is Granted:** Undergraduate, Other **Number Awarded:** 1 winner and 4 runners-up are selected each year. **Funds Available:** Each year, prizes include scholarships, gifts, a cruise to the Bahamas, a trip to Las Vegas, a modeling contract, and use of an apartment in Miami. The total value is more than $100,000. **Duration:** The pageant is held annually
Eligibility Requirements: This program is open to women between 18 and 29 years of age who are at least 25% Hispanic. Applicants may be single, married, or divorced, and they may have children. They appear in a nationally-televised pageant where selection is based one third on an interview, one third on swimsuit appearances, and one third on evening gown appearances. Height and weight are not factors, but contestants should be proportionate. Pageant experience and fluency in Spanish are not required.

1476 ■ DAWN RAMOS PRODUCTIONS

607 South Loving Avenue
Sherman, TX 75090-6743
Tel: (903)891-9761
E-mail: info@misslatina.com
Web Site: http://www.misslatina.com
To recognize and reward teen-aged Latina women who compete in a national beauty pageant.
Title of Award: Teen Latina USA **Area, Field, or Subject:** General studies/Field of study not specified **Level of Education for which Award is Granted:** Undergraduate **Number Awarded:** 1 winner and 4 runners-up are selected each year. **Funds Available:** Each year, prizes

include scholarships, gifts, a cruise to the Bahamas, a trip to Las Vegas, a modeling contract, and use of an apartment in Miami. The total value is more than $25,000. **Duration:** The pageant is held annually
Eligibility Requirements: This program is open to women between 13 and 17 years of age who are at least 25% Hispanic. Applicants must be single and they may not have children. They appear in a nationally-televised pageant where selection is based one third on an interview, one third on swimsuit appearances, and one third on evening gown appearances. Height and weight are not factors, but contestants should be proportionate. Pageant experience and fluency in Spanish are not required.

1477 ■ JAY RAMSDELL FOUNDATION

Attn: Daniel Lay
First National Bank
Trust Department
P.O. Box 258
Bar Harbor, ME 04609
E-mail: oct60@acadia.net
Web Site: http://www.jramsdellfoundation.org
To provide financial assistance for college to high school seniors in Maine who have been active in athletics.
Title of Award: Jay Ramsdell Scholarships **Area, Field, or Subject:** General studies/Field of study not specified **Level of Education for which Award is Granted:** Undergraduate **Number Awarded:** 1 each year. **Funds Available:** The stipend is $5,000. Funds are paid to the college or university after the recipient has successfully completed the first semester and is enrolled for the second semester. **Duration:** 1 year; recipients may reapply.
Eligibility Requirements: This program is open to residents of Maine who are seniors graduating from a high school in the state. Students must be nominated by the athletic director at their high school; each director may nominate 1 student. Nominees must have been active in athletics; special attention is paid to team managers and statisticians. Financial need must be demonstrated, although need is not the primary consideration in making the award. **Additional Information:** These scholarships were first awarded in 1990.

1478 ■ JIMMY RANE FOUNDATION

1100 Highway 431 North
P.O. Box 40
Abbeville, AL 36310
Tel: (334)585-9505; (866)606-2470
E-mail: info@jimmyranefoundation.org
Web Site: http://www.jimmyranefoundation.org
To provide financial assistance for college to students who can demonstrate financial need.
Title of Award: Jimmy Rane Foundation Scholarships **Area, Field, or Subject:** General studies/Field of study not specified **Level of Education for which Award is Granted:** Undergraduate **Number Awarded:** Varies each year; recently, 17 of these scholarships were awarded. **Funds Available:** 1 year; may be renewed up to 3 additional years. **Duration:** The stipend depends on the need of the recipient.
Eligibility Requirements: This program is open to high school seniors and students enrolled in college or vocational institutions; preference is given to high school seniors. Applicants must submit a biography that includes school and unpaid community activities, special awards, honors, and offices held; an essay on why they feel they should be awarded this scholarship, including their plans as they relate to their education, career, and long-term goals; 3 letters of recommendation; and documentation of financial need. **Deadline for Receipt:** February of each year. **Additional Information:** This program was established in 2002.

1479 ■ JEANNETTE RANKIN FOUNDATION, INC.

P.O. Box 6653
Athens, GA 30604-6653
Tel: (706)208-1211
Fax: (706)548-0202
E-mail: info@rankinfoundation.org
Web Site: http://www.rankinfoundation.org
To provide financial assistance for college to women who are 35 years or older.
Title of Award: Jeannette Rankin Award **Area, Field, or Subject:** General studies/Field of study not specified **Level of Education for**

which **Award is Granted:** Undergraduate **Number Awarded:** Varies each year; recently, 45 of these scholarships were awarded. **Funds Available:** The stipend is $2,000. **Duration:** 1 year; nonrenewable.
Eligibility Requirements: Women who are 35 years of age or older are eligible to apply for this scholarship if they are in financial need and have clear educational goals. They must be U.S. citizens and enrolled in a certified program of technical/vocational training or undergraduate education. **Deadline for Receipt:** February of each year. **Additional Information:** This program began in 1978. Awards are not given to students enrolled in graduate courses or working on a second undergraduate degree.

1480 ■ REBEKAH ASSEMBLY OF TEXAS
Attn: Scholarship Committee
16400 KC Road 4060
Scurry, TX 75158
To provide financial assistance for college to high school seniors in Texas.
Title of Award: Irma Gesche Scholarship **Area, Field, or Subject:** General studies/Field of study not specified **Level of Education for which Award is Granted:** Undergraduate **Number Awarded:** 1 each year. **Funds Available:** The stipend is $1,000. **Duration:** 1 year.
Eligibility Requirements: This scholarship is available to Texas high school seniors who are interested in attending a 2-year or 4-year college or university in the state. Selection is based on academic ability, community service, personal development, and financial need. Applicants must submit a completed application along with a high school transcript, a typed letter describing their educational goals, and 3 letters of recommendation. **Deadline for Receipt:** December of each year.

1481 ■ RECORDING FOR THE BLIND AND DYSLEXIC
Attn: Strategic Communications Department
Anne T. Macdonald Center
20 Roszel Road
Princeton, NJ 08540
Tel: (609)520-8044; (866)RFBD-585
E-mail: jhaggith@rfbd.org
Web Site: http://www.rfbd.org/applications_awards.htm
To provide financial assistance to outstanding high school students with learning disabilities who plan to continue their education.
Title of Award: Marion Huber Learning through Listening Awards **Area, Field, or Subject:** General studies/Field of study not specified **Level of Education for which Award is Granted:** Undergraduate **Number Awarded:** 6 each year: 3 at $6,000 and 3 at $2,000. **Funds Available:** Stipends are $6,000 or $2,000. **Duration:** 1 year.
Eligibility Requirements: This program is open to seniors graduating from public or private high schools in the United States or its territories who have a specific learning disability (visual impairment alone does not satisfy this requirement). Applicants must be planning to continue their education at a 2-year or 4-year college or vocational school. They must be registered Recording for the Blind and Dyslexic borrowers and have earned a GPA of 3.0 or higher in grades 10-12. Selection is based on outstanding scholastic achievement, leadership, enterprise, and service to others. **Deadline for Receipt:** February of each year. **Additional Information:** This program was established in 1992.

1482 ■ RECORDING FOR THE BLIND AND DYSLEXIC
Attn: Strategic Communications Department
Anne T. Macdonald Center
20 Roszel Road
Princeton, NJ 08540
Tel: (609)520-8044; (866)RFBD-585
E-mail: jhaggith@rfbd.org
Web Site: http://www.rfbd.org/applications_awards.htm
To recognize and reward the outstanding academic achievements of blind college seniors.
Title of Award: Mary P. Oenslager Scholastic Achievement Awards **Area, Field, or Subject:** General studies/Field of study not specified **Level of Education for which Award is Granted:** Four Year College, Professional **Number Awarded:** 9 each year: 3 Top winners, 3 Special Honors winners, and 3 Honors winners. **Funds Available:** Top winners receive $6,000 each, Special Honors winners $3,000 each, and Honors winners $1,000 each. **Duration:** The awards are presented annually.
Eligibility Requirements: To be eligible for this award, candidates must 1) be legally blind; 2) have received, or will receive, a bachelor's degree

from a 4-year accredited college or university in the United States or its territories during the year the award is given; 3) have an overall academic average of 3.0 or higher; and 4) have been registered borrowers from Recording for the Blind and Dyslexic for at least 1 year and have borrowed at least 1 of its audiobooks during that time. Selection is based on evidence of leadership, enterprise, and service to others. **Deadline for Receipt:** February of each year. **Additional Information:** These awards are named for the founder of the program who established it in 1959 and endowed it with a gift of $1 million in 1990.

1483 ■ RED RIVER VALLEY ASSOCIATION FOUNDATION
P.O. Box 1916
Harrisonburg, VA 22801
Tel: (540)442-7782
Fax: (540)443-3105
E-mail: afbridger@aol.com
Web Site: http://www.river-rats.org
To provide financial assistance for college or graduate school to the spouses and children of selected service personnel and members of the Red River Valley Fighter Pilots Association.
Title of Award: Red River Valley Fighter Pilots Association Scholarship Grant Program **Area, Field, or Subject:** General studies/Field of study not specified **Level of Education for which Award is Granted:** Graduate, Undergraduate **Number Awarded:** Varies each year; since this program was established, it has awarded more than 900 scholarships worth nearly $1,500,000. **Funds Available:** The amount awarded varies, depending upon the need of the recipient. Recently, undergraduate stipends have ranged from $500 to $3,500 and averaged $1,725; graduate stipends have ranged from $500 to $2,000 and averaged $1,670. Funds are paid directly to the recipient's institution and are to be used for tuition, fees, books, and room and board for full-time students. **Duration:** 1 year.
Eligibility Requirements: This program is open to the spouses and children of 1) service members missing in action (MIA) or killed in action (KIA) in armed conflicts by U.S. forces since August 1964, including those lost in the World Trade Center or Pentagon on September 11, 2001; 2) surviving dependents of U.S. military aircrew members killed in a non-combat aircraft accident in which they were performing aircrew duties; and 3) current members of the association and deceased members who were in good standing at the time of their death. Applicants must be interested in attending an accredited college or university to work on an undergraduate or graduate degree. Selection is based on demonstrated academic achievement, college entrance examination scores, financial need, and accomplishments in school, church, civic, and social activities. **Deadline for Receipt:** May of each year. **Additional Information:** This program was established in 1970, out of concern for the families of aircrews (known as "River Rats") who were killed or missing in action in the Red River Valley of North Vietnam. Information is also available from Herm Davis, 16728 Frontenac Terrace, Rockville, MD 20855, (301) 548-9423.

1484 ■ CLIFFORD H. "TED" REES, JR. SCHOLARSHIP FOUNDATION
Attn: ARI Director of Education
4100 North Fairfax Drive, Suite 200
Arlington, VA 22203
Tel: (703)524-8800
Fax: (703)528-3816
E-mail: rmach@ari.org
Web Site: http://www.reesscholarship.org
To provide financial assistance to students preparing for a career as a heating, ventilation, air-conditioning, and refrigeration (HVACR) technician.
Title of Award: Clifford H. "Ted" Rees, Jr. Scholarship **Area, Field, or Subject:** Heating, air conditioning, and refrigeration **Level of Education for which Award is Granted:** Vocational/Occupational **Number Awarded:** 2 each year. **Funds Available:** The stipend is $2,000. **Duration:** 1 year; nonrenewable.
Eligibility Requirements: This program is open to U.S. citizens and permanent residents who are enrolled in a program for preparation for a career in residential air-conditioning and heating, light commercial air-conditioning and heating, or commercial refrigeration. They must be enrolled in a training program at an institutionally accredited school. Along

with their application, they must submit an essay of 150 to 200 words on why this scholarship should be awarded to them. **Deadline for Receipt:** October of each year.

1485 ■ THE RETIRED ENLISTED ASSOCIATION

Attn: National Scholarship Committee
1111 South Abilene Court
Aurora, CO 80012-4909
Tel: (303)752-0660
Free: 800-338-9337
Fax: (303)752-0835
E-mail: treahq@trea.org
Web Site: http://www.trea.org/scholarship/index.html
To provide financial assistance for college to the dependents of members of The Retired Enlisted Association (TREA).

Title of Award: TREA National Scholarships **Area, Field, or Subject:** General studies/Field of study not specified **Level of Education for which Award is Granted:** Undergraduate **Number Awarded:** 40 each year. **Funds Available:** The stipends are $1,000 per year. **Duration:** 1 year; recipients may reapply.
Eligibility Requirements: This program is open to dependent children and grandchildren of association or auxiliary members who are high school seniors or full-time college students and interested in pursuing postsecondary education. Selection is based on a 300-word essay on "What Higher Education Means to Me," 2 letters of recommendation, educational accomplishments, extracurricular activities, work experience, and financial need. **Deadline for Receipt:** April of each year. **Additional Information:** Recipients may attend technical schools, 4-year colleges, or universities.

1486 ■ RHODE ISLAND FOUNDATION

Attn: Scholarship Coordinator
One Union Station
Providence, RI 02903
Tel: (401)274-4564
Fax: (401)331-8085
E-mail: libbym@rifoundation.org
Web Site: http://www.rifoundation.org
To provide financial assistance for college to students in Rhode Island whose parents did not attend college.

Title of Award: Patty & Melvin Alperin First Generation Scholarship **Area, Field, or Subject:** General studies/Field of study not specified **Level of Education for which Award is Granted:** Undergraduate **Number Awarded:** Varies each year. Recently, 13 of these scholarships were awarded: 4 new awards and 9 renewals. **Funds Available:** The stipend ranges up to $1,000. **Duration:** 1 year; may be renewed for up to 3 additional years if the recipient maintains good academic standing.
Eligibility Requirements: This program is open to college-bound Rhode Island high school seniors and graduates whose parents did not have the benefit of attending college. Applicants must intend to work on either a 2-year degree at an accredited nonprofit postsecondary institution or a 4-year college degree. Along with their application, they must submit an essay (up to 300 words) on what it means to them to be of the first generation in their family to work on a college degree. Selection is based on academic excellence, character, and financial need. **Deadline for Receipt:** May of each year.

1487 ■ RHODE ISLAND FOUNDATION

Attn: Scholarship Coordinator
One Union Station
Providence, RI 02903
Tel: (401)274-4564
Fax: (401)331-8085
E-mail: libbym@rifoundation.org
Web Site: http://www.rifoundation.org
To provide financial assistance for college to spouses and dependents of workers insured by Beacon Mutual Insurance Company who were killed or permanently disabled in industrial accidents.
Title of Award: Beacon Brighter Tomorrows Scholarship **Area, Field, or Subject:** General studies/Field of study not specified **Level of Education for which Award is Granted:** Undergraduate **Number Awarded:** 1 to 2 each year. **Funds Available:** Stipends range from $1,000 to $2,000.
Eligibility Requirements: This program is open to spouses and/or legal dependents of workers insured by the company who were killed or permanently disabled in an industrial accident. Applicants must have been accepted into an accredited postsecondary institution on a full- or part-time basis. They must submit an essay (up to 300 words) on what they hope they will be doing in their professional life 10 years from now. Financial need is considered in the selection process. **Deadline for Receipt:** May of each year.

1488 ■ RHODE ISLAND FOUNDATION

Attn: Scholarship Coordinator
One Union Station
Providence, RI 02903
Tel: (401)274-4564
Fax: (401)331-8085
E-mail: libbym@rifoundation.org
Web Site: http://www.rifoundation.org
To provide financial assistance to college students in Rhode Island for nontraditional enrichment experiences.

Title of Award: Michael P. Metcalf Memorial Scholarship **Area, Field, or Subject:** General studies/Field of study not specified **Level of Education for which Award is Granted:** Undergraduate **Number Awarded:** Varies each year; recently, 3 of these awards were granted. **Funds Available:** Stipends range up to $5,000. **Duration:** These are 1-time awards.
Eligibility Requirements: This program is open to college sophomores and juniors who are legal residents of Rhode Island. They may apply for grants to subsidize experiences intended to broaden their perspective and enhance their personal growth. These may include, but are not limited to, travel in this country and abroad and a variety of internship and public service programs. Traditional programs and those that are a regular part of the applicant's curriculum (e.g., junior year abroad, departmentally-sponsored summer research program) are not funded. Grants may not be used to purchase equipment. Applicants must show financial need. Criteria for evaluating applications include: clarity and thoughtfulness of application, creativity and motivation of proposed project, evidence of self direction and initiative, and financial need. **Deadline for Receipt:** January of each year. **Additional Information:** This award was established in 1989 to honor the memory of Michael P. Metcalf, publisher of the *Providence Journal*.

1489 ■ RHODE ISLAND FOUNDATION

Attn: Scholarship Coordinator
One Union Station
Providence, RI 02903
Tel: (401)274-4564
Fax: (401)331-8085
E-mail: libbym@rifoundation.org
Web Site: http://www.rifoundation.org
To provide financial assistance for college to graduating high school seniors in Rhode Island who have been involved in public service activities.

Title of Award: Rhode Island Association of Former Legislators Scholarship **Area, Field, or Subject:** General studies/Field of study not specified **Level of Education for which Award is Granted:** Undergraduate **Number Awarded:** 5 each year. **Funds Available:** The stipend is $1,500 per year. **Duration:** 1 year; nonrenewable.
Eligibility Requirements: This program is open to graduating high school seniors who are Rhode Island residents. Applicants must have distinguished themselves by their outstanding involvement in community service, have been accepted into an accredited postsecondary institution, and be able to demonstrate financial need. Along with their application, they must submit an essay (up to 300 words), explaining the nature of their community service participation, the work's influence on them, and how they plan to continue their public service work into the future. **Deadline for Receipt:** May of each year.

1490 ■ RHODE ISLAND FOUNDATION

Attn: Scholarship Coordinator
One Union Station
Providence, RI 02903
Tel: (401)274-4564
Fax: (401)331-8085
E-mail: libbym@rifoundation.org
Web Site: http://www.rifoundation.org

To provide financial assistance to students at colleges and universities in Rhode Island who are older than 45 years of age.
Title of Award: Lily and Catello Sorrentino Memorial Scholarship **Area, Field, or Subject:** General studies/Field of study not specified **Level of Education for which Award is Granted:** Undergraduate **Number Awarded:** Varies each year; recently, 2 of these scholarships were awarded. **Funds Available:** Stipends range from $350 to $1,000 per year. **Duration:** 1 year.
Eligibility Requirements: This program is open to Rhode Island residents older than 45 years of age who are enrolled at a degree-conferring non-parochial college or university in the state to complete an undergraduate degree. Applicants must be able to demonstrate financial need. They must submit a 500-word essay describing their reasons for returning to school, the course of study they plan to pursue, how that relates to their career goals, and how they plan to finance the continuation of their educational program. Preference is given to first-time applicants. **Deadline for Receipt:** May of each year. **Additional Information:** This program was established in 1978.

1491 ■ RHODE ISLAND FOUNDATION

Attn: Scholarship Coordinator
One Union Station
Providence, RI 02903
Tel: (401)274-4564
Fax: (401)331-8085
E-mail: libbym@rifoundation.org
Web Site: http://www.rifoundation.org
To provide financial assistance for college in Rhode Island to single parents.
Title of Award: Bruce and Marjorie Sundlun Scholarship **Area, Field, or Subject:** General studies/Field of study not specified **Level of Education for which Award is Granted:** Undergraduate **Number Awarded:** 3 to 5 each year. **Funds Available:** Stipends range from $250 to $1,000 per year. **Duration:** 1 year; nonrenewable.
Eligibility Requirements: This program is open to single parents (men and women) with low incomes who are seeking to upgrade their potential career skills by returning to school in Rhode Island for an academic, trade, or vocational program. Applicants must be Rhode Island residents who can demonstrate financial need. As part of the selection process, they must submit an essay (up to 500 words) on their reasons for returning to school, how they chose their intended career or job training, how this scholarship can help them achieve their goals, and specifically how the money will be used. Preference is given to parents who are currently receiving public assistance, have recently received public assistance, are completing their first degree or certificate program, or will soon be released from prison. **Deadline for Receipt:** June of each year. **Additional Information:** This program was established in 1990.

1492 ■ RHODE ISLAND HIGHER EDUCATION ASSISTANCE AUTHORITY

Attn: Scholarship and Grant Division
560 Jefferson Boulevard
Warwick, RI 02886
Tel: (401)736-1170
Free: 800-922-9855
Fax: (401)732-3541
E-mail: scholarships@riheaa.org
Web Site: http://www.riheaa.org/borrowers/scholarships
To provide financial assistance for college to high school seniors in Rhode Island who can demonstrate academic promise.
Title of Award: CollegeBound*fund* Academic Promise Scholarship **Area, Field, or Subject:** General studies/Field of study not specified **Level of Education for which Award is Granted:** Undergraduate **Number Awarded:** Varies each year. **Funds Available:** The stipend is $2,500. **Duration:** 1 year; may be renewed for up to 3 additional years provided the recipient maintains a cumulative GPA of 3.0 or minimum GPAs of 2.50 for the first year, 2.75 for the second year, or 3.0 for the third year.
Eligibility Requirements: This program is open to U.S. citizens and permanent residents who have been residents of Rhode Island since the beginning of the year prior to the academic year in which they enroll in college. Applicants must be high school seniors accepted for full-time enrollment in a program that leads to a certificate or degree, not owe a refund on a federal Title IV grant, not be in default on a Title IV loan, and

not already possess a bachelor's degree. They must file a Free Application for Federal Student Aid (FAFSA) and take the SAT or ACT test. Selection is based on those test scores and high school GPA. **Deadline for Receipt:** February of each year.

1493 ■ RHODE ISLAND HIGHER EDUCATION ASSISTANCE AUTHORITY

Attn: Scholarship and Grant Division
560 Jefferson Boulevard
Warwick, RI 02886
Tel: (401)736-1170
Free: 800-922-9855
Fax: (401)732-3541
E-mail: grants@riheaa.org
Web Site: http://www.riheaa.org/borrowers/grants
To provide financial assistance for college to residents of Rhode Island who can demonstrate financial need.
Title of Award: Rhode Island State Grant Program **Area, Field, or Subject:** General studies/Field of study not specified **Level of Education for which Award is Granted:** Undergraduate **Number Awarded:** Varies each year. **Funds Available:** Stipends range from $300 to $1,400 per year, depending on the recipient's financial need. **Duration:** 1 year; may be renewed for up to 3 additional years (or 4 years for a bona fide 5-year program of study) as long as the recipient files a new FAFSA, continues to meet all eligibility requirements, and maintains satisfactory progress as defined by the institution.
Eligibility Requirements: This program is open to U.S. citizens and permanent residents who have been residents of Rhode Island since the beginning of the year prior to the academic year in which they enroll in college. Applicants must be enrolled or accepted for enrollment in a program that leads to a certificate or degree, not owe a refund on a federal Title IV grant, not be in default on a Title IV loan, and not already possess a bachelor's degree. If they are already enrolled in college, they must be making satisfactory academic progress as defined by their school's academic progress policy. The only application procedure is filing a Free Application for Federal Student Aid (FAFSA); all Rhode Island residents who submit that form are automatically considered for these grants. Applicants must be interested in attending an eligible school in the United States, Canada, or Mexico on at least a half-time basis. **Deadline for Receipt:** February of each year.

1494 ■ RHODE ISLAND NATIONAL GUARD

Command Readiness Center
Attn: TAGRI-DP/ED
645 New London Avenue
Cranston, RI 02920-3097
Tel: (401)275-4109
Fax: (401)275-4014
E-mail: sharon.harmon@ri.ngb.army.mil
Web Site: http://www.riguard.com/education
To provide financial assistance for college or graduate school to members of the National Guard in Rhode Island.
Title of Award: Rhode Island National Guard State Tuition Assistance Program **Area, Field, or Subject:** General studies/Field of study not specified **Level of Education for which Award is Granted:** Master's, Undergraduate **Number Awarded:** Varies each year. **Funds Available:** Qualified Guard members receive payment of tuition for up to 3 courses per semester. **Duration:** 1 semester; may be renewed.
Eligibility Requirements: This program is open to active members of the Rhode Island National Guard in good standing who are currently satisfactorily participating in all unit training assemblies and annual training periods. Applicants must have at least 1 year of service remaining. They must be enrolled in or planning to enroll in an associate, bachelor's, or master's degree program at a public institution in the state. **Additional Information:** This program was established in 1999.

1495 ■ RHODE ISLAND NATIONAL GUARD

Command Readiness Center
Attn: TAGRI-DP/ED
645 New London Avenue
Cranston, RI 02920-3097
Tel: (401)275-4109
Fax: (401)275-4014

E-mail: sharon.harmon@ri.ngb.army.mil

Web Site: http://www.riguard.com/education

To provide financial assistance to members of the Rhode Island National Guard who attend public institutions in the state.

Title of Award: Rhode Island National Guard State Tuition Exemption Program **Area, Field, or Subject:** General studies/Field of study not specified **Level of Education for which Award is Granted:** Undergraduate **Number Awarded:** Varies each year. **Funds Available:** Qualified Guard members are entitled to tuition-free classes at public institutions in Rhode Island. The waiver does not cover books or fees. **Duration:** Upon enrollment, Guard members are entitled to 4 tuition-free classes (1 in the fall semester, 1 in the spring semester, and 2 in the summer). For each year they extend their enlistment, they become entitled to an additional 4 tuition-free classes.

Eligibility Requirements: This program is open to active members of the Rhode Island National Guard who attend all required unit training assemblies and annual training. Applicants must be residents of Rhode Island working toward an associate or bachelor's degree at a designated public institution in the state. They must pass the Guard's height and weight standards, weapons qualification, and the APFT. They may not have more than 4 unexcused absences from military duty within a 12-month period or have tested positive for any illegal drug. **Additional Information:** This program was established in 1994. The designated institutions are the University of Rhode Island, Rhode Island College, and the Community College of Rhode Island.

1496 ■ RIO GRANDE VALLEY LIVESTOCK SHOW

1000 North Texas

P.O. Box 867

Mercedes, TX 78570

Tel: (956)565-2456

Fax: (956)565-3005

E-mail: info@rgvlivestockshow.com

Web Site: http://www.rgvlivestockshow.org

To provide financial assistance for college to Texas high school seniors who exhibit at the Rio Grande Valley Livestock Show (RGVLS).

Title of Award: Rio Grande Valley Livestock Show Champs for Champions Scholarship Program **Area, Field, or Subject:** General studies/Field of study not specified **Level of Education for which Award is Granted:** Undergraduate **Number Awarded:** Varies each year; recently, 39 of these scholarships were awarded. **Funds Available:** A stipend is awarded (amount not specified). **Duration:** 1 year.

Eligibility Requirements: This program is open to senior graduating from Texas high schools who have exhibited at the RGVLS. Applicants must have scores of at least 800 on the mathematics and critical reading sections of the SAT or 18 on the ACT. They must have applied for admission to a college or university. Along with their application, they must submit a 1-page narrative about themselves. Selection is based on the narrative (10 points), participation in the RBVLS (10 points for livestock projects, 10 points for projects other than livestock), leadership (10 points), honors and awards (7 points), citizenship (5 points), academics (40 points), and an interview (8 points). **Deadline for Receipt:** January of each year.

1497 ■ RIO GRANDE VALLEY LIVESTOCK SHOW

1000 North Texas

P.O. Box 867

Mercedes, TX 78570

Tel: (956)565-2456

Fax: (956)565-3005

E-mail: info@rgvlivestockshow.com

Web Site: http://www.rgvlivestockshow.org

To provide financial assistance for college to Texas students who exhibit champion projects at the Rio Grande Valley Livestock Show (RGVLS).

Title of Award: Rio Grande Valley Livestock Show Exhibitors Scholarship Program **Area, Field, or Subject:** General studies/Field of study not specified **Level of Education for which Award is Granted:** Undergraduate **Number Awarded:** Varies each year, depending on the number of entries in various categories. **Funds Available:** Recipients may redeem up to $2,000 in scholarships per semester. **Duration:** 1 semester; exhibitors may accumulate up to $10,000 in scholarships during their entire participation in RGVLS events. Continued redemption of scholarships requires the recipient to remain enrolled full time at an accredited college, university, or vocational/trade school with a GPA of 2.0 or higher. Funds are paid directly to the institution.

Eligibility Requirements: This program is open to students graduating from Texas high schools who exhibit a project that they own at the RGVLS. Students must be planning to attend an accredited college, university, or vocational/trade school. Scholarships are awarded to exhibitors of breed champions in the market animal divisions, exhibitors of the grand champion and the reserve grand champion in the horticulture division, exhibitors of the grand champion and reserve grand champion in the junior and senior divisions of the All Valley Cotton Style Show, and high point individuals of the junior and senior divisions of the livestock judging contest. For some of the market animal divisions, scholarships are only awarded if a sufficient number of entries are received. **Deadline for Receipt:** February of each year.

1498 ■ RIO GRANDE VALLEY LIVESTOCK SHOW

1000 North Texas

P.O. Box 867

Mercedes, TX 78570

Tel: (956)565-2456

Fax: (956)565-3005

E-mail: info@rgvlivestockshow.com

Web Site: http://www.rgvlivestockshow.org

To provide financial assistance for college to Texas high school seniors who exhibit Simbrah/Simmental cattle at the Rio Grande Valley Livestock Show (RGVLS).

Title of Award: Rio Grande Valley Simbrah/Simmental Association Scholarship **Area, Field, or Subject:** General studies/Field of study not specified **Level of Education for which Award is Granted:** Undergraduate **Number Awarded:** At least 1 each year. **Funds Available:** The stipend is $1,000. **Duration:** 1 year.

Eligibility Requirements: This program is open to senior graduating from Texas high schools who exhibit in the junior Simbrah/Simmental cattle division at the RGVLS. Applicants must be planning to attend an accredited college, university, or vocational/technical school within 1 year after graduation. Selection is based on attitude and cooperativeness at the show, desire and interest in furthering education beyond high school, involvement in FFA and/or 4-H, involvement in extracurricular activities not including FFA or 4-H, high school grades, and financial need. **Deadline for Receipt:** February of each year.

1499 ■ JACKIE ROBINSON FOUNDATION

Attn: Education and Leadership Development Program

3 West 35th Street, 11th Floor

New York, NY 10001-2204

Tel: (212)290-8600

Fax: (212)290-8081

E-mail: general@jackierobinson.org

Web Site: http://www.jackierobinson.org

To provide financial assistance for college to minority high school seniors.

Title of Award: Jackie Robinson Scholarships **Area, Field, or Subject:** General studies/Field of study not specified **Level of Education for which Award is Granted:** Four Year College **Number Awarded:** 100 or more each year. **Funds Available:** The stipend is $6,000 per year. **Duration:** 4 years.

Eligibility Requirements: This program is open to members of an ethnic minority group who are high school seniors accepted at a 4-year college or university. Applicants must be able to demonstrate high academic achievement (SAT score of 900 or higher or ACT score of 21 or higher), financial need, and leadership potential. U.S. citizenship is required. **Deadline for Receipt:** March of each year. **Additional Information:** The program also offers personal and career counseling on a year-round basis, a week of interaction with other scholarship students from around the country, and assistance in obtaining summer jobs and permanent employment after graduation. It was established in 1973 by a grant from Chesebrough-Pond.

1500 ■ ROCKY MOUNTAIN ELK FOUNDATION

2291 West Broadway

P.O. Box 8249

Missoula, MT 59807-8249

Tel: (406)523-4500

Free: 800-CALL

Fax: (406)523-4550

Web Site: http://www.rmef.org/pages/HSH.html

To provide financial assistance for college to high school seniors who have participated in the High Schools for Habitat program of the Rocky Mountain Elk Foundation.

Title of Award: High Schools For Habitat Conservation Scholarships **Area, Field, or Subject:** General studies/Field of study not specified **Level of Education for which Award is Granted:** Undergraduate **Number Awarded:** 10 each year. **Funds Available:** The stipend is $1,000. In addition, recipients are given an engraved plaque and a 1-year membership in the foundation. **Duration:** 1 year; nonrenewable.

Eligibility Requirements: This program is open to high school seniors and graduates who are planning to enroll full time as a freshman in an accredited undergraduate program. Applicants must have participated actively in the High Schools for Habitat program for at least 2 years. Selection is based on a 100-word statement of their personal and educational life goals (10 points), leadership activities in High Schools for Habitat (30 points), other leadership activities (10 points), hobbies and leisure activities (5 points), and a 500-word essay on their understanding of a citizen conservationist (30 points). **Deadline for Receipt:** February of each year. **Additional Information:** This program, established in 2000, currently operates in 40 high schools in 20 states and 2 Canadian provinces. Information is also available from Carole Biletnikoff, HSH Program Coordinator, 5665 Sterrettania Road, Fairview, PA 16415, (814) 833-7996, Fax: (814) 833-8996, E-mail: carole@highschoolsforhabitat.org.

1501 ■ ROCKY MOUNTAIN FARMERS UNION

Attn: Education Department
5655 South Yosemite Street, Suite 400
Greenwood Village, CO 80111
Tel: (303)752-5800
Free: 800-373-7638
Fax: (303)752-5810
E-mail: rmfu@rmfu.org
Web Site: http://www.rmfu.org

To provide financial assistance for college to members of the Rocky Mountain Farmers Union (RMFU).

Title of Award: Rocky Mountain Farmers Union Scholarships **Area, Field, or Subject:** General studies/Field of study not specified **Level of Education for which Award is Granted:** Undergraduate **Number Awarded:** Varies each year. Recently, 11 of these scholarships were awarded: 10 at $1,000 and 1 at $500. **Funds Available:** Stipends are $1,000 or $500. **Duration:** 1 year; nonrenewable.

Eligibility Requirements: This program is open to regular and associate members of the RMFU who are high school seniors or currently enrolled in an institution of higher learning; applicants need not have a membership in their own name if their parents are members. Along with their application, they must submit a current high school or college transcript, ACT or SAT scores, 2 letters of recommendation, and a letter of at least 100 words demonstrating their knowledge of Farmers Union and explaining their financial need. Some scholarships also have specific residency requirements. **Deadline for Receipt:** March of each year. **Additional Information:** The RMFU operates in Colorado, New Mexico, and Wyoming. This program includes the Joey Skurich Memorial Scholarship, the Perry and Donna Jackson Farmers Union Scholarship, the Dale Smith Memorial Scholarship, the James G. Patton Memorial Scholarship, the Hazel Hemphill Memorial Scholarship, the Maurice Parker Memorial Scholarship, and the Edna Buchanan Memorial Scholarship.

1502 ■ ROBIN ROMANO MEMORIAL FUND

c/o Ken Fratus
Boston Globe Sports
135 Morrissey Boulevard
P.O. Box 55819
Boston, MA 02105-5819
Tel: (617)929-7949
Free: 800-628-6214

To provide financial assistance for college to high school seniors and graduates who are cancer survivors.

Title of Award: Robin Romano Memorial Scholarship **Area, Field, or Subject:** General studies/Field of study not specified **Level of Education for which Award is Granted:** Undergraduate **Number Awarded:** 1 or more each year. **Funds Available:** The stipend is $7,500. **Duration:** Up to 4 years.

Eligibility Requirements: Eligible to apply for this support are high school seniors, high school graduates, and currently-enrolled college students who are cancer survivors. **Additional Information:** Partial scholarships are often awarded to other students. This program was started in 2000. Since then, the fund has raised nearly $150,000 and has awarded full or partial scholarships to 10 students.

1503 ■ PAUL F. RONCI MEMORIAL TRUST

c/o Mary Lou Fonseca
P.O. Box 515
Harmony, RI 02829-0515
Tel: (401)349-4404
Fax: (401)349-4404
Web Site: http://www.paulfroncischolarship.org

To provide financial assistance to undergraduate and graduate students from Rhode Island.

Title of Award: Paul F. Ronci Memorial Scholarships **Area, Field, or Subject:** General studies/Field of study not specified **Level of Education for which Award is Granted:** Graduate, Undergraduate **Number Awarded:** 1 each year. **Funds Available:** Stipends range from $500 up to full payment of tuition. **Duration:** 1 year; recipients may reapply.

Eligibility Requirements: This program is open to full-time undergraduate and graduate students who have been residents of Rhode Island for at least 10 of the last 12 years. Applicants must rank in the top 10% of their class. Along with their application, they must submit documentation of financial need and an essay on their goals, ambitions, and desires, with specific reference to what they intend to accomplish for the good of humanity. **Deadline for Receipt:** March of each year.

1504 ■ ROPAGE GROUP LLC

8877 North 107th Avenue, Suite 302
P.O. Box 287
Peoria, AZ 85345
E-mail: questions@patricias-scholarship.org
Web Site: http://www.patricias-scholarship.org

To provide financial assistance for college to students who have overcome great obstacles.

Title of Award: Patricia M. McNamara Memorial Scholarship **Area, Field, or Subject:** General studies/Field of study not specified **Level of Education for which Award is Granted:** Undergraduate **Number Awarded:** 1 each year. **Funds Available:** The stipend is $1,000. **Duration:** 1 year.

Eligibility Requirements: This program is open to students who are attending or planning to attend an institution of higher education. Applicants must submit a short essay about 1 of the greatest obstacles they have had to overcome. **Deadline for Receipt:** December of each year. **Additional Information:** This scholarship was first awarded in 2006.

1505 ■ ROYAL NEIGHBORS OF AMERICA

Attn: Fraternal Services
230 16th Street
Rock Island, IL 61201-8645
Tel: (309)788-4561
Free: 800-627-4762
E-mail: contact@royalneighbors.org
Web Site: http://www.royalneighbors.org/MemberBenefits/scholarships.cfm

To provide financial assistance for college to women members of the Royal Neighbors of America who have been involved in the sport of volleyball.

Title of Award: Dreams Can Come True Scholarships **Area, Field, or Subject:** General studies/Field of study not specified **Level of Education for which Award is Granted:** Undergraduate **Number Awarded:** 5 each year. **Funds Available:** The stipend is $2,000 per year. **Duration:** 4 years.

Eligibility Requirements: This program is open to women members of the society who are graduating high school seniors or college students of any age. Applicants must have participated in the sport of volleyball. Selection is based on academic performance. **Deadline for Receipt:** December of each year. **Additional Information:** This program was established in 2004.

1506 ■ ROYAL NEIGHBORS OF AMERICA

Attn: Fraternal Services
230 16th Street
Rock Island, IL 61201-8645

Tel: (309)788-4561
Free: 800-627-4762
E-mail: contact@royalneighbors.org
Web Site: http://www.royalneighbors.org/MemberBenefits/
scholarships.cfm
To provide financial assistance for college to women members of the
Royal Neighbors of America.
Title of Award: Marie Kirkland Scholarship **Area, Field, or Subject:**
General studies/Field of study not specified **Level of Education for
which Award is Granted:** Four Year College **Number Awarded:** 1 each
year. **Funds Available:** The stipend is $2,500 per year. **Duration:** 4
years.
Eligibility Requirements: Applicants must have been members of the
society for at least 2 years immediately prior to the application deadline,
be high school seniors recommended by their local lodge and field
representative, be in the top quarter of their graduating class, and have
been admitted to an accredited 4-year college or university as a full-time
student. Selection is based on character and personal goals, school and
community activities, ability to meet the specific entrance requirements of
the accredited college or university selected, and general aptitude for college work as indicated by aptitude tests or scholastic records. The recipient is the woman judged to be most qualified from all applicants for Royal
Neighbors of America scholarships. **Deadline for Receipt:** December of
each year. **Additional Information:** This program was established in
1998.

1507 ■ ROYAL NEIGHBORS OF AMERICA

Attn: Fraternal Services
230 16th Street
Rock Island, IL 61201-8645
Tel: (309)788-4561
Free: 800-627-4762
E-mail: contact@royalneighbors.org
Web Site: http://www.royalneighbors.org/MemberBenefits/
scholarships.cfm
To provide financial assistance for college to members of the Royal
Neighbors of America who are nontraditional students.
Title of Award: Royal Neighbors of America Nontraditional Scholarships
Area, Field, or Subject: General studies/Field of study not specified
Level of Education for which Award is Granted: Undergraduate
Number Awarded: 15 each year. **Funds Available:** The stipend is
$1,000 per year for full-time students or $500 per year for part-time
students. **Duration:** 1 year; nonrenewable.
Eligibility Requirements: Applicants must have been members of the
society for at least 2 years immediately prior to the application deadline,
be 23 years of age or older, provide (if currently an undergraduate
student) a transcript of college grades, and have been admitted to an accredited college, university, community college, or vocational school.
Selection is based on character and personal goals, participation in
school and community activities, ability to meet the specific entrance
requirements of the accredited college or university or of the vocational
school selected, and financial need. **Deadline for Receipt:** December of
each year.

1508 ■ ROYAL NEIGHBORS OF AMERICA

Attn: Fraternal Services
230 16th Street
Rock Island, IL 61201-8645
Tel: (309)788-4561
Free: 800-627-4762
E-mail: contact@royalneighbors.org
Web Site: http://www.royalneighbors.org/MemberBenefits/
scholarships.cfm
To provide financial assistance for college to members of the Royal
Neighbors of America in designated states.
Title of Award: Royal Neighbors of America State/Territorial Scholarships
Area, Field, or Subject: General studies/Field of study not specified
Level of Education for which Award is Granted: Undergraduate
Number Awarded: More than 20 each year. **Funds Available:** Stipends
are $1,000 or $500 per year. **Duration:** 1 year; nonrenewable.
Eligibility Requirements: Applicants must have been members of the
society for at least 2 years immediately prior to the application deadline,
be high school seniors recommended by their local lodge and field

representative, be in the top third of their graduating class, and have been
admitted to an accredited college, university, community college, or
vocational school as a full-time student. Selection is based on character
and personal goals, school and community activities, ability to meet the
specific entrance requirements of the accredited college or university or of
the vocational school selected, and general aptitude for college work as
indicated by aptitude tests or scholastic records. **Deadline for Receipt:**
December of each year. **Additional Information:** These scholarships are
currently available in the following states or territories that offer a state
scholarship: California, Colorado, Florida, CMA Illinois, Northern Illinois,
Southern Illinois, Indiana, Iowa, Kansas, Michigan, Minnesota, Missouri,
Montana, Nebraska, North Dakota, Oklahoma, Oregon, Pennsylvania,
South Dakota, Texas, Washington, Wisconsin, and Wyoming.

1509 ■ ROYAL NEIGHBORS OF AMERICA

Attn: Fraternal Services
230 16th Street
Rock Island, IL 61201-8645
Tel: (309)788-4561
Free: 800-627-4762
E-mail: contact@royalneighbors.org
Web Site: http://www.royalneighbors.org/MemberBenefits/
scholarships.cfm
To provide financial assistance for college to members of the Royal
Neighbors of America (RNA).
Title of Award: Royal Neighbors of America Traditional Scholarships
Area, Field, or Subject: General studies/Field of study not specified
Level of Education for which Award is Granted: Four Year College
Number Awarded: 10 each year. **Funds Available:** The stipend is
$2,000 per year. **Duration:** 4 years.
Eligibility Requirements: This program is open to high school seniors
who have a qualifying RNA benefit certificate. Applicants must be recommended by their local lodge and field representative, be in the top quarter
of their graduating class, and have been admitted to an accredited 4-year
college or university as a full-time student. Selection is based on
character and personal goals, school and community activities, ability to
meet the specific entrance requirements of the accredited college or
university selected, and general aptitude for college work as indicated by
aptitude tests or scholastic records. **Deadline for Receipt:** December of
each year.

1510 ■ ROYAL NEIGHBORS OF AMERICA

Attn: Fraternal Services
230 16th Street
Rock Island, IL 61201-8645
Tel: (309)788-4561
Free: 800-627-4762
E-mail: contact@royalneighbors.org
Web Site: http://www.royalneighbors.org/MemberBenefits/
scholarships.cfm
To provide financial assistance for college to members of the Royal
Neighbors of America who have been involved in volunteer activities.
Title of Award: Volunteer Regional Scholarships **Area, Field, or Subject:**
General studies/Field of study not specified **Level of Education for
which Award is Granted:** Undergraduate **Number Awarded:** 8 each
year: 1 in each of the society's regions. **Funds Available:** The stipend is
$1,000 per year. **Duration:** 4 years.
Eligibility Requirements: This program is open to members of the
society who are graduating high school seniors. Applicants must
demonstrate outstanding and significant volunteer qualities. **Deadline for
Receipt:** December of each year. **Additional Information:** This program
was established in 2004.

1511 ■ RURITAN NATIONAL FOUNDATION

5451 Lyons Road
P.O. Box 487
Dublin, VA 24084
Tel: (540)674-9441; 877-787-8727
Fax: (540)674-2304
E-mail: office@ruritan.org
Web Site: http://www.ruritan.org
To provide financial assistance for college to students who are recom-
mended by active members of Ruritan.

Title of Award: Ruritan National Foundation Scholarship Program **Area, Field, or Subject:** General studies/Field of study not specified **Level of Education for which Award is Granted:** Undergraduate **Number Awarded:** Varies each year. **Funds Available:** Stipends depend on the need of the recipient and the availability of funds. **Duration:** 1 year. **Eligibility Requirements:** All students pursuing a postsecondary education are eligible to apply for a scholarship, but they must have 2 written recommendations from active Ruritan members. Preference is given to freshmen and sophomores. Students who live in communities without a local Ruritan club are not eligible unless they are already associated with 2 members. Selection is based on financial need, character, scholarship, academic promise, and desire of the applicant for further education or training. **Deadline for Receipt:** March of each year.

1512 ■ SALEM UNITED METHODIST CHURCH

Attn: Robert D. Thompson, Trust Administrator
225 First Avenue, S.W.
Cedar Rapids, IA 52405
Tel: (319)396-5479
E-mail: robertdtia@msn.com
To provide financial assistance to Baptist, Congregational, Methodist, and Presbyterian college and seminary students from Iowa.
Title of Award: Adora S. Jones Ministerial Trust Scholarships **Area, Field, or Subject:** Religion **Level of Education for which Award is Granted:** Master's, Undergraduate **Number Awarded:** 1 or more each year. **Funds Available:** Stipends range from $1,000 to $4,000. **Duration:** 1 year.
Eligibility Requirements: This program is open to residents of Iowa who are attending a college or seminary to prepare for a career in ministry and preaching the Gospel. Applicants must be members of a Baptist, Congregational, United Methodist, or Presbyterian church. They must be able to demonstrate financial need. **Deadline for Receipt:** October of each year.

1513 ■ SALLIE MAE 911 EDUCATION FUND

c/o The Community Foundation
1201 15th Street, N.W., Suite 420
Washington, DC 20005-2842
Tel: (202)955-5890
Free: 800-441-4043
Fax: (202)955-8084
Web Site: http://www.thesalliemaefund.org
To provide financial assistance for college to children of those killed or disabled in the terrorist attacks of September 11, 200l.
Title of Award: Sallie Mae 911 Education Fund Scholarship Program **Area, Field, or Subject:** General studies/Field of study not specified **Level of Education for which Award is Granted:** Undergraduate **Number Awarded:** Varies each year. **Funds Available:** The stipend is $2,500 per year. **Duration:** 1 year; may be renewed up to 3 additional years.
Eligibility Requirements: This program is open to the children of the victims of the September 11, 2001 terrorist attacks, including children of people killed in airplanes or buildings as well as police, fire safety, or medical personnel killed or disabled as a result of the attacks. Applicants must be enrolled or planning to enroll full time as an undergraduate student at a public or private 2-year or 4-year college or university. **Deadline for Receipt:** May of each year.

1514 ■ LEOPOLD SCHEPP FOUNDATION

551 Fifth Avenue, Suite 3000
New York, NY 10176-2597
Tel: (212)692-0191
To provide financial assistance to undergraduate and graduate students.
Title of Award: Leopold Schepp Foundation Scholarships **Area, Field, or Subject:** General studies/Field of study not specified **Level of Education for which Award is Granted:** Graduate, Undergraduate **Number Awarded:** Approximately 200 each year. **Funds Available:** The maximum stipend is $8,000 per year. **Duration:** 1 year; may be renewed.
Eligibility Requirements: This program is open to undergraduates under 30 years of age and graduate students under 40 years of age. Applicants must either be currently enrolled full time or have completed 1 year of undergraduate work at an accredited college or university. They must have a GPA of 3.0 or higher. High school seniors, graduate students

completing a dissertation and not enrolled in class, and students working on a second degree at the same level, are not eligible. U.S. citizenship or permanent resident status is required. Selection is based on character, ability, and financial need. **Deadline for Receipt:** The foundation stops accepting applications when a sufficient number has been received, usually in January. **Additional Information:** Finalists may be required to travel to New York at their own expense for an interview. Requests for applications must be accompanied by a self-addressed stamped envelope.

1515 ■ SCHOLARSHIP ADMINISTRATIVE SERVICES, INC.

Attn: MEFUSA Program
2000 Rock Street, Suite 3
Mountain View, CA 94043
To provide financial assistance to African American high school seniors who are interested in attending a community college.
Title of Award: African American Community College Scholarship **Area, Field, or Subject:** General studies/Field of study not specified **Level of Education for which Award is Granted:** Two Year College **Number Awarded:** Up to 100 each year. **Funds Available:** The stipend is $5,000 per year. **Duration:** 1 year; may be renewed 1 additional year if the recipient maintains full-time enrollment and a GPA of 2.5 or higher.
Eligibility Requirements: This program is open to African Americans graduating from high schools anywhere in the United States. Applicants must be planning to attend a community college on a full-time basis. Along with their application, they must submit a 1,000-word essay on their educational and career goals, how a community college education will help them to achieve those goals, and how they plan to serve the African American community after completing their education. Selection is based on the essay, high school GPA (2.5 or higher), SAT or ACT scores, involvement in the African American community, and financial need. **Deadline for Receipt:** April of each year. **Additional Information:** This program is sponsored by the Minority Educational Foundation of the United States of America (MEFUSA) and administered by Scholarship Administrative Services, Inc. MEFUSA was established in 2001 to meet the needs of minority students who "show a determination to get a college degree," but who, for financial or other personal reasons, are not able to attend a 4-year college or university. Requests for applications should be accompanied by a self-addressed stamped envelope, the student's e-mail address, and the source where they found the scholarship information.

1516 ■ SCHOLARSHIP ADMINISTRATIVE SERVICES, INC.

Attn: MEFUSA Program
2000 Rock Street, Suite 3
Mountain View, CA 94043
To provide financial assistance to American Indian high school seniors who are interested in attending a community college.
Title of Award: American Indian Community College Scholarship **Area, Field, or Subject:** General studies/Field of study not specified **Level of Education for which Award is Granted:** Two Year College **Number Awarded:** Up to 100 each year. **Funds Available:** The stipend is $5,000 per year. **Duration:** 1 year; may be renewed 1 additional year if the recipient maintains full-time enrollment and a GPA of 2.5 or higher.
Eligibility Requirements: This program is open to American Indian seniors graduating from high schools anywhere in the United States. Applicants must be enrolled members of a federally-recognized tribal organization and planning to attend a community college on a full-time basis. Along with their application, they must submit a 1,000-word essay on their educational and career goals, how a community college education will help them to achieve those goals, and how they plan to serve the American Indian community after completing their education. Selection is based on the essay, high school GPA (2.5 or higher), SAT or ACT scores, involvement in the American Indian community, and financial need. **Deadline for Receipt:** April of each year. **Additional Information:** This program is sponsored by the Minority Educational Foundation of the United States of America (MEFUSA) and administered by Scholarship Administrative Services, Inc. MEFUSA was established in 2001 to meet the needs of minority students who "show a determination to get a college degree," but who, for financial or other personal reasons, are not able to attend a 4-year college or university. Requests for applications should be

accompanied by a self-addressed stamped envelope, the student's e-mail address, and the source where they found the scholarship information.

1517 ■ SCHOLARSHIP ADMINISTRATIVE SERVICES, INC.

Attn: MEFUSA Program
2000 Rock Street, Suite 3
Mountain View, CA 94043
To provide financial assistance to Asian American high school seniors who are interested in attending a community college.
Title of Award: Asian American Community College Scholarship **Area, Field, or Subject:** General studies/Field of study not specified **Level of Education for which Award is Granted:** Two Year College **Number Awarded:** Up to 100 each year. **Funds Available:** The stipend is $5,000 per year. **Duration:** 1 year; may be renewed 1 additional year if the recipient maintains full-time enrollment and a GPA of 2.5 or higher.
Eligibility Requirements: This program is open to Asian American seniors graduating from high schools anywhere in the United States. Applicants must be planning to attend a community college on a full-time basis. Along with their application, they must submit a 1,000-word essay on their educational and career goals, how a community college education will help them to achieve those goals, and how they plan to serve the Asian American community after completing their education. Selection is based on the essay, high school GPA (2.5 or higher), SAT or ACT scores, involvement in the Asian American community, and financial need.
Deadline for Receipt: April of each year. **Additional Information:** This program is sponsored by the Minority Educational Foundation of the United States of America (MEFUSA) and administered by Scholarship Administrative Services, Inc. MEFUSA was established in 2001 to meet the needs of minority students who "show a determination to get a college degree," but who, for financial or other personal reasons, are not able to attend a 4-year college or university. Requests for applications should be accompanied by a self-addressed stamped envelope, the student's e-mail address, and the source where they found the scholarship information.

1518 ■ SCHOLARSHIP ADMINISTRATIVE SERVICES, INC.

Attn: MEFUSA Program
2000 Rock Street, Suite 3
Mountain View, CA 94043
To provide financial assistance to Chicano/Latino high school seniors who are interested in attending a community college.
Title of Award: Chicano/Latino Community College Scholarship **Area, Field, or Subject:** General studies/Field of study not specified **Level of Education for which Award is Granted:** Two Year College **Number Awarded:** Up to 100 each year. **Funds Available:** The stipend is $5,000 per year. **Duration:** 1 year; may be renewed 1 additional year if the recipient maintains full-time enrollment and a GPA of 2.5 or higher.
Eligibility Requirements: This program is open to Chicano/Latino seniors graduating from high schools anywhere in the United States. Applicants must be planning to attend a community college on a full-time basis. Along with their application, they must submit a 1,000-word essay on their educational and career goals, how a community college education will help them to achieve those goals, and how they plan to serve the Chicano/Latino community after completing their education. Selection is based on the essay, high school GPA (2.5 or higher), SAT or ACT scores, involvement in the Chicano/Latino community, and financial need.
Deadline for Receipt: April of each year. **Additional Information:** This program is sponsored by the Minority Educational Foundation of the United States of America (MEFUSA) and administered by Scholarship Administrative Services, Inc. MEFUSA was established in 2001 to meet the needs of minority students who "show a determination to get a college degree," but who, for financial or other personal reasons, are not able to attend a 4-year college or university. Requests for applications should be accompanied by a self-addressed stamped envelope, the student's e-mail address, and the source where they found the scholarship information.

1519 ■ SCHOLARSHIP AMERICA

Attn: Scholarship Management Services
One Scholarship Way
P.O. Box 297
St. Peter, MN 56082
Tel: (507)931-1682
Free: 800-537-4180
Fax: (507)931-9168

E-mail: axaachievement@scholarshipamerica.org
Web Site: http://www.axa-achievement.com
To provide financial assistance for college to high school seniors who demonstrate outstanding achievement.
Title of Award: AXA Achievement Scholarships **Area, Field, or Subject:** General studies/Field of study not specified **Level of Education for which Award is Granted:** Undergraduate **Number Awarded:** 52 each year: 1 from each state, the District of Columbia, and Puerto Rico. Of those 52, 10 are designated as national AXA Achievers. **Funds Available:** The stipend is $10,000. Funds may be used only for undergraduate educational expenses. Students selected as national AXA Achievers receive an additional stipend of $15,000, a computer, and the offer of an internship. **Duration:** 1 year. Awards are not renewable, but recipients may arrange to receive payment in installments over multiple years as long as they continue to meet eligibility requirements.
Eligibility Requirements: This program is open to graduating high school seniors who plan to enroll full time in an accredited 2-year or 4-year college or university in the United States. Applicants must demonstrate ambition and achievement in school and community activities or work experience. In the selection process, primary consideration is given to the demonstrated achievement as reported by the applicant and supported by an appraisal completed by an adult professional who is not a relative. Other factors considered include extracurricular activities in school and community, work experience, and academic record. From among the recipients, students whose achievements are especially noteworthy are designated as national AXA Achievers. **Deadline for Receipt:** December of each year. **Additional Information:** This program, established in 2002, is supported by the AXA Foundation, in association with the *U.S. News and World Report.*

1520 ■ SCHOLARSHIP AMERICA

Attn: Scholarship Management Services
One Scholarship Way
P.O. Box 297
St. Peter, MN 56082
Tel: (507)931-1682
Free: 800-537-4180
Fax: (507)931-9168
E-mail: bestbuy@scholarshipamerica.org
Web Site: http://bestbuy.scholarshipamerica.org/index.php
To provide financial assistance for college to high school seniors who demonstrate outstanding volunteer community service.
Title of Award: Best Buy Scholarships **Area, Field, or Subject:** General studies/Field of study not specified **Level of Education for which Award is Granted:** Undergraduate **Number Awarded:** Up to 1,308 each year. In each of the 435 Congressional districts in the United States plus the District of Columbia, up to 3 scholarships are awarded: 2 at $2,000 to the top qualifying students and 1 at $1,000 to the next qualifying applicant. **Funds Available:** The stipend is $2,000 or $1,000. **Duration:** 1 year; nonrenewable.
Eligibility Requirements: This program is open to graduating high school seniors who plan to enroll full time at an accredited 2-year or 4-year college or university or vocational/technical school in the United States. Applicants must be able to demonstrate "solid academic performance and exemplary community service." Consideration may also be given to participation in school activities and work experience, but financial need is not considered. **Deadline for Receipt:** February of each year. **Additional Information:** This program is supported by the Best Buy Children's Foundation.

1521 ■ SCHOLARSHIP AMERICA

Attn: Scholarship Management Services
One Scholarship Way
P.O. Box 297
St. Peter, MN 56082
Tel: (507)931-1682
Free: 800-537-4180
Fax: (507)931-9168
To provide financial assistance for college to high school seniors in Rhode Island and southeastern Massachusetts.
Title of Award: Dunkin' Donuts Scholarships **Area, Field, or Subject:** General studies/Field of study not specified **Level of Education for which Award is Granted:** Undergraduate **Number Awarded:** 100 each year. **Funds Available:** The stipend is $1,000. **Duration:** 1 year.

Eligibility Requirements: This program is open to 1) seniors graduating from high schools in Rhode Island and Bristol County, Massachusetts, and 2) recent graduates of those high schools already enrolled in college. Applicants must be able to demonstrate academic excellence, leadership qualities, community involvement, and a clear goal for their future. **Deadline for Receipt:** April of each year. **Additional Information:** This program began in 1996.

1522 ■ SCHOLARSHIP AMERICA

Attn: Scholarship Management Services
One Scholarship Way
P.O. Box 297
St. Peter, MN 56082
Tel: (507)931-1682; 877-862-0136
Fax: (507)931-9168
E-mail: familiesoffreedom@csfa.org
Web Site: http://www.familiesoffreedom.org
To provide college scholarships to financially-needy individuals and the families of individuals who were victims of the terrorist attacks on September 11, 2001.
Title of Award: Families of Freedom Scholarship Fund **Area, Field, or Subject:** General studies/Field of study not specified **Level of Education for which Award is Granted:** Undergraduate **Number Awarded:** This is an entitlement program; all eligible students will receive funding. Recently 180 students received nearly $1.6 million in scholarship funds. **Funds Available:** Stipends range from $1,000 to $28,000 per year, depending upon the need of the recipient. Recently, awards averaged $13,100 per academic year. Funds are distributed annually, in 2 equal installments. Checks are made payable jointly to the student and the student's school. **Duration:** 1 year; may be renewed.
Eligibility Requirements: This program is open to the individuals who were disabled as a result of the terrorist attacks on September 11, 2001 and to the relatives of those individuals who were killed or permanently disabled during the attacks. Primarily, the fund will benefit dependents (including spouses and children) of the following groups: airplane crew and passengers; World Trade Center workers and visitors; Pentagon workers and visitors; and rescue workers, including fire fighters, emergency medical personnel, and law enforcement personnel. Applicants must be enrolled or planning to enroll in an accredited 2- or 4-year college, university, or vocational/technical school in the United States. They must be able to demonstrate financial need. **Deadline for Receipt:** Applications may be submitted at any time. **Additional Information:** This program was established on September 17, 2001. The fundraising goal of $100 million was reached on September 4, 2002. The fund will operate until December 31, 2030.

1523 ■ SCHOLARSHIP AMERICA

Attn: Scholarship Management Services
One Scholarship Way
P.O. Box 297
St. Peter, MN 56082
Tel: (507)931-1682
Free: 800-537-4180
Fax: (507)931-9168
E-mail: scholarship@usafunds.org
Web Site: http://www.usafunds.org/planning/
access_to_education_scholarship/index.html
To provide financial assistance to undergraduate and graduate students, especially those who are members of ethnic minority groups or have physical disabilities.
Title of Award: USA Funds Access to Education Scholarships **Area, Field, or Subject:** General studies/Field of study not specified **Level of Education for which Award is Granted:** Graduate, Undergraduate **Number Awarded:** Varies each year; recently, a total of $3 million was available for this program. **Funds Available:** The stipend is $1,500 per year for full-time undergraduate or graduate students or $750 per year for half-time undergraduate students. Funds are paid jointly to the student and the school. **Duration:** 1 year; may be renewed until the student receives a final degree or certificate or until the total award to a student reaches $6,000, whichever comes first. Renewal requires the recipient to maintain a GPA of 2.5 or higher.
Eligibility Requirements: This program is open to high school seniors and graduates who plan to enroll or are already enrolled in full-time undergraduate or graduate course work at an accredited 2- or 4-year college, university, or vocational/technical school. Half-time undergraduate students are also eligible. Up to 50% of the awards are targeted at students who have a documented physical disability or are a member of an ethnic minority group, including but not limited to Native Hawaiian, Alaskan Native, Black/African American, Asian, Pacific Islander, American Indian, or Hispanic/Latino. Residents of all 50 states, the District of Columbia, Puerto Rico, Guam, the U.S. Virgin Islands, and all U.S. territories and commonwealths are eligible. Applicants must also be U.S. citizens or eligible noncitizens and come from a family with an annual adjusted gross income of $35,000 or less. In addition to financial need, selection is based on past academic performance and future potential, leadership and participation in school and community activities, work experience, career and educational aspirations, and goals. **Deadline for Receipt:** February of each year. **Additional Information:** This program, established in 2000, is sponsored by USA Funds, which serves as the education loan guarantor and administrator in selected states.

1524 ■ SCHOLARSHIP AMERICA

Attn: Scholarship Management Services
One Scholarship Way
P.O. Box 297
St. Peter, MN 56082
Tel: (507)931-1682
Free: 800-537-4180
Fax: (507)931-9168
E-mail: scholarship@usafunds.org
Web Site: http://www.usafunds.org/Borrowers/
Access_to_Education_hawaii.html
To provide financial assistance to undergraduate and graduate students from Arizona, especially those who are members of ethnic minority groups or have physical disabilities.
Title of Award: USA Funds Arizona Silver Anniversary Scholarships **Area, Field, or Subject:** General studies/Field of study not specified **Level of Education for which Award is Granted:** Graduate, Undergraduate **Number Awarded:** Varies each year; recently, a total of $500,000 was available for this program. **Funds Available:** The stipend is $1,500 per year for full-time undergraduate or graduate students or $750 per year for half-time undergraduate students. Funds are paid jointly to the student and the school. **Duration:** 1 year; may be renewed until the student receives a final degree or certificate or until the total award to a student reaches $6,000, whichever comes first. Renewal requires the recipient to maintain a GPA of 2.5 or higher.
Eligibility Requirements: This program is open to high school seniors and graduates who are residents of Arizona planning to enroll or already enrolled in full-time undergraduate or graduate course work at an accredited 2- or 4-year college, university, or vocational/technical school. Half-time undergraduate students are also eligible. Up to 50% of the awards are targeted at students who have a documented physical disability or are a member of an ethnic minority group, including but not limited to Native Hawaiian, Alaskan Native, Black/African American, Asian, Pacific Islander, American Indian, or Hispanic/Latino. Applicants must also be U.S. citizens or eligible noncitizens and come from a family with an annual adjusted gross income of $35,000 or less. In addition to financial need, selection is based on past academic performance and future potential, leadership and participation in school and community activities, work experience, career and educational aspirations, and goals. **Deadline for Receipt:** February of each year. **Additional Information:** This program is sponsored by USA Funds, which serves as the education loan guarantor and administrator in Arizona.

1525 ■ SCOTTISH RITE FOUNDATION OF WYOMING

1820 Capitol Avenue
Cheyenne, WY 82001
To provide financial assistance to students currently enrolled in their second year in a Wyoming community college.
Title of Award: Wyoming Scottish Rite Foundation Scholarships **Area, Field, or Subject:** General studies/Field of study not specified **Level of Education for which Award is Granted:** Two Year College **Number Awarded:** 7 each year. **Funds Available:** The stipend is $1,000. **Duration:** 1 year.
Eligibility Requirements: Each community college may recommend at least 6 applicants. Nominees must be graduates of a Wyoming high

school or hold a Wyoming GED. They must have sophomore standing at a Wyoming community college and be enrolled full time. Selection is based on leadership potential activities, GPA, and financial need. **Deadline for Receipt:** May of each year. **Additional Information:** Scholarships are nontransferable between colleges.

1526 ■ SCREEN ACTORS GUILD FOUNDATION

Attn: Administrative Director
5757 Wilshire Boulevard
Los Angeles, CA 90036-3600
Tel: (323)549-6649
Fax: (323)549-6710
E-mail: dlloyd@sag.org
Web Site: http://www.sagfoundation.org/scholarship/standard.shtml
To provide financial assistance for college to members and children of members of the Screen Actors Guild (SAG).
Title of Award: John L. Dales Standard Scholarships **Area, Field, or Subject:** General studies/Field of study not specified **Level of Education for which Award is Granted:** Undergraduate **Number Awarded:** Varies each year. **Funds Available:** The amount of the awards depends on the availability of funds. **Duration:** 1 year; recipients may reapply.
Eligibility Requirements: Applicants must have been members of SAG for at least 5 years and have aggregate earnings under guild jurisdiction of at least $30,000. The children of a parent who has been a member for at least 10 years and have aggregate earnings under guild jurisdiction of at least $60,000 are also eligible. Applicants must submit transcripts of high school and college work, SAT scores, information on academic and extracurricular activities, 2 letters of recommendation, information on financial need, and an essay of 250 to 500 words on a topic of their choice. **Deadline for Receipt:** March of each year. **Additional Information:** This program was established in 1973.

1527 ■ SEABEE MEMORIAL SCHOLARSHIP ASSOCIATION

P.O. Box 6574
Silver Spring, MD 20916
Tel: (301)570-2850
Fax: (301)570-2873
E-mail: smsa@erols.com
Web Site: http://www.seabee.org
To provide financial assistance for college to the children or grandchildren of active or deceased members of the Naval Construction Battalion (Seabees) or Navy Civil Engineering Corps.
Title of Award: Seabee Memorial Scholarship Association Program **Area, Field, or Subject:** General studies/Field of study not specified **Level of Education for which Award is Granted:** Four Year College **Number Awarded:** Varies each year; recently, 18 new scholarships were awarded through this program. **Funds Available:** The stipend is $2,200 per year. **Duration:** 1 year; may be renewed for 3 additional years.
Eligibility Requirements: This program is open to the children, stepchildren, and grandchildren of regular, Reserve, retired, or deceased officers and enlisted members who are now serving or have been honorably discharged from the Naval Construction Force (Seabees) or Navy Civil Engineering Corps. Applicants may be high school seniors, high school graduates, or students currently enrolled in a 4-year college or university. Full-time college enrollment is required. Selection is based on financial need, character, good citizenship, leadership, and scholastic record. **Deadline for Receipt:** April of each year.

1528 ■ LISA SECHRIST MEMORIAL FOUNDATION

Attn: Kim Mackmin, Scholarship Selection Committee
Brookfield Homes
8500 Executive Park Avenue, Suite 300
Fairfax, VA 22031
Web Site: http://www.lisasechrist.com/scholarship.html
To provide financial assistance for college to female high school seniors from Virginia who come from disadvantaged backgrounds.
Title of Award: Lisa Sechrist Memorial Foundation Scholarship **Area, Field, or Subject:** General studies/Field of study not specified **Level of Education for which Award is Granted:** Undergraduate **Number Awarded:** 1 each year. **Funds Available:** The stipend is $2,500 per year. **Duration:** 4 years, provided the recipient maintains a GPA of 2.5 or higher.
Eligibility Requirements: This program is open to women graduating from high schools in Virginia who come from a disadvantaged back-

ground. Applicants should be able to demonstrate membership in honor societies, participation in sports or other extracurricular activities, citizenship and service within the community, and/or leadership skills within the school or community. Selection is based on merit, integrity, academic potential, and financial need. **Deadline for Receipt:** March of each year.

1529 ■ SECOND BOMBARDMENT ASSOCIATION

c/o Kemp F. Martin
806 Oak Valley Drive
Houston, TX 77024
Tel: (713)464-0401
To provide financial assistance for college to the children of members of the Second Bombardment Association.
Title of Award: Second Bombardment Association Scholarship **Area, Field, or Subject:** General studies/Field of study not specified **Level of Education for which Award is Granted:** Undergraduate **Number Awarded:** 2 each year: 1 from an officer's family and 1 from an enlisted person's family. **Funds Available:** The stipend is $1,000. **Duration:** 1 year.
Eligibility Requirements: High school seniors, graduates, and currently-enrolled college students are eligible to apply if at least 1 parent is a member of the Second Bombardment Association and is on duty at Barksdale. **Additional Information:** Further information is available from the Air Force Aid Society, 1745 Jefferson Davis Highway, Suite 202, Arlington, VA 22202.

1530 ■ SECOND (INDIANHEAD) DIVISION ASSOCIATION

Attn: Scholarship Foundation
c/o Ed Mize
4848 Highland Drive, Number 613
Salt Lake City, UT 84117-6007
Tel: (801)277-7901
E-mail: mizedjean@hotmail.com
Web Site: http://www.swiftsite.com/2IDA
To provide financial assistance for college to children and grandchildren of members of the Second (Indianhead) Division Association.
Title of Award: Indianhead Division Scholarships **Area, Field, or Subject:** General studies/Field of study not specified **Level of Education for which Award is Granted:** Undergraduate **Number Awarded:** 1 or more each year. **Funds Available:** The stipend is usually $1,000 per year. **Duration:** 1 year; may be renewed.
Eligibility Requirements: This program is open to 1) children and grandchildren of veterans who have been members of the association for the past 3 years and have a current membership, and 2) children and grandchildren of men or women killed in action while serving with the Second Division. Applicants may be high school seniors or currently-enrolled college students. They must submit a personal letter giving reasons for the request and plans for the future; a high school and, if appropriate, college transcript; ACT or SAT test scores; a statement from their school principal attesting to their character and involvement in extracurricular activities; 2 letters of recommendation from current teachers or professors; a 200- to 300-word essay on such subjects as "What Being an American Means to Me," "Why I Should Receive This Scholarship," or "What Significant Part of U.S. Army History Has the Second Infantry Division Contributed;" and a statement from their parents or guardians on the financial support they will be able to provide the applicant. **Deadline for Receipt:** May of each year.

1531 ■ SECOND MARINE DIVISION ASSOCIATION

Attn: Memorial Scholarship Fund
P.O. Box 8180
Camp Lejeune, NC 28547-8180
Tel: (910)451-3167
To provide financial assistance for college to the children and grandchildren of veterans or members of the Second Marine Division.
Title of Award: Second Marine Division Association Memorial Scholarship **Area, Field, or Subject:** General studies/Field of study not specified **Level of Education for which Award is Granted:** Undergraduate **Number Awarded:** Varies each year. **Funds Available:** The award is $1,000 per year. **Duration:** 1 year; may be renewed.
Eligibility Requirements: This program is open to unmarried dependent children and grandchildren of individuals who are serving or have served in the Second Marine Division or in a unit attached to it. Applicants must

be high school seniors, high school graduates, or full-time undergraduate students in accredited colleges or vocational/technical schools. They must have a family income of less than $50,000 and a GPA of 2.5 or higher. **Deadline for Receipt:** March of each year. **Additional Information:** For an application, send a self-addressed stamped envelope to David Dowdakin, Board of Trustees, SMDA Memorial Scholarship Fund, 3933 S.E. Oak Street, Portland, OR 97214.

1532 ■ ABE AND ANNIE SEIBEL FOUNDATION

c/o Frost Bank
Trust Department
P.O. Box 8210
Galveston, TX 77553-8210
Tel: (409)770-5665
To loan money to students in Texas who are interested in attending college.
Title of Award: Abe and Annie Seibel Foundation Loans **Area, Field, or Subject:** General studies/Field of study not specified **Level of Education for which Award is Granted:** Undergraduate **Number Awarded:** Varies each year. **Funds Available:** The maximum loan is $4,000 per year. The lifetime maximum is $16,000. Loans are interest free. Repayment must begin at the rate of $35 per month while the student is still enrolled in college; following graduation, repayment must be completed within 6 years or a minimum of $50 per month, whichever is higher. **Duration:** Up to 4 years.
Eligibility Requirements: Applicants must be U.S. citizens and Texas residents (high school seniors or college students) who are planning to attend or are attending a Texas college or university. High school seniors who are in the top 10% of their graduating class may have any SAT or ACT score; if they are in the top 15%, they must have at least 22 on the ACT (or SAT equivalent); if they are in the second quarter of their graduating class, they must have at least 25 on the ACT (or SAT equivalent); if they are in the third or fourth quarters of their class, they must have at least 27 on the ACT (or SAT equivalent). Current college students must have a GPA of 2.75 or higher. **Deadline for Receipt:** February of each year. **Additional Information:** Recipients must attend college in Texas on a full-time basis.

1533 ■ SENECA NATION OF INDIANS

Attn: Allegany Education Department
P.O. Box 231
Salamanca, NY 14779
Tel: (716)945-1790
Fax: (716)945-7170
E-mail: fwhite@sni.org
Web Site: http://www.sni.org
To provide financial assistance to Seneca Nation members who are interested in working on an undergraduate or graduate degree.
Title of Award: Seneca Nation of Indians Higher Education Program **Area, Field, or Subject:** General studies/Field of study not specified **Level of Education for which Award is Granted:** Graduate, Undergraduate **Number Awarded:** Varies each year. **Funds Available:** The maximum annual stipends are $11,000 for first-priority students, $8,000 for second-priority students, or $6,000 for third-priority students. **Duration:** 1 year; may be renewed if the recipient maintains a GPA of 2.0 or higher.
Eligibility Requirements: Enrolled members of the Seneca Nation are eligible to apply if they are in financial need and accepted in an accredited program of study at the graduate or undergraduate level. First priority is given to students with permanent residence on the reservation, second priority to students with permanent residence within New York state, and third priority to students with permanent residence outside New York state. **Deadline for Receipt:** June of each year for fall semester; July of each year for fall quarter or trimester; October of each year for winter quarter or trimester; November of each year for spring semester; January of each year for spring quarter or trimester; April of each year for summer term.

1534 ■ SENIOR ENLISTED ACADEMY ALUMNI ASSOCIATION

Attn: CPO Scholarship Fund
1269 Elliot Avenue
Newport, RI 02841-1525
E-mail: john@seaaa.org

Web Site: http://www.cposf.org
To provide financial assistance for college to the dependents of Navy Chief Petty Officers (CPOs).
Title of Award: CPO Scholarship Fund **Area, Field, or Subject:** General studies/Field of study not specified **Level of Education for which Award is Granted:** Undergraduate **Number Awarded:** 10 each year: 2 in each of the categories. **Funds Available:** The amount of the stipend depends on the availability of funds; awards are sent directly to the recipient's school. **Duration:** 1 year.
Eligibility Requirements: This program is open to the spouses and children (natural born, adopted, or step) of active, Reserve, retired, and deceased Navy CPOs. Applicants must be high school graduates or seniors planning to graduate and must intend to enter their first year of college or university with the goal of obtaining an associate, bachelor's, or graduate degree. Members of the armed services are not eligible. Scholarships are awarded in 5 categories: 1) active duty East Coast (stationed East of or at Great Lakes, Illinois); 2) active duty West coast (stationed West of Great Lakes, Illinois); 3) active duty stationed outside the continental United States; 4) Reserve; and 5) retired and deceased. Applicants must submit an essay of 250 to 300 words on "How my education will help society." Selection is based on the essay, honors and awards received during high school, extracurricular activities, community activities, and employment experience. **Deadline for Receipt:** March of each year. **Additional Information:** Information is also available from Duane Bushey, Chief Executive Officer, CPOSF, 1034 Creamer Road, Norfolk, VA 23503, E-mail: kiddercorp@cox.net.

1535 ■ SERTOMA INTERNATIONAL

Attn: Director of Finance and Administration
1912 East Meyer Boulevard
Kansas City, MO 64132-1174
Tel: (816)333-8300
Fax: (816)333-4320
E-mail: aellington@sertoma.org
Web Site: http://www.sertoma.org
To provide financial assistance for college to members of Serteens.
Title of Award: Serteens Scholarships **Area, Field, or Subject:** General studies/Field of study not specified **Level of Education for which Award is Granted:** Undergraduate **Number Awarded:** 4 each year. **Funds Available:** The stipend is $1,000 per year. **Duration:** 1 year.
Eligibility Requirements: This program is open to members of the organization in the United States who are graduating from high school and planning to attend college in the following fall. Applicants must have maintained a GPA of 3.0 or higher during their sophomore, junior, and senior years of high school. Along with their application, they must submit a 1-page statement explaining how this scholarship will help them achieve their goals. U.S. citizenship is required. Selection is based on academic achievement, participation in Serteen Club activities, and participation in non-Serteen service activities. **Deadline for Receipt:** March of each year. **Additional Information:** Serteens is the high school affiliate of Sertoma, which stands for SERvice TO MAnkind, a volunteer service organization with 25,000 members in 800 clubs across North America.

1536 ■ SERTOMA INTERNATIONAL

Attn: Director of Finance and Administration
1912 East Meyer Boulevard
Kansas City, MO 64132-1174
Tel: (816)333-8300
Fax: (816)333-4320
E-mail: aellington@sertoma.org
Web Site: http://www.sertoma.org
To provide financial assistance for college to members of Sertoma Collegiate Club.
Title of Award: Sertoma Collegiate Club Scholarships **Area, Field, or Subject:** General studies/Field of study not specified **Level of Education for which Award is Granted:** Four Year College **Number Awarded:** 4 each year. **Funds Available:** The stipend is $1,000 per year. **Duration:** 1 year.
Eligibility Requirements: This program is open to U.S. citizens who are active members of the organization. Applicants must be working full time on a bachelor's degree with a cumulative GPA of 3.2 or higher. Associate degrees, community colleges, and vocational programs do not qualify. Along with their application, they must submit a 1-page statement of

purpose describing how this scholarship will help them achieve their goals. Selection is based on academic achievement and participation in both Sertoma Collegiate Club programs and non-Sertoma service activities. **Deadline for Receipt:** March of each year. **Additional Information:** Sertoma, which stands for SERvice TO MAnkind, is a volunteer service organization with 25,000 members in 800 clubs across North America.

1537 ■ SERTOMA INTERNATIONAL
Attn: Director of Finance and Administration
1912 East Meyer Boulevard
Kansas City, MO 64132-1174
Tel: (816)333-8300
Fax: (816)333-4320
E-mail: aellington@sertoma.org
Web Site: http://www.sertoma.org
To provide financial assistance for college to hearing impaired students.

Title of Award: Sertoma Scholarships for Hearing-Impaired Students **Area, Field, or Subject:** General studies/Field of study not specified **Level of Education for which Award is Granted:** Four Year College **Number Awarded:** 20 each year. **Funds Available:** The stipend is $1,000 per year. **Duration:** 1 year; may be renewed up to 4 times.

Eligibility Requirements: This program is open to students who have a minimum 40dB bilateral hearing loss and are interested in working full time on a bachelor's degree at a 4-year college or university. Students working on a community college degree, associate degree, or vocational program degree are ineligible. Applicants must be able to document their hearing loss. They must be entering or continuing undergraduate studies in the United States. A GPA of at least 3.2 and U.S. citizenship are required. Selection is based on past academic performance, goals, a statement of purpose, and overall merit. Financial need is not considered. **Deadline for Receipt:** April of each year. **Additional Information:** Sertoma, which stands for SERvice TO MAnkind, is a volunteer service organization with 25,000 members in 800 clubs across North America. Funding for this program is provided by Oticon, Inc. and the Sertoma Foundation. To request an application, students must send a self-addressed, stamped envelope.

1538 ■ SERVICE EMPLOYEES INTERNATIONAL UNION
Attn: Education Department
1313 L Street, N.W.
Washington, DC 20005
Tel: (202)898-3326
Free: 800-448-SEIU
Fax: (202)898-3348
Web Site: http://www.seiu.org/mbe/scholarships/jessejackson.cfm
To provide financial assistance for college to members and children of members of the Service Employees International Union (SEIU) who share the vision of a "more just and humane society" held by the Rev. Jesse Jackson.

Title of Award: Jesse Jackson Scholarship Program **Area, Field, or Subject:** General studies/Field of study not specified **Level of Education for which Award is Granted:** Undergraduate **Number Awarded:** 1 each year. **Funds Available:** The stipend is $5,000 per year. **Duration:** 1 year; may be renewed up to 3 additional years.

Eligibility Requirements: This program is open to members of an SEIU local or affiliated union and their children. Applicants must be working on or planning to work on a degree at a 2-year community or junior college or 4-year college or university. Their record of work and aspirations for economic and social justice must "reflect the values and accomplishments of the Rev. Jesse Jackson." Along with their application, they must submit a personal statement of 500 words or less that describes what the labor movement has meant to them and their family; their social justice, labor, or political activism; goals for working for social and economic justice within an organization; and their plans to carry out this activism in their career after graduation. Selection is based on originality, clarity, and commitment to social and economic justice in the workplace. **Deadline for Receipt:** February of each year. **Additional Information:** This program is administered by Scholarship Program Administrators, Inc., 1201 Eighth Avenue South, P.O. Box 23737, Nashville, TN 27202-3737, (615) 320-3149, Fax: (615) 320-3151, E-mail: info@spaprog.com. The recipient must agree to participate in some paid or course credit internships or work experiences in social change organizations during the years they receive this award.

1539 ■ SERVICE EMPLOYEES INTERNATIONAL UNION
Attn: Education Department
1313 L Street, N.W.
Washington, DC 20005
Tel: (202)898-3326
Free: 800-448-SEIU
Fax: (202)898-3348
Web Site: http://www.seiu.org/mbe/scholarships/classic_program.cfm
To provide financial assistance for continuing education to members and children of members of the Service Employees International Union (SEIU).

Title of Award: SEIU 1-Year Scholarships **Area, Field, or Subject:** General studies/Field of study not specified **Level of Education for which Award is Granted:** Undergraduate **Number Awarded:** 33 each year. **Funds Available:** The stipend is $1,500. **Duration:** 1 year; may not be renewed.

Eligibility Requirements: All members of SEIU in good standing for 3 continuous years or the children of those members are eligible. Applicants must be 1) returning to an accredited college or university as a sophomore, junior, or senior; or 2) attending an accredited community college, trade school, or technical school. As part of the application process, they must read the online essay "Uniting Our Strength to Win Big" and answer questions pertaining to the essay. Applicants who pass the test are eligible for a lottery drawing, from which winners are selected. **Deadline for Receipt:** February of each year. **Additional Information:** This program is administered by Scholarship Program Administrators, Inc., 1201 Eighth Avenue South, P.O. Box 23737, Nashville, TN 27202-3737, (615) 320-3149, Fax: (615) 320-3151, E-mail: info@spaprog.com.

1540 ■ SERVICE EMPLOYEES INTERNATIONAL UNION
Attn: Education Department
1313 L Street, N.W.
Washington, DC 20005
Tel: (202)898-3326
Free: 800-448-SEIU
Fax: (202)898-3348
Web Site: http://www.seiu.org/mbe/scholarships/classic_program.cfm
To provide financial assistance for undergraduate education to members and children of members of the Service Employees International Union (SEIU).

Title of Award: SEIU 4-Year Scholarships **Area, Field, or Subject:** General studies/Field of study not specified **Level of Education for which Award is Granted:** Four Year College **Number Awarded:** 15 each year. **Funds Available:** The stipend is $1,000 per year. **Duration:** 4 years.

Eligibility Requirements: This program is open to members of SEIU in good standing for 3 continuous years and the children of those members. Applicants must be graduating from high school or a GED program and planning to enroll as a freshman at an accredited 4-year college or university. Students who plan to attend a 2-year program or trade school are not eligible. As part of the application process, As part of the application process, they must read the online essay "Uniting Our Strength to Win Big" and answer questions pertaining to the essay. Applicants who pass the test are eligible for a lottery **Deadline for Receipt:** February of each year. **Additional Information:** This program is administered by Scholarship Program Administrators, Inc., 1201 Eighth Avenue South, P.O. Box 23737, Nashville, TN 27202-3737, (615) 320-3149, Fax: (615) 320-3151, E-mail: info@spaprog.com.

1541 ■ SHOPKO STORES INC.
700 Pilgrim Way
P.O. Box 19060
Green Bay, WI 54307-9060
Tel: (920)497-2211
Web Site: http://www.shopko.com
To provide financial assistance for college to residents of states where ShopKo stores operate.

Title of Award: ShopKo Scholarships **Area, Field, or Subject:** General studies/Field of study not specified **Level of Education for which Award is Granted:** Undergraduate **Number Awarded:** 100 each year. **Funds Available:** The stipend is $1,000 per year. **Duration:** 1 year; nonrenewable.

Eligibility Requirements: This program is open to residents of California, Colorado, Idaho, Illinois, Iowa, Michigan, Minnesota, Montana, Nebraska,

Nevada, Oregon, South Dakota, Utah, Washington, and Wisconsin. Applicants must be high school seniors or graduates who plan to enroll or students who are already enrolled in a full-time undergraduate course of study at an accredited 2-year or 4-year college, university, or vocational/technical school. Selection is based on academic record, potential to succeed, leadership and participation in school and community activities, honors, work experience, a statement of educational and career goals, and an outside appraisal. Financial need is not considered. **Deadline for Receipt:** November of each year. **Additional Information:** This program is managed by Scholarships Inc, P.O. Box 1873, Green Bay, WI 54305.

1542 ■ SICKLE CELL DISEASE ASSOCIATION OF AMERICA

Attn: Scholarship Committee
16 South Calvert Street, Suite 600
Baltimore, MD 21202-1314
Tel: (410)528-1555
Free: 800-421-8453
Fax: (410)528-1495
E-mail: scdaa@sicklecelldisease.org
Web Site: http://www.sicklecelldisease.org/programs/nash_scholarship.phtml
To provide financial assistance for college to graduating high school seniors who have sickle cell disease.
Title of Award: Kermit B. Nash Academic Scholarship **Area, Field, or Subject:** General studies/Field of study not specified **Level of Education for which Award is Granted:** Four Year College **Number Awarded:** 1 each year. **Funds Available:** The stipend is $5,000 per year. **Duration:** Up to 4 years.
Eligibility Requirements: This program is open to graduating high school seniors who have sickle cell disease (not the trait). Applicants must have a GPA of 3.0 or higher and be U.S. citizens or permanent residents planning to attend an accredited 4-year college or university as a full-time student. They must submit a personal essay, up to 1,000 words, on an aspect of the impact of the disease on their lives or on society. Selection is based on GPA, general academic achievement and promise, SAT scores, leadership and community service, severity of academic challenges and obstacles posed by sickle cell disease, and the quality of their essay. **Deadline for Receipt:** June of each year. **Additional Information:** The Sickle Cell Disease Association of America (SCDAA) was formerly the National Association for Sickle Cell Disease. It established this program in 1999. Requests for applications must be submitted in writing; telephone requests are not honored.

1543 ■ SICKLE CELL DISEASE ASSOCIATION OF AMERICA-CONNECTICUT CHAPTER

Attn: Garey E. Coleman
114 Woodland Street, Suite 2101
Hartford, CT 06105-1299
Tel: (860)714-5540
Free: 800-379-0119
Fax: (860)714-8007
E-mail: scdaa@iconn.net
Web Site: http://www.sicklecellct.org/programs
To provide financial assistance for college to high school seniors in Connecticut who have sickle cell disease.
Title of Award: I.H. McLendon Memorial Scholarship **Area, Field, or Subject:** General studies/Field of study not specified **Level of Education for which Award is Granted:** Undergraduate **Number Awarded:** 1 each year. **Funds Available:** The stipend is $1,000. **Duration:** 1 year.
Eligibility Requirements: This program is open to Connecticut residents who have sickle cell disease. Applicants must be graduating high school seniors, have a GPA of 3.0 or higher, be in the top third of their class, and be interested in attending a 2- or 4-year college or university. Along with their application, they must submit a statement outlining their personal and career goals and how the scholarship will help them achieve those goals, 3 letters of recommendation, and a letter from their physician attesting to existence of sickle cell disease. Finalists are interviewed. **Deadline for Receipt:** April of each year.

1544 ■ SIGMA ALPHA IOTA PHILANTHROPIES, INC.

One Tunnel Road
Asheville, NC 28805
Tel: (828)251-0606
Fax: (828)251-0644
E-mail: philonline@sai-national.org
Web Site: http://www.sai-national.org/phil/philsch1.html
To provide financial assistance to members of Sigma Alpha Iota (an organization of women musicians) who are interested in working on an undergraduate or graduate degree in music therapy.
Title of Award: Music Therapy Scholarship **Area, Field, or Subject:** Music therapy **Level of Education for which Award is Granted:** Graduate, Undergraduate **Number Awarded:** 1 each year. **Funds Available:** The stipend is $1,000. **Duration:** 1 year.
Eligibility Requirements: Members of the organization may apply for these scholarships if they wish to study music therapy at the undergraduate or graduate level. Applicants must submit an essay the includes their personal definition of music therapy, their career plans and professional goals as a music therapist, and why they feel they are deserving of this scholarship. Selection is based on music therapy skills, musicianship, fraternity service, community service, leadership, self-reliance, and dedication to the field of music therapy as a career. **Deadline for Receipt:** March of each year. **Additional Information:** There is a $25 nonrefundable application fee.

1545 ■ SIMON YOUTH FOUNDATION

115 West Washington Street, Suite 1325
Indianapolis, IN 46204
Tel: (317)263-2361
Free: 800-509-3676
Fax: (317)263-2371
E-mail: syf@simon.com
Web Site: http://www.simonyouth.scholarshipamerica.org
To provide financial assistance for college to high school seniors in communities with a shopping mall owned and/or operated by Simon Property Group Inc.
Title of Award: Simon Youth Foundation Community Scholarship Program **Area, Field, or Subject:** General studies/Field of study not specified **Level of Education for which Award is Granted:** Undergraduate **Number Awarded:** Up to 206 per year, including 190 at $1,200 to students in communities with malls, 8 at $1,200 to students in communities with Community Centers, and 8 at $2,500 per year to students in the 8 designated mall regions. **Funds Available:** Stipends are $2,500 per year or $1,200. **Duration:** 1 year; the $2,500 awards may be renewed up to 3 additional years; the $1,200 awards are nonrenewable.
Eligibility Requirements: This program is open to seniors at high schools in communities that host a Simon Property Mall or Community Center (strip mall). Renewable scholarships are available to students in the following mall regions: Atlanta (Georgia), Boston (Massachusetts), Dallas (Texas), Indianapolis (Indiana), Miami (Florida), New York (New York), Orange County (California), and Orlando (Florida). Applicants must plan to enroll in a full-time undergraduate course of study at an accredited 2- or 4-year college, university, or vocational/technical school. Selection is based on academic record, demonstrated leadership and participation in school and community activities, honors, work experience, a statement of goals and aspirations, an outside appraisal, and financial need. **Deadline for Receipt:** November of each year. **Additional Information:** This program is managed by Scholarship America, One Scholarship Way, P.O. Box 297, St. Peter, MN 56082, (507) 931-1682, (800) 537-4180, Fax: (507) 931-9168, E-mail: smsinfo@csfa.org. Applications are available through the Simon Marketplace in each Simon mall.

1546 ■ SIOUX FALLS AREA COMMUNITY FOUNDATION

Attn: Scholarship Coordinator
300 North Phillips Avenue, Suite 120
Sioux Falls, SD 57104-6006
Tel: (605)336-7055
Fax: (605)336-0038
E-mail: sbrown@sfacf.org
Web Site: http://www.sfacf.org
To provide financial assistance for college to high school seniors in South Dakota.
Title of Award: Fred and Marie Christopherson Scholarship **Area, Field, or Subject:** General studies/Field of study not specified **Level of Education for which Award is Granted:** Four Year College **Number Awarded:** Varies each year; recently, 3 of these scholarships were awarded. **Funds Available:** The stipend is $2,500 the first year and $1,000 in subsequent

years. Funds are paid annually in 2 equal installments and are to be used for tuition, fees, and/or books. **Duration:** 1 year; may be renewed for 3 additional years if the recipient maintains a GPA of 3.0 or higher and full-time enrollment.

Eligibility Requirements: This program is open to seniors graduating from a high school in South Dakota. Applicants must be interested in attending a 4-year college or university in the state. They must have a GPA of 3.9 or higher and an ACT score of at least 28. Along with their application, they must submit an essay on their educational and career goals, 2 letters of recommendation, and an official transcript. **Deadline for Receipt:** March of each year. **Additional Information:** This program was established in 1989.

1547 ■ SIOUX FALLS AREA COMMUNITY FOUNDATION

Attn: Scholarship Coordinator
300 North Phillips Avenue, Suite 120
Sioux Falls, SD 57104-6006
Tel: (605)336-7055
Fax: (605)336-0038
E-mail: sbrown@sfacf.org
Web Site: http://www.sfacf.org
To provide financial assistance for college to high school seniors in South Dakota.

Title of Award: Joe Foss, An American Hero Scholarship **Area, Field, or Subject:** General studies/Field of study not specified **Level of Education for which Award is Granted:** Undergraduate **Number Awarded:** Varies each year; recently, 6 of these scholarships were awarded. **Funds Available:** The stipend is $1,000. Funds are paid in 2 equal installments and are to be used for tuition, fees, and/or books. **Duration:** 1 year.

Eligibility Requirements: This program is open to seniors graduating from high schools in South Dakota. Applicants must have a GPA of 3.5 or higher and an ACT score of at least 21. They must be able to demonstrate the characteristics of an American patriot. Along with their application, they must submit an essay either on "What is an American Patriot," or an event or individual that was helpful to them in forming their value system. **Deadline for Receipt:** March of each year. **Additional Information:** This program was established in 1992.

1548 ■ THE SISTERS OF PERPETUAL INDULGENCE, INC.

Attn: Scholarship Fund Committee Chair
584 Castro Street
PMB 392
San Francisco, CA 94114
Web Site: http://www.SisterFund.com
To provide financial assistance for college or graduate school to students who are committed to working for social and economic justice.

Title of Award: The Sisters' Economic and Social Justice Scholarship Fund **Area, Field, or Subject:** General studies/Field of study not specified **Level of Education for which Award is Granted:** Graduate, Undergraduate **Number Awarded:** Varies each year; recently, 23 of these scholarships were awarded. **Funds Available:** Stipends are either $1,000 or $500. **Duration:** 1 year.

Eligibility Requirements: This program is open to students enrolled in an accredited college or university and working on a bachelor's, master's, M.D., J.D., or Ph.D. degree. Applicants must be able to demonstrate a history of working for social and economic justice in their local or national community and be able to describe their plans to use their education to further economic and social justice. Ineligible students include those who are attending 1) military schools, law enforcement academies, or related preparatory programs; 2) institutions associated with religious groups known for discrimination or intolerance; or 3) institutions that, either through intentional or unintentional action or inaction, promote, encourage, or foster social or economic injustice. Selection is based on financial need, prior community involvement, future community involvement, and commitment to economic and social justice issues. Age, ethnicity, race or national origin, gender, and sexual orientation are not considered. **Deadline for Receipt:** November of each year. **Additional Information:** The Sisters of Perpetual Indulgence is an organization of gay men

established in San Francisco in 1979. It began offering scholarships in 2001. Applications must be submitted online.

1549 ■ SITNASUAK NATIVE CORPORATION

Attn: Sitnasuak Foundation
P.O. Box 905
Nome, AK 99762
Tel: (907)443-2632
Fax: (907)443-3063
E-mail: foundation@snc.org
Web Site: http://snc.org/foundationtext.htm
To provide financial assistance for college or graduate school to members of the Sitnasuak Native Corporation and other residents of the Bering Straits region of Alaska.

Title of Award: Sitnasuak Foundation Scholarships **Area, Field, or Subject:** General studies/Field of study not specified **Level of Education for which Award is Granted:** Graduate, Undergraduate **Number Awarded:** Varies each year. **Funds Available:** For full-time students, the stipend is $600 per semester for those with a GPA of 3.0 or higher, $500 per semester for those with a GPA of 2.5 to 2.9, or $400 per semester for those with a GPA of 2.0 to 2.4. For part-time students, the stipend is $200 per semester. For vocational training students, the stipend is $400 per semester or $800 per year. **Duration:** 1 year; may be renewed if undergraduate students maintain a GPA of 2.0 or higher, if graduate students maintain a GPA of 2.5 or higher, and if vocational students provide a progress report at the end of each term.

Eligibility Requirements: This program is open to students in the following order of priority: 1) residents of the Bering Straits region of Alaska with plans to return and contribute to the development of the region; 2) shareholders of the Sitnasuak Native Corporation and their descendants; and 3) continuing students. Applicants must be enrolled or accepted for enrollment in a college, graduate school, or vocational program. They must have earned a GED or high school diploma with a GPA of 2.0 or higher and be able to demonstrate financial need. Along with their application, they must submit a 2-page essay describing their educational goals and future plans to contribute to the development of the Bering Straits region. **Deadline for Receipt:** High school seniors and other first-time applicants must submit applications by April of each year. Continuing students must submit applications by July or November of each year. **Additional Information:** The Sitnasuak Native Corporation is the largest of 16 native village corporations in the Bering Straits region of Alaska.

1550 ■ SIXTH MARINE DIVISION ASSOCIATION

c/o Marine Corps Scholarship Foundation
P.O. Box 3008
Princeton, NJ 08543-3008
Tel: (609)921-3534
Free: 800-292-7777
Fax: (609)452-2259
E-mail: mcsfnj@mcsf.org
Web Site: http://www.marine-scholars.org
To provide financial assistance for college to the grandchildren of veterans who served with the Sixth Marine Division during World War II.

Title of Award: Sixth Marine Division Association Scholarship **Area, Field, or Subject:** General studies/Field of study not specified **Level of Education for which Award is Granted:** Undergraduate **Number Awarded:** Varies each year. **Funds Available:** Stipends depend on the need of the recipient and the availability of funds. **Duration:** 1 year; may be renewed for up to 3 additional years.

Eligibility Requirements: This program is open to grandchildren of veterans who served with the Sixth Marine Division during World War II and are or were members of the Sixth Marine Division Association. Applicants must submit academic transcripts, a copy of their grandparent's honorable discharge, and a 300-word essay on topics that change periodically. Recently, they were invited to write on the topic, "What is the most valuable lesson you have learned and who was responsible for teaching it?" Only undergraduate study is supported. The family income of applicants must be less than $63,000 per year. **Deadline for Receipt:** April of each year.

1551 ■ SKANDALARIS FAMILY FOUNDATION

P.O. Box 2061
Venice, FL 34284

Tel: (941)544-8659
Fax: (941)408-9526
E-mail: info@skandalaris.com
Web Site: http://www.skandalaris.com
To provide financial assistance for college to high school seniors and current college students, especially those from Michigan.

Title of Award: Skandalaris Family Foundation Scholarships **Area, Field, or Subject:** General studies/Field of study not specified **Level of Education for which Award is Granted:** Undergraduate **Number Awarded:** Varies each year; recently, 115 of these scholarships were awarded. **Funds Available:** The stipend is at least $2,000. **Duration:** 1 year; may be renewed.

Eligibility Requirements: This program is open to graduating high school seniors and students already enrolled in college. The majority of the scholarships are awarded to residents of Michigan. High school seniors must have a GPA of 3.5 or higher, minimum scores of 1200 on the SAT or 24 on the ACT, and a record of involvement in school, athletic, and community activities. College students must have a cumulative GPA of 3.4 or higher and a record of active involvement in university, athletic, or community services. All applicants must be U.S. citizens and able to demonstrate financial need. **Deadline for Receipt:** April of each year.

1552 ■ SLOVAK CATHOLIC SOKOL

Attn: Membership Memorial Scholarship Fund
205 Madison Street
P.O. Box 899
Passaic, NJ 07055-0899
Tel: (973)777-2605
Free: 800-886-7656
Fax: (973)779-8245
E-mail: sokol205@aol.com
Web Site: http://www.slovakcatholicsokol.org/members/scholarships.htm
To provide financial assistance for college or graduate school to members of the Slovak Catholic Sokol.

Title of Award: Slovak Catholic Sokol College Scholarship Grants **Area, Field, or Subject:** General studies/Field of study not specified **Level of Education for which Award is Granted:** Graduate, Undergraduate **Number Awarded:** 30 each year. **Funds Available:** The stipend is $1,000 per year. **Duration:** 1 year; may be renewed 1 additional year.

Eligibility Requirements: This program is open to members of the Slovak Catholic Sokol who have completed at least 1 semester of college and are currently enrolled full time as an undergraduate or graduate student at an accredited college, university, or professional school. Applicants must have been a member for at least 5 years, have at least $3,000 permanent life insurance coverage, and have at least 1 parent who is a member. **Deadline for Receipt:** February of each year. **Additional Information:** Slovak Catholic Sokol was founded as a fraternal benefit society in 1905. It is licensed to operate in the following states: Connecticut, Illinois, Indiana, Massachusetts, Michigan, New Jersey, New York, Ohio, Pennsylvania, and Wisconsin. This program was established in 2003.

1553 ■ SLOVENE NATIONAL BENEFIT SOCIETY

247 West Allegheny Road
Imperial, PA 15126-9774
Tel: (724)695-1100
Free: 800-THE-SNPJ
Fax: (724)695-1555
E-mail: snpj@snpj.com
Web Site: http://snpj.org/Fraternal%20Pages/snpj_scholar_02.html
To provide financial assistance for college to members of the Slovene National Benefit Society (SNPJ).

Title of Award: Slovene National Benefit Society Scholarships **Area, Field, or Subject:** General studies/Field of study not specified **Level of Education for which Award is Granted:** Undergraduate **Number Awarded:** Varies each year. **Funds Available:** A stipend is awarded (amount not specified). **Duration:** 1 year; may be renewed provided the recipient demonstrates normal academic progress.

Eligibility Requirements: This program is open to members of the SNPJ who are enrolled in an accredited college, university, or trade school. Applicants must have a minimum of $5,000 permanent SNPJ insurance ($2,000 if purchased prior to 1996) at the date of application and have been a member of the society for at least 2 years. Selection is based on

academic achievement, financial need, and involvement in SNPJ-approved activities. **Additional Information:** The society is licensed to conduct business in the following states: Arizona, California, Colorado, Florida, Illinois, Indiana, Kansas, Michigan, Minnesota, Missouri, Montana, New Mexico, New York, Ohio, Oregon, Pennsylvania, Utah, Washington, West Virginia, Wisconsin, and Wyoming.

1554 ■ J. CRAIG AND PAGE T. SMITH SCHOLARSHIP FOUNDATION

505 20th Street North, Suite 1800
Birmingham, AL 35203
Tel: (205)250-6669
E-mail: scholarships@jcraigsmithfoundation.org
Web Site: http://www.jcraigsmithfoundation.org
To provide financial assistance to high school seniors in Alabama, especially those who are the first in their family to attend college.

Title of Award: Alabama First in Family Scholarships **Area, Field, or Subject:** General studies/Field of study not specified **Level of Education for which Award is Granted:** Four Year College **Number Awarded:** Approximately 10 each year. **Funds Available:** Funding covers full payment of tuition, campus room, board, and books. **Duration:** 4 years, provided the recipient remains enrolled full time, makes significant progress toward completion of an undergraduate degree, verifies community service during the school year, and maintains a GPA of at least "C+."

Eligibility Requirements: This program is open to seniors graduating from high schools in Alabama who have a GPA of 2.0 or higher. Applicants must be planning to attend a 4-year college or university in the state as a full-time student. They must submit an essay on their future plans or goals of accomplishment for themselves, an essay documenting community and civic-oriented activities or assistance to family members, an official transcript, ACT or SAT scores (no minimum is required), and documentation of financial need. Special consideration is given to applicants who will be the first in either their mother's or father's (or both parents') families to attend college. **Deadline for Receipt:** January of each year. **Additional Information:** This program began in 2005.

1555 ■ SOCIETY OF DAUGHTERS OF THE UNITED STATES ARMY

c/o Mary P. Maroney,
Chair, Memorial and Scholarship Funds
11804 Grey Birch Place
Reston, VA 20191-4223
To provide financial assistance for college to daughters and granddaughters of active, retired, or deceased career Army warrant and commissioned officers.

Title of Award: Society of Daughters of the United States Army Scholarships **Area, Field, or Subject:** General studies/Field of study not specified **Level of Education for which Award is Granted:** Undergraduate **Number Awarded:** Varies each year. **Funds Available:** Scholarships, to a maximum of $1,000, are paid directly to the college or school for tuition, laboratory fees, books, or other expenses. **Duration:** 1 year; may be renewed up to 4 additional years if the recipient maintains at least a 3.0 GPA.

Eligibility Requirements: This program is open to the daughters, adopted daughters, stepdaughters, or granddaughters of career commissioned officers or warrant officers of the U.S. Army (active, regular, or Reserve) who 1) are currently on active duty, 2) retired after 20 years of active duty or were medically retired, or 3) died while on active duty or after retiring from active duty with 20 or more years of service. Applicants must have at least a 3.0 GPA and be studying or planning to study at the undergraduate level. Selection is based on depth of character, leadership, seriousness of purpose, academic achievement, and financial need. **Deadline for Receipt:** February of each year. **Additional Information:** Recipients may attend any accredited college, professional, or vocational school. This program includes named scholarships from the following funds: the Colonel Hayden W. Wagner Memorial Fund, the Eugenia Bradford Roberts Memorial Fund, the Daughters of the U.S. Army Scholarship Fund, the Gladys K. and John K. Simpson Scholarship Fund, and the Margaret M. Prickett Scholarship Fund. Requests for applications must be accompanied by a self-addressed stamped envelope.

1556 ■ SOLVAY PHARMACEUTICALS, INC.

Attn: Creon Family Scholarship Program
901 Sawyer Road
Marietta, GA 30062

Tel: (770)578-5898
Free: 800-354-0026
Fax: (770)578-5586
Web Site: http://www.solvaypharmaceuticals-us.com
To provide financial assistance for college to students with Cystic Fibrosis (CF).

Title of Award: Creon Family Scholarship Program **Area, Field, or Subject:** General studies/Field of study not specified **Level of Education for which Award is Granted:** Undergraduate **Number Awarded:** 30 each year. **Funds Available:** The stipend is $2,000 per year. **Duration:** 2 years.

Eligibility Requirements: This program is open to high school seniors, vocational school students, and college students with CF. U.S. citizenship is required. Applicants must submit an academic transcript, documentation of financial need, a photograph, 2 letters of recommendation, and a creative representation (essay, poem, photograph, painting, sculpture, video, cassette tape, etc.) on what they have learned from living with CF. Selection is based on academic excellence, extracurricular activities, the creative representation, the ability to serve as a role model to others with CF, and financial need. **Deadline for Receipt:** June of each year. **Additional Information:** This program started in 1992. Winners, upon mailing in a prescription from their prescribers, also receive a 1-year supply of CREON MINIMICROSPHERES (Pancrelipase Delayed-Release Capsules, USP) Brand pancreatic enzymes.

1557 ■ SONLIGHT CURRICULUM, LTD.

Attn: Scholarship Committee
8042 South Grant Way
Littleton, CO 80122
Tel: (303)730-6292
Fax: (303)795-8668
E-mail: scholarship@sonlight.com
Web Site: http://www.sonlight.com/scholarships.html
To provide financial assistance for college to home-schooled students who have utilized Sonlight Core programs.

Title of Award: Sonlight Scholarships **Area, Field, or Subject:** General studies/Field of study not specified **Level of Education for which Award is Granted:** Undergraduate **Number Awarded:** 8 each year: 1 at $5,000 per year, 2 at $2,500 per year, and 5 at $1,000 per year. **Funds Available:** Stipends are $20,000 ($5,000 per year), $10,000 ($2,500 per year), or $4,000 ($1,000 per year). **Duration:** 4 years, provided the recipients maintain a GPA of 3.5 or higher and provide the sponsor with a copy of their college transcript.

Eligibility Requirements: This program is open to high school seniors and current college students who have been home-schooled and used at least 3 Sonlight Core programs. Preference is given to students who have used the curriculum most recently and at the higher levels. Applicants must demonstrate a heart for learning, mission mindedness, spiritual mindedness, balance in their activities and interests, and leadership. They must submit a 2-page personal essay on how their future plans and aspirations fit in with the purposes of God (including references to seeking God's Kingdom, asserting the crown rights of King Jesus, and how their future plans or purposes will help extend His Kingdom) and a 3-page argumentative essay that they have written. Selection is based on those essays, academic achievement, extracurricular activities, and 3 reference letters. **Deadline for Receipt:** December of each year.

1558 ■ SONS OF UNION VETERANS OF THE CIVIL WAR

P.O. Box 1865
Harrisburg, PA 17105
Tel: (717)232-7000
E-mail: suvcinc@aol.com
Web Site: http://www.suvcw.org/scholar.htm
To provide financial assistance for college to descendants of Union Civil War veterans.

Title of Award: Sons of Union Veterans of the Civil War Scholarships **Area, Field, or Subject:** General studies/Field of study not specified **Level of Education for which Award is Granted:** Four Year College **Number Awarded:** 2 each year. **Funds Available:** The stipend is $1,000. Funds are to be used for tuition and books. Checks are mailed directly to the recipient's school. **Duration:** 1 year.

Eligibility Requirements: This program is open to both high school seniors and currently-enrolled 4-year college students. Applicants should

1) be a descendant of a Union Civil War veteran who was honorably discharged or who died while in service; 2) rank in the upper quarter of their high school graduating class (preferably in the upper tenth); 3) have a record of performance in school and community activities; 4) have an interest in and positive attitude toward college; 5) provide 3 letters of recommendation; and 6) submit an official grade transcript. Financial need is not considered in the selection process. **Deadline for Receipt:** March of each year. **Additional Information:** Information is also available from John M. McNulty, 2501 Edgecomb Avenue, Glenside, PA 19038, (215) 884-3487, E-mail: jmm6@psu.edu. Recipients must attend a 4-year college or university.

1559 ■ SOROPTIMIST INTERNATIONAL OF THE AMERICAS

Attn: Program Department
1709 Spruce Street
Philadelphia, PA 19103-6103
Tel: (215)893-9000
Fax: (215)893-5200
E-mail: siahq@soroptimist.org
Web Site: http://www.soroptimist.org
To help women reentering the job market upgrade their employment status through education.

Title of Award: Women's Opportunity Awards Program **Area, Field, or Subject:** General studies/Field of study not specified **Level of Education for which Award is Granted:** Undergraduate **Number Awarded:** In each of the 28 regions, the winner receives an award of $5,000; most regions grant additional $3,000 awards. From among the regional winners, 3 receive an additional award of $10,000 from Soroptimist International of the Americas. Since the program was established, about 1,640 women have been assisted. **Funds Available:** Awards are $10,000, $5,000, or $3,000. **Duration:** The awards are issued each year and are nonrenewable.

Eligibility Requirements: This program is open to mature women who are the heads of their households with financial responsibility for their family. They may be interested in vocational or technical training or completing an undergraduate degree. Applicants must describe their career goals, how those relate to their educational or training goals, the economic and social barriers and personal hardships they have faced, and their financial need. **Deadline for Receipt:** Applications must be submitted to local clubs by December of each year. **Additional Information:** This program, established in 1972, was formerly known as the Training Awards Program. The awards may not be used for graduate study or international travel. Applications are to be processed through the local Soroptimist club. Applicants must reside in and attend an accredited college or university within the countries represented in the federation: Argentina, Bolivia, Brazil, Canada, Chile, Costa Rica, Ecuador, Guam, Japan, Republic of Korea, Mexico, Panama, Paraguay, Peru, Philippines, Puerto Rico, Taiwan, United States, or Venezuela.

1560 ■ SOUTH CAROLINA COMMISSION ON HIGHER EDUCATION

Attn: Director of Student Services
1333 Main Street, Suite 200
Columbia, SC 29201
Tel: (803)737-2280; 877-349-7183
Fax: (803)737-2297
E-mail: srhyne@che.sc.gov
Web Site: http://www.che.sc.gov
To provide financial assistance for college to residents of South Carolina.

Title of Award: Legislative Incentive for Future Excellence (LIFE) Scholarship Program **Area, Field, or Subject:** General studies/Field of study not specified **Level of Education for which Award is Granted:** Undergraduate **Number Awarded:** Varies each year; recently, 28,390 of these scholarships, worth more than $127 million, were awarded. **Funds Available:** The stipend is $4,700 per year, plus a $300 book allowance, at 4-year colleges or universities. Students at public and private 2-year colleges receive a stipend of the cost of tuition at a regional campus of the University of South Carolina plus a $300 book allowance. Technical school students receive the cost of tuition plus a $300 book allowance. Funds may be applied only toward the cost of attendance at an eligible South Carolina institution. **Duration:** 1 year; may be renewed up to a total of 10 semesters for a 5-year program, 8 semesters for a 4-year program, 4 semesters for a 2-year program, or 2 semesters for a 1-year certificate or diploma program.

Eligibility Requirements: This program is open to residents of South Carolina who graduate from high school or complete a home-school program and attend an eligible South Carolina public or private college or university. As an entering freshman at a 4-year college or university, they must meet any 2 of the following requirements: 1) have earned a GPA of 3.0 or higher in high school; 2) score at least 1100 on the mathematics and critical reading sections of the SAT or 24 on the ACT; and/or 3) graduate in the top 30% of their high school class. Students entering a 2-year or technical institution must have a high school GPA of 3.0 or higher. Continuing college students must have completed an average of 30 credit hours for each academic year and maintained a GPA of 3.0 or higher. Students transferring must have completed 30 credit hours for a second-year transfer, 60 for a third-year transfer, or 90 for a fourth-year transfer; their cumulative GPA must be 3.0 or higher. U.S. citizenship or permanent resident status is required. Applicants may not have been convicted of any felonies or alcohol- or drug-related charges. **Additional Information:** The South Carolina General Assembly established this program in 1998.

1561 ■ SOUTH CAROLINA COMMISSION ON HIGHER EDUCATION

Attn: Director of Student Services
1333 Main Street, Suite 200
Columbia, SC 29201
Tel: (803)737-2262; 877-349-7183
Fax: (803)737-2297
E-mail: shubbard@che.sc.gov
Web Site: http://www.che.sc.gov
To provide financial assistance for college to high school students in South Carolina who have achieved a high score on a college entrance examination.
Title of Award: Palmetto Fellows Scholarships **Area, Field, or Subject:** General studies/Field of study not specified **Level of Education for which Award is Granted:** Four Year College **Number Awarded:** Varies each year; recently, 3,727 of these scholarships, worth more than $24 million, were awarded. **Funds Available:** Grants up to $6,700 per year are available, half provided by the South Carolina Commission on Higher Education and half by the institution the student attends. **Duration:** 1 year; may be renewed for 3 additional years provided the recipient maintains full-time enrollment and a GPA of 3.0 or higher.
Eligibility Requirements: This program is open to residents of South Carolina who are enrolled in a public or private high school or an approved home-school program. Applicants must be planning to attend a 4-year public or private college or university in South Carolina during the fall immediately following graduation. They must either 1) score at least 1200 on the mathematics and critical reading sections of the SAT or 27 on the ACT, have a GPA of 3.5 or higher, and rank in the top 6% of their class; or 2) score at least 1400 on the mathematics and critical reading sections of the SAT or 32 on the ACT and have a GPA of 4.0. Early awards are based on test scores, GPA, and class rank at the end of the junior year; final awards are based on test scores, GPA, and class rank at the end of the senior year. U.S. citizenship or permanent resident status is required. **Deadline for Receipt:** December of each year for early awards; June of each year for final awards. **Additional Information:** Applications are forwarded to principals at high schools attended by students who attain the qualifying examination scores.

1562 ■ SOUTH CAROLINA COMMISSION ON HIGHER EDUCATION

Attn: Director of Student Services
1333 Main Street, Suite 200
Columbia, SC 29201
Tel: (803)737-2280; 877-349-7183
Fax: (803)737-2297
E-mail: srhyne@che.sc.gov
Web Site: http://www.che.sc.gov
To provide financial assistance to underrepresented students at public colleges or universities in South Carolina.
Title of Award: South Carolina Access and Equity Undergraduate Scholars Program **Area, Field, or Subject:** General studies/Field of study not specified **Level of Education for which Award is Granted:** Undergraduate **Number Awarded:** Varies each year, but no more than 20% of the grant funds at each institution may be used for entering freshmen. **Funds Available:** Stipends of up to $1,000 per year are provided, funding permitting. **Duration:** 1 year; may be renewed.
Eligibility Requirements: Eligible to apply are residents of South Carolina who are members of a traditionally underrepresented group at

the senior institution, regional campus of the University of South Carolina, or South Carolina technical college they are or will be attending. Full-time entering freshmen must have a high school GPA of at least 3.0; continuing full-time college students must have a cumulative GPA of at least 2.0; part-time students must have completed at least 12 hours of college work with a GPA of at least 2.0 and be at least 21 years old or have been out of school at least 2 years prior to reenrolling. Priority is given to full-time students. U.S. citizenship is required.

1563 ■ SOUTH CAROLINA COMMISSION ON HIGHER EDUCATION

Attn: Director of Student Services
1333 Main Street, Suite 200
Columbia, SC 29201
Tel: (803)737-4544; 877-349-7183
Fax: (803)737-2297
E-mail: kwham@che.sc.gov
Web Site: http://www.che.sc.gov
To provide financial assistance to high school seniors in South Carolina who plan to attend a 4-year institution in the state.
Title of Award: South Carolina HOPE Scholarships **Area, Field, or Subject:** General studies/Field of study not specified **Level of Education for which Award is Granted:** Four Year College **Number Awarded:** Varies each year; recently, 2,521 students received more than $6 million in support from this program. **Funds Available:** The maximum stipend is $2,650, including a $150 book allowance. **Duration:** 1 year; nonrenewable.
Eligibility Requirements: This program is open to seniors graduating from high schools or completing a home-school program in South Carolina. Applicants must be planning to attend a 4-year public or private college or university in the state and have a GPA of 3.0 or higher. They may not have been convicted of any felony or drug- or alcohol-related misdemeanor during the past academic year and may not be eligible for the Palmetto Fellows or LIFE Scholarship Programs. U.S. citizenship or permanent resident status is required. Selection is based on merit. **Additional Information:** This program was established in 2001.

1564 ■ SOUTH CAROLINA COMMISSION ON HIGHER EDUCATION

Attn: Director of Student Services
1333 Main Street, Suite 200
Columbia, SC 29201
Tel: (803)737-4544; 877-349-7183
Fax: (803)737-2297
E-mail: kwham@che.sc.gov
Web Site: http://www.che.sc.gov
To provide financial assistance to needy students at 2-year colleges in South Carolina.
Title of Award: South Carolina Lottery Tuition Assistance Program **Area, Field, or Subject:** General studies/Field of study not specified **Level of Education for which Award is Granted:** Two Year College, Vocational/Occupational **Number Awarded:** Varies each year; recently, 33,219 students received more than $33.2 million in support from this program. **Funds Available:** The amount of the assistance varies each year. Recently, full-time students were eligible for up to $924 per semester and part-time students were eligible for up to $77 per credit hour. **Duration:** 1 semester; may be renewed.
Eligibility Requirements: This program is open to students at 2-year public and private colleges and technical schools in South Carolina who meet the qualifications of financial need as established by the financial aid office at the institution they are attending. Applicants must be U.S. citizens or permanent residents and residents of South Carolina. They may not be receiving other scholarship assistance from the South Carolina Commission on Higher Education. **Additional Information:** Information on this program at technical colleges in South Carolina is available from the South Carolina State Board for Technical and Comprehensive Education, 111 Executive Center Drive, Columbia, SC 29210, (803) 896-5320.

1565 ■ SOUTH CAROLINA COMMISSION ON HIGHER EDUCATION

Attn: Director of Student Services
1333 Main Street, Suite 200
Columbia, SC 29201
Tel: (803)737-2280; 877-349-7183
Fax: (803)737-2297
E-mail: srhyne@che.sc.gov

Web Site: http://www.che.sc.gov
To provide financial assistance for college to South Carolina residents with financial need.

Title of Award: South Carolina Need-Based Grants Program **Area, Field, or Subject:** General studies/Field of study not specified **Level of Education for which Award is Granted:** Undergraduate **Number Awarded:** Varies each year; recently, 26,936 students received more than $18.5 million in support from this program. **Funds Available:** Grants up to $2,500 per academic year are available to full-time students and up to $1,250 per academic year to part-time students. **Duration:** 1 year; may be renewed for up to 8 full-time equivalent terms.

Eligibility Requirements: This program is open to residents of South Carolina who meet the qualifications of financial need as established by the financial aid office at the college or university in South Carolina that they are attending or planning to attend. Assistance is provided at participating South Carolina public or private 2- or 4-year colleges and universities. Applicants must be enrolled for their first 1-year program, first associate degree, first 2-year program leading to a bachelor's degree, first bachelor's degree, or first professional degree. **Additional Information:** Further information on this program is available from college financial aid offices in South Carolina.

1566 ■ SOUTH CAROLINA HIGHER EDUCATION TUITION GRANTS COMMISSION

Attn: Executive Director
101 Business Park Boulevard, Suite 2100
Columbia, SC 29203-9498
Tel: (803)896-1120
Fax: (803)896-1126
E-mail: info@sctuitiongrants.org
Web Site: http://www.sctuitiongrants.com
To provide financial assistance to students at independent colleges and universities in South Carolina.

Title of Award: South Carolina Tuition Grants Program **Area, Field, or Subject:** General studies/Field of study not specified **Level of Education for which Award is Granted:** Undergraduate **Number Awarded:** Varies each year; recently, 3,154 new scholarships were awarded through this program. **Funds Available:** The amounts of the awards depend on the need of the recipient and the tuition and fees at the institution to be attended. Recently, the average grant was approximately $2,300. Funds may not be used for part-time enrollment, room and board charges, summer school enrollment, or graduate school enrollment. **Duration:** 1 year; may be renewed.

Eligibility Requirements: Eligible to apply are residents of South Carolina who are attending or accepted for enrollment as full-time students at eligible private institutions in the state. Applicants must 1) graduate in the upper 75% of their high school class, 2) score 900 or above on the SAT or 19 or above on the ACT, or 3) graduate with a high school GPA of 2.0 or higher. Selection is based on financial need. **Deadline for Receipt:** June of each year. **Additional Information:** This program was established in 1970. Further information is available from college financial aid offices at the 20 participating private institutions in South Carolina.

1567 ■ SOUTH CAROLINA OFFICE OF VETERANS AFFAIRS

1205 Pendleton Street, Suite 369
Columbia, SC 29201-3789
Tel: (803)734-0200
Fax: (803)734-0197
E-mail: va@oepp.sc.gov
Web Site: http://www.govoepp.state.sc.us/vetaff.htm
To provide free college tuition to the children of disabled and other South Carolina veterans.

Title of Award: South Carolina Tuition Program for Children of Certain War Veterans **Area, Field, or Subject:** General studies/Field of study not specified **Level of Education for which Award is Granted:** Undergraduate **Number Awarded:** Varies each year. **Funds Available:** Children who qualify are eligible for free tuition at any South Carolina state-supported college, university, or postsecondary technical education institution. The waiver applies to tuition only. The costs of room and board, certain fees, and books are not covered. **Duration:** Students are eligible to receive this support as long as they are younger than 26 years of age and working on an undergraduate degree.

Eligibility Requirements: This program is open to the children of wartime veterans who were legal residents of South Carolina both at the time of entry into military or naval service and during service, or who have been residents of South Carolina for at least 1 year. Veteran parents must 1) be permanently and totally disabled as determined by the U.S. Department of Veterans Affairs; 2) have been a prisoner of war; 3) have been killed in action; 4) have died from other causes while in service; 5) have died of a disease or disability resulting from service; 6) be currently missing in action; 7) have received the Congressional Medal of Honor; 8) have received the Purple Heart Medal from wounds received in combat; or 9) be now deceased but qualified under categories 1 or 2 above. The veteran's child must be 26 years of age or younger and working on an undergraduate degree.

1568 ■ SOUTH CAROLINA SHERIFFS' ASSOCIATION

Attn: Executive Director
112 West Park Boulevard
Columbia, SC 29210
Tel: (803)772-1101
Fax: (803)772-1197
E-mail: sheriffsc@aol.com
Web Site: http://www.sheriffsc.com
To provide financial assistance to seniors graduating from South Carolina high schools who are interested in attending college in the state.

Title of Award: South Carolina Sheriffs' Association Scholarships **Area, Field, or Subject:** General studies/Field of study not specified **Level of Education for which Award is Granted:** Undergraduate **Number Awarded:** 4 each year. **Funds Available:** The stipend is $1,000. **Duration:** 1 year.

Eligibility Requirements: This program is open to graduating high school seniors from South Carolina who are interested in attending a college within the state. Applicants must submit an essay on a topic that changes annually; recently, they were invited to write on "The Sheriff's Office and Domestic Violence." Financial need is not considered in the selection process. **Deadline for Receipt:** February of each year.

1569 ■ SOUTH CAROLINA STUDENT LOAN CORPORATION

Interstate Center
16 Berryhill Road, Suite 210
P.O. Box 21487
Columbia, SC 29221-1487
Tel: (803)798-0916
Free: 800-347-2752
Fax: (803)772-9410
Web Site: http://www.slc.sc.edu
To provide supplemental educational loans to undergraduate students from South Carolina.

Title of Award: Palmetto Assistance Loans **Area, Field, or Subject:** General studies/Field of study not specified **Level of Education for which Award is Granted:** Undergraduate **Number Awarded:** Varies each year. **Funds Available:** Loans range up to the actual cost of attendance, less any other financial aid received. There is no application fee. Interest rates are variable, equal to the prime rate. Borrowers have 6 months after they drop below half time or until completion of residency before repayment begins. Repayment must be completed within 12 years for loan totals less than $9,999, within 15 years for loan totals from $10,000 to $19,999, within 20 years for loan totals from $20,000 to $39,999, within 25 years for loan totals from $40,000 to $59,999, or within 30 years for loan totals of $60,000 or more. **Duration:** 1 year; may be renewed.

Eligibility Requirements: This program is open to residents of South Carolina who are enrolled in a undergraduate certificate or degree-granting program at least half time. Applicants must be U.S. citizens or permanent residents with a high school diploma or GED. They must be creditworthy and in good standing on all other educational loans.

1570 ■ SOUTH DAKOTA ASSOCIATION OF TOWNS AND TOWNSHIPS

351 Wisconsin, S.W., Suite 101
P.O. Box 903
Huron, SD 57350-0903
Tel: (605)353-1439
Fax: (605)352-5322

E-mail: sdatat@basec.net
To provide financial assistance for college to high school seniors in South Dakota.

Title of Award: SDATAT Scholarship **Area, Field, or Subject:** General studies/Field of study not specified **Level of Education for which Award is Granted:** Undergraduate **Number Awarded:** 1 each year. **Funds Available:** The stipend is $1,000. **Duration:** 1 year.
Eligibility Requirements: This program is open to seniors graduating from high schools in South Dakota or who are home-schooled. Applicants must be planning to attend a university, college, or technical school in South Dakota. Along with their application, they must submit a 500-word essay on "Local Government Consolidation: What Happens to Local Control?" **Deadline for Receipt:** March of each year.

1571 ■ SOUTH DAKOTA BOARD OF REGENTS

Attn: Scholarship Committee
306 East Capitol Avenue, Suite 200
Pierre, SD 57501-2545
Tel: (605)773-3455
Fax: (605)773-2422
E-mail: info@ris.sdbor.edu
Web Site: http://www.sdbor.edu
To provide financial assistance for college to the dependents of disabled and deceased members of the South Dakota National Guard.

Title of Award: Free Tuition for Dependents of Disabled or Deceased South Dakota National Guard Members **Area, Field, or Subject:** General studies/Field of study not specified **Level of Education for which Award is Granted:** Undergraduate **Number Awarded:** Varies each year. **Funds Available:** Qualifying applicants are eligible to attend a state-supported postsecondary institution in South Dakota without payment of tuition. **Duration:** 8 semesters or 12 quarters of either full- or part-time study.
Eligibility Requirements: This program is open to the spouses and children of members of the South Dakota Army or Air National Guard who died or sustained a total and permanent disability while on state active duty or any authorized duty training. Applicants must be younger than 25 years of age and proposing to work on an undergraduate degree at a public institution of higher education in South Dakota.

1572 ■ SOUTH DAKOTA BOARD OF REGENTS

Attn: Scholarship Committee
306 East Capitol Avenue, Suite 200
Pierre, SD 57501-2545
Tel: (605)773-3455
Fax: (605)773-2422
E-mail: info@ris.sdbor.edu
Web Site: http://www.ris.sdbor.edu
To provide financial assistance for college to members of the South Dakota National Guard.

Title of Award: Reduced Tuition for South Dakota National Guardmembers **Area, Field, or Subject:** General studies/Field of study not specified **Level of Education for which Award is Granted:** Undergraduate **Number Awarded:** Varies each year. **Funds Available:** Qualifying Guard members are eligible for a 50% reduction in tuition at any state-supported postsecondary institution in South Dakota. **Duration:** This assistance is available for up to 4 academic years.
Eligibility Requirements: Eligible to apply for this assistance are members of the South Dakota Army or Air National Guard who are South Dakota residents, have satisfactorily completed Initial Active Duty for Training (IADT), meet the entrance requirements at 1 of the 6 state educational institutions or 4 state vocational/technical schools, attend 90% of drills and training periods, and maintain a satisfactory academic grade level. **Additional Information:** Students participating in the Army Continuing Education Systems (ACES) or the Montgomery GI Bill are not authorized to use this program.

1573 ■ SOUTH DAKOTA BOARD OF REGENTS

Attn: Scholarship Committee
306 East Capitol Avenue, Suite 200
Pierre, SD 57501-2545
Tel: (605)773-3455
Fax: (605)773-2422
E-mail: info@ris.sdbor.edu

Web Site: http://www.sdbor.edu/administration/academics/ Scholarships.htm
To provide financial assistance to students at public universities in South Dakota who are entering their junior year.

Title of Award: Marlin R. Scarborough Memorial Scholarship **Area, Field, or Subject:** General studies/Field of study not specified **Level of Education for which Award is Granted:** Four Year College **Number Awarded:** 1 each year. **Funds Available:** The stipend is $1,500; funds are allocated to the institution for distribution to the student. **Duration:** 1 year; nonrenewable.
Eligibility Requirements: This program is open to students entering their junior year at public universities in South Dakota. Applicants must have a GPA of 3.5 or higher. They must be nominated by their university. Along with their application, they must submit an essay explaining their leadership and academic qualities, career plans, and educational interests.

1574 ■ SOUTH DAKOTA BOARD OF REGENTS

Attn: Scholarship Committee
306 East Capitol Avenue, Suite 200
Pierre, SD 57501-2545
Tel: (605)773-3455
Fax: (605)773-2422
E-mail: info@ris.sdbor.edu
Web Site: http://www.sdbor.edu
To provide free tuition at South Dakota public colleges and universities to children of military personnel who died while in service.

Title of Award: South Dakota Free Tuition for Children of Residents Who Died During Service in the Armed Forces **Area, Field, or Subject:** General studies/Field of study not specified **Level of Education for which Award is Granted:** Undergraduate **Number Awarded:** Varies each year. **Funds Available:** Eligible children are entitled to attend any South Dakota state-supported institution of higher education or state-supported technical or vocational school free of tuition and mandatory fees. **Duration:** 8 semesters or 12 quarters of either full- or part-time study.
Eligibility Requirements: This program is open to residents of South Dakota younger than 25 years of age. The applicant's parent must have been killed in action or died of other causes while on active duty and must have been a resident of South Dakota for at least 6 months immediately preceding entry into active service.

1575 ■ SOUTH DAKOTA BOARD OF REGENTS

Attn: Scholarship Committee
306 East Capitol Avenue, Suite 200
Pierre, SD 57501-2545
Tel: (605)773-3455
Fax: (605)773-2422
E-mail: info@ris.sdbor.edu
Web Site: http://www.sdbor.edu
To provide free tuition at South Dakota public colleges and universities to dependents of prisoners of war (POWs) and persons missing in action (MIAs).

Title of Award: South Dakota Free Tuition for Dependents of Prisoners or Missing in Action **Area, Field, or Subject:** General studies/Field of study not specified **Level of Education for which Award is Granted:** Undergraduate **Number Awarded:** Varies each year. **Funds Available:** Eligible dependents are entitled to attend any South Dakota state-supported institution of higher education or state-supported technical or vocational school free of tuition and mandatory fees. **Duration:** 8 semesters or 12 quarters of either full- or part-time study.
Eligibility Requirements: This program is open to residents of South Dakota who are the spouses or children of POWs or of MIAs. Applicants may not be eligible for equal or greater benefits from any federal financial assistance program. **Additional Information:** Recipients must attend a state-supported school in South Dakota.

1576 ■ SOUTH DAKOTA BOARD OF REGENTS

Attn: Scholarship Committee
306 East Capitol Avenue, Suite 200
Pierre, SD 57501-2545
Tel: (605)773-3455
Fax: (605)773-2422
E-mail: info@ris.sdbor.edu

Web Site: http://www.sdbor.edu

To provide free tuition at South Dakota public colleges and universities to children of deceased fire fighters, law enforcement officers, and emergency medical technicians.

Title of Award: South Dakota Free Tuition for Survivors of Deceased Fire Fighters, Certified Law Enforcement Officers, and Emergency Medical Technicians **Area, Field, or Subject:** General studies/Field of study not specified **Level of Education for which Award is Granted:** Undergraduate **Number Awarded:** Varies each year. **Funds Available:** Eligible survivors are entitled to attend any South Dakota state-supported institution of higher education or state-supported technical or vocational school free of tuition. **Duration:** Until completion of a bachelor's or vocational degree; the degree must be earned within 36 months or 8 semesters.

Eligibility Requirements: This program is open to residents of South Dakota who are the survivor of a fire fighter, certified law enforcement officer, or emergency medical technician who died as a direct result of injuries received in performance of official duties. Applicants must have been accepted for enrollment at a state-supported institution of higher education or technical or vocational school.

1577 ■ SOUTH DAKOTA BOARD OF REGENTS

Attn: Scholarship Committee
306 East Capitol Avenue, Suite 200
Pierre, SD 57501-2545
Tel: (605)773-3455
Fax: (605)773-2422
E-mail: info@ris.sdbor.edu
Web Site: http://www.sdbor.edu

To provide free tuition at South Dakota public colleges and universities to certain veterans.

Title of Award: South Dakota Free Tuition for Veterans and Others Who Performed War Service **Area, Field, or Subject:** General studies/Field of study not specified **Level of Education for which Award is Granted:** Undergraduate **Number Awarded:** Varies each year. **Funds Available:** Eligible veterans are entitled to attend any South Dakota state-supported institution of higher education or state-supported technical or vocational school free of tuition and mandatory fees. **Duration:** Eligible veterans are entitled to receive 1 month of free tuition for each month of qualifying service, from a minimum of 1 year to a maximum of 4 years.

Eligibility Requirements: This program is open to current residents of South Dakota who have been discharged from the military forces of the United States under honorable conditions. Applicants must meet 1 of the following criteria: 1) served on active duty at any time between August 2, 1990 and March 3, 1991; 2) received an Armed Forces Expeditionary Medal, Southwest Asia Service Medal, or other U.S. campaign or service medal for participation in combat operations against hostile forces outside the boundaries of the United States; or 3) have a service-connected disability rating of at least 10%. They may not be eligible for any other educational assistance from the U.S. government. Qualifying veterans must apply for this benefit within 20 years after the date proclaimed for the cassation of hostilities or within 6 years from and after the date of their discharge from military service, whichever is later.

1578 ■ SOUTH DAKOTA BOARD OF REGENTS

Attn: Scholarship Committee
306 East Capitol Avenue, Suite 200
Pierre, SD 57501-2545
Tel: (605)773-3455
Fax: (605)773-2422
E-mail: info@ris.sdbor.edu
Web Site: http://www.sdbor.edu

To provide financial assistance for college or graduate school to visually impaired residents of South Dakota.

Title of Award: South Dakota Free Tuition for Visually Impaired Persons **Area, Field, or Subject:** General studies/Field of study not specified **Level of Education for which Award is Granted:** Graduate, Undergraduate **Number Awarded:** Varies each year. **Funds Available:** Qualified applicants may attend any institution under the supervision of the South Dakota Board of Regents without payment of tuition, library fees, registration fees, or any other fees. **Duration:** Benefits are provided until the recipient has earned 225 semester hours of credit or the equivalent.

Eligibility Requirements: Eligible for this program is any visually impaired resident of South Dakota who can meet the entrance require-

ments for admission to a postsecondary educational institution (including graduate school and medical school) under the supervision of the state board of regents. For purposes of the program, "visual impairment" means that the person cannot, with use of correcting glasses, see sufficiently well to perform ordinary activities for which eyesight is essential. This program does not extend to visually impaired persons who are entitled to receive tuition and fee support from the state's department of vocational rehabilitation. **Additional Information:** Applicants should contact the financial aid director at the South Dakota college or university they plan to attend, not the sponsor. The exemption from charges does not apply if a course is repeated because of unsatisfactory work, unless the problem was caused by illness or some other circumstance for which the student had no responsibility.

1579 ■ SOUTH DAKOTA BOARD OF REGENTS

Attn: Scholarship Committee
306 East Capitol Avenue, Suite 200
Pierre, SD 57501-2545
Tel: (605)773-3455
Fax: (605)773-2422
E-mail: info@ris.sdbor.edu
Web Site: http://www.sdbor.edu/SDOpportunityScholarship.htm

To provide financial assistance to South Dakota high school seniors who plan to attend college in the state.

Title of Award: South Dakota Opportunity Scholarship **Area, Field, or Subject:** General studies/Field of study not specified **Level of Education for which Award is Granted:** Undergraduate **Number Awarded:** Varies each year. **Funds Available:** The stipend is $1,000 per year for the first 3 years and $2,000 for the fourth year. **Duration:** 4 years, provided they maintain a GPA of 3.0 or higher and full-time enrollment.

Eligibility Requirements: This program is open to seniors who are graduating from high schools South Dakota and have completed the Regents Scholar curriculum. Applicants may have received no grade below a "C" and must have a cumulative high school GPA of 3.0 or higher as well as a score of at least 24 on the ACT or 1100 on the critical reading and mathematics portions of the SAT. **Deadline for Receipt:** August of each year. **Additional Information:** These scholarships were first awarded in 2004.

1580 ■ SOUTH DAKOTA DEPARTMENT OF EDUCATION

Attn: Office of the Secretary
700 Governors Drive
Pierre, SD 57501
Tel: (605)773-3134
Fax: (605)773-6139
Web Site: http://doe.sd.gov/scholarships/hagen

To provide financial assistance for college to American Indians whose reservation is located in South Dakota.

Title of Award: Richard Hagen-Minerva Harvey Memorial Scholarship **Area, Field, or Subject:** General studies/Field of study not specified **Level of Education for which Award is Granted:** Undergraduate **Number Awarded:** Up to 7 each year. **Funds Available:** The stipend is at least $1,000 per year for the first 2 years of college, at least $1,500 for the third year, and at least $2,500 for the fourth year. **Duration:** 4 years, provided the recipient maintains a cumulative GPA of 2.5 or higher.

Eligibility Requirements: This program is open to enrolled members of American Indian tribes whose reservation is located in whole or part in South Dakota. Applicants must be attending or planning to attend a public or non-public accredited college, university, or technical institute in South Dakota. They must apply within 5 years after high school graduation or within 1 year after release from active military duty (if that release is within 5 years of high school graduation). Along with their application, they must submit high school and/or college transcripts, verification of tribal enrollment, ACT scores, and an essay explaining why they deserve to receive this scholarship. **Deadline for Receipt:** April of each year.

1581 ■ SOUTH DAKOTA GOLF ASSOCIATION

Attn: Junior Golf Foundation
307 West 41st Street, Suite 8
Sioux Falls, SD 57105
Tel: (605)338-7499
E-mail: sdga@sdga.org
Web Site: http://www.sdga.org/foundation.php

To provide financial assistance for college to high school seniors in South Dakota who have participated in golf.

Title of Award: South Dakota Junior Golf Foundation Scholarships **Area, Field, or Subject:** General studies/Field of study not specified **Level of Education for which Award is Granted:** Four Year College **Number Awarded:** 4 each year. **Funds Available:** The stipend is $1,000. **Duration:** 1 year.

Eligibility Requirements: This program is open to seniors graduating from high schools in South Dakota who plan to attend a 4-year college, university, or accredited postsecondary institution in the state. Applicants must have resided in South Dakota for at least the past 2 years. Along with their application, they must provide a history of their golf participation and accomplishments and their future plans in the game. **Deadline for Receipt:** June of each year.

1582 ■ SOUTH DAKOTA NATIONAL GUARD ENLISTED ASSOCIATION

c/o Bruce Anderson, Executive Director
25790 Country Lane
Renner, SD 57055
Tel: (605)988-5414
E-mail: bcres@sio.midco.net
Web Site: http://www.sdngea.com/scholarship.html

To provide financial assistance for college to members of the South Dakota National Guard Enlisted Association (SDNGEA), the National Guard Association of South Dakota (NGASD), and their dependents.

Title of Award: Major General Duane L. "Duke" Corning Memorial Scholarship **Area, Field, or Subject:** General studies/Field of study not specified **Level of Education for which Award is Granted:** Undergraduate **Number Awarded:** 2 each year: 1 sponsored by SDNGEA for enlisted members and 1 sponsored by NGASD for officers. **Funds Available:** Stipends are $1,000 or $500. **Duration:** 1 year; nonrenewable.

Eligibility Requirements: This program is open to current and retired members of the SDNGEA and the NGASD and the dependents of current and retired members of those associations. Applicants must be graduating high school seniors or undergraduate students. They must submit a 300-page autobiography that includes their experiences to date and their hopes and plans for the future. Selection is based on the essay; awards, honors, and offices in high school, college, or trade school; GPA and ACT/SAT scores; letters of recommendation; and extracurricular and community activities and honors. **Deadline for Receipt:** February of each year. **Additional Information:** Information is also available from Randy Decker, 23009 Candlelight Drive, Rapid City, SD 57703, (605) 737-6391, E-mail: randal.decker@sd.ngb.army.mil.

1583 ■ SOUTHERN REGIONAL EDUCATION BOARD

592 10th Street N.W.
Atlanta, GA 30318-5790
Tel: (404)875-9211
Fax: (404)872-1477
E-mail: acm-rcp@sreb.org
Web Site: http://www.sreb.org/programs/acm/acmindex.asp

To enable students from southern states to attend a public college or university in another southern state at reduced tuition.

Title of Award: SREB Academic Common Market **Area, Field, or Subject:** General studies/Field of study not specified **Level of Education for which Award is Granted:** Undergraduate **Number Awarded:** Varies each year; recently, more than 2,200 students participated in this program. **Funds Available:** Participants pay only the in-state tuition at the institution outside their home state while they are studying in a program not available in their home state. **Duration:** 1 year; may be renewed.

Eligibility Requirements: Eligible are residents of 16 southern states (Alabama, Arkansas, Delaware, Florida, Georgia, Kentucky, Louisiana, Maryland, Mississippi, North Carolina, Oklahoma, South Carolina, Tennessee, Texas, Virginia, and West Virginia) who wish to study in a program not available at any public institution of higher education in their home state. If their state has made arrangements to send students to another state, they may participate in this program.

1584 ■ SPECIAL OPERATIONS WARRIOR FOUNDATION

4409 El Prado Boulevard
P.O. Box 14385
Tampa, FL 33690

Tel: (813)805-9400; 877-337-7693
Fax: (813)805-0567
E-mail: warrior@specialops.org
Web Site: http://www.specialops.org

To provide financial assistance for college to the children of Special Operations personnel who died in training or operational missions.

Title of Award: Special Operations Warrior Foundation Scholarships **Area, Field, or Subject:** General studies/Field of study not specified **Level of Education for which Award is Granted:** Undergraduate **Number Awarded:** Varies each year. Recently, the foundation provided more than $220,000 in scholarship grants and academic and financial aid counseling. **Funds Available:** A stipend is awarded (amount not specified). Funding is based on need and is intended to ensure payment of the full cost of tuition, fees, room, board, books, and supplies. **Duration:** 4 years or more.

Eligibility Requirements: This program is open to the children of parents who served in Special Operations and were killed in a training accident or an operational mission. This is an entitlement program; all eligible students receive support. **Deadline for Receipt:** Applications may be submitted at any time. **Additional Information:** This program was established in 1980 because of the high casualty rates experienced by personnel of U.S. Special Operations Command. Recently, the foundation calculated that 376 Special Operations personnel had lost their lives and that 418 surviving children were eligible for support.

1585 ■ SPINA BIFIDA ASSOCIATION OF AMERICA

Attn: Scholarship Committee
4590 MacArthur Boulevard, N.W., Suite 250
Washington, DC 20007-4226
Tel: (202)944-3285
Free: 800-621-3141
Fax: (202)944-3295
E-mail: sbaa@sbaa.org
Web Site: http://www.sbaa.org

To provide financial assistance to members of the Spina Bifida Association of America (SBAA) who are planning to attend a 4-year college or university.

Title of Award: Four-Year SBAA Educational Scholarship Fund **Area, Field, or Subject:** General studies/Field of study not specified **Level of Education for which Award is Granted:** Four Year College **Number Awarded:** 1 each year. **Funds Available:** The stipend is $5,000 per year. Funds may be used for tuition, room, and board. **Duration:** 4 years.

Eligibility Requirements: Eligible to apply for these scholarships are persons born with spina bifida who are current members of the association. Applicants must be high school juniors or seniors planning to attend a 4-year college or university. Selection is based on academic record, other efforts shown in school, financial need, work history, community service, leadership, and commitment to personal goals. **Deadline for Receipt:** February of each year. **Additional Information:** This program was established in 1998. The sponsor also offers a number of named scholarships, including the Lazof Family Foundation Scholarship, and a 1-year SBAA Educational Scholarship (which is for both undergraduate and graduate students).

1586 ■ SPJST SUPREME LODGE

Attn: Scholarship Department
P.O. Box 100
Temple, TX 76503
Tel: (254)773-1575
Free: 800-727-7578
Web Site: http://www.spjst.com/scholarship.html

To provide financial assistance for college to members or the children of members of the SPJST Supreme Lodge.

Title of Award: SPJST General Scholarship and Leadership Grant **Area, Field, or Subject:** General studies/Field of study not specified **Level of Education for which Award is Granted:** Undergraduate **Number Awarded:** Varies each year. **Funds Available:** A stipend is awarded (amount not specified). **Duration:** 1 year.

Eligibility Requirements: This program is open to members and the children of members who have had an active SPJST insurance certificate in force for at least 1 year. Applicants must be attending or planning to attend a college or university as an undergraduate student. They must submit an official transcript, SAT or ACT scores, a personal statement explaining why they wish to go to college and how the scholarship will help them (up to 300 words), 3 references, and a photography and biography. Selection is based on academic record, references, the personal statement and SPJST involvement. **Deadline for Receipt:** January of each year. **Additional Information:** SPJST was founded as a fraternal benefit society in 1897 by Czech pioneers in Texas and currently operates under Texas insurance laws. It established its general scholarships in 1982 and leadership grants in 1996.

1587 ■ SPORTS TURF MANAGERS ASSOCIATION

Attn: SAFE Foundation
805 New Hampshire, Suite E
Lawrence, KS 66044
800-323-3875
Fax: 800-366-0391
E-mail: stmainfo@sportsturfmanager.com
Web Site: http://www.sportsturfmanager.org
To provide financial assistance to student members of the Sports Turf Managers Association (STMA) who are interested in preparing for a career in the turf management industry.
Title of Award: SAFE Foundation Scholarships **Area, Field, or Subject:** Turfgrass management **Level of Education for which Award is Granted:** Undergraduate **Number Awarded:** 1 or more each year. **Funds Available:** The stipend is $1,000. Winners also receive $500 for travel or lodging expenses to attend the annual conference of the STMA. **Duration:** 1 year.
Eligibility Requirements: This program is open to STMA student members who are preparing for a career in the sports turf industry (excluding golf course management). Applicants must submit lists of 1) awards, honors, or scholarships that they have received; 2) activities in which they have participated related to their school, department, or community; and 3) professional associations and university organizations to which they belong. Selection is based on academic preparation, cumulative GPA, experience in sports turf management, and references. Financial need is not considered. **Deadline for Receipt:** September of each year. **Additional Information:** The SAFE (Safer Athletic Field Environments) Foundation was established in 2000.

1588 ■ STATE STUDENT ASSISTANCE COMMISSION OF INDIANA

Attn: Grant Division
150 West Market Street, Suite 500
Indianapolis, IN 46204-2811
Tel: (317)232-2350; 888-528-4719
Fax: (317)232-3260
E-mail: grants@ssaci.state.in.us
Web Site: http://www.in.gov/ssaci/programs/cvo.html
To provide financial assistance for undergraduate or graduate education to students in Indiana who are 1) the children of disabled or other veterans, and 2) the children and spouses of certain deceased or disabled public safety officers.
Title of Award: Indiana Child of Veteran and Public Safety Officer Supplemental Grant Program **Area, Field, or Subject:** General studies/Field of study not specified **Level of Education for which Award is Granted:** Graduate, Undergraduate **Number Awarded:** Varies each year. **Funds Available:** Qualified applicants receive a 100% remission of tuition and all mandatory fees for undergraduate or graduate work at state-supported postsecondary schools and universities in Indiana. It does not cover such fees as room and board. **Duration:** Up to 124 semester hours of study.
Eligibility Requirements: The veterans portion of this program is open to Indiana residents who are the natural or adopted children of veterans who served in the active-duty U.S. armed forces during a period of wartime. Applicants may be of any age; parents must have lived in Indiana for at least 3 years during their lifetime. The veteran parent must also 1) have a service-connected disability as determined by the U.S. Department of Veterans Affairs or the Department of Defense; 2) have received a Purple Heart Medal; or 3) have been a resident of Indiana at the time of entry into the service and declared a POW or MIA after January 1, 1960. Students at the Indiana Soldiers' and Sailors' Children's Home are also eligible. The public safety officer portion of this program is open to 1) the children and spouses of regular law enforcement officers, regular fire fighters, volunteer fire fighters, county police reserve officers, city police reserve officers, paramedics, emergency medical technicians, and advanced

emergency medical technicians killed in the line of duty, and 2) the children and spouses of Indiana state police troopers permanently and totally disabled in the line of duty. Children must be younger than 23 years of age and enrolled full time in an undergraduate or graduate degree program. Spouses must be enrolled in an undergraduate program and must have been married to the covered public safety officer at the time of death or disability. **Deadline for Receipt:** Applications must be submitted at least 30 days before the start of the college term. **Additional Information:** The veterans portion of this program is administered by the Indiana Department of Veterans' Affairs, 302 West Washington Street, Room E-120, Indianapolis, IN 46204-2738, (317) 232-3910, (800) 400-4520, Fax: (317) 232-7721, E-mail: jkiser@dva.state.in.us.

1589 ■ STATE STUDENT ASSISTANCE COMMISSION OF INDIANA

Attn: Grant Division
150 West Market Street, Suite 500
Indianapolis, IN 46204-2811
Tel: (317)232-2350; 888-528-4719
Fax: (317)232-3260
E-mail: grants@ssaci.state.in.us
Web Site: http://www.in.gov/ssaci/programs/ngsg.html
To provide financial assistance for college to members of the Indiana National Guard.
Title of Award: Indiana National Guard Supplemental Grant Program **Area, Field, or Subject:** General studies/Field of study not specified **Level of Education for which Award is Granted:** Undergraduate **Number Awarded:** Varies each year. **Funds Available:** The award provides payment of 100% of the tuition costs at state-funded colleges and universities in Indiana. No funding is provided for books, room, or board. **Duration:** 1 year; may be renewed.
Eligibility Requirements: This program is open to members of the Indiana Air and Army National Guard who are in active drilling status and have not been AWOL at any time during the preceding 12 months. Applicants must be high school graduates seeking their first associate or bachelor's degree. Allowances may be made for students who earned a GED certificate or were home-schooled, but only on a case-by-case basis following a written appeal. As part of the application process, students must file the Free Application for Federal Student Aid (FAFSA). If they qualify as dependent students based on FAFSA data, their parents must be residents of Indiana; if the FAFSA standards define them as independent students, they must be Indiana residents. **Deadline for Receipt:** March of each year. **Additional Information:** This assistance may be used only at the following state funded colleges and universities: Ball State University, Indiana State University, Indiana University, Ivy Tech State College, Purdue University, University of Southern Indiana, and Vincennes University.

1590 ■ STATE STUDENT ASSISTANCE COMMISSION OF INDIANA

Attn: Grant Division
150 West Market Street, Suite 500
Indianapolis, IN 46204-2811
Tel: (317)232-2350; 888-528-4719
Fax: (317)232-3260
E-mail: grants@ssaci.state.in.us
Web Site: http://www.in.gov/ssaci/programs/parttime.html
To provide financial assistance to Indiana residents who are working part time on an undergraduate degree.
Title of Award: Indiana Part-Time Grant Program **Area, Field, or Subject:** General studies/Field of study not specified **Level of Education for which Award is Granted:** Undergraduate **Number Awarded:** Varies each year. **Funds Available:** The amount of the award depends on the availability of funds and the number of credit hours taken. **Duration:** 1 term (quarter or semester); may be renewed.
Eligibility Requirements: This program is open to Indiana residents who are high school seniors, high school graduates, or GED certificate recipients. Applicants must be attending or planning to attend an eligible Indiana postsecondary institution as a part-time undergraduate student working on an associate or first bachelor's degree. They must be able to

demonstrate financial need for tuition assistance. **Additional Information:** Recipients must attend school, on a part-time basis, in Indiana.

1591 ■ STATE STUDENT ASSISTANCE COMMISSION OF INDIANA

Attn: Office of Twenty-first Century Scholars
150 West Market Street, Suite 500
Indianapolis, IN 46204-2811
Tel: (317)233-2100
Free: 800-992-2076
Fax: (317)232-3260
E-mail: scholars@scholars.indiana.edu
Web Site: http://www.in.gov/ssaci/programs/21st/index.html
To provide financial assistance for college education to students in Indiana currently in junior high school.

Title of Award: Indiana Twenty-first Century Scholars Program **Area, Field, or Subject:** General studies/Field of study not specified **Level of Education for which Award is Granted:** Undergraduate **Number Awarded:** Varies each year. **Funds Available:** As college students, participants who comply with program requirements receive 1) full tuition if they attend a participating Indiana public college or university, or 2) an award equal to tuition at a public institution if they attend a private institution. **Duration:** Until completion of an undergraduate degree.
Eligibility Requirements: This program is open to Indiana residents currently enrolled in the 7th or 8th grade at an Indiana public or accredited private school who demonstrate financial need. Students must fulfill a pledge to graduate from an Indiana high school with a GPA of 2.0 or higher, to abstain from the illegal use of drugs or alcohol and from criminal activity, to be admitted to an eligible Indiana college or university, and to apply for other federal and state financial assistance during their senior year in high school. **Deadline for Receipt:** Participants must file an affirmation that they have complied with their pledge by March of their senior year in high school. **Additional Information:** This program began in 1990 and the first group of scholars entered college in 1995. Participants must attend an Indiana college or university as a full-time student.

1592 ■ STATE STUDENT ASSISTANCE COMMISSION OF INDIANA

Attn: Grant Division
150 West Market Street, Suite 500
Indianapolis, IN 46204-2811
Tel: (317)232-2350; 888-528-4719
Fax: (317)232-3260
E-mail: grants@ssaci.state.in.us
Web Site: http://www.in.gov/ssaci/programs/hea.html
To provide financial assistance to Indiana residents who are working full time on an undergraduate degree.

Title of Award: Frank O'Bannon Grant Program **Area, Field, or Subject:** General studies/Field of study not specified **Level of Education for which Award is Granted:** Undergraduate **Number Awarded:** Varies each year. **Funds Available:** This program offers tuition assistance from $200 to several thousand dollars per year, depending on the level of appropriations, the number of eligible students making application, the calculation of student's financial need, and the cost of tuition and fees at the schools of choice. **Duration:** 1 year.
Eligibility Requirements: This program is open to Indiana residents who are high school seniors, high school graduates, or GED certificate recipients. Applicants must be attending or planning to attend an eligible Indiana postsecondary institution as a full-time undergraduate student working on an associate or first bachelor's degree. They must be able to demonstrate financial need for tuition assistance. U.S. citizenship or permanent resident status is required. **Deadline for Receipt:** March of each year. **Additional Information:** This program was formerly known as the Indiana Higher Education Grant Program. Recipients must attend school, on a full-time basis, in Indiana.

1593 ■ STATE UNIVERSITY SYSTEM OF FLORIDA

Attn: Office of Academic and Student Affairs
325 West Gaines Street, Suite 1501
Tallahassee, FL 32399-1950
Tel: (850)245-0467
Fax: (850)245-9667
E-mail: we're.listening@fldoe.org
Web Site: http://www.fldoe.org

To provide financial assistance to Florida undergraduate students with disabilities.
Title of Award: Theodore R. and Vivian M. Johnson Scholarship Program **Area, Field, or Subject:** General studies/Field of study not specified **Level of Education for which Award is Granted:** Four Year College **Number Awarded:** Several each year. **Funds Available:** The stipend depends on the availability of funds. **Duration:** 1 year; may be renewed if recipient maintains a GPA of 2.0 or higher and enrolls in at least 18 credits each academic year.
Eligibility Requirements: This program is open to students with disabilities enrolled at a State University System of Florida institution. Applicants must submit an official transcript (with GPA of 2.0 or higher); documentation of the nature and/or extent of their disability, which may be in 1 or more of the following classifications: hearing impairment, physical impairment, specific learning disability, speech/language impairment, visual impairment, or other impairment; and documentation of financial need. **Deadline for Receipt:** May of each year. **Additional Information:** This program is administered by the equal opportunity program at each of the 11 State University System of Florida 4-year institutions. Contact that office for further information. Funding is provided by the Theodore R. and Vivian M. Johnson Foundation with matching funding from the Florida Legislature.

1594 ■ STATEWIDE HISPANIC CHAMBER OF COMMERCE OF NEW JERSEY

Attn: Scholarship Selection Committee
150 Warren Street, Suite 110
Jersey City, NJ 07302
Tel: (201)451-9512
Fax: (201)451-9547
E-mail: shccnj@att.net
Web Site: http://www.shccnj.org
To provide financial assistance for college to Hispanic residents of New Jersey.

Title of Award: Statewide Hispanic Chamber of Commerce of New Jersey Scholarships **Area, Field, or Subject:** Business administration **Level of Education for which Award is Granted:** Undergraduate **Number Awarded:** 1 or more each year. **Funds Available:** A stipend is awarded (amount not specified). **Duration:** 1 year.
Eligibility Requirements: This program is open to residents of New Jersey who are Hispanic (at least 1 parent must be fully Hispanic) and U.S. citizens or permanent residents. Applicants must be full-time college freshmen or high school seniors with a GPA of 3.0 or higher. They must be intending to major in business or a business technology-related program at a 2- or 4-year college in New Jersey. Along with their application, they must submit short answers to questions about their community and the environment in which they have lived during the past 4 years, their high school experience and an important aspect of their high school career, their involvement in extracurricular activities in school and/or their community, their family and how it has shaped their development, and their willingness to participate in internship and mentoring activities that may be available through the scholarship program. Financial need is also considered in the selection process. **Deadline for Receipt:** September of each year.

1595 ■ STUDENT AID FOUNDATION

2520 East Piedmont Road, Suite F
PMB 180
Marietta, GA 30062
Tel: (770)973-7077
Fax: (770)973-2220
E-mail: studentaid@bellsouth.net
Web Site: http://www.studentaidfoundation.org
To provide loans to women in Georgia who need financial assistance in order to continue their education beyond the high school level.

Title of Award: Student Aid Foundation Loans **Area, Field, or Subject:** General studies/Field of study not specified **Level of Education for which Award is Granted:** Graduate, Undergraduate **Number Awarded:** Approximately 35 each year. **Funds Available:** Loans range from $3,500 to $4,500 per year for undergraduates and up to $5,000 per year for graduate students. Loans are not granted to cover all necessary expenses but to supplement what parents can provide or the recipient can earn or receive from scholarships. No interest on loans is charged while

the student is in college or in training. Interest at 6% begins 3 months after the borrower completes her course of study or leaves school for any reason. If the loan is not repaid within 4 years, the interest rate increases to 12%. The minimum monthly repayment is $100 or $20 per $1,000 borrowed, whichever is greater. **Duration:** 1 academic year; renewable for 1 additional year.
Eligibility Requirements: This program is open to full-time traditional or nontraditional women students who are residents of Georgia or who are currently attending a school in the state. Applicants must have a GPA of 2.5 or higher. Selection is based on financial need, academic ability, and the desire to succeed in obtaining an education. **Deadline for Receipt:** April of each year. **Additional Information:** This program began in 1908. Recipients are expected to complete their training and become self-supporting within 4 years, unless there are unusual circumstances to warrant a deviation from this general rule. If a payment cannot be made when due, a letter of explanation must be sent to the office. Also, the office must be informed of marriage, change of address, or any other pertinent changes.

1596 ■ STUDENT INSIGHTS
136 Justice Drive
Valencia, PA 16059
Tel: (724)612-3685
E-mail: contact@studentinsights.com
Web Site: http://www.student-view.com
To provide financial assistance for college to high school seniors in selected states who complete an online questionnaire about schools in their area.
Title of Award: Student-View Scholarship **Area, Field, or Subject:** General studies/Field of study not specified **Level of Education for which Award is Granted:** Undergraduate **Number Awarded:** 1 each year. **Funds Available:** The stipend is $5,000. **Duration:** 1 year.
Eligibility Requirements: This program is open to college-bound high school seniors in Connecticut, Delaware, the District of Columbia, Illinois, Indiana, Kentucky, Maryland, Michigan, New York, New Jersey, North Carolina, Ohio, Pennsylvania, Tennessee, Virginia, West Virginia, and Wisconsin. Applicants must complete an online questionnaire in which they rate their awareness of a number of colleges in their region, including their academic strength, tuition cost, etc. They must also submit an essay, up to 250 words, on their own college search experience. **Additional Information:** The sponsor is a firm that provides market information to colleges and universities.

1597 ■ STUDENT LOAN FINANCE CORPORATION
105 First Avenue S.W.
Aberdeen, SD 57401-4173
Tel: (605)622-4400
Free: 800-592-1270
Fax: (605)622-4547
E-mail: service@slfc.com
Web Site: http://www.slfc.com
To provide financial assistance for college to high school seniors in South Dakota.
Title of Award: Tom Steele Memorial Scholarships **Area, Field, or Subject:** General studies/Field of study not specified **Level of Education for which Award is Granted:** Undergraduate **Number Awarded:** Up to 220 each year: 1 to a senior at each high school in South Dakota. **Funds Available:** The stipend is $1,000. **Duration:** 1 year.
Eligibility Requirements: This program is open to seniors graduating from high schools in South Dakota who plan to enroll full time at an accredited 2-year or 4-year college, university, or technical/vocational school. Selection is based on academic achievement (GPA of 3.25 or higher); work experience; activities, awards, and honors; a brief statement of educational and career objectives and long-term goals; and a statement of unusual family or personal circumstances that have affected achievement in school, work experience, or participation in school and community activities. Financial need is not considered. **Deadline for Receipt:** January of each year. **Additional Information:** This program was established in 2004 to honor a long-time official of the sponsor, the state educational loan agency for South Dakota. It is managed by Scholarship America, One Scholarship Way, P.O. Box 297, St. Peter, MN 56082, (507) 931-1682, (800) 537-4180, Fax: (507) 931-9168, E-mail: smsinfo@csfa.org.

1598 ■ COMMANDER WILLIAM S. STUHR SCHOLARSHIP FUND
c/o Joseph A. LaRivere, Executive Director
1200 Fifth Avenue, Suite 9-D
New York, NY 10029
E-mail: stuhrstudents@earthlink.net
To provide financial assistance for college to the dependent children of retired or active-duty military personnel.
Title of Award: Commander William S. Stuhr Scholarships **Area, Field, or Subject:** General studies/Field of study not specified **Level of Education for which Award is Granted:** Four Year College **Number Awarded:** 5 each year: 1 for a child of a military servicemember from each of the 5 branches (Air Force, Army, Coast Guard, Marine Corps, and Navy). **Funds Available:** The stipend is $1,125 per year. **Duration:** 4 years, provided the recipient makes the dean's list at their college at least once during their first 2 years.
Eligibility Requirements: This program is open to the dependent children of military personnel who are serving on active duty or retired with pay after 20 years' service (not merely separated from service). Applicants must be high school seniors who rank in the top 10% of their class for their junior year and the first half of their senior year. They must plan to attend a 4-year accredited college. Selection is based on academic performance, extracurricular activities, demonstrated leadership potential, and financial need. **Deadline for Receipt:** February of each year. **Additional Information:** This program was established in 1965. Recipients and their families attend a scholarship awards function in late May or early June; the fund pays air transportation to the event. Applications may be obtained only by writing and enclosing a self-addressed stamped envelope. The fund does not respond to telephone, fax, or e-mail inquiries.

1599 ■ SUNKIST GROWERS
Attn: Administrator
P.O. Box 7888
Van Nuys, CA 91409-7888
Tel: (818)986-4800
Web Site: http://www.sunkist.com/about/bodine_scholarship.asp
To provide financial assistance to undergraduate students in California and Arizona who have an agricultural background and need financial assistance to further their education.
Title of Award: A.W. Bodine-Sunkist Memorial Scholarship **Area, Field, or Subject:** General studies/Field of study not specified **Level of Education for which Award is Granted:** Undergraduate **Number Awarded:** Varies each year; recently, 16 of these scholarships were awarded. Since the establishment of the program, more than 275 scholarships have been awarded. **Funds Available:** Stipends average $2,000 per year. **Duration:** 1 year; may be renewed for up to 3 additional years provided the recipients carry at least 12 units per term and earn a minimum GPA of 2.7.
Eligibility Requirements: This program is open to students entering an undergraduate program at any level. Applicants must have a background in California or Arizona agriculture (i.e., the student or someone in the student's immediate family must derive the majority of income from agriculture). They must have earned a 3.0 GPA and be able to demonstrate financial need. Along with their application, they must submit a 500-word essay on their background and goals. Selection is based on the essay, financial need, college board test scores, GPA, and recommendations. **Deadline for Receipt:** April of each year. **Additional Information:** This program was established in 1990.

1600 ■ SUNNYSIDE FOUNDATION, INC.
8222 Douglas Avenue, Suite 501
Dallas, TX 75225
Tel: (214)692-5686; 888-663-8362
Fax: (214)692-1968
E-mail: sunnysd@airmail.net
To provide financial assistance for education and other needs to Christian Scientists in Texas.
Title of Award: Sunnyside Foundation Financial Assistance Program **Area, Field, or Subject:** General studies/Field of study not specified **Level of Education for which Award is Granted:** Undergraduate, Other **Number Awarded:** Varies each year. **Funds Available:** The amount awarded depends upon the needs of the recipient.
Eligibility Requirements: Any Christian Scientist who is a Texas resident and regularly attends a Christian Science church or Sunday school is

eligible to apply. Applications for financial assistance may be submitted for a variety of purposes, including college, educational needs, food and clothing, shelter, child care, summer camp, nursing care, practitioner fees, emergency situations, and special opportunities. **Deadline for Receipt:** Applications may be submitted at any time. **Additional Information:** All requests for assistance are strictly confidential.

1601 ■ SUNSHINE LADY FOUNDATION, INC.

Attn: WISP Program
4900 Randall Parkway, Suite H
Wilmington, NC 28403
Tel: (910)397-7742; (866)255-7742
Fax: (910)397-0023
E-mail: nancy@sunshineladyfdn.org
Web Site: http://www.sunshineladyfdn.org/wisp.html
To provide financial assistance for college or graduate school to women who are victims of partner abuse.
Title of Award: Women's Independence Scholarship Program **Area, Field, or Subject:** General studies/Field of study not specified **Level of Education for which Award is Granted:** Graduate, Undergraduate **Number Awarded:** Varies each year. **Funds Available:** Stipends depend on the need of the recipient, but they are at least $250 and average $2,500. First priority is given to funding for direct educational expenses (tuition, books, and fees), which is paid directly to the educational institution. Second priority is for assistance in reducing indirect financial barriers to education (e.g., child care, transportation), which is paid directly to the sponsoring agency. **Duration:** 1 year; may be renewed if the recipient maintains a GPA of 3.0 or higher.
Eligibility Requirements: This program is open to women who are victims of partner abuse and have worked for at least 1 month with a nonprofit domestic violence victim services provider that is willing to sponsor them. Applicants must be interested in attending a vocational school, community college, 4-year college or university, or (in exceptional circumstances) graduate school as a full or part time student. They should have left an abusive partner within the past 2 years; women who have been parted from their batterer for more than 2 years are also eligible but funding for such applicants may be limited. Preference is given to single mothers with young children. Special consideration is given to applicants who plan to use their education to further the rights of, and options for, women and girls. Selection is based primarily on financial need. **Deadline for Receipt:** Applications may be submitted at any time, but they must be received at least 3 months before the start of the intended program. **Additional Information:** This program was established in 1999.

1602 ■ SUPERSIBS!

Attn: Scholarship Committee
4300 Lincoln Avenue, Suite I
Rolling Meadows, IL 60008
Tel: (847)705-SIBS; (866)444-SIBS
Fax: (847)776-7084
E-mail: info@supersibs.org
Web Site: http://www.supersibs.org
To provide financial assistance for college to siblings of children with cancer.
Title of Award: SuperSibs! Scholarships **Area, Field, or Subject:** General studies/Field of study not specified **Level of Education for which Award is Granted:** Undergraduate **Number Awarded:** Up to 5 each year. **Funds Available:** The stipend is $5,000. **Duration:** 1 year.
Eligibility Requirements: This program is open to seniors graduating from high schools in the United States, Puerto Rico, or the Virgin Islands with a GPA of 2.0 or higher. Applicants must be the siblings of children who have or have had cancer. They must be planning to attend an accredited college, university, or vocational institution in the following fall. Half-siblings and stepsiblings who reside in the same home as the cancer patient are also eligible. Along with their application, they must submit an essay, up to 1,000 words, on what they learned from their experience as the sibling of a brother or sister with cancer, how they will apply those learnings in their life and the lives of others, the advice they can share with other siblings to help them manage through this challenging time, how this scholarship will make a difference in their life, and anything else they would like the sponsor to know about them. Selection is based on the essay (60 points), a high school transcript (10 points), and a letter of recommendation (30 points). **Additional Information:** The sponsor also

offers another $5,000 scholarship to the siblings of children with cancer (the Manne Family Foundation Scholarship), but that one requires applicants to demonstrate financial need. **Deadline for Receipt:** March of each year.

1603 ■ SUPREME EMBLEM CLUB OF THE UNITED STATES OF AMERICA

c/o Gail Stankiewicz, Supreme Corresponding Secretary
505 Grassy Brook Road
Brookline, VT 05345
Tel: (802)365-7292
E-mail: gailvt@sover.net
Web Site: http://www.emblemclub.com
To provide financial aid for college to members or the children of members of the Supreme Emblem Club of the United States of America who have a physically challenging condition.
Title of Award: Supreme Emblem Club of the United States of America Grant-in-Aid Awards **Area, Field, or Subject:** General studies/Field of study not specified **Level of Education for which Award is Granted:** Undergraduate **Number Awarded:** Varies each year. **Funds Available:** The amount awarded varies each year. Funds must be used for tuition, books, or fees. **Duration:** 1 year.
Eligibility Requirements: This program is open to high school graduates or those already in college. Applicants must be sponsored by the Emblem Club in which the student or the student's mother or grandmother is a member. They must be serious about continuing their education but, because of a physically challenging situation, are unable to meet the high criteria applied to the Emblem Club's Scholarship Program. **Deadline for Receipt:** March of each year. **Additional Information:** The sponsoring Emblem Club must be a current contributor to the regular scholarship fund for the applicant to be considered for an award.

1604 ■ SUPREME EMBLEM CLUB OF THE UNITED STATES OF AMERICA

c/o Gail Stankiewicz, Supreme Corresponding Secretary
505 Grassy Brook Road
Brookline, VT 05345
Tel: (802)365-7292
E-mail: gailvt@sover.net
Web Site: http://www.emblemclub.com
To provide financial aid for college to members or the children of members of the Supreme Emblem Club of the United States of America.
Title of Award: Supreme Emblem Club of the United States of America Scholarships **Area, Field, or Subject:** General studies/Field of study not specified **Level of Education for which Award is Granted:** Undergraduate **Number Awarded:** Varies each year. **Funds Available:** The amount awarded varies each year. Funds must be used for tuition, books, or fees. **Duration:** 1 year.
Eligibility Requirements: This program is open to high school graduates or those already in college. Each applicant is required to apply for and take either the SAT or ACT not later than November. Applicants must be sponsored by the Emblem Club in which the student or the student's mother or grandmother is a member. **Deadline for Receipt:** March of each year. **Additional Information:** This program was established in 1934. The sponsoring Emblem Club must be a current contributor to the regular scholarship fund for the applicant to be considered for an award.

1605 ■ SURFACE NAVY ASSOCIATION

2550 Huntington Avenue, Suite 202
Alexandria, VA 22303
Tel: (703)960-6800
Free: 800-NAVY-SNA
Fax: (703)960-6807
E-mail: navysna@aol.com
Web Site: http://www.navysna.org/awards/index.html
To provide financial assistance for college or graduate school to members of the Surface Navy Association (SNA) and their dependents.
Title of Award: VADM Robert L. Walters Scholarship **Area, Field, or Subject:** General studies/Field of study not specified **Level of Education for which Award is Granted:** Graduate, Undergraduate **Number Awarded:** Varies each year. **Funds Available:** The stipend is $2,000 per year. **Duration:** 4 years, provided the recipient maintains a GPA of 3.0 or higher.

Eligibility Requirements: This program is open to SNA members and their children, stepchildren, wards, and spouses. The SNA member must 1) be in the second or subsequent consecutive year of membership; 2) be serving, retired, or honorably discharged; 3) be a Surface Warfare Officer or Enlisted Surface Warfare Specialist; and 4) have served for at least 3 years on a surface ship of the U.S. Navy or Coast Guard. Applicants must be studying or planning to study at an accredited undergraduate or graduate institution. Along with their application, they must submit a 200-word essay about themselves; a list of their extracurricular activities, community service activities, academic honors and/or positions of leadership that represent their interests, with an estimate of the amount of time involved with each activity; and 3 letters of reference. High school seniors should also include a transcript of high school grades and a copy of ACT or SAT scores. Applicants who are on active duty or drilling Reservists should also include a letter from their commanding officer commenting on their military service and leadership potential, a transcript of grades from their most recent 4 semesters of school, a copy of their ACT or SAT scores if available, and an indication of whether they have applied for or are enrolled in the Enlisted Commissioning Program. Applicants who are not high school seniors, active duty, or drilling Reservists should also include a transcript of the grades from their most recent 4 semesters of school and a copy of ACT or SAT test scores (unless they are currently attending a college or university). Selection is based on demonstrated leadership, community service, academic achievement, and commitment to pursuing higher educational objectives. **Deadline for Receipt:** January of each year.

1606 ■ TAILHOOK EDUCATIONAL FOUNDATION

9696 Businesspark Avenue
P.O. Box 26626
San Diego, CA 92196-0626
Tel: (858)689-9223
Free: 800-269-8267
E-mail: thookassn@aol.com
Web Site: http://www.tailhook.org/Foundation.html
To provide financial assistance for college to personnel associated with naval aviation and their children.
Title of Award: Tailhook Educational Foundation Scholarships **Area, Field, or Subject:** General studies/Field of study not specified **Level of Education for which Award is Granted:** Undergraduate **Number Awarded:** Varies each year; recently, 43 of these scholarships were awarded. **Funds Available:** The stipend ranges from $2,000 to $3,000. **Duration:** 1 year.
Eligibility Requirements: This program is open to 1) the children (natural, step, and adopted) of current or former U.S. Navy personnel who served as a naval aviator, naval flight officer, or designated naval air crewman, or 2) personnel and children of personnel who are serving or have served on board a U.S. Navy aircraft carrier as a member of the ship's company or assigned airwing. Applicants must be enrolled or accepted for enrollment at an accredited college or university. Selection is based on educational and extracurricular achievements, merit, and citizenship. **Deadline for Receipt:** March of each year.

1607 ■ MAMORU AND AIKO TAKITANI FOUNDATION

P.O. Box 10687
Honolulu, HI 96816-0687
E-mail: info@takitani.org
Web Site: http://www.takitani.org
To provide financial assistance for college to needy high school seniors in Hawaii.
Title of Award: Mamoru and Aiko Takitani Foundation Scholarships **Area, Field, or Subject:** General studies/Field of study not specified **Level of Education for which Award is Granted:** Undergraduate **Number Awarded:** Each qualifying high school in the state (approximately 60) awards 1 of these scholarships. Semifinalist awards are presented to 10 students. The finalist awards include 2 at $10,000 and 1 at $5,000. **Funds Available:** The stipend for each high school winner is $1,000. Semifinalists receive an additional $1,000 scholarship. Finalists receive stipends of $10,000 or $5,000. **Duration:** 1 year.
Eligibility Requirements: This program is open to college-bound seniors graduating from high schools in Hawaii. Applicants must prepare a 1-page essay describing their personal goals and how this scholarship would help them attain those, their plans for serving the community after graduation,

and any financial or unique circumstances that the sponsor should consider. They must submit those essays and other application materials to their college counselor or senior advisor. Selection is based on academic and extracurricular achievement, the personal essay, the applicant's unique circumstances, and financial need. Each school selects its own winner. From those, 6 semifinalists are selected from each school district, 1 from the Hawaii Catholic Schools, and 2 from the Hawaii Association of Independent Schools. From among those semifinalists, the sponsor's board of directors selects finalists. **Deadline for Receipt:** February of each year. **Additional Information:** This program was established in 1993. The finalist awards are designated the Mamoru Takitani Distinguished Student Award (at $10,000), the Aiko Takitani Distinguished Student Award (at $10,000), and the Karen Uno Outstanding Student Award (at $5,000).

1608 ■ TECHNOLOGY STUDENT ASSOCIATION

1914 Association Drive
Reston, VA 20191-1540
Tel: (703)860-9000
Fax: (703)758-4852
E-mail: general@tsaweb.org
Web Site: http://www.tsaweb.org
To provide financial support for college to members of the Technology Student Association (TSA).
Title of Award: ECI Scholarship Foundation Scholarship for the Technology Student Association **Area, Field, or Subject:** General studies/Field of study not specified **Level of Education for which Award is Granted:** Undergraduate **Number Awarded:** 1 each year. **Funds Available:** The stipend is $1,000. **Duration:** 1 year.
Eligibility Requirements: This program is open to TSA members who are rising high school seniors and have taken the SAT or ACT examination. Selection is based on those aptitude test scores, cumulative GPA, community involvement, demonstrated leadership, and financial need. **Deadline for Receipt:** May of each year. **Additional Information:** This program, established in 2003, is sponsored by the ECI Scholarship Foundation of Educational Communications Inc. Information is also available from ECISF-TSA, Attn: Rebecca Garcia, 1701 Directors Boulevard, Suite 920, P.O. Box 149319, Austin, TX 78714-9319.

1609 ■ TENNESSEE FUNERAL DIRECTORS ASSOCIATION

Attn: Scholarship Committee
1616 Church Street
Nashville, TN 37203
Tel: (615)321-8792
Free: 800-537-1599
Fax: (615)321-8794
E-mail: tnfuneral@xspedius.net
Web Site: http://www.tnfda.org
To provide financial assistance to Tennessee residents who are preparing for a career in funeral service.
Title of Award: Tennessee Funeral Directors Association Memorial Scholarship Program **Area, Field, or Subject:** Mortuary science **Level of Education for which Award is Granted:** Undergraduate **Number Awarded:** 2 each year. **Funds Available:** The stipend is $1,000. **Duration:** 1 year.
Eligibility Requirements: Applicants must be U.S. citizens and Tennessee residents who are enrolled in school on a full-time basis and have completed 2 semesters or one half of their course of study at a college accredited by the American Board of Funeral Service Education. They must have expressed the intent to enter funeral service upon graduation. As part of the application process, students must submit a completed application form, the latest family federal income tax return, college transcripts, 2 letters of recommendation, and a 2-page handwritten essay about themselves. Selection is based on financial need, academic record, recommendations, extracurricular and community activities, and the required essay. **Additional Information:** This program was established in 1997.

1610 ■ TENNESSEE STUDENT ASSISTANCE CORPORATION

Parkway Towers
404 James Robertson Parkway, Suite 1950
Nashville, TN 37243-0820
Tel: (615)741-1346

Free: 800-342-1663
Fax: (615)741-6101
E-mail: tsac@mail.state.tn.us
Web Site: http://www.tnscholardollars.com/mon_college/
ned_mc_shcolar.htm
To provide financial assistance to outstanding Tennessee high school seniors and recent graduates who plan to attend college in the state.
Title of Award: Ned McWherter Scholars Program **Area, Field, or Subject:** General studies/Field of study not specified **Level of Education for which Award is Granted:** Undergraduate **Number Awarded:** Approximately 50 each year. **Funds Available:** Stipends up to $6,000 per year are provided. **Duration:** 1 year; may be renewed for up to 3 additional years if the recipient remains a full-time student and maintains a minimum GPA of 3.0 per term and 3.2 per year.
Eligibility Requirements: This program is open to recent high school graduates and high school seniors in Tennessee who are residents of the state, whose parents are residents of the state, who ranked in the top 5% on the ACT or SAT tests (recently, 29 on the ACT or 1280 on the SAT), and who earned a GPA of 3.5 or higher in high school. Selection is based on academic record, test scores, and demonstrated leadership. **Deadline for Receipt:** February of each year. **Additional Information:** This program was established in 1986. Recipients must attend a college or university in Tennessee.

1611 ■ TENNESSEE STUDENT ASSISTANCE CORPORATION
Parkway Towers
404 James Robertson Parkway, Suite 1950
Nashville, TN 37243-0820
Tel: (615)741-1346
Free: 800-342-1663
Fax: (615)741-6101
E-mail: tsac@mail.state.tn.us
Web Site: http://www.tnscholardollars.com/mon_college/
depend_child_scholar.htm
To provide financial assistance for college to the dependent children of disabled or deceased Tennessee law enforcement officers, fire fighters, or emergency medical service technicians.
Title of Award: Tennessee Dependent Children Scholarship **Area, Field, or Subject:** General studies/Field of study not specified **Level of Education for which Award is Granted:** Undergraduate **Number Awarded:** Varies each year; recently, 19 students received $77,786 in support from this program **Funds Available:** The award covers tuition and fees, books, supplies, and room and board, minus any other financial aid for which the student is eligible. **Duration:** 1 year; may be renewed for up to 3 additional years or until completion of a program of study.
Eligibility Requirements: This program is open to Tennessee residents who are the dependent children of a Tennessee law enforcement officer, fire fighter, or emergency medical service technician who was killed or totally and permanently disabled in the line of duty. Applicants must be enrolled or accepted for enrollment as a full-time undergraduate student at a college or university in Tennessee. **Deadline for Receipt:** July of each year. **Additional Information:** This program was established in 1990.

1612 ■ TENNESSEE STUDENT ASSISTANCE CORPORATION
Parkway Towers
404 James Robertson Parkway, Suite 1950
Nashville, TN 37243-0820
Tel: (615)741-1346
Free: 800-342-1663
Fax: (615)741-6101
E-mail: tsac@mail.state.tn.us
Web Site: http://www.tnscholardollars.com/mon_college/gams.htm
To provide supplemental financial assistance for college to high school seniors in Tennessee who meet academic requirements in excess of those for the Tennessee HOPE Scholarships.
Title of Award: Tennessee General Assembly Merit Scholarships **Area, Field, or Subject:** General studies/Field of study not specified **Level of Education for which Award is Granted:** Undergraduate **Number Awarded:** Varies each year. **Funds Available:** The stipend is an additional $1,000, so the total award is $4,000 per year for students at 4-year colleges and universities or $2,500 per year for students at 2-year schools. **Duration:** 1 year; students may receive this supplemental funding only once.

Eligibility Requirements: This program is open to seniors graduating from public and private high schools in Tennessee and other residents of the state who qualify for a Tennessee HOPE Scholarship. Applicants for this supplemental funding must have higher levels of academic achievement: ACT scores of at least 29 (instead of 21), SAT scores of at least 1280 (instead of 980), and GPA of 3.75 or higher (instead of 3.0). The GPA may be weighted to include extra credit for AP or other advanced courses. They must be planning to attend an accredited public or private college or university in Tennessee. **Deadline for Receipt:** April of each year. **Additional Information:** This program is part of the Tennessee Education Lottery Scholarship Program, which began in 2004.

1613 ■ TENNESSEE STUDENT ASSISTANCE CORPORATION
Parkway Towers
404 James Robertson Parkway, Suite 1950
Nashville, TN 37243-0820
Tel: (615)741-1346
Free: 800-342-1663
Fax: (615)741-6101
E-mail: tsac@mail.state.tn.us
Web Site: http://www.tnscholardollars.com/mon_college/hope_grant.htm
To provide financial assistance for college to high school seniors in Tennessee who do not qualify for the Tennessee HOPE Scholarships but meet other academic and income requirements.
Title of Award: Tennessee HOPE Access Grants **Area, Field, or Subject:** General studies/Field of study not specified **Level of Education for which Award is Granted:** Undergraduate **Number Awarded:** Varies each year. **Funds Available:** The stipend is $2,000 per year for students at 4-year colleges and universities or $1,250 per year for students at 2-year schools. **Duration:** 1 year; this grant is nonrenewable but recipients may apply for a Tennessee HOPE Scholarship after 1 year of college if they have a cumulative GPA of 2.75 or higher.
Eligibility Requirements: This program is open to seniors graduating from public and private high schools in Tennessee who have an unweighted GPA of 2.75 or higher and an ACT score of at least 18 or an SAT score of at least 860. Applicants must have an annual family income of $36,000 or less. They must be planning to attend an accredited public or private college or university in Tennessee. **Deadline for Receipt:** April of each year. **Additional Information:** This program is part of the Tennessee Education Lottery Scholarship Program, which began in 2004.

1614 ■ TENNESSEE STUDENT ASSISTANCE CORPORATION
Parkway Towers
404 James Robertson Parkway, Suite 1950
Nashville, TN 37243-0820
Tel: (615)741-1346
Free: 800-342-1663
Fax: (615)741-6101
E-mail: tsac@mail.state.tn.us
Web Site: http://www.tnscholardollars.com/mon_college/
hope_scholar.htm
To provide financial assistance for college to high school seniors in Tennessee.
Title of Award: Tennessee HOPE Scholarships **Area, Field, or Subject:** General studies/Field of study not specified **Level of Education for which Award is Granted:** Undergraduate **Number Awarded:** Varies each year. **Funds Available:** The stipend is $3,000 per year for students at 4-year colleges and universities or $1,500 per year for students at 2-year schools. **Duration:** 1 year; may be renewed up to 4 additional years if the recipient maintains a cumulative GPA of 2.75 or higher.
Eligibility Requirements: This program is open to seniors graduating from public and private high schools in Tennessee, students in Tennessee who have completed a home-school program, and residents of Tennessee who have attained a GED. High school seniors must have an ACT score of at least 21 (or SAT score of at least 980) or an unweighted GPA of 3.0 or higher; home-school students must have an ACT score of at least 21 (or SAT score of at least 980); and GED recipients must have a GED score of at least 525 and an ACT score of at least 21 (or SAT score of at least 980). Applicants must be planning to attend an accredited public or private college or university in Tennessee. **Deadline for Receipt:** April of

each year. **Additional Information:** This program is part of the Tennessee Education Lottery Scholarship Program, which began in 2004.

1615 ■ TENNESSEE STUDENT ASSISTANCE CORPORATION
Parkway Towers
404 James Robertson Parkway, Suite 1950
Nashville, TN 37243-0820
Tel: (615)741-1346
Free: 800-342-1663
Fax: (615)741-6101
E-mail: tsac@mail.state.tn.us
Web Site: http://www.tnscholardollars.com/mon_college/
need_based_award.htm
To provide supplemental financial assistance for college to high school seniors in Tennessee who qualify for the Tennessee HOPE Scholarships and also demonstrate financial need.
Title of Award: Tennessee Need-Based Supplemental Awards **Area, Field, or Subject:** General studies/Field of study not specified **Level of Education for which Award is Granted:** Undergraduate **Number Awarded:** Varies each year. **Funds Available:** The stipend is an additional $1,000, so the total award is $4,000 per year for students at 4-year colleges and universities or $2,500 per year for students at 2-year schools. **Duration:** 1 year; students may receive this supplemental funding only once.
Eligibility Requirements: This program is open to seniors graduating from public and private high schools in Tennessee and other residents of the state who qualify for a Tennessee HOPE Scholarship. Applicants must have an annual family income of $36,000 or less. They must be planning to attend an accredited public or private college or university in Tennessee. **Deadline for Receipt:** April of each year. **Additional Information:** This program is part of the Tennessee Education Lottery Scholarship Program, which began in 2004.

1616 ■ TENNESSEE STUDENT ASSISTANCE CORPORATION
Parkway Towers
404 James Robertson Parkway, Suite 1950
Nashville, TN 37243-0820
Tel: (615)741-1346
Free: 800-342-1663
Fax: (615)741-6101
E-mail: tsac@mail.state.tn.us
Web Site: http://www.tnscholardollars.com/mon_college/tsa_award.htm
To provide financial assistance to students in Tennessee who have financial need.
Title of Award: Tennessee Student Assistance Awards **Area, Field, or Subject:** General studies/Field of study not specified **Level of Education for which Award is Granted:** Undergraduate **Number Awarded:** Varies each year. **Funds Available:** Recently, the maximum award was $2,322 at eligible Tennessee public postsecondary institutions or $5,538 at eligible Tennessee independent postsecondary institutions. **Duration:** 1 year; nonrenewable.
Eligibility Requirements: This program is open to students in Tennessee who are U.S. citizens, are Tennessee residents, are enrolled at least half time as undergraduate students, and can demonstrate financial need (expected family contribution of $2,100 or less). **Deadline for Receipt:** April of each year. **Additional Information:** This program was established in 1976.

1617 ■ TENNESSEE STUDENT ASSISTANCE CORPORATION
Parkway Towers
404 James Robertson Parkway, Suite 1950
Nashville, TN 37243-0820
Tel: (615)741-1346
Free: 800-342-1663
Fax: (615)741-6101
E-mail: tsac@mail.state.tn.us
Web Site: http://www.tnscholardollars.com/mon_college/
wilder_naifeh.htm
To provide financial assistance to students enrolled at Tennessee Technology Centers.
Title of Award: Wilder-Naifeh Technical Skills Grants **Area, Field, or Subject:** General studies/Field of study not specified **Level of Education**

for which **Award is Granted:** Vocational/Occupational **Number Awarded:** Varies each year. **Funds Available:** The stipend is $1,250 per year. **Duration:** 1 year.
Eligibility Requirements: This program is open to students working on a certificate or diploma at a Tennessee Technology Center. Applicants must be enrolled full time, but they are not required to meet any GPA or ACT minimum scores. **Deadline for Receipt:** April of each year. **Additional Information:** This program is part of the Tennessee Education Lottery Scholarship Program, which began in 2004.

1618 ■ TENTH MOUNTAIN DIVISION ASSOCIATION
Attn: Foundation
133 South Van Gordon Street, Suite 200
Lakewood, CO 80228
Tel: (303)756-8486
Fax: (303)988-3005
E-mail: tenthmtnfdn@nsp.org
Web Site: http://www.10thmtndivassoc.org/foundation.html
To provide financial assistance for college or graduate school to children and grandchildren of former members of the Tenth Mountain Division.
Title of Award: Tenth Mountain Division Association College Assistance Scholarships **Area, Field, or Subject:** General studies/Field of study not specified **Level of Education for which Award is Granted:** Graduate, Undergraduate **Number Awarded:** Varies each year; recently, the foundation was supporting 27 students: 1 graduate student, 13 seniors, 5 juniors, 7 sophomores, and 1 freshman. **Funds Available:** Scholarships are awarded up to $1,250 per year, depending on need. **Duration:** 1 year; may be renewed up to 3 additional years.
Eligibility Requirements: Eligible to apply for these scholarships are the children and grandchildren of veterans who served in the Tenth Mountain Division during World War II. Applicants must meet the academic requirements of the college or university they choose to attend and must demonstrate financial need. **Deadline for Receipt:** June of each year. **Additional Information:** Since this program was established in 1966, more than 600 scholarships have been awarded.

1619 ■ TET '68, INC.
Attn: Scholarship Competition
P.O. Box 31885
Richmond, VA 23294
Tel: (804)550-3692
E-mail: Tet68Info@tet68.org
Web Site: http://www.tet68.org/TET68sch.html
To provide financial assistance for college to high school seniors whose parent served in Vietnam.
Title of Award: TET '68 Scholarship **Area, Field, or Subject:** General studies/Field of study not specified **Level of Education for which Award is Granted:** Undergraduate **Number Awarded:** 3 or 4 each year. **Funds Available:** The stipend is $1,000. **Duration:** 1 year.
Eligibility Requirements: This program is open to high school seniors whose parent or stepparent is a Vietnam veteran. Applicants must submit a 500-word essay on "What is Freedom;" a copy of the parent's or stepparent's DD214 showing Vietnam service with Campaign Ribbon Award; a cover sheet that includes their full name and contact information for themselves, a person at their high school, and a person at their chosen college; and a statement verifying that they will graduate from high school in the following spring. **Deadline for Receipt:** March of each year. **Additional Information:** This program began in 1988.

1620 ■ TEXAS 4-H YOUTH DEVELOPMENT FOUNDATION
Attn: Executive Director
Texas A&M University
7606 Eastmark Drive, Suite 101
College Station, TX 77843-2473
Tel: (979)845-1213
Fax: (979)845-6495
E-mail: texas4-hscholarships@tamu.edu
Web Site: http://texas4-h.tamu.edu/scholarships
To provide financial assistance for college to 4-H members in Texas.
Title of Award: Houston Livestock Show and Rodeo 4-H Scholarships **Area, Field, or Subject:** General studies/Field of study not specified **Level of Education for which Award is Granted:** Undergraduate **Number Awarded:** 70 each year. **Funds Available:** The stipend is $2,500 per year. **Duration:** 4 years.

Eligibility Requirements: This program is open to graduating seniors at public high schools in Texas who have been actively participating in 4-H. Applicants must be in the top quarter of their class and have minimum scores of 910 on the combined mathematics and critical reading sections of the SAT or 19 on the ACT. They must be U.S. citizens planning to attend a college or university in Texas and major in any field. Selection is based on GPA (20%), test scores (15%), 4-H experience (35%), financial need (20%), and a personal interview (10%). **Deadline for Receipt:** Students submit their applications to their county extension office, which must forward them to the district extension office by February of each year. **Additional Information:** Funding for this program is provided by the Houston Livestock Show and Rodeo. Students who apply to the Texas FFA Association or the Texas chapter of Family, Career and Community Leaders of America (FCCLA) for a scholarship will have their 4-H application voided.

1621 ■ TEXAS 4-H YOUTH DEVELOPMENT FOUNDATION
Attn: Executive Director
Texas A&M University
7606 Eastmark Drive, Suite 101
College Station, TX 77843-2473
Tel: (979)845-1213
Fax: (979)845-6495
E-mail: texas4-hscholarships@tamu.edu
Web Site: http://texas4-h.tamu.edu/scholarships
To provide financial assistance to 4-H members in Texas who plan to work on a baccalaureate degree in any field at a college or university in the state.
Title of Award: Texas 4-H Baccalaureate Scholarship Program **Area, Field, or Subject:** General studies/Field of study not specified **Level of Education for which Award is Granted:** Four Year College **Number Awarded:** The foundation awards approximately 170 scholarships, worth more than $1.2 million, for all of its programs each year. **Funds Available:** Stipends range from $1,500 to $15,000, depending on the contributions from various donors. **Duration:** 1 year.
Eligibility Requirements: This program is open to graduating seniors at high schools in Texas who have been actively participating in 4-H and plan to attend a college or university in the state to work on a baccalaureate degree. Applicants must have passed all sections of the TAAS, THEA, and/or TAKS test and have minimum scores of 910 on the combined mathematics and critical reading sections of the SAT or 19 on the ACT. Some scholarships require applicants to demonstrate financial need; selection for those awards is based on GPA (20%), test scores (15%), 4-H experience (35%), financial need (20%), and a personal interview (10%). For other scholarships, selection is based on GPA (20%), test scores (15%), 4-H experience (55%), and a personal interview (10%). Some scholarships require a major in agriculture; others are unrestricted. **Deadline for Receipt:** Students submit their applications to their county extension office, which must forward them to the district extension office by February of each year. **Additional Information:** Students submit 1 application. The foundation determines the scholarships for which they are eligible, based on the specific requirements established by particular sponsors. Students who apply to the Texas FFA Association or the Texas chapter of Family, Career and Community Leaders of America (FCCLA) for a scholarship will have their 4-H application voided.

1622 ■ TEXAS ELECTRIC COOPERATIVES, INC.
Attn: Vice President of Member Services
2550 South IH-35
Austin, TX 78704
Tel: (512)454-0311
E-mail: twortham@texas-ec.org
Web Site: http://www.texas-ec.org/resources/youth/pages/twrea.aspx
To provide financial assistance for college to members and children of members of the Texas Rural Electric Women's Association (TREWA).
Title of Award: TREWA Scholarships **Area, Field, or Subject:** General studies/Field of study not specified **Level of Education for which Award is Granted:** Undergraduate **Number Awarded:** 7 each year. **Funds Available:** The stipend is $1,000. Funds are paid directly to the recipient's institution, half at the beginning of the first semester and half upon verification of completion of the first semester with passing grades. **Duration:** 1 year; nonrenewable.
Eligibility Requirements: Eligible are current members of the association, their children, and employees of electric cooperatives that are current

members. Applicants may be enrolled or planning to enroll in an accredited college, university, junior or community college, trade/technical school, or business school of their choice to work on a degree, certificate, diploma, or license. Grades received in high school are not the deciding factor in the selection process; leadership qualities, career focus, energy awareness, a 250-word essay on the applicant's plans and goals, and general knowledge of the rural electric problem are considered. **Deadline for Receipt:** April of each year. **Additional Information:** This scholarship is sponsored by TREWA and administered by Texas Electric Cooperatives, Inc. Recipients may attend any accredited college, university, junior college, community college, trade/technical school, or business school of their choice.

1623 ■ TEXAS HIGHER EDUCATION COORDINATING BOARD
Attn: Grants and Special Programs
1200 East Anderson Lane
P.O. Box 12788, Capitol Station
Austin, TX 78711-2788
Tel: (512)427-6323
Free: 800-242-3062
Fax: (512)427-6127
E-mail: grantinfo@thecb.state.tx.us
Web Site: http://www.collegefortexans.com
To provide financial assistance at Texas public institutions to students from Western Hemisphere countries.
Title of Award: Good Neighbor Scholarship Program **Area, Field, or Subject:** General studies/Field of study not specified **Level of Education for which Award is Granted:** Undergraduate **Number Awarded:** Varies each year; recently, 235 of these scholarships were awarded. **Funds Available:** Eligible students are exempted from the payment of all tuition charges at publicly-supported colleges and universities in Texas. **Duration:** 1 year.
Eligibility Requirements: This program is open to native-born citizens and residents of nations of the Western Hemisphere (other than Cuba or the United States). Applicants must be interested in attending a public college or university in Texas. They must be certified by their native country, be scholastically qualified for admission to a participating public college or university in Texas, intend to return to their home country upon completion of their program of study, and be nominated by their college. **Deadline for Receipt:** March of each year. **Additional Information:** Applications must be submitted through the financial aid office or international student office at the college or university attended.

1624 ■ TEXAS HIGHER EDUCATION COORDINATING BOARD
Attn: Grants and Special Programs
1200 East Anderson Lane
P.O. Box 12788, Capitol Station
Austin, TX 78711-2788
Tel: (512)427-6101
Free: 800-242-3062
Fax: (512)427-6127
E-mail: grantinfo@thecb.state.tx.us
Web Site: http://www.collegefortexans.com
To exempt children of deceased veterans from payment of tuition at public universities in Texas.
Title of Award: Hazlewood Exemption for Dependents of Texas Veterans **Area, Field, or Subject:** General studies/Field of study not specified **Level of Education for which Award is Granted:** Undergraduate **Number Awarded:** Varies each year; recently, 8 of these awards were granted. **Funds Available:** Eligible students are exempt from payment of tuition, dues, fees, and charges at state-supported colleges and universities in Texas. **Duration:** 1 year; may be renewed for a cumulative total of 150 credit hours.
Eligibility Requirements: This program is open to the children of Texas servicemen who died in the line of duty or as a result of injury or illness directly related to service in the U.S. military or the National Guard. Applicants must have used up all federal educational benefits for which they are eligible. They must have resided in Texas for at least 12 months and be attending or planning to attend a public college or university in the state.

1625 ■ TEXAS HIGHER EDUCATION COORDINATING BOARD
Attn: Grants and Special Programs
1200 East Anderson Lane

P.O. Box 12788, Capitol Station
Austin, TX 78711-2788
Tel: (512)427-6101
Free: 800-242-3062
Fax: (512)427-6127
E-mail: grantinfo@thecb.state.tx.us
Web Site: http://www.collegefortexans.com
To exempt Texas veterans from payment of tuition for undergraduate or graduate study at public universities in the state.

Title of Award: Hazlewood Exemption for Texas Veterans **Area, Field, or Subject:** General studies/Field of study not specified **Level of Education for which Award is Granted:** Graduate, Undergraduate **Number Awarded:** Varies each year; recently, 8.858 of these awards were granted. **Funds Available:** Veterans who are eligible for this benefit are entitled to free tuition and fees at state-supported colleges and universities in Texas. **Duration:** Exemptions may be claimed up to a cumulative total of 150 credit hours, including undergraduate and graduate study.

Eligibility Requirements: This program is open to veterans who were legal residents of Texas at the time they entered the U.S. armed forces and served for at least 181 days of active military duty, excluding basic training. Applicants must have received an honorable discharge or separation or a general discharge under honorable conditions. They must be enrolled at a public college or university in Texas but have used up all other federal education benefits (e.g., Montgomery Bill, Pell grants, federal SEOG grants).

1626 ■ TEXAS HIGHER EDUCATION COORDINATING BOARD
Attn: Hinson-Hazlewood College Student Loan Program
1200 East Anderson Lane
P.O. Box 12788, Capitol Station
Austin, TX 78711-2788
Tel: (512)427-6340
Free: 800-242-3062
Fax: (512)427-6423
E-mail: loaninfo@thecb.state.tx.us
Web Site: http://www.hhloans.com
To provide educational loans to students in Texas who cannot qualify for need-based assistance.

Title of Award: Hinson-Hazlewood College Access Loan Program **Area, Field, or Subject:** General studies/Field of study not specified **Level of Education for which Award is Granted:** Graduate, Undergraduate **Number Awarded:** Varies each year. **Funds Available:** Loans up to $10,000 per year, or the cost of education, are available. No guarantee fee is charged, but there is a 3% origination fee. After a grace period of 6 months, repayment must be completed within 10 years at a minimum monthly payment of $50. The current interest rate is 5.25%. **Duration:** 1 year; may be renewed up to 3 additional years for a total loan of $45,000.

Eligibility Requirements: This program is open to students who qualify as Texas residents and meet the academic requirements of a public or private college or university in the state. Applicants must enroll at least half time in an associate, bachelor's, or higher degree program. Promissory notes must be cosigned by a credit-worthy person. Applicants do not need to show financial need and may use these loan funds to cover the family's expected contribution on other loan programs. **Additional Information:** Applications must be submitted through the financial aid office at the college or university attended.

1627 ■ TEXAS HIGHER EDUCATION COORDINATING BOARD
Attn: Grants and Special Programs
1200 East Anderson Lane
P.O. Box 12788, Capitol Station
Austin, TX 78711-2788
Tel: (512)427-6101
Free: 800-242-3062
Fax: (512)427-6127
E-mail: grantinfo@thecb.state.tx.us
Web Site: http://www.collegefortexans.com
To provide educational assistance to the spouses and children of Texas military personnel assigned elsewhere.

Title of Award: Military Tuition Waiver During Assignment After Texas **Area, Field, or Subject:** General studies/Field of study not specified **Level of Education for which Award is Granted:** Undergraduate **Number Awarded:** Varies each year. **Funds Available:** Eligible students

are entitled to pay tuition and fees at the resident rate at publicly-supported colleges and universities in Texas. **Duration:** The waiver remains in effect for the duration of the member's first assignment outside of Texas.

Eligibility Requirements: This program is open to the spouses and dependent children of members of the U.S. armed forces or commissioned officers of the Public Health Service who remain in Texas when the member is reassigned to duty outside of the state. The spouse or dependent child must reside continuously in Texas. Applicants must be attending or planning to attend a Texas public college or university. **Additional Information:** This program became effective in September, 2003.

1628 ■ TEXAS HIGHER EDUCATION COORDINATING BOARD
Attn: Grants and Special Programs
1200 East Anderson Lane
P.O. Box 12788, Capitol Station
Austin, TX 78711-2788
Tel: (512)427-6101
Free: 800-242-3062
Fax: (512)427-6127
E-mail: grantinfo@thecb.state.tx.us
Web Site: http://www.collegefortexans.com
To provide a tuition exemption to blind and/or deaf residents of Texas.

Title of Award: Texas Blind/Deaf Student Exemption Program **Area, Field, or Subject:** General studies/Field of study not specified **Level of Education for which Award is Granted:** Undergraduate **Number Awarded:** Varies each year; recently, 3,278 students received support through this program. **Funds Available:** Eligible students are exempted from the payment of all dues, fees, and tuition charges at publicly-supported colleges and universities in Texas. **Duration:** Up to 8 semesters.

Eligibility Requirements: This program is open to Texas residents who can present certification from the Department of Assistive and Rehabilitative Services of their deafness or blindness. Applicants must present to the registrar of a public college or university in Texas a copy of their high school transcript, a letter of recommendation, proof that they have met all admission requirements, and a statement of purpose that indicates the certificate, degree program, or professional enhancement that they intend to pursue.

1629 ■ TEXAS HIGHER EDUCATION COORDINATING BOARD
Attn: Grants and Special Programs
1200 East Anderson Lane
P.O. Box 12788, Capitol Station
Austin, TX 78711-2788
Tel: (512)427-6101
Free: 800-242-3062
Fax: (512)427-6127
E-mail: grantinfo@thecb.state.tx.us
Web Site: http://www.collegefortexans.com
To provide educational assistance to the children of disabled or deceased Texas fire fighters, peace officers, game wardens, and employees of correctional institutions.

Title of Award: Texas Children of Disabled or Deceased Firemen, Peace Officers, Game Wardens, and Employees of Correctional Institutions Exemption Program **Area, Field, or Subject:** General studies/Field of study not specified **Level of Education for which Award is Granted:** Undergraduate **Number Awarded:** Varies each year; recently, 116 students received support through this program. **Funds Available:** Eligible students are exempted from the payment of all dues, fees, and tuition charges at publicly-supported colleges and universities in Texas. **Duration:** Support is provided for up to 120 semester credit hours of undergraduate study or until the recipient reaches 26 years of age, whichever comes first.

Eligibility Requirements: Eligible are children of Texas paid or volunteer fire fighters; paid municipal, county, or state peace officers; custodial employees of the Department of Corrections; or game wardens. The parent must have suffered an injury in the line of duty, resulting in disability or death. Applicants must be under 21 years of age.

1630 ■ TEXAS HIGHER EDUCATION COORDINATING BOARD
Attn: Grants and Special Programs
1200 East Anderson Lane

P.O. Box 12788, Capitol Station
Austin, TX 78711-2788
Tel: (512)427-6101
Free: 800-242-3062
Fax: (512)427-6127
E-mail: grantinfo@thecb.state.tx.us
Web Site: http://www.collegefortexans.com
To provide educational assistance to the children of Texas military person-
nel declared prisoners of war or missing in action.
Title of Award: Texas Children of U.S. Military Who Are Missing in Action
or Prisoners of War Exemption Program **Area, Field, or Subject:** General
studies/Field of study not specified **Level of Education for which Award
is Granted:** Undergraduate **Number Awarded:** Varies each year;
recently, 2 of these exemptions were granted. **Funds Available:** Eligible
students are exempted from the payment of all dues, fees, and tuition
charges at publicly-supported colleges and universities in Texas. **Duration:** Up to 8 semesters.
Eligibility Requirements: Eligible are dependent children of Texas
residents who are either prisoners of war or missing in action. Applicants
must be under 21 years of age, or under 25 if they receive the majority of
support from their parent(s).

1631 ■ TEXAS HIGHER EDUCATION COORDINATING BOARD

Attn: Grants and Special Programs
1200 East Anderson Lane
P.O. Box 12788, Capitol Station
Austin, TX 78711-2788
Tel: (512)427-6387
Free: 800-242-3062
Fax: (512)427-6127
E-mail: grantinfo@thecb.state.tx.us
Web Site: http://www.collegefortexans.com
To provide financial assistance to students in Texas who are planning to
attend college after completing high school in less than specified times.
Title of Award: Texas Early High School Graduation Scholarships **Area,
Field, or Subject:** General studies/Field of study not specified **Level of
Education for which Award is Granted:** Undergraduate **Number
Awarded:** Varies each year; recently, 232 of these scholarships were
awarded. **Funds Available:** Stipends are 1) $2,000 for students who
complete the requirements within 36 months (an additional $1,000 is
awarded if the student also graduates with at least 15 hours of college
credit); 2) $500 for students who complete the requirements in more than
36 but less than 41 months (an additional $1,000 is awarded if the student
also graduates with at least 30 hours of college credit); or 3) $1,000 for
students who complete the requirements in more than 41 but less than 46
months and also have at least 30 hours of college credit. If the award is
used at a private college or university, the school must provide a matching
scholarship. **Duration:** 1 year; nonrenewable.
Eligibility Requirements: This program is open to residents of Texas
who have attended high school in the state and plan to attend a Texas
public or private college or university. Applicants must have completed
either the recommended high school curriculum or the distinguished
achievement high school curriculum in no more than 36 consecutive
months. Smaller awards are available to applicants who 1) complete the
requirements for grades 9-12 within 41 months, or 2) complete the
requirements within 46 months and also earn at least 30 hours of college
credit. **Additional Information:** Interested students should contact their
high school counselor. This program was established in 1995 and
amended in 2003.

1632 ■ TEXAS HIGHER EDUCATION COORDINATING BOARD

Attn: Grants and Special Programs
1200 East Anderson Lane
P.O. Box 12788, Capitol Station
Austin, TX 78711-2788
Tel: (512)427-6101
Free: 800-242-3062
Fax: (512)427-6127
E-mail: grantinfo@thecb.state.tx.us
Web Site: http://www.collegefortexans.com
To provide financial assistance for college to students in Texas who have
been in foster care.
Title of Award: Texas Education and Training Vouchers for Youths Aging
Out of Foster Care **Area, Field, or Subject:** General studies/Field of

study not specified **Level of Education for which Award is Granted:**
Undergraduate **Number Awarded:** Varies each year. **Funds Available:**
Vouchers can be used to cover the cost of attendance (tuition and fees,
books and supplies, room and board, transportation, child care, and some
personal expenses) or $5,000 per year, whichever amount is less. **Dura-
tion:** 1 year. Participants in the program remain eligible until age 23 ad
long as they are enrolled and making satisfactory progress toward
completing their postsecondary education or training program.
Eligibility Requirements: This program is open to residents of Texas
who 1) are between 16 and 21 years of age, have a high school diploma
or equivalent, and are attending a Texas public or private college that
provides a bachelor's degree or not less than a 2-year program that
provides credit towards an associate degree or certificate; 2) are beyond
the age of compulsory school attendance (age 18) and are attending an
accredited or preaccredited program that provides not less than 1 year of
training toward gainful employment; 3) are in foster care of the Texas
Department of Family and Protective Services (TDFPS), are at least 16
years of age, and are likely to remain in foster care until turning 18; 4)
have aged out of TDFPS foster care but have not yet turned 21; or 5) are
adopted from TDFPS foster care after turning 16 years of age but are not
yet 21. Applicants must be attending or planning to attend a Texas public
or private educational institution that is accredited or granted preaccredited status. **Additional Information:** Information is also available from
TDFPS, 701 West 51st Street, P.O. Box 149030, Austin, TX 78714-9030,
(800) 233-3405, E-mail: beth.engelking@dfps.state.tx.us.

1633 ■ TEXAS HIGHER EDUCATION COORDINATING BOARD

Attn: Grants and Special Programs
1200 East Anderson Lane
P.O. Box 12788, Capitol Station
Austin, TX 78711-2788
Tel: (512)427-6101
Free: 800-242-3062
Fax: (512)427-6127
E-mail: grantinfo@thecb.state.tx.us
Web Site: http://www.collegefortexans.com
To provide financial assistance to students entering a public 2-year col-
lege in Texas.
Title of Award: Texas Educational Opportunity Grant Program **Area,
Field, or Subject:** General studies/Field of study not specified **Level of
Education for which Award is Granted:** Two Year College **Number
Awarded:** Varies each year; recently, 4,512 of these grants were
awarded. **Funds Available:** Full-time stipends are approximately $1,795
per semester for public state college students, $635 per semester for
community college students, or $990 per semester for technical college
students. **Duration:** 1 year. Students can receive awards for up to 75
semester credit hours, for 4 years, or until they receive an associate
degree, whichever occurs first. Renewal requires completion of at least
75% of the hours taken in the prior year plus a cumulative college GPA of
2.5 or higher.
Eligibility Requirements: This program is open to residents of Texas
enrolled at least half time in the first 30 credit hours at a public community
college, public technical college, or public state college in Texas. Applicants must have an expected family contribution of no more than
$2,000. **Additional Information:** Information and application forms may
be obtained from the director of financial aid at the college in Texas the
applicant attends. This program was established in 1999 as the TEXAS
(an acronym for Towards EXcellence, Access, and Success) Grant II. The
eligible public state colleges are Lamar State College at Orange, Lamar
State College at Port Arthur, and Lamar Institute of Technology.

1634 ■ TEXAS HIGHER EDUCATION COORDINATING BOARD

Attn: Grants and Special Programs
1200 East Anderson Lane
P.O. Box 12788, Capitol Station
Austin, TX 78711-2788
Tel: (512)427-6101
Free: 800-242-3062
Fax: (512)427-6127
E-mail: grantinfo@thecb.state.tx.us
Web Site: http://www.collegefortexans.com
To recognize and reward the top students in Texas high schools.
Title of Award: Texas Exemption for Highest Ranking High School
Graduate Program **Area, Field, or Subject:** General studies/Field of

study not specified **Level of Education for which Award is Granted:** Undergraduate **Number Awarded:** Varies each year; recently, 1,102 of these exemptions were granted. **Funds Available:** Tuition is waived for award winners at any public college or university in Texas. **Duration:** 1 year; nonrenewable.

Eligibility Requirements: This award is presented to the highest ranking graduate (i.e., valedictorians) of accredited high schools in Texas. Applicants may be Texas residents, nonresidents, or foreign students.

1635 ■ TEXAS HIGHER EDUCATION COORDINATING BOARD

Attn: Grants and Special Programs
1200 East Anderson Lane
P.O. Box 12788, Capitol Station
Austin, TX 78711-2788
Tel: (512)427-6101
Free: 800-242-3062
Fax: (512)427-6127
E-mail: grantinfo@thecb.state.tx.us
Web Site: http://www.collegefortexans.com
To provide educational assistance to disabled Texas peace officers.

Title of Award: Texas Exemption for Peace Officers Disabled in the Line of Duty **Area, Field, or Subject:** General studies/Field of study not specified **Level of Education for which Award is Granted:** Professional, Undergraduate **Number Awarded:** Varies each year; recently, 23 of these exemptions were awarded. **Funds Available:** Eligible students are exempted from the payment of all dues, fees, and tuition charges at publicly-supported colleges and universities in Texas. **Duration:** Up to 12 semesters.

Eligibility Requirements: This program is open to Texas residents permanently disabled as a result of an injury suffered as a peace officer who are unable to continue employment as a peace officer because of the disability. Applicants must be planning to attend a publicly-supported college or university in Texas as an undergraduate student. **Additional Information:** For more information, students should contact the admission office at the institution they plan to attend.

1636 ■ TEXAS HIGHER EDUCATION COORDINATING BOARD

Attn: Grants and Special Programs
1200 East Anderson Lane
P.O. Box 12788, Capitol Station
Austin, TX 78711-2788
Tel: (512)427-6101
Free: 800-242-3062
Fax: (512)427-6127
E-mail: grantinfo@thecb.state.tx.us
Web Site: http://www.collegefortexans.com
To provide educational assistance to students in Texas who once were in foster or other residential care and have been adopted.

Title of Award: Texas Exemption Program for Adopted Students Formerly in Foster or Other Residential Care **Area, Field, or Subject:** General studies/Field of study not specified **Level of Education for which Award is Granted:** Undergraduate **Number Awarded:** Varies each year; recently, 11 students received support through this program. **Funds Available:** Eligible students are exempted from the payment of all dues, fees, and tuition charges at publicly-supported colleges and universities in Texas. **Duration:** 1 year; may be renewed.

Eligibility Requirements: Eligible are students who have been in foster care or other residential care under the conservatorship of the Texas Department of Family and Protective Services and have been adopted. Applicants must be attending or planning to attend a public college or university in Texas. **Additional Information:** This program was established in 2003.

1637 ■ TEXAS HIGHER EDUCATION COORDINATING BOARD

Attn: Grants and Special Programs
1200 East Anderson Lane
P.O. Box 12788, Capitol Station
Austin, TX 78711-2788
Tel: (512)427-6101
Free: 800-242-3062
Fax: (512)427-6127
E-mail: grantinfo@thecb.state.tx.us
Web Site: http://www.collegefortexans.com

To provide educational assistance to the children and spouses of certain deceased Texas public employees.

Title of Award: Texas Exemption for Surviving Spouses and Dependent Children of Certain Deceased Public Servants **Area, Field, or Subject:** General studies/Field of study not specified **Level of Education for which Award is Granted:** Undergraduate **Number Awarded:** Varies each year; recently, 65 students received support through this program. **Funds Available:** Eligible students are exempted from the payment of all dues, fees, and tuition charges at publicly-supported colleges and universities in Texas. In addition, the institution provides them with an allowance for textbooks. If the student qualifies to live in the institution's housing, the institution must provide either free room and board or an equivalent room and board stipend. **Duration:** 1 year; may be renewed.

Eligibility Requirements: This program is open to residents of Texas whose parent or spouse was killed in the line of duty in certain public service positions after September 1, 2000. Eligible public service positions include peace officers, probation officers, parole officers, jailers, members of organized police reserve and auxiliary units, juvenile correctional employees, paid and volunteer fire fighters, and emergency medical service volunteers and paid personnel. Applicants must be enrolled or planning to enroll full time at a Texas public college or university.

1638 ■ TEXAS HIGHER EDUCATION COORDINATING BOARD

Attn: Grants and Special Programs
1200 East Anderson Lane
P.O. Box 12788, Capitol Station
Austin, TX 78711-2788
Tel: (512)427-6101
Free: 800-242-3062
Fax: (512)427-6127
E-mail: grantinfo@thecb.state.tx.us
Web Site: http://www.collegefortexans.com
To provide financial assistance to accounting students attending college in Texas.

Title of Award: Texas Fifth-Year Accounting Student Scholarship Program **Area, Field, or Subject:** Accounting **Level of Education for which Award is Granted:** Four Year College **Number Awarded:** Varies each year; recently, 328 of these scholarships were awarded. **Funds Available:** The maximum stipend is $3,000. **Duration:** 1 year.

Eligibility Requirements: This program is open to both residents and nonresidents of Texas. Applicants must be enrolled at least half time and have completed at least 120 hours of college course work, including at least 15 semester credit hours of accounting. They may not have already taken the C.P.A. exam, but they must plan to take it in Texas and be willing to sign a written statement confirming their intent to take the written examination conducted by the Texas State Board of Public Accountancy to become a certified public accountant. Selection is based on financial need and scholastic ability and performance. **Additional Information:** Information and application forms may be obtained from the director of financial aid at the public college or university in Texas the applicant attends. Information is also available from the Texas State Board of Public Accountancy, 333 Guadalupe, Tower III, Suite 900, Austin, TX 78701-3900, (512) 305-7850, Fax: (512) 305-7875, E-mail: exam@tsbpa.state.tx.us. This program began in 1996. Study must be conducted in Texas; funds cannot be used to support attendance at an out-of-state institution.

1639 ■ TEXAS HIGHER EDUCATION COORDINATING BOARD

Attn: Grants and Special Programs
1200 East Anderson Lane
P.O. Box 12788, Capitol Station
Austin, TX 78711-2788
Tel: (512)427-6101
Free: 800-242-3062
Fax: (512)427-6127
E-mail: grantinfo@thecb.state.tx.us
Web Site: http://www.collegefortexans.com
To exempt students in Texas who were in foster care when they became 18 years of age from payment of tuition at public colleges and universities in the state.

Title of Award: Texas Foster Care Exemption Program **Area, Field, or Subject:** General studies/Field of study not specified **Level of Education for which Award is Granted:** Undergraduate **Number Awarded:** Varies each year; recently, 950 students received support through this program.

Funds Available: Eligible students are exempted from the payment of all dues, fees, and tuition charges at publicly-supported colleges and universities in Texas. **Duration:** 1 year.

Eligibility Requirements: Eligible are students who have been in the care or conservatorship of the Texas Department of Family and Protective Services 1) on the day before their 18th birthday, the day they graduated from high school, or the day they received a GED certificate; or 2) through their 14th birthday and were then adopted. Applicants must enroll as an undergraduate at a public college or university in Texas within 3 years of that relevant date, but no later than their 21st birthday.

1640 ■ TEXAS HIGHER EDUCATION COORDINATING BOARD

Attn: Grants and Special Programs
1200 East Anderson Lane
P.O. Box 12788, Capitol Station
Austin, TX 78711-2788
Tel: (512)427-6101
Free: 800-242-3062
Fax: (512)427-6127
E-mail: grantinfo@thecb.state.tx.us
Web Site: http://www.collegefortexans.com
To provide financial assistance to undergraduate students entering college in Texas from high school or a community college.

Title of Award: TEXAS Grant **Area, Field, or Subject:** General studies/Field of study not specified **Level of Education for which Award is Granted:** Undergraduate **Number Awarded:** Varies each year. **Funds Available:** Full-time stipends are approximately $1,795 per semester for public university students, $635 per semester for community college students, or $990 per semester for technical college students. Stipends at private institutions are based on the public university amount. **Duration:** 1 year. Students who qualify on the basis of their high school curriculum can receive awards for up to 150 semester credit hours, for 6 years, or until their receive their bachelor's degree, whichever occurs first. Students who qualify on the basis of an associate degree can receive awards for up to 90 semester credit hours, for 4 years, or until they complete a baccalaureate degree, whichever occurs first. Renewal requires completion of at least 75% of the hours taken in the prior year plus a cumulative college GPA of 2.5 or higher.

Eligibility Requirements: This program is open to residents of Texas enrolled at a college or university in the state who have applied for other financial assistance and have an expected family contribution of no more than $4,000. Applicants may be 1) enrolled in the first 30 credit hours, having graduated from high school no earlier than the 1998-99 school year, where they completed the recommended or distinguished achievement high school curriculum or its equivalent, and having enrolled at an eligible Texas college or university within 16 months of high school graduation; or 2) transferring from a community college from which they received their first associate degree in May 2001 or later and enrolling in a higher level undergraduate program within 12 months of receiving their associate degree. At least three-quarter time enrollment is required. **Additional Information:** Information and application forms may be obtained from the director of financial aid at the college or university in Texas the applicant attends. This program was established in 1999 as an acronym for Towards EXcellence, Access, and Success.

1641 ■ TEXAS HIGHER EDUCATION COORDINATING BOARD

Attn: Grants and Special Programs
1200 East Anderson Lane
P.O. Box 12788, Capitol Station
Austin, TX 78711-2788
Tel: (512)427-6101
Free: 800-242-3062
Fax: (512)427-6127
E-mail: grantinfo@thecb.state.tx.us
Web Site: http://www.collegefortexans.com
To provide financial assistance to undergraduate and graduate students at colleges and universities in Texas who are also receiving other state funds.

Title of Award: Texas Leveraging Educational Assistance Partnership Program **Area, Field, or Subject:** General studies/Field of study not specified **Level of Education for which Award is Granted:** Graduate, Undergraduate **Number Awarded:** Varies each year. **Funds Available:** The stipend depends on the need of the recipient, to a maximum of $1,250. **Duration:** 1 year; may be renewed.

Eligibility Requirements: This program is open to Texas residents who are enrolled or accepted for enrollment at least half time at a college or university in Texas on the undergraduate or graduate level. Financial need must be demonstrated. Applicants must also be receiving funding from another state program (either the Texas Student Incentive Grant Program for students at public colleges and universities or the Texas Tuition Equalization Grant Program for students at private colleges and universities).

1642 ■ TEXAS HIGHER EDUCATION COORDINATING BOARD

Attn: Grants and Special Programs
1200 East Anderson Lane
P.O. Box 12788, Capitol Station
Austin, TX 78711-2788
Tel: (512)427-6323
Free: 800-242-3062
Fax: (512)427-6127
E-mail: grantinfo@thecb.state.tx.us
Web Site: http://www.collegefortexans.com
To provide financial assistance for college or technical school to members of the Texas National Guard.

Title of Award: Texas National Guard Tuition Assistance Program **Area, Field, or Subject:** General studies/Field of study not specified **Level of Education for which Award is Granted:** Graduate, Undergraduate **Number Awarded:** Varies each year; recently, 2,200 Guard members participated in this program. **Funds Available:** Eligible Guard members receive exemption from tuition at Texas public colleges and universities. For students who attend a private, nonprofit institution, the award is based on public university tuition charges for 6 semester credit hours at the resident rate. **Duration:** Tuition assistance is available for up to 9 semester credit hours per semester for up to 10 semesters or 5 academic years, whichever occurs first.

Eligibility Requirements: This program is open to Texas residents who are active, drilling members of the Texas National Guard, Texas Air Guard, or the State Guard. Applicants must have a 3-year enlistment and the rank of enlisted, W01-CW3, or second lieutenant through captain. They must be attending, enrolled at, or planning to attend a public, private, or independent institution of higher education in Texas for undergraduate, vocational, or technical courses. **Deadline for Receipt:** June of each year for the fall semester; November of each year for the spring semester. **Additional Information:** Information is also available from the Office of the Adjutant General, Education Services Office, Camp Mabry, Building 34, P.O. Box 5218, Austin, TX 78763-5218, (512) 465-5001, E-mail: education.office@tx.ngb.army.mil.

1643 ■ TEXAS HIGHER EDUCATION COORDINATING BOARD

Attn: Grants and Special Programs
1200 East Anderson Lane
P.O. Box 12788, Capitol Station
Austin, TX 78711-2788
Tel: (512)427-6101
Free: 800-242-3062
Fax: (512)427-6127
E-mail: grantinfo@thecb.state.tx.us
Web Site: http://www.collegefortexans.com
To provide financial assistance to undergraduate and graduate students in Texas.

Title of Award: Texas Public Educational Grant Program **Area, Field, or Subject:** General studies/Field of study not specified **Level of Education for which Award is Granted:** Graduate, Undergraduate **Number Awarded:** Varies each year; recently, 102,696 of these grants were awarded. **Funds Available:** The amount awarded varies, depending upon the financial need of the recipient. No award may exceed the student's unmet financial need. Each institution sets its own maximum award amounts. **Duration:** 1 year; may be renewed.

Eligibility Requirements: This program is open to residents of Texas, nonresidents, and foreign students. Applicants may be undergraduate or graduate students. They must be attending a public college or university in Texas. Financial need is considered as part of the selection process. **Additional Information:** Information and application forms may be obtained from the director of financial aid at the public college or university in Texas the applicant attends. Study must be conducted in Texas; funds cannot be used to support attendance at an out-of-state institution.

1644 ■ TEXAS HIGHER EDUCATION COORDINATING BOARD
Attn: Grants and Special Programs
1200 East Anderson Lane
P.O. Box 12788, Capitol Station
Austin, TX 78711-2788
Tel: (512)427-6101
Free: 800-242-3062
Fax: (512)427-6127
E-mail: grantinfo@thecb.state.tx.us
Web Site: http://www.collegefortexans.com
To provide educational assistance to students in Texas whose families are receiving Temporary Assistance to Needy Families (TANF).
Title of Award: Texas TANF Exemption Program **Area, Field, or Subject:** General studies/Field of study not specified **Level of Education for which Award is Granted:** Undergraduate **Number Awarded:** Varies each year; recently, 106 students received this assistance. **Funds Available:** Eligible students are exempt from the payment of all fees (other than building use fees) and tuition charges at publicly-supported colleges and universities in Texas. **Duration:** 1 year; nonrenewable.
Eligibility Requirements: Eligible are students who graduated from a public high school in Texas and are dependent children whose parents received, during the year of their high school graduation, TANF for at least 6 months. Applicants must be younger than 22 years of age at the time of enrollment in college and must enroll in college within 24 months of high school graduation.

1645 ■ TEXAS HIGHER EDUCATION COORDINATING BOARD
Attn: Grants and Special Programs
1200 East Anderson Lane
P.O. Box 12788, Capitol Station
Austin, TX 78711-2788
Tel: (512)427-6101
Free: 800-242-3062
Fax: (512)427-6127
E-mail: grantinfo@thecb.state.tx.us
Web Site: http://www.collegefortexans.com
To provide financial assistance to undergraduate and graduate students attending private postsecondary schools in Texas.
Title of Award: Texas Tuition Equalization Grant Program **Area, Field, or Subject:** General studies/Field of study not specified **Level of Education for which Award is Granted:** Graduate, Undergraduate **Number Awarded:** Varies each year; recently, 27,994 of these grants were awarded. **Funds Available:** The maximum awarded is the lesser of the student's unmet need or the amount they would pay at a public institution (currently, $3,653). **Duration:** 1 year; may be renewed.
Eligibility Requirements: This program is open to 1) residents of Texas, and 2) residents of other states who are National Merit Scholarship finalists. Applicants must be enrolled at least half time as an undergraduate or graduate student at an eligible nonprofit independent college in the state. They may not be receiving an athletic scholarship. Financial need is considered in the selection process. **Additional Information:** Information and application forms may be obtained from the director of financial aid at any participating nonprofit independent college or university in Texas.

1646 ■ TEXAS HIGHER EDUCATION COORDINATING BOARD
Attn: Grants and Special Programs
1200 East Anderson Lane
P.O. Box 12788, Capitol Station
Austin, TX 78711-2788
Tel: (512)427-6101
Free: 800-242-3062
Fax: (512)427-6127
E-mail: grantinfo@thecb.state.tx.us
Web Site: http://www.collegefortexans.com
To exempt military personnel stationed in Texas and their dependents from the payment of nonresident tuition at public institutions of higher education in the state.
Title of Award: Texas Waivers of Nonresident Tuition for Military Personnel and Their Dependents **Area, Field, or Subject:** General studies/Field of study not specified **Level of Education for which Award is Granted:** Graduate, Undergraduate **Number Awarded:** Varies each year; recently, 10,333 students received these waivers. **Funds Available:** Although persons eligible under this program are classified as nonresidents, they are entitled to pay the resident tuition at Texas institutions of higher

education, regardless of their length of residence in Texas. **Duration:** 1 year; may be renewed.
Eligibility Requirements: Eligible for these waivers are members of the U.S. armed forces and commissioned officers of the Public Health Service from states other than Texas, their spouses, and dependent children. Applicants must be assigned to Texas and attending or planning to attend a public college or university in the state.

1647 ■ TEXAS HIGHER EDUCATION COORDINATING BOARD
Attn: Grants and Special Programs
1200 East Anderson Lane
P.O. Box 12788, Capitol Station
Austin, TX 78711-2788
Tel: (512)427-6101
Free: 800-242-3062
Fax: (512)427-6127
E-mail: grantinfo@thecb.state.tx.us
Web Site: http://www.collegefortexans.com
To provide a partial tuition exemption to the surviving spouses and dependent children of deceased military personnel who move to Texas following the service member's death.
Title of Award: Texas Waivers of Nonresident Tuition for Military Survivors **Area, Field, or Subject:** General studies/Field of study not specified **Level of Education for which Award is Granted:** Undergraduate **Number Awarded:** Varies each year. **Funds Available:** Although persons eligible under this program are still classified as nonresidents, they are entitled to pay the resident tuition at Texas institutions of higher education on an immediate basis. **Duration:** 1 year.
Eligibility Requirements: Eligible for these waivers are the surviving spouses and dependent children of members of the U.S. armed forces and commissioned officers of the Public Health Service who died while in service. Applicants must move to Texas within 60 days of the date of the death of the service member. They must be attending or planning to attend a public college or university in the state. Children are eligible even if the surviving parent does not accompany them to Texas. **Additional Information:** This program became effective in 2003.

1648 ■ TEXAS HIGHER EDUCATION COORDINATING BOARD
Attn: Grants and Special Programs
1200 East Anderson Lane
P.O. Box 12788, Capitol Station
Austin, TX 78711-2788
Tel: (512)427-6101
Free: 800-242-3062
Fax: (512)427-6127
E-mail: grantinfo@thecb.state.tx.us
Web Site: http://www.collegefortexans.com
To exempt veterans who move to Texas and their dependents from the payment of nonresident tuition at public institutions of higher education in the state.
Title of Award: Texas Waivers of Nonresident Tuition for Veterans and Their Dependents **Area, Field, or Subject:** General studies/Field of study not specified **Level of Education for which Award is Granted:** Undergraduate **Number Awarded:** Varies each year. **Funds Available:** Although persons eligible under this program are still classified as nonresidents, they are entitled to pay the resident tuition at Texas institutions of higher education on an immediate basis. **Duration:** 1 year.
Eligibility Requirements: Eligible for these waivers are former members of the U.S. armed forces and commissioned officers of the Public Health Service who are retired or have been honorably discharged, their spouses, and dependent children. Applicants must have moved to Texas upon separation from the service and be attending or planning to attend a public college or university in the state. They must have indicated an intent to become a Texas resident by registering to vote and doing 1 of the following: owning real property in Texas, registering an automobile in Texas, or executing a will indicating that they are a resident of the state.

1649 ■ TEXAS HIGHER EDUCATION COORDINATING BOARD
Attn: Grants and Special Programs
1200 East Anderson Lane
P.O. Box 12788, Capitol Station
Austin, TX 78711-2788
Tel: (512)427-6101

Free: 800-242-3062
Fax: (512)427-6127
E-mail: grantinfo@thecb.state.tx.us
Web Site: http://www.collegefortexans.com
To exempt dependents of military personnel who move to Texas from the payment of nonresident tuition at public institutions of higher education in the state.
Title of Award: Waivers of Nonresident Tuition for Dependents of Military Personnel Moving to Texas **Area, Field, or Subject:** General studies/Field of study not specified **Level of Education for which Award is Granted:** Undergraduate **Number Awarded:** Varies each year. **Funds Available:** Although persons eligible under this program are still classified as nonresidents, they are entitled to pay the resident tuition at Texas institutions of higher education on an immediate basis. **Duration:** 1 year.
Eligibility Requirements: Eligible for these waivers are the spouses and dependent children of members of the U.S. armed forces and commissioned officers of the Public Health Service who move to Texas while the service member remains assigned to another state. Applicants must be attending or planning to attend a public college or university in the state. They must indicate their intent to become a Texas resident. For dependent children to qualify, the spouse must also move to Texas. **Additional Information:** This program became effective in September 2003.

1650 ■ TEXAS HIGHER EDUCATION COORDINATING BOARD

Attn: Grants and Special Programs
1200 East Anderson Lane
P.O. Box 12788, Capitol Station
Austin, TX 78711-2788
Tel: (512)427-6101
Free: 800-242-3062
Fax: (512)427-6127
E-mail: grantinfo@thecb.state.tx.us
Web Site: http://www.collegefortexans.com
To provide a partial tuition exemption to the spouses and dependent children of military personnel who are Texas residents but are not assigned to duty in the state.
Title of Award: Waivers of Nonresident Tuition for Dependents of Military Personnel Who Previously Lived in Texas **Area, Field, or Subject:** General studies/Field of study not specified **Level of Education for which Award is Granted:** Undergraduate **Number Awarded:** Varies each year. **Funds Available:** Although persons eligible under this program are classified as nonresidents, they are entitled to pay the resident tuition at Texas institutions of higher education, regardless of their length of residence in Texas. **Duration:** 1 year.
Eligibility Requirements: Eligible for these waivers are the spouses and dependent children of members of the U.S. armed forces who are not assigned to duty in Texas but have previously resided in the state for at least 6 months. Service members must verify that they remain Texas residents by designating Texas as their place of legal residence for income tax purposes, registering to vote in the state, and doing 1 of the following: owning real property in Texas, registering an automobile in Texas, or executing a will indicating that they are a resident of the state. The spouse or dependent child must be attending or planning to attend a Texas public college or university.

1651 ■ TEXAS MOTOR TRANSPORTATION ASSOCIATION

Attn: Texas Motor Transportation Foundation
700 East 11th Street
Austin, TX 78701-2623
Tel: (512)478-2541
Free: 800-727-7135
Fax: (512)474-6494
E-mail: info@tmta.com
Web Site: http://www.tmta.com/Foundation/AboutFoundation.asp
To provide financial assistance for college to employees and dependents of employees of companies that are members of the Texas Motor Transportation Association (TMTA).
Title of Award: Texas Motor Transportation Foundation Scholarships **Area, Field, or Subject:** General studies/Field of study not specified **Level of Education for which Award is Granted:** Undergraduate **Number Awarded:** 1 or more each year. **Funds Available:** A stipend is awarded (amount not specified). **Duration:** 1 year; may be renewed.
Eligibility Requirements: This program is open to high school seniors and graduates who employees or dependents of employees of TMTA

member companies. Applicants must be attending or planning to attend a college, university, or trade school. Along with their application, they must submit a cover letter that includes information on their current and planned studies, career goals, interests, and reasons for applying for this scholarship. Selection is based on academic achievement, community involvement, and financial need. **Deadline for Receipt:** June of each year.

1652 ■ TEXAS MUTUAL INSURANCE COMPANY

Attn: Office of the President
6210 East Highway 290
Austin, TX 78723-1098
Tel: (512)224-3820
Free: 800-859-5995
Fax: (512)224-3889
E-mail: information@texasmutual.com
Web Site: http://www.texasmutual.com/workers/scholarship.shtm
To provide financial assistance for college to workers and their families covered by workers' compensation insurance in Texas.
Title of Award: Texas Mutual Scholarship Program **Area, Field, or Subject:** General studies/Field of study not specified **Level of Education for which Award is Granted:** Undergraduate **Number Awarded:** Varies each year. **Funds Available:** Scholarships are intended to cover normal undergraduate, technical, or vocational school tuition and fees, to a maximum of $4,000 per semester. Those funds are paid directly to the college or vocational school. The cost of course-related books and fees are also reimbursed, up to a maximum of $500 per semester. Those funds are paid directly to the student. **Duration:** 1 year; may be renewed if the recipient maintains a GPA of 2.5 or higher.
Eligibility Requirements: This program is open to 1) employees who qualify for lifetime income benefits as a result of injuries suffered on the job as covered by the Texas Workers' Compensation Act; 2) children and spouses of injured workers; and 3) children and unmarried spouses of employees who died as a result of a work-related injury. Workers must be covered by the Texas Mutual Insurance Company, formerly the Texas Workers' Compensation Insurance Fund. Children must be between 16 and 25 years of age. Surviving spouses must still be eligible for workers' compensation benefits. Financial need is considered in the selection process. **Deadline for Receipt:** Applications may be submitted at any time.

1653 ■ THIRD MARINE DIVISION ASSOCIATION, INC.

P.O. Box 254
Chalfont, PA 18914-0254
E-mail: ThrdMarDiv@aol.com
Web Site: http://www.caltrap.com
To provide financial assistance for college to the dependents of certain military personnel who served in the Third Marine Division during the Vietnam War.
Title of Award: Third Marine Division Association Memorial Scholarship Fund **Area, Field, or Subject:** General studies/Field of study not specified **Level of Education for which Award is Granted:** Undergraduate **Number Awarded:** 20 to 25 each year. **Funds Available:** Awards range from $400 to $2,400, depending upon need. **Duration:** 1 year; may be renewed for up to 3 additional years for undergraduate study.
Eligibility Requirements: This program is open to dependent children of 1) Third Marine Division members who lost their lives while serving in Vietnam; 2) deceased 100% service-connected disabled veterans of any period of Division service, provided the veteran's death resulted from his service-connected disability; 3) certified association members, living or deceased, whose membership extended for at least 2 years prior to death, if deceased, or date of application, if living; and 4) Third Marine Division members who lost their lives while serving in Desert Shield or Desert Storm. All applicants must be between 16 and 23 years of age and able to demonstrate financial need. Their military sponsor must have been a member of the Third Marine Division Association for at least 2 years. **Deadline for Receipt:** April of each year. **Additional Information:** This program was established in 1969 to serve the first category of applicants; it was expanded in 1988 to serve the second and third categories and in

1991 to serve the fourth category. Information is also available from Ben Dowdey, E-mail: bdowdey@wans.net.

1654 ■ THIRD WAVE FOUNDATION

511 West 25th Street, Suite 301
New York, NY 10002
Tel: (212)675-0700
Fax: (212)255-6653
E-mail: info@thirdwavefoundation.org
Web Site: http://www.thirdwavefoundation.org/programs/scholarships.html
To provide educational assistance to undergraduate and graduate women who have been involved as social change activists.
Title of Award: Scholarship Program for Young Women and Transgender Activists **Area, Field, or Subject:** General studies/Field of study not specified **Level of Education for which Award is Granted:** Graduate, Undergraduate **Number Awarded:** Varies each year; recently, 4 undergraduates and 3 graduate students received a total of $12,000 in support through this program. **Funds Available:** Stipends range from $500 to $5,000 per year. **Duration:** 1 year.
Eligibility Requirements: This program is open to full-time and part-time students under 30 years of age who are enrolled in, or have been accepted to, an accredited university, college, vocational/technical school, community college, or graduate school. Women and transgender students of all races and ethnicities are eligible. Applicants should have been involved as activists, artists, or cultural workers on such issues as racism, homophobia, sexism, or other forms of inequality. They must submit 500-word essays on 1) their current social change involvement and how it relates to their educational and life goals; and 2) if they would describe themselves as a feminist and why. Graduate students and students planning to study abroad through a U.S. university program are also eligible. Selection is based on financial need and commitment to social justice work. **Deadline for Receipt:** March or September of each year.

1655 ■ THIRD WAVE FOUNDATION

511 West 25th Street, Suite 301
New York, NY 10002
Tel: (212)675-0700
Fax: (212)255-6653
E-mail: info@thirdwavefoundation.org
Web Site: http://www.thirdwavefoundation.org/programs/scholarships.html
To provide educational assistance to undergraduate and graduate women of color who have been involved as social change activists.
Title of Award: Third Wave Foundation Woodlake Scholarships **Area, Field, or Subject:** General studies/Field of study not specified **Level of Education for which Award is Granted:** Graduate, Undergraduate **Number Awarded:** Varies each year. Recently, 8 of these scholarships were awarded: 6 at $3,000 and 2 at $1,000. **Funds Available:** Stipends are $3,000 or $1,000 per year. **Duration:** 1 year.
Eligibility Requirements: This program is open to full-time and part-time students under 30 years of age who are enrolled in, or have been accepted to, an accredited university, college, vocational/technical school, community college, or graduate school. Applicants must be women of color who place greater emphasis on social justice and the struggle for justice and equality over academic performance and who integrate social justice into all areas of their lives. They must submit 500-word essays on 1) their current social change involvement and how it relates to their educational and life goals; and 2) if they would describe themselves as a feminist and why. Graduate students and students planning to study abroad through a U.S. university program are also eligible. Selection is based on financial need and commitment to social justice work. **Deadline for Receipt:** March or September of each year.

1656 ■ THORNTON SISTERS FOUNDATION

P.O. Box 21
Atlantic Highlands, NJ 07716
Tel: (732)872-1353
E-mail: tsfoundation2001@yahoo.com
Web Site: http://www.thorntonsisters.com/ttsf.htm
To provide financial assistance for college to women of color in New Jersey.
Title of Award: Donald and Itasker Thornton Memorial Scholarship **Area, Field, or Subject:** General studies/Field of study not specified **Level of**

Education for which Award is Granted: Four Year College **Number Awarded:** 1 or more each year. **Funds Available:** A stipend is awarded (amount not specified). Funds are to be used for tuition and/or books. **Duration:** 1 year; nonrenewable.
Eligibility Requirements: This program is open to women of color (defined as African Americans, Latino Americans, Caribbean Americans, and Native Americans) who are graduating from high schools in New Jersey. Applicants must have a GPA of "C+" or higher and be able to document financial need. They must be planning to attend an accredited 4-year college or university. Along with their application, they must submit a 500-word essay describing their family background, personal and/or economic disadvantages, honors or academic distinctions, and community involvement and activities. **Deadline for Receipt:** May of each year.

1657 ■ TOURISM CARES FOR TOMORROW

Attn: Program Manager
585 Washington Street
Canton, MA 02021
Tel: (781)821-5990
Fax: (781)821-8949
E-mail: info@tourismcares.org
Web Site: http://www.tourismcares.org
To provide financial assistance to upper-division students from Quebec who are majoring in tourism.
Title of Award: Societe des casinos du Quebec Scholarship **Area, Field, or Subject:** Travel and tourism **Level of Education for which Award is Granted:** Four Year College **Number Awarded:** 1 each year. **Funds Available:** The stipend is $1,000. **Duration:** 1 year.
Eligibility Requirements: This program is open to residents of Quebec entering their junior or senior year at an accredited 4-year college or university in the United States or Canada. Applicants must be working on a degree in a travel and tourism-related program and have a GPA of 3.0 or higher. Along with their application, they must submit a 2-page essay on 1 of the following topics: international inbound tourism, intergenerational travel, effects of technological advancements on tourism, cultural diversity, impact of group tourism, career opportunities in the industry, niche marketing, or heritage tourism. Financial need is not considered in the selection process. **Deadline for Receipt:** March of each year. **Additional Information:** This program is sponsored by the Societe des casinos du Quebec.

1658 ■ TRANSPORT WORKERS UNION OF AMERICA

1700 Broadway, Second Floor
New York, NY 10019-5905
Tel: (212)259-4900
Web Site: http://www.twu.org/about/scholarships.html
To provide financial assistance for college to high school seniors who are dependents of members of the Transport Workers Union of America (TWU).
Title of Award: Michael J. Quill Scholarship Fund **Area, Field, or Subject:** General studies/Field of study not specified **Level of Education for which Award is Granted:** Undergraduate **Number Awarded:** 10 each year. **Funds Available:** The stipend is $1,200 per year. **Duration:** 1 year; may be renewed for up to 3 additional years upon successful completion of a regular course of studies in the preceding year.
Eligibility Requirements: This program is open to high school seniors who are the children or dependent siblings of present, retired, or deceased TWU members. Applicants must be entering an accredited college in the following fall. Winners are selected from eligible applicants in a public drawing held in May of each year. **Deadline for Receipt:** April of each year.

1659 ■ TRANSPORTATION CLUBS INTERNATIONAL

Attn: Gay Fielding
7031 Manchester Street
New Orleans, LA 70126
E-mail: GayFielding@bellsouth.net
Web Site: http://www.transportationclubsinternational.com
To provide financial assistance to college students of Canadian nationality who are interested in preparing for a career in fields related to transportation.
Title of Award: Ginger & Fred Deines Canada Scholarship **Area, Field, or Subject:** Transportation **Level of Education for which Award is**

Granted: Undergraduate **Number Awarded:** 1 each year. **Funds Available:** The stipend is $1,500. **Duration:** 1 year.

Eligibility Requirements: This program is open to students enrolled in an academic institution that offers courses in transportation, logistics, traffic management, or related fields. Applicants must intend to prepare for a career in those fields. They must be of Canadian nationality but may be attending school in the United States or in Canada. Selection is based on scholastic ability, potential, professional interest, character, and financial need. **Deadline for Receipt:** April of each year. **Additional Information:** Requests for applications must be accompanied by a stamped self-addressed envelope.

1660 ■ TRANSPORTATION CLUBS INTERNATIONAL

Attn: Gay Fielding
7031 Manchester Street
New Orleans, LA 70126
E-mail: GayFielding@bellsouth.net
Web Site: http://www.transportationclubsinternational.com
To provide financial assistance to college students interested in preparing for a career in fields related to transportation.
Title of Award: Hooper Memorial Scholarship **Area, Field, or Subject:** Transportation **Level of Education for which Award is Granted:** Undergraduate **Number Awarded:** 1 or more each year. **Funds Available:** The stipend is $1,500. **Duration:** 1 year.

Eligibility Requirements: This program is open to students enrolled in an academic institution that offers courses in transportation, logistics, traffic management, or related fields. Applicants must intend to prepare for a career in those fields. Selection is based on scholastic ability, character, potential, professional interest, and financial need. **Deadline for Receipt:** April of each year. **Additional Information:** Requests for applications must be accompanied by a stamped self-addressed envelope.

1661 ■ TRANSPORTATION CLUBS INTERNATIONAL

Attn: Gay Fielding
7031 Manchester Street
New Orleans, LA 70126
E-mail: GayFielding@bellsouth.net
Web Site: http://www.transportationclubsinternational.com
To provide financial assistance to college students interested in preparing for a career in fields related to transportation.
Title of Award: Texas Transportation Scholarship **Area, Field, or Subject:** Transportation **Level of Education for which Award is Granted:** Undergraduate **Number Awarded:** 1 each year. **Funds Available:** The stipend is $1,000. **Duration:** 1 year.

Eligibility Requirements: This program is open to students enrolled in an academic institution that offers courses in transportation, logistics, traffic management, or related fields. Applicants must intend to prepare for a career in those fields. They must have been enrolled in a school in Texas during some phase of their education (elementary or secondary). Selection is based on scholastic ability, potential, character, professional interest, and financial need. **Deadline for Receipt:** April of each year. **Additional Information:** Requests for applications must be accompanied by a stamped self-addressed envelope.

1662 ■ TRANSPORTATION CLUBS INTERNATIONAL

Attn: Gay Fielding
7031 Manchester Street
New Orleans, LA 70126
E-mail: GayFielding@bellsouth.net
Web Site: http://www.transportationclubsinternational.com
To provide financial assistance to college students interested in preparing for a career in fields related to transportation.
Title of Award: Alice Glaisyer Warfield Memorial Scholarship **Area, Field, or Subject:** Transportation **Level of Education for which Award is Granted:** Undergraduate **Number Awarded:** 1 or more each year. **Funds Available:** The stipend is $1,000. **Duration:** 1 year.

Eligibility Requirements: This program is open to students enrolled in an academic institution that offers courses in transportation, logistics, traffic management, or related fields. Applicants must intend to prepare for a career in those fields. Selection is based on scholastic ability, character, potential, professional interest, and financial need. **Deadline for Receipt:** April of each year. **Additional Information:** Requests for applications must be accompanied by a stamped self-addressed envelope.

1663 ■ TRANSPORTATION CLUBS INTERNATIONAL

Attn: Gay Fielding
7031 Manchester Street
New Orleans, LA 70126
E-mail: GayFielding@bellsouth.net
Web Site: http://www.transportationclubsinternational.com
To provide financial assistance to college students interested in preparing for a career in a field related to transportation.
Title of Award: Charlotte Woods Memorial Scholarship **Area, Field, or Subject:** Transportation **Level of Education for which Award is Granted:** Undergraduate **Number Awarded:** 1 each year. **Funds Available:** The stipend is $1,000. **Duration:** 1 year.

Eligibility Requirements: This program is open to students enrolled in an academic institution (vocational or degree program) that offers courses in transportation, logistics, traffic management, or related fields. Applicants must be a member of Transportation Clubs International (or the dependent of a member) planning a career in those fields. Selection is based on scholastic ability, potential, professional interest, character, and financial need. **Deadline for Receipt:** April of each year. **Additional Information:** Requests for applications must be accompanied by a stamped self-addressed envelope.

1664 ■ TRAVEL INDUSTRY ASSOCIATION OF AMERICA

Attn: TIA Foundation
1100 New York Avenue, N.W., Suite 450
Washington, DC 20005-3934
Tel: (202)408-8422
Fax: (202)408-1255
Web Site: http://www.tia.org
To provide financial assistance to minority undergraduate students interested in studying travel and tourism.
Title of Award: Ronald H. Brown Memorial Scholarship **Area, Field, or Subject:** Travel and tourism **Level of Education for which Award is Granted:** Four Year College **Number Awarded:** 1 each year. **Funds Available:** The stipend is $3,000 per year. **Duration:** 1 year.

Eligibility Requirements: This program is open to minorities who are interested in working on an undergraduate degree in the travel and tourism field. Candidates must first be nominated by a department head at a 4-year college or university that has a travel and tourism program. Nominees are then contacted by the foundation and invited to complete an application, including an essay on what segment of the tourism industry interests them and why.

1665 ■ TRAVEL INDUSTRY ASSOCIATION OF AMERICA

Attn: TIA Foundation
1100 New York Avenue, N.W., Suite 450
Washington, DC 20005-3934
Tel: (202)408-8422
Fax: (202)408-1255
Web Site: http://www.tia.org/about/foundation_scholarships.html
To provide financial assistance to undergraduate students majoring in travel and tourism.
Title of Award: TIA Foundation Undergraduate Scholarships **Area, Field, or Subject:** Travel and tourism **Level of Education for which Award is Granted:** Four Year College **Number Awarded:** 6 each year. **Funds Available:** The stipend is $3,000. **Duration:** 1 year.

Eligibility Requirements: This program is open to students who are interested in working on an undergraduate degree in the travel and tourism field. Candidates must first be nominated by a department head at a 4-year college or university that has a travel and tourism program. Nominees are then contacted by the foundation and invited to complete an application that includes an essay on what segment of the tourism industry interests them and why. **Additional Information:** This program, which began in 1993, includes the National Council of Destination Organizations (NCDO) Undergraduate Scholarship, the Shop America Alliance Scholarship, the Tourism Works for America Legacy Scholarship, and the William S. Norman Scholarship.

1666 ■ TRAVEL INDUSTRY ASSOCIATION OF AMERICA

Attn: TIA Foundation
1100 New York Avenue, N.W., Suite 450
Washington, DC 20005-3934
Tel: (202)408-8422

Fax: (202)408-1255
Web Site: http://www.tia.org/about/foundation_scholarships.html
To provide financial assistance to graduate students majoring in travel and tourism.

Title of Award: Travel Industry Association of America Graduate Scholarships **Area, Field, or Subject:** Travel and tourism **Level of Education for which Award is Granted:** Four Year College, Graduate **Number Awarded:** 7 each year. **Funds Available:** The stipend is $4,000. **Duration:** 1 year.

Eligibility Requirements: This program is open to students who are interested in working on a graduate degree in the travel and tourism field. Candidates must first be nominated by a department head at a 4-year college or university that has a travel and tourism program. Nominees are then contacted by the foundation and invited to complete an application that includes an essay on what segment of the tourism industry interests them and why. **Additional Information:** This program includes the William D. Toohey Scholarship, the National Council of Destination Organizations (NCDO) Graduate Scholarship, and the Choice Hotels International Scholarship.

1667 ■ TRAVIS OFFICERS' SPOUSES' CLUB

P.O. Box 1475
101 Randolph Street
Travis AFB, CA 94535
To provide financial assistance for college to children and spouses of military personnel association with Travis Air Force Base (AFB). California.

Title of Award: Travis Officers' Spouses' Club Scholarships **Area, Field, or Subject:** General studies/Field of study not specified **Level of Education for which Award is Granted:** Undergraduate **Number Awarded:** Varies each year. Recently, 8 high school scholarships (1 each at $1,800, $1,700, $1,550, $1,100, $850, $700, $500, and $300) and 3 continuing education spouse scholarships (1 each at $750, $650, and $200) were awarded. **Funds Available:** Stipends range from $200 to $1,800. **Duration:** 1 year.

Eligibility Requirements: This program is open to 1) high school seniors who are dependent children of Travis AFB military personnel planning to attend college; and 2) spouses of Travis AFB military personnel interested in continuing education. Applicants must submit school transcripts, standardized test scores, written essays, and letters of recommendation. Selection is based on responsibility, leadership, scholastics, citizenship, and diversity of interest.

1668 ■ TUSKEGEE AIRMEN, INC.

1501 Lee Highway, Suite 130
Arlington, VA 22209-1109
Tel: (703)522-8590
Fax: (703)522-8542
E-mail: hqtai@tuskegeeairmen.org
Web Site: http://www.tuskegeeairmen.org/youthinaviation/scholarships.html
To provide financial assistance for college to high school seniors and graduates who submit an essay on the history of Tuskegee Airmen, a group of African Americans who served as pilots in World War II.

Title of Award: Tuskegee Airmen Scholarships **Area, Field, or Subject:** General studies/Field of study not specified **Level of Education for which Award is Granted:** Undergraduate **Number Awarded:** Varies each year; recently, 41 of these scholarships were available. **Funds Available:** The stipend is $1,500. **Duration:** 1 year; nonrenewable.

Eligibility Requirements: This program is open to students who have graduated or will graduate from high school in the current year with a GPA of 3.0 or higher. Applicants must submit a 1-page essay entitled "The Tuskegee Airmen" that reflects an overview of their history. They must also submit documentation of financial need and a 2-page essay that includes a brief autobiographical sketch, educational aspirations, career goals, and an explanation of why financial assistance is essential. Applications must be submitted to individual chapters of Tuskegee Airmen, Inc. which verify them as appropriate, evaluate them, and forward those considered worthy of further consideration to the national competition. Selection is based on academic achievement, extracurricular and community activities, financial need, recommendations, and both essays. **Deadline for Receipt:** February of each year. **Additional Information:** This program was established in 1978. Information is also available from the Tuskegee Airmen National Scholarship Fund, P.O. Box 78967, Los Angeles, CA 90016.

1669 ■ TWO/TEN INTERNATIONAL FOOTWEAR FOUNDATION

Attn: Scholarship Director
1466 Main Street
Waltham, MA 02451
Tel: (781)736-1500
Free: 800-FIND-210
Fax: (781)736-1555
E-mail: scholarship@twoten.org
Web Site: http://www.twoten.org/ClassicScholarships.aspx
To provide financial assistance to full-time undergraduate students who work, or whose parent works, in the footwear, leather, or allied industries.

Title of Award: Two/Ten International Footwear Foundation College Scholarship Program **Area, Field, or Subject:** General studies/Field of study not specified **Level of Education for which Award is Granted:** Undergraduate **Number Awarded:** Varies; generally, more than 200 new awards and 300 renewals each year. **Funds Available:** Classic scholarships range up to $3,000 per year, depending on the need of the recipient. For students who demonstrate exceptional financial need, stipends up to $15,000 per year are available. Funds are sent directly to the recipient's school. **Duration:** 1 year; may be renewed up to 3 additional years.

Eligibility Requirements: This program is open to students attending or planning to attend a college, university, nursing school, or vocational/technical school to work on a 2-year or 4-year undergraduate degree. Either their parent (natural, step, or adopted) must be employed (for at least 2 years) in the footwear, leather, or allied industries or the applicants must be employed for at least 500 hours in 1 of those industries. The employer must do 50% of its business in footwear, or the applicant or parent must work in a specific footwear division. U.S. citizenship or permanent resident status is required. Selection is based on academic record, personal promise, character, and financial need. **Deadline for Receipt:** January of each year. **Additional Information:** Awards may be used only in 2- or 4-year accredited programs of study.

1670 ■ UCB PHARMA, INC.

Keppra Scholarship Program
c/o S&R Communications Group
2511 Old Cornwallis Road, Suite 200
Durham, NC 27713
888-275-7928
E-mail: kepprascholarship@srcomgroup.com
Web Site: http://www.keppra.com/pc/other_resources/scholarshipProgram.aspx
To provide financial assistance for college or graduate school to epilepsy patients and their family members and caregivers.

Title of Award: Keppra Family Epilepsy Scholarship Program **Area, Field, or Subject:** General studies/Field of study not specified **Level of Education for which Award is Granted:** Graduate, Undergraduate **Number Awarded:** 30 each year: 20 to epilepsy patients and 10 to family members or caregivers. **Funds Available:** The stipend is $50,000. **Duration:** 1 year; nonrenewable.

Eligibility Requirements: This program is open to epilepsy patients and their family members and caregivers. Applicants must be working on or planning to work on an undergraduate or graduate degree at an institution of higher education in the United States. They must be able to demonstrate academic achievement, a record of participation in activities outside of school, and service as a role model. Along with their application, they must submit a 1-page essay explaining why they should be selected for the scholarship, how epilepsy has impacted their life either as a patient or as a family member or caregiver, and how they will benefit from the scholarship. **Deadline for Receipt:** May of each year.

1671 ■ ULMAN CANCER FUND FOR YOUNG ADULTS

Attn: Scholarship Committee
4725 Dorsey Hall Drive, Suite A
PMB 505
Ellicott City, MD 21042
Tel: (410)964-0202; 888-393-FUND
E-mail: scholarship@ulmanfund.org
Web Site: http://www.ulmanfund.org/Services/Scholarship/tabid/73/Default.aspx

To provide financial assistance for college to cancer survivors, patients, and caregivers.

Title of Award: Cancer Teaches Us Survivorship Award **Area, Field, or Subject:** General studies/Field of study not specified **Level of Education for which Award is Granted:** Undergraduate **Number Awarded:** 1 or more each year. **Funds Available:** The stipend is $1,000. **Duration:** 1 year.

Eligibility Requirements: This program is open to young adults who are cancer survivors, patients, or caregivers and survivors of childhood cancer. Applicants must be able to demonstrate financial need. They must be between 15 and 40 years of age and working on, or planning to work on, an academic or professional degree. Along with their application, they must submit a 500-word essay on 1 of 4 assigned topics that relate to cancer. Selection is based on the quality of the essay, recommendations, their overall story of cancer survivorship, and financial need. **Deadline for Receipt:** March of each year.

1672 ■ ULMAN CANCER FUND FOR YOUNG ADULTS

Attn: Scholarship Committee
4725 Dorsey Hall Drive, Suite A
PMB 505
Ellicott City, MD 21042
Tel: (410)964-0202; 888-393-FUND
E-mail: scholarship@ulmanfund.org
Web Site: http://www.ulmanfund.org/Services/Scholarship/tabid/73/Default.aspx
To provide financial assistance for college to undergraduates who have had cancer.

Title of Award: Matt Stauffer Memorial Scholarships **Area, Field, or Subject:** General studies/Field of study not specified **Level of Education for which Award is Granted:** Undergraduate **Number Awarded:** Varies each year; recently, 12 of these scholarships were awarded. **Funds Available:** The stipend is $1,000. **Duration:** 1 year.

Eligibility Requirements: This program is open to students who are battling, or have overcome, cancer. Applicants must be able to demonstrate financial need. They must be between 15 and 40 years of age and working on, or planning to work on, an academic or professional degree. Along with their application, they must submit a 500-word essay on 1 of 4 assigned topics that relate to cancer. Selection is based on the quality of the essay, recommendations, their overall story of cancer survivorship, and financial need. **Deadline for Receipt:** March of each year. **Additional Information:** These scholarships were first awarded in 1998.

1673 ■ ULMAN CANCER FUND FOR YOUNG ADULTS

Attn: Scholarship Committee
4725 Dorsey Hall Drive, Suite A
PMB 505
Ellicott City, MD 21042
Tel: (410)964-0202; 888-393-FUND
E-mail: scholarship@ulmanfund.org
Web Site: http://www.ulmanfund.org/Services/Scholarship/tabid/73/Default.aspx
To provide financial assistance to college students who have a parent with cancer.

Title of Award: Marilyn Yetso Memorial Scholarship **Area, Field, or Subject:** General studies/Field of study not specified **Level of Education for which Award is Granted:** Undergraduate **Number Awarded:** Varies each year; recently, 10 of these scholarships were awarded. **Funds Available:** The stipend is $1,000. **Duration:** 1 year.

Eligibility Requirements: This program is open to students who have or have lost a parent to cancer. Applicants must be able to demonstrate financial need. They must be between 15 and 40 years of age and working on, or planning to work on, an academic or professional degree. Along with their application, they must submit a 500-word essay on 1 of 4 assigned topics that relate to cancer. Selection is based on the quality of the essay, recommendations, their overall story of cancer survivorship, and financial need. **Deadline for Receipt:** March of each year. **Additional Information:** These scholarships were first awarded in 2002.

1674 ■ UNITED COMPANIES, INC.

Attn: Scholarship Program
5450 A Street
Anchorage, AK 99518

Tel: (907)561-1674
Free: 800-478-2020
Fax: (907)563-3185
E-mail: unicom@unicom-alaska.com
Web Site: http://www.unicom-alaska.com/scholarship.html
To provide financial assistance for college to residents of selected Native communities in Alaska.

Title of Award: United Companies Scholarships **Area, Field, or Subject:** General studies/Field of study not specified **Level of Education for which Award is Granted:** Undergraduate **Number Awarded:** Varies each year; recently, 144 of these scholarships were awarded. **Funds Available:** A stipend is awarded (amount not specified). **Duration:** 1 year.

Eligibility Requirements: This program is open to high school seniors and graduates who live in a Native Alaska community where affiliates of United Companies, Inc. provide communications services. Applicants must be planning to enroll in a college, university, or vocational/trade school. Along with their application, they must submit a current transcript with GPA, the name of the college they plan to attend, estimated cost of education for 1 year, intended major or course of study, and an essay describing their future plans and goals. **Deadline for Receipt:** April of each year. **Additional Information:** United Companies, Inc. is owned by Alaska native corporations. Through its affiliates (United Utilities, Inc., United-KUC, and Unicom, Inc.), it provides communications services to 61 native communities in Alaska.

1675 ■ UNITED DAUGHTERS OF THE CONFEDERACY

Attn: Education Director
328 North Boulevard
Richmond, VA 23220-4057
Tel: (804)355-1636
Fax: (804)353-1396
E-mail: hqudc@rcn.com
Web Site: http://www.hqudc.org/scholarships/scholarships.html
To provide financial assistance for college to lineal descendants of Confederate veterans, especially those from New York.

Title of Award: Charlotte M.F. Bentley/New York Chapter 103 Scholarship **Area, Field, or Subject:** General studies/Field of study not specified **Level of Education for which Award is Granted:** Undergraduate **Number Awarded:** 1 each year. **Funds Available:** The amount of this scholarship depends on the availability of funds. **Duration:** 1 year; may be renewed.

Eligibility Requirements: Eligible to apply for these scholarships are lineal descendants of worthy Confederates or collateral descendants who are current or former members of the Children of the Confederacy or current members of the United Daughters of the Confederacy. Preference is given to members from New York. Applicants must submit a family financial report and certified proof of the Confederate record of 1 ancestor, with the company and regiment in which he served. They must have at least a 3.0 GPA in high school. **Deadline for Receipt:** March of each year. **Additional Information:** Information is also available from Mrs. Robert C. Kraus, Second Vice President General, 239 Deerfield Lane, Franklin, NC 28734-0112. Members of the same family may not hold scholarships simultaneously, and only 1 application per family will be accepted within any 1 year. All requests for applications must be accompanied by a self-addressed stamped envelope.

1676 ■ UNITED DAUGHTERS OF THE CONFEDERACY

Attn: Education Director
328 North Boulevard
Richmond, VA 23220-4057
Tel: (804)355-1636
Fax: (804)353-1396
E-mail: hqudc@rcn.com
Web Site: http://www.hqudc.org/scholarships/scholarships.html
To provide financial assistance for college to women, particularly in selected areas of Arkansas or Texas, who are lineal descendants of Confederate veterans.

Title of Award: Eloise Campbell Memorial Scholarships **Area, Field, or Subject:** General studies/Field of study not specified **Level of Education for which Award is Granted:** Undergraduate **Number Awarded:** 1 each year. **Funds Available:** The amount of the scholarship depends on the availability of funds. **Duration:** 1 year; may be renewed for up to 3 additional years.

Eligibility Requirements: Eligible to apply for these scholarships are lineal descendants of worthy Confederates or collateral descendants who are members of the Children of the Confederacy or the United Daughters of the Confederacy. Applicants must be female and have at least a 3.0 GPA in high school. Preference is given to candidates from Bowie County, Texas and Miller County, Arkansas. Applications must be accompanied by a family financial report and certified proof of the Confederate military record of 1 ancestor, with the company and regiment in which he served. **Deadline for Receipt:** March of each year. **Additional Information:** Information is also available from Mrs. Robert C. Kraus, Second Vice President General, 239 Deerfield Lane, Franklin, NC 28734-0112. Members of the same family may not hold scholarships simultaneously, and only 1 application per family will be accepted within any 1 year. Requests for applications must be accompanied by a self-addressed stamped envelope.

1677 ■ UNITED DAUGHTERS OF THE CONFEDERACY
Attn: Education Director
328 North Boulevard
Richmond, VA 23220-4057
Tel: (804)355-1636
Fax: (804)353-1396
E-mail: hqudc@rcn.com
Web Site: http://www.hqudc.org/scholarships/scholarships.html
To provide financial assistance for college to lineal descendants of Confederate veterans in Alabama.
Title of Award: Lola B. Curry Scholarship **Area, Field, or Subject:** General studies/Field of study not specified **Level of Education for which Award is Granted:** Undergraduate **Number Awarded:** 1 each year. **Funds Available:** The amount of the scholarship depends on the availability of funds. **Duration:** 1 year; may be renewed.
Eligibility Requirements: Eligible to apply for these scholarships are Alabama residents who are lineal descendants of worthy Confederates or collateral descendants who are members of the Children of the Confederacy or the United Daughters of the Confederacy. Applicants must submit a family financial report and certified proof of the Confederate record of 1 ancestor, with the company and regiment in which he served. They must have a GPA of 3.0 or higher in high school. **Deadline for Receipt:** March of each year. **Additional Information:** Information is also available from Mrs. Robert C. Kraus, Second Vice President General, 239 Deerfield Lane, Franklin, NC 28734-0112. Members of the same family may not hold scholarships simultaneously, and only 1 application per family will be accepted within any 1 year. Requests for applications must be accompanied by a self-addressed stamped envelope.

1678 ■ UNITED DAUGHTERS OF THE CONFEDERACY
Attn: Education Director
328 North Boulevard
Richmond, VA 23220-4057
Tel: (804)355-1636
Fax: (804)353-1396
E-mail: hqudc@rcn.com
Web Site: http://www.hqudc.org/scholarships/scholarships.html
To provide financial assistance for college to lineal descendants of Confederate veterans who are members of the Children of the Confederacy.
Title of Award: Winnie C. Davis Children of the Confederacy Scholarship **Area, Field, or Subject:** General studies/Field of study not specified **Level of Education for which Award is Granted:** Undergraduate **Number Awarded:** 1 each year. **Funds Available:** The amount of this scholarship depends on the availability of funds. **Duration:** 1 year; may be renewed for up to 3 additional years.
Eligibility Requirements: Eligible to apply for these scholarships are lineal descendants of worthy Confederates or collateral descendants. Applicants must submit a family financial report and certified proof of the Confederate record of 1 ancestor, with the company and regiment in which he served. In addition, applicants themselves must be, or have been until age 18, participating members of the Children of the Confederacy. They must have at least a 3.0 GPA in high school. **Deadline for Receipt:** March of each year. **Additional Information:** Information is also available from Mrs. Robert C. Kraus, Second Vice President General, 239 Deerfield Lane, Franklin, NC 28734-0112. Members of the same family may not hold scholarships simultaneously, and only 1 application per

family will be accepted within any 1 year. All requests for applications must be accompanied by a self-addressed stamped envelope.

1679 ■ UNITED DAUGHTERS OF THE CONFEDERACY
Attn: Education Director
328 North Boulevard
Richmond, VA 23220-4057
Tel: (804)355-1636
Fax: (804)353-1396
E-mail: hqudc@rcn.com
Web Site: http://www.hqudc.org/scholarships/scholarships.html
To provide financial assistance for college to lineal descendants of Confederate veterans who have been members of the Children of the Confederacy for at least 3 years.
Title of Award: Elizabeth and Wallace Kingsbury Scholarship **Area, Field, or Subject:** General studies/Field of study not specified **Level of Education for which Award is Granted:** Undergraduate **Number Awarded:** 1 each year. **Funds Available:** The amount of the scholarship depends on the availability of funds. **Duration:** 1 year; may be renewed for up to 3 additional years.
Eligibility Requirements: Eligible to apply for these scholarships are lineal descendants of worthy Confederates or collateral descendants who have been members of the Children of the Confederacy for at least 3 years. Applicants must submit a family financial report and certified proof of the Confederate record of 1 ancestor, with the company and regiment in which he served. They must have at least a 3.0 GPA in high school. **Deadline for Receipt:** March of each year. **Additional Information:** Information is also available from Mrs. Robert C. Kraus, Second Vice President General, 239 Deerfield Lane, Franklin, NC 28734-0112. Members of the same family may not hold scholarships simultaneously, and only 1 application per family will be accepted within any 1 year. Requests for applications must be accompanied by a self-addressed stamped envelope.

1680 ■ UNITED DAUGHTERS OF THE CONFEDERACY
Attn: Education Director
328 North Boulevard
Richmond, VA 23220-4057
Tel: (804)355-1636
Fax: (804)353-1396
E-mail: hqudc@rcn.com
Web Site: http://www.hqudc.org/scholarships/scholarships.html
To provide financial assistance for college to lineal descendants of Confederate veterans who are residents of Texas, Mississippi, or Louisiana.
Title of Award: Gertrude Botts Saucier Scholarship **Area, Field, or Subject:** General studies/Field of study not specified **Level of Education for which Award is Granted:** Undergraduate **Number Awarded:** 1 each year. **Funds Available:** The amount of the scholarship depends on the availability of funds. **Duration:** 1 year; may be renewed for up to 3 additional years.
Eligibility Requirements: Eligible to apply for these scholarships are lineal descendants of worthy Confederates or collateral descendants who are members of the Children of the Confederacy or the United Daughters of the Confederacy. Applicants must reside in Texas, Mississippi, or Louisiana and must submit a family financial report and certified proof of the Confederate record of 1 ancestor, with the company and regiment in which he served. They must have at least a 3.0 GPA in high school. **Deadline for Receipt:** March of each year. **Additional Information:** Information is also available from Mrs. Robert C. Kraus, Second Vice President General, 239 Deerfield Lane, Franklin, NC 28734-0112. Members of the same family may not hold scholarships simultaneously, and only 1 application per family will be accepted within any 1 year. Requests for applications must be accompanied by a self-addressed stamped envelope.

1681 ■ UNITED DAUGHTERS OF THE CONFEDERACY
Attn: Education Director
328 North Boulevard
Richmond, VA 23220-4057
Tel: (804)355-1636
Fax: (804)353-1396
E-mail: hqudc@rcn.com

Web Site: http://www.hqudc.org/scholarships/scholarships.html
To provide financial assistance for college to lineal descendants of Confederate veterans.

Title of Award: United Daughters of the Confederacy Scholarships **Area, Field, or Subject:** General studies/Field of study not specified **Level of Education for which Award is Granted:** Undergraduate **Number Awarded:** 17 unrestricted scholarships are available; another 11 scholarships with varying restrictions are also offered. **Funds Available:** The amount of the scholarships depends on the availability of funds. **Duration:** 1 year; may be renewed up to 3 additional years.

Eligibility Requirements: Eligible to apply for these scholarships are lineal descendants of worthy Confederates or collateral descendants who are members of the Children of the Confederacy or the United Daughters of the Confederacy. Applicants must be high school seniors or college students and submit a family financial report and certified proof of the Confederate record of 1 ancestor, with the company and regiment in which he served. They must have a high school GPA of 3.0 or higher. **Deadline for Receipt:** March of each year. **Additional Information:** Applications must be submitted through the division or chapter of their home state. Each division or chapter may present only 1 candidate for any 1 scholarship. Unrestricted scholarships are named the Admiral Raphael Semmes Memorial Scholarship, the Janet B. Seippel Scholarship, the Cody Bachman Memorial Scholarship, the Donor Scholarship, the Cora Bell Wesley Memorial Scholarship, the Cornelia Branch Stone Scholarship, the David Stephen Wylie Scholarship, the Henry Clay Darsey Memorial Scholarship, the Hector W. Church Memorial Scholarship, the Major Madison Bell Scholarship, the Mary B. Poppenheim Memorial Scholarship, the Matthew Fontaine Maury Scholarship, the Mrs. Ella M. Franklin Memorial Scholarship, the Mrs. L.H. Raines Memorial Scholarship, the S.A. Cunningham Scholarship, the Dorothy Williams Scholarships, the Barbara Jackson Sichel Memorial Scholarship, and the Stonewall Jackson Scholarship. The unrestricted scholarships may be used at any institution approved by the Education Committee of the United Daughters of the Confederacy. Information is also available from Mrs. Robert C. Kraus, Second Vice President General, 239 Deerfield Lane, Franklin, NC 28734-0112. Members of the same family may not hold scholarships simultaneously, and only 1 application per family will be accepted within a current year. All requests for applications must be accompanied by a self-addressed stamped envelope.

1682 ■ UNITED DAUGHTERS OF THE CONFEDERACY-TEXAS DIVISION

c/o Sally E. Peterson, Education Committee Chair
11830 Spruce Hill
Houston, TX 77077-4927
Tel: (281)556-1451
E-mail: sepfromlsu@houston.rr.com
Web Site: http://txudc.org/education.htm
To provide financial assistance to the descendants of Confederate veterans who are interested in attending college in Texas.

Title of Award: Texas Division Scholarships **Area, Field, or Subject:** General studies/Field of study not specified **Level of Education for which Award is Granted:** Undergraduate **Number Awarded:** Varies each year. **Funds Available:** Stipends range up to $1,000. Funds are paid directly to the recipient's university. **Duration:** Up to 4 years, as long as the recipient remains enrolled full time with a GPA of 3.0 or higher.

Eligibility Requirements: This program is open to high school seniors and current college students who are lineal or collateral descendants of men who served in the Confederate military. Collateral descendants must be members of the United Daughters of the Confederacy (UDC) or Children of the Confederacy (CofC). Applicants must be endorsed by officials of their local UDC Chapter in Texas. They must be attending or planning to attend an accredited college or university in Texas. Along with their application, they must submit a 300-word letter pledging to make the best possible use of the opportunity offered through the scholarship and outlining goals and plans for obtaining them; the letter should evaluate the significance of a Southern heritage in today's world. Financial need is also considered in the selection process. **Deadline for Receipt:** February of each year. **Additional Information:** This program includes the following named awards: the Barthold Scholarship, the Bounds-Stone Scholarship, the Audie Murphy Scholarship, the Katie Cabell Muse Scholarship, the Johnie May Myers Scholarship, the Ralph W. Widener Scholarship, the Ralph Widener, Sr. Scholarship, and the Kathryn Noble Wilcox Scholar-

ship. Some of the scholarships may be used only at specified Texas universities.

1683 ■ UNITED DAUGHTERS OF THE CONFEDERACY-VIRGINIA DIVISION

c/o Suzie Snyder, Education Committee Chair
8440 Bradshaw Road
Salem, VA 24153-2246
Tel: (540)384-6884
E-mail: Suzienotes@aol.com
Web Site: http://users.erols.com/va-udc/scholarships.html
To provide financial assistance for college to Confederate descendants from Virginia.

Title of Award: Howard Stiles Nuchols Scholarship **Area, Field, or Subject:** General studies/Field of study not specified **Level of Education for which Award is Granted:** Undergraduate **Number Awarded:** This scholarship is offered whenever a prior recipient graduates or is no longer eligible. **Funds Available:** The amount of the stipend depends on the availability of funds. Payment is made directly to the college or university the recipient attends. **Duration:** 1 year; may be renewed up to 3 additional years if the recipient maintains a GPA of 3.0 or higher.

Eligibility Requirements: This program is open to residents of Virginia who are 1) lineal descendants of Confederates, or 2) collateral descendants and also members of the Children of the Confederacy or the United Daughters of the Confederacy (UDC). Applicants must submit proof of the Confederate military record of at least 1 ancestor, with the company and regiment in which he served. They must also submit a personal letter pledging to make the best possible use of the scholarship; describing their health, social, family, religious, and fraternal connections within the community; and reflecting on what a Southern heritage means to them (using the term "War Between the States" in lieu of "Civil War"). They must have a GPA of 3.0 or higher and be able to demonstrate financial need. Preference is given to applicants who are current or former members of the Virginia division of the Children of the Confederacy. **Deadline for Receipt:** May of years in which the scholarship is available. **Additional Information:** Information on this scholarship is also available from the UDC Virginia Division Director, Samba Lougheed, E-mail jslougheed@erols.com.

1684 ■ UNITED DAUGHTERS OF THE CONFEDERACY-VIRGINIA DIVISION

c/o Suzie Snyder, Education Committee Chair
8440 Bradshaw Road
Salem, VA 24153-2246
Tel: (540)384-6884
E-mail: Suzienotes@aol.com
Web Site: http://users.erols.com/va-udc/scholarships.html
To provide financial assistance for college to Confederate descendants from Virginia.

Title of Award: Virginia Division Gift Scholarships **Area, Field, or Subject:** General studies/Field of study not specified **Level of Education for which Award is Granted:** Undergraduate **Number Awarded:** These scholarships are offered whenever a prior recipient graduates or is no longer eligible. **Funds Available:** The amount of the stipend depends on the availability of funds. Payment is made directly to the college or university the recipient attends. **Duration:** 1 year; may be renewed up to 3 additional years if the recipient maintains a GPA of 3.0 or higher.

Eligibility Requirements: This program is open to residents of Virginia who are 1) lineal descendants of Confederates, or 2) collateral descendants and also members of the Children of the Confederacy or the United Daughters of the Confederacy. Applicants must submit proof of the Confederate military record of at least 1 ancestor, with the company and regiment in which he served. They must also submit a personal letter pledging to make the best possible use of the scholarship; describing their health, social, family, religious, and fraternal connections within the community; and reflecting on what a Southern heritage means to them (using the term "War Between the States" in lieu of "Civil War"). They must have a GPA of 3.0 or higher and be able to demonstrate financial need. **Deadline for Receipt:** May of years in which any of the scholarships is available. **Additional Information:** This program includes the following named scholarships: the Mary Custis Lee Memorial Scholarship, the Matthew Fontaine Maury Scholarship, the Catherine Custis Taylor Goffigan Scholarship, the Rives Cosby Ford Memorial Fellowship, the Margaret

Hart Barnes Memorial Scholarship, and the Jennie Gunn Ball Scholarship. Information is also available from Mrs. George W. Bryson, 10103 Rixeyville Road, Culpeper, VA 22701-4422, E-mail: brysdale@aol.com.

1685 ■ UNITED FOOD AND COMMERCIAL WORKERS INTERNATIONAL UNION
Attn: Scholarship Program
1775 K Street, N.W.
Washington, DC 20006-1598
Tel: (202)223-3111
Fax: (202)466-1562
E-mail: scholarship@ufcw.org
Web Site: http://www.ufcw.org/scholarship/test_cfm.cfm
To provide financial assistance for college to members of the United Food and Commercial Workers International Union (UFCW) and their children.
Title of Award: United Food and Commercial Workers International Union Scholarship Program **Area, Field, or Subject:** General studies/Field of study not specified **Level of Education for which Award is Granted:** Undergraduate **Number Awarded:** 7 each year. **Funds Available:** The stipend is $1,000 per year. **Duration:** 4 years.
Eligibility Requirements: This program is open to UFCW members who have been in good standing for at least 1 year and their unmarried children. Applicants must be under 20 years of age, be high school seniors, and have taken the SAT or the ACT examination. Selection is based on test scores, scholastic records and achievements, personal qualifications, and merit. **Deadline for Receipt:** Preliminary applications must be completed by the end of December; the additional form necessary to complete the application process must be submitted by mid-March.

1686 ■ U.S. AIR FORCE
Attn: Headquarters AFROTC/RRUC
551 East Maxwell Boulevard
Maxwell AFB, AL 36112-5917
Tel: (334)953-2091; (866)423-7682
Fax: (334)953-6167
Web Site: http://www.afrotc.com/scholarships/incolschol/minority/hsi.php
To provide financial assistance to students at designated Hispanic Serving Institutions (HSIs) who are willing to join Air Force ROTC in college and serve as Air Force officers following completion of their bachelor's degree.
Title of Award: Air Force Enhanced ROTC Hispanic Serving Institution Scholarship Program **Area, Field, or Subject:** General studies/Field of study not specified **Level of Education for which Award is Granted:** Undergraduate **Number Awarded:** Up to 120 each year: 15 at each of the participating AFROTC units. **Funds Available:** Awards are type 2 AFROTC scholarships that provide for payment of tuition and fees, to a maximum of $15,000 per year, plus an annual book allowance of $600. Recipients are also awarded a tax-free subsistence allowance for 10 months of each year that is $300 per month during the sophomore year, $350 during the junior year, and $400 during the senior year. **Duration:** Up to 3 and a half years (beginning as early as the spring semester of the freshman year).
Eligibility Requirements: This program is open to U.S. citizens who are at least 17 years of age and currently enrolled at 1 of 8 designated HSIs that have an Air Force ROTC unit on campus. Applicants do not need to be Hispanic as long as they are enrolled at the university and have a cumulative GPA of 2.5 or higher. At the time of commissioning, they may be no more than 31 years of age. They must be able to pass the Air Force Officer Qualifying Test (AFOQT) and the Air Force ROTC Physical Fitness Test. Currently, the program is accepting applications from students with any major. **Deadline for Receipt:** Applications may be submitted at any time. **Additional Information:** The designated universities are California State University at Fresno, California State University at San Bernardino, New Mexico State University, the University of Miami, the University of New Mexico, the University of Puerto Rico at Río Piedras, the University of Puerto Rico at Mayaguez, and the University of Texas at San Antonio. While scholarship recipients can major in any subject, they must complete 4 years of aerospace studies courses. They must also attend a 4-week summer training camp at an Air Force base, usually between their sophomore and junior years; 2-year scholarship awardees attend in the summer after their junior year. Current military personnel are eligible for early release from active duty in order to enter the Air Force ROTC program. Following completion of their bachelor's degree, scholarship

recipients earn a commission as a second lieutenant in the Air Force and serve at least 4 years.

1687 ■ U.S. AIR FORCE
Attn: Headquarters AFROTC/RRUC
551 East Maxwell Boulevard
Maxwell AFB, AL 36112-5917
Tel: (334)953-2091; (866)423-7682
Fax: (334)953-6167
Web Site: http://www.afrotc.com/scholarships/incolschol/minority/hbcu.php
To provide financial assistance to students at designated Historically Black Colleges and Universities (HBCUs) who are willing to join Air Force ROTC and serve as Air Force officers following completion of their bachelor's degree.
Title of Award: Air Force Enhanced ROTC Historically Black Colleges and Universities Scholarship Program **Area, Field, or Subject:** General studies/Field of study not specified **Level of Education for which Award is Granted:** Undergraduate **Number Awarded:** Up to 120 each year: 15 at each of the participating AFROTC units. **Funds Available:** Awards are type 2 AFROTC scholarships that provide for payment of tuition and fees, to a maximum of $15,000 per year, plus an annual book allowance of $600. Recipients are also awarded a tax-free subsistence allowance for 10 months of each year that is $300 per month during the sophomore year, $350 during the junior year, and $400 during the senior year. **Duration:** Up to 3 and a half years (beginning as early as the spring semester of the freshman year).
Eligibility Requirements: This program is open to U.S. citizens at least 17 years of age who are currently enrolled as freshmen at 1 of the 8 HBCUs that has an Air Force ROTC unit on campus. Applicants do not need to be African American as long as they are attending an HBCU and have a cumulative GPA of 2.5 or higher. At the time of commissioning, they may be no more than 31 years of age. They must be able to pass the Air Force Officer Qualifying Test (AFOQT) and the Air Force ROTC Physical Fitness Test. Currently, the program is accepting applications from students with any major. **Deadline for Receipt:** Applications may be submitted at any time. **Additional Information:** The participating HBCUs are Tuskegee University (Tuskegee, Alabama), Alabama State University (Montgomery, Alabama), Howard University (Washington, D.C.), Grambling State University (Grambling, Louisiana), North Carolina A&T State University (Greensboro, North Carolina), Fayetteville State University (Fayetteville, North Carolina), Tennessee State University (Nashville, Tennessee), and Jackson State University (Jackson, Mississippi). While scholarship recipients can major in any subject, they must complete 4 years of aerospace studies courses at 1 of the HBCUs that have an Air Force ROTC unit on campus. Recipients must also attend a 4-week summer training camp at an Air Force base, usually between their sophomore and junior years; 2-year scholarship awardees attend in the summer after their junior year. Current military personnel are eligible for early release from active duty in order to enter the Air Force ROTC program. Following completion of their bachelor's degree, scholarship recipients earn a commission as a second lieutenant in the Air Force and serve at least 4 years.

1688 ■ U.S. AIR FORCE
Attn: HQ USAF/JAX
1420 Air Force
Pentagon, Room 5B269
Washington, DC 20330-1420
Tel: (703)614-5941
Free: 800-JAG-USAF
E-mail: joseph.dene@pentagon.af.mil
Web Site: http://www.jagusaf.hq.af.mil/EDprgrms/oycp.htm
To provide financial assistance to law students who are willing to join Air Force ROTC and serve as Air Force Judge Advocates following completion of their studies.
Title of Award: Air Force One-Year College Program (OYCP) **Area, Field, or Subject:** General studies/Field of study not specified **Level of Education for which Award is Granted:** Four Year College, Doctorate **Number Awarded:** Varies each year. **Funds Available:** Participants receive a stipend for 10 months of the year at $400 per month and a salary during summer field training. No other scholarship assistance is available. **Duration:** 1 year.

Eligibility Requirements: This program is open to students in their second year of law school or law students working on a joint or LL.M. degree with at least 1 year of study in their degree program. Applicants must 1) be attending an ABA-approved law school that has, or is located near, an AFROTC detachment; 2) be in good academic standing; and 3) be able to meet AFROTC entry standards (U.S. citizenship, weight and medical qualifications, and Air Force Officer Qualification Test minimum score). They must be younger than 35 years of age upon commissioning and entering active duty. **Deadline for Receipt:** March of each year. **Additional Information:** Selectees with no prior military experience attend field training encampment during the summer prior to entering the AFROTC program as contract cadets. Upon completion of their degree and legal licensing requirements, participants enter active duty as first lieutenants in the U.S. Air Force Judge Advocate General's Department. After 6 months of active duty, they are promoted to captain. The initial required active-duty service obligation is 4 years.

1689 ■ U.S. AIR FORCE
Attn: Headquarters AFROTC/RRUC
551 East Maxwell Boulevard
Maxwell AFB, AL 36112-5917
Tel: (334)953-2091; (866)423-7682
Fax: (334)953-6167
Web Site: http://www.afrotc.com/scholarships/incolschol/minority/hsi.php
To provide financial assistance to students at Hispanic Serving Institutions (HSIs) who are willing to join Air Force ROTC in college and serve as Air Force officers following completion of their bachelor's degree.
Title of Award: Air Force Regular ROTC Hispanic Serving Institution Scholarship Program **Area, Field, or Subject:** General studies/Field of study not specified **Level of Education for which Award is Granted:** Undergraduate **Number Awarded:** Varies each year. AFROTC units at every HSI may nominate an unlimited number of cadets to receive these scholarships. **Funds Available:** Awards are type 2 AFROTC scholarships that provide for payment of tuition and fees, to a maximum of $15,000 per year, plus an annual book allowance of $600. Recipients are also awarded a tax-free subsistence allowance for 10 months of each year that is $300 per month during the sophomore year, $350 during the junior year, and $400 during the senior year. **Duration:** 2 to 3 years, beginning during the current term.
Eligibility Requirements: This program is open to U.S. citizens at least 17 years of age who are currently enrolled at 1 of the 42 HSIs that has an Air Force ROTC unit on campus or that has a cross-enrollment agreement with another school that hosts a unit. Applicants do not need to be Hispanic as long as they are attending an HSI and have a cumulative GPA of 2.5 or higher. At the time of commissioning, they may be no more than 31 years of age. They must be able to pass the Air Force Officer Qualifying Test (AFOQT) and the Air Force ROTC Physical Fitness Test. Currently, the program is accepting applications from students with any major. **Deadline for Receipt:** Applications may be submitted at any time. **Additional Information:** While scholarship recipients can major in any subject, they must complete 4 years of aerospace studies courses. They must also attend a 4-week summer training camp at an Air Force base, usually between their sophomore and junior years; 2-year scholarship awardees attend in the summer after their junior year. Current military personnel are eligible for early release from active duty in order to enter the Air Force ROTC program. Following completion of their bachelor's degree, scholarship recipients earn a commission as a second lieutenant in the Air Force and serve at least 4 years.

1690 ■ U.S. AIR FORCE
Attn: Headquarters AFROTC/RRUC
551 East Maxwell Boulevard
Maxwell AFB, AL 36112-5917
Tel: (334)953-2091; (866)423-7682
Fax: (334)953-6167
Web Site: http://www.afrotc.com/scholarships/incolschol/minority/hbcu.php
To provide financial assistance to students at Historically Black Colleges and Universities (HBCUs) who are willing to serve as Air Force officers following completion of their bachelor's degree.
Title of Award: Air Force Regular ROTC Historically Black Colleges and Universities Scholarship Program **Area, Field, or Subject:** General studies/Field of study not specified **Level of Education for which Award**

is Granted: Undergraduate **Number Awarded:** Varies each year. AFROTC units at every HBCU may nominate an unlimited number of cadets to receive these scholarships. **Funds Available:** Awards are type 2 AFROTC scholarships that provide for payment of tuition and fees, to a maximum of $15,000 per year, plus an annual book allowance of $600. Recipients are also awarded a tax-free subsistence allowance for 10 months of each year that is $300 per month during the sophomore year, $350 during the junior year, and $400 during the senior year. **Duration:** 2 to 3 years, beginning during the current term.
Eligibility Requirements: This program is open to U.S. citizens at least 17 years of age who are currently enrolled at 1 of the 48 HBCUs that has an Air Force ROTC unit on campus or that has a cross-enrollment agreement with another school that hosts a unit. Applicants do not need to be African American as long as they are attending an HBCU and have a cumulative GPA of 2.5 or higher. At the time of commissioning, they may be no more than 31 years of age. They must be able to pass the Air Force Officer Qualifying Test (AFOQT) and the Air Force ROTC Physical Fitness Test. Currently, the program is accepting applications from students with any major. **Deadline for Receipt:** Applications may be submitted at any time. **Additional Information:** While scholarship recipients can major in any subject, they must complete 4 years of aerospace studies courses at 1 of the HBCUs that have an Air Force ROTC unit on campus. Recipients must also attend a 4-week summer training camp at an Air Force base, usually between their sophomore and junior years; 2-year scholarship awardees attend in the summer after their junior year. Current military personnel are eligible for early release from active duty in order to enter the Air Force ROTC program. Following completion of their bachelor's degree, scholarship recipients earn a commission as a second lieutenant in the Air Force and serve at least 4 years.

1691 ■ U.S. AIR FORCE
Attn: Headquarters AFROTC/RRUC
551 East Maxwell Boulevard
Maxwell AFB, AL 36112-5917
Tel: (334)953-2091; (866)423-7682
Fax: (334)953-6167
Web Site: http://www.afrotc.com/overview/programs.php
To provide financial assistance to college sophomores interested in joining Air Force ROTC and serving as Air Force officers following completion of their bachelor's degree.
Title of Award: Air Force ROTC General Military Course Incentive **Area, Field, or Subject:** General studies/Field of study not specified **Level of Education for which Award is Granted:** Undergraduate **Funds Available:** Selected cadets receive up to $1,500 for tuition and a stipend of $250 per month. **Duration:** 1 semester (the spring semester of junior year); nonrenewable.
Eligibility Requirements: This program is open to U.S. citizens who are entering the spring semester of their sophomore year in the general military course at a college or university with an Air Force ROTC unit on campus or a college with a cross-enrollment agreement with such a school. Applicants must be full-time students, have a GPA of 2.0 or higher both cumulatively and during the prior term, be enrolled in both the Aerospace Studies 200 class and the Leadership Laboratory, pass the Air Force Officer Qualifying Test, meet Air Force physical fitness and weight requirements, and be able to be commissioned before they become 31 years of age. They must agree to serve for at least 4 years as active-duty Air Force officers following graduation from college. **Additional Information:** Upon successful completion of their sophomore year, recipients of these scholarships may upgrade to the Professional Officer Course Incentive. They also remain eligible to apply for other AFROTC in-college scholarship programs.

1692 ■ U.S. AIR FORCE
Attn: Air Force Personnel Center
Headquarters USAF/DPPAT
550 C Street West, Suite 10
Randolph AFB, TX 78150-4712
Fax: (210)565-2328
Web Site: http://www.airforce.com/education/enlisted/moneyForSchool.php
To provide financial assistance for college or graduate school to active-duty Air Force personnel.
Title of Award: Air Force Tuition Assistance Program **Area, Field, or Subject:** General studies/Field of study not specified **Level of Education**

for which Award is Granted: Graduate, Undergraduate **Number Awarded:** Varies each year. **Funds Available:** Air Force personnel chosen for participation in this program continue to receive their regular Air Force pay. The Air Force will pay 100% of the tuition costs in an approved program, to a maximum of $4,500 per year or $250 per semester hour, whichever is less. **Duration:** Up to 4 years.

Eligibility Requirements: Eligible to apply for this program are active-duty Air Force personnel who have completed 2 years of their service obligation. **Additional Information:** Applications and further information about this program are available from counselors at the education centers on Air Force bases. Most Air Force personnel who receive tuition assistance participate in the Community College of the Air Force; there, participants earn a 2-year associate degree by combining on-the-job technical training or attendance at Air Force schools with enrollment in college courses at a civilian institution during off-duty hours. In addition, each Air Force base offers at least 4 subject areas in which selected Air Force personnel can receive tuition assistance for study leading to a bachelor's degree, and 2 disciplines in which they can pursue graduate study.

1693 ■ U.S. AIR FORCE
Attn: Headquarters AFROTC/RRUE
Enlisted Commissioning Section
551 East Maxwell Boulevard
Maxwell AFB, AL 36112-5917
Tel: (334)953-2091; (866)423-7682
Fax: (334)953-6167
E-mail: enlisted@afrotc.com
Web Site: http://www.afoats.af.mil/AFROTC/EnlistedComm/SOAR.asp
To allow selected enlisted Air Force personnel to earn a bachelor's degree by providing financial assistance for full-time college study.

Title of Award: Scholarships for Outstanding Airmen to ROTC (SOAR) **Area, Field, or Subject:** General studies/Field of study not specified **Level of Education for which Award is Granted:** Undergraduate **Number Awarded:** Approximately 50 each year. **Funds Available:** A limited number of selectees receive type 1 AFROTC scholarships that provide payment of full tuition and required educational fees plus an allowance of $600 per year for books. Other selectees receive type 2 scholarships that pay the same benefits except tuition is capped at $15,000 per year. All recipients are also awarded a tax-free subsistence allowance for 10 months of each year that is $250 per month during the freshman year, $300 per month during the sophomore year, $350 per month during the junior year, and $400 per month during the senior year. **Duration:** 2 to 4 years.

Eligibility Requirements: Eligible to participate in this program are enlisted members of the Air Force who have completed from 1 to 6 years of active duty and have at least 1 year time-on-station. Candidates must be nominated by their commanding officers and be accepted at a college or university offering the AFROTC 4-year program. Airmen with 24 semester hours or more of graded college credit must have a cumulative GPA of 2.5 or higher; airmen with less than 24 semester hours must have an ACT score of 24 or higher or an SAT score of 1100 or higher. All applicants must earn Air Force Officer Qualifying Test (AFOQT) scores of 15 or more on the verbal scale and 10 or more on the quantitative scale. U.S. citizenship is required. When the recipients complete the program, they may be no more than 27 years of age (extendable to 30 years if the applicant has prior active-duty service). All academic majors are eligible. **Deadline for Receipt:** October of each year. **Additional Information:** Upon completing their degree, selectees are commissioned as officers in the Air Force with a 4-year service obligation. Further information is available from base education service officers or an Air Force ROTC unit.

1694 ■ U.S. ARMY
Human Resources Command
AHRC-PDE-EI
Attn: Education Incentives and Counseling Branch
200 Stovall Street, Suite 3N17
Alexandria, VA 22332-0472
Tel: (703)325-0285
Free: 800-872-8272
Fax: (703)325-6599
E-mail: pdeei@hoffman.army.mil
Web Site: http://www.hrc.army.mil/site/education/Text/ACF.html

To provide financial assistance for college to Army enlistees after they have completed their service obligation.

Title of Award: Army College Fund **Area, Field, or Subject:** General studies/Field of study not specified **Level of Education for which Award is Granted:** Undergraduate **Number Awarded:** Varies each year. **Funds Available:** The Army College Fund (ACF) provides money for college in addition to that which the enlistee receives under the Montgomery GI Bill. The maximum benefit is $26,500 for a 2-year enlistment, $33,000 for a 3-year enlistment, or $40,000 for a 4-year enlistment. For specified MOSs, the maximum benefit (including payments under the Montgomery GI Bill) is $50,000. **Duration:** 36 months; funds must be utilized within 10 years of leaving the Army.

Eligibility Requirements: Eligible for this program are high school seniors or graduates who enlist in an approved military occupational specialty (MOS) for at least 2 years, score 50 or above on the Armed Forces Qualification Test (AFQT), enroll in the Montgomery GI Bill, and attend a Department of Veterans Affairs-approved postsecondary educational institution on a full-time basis after completion of their service obligation. **Deadline for Receipt:** Applications may be submitted at any time. **Additional Information:** Applications and further information are available from local Army recruiters.

1695 ■ U.S. ARMY
ROTC Cadet Command
Attn: ATCC-OP-I-S
55 Patch Road, Building 56
Fort Monroe, VA 23651-1052
Tel: (757)727-4558
Free: 800-USA-ROTC
E-mail: atccps@usaac.army.mil
Web Site: http://www.rotc.usaac.army.mil/scholarship_HPD2/fouryear/program.htm
To provide financial assistance to high school seniors or graduates who are interested in enrolling in Army ROTC in college.

Title of Award: Army ROTC 4-Year Scholarships **Area, Field, or Subject:** General studies/Field of study not specified **Level of Education for which Award is Granted:** Four Year College **Number Awarded:** Approximately 1,500 each year. **Funds Available:** This scholarship provides financial assistance of up to $20,000 per year for college tuition and educational fees or for room and board, whichever the student selects. In addition, a flat rate of $600 per year is provided for the purchase of textbooks, classroom supplies and equipment. Recipients are also awarded a stipend for up to 10 months of each year that is $250 per month during their freshman year; $300 per month during their sophomore year $350 per month during their junior year, and $400 per month during their senior year. **Duration:** 4 years, until completion of a baccalaureate degree.

Eligibility Requirements: Applicants for this program must 1) be U.S. citizens; 2) be at least 17 years of age by October of the year in which they are seeking a scholarship; 3) be able to complete a college degree and receive their commission before their 31st birthday; 4) score at least 920 on the SAT or 19 on the ACT; 5) have a high school GPA of 2.5 or higher; and 6) meet medical and other regulatory requirements. Current college or university students may apply if their school considers them beginning freshmen with 4 academic years remaining for a bachelor's degree. **Deadline for Receipt:** November of each year. **Additional Information:** Scholarship recipients participate in the Army ROTC program as part of their college curriculum by enrolling in 4 years of military science classes and attending a 6-week summer camp between the junior and senior years. Following graduation, they receive a commission as a Regular Army, Army Reserve, or Army National Guard officer. Scholarship winners must serve in the military for 8 years. That service obligation may be fulfilled 1) by serving on active duty for 4 years followed by service in the Army National Guard (ARNG), the United States Army Reserve (USAR), or the Inactive Ready Reserve (IRR) for the remainder of the 8 years; or 2) by serving 8 years in an ARNG or USAR troop program unit that includes a 3- to 6-month active-duty period for initial training.

1696 ■ U.S. ARMY
ROTC Cadet Command
Attn: ATCC-OP-I-S
55 Patch Road, Building 56
Fort Monroe, VA 23651-1052

Tel: (757)727-4558
Free: 800-USA-ROTC
E-mail: atccps@usaac.army.mil
Web Site: http://www.rotc.usaac.army.mil/scholarship_HPD2/index.asp
To provide financial assistance to non-scholarship participants in the Army ROTC Program who have qualified for the Advanced Course.

Title of Award: Army ROTC Advanced Course **Area, Field, or Subject:** General studies/Field of study not specified **Level of Education for which Award is Granted:** Four Year College **Number Awarded:** Varies each year. **Funds Available:** Participants receive a stipend of $350 per month during their junior year and $400 per month during their senior year, as well as pay for attending the 6-week advanced camp during the summer between the junior and senior years of college. **Duration:** 2 years.

Eligibility Requirements: Non-scholarship cadets in the ROTC Program are eligible to apply for this program if they have qualified for the ROTC Advanced Course. The Advanced Course is usually taken during the final 2 years of college. **Additional Information:** Non-scholarship graduates may serve 3 years on active duty and 5 years in the Reserve Forces, or they may select or be selected to serve all 8 years on Reserve Forces Duty (RFD). If RFD is selected, graduates attend an Officer Basic Course and spend the remainder of their 8-year obligation in the Reserve Forces.

1697 ■ U.S. ARMY
ROTC Cadet Command
Attn: ATCC-OP-I-S
55 Patch Road, Building 56
Fort Monroe, VA 23651-1052
Tel: (757)727-4558
Free: 800-USA-ROTC
E-mail: atccps@usaac.army.mil
Web Site: http://www.rotc.usaac.army.mil/scholarship_HPD2/index.asp
To provide financial assistance to students who are or will be enrolled in Army ROTC.

Title of Award: Army ROTC College Scholarship Program **Area, Field, or Subject:** General studies/Field of study not specified **Level of Education for which Award is Granted:** Four Year College **Number Awarded:** Varies each year; a recent allocation provided for 700 4-year scholarships, 1,800 3-year scholarships, and 2,800 2-year scholarships. **Funds Available:** These scholarships provide financial assistance for college tuition and educational fees, up to an annual amount of $16,000. In addition, a flat rate of $510 is provided for the purchase of textbooks, classroom supplies, and equipment. Recipients are also awarded a stipend for up to 10 months of each year that is $300 per month during their sophomore year, $350 per month during their junior year, and $400 per month during their senior year. **Duration:** 2 or 3 years, until the recipient completes the bachelor's degree.

Eligibility Requirements: This program is open to U.S. citizens at least 17 years of age who have already completed 1 or 2 years in a college or university with an Army ROTC unit on campus or in a college with a cross-enrollment agreement with a college with an Army ROTC unit on campus. Applicants must have 2 or 3 years remaining for their bachelor's degree (or 4 years of a 5-year bachelor's program) and must be able to complete that degree before their 31st birthday. They must have a GPA of 2.5 or higher in their previous college study and scores of at least 920 on the SAT or 19 on the ACT. **Deadline for Receipt:** December of each year. **Additional Information:** Applications must be made through professors of military science at 1 of the schools hosting the Army ROTC program. Preference is given to students who have already enrolled as non-scholarship students in military science classes at 1 of the more than 270 institutions with an Army ROTC unit on campus, at 1 of the 75 college extension centers, or at 1 of the more than 1,000 colleges with cross-enrollment or extension agreements with 1 of the colleges with an Army ROTC unit. Scholarship winners must serve in the military for 8 years. That service obligation may be fulfilled 1) by serving on active duty for 4 years followed by service in the Army National Guard (ARNG), the United States Army Reserve (USAR), or the Inactive Ready Reserve (IRR) for the remainder of the 8 years; or 2) by serving 8 years in an ARNG or USAR troop program unit that includes a 3- to 6-month active-duty period for initial training.

1698 ■ U.S. ARMY
Human Resources Command
AHRC-PDE-EI

Attn: Education Incentives and Counseling Branch
200 Stovall Street, Suite 3N17
Alexandria, VA 22332-0472
Tel: (703)325-0285
Free: 800-872-8272
Fax: (703)325-6599
E-mail: pdeei@hoffman.army.mil
Web Site: http://www.hrc.army.mil/site/education/Text/TA.html
To provide financial assistance to Army personnel interested in working on an undergraduate or graduate degree.

Title of Award: Army Tuition Assistance Benefits **Area, Field, or Subject:** General studies/Field of study not specified **Level of Education for which Award is Granted:** Graduate, Undergraduate **Number Awarded:** Varies each year. **Funds Available:** Those selected for participation in this program receive their regular Army pay and 100% of tuition at the postsecondary educational institution of their choice, but capped at $4,500 per year or $250 per semester hour, whichever is less. **Duration:** Until completion of a bachelor's or graduate degree.

Eligibility Requirements: This program is open to active-duty Army personnel, including members of the Army National Guard and Army Reserve on active duty. Applicants must first visit an education counselor to declare an educational goal and establish an educational plan. Applicants may enroll in up to 15 semester hours of college courses. **Additional Information:** This program is part of the Army Continuing Education System (ACES). Further information is available from counselors at the education centers at all Army installations with a troop strength of 750 or more.

1699 ■ U.S. ARMY
ROTC Cadet Command
Attn: ATCC-OP-I-S
55 Patch Road, Building 56
Fort Monroe, VA 23651-1052
Tel: (757)727-4558
Free: 800-USA-ROTC
E-mail: atccps@usaac.army.mil
Web Site: http://www.rotc.usaac.army.mil/scholarship_HPD2/GRFD/grfd%20main.htm
To provide financial assistance to college and graduate students who are interested in enrolling in Army ROTC and serve in the Army National Guard following graduation.

Title of Award: Dedicated Army National Guard (DedARNG) Scholarships **Area, Field, or Subject:** General studies/Field of study not specified **Level of Education for which Award is Granted:** Four Year College, Graduate **Number Awarded:** 594 each year (11 in each state or U.S. territory). **Funds Available:** Participants receive reimbursement of tuition (up to $28,000 per year), a grant of $600 per year for books, plus an ROTC stipend for 10 months of the year at $350 per month during their junior year and $400 per month during their senior year. As a member of the Army National Guard, they also receive weekend drill pay at the pay grade of E-5 during their junior year or E-6 during their senior year. **Duration:** Normally 2 years. Students who convert to this program may be eligible for support up to 4 years.

Eligibility Requirements: This program is open to full-time students entering their junior year of college with a GPA of 2.5 or higher. Graduate students are also eligible if they have only 2 years remaining for completion of their graduate degree. Students who have been awarded an ROTC campus-based scholarship may apply to convert to this program during their freshman year. Applicants must meet all medical and moral character requirements for enrollment in Army ROTC. They must be willing to enroll in the Simultaneous Membership Program (SMP) of an ROTC unit on their campus; the SMP requires simultaneous membership in Army ROTC and the Army National Guard. **Additional Information:** After graduation, participants serve 3 to 6 months on active duty in the Officer Basic Course (OBC). Following completion of OBC, they are released from active duty and are obligated to serve 8 years in the Army National Guard.

1700 ■ U.S. ARMY
Human Resources Command
Attn: AHRC-OPL-L
200 Stovall Street
Alexandria, VA 22332-0414
Tel: (703)325-3138

Fax: (703)325-5463

Web Site: http://www.hrc.army.mil/site/Active/opfamacs/DCP01.htm

To enable Army warrant and commissioned officers to complete an academic degree while receiving their regular pay and allowances.

Title of Award: Degree Completion Program of the U.S. Army **Area, Field, or Subject:** General studies/Field of study not specified **Level of Education for which Award is Granted:** Graduate, Undergraduate **Number Awarded:** Varies each year. **Funds Available:** Participants continue to receive regular Army salary and allowances, but they are required to pay all educational expenses out of their own funds. They are not eligible for Army Tuition Assistance Benefits, but they may use any Montgomery GI Bill or VEAP benefits to which they are entitled. **Duration:** The period of schooling is generally limited to 12 months, although up to 18 months may be authorized on an individual basis.

Eligibility Requirements: This program is open to Army warrant and commissioned officers who wish to complete a bachelor's or graduate degree at an approved civilian institution on a full-time basis. Commissioned officers must be on active duty and have less than 19 years of active federal commissioned service (AFCS). Warrant officers must be in a voluntary indefinite status or Regular Army and have at least 3 years of AFCS. Those who are in voluntary indefinite status must have less than 16 years of active federal service (AFS); those who are Regular Army must have less than 24 years of active warrant officer service (AWOS). All applicants must have enough service time left after completing degree requirements to fulfill the service obligation. **Deadline for Receipt:** Applications may be submitted at any time, but they must be received at least 5 months prior to the starting date of the proposed schooling. **Additional Information:** Participants in this program incur an additional service obligation of 3 days of service for each day of educational leave.

1701 ■ U.S. ARMY

ROTC Cadet Command

Attn: ATCC-OP-I-S

55 Patch Road, Building 56

Fort Monroe, VA 23651-1052

Tel: (757)727-4558

Free: 800-USA-ROTC

E-mail: atccps@usaac.army.mil

Web Site: http://www.rotc.usaac.army.mil/scholarship_HPD2/green/index.asp

To provide financial assistance to soldiers who wish to obtain an early discharge from the Army and return to college to participate in the Army Reserve Officers' Training Corps (ROTC).

Title of Award: Green to Gold Non-Scholarship Program **Area, Field, or Subject:** General studies/Field of study not specified **Level of Education for which Award is Granted:** Undergraduate **Number Awarded:** Varies each year. **Funds Available:** Cadets receive a stipend for 10 months of the year that is $350 per month during their junior year and $400 per month during their senior year, as well as pay for attending the 6-week Leader Development and Assessment Course (LDAC) during the summer between the junior and senior year of college. **Duration:** 2 years.

Eligibility Requirements: This program is open to enlisted soldiers who have served at least 2 years on active duty and have also completed at least 2 years of college with a GPA of 2.0 or higher. Applicants must be under 30 years of age when they graduate (waivers up to 32 years of age are available). They apply for this program to obtain an early discharge from active duty in order to enroll in a baccalaureate degree program. **Deadline for Receipt:** March or September of each year. **Additional Information:** Cadets who had previously qualified for benefits from the Army College Fund and/or the Montgomery GI Bill are still entitled to receive those in addition to any benefits from this program. Cadets are also entitled to participate in the Simultaneous Membership Program and serve with pay in a drilling unit of the Army Reserve or Army National Guard. Upon graduation from college, cadets are commissioned as second lieutenants and are required to serve in the military for 8 years. That obligation may be fulfilled by serving 3 years on active duty and 5 years in the Inactive Ready Reserve (IRR).

1702 ■ U.S. ARMY

ROTC Cadet Command

Attn: ATCC-OP-I-S

55 Patch Road, Building 56

Fort Monroe, VA 23651-1052

Tel: (757)727-4558

Free: 800-USA-ROTC

E-mail: atccps@usaac.army.mil

Web Site: http://www.rotc.usaac.army.mil/scholarship_HPD2/green/index.asp

To provide scholarships and other payments to soldiers who wish to obtain an early discharge from the Army and return to college to participate in the Army Reserve Officers' Training Corps (ROTC).

Title of Award: Green to Gold Scholarship Program **Area, Field, or Subject:** General studies/Field of study not specified **Level of Education for which Award is Granted:** Undergraduate **Number Awarded:** Varies each year; recently, 224 of these scholarships were awarded, including 76 for 2 years, 91 for 3 years, 51 for 4 years, and 6 for graduate study. **Funds Available:** Scholarship winners receive up to $20,000 per year as support for tuition and fees or for room and board, whichever the recipient selects; additional support up to $900 per year for textbooks, supplies, and equipment; a stipend for 10 months of the year that is $300 per month during their sophomore year, $350 per month during their junior year, and $400 per month during their senior year; and pay for attending the 6-week Leader Development and Assessment Course (LDAC) during the summer between the junior and senior year of college. **Duration:** Scholarships are for 2, 3, or 4 years; soldiers without prior college credit or whose colleges accept them as academic freshmen are eligible for 4-year scholarships; soldiers with 1 year of college completed are eligible for 3-year scholarships; soldiers with 2 years of college completed are eligible for 2-year scholarships.

Eligibility Requirements: Enlisted soldiers who have served at least 2 years on active duty may apply for this program to obtain an early discharge from active duty in order to enroll in a baccalaureate degree program. Applicants must have a cumulative high school or college GPA of 2.5 or higher, a General Technical (GT) score of 110 or higher, and an Army Physical Fitness Test (APFT) score of 180 or higher (including 60 points in each event). They may have no more than 3 dependents including a spouse (that requirement may be waived) and must be under 31 years of age when they graduate and are commissioned. **Deadline for Receipt:** March or September of each year. **Additional Information:** Recipients who had previously qualified for benefits from the Army College Fund and/or the Montgomery GI Bill are still entitled to receive those in addition to any benefits from this program. Upon graduation from college, scholarship winners are commissioned as second lieutenants and are required to serve in the military for 8 years. That obligation may be fulfilled by serving 4 years on active duty followed by 4 years in the Inactive Ready Reserve (IRR).

1703 ■ U.S. ARMY

ROTC Cadet Command

Attn: ATCC-OP-I-S

55 Patch Road, Building 56

Fort Monroe, VA 23651-1052

Tel: (757)727-4558

Free: 800-USA-ROTC

E-mail: atccps@usaac.army.mil

Web Site: http://www.rotc.usaac.army.mil/scholarship_HPD2/GRFD/grfd%20main.htm

To provide financial assistance to college and graduate students who are willing to enroll in Army ROTC and serve in a Reserve component of the Army following graduation.

Title of Award: Guaranteed Reserve Forces Duty (GRFD) Scholarships **Area, Field, or Subject:** General studies/Field of study not specified **Level of Education for which Award is Granted:** Four Year College, Graduate **Number Awarded:** 54 each year (1 in each state or U.S. territory). **Funds Available:** Participants receive reimbursement of tuition (up to $28,000 per year), a grant of $600 per year for books, plus an ROTC stipend for 10 months of the year at $350 per month during their junior year and $400 per month during their senior year. As a member of the Army National Guard or Army Reserve, they also receive weekend drill pay at the pay grade of E-5 during their junior year or E-6 during their senior year. **Duration:** 2 years.

Eligibility Requirements: This program is open to full-time students entering their junior year of college with a GPA of 2.5 or higher. Graduate students are also eligible if they have only 2 years remaining for completion of their graduate degree. Applicants must meet all other medical and moral character requirements for enrollment in Army ROTC). They must be willing to enroll in the Simultaneous Membership Program (SMP) of an ROTC unit on their campus; the SMP requires simultaneous membership in Army ROTC and the Army National Guard or Army Reserve. **Additional Information:** After graduation, participants serve 3 to 6 months on active duty in the Officer Basic Course (OBC). Following completion of OBC, they are released from active duty and are obligated to serve 8 years in the Army National Guard or Army Reserve.

1704 ■ U.S. ARMY
ROTC Cadet Command
Attn: ATCC-OP-I-S
55 Patch Road, Building 56
Fort Monroe, VA 23651-1052
Tel: (757)727-4558
Free: 800-USA-ROTC
E-mail: atccps@usaac.army.mil
Web Site: http://www.rotc.usaac.army.mil/scholarship_HPD2/fouryear/hbcu.htm
To provide financial assistance to high school seniors or graduates who are interested in enrolling in Army ROTC at an Historically Black College or University (HBCU).
Title of Award: Historically Black Colleges/Universities Scholarship Program **Area, Field, or Subject:** General studies/Field of study not specified **Level of Education for which Award is Granted:** Undergraduate **Number Awarded:** A limited number of these scholarships is offered each year. **Funds Available:** This scholarship provides financial assistance of up to $20,000 per year for college tuition and educational fees or for room and board, whichever the student selects. In addition, a flat rate of $600 per year is provided for the purchase of textbooks, classroom supplies and equipment. Recipients are also awarded a stipend for up to 10 months of each year that is $250 per month during their freshman year; $300 per month during their sophomore year $350 per month during their junior year, and $400 per month during their senior year. **Duration:** 4 years.
Eligibility Requirements: Applicants for this program must 1) be U.S. citizens; 2) be at least 17 years of age by October of the year in which they are seeking a scholarship; 3) be able to complete a college degree and receive their commission before their 31st birthday; 4) score at least 920 on the SAT or 19 on the ACT; 5) have a high school GPA of 2.5 or higher; 6) meet medical and other regulatory requirements; and 7) be planning to attend 1 of 73 designated HBCUs that has an ROTC detachment or a cross-town agreement with a college or university that does. Current college or university students may apply if their school considers them beginning freshmen with 4 academic years remaining for a bachelor's degree. **Deadline for Receipt:** November of each year. **Additional Information:** Scholarship recipients participate in the Army ROTC program as part of their college curriculum by enrolling in 4 years of military science classes, pursuing an Army-approved academic discipline, and attending a 6-week summer camp between the junior and senior years. Following graduation, they receive a commission as a Regular Army, Army Reserve, or Army National Guard officer. Scholarship winners must serve in the military for 8 years. That service obligation may be fulfilled 1) by serving on active duty for 4 years followed by service in the Army National Guard (ARNG), the United States Army Reserve (USAR), or the Inactive Ready Reserve (IRR) for the remainder of the 8 years; or 2) by serving 8 years in an ARNG or USAR troop program unit that includes a 3to 6-month active duty period for initial training.

1705 ■ U.S. ARMY
ROTC Cadet Command
Attn: ATCC-OP-I-S
55 Patch Road, Building 56
Fort Monroe, VA 23651-1052
Tel: (757)727-4558
Free: 800-USA-ROTC
E-mail: atccps@usaac.army.mil
Web Site: http://www.rotc.usaac.army.mil/scholarship_HPD2/index.asp
To provide financial assistance to individuals who serve simultaneously in the Army National Guard or Army Reserve and the Army Reserve Officers' Training Corps (ROTC) while they are in college.
Title of Award: Simultaneous Membership Program (SMP) **Area, Field, or Subject:** General studies/Field of study not specified **Level of Education for which Award is Granted:** Undergraduate **Number Awarded:**

Varies each year. **Funds Available:** Advanced ROTC Simultaneous Membership Program (SMP) participants are paid at the rate of at least a Sergeant E-5 for their Guard or Reserve training assemblies (recently, $216 per month), plus an ROTC stipend for 10 months of the year at $350 per month during their junior year and $400 per month during their senior year. **Duration:** Up to 2 years.
Eligibility Requirements: Students who are members of the Army National Guard or the Army Reserve and Army ROTC at the same time are eligible for this assistance. Applicants must have completed basic training or the equivalent, have at least 4 years remaining on their current military obligation, be full-time students as college juniors, have a GPA of 2.0 or higher, and be U.S. citizens. **Additional Information:** Participants serve as officer trainees in their Guard or Reserve units and, under the close supervision of a commissioned officer, perform duties commensurate with those of a second lieutenant. Cadets who successfully complete the SMP program graduate with a commission as a second lieutenant. Once commissioned, they may continue to serve in their Guard or Reserve units, or they may apply for active duty in the U.S. Army.

1706 ■ U.S. ARMY NATIONAL GUARD
c/o DANTES
6490 Saufley Field Road
Pensacola, FL 32509-5243
Tel: (850)452-1085
Fax: (850)452-1161
E-mail: tahelp@voled.doded.mil
Web Site: http://www.1800goguard.com/education/edu_tuition.html
To provide financial assistance for college or graduate school to members of the Army National Guard in each state.
Title of Award: Army National Guard Tuition Assistance **Area, Field, or Subject:** General studies/Field of study not specified **Level of Education for which Award is Granted:** Graduate, Undergraduate **Number Awarded:** Varies each year; recently, more than 22,000 Guard members received tuition assistance. **Funds Available:** Assistance provides up to 100% of tuition (to a maximum of $250 per semester hour or $4,500 per person per fiscal year). **Duration:** Participants in Office Candidate School (OCS), Warrant Officer Candidate School (WOCS), and ROTC Simultaneous Membership Program (SMP) may enroll in up to 15 semester hours per year until completion of a baccalaureate degree. Warrant Officers are funded to complete an associate degree.
Eligibility Requirements: This program is open to members of the Army National Guard in every state who are interested in attending a college, community college, or university within the state. Applicants must have sufficient time to complete the course before their Expiration Time of Service (ETS) date. They must be interested in working on a high school diploma or equivalent (GED), certificate, associate degree, bachelor's degree, master's degree, or first professional degree, including those in architecture, certified public accountant, podiatry, dentistry (D.D.S. or D.M.D.), medicine (M.D.), optometry, osteopathic medicine, pharmacy (Pharm.D.), or theology (M.Div. or M.H.L.). Commissioned officers must agree to remain in the Guard for at least 4 years following completion of the course for which assistance is provided, unless they are involuntarily separated from the service. **Additional Information:** Tuition assistance may be used along with federal Pell Grants but not with Montgomery GI Bill benefits. State tuition assistance programs can be used concurrently with this program, but not to exceed 100% of tuition costs.

1707 ■ U.S. ARMY ORDNANCE CORPS ASSOCIATION
Attn: Heiser Scholarship
P.O. Box 377
Aberdeen Proving Ground, MD 21005-0377
Tel: (410)272-8540
Fax: (410)272-8425
Web Site: http://www.usaoca.org/heiser.html
To provide financial assistance for college to students who submit, along with their application, an essay on the U.S. Army.
Title of Award: LTG and Mrs. Joseph M. Heiser Scholarship **Area, Field, or Subject:** General studies/Field of study not specified **Level of Education for which Award is Granted:** Undergraduate **Number Awarded:** Varies each year; recently, 4 of these scholarships were awarded. **Funds Available:** The stipend is $1,000. **Duration:** 1 year.
Eligibility Requirements: This program is open to high school seniors and students already enrolled in college. Applicants must submit an essay

of 1,000 to 1,500 words on a topic related to the history or heritage of the U.S. Army, a statement describing any circumstances that would impact their attending college, letters of recommendation, transcripts, and an essay of 300 to 500 words on their educational and career goals. **Deadline for Receipt:** June of each year.

1708 ■ UNITED STATES ARMY WARRANT OFFICERS ASSOCIATION

Attn: USAWOA Scholarship Foundation
462 Herndon Parkway, Suite 207
Herndon, VA 20170-5235
Tel: (703)742-7727
Free: 800-5-USAWOA
Fax: (703)742-7728
E-mail: usawoasf@cavetel.net
Web Site: http://www.penfed.org/usawoa/WOASF/index.html
To provide financial assistance for college to dependents of members of the United States Army Warrant Officers Association.
Title of Award: United States Army Warrant Officers Association Family Member Scholarship Program **Area, Field, or Subject:** General studies/ Field of study not specified **Level of Education for which Award is Granted:** Undergraduate **Number Awarded:** Varies each year; recently, 3 of these scholarships were awarded. **Funds Available:** The stipend is at least $1,000. **Duration:** 1 year; may be renewed.
Eligibility Requirements: This program is open to children and dependent stepchildren, under 23 years of age, of regular members of the association. Spouses of members are also eligible. Applicants must plan to attend an accredited U.S. college, university, or vocational/technical institution on a full-time basis. They must have a GPA of 3.0 or higher. **Deadline for Receipt:** April of each year. **Additional Information:** This program includes the Carrie A. Clayburn Memorial Scholarship and the Pentagon Federal Credit Union USAWOA Scholarship.

1709 ■ U.S. BANCORP

U.S. Bancorp Center
800 Nicollet Mall
Minneapolis, MN 55402
Tel: (612)US-BANKS
Free: 800-US-BANKS
Web Site: http://www.usbank.com/cgi_w/cfm/studentloans/marketing.cfm
To provide financial assistance for college to high school seniors who apply through an online procedure.
Title of Award: U.S. Bank Internet Scholarship Program **Area, Field, or Subject:** General studies/Field of study not specified **Level of Education for which Award is Granted:** Undergraduate **Number Awarded:** Up to 30 each year. **Funds Available:** The stipend is $1,000. **Duration:** 1 year; nonrenewable.
Eligibility Requirements: This program is open to high school seniors planning to enroll full time at a 2-year or 4-year accredited college or university that participates in the Federal Family Education Loan Program (FFELP). U.S. citizenship or permanent resident status is required. Applications are available only through an online procedure. Selection is based on a random drawing. **Deadline for Receipt:** February of each year. **Additional Information:** This program began in 1997.

1710 ■ UNITED STATES BOWLING CONGRESS

Attn: SMART Program
5301 South 76th Street
Greendale, WI 53129-1192
Tel: (414)423-3223
Free: 800-514-BOWL
Fax: (414)421-3014
E-mail: smart@bowl.com
Web Site: http://www.bowl.com/scholarships/main.aspx
To recognize and reward, with college scholarships, young bowlers who demonstrate outstanding community service.
Title of Award: Annual Zeb Scholarship **Area, Field, or Subject:** General studies/Field of study not specified **Level of Education for which Award is Granted:** Undergraduate **Number Awarded:** 1 each year. **Funds Available:** The award consists of a $2,500 college scholarship. **Duration:** The award is presented annually.
Eligibility Requirements: This award is presented to United States Bowling Congress (USBC) Youth members in the junior or senior year of high

school. Applicants must have a GPA of 2.0 or higher and not have competed in a professional bowling tournament. Along with their application, they must submit an essay of 500 words on a topic of their choosing. Selection is based on the essay, grades, letters of reference, and academic and community involvement. **Deadline for Receipt:** March of each year. **Additional Information:** This award, named in honor or Jim Zebehazy, executive director of the Young American Bowling alliance prior to its merger with the USBC, is presented at the USBC Junior Gold Championships award ceremony. Travel and hotel expenses for the awardee and a parent or guardian to attend the ceremony are also provided.

1711 ■ UNITED STATES BOWLING CONGRESS

Attn: SMART Program
5301 South 76th Street
Greendale, WI 53129-1192
Tel: (414)423-3223
Free: 800-514-BOWL
Fax: (414)421-3014
E-mail: smart@bowl.com
Web Site: http://www.bowl.com/scholarships/main.aspx
To provide financial assistance for college to members of the United States Bowling Congress (USBC) Youth who demonstrate outstanding community service and financial need.
Title of Award: Earl Anthony Memorial Scholarships **Area, Field, or Subject:** General studies/Field of study not specified **Level of Education for which Award is Granted:** Undergraduate **Number Awarded:** 5 each year. **Funds Available:** The stipend is $5,000. **Duration:** 1 year; nonrenewable.
Eligibility Requirements: This program is open to USBC Youth members who are seniors in high school or current college students. Applicants must have a GPA of 2.5 or higher and not have competed in a professional bowling tournament. Along with their application, they must submit an essay of 500 words on how their bowling, community service, and educational achievements have influenced their life and their goals for the future. Financial need is also considered in the selection process. **Deadline for Receipt:** April of each year.

1712 ■ UNITED STATES BOWLING CONGRESS

Attn: SMART Program
5301 South 76th Street
Greendale, WI 53129-1192
Tel: (414)423-3343
Free: 800-514-BOWL
Fax: (414)421-3014
E-mail: smart@bowl.com
Web Site: http://www.bowl.com/scholarships/main.aspx
To provide financial assistance for college to outstanding women bowlers.
Title of Award: Alberta E. Crowe Star of Tomorrow Award **Area, Field, or Subject:** General studies/Field of study not specified **Level of Education for which Award is Granted:** Undergraduate **Number Awarded:** 1 each year. **Funds Available:** The stipend is $1,500 per year. **Duration:** 1 year; may be renewed for 3 additional years.
Eligibility Requirements: This program is open to women amateur bowlers who are current members in good standing of the United States Bowling Congress (USBC) or USBC Youth and competitors in events sanctioned by those organizations. Applicants must be high school or college students younger than 22 years of age, have a GPA of 2.5 or higher, and have a bowling average of 175 or greater. They may not have competed in a professional bowling tournament. Along with their application, they must submit an essay, up to 500 words, on how this scholarship will influence their bowling, academic, and personal goals. Selection is based on bowling performances on local, regional, state, and national levels; academic achievement; and extracurricular involvement. **Deadline for Receipt:** September of each year.

1713 ■ UNITED STATES BOWLING CONGRESS

Attn: SMART Program
5301 South 76th Street
Greendale, WI 53129-1192
Tel: (414)423-3343
Free: 800-514-BOWL
Fax: (414)421-3014

E-mail: smart@bowl.com
Web Site: http://www.bowl.com/scholarships/main.aspx
To provide financial assistance for college to members of the United State Bowling Congress (USBC) who demonstrate a financial hardship.
Title of Award: Gift for Life Scholarships **Area, Field, or Subject:** General studies/Field of study not specified **Level of Education for which Award is Granted:** Undergraduate **Number Awarded:** 12 each year: 6 specifically for females and 6 for males. That includes 2 awards reserved for children (1 daughter and 1 son) of fire/police/emergency rescue department employees. **Funds Available:** The stipend is $1,000. **Duration:** Scholarships are presented annually. Students may apply each year they are eligible and may win 1 scholarship each year before their high school graduation.
Eligibility Requirements: This program is open to USBC members who are high school students (grades 9-12) and who have not yet competed in a professional bowling tournament. Applicants must be able to demonstrate a financial hardship, defined as residing in a household where the number of children, the income level of their parents, and possible extenuating circumstances make obtaining a college education financially unlikely. They must submit an essay, up to 500 words, explaining how their financial situation could hinder or stop them from achieving their educational goals. Other factors considered in the selection process include GPA (2.0 or higher required), scholastic honors, extracurricular activities, and bowling activities. Applications from males and females are evaluated separately. In honor of the heroes of September 11, 2001, 2 scholarships are reserved for a son and a daughter of fire/police/emergency rescue personnel. **Deadline for Receipt:** March of each year.

1714 ■ UNITED STATES BOWLING CONGRESS

Attn: SMART Program
5301 South 76th Street
Greendale, WI 53129-1192
Tel: (414)423-3343
Free: 800-514-BOWL
Fax: (414)421-3014
E-mail: smart@bowl.com
Web Site: http://www.bowl.com/scholarships/main.aspx
To provide financial assistance for college to outstanding male bowlers.
Title of Award: Chuck Hall Star of Tomorrow Award **Area, Field, or Subject:** General studies/Field of study not specified **Level of Education for which Award is Granted:** Undergraduate **Number Awarded:** 1 each year. **Funds Available:** The stipend is $1,250 per year. **Duration:** 1 year; may be renewed up to 3 additional years.
Eligibility Requirements: This program is open to men amateur bowlers who are current members in good standing of the United States Bowling Congress (USBC) or USBC Youth and competitors in events sanctioned by those organizations. Applicants must be high school or college students younger than 22 years of age, have a GPA of 2.5 or higher, and have a bowling average of 175 or greater. They may not have competed in a professional bowling tournament. Along with their application, they must submit an essay, up to 500 words, on how bowling has influenced their life, academic, and personal goals. Selection is based on bowling performances on local, state, and national levels; academic achievement; and community involvement. **Deadline for Receipt:** November of each year.

1715 ■ UNITED STATES BOWLING CONGRESS

Attn: Pepsi-Cola Youth Bowling Event Manager
5301 South 76th Street
Greendale, WI 53129-1192
Tel: (414)423-3442
Free: 800-514-BOWL
Fax: (414)421-3014
E-mail: maureen.vicena@bowl.com
Web Site: http://www.bowl.com/tournaments/youth/pepsi/main.aspx
To recognize and reward (with college scholarships) members of the United States Bowling Congress (USBC) who achieve high scores in an international competition.
Title of Award: Pepsi USBC Youth Bowling Championships **Area, Field, or Subject:** General studies/Field of study not specified **Level of Education for which Award is Granted:** Undergraduate **Number Awarded:** Each year, 16 scholarships are awarded: 8 are set aside for girls (4 in each division) and 8 for boys (4 in each division). **Funds Available:** At the

international finals, the top finishers in each division receive scholarships of $2,000, $1,500, $1,000, and $500, respectively. **Duration:** The competition is held annually.
Eligibility Requirements: This competition is open to USBC members in the United States, Puerto Rico, U.S. military zones, and Canada. Applicants enter in 1 of 6 categories: 11 and under boys' handicap, 12 and above boys' handicap, 12 and above boys' scratch, 11 and under girls' handicap, 12 and above girls' handicap, and 12 and above girls' scratch. Based on their bowling scores in state and zone competitions, the top bowlers in the 12 and above boys' and girls' handicap categories advance to the international finals. Also advancing to the international finals are the state and zone winners in the 12 and above boys' and girls' scratch categories who are also USBC Junior Gold members (boys must have an average of 175 or above, girls must have an average of 165 or above). All selected finalists (more than 200 qualify each year), are then assigned to Division I or Division II for the international competition, held annually at a site in the United States; assignment is based on their adjusted score from year-end averages and state and zone competitions. Bowlers whose scores are in the top half are assigned to Division I and bowlers whose scores are in the bottom half are assigned to Division II. Scholarships are awarded solely on the basis of bowling performance in the international finals. **Deadline for Receipt:** Qualifying tournaments are held in bowling centers from October through February of each year. Center and section qualifying takes place in March and April. State and zone qualifying competitions take place through the end of May. The national finals are held in July.
Additional Information: This competition is sponsored by the Pepsi-Cola Company and conducted by the USBC. More than $300,000 is scholarships is awarded at state and zone competitions for all 6 categories. USBC also awards a $400 stipend to each competitor at the international finals (Canadian athletes are not eligible for the stipend and competitors from U.S. military bases must pay for their own transportation to the United States); the stipend is intended to assist with the cost of travel, meals, and housing.

1716 ■ UNITED STATES BOWLING CONGRESS

Attn: SMART Program
5301 South 76th Street
Greendale, WI 53129-1192
Tel: (414)423-3343
Free: 800-514-BOWL
Fax: (414)421-3014
E-mail: smart@bowl.com
Web Site: http://www.bowl.com/scholarships/main.aspx
To provide financial assistance for college and other educational activities to young bowlers.
Title of Award: SMART Program Scholarships **Area, Field, or Subject:** General studies/Field of study not specified **Level of Education for which Award is Granted:** Professional, Undergraduate **Number Awarded:** Varies each year; recently, more than 35,000 bowlers received scholarships. **Funds Available:** The awards vary; recently, a total of $2,914,100 was awarded through this program. Some scholarships must be used at accredited colleges and universities for tuition, housing, and books. Other uses that are specified include: bowling camps and lessons; bowling coaching seminars; business, technical, or trade schools; continuing education classes; and educational camps in mathematics, science, art, or computers.
Eligibility Requirements: These awards are presented to bowlers throughout the United States and Canada. Some scholarships are presented to winners of bowling tournaments, but others require written applications. Some require demonstrations of financial need, but others are based on bowling and/or academic accomplishments. Some are limited to students, but others are open to bowlers at other levels. All scholarships must conform to standards of the Scholarship Management and Accounting Reports for Tenpins (SMART) program of the United States Bowling Congress (USBC). **Additional Information:** For a complete list of all scholarship opportunities, contact the sponsor.

1717 ■ UNITED STATES BOWLING CONGRESS

Attn: Junior Gold Program
5301 South 76th Street
Greendale, WI 53129-1192
Tel: (414)423-3171
Free: 800-514-BOWL

Fax: (414)421-3014
E-mail: USBCjuniorgold@bowl.com
Web Site: http://www.bowl.com/bowl/yaba
To recognize and reward, with college scholarships, United States Bowling Congress (USBC) Junior Gold program members who achieve high scores in a national competition.
Title of Award: USBC Junior Gold Championships **Area, Field, or Subject:** General studies/Field of study not specified **Level of Education for which Award is Granted:** Undergraduate **Number Awarded:** Varies each year. Recently, a total of 1,458 spots were available at the national tournament and scholarships were provided to approximately 10% of the competitors. For bowlers from the Pepsi competition, 4 girls and 4 boys win scholarships. **Funds Available:** Scholarships depend on the availability of funding provided by sponsors. Recently, more than $50,000 in scholarships was awarded. Another $15,000 in scholarships was awarded to Junior Gold participants who qualified for the national tournament through the Pepsi competition. That includes $3,000 for first, $2,000 for second, $1,500 for third, and $1,000 for fourth for boys and girls. **Duration:** The competition is held annually.
Eligibility Requirements: This program is open to USBC members who qualify for the Junior Gold program by maintaining a bowling average score of 165 for girls or 175 for boys, based on at least 21 games. Competitions for Junior Gold members are held throughout the season at bowling centers and in bowling leagues in the United States. Each approved competition may enter its top 10% of scorers in the Junior Gold Championships, held annually at a site in the United States. In addition, USBC Junior Gold members who participate in the Pepsi USBC Youth Bowling Championship in the girls' and boys' 12 and over scratch categories and achieve high scores in state and zone competitions are eligible to advance to the national tournament of this program. They compete in separate divisions for boys and girls. Scholarships are awarded solely on the basis of bowling performance in the national tournament. **Deadline for Receipt:** Applications must by submitted by May of each year. The national finals are held in July. **Additional Information:** This competition was first held in 1998. The sponsoring league or center must pay a fee of $150 for each participant who advances to the national tournament.

1718 ■ UNITED STATES BOWLING CONGRESS

Attn: SMART Program
5301 South 76th Street
Greendale, WI 53129-1192
Tel: (414)423-3223
Free: 800-514-BOWL
Fax: (414)421-3014
E-mail: smart@bowl.com
Web Site: http://www.bowl.com/scholarships/main.aspx
To recognize and reward, with college scholarships, outstanding young bowlers.
Title of Award: USBC Youth Leaders of the Year Awards **Area, Field, or Subject:** General studies/Field of study not specified **Level of Education for which Award is Granted:** Undergraduate **Number Awarded:** 2 each year: 1 for a female and 1 for a male. **Funds Available:** The awards consist of $1,500 college scholarships. **Duration:** The awards are presented annually.
Eligibility Requirements: These awards are presented to participants in the Youth Leader program of the United States Bowling Congress (USBC) who are 18 years of age or older. Males and females are considered in separate competitions. Selection is based on exemplary Youth Leader activities and contributions to the sport of bowling. **Deadline for Receipt:** Nominations must be submitted by January of each year. **Additional Information:** Awardees also serve for 2 years on the USBC Board of Directors.

1719 ■ UNITED STATES BOWLING CONGRESS

Attn: SMART Program
5301 South 76th Street
Greendale, WI 53129-1192
Tel: (414)423-3223
Free: 800-514-BOWL
Fax: (414)421-3014
E-mail: smart@bowl.com
Web Site: http://www.bowl.com/scholarships/main.aspx

To provide financial assistance for college to members of the United States Bowling Congress (USBC) Youth who are also recognized in *Who's Who Among American High School Students-Sports Edition.*
Title of Award: Who's Who Sports Edition All-Academic Bowling Team Scholarships **Area, Field, or Subject:** General studies/Field of study not specified **Level of Education for which Award is Granted:** Undergraduate **Number Awarded:** Up to 20 each year. **Funds Available:** The stipend is $1,000. **Duration:** 1 year; nonrenewable.
Eligibility Requirements: This program is open to USBC Youth members who are juniors or seniors in high school. Applicants must have a GPA of 2.5 or higher and not have competed in a professional bowling tournament. They must be listed in the current edition of *Who's Who Among American High School Students-Sports Edition.* Along with their application, they must submit an essay of 500 words on how their involvement in bowling has influenced their life, academic, and personal goals. Financial need is not considered in the selection process. **Deadline for Receipt:** March of each year.

1720 ■ UNITED STATES CHESS FEDERATION

Attn: Scholastic Department
3054 U.S. Route 9W
New Windsor, NY 12553
Tel: (845)562-8350
Free: 800-388-KING
Fax: (845)561-CHES
E-mail: clubs@uschess.org
Web Site: http://www.uschess.org
To recognize and reward, with college scholarships, high school students who excel in academics, chess play, and sportsmanship.
Title of Award: USCF Scholar-Chessplayer Outstanding Achievement Awards **Area, Field, or Subject:** General studies/Field of study not specified **Level of Education for which Award is Granted:** Undergraduate **Number Awarded:** 7 each year. **Funds Available:** First place is $2,000, second $1,000, third $700, fourth $500, fifth $400, and sixth and seventh $200 each. **Duration:** 1 year.
Eligibility Requirements: This program is open to high school juniors and seniors who are members of the United States Chess Federation (USCF) and have shown outstanding merit in academics, sportsmanship, and chess. Applicants must submit a high school transcript, a letter of recommendation from a chess coach, a letter of recommendation from a teacher, a recent photograph, and an essay (up to 500 words) describing the positive influence that chess has had on their life. Financial need is not considered in the selection process. **Deadline for Receipt:** February of each year.

1721 ■ U.S. COAST GUARD

Attn: Coast Guard Recruiting
4200 Wilson Boulevard, Suite 450
Arlington, VA 22203
877-NOW-USCG
Web Site: http://www.gocoastguard.com/scholarships.html
To provide financial assistance to college students at minority institutions willing to serve in the Coast Guard following graduation.
Title of Award: College Student Pre-Commissioning Initiative **Area, Field, or Subject:** General studies/Field of study not specified **Level of Education for which Award is Granted:** Four Year College **Number Awarded:** Varies each year. **Funds Available:** Those selected to participate receive full payment of tuition, books, and fees; monthly housing and food allowances; medical and life insurance; special training in leadership, management, law enforcement, navigation, and marine science; 30 days paid vacation per year; and a monthly salary of up to $2,200. **Duration:** 2 years.
Eligibility Requirements: This program is open to students enrolled as sophomores or juniors at approved 4-year Historically Black Colleges and Universities (HBCUs), Hispanic Serving Institutions (HSIs), and other approved minority institutions of higher learning. Applicants must be U.S. citizens; have a GPA of 2.5 or higher; have scores of 1000 or higher on the SAT, 1100 or higher on the SAT I, 23 or higher on the ACT, or 110 or higher on the ASVAB GT; be between 21 and 26 years of age at the time of college graduation; and meet all physical requirements for a Coast Guard commission. They must agree to attend the Coast Guard Officer Candidate School following graduation and serve on active duty as an officer for at least 3 years. **Deadline for Receipt:** February of each year.

1722 ■ U.S. COAST GUARD INSTITUTE

Attn: Commanding Officer
5900 S.W. 64th Street
Oklahoma City, OK 73169-6990
Tel: (405)954-1360; 888-53-BUCKS
Fax: (405)954-7249
Web Site: http://www.uscg.mil/hq/cgi/tuition/ta.html
To provide financial assistance to members and employees of the Coast Guard who are interested in pursuing additional education during their off-duty hours.

Title of Award: Coast Guard Tuition Assistance Program **Area, Field, or Subject:** General studies/Field of study not specified **Level of Education for which Award is Granted:** Graduate, Undergraduate **Number Awarded:** Varies each year; recently, more than 10,000 Coast Guard active-duty members, Reservists, and civilian employees received tuition assistance. **Funds Available:** Active-duty, Reserve, and civilian Coast Guard members receive full payment of all expenses for completion of a high school degree or equivalent. For college courses (vocational/technical, undergraduate, and graduate), 100% of the cost of tuition is reimbursed, to a maximum of $250 per semester hour or $4,500 per fiscal year. **Duration:** Until completion of a bachelor's or graduate degree.

Eligibility Requirements: This program is open to Coast Guard members who are interested in pursuing additional education at the high school, vocational/technical, undergraduate, graduate, or professional level. Civilian employees with at least 90 days of Coast Guard service and Selected Reservists are also eligible. Enlisted members must have at least 12 months remaining on their active-duty contracts or Selected Reserve obligation after completion of the course. Officers must agree not to request release, separation, retirement, or termination of Selected Reserve status for 12 months after completing a course. Civilian employees must agree to retain employment with the Coast Guard for 1 month for each completed course credit hour. For military personnel, the command education services officer (ESO) must certify that the course of instruction is Coast Guard mission or career related. The supervisor of civilian employees must certify that the education is career related. All courses must be related to the mission of the Coast Guard or the individual's career or professional development. **Deadline for Receipt:** Applications may be submitted at any time. **Additional Information:** Information is also available from the Commanding Officer, NETPDTC (USCG Group), 6490 Saufley Field Road, Pensacola, FL 32509-5241, (850) 452-1293, Fax: (850) 452-1149. Graduate students must earn a grade of "B" or higher to receive reimbursement; undergraduates must earn a grade of "D" or higher.

1723 ■ U.S. JCI SENATE

Attn: Foundation
7447 South Lewis Avenue
P.O. Box 7
Tulsa, OK 74102-0007
Tel: (918)584-2481
Free: 800-JAY-CEES
Fax: (918)584-4422
Web Site: http://www.usjcisenate.org/modules/scholarship
To provide financial assistance for college to high school seniors.

Title of Award: U.S. JCI Senate Scholarship Grants **Area, Field, or Subject:** General studies/Field of study not specified **Level of Education for which Award is Granted:** Undergraduate **Number Awarded:** Varies each year; recently, 20 of these scholarships were awarded. **Funds Available:** The stipend is $1,000. **Duration:** 1 year; nonrenewable.

Eligibility Requirements: This program is open to graduating high school seniors who plan to continue their education at an accredited college, university, or vocational school as a full-time student. Applicants must submit information on leadership positions and offices in school, church, volunteer, and community activities; memberships and participation in school, church, volunteer, and community activities; honors and awards received during high school; employment experience; and family financial situation. They must also submit a personal statement of 100 to 300 words on their chosen field of college study, their reasons for this choice, and pertinent experiences, activities, and accomplishments. Applications are submitted to the JCI Senate in their state. Each state organization selects the 2 highest-ranked applications and forwards them to the national organization. **Deadline for Receipt:** January of each year. **Additional Information:** These scholarships were first awarded in 1987.

1724 ■ UNITED STATES JUNIOR CHAMBER OF COMMERCE

Attn: War Memorial Fund
7447 South Lewis Avenue
P.O. Box 7
Tulsa, OK 74102-0007
Tel: (918)584-2481
Free: 800-JAY-CEES
Fax: (918)584-4422
Web Site: http://www.usjaycees.org
To provide financial assistance to members of the United States Junior Chamber of Commerce (Jaycees) who are interested in returning to college.

Title of Award: Charles R. Ford Scholarship **Area, Field, or Subject:** General studies/Field of study not specified **Level of Education for which Award is Granted:** Undergraduate **Number Awarded:** 1 each year. **Funds Available:** The stipend is $2,500 per year. Funds are sent directly to the recipient's college or university. **Duration:** 1 year; nonrenewable.

Eligibility Requirements: This program is open to Jaycee members who are interested in returning to college to completed their formal education. Applicants must be U.S. citizens, possess academic potential and leadership qualities, and demonstrate financial need. Applications must be sent to the Jaycee state president, who then selects 1 semifinalist and forwards the application to the national office. **Deadline for Receipt:** Requests for applications must be received by January of each year. **Additional Information:** Requests for applications must be accompanied by a self-addressed stamped envelope and a $10 application fee.

1725 ■ UNITED STATES JUNIOR CHAMBER OF COMMERCE

Attn: War Memorial Fund
7447 South Lewis Avenue
P.O. Box 7
Tulsa, OK 74102-0007
Tel: (918)584-2481
Free: 800-JAY-CEES
Fax: (918)584-4422
Web Site: http://www.usjaycees.org
To provide financial assistance for college to deserving students.

Title of Award: Jaycee War Memorial Fund Scholarship Program **Area, Field, or Subject:** General studies/Field of study not specified **Level of Education for which Award is Granted:** Undergraduate **Number Awarded:** 25 each year. **Funds Available:** The stipend is $1,000 per year. Funds are sent directly to the recipient's college or university. **Duration:** 1 year.

Eligibility Requirements: Applicants for these scholarships must be U.S. citizens, possess academic potential and leadership, and demonstrate financial need. Applications must be first submitted to the student's respective state Junior Chamber of Commerce organization. **Deadline for Receipt:** Requests for applications must be received by January of each year. **Additional Information:** This program was established in 1944. Requests for applications must be accompanied by a self-addressed stamped envelope and a $10 application fee.

1726 ■ UNITED STATES JUNIOR CHAMBER OF COMMERCE

Attn: War Memorial Fund
7447 South Lewis Avenue
P.O. Box 7
Tulsa, OK 74102-0007
Tel: (918)584-2481
Free: 800-JAY-CEES
Fax: (918)584-4422
Web Site: http://www.usjaycees.org
To provide financial assistance for college to members of the United States Junior Chamber of Commerce (Jaycees) and their children.

Title of Award: Thomas Wood Baldridge Scholarship **Area, Field, or Subject:** General studies/Field of study not specified **Level of Education for which Award is Granted:** Undergraduate **Number Awarded:** 1 each year. **Funds Available:** The stipend is $3,000 per year. Funds are sent directly to the recipient's college or university. **Duration:** 1 year; nonrenewable.

Eligibility Requirements: This program is open to Jaycee members and the immediate family members of Jaycees. Applicants must be enrolled in or accepted for admission to a college or university. They must be U.S.

citizens, possess academic potential and leadership qualities, and demonstrate financial need. Applications must be sent to the Jaycee state president, who then selects 1 semifinalist and forwards the application to the national office. **Deadline for Receipt:** Requests for applications must be received by January of each year. **Additional Information:** Requests for applications must be accompanied by a self-addressed stamped envelope and a $10 application fee.

1727 ■ U.S. MARINE CORPS

Manpower and Reserve Affairs (MMOA-5)
Attn: Undergraduate and Graduate Education Programs
3280 Russell Road
Quantico, VA 22134-5103
Tel: (703)784-9284
Fax: (703)784-9844
E-mail: ellisdl@manpower.usmc.mil
Web Site: http://www.usmc.mil

To allow selected commissioned Marine Corps officers to earn a bachelor's degree by pursuing full-time college study while continuing to receive their regular pay and allowances.

Title of Award: Marine Corps College Degree Program **Area, Field, or Subject:** General studies/Field of study not specified **Level of Education for which Award is Granted:** Undergraduate **Number Awarded:** Varies each year; recently, 8 officers were selected to participate in this program. **Funds Available:** Commissioned officers selected to participate in this program receive their regular Marine Corps pay while attending college or university on a full-time basis, but they must pay for tuition and books. **Duration:** Up to the equivalent of 2 academic years. **Eligibility Requirements:** Eligible to participate in this program are commissioned Marine Corps officers, including regular officers, extended duty Reservists, officers serving with a Standard Written Agreement (SWAG) of 3 years or on Extended Active Duty (EAD), and officers serving with a SWAG of 3 years or on an EAD of 3 to 5 years awarded by the Officer Retention Board (ORB). Applicants must have been accepted at an accredited institution as a full-time student. **Deadline for Receipt:** February of each year. **Additional Information:** Officers must agree not to resign or request retirement while enrolled in the program. They must also agree to remain on active duty, after completion of degree requirements or upon separation from the program for any other reason, for 3 years or, if the enrollment in school is longer than 1 calendar year, for 4 years.

1728 ■ U.S. MARINE CORPS

Attn: Marine Corps Recruiting Command (ON/E)
3280 Russell Road
Quantico, VA 22134-5103
Tel: (703)784-9446
Fax: (703)784-9859
E-mail: darlanddk@mcrc.usmc.mil
Web Site: http://www.marines.com

To allow selected enlisted Marine Corps personnel to earn a bachelor's degree and become a commissioned officer by pursuing full-time college study while continuing to receive their regular pay and allowances.

Title of Award: Marine Corps Enlisted Commissioning Education Program **Area, Field, or Subject:** General studies/Field of study not specified **Level of Education for which Award is Granted:** Undergraduate **Number Awarded:** Varies each year; recently, 110 Marines participated in this program. **Funds Available:** Participants receive regular Marine Corps pay while attending school on a full-time basis but are responsible for payment of all tuition and fees. They are not eligible for the Marine Corps Tuition Assistance Program but may use in-service Montgomery GI Bill education benefits and student loans. **Duration:** Until completion of a bachelor's degree. **Eligibility Requirements:** Eligible to participate in this program are enlisted members of the Marine Corps on active duty and in the Active Reserve program at the rank of corporal or above. Applicants must have an SAT score of 1000 or higher, a combined English and mathematics ACT score of 45 or higher, or an AFQT score of 74 or higher. They must be between 20 and 26 years of age (although an age waiver may be requested) and have ranked in the top half of their high school graduating class. Selection is based on potential for commissioned service as demonstrated by their service record, previous academic record, and evidence of career and academic self-improvement. **Deadline for Receipt:** September of each year. **Additional Information:** Participants are assigned to a 9-week preparatory school in San Diego, California

before reporting to their college or university. If they successfully obtain a bachelor's degree and complete officer candidate training, they are commissioned second lieutenants in the Regular Marine Corps. Selectees are required to extent or reenlist in order to have at least 6 years of obligated service before they enter this program. They must serve at least 4 years of active commissioned service.

1729 ■ U.S. MARINE CORPS

Attn: Marine Corps Recruiting Command (ON/E)
3280 Russell Road
Quantico, VA 22134-5103
Tel: (703)784-9442
Fax: (703)784-9859
E-mail: braniganga@mcrc.usmc.mil
Web Site: http://www.marines.com

To allow Marine Corps commanders to nominate enlisted personnel to earn a bachelor's degree and become a commissioned officer by pursuing full-time college study while continuing to receive their regular pay and allowances.

Title of Award: Marine Corps Meritorious Commissioning Program **Area, Field, or Subject:** General studies/Field of study not specified **Level of Education for which Award is Granted:** Undergraduate **Number Awarded:** Varies each year. **Funds Available:** Participants receive regular Marine Corps pay while attending school on a full-time basis but are responsible for payment of all tuition and fees. They are not eligible for the Marine Corps Tuition Assistance Program but may use in-service Montgomery GI Bill education benefits and student loans. **Duration:** Selected Marines have up to 18 months of full-time study to complete their baccalaureate degree. **Eligibility Requirements:** Marine Corps commanding officers are invited to nominated enlisted personnel for this program. Nominees must have completed at least 75 semester hours of college course work and have minimum scores of 1000 on the SAT, 45 on the ACT, or 74 on the AFQT. They must be between 21 and 30 years of age and have been accepted at a college or university affiliated with the Navy ROTC program. **Deadline for Receipt:** May or September of each year. **Additional Information:** Following acceptance into this program, Marines complete a 10-week class at Officer Candidates School, then enter college to complete their baccalaureate degree. Upon graduation from college, they are commissioned and assigned to the Basic School. After graduation and commissioning, participants are required to serve at least 4 years on active duty.

1730 ■ U.S. MARINE CORPS

Attn: Lifelong Learning Center
3098 Range Road
Quantico, VA 22134-5028
Tel: (703)784-9550
Web Site: http://www.usmc-mccs.org/education/mta.cfm

To provide financial assistance for undergraduate or graduate study to Marine Corps personnel.

Title of Award: Marine Corps Tuition Assistance Program **Area, Field, or Subject:** General studies/Field of study not specified **Level of Education for which Award is Granted:** Graduate, Undergraduate **Number Awarded:** Varies each year; in recent years, approximately 20,000 Marines availed themselves of this program. **Funds Available:** Those selected for participation in this program receive their regular Marine Corps pay and 100% of tuition at the postsecondary educational institution of their choice, but capped at $4,500 per year or $250 per semester hour, whichever is less. **Duration:** Until completion of a bachelor's or graduate degree. **Eligibility Requirements:** Eligible for assistance under this program are active-duty Marines who wish to take college courses for academic credit during off-duty time. Funding is available for vocational/technical, undergraduate, graduate, undergraduate development, independent study, and distance learning programs. Commissioned officers must agree to remain on active duty for 2 years after the completion of any funded courses. All students must successfully complete their courses with a satisfactory grade.

1731 ■ U.S. NAVAL ACADEMY CLASS OF 1963 FOUNDATION

c/o David B. Puckett
5051 Chatham Valley
Toledo, OH 43615

E-mail: dpuckett@buckeye-express.com
Web Site: http://www.USNA63.org
To provide financial assistance for college or graduate school to the widows and children of deceased members of the U.S. Naval Academy's class of 1963.
Title of Award: U.S. Naval Academy Class of 1963 Foundation Scholarship **Area, Field, or Subject:** General studies/Field of study not specified **Level of Education for which Award is Granted:** Graduate, Undergraduate **Number Awarded:** Varies each year. **Funds Available:** The stipend is $3,750 per year for undergraduate students or $1,000 per year for graduate students. Funds are paid directly to the recipient's college or vocational school to be applied for any purpose, including tuition, fees, books, room, board, etc. **Duration:** 1 year; may be renewed for 3 additional years of undergraduate study or 2 years of graduate study.
Eligibility Requirements: Eligible to apply for these scholarships are the widows and children of deceased members of the U.S. Naval Academy class of 1963, including those who enrolled in the class originally and those who joined it later. Applicants must be enrolled in or accepted at an accredited college or university offering a 2-year or 4-year course of study (including graduate work), or a qualified technical or vocational school. Financial need is not considered. **Deadline for Receipt:** April of each year.

1732 ■ U.S. NAVY

Attn: Navy Exchange Service Command
3280 Virginia Beach Boulevard
Virginia Beach, VA 23452-5724
800-NAV-EXCH
Web Site: http://www.navy-nex.com/command/about_us/
a.ok.program.html
To provide financial assistance for college to children of active and retired military personnel who shop at Navy Exchange (NEX) stores.
Title of Award: A-OK Student Reward Program **Area, Field, or Subject:** General studies/Field of study not specified **Level of Education for which Award is Granted:** Undergraduate **Number Awarded:** 16 each year: at each drawing, 1 savings bond for each of the 4 denominations is awarded. **Funds Available:** Winners receive savings bonds for $5,000, $3,000, $2,000, or $1,000. Funds are intended to help pay expenses of college. **Duration:** Drawings are held 4 times a year (in February, May, August, and November).
Eligibility Requirements: This program is open to dependent children of active-duty military members, Reservists, and military retirees who are enrolled in grades 1-12 and have a GPA of 3.0 or higher. Applicants submit an entry at the service desk of their NEX store. Winners are selected in a drawing. **Additional Information:** This program was established in 1997.

1733 ■ U.S. NAVY

Attn: Commander, Naval Service Training Command
250 Dallas Street, Suite A
Pensacola, FL 32508-5268
Tel: (850)452-9563
Fax: (850)452-2486
E-mail: PNSC-STA21@navy.mil
Web Site: http://www.navy.com/careers/officerplanner/enlistedtoofficer
To allow outstanding enlisted Navy personnel to complete a bachelor's degree and receive a commission as a naval flight officer (NFO).
Title of Award: Naval Flight Officer Option of the Seaman to Admiral-21 Program **Area, Field, or Subject:** General studies/Field of study not specified **Level of Education for which Award is Granted:** Four Year College **Number Awarded:** Varies each year. **Funds Available:** Awardees continue to receive their regular Navy pay and allowances while they attend college on a full-time basis. They also receive reimbursement for tuition, fees, and books up to $10,000 per year. If base housing is available, they are eligible to live there. Participants are not eligible to receive benefits under the Navy's Tuition Assistance Program (TA), the Montgomery GI Bill (MGIB), Navy College Fund, or the Veterans Educational Assistance Program (VEAP). **Duration:** Selectees are supported for up to 36 months of full-time, year-round study or completion of a bachelor's degree, as long as they maintain a GPA of 2.5 or higher.
Eligibility Requirements: This program is open to U.S. citizens who are currently serving on active duty in the U.S. Navy or Naval Reserve, including Training and Administration of the Reserves (TAR), Selected Reserves

(SELRES), and Navy Reservists on active duty except for those on active for training (ACDUTRA). Applicants must be high school graduates (or GED recipients) who are able to complete requirements for a baccalaureate degree in 36 months or less. When they complete their degree requirements, they must be younger than 27 years of age (may be adjusted to 31 years of age for prior active-duty service). Within the past 3 years, they must have taken the SAT test (and achieved scores of at least 500 on the mathematics section and 500 on the verbal or critical reading section) or the ACT test (and achieved a score of 41 or higher, including at least 21 on the mathematics portion and 20 on the English portion). They must also achieve a score of at least the following: AQR (3), FOFAR (4) on the Aviation Selection Test Battery. **Deadline for Receipt:** July of each year. **Additional Information:** This program was established in 2001 as a replacement for the Aviation Enlisted Commissioning Program (AECP). Upon acceptance into the program, selectees attend the Naval Science Institute (NSI) in Newport, Rhode Island for an 8-week program in the fundamental core concepts of being a naval officer (navigation, engineering, weapons, military history and justice, etc.). They then enter a college or university with an NROTC unit or affiliation and pursue full-time study for a bachelor's degree. They become members of and drill with the NROTC unit. When they complete their degree, they are commissioned as ensigns in the United States Naval Reserve and assigned to flight training. After commissioning, participants incur an active duty obligation of 6 years after designation as a Naval Flight Officer or 6 years from the date of disenrollment from flight training.

1734 ■ U.S. NAVY

Attn: Navy Personnel Command (PERS-675)
5720 Integrity Drive
Millington, TN 38055-6040
Tel: (901)874-4258; (866)U-ASK-NPC
Fax: (901)874-2052
E-mail: MILL_MGIB@navy.mil
Web Site: http://www.npc.navy.mil/CareerInfo/Education/GIBill/
NavyCollegeFundProgram.htm
To provide financial assistance for college to Navy enlistees during and after they have completed their service obligation.
Title of Award: Navy College Fund **Area, Field, or Subject:** General studies/Field of study not specified **Level of Education for which Award is Granted:** Undergraduate **Number Awarded:** Varies each year. **Funds Available:** The Navy College Fund provides, in addition to the Montgomery GI Bill, up to $15,000 for college tuition and expenses. **Duration:** Enlistees may begin using this educational benefit on a part-time basis after 2 years of continuous active duty. Funds must be utilized within 10 years of leaving the Navy.
Eligibility Requirements: Eligible for this program are high school seniors and graduates between 17 and 35 years of age who enlist in the Navy for 3 to 4 years of active duty. They must score 50 or above on the AFQT and also enroll in the Montgomery GI Bill. Sailors currently on active duty in selected Navy ratings with critical personnel shortages are also eligible. Applicants must be interested in attending a Department of Veterans Affairs-approved postsecondary educational institution on a full-time basis after completion of their service obligation. **Deadline for Receipt:** Applications may be submitted at any time. **Additional Information:** Applications and further information are available from local Navy recruiters and from the Navy Recruiting Command, 801 North Randolph Street, Arlington, VA 22203-1991.

1735 ■ U.S. NAVY

Attn: Naval Education and Training Center
Code N8115
6490 Saufley Field Road
Pensacola, FL 32509-5241
877-253-7122
Fax: (850)452-1149
E-mail: SFLY_TA.navy@navy.mil
Web Site: http://www.npc.navy.mil/CareerInfo/Education
To provide financial assistance for high school, vocational, undergraduate, or graduate education to Navy personnel.
Title of Award: Navy Tuition Assistance Program **Area, Field, or Subject:** General studies/Field of study not specified **Level of Education for which Award is Granted:** Graduate, Undergraduate **Number Awarded:** Varies each year. **Funds Available:** Those selected for

participation in this program receive their regular Navy pay and 100% of tuition at the postsecondary educational institution of their choice, but capped at $250 per semester hour and 12 semester hours per fiscal year (the 12-semester hour limit may be waived upon application). **Duration:** Until completion of a bachelor's or graduate degree.

Eligibility Requirements: This program is open to active-duty Navy offices and enlisted personnel, including Naval Reservists on continuous active duty, enlisted Naval Reservists ordered to active duty for 120 days or more, and Naval Reservist officers ordered to active duty for 2 years or more. Applicants must register to take courses at accredited civilian schools during off-duty time. Tuition assistance is provided for courses taken at accredited colleges, universities, vocational/technical schools, private schools, and through independent study/distance learning (but not for flight training). **Additional Information:** This program is supported by the Naval Education and Training Command, Educational Programs Building 628, 250 Dallas Street, Pensacola, FL 32509-5220, Fax: (850) 452-2510, E-mail: NCC@cnet.navy.mil. Officers must agree to remain on active duty for at least 2 years after completion of courses funded by this program.

1736 ■ U.S. NAVY

Attn: Commander, Naval Service Training Command
250 Dallas Street, Suite A
Pensacola, FL 32508-5268
Tel: (850)452-9563
Fax: (850)452-2486
E-mail: PNSC-STA21@navy.mil
Web Site: http://www.navy.com/careers/officerplanner/enlistedtoofficer
To allow outstanding enlisted Navy personnel to complete a bachelor's degree and receive a commission as a pilot.

Title of Award: Pilot Option of the Seaman to Admiral-21 Program **Area, Field, or Subject:** General studies/Field of study not specified **Level of Education for which Award is Granted:** Four Year College **Number Awarded:** Varies each year. **Funds Available:** Awardees continue to receive their regular Navy pay and allowances while they attend college on a full-time basis. They also receive reimbursement for tuition, fees, and books up to $10,000 per year. If base housing is available, they are eligible to live there. Participants are not eligible to receive benefits under the Navy's Tuition Assistance Program (TA), the Montgomery GI Bill (MGIB), Navy College Fund, or the Veterans Educational Assistance Program (VEAP). **Duration:** Selectees are supported for up to 36 months of full-time, year-round study or completion of a bachelor's degree, as long as they maintain a GPA of 2.5 or higher.

Eligibility Requirements: This program is open to U.S. citizens who are currently serving on active duty in the U.S. Navy or Naval Reserve, including Training and Administration of the Reserves (TAR), Selected Reserves (SELRES), and Navy Reservists on active duty except for those on active for training (ACDUTRA). Applicants must be high school graduates (or GED recipients) who are able to complete requirements for a baccalaureate degree in 36 months or less. When they complete their degree requirements, they must be younger than 27 years of age (may be adjusted to 29 years of age for prior active-duty service). Within the past 3 years, they must have taken the SAT test (and achieved scores of at least 500 on the mathematics section and 500 on the verbal or critical reading section) or the ACT test (and achieved a score of 41 or higher, including at least 21 on the mathematics portion and 20 on the English portion). They must also achieve a score of at least the following: AQR (3), PFAR (4) on the Pilot Flight Aptitude Rating (PFAR) portions of the Aviation Selection Test Battery. **Deadline for Receipt:** July of each year. **Additional Information:** This program was established in 2001 as a replacement for the Aviation Enlisted Commissioning Program (AECP). Upon acceptance into the program, selectees attend the Naval Science Institute (NSI) in Newport, Rhode Island for an 8-week program in the fundamental core concepts of being a naval officer (navigation, engineering, weapons, military history and justice, etc.). They then enter a college or university with an NROTC unit or affiliation and pursue full-time study for a bachelor's degree. They become members of and drill with the NROTC unit. When they complete their degree, they are commissioned as ensigns in the United States Naval Reserve and assigned to flight training. After

commissioning, participants incur an active duty obligation of 8 years after designation as a Naval Aviator or 6 years from the date of disenrollment from flight training.

1737 ■ U.S. NAVY

Attn: Commander, Naval Service Training Command
250 Dallas Street, Suite A
Pensacola, FL 32508-5268
Tel: (850)452-9563
Fax: (850)452-2486
E-mail: PNSC-STA21@navy.mil
Web Site: http://www.navy.com/careers/officerplanner/enlistedtoofficer
To allow outstanding enlisted Navy personnel to complete a bachelor's degree and receive a commission.

Title of Award: Seaman to Admiral-21 Program **Area, Field, or Subject:** General studies/Field of study not specified **Level of Education for which Award is Granted:** Four Year College **Number Awarded:** Varies each year. **Funds Available:** Awardees continue to receive their regular Navy pay and allowances while they attend college on a full-time basis. They also receive reimbursement for tuition, fees, and books up to $10,000 per year. If base housing is available, they are eligible to live there. Participants are not eligible to receive benefits under the Navy's Tuition Assistance Program (TA), the Montgomery GI Bill (MGIB), Navy College Fund, or the Veterans Educational Assistance Program (VEAP). **Duration:** Selectees are supported for up to 36 months of full-time, year-round study or completion of a bachelor's degree, as long as they maintain a GPA of 2.5 or higher.

Eligibility Requirements: This program is open to U.S. citizens who are currently serving on active duty in the U.S. Navy or Naval Reserve, including Training and Administration of the Reserves (TAR), Selected Reserves (SELRES), and Navy Reservists on active duty except for those on active for training (ACDUTRA). Applicants must be high school graduates (or GED recipients) who are able to complete requirements for a baccalaureate degree in 36 months or less. When they complete their degree requirements, they must be younger than 31 years of age. Within the past 3 years, they must have taken the SAT test (and achieved scores of at least 500 on the mathematics section and 500 on the verbal or critical reading section) or the ACT test (and achieved a score of 41 or higher, including at least 21 on the mathematics portion and 20 on the English portion). **Deadline for Receipt:** July of each year. **Additional Information:** This program was established in 2001 as a replacement for the Seaman to Admiral Program (established in 1994), the Enlisted Commissioning Program, and other specialized programs for sailors to earn a commission. Upon acceptance into the program, selectees attend the Naval Science Institute (NSI) in Newport, Rhode Island for an 8-week program in the fundamental core concepts of being a naval officer (navigation, engineering, weapons, military history and justice, etc.). They then enter a college or university with an NROTC unit or affiliation and pursue full-time study for a bachelor's degree. They become members of and drill with the NROTC unit. When they complete their degree, they are commissioned as ensigns in the United States Naval Reserve and assigned to initial training for their officer community. After commissioning, 5 years of active service are required.

1738 ■ U.S. NAVY

Attn: Commander, Naval Service Training Command
250 Dallas Street, Suite A
Pensacola, FL 32508-5268
Tel: (850)452-9563
Fax: (850)452-2486
E-mail: PNSC-STA21@navy.mil
Web Site: http://www.navy.com/careers/officerplanner/enlistedtoofficer
To allow outstanding enlisted Navy personnel to complete a bachelor's degree and receive a commission as a special duty officer (cryptology).

Title of Award: Special Duty Officer (Information Warfare) Option of the Seaman to Admiral-21 Program **Area, Field, or Subject:** General studies/Field of study not specified **Level of Education for which Award is Granted:** Four Year College **Number Awarded:** Varies each year. **Funds Available:** Awardees continue to receive their regular Navy pay and allowances while they attend college on a full-time basis. They also receive reimbursement for tuition, fees, and books up to $10,000 per year. If base housing is available, they are eligible to live there. Participants are not eligible to receive benefits under the Navy's Tuition Assistance Program

(TA), the Montgomery GI Bill (MGIB), Navy College Fund, or the Veterans Educational Assistance Program (VEAP). **Duration:** Selectees are supported for up to 36 months of full-time, year-round study or completion of a bachelor's degree, as long as they maintain a GPA of 2.5 or higher.
Eligibility Requirements: This program is open to U.S. citizens who are currently serving on active duty in the U.S. Navy or Naval Reserve, including Training and Administration of the Reserves (TAR), Selected Reserves (SELRES), and Navy Reservists on active duty except for those on active for training (ACDUTRA). Applicants must be high school graduates (or GED recipients) who are at least 18 years of age and able to complete requirements for a baccalaureate degree in 36 months or less. They must currently be active duty enlisted personnel possessing information warfare skills in the areas of signals, foreign languages (emphasis on Middle and Far Eastern languages), and information systems technologies and networks. When they complete their degree requirements, they must be younger than 35 years of age. Within the past 3 years, they must have taken the SAT test (and achieved scores of at least 500 on the mathematics section and 500 on the verbal or critical reading section) or the ACT test (and achieved a score of 41 or higher, including at least 21 on the mathematics portion and 20 on the English portion). They must also pass relevant medical standards. **Deadline for Receipt:** July of each year. **Additional Information:** This program was established in 2001 as a replacement for the Seaman to Admiral Program (established in 1994), the Enlisted Commissioning Program, and other specialized programs for sailors to earn a commission. Upon acceptance into the program, selectees attend the Naval Science Institute (NSI) in Newport, Rhode Island for an 8-week program in the fundamental core concepts of being a naval officer (navigation, engineering, weapons, military history and justice, etc.). They then enter a college or university with an NROTC unit or affiliation and pursue full-time study for a bachelor's degree. They become members of and drill with the NROTC unit. When they complete their degree, they are commissioned as ensigns in the United States Naval Reserve and assigned to initial training as a special duty officer (cryptology). After commissioning, 5 years of active service are required.

1739 ■ U.S. NAVY

Attn: Commander, Naval Service Training Command
250 Dallas Street, Suite A
Pensacola, FL 32508-5268
Tel: (850)452-9563
Fax: (850)452-2486
E-mail: PNSC-STA21@navy.mil
Web Site: http://www.navy.com/careers/officerplanner/enlistedtoofficer
To allow outstanding enlisted Navy personnel to complete a bachelor's degree and receive a commission as a special duty officer (intelligence).
Title of Award: Special Duty Officer (Intelligence) Option of the Seaman to Admiral-21 Program **Area, Field, or Subject:** General studies/Field of study not specified **Level of Education for which Award is Granted:** Four Year College **Number Awarded:** Varies each year. **Funds Available:** Awardees continue to receive their regular Navy pay and allowances while they attend college on a full-time basis. They also receive reimbursement for tuition, fees, and books up to $10,000 per year. If base housing is available, they are eligible to live there. Participants are not eligible to receive benefits under the Navy's Tuition Assistance Program (TA), the Montgomery GI Bill (MGIB), Navy College Fund, or the Veterans Educational Assistance Program (VEAP). **Duration:** Selectees are supported for up to 36 months of full-time, year-round study or completion of a bachelor's degree, as long as they maintain a GPA of 2.5 or higher.
Eligibility Requirements: This program is open to U.S. citizens who are currently serving on active duty in the U.S. Navy or Naval Reserve, including Training and Administration of the Reserves (TAR), Selected Reserves (SELRES), and Navy Reservists on active duty except for those on active for training (ACDUTRA). Applicants must be high school graduates (or GED recipients) who are at least 19 years of age and able to complete requirements for a baccalaureate degree in 36 months or less. They must currently be active duty enlisted personnel of occupational field 21 (intelligence specialist). When they complete their degree requirements, they must be younger than 35 years of age. Within the past 3 years, they must have taken the SAT test (and achieved scores of at least 500 on the mathematics section and 500 on the verbal or critical reading section) or the ACT test (and achieved a score of 41 or higher, including at least 21 on the mathematics portion and 20 on the English portion). They must also pass relevant medical standards. **Deadline for Receipt:** July of each

year. **Additional Information:** This program was established in 2001 as a replacement for the Seaman to Admiral Program (established in 1994), the Enlisted Commissioning Program, and other specialized programs for sailors to earn a commission. Upon acceptance into the program, selectees attend the Naval Science Institute (NSI) in Newport, Rhode Island for an 8-week program in the fundamental core concepts of being a naval officer (navigation, engineering, weapons, military history and justice, etc.). They then enter a college or university with an NROTC unit or affiliation and pursue full-time study for a bachelor's degree. They become members of and drill with the NROTC unit. When they complete their degree, they are commissioned as ensigns in the United States Naval Reserve and assigned to initial training as a special duty officer (intelligence). After commissioning, 5 years of active service are required.

1740 ■ U.S. NAVY

Attn: Commander, Naval Service Training Command
250 Dallas Street, Suite A
Pensacola, FL 32508-5268
Tel: (850)452-9563
Fax: (850)452-2486
E-mail: PNSC-STA21@navy.mil
Web Site: http://www.navy.com/careers/officerplanner/enlistedtoofficer
To allow outstanding enlisted Navy personnel to complete a bachelor's degree and receive a commission as a special operations officer.
Title of Award: Special Operations Option of the Seaman to Admiral-21 Program **Area, Field, or Subject:** General studies/Field of study not specified **Level of Education for which Award is Granted:** Four Year College **Number Awarded:** Varies each year. **Funds Available:** Awardees continue to receive their regular Navy pay and allowances while they attend college on a full-time basis. They also receive reimbursement for tuition, fees, and books up to $10,000 per year. If base housing is available, they are eligible to live there. Participants are not eligible to receive benefits under the Navy's Tuition Assistance Program (TA), the Montgomery GI Bill (MGIB), Navy College Fund, or the Veterans Educational Assistance Program (VEAP). **Duration:** Selectees are supported for up to 36 months of full-time, year-round study or completion of a bachelor's degree, as long as they maintain a GPA of 2.5 or higher.
Eligibility Requirements: This program is open to U.S. citizens who are currently serving on active duty in the U.S. Navy or Naval Reserve, including Training and Administration of the Reserves (TAR), Selected Reserves (SELRES), and Navy Reservists on active duty except for those on active for training (ACDUTRA). Applicants must have 1 of the following NECs: 5332, 5333, 5334, 5335, 5336, 5337, 5342, or 5343. They must be high school graduates (or GED recipients) who are able to complete requirements for a baccalaureate degree in 36 months or less. When they complete their degree requirements, they must be younger than 29 years of age. That age limitation may be adjusted upward for active service on a month for month basis up to 24 months, and waivers are considered for enlisted personnel who possess particularly exceptional qualifications if they can complete their degree prior to their 35th birthday. Within the past 3 years, they must have taken the SAT test (and achieved scores of at least 500 on the mathematics section and 500 on the verbal or critical reading section) or the ACT test (and achieved a score of 41 or higher, including at least 21 on the mathematics portion and 20 on the English portion). They must also pass physical regulations that include qualification for diving duty and/or combat swimmer. **Deadline for Receipt:** July of each year. **Additional Information:** This program was established in 2001 as a replacement for the Seaman to Admiral Program (established in 1994), the Enlisted Commissioning Program, and other specialized programs for sailors to earn a commission. Upon acceptance into the program, selectees attend the Naval Science Institute (NSI) in Newport, Rhode Island for an 8-week program in the fundamental core concepts of being a naval officer (navigation, engineering, weapons, military history and justice, etc.). They then enter a college or university with an NROTC unit or affiliation and pursue full-time study for a bachelor's degree. They become members of and drill with the NROTC unit. When they complete their degree, they are commissioned as ensigns in the United States Naval Reserve and assigned to initial training as a special operations officer. After commissioning, 5 years of active service are required.

1741 ■ U.S. NAVY

Attn: Commander, Naval Service Training Command
250 Dallas Street, Suite A
Pensacola, FL 32508-5268

Tel: (850)452-9563
Fax: (850)452-2486
E-mail: PNSC-STA21@navy.mil
Web Site: http://www.navy.com/careers/officerplanner/enlistedtoofficer
To allow outstanding enlisted Navy personnel to complete a bachelor's degree and receive a commission as a special warfare officer.
Title of Award: Special Warfare Option of the Seaman to Admiral-21 Program **Area, Field, or Subject:** General studies/Field of study not specified **Level of Education for which Award is Granted:** Four Year College **Number Awarded:** Varies each year. **Funds Available:** Awardees continue to receive their regular Navy pay and allowances while they attend college on a full-time basis. They also receive reimbursement for tuition, fees, and books up to $10,000 per year. If base housing is available, they are eligible to live there. Participants are not eligible to receive benefits under the Navy's Tuition Assistance Program (TA), the Montgomery GI Bill (MGIB), Navy College Fund, or the Veterans Educational Assistance Program (VEAP). **Duration:** Selectees are supported for up to 36 months of full-time, year-round study or completion of a bachelor's degree, as long as they maintain a GPA of 2.5 or higher.
Eligibility Requirements: This program is open to U.S. citizens who are currently serving on active duty in the U.S. Navy or Naval Reserve, including Training and Administration of the Reserves (TAR), Selected Reserves (SELRES), and Navy Reservists on active duty except for those on active for training (ACDUTRA). Only males are eligible for this option. They must have 1 of the following NECs: 5323, 5326, 8491, or 8492. Applicants must be high school graduates (or GED recipients) who are able to complete requirements for a baccalaureate degree in 36 months or less. When they complete their degree requirements, they must be younger than 29 years of age. That age limitation may be adjusted upward for active service on a month for month basis up to 24 months, and waivers are considered for enlisted personnel who possess particularly exceptional qualifications if they can complete their degree prior to their 35th birthday. Within the past 3 years, they must have taken the SAT test (and achieved scores of at least 500 on the mathematics section and 500 on the verbal or critical reading section) or the ACT test (and achieved a score of 41 or higher, including at least 21 on the mathematics portion and 20 on the English portion). They must also pass physical regulations that include qualification for diving duty and/or combat swimmer. **Deadline for Receipt:** July of each year. **Additional Information:** This program was established in 2001 as a replacement for the Seaman to Admiral Program (established in 1994), the Enlisted Commissioning Program, and other specialized programs for sailors to earn a commission. Upon acceptance into the program, selectees attend the Naval Science Institute (NSI) in Newport, Rhode Island for an 8-week program in the fundamental core concepts of being a naval officer (navigation, engineering, weapons, military history and justice, etc.). They then enter a college or university with an NROTC unit or affiliation and pursue full-time study for a bachelor's degree. They become members of and drill with the NROTC unit. When they complete their degree, they are commissioned as ensigns in the United States Naval Reserve and assigned to initial training as a special warfare officer. After commissioning, 5 years of active service are required.

1742 ■ U.S. NAVY

Attn: Commander, Naval Service Training Command
250 Dallas Street, Suite A
Pensacola, FL 32508-5268
Tel: (850)452-9563
Fax: (850)452-2486
E-mail: PNSC-STA21@navy.mil
Web Site: http://www.navy.com/careers/officerplanner/enlistedtoofficer
To allow outstanding enlisted Navy personnel to complete a bachelor's degree and receive a commission as a surface warfare officer (SWO).
Title of Award: Surface Warfare Officer Option of the Seaman to Admiral-21 Program **Area, Field, or Subject:** General studies/Field of study not specified **Level of Education for which Award is Granted:** Four Year College **Number Awarded:** Varies each year. **Funds Available:** Awardees continue to receive their regular Navy pay and allowances while they attend college on a full-time basis. They also receive reimbursement for tuition, fees, and books up to $10,000 per year. If base housing is available, they are eligible to live there. Participants are not eligible to receive benefits under the Navy's Tuition Assistance Program (TA), the Montgomery GI Bill (MGIB), Navy College Fund, or the Veterans Educational Assistance Program (VEAP). **Duration:** Selectees are sup-

ported for up to 36 months of full-time, year-round study or completion of a bachelor's degree, as long as they maintain a GPA of 2.5 or higher.
Eligibility Requirements: This program is open to U.S. citizens who are currently serving on active duty in the U.S. Navy or Naval Reserve, including Training and Administration of the Reserves (TAR), Selected Reserves (SELRES), and Navy Reservists on active duty except for those on active for training (ACDUTRA). Applicants must be high school graduates (or GED recipients) who are able to complete requirements for a baccalaureate degree in 36 months or less. When they complete their degree requirements, they must be younger than 31 years of age. That age limitation may be adjusted upward for active service on a month for month basis up to 24 months, and waivers are considered for enlisted personnel who possess particularly exceptional qualifications if they can complete their degree prior to their 35th birthday. Within the past 3 years, they must have taken the SAT test (and achieved scores of at least 500 on the mathematics section and 500 on the verbal or critical reading section) or the ACT test (and achieved a score of 41 or higher, including at least 21 on the mathematics portion and 20 on the English portion). They must also pass relevant medical standards. **Deadline for Receipt:** July of each year. **Additional Information:** This program was established in 2001 as a replacement for the Seaman to Admiral Program (established in 1994), the Enlisted Commissioning Program, and other specialized programs for sailors to earn a commission. Upon acceptance into the program, selectees attend the Naval Science Institute (NSI) in Newport, Rhode Island for an 8-week program in the fundamental core concepts of being a naval officer (navigation, engineering, weapons, military history and justice, etc.). They then enter a college or university with an NROTC unit or affiliation and pursue full-time study for a bachelor's degree. They become members of and drill with the NROTC unit. When they complete their degree, they are commissioned as ensigns in the United States Naval Reserve and assigned to initial training as a surface warfare officer. After commissioning, 5 years of active service are required.

1743 ■ UNITED STATES SUBMARINE VETERANS, INC.

Attn: National Office
P.O. Box 3870
Silverdale, WA 98383-3870
Tel: (360)337-2978
E-mail: ussvi@telebyte.net
Web Site: http://www.ussvcf.org/scolchr1.htm
To provide financial assistance for college to the children and grandchildren of members of the United States Submarine Veterans, Inc. (USSVI).
Title of Award: USSVI Scholarships **Area, Field, or Subject:** General studies/Field of study not specified **Level of Education for which Award is Granted:** Undergraduate **Number Awarded:** Varies each year; recently, a total of $7,700 in scholarships was awarded. **Funds Available:** The stipend depends on the availability of funds and the need of the recipient. **Duration:** 1 year.
Eligibility Requirements: This program is open to children and grandchildren of USSVI members who are high school seniors planning to attend college or already enrolled as college students. Applicants must be unmarried and under 21 years of age (or 23 if currently enrolled in a full-time course of study). Selection is based on academic proficiency, participation in extracurricular activities that benefit their school and community, recognition of volunteer activities as demonstrated by awards, and financial need. **Deadline for Receipt:** April of each year. **Additional Information:** Information is also available from the Scholarship Chairman, Paul W. Orstad, 30 Surrey Lane, Norwich, CT 06369-6541, (860) 889-4750, E-mail: hogan343@aol.com.

1744 ■ UNIVERSITY INTERSCHOLASTIC LEAGUE

Attn: Texas Interscholastic League Foundation
1701 Manor Road
P.O. Box 8028
Austin, TX 78713
Tel: (512)232-4938
Fax: (512)471-5908
E-mail: carolyn.scott@mail.utexas.edu
Web Site: http://www.uil.utexas.edu/tilf/scholarships.html
To provide financial assistance to students who participate in programs of the Texas Interscholastic League Foundation (TILF) and have competed in girls' high school varsity basketball.
Title of Award: Leta Andrews Scholarship **Area, Field, or Subject:** General studies/Field of study not specified **Level of Education for**

which **Award is Granted:** Undergraduate **Number Awarded:** 1 each year. **Funds Available:** The stipend is $1,000 per year. **Duration:** 1 year; nonrenewable.

Eligibility Requirements: This program is open to students who have competed in girl's high school varsity basketball and meet the 5 basic requirements of the TILF: 1) graduate from high school during the current year and begin college or university in Texas by the following fall; 2) enroll full time and maintain a GPA of 2.5 or higher during the first semester; 3) compete in a University Interscholastic League (UIL) academic state meet contest in accounting, calculator applications, computer applications, computer science, current issues and events, debate (cross-examination and Lincoln-Douglas), journalism (editorial writing, feature writing, headline writing, and news writing), literary criticism, mathematics, number sense, 1-act play, ready writing, science, social studies, speech (prose interpretation, poetry interpretation, informative speaking, and persuasive speaking), or spelling and vocabulary; 4) submit high school transcripts that include SAT and/or ACT scores; and 5) submit parents' latest income tax returns. **Deadline for Receipt:** May of each year. **Additional Information:** This program is sponsored by Whataburger Inc. and Southwest Shootout Inc.

1745 ■ UNIVERSITY INTERSCHOLASTIC LEAGUE

Attn: Texas Interscholastic League Foundation
1701 Manor Road
P.O. Box 8028
Austin, TX 78713
Tel: (512)232-4938
Fax: (512)471-5908
E-mail: carolyn.scott@mail.utexas.edu
Web Site: http://www.uil.utexas.edu/tilf/scholarships.html
To provide financial assistance to students who participate in programs of the Texas Interscholastic League Foundation (TILF) and plan to attend college or university in Texas.

Title of Award: TILF Scholarships **Area, Field, or Subject:** General studies/Field of study not specified **Level of Education for which Award is Granted:** Undergraduate **Number Awarded:** Varies each year; recently, 262 new scholarships (worth $1,171,000) and 271 renewal scholarships were awarded. **Funds Available:** Stipends range from $3,500 to $500 per year. **Duration:** 1 year; some programs may be renewed up to 4 additional years.

Eligibility Requirements: This program is open to students who meet the 5 basic requirements of the TILF: 1) graduate from high school during the current year and begin college or university in Texas by the following fall; 2) enroll full time and maintain a GPA of 2.5 or higher during the first semester; 3) compete in a University Interscholastic League (UIL) academic state meet contest in accounting, calculator applications, computer applications, computer science, current issues and events, debate (cross-examination and Lincoln-Douglas), journalism (editorial writing, feature writing, headline writing, and news writing), literary criticism, mathematics, number sense, 1-act play, ready writing, science, social studies, speech (prose interpretation, poetry interpretation, informative speaking, and persuasive speaking), or spelling and vocabulary; 4) submit high school transcripts that include SAT and/or ACT scores; and 5) submit parents' latest income tax returns. **Deadline for Receipt:** May of each year. **Additional Information:** Some scholarships within this program include additional specific eligibility requirements, such as college majors or regions in the state where students must live.

1746 ■ UNIVERSITY INTERSCHOLASTIC LEAGUE

Attn: Texas Interscholastic League Foundation
1701 Manor Road
P.O. Box 8028
Austin, TX 78713
Tel: (512)232-4938
Fax: (512)471-5908
E-mail: carolyn.scott@mail.utexas.edu
Web Site: http://www.uil.utexas.edu/tilf/scholarships.html
To provide financial assistance to students who participate in programs of the Texas Interscholastic League Foundation (TILF) and have competed in girls' high school varsity basketball.

Title of Award: Dean Weese Scholarship **Area, Field, or Subject:** General studies/Field of study not specified **Level of Education for which Award is Granted:** Undergraduate **Number Awarded:** 1 each

year. **Funds Available:** The stipend is $1,000 per year. **Duration:** 1 year; nonrenewable.

Eligibility Requirements: This program is open to students who have competed in girl's high school varsity basketball and meet the 5 basic requirements of the TILF: 1) graduate from high school during the current year and begin college or university in Texas by the following fall; 2) enroll full time and maintain a GPA of 2.5 or higher during the first semester; 3) compete in a University Interscholastic League (UIL) academic state meet contest in accounting, calculator applications, computer applications, computer science, current issues and events, debate (cross-examination and Lincoln-Douglas), journalism (editorial writing, feature writing, headline writing, and news writing), literary criticism, mathematics, number sense, 1-act play, ready writing, science, social studies, speech (prose interpretation, poetry interpretation, informative speaking, and persuasive speaking), or spelling and vocabulary; 4) submit high school transcripts that include SAT and/or ACT scores; and 5) submit parents' latest income tax returns. **Deadline for Receipt:** May of each year. **Additional Information:** This program is sponsored by Whataburger Inc. and Southwest Shootout Inc.

1747 ■ URBAN LEAGUE OF NEBRASKA, INC.

Attn: Scholarships
3022 North 24th Street
Omaha, NE 68110
Tel: (402)453-9730
Fax: (402)453-9676
Web Site: http://www.urbanleagueneb.org
To provide financial assistance for college to African American residents of Nebraska.

Title of Award: Jerry Morris and Summer Houston Memorial Scholarship **Area, Field, or Subject:** General studies/Field of study not specified **Level of Education for which Award is Granted:** Undergraduate **Number Awarded:** 1 or more each year. **Funds Available:** The stipend is $1,000. **Duration:** 1 year; may be renewed 1 additional year.

Eligibility Requirements: This program is open to African American residents of Nebraska who are seniors in high school or full-time freshmen or sophomores in college. Applicants must have a GPA of 2.5 or higher, a record of active involvement in school and community activities, and demonstrated social awareness and involvement. Selection is based primarily on academic ability and leadership, although personal and family financial situations may also be considered. U.S. citizenship is required. **Deadline for Receipt:** April of each year. **Additional Information:** This program is supported by the Union Pacific Railroad Black Employee Network.

1748 ■ URBAN LEAGUE OF NEBRASKA, INC.

Attn: Scholarships
3022 North 24th Street
Omaha, NE 68110
Tel: (402)453-9730
Fax: (402)453-9676
Web Site: http://www.urbanleagueneb.org
To provide financial assistance for college to residents of Nebraska, especially minority students.

Title of Award: Multicultural Association Scholarship **Area, Field, or Subject:** General studies/Field of study not specified **Level of Education for which Award is Granted:** Undergraduate **Number Awarded:** 1 or more each year. **Funds Available:** A stipend is awarded (amount not specified). **Duration:** 1 year.

Eligibility Requirements: This program is open to Nebraska residents who are seniors in high school or students currently enrolled in college. Applicants must have a GPA of 2.5 or higher. Preference is given to students from a multicultural (American Indian, African American, Asian American, Hispanic American) background. **Deadline for Receipt:** March of each year. **Additional Information:** This program is supported by employees of the Omaha Public Power District.

1749 ■ URBAN LEAGUE OF NEBRASKA, INC.

Attn: Scholarships
3022 North 24th Street
Omaha, NE 68110
Tel: (402)453-9730
Fax: (402)453-9676

Web Site: http://www.urbanleagueneb.org

To provide financial assistance for college to residents of Nebraska.

Title of Award: Osborne Scholarship **Area, Field, or Subject:** General studies/Field of study not specified **Level of Education for which Award is Granted:** Undergraduate **Number Awarded:** 1 or more each year. **Funds Available:** A stipend is awarded (amount not specified). **Duration:** 1 year.

Eligibility Requirements: This program is open to Nebraska residents who are seniors in high school or students currently enrolled in college. Applicants must have a GPA of 2.5 or higher and be able to demonstrate financial need. They must be able to demonstrate at least 5 to 10 hours of community involvement. Along with their application, they must submit a 500-word essay on their goals and ambitions and the reasons they should receive this scholarship. **Deadline for Receipt:** March of each year.

1750 ■ URBAN LEAGUE OF NEBRASKA, INC.

Attn: Scholarships
3022 North 24th Street
Omaha, NE 68110
Tel: (402)453-9730
Fax: (402)453-9676
Web Site: http://www.urbanleagueneb.org

To provide financial assistance for college to residents of Nebraska.

Title of Award: Charles B. Washington Scholarship **Area, Field, or Subject:** General studies/Field of study not specified **Level of Education for which Award is Granted:** Undergraduate **Number Awarded:** 1 or more each year. **Funds Available:** A stipend is awarded (amount not specified). **Duration:** 1 year.

Eligibility Requirements: This program is open to Nebraska residents who are seniors in high school or students currently enrolled in college. Applicants must have a GPA of 2.5 or higher and be able to demonstrate financial need. They must be able to demonstrate at least 5 to 10 hours of community involvement. Along with their application, they must submit a 500-word essay on their goals and ambitions and the reasons they should receive this scholarship. **Deadline for Receipt:** March of each year.

1751 ■ US PAN ASIAN AMERICAN CHAMBER OF COMMERCE

Attn: Scholarship Coordinator
1329 18th Street, N.W.
Washington, DC 20036
Tel: (202)296-5221
Fax: (202)296-5225
E-mail: administrator@uspaacc.com
Web Site: http://www.uspaacc.com/web/programs/
aa_supplier_council.htm

To provide financial assistance for college to Asian American high school seniors who demonstrate financial need.

Title of Award: Asian American Scholarship **Area, Field, or Subject:** General studies/Field of study not specified **Level of Education for which Award is Granted:** Undergraduate **Number Awarded:** 1 each year. **Funds Available:** The maximum stipend is $5,000. Funds are paid directly to the recipient's college or university. **Duration:** 1 year.

Eligibility Requirements: This program is open to high school seniors of Asian heritage who are U.S. citizens or permanent residents. Applicants must be planning to begin full-time study at an accredited postsecondary educational institution in the United States. Along with their application, they must submit a 500-word essay on "Why I need this scholarship." Selection is based on academic excellence (GPA of 3.3 or higher), leadership in extracurricular activities, community service involvement, and financial need. **Deadline for Receipt:** February of each year. **Additional Information:** This program was established in 1989. Funding is not provided for correspondence courses, Internet courses, or study in a country other than the United States.

1752 ■ US PAN ASIAN AMERICAN CHAMBER OF COMMERCE

Attn: Scholarship Coordinator
1329 18th Street, N.W.
Washington, DC 20036
Tel: (202)296-5221
Fax: (202)296-5225
E-mail: administrator@uspaacc.com
Web Site: http://www.uspaacc.com/web/programs/jackie_chan.htm

To provide financial assistance for college to Asian American high school seniors who demonstrate special talents.

Title of Award: Jackie Chan Scholarships **Area, Field, or Subject:** General studies/Field of study not specified **Level of Education for which Award is Granted:** Undergraduate **Number Awarded:** 2 each year. **Funds Available:** The maximum stipend is $8,000. Funds are paid directly to the recipient's college or university. **Duration:** 1 year.

Eligibility Requirements: This program is open to high school seniors of Asian heritage who are U.S. citizens or permanent residents. Applicants must be planning to begin full-time study at an accredited postsecondary educational institution in the United States. Along with their application, they must submit a 500-word essay on "How do you plan to use your special talents to achieve your professional goals?" Selection is based on academic excellence (GPA of 3.3 or higher), leadership in extracurricular activities, community service involvement, and financial need. **Deadline for Receipt:** February of each year. **Additional Information:** Funding is not provided for correspondence courses, Internet courses, or study in a country other than the United States.

1753 ■ US PAN ASIAN AMERICAN CHAMBER OF COMMERCE

Attn: Scholarship Coordinator
1329 18th Street, N.W.
Washington, DC 20036
Tel: (202)296-5221
Fax: (202)296-5225
E-mail: administrator@uspaacc.com
Web Site: http://www.uspaacc.com/web/programs/ruth_mu_lan.htm

To provide financial assistance for college to female Asian American high school seniors who demonstrate financial need.

Title of Award: Ruth Mu-Lan Chu and James S.C. Chao Scholarship **Area, Field, or Subject:** General studies/Field of study not specified **Level of Education for which Award is Granted:** Undergraduate **Number Awarded:** 1 each year. **Funds Available:** The maximum stipend is $5,000. Funds are paid directly to the recipient's college or university. **Duration:** 1 year.

Eligibility Requirements: This program is open to female high school seniors of Asian heritage who are U.S. citizens or permanent residents. Applicants must be planning to begin full-time study at an accredited postsecondary educational institution in the United States. Along with their application, they must submit a 500-word essay on "Why I need this scholarship." Selection is based on academic excellence (GPA of 3.5 or higher), community service involvement, and financial need. **Deadline for Receipt:** February of each year. **Additional Information:** Funding is not provided for correspondence courses, Internet courses, or study in a country other than the United States.

1754 ■ US PAN ASIAN AMERICAN CHAMBER OF COMMERCE

Attn: Scholarship Coordinator
1329 18th Street, N.W.
Washington, DC 20036
Tel: (202)296-5221
Fax: (202)296-5225
E-mail: administrator@uspaacc.com
Web Site: http://www.uspaacc.com/web/programs/bruce_lee.htm

To provide financial assistance for college to high school seniors who have persevered over adversity.

Title of Award: Bruce Lee Scholarship **Area, Field, or Subject:** General studies/Field of study not specified **Level of Education for which Award is Granted:** Undergraduate **Number Awarded:** 1 each year. **Funds Available:** The maximum stipend is $5,000. Funds are paid directly to the recipient's college or university. **Duration:** 1 year.

Eligibility Requirements: This program is open to high school seniors who are U.S. citizens or permanent residents. Applicants must be planning to begin full-time study at an accredited postsecondary educational institution in the United States. Along with their application, they must submit a 500-word essay on "What adversities have you overcome?" Selection is based on academic excellence (GPA of 3.0 or higher), character, ability to persevere and prevail over adversity, community service involvement, and financial need. **Deadline for Receipt:** February of each year. **Additional Information:** Funding is not provided for correspondence courses, Internet courses, or study in a country other than the United States.

1755 ■ US PAN ASIAN AMERICAN CHAMBER OF COMMERCE

Attn: Scholarship Coordinator
1329 18th Street, N.W.
Washington, DC 20036
Tel: (202)296-5221
Fax: (202)296-5225
E-mail: administrator@uspaacc.com
Web Site: http://www.uspaacc.com/web/programs/dr_poh_shien.htm
To provide financial assistance for college to Asian American high school seniors who demonstrate financial need.
Title of Award: Drs. Poh Shien and Judy Young Scholarship **Area, Field, or Subject:** General studies/Field of study not specified **Level of Education for which Award is Granted:** Undergraduate **Number Awarded:** 1 each year. **Funds Available:** The maximum stipend is $4,000. Funds are paid directly to the recipient's college or university. **Duration:** 1 year.
Eligibility Requirements: This program is open to high school seniors of Asian heritage who are U.S. citizens or permanent residents. Applicants must be planning to begin full-time study at an accredited postsecondary educational institution in the United States. Along with their application, they must submit a 500-word essay on "Why I need this scholarship." Selection is based on academic excellence (GPA of 3.5 or higher), leadership in extracurricular activities, community service involvement, and financial need. **Deadline for Receipt:** February of each year. **Additional Information:** Funding is not provided for correspondence courses, Internet courses, or study in a country other than the United States.

1756 ■ US PAN ASIAN AMERICAN CHAMBER OF COMMERCE

Attn: Scholarship Coordinator
1329 18th Street, N.W.
Washington, DC 20036
Tel: (202)296-5221
Fax: (202)296-5225
E-mail: administrator@uspaacc.com
Web Site: http://www.uspaacc.com/sodexho
To provide financial assistance and work experience to Asian American college students
Title of Award: Sodexho Pan Asian Network Group Scholarship **Area, Field, or Subject:** General studies/Field of study not specified **Level of Education for which Award is Granted:** Four Year College **Number Awarded:** 1 each year. **Funds Available:** The stipend is $5,000. Funds are paid directly to the recipient's college or university. An additional stipend is paid for the internship. **Duration:** 1 academic year for the scholarship; 8 weeks for the internship.
Eligibility Requirements: This program is open to college sophomores and juniors of Asian heritage who are U.S. citizens or permanent residents. Applicants must be enrolled in full-time study at an accredited 4-year college or university in the United States and working on a degree in business management, preferably food service management, hotel restaurant institution management, facilities management, or similar program leading to a bachelor's degree. They must be willing to commit to a paid internship with Sodexho during the summer. Along with their application, they must submit a 500-word essay on how they plan to use their special talents to achieve their professional goals. Selection is based on academic excellence (GPA of 3.0 or higher), leadership in extracurricular activities, community service involvement. **Deadline for Receipt:** February of each year. **Additional Information:** This program, established in 2005, is sponsored by Sodexho USA and its Pan Asian Network Group (PANG). Funding is not provided for correspondence courses, Internet courses, or study in a country other than the United States.

1757 ■ US PAN ASIAN AMERICAN CHAMBER OF COMMERCE

Attn: Scholarship Coordinator
1329 18th Street, N.W.
Washington, DC 20036
Tel: (202)296-5221
Fax: (202)296-5225
E-mail: administrator@uspaacc.com
Web Site: http://www.uspaacc.com/web/programs/telamon.htm

To provide financial assistance for college to Asian American high school seniors.
Title of Award: Telamon Scholarship **Area, Field, or Subject:** General studies/Field of study not specified **Level of Education for which Award is Granted:** Undergraduate **Number Awarded:** 1 each year. **Funds Available:** The maximum stipend is $3,500. Funds are paid directly to the recipient's college or university. **Duration:** 1 year.
Eligibility Requirements: This program is open to high school seniors of Asian heritage who are U.S. citizens or permanent residents. Applicants must be planning to begin full-time study at an accredited postsecondary educational institution in the United States. Along with their application, they must submit a 500-word essay on "What are the characteristics or qualities needed in order to achieve success?" Selection is based on academic excellence (GPA of 3.5 or higher), leadership in extracurricular activities, community service involvement, and financial need. **Deadline for Receipt:** February of each year. **Additional Information:** This program was established in 2001. Funding is not provided for correspondence courses, Internet courses, or study in a country other than the United States.

1758 ■ USO WORLD HEADQUARTERS

Attn: Scholarship Program
Washington Navy Yard, Building 198
901 M Street, S.E.
Washington, DC 20374
Tel: (202)610-5700
Fax: (202)610-5699
Web Site: http://www.desert-storm.com/soldiers/uso.html
To provide financial assistance for academic or vocational education to spouses and children of military personnel who died in the Persian Gulf War.
Title of Award: USO Desert Storm Education Fund **Area, Field, or Subject:** General studies/Field of study not specified **Level of Education for which Award is Granted:** Undergraduate **Number Awarded:** All eligible survivors will receive funding. **Funds Available:** It is the purpose of the fund to provide as much financial support as possible to all eligible persons. To this end, USO will distribute all of the fund to the eligible persons in equal amounts. **Duration:** This will be a 1-time distribution of these funds.
Eligibility Requirements: This program is open to the spouses and children of armed service personnel killed, either through accidental causes or in combat, during Operations Desert Shield and Desert Storm. Department of Defense guidelines will be used to determine those service personnel who were taking part in either of these operations at the time of their deaths. This is an entitlement program; neither financial need nor academic achievement are factors in allocating support from the fund. All eligible candidates are contacted directly.

1759 ■ U.S.S. INTREPID ASSOCIATION, INC.

86 North River Pier
New York, NY 10036-1012
800-343-CV11
E-mail: cv11men@aol.com
Web Site: http://www.ussintrepid.com/intrepid.html
To provide financial assistance for college to the relatives of members of the U.S.S. Intrepid Association.
Title of Award: U.S.S. Intrepid Scholarships **Area, Field, or Subject:** General studies/Field of study not specified **Level of Education for which Award is Granted:** Undergraduate **Number Awarded:** Varies each year; recently, 4 of these scholarships were awarded. **Funds Available:** The stipend is $1,000. **Duration:** 1 year.
Eligibility Requirements: This program is open to the relatives (children, grandchildren, etc.) of association members. **Additional Information:** Information is also available from Alan Sasloff, 3333 Henry Hudson Parkway, Riverdale, NY 10463, (718) 549-0518, E-mail: AMSasloff@aol.com.

1760 ■ USS LAKE CHAMPLAIN FOUNDATION

c/o Captain R.K. Martin, USN (ret)
P.O. Box 233
Keeseville, NY 12944
Tel: (518)834-7660
Web Site: http://www.usslakechamplainfoundation.com

To provide financial assistance for college to naval personnel who are (or have been) attached to the *USS Lake Champlain* and to their dependents. **Title of Award:** USS Lake Champlain (CG-57) Scholarship Fund **Area, Field, or Subject:** General studies/Field of study not specified **Level of Education for which Award is Granted:** Undergraduate **Number Awarded:** Varies each year. Recently, 11 of these scholarships were awarded: 3 at $100, 3 at $250, and 5 at $1,000. **Funds Available:** Stipends range from $100 to $1,000. Scholarships greater than $250 are paid in 2 installments: 1 at the beginning of the fall semester and 1 at the beginning of the second semester upon verification of satisfactory completion of the first semester and continued enrollment. Funds are paid directly to the academic institution. **Duration:** 1 year.

Eligibility Requirements: Eligible to apply are 1) past and present crew members of the *USS Lake Champlain;* 2) spouses and dependent children of officers and enlisted personnel currently serving aboard the *USS Lake Champlain;* and 3) spouses and dependent children of officers and enlisted personnel on active duty, retired with pay, or deceased who were previously assigned to the *USS Lake Champlain* since commissioning on August 12, 1988. Applicants must submit an essay on their career objectives, why they are interested in that career, and how furthering their education will lead to their accomplishing their career objective. Selection is based on that essay, financial need, high school and/or college transcripts, 2 letters of recommendation, extracurricular activities and awards, and work experience. **Deadline for Receipt:** May of each year.

1761 ■ USS LITTLE ROCK ASSOCIATION
P.O. Box 16846
Stamford, CT 06905-8846
E-mail: littlerocksol@acsworld.com
Web Site: http://www.usslittlerock.org/scholarship.html
To provide financial assistance to Naval ROTC midshipmen who have a personal or family connection to the sea services or are members of the USS Little Rock Association.

Title of Award: USS Little Rock Association NROTC Scholarship Program **Area, Field, or Subject:** General studies/Field of study not specified **Level of Education for which Award is Granted:** Four Year College **Number Awarded:** 1 or 2 each year. **Funds Available:** The stipend is $1,000 per year. **Duration:** 1 year; may be renewed 1 additional year.

Eligibility Requirements: This program is open to students entering their third academic year of an NROTC program (scholarship, college program, Enlisted Commissioning Program, or Seaman to Admiral). Applicants must 1) be children or direct descendants of active, retired, or honorably discharged members of the sea services (U.S. Navy, U.S. Marine Corps, or U.S. Coast Guard) or their Reserve components; 2) themselves be serving or have served in any of the regular or Reserve sea services; or 3) have been Junior Associate members of the USS Little Rock Association for at least 2 years. They must have a GPA of 3.0 or higher and have demonstrated superior leadership qualities and aptitude for service in all of their NROTC activities. Along with their application, they must submit a 500-word letter describing why they consider themselves worthy of the award. **Deadline for Receipt:** May of each year. **Additional Information:** This program was initiated in 2001.

1762 ■ UTAH ARMY NATIONAL GUARD
Attn: UT-G1-ESO
12953 South Minuteman Drive
P.O. Box 1776
Draper, UT 84020-1776
Tel: (801)523-4537
Web Site: http://www.ut.ngb.army.mil/education2
To provide tuition assistance to currently-enrolled members of the Utah National Guard.

Title of Award: Utah National Guard Tuition Waiver **Area, Field, or Subject:** General studies/Field of study not specified **Level of Education for which Award is Granted:** Undergraduate **Number Awarded:** Varies each year. Each participating college and university is required to set aside 2.5% of the instate scholarships they award each year for members of the Utah National Guard. **Funds Available:** Qualified Guard members receive tuition waivers that pay 100% of tuition at the designated public colleges and universities. **Duration:** 1 semester; recipients may renew.

Eligibility Requirements: This program is open to Utah residents who are MOS/AFSC qualified members of the Utah National Guard. Applicants

must have been accepted as a full-time student at 1 of the following schools: University of Utah, Utah State University, Southern Utah University, College of Eastern Utah, Dixie State College, Salt Lake Community College, Snow College, Utah Valley State College, or Weber State University. Along with their application, they must submit a short essay on "How have the events of 9/11 effected the citizen soldier?" Guard members who already have a 4-year college degree or who are assigned to active duty are not eligible. **Deadline for Receipt:** May of each year. **Additional Information:** Information is also available from the Utah Air National Guard, Attn: 151st MSF-DPH, 765 North 2200 West, Salt Lake City, UT 84116, (801) 245-2441.

1763 ■ UTAH ASSOCIATION OF INDEPENDENT INSURANCE AGENTS
4885 South 900 East, Suite 302
Salt Lake City, UT 84117
Tel: (801)269-1200
Fax: (801)269-1265
E-mail: elainejones@mcleodusa.net
Web Site: http://www.uaiia.org/_private/scholarship.htm
To provide financial assistance to high school seniors in Utah who are interested in attending college to prepare for a career in business or insurance.

Title of Award: Utah Association of Independent Insurance Agents Scholarship Program **Area, Field, or Subject:** Actuarial science; Business administration; Insurance and insurance-related fields **Level of Education for which Award is Granted:** Undergraduate **Number Awarded:** Varies each year; 1 scholarship is reserved for a student preparing for an insurance career and others (recently, 7 other scholarships were awarded) for students working on a degree in insurance or business. **Funds Available:** The stipend is $1,000. **Duration:** 1 year.

Eligibility Requirements: This program is open to seniors graduating from high schools in Utah with a GPA of 3.0 or higher. Applicants must be planning to attend college to prepare for an insurance career and/or work on a degree in insurance or business. Along with their application, they must submit answers to questions about why they are preparing for either an insurance or their chosen career, how their selected major will prepare them for either an insurance or a successful career, why they feel they should receive this scholarship, their 3 top priority goals, and what they want to be doing 6 years from now. Financial need is also considered in the selection process. **Deadline for Receipt:** March of each year.

1764 ■ UTAH ELKS ASSOCIATION
c/o Jim Fugua, Scholarship Chair
Provo Lodge 849
1000 South University Avenue
P.O. Box 83
Provo, UT 84603
Tel: (801)373-0849
Web Site: http://www.utahelks.org
To provide financial assistance for college to high school seniors in Utah.

Title of Award: Utah Elks Association Scholarship Program **Area, Field, or Subject:** General studies/Field of study not specified **Level of Education for which Award is Granted:** Four Year College **Number Awarded:** Varies each year, recently, the program awarded 4 scholarships (2 to males and 2 to females) at $4,000, 16 (8 to males and 8 to females) at $800, and 16 (8 to males and 8 to females) at $700. **Funds Available:** Stipends are $4,000, $800, or $700. **Duration:** 1 year.

Eligibility Requirements: This program is open to seniors graduating from high schools in Utah. Applicants must submit a 500-word essay on their career and life goals and their plan to achieve those. Selection is based on that essay, academic achievement, community service, honors and awards, leadership, and financial need. U.S. citizenship is required. **Deadline for Receipt:** January of each year.

1765 ■ UTAH ELKS ASSOCIATION
c/o Jim Fugua, Scholarship Chair
Provo Lodge 849
1000 South University Avenue
P.O. Box 83
Provo, UT 84603
Tel: (801)373-0849
Web Site: http://www.utahelks.org

To provide financial assistance for college to high school seniors in Utah who have a disability or other special need.

Title of Award: Utah Elks Association Special Needs Student Scholarship Award **Area, Field, or Subject:** General studies/Field of study not specified **Level of Education for which Award is Granted:** Undergraduate **Number Awarded:** Varies each year, depending upon the funds available. **Funds Available:** A stipend is awarded (amount not specified). **Duration:** 1 year.

Eligibility Requirements: This program is open to seniors graduating from high schools in Utah who have a special need, such as a disability. Applicants must submit 1) a supporting letter from a doctor or professional person stating the nature of the special need, and 2) a 500-word essay on their career and life goals and their plan to achieve those. Selection is based on that essay, academic achievement, community service, honors and awards, leadership, and financial need. U.S. citizenship is required. **Deadline for Receipt:** January of each year.

1766 ■ UTAH HEMOPHILIA FOUNDATION

880 East 3375 South
Salt Lake City, UT 84106
Tel: (801)484-0325; 877-INFO-VWD
Fax: (801)484-4177
E-mail: info@hemophiliautah.org
Web Site: http://www.hemophiliautah.org/Programs/programs.html
To provide financial assistance for college to residents of Utah with bleeding disorders and their families.

Title of Award: Utah Hemophilia Foundation Scholarships **Area, Field, or Subject:** General studies/Field of study not specified **Level of Education for which Award is Granted:** Undergraduate **Number Awarded:** Varies each year, Recently, 7 of these scholarships were awarded: 5 at $1,500 and 2 at $500. **Funds Available:** Stipends are $1,500 or $500. **Duration:** 1 year.

Eligibility Requirements: This program is open to people in Utah with bleeding disorders and to their spouses, children, and parents. Applicants must be attending or planning to attend a college, university, trade school, or technical program. **Additional Information:** This program includes the Choice Source Therapeutics Scholarships (sponsored by Choice Source Therapeutics) and the Chris Townsend Memorial Scholarship.

1767 ■ UTAH HIGHER EDUCATION ASSISTANCE AUTHORITY

Board of Regents Building, The Gateway
60 South 400 West
Salt Lake City, UT 84101-1284
Tel: (801)321-7294; 877-336-7378
Fax: (801)321-7299
E-mail: uheaa@utahsbr.edu
Web Site: http://www.uheaa.org/grants.htm
To provide financial assistance and work-study to students at designated Utah institutions.

Title of Award: Utah Centennial Opportunity Program for Education **Area, Field, or Subject:** General studies/Field of study not specified **Level of Education for which Award is Granted:** Undergraduate **Number Awarded:** Varies each year. **Funds Available:** The maximum award to each eligible student is $5,000, of which no more than $2,500 may be a grant and the remainder provided in the form of a work study award. For the work-study portion, students receive the current federal minimum wage. **Duration:** 1 year; may be renewed.

Eligibility Requirements: Students at participating colleges in Utah may request an application directly from their college's financial aid offices. The participating institutions in Utah are: Brigham Young University, College of Eastern Utah, Dixie State College, LDS Business College, Salt Lake Community College, Snow College, Southern Utah University, University of Utah, Utah State University, Utah Valley State College, Weber State University, and Westminster College. Applicants must meet the federal guidelines for financial need. They must also be willing to accept a work-study assignment in 1) an institutional job on campus; 2) school assistant jobs, as tutors, mentors, or teacher assistants, to work with educationally disadvantaged and high risk school pupils, by contract, at individual schools or school districts; 3) community service jobs, with

volunteer community service organizations; or 4) matching jobs, by contract with government agencies, private businesses, or nonprofit corporations.

1768 ■ UTAH HIGHER EDUCATION ASSISTANCE AUTHORITY

Board of Regents Building, The Gateway
60 South 400 West
Salt Lake City, UT 84101-1284
Tel: (801)321-7294; 877-336-7378
Fax: (801)321-7299
E-mail: uheaa@utahsbr.edu
Web Site: http://www.uheaa.org/scholarships.htm
To provide financial assistance for college to Utah residents who graduate from high school early.

Title of Award: Utah Centennial Scholarship for Early Graduation **Area, Field, or Subject:** General studies/Field of study not specified **Level of Education for which Award is Granted:** Undergraduate **Number Awarded:** Varies each year. **Funds Available:** Stipends are $1,000 for students who graduate after their junior year, $750 after the first quarter of their senior year, $500 after the second quarter of their senior year, or $250 after the third quarter of their senior year. Funds are sent directly to the student's postsecondary institution. **Duration:** These are 1-time awards.

Eligibility Requirements: This program is open to public high school students in Utah who complete early graduation having completed all required courses and demonstrated mastery of required skills and competencies. Applicants must enroll full time in an accredited Utah college or university within 1 calendar year of high school graduation. **Additional Information:** Information is also available from the Utah State Office of Education, Attn: Curriculum Coordinator, 250 East 500 South, P.O. Box 144200, Salt Lake City, UT 84114-4200, (801) 538-7884.

1769 ■ UTAH HIGHER EDUCATION ASSISTANCE AUTHORITY

Board of Regents Building, The Gateway
60 South 400 West
Salt Lake City, UT 84101-1284
Tel: (801)321-7294; 877-336-7378
Fax: (801)321-7299
E-mail: uheaa@utahsbr.edu
Web Site: http://www.uheaa.org/grants.htm
To provide financial assistance for college to students in Utah with financial need.

Title of Award: Utah Leveraging Educational Assistance Partnership Program **Area, Field, or Subject:** General studies/Field of study not specified **Level of Education for which Award is Granted:** Undergraduate **Number Awarded:** Varies each year. **Funds Available:** The maximum stipend is $2,500. **Duration:** 1 year; may be renewed.

Eligibility Requirements: Students at participating colleges in Utah may request an application directly from their college's financial aid offices. The participating colleges in Utah are: College of Eastern Utah, Dixie State College, Salt Lake Community College, Snow College, Southern Utah University, University of Utah, Utah State University, Utah Valley State College, Weber State University, and Westminster College. Applicants must have substantial financial need. Students taking correspondence courses are not eligible.

1770 ■ UTAH HIGHER EDUCATION ASSISTANCE AUTHORITY

Board of Regents Building, The Gateway
60 South 400 West
Salt Lake City, UT 84101-1284
Tel: (801)321-7107; 877-336-7378
Fax: (801)321-7299
E-mail: uheaa@utahsbr.edu
Web Site: http://www.uheaa.org/scholarships.htm
To provide financial assistance for college to Utah residents who complete an associate degree at a community college while still enrolled in high school.

Title of Award: Utah New Century Scholarship Program **Area, Field, or Subject:** General studies/Field of study not specified **Level of Education for which Award is Granted:** Undergraduate **Number Awarded:** Varies each year. **Funds Available:** Stipends equal 75% of an eligible student's tuition cost at a Utah public institution of higher education that offers a bachelor's degree, or an equivalent amount at designated private institu-

tions. **Duration:** Up to 2 years, provided the student maintains at least a 3.0 GPA.
Eligibility Requirements: This program is open to high school students in Utah who take classes at a local community college and complete an associate degree by September of the year their class graduates from high school. Applicants must be planning to attend an accredited college or university in the states. **Additional Information:** This program was established in 1999.

1771 ■ UTAH SPORTS HALL OF FAME FOUNDATION
Attn: Scholarship Chair
2248 Texas Street
Salt Lake City, UT 84109
Tel: (801)484-0666
To recognize and reward outstanding high school seniors in Utah who have been involved in athletics and are interested in attending college in the state.
Title of Award: Ream's Food Stores Scholarships **Area, Field, or Subject:** General studies/Field of study not specified **Level of Education for which Award is Granted:** Undergraduate **Number Awarded:** 6 each year: 3 boys and 3 girls. **Funds Available:** The stipend is $2,000. Funds are paid to the recipient's institution. **Duration:** 1 year; nonrenewable.
Eligibility Requirements: Each high school in Utah may nominate 1 boy and 1 girl who are graduating this year. Nominees must be planning to attend college in the state. Selection is based on academic record, personal character, financial need, leadership qualities, and involvement in athletic activities, including football, basketball, cross country, volleyball, tennis, track and field, soccer, rodeo, baseball, swimming, wrestling, officiating, or community recreation. **Deadline for Receipt:** March of each year. **Additional Information:** Additional information is also available from Berdean Jarman, 873 West 1200 North, Orem, UT 84057. Formerly, the sponsoring organization was known as the Old Time Athletes Association. Recipients must attend an academic institution in Utah.

1772 ■ UTAH SPORTS HALL OF FAME FOUNDATION
Attn: Scholarship Chair
2248 Texas Street
Salt Lake City, UT 84109
Tel: (801)484-0666
To recognize and reward outstanding Native American high school seniors in Utah who have been involved in athletics and are interested in attending college in the state.
Title of Award: Utah Sports Hall of Fame Native American Scholarships **Area, Field, or Subject:** General studies/Field of study not specified **Level of Education for which Award is Granted:** Undergraduate **Number Awarded:** 2 each year. **Funds Available:** The stipend is $2,000. Funds are paid to the recipient's institution. **Duration:** 1 year; nonrenewable.
Eligibility Requirements: Each high school in Utah may nominate 1 Native American high school senior. Nominees must be planning to attend college in the state. Selection is based on academic record, personal character, financial need, leadership qualities, and involvement in athletic activities, including football, basketball, cross country, volleyball, tennis, track and field, soccer, rodeo, baseball, swimming, wrestling, officiating, or community recreation. **Deadline for Receipt:** March of each year. **Additional Information:** Additional information is also available from Berdean Jarman, 873 West 1200 North, Orem, UT 84057. Formerly, the sponsoring organization was known as the Old Time Athletes Association. Recipients must attend an academic institution in Utah.

1773 ■ UTILITY WORKERS UNION OF AMERICA
Attn: Merit Scholarships Awards Program
815 16th Street, N.W., Suite 605
Washington, DC 20006
Tel: (202)974-8200
Fax: (202)974-8201
Web Site: http://uwua.net
To provide financial assistance for college to the children of members of the Utility Workers Union of America.
Title of Award: Utility Workers Union of America Merit Scholarships **Area, Field, or Subject:** General studies/Field of study not specified **Level of Education for which Award is Granted:** Undergraduate **Number Awarded:** 2 each year. **Funds Available:** The stipend ranges from $500

to $2,000 per year. **Duration:** Up to 4 years or until completion of the bachelor's degree, whichever occurs first.
Eligibility Requirements: Eligible are children of members of the Utility Workers Union of America who plan to graduate from high school in spring following application and enroll full time in college in the following fall. Applicants must take the Preliminary Scholastic Assessment Test/ National Merit Scholarship Qualifying Test in the fall, prior to applying. Selection is based on academic record, activities and contributions to the school and community, test scores, school recommendation, and an essay. Family financial circumstances are not considered. **Deadline for Receipt:** December of each year. **Additional Information:** This program was established in 1961.

1774 ■ VASA ORDER OF AMERICA
Attn: Vice Grand Master
3236 Berkeley Avenue
Cleveland Heights, OH 44118-2055
Tel: (216)371-5141
E-mail: rolf.bergman@sbcglobal.net
Web Site: http://www.vasaorder.com
To provide financial assistance for college to members of the Vasa Order of America from designated states.
Title of Award: Gladys A. and Russell M. Birtwistle Award **Area, Field, or Subject:** General studies/Field of study not specified **Level of Education for which Award is Granted:** Undergraduate **Number Awarded:** 1 each year. **Funds Available:** The stipend is $1,500. **Duration:** 1 year.
Eligibility Requirements: Applicants must have been members of the organization for at least 1 year and live in districts 1 (Connecticut), 2 (Massachusetts), or 3 (Rhode Island). They must be high school seniors or college undergraduates who plan to continue their education on a full-time basis at an accredited institution. Selection is based on a grade transcript, letters of recommendation from school and local Vasa lodge officials, and an essay of up to 1,000 words on a topic related to Vasa. **Deadline for Receipt:** February of each year. **Additional Information:** Vasa Order of America is a Swedish American fraternal organization incorporated in 1899.

1775 ■ VASA ORDER OF AMERICA
Attn: Vice Grand Master
3236 Berkeley Avenue
Cleveland Heights, OH 44118-2055
Tel: (216)371-5141
E-mail: rolf.bergman@sbcglobal.net
Web Site: http://www.vasaorder.com
To provide financial assistance for undergraduate or graduate study to members of the Vasa Order of America.
Title of Award: Irma and Knute Carlson Award **Area, Field, or Subject:** General studies/Field of study not specified **Level of Education for which Award is Granted:** Four Year College, Graduate **Number Awarded:** 1 each year. **Funds Available:** The stipend is $1,000. **Duration:** 1 year.
Eligibility Requirements: Applicants must have been members of the organization for at least 1 year. They may be college juniors, seniors, or graduate students. Selection is based on a transcript, letters of recommendation from school and local Vasa lodge officials, and an essay of up to 1,000 words on a topic related to Vasa. **Deadline for Receipt:** February of each year. **Additional Information:** Vasa Order of America is a Swedish American fraternal organization incorporated in 1899.

1776 ■ VASA ORDER OF AMERICA
Attn: Vice Grand Master
3236 Berkeley Avenue
Cleveland Heights, OH 44118-2055
Tel: (216)371-5141
E-mail: rolf.bergman@sbcglobal.net
Web Site: http://www.vasaorder.com
To provide financial assistance for college or graduate school to students of Swedish heritage.
Title of Award: Oscar and Mildred Larson Award **Area, Field, or Subject:** General studies/Field of study not specified **Level of Education for which Award is Granted:** Graduate, Undergraduate **Number Awarded:** 1 each year. **Funds Available:** The stipend is $3,000 per year. **Duration:** 1 year; may be renewed up to 3 additional years for a total award of $16,000.

Eligibility Requirements: Applicants must be Swedish born or of Swedish ancestry; residents of the United States, Canada, or Sweden; and enrolled or accepted as full-time undergraduate or graduate students in an accredited 4-year college or university in the United States. Membership in Vasa Order of America is not required. Selection is based on a grade transcript, letters of recommendation from school and local Vasa lodge officials, and an essay of up to 1,000 words on a topic related to Vasa. **Deadline for Receipt:** February of each year. **Additional Information:** Vasa Order of America is a Swedish American fraternal organization incorporated in 1899.

1777 ■ VASA ORDER OF AMERICA

Attn: Vice Grand Master
3236 Berkeley Avenue
Cleveland Heights, OH 44118-2055
Tel: (216)371-5141
E-mail: rolf.bergman@sbcglobal.net
Web Site: http://www.vasaorder.com
To provide financial assistance for college to members of the Vasa Order of America from designated states.
Title of Award: L. Einar and Edith L. Nilsson Award **Area, Field, or Subject:** General studies/Field of study not specified **Level of Education for which Award is Granted:** Undergraduate **Number Awarded:** 1 each year. **Funds Available:** The stipend is $1,500. **Duration:** 1 year.
Eligibility Requirements: Applicants must have been members of the organization for at least 1 year and live in district 1 (Connecticut), district 2 (Massachusetts), or district 3 (Rhode Island). They must be high school seniors or college undergraduates who plan to continue their education on a full-time basis at an accredited institution. Selection is based on a grade transcript, letters of recommendation from school and local Vasa lodge officials, and an essay of up to 1,000 words on a topic related to Vasa. **Deadline for Receipt:** February of each year. **Additional Information:** Vasa Order of America is a Swedish American fraternal organization incorporated in 1899.

1778 ■ VASA ORDER OF AMERICA

Attn: Vice Grand Master
3236 Berkeley Avenue
Cleveland Heights, OH 44118-2055
Tel: (216)371-5141
E-mail: rolf.bergman@sbcglobal.net
Web Site: http://www.vasaorder.com
To provide financial assistance for college or vocational education to members of the Vasa Order of America.
Title of Award: Vasa Order of America College or Vocational School Scholarships **Area, Field, or Subject:** General studies/Field of study not specified **Level of Education for which Award is Granted:** Undergraduate **Number Awarded:** 10 each year. **Funds Available:** Stipends are $1,000. **Duration:** 1 year.
Eligibility Requirements: Applicants must have been members of the organization for at least 1 year. They must be planning to continue their academic or vocational education on a full-time basis. Selection is based on a grade transcript, letters of recommendation from school and local Vasa lodge officials, and an essay of up to 1,000 words on a topic related to Vasa. **Deadline for Receipt:** February of each year. **Additional Information:** Vasa Order of America is a Swedish American fraternal organization incorporated in 1899.

1779 ■ VERMONT GROCERS' ASSOCIATION

Attn: Director of Communications and Events
33 Lafayette Street
Rutland, VT 05701-4167
Tel: (802)775-5460
Free: 800-VGA-8503
Fax: (802)773-2242
E-mail: info@vtgrocers.org
Web Site: http://www.vtgrocers.org
To provide financial assistance for college to high school seniors who are either an employee of or the dependent of an employee affiliated with the Vermont Grocers' Association (VGA).
Title of Award: Donna Hogan Award **Area, Field, or Subject:** General studies/Field of study not specified **Level of Education for which Award is Granted:** Undergraduate **Number Awarded:** 1 each year. **Funds**

Available: The stipend is $1,000 for the first year and $500 for the following years. **Duration:** 4 years, provided the recipient maintains a GPA of 3.0 or higher.
Eligibility Requirements: This program is open to high school seniors who are either residents of Vermont or affiliated with a member of the VGA. All applicants must meet 1 of more of the following criteria: 1) dependent of a VGA associate or retail member store/company owner; 2) dependent of a VGA associate or retail member store/company employee; or 3) employee of a VGA retail member store/associate member company. The qualifying employee must be employed at least 15 hours per week or 750 hours per year in a VGA associate or retail member store/company and have been employed there for at least 1 year. Selection is based on academic record, extracurricular activities, financial need, and letters of recommendation. **Deadline for Receipt:** April of each year. **Additional Information:** This award was established in 2002.

1780 ■ VERMONT GROCERS' ASSOCIATION

Attn: Director of Communications and Events
33 Lafayette Street
Rutland, VT 05701-4167
Tel: (802)775-5460
Free: 800-VGA-8503
Fax: (802)773-2242
E-mail: info@vtgrocers.org
Web Site: http://www.vtgrocers.org
To provide financial assistance for college to high school seniors who are either an employee of or the dependent of an employee affiliated with the Vermont Grocers' Association (VGA).
Title of Award: Ernest Hurst Memorial Award **Area, Field, or Subject:** General studies/Field of study not specified **Level of Education for which Award is Granted:** Undergraduate **Number Awarded:** 1 each year. **Funds Available:** The stipend is $1,000 for the first year and $500 for the following years. **Duration:** 4 years, provided the recipient maintains a GPA of 3.0 or higher.
Eligibility Requirements: This program is open to high school seniors who are either residents of Vermont or affiliated with a member of the VGA. All applicants must meet 1 of more of the following criteria: 1) dependent of a VGA associate or retail member store/company owner; 2) dependent of a VGA associate or retail member store/company employee; or 3) employee of a VGA retail member store/associate member company. The qualifying employee must be employed at least 15 hours per week or 750 hours per year in a VGA associate or retail member store/company and have been employed there for at least 1 year. Selection is based on academic record, extracurricular activities, financial need, and letters of recommendation. **Deadline for Receipt:** April of each year. **Additional Information:** This award was established in 1998.

1781 ■ VERMONT GROCERS' ASSOCIATION

Attn: Director of Communications and Events
33 Lafayette Street
Rutland, VT 05701-4167
Tel: (802)775-5460
Free: 800-VGA-8503
Fax: (802)773-2242
E-mail: info@vtgrocers.org
Web Site: http://www.vtgrocers.org
To provide financial assistance for college to high school seniors who are either an employee of or the dependent of an employee affiliated with the Vermont Grocers' Association (VGA).
Title of Award: Vermont Grocers' Association Scholarship **Area, Field, or Subject:** General studies/Field of study not specified **Level of Education for which Award is Granted:** Undergraduate **Number Awarded:** Varies each year; recently, 10 of these scholarships were awarded, including 3 that were based on merit only. **Funds Available:** The stipend is $1,000 for the first year and $500 for the second year. **Duration:** 2 years, provided the recipient maintains a GPA of 3.0 or higher during the first year.
Eligibility Requirements: This program is open to high school seniors who are either residents of Vermont or affiliated with a member of the VGA. All applicants must meet 1 of more of the following criteria: 1) dependent of a VGA associate or retail member store/company owner; 2) dependent of a VGA associate or retail member store/company employee; or 3) employee of a VGA retail member store/associate member company. The qualifying employee must be employed at least 15 hours

per week or 750 hours per year in a VGA associate or retail member store/company and have been employed there for at least 1 year. Selection is based on academic record, extracurricular activities, and letters of recommendation. While most of the scholarships are also based on financial need, some are awarded irrespective of income. **Deadline for Receipt:** April of each year.

1782 ■ VERMONT STUDENT ASSISTANCE CORPORATION
Champlain Mill
Attn: Scholarship Programs
P.O. Box 2000
Winooski, VT 05404-2601
Tel: (802)654-3798; 888-253-4819
Fax: (802)654-3765
E-mail: info@vsac.org
Web Site: http://www.vsac.org
To provide financial assistance to Vermont residents who are interested in attending a culinary arts program.
Title of Award: Cabot Creamery Culinary Scholarship **Area, Field, or Subject:** Culinary arts **Level of Education for which Award is Granted:** Undergraduate **Number Awarded:** Either 1 at $1,000 or 2 at $500 each year. **Funds Available:** The stipend is either $1,000 or $500. **Duration:** 1 year.
Eligibility Requirements: This scholarship is available to residents of Vermont who are high school seniors, high school graduates, or currently-enrolled college students. Applicants must be enrolled or planning to enroll in an academic, vocational, technical, or advanced training program related to the culinary arts. Selection is based on academic achievement, required essays, a letter of recommendation, and financial need. **Deadline for Receipt:** March of each year.

1783 ■ VERMONT STUDENT ASSISTANCE CORPORATION
Champlain Mill
Attn: Scholarship Programs
P.O. Box 2000
Winooski, VT 05404-2601
Tel: (802)654-3798; 888-253-4819
Fax: (802)654-3765
E-mail: info@vsac.org
Web Site: http://www.vsac.org
To provide financial assistance for college to single parent mothers in Vermont.
Title of Award: Sister Elizabeth Candon Scholarship **Area, Field, or Subject:** General studies/Field of study not specified **Level of Education for which Award is Granted:** Undergraduate **Number Awarded:** 1 each year. **Funds Available:** The stipend is $1,000 per year. **Duration:** 1 year; may be renewed up to 3 additional years.
Eligibility Requirements: This program is open to women residents of Vermont who are single parents with primary custody of at least 1 child 12 years of age or younger. Applicants must be enrolled at least half time in an accredited undergraduate degree program. Selection is based on financial need, a letter of recommendation, and required essays. **Deadline for Receipt:** June of each year.

1784 ■ VERMONT STUDENT ASSISTANCE CORPORATION
Champlain Mill
Attn: Scholarship Programs
P.O. Box 2000
Winooski, VT 05404-2601
Tel: (802)654-3798; 888-253-4819
Fax: (802)654-3765
E-mail: info@vsac.org
Web Site: http://www.vsac.org
To provide financial assistance for college to high school seniors in Vermont.
Title of Award: Chittenden Bank Scholarship **Area, Field, or Subject:** General studies/Field of study not specified **Level of Education for which Award is Granted:** Undergraduate **Number Awarded:** 2 each year. **Funds Available:** The stipend is $2,500 per year. **Duration:** 1 year; may be renewed up to 3 additional years.
Eligibility Requirements: This scholarship is available to U.S. citizens who are residents of Vermont and graduating from a high school in the state. Applicants must be planning to attend an accredited 2-year or

4-year college or university. Selection is based on letters of recommendation, required essays, academic achievement, and financial need. **Deadline for Receipt:** April of each year.

1785 ■ VERMONT STUDENT ASSISTANCE CORPORATION
Champlain Mill
Attn: Scholarship Programs
P.O. Box 2000
Winooski, VT 05404-2601
Tel: (802)654-3798; 888-253-4819
Fax: (802)654-3765
E-mail: info@vsac.org
Web Site: http://www.vsac.org
To provide financial assistance for college to high school seniors in Vermont whose parent is a police officer in the state.
Title of Award: Herbert Fullam Scholarship **Area, Field, or Subject:** General studies/Field of study not specified **Level of Education for which Award is Granted:** Undergraduate **Number Awarded:** 1 each year. **Funds Available:** The stipend is $1,000. **Duration:** 1 year.
Eligibility Requirements: This scholarship is available to high school seniors in Vermont who are planning to enroll in a degree program in a 2-year or 4-year college. Applicants must be the child of a Vermont police officer. Selection is based on required essays and financial need. **Deadline for Receipt:** April of each year. **Additional Information:** This program was established by the Vermont Police Association, which is responsible for selecting the recipients.

1786 ■ VERMONT STUDENT ASSISTANCE CORPORATION
Champlain Mill
Attn: Scholarship Programs
P.O. Box 2000
Winooski, VT 05404-2601
Tel: (802)654-3798; 888-253-4819
Fax: (802)654-3765
E-mail: info@vsac.org
Web Site: http://www.vsac.org
To provide financial assistance for college to high school seniors in Vermont whose parents belong to the Vermont Police Association.
Title of Award: Gene Gaiotti Memorial Scholarship **Area, Field, or Subject:** General studies/Field of study not specified **Level of Education for which Award is Granted:** Undergraduate **Number Awarded:** 1 each year. **Funds Available:** The stipend is $1,000. **Duration:** 1 year.
Eligibility Requirements: This scholarship is available to high school seniors in Vermont who are planning to enroll in a degree program at a 2-year or 4-year college. Applicants must be the child of a police officer who is a member of the Vermont Police Association. Selection is based on required essays and financial need. **Deadline for Receipt:** April of each year. **Additional Information:** This program was established by the Vermont Police Association, which is responsible for selecting the recipients.

1787 ■ VERMONT STUDENT ASSISTANCE CORPORATION
Champlain Mill
Attn: Scholarship Programs
P.O. Box 2000
Winooski, VT 05404-2601
Tel: (802)654-3798; 888-253-4819
Fax: (802)654-3765
E-mail: info@vsac.org
Web Site: http://www.vsac.org
To provide financial assistance to adults in Vermont who are interested in attending college to upgrade their employment skills.
Title of Award: Bette Matkowski Scholarship **Area, Field, or Subject:** General studies/Field of study not specified **Level of Education for which Award is Granted:** Undergraduate **Number Awarded:** 2 each year. **Funds Available:** The stipend is $1,000. **Duration:** 1 year.
Eligibility Requirements: This scholarship is available to adults in Vermont who wish to attend an accredited college or university in order to upgrade their employment skills. Selection is based on financial need and required essays. **Deadline for Receipt:** July of each year. **Additional**

Information: The Vermont Student Assistance Corporation established this scholarship in 2002 to honor a former board member.

1788 ■ VERMONT STUDENT ASSISTANCE CORPORATION
Champlain Mill
Attn: Scholarship Programs
P.O. Box 2000
Winooski, VT 05404-2601
Tel: (802)654-3798; 888-253-4819
Fax: (802)654-3765
E-mail: info@vsac.org
Web Site: http://www.vsac.org
To provide financial assistance for college to needy residents of Vermont.
Title of Award: Vermont Incentive Grants **Area, Field, or Subject:** General studies/Field of study not specified **Level of Education for which Award is Granted:** Undergraduate **Number Awarded:** Varies each year. **Funds Available:** Stipends range from $500 to $9,100 per year. **Duration:** 1 year; may be renewed.
Eligibility Requirements: This program is open to residents of Vermont who wish to attend college, either within or outside Vermont, as a full-time undergraduate student. U.S. citizenship or permanent resident status is required. Selection is based on financial need.

1789 ■ VERMONT STUDENT ASSISTANCE CORPORATION
Champlain Mill
Attn: Scholarship Programs
P.O. Box 2000
Winooski, VT 05404-2601
Tel: (802)654-3798; 888-253-4819
Fax: (802)654-3765
E-mail: info@vsac.org
Web Site: http://www.vsac.org
To provide scholarship/loans to members of the Vermont National Guard.
Title of Award: Vermont National Guard Scholarship Program **Area, Field, or Subject:** General studies/Field of study not specified **Level of Education for which Award is Granted:** Undergraduate **Number Awarded:** 100 each year. **Funds Available:** Up to $2,500 is available as an interest-free educational loan. Partial or complete cancellation of the loan is provided if the recipient completes and passes the courses and completes 2 years of service in the Vermont National Guard for each full academic award received. **Duration:** 1 year.
Eligibility Requirements: This program is open to all members of the Vermont Army National Guard or Vermont Air National Guard who have successfully completed basic training or commissioning. Applicants must have been residents of Vermont for at least 1 year and be interested in attending a college, university, vocational school, or technical school in the state. Financial need is not considered. **Deadline for Receipt:** June of each year. **Additional Information:** This program, established in 1998, is sponsored by the Vermont National Guard, Green Mountain Armory, Colchester, VT 05446-3004, (802) 338-3348, (800) 4VT-ARNG.

1790 ■ VERMONT STUDENT ASSISTANCE CORPORATION
Champlain Mill
Attn: Scholarship Programs
P.O. Box 2000
Winooski, VT 05404-2601
Tel: (802)654-3798; 888-253-4819
Fax: (802)654-3765
E-mail: info@vsac.org
Web Site: http://www.vsac.org
To provide financial assistance to needy residents of Vermont who wish to attend college on a part-time basis.
Title of Award: Vermont Part-Time Grants **Area, Field, or Subject:** General studies/Field of study not specified **Level of Education for which Award is Granted:** Undergraduate **Number Awarded:** Varies each year. **Funds Available:** The amounts of the awards depend on the number of credit hours and the need of the recipient. **Duration:** 1 year; may be renewed.
Eligibility Requirements: This program is open to residents of Vermont who are enrolled or accepted for enrollment in an undergraduate degree, diploma, or certificate program. Applicants must be taking fewer than 12 credits per semester and not have received a baccalaureate degree. Financial need is considered in the selection process.

1791 ■ VERTICAL FLIGHT FOUNDATION
Attn: Scholarship Coordinator
217 North Washington Street
Alexandria, VA 22314-2538
Tel: (703)684-6777
Fax: (703)739-9279
E-mail: Staff@vtol.org
Web Site: http://www.vtol.org/vff.html
To provide financial assistance for college to high school seniors in the area of the Federal City chapter of the American Helicopter Society (AHS).
Title of Award: Daniel L. Peduzzi Memorial Scholarship **Area, Field, or Subject:** General studies/Field of study not specified **Level of Education for which Award is Granted:** Undergraduate **Number Awarded:** 1 each year. **Funds Available:** The stipend is $2,000. **Duration:** 1 year.
Eligibility Requirements: This program is open to seniors graduating from high schools in the Federal City chapter area, which covers Washington, D.C., Maryland (except zip codes 20600-20699), and Virginia (except zip codes 22000-22499). Applicants must have been accepted as a freshman at an accredited college or university. They must submit a narrative covering their future academic interest, their future career interest, and other reasons why they should be considered for this scholarship. Selection is based only on merit. **Deadline for Receipt:** May of each year. **Additional Information:** This program was established in 1992.

1792 ■ VETERANS OF FOREIGN WARS OF THE UNITED STATES
VFW Building
406 West 34th Street
Kansas City, MO 64111
Tel: (816)968-1117
Fax: (816)968-1149
E-mail: SWilson@vfw.org
Web Site: http://www.vfw.org
To provide financial assistance for college to children and grandchildren of veterans and military personnel who have been active in programs of the Veterans of Foreign Wars (VFW).
Title of Award: Veterans Tribute Scholarships **Area, Field, or Subject:** General studies/Field of study not specified **Level of Education for which Award is Granted:** Undergraduate **Number Awarded:** 3 each year. **Funds Available:** The highest ranked applicant receives a $10,000 scholarship, second a $5,000 scholarship, and third a $3,000 scholarship. **Duration:** 1 year.
Eligibility Requirements: This program is open to students between 15 and 18 years of age who are children or grandchildren of living U.S. military veterans, as well as those currently serving (active duty, Reserves, or National Guard). Selection is based on the number of points that applicants achieve out of a possible total of 1,500. Points are awarded for GPA (50 for 2.0 to 2.4, 75 for 2.5 to 2.9, 100 for 3.0 to 3.4, 125 for 3.5 to 3.9, or 150 for 4.0+); 100 for participation in the VFW's Voice of Democracy Scholarship Program; 100 for participation in the VFW's Patriot's Pen Youth Essay Contest; 100 for participation in the VFW Auxiliary's Outstanding Young Volunteer of the Year Program; 100 for participation in the VFW Auxiliary's Young American Creative Patriotic Art program; up to 100 for documented community service (at least 50 hours); 50 if the parent served in the U.S. military overseas; 10 to 100 if the veteran has a service-connected disability (based on the degree of disability); 300 if the veteran is a VFW member; 200 if the veteran is a VFW life member; 100 if the veteran's spouse is a member of the Ladies or Men's Auxiliary to the VFW; and 100 if the veteran has held or holds a VFW office. **Deadline for Receipt:** December of each year.

1793 ■ VETERANS OF FOREIGN WARS OF THE UNITED STATES OF MEXICAN ANCESTRY
Central California Committee
c/o Manuel Hernandez
6719 Lindsey Avenue
Pico Rivera, CA 90660-3638
To provide financial assistance for college to Mexican American high school students in California.
Title of Award: Veterans of Foreign Wars of Mexican Ancestry Scholarship Program **Area, Field, or Subject:** General studies/Field of study not specified **Level of Education for which Award is Granted:** Undergraduate **Number Awarded:** Varies; a total of $9,000 is available for these

scholarships each year: $3,000 in each of the 3 districts. **Funds Available:** Stipends range from $500 to $1,000. **Duration:** 1 year.
Eligibility Requirements: This program is open to high school seniors of Mexican descent who reside in California. They must have earned a GPA of 3.5 or higher and need financial assistance to attend college. Preference is given to the children of veterans. **Deadline for Receipt:** March of each year. **Additional Information:** Students who live in the central portion of California (from Los Angeles to Fresno) should write to the Central California Committee to obtain an application; students who live north of there should contact Robert Gonzalez, 3210 Santa Maria Avenue, Santa Clara, CA 95051-1622, (408) 248-1677; students who live south of there should contact Gilbert Castorena, 3981 Coleman Avenue, San Diego, CA 92154-2516, (619) 690-0907.

1794 ■ VETERANS OF THE VIETNAM WAR, INC.

Attn: Assistance in Education Program
805 South Township Boulevard
Pittston, PA 18640-3327
Tel: (570)603-9740
Fax: (570)603-9741
Web Site: http://www.vvnw.org/Educational_Material/Scholarship/scholarship.htm
To provide financial assistance for college to members of Veterans of the Vietnam War (VVnW) and their families.
Title of Award: Veterans of the Vietnam War National Scholarship Program **Area, Field, or Subject:** General studies/Field of study not specified **Level of Education for which Award is Granted:** Undergraduate **Number Awarded:** 1 or more each year, depending on the availability of funds. **Funds Available:** The stipend is $1,000. Funds are paid directly to the recipient. **Duration:** 1 year.
Eligibility Requirements: This program is open to members of the VVnW in good standing for at least 1 year and their spouses, children, adopted children, foster children, and other immediate descendants. Applicants must be enrolled in or accepted to a program of postsecondary education. Selection is based on a random drawing; financial need, merit, and course of study are not considered. **Deadline for Receipt:** October of each year.

1795 ■ VIETNAM VETERANS OF AMERICA

Attn: Mike Nash Scholarship Program
8605 Cameron Street, Suite 400
Silver Spring, MD 20910-3710
Tel: (301)585-4000
Free: 800-VVA-1316
E-mail: finance@vva.org
Web Site: http://www.vva.org/Scholarship/index.htm
To provide financial assistance for college to members of Vietnam Veterans of America (VVA), their families, and the families of other Vietnam veterans.
Title of Award: Mike Nash Memorial Scholarship Fund **Area, Field, or Subject:** General studies/Field of study not specified **Level of Education for which Award is Granted:** Undergraduate **Number Awarded:** Varies each year; recently, 9 of these scholarships were awarded. **Funds Available:** The stipend is $1,000 per year. **Duration:** 1 year; may be renewed for up to 3 additional years.
Eligibility Requirements: This program is open to 1) members of VVA; 2) the spouses, children, stepchildren, and grandchildren of VVA members; and 3) the spouses, children, stepchildren, and grandchildren of MIA, KIA, or deceased Vietnam veterans. Applicants must be enrolled or planning to enroll at least half time at an accredited college, university, or technical institution. Along with their application, they must submit high school or college transcripts; SAT, ACT, or other recognized test scores; a letter of recommendation from a VVA state council, chapter, or national; 2 letters of recommendation; a letter describing their current educational goals and objectives, individual accomplishments, and any other personal information that may assist in the selection process; and documentation of financial need. **Deadline for Receipt:** June of each year. **Additional Information:** This program was established in 1991 and given its current name in 1997.

1796 ■ VIETNOW NATIONAL HEADQUARTERS

1835 Broadway
Rockford, IL 61104-5409

Tel: (815)227-5100
Free: 800-837-VNOW
Fax: (815)227-5127
E-mail: vnnatl@inwave.com
Web Site: http://www.vietnow.com
To provide financial assistance for college to dependents of certain veterans.
Title of Award: VietNow Scholarships **Area, Field, or Subject:** General studies/Field of study not specified **Level of Education for which Award is Granted:** Undergraduate **Number Awarded:** Varies each year; recently, 9 of these scholarships were awarded. **Funds Available:** The stipend is $1,000 per year. **Duration:** 1 year.
Eligibility Requirements: Applicants must be either 1) a dependent (biological child, stepchild, adopted child, or foster child) under the age of 35 of a VietNow member in good standing, or 2) a dependent of a veteran listed as missing in action, prisoner of war, or killed in action. Selection is based on academic achievement, ability, and extracurricular activities; financial need is a minor consideration. **Deadline for Receipt:** March of each year.

1797 ■ VII CORPS DESERT STORM VETERANS ASSOCIATION

Attn: Scholarship Committee
Army Historical Foundation
2425 Wilson Boulevard
Arlington, VA 22201
Tel: (703)604-6565
E-mail: viicorpsdsva@aol.com
Web Site: http://www.desertstormvets.org/scholarship/index.cfm
To provide financial assistance for college to students who served, or are the family members of individuals who served, with VII Corps in Operations Desert Shield, Desert Storm, or related activities.
Title of Award: VII Corps Desert Storm Veterans Association Scholarship **Area, Field, or Subject:** General studies/Field of study not specified **Level of Education for which Award is Granted:** Undergraduate **Number Awarded:** 3 each year. **Funds Available:** The stipend is $5,000 per year. Funds are paid to the recipients upon proof of admission or registration at an accredited institution, college, or university. **Duration:** 1 year; recipients may reapply.
Eligibility Requirements: Applicants must have served, or be a family member of those who served, with VII Corps in Operations Desert Shield/Desert Storm, Provide Comfort, or 1 of the support base activities. Scholarships are limited to students entering or enrolled in accredited technical institutions (trade or specialty), 2-year colleges, and 4-year colleges or universities. Awards will not be made to individuals receiving military academy appointments or full 4-year scholarships. Letters of recommendation and a transcript are required. Selection is not based solely on academic standing; consideration is also given to extracurricular activities and other self-development skills and abilities obtained through on-the-job training or correspondence courses. Priority is given to survivors of VII Corps soldiers who died during Operations Desert Shield/Desert Storm or Provide Comfort, veterans who are also members of the VII Corps Desert Storm Veterans Association, and family members of veterans who are also members of the VII Corps Desert Storm Veterans Association. **Deadline for Receipt:** January of each year. **Additional Information:** This program began in 1998.

1798 ■ VIRGINIA ARMY/AIR NATIONAL GUARD ENLISTED ASSOCIATION

Attn: Executive Secretary
2503 Ravenwood Avenue, N.W.
Roanoke, VA 24012-3245
Tel: (540)366-5133
Fax: (540)362-4417
E-mail: sfcjj@aol.com
Web Site: http://www.staunton.com/vaaangea/Education/learn.html
To provide financial assistance for college to members of the Virginia Army/Air National Guard Enlisted Association (VaA/ANGEA) and to members of their families.
Title of Award: Virginia Army/Air National Guard Enlisted Association Scholarship **Area, Field, or Subject:** General studies/Field of study not specified **Level of Education for which Award is Granted:** Undergraduate **Number Awarded:** Generally, 2 scholarships at $1,000 and 4 scholarships at $500 are awarded each year. **Funds Available:** Generally,

stipends are either $1,000 or $500. **Duration:** 1 year; recipients may reapply.

Eligibility Requirements: This program is open to 1) enlisted soldiers or enlisted airmen currently serving as a member of the Virginia National Guard (VNG) who are also a member of the VaA/ANGEA; 2) retired enlisted soldiers or retired enlisted airmen of the VNG who are also a member of the VaA/ANGEA; 3) spouses of current enlisted soldiers or enlisted airmen of the VNG who are also a member of the VaA/ANGEA; 4) spouses of retired enlisted soldiers or retired enlisted airmen of the VNG who are also a member of the VaA/ANGEA; and 5) dependents of current or retired enlisted soldiers or airmen of the VNG (a copy of the dependency decree may be required) who are also members of the VaA/ANGEA. Applicants must submit a copy of their school transcript (high school or college), a letter with facts on their desire to continue their education and their need for assistance, 3 letters of recommendation, a letter of academic reference, and a photocopy of their VaA/ANGEA membership card. Selection is based on academics (15 points), personal letter (15 points), letters of recommendation (16 points), school involvement (15 points), community involvement (15 points), responsibility (15 points), and financial need (9 points). **Deadline for Receipt:** February of each year. **Additional Information:** Recipients may attend school on either a part-time or full-time basis. Information is also available from CMS Charles P. Smith, 10163 Tunstall Road, New Kent, VA 23124.

1799 ■ VIRGINIA ASSOCIATION FOR PUPIL TRANSPORTATION

c/o David L. Pace, Scholarship Chair
2650 Leroy Road, Building 1
Virginia Beach, VA 23456
Tel: (757)263-1569
E-mail: dpace@vbcps.k12.va.us
Web Site: http://www.pen.k12.va.us/VDOE/Finance/VAPT/scholarship.htm
To provide financial assistance for college to high school seniors in Virginia who have a parent or grandparent employed in a public school pupil transportation field in the state.
Title of Award: Clyde W. Morris Memorial Scholarship **Area, Field, or Subject:** General studies/Field of study not specified **Level of Education for which Award is Granted:** Undergraduate **Number Awarded:** 1 or more each year. **Funds Available:** The stipend is $1,000. **Duration:** 1 year.
Eligibility Requirements: This program is open to seniors at public high schools in Virginia who have a parent or grandparent employed in a public school pupil transportation field in the state. Applicants should have a GPA of 3.0 or higher. As part of the application process, they must write a 500-word essay on why they applied for the scholarship and how the funds will be used. Selection is based on academic record, leadership, citizenship, service, and the essay. **Deadline for Receipt:** April of each year. **Additional Information:** This scholarship was first awarded in 1996.

1800 ■ VIRGINIA ASSOCIATION OF SCHOOL BUSINESS OFFICIALS

c/o Steven R. Bateson, Scholarship Chair
Chesterfield County Public Schools
P.O. Box 10
Chesterfield, VA 23832
Tel: (804)748-1405
E-mail: batesons@chesterfield.gov
Web Site: http://www.vasbo.org/scholarship.htm
To provide financial assistance for college to children and grandchildren of members of the Virginia Association of School Business Officials (VASBO).
Title of Award: VASBO Scholarships **Area, Field, or Subject:** General studies/Field of study not specified **Level of Education for which Award is Granted:** Undergraduate **Number Awarded:** 2 each year. **Funds Available:** The stipend is $1,500. **Duration:** 1 year.
Eligibility Requirements: This program is open to high school seniors who are children or grandchildren of VASBO members. Applicants must be interested in attending an accredited 2-year or 4-year college or

university. Selection is based on academic achievement, character, school and community service, and career goals. **Deadline for Receipt:** February of each year.

1801 ■ VIRGINIA ATHLETIC TRAINERS ASSOCIATION

c/o Terry Zablocki, Scholarship Committee Chair
Maury High School
322 Shirley Avenue
Norfolk, VA 23517
Tel: (757)628-9189
E-mail: tzablocki@nps.k12.va.us
Web Site: http://www.vata.org/scholarship/index.htm
To provide financial assistance to high school seniors in Virginia who are interested in preparing for a career as an athletic trainer.
Title of Award: Virginia Athletic Trainers Association Scholarship Award **Area, Field, or Subject:** Athletics **Level of Education for which Award is Granted:** Undergraduate **Number Awarded:** 2 each year: 1 at $1,000 and 1 at $500. **Funds Available:** Stipends are $1,000 or $500. **Duration:** 1 year.
Eligibility Requirements: This program is open to seniors graduating from high schools in Virginia who intend to study athletic training in college. Applicants must provide evidence of interest in athletic training through experience as a high school student athletic trainer and/or attendance at an athletic training seminar or workshop. Along with their application, they must submit an essay of 250 to 500 words on their interest in a career in the allied health profession of athletic training. Selection is based on academic ability, leadership ability, responsible citizenship, and dedication and interest in athletic training. **Deadline for Receipt:** March of each year.

1802 ■ VIRGINIA DEPARTMENT OF VETERANS' AFFAIRS

270 Franklin Road, S.W., Room 503
Roanoke, VA 24011-2215
Tel: (540)857-7104
Fax: (540)857-7573
Web Site: http://www.dvs.virginia.gov/education_benefits.htm
To provide educational assistance to the children of disabled and other Virginia veterans or service personnel.
Title of Award: Virginia War Orphans Education Program **Area, Field, or Subject:** General studies/Field of study not specified **Level of Education for which Award is Granted:** Graduate, Undergraduate **Number Awarded:** Varies; generally more than 150 each year. **Funds Available:** Eligible individuals receive free tuition and are exempted from any fees charged by state-supported schools in Virginia. **Duration:** Entitlement extends to a maximum of 48 months.
Eligibility Requirements: This program is open to residents of Virginia who have at least 1 parent who served in the U.S. armed forces and is permanently and totally disabled due to an injury or disease incurred in a time of war or other period of armed conflict, has died as a result of war or other armed conflict, or is listed as a prisoner of war or missing in action. Applicants must be between 16 and 25 years of age and be accepted at a public secondary or postsecondary educational institution in Virginia. The veteran parent must have been a resident of Virginia at the time of entry into active military service or for at least 5 consecutive years immediately prior to the date of application or death. The surviving parent must have been a resident of Virginia for at least 5 years prior to marrying the deceased parent or for at least 5 years immediately prior to the date on which the application was submitted. **Additional Information:** Individuals entitled to this benefit may use it to pursue any vocational, technical, undergraduate, or graduate program of instruction. Generally, programs listed in the academic catalogs of state-supported institutions are acceptable, provided they have a clearly defined educational objective (such as a certificate, diploma, or degree).

1803 ■ VIRGINIA HIGH SCHOOL LEAGUE

1642 State Farm Boulevard
Charlottesville, VA 22911
Tel: (434)977-8475
Fax: (434)977-5943
Web Site: http://www.vfbinsurance.com/VHSL/VHSLAbout.asp
To provide financial assistance for college to high school seniors who have participated in activities of the Virginia High School League (VHSL).
Title of Award: Farm Bureau Insurance-VHSL Achievement Awards **Area, Field, or Subject:** General studies/Field of study not specified

Level of Education for which Award is Granted: Undergraduate **Number Awarded:** 10 each year. For each of the 3 groups (A, AA, and AAA), 1 female athlete, 1 male athlete, and 1 academic participant are selected. In addition, 1 courageous achievement candidate is selected statewide. **Funds Available:** The stipend is $1,000. **Duration:** 1 year. **Eligibility Requirements:** This program is open to college-bound seniors graduating from high schools that are members of the VHSL. Applicants must have participated in 1 or more VHSL athletic activities (baseball, basketball, cheer, cross country, field hockey, football, golf, gymnastics, soccer, softball, swimming, tennis, indoor and outdoor track, volleyball, wrestling) and/or academic activities (student publications, creative writing, theater, forensics, debate, scholastic bowl). They must have a GPA of 3.0 or higher. Each school may nominate up to 4 students: 1 female athlete, 1 male athlete, 1 academic participant, and 1 courageous achievement candidate. The courageous achievement category is reserved for students who have overcome serious obstacles to make significant contributions to athletic and/or academic activities. The obstacles may include a serious illness, injury, or disability; a challenging social or home situation; or another extraordinary situation where the student has displayed tremendous courage against overwhelming odds. Along with their application, students must submit a 500-word essay describing how extracurricular activities have enhanced their educational experience. Candidates are judged separately in the 3 VHSL groups (A, AA, and AAA). Selection is based on the essay; involvement in other school-sponsored activities; involvement in activities outside of school; and 2 letters of support. **Deadline for Receipt:** March of each year. **Additional Information:** This program, which began in 1992, is supported by Farm Bureau Insurance. The courageous achievement category, designated the Andrew Mullins Courageous Achievement Award, was added in 2002.

1804 ■ VIRGINIA HIGH SCHOOL LEAGUE

1642 State Farm Boulevard
Charlottesville, VA 22911
Tel: (434)977-8475
Fax: (434)977-5943
Web Site: http://www.vhsl.org
To provide financial assistance for college to high school seniors who have participated in activities of the Virginia High School League (VHSL).
Title of Award: Wachovia Citizenship Awards **Area, Field, or Subject:** General studies/Field of study not specified **Level of Education for which Award is Granted:** Undergraduate **Number Awarded:** 6 each year: a female and a male in each of the 3 VHSL groups. **Funds Available:** The stipend is $1,000. **Duration:** 1 year.
Eligibility Requirements: This program is open to college-bound seniors graduating from high schools that are members of the VHSL. Applicants must have participated in 1 or more of the following VHSL activities: baseball, basketball, cheer, creative writing, cross country, debate, drama, field hockey, football, forensics, golf, gymnastics, lacrosse, leaders conference, magazines, newspapers/newsmagazines, scholastic bowl, soccer, softball, sportsmanship summit/committee, swimming and diving, tennis, track (indoor and outdoor), volleyball, wrestling, and yearbook. They must submit an essay (from 500 to 1,000 words) on what they have done that meets a definition of citizenship and how others have benefited. Each school may nominate 1 female and 1 male. Candidates are judged separately in the 3 VHSL groups (A, AA, and AAA). Selection is based on the essay; contributions to family, school, and community; promotion of good citizenship and sportsmanship; and 2 letters of support. **Deadline for Receipt:** March of each year. **Additional Information:** This program is supported by Wachovia Bank.

1805 ■ VIRGINIA NATIONAL GUARD

Attn: Educational Services Officer
Fort Pickett, Building 316
Blackstone, VA 23824-6316
Tel: (434)298-6222
Fax: (434)298-6296
E-mail: jeremy.serafin@va.ngb.army.mil
Web Site: http://www.virginiaguard.com
To provide financial assistance for college to members of the Virginia National Guard.
Title of Award: Virginia National Guard Tuition Assistance Program **Area, Field, or Subject:** General studies/Field of study not specified **Level of**

Education for which Award is Granted: Undergraduate **Number Awarded:** Varies each year. **Funds Available:** The program provides reimbursement of tuition at approved colleges, universities, and vocational/technical schools in Virginia, to a maximum of $2,100 per semester or $4,200 per year. **Duration:** 1 semester; may be renewed. **Eligibility Requirements:** This program is open to active members of the Virginia National Guard who are residents of Virginia and interested in attending college in the state. **Deadline for Receipt:** March of each year for summer session; June of each year for fall semester; October of each year for spring semester. **Additional Information:** This program was established in 1983. Recipients must remain in the Guard for at least 2 years after being funded.

1806 ■ VIRGINIA NATIONAL GUARD ASSOCIATION

Attn: Scholarship Committee
5901 Beulah Road
Sandston, VA 23150-6112
Tel: (804)328-0037; 888-703-0037
Fax: (804)328-3020
E-mail: vnga@worldnet.att.net
Web Site: http://www.vnga.org/scholarship/home.htm
To provide financial assistance for college to members of the Virginia National Guard Association (VNGA) and their children.
Title of Award: Virginia National Guard Association Scholarship **Area, Field, or Subject:** General studies/Field of study not specified **Level of Education for which Award is Granted:** Undergraduate **Number Awarded:** Varies each year. **Funds Available:** A stipend is awarded; the amount is determined annually. **Duration:** 1 year; may be renewed for 2 additional years.
Eligibility Requirements: Applicants must have been enrolled in a college or university for 1 year and qualify under 1 of the following conditions: 1) an officer or warrant officer in the Virginia National Guard and a VNGA member; 2) the child of an officer or warrant officer in the Virginia National Guard who is a VNGA member; 3) the child of a retired officer or warrant officer who is a VNGA member; 4) the child of a deceased retired officer or warrant officer, or 5) the child of a Virginia National Guard officer or warrant officer who died while in the Virginia National Guard. Along with their application, they must submit a brief description of their educational and/or military objectives, a list of their leadership positions and honors, and a brief statement of their financial need. **Deadline for Receipt:** September of each year. **Additional Information:** The association also offers a special scholarship in memory of CW4 William C. Singletary who, in rescuing 2 elderly women from drowning, gave his own life. Information is also available from the scholarship committee, 50 Falcon Road, Suite 37-F, Sandston, VA 23150-2524, (804) 236-6592.

1807 ■ VIRGINIA PUBLIC SAFETY FOUNDATION, INC.

P.O. Box 1355
Richmond, VA 23218
Tel: (804)282-0148
Fax: (804)282-2127
E-mail: vpsf@globalweb.net
Web Site: http://
To provide financial assistance for college to the children of current and selected former Virginia public safety officers.
Title of Award: Virginia Public Safety Foundation Scholarships **Area, Field, or Subject:** General studies/Field of study not specified **Level of Education for which Award is Granted:** Undergraduate **Number Awarded:** Varies each year; recently 29 were awarded. **Funds Available:** Stipends range up to $3,000 per year. **Duration:** 1 year; nonrenewable. **Eligibility Requirements:** Eligible to apply for support are the children of all active-duty Virginia public safety officers and those officers forced to retire because of an injury incurred in the line of duty. "Public safety" officers are defined as state and local police, sheriffs, their deputies, corrections and jail officers, fire fighters, agents of the Alcoholic Beverage Control Department, and volunteer members of a fire company or rescue squad. Applicants may be high school seniors or currently enrolled in college. Selection is based on merit (academic record, character, personal and career goals, extracurricular activities, and school service). Financial need is not considered in the selection process. **Deadline for Receipt:** February of each year. **Additional Information:** This program was originally created in 1987 by the Virginia Police Foundation, which subsequently merged with the Virginia Public Safety Foundation. To date,

more than $200,000 in scholarships has been awarded. Recipients may attend school in any state.

1808 ■ VIRGINIA STATE GOLF ASSOCIATION

Attn: Virginia Golf Foundation, Inc.
600 Founders Bridge Boulevard
Midlothian, VA 23113
Tel: (804)378-2300
Fax: (804)378-8216
E-mail: info@vsga.org
Web Site: http://www.vsga.org
To provide financial assistance for college to young Virginians who have an interest in golf.
Title of Award: Virginia Golf Foundation Scholarship Program **Area, Field, or Subject:** General studies/Field of study not specified; Turfgrass management **Level of Education for which Award is Granted:** Undergraduate **Number Awarded:** Varies each year. Recently, 35 of these scholarships were awarded: 2 at $5,000 (the Spencer-Wilkinson Award for a woman and the C. Dan Keffer Award for a man), 7 at $3,000, 3 at $2,500, 4 at $2,000 (including the David A. King Merit Award and the VSGA Women's Division Merit Award), 10 at $1,000, and 9 at $500. That included 14 scholarships for 4 years, 16 merit awards for 1 year, and 5 scholarships for turfgrass management students at Virginia Tech. **Funds Available:** Stipends range from $500 to $5,000. Funds may be used only for tuition, room, and other approved educational expenses. **Duration:** The program includes 4-year scholarships and 1-year merit awards.
Eligibility Requirements: This program is open to high school seniors in Virginia who are interested in golf and wish to attend a college or university in the state. Applicants must submit an essay of 500 words or less on how golf has influenced their life, the role it will play in their future plans, why they are applying for this scholarship, and their career plans following graduation. Selection is based on the essay, interest in golf (excellence and ability are not considered), academic achievement, citizenship, character, and financial need. Applications must be made on behalf of the candidate by a member club of the Virginia State Golf Association (VSGA). Some scholarships are reserved for students working on degrees in turfgrass management at Virginia Polytechnic Institute and State University. The David A. King Merit award is presented to an outstanding applicant. The VSGA Women's Division Merit Award and the Spencer-Wilkinson Award are set aside specifically for women and the C. Dan Keffer Award is set aside specifically for men. **Deadline for Receipt:** February of each year. **Additional Information:** This program was established in 1984. Since then, more than 480 students have received a total of $1,168,600 in scholarships.

1809 ■ VOCATIONAL FOUNDATION OF NEBRASKA

P.O. Box 22607
Lincoln, NE 68542-2607
Tel: (402)423-6786
To provide financial assistance to career and technical students in Nebraska.
Title of Award: Outstanding Secondary Career and Technical Education Student Award **Area, Field, or Subject:** General studies/Field of study not specified **Level of Education for which Award is Granted:** Vocational/Occupational **Number Awarded:** 1 each year. **Funds Available:** The award is a $1,000 scholarship. Funds must be used for attendance at a Nebraska postsecondary institution. **Duration:** The award is presented annually.
Eligibility Requirements: This program is open to students who are currently enrolled in career and technical education in Nebraska or have been enrolled within the past 12 months. Students must be nominated by a teacher who 1) describes how they have demonstrated a high level of competence in the program through classroom, work experience, laboratory training, related projects, or extracurricular activities, and 2) explains what distinguishes them from others in terms of capability, motivation, achievements, performances, and contributions. Nominees must also complete an application in which they describe how they will apply their career and technical education to their future plans and list projects or experiences that have seemed most interesting or important to them,

school and community activities, and honors or awards. **Deadline for Receipt:** Nominations must be submitted by March of each year.

1810 ■ VOCATIONAL FOUNDATION OF NEBRASKA

P.O. Box 22607
Lincoln, NE 68542-2607
Tel: (402)423-6786
To provide financial assistance to career and technical students in Nebraska who are members of groups defined as "special populations."
Title of Award: Outstanding Secondary Special Populations Career and Technical Education Student Award **Area, Field, or Subject:** General studies/Field of study not specified **Level of Education for which Award is Granted:** Vocational/Occupational **Number Awarded:** 1 each year. **Funds Available:** The award is a $1,000 scholarship. Funds must be used for attendance at a Nebraska postsecondary institution. **Duration:** The award is presented annually.
Eligibility Requirements: This program is open to students who are currently enrolled in career and technical education in Nebraska or have been enrolled within the past 12 months. Students must be members of a "special populations" group, including individuals with disabilities and economically and academically disadvantaged individuals. They must be nominated by a teacher who 1) describes how they have demonstrated a high level of competence in the program through classroom, work experience, laboratory training, related projects, or extracurricular activities, and 2) explains what distinguishes them from others in terms of capability, motivation, achievements, performances, and contributions. Nominees must also complete an application in which they describe how they will apply their career and technical education to their future plans and list projects or experiences that have seemed most interesting or important to them and school and community activities. **Deadline for Receipt:** Nominations must be submitted by March of each year.

1811 ■ DANA WALTERS SCHOLARSHIP FOUNDATION

P.O. Box 723243
Atlanta, GA 31139
Tel: (770)436-0190
E-mail: sonickaren@aol.com
Web Site: http://www.dwscholarship.com/scholar.html
To provide financial assistance for college to residents of Georgia who have cystic fibrosis (CF) and members of their immediate families.
Title of Award: Dana Walters Scholarships **Area, Field, or Subject:** General studies/Field of study not specified **Level of Education for which Award is Granted:** Undergraduate **Number Awarded:** 1 or more each year. **Funds Available:** The stipend is $1,000. Funds are paid directly to the recipient's college. **Duration:** 1 year; may be renewed.
Eligibility Requirements: This program is open to residents of Georgia who have CF or are a member of a family (including parents) of a person who has CF. Applicants must be graduating high school seniors or already have a high school diploma. They must have a combined SAT score of at least 900 and either a GPA of 2.7 or higher or a rank in the top 30% of their class. Financial need is not considered in the selection process. **Deadline for Receipt:** March of each year.

1812 ■ WAMPANOAG TRIBE OF GAY HEAD

Attn: Education Director
20 Black Brook Road
Aquinnah, MA 02535-1546
Tel: (508)645-9265
Fax: (508)645-3790
Web Site: http://www.wampanoagtribe.net/education/higher.htm
To provide financial assistance for college or graduate school to members of the Wampanoag Tribe of Gay Head.
Title of Award: Wampanoag Higher Education Scholarship Program **Area, Field, or Subject:** General studies/Field of study not specified **Level of Education for which Award is Granted:** Graduate, Undergraduate **Number Awarded:** Varies each year. **Funds Available:** The stipend depends on the need of the recipient. **Duration:** 1 year; may be renewed.
Eligibility Requirements: This program is open to enrolled members of the Wanpanoag Tribe of Gay Head who are working on or planning to work on a baccalaureate or advanced degree. Applicants must submit a letter of acceptance from a college or university and documentation of financial need. **Deadline for Receipt:** July of each year.

1813 ■ WASHINGTON COUNCIL OF THE BLIND

P.O. Box 6996
Kennewick, WA 99336
Tel: (206)283-4276
Free: 800-255-1147
E-mail: info@wcbinfo.org
Web Site: http://www.wcbinfo.org
To provide financial aid for college or graduate school to blind students in Washington.

Title of Award: Washington Council of the Blind Scholarships **Area, Field, or Subject:** General studies/Field of study not specified **Level of Education for which Award is Granted:** Graduate, Undergraduate **Number Awarded:** 1 or more each year. **Funds Available:** The stipend is at least $2,000 per year. **Duration:** 1 year.

Eligibility Requirements: This program is open to blind residents of Washington state. Applicants must be attending or planning to attend a college, university, or vocational school within the Pacific Northwest (Washington, Oregon, Idaho, Alaska, and Montana), a college or university with a branch campus in Washington, or a distance learning program. Along with their application, they must submit 2 letters of recommendation, proof of legal blindness, and a 1- to 3-page statement of their reasons for applying for this scholarship and how it will assist them to achieve their goals. The statement should include a brief description of their background, education, work experience, economic status, strengths, weaknesses, and personal goals for the next 5 to 10 years. **Deadline for Receipt:** June of each year. **Additional Information:** Additional information is available from Alan Bentson, Scholarship Committee Chair, 7356 34th Avenue, N.E., Seattle, WA 98115, (206) 527-4527, E-mail: alan@wtbbi.org.

1814 ■ WASHINGTON EDUCATION FOUNDATION

1605 N.W. Sammamish Road, Suite 100
Issaquah, WA 98027
Tel: (425)416-2000; 877-655-4097
Fax: (425)416-2001
E-mail: info@waedfoundation.org
Web Site: http://www.waedfoundation.org
To provide financial assistance to students at community and technical colleges in Washington who plan to transfer to a 4-year institution in the state.

Title of Award: Take Aim Transfer Scholarships **Area, Field, or Subject:** General studies/Field of study not specified **Level of Education for which Award is Granted:** Four Year College **Number Awarded:** Varies each year. **Funds Available:** The stipend is $2,000. **Duration:** 1 year.

Eligibility Requirements: This program is open to students currently enrolled at community and technical colleges in Washington. Applicants must be planning to complete their associate degree in the year they apply and then transfer to a 4-year college or university in the state to complete their bachelor's degree. They must be able to demonstrate financial need. Each college in Washington may nominate 3 to 5 students. **Additional Information:** This program, established in 2004, is supported by Northwest Education Loan Association (NELA).

1815 ■ WASHINGTON EDUCATION FOUNDATION

1605 N.W. Sammamish Road, Suite 100
Issaquah, WA 98027
Tel: (425)416-2000
Fax: (425)416-2001
E-mail: info@waedfoundation.org
Web Site: http://www.waedfoundation.org/achievers/index.htm
To provide financial assistance for college to low-income students at selected high schools in Washington state.

Title of Award: Washington State Achievers Program **Area, Field, or Subject:** General studies/Field of study not specified **Level of Education for which Award is Granted:** Undergraduate **Number Awarded:** Approximately 500 each year. **Funds Available:** Stipends are approximately $5,000 per year. **Duration:** 4 years.

Eligibility Requirements: This program is open to students currently classified as juniors at 16 designated high schools in Washington. The schools were selected because they serve large populations of low-income students and because they agreed to implement a redesign program that facilitates high academic achievement and increased college enrollment among their students. Students must intend to obtain a 4-year college degree as a full-time student, with at least the first 2 years of attendance at an eligible Washington public or independent college or university. They must also have a family income less than specified amounts, ranging from $33,900 for a family of 2 to $67,400 for a family of 7. Selection is based on the student's academic record; overcoming hardships or unusual circumstances; motivation, tenacity, and initiative; leadership potential; demonstrated concern for others and the community; persistence and potential for success in degree completion; and intellectual curiosity and creative achievement. **Deadline for Receipt:** November of each year. **Additional Information:** These scholarships were first awarded in 2001. Support for this program is provided by the Bill and Melinda Gates Foundation. Recipients are expected to utilize their senior year in high school to enroll in additional college preparatory classes, consider possible colleges, apply for financial aid, and pursue other scholarships as needed. After high school graduation, they may attend a community or technical college, but only if they enroll in approved programs that will transfer with junior status to a 4-year degree program at an eligible college or university.

1816 ■ WASHINGTON EDUCATION FOUNDATION

1605 N.W. Sammamish Road, Suite 100
Issaquah, WA 98027
Tel: (425)416-2000; 877-655-4097
Fax: (425)416-2001
E-mail: info@waedfoundation.org
Web Site: http://www.waedfoundation.org/gs/index.htm
To provide financial assistance for college to high school seniors in Washington state who have been in foster, group, or kinship care.

Title of Award: Washington State Governor's Scholarship for Foster Youth **Area, Field, or Subject:** General studies/Field of study not specified **Level of Education for which Award is Granted:** Undergraduate **Number Awarded:** Between 20 and 30 each year. **Funds Available:** Stipends range from $1,000 to $5,000 per year and average $4,000. **Duration:** 1 year; may be renewed up to 3 additional years if the recipient continues to demonstrate financial need and satisfactory progress toward a degree.

Eligibility Requirements: This program is open to dependent youth who are, or have been until emancipation, in state, tribal, or federally-recognized foster, group, or kinship care in the state of Washington. Applicants must be high school seniors with a GPA of 2.0 or higher and planning to enroll full time at an accredited public or private nonprofit college or university in Washington. Selection is based on academic preparedness; motivation and commitment to play a significant role in an activity, group, organization, or family; willingness to seek and use support from others when needed; ability to set educational and career goals and take the intermediate steps to reach those goals; ability to persist toward goals in the face of obstacles or challenges; and financial need. **Deadline for Receipt:** February of each year. **Additional Information:** This program was established by Governor Gary Locke in 2001.

1817 ■ WASHINGTON HIGHER EDUCATION COORDINATING BOARD

917 Lakeridge Way
P.O. Box 43430
Olympia, WA 98504-3430
Tel: (360)753-7851; 888-535-0747
Fax: (360)753-7808
E-mail: info@hecb.wa.gov
Web Site: http://www.hecb.wa.gov/financialaid/wave/waveindex.asp
To provide financial assistance to Washington residents who are attending vocational/technical schools.

Title of Award: Washington Award for Vocational Excellence **Area, Field, or Subject:** General studies/Field of study not specified **Level of Education for which Award is Granted:** Vocational/Occupational **Number Awarded:** Up to 147 each year: 3 in each state legislative district. **Funds Available:** Awards do not exceed the annual undergraduate tuition and fees at public research universities in the state (approximately $3,700 per year). **Duration:** Up to 6 quarters or 4 semesters, provided the student maintains a GPA of 3.0 or higher.

Eligibility Requirements: High schools, skills centers, and community and technical colleges nominate students who are engaged in vocational or technical training for these awards. Nominees must 1) graduate from high school having completed at least 360 hours in a single, approved vocational program, or 2) be enrolled in a public community or technical college and complete at least 1 year (360 hours) in an approved vocational program. They may be planning to attend a public 2 or 4-year college or university or an accredited private college, university, or vocational school in Washington. Selection is based on financial need (25 points), leadership (20 points), community service (20 points), vocational plans (30 points), other work experience (15 points), and a student narrative on what vocational education has meant to them (30 points). **Deadline for Receipt:** February of each year. **Additional Information:** This program, established in 1984, is jointly administered with the Washington Workforce Training and Education Coordinating Board, 128 Tenth Avenue, S.W., P.O. Box 43105, Olympia, WA 98504-3105, (360) 753-0892, E-mail: ddonahoo@wtb.wa.gov.

1818 ■ WASHINGTON HIGHER EDUCATION COORDINATING BOARD

917 Lakeridge Way
P.O. Box 43430
Olympia, WA 98504-3430
Tel: (360)753-7851
Fax: (360)753-7808
E-mail: info@hecb.wa.gov
Web Site: http://www.hecb.wa.gov/financialaid/wsp/wspindex.asp
To provide financial assistance for education at colleges and universities in Washington to the top 1% of students who graduate from high schools in the state.

Title of Award: Washington Scholars Program **Area, Field, or Subject:** General studies/Field of study not specified **Level of Education for which Award is Granted:** Undergraduate **Number Awarded:** Up to 147 each year: 3 in each state legislative district. **Funds Available:** Awards provide payment of full-time undergraduate resident tuition and fees, or approximately $3,700 per year. **Duration:** Aid is provided for 12 quarters or 8 semesters of undergraduate study.

Eligibility Requirements: High school principals in Washington may nominate graduating seniors in the top 1% of their class for this program. Students are selected to receive awards based on academic accomplishments, leadership, and community service. **Additional Information:** Recipients may study at an independent or public college or university in Washington.

1819 ■ WASHINGTON HIGHER EDUCATION COORDINATING BOARD

917 Lakeridge Way
P.O. Box 43430
Olympia, WA 98504-3430
Tel: (360)753-7843
Fax: (360)753-7808
E-mail: aies@hecb.wa.gov
Web Site: http://www.hecb.wa.gov/financialaid/other/indian.asp
To provide financial assistance to American Indian undergraduate and graduate students in Washington.

Title of Award: Washington State American Indian Endowed Scholarship Program **Area, Field, or Subject:** General studies/Field of study not specified **Level of Education for which Award is Granted:** Graduate, Undergraduate **Number Awarded:** Approximately 15 new and 10 renewal scholarships are awarded each year. **Funds Available:** Stipends range from about $1,000 to $2,000 per year. **Duration:** 1 year, may be renewed up to 4 additional years.

Eligibility Requirements: American Indian students who are Washington residents are eligible for this program if they have close social and cultural ties to an American Indian tribe and/or community in the state and agree to use their education to benefit other American Indians. They must demonstrate financial need, be enrolled, or intend to enroll, as a full-time undergraduate or graduate student at a Washington state public or independent college, university, or career school; students who are working on a degree in religious, seminarian, or theological academic studies are not eligible. **Deadline for Receipt:** May of each year. **Additional Information:** This program was created by the Washington legislature in

1990 with a state appropriation to an endowment fund and matching contributions from tribes, individuals, and organizations.

1820 ■ WASHINGTON HIGHER EDUCATION COORDINATING BOARD

917 Lakeridge Way
P.O. Box 43430
Olympia, WA 98504-3430
Tel: (360)753-7851
Fax: (360)753-7808
E-mail: info@hecb.wa.gov
Web Site: http://www.hecb.wa.gov/financialaid/sng/sngindex.asp
To provide financial assistance for undergraduate study to Washington residents who come from a low-income or disadvantaged family.

Title of Award: Washington State Need Grant **Area, Field, or Subject:** General studies/Field of study not specified **Level of Education for which Award is Granted:** Undergraduate **Number Awarded:** Varies each year; recently, more than 49,000 students received about $106 million in benefits from this program. **Funds Available:** The stipend depends on the type of institution the recipient attends. Recently, it was $1,908 per year at community, technical, and private career colleges; $3,026 at public comprehensive universities (Central Washington University, Eastern Washington University, The Evergreen State College, and Western Washington University); $3,798 at public research universities (University of Washington and Washington State University); or $4,032 at independent universities. **Duration:** 1 academic year; renewal is possible for up to 3 additional years.

Eligibility Requirements: This program is open to residents of Washington whose family income is equal to or less than 55% of the state median (currently defined as $18,000 for a family of 1 ranging to $48,000 for a family of 8) or who are disadvantaged (defined to mean a student who by reasons of adverse cultural, educational, environmental, experiential, or familial circumstance is unlikely to aspire to, or enroll in, higher education). Applicants must be enrolled or planning to enroll at least half time in an eligible certificate, bachelor's degree, or first associate degree program. They may not be working on a degree in theology. **Deadline for Receipt:** Varies according to the participating institution; generally in October of each year. **Additional Information:** Consideration is automatic with the institution's receipt of the student's completed financial aid application. This program began in 1969.

1821 ■ WASHINGTON METROPOLITAN SCHOLARS

1220 L Street
Washington, DC 20005-4018
Tel: (202)270-1762
E-mail: avis@wmscholars.org
Web Site: http://www.wmscholars.org
To provide financial assistance for college to African American high school seniors in the Washington, D.C. area.

Title of Award: Carl T. Rowan Awards **Area, Field, or Subject:** General studies/Field of study not specified **Level of Education for which Award is Granted:** Four Year College **Number Awarded:** 3 each year: 1 each to students from Maryland, Virginia, and Washington, D.C. **Funds Available:** The stipend is $5,000 per year. **Duration:** 1 year.

Eligibility Requirements: This program is open to African American high school seniors in the Washington, D.C. area (including Montgomery and Prince George's counties in Maryland and Alexandria, Arlington County, Fairfax County, and Falls Church City in Virginia) who are interested in attending a 4-year college or university. Applicants have a GPA of 3.5 or higher. They may not apply directly; they must be nominated by their high school. Each public, private, and parochial school in the area may nominate 10 students. Nomination materials must include official transcripts (including class rank, SAT scores, final junior class grades, and first-semester senior class grades), 2 letters of recommendation, and an essay of 200 to 250 words by the student on a topic of his or her choice. Selection is based on merit and financial need. **Deadline for Receipt:** High schools must submit nominations in early November of each year. **Additional Information:** This program was established in 2004 as the successor to Project Excellence, founded in 1987 by the columnist Carl T. Rowan. Recipients may use the scholarship at the university or college of their choice.

1822 ■ WASHINGTON NATIONAL GUARD

Attn: Education Services Officer
Building 1
Camp Murray
Tacoma, WA 98430-5073
Tel: (253)512-8899
Free: 800-606-9843
Fax: (253)512-8497
E-mail: Mark.Rhoden@wa.ngb.army.mil
Web Site: http://www.washingtonguard.com/Education/state.html
To provide forgivable loans to members of the Washington National Guard who wish to attend college or graduate school.
Title of Award: Washington National Guard Scholarship Program **Area, Field, or Subject:** General studies/Field of study not specified **Level of Education for which Award is Granted:** Graduate, Undergraduate **Number Awarded:** Varies; scholarships are awarded on a first-come, first-served basis as long as funds are available. **Funds Available:** This program provides a stipend that is based on the number of credits completed but does not exceed $4,003 per school year. Recipients incur a service obligation of 1 additional year in the Guard for the initial scholarship award and 1 additional year for each full year of academic credit completed with this assistance. The grant serves as a loan which is forgiven if the recipient completes the contracted service time in the Washington National Guard. Failure to meet the service obligation requires the recipient to repay the loan plus 8% interest. **Duration:** 1 year; may be renewed.
Eligibility Requirements: This program is open to members of the Washington National Guard who have already served for at least 1 year and have at least 2 years remaining on their current contract. Applicants may be enlisted, warrant, or commissioned officers below Major. They must be attending an accredited college as a resident of Washington state and must already have utilized all available federal educational benefits. Army Guard members must have completed BCT/AIT and awarded initial MOS; Air Guard members who have completed BMT/initial tech school and awarded "3-Level" AFSC. Graduate students are eligible, but undergraduates receive preference as long as they are making satisfactory progress toward a baccalaureate degree. The minimum GPA requirement is 2.5 for undergraduates or 3.0 for graduate students. **Deadline for Receipt:** Applications may be submitted at any time.

1823 ■ WASHINGTON NATIONAL GUARD

Attn: Education Services Officer
Building 1
Camp Murray
Tacoma, WA 98430-5073
Tel: (253)512-8899
Free: 800-606-9843
Fax: (253)512-8497
E-mail: Mark.Rhoden@wa.ngb.army.mil
Web Site: http://www.washingtonguard.com/Education/state.html
To enable members of the Washington National Guard to attend public colleges and universities in the state without payment of tuition.
Title of Award: Washington State Employee Tuition Waiver **Area, Field, or Subject:** General studies/Field of study not specified **Level of Education for which Award is Granted:** Undergraduate **Number Awarded:** Varies each year. **Funds Available:** Participating colleges and universities waive all or a portion of tuition and fees for members of the Washington National Guard on a space available basis. **Duration:** 1 class; depending on the school, additional waivers may be granted.
Eligibility Requirements: This program is open to members of the Washington National Guard who are interested in attending state universities, regional universities, and community colleges in Washington. **Deadline for Receipt:** Each participating college and university determines the deadline for its applicants. **Additional Information:** This program, also known as the House Bill 1601 Program, was established in 1996 when the state legislature expanded existing law, which applied to state employees, to include members of the National Guard. Each public college and university in the state decides if it wishes to support the program and terms under which it does so.

1824 ■ WASHINGTON STATE BUSINESS EDUCATION ASSOCIATION

c/o Jackie Floetke, Awards & Scholarship Chair
P.O. Box 138
Wilson Creek, WA 98860
Tel: (509)345-2541
E-mail: jfloetke@wilsoncreek.org
Web Site: http://www.wsbea.org/scholarships.htm
To provide financial assistance for college to members of Future Business Leaders of America (FBLA) in Washington.
Title of Award: Dr. Eugene Kosy Scholarship **Area, Field, or Subject:** General studies/Field of study not specified **Level of Education for which Award is Granted:** Four Year College **Number Awarded:** 1 or more each year. **Funds Available:** The stipend is $1,000. **Duration:** 1 year.
Eligibility Requirements: This program is open to members of FBLA who are seniors graduating from high schools in Washington. They must be nominated by their adviser, who must be a member of the Washington State Business Education Association (WSBEA). Along with their application, they must submit a statement of their need for this scholarship, a description of their leadership activities, a description of their FBLA activities, a description of their community service accomplishments, information on their work experience, and a 300-word essay on what FBLA has meant to them **Deadline for Receipt:** February of each year.

1825 ■ WASHINGTON STATE FBLA

Attn: Scholarship Program
P.O. Box 1992
Olympia, WA 98507-1992
Tel: (360)753-5666
E-mail: Judy@wafbla.org
Web Site: http://www.wafbla.org
To provide financial assistance for college to members of Future Business Leaders of America (FBLA) in Washington.
Title of Award: Washington FBLA Scholarship **Area, Field, or Subject:** General studies/Field of study not specified **Level of Education for which Award is Granted:** Four Year College **Number Awarded:** 1 or more each year. **Funds Available:** The stipend is $1,000. **Duration:** 1 year.
Eligibility Requirements: This program is open to members of FBLA who are seniors graduating from high schools in Washington. They must be nominated by their adviser. Along with their application, they must submit a statement of their need for this scholarship, a description of their leadership activities, a description of their FBLA activities, a description of their community service accomplishments, information on their work experience, and a 300-word essay on how participation in FBLA has helped them in the pursuit of their academic and personal goals. **Deadline for Receipt:** March of each year.

1826 ■ WASHINGTON STATE FEDERATION OF BUSINESS AND PROFESSIONAL WOMEN

Attn: Foundation
c/o Virginia Murphy, Scholarship Committee Chair
P.O. Box 631
Chelan, WA 98816-0631
E-mail: vamurf@nwi.net
Web Site: http://www.bpwwa.org
To provide financial assistance to women in Washington who are single parents and interested in continuing their education beyond high school
Title of Award: Single Parent Scholarship **Area, Field, or Subject:** General studies/Field of study not specified **Level of Education for which Award is Granted:** Undergraduate **Number Awarded:** Varies each year; recently, 4 of these scholarships were awarded. **Funds Available:** The stipend is $1,000. **Duration:** 1 year.
Eligibility Requirements: This program is open to women who have been residents of Washington for 2 or more years and have been accepted into a program or course of study at an accredited school in the state. Applicants may be of any age, but they must have 1 or more dependent children, under 18 years of age, living at home. They must be able to demonstrate scholastic ability and financial need. Along with their application, they must submit a 300-word essay on their specific short-term goals and how the proposed training will help them accomplish those goals and make a difference in their professional career. U.S. citizenship

is required. **Deadline for Receipt:** March of each year.

1827 ■ WASHINGTON STATE PTA

Attn: WSPTA Scholarship Foundation
2003 65th Avenue West
Tacoma, WA 98466-6215
Tel: (253)565-2153
Free: 800-562-3804
Fax: (253)565-7753
E-mail: wapta@wastatepta.org
Web Site: http://www.wastatepta.org
To provide financial assistance for college to graduates of Washington public high schools.

Title of Award: Washington State PTA Scholarships **Area, Field, or Subject:** General studies/Field of study not specified **Level of Education for which Award is Granted:** Undergraduate **Number Awarded:** Varies each year. Recently, 37 of these scholarships were awarded: 29 at $2,000 to 4-year college students and 8 at $1,000 to community college and vocational/technical school students. **Funds Available:** Stipends are $2,000 at 4-year colleges or universities or $1,000 at community colleges, vocational/technical schools, or other accredited institutions. **Duration:** 1 year; nonrenewable.

Eligibility Requirements: This program is open to graduates of public high schools in Washington State who are entering postsecondary institutions; applicants may be current graduating seniors or graduates from prior years entering their freshman year as a full-time student. Selection is based primarily on financial need; academic criteria are not considered as long as the candidates are able to meet the admission requirements of the school they wish to attend. **Deadline for Receipt:** February of each year. **Additional Information:** Information is also available directly from the Washington State PTA Scholarship Foundation, P.O. Box 53306, Bellevue, WA 98015.

1828 ■ WASIE FOUNDATION

Attn: Program Officer
4999 France Avenue South, Suite 250
Minneapolis, MN 55410-1711
Tel: (612)455-6880
Fax: (612)455-6888
To provide financial assistance to undergraduates who are attending selected academic institutions in Minnesota.

Title of Award: Wasie Foundation Scholarship Program **Area, Field, or Subject:** General studies/Field of study not specified **Level of Education for which Award is Granted:** Undergraduate, Graduate **Number Awarded:** Generally, 9 each year. **Funds Available:** A stipend is awarded (amount not specified). **Duration:** 1 year; recipients may reapply.

Eligibility Requirements: This program is open to U.S. citizens who have been accepted as full-time students at 1 of the participating schools in Minnesota: College of St. Benedict, College of St. Catherine, College of St. Scholastica, Dunwoody College of Technology, Hamline University, Mayo Medical School, St. John's University, St. Mary's University of Minnesota, University of Minnesota, University of St. Thomas, and William Mitchell College of Law. A personal statement, academic transcripts, and a photograph must be submitted with the complete application. Preference is given to individuals of Polish ancestry who are members of the Christian faith. Preference is also given to individuals from north and northeast Minneapolis and surrounding communities. Selection is based on financial need, academic ability, education and career goals, leadership qualities, and involvement in volunteer and extracurricular activities. **Deadline for Receipt:** March of each year. **Additional Information:** This program started in the 1960s. The Wasie Scholarship is very competitive. In the past, only 20% of the applicants have received scholarships. Recipients must attend school on a full-time basis.

1829 ■ WATTS CHARITY ASSOCIATION, INC.

6245 Bristol Parkway, Suite 224
Culver City, CA 90230
Tel: (323)671-0394
Fax: (323)778-2613
E-mail: wattscharity@yahoo.com
Web Site: http://4watts.tripod.com/id5.html
To provide financial assistance to upper-division college students interested in preparing for a career as a minister.

Title of Award: Frank Watts Scholarship **Area, Field, or Subject:** Religion **Level of Education for which Award is Granted:** Four Year College **Number Awarded:** 1 each year. **Funds Available:** A stipend is awarded (amount not specified). **Duration:** 1 year.

Eligibility Requirements: This program is open to U.S. citizens of African American descent who are enrolled full time as a college or university junior. Applicants must be studying to become a minister. They must have a GPA of 3.0 or higher, be between 17 and 24 years of age, and be able to demonstrate that they intend to continue their education for at least 2 years. Along with their application, they must submit 1) a 1-paragraph statement on why they should be awarded a Watts Foundation scholarship, and 2) a 1- to 2-page essay on a specific type of cancer, based either on how it has impacted their life or on researched information. **Deadline for Receipt:** May of each year. **Additional Information:** Royce R. Watts, Sr. established the Watts Charity Association after he learned he had cancer in 2001.

1830 ■ G.H. WEEMS EDUCATIONAL FUND

Weems Building
124 East Main Street
Waverly, TN 37185
Tel: (931)296-3487
Web Site: http://www.slaydenbrothers.org/weemsfoundation.htm
To provide "honor loans" for college to students from selected counties in Tennessee and other areas of the country.

Title of Award: G.H. Weems Honor Loans **Area, Field, or Subject:** General studies/Field of study not specified **Level of Education for which Award is Granted:** Undergraduate **Number Awarded:** Varies each year; recently, 4 of these loans were granted. **Funds Available:** The amount loaned varies, but quarterly installments do not exceed $500. Funds are made available on an honor loan basis. The honor of the recipient is the basis on which the fund relies for proper use and repayment of the loan. Recipients are asked to pledge "upon their honor" to repay the loan as soon as possible, so that others can benefit from the fund. Small amounts repaid at regular or irregular intervals are encouraged. No interest is charged while the recipient attends school or for 5 years after graduation. **Duration:** 1 year; may be renewed.

Eligibility Requirements: This program is open to students in any state; however, preference is given to applicants from Dickson, Humphreys, and Montgomery counties (Tennessee). Applicants must be needy (i.e., financial assistance is required from sources outside their family), worthy (i.e., someone who can use wisely and profit greatly from the assistance), and deserving (i.e., their conduct, character, and reputation must merit the trust and confidence of the fund). These loans are not intended to provide the sole financial assistance for the recipient. It is the aim of the fund to supply only minimum essential financial aid to applicants who have already exhibited great energy and ambition in attaining their education. The amount applied for should be the minimum needed to accomplish the applicant's plan. In fact, a carefully thought-out and practical plan for financing and accomplishing an education is 1 of the most convincing justifications for the extension of an honor loan. **Deadline for Receipt:** Applications may be submitted at any time. **Additional Information:** This fund was started in 1939 as a fund for the education of younger members of the Weems family. Within a few years, its scope was expanded to provide "aid and assistance to needy, worthy and deserving students who are not financially able to secure the proper preparation for a more useful life." Information is also available from William M. Slayden, III, Executive Director, G.H. Weems Educational Fund, 122 Debusk Lane, Knoxville, TN 37922.

1831 ■ WELLS FARGO EDUCATION FINANCIAL SERVICES

301 East 58th Street North
Sioux Falls, SD 57104
800-658-3567
Fax: 800-456-0561
E-mail: studentloans@wellsfargoefs.com
Web Site: http://www.wellsfargo.com/collegesteps
To provide financial assistance for college to high school seniors who enroll in the CollegeSTEPS program sponsored by Wells Fargo Bank.

Title of Award: CollegeSTEPS Program Scholarships **Area, Field, or Subject:** General studies/Field of study not specified **Level of Education for which Award is Granted:** Undergraduate **Number Awarded:** 100 each year. **Funds Available:** Each prize is a $1,000 tuition scholarship.

Funds are paid jointly to the winner and the U.S. institution of higher learning. **Duration:** Scholarships are for 1 year.

Eligibility Requirements: This program is open to residents of the United States (except New York and Florida) who are seniors in high school. Applicants must be actively enrolled in the CollegeSTEPS program. They must have access to the Internet and an active E-mail account. Selection is based on random drawings, held monthly from October through May in 6 regions of the country. **Deadline for Receipt:** Entries may be submitted any month between October and May each year.

1832 ■ PROFESSOR CHEN WEN-CHEN MEMORIAL FOUNDATION
Attn: Scholarship Committee
P.O. Box 6223
Lawrenceville, NJ 08648
Tel: (609)936-1352
E-mail: mkao@comcast.net
Web Site: http://www.cwcmf.org
To provide financial assistance to students at North American colleges and universities who have been involved in the Taiwanese community and are physically challenged or have physically challenged or single parents.
Title of Award: Dr. Ho Da-Fu Scholarship **Area, Field, or Subject:** General studies/Field of study not specified **Level of Education for which Award is Granted:** Undergraduate **Number Awarded:** 2 each year. **Funds Available:** The stipend is $1,500. **Duration:** 1 year.
Eligibility Requirements: This program is open to students who have participated in Taiwanese social-political movements or have made significant contributions to the Taiwanese community in North America. Applicants must be currently enrolled at a college or university in North America. They must 1) be physically challenged, 2) have physically-challenged parents, or 3) have single parents. Selection is based on academic achievement. **Deadline for Receipt:** May of each year. **Additional Information:** Information is also available from Dr. Long R. Mark Kao, 3 Worchester Lane, Princeton Junction, NJ 08550.

1833 ■ PROFESSOR CHEN WEN-CHEN MEMORIAL FOUNDATION
Attn: Scholarship Committee
P.O. Box 6223
Lawrenceville, NJ 08648
Tel: (609)936-1352
E-mail: mkao@comcast.net
Web Site: http://www.cwcmf.org
To provide financial assistance to students at North American colleges and universities who have been involved in the Taiwanese community.
Title of Award: Professor Chen Wen-Chen Scholarships **Area, Field, or Subject:** General studies/Field of study not specified **Level of Education for which Award is Granted:** Undergraduate **Number Awarded:** 4 each year. **Funds Available:** The stipend is $1,500. **Duration:** 1 year.
Eligibility Requirements: This program is open to students who have participated in Taiwanese social-political movements or have made significant contributions to the Taiwanese community in North America. Applicants must be currently enrolled at a college or university in North America. Selection is based on academic achievement. **Deadline for Receipt:** May of each year. **Additional Information:** Information is also available from Dr. Long R. Mark Kao, 3 Worchester Lane, Princeton Junction, NJ 08550.

1834 ■ WEST VIRGINIA DIVISION OF VETERANS' AFFAIRS
Charleston Human Resource Center
1321 Plaza East, Suite 101
Charleston, WV 25301-1400
Tel: (304)558-3661; 888-838-2332
Fax: (304)558-3662
E-mail: wvdva@state.wv.us
Web Site: http://www.wvs.state.wv.us/va/state_fed.htm
To provide financial assistance for college to the children of deceased West Virginia veterans.
Title of Award: West Virginia State War Orphans Educational Program **Area, Field, or Subject:** General studies/Field of study not specified **Level of Education for which Award is Granted:** Undergraduate **Number Awarded:** Varies each year. **Funds Available:** High school students are eligible for a grant of $110 to $250 per semester. Students attending a state-supported college, university, or vocational school in West Virginia who are not receiving any aid from the U.S. Department of

Veterans Affairs (VA) are entitled to a waiver of tuition and also to receive up to $500 per year for fees, board, room, books, supplies, and other expenses. Students attending a state-supported postsecondary institution who are getting VA assistance receive waiver of tuition and registration fees only. Students attending a private postsecondary school in West Virginia are only eligible for the monetary grant of $500 per year if they are not receiving any VA assistance. **Duration:** 1 year; may be renewed upon reapplication if the student maintains a cumulative GPA of at least 2.0.
Eligibility Requirements: Applicants must have been residents of West Virginia for at least 1 year, be between the ages of 16 and 23, and have a veteran parent who entered service as a resident of West Virginia, served during World War I, World War II, the Korean Conflict, the Vietnam Era from August 5, 1964 to May 7, 1975, or any other time of conflict declared by Congress, and died of injuries or disease as a result of that service. **Deadline for Receipt:** July for the fall semester; November for the spring semester.

1835 ■ WEST VIRGINIA FUNERAL DIRECTORS ASSOCIATION
815 Quarrier Street, Suite 215
Charleston, WV 25301-2641
Tel: (304)345-4711
Fax: (304)346-6416
E-mail: info@wvfda.org
Web Site: http://www.wvfda.org
To provide financial assistance to residents of West Virginia who are currently enrolled in a mortuary school.
Title of Award: West Virginia Funeral Directors Association Scholarships **Area, Field, or Subject:** Mortuary science **Level of Education for which Award is Granted:** Undergraduate **Number Awarded:** 1 or 2 each year. **Funds Available:** The stipend is $1,000. **Duration:** 1 year.
Eligibility Requirements: This program is open to students currently enrolled in a mortuary school who have been residents of West Virginia for at least 2 years. Applicants must have completed at least 1 semester or quarter of their mortuary science program, have earned at least a 2.5 GPA in the program, have met state licensing requirements, and be able to demonstrate financial need.

1836 ■ WEST VIRGINIA HIGHER EDUCATION POLICY COMMISSION
Attn: Office of Financial Aid and Outreach Services
1018 Kanawha Boulevard, East, Suite 700
Charleston, WV 25301-2827
Tel: (304)558-4614; 888-825-5707
Fax: (304)558-4622
E-mail: kee@hepc.wvnet.edu
Web Site: http://www.hepc.wvnet.edu/students/heaps.html
To provide financial assistance to West Virginia residents who are working on a college degree or certificate in the state on a part-time basis.
Title of Award: West Virginia Higher Education Adult Part-Time Student Grant Program **Area, Field, or Subject:** General studies/Field of study not specified **Level of Education for which Award is Granted:** Undergraduate **Number Awarded:** Varies each year; recently, more than 3,000 students received more than $3 million in aid through this program. **Funds Available:** For students enrolled at a public college or university, the stipend is based on the actual per credit tuition and fees. For students at other eligible institutions, the award is based on the average per credit tuition and fees charged by all of the public undergraduate institutions of higher education during the previous year. The maximum award recently was $2,770 per year. **Duration:** 1 year; may be renewed until the program of study is completed, up to a maximum of 9 additional years.
Eligibility Requirements: This program is open to West Virginia residents who are U.S. citizens or permanent residents. Applicants must be enrolled or accepted for enrollment in a certificate, associate, or bachelor's degree program on a part-time basis at an eligible West Virginia institution, including a community college, a technical college, an adult technical preparatory education program or training, a state college or university, an independent college or university, or an approved distance education program (including web-based courses). Students who are financially dependent upon parents or a spouse may qualify if they demonstrate financial need and are otherwise eligible. Traditional college age students are also eligible. Applicants must be eligible to participate in the federal Pell Grant program, demonstrate financial need, not be in default on a higher education loan, and demonstrate that they

have applied for or accepted other student financial assistance in compliance with federal financial aid rules. **Deadline for Receipt:** Applications may be submitted at any time. **Additional Information:** This program was established in 1999.

1837 ■ WEST VIRGINIA HIGHER EDUCATION POLICY COMMISSION

Attn: Office of Financial Aid and Outreach Services
1018 Kanawha Boulevard, East, Suite 700
Charleston, WV 25301-2827
Tel: (304)558-4614; 888-825-5707
Fax: (304)558-4622
E-mail: wicks@hepc.wvnet.edu
Web Site: http://www.hepc.wvnet.edu/students/wvgrant.html
To provide financial assistance to West Virginia residents who wish to attend an approved institution of higher education in West Virginia or Pennsylvania.
Title of Award: West Virginia Higher Education Grant Program **Area, Field, or Subject:** General studies/Field of study not specified **Level of Education for which Award is Granted:** Undergraduate **Number Awarded:** Varies each year; recently, approximately 11,000 students received assistance worth $20.7 million. **Funds Available:** Awards are limited to payment of tuition and fees, from $350 to $2,718 per year. Funds are sent directly to the institution. **Duration:** 1 year; may be renewed for up to 3 additional years.
Eligibility Requirements: This program is open to U.S. citizens who have been residents of West Virginia for at least 1 year prior to applying. Applicants must plan to enroll as full-time undergraduate students at an approved college or university in West Virginia or Pennsylvania. Selection is based on financial need and academic performance. **Deadline for Receipt:** February of each year.

1838 ■ WEST VIRGINIA HIGHER EDUCATION POLICY COMMISSION

Attn: PROMISE Scholarship Program
1018 Kanawha Boulevard, East, Suite 700
Charleston, WV 25301-2827
Tel: (304)558-4417; 877-WV-PROMISE
Fax: (304)558-3264
E-mail: morgenstern@hepc.wvnet.edu
Web Site: http://www.promisescholarships.org
To provide financial assistance for college to high school seniors in West Virginia who have complied with core academic requirements.
Title of Award: West Virginia PROMISE Scholarships **Area, Field, or Subject:** General studies/Field of study not specified **Level of Education for which Award is Granted:** Undergraduate **Number Awarded:** Varies each year; recently, a total of $17 million was appropriated for this program. A total of 4,300 students were eligible for these scholarships, of whom 1,200 were eligible for supplemental grant funding. **Funds Available:** Students who attend a West Virginia state college or university receive a full tuition scholarship. Students who attend a West Virginia private college receive an equivalent dollar scholarship, recently for $2,800. Grant recipients receive funding for other education expenses. **Duration:** 1 year; may be renewed for 1 additional year in an associate degree program, for 3 additional years in a baccalaureate degree program, or for 4 additional years in an approved 5-year undergraduate degree program. Recipients must maintain a GPA of 2.75 or higher during the first year of college and at least 3.0 cumulatively in successive years.
Eligibility Requirements: This program is open to high school seniors in West Virginia who have earned a GPA of 3.0 or higher in core courses (4 credits of English/language arts, 3 credits of mathematics, 3 credits of social sciences, and 3 credits of natural sciences) and overall. All applicants (including those who earn a GED or who are home-schooled) must attain a composite score of 21 or higher on the ACT or a combined score of 1000 or higher on the SAT. High school graduates must apply for this program within 2 years of high school graduation if they still qualify as an entering college freshman. GED recipients must have earned the GED within 2 years of the date their high school class would normally have graduated and must apply for this program within 2 years after attaining the GED; they must have earned a score of 250 or higher on the GED examination. Home-schooled students must have attained a score of 250 or higher on the GED examination and must have earned the GED within 1 year of the time of completion of instruction, but not later than 20 years of age. All applicants must have lived in West Virginia for at least 12 months immediately preceding application for this program. Half of the

credits required for high school graduation must have been completed in a public or private high school in West Virginia. Home-schooled students must have been provided instruction in West Virginia for 2 years immediately preceding application. Selection is based on merit; financial need is not considered. Additional funding, in the form of grants, is available to scholars whose family EFC is $4,000 or less. **Deadline for Receipt:** January of each year. **Additional Information:** This program was approved by the West Virginia legislature in 1999. The first scholarships were awarded to the high school class of 2002. PROMISE stands for Providing Real Opportunities for Maximizing In-state Student Excellence.

1839 ■ WESTERN CATHOLIC UNION

510 Maine
P.O. Box 410
Quincy, IL 62306-0410
Tel: (217)223-9721
Free: 800-223-4WCU
Fax: (217)223-9726
E-mail: info@wculife.com
Web Site: http://www.westerncatholicunion.org/benefits.htm
To provide financial assistance to members of Western Catholic Union (WCU) who are preparing for a religious vocation.
Title of Award: Gerald A. Wiewel Vocation Scholarship **Area, Field, or Subject:** Religion **Level of Education for which Award is Granted:** Master's, Undergraduate **Number Awarded:** 2 each year. **Funds Available:** The stipend is $1,000. **Duration:** 1 year.
Eligibility Requirements: This program is open to WCU members who are enrolled in a seminary or convent to prepare for a religious vocation. Applicants must submit a 500-word essay on why they are qualified to receive this grant, including a statement of their future goals and aspirations. Selection is based on that essay, academic achievement, religious activities, community involvement, and financial need. **Deadline for Receipt:** February of each year. **Additional Information:** Western Catholic Union was established in 1877 as a fraternal benefit society.

1840 ■ WESTERN GOLF ASSOCIATION

Attn: Evans Scholars Foundation
1 Briar Road
Golf, IL 60029-0301
Tel: (847)724-4600
Fax: (847)724-7133
E-mail: evansscholars@wgaesf.com
Web Site: http://www.evansscholarsfoundation.com
To provide financial assistance for college to students who have worked as golf caddies.
Title of Award: Chick Evans Caddie Scholarships **Area, Field, or Subject:** General studies/Field of study not specified **Level of Education for which Award is Granted:** Undergraduate **Number Awarded:** Varies each year; recently, 820 caddies were receiving support from this program. **Funds Available:** The awards cover tuition and housing at universities approved by the scholarship committee. **Duration:** 1 year; may be renewed for up to 3 additional years.
Eligibility Requirements: Candidates for these scholarships must have completed their junior year in high school, rank in the upper quarter of their graduating class, have a GPA of 3.0 or higher, have taken the SAT or ACT test, be able to demonstrate financial need, and have been a full-time caddie on a regular basis for at least 2 years. Applicants from 12 states (Colorado, Illinois, Indiana, Michigan, Minnesota, Missouri, Ohio, Oregon, Pennsylvania, Virginia, Washington, and Wisconsin) must attend designated universities; applicants from other states must attend their state university, as approved by the scholarship committee. Selection is based on character, integrity, leadership, and financial need. **Deadline for Receipt:** September of each year. **Additional Information:** Applicants from the 12 designated states must attend the following universities: the University of Colorado at Boulder, Northwestern University, the University of Illinois at Urbana-Champaign, Northern Illinois University, Purdue University, Indiana University, University of Missouri at Columbia; University of Michigan, Michigan State University, University of Minnesota, Ohio State University, Miami University, University of Oregon, Oregon State University, Pennsylvania State University; University of Washington, Marquette University, or University of Wisconsin at Madison. At 14 of those universities (Colorado, Northwestern, Illinois, Marquette, Northern

Illinois, Purdue, Indiana, Missouri, Michigan, Michigan State, Minnesota, Ohio State, Miami, and Wisconsin), Evans Scholars reside in Chapter Houses maintained by the foundation. At other universities, they reside on campus. Applications are sent only to sponsoring clubs where the candidate caddies and which documents the caddie record.

1841 ■ WESTERN INTERSTATE COMMISSION FOR HIGHER EDUCATION

Attn: Student Exchange Programs
3035 Center Green Drive
P.O. Box 9752
Boulder, CO 80301-9752
Tel: (303)541-0214
Fax: (303)541-0291
E-mail: info-sep@wiche.edu
Web Site: http://www.wiche.edu/sep/wue
To underwrite some of the cost of out-of-state undergraduate schooling for students in selected western states.
Title of Award: Western Undergraduate Exchange **Area, Field, or Subject:** General studies/Field of study not specified **Level of Education for which Award is Granted:** Undergraduate **Number Awarded:** Varies each year; recently, more than 20,000 students (approximately 3,400 at 2-year colleges and 16,600 at 4 year universities) were enrolled at 127 campuses in the 15 states. **Funds Available:** Participants in this program attend out-of-state institutions but pay only 150% of resident tuition instead of the regular full nonresident tuition. **Duration:** 1 year; may be renewed.
Eligibility Requirements: This program is open to residents of states that participate in the Western Undergraduate Exchange (WUE): Alaska, Arizona, California, Colorado, Hawaii, Idaho, Montana, Nevada, New Mexico, North Dakota, Oregon, South Dakota, Utah, Washington, and Wyoming. To be eligible, students should be resident in 1 of these states for at least 1 year before applying and be interested in enrolling in a participating 2-year or 4-year college or university in 1 of the other states. The financial status of the applicants is not considered. Interested students apply for admission and for WUE assistance directly from the institution of their choice. **Deadline for Receipt:** Deadline dates vary; check with the institution you wish to attend. **Additional Information:** Some limitations apply. For instance, students from California are eligible for selected programs only in Alaska, Hawaii, New Mexico, North Dakota, South Dakota, Washington, and Wyoming; only 1 institution in California (the California Maritime Academy) participates in the program; residents of Hawaii may enroll as WUE students in 4-year programs only. Information on additional restrictions is available from the program office or the admissions office of participating institutions.

1842 ■ WICHITA AND AFFILIATED TRIBES

Attn: Higher Education
P.O. Box 729
Anadarko, OK 73005
Tel: (405)247-2425
Fax: (405)247-2430
E-mail: Info@wichita.nsn.us
Web Site: http://www.wichita.nsn.us/he.htm
To provide financial assistance for college to Wichita tribal members.
Title of Award: Wichita Higher Education Program **Area, Field, or Subject:** General studies/Field of study not specified **Level of Education for which Award is Granted:** Undergraduate **Number Awarded:** Varies each year. **Funds Available:** Stipends depend on the need of the recipient. **Duration:** 1 year; may be renewed as long as the recipient remains enrolled full time with a GPA of 2.0 or higher.
Eligibility Requirements: This program is open to Wichita tribal members who have been accepted to a college or university as a full-time student. Applicants must submit high school and/or college transcripts, tribal identification, and a letter of intent. Preference is given to students who are eligible for federal Pell grants.

1843 ■ WINGS OVER AMERICA SCHOLARSHIP FOUNDATION

1551 Dillingham Boulevard
Norfolk, VA 23511
E-mail: info@wingsoveramerica.us
Web Site: http://www.wingsoveramerica.us

To provide financial assistance for college to dependents of naval aviators.
Title of Award: Wings Over America Scholarships **Area, Field, or Subject:** General studies/Field of study not specified **Level of Education for which Award is Granted:** Undergraduate **Number Awarded:** Varies each year; recently, 31 of these scholarships were awarded. **Funds Available:** A stipend is awarded (amount not specified). **Duration:** 1 year.
Eligibility Requirements: This program is open to dependent children and spouses of naval air command personnel. Applicants must be planning to continue their education. Selection is based on academic merit, community service, and financial need. **Additional Information:** This foundation was established as Wings Over the Atlantic in 1986 and began awarding scholarships in 2000.

1844 ■ WINSTON-SALEM FOUNDATION

Attn: Director, Student Aid
860 West Fifth Street
Winston-Salem, NC 27101-2506
Tel: (336)714-3445
Fax: (336)727-0581
E-mail: info@wsfoundation.org
Web Site: http://www.wsfoundation.org/student_aid_loan_funds.php
To provide loans for college to residents of North Carolina.
Title of Award: Paul Holcomb Murphy Memorial Fund **Area, Field, or Subject:** General studies/Field of study not specified **Level of Education for which Award is Granted:** Undergraduate **Number Awarded:** 1 or more each year. **Funds Available:** The maximum loan is $5,000 per year. Repayment of the principal is deferred until the student borrower leaves school. There is a 60-day grace period before repayment begins. The interest rate is 4%. **Duration:** 1 year; may be renewed.
Eligibility Requirements: This program is open to college-bound high school seniors in North Carolina. Applicants must be U.S. citizens. Selection is based on career plans and goals, academic promise, financial need, indication of ability to repay the loan, and current income and debts. **Additional Information:** There is a $20 application fee (waived if the applicant is unable to pay).

1845 ■ WISCONSIN COUNCIL OF THE BLIND

754 Williamson Street
Madison, WI 53703
Tel: (608)255-1166
Free: 800-783-5213
Fax: (608)255-3301
E-mail: info@wcblind.org
Web Site: http://www.wcblind.org/Scholarships.htm
To provide financial assistance for college to blind students from Wisconsin.
Title of Award: Wisconsin Council of the Blind Scholarships **Area, Field, or Subject:** General studies/Field of study not specified **Level of Education for which Award is Granted:** Undergraduate **Number Awarded:** 7 each year. **Funds Available:** The stipend is $1,000. **Duration:** 1 year.
Eligibility Requirements: This program is open to legally blind residents of Wisconsin who have completed at least 1 year of college or technical schooling. Applicants must be full-time students who have at least a 2.5 GPA. **Deadline for Receipt:** September of each year. **Additional Information:** Information is also available from Sue Barber, E-mail: sue@wcblind.org

1846 ■ WISCONSIN DEPARTMENT OF VETERANS AFFAIRS

30 West Mifflin Street
P.O. Box 7843
Madison, WI 53707-7843
Tel: (608)266-1311
Free: 800-WIS-VETS
Fax: (608)267-0403
E-mail: wdvaweb@dva.state.wi.us
Web Site: http://dva.state.wi.us/Ben_education.asp
To provide financial assistance for college or graduate school to Wisconsin veterans and their dependents.
Title of Award: Wisconsin G.I. Bill **Area, Field, or Subject:** General studies/Field of study not specified **Level of Education for which Award is Granted:** Graduate, Undergraduate **Number Awarded:** Varies each year. **Funds Available:** Veterans who qualify as a Wisconsin resident for

tuition purposes are eligible for a remission of 50% of tuition and fees at a UW or WCTS institution. Veterans who qualify as a Wisconsin veteran for purposes of this program but for other reasons fail to meet the definition of a Wisconsin resident for tuition purposes at the UW system are eligible for a remission of 100% of non-resident fees. Spouses and children of deceased or disabled veterans are entitled to a remission of 100% of tuition and fees at a UW or WCTS institution. **Duration:** Up to 8 semesters or 128 credits, whichever is greater.

Eligibility Requirements: This program is open to current residents of Wisconsin who 1) were residents of the state when they entered or reentered active duty in the U.S. armed forces, or 2) have moved to the state and have been residents for any consecutive 12-month period after entry or reentry into service. Applicants must have served on active duty for at least 2 continuous years or for at least 90 days during specified wartime periods. Also eligible are 1) qualifying children and unremarried surviving spouses of Wisconsin veterans who died in the line of duty; and 2) children and spouses of Wisconsin veterans who have a service-connected disability rated by the U.S. Department of Veterans Affairs as 30% or greater. Children must be between 18 and 26 years of age (regardless of the date of the veteran's death or initial disability rating), be a Wisconsin resident for tuition purposes, and register as a full-time student. Spouses remain eligible for 10 years following the date of the veteran's death or initial disability rating; they must be Wisconsin residents for tuition purposes but they may enroll full or part time. Students may attend any institution, center, or school within the University of Wisconsin (UW) System or the Wisconsin Technical College System (WCTS). There are no income limits, delimiting periods following military service during which the benefit must be used, or limits on the level of study (e.g., vocational, undergraduate, professional, or graduate). **Deadline for Receipt:** Applications may be submitted at any time, but they should be received as early as possible prior to the intended date of enrollment. **Additional Information:** This program was established in 2005 as a replacement for Wisconsin Tuition and Fee Reimbursement Grants.

1847 ■ WISCONSIN DEPARTMENT OF VETERANS AFFAIRS

30 West Mifflin Street
P.O. Box 7843
Madison, WI 53707-7843
Tel: (608)266-1311
Free: 800-WIS-VETS
Fax: (608)267-0403
E-mail: wdvaweb@dva.state.wi.us
Web Site: http://dva.state.wi.us/Ben_retraininggrants.asp
To provide funds to recently unemployed Wisconsin veterans or their families who need financial assistance while being retrained for employment.

Title of Award: Wisconsin Job Retraining Grants **Area, Field, or Subject:** General studies/Field of study not specified **Level of Education for which Award is Granted:** Graduate, Undergraduate **Number Awarded:** Varies each year. **Funds Available:** The maximum grant is $3,000 per year; the actual amount varies, depending upon the amount of the applicant's unmet need. In addition to books, fees, and tuition, the funds may be used for living expenses. **Duration:** 1 year; may be renewed 1 additional year.

Eligibility Requirements: This program is open to current residents of Wisconsin who 1) were residents of the state when they entered or reentered active duty in the U.S. armed forces, or 2) have moved to the state and have been residents for any consecutive 12-month period after entry or reentry into service. Applicants must have served on active duty for at least 2 continuous years or for at least 90 days during specified wartime periods. Unremarried spouses and minor or dependent children of deceased veterans who would have been eligible for the grant if they were living today may also be eligible. The applicant must, within the year prior to the date of application, have become unemployed (involuntarily laid off or discharged, not due to willful misconduct) or underemployed (experienced an involuntary reduction of income). Underemployed applicants must have current annual income from employment that does not exceed federal poverty guidelines. All applicants must be retraining at accredited schools in Wisconsin or in a structured on-the-job program. Course work toward a college degree does not qualify. Training does not have to be full time, but the program must be completed within 2 years and must reasonably be expected to lead to employment. **Deadline for**

Receipt: Applications may be submitted at any time.

1848 ■ WISCONSIN DEPARTMENT OF VETERANS AFFAIRS

30 West Mifflin Street
P.O. Box 7843
Madison, WI 53707-7843
Tel: (608)266-1311
Free: 800-WIS-VETS
Fax: (608)267-0403
E-mail: wdvaweb@dva.state.wi.us
Web Site: http://dva.state.wi.us/Ben_VetEd.asp
To provide financial assistance for undergraduate education to Wisconsin veterans.

Title of Award: Wisconsin Veterans Education (VetEd) Reimbursement Grants **Area, Field, or Subject:** General studies/Field of study not specified **Level of Education for which Award is Granted:** Undergraduate **Number Awarded:** Varies each year. **Funds Available:** Eligible veterans are entitled to reimbursement of 100% of the costs of tuition and fees not covered by other grants, scholarships, or remissions, to a maximum of the UW-Madison rate for the same number of credits. **Duration:** The amount of reimbursement depends on the time the veteran served on active duty: 30 credits or 2 semesters for 90 to 180 days of active service, 60 credits or 4 semesters for 181 to 730 days of active service, or 120 credits or 8 semesters for 731 days or more of active service.

Eligibility Requirements: This program is open to current residents of Wisconsin who 1) were residents of the state when they entered or reentered active duty in the U.S. armed forces, or 2) have moved to the state and have been residents for any consecutive 12-month period after entry or reentry into service. Applicants must have served on active duty for at least 2 continuous years or for at least 90 days during specified wartime periods. They must be working full or part time on a degree, certificate of graduation, or course completion at an eligible campus of the University of Wisconsin, technical college, or approved private institution of higher education in Wisconsin or Minnesota. Their household income must be below $50,000 plus $1,000 for each dependent in excess of 2 dependents. Veterans seeking reimbursement through this program must first apply for Wisconsin G.I. Bill benefits. To qualify for reimbursement, they must achieve at least a 2.0 GPA or an average grade of "C" in the semester for which reimbursement is requested. Veterans may use this program up to 10 years after leaving active duty. Once a veteran reaches the 10-year delimiting date, he or she may "bank" up to 60 unused credits for part-time study. **Deadline for Receipt:** Veterans must make a pre-application within 30 days of the start of the semester or term to be eligible for reimbursement. End of semester applications must be received within 60 days of the end of the semester or term. **Additional Information:** This program was established in 2005 as a replacement for the former Wisconsin Part-Time Study Grants. Reimbursement is not provided to students for payment amounts for which they are eligible under other programs, including the Wisconsin G.I. Bill.

1849 ■ WISCONSIN FOUNDATION FOR INDEPENDENT COLLEGES, INC.

Attn: Program Manager
735 North Water Street, Suite 600
Milwaukee, WI 53202-4100
Tel: (414)273-5980
Fax: (414)273-5995
E-mail: wfic@wficweb.org
Web Site: http://www.wficweb.org/scholar.html
To provide financial assistance to students from selected states who are enrolled or planning to enroll at member institutions of the Wisconsin Foundation for Independent Colleges (WFIC).

Title of Award: American Family Insurance Community Involvement Scholarship **Area, Field, or Subject:** General studies/Field of study not specified **Level of Education for which Award is Granted:** Four Year College **Number Awarded:** 1 or more each year. **Funds Available:** The stipend is $1,000. **Duration:** 1 year.

Eligibility Requirements: This program is open to students enrolled or planning to enroll at a WFIC member college or university on a full-time basis. Applicants must be residents of Arizona, Colorado, Idaho, Illinois, Indiana, Iowa, Kansas, Minnesota, Missouri, Nebraska, Nevada, North Dakota, Ohio, Oregon, South Dakota, Utah, or Wisconsin. Along with their application, they must submit a 1-page autobiography that includes their future plans, a listing of their campus and community involvement including time committed to each, a listing of their academic honors and achievements, and a letter of recommendation. Selection is based on academic achievement (GPA of 3.0 or higher or ranking in the top 25% of high school class for entering freshmen), involvement in campus and community, and financial need. **Deadline for Receipt:** Each participating college sets its own deadline. **Additional Information:** The WFIC member schools are Alverno College, Beloit College, Cardinal Stritch University, Carroll College, Carthage College, Concordia University of Wisconsin, Edgewood College, Lakeland College, Lawrence University, Marian College, Marquette University, Milwaukee Institute of Art & Design, Milwaukee School of Engineering, Mount Mary College, Northland College, Ripon College, St. Norbert College, Silver Lake College, Viterbo University, and Wisconsin Lutheran College. This program is supported by American Family Insurance.

1850 ■ WISCONSIN FOUNDATION FOR INDEPENDENT COLLEGES, INC.
Attn: Program Manager
735 North Water Street, Suite 600
Milwaukee, WI 53202-4100
Tel: (414)273-5980
Fax: (414)273-5995
E-mail: wfic@wficweb.org
Web Site: http://www.wficweb.org/scholar.html
To provide financial assistance to students attending or planning to attend a member institution of the Wisconsin Foundation for Independent Colleges (WFIC).
Title of Award: Rath Distinguished Scholarships **Area, Field, or Subject:** General studies/Field of study not specified **Level of Education for which Award is Granted:** Four Year College **Number Awarded:** 1 or more each year. **Funds Available:** The stipend is $10,000. **Duration:** 1 year.
Eligibility Requirements: This program is open to students enrolled or planning to enroll at a WFIC member college or university on a full-time basis. Applicants must have a GPA of 3.0 or higher; entering freshmen must rank in the top 25% of their high school class. They must be able to demonstrate financial need and campus and community leadership. Preference is given to students from Wisconsin, but residency is not required. **Deadline for Receipt:** Each participating college sets its own deadline. **Additional Information:** The WFIC member schools are Alverno College, Beloit College, Cardinal Stritch University, Carroll College, Carthage College, Concordia University of Wisconsin, Edgewood College, Lakeland College, Lawrence University, Marian College, Marquette University, Milwaukee Institute of Art & Design, Milwaukee School of Engineering, Mount Mary College, Northland College, Ripon College, St. Norbert College, Silver Lake College, Viterbo University, and Wisconsin Lutheran College. This program is supported by the Rath Foundation.

1851 ■ WISCONSIN FOUNDATION FOR INDEPENDENT COLLEGES, INC.
Attn: Program Manager
735 North Water Street, Suite 600
Milwaukee, WI 53202-4100
Tel: (414)273-5980
Fax: (414)273-5995
E-mail: wfic@wficweb.org
Web Site: http://www.wficweb.org/scholar.html
To provide financial assistance to students attending or planning to attend member institutions of the Wisconsin Foundation for Independent Colleges (WFIC).
Title of Award: United Parcel Service Scholarships **Area, Field, or Subject:** General studies/Field of study not specified **Level of Education for which Award is Granted:** Four Year College **Number Awarded:** Each WFIC institution may award 1 scholarship at $2,500 or 2 at $1,250. **Funds Available:** Stipends are $2,500 or $1,250. **Duration:** 1 year.
Eligibility Requirements: This program is open to students enrolled or planning to enroll at WFIC member colleges and universities on a full-time basis. Applicants may be majoring in any field, but they must have a GPA of 3.0 or higher; entering freshmen must rank in the top 25% of their high school class. Recipients are selected by the participating schools. Financial need is considered in the selection process. **Deadline for**

Receipt: Each participating college sets its own deadline. **Additional Information:** The WFIC member schools are Alverno College, Beloit College, Cardinal Stritch University, Carroll College, Carthage College, Concordia University of Wisconsin, Edgewood College, Lakeland College, Lawrence University, Marian College, Marquette University, Milwaukee Institute of Art & Design, Milwaukee School of Engineering, Mount Mary College, Northland College, Ripon College, St. Norbert College, Silver Lake College, Viterbo University, and Wisconsin Lutheran College. This program is supported by the UPS Foundation.

1852 ■ WISCONSIN FUNERAL DIRECTORS ASSOCIATION
Attn: Wisconsin Funeral Directors Foundation, Ltd.
2300 North Mayfair Road, Suite 595
Wauwatosa, WI 53226-1508
Tel: (414)453-3060
Fax: (414)453-9860
E-mail: info@wfda.org
Web Site: http://www.wfda.org/public/careers.html
To provide financial assistance to funeral service students in Wisconsin.
Title of Award: Wisconsin Funeral Directors Foundation Scholarship Program **Area, Field, or Subject:** Mortuary science **Level of Education for which Award is Granted:** Undergraduate **Number Awarded:** 1 each year. **Funds Available:** The stipend is $1,000. **Duration:** 1 year.
Eligibility Requirements: This program is open to residents of Wisconsin who have completed 1 year of mortuary college with a GPA of 3.0 or higher (for at least 30 semester or 45 quarter credits). Applicants must submit a statement (up to 500 words) on their goals in funeral service and how they plan to accomplish these goals. **Deadline for Receipt:** May of each year. **Additional Information:** Information is also available from Gary Langendorf, Draeger-Langendorf Funeral Home, 1910 Taylor Avenue, Racine, WI 53403, (262) 637-6514, Fax: (262) 637-6204.

1853 ■ WISCONSIN HIGHER EDUCATIONAL AIDS BOARD
131 West Wilson Street, Room 902
P.O. Box 7885
Madison, WI 53707-7885
Tel: (608)267-2213
Fax: (608)267-2808
E-mail: nancy.wilkison@heab.state.wi.us
Web Site: http://heab.state.wi.us/programs.html
To provide financial assistance for college to Wisconsin high school seniors with the highest GPAs in their schools.
Title of Award: Wisconsin Academic Excellence Scholarship Program **Area, Field, or Subject:** General studies/Field of study not specified **Level of Education for which Award is Granted:** Undergraduate **Number Awarded:** The number of scholarships allotted to each high school is based on total student enrollment, ranging from 1 scholarship for schools with enrollment of 80 to 499 up to 6 scholarships for schools with enrollment greater than 2,500. Students at schools with enrollment less than 80 compete statewide for an additional 10 scholarships. **Funds Available:** The awards provide full tuition, up to $2,250 per year, during the first 3 years of undergraduate study; for subsequent years, the maximum award is equal to full tuition and fees at a campus of the University of Wisconsin. **Duration:** Up to 10 semesters.
Eligibility Requirements: This program is open to seniors at each public and private high school throughout Wisconsin who have the highest GPAs. Applicants must plan to attend a branch of the University of Wisconsin, a Wisconsin technical college, or an independent institution in the state as a full-time student in the following fall.

1854 ■ WISCONSIN HIGHER EDUCATIONAL AIDS BOARD
131 West Wilson Street, Room 902
P.O. Box 7885
Madison, WI 53707-7885
Tel: (608)266-0888
Fax: (608)267-2808
E-mail: sandy.thomas@heab.state.wi.us
Web Site: http://heab.state.wi.us/programs.html
To provide financial support for undergraduate study to Wisconsin residents who are legally deaf or blind.
Title of Award: Wisconsin Hearing and Visually Handicapped Student Grant Program **Area, Field, or Subject:** General studies/Field of study not specified **Level of Education for which Award is Granted:**

Undergraduate **Number Awarded:** Varies each year. **Funds Available:** Grants range from $250 to $1,800 per academic year. **Duration:** 1 year; may be renewed up to 4 additional years.

Eligibility Requirements: To be eligible for a grant, the student must be a Wisconsin resident, must have financial need as determined by the institution the student attends, must submit evidence of a severe or profound hearing or visual impairment certified by a medical examiner, and must be enrolled in a nonprofit, accredited public or private college, university, or vocational/technical school located in Wisconsin. **Additional Information:** If the disability prevents the student from studying in a Wisconsin institution, he or she may attend an out-of-state institution that specializes in the training of deaf and/or blind students.

1855 ■ WISCONSIN HIGHER EDUCATIONAL AIDS BOARD

131 West Wilson Street, Room 902
P.O. Box 7885
Madison, WI 53707-7885
Tel: (608)266-0888
Fax: (608)267-2808
E-mail: sandy.thomas@heab.state.wi.us
Web Site: http://heab.state.wi.us/programs.html

To provide financial assistance to financially needy undergraduate students attending public institutions of higher education in Wisconsin.

Title of Award: Wisconsin Higher Education Grant **Area, Field, or Subject:** General studies/Field of study not specified **Level of Education for which Award is Granted:** Undergraduate **Number Awarded:** Varies each year. **Funds Available:** Awards range from $250 to $1,800 per year. **Duration:** Up to 10 semesters.

Eligibility Requirements: Eligible are Wisconsin residents enrolled at least half time at any branch of the University of Wisconsin, at any vocational/technical institution in the state, or at any Tribal College in the state. Selection is based on financial need.

1856 ■ WISCONSIN HIGHER EDUCATIONAL AIDS BOARD

131 West Wilson Street, Room 902
P.O. Box 7885
Madison, WI 53707-7885
Tel: (608)266-0888
Fax: (608)267-2808
E-mail: sandy.thomas@heab.state.wi.us
Web Site: http://heab.state.wi.us/programs.html

To provide financial aid for college or graduate school to Native Americans in Wisconsin.

Title of Award: Wisconsin Indian Student Assistance Grants **Area, Field, or Subject:** General studies/Field of study not specified **Level of Education for which Award is Granted:** Graduate, Undergraduate **Funds Available:** Awards range from $250 to $1,100 per year. Additional funds are available on a matching basis from the U.S. Bureau of Indian Affairs. **Duration:** Up to 5 years.

Eligibility Requirements: Wisconsin residents who have at least 25% Native American blood (of a certified tribe or band) are eligible to apply if they are able to demonstrate financial need and are interested in attending college on the undergraduate or graduate school level. Applicants must attend a Wisconsin institution (public, independent, or proprietary). They may be enrolled either full or part time. **Deadline for Receipt:** Generally, applications can be submitted at any time.

1857 ■ WISCONSIN HIGHER EDUCATIONAL AIDS BOARD

131 West Wilson Street, Room 902
P.O. Box 7885
Madison, WI 53707-7885
Tel: (608)267-2212
Fax: (608)267-2808
E-mail: mary.kuzdas@heab.state.wi.us
Web Site: http://heab.state.wi.us/programs.html

To provide financial assistance to minorities in Wisconsin who are currently enrolled in college.

Title of Award: Wisconsin Minority Undergraduate Retention Grants **Area, Field, or Subject:** General studies/Field of study not specified **Level of Education for which Award is Granted:** Undergraduate **Number Awarded:** Varies each year. **Funds Available:** Stipends range from $250 to $2,500 per year, depending on the need of the recipient. **Duration:** Up to 4 years.

Eligibility Requirements: African Americans, Hispanic Americans, and American Indians in Wisconsin are eligible to apply if they are enrolled as sophomores, juniors, seniors, or fifth-year undergraduates in a 4-year nonprofit institution or as second-year students in a 2-year program at a public vocational institution in the state. Grants are also available to students who were admitted to the United States after December 31, 1975 and who are a former citizen of Laos, Vietnam, or Cambodia or whose ancestor was a citizen of 1 of those countries. They must be nominated by their institution and be able to demonstrate financial need. **Deadline for Receipt:** Deadline dates vary by institution; check with your school's financial aid office. **Additional Information:** The Wisconsin Higher Educational Aids Board administers this program for students in private nonprofit institutions and public vocational institutions. The University of Wisconsin has a similar program for students attending any of the branches of that system. Eligible students should apply through their school's financial aid office.

1858 ■ WISCONSIN HIGHER EDUCATIONAL AIDS BOARD

131 West Wilson Street, Room 902
P.O. Box 7885
Madison, WI 53707-7885
Tel: (608)266-1665
Fax: (608)267-2808
E-mail: john.whitt@heab.state.wi.us
Web Site: http://heab.state.wi.us/programs.html

To provide financial assistance for college to needy and educationally disadvantaged students in Wisconsin.

Title of Award: Wisconsin Talent Incentive Program (TIP) Grants **Area, Field, or Subject:** General studies/Field of study not specified **Level of Education for which Award is Granted:** Undergraduate **Number Awarded:** Varies each year. **Funds Available:** Grants range up to $1,800 per year. **Duration:** 1 year; may be renewed up to 4 additional years provided the recipient continues to be a Wisconsin resident enrolled at least half time in a degree or certificate program, makes satisfactory academic progress, demonstrates financial need, and remains enrolled continuously from semester to semester and from year to year. If recipients withdraw from school or cease to attend classes for any reason (other than medical necessity), they may not reapply.

Eligibility Requirements: This program is open to residents of Wisconsin entering a college or university in the state who meet requirements of both financial need and educational disadvantage. Financial need qualifications include 1) family contribution (a dependent student whose expected parent contribution is $200 or less, an independent student with dependents whose academic year contribution is $200 or less, or an independent student with no dependents whose maximum contribution is $200 or less); 2) TANF or W2 benefits (a dependent student whose family is receiving TANF or W2 benefits or an independent student who is receiving TANF or W2 benefits); or 3) unemployment (a dependent student whose parents are ineligible for unemployment compensation and have no current income from employment, or an independent student and spouse, if married, who are ineligible for unemployment compensation and have no current income from employment). Educational disadvantage qualifications include students who are 1) minorities (African American, Native American, Hispanic, or southeast Asian); 2) enrolled in a special academic support program due to insufficient academic preparation; 3) a first-generation college student (neither parent graduated from a 4-year college or university); 4) disabled according to the Department of Workforce Development, Division of Vocational Rehabilitation or according to a Wisconsin college or university that uses the Americans with Disabilities Act definition; 5) currently or formerly incarcerated in a correctional institution; or 6) from an environmental and academic background that deters the pursuit of educational plans. Students already in college are not eligible.

1859 ■ WISCONSIN HIGHER EDUCATIONAL AIDS BOARD

131 West Wilson Street, Room 902
P.O. Box 7885
Madison, WI 53707-7885
Tel: (608)267-2212
Fax: (608)267-2808
E-mail: mary.kuzdas@heab.state.wi.us
Web Site: http://heab.state.wi.us/programs.html

To provide assistance to financially needy undergraduate students attending private institutions of higher education in Wisconsin.
Title of Award: Wisconsin Tuition Grant **Area, Field, or Subject:** General studies/Field of study not specified **Level of Education for which Award is Granted:** Undergraduate **Number Awarded:** Varies each year. **Funds Available:** Awards are based on financial need, but may not exceed tuition charged at the University of Wisconsin at Madison. **Duration:** Up to 10 semesters.
Eligibility Requirements: Eligible are Wisconsin residents enrolled in independent nonprofit colleges and universities in Wisconsin. Selection is based on financial need.

1860 ■ WISCONSIN HISPANIC SCHOLARSHIP FOUNDATION, INC.

1220 West Windlake Avenue
Milwaukee, WI 53215
Tel: (414)383-7066
Fax: (414)383-6677
E-mail: fiestamilw@aol.com
Web Site: http://www.mexicanfiesta.org/about.php
To provide financial assistance to Hispanic American students in Wisconsin who are interested in attending college or graduate school.
Title of Award: Mexican Fiesta Scholarships **Area, Field, or Subject:** General studies/Field of study not specified **Level of Education for which Award is Granted:** Graduate, Undergraduate **Number Awarded:** Varies; a total of $20,000 is awarded in scholarships each year. **Funds Available:** The amount of the stipend depends on the number of students selected. **Duration:** 1 year; recipients may reapply.
Eligibility Requirements: Applicants must be at least 50% Hispanic, be high school seniors or full-time undergraduate or graduate students, have earned a GPA of 2.75 or higher, be Wisconsin residents, and be bilingual in Spanish and English. **Deadline for Receipt:** March of each year. **Additional Information:** Recipients can attend college in any state. Funds for this program are raised each year at the Mexican Fiesta, held in Milwaukee for 3 days each August. Recipients must perform 20 hours of volunteer work in the Hispanic community.

1861 ■ WISCONSIN INDIAN EDUCATION ASSOCIATION

Attn: Scholarship Coordinator
P.O. Box 910
Keshena, WI 54135
Tel: (715)799-5110
Fax: (715)799-1364
E-mail: vnuske@mitw.org
Web Site: http://www.wiea.org
To provide financial assistance for undergraduate or graduate study to members of Wisconsin Indian tribes.
Title of Award: WIEA Scholarships **Area, Field, or Subject:** General studies/Field of study not specified **Level of Education for which Award is Granted:** Graduate, Undergraduate **Number Awarded:** 4 each year: 1 in each of the 4 categories. **Funds Available:** The stipend is $1,000 per year. **Duration:** 1 year.
Eligibility Requirements: This program is open to residents of Wisconsin who can provide proof of tribal enrollment. Applicants must fall into 1 of the following categories: 1) graduating high school senior; 2) new or continuing student at a tribal or technical/vocational college; 3) undergraduate student at a 4-year college; or 4) graduate or Ph.D. student. All applicants must be full-time students. Selection is based on letters of recommendation (10 points), a personal essay on how applicants will apply their education (25 points), GPA of 2.5 to 2.99 (5 points), GPA of 3.0 to 3.49 (10 points), and GPA of 3.5 to 4.0 (15 points). Financial need is not considered. **Deadline for Receipt:** March of each year. **Additional Information:** Eligible tribes include Menominee, Oneida, Stockbridge/Munsee, Mole Lake, Potowatomi, Ho-Chunk, Ba Chippewa, LCO Chippewa, St. Croix Chippewa, Red Cliff Chippewa, Sakoagon Chippewa, Brotherton, and Lac du Flam Chippewa.

1862 ■ WISCONSIN NATIONAL GUARD ENLISTED ASSOCIATION

Attn: SGM Bonnie Moser
2400 Wright Street
Madison, WI 53704
Tel: (608)242-3112
E-mail: WNGEA@yahoo.com

To provide financial assistance for college to members of the Wisconsin National Guard Enlisted Association (WNGEA) and to their spouses and children.
Title of Award: Wisconsin National Guard Enlisted Association College Grant Program **Area, Field, or Subject:** General studies/Field of study not specified **Level of Education for which Award is Granted:** Undergraduate **Number Awarded:** Varies each year. Recently, 7 of these scholarships were awarded: the Raymond A. Matera Scholarship at $1,000, the USAA Todd Olsen Memorial Award (sponsored by the USAA Insurance Corporation) at $500, the Charles Kaufman Memorial Award at $500, and 4 others at $500 each. **Funds Available:** Stipends are $1,000 or $500 per year. **Duration:** 1 year; recipients may not reapply for 2 years.
Eligibility Requirements: This program is open to WNGEA members, the unmarried children of WNGEA members, the spouses of WNGEA members, and the unmarried children and spouses of deceased WNGEA members. WNGEA member applicants, as well as the parents or guardians of unmarried children who are applicants, must have at least 1 year remaining on their enlistment following completion of the school year for which application is submitted (or they must have 20 or more years of service). Applicants must be enrolled at a college, university, trade school, or business school (graduate students are not eligible for these grants). Selection is based on financial need, leadership, and good moral character. **Deadline for Receipt:** May of each year.

1863 ■ WISCONSIN SCHOOL COUNSELOR ASSOCIATION

c/o Elizabeth Disch, Scholarship Chair
300 12th Avenue
P.O. Box 252
New Glarus, WI 53574
Tel: (608)967-2372
Web Site: http://www.wscaweb.com
To provide financial assistance for college to high school seniors in Wisconsin.
Title of Award: WSCA/TCF Bank Scholarship **Area, Field, or Subject:** General studies/Field of study not specified **Level of Education for which Award is Granted:** Undergraduate **Number Awarded:** 4 each year. **Funds Available:** The stipend is $1,000. **Duration:** 1 year.
Eligibility Requirements: This program is open to graduating seniors at public and private high schools in Wisconsin. Applicants must be planning to attend a 2-year or 4-year college or university. Along with their application, they must submit a 1-page essay describing how a school counselor or school counseling program has helped them plan, decide, resolve, or grow in some area of their life. **Deadline for Receipt:** November of each year. **Additional Information:** This program is jointly sponsored by the Wisconsin School Counselor Association (WSCA) and TCF Bank.

1864 ■ WOMAN'S LIFE INSURANCE SOCIETY

1338 Military Street
P.O. Box 5020
Port Huron, MI 48061-5020
Tel: (810)985-5191
Free: 800-521-9292
Fax: (810)985-6970
E-mail: info@womanslifeins.com
Web Site: http://www.womanslifeins.com/html/navbar/bensch.html
To provide financial assistance for college to high school seniors who are members of the Woman's Life Insurance Society.
Title of Award: Woman's Life Merit Scholarships **Area, Field, or Subject:** General studies/Field of study not specified **Level of Education for which Award is Granted:** Undergraduate **Number Awarded:** 5 each year. **Funds Available:** The stipend is $1,000. **Duration:** 1 year.
Eligibility Requirements: This program is open to members of this fraternal benefit society who are graduating high school seniors. Selection is based on merit. **Additional Information:** The sponsor's origins date to 1892, when it was founded as a society of women helping women.

1865 ■ WOMAN'S LIFE INSURANCE SOCIETY

1338 Military Street
P.O. Box 5020
Port Huron, MI 48061-5020
Tel: (810)985-5191
Free: 800-521-9292
Fax: (810)985-6970

E-mail: info@womanslifeins.com
Web Site: http://www.womanslifeins.com/html/navbar/bensch.html
To provide financial assistance for college to financially needy undergraduates who are members of the Woman's Life Insurance Society.
Title of Award: Woman's Life Need Scholarships **Area, Field, or Subject:** General studies/Field of study not specified **Level of Education for which Award is Granted:** Undergraduate **Number Awarded:** 5 each year. **Funds Available:** The stipend is $1,000. **Duration:** 1 year.
Eligibility Requirements: This program is open to members of this fraternal benefit society who are working on an undergraduate degree. Selection is based on financial need. **Additional Information:** The sponsor's origins date to 1892, when it was founded as a society of women helping women.

1866 ■ WOMEN NATIONALLY ACTIVE FOR CHRIST

National Association of Free Will Baptists
5233 Mt. View Road
P.O. Box 5002
Antioch, TN 37011-5002
Tel: (615)731-6812; 877-767-7659
Fax: (615)731-0771
E-mail: exoff@nafwb.org
Web Site: http://www.nafwb.org/wnac
To provide financial assistance to Free Will Baptists from other countries who wish to attend college in their own country.
Title of Award: Cleo Pursell Foreign Student Scholarship **Area, Field, or Subject:** Religion **Level of Education for which Award is Granted:** Undergraduate **Number Awarded:** 3 or more each year. **Funds Available:** Stipends generally do not exceed $1,250 per year; the exact amount depends upon the student's individual need. **Duration:** 1 year.
Eligibility Requirements: Eligible to apply for this support are students from a Free Will Baptist church or mission in a country other than the United States. They must be enrolled in a Bible institute, Bible college, or seminary (generally in their own country) and be training to serve in a Free Will Baptist church, Free Will Baptist school, or a Free Will Baptist mission. In most cases, applicants should be planning to study in their own language.

1867 ■ WOMEN'S ARMY CORPS VETERANS' ASSOCIATION

P.O. Box 5577
Fort McClellan, AL 36205-5577
E-mail: info@armywomen.org
Web Site: http://www.armywomen.org
To provide financial assistance for college to the relatives of Army military women.
Title of Award: Women's Army Corps Veterans' Association Scholarship **Area, Field, or Subject:** General studies/Field of study not specified **Level of Education for which Award is Granted:** Undergraduate **Number Awarded:** 1 or more each year. **Funds Available:** The stipend is $1,500. **Duration:** 1 year.
Eligibility Requirements: This program is open to high school seniors who are the children, grandchildren, nieces, or nephews of Army service women. Applicants must have a cumulative GPA of 3.5 or higher and be planning to enroll as a full-time student at an accredited college or university in the United States. They must submit a 500-word biographical sketch that includes their future goals and how the scholarship would be used. Selection is based on academic achievement, leadership ability as expressed through cocurricular activities and community involvement, the biographical sketch, and recommendations. Financial need is not considered in the selection process. **Deadline for Receipt:** April of each year.

1868 ■ WOMEN'S BASKETBALL COACHES ASSOCIATION

Attn: Manager of Office Administration and Awards
4646 Lawrenceville Highway
Lilburn, GA 30247-3620
Tel: (770)279-8027
Fax: (770)279-8473
E-mail: wwade@wbca.org
Web Site: http://www.wbca.org/WBCAScholarAward.asp
To provide financial assistance for undergraduate or graduate study to women's basketball players.
Title of Award: Women's Basketball Coaches Association Scholarship Awards **Area, Field, or Subject:** General studies/Field of study not speci-

fied **Level of Education for which Award is Granted:** Graduate, Undergraduate **Number Awarded:** 2 each year. **Funds Available:** The stipend is $1,000 per year. **Duration:** 1 year.
Eligibility Requirements: This program is open to women's basketball players who are competing in any of the 4 intercollegiate divisions (NCAA Divisions I, II, and III, and NAIA). Applicants must be interested in completing an undergraduate degree or beginning work on an advanced degree. They must be nominated by a member of the Women's Basketball Coaches Association (WBCA). Selection is based on sportsmanship, commitment to excellence as a student-athlete, honesty, ethical behavior, courage, and dedication to purpose.

1869 ■ WOODHOLME FOUNDATION

Attn: Sheila Lewis, Co-Chair
P.O. Box 651
Owings Mills, MD 21117
Tel: (410)356-0800
To provide financial assistance to underachieving high school seniors interested in attending an Historically Black College or University (HBCU).
Title of Award: Second Chance Award **Area, Field, or Subject:** General studies/Field of study not specified **Level of Education for which Award is Granted:** Undergraduate **Number Awarded:** Varies each year. **Funds Available:** A stipend is awarded (amount not specified). **Duration:** 1 year.
Eligibility Requirements: This program is open to seniors graduating from high schools with a GPA of 2.0 or lower. Students must be nominated by a principal, counselor, or teacher who can verify that the their low grades are the result of factors beyond their control and that they deserve a second chance. Nominees must be interested in attending a pre-selected HBCU. **Deadline for Receipt:** April of each year.

1870 ■ WORKER'S COMPENSATION ASSOCIATION OF NEW MEXICO

Attn: Brock Carter
P.O. Box 35757, Station D
Albuquerque, NM 87176
Tel: (505)881-1112
Free: 800-640-0724
E-mail: batcbear@aol.com
Web Site: http://www.wcaofnm.com
To provide financial assistance for college to residents of New Mexico whose parent was permanently disabled or killed in an employment-related accident.
Title of Award: Toby Wright Scholarship Fund **Area, Field, or Subject:** General studies/Field of study not specified **Level of Education for which Award is Granted:** Undergraduate **Number Awarded:** Varies each year. **Funds Available:** A stipend is awarded (amount not specified). Funds may be used for tuition, books, housing, meals, and course fees. **Duration:** 1 semester or quarter; may be renewed if the recipient maintains a GPA of 2.5 or higher and full-time enrollment.
Eligibility Requirements: This program is open to residents of New Mexico between 16 and 25 years of age who attending or planning to attend a college, university, or trade school in the state. Applicants must have a parent who was permanently or catastrophically injured or killed in an employment-related accident that resulted in a New Mexico workers' compensation claim. The parent's death or injury must have resulted in a substantial decline in the family income.

1871 ■ WORKERS COMPENSATION FUND

392 East 6400 South
P.O. Box 57929
Salt Lake City, UT 84157-0929
Tel: (801)288-8000
Free: 800-446-2667
E-mail: cmorris@wcfgroup.com
Web Site: http://www.wcfgroup.com
To provide financial assistance for college to children and spouses of workers who died in work-related accidents in Utah.
Title of Award: Legacy of Learning Scholarships **Area, Field, or Subject:** General studies/Field of study not specified **Level of Education for which Award is Granted:** Undergraduate **Number Awarded:** Varies each year; recently, 52 students received these scholarships. **Funds Available:** The stipend is $1,500 per year. **Duration:** 1 year; may be renewed as long as the recipient remains in college.

Eligibility Requirements: This program is open to Utah residents who are the children and spouses of workers who died in accidents that occurred on job sites covered by the sponsoring company. Applicants must be attending or planning to attend an accredited college or university. Selection is based on GPA, standard test scores, general character, community involvement, and financial need. **Additional Information:** This program was established in 1990.

1872 ■ WORKFORCE SAFETY & INSURANCE

1600 East Century Avenue, Suite 1
P.O. Box 5585
Bismarck, ND 58506-5585
Tel: (701)328-3828
Free: 800-440-3796
Fax: (701)328-3820
Web Site: http://www.workforcesafety.com/workers/typesofbenefits.asp
To provide financial assistance for college to injured workers in North Dakota.

Title of Award: Exceptional Circumstances Scholarships **Area, Field, or Subject:** General studies/Field of study not specified **Level of Education for which Award is Granted:** Undergraduate **Number Awarded:** Varies each year. **Funds Available:** The maximum stipend is $10,000 per year. **Duration:** 1 year; may be renewed up to 4 additional years provided the recipient reapplies and maintains a satisfactory GPA.
Eligibility Requirements: This program is open to injured workers in North Dakota who can demonstrate that a program of higher or technical education would be beneficial and appropriate because of exceptional circumstances. Applicants must have completed a rehabilitation process with Workforce Safety & Insurance (WSI) and have not outstanding litigation on any rehabilitation plan. **Additional Information:** This program was established in 1997. The sponsoring company was formerly North Dakota Workers Compensation.

1873 ■ WORKFORCE SAFETY & INSURANCE

1600 East Century Avenue, Suite 1
P.O. Box 5585
Bismarck, ND 58506-5585
Tel: (701)328-3828
Free: 800-440-3796
Fax: (701)328-3820
Web Site: http://www.workforcesafety.com/workers/typesofbenefits.asp
To provide financial assistance for college to children and spouses of workers who died in work-related accidents in North Dakota.

Title of Award: Guardian Scholarships **Area, Field, or Subject:** General studies/Field of study not specified **Level of Education for which Award is Granted:** Undergraduate **Number Awarded:** Varies each year; recently, 32 of these scholarships were awarded. **Funds Available:** The maximum stipend is $4,000 per year. **Duration:** 1 year; may be renewed up to 4 additional years.
Eligibility Requirements: This program is open to spouses and dependent children of workers who lost their lives in work-related accidents in North Dakota. Applicants must be attending or planning to attend an accredited college, university, or technical school. **Additional Information:** This program was established in 1997. The sponsoring company was formerly North Dakota Workers Compensation.

1874 ■ WORKFORCE SAFETY & INSURANCE

1600 East Century Avenue, Suite 1
P.O. Box 5585
Bismarck, ND 58506-5585
Tel: (701)328-3800
Free: 800-777-5033
Fax: (701)328-3820
Web Site: http://www.workforcesafety.com/workers/typesofbenefits.asp
To provide educational loans to workers in North Dakota who have sustained a compensable injury.

Title of Award: WSI Education Loan Fund **Area, Field, or Subject:** General studies/Field of study not specified **Level of Education for which Award is Granted:** Undergraduate **Number Awarded:** Varies each year. **Funds Available:** The loan depends on the demonstrated need of the recipient. The interest rate is 1% below the Bank of North Dakota's prime rate. It is fixed and is based on the rate applicable on the date of first disbursement, the day immediately following withdrawal date,

or last date of attendance, whichever is lowest. **Duration:** 1 year; may be renewed.
Eligibility Requirements: This program is open to workers in North Dakota who have suffered an injury compensable by the state's Workforce Safety & Insurance (WSI). Applicants must be enrolled at an accredited institution of higher or technical education to enhance their employment. They must have obtained a high school diploma or equivalent and either must be ineligible for retraining by state statute or have exhausted training and education benefits. **Additional Information:** This program was established in 1997. The sponsoring company was formerly North Dakota Workers Compensation.

1875 ■ WORLD TEAM TENNIS, INC.

Attn: Billie Jean King WTT Charities
1776 Broadway, Suite 600
New York, NY 10019
Tel: (212)586-3444
Fax: (212)586-6277
Web Site: http://www.wtt.com/charities/donnelly.asp
To recognize and reward young tennis players who have diabetes.

Title of Award: Novo Nordisk Donnelly Awards **Area, Field, or Subject:** General studies/Field of study not specified **Level of Education for which Award is Granted:** Undergraduate **Number Awarded:** 2 each year. **Funds Available:** The award is $5,000; funds may be used for education, tennis development, and/or medical care. **Duration:** The nonrenewable awards are presented annually.
Eligibility Requirements: This program is open to scholar/athletes between 14 and 21 years of age who play tennis competitively either on a school team or as a ranked tournament player and have type I diabetes. Applicants must submit a 500-word essay on the significance of diabetes in their lives. Selection is based on values, commitment, sportsmanship, community involvement, and financial need. **Deadline for Receipt:** April of each year. **Additional Information:** This program was established in 1998 by the Billie Jean King Foundation in cooperation with the American Diabetes Association. It includes 2 scholarships named after sisters, Diane Donnelly Stone and Tracey Donnelly Maltby, who have had diabetes since childhood and have played tennis competitively. Novo Nordisk sponsors the program. Information is also available from Billie Jean King WTT Charities, Inc., Attn: Diane Donnelly Stone, 960 Harlem Avenue, Glenview, IL 60025, Fax: (847) 904-7362, E-mail: dstone.wtt. com.

1876 ■ WSA FRATERNAL LIFE

Attn: Scholarship Program
9025 Grant Street, Suite 201
Thornton, CO 80229
Tel: (303)451-1494
Free: 800-WSA-LIFE
Fax: (303)451-5112
E-mail: info@wsalife.com
Web Site: http://www.wsa-life.com/benefits/scholarship.php
To provide financial assistance to high school seniors in selected states who are members of WSA Fraternal Life.

Title of Award: WSA Scholarship Program **Area, Field, or Subject:** General studies/Field of study not specified **Level of Education for which Award is Granted:** Undergraduate **Number Awarded:** Varies each year; recently, 11 new scholarships were awarded. **Funds Available:** The stipend is $2,000 per year. **Duration:** 1 year; may be renewed up to 3 additional years if the recipient remains enrolled as a full-time student, maintains WSA Fraternal Life membership, and earns a GPA of 2.5 or higher.
Eligibility Requirements: This program is open to graduating high school seniors who have been members of WSA Fraternal Life for at least 4 continuous years. Applicants must have a high school GPA of 2.0 or higher and a letter of acceptance from an accredited college or university. They must have completed 40 hours of community service during their senior year of high school. **Deadline for Receipt:** June of each year. **Additional Information:** WSA Fraternal Life was incorporated in 1908 as the Western Slavonic Association. It adopted its current name in 1989 and began the scholarship program in 1995. The states in which it is licensed

to operate are Colorado, Illinois, Minnesota, New Mexico, Ohio, Pennsylvania, South Dakota, and Utah.

1877 ■ WYETH PHARMACEUTICALS

Attn: Wyeth Hemophilia Hotline
5 Giralda Farms
Madison, NJ 07940
888-999-2349
Web Site: http://www.hemophiliavillage.com/programs_scholar.asp
To provide financial assistance for college or graduate school to persons with hemophilia.
Title of Award: Soozie Courter Sharing a Brighter Tomorrow Hemophilia Scholarship **Area, Field, or Subject:** General studies/Field of study not specified **Level of Education for which Award is Granted:** Graduate, Undergraduate **Number Awarded:** 19 each year: 16 to undergraduates, 2 to graduate students, and 1 to a vocational student. **Funds Available:** The stipends are $5,000 for undergraduate students, $7,500 for graduate students, or $2,500 for recipients at a vocational school. **Duration:** 1 year. **Eligibility Requirements:** This program is open to persons with hemophilia (A or B) who are high school seniors, have a GED, or are currently attending an accredited college, university, junior college, vocational school, or graduate school. They must need financial assistance to work on an undergraduate degree. **Deadline for Receipt:** April of each year. **Additional Information:** This program was established in 1998 and given its current name in 2000.

1878 ■ WYOMING NATIONAL GUARD

Attn: Education Services Officer
5500 Bishop Boulevard
Cheyenne, WY 82009-3320
Tel: (307)772-5262
Free: 800-832-1959
E-mail: shellie.franklin@wy.ngb.army.mil
Web Site: http://www.wy.ngb.army.mil/education
To provide financial assistance for college or graduate school to members of the Wyoming National Guard.
Title of Award: Wyoming National Guard Educational Assistance Plan **Area, Field, or Subject:** General studies/Field of study not specified **Level of Education for which Award is Granted:** Graduate, Undergraduate **Number Awarded:** Varies each year. **Funds Available:** The program provides full payment of tuition at eligible institutions. **Duration:** Guard members may continue to receive these benefits as long as they maintain a "C" average, keep up with Guard standards for drill attendance, and remain in good standing with the Guard. **Eligibility Requirements:** This program is open to members of the Wyoming Army National Guard and the Wyoming Air National Guard who have spent at least 6 years in the Guard or are currently serving under their initial 6-year enlistment period. New enlistees who commit to serving 6 years are also eligible. Applicants may be pursuing, or planning to pursue, a degree at any level at the University of Wyoming, a Wyoming community college, or an approved technical institution in Wyoming. **Additional Information:** The Wyoming legislature created this program in 2001. Recipients must agree to serve in the Guard for at least 2 years after they graduate or stop using the plan.

1879 ■ WYOMING NATIONAL GUARD ASSOCIATION

Attn: Scholarship Committee Chair
P.O. Box 20172
Cheyenne, WY 82003
Tel: (307)772-5262
Free: 800-832-1959
E-mail: shellie.franklin@wy.ngb.army.mil
Web Site: http://www.wynga.org/scholarships.htm
To provide financial assistance for college to members of the Wyoming National Guard Association (WYNGA) and their families.
Title of Award: Wyoming National Guard Association Scholarships **Area, Field, or Subject:** General studies/Field of study not specified **Level of Education for which Award is Granted:** Undergraduate **Number Awarded:** Varies each year; recently, 7 of these scholarships were awarded. **Funds Available:** Stipends are $500. **Duration:** 1 year. **Eligibility Requirements:** This program is open to enlisted and officer members of the WYNGA and their spouses and unmarried children. Applicants must be attending or planning to attend an accredited institution

of higher education. Along with their application, they must submit a cover letter that includes information on their educational career goals, their need for this scholarship, and a list of awards, honors, extracurricular activities, and organizations in which they have participated. **Deadline for Receipt:** May of each year. **Additional Information:** This program includes the following named scholarships: the Colonel Weston Peterson Memorial Scholarship, the MG Charles J. Wing Family Program Scholarship, the Bev Holmes Appreciation & Service Award Scholarship, the F.E. Warren AFB Federal Credit Union Scholarship, and the USAA Insurance Company Scholarship.

1880 ■ WYOMING VETERANS' COMMISSION

Wyoming Army National Guard Armory
5905 CY Avenue, Room 101
Casper, WY 82604
Tel: (307)265-7372
Free: 800-833-5987
Fax: (307)265-7392
E-mail: wvac@bresnan.net
To provide financial assistance for college to dependents of deceased and disabled members of the Wyoming National Guard.
Title of Award: Wyoming Education Benefits for National Guard Family Members **Area, Field, or Subject:** General studies/Field of study not specified **Level of Education for which Award is Granted:** Undergraduate **Number Awarded:** Varies each year. **Funds Available:** Payment of tuition and fees is provided by this program. **Eligibility Requirements:** This program is open to children and spouses of Wyoming National Guard members who have died or sustained permanent total disability from duty as a Guard member while on state active duty or another authorized training duty. Applicants must be attending or planning to attend the University of Wyoming or a junior college or vocational training institution in the state. **Deadline for Receipt:** Applications may be submitted at any time, but they should be received 2 or 3 weeks before the beginning of the semester. **Additional Information:** Applications may be obtained from the institution the applicant is attending or planning to attend.

1881 ■ WYOMING VETERANS' COMMISSION

Wyoming Army National Guard Armory
5905 CY Avenue, Room 101
Casper, WY 82604
Tel: (307)265-7372
Free: 800-833-5987
Fax: (307)265-7392
E-mail: wvac@bresnan.net
Web Site: http://uwadmnweb.uwyo.edu/sfa/Vet/vietnam.asp
To provide financial assistance for college to Wyoming veterans who served during the Vietnam era.
Title of Award: Wyoming Vietnam Veterans' Awards **Area, Field, or Subject:** General studies/Field of study not specified **Level of Education for which Award is Granted:** Undergraduate **Number Awarded:** Varies each year. **Funds Available:** Qualifying veterans may be eligible for free resident tuition at the University of Wyoming or at any of the state's community colleges. **Duration:** Up to 10 semesters. **Eligibility Requirements:** Eligible to apply for these scholarships are Wyoming veterans who 1) served on active duty with the U.S. armed forces between August 5, 1964 and May 7, 1975; 2) received a Vietnam service medal between those dates; 3) received an honorable discharge; 4) have lived in Wyoming for at least 1 year; and 5) have exhausted their veterans' benefits entitlement or for some other reason are no longer eligible for U.S. Department of Veterans Affairs benefits. **Deadline for Receipt:** Applications may be submitted at any time, but they should be received 2 or 3 weeks before the beginning of the semester. **Additional Information:** Applications may be obtained from the institution the applicant is attending or planning to attend.

1882 ■ WYOMING VETERANS' COMMISSION

Wyoming Army National Guard Armory
5905 CY Avenue, Room 101
Casper, WY 82604
Tel: (307)265-7372
Free: 800-833-5987
Fax: (307)265-7392

E-mail: wvac@bresnan.net

Web Site: http://uwadmnweb.uwyo.edu/sfa

To provide financial assistance for college to children of deceased, POW, or MIA Wyoming veterans.

Title of Award: Wyoming War Orphans Scholarships **Area, Field, or Subject:** General studies/Field of study not specified **Level of Education for which Award is Granted:** Undergraduate **Number Awarded:** Varies each year. **Funds Available:** Qualifying veterans' children may be eligible for free resident tuition at the University of Wyoming or at any of the state's community colleges. **Duration:** Up to 10 semesters.

Eligibility Requirements: This program is open to children of veterans whose parent was a resident of Wyoming at the time of entering service and 1) died while in service during a period of war defined by law; 2) is listed officially as being a POW or MIA in the Korean or Vietnam conflicts; or 3) was honorably discharged from the military and subsequently died of an injury or disease incurred while in service and was a Wyoming resident at the time of death. Applicants must be attending or planning to attend the University of Wyoming or a community college in the state. **Deadline for Receipt:** Applications may be submitted at any time, but they should be received 2 or 3 weeks before the beginning of the semester. **Additional Information:** Applications may be obtained from the institution the applicant is attending or planning to attend.

1883 ■ YUKON DELTA FISHERIES DEVELOPMENT ASSOCIATION

Attn: Vocational Training Program

P.O. Box 210

Emmonak, AK 99581

Tel: (907)949-1202; 877-985-6625

Fax: (907)949-1203

Web Site: http://www.ydfda.org/development/
development.aspx?pg=education

To provide financial assistance for vocational training to residents of Alaska Native villages served by the Yukon Delta Fisheries Development Association (YDFDA):

Title of Award: YDFDA Vocational Training Grants **Area, Field, or Subject:** General studies/Field of study not specified **Level of Education for which Award is Granted:** Vocational/Occupational **Number Awarded:** Varies each year; recently, 9 of these grants were awarded. **Funds Available:** The stipend depends on the cost of the program and the need of the recipient. **Duration:** At least 3 months.

Eligibility Requirements: This program is open to students who are interested in vocational training and have been residents for at least 5 continuous years of a Native village in the Lower Yukon Delta region of Alaska. Applicants must have a subsistence and/or commercial fishing relationship to the Lower Yukon Delta region. Selection criteria include motivation, academic achievement, and leadership potential. **Deadline for Receipt:** Applications may be submitted at any time, but they must be received at least 2 months prior to the start of the program. **Additional Information:** YDFDA serves the Lower Delta Yukon region as 1 of 6 Community Development Quota (CDQ) organizations in the state.

1884 ■ ZAMI, INC.

P.O. Box 2502

Decatur, GA 30031

Tel: (404)370-0920

E-mail: zami@zami.org

Web Site: http://www.zami.org/scholarship.htm

To provide financial assistance to lesbians and gay men of African descent who are entering or attending a college or university as a graduate or undergraduate student.

Title of Award: Audre Lorde Scholarship Fund **Area, Field, or Subject:** General studies/Field of study not specified **Level of Education for which Award is Granted:** Graduate, Undergraduate **Number Awarded:** Varies each year; recently, 21 of these scholarships were awarded. **Funds Available:** The stipend is $1,000. Funds are paid directly to the academic institution. **Duration:** 1 year.

Eligibility Requirements: This program is open to "out" lesbians and gay men of African descent who are graduating high school seniors or enrolled in a technical, undergraduate, or graduate program located in the United States. Applicants must have a GPA of 2.5 or higher. They must submit 2 essays of 300 words or less on from a list of 5 topics that relate to their experiences being "out," their dreams for the future, how their friends would characterize them as a lesbian or gay person, their favorite books or other works of art, or the most difficult time in their life. Lesbians and gay men who are over 40 years of age are especially encouraged to apply. **Deadline for Receipt:** May of each year. **Additional Information:** This fund was established in 1995; the first scholarships were awarded in 1997. Each year, named scholarships are awarded to honor the donors whose support makes the program possible.

1885 ■ ZLB BEHRING

Attn: Choice Member Support Center

1020 First Avenue

P.O. Box 61501

King of Prussia, PA 19406

Tel: (610)878-4000; 888-508-6978

Fax: (610)878-4009

E-mail: AventisBehringChoice@ZLBBehring.com

Web Site: http://www.zlbbehring.com

To provide financial assistance for college to students with bleeding disorders who are members of the Aventis Behring Choice program.

Title of Award: Arthur B. Kane Memorial Scholarships **Area, Field, or Subject:** General studies/Field of study not specified **Level of Education for which Award is Granted:** Undergraduate **Number Awarded:** At least 4 each year. **Funds Available:** The stipend is $6,250 per year. **Duration:** Up to 4 years, provided the recipient maintains full-time enrollment and satisfactory progress towards a degree.

Eligibility Requirements: This program is open to participants in the program who are attending or planning to attend a college, university, or vocational/trade school. Applicants must have hemophilia A or B or von Willebrand's disease. **Deadline for Receipt:** March of each year. **Additional Information:** This program, offered by a pharmaceutical manufacturer, provides the largest scholarship awards available to the bleeding disorders community. Recipients must spend 2 to 4 hours each year mentoring teenagers with bleeding disorders and encouraging them in their pursuit of higher education.

African Studies

1886 ■ HBCUCONNECT.COM, LLC.
Attn: Scholarship Administrator
5300 East Main Street
Columbus, OH 43213-2580
Tel: (614)864-4446
E-mail: scholarship@hbcuconnect.com
Web Site: http://hbcuconnect.com/scholarships.shtml
To provide financial assistance to underrepresented minority students attending or planning to attend an Historically Black College or University (HBCU).
Title of Award: HBCU Minority Student Scholarships **Area, Field, or Subject:** Actuarial science; African studies; General studies/Field of study not specified; Insurance and insurance-related fields **Level of Education for which Award is Granted:** Four Year College **Number Awarded:** Varies each year; recently, 4 of these scholarships were awarded. **Funds Available:** The stipend is $1,000. **Duration:** 1 year.
Eligibility Requirements: This program is open to high school seniors and current full-time college students who are members of an underrepresented minority group (African American, Hispanic American, Native American). Applicants must be attending or interested in attending an HBCU to work on a 4-year degree. Preference is given to students planning to major in actuarial science or African studies. Along with their application, they must submit 4 essays: why they decided to attend an HBCU, what they want to do once they receive their degree, a situation that demonstrates initiative and their willingness to go above and beyond, and how they are currently funding their college education. **Deadline for Receipt:** July or December of each year.

1887 ■ U.S. AIR FORCE
Attn: Headquarters AFROTC/RRUE
Enlisted Commissioning Section
551 East Maxwell Boulevard
Maxwell AFB, AL 36112-5917
Tel: (334)953-2091; (866)423-7682
Fax: (334)953-6167
E-mail: enlisted@afrotc.com
Web Site: http://www.afoats.af.mil/AFROTC/EnlistedComm/AECP.asp
To allow selected enlisted Air Force personnel to earn a bachelor's degree in approved majors by providing financial assistance for full-time college study.
Title of Award: Airman Education and Commissioning Program **Area, Field, or Subject:** African studies; Asian studies; Computer and information sciences; Engineering; Foreign languages; Mathematics and mathematical sciences; Meteorology; Near Eastern studies; Nursing; Physics; Russian studies **Level of Education for which Award is Granted:** Undergraduate **Number Awarded:** Approximately 60 each year. **Funds Available:** While participating in this program, cadets remain on active duty in the Air Force and receive their regular salary and benefits. They also receive payment of tuition and fees up to $15,000 per year and an annual textbook allowance of $600. **Duration:** 1 to 3 years, until completion of a bachelor's degree.
Eligibility Requirements: Eligible to participate in this program are enlisted members of the Air Force who have been accepted at a university

or college (or approved crosstown institution) that is associated with AFROTC and that offers an approved major. The majors currently supported are computer science, all ABET-accredited engineering fields (not engineering technology), foreign area studies (limited to Middle East, Africa, Asia, Russia/Eurasia), foreign languages (limited to Arabic, Armenian, Azeri, Chinese, French, Georgian, Hebrew, Hindi, Indonesian, Kazakh, Pashto, Persian Farsi, Russian, Swahili, and Turkish), mathematics, meteorology, nursing, and physics. Applicants must have completed at least 1 year of time-in-service and 1 year of time-on-station. They must have scores on the Air Force Officer Qualifying Test of at least 15 on the verbal and 10 on the quantitative and be able to pass the Air Force ROTC Physical Fitness Test. Normally they should have completed at least 30 semester hours of college study with a GPA of 2.75 or higher. They must be younger than 31 years of age or otherwise able to be commissioned before they become 35 years of age. **Deadline for Receipt:** February of each year. **Additional Information:** While attending college, participants in this program attend ROTC classes at their college or university. Upon completing their degree, they are commissioned to serve in the Air Force in their area of specialization with an active-duty service commitment of at least 4 years. Further information is available from base education service officers or an Air Force ROTC unit. This program does not provide for undergraduate flying training.

1888 ■ WISCONSIN FOUNDATION FOR INDEPENDENT COLLEGES, INC.
Attn: College-to-Work Program
735 North Water Street, Suite 600
Milwaukee, WI 53202-4100
Tel: (414)273-5980
Fax: (414)273-5995
E-mail: wfic@wficweb.org
Web Site: http://www.wficweb.org/work.html
To provide financial assistance and work experience to students majoring in fields related to history at member institutions of the Wisconsin Foundation for Independent Colleges (WFIC).
Title of Award: Milton Historical Society College-to-Work Program **Area, Field, or Subject:** African-American studies; Education; History, American; Museum science **Level of Education for which Award is Granted:** Four Year College **Number Awarded:** 1 each year. **Funds Available:** The stipends are $3,500 for the scholarship and $1,500 for the internship. **Duration:** 1 year for the scholarship; 10 weeks during the summer for the internship.
Eligibility Requirements: This program is open to full-time sophomores, juniors, and seniors at WFIC member colleges and universities. Preference is given to students majoring in African American studies, American history, museum science, or history education. Applicants must be interested in an internship at the Milton Historical Society in Milton, Wisconsin. Along with their application, they must submit a 1-page essay that includes why they are applying for the internship, why they have selected their major and what interests them about it, why they are attending their chosen college or university, and their future career objectives. **Deadline for Receipt:** February of each year. **Additional Information:** The WFIC member schools are Alverno College, Beloit College, Cardinal Stritch University, Carroll College, Carthage College, Concordia University of Wisconsin, Edgewood College, Lakeland College, Lawrence University,

Marian College, Marquette University, Milwaukee Institute of Art & Design, Milwaukee School of Engineering, Mount Mary College, Northland College, Ripon College, St. Norbert College, Silver Lake College, Viterbo University, and Wisconsin Lutheran College. This program is sponsored by the Milton Historical Society.

American Studies

1889 ■ ARIZONA SOCIETY DAUGHTERS OF THE AMERICAN REVOLUTION

c/o Jean Oracheff, Scholarship Chair
5217 West Creedance Boulevard
Glendale, AZ 85310
E-mail: vglortho@aol.com
Web Site: http://arizonasocietydar.homestead.com/Scholarships.html
To provide financial assistance to high school seniors in Arizona interested in studying U.S. history in college.
Title of Award: Mary Ann Tallman Scholarship Endowment **Area, Field, or Subject:** History, American **Level of Education for which Award is Granted:** Undergraduate **Number Awarded:** 1 each year. **Funds Available:** A stipend is awarded (amount not specified). **Duration:** 1 year.
Eligibility Requirements: This program is open to seniors graduating from high schools in Arizona and preparing to enter an institution of higher learning. Applicants must be planning to major or minor in American history. They must submit a letter describing their leadership experiences, evidence of patriotism, and plans for the future. **Deadline for Receipt:** January of each year.

1890 ■ CALIFORNIA STATE UNIVERSITY

Office of the Chancellor
Attn: Lori Redfearn, Vice President
401 Golden Shore, Sixth Floor
Long Beach, CA 90802-4210
Tel: (562)951-4815
E-mail: lredfearn@calstate.edu
Web Site: http://www.calstate.edu/foundation/scholarship.shtml
To provide financial assistance to graduate students majoring in designated fields at campuses of the California State University (CSU) system.
Title of Award: Glenn and Dorothy Dumke Fellowship **Area, Field, or Subject:** Economics; History, American; Library and archival sciences; Political science; Public administration **Level of Education for which Award is Granted:** Four Year College, Master's **Number Awarded:** 1 each year. **Funds Available:** The stipend is $1,000 per year. **Duration:** 1 year.
Eligibility Requirements: This program is open to students working on a graduate degree at CSU campuses in public policy, American history, economics, archival management, or government.

1891 ■ CHICKASAW FOUNDATION

P.O. Box 1726
Ada, OK 74821-1726
Tel: (580)421-9030
Fax: (580)421-9031
Web Site: http://www.cflink.org
To provide financial assistance to members of the Chickasaw Nation who are majoring or minoring in American history.
Title of Award: Colbert "Bud" Baker Scholarship **Area, Field, or Subject:** Education; History, American; Law; Native American studies **Level of Education for which Award is Granted:** Four Year College **Number Awarded:** 1 each year. **Funds Available:** The stipend is $1,000 per year. **Duration:** 1 year.
Eligibility Requirements: This program is open to Chickasaw students who are currently enrolled full time at an accredited institution of higher education. Applicants must be classified as juniors or seniors at a 4-year college. They must be majoring in history or majoring in education or pre-law with a minor in history. The history emphasis must be on Chickasaw tribal history or Native American studies. Along with their application, they must submit high school or college transcripts, 2 letters of recommendation, a copy of their Certificate of Degree of Indian Blood, a copy of their Chickasaw Nation citizenship card, and a 1-page essay on their long-term goals and plans for achieving them. Financial need is not considered in the selection process. **Deadline for Receipt:** May of each year.

1892 ■ COOK INLET REGION, INC.

Attn: CIRI Foundation
2600 Cordova Street, Suite 206
Anchorage, AK 99503
Tel: (907)263-5582
Free: 800-764-3382
Fax: (907)263-5588
E-mail: tcf@ciri.com
Web Site: http://www.thecirifoundation.org/scholarship.html
To provide financial assistance for undergraduate or graduate studies to Alaska Natives who are original enrollees to Cook Inlet Region, Inc. (CIRI) and their lineal descendants.
Title of Award: Peter Kalifornsky Memorial Endowment Scholarship Fund **Area, Field, or Subject:** General studies/Field of study not specified; Native American studies **Level of Education for which Award is Granted:** Four Year College, Graduate **Number Awarded:** Varies each year; recently, 1 of these scholarships (at $2,000 per semester) was awarded. **Funds Available:** The stipend is $9,000 per year, $7,000 per year, or $2,000 per semester, depending on GPA. **Duration:** 1 year (2 semesters).
Eligibility Requirements: This program is open to Alaska Native enrollees to CIRI under the Alaska Native Claims Settlement Act (ANCSA) of 1971 and their lineal descendants. There are no Alaska residency requirements or age limitations. Applicants must be accepted or enrolled full time in a 4-year undergraduate or a graduate degree program. Preference is given to students in Alaska Native studies. They must have a GPA of 2.5 or higher. Selection is based on academic achievement, rigor of course work or degree program, quality of a statement of purpose, student financial contribution, financial need, grade level, previous work performance, education and community activities, letters of recommendation, seriousness of purpose, and practicality of educational and professional goals. **Deadline for Receipt:** May of each year. **Additional Information:** This program was established in 1993. Recipients must attend school on a full-time basis.

1893 ■ DAUGHTERS OF THE AMERICAN REVOLUTION-COLORADO STATE SOCIETY

c/o Marilyn Fishburn, State Scholarship Chair
1546 West 28th Street
Loveland, CO 80538
E-mail: admin@coloradodar.org
Web Site: http://www.coloradodar.org/scholarships.htm
To provide financial assistance to high school seniors in Colorado who are interested in majoring in American history in college.
Title of Award: Honorary State Regents' American History Scholarship **Area, Field, or Subject:** History, American **Level of Education for which Award is Granted:** Undergraduate **Number Awarded:** 1 each year. **Funds Available:** The maximum stipend is $2,500. Funds are paid directly to the students' school. **Duration:** 1 year; nonrenewable.
Eligibility Requirements: Eligible to apply are graduating high school seniors in Colorado who are 1) American citizens; 2) in the upper third of their graduating class; 3) accepted at an accredited college or university (in any state); and 4) planning to major in American history. Interested students are invited to submit their complete application to the state scholarship chair (c/o the sponsor's address); they must include a statement of their career interest and goals (up to 500 words), 2 character references, their college transcripts, a letter of sponsorship from the Daughters of the American Revolution's Colorado chapter, and a list of their scholastic achievements, extracurricular activities, honors, and other significant accomplishments. Selection is based on academic record and financial need. **Deadline for Receipt:** January of each year.

1894 ■ DAUGHTERS OF THE AMERICAN REVOLUTION-NEW YORK STATE ORGANIZATION

c/o Layla Voll
311 West 21st Street
New York, NY 10011
E-mail: Layla_Voll@hotmail.com
Web Site: http://www.nydar.org/education/desimone.html
To provide financial assistance to high school seniors in New York who plan to study American history in college.
Title of Award: Damaris Smith Desimone Scholarship **Area, Field, or Subject:** History, American **Level of Education for which Award is**

Granted: Four Year College **Number Awarded:** 1 each year. **Funds Available:** The stipend is $1,000. **Duration:** 1 year; nonrenewable.
Eligibility Requirements: This program is open to seniors graduating from high schools in New York who plan to attend an accredited 4-year college or university in the state. Applicants must be intending to major in U.S. history. Selection is based on merit, including achievement in high school and the community and personal and academic interests. **Deadline for Receipt:** January of each year.

1895 ■ DAUGHTERS OF THE AMERICAN REVOLUTION-
WASHINGTON STATE SOCIETY
c/o Margaret Hamby, State Scholarship Chair
1307 144th Avenue, N.E.
Bellevue, WA 98007
E-mail: marghamby@msn.com
Web Site: http://www.rootsweb.com/~wassdar/scholars.html
To provide financial assistance to American history majors entering their senior year at designated universities in Washington.
Title of Award: Sarah Soule Patton Scholarship **Area, Field, or Subject:** History, American **Level of Education for which Award is Granted:** Four Year College **Number Awarded:** 1 each year. **Funds Available:** The stipend is $2,000. **Duration:** 1 year.
Eligibility Requirements: This program is open to students entering their senior year at Washington State University, Whitman College, St. Martin University, Pacific Lutheran University, University of Puget Sound, Gonzaga University, Whitworth College, Eastern Washington University, Seattle Pacific University, University of Washington, Western Washington University, Central Washington University, and Seattle University. Applicants must be majoring in American history, U.S. citizens, able to demonstrate financial need and good character, and recommended by the financial aid office at their college or university. **Deadline for Receipt:** January of each year.

1896 ■ IOWA FEDERATION OF LABOR, AFL-CIO
Attn: Scholarship Program
2000 Walker Street, Suite A
Des Moines, IA 50317-5290
Tel: (515)262-9571
Free: 800-372-4817
Fax: (515)262-9573
E-mail: ifl@iowaaflcio.org
Web Site: http://www.iowaaflcio.org
To recognize and reward outstanding essays on a labor-related topic written by high school seniors in Iowa.
Title of Award: Iowa Federation of Labor Scholarships **Area, Field, or Subject:** History, American; Industrial and labor relations; Writing **Level of Education for which Award is Granted:** Undergraduate **Number Awarded:** 3 each year. **Funds Available:** First prize is $1,500, second prize is $1,000, and third prize is $500. Funds may be used as a scholarship at the college or university of the recipient's choice. **Duration:** The competition is held annually.
Eligibility Requirements: This competition is open to all seniors in accredited high schools in Iowa (public, private, and parochial). Students must write an essay (from 500 to 750 words) on the history of the labor movement in the United States. It is recommended that competitors read *A History of the Labor Movement in the United States* before writing the essay. **Deadline for Receipt:** March of each year.

1897 ■ KONIAG INCORPORATED
Attn: Koniag Education Foundation
6927 Old Seward Highway, Suite 103
Anchorage, AK 99518-2283
Tel: (907)562-9093; 888-562-9093
Fax: (907)562-9023
E-mail: kef@alaska.net
Web Site: http://www.koniageducation.org
To provide financial assistance to Alaska Natives of the Koniag region who are enrolled in undergraduate or graduate study in a field related to Alutiiq culture.
Title of Award: Larry Matfay Cultural Heritage Scholarship **Area, Field, or Subject:** Anthropology; History; Native American studies **Level of Education for which Award is Granted:** Four Year College, Graduate **Number Awarded:** 1 each year. **Funds Available:** The stipend is $1,000.

Funds are sent directly to the recipient's school and may be used for tuition, books, supplies, room, board, and transportation. **Duration:** 1 year; may be renewed.
Eligibility Requirements: This program is open to college juniors, seniors, and graduate students who are 1) Alaska Natives enrolled under Section 5 of the Alaska Native Claims Settlement Act to the Koniag region, or 2) direct or legally adopted descendants of those original enrollees. Applicants must supply proof of eligibility and documentation of financial need. They must have a GPA of 2.5 or higher cumulatively (3.0 or higher within their major) and be majoring in anthropology, history, Alaska Native or American Indian studies, or another discipline that involves research and learning about Alutiiq culture. Along with their application, they must submit 1) a 300- to 600-word letter that includes their personal and family history, their schooling or work history, and their educational and life goals; and 2) a 200- to 400-word essay on how their education may benefit the Alutiiq people. **Deadline for Receipt:** March of each year. **Additional Information:** Recipients are also eligible to apply for a Koniag Education Foundation Academic Achievement/Graduate Scholarship. The Koniag Education Foundation was established in 1993 by the directors of Koniag, Inc. The Koniag region covers Kodiak Island, many smaller islands, and a portion of the Alaska Peninsula.

1898 ■ GILDER LEHRMAN INSTITUTE OF AMERICAN HISTORY
Attn: Prize in American History
19 West 44th Street, Suite 500
New York, NY 10036
Tel: (646)366-9666
Fax: (646)366-9669
E-mail: info@gilderlehrman.org
Web Site: http://www.gilderlehrman.org
To recognize and reward high school students who write outstanding essays on topics related to U.S. history.
Title of Award: Gilder Lehrman Prize in American History **Area, Field, or Subject:** History, American; Writing **Level of Education for which Award is Granted:** Undergraduate **Number Awarded:** 3 cash prizes are awarded each year. **Funds Available:** First prize is $5,000, second $3,000, and third $1,000. **Duration:** The competition is held annually.
Eligibility Requirements: This competition is open to students at high schools in the United States. Candidates submit essays on topics related to American history to the *Concord Review*. The editors of that journal then select 10 outstanding essays on U.S. history and refer them to the sponsors of this competition. **Additional Information:** This competition began in 2000. Information on the *Concord Review* is available from its Editor, 730 Boston Post Road, Suite 24, Sudbury, MA 01776, (800) 331-5007, E-mail: fitzhugh@tcr.org.

1899 ■ NEW YORK STATE ARCHIVES
Attn: Coordinator of Educational Programs
Cultural Education Center, Suite 9B52
Albany, NY 12230
Tel: (518)474-6926
E-mail: jdaniels@mail.nysed.gov
Web Site: http://www.archives.nysed.gov/a/grantsawards/ga_student_sraguidelines.shtml
To recognize and reward outstanding historical research conducted by students in grades 4 through 12 in New York State.
Title of Award: New York State Archives Student Research Award **Area, Field, or Subject:** Creative writing; History, American; Playwriting; Writing **Level of Education for which Award is Granted:** Undergraduate **Number Awarded:** 3 each year: 1 in each grade level category. **Funds Available:** The award in each category consists of a certificate and a cash prize. **Duration:** The competition is held annually.
Eligibility Requirements: This is a statewide competition open to students in New York in 3 categories: grades 4-5, grades 6-8, and grades 9-12. Individual students and groups of students (including entire classes) may be nominated. All nominations for the award must be made by a teacher or administrator in the school attended by the entrants. Research projects prepared for other competitions (e.g., History Day) are eligible if they meet other relevant criteria, especially the use of historical records. An annotated bibliography is required for all entries. A substantial portion of the research must be based on historical records from archives, museums, historical societies, libraries, local governments, community organizations, businesses, families, and/or individuals. The product of the

student research may be any of the following: research paper; exhibit; audiovisual production; performance; proposal for designation of historic marker, property, or district; or web sites, PowerPoint presentations, and other computer-based entries. Oral history interviews are not eligible for this award program. **Deadline for Receipt:** May of each year. **Additional Information:** This program began in 1990.

1900 ■ MORRIS K. UDALL FOUNDATION
130 South Scott Avenue
Tucson, AZ 85701-1922
Tel: (520)670-5529
Fax: (520)670-5530
Web Site: http://www.udall.gov/scholarship
To provide financial assistance to 1) college sophomores and juniors who intend to prepare for a career in environmental public policy and 2) Native American and Alaska Native students who intend to prepare for a career in health care or tribal public policy.
Title of Award: Morris K. Udall Scholarships **Area, Field, or Subject:** Business administration; Economics; Education; Environmental conservation; Environmental science; Health care services; Native American studies; Natural resources; Political science; Public administration; Public health; Urban affairs/design/planning **Level of Education for which Award is Granted:** Undergraduate **Number Awarded:** Approximately 80 scholarships and 50 honorable mentions are awarded each year. **Funds Available:** The maximum stipend for scholarship winners is $5,000 per year. Funds are to be used for tuition, fees, books, and room and board. Honorable mention stipends are $350. **Duration:** 1 year; recipients nominated as sophomores may be renominated in their junior year.
Eligibility Requirements: Each 2-year and 4-year college and university in the United States and its possessions may nominate up to 6 sophomores or juniors from either or both categories of this program: 1) students who intend to prepare for a career in environmental public policy, and 2) Native American and Alaska Native students who intend to prepare for a career in health care or tribal public policy. For the first category, the program seeks future leaders across a wide spectrum of environmental fields, such as policy, engineering, science, education, urban planning and renewal, business, health, justice, and economics. For the second category, the program seeks future Native American and Alaska Native leaders in public and community health care, tribal government, and public policy affecting Native American communities, including land and resource management, economic development, and education. Nominees must be U.S. citizens, nationals, or permanent residents with a GPA of 3.0 or higher. Along with their application, they must submit an 800-word essay discussing a significant public speech, legislative act, or public policy statement by former Congressman Morris K. Udall and its impact on their field of study, interests, and career goals. Selection is based on demonstrated commitment to 1) environmental issues through substantial commitment to and participation in 1 or more of the following: campus activities, research, community service, or public service; or 2) tribal public policy or Native American health through substantial contributions to and participation in 1 or more of the following: campus activities, tribal involvement, community or public service, or research; a course of study and proposed career likely to lead to position where nominee can make significant contributions to the shaping of environmental, tribal public policy, or Native American health care issues, whether through scientific advances, public or political service, or community action; and leadership, character, desire to make a difference, and general well-roundedness.
Deadline for Receipt: Faculty representatives must submit their nominations by early March of each year.

1901 ■ UNITED DAUGHTERS OF THE CONFEDERACY
Attn: Education Director
328 North Boulevard
Richmond, VA 23220-4057
Tel: (804)355-1636
Fax: (804)353-1396
E-mail: hqudc@rcn.com
Web Site: http://www.hqudc.org/scholarships/scholarships.html
To provide financial assistance to lineal descendants of Confederate veterans in certain southern states who are interested in majoring in southern history or literature.
Title of Award: Helen James Brewer Scholarship **Area, Field, or Subject:** English language and literature; History, American; Literature;

United States studies **Level of Education for which Award is Granted:** Undergraduate **Number Awarded:** 1 each year. **Funds Available:** The amount of this scholarship depends on the availability of funds. **Duration:** 1 year; may be renewed.
Eligibility Requirements: Eligible to apply for these scholarships are lineal descendants of worthy Confederates or collateral descendants who are current or former members of the Children of the Confederacy or current members of the United Daughters of the Confederacy. Applicants must intend to study English or southern history and literature and must submit a family financial report and certified proof of the Confederate record of 1 ancestor, with the company and regiment in which he served. They must have at least a 3.0 GPA in high school. Residency in Alabama, Florida, Georgia, South Carolina, Tennessee, or Virginia is required. **Deadline for Receipt:** March of each year. **Additional Information:** Information is also available from Mrs. Robert C. Kraus, Second Vice President General, 239 Deerfield Lane, Franklin, NC 28734-0112. Members of the same family may not hold scholarships simultaneously, and only 1 application per family will be accepted within any 1 year. All requests for applications must be accompanied by a self-addressed stamped envelope.

1902 ■ VIRGINIA DAUGHTERS OF THE AMERICAN REVOLUTION
c/o Catherine Rafferty, Scholarship Chair
10101 Sanders Court
Great Falls, VA 22066-2526
Web Site: http://www.vadar.org/vadarscholarships.htm
To provide financial assistance to high school seniors in Virginia who wish to study American history in college.
Title of Award: Virginia DAR American History Scholarships **Area, Field, or Subject:** History, American **Level of Education for which Award is Granted:** Undergraduate **Number Awarded:** 2 each year: 1 at $1,000 and 1 at $500. **Funds Available:** Stipends are $1,000 or $500. **Duration:** 1 year.
Eligibility Requirements: This program is open to seniors graduating from high schools in Virginia in the top third of their class. Applicants must be planning to major in American history in college. Along with their application, they must submit a 1,000-word letter giving their reasons for desiring an education in American history, a transcript of grades, SAT or ACT scores, extracurricular activities, honors received, and documentation of financial need. **Deadline for Receipt:** January of each year. **Additional Information:** The top winner of this scholarship is nominated for consideration for the American History Scholarship awarded by the National Society Daughters of the American Revolution.

1903 ■ VIRGINIA DAUGHTERS OF THE AMERICAN REVOLUTION
c/o Catherine Rafferty, Scholarship Chair
10101 Sanders Court
Great Falls, VA 22066-2526
Web Site: http://www.vadar.org/vadarscholarships.htm
To provide financial assistance to high school seniors in Virginia who wish to study designated fields in college.
Title of Award: Virginia DAR Scholarships **Area, Field, or Subject:** Environmental conservation; Environmental science; Forestry; Genealogy; History, American; Home Economics; Medicine; Science **Level of Education for which Award is Granted:** Undergraduate **Number Awarded:** 2 each year: 1 at $1,000 and 1 at $500. **Funds Available:** Stipends are $1,000 or $500. **Duration:** 1 year.
Eligibility Requirements: This program is open to seniors graduating from high schools in Virginia who plan to attend a Virginia college or university. Applicants must be planning to work on a degree in the field of science, medicine, conservation, ecology, forestry, home arts, genealogical research, or American history. Along with their application, they must submit a 1,000-word letter giving their reasons for interest in the scholarship, a transcript of grades, a letter of recommendation from a teacher in their chosen field, and documentation of financial need. **Deadline for Receipt:** January of each year.

1904 ■ WISCONSIN FOUNDATION FOR INDEPENDENT COLLEGES, INC.
Attn: College-to-Work Program
735 North Water Street, Suite 600
Milwaukee, WI 53202-4100
Tel: (414)273-5980

Fax: (414)273-5995
E-mail: wfic@wficweb.org
Web Site: http://www.wficweb.org/work.html
To provide financial assistance and work experience to students majoring in fields related to history at member institutions of the Wisconsin Foundation for Independent Colleges (WFIC).

Title of Award: Milton Historical Society College-to-Work Program **Area, Field, or Subject:** African-American studies; Education; History, American; Museum science **Level of Education for which Award is Granted:** Four Year College **Number Awarded:** 1 each year. **Funds Available:** The stipends are $3,500 for the scholarship and $1,500 for the internship. **Duration:** 1 year for the scholarship; 10 weeks during the summer for the internship.

Eligibility Requirements: This program is open to full-time sophomores, juniors, and seniors at WFIC member colleges and universities. Preference is given to students majoring in African American studies, American history, museum science, or history education. Applicants must be interested in an internship at the Milton Historical Society in Milton, Wisconsin. Along with their application, they must submit a 1-page essay that includes why they are applying for the internship, why they have selected their major and what interests them about it, why they are attending their chosen college or university, and their future career objectives. **Deadline for Receipt:** February of each year. **Additional Information:** The WFIC member schools are Alverno College, Beloit College, Cardinal Stritch University, Carroll College, Carthage College, Concordia University of Wisconsin, Edgewood College, Lakeland College, Lawrence University, Marian College, Marquette University, Milwaukee Institute of Art & Design, Milwaukee School of Engineering, Mount Mary College, Northland College, Ripon College, St. Norbert College, Silver Lake College, Viterbo University, and Wisconsin Lutheran College. This program is sponsored by the Milton Historical Society.

1905 ■ WORLDSTUDIO FOUNDATION

200 Varick Street, Suite 507
New York, NY 10014
Tel: (212)366-1317
Fax: (212)807-0024
E-mail: scholarshipcoordinator@worldstudio.org
Web Site: http://www.worldstudio.org/schol/index.html
To provide financial support for college or graduate school to art students of Native American heritage.

Title of Award: Worldstudio Foundation Indigenous Peoples Award **Area, Field, or Subject:** Art; Art industries and trade; Crafts; Native American studies **Level of Education for which Award is Granted:** Graduate, Undergraduate **Number Awarded:** 1 or more each year. **Funds Available:** The stipend ranges from $1,000 to $2,000. **Duration:** 1 academic year. Recipients may reapply.

Eligibility Requirements: This program is open to art students affiliated with Native American, Alaska Native/Inuit, or other indigenous tribes of the Americas. Applicants must be interested in maintaining traditional art, designs, or crafts. They must be undergraduate or graduate students at an accredited college or university in the United States with a GPA of 2.0 or higher. Selection is based on the quality of submitted work, a written statement of purpose, financial need, and academic record. **Deadline for Receipt:** March of each year.

Asian Studies

1906 ■ CHINESE HISTORICAL SOCIETY OF SOUTHERN CALIFORNIA

Attn: Scholarship Chair
415 Bernard Street
P.O. Box 862647
Los Angeles, CA 90086-2647
Tel: (323)222-0856
E-mail: chssc@chssc.org
Web Site: http://www.chssc.org
To provide financial assistance to students from any state who who attending college in southern California and interested in majoring in Chinese American studies.

Title of Award: CHSSC Scholarship **Area, Field, or Subject:** Asian studies; Humanities; Social sciences **Level of Education for which Award is**

Granted: Graduate, Undergraduate **Number Awarded:** 1 each year. **Funds Available:** The stipend is $1,000. **Duration:** 1 year.

Eligibility Requirements: This program is open to undergraduate and graduate students from any state who are attending an accredited college or university in southern California on a full-time basis, have earned at least a 3.0 GPA, and are have an academic interest related to Chinese American studies in the humanities or social sciences. Applicants must submit a 300- to 500-word essay in English on the importance to them of Chinese American studies; a statement of additional factors, such as financial need, family circumstances, employment history, and campus and community activities that may advance their application; transcripts; and an optional letter of recommendation. Finalists are interviewed. **Deadline for Receipt:** March of each year. **Additional Information:** This program began in 1992. Information is also available from Susie Ling, E-mail: shling@pasadena.edu.

1907 ■ NATIONAL SECURITY AGENCY

Attn: Office of Recruitment and Staffing (Roberts)
9800 Savage Road, Suite 6779
P.O. Box 1661, Suite 6779
Fort Meade, MD 20755-6779
Tel: (410)854-4725; (866)672-4473
Web Site: http://www.nsa.gov/careers/students_4.cfm
To provide financial assistance to college juniors interested in preparing for a career with the National Security Agency (NSA) as an intelligence analyst.

Title of Award: Pat Roberts Intelligence Scholars Program for Intelligence Analysts **Area, Field, or Subject:** Asian studies; Banking; Finance; Foreign languages; Geography; Information science and technology; International affairs and relations; Library and archival sciences; Near Eastern studies; South Asian studies; Telecommunications systems **Level of Education for which Award is Granted:** Four Year College **Number Awarded:** Varies each year. **Funds Available:** The stipend is $25,000 per year. After graduation, recipients have an employment obligation to NSA equal to 1.5 times the length of educational support provided. **Duration:** 1 year (the senior year of college).

Eligibility Requirements: This program is open to college juniors whose academic program includes 1 of the following areas of emphasis: 1) regional studies (Middle East or south, east, or central Asia); 2) topical studies (terrorism, proliferation or related sciences, international banking and finance, or telecommunications and information systems networks); or 3) disciplines (intelligence analysis, philosophy, or international relations; familiarity with foreign languages, particularly Arabic, Chinese, Dari, Farsi, Hindi, Korean, Pashto, Urdu, or a central Asian language is desirable; highly qualified applicants studying social network analysis, library science, or geographic information systems may also be considered). Applicants must be enrolled full time with a GPA of 3.0 or higher. Along with their application, they must submit a 1-page essay describing how the proposed program of study will improve their ability to analyze information and to think and write critically. U.S. citizenship and eligibility to obtain a high-level security clearance are required **Deadline for Receipt:** October of each year. **Additional Information:** After graduation, participants enter NSA's Intelligence Analysis Development Program as a full-time employee.

1908 ■ NATIONAL SECURITY AGENCY

Attn: Office of Recruitment and Staffing (Stokes)
9800 Savage Road, Suite 6779
P.O. Box 1661, Suite 6779
Fort Meade, MD 20755-6779
Tel: (410)854-4725; (866)672-4473
Web Site: http://www.nsa.gov/careers/students_4.cfm
To provide minority and other high school seniors and college sophomores with scholarship/loans and work experience at the National Security Agency (NSA).

Title of Award: Stokes Educational Scholarship Program **Area, Field, or Subject:** Asian studies; Computer and information sciences; Engineering, Computer; Engineering, Electrical; Finance; Foreign languages; International affairs and relations; Mathematics and mathematical sciences; Near Eastern studies; South Asian studies **Level of Education for which Award is Granted:** Undergraduate **Number Awarded:** Varies each year. **Funds Available:** Participants receive college tuition for up to 4 years, reimbursement for books and certain fees, a year-round salary, and a housing allowance and travel reimbursement during summer employment if the distance between the agency and school exceeds 75 miles. Following graduation, participants must work for the agency for 1 and a half times their length of study, usually 5 years. Students who leave agency employment earlier must repay the tuition cost. **Duration:** Up to 4 years, followed by employment at the agency for 5 years.

Eligibility Requirements: This program is open to graduating high school seniors, particularly minorities, who 1) are planning a college major in electrical or computer engineering, computer science, international affairs, international finance, mathematics, area studies (Middle East or south, east, or central Asia), foreign languages (recent language interests included Arabic, Chinese, Farsi, and Korean); 2) have minimum scores of 1600 on the SAT (1100 on critical reading and mathematics, 500 in writing) or 25 on the ACT; 3) have a GPA of 3.0 or higher; 4) are U.S. citizens; and 5) demonstrate leadership abilities. Also eligible are college sophomores who are U.S. citizens, have a GPA of 3.0 or higher, and are majoring in the eligible fields. Applicants must include a 1-page essay on why they want to have a career with the NSA. **Deadline for Receipt:** November of each year. **Additional Information:** Participants must attend classes full time and work at the agency during the summer in jobs tailored to their course of study. They must maintain at least a 3.0 GPA. This program, established in 1986, was formerly known as the National Security Agency Undergraduate Training Program.

1909 ■ U.S. AIR FORCE
Attn: Headquarters AFROTC/RRUE
Enlisted Commissioning Section
551 East Maxwell Boulevard
Maxwell AFB, AL 36112-5917
Tel: (334)953-2091; (866)423-7682
Fax: (334)953-6167
E-mail: enlisted@afrotc.com
Web Site: http://www.afoats.af.mil/AFROTC/EnlistedComm/AECP.asp
To allow selected enlisted Air Force personnel to earn a bachelor's degree in approved majors by providing financial assistance for full-time college study.

Title of Award: Airman Education and Commissioning Program **Area, Field, or Subject:** African studies; Asian studies; Computer and information sciences; Engineering; Foreign languages; Mathematics and mathematical sciences; Meteorology; Near Eastern studies; Nursing; Physics; Russian studies **Level of Education for which Award is Granted:** Undergraduate **Number Awarded:** Approximately 60 each year. **Funds Available:** While participating in this program, cadets remain on active duty in the Air Force and receive their regular salary and benefits. They also receive payment of tuition and fees up to $15,000 per year and an annual textbook allowance of $600. **Duration:** 1 to 3 years, until completion of a bachelor's degree.

Eligibility Requirements: Eligible to participate in this program are enlisted members of the Air Force who have been accepted at a university or college (or approved crosstown institution) that is associated with AFROTC and that offers an approved major. The majors currently supported are computer science, all ABET-accredited engineering fields (not engineering technology), foreign area studies (limited to Middle East, Africa, Asia, Russia/Eurasia), foreign languages (limited to Arabic, Armenian, Azeri, Chinese, French, Georgian, Hebrew, Hindi, Indonesian, Kazakh, Pashto, Persian Farsi, Russian, Swahili, and Turkish), mathematics, meteorology, nursing, and physics. Applicants must have completed at least 1 year of time-in-service and 1 year of time-on-station. They must have scores on the Air Force Officer Qualifying Test of at least 15 on the verbal and 10 on the quantitative and be able to pass the Air Force ROTC Physical Fitness Test. Normally they should have completed at least 30 semester hours of college study with a GPA of 2.75 or higher. They must be younger than 31 years of age or otherwise able to be commissioned before they become 35 years of age. **Deadline for Receipt:** February of each year. **Additional Information:** While attending college, participants in this program attend ROTC classes at their college or university. Upon completing their degree, they are commissioned to serve in the Air Force in their area of specialization with an active-duty service commitment of at

least 4 years. Further information is available from base education service officers or an Air Force ROTC unit. This program does not provide for undergraduate flying training.

Canadian Studies

1910 ■ CANADIAN INSTITUTE OF UKRAINIAN STUDIES
c/o University of Alberta
450 Athabasca Hall
Edmonton, AB, Canada T6G 2E8
E-mail: cius@ualberta.ca
Web Site: http://www.ualberta.ca/CIUS/cius-grants.htm
To provide financial assistance to Canadian undergraduate students majoring in a field related to Ukrainian or Ukrainian Canadian studies.

Title of Award: Leo J. Krysa Family Undergraduate Scholarship **Area, Field, or Subject:** Canadian studies; Education; European studies; Humanities; Social sciences; Ukrainian studies **Level of Education for which Award is Granted:** Four Year College **Number Awarded:** 1 each year. **Funds Available:** The maximum stipend is $C3,500. **Duration:** 8 months; nonrenewable.

Eligibility Requirements: This program is open to Canadian citizens and permanent residents who are entering the final year of study for an undergraduate degree at a college or university in Canada. Applicants' programs must emphasize Ukrainian and/or Ukrainian Canadian studies, through a combination of Ukrainian and east European or Canadian courses in education, history, humanities, or the social sciences. Selection is based on overall academic record, performance in Ukrainian-content courses, a working sample, and community involvement. **Deadline for Receipt:** February of each year. **Additional Information:** Recipients may attend any Canadian university.

Chinese Studies

1911 ■ US PAN ASIAN AMERICAN CHAMBER OF COMMERCE
Attn: Scholarship Coordinator
1329 18th Street, N.W.
Washington, DC 20036
Tel: (202)296-5221
Fax: (202)296-5225
E-mail: administrator@uspaacc.com
Web Site: http://www.uspaacc.com/web/programs/
bernadette_Wong_yu.htm
To provide financial assistance to high school seniors who are interested in studying Chinese language or Chinese studies at a college or university in the United States or China.

Title of Award: Bernadette Wong Yu Scholarship **Area, Field, or Subject:** Chinese studies; Foreign languages **Level of Education for which Award is Granted:** Undergraduate **Number Awarded:** 1 each year. **Funds Available:** The maximum stipend is $3,000. Funds are paid directly to the recipient's college or university. **Duration:** 1 year.

Eligibility Requirements: This program is open to high school seniors who are U.S. citizens or permanent residents. Applicants must be planning to begin full-time study of Chinese language or Chinese studies at an accredited postsecondary educational institution in the United States or China. Along with their application, they must submit a 500-word essay on "Why I am interested in the Chinese culture." Selection is based on academic excellence (GPA of 3.3 or higher), community service involvement, and financial need. **Deadline for Receipt:** February of each year. **Additional Information:** Funding is not provided for correspondence courses, Internet courses, or study in a country other than the United States or China.

East European Studies

1912 ■ AMERICAN HUNGARIAN FOUNDATION
Attn: President
300 Somerset Street
P.O. Box 1084
New Brunswick, NJ 08903-1084

Tel: (732)846-5777
Fax: (732)249-7033
E-mail: info@ahfoundation.org
Web Site: http://www.ahfoundation.org
To support the training or research of students, professionals, and postdoctorates who are interested in careers in Hungarian studies.
Title of Award: American Hungarian Foundation Fellowships and Scholarships **Area, Field, or Subject:** East European studies **Level of Education for which Award is Granted:** Graduate, Professional, Postdoctoral, Undergraduate **Number Awarded:** 1 or more each year. **Funds Available:** Fellowship awards vary in amount, according to demonstrated need and availability of funds. **Duration:** Up to 1 year.
Eligibility Requirements: Applicants must be either 1) currently-enrolled full-time undergraduate or graduate students at academic institutions in the United States or Canada or 2) individuals who are well established in an academic or professional position. They must be interested in conducting scientific research that increases the existing stock of knowledge about Hungary and the Hungarian people; in pursuing advanced studies about the Hungarian culture; or in publishing works that describe the results of existing research studies. No age limit is set for applicants, but fellowships are generally not offered to persons under 18 years of age. The funded project may take place in Hungary, the United States, or any other appropriate location.

1913 ■ CANADIAN INSTITUTE OF UKRAINIAN STUDIES
c/o University of Alberta
450 Athabasca Hall
Edmonton, AB, Canada T6G 2E8
E-mail: cius@ualberta.ca
Web Site: http://www.ualberta.ca/CIUS/cius-grants.htm
To provide financial assistance to Canadian undergraduate students majoring in a field related to Ukrainian or Ukrainian Canadian studies.
Title of Award: Leo J. Krysa Family Undergraduate Scholarship **Area, Field, or Subject:** Canadian studies; Education; European studies; Humanities; Social sciences; Ukrainian studies **Level of Education for which Award is Granted:** Four Year College **Number Awarded:** 1 each year. **Funds Available:** The maximum stipend is $C3,500. **Duration:** 8 months; nonrenewable.
Eligibility Requirements: This program is open to Canadian citizens and permanent residents who are entering the final year of study for an undergraduate degree at a college or university in Canada. Applicants' programs must emphasize Ukrainian and/or Ukrainian Canadian studies, through a combination of Ukrainian and east European or Canadian courses in education, history, humanities, or the social sciences. Selection is based on overall academic record, performance in Ukrainian-content courses, a working sample, and community involvement. **Deadline for Receipt:** February of each year. **Additional Information:** Recipients may attend any Canadian university.

1914 ■ U.S. AIR FORCE
Attn: Headquarters AFROTC/RRUE
Enlisted Commissioning Section
551 East Maxwell Boulevard
Maxwell AFB, AL 36112-5917
Tel: (334)953-2091; (866)423-7682
Fax: (334)953-6167
E-mail: enlisted@afrotc.com
Web Site: http://www.afoats.af.mil/AFROTC/EnlistedComm/AECP.asp
To allow selected enlisted Air Force personnel to earn a bachelor's degree in approved majors by providing financial assistance for full-time college study.
Title of Award: Airman Education and Commissioning Program **Area, Field, or Subject:** African studies; Asian studies; Computer and information sciences; Engineering; Foreign languages; Mathematics and mathematical sciences; Meteorology; Near Eastern studies; Nursing; Physics; Russian studies **Level of Education for which Award is Granted:** Undergraduate **Number Awarded:** Approximately 60 each year. **Funds Available:** While participating in this program, cadets remain on active duty in the Air Force and receive their regular salary and benefits. They also receive payment of tuition and fees up to $15,000 per year and an annual textbook allowance of $600. **Duration:** 1 to 3 years, until completion of a bachelor's degree.
Eligibility Requirements: Eligible to participate in this program are enlisted members of the Air Force who have been accepted at a university

or college (or approved crosstown institution) that is associated with AFROTC and that offers an approved major. The majors currently supported are computer science, all ABET-accredited engineering fields (not engineering technology), foreign area studies (limited to Middle East, Africa, Asia, Russia/Eurasia), foreign languages (limited to Arabic, Armenian, Azeri, Chinese, French, Georgian, Hebrew, Hindi, Indonesian, Kazakh, Pashto, Persian Farsi, Russian, Swahili, and Turkish), mathematics, meteorology, nursing, and physics. Applicants must have completed at least 1 year of time-in-service and 1 year of time-on-station. They must have scores on the Air Force Officer Qualifying Test of at least 15 on the verbal and 10 on the quantitative and be able to pass the Air Force ROTC Physical Fitness Test. Normally they should have completed at least 30 semester hours of college study with a GPA of 2.75 or higher. They must be younger than 31 years of age or otherwise able to be commissioned before they become 35 years of age. **Deadline for Receipt:** February of each year. **Additional Information:** While attending college, participants in this program attend ROTC classes at their college or university. Upon completing their degree, they are commissioned to serve in the Air Force in their area of specialization with an active-duty service commitment of at least 4 years. Further information is available from base education service officers or an Air Force ROTC unit. This program does not provide for undergraduate flying training.

European Studies

1915 ■ CANADIAN INSTITUTE OF UKRAINIAN STUDIES
c/o University of Alberta
450 Athabasca Hall
Edmonton, AB, Canada T6G 2E8
E-mail: cius@ualberta.ca
Web Site: http://www.ualberta.ca/CIUS/cius-grants.htm
To provide financial assistance to Canadian undergraduate students majoring in a field related to Ukrainian or Ukrainian Canadian studies.
Title of Award: Leo J. Krysa Family Undergraduate Scholarship **Area, Field, or Subject:** Canadian studies; Education; European studies; Humanities; Social sciences; Ukrainian studies **Level of Education for which Award is Granted:** Four Year College **Number Awarded:** 1 each year. **Funds Available:** The maximum stipend is $C3,500. **Duration:** 8 months; nonrenewable.
Eligibility Requirements: This program is open to Canadian citizens and permanent residents who are entering the final year of study for an undergraduate degree at a college or university in Canada. Applicants' programs must emphasize Ukrainian and/or Ukrainian Canadian studies, through a combination of Ukrainian and east European or Canadian courses in education, history, humanities, or the social sciences. Selection is based on overall academic record, performance in Ukrainian-content courses, a working sample, and community involvement. **Deadline for Receipt:** February of each year. **Additional Information:** Recipients may attend any Canadian university.

1916 ■ CLAN SCOTT SOCIETY, INC.
P.O. Box 13021
Austin, TX 78711-3021
To provide financial assistance to individuals under the age of 19 who are interested in study or training in the Scottish performing arts.
Title of Award: Clan Scott Society Scholarship **Area, Field, or Subject:** Dance; Music; Scottish studies **Level of Education for which Award is Granted:** Undergraduate **Number Awarded:** Varies each year. **Funds Available:** The amount awarded depends upon the needs of the recipient and the funds available. Funds are paid directly to the individual or organization providing the training or education to the scholarship recipient. **Duration:** Up to 1 year.
Eligibility Requirements: This program is open to children, aged 18 or younger, who need financial assistance to support their education, training, or development in the Scottish performing arts. For the purposes of this program, these arts are defined as the traditional music or dance of Scotland as typically performed in competition at Scottish games and gatherings (including, but not restricted to, Scottish bagpipes, drumming, fiddle, harp, and Highland dance). Preference is given to members of the society and to their families. All applications must be submitted in writing and identify the applicant's name, the Scottish performing art for which the scholarship will be used, the person or organization providing the training

or education, the dates or time period during which the training will occur, the cost of the training or education, and a brief explanation of why the applicant deserves the scholarship. **Deadline for Receipt:** Applications may be submitted at any time.

1917 ■ DREW UNIVERSITY

Attn: Office of International and Off-Campus Programs
Brothers College Room 115
36 Madison Avenue
Madison, NJ 07940-4036
Tel: (973)408-3438
Fax: (973)408-3768
E-mail: intlprog@drew.edu
Web Site: http://depts.drew.edu/offcamp/non-DrewScholarships.htm
To provide financial assistance to students from any college who wish to participate in the off-campus programs in the United States or abroad sponsored by Drew University.
Title of Award: Drew University Off Campus Programs Scholarships **Area, Field, or Subject:** Art; British studies; English language and literature; European studies; General studies/Field of study not specified; Performing arts; Political science **Level of Education for which Award is Granted:** Undergraduate **Number Awarded:** Varies each year. **Funds Available:** Grants up to $3,000 per semester are available to be applied to the cost of the programs. **Duration:** 1 semester.
Eligibility Requirements: Students from any American college or university who have been accepted to participate in 1 of the off-campus programs sponsored by Drew University may apply for financial aid if the university's financial aid office determines that they meet the standards of financial need. Applicants for semester programs must be entering their junior or senior year and have a GPA of 2.7 or higher. **Deadline for Receipt:** April of each year for the fall semester; November of each year for the spring semester. **Additional Information:** The programs available recently included a Washington semester on American politics, a semester on the United Nations in New York, a New York semester on contemporary art and culture, a semester on the new Europe, a program in Eritrea on developing countries, and a London semester on British politics, history, drama, or literature.

1918 ■ LUSO-AMERICAN EDUCATION FOUNDATION

Attn: Administrative Director
7080 Donlon Way, Suite 202
P.O. Box 2967
Dublin, CA 94568
Tel: (925)828-3883
Fax: (925)828-3883
Web Site: http://www.luso-american.org/laef
To provide financial assistance for undergraduate study in Portuguese language to students in California.
Title of Award: Herbert Fernandes Scholarship **Area, Field, or Subject:** Foreign languages; Portuguese studies **Level of Education for which Award is Granted:** Four Year College **Number Awarded:** 1 each year. **Funds Available:** The stipend is $1,000. **Duration:** 1 year; renewable.
Eligibility Requirements: This program is open to students of Portuguese descent who are sophomores, juniors, or seniors at 4-year colleges or universities with a GPA of 3.5 or higher. Applicants must be California residents who are interested or involved in the Luso-American community and have taken or will enroll in Portuguese language classes. Selection is based on promise of success in college, financial need, qualities of leadership, vocational promise, and sincerity of purpose. **Deadline for Receipt:** February of each year.

1919 ■ ST. ANDREW'S SOCIETY OF WASHINGTON, D.C.

Charity and Education Fund Scholarship Committee
Attn: T.J. Holland, Chair
1443 Laurel Hill Road
Vienna, VA 22182-1711
E-mail: tjholland@bfsfcu.org
Web Site: http://www.accessenter.com/saintandrews/scholarships.htm
To provide financial assistance for college or graduate school to students in Scotland and to U.S. students of Scottish descent.
Title of Award: St. Andrew's Society of Washington Scholarships **Area, Field, or Subject:** General studies/Field of study not specified; Scottish studies **Level of Education for which Award is Granted:** Four Year College, Graduate **Number Awarded:** Varies each year; recently, 10 of these scholarships were awarded. **Funds Available:** The amounts of the awards depend on the availability of funds. Recently, stipends averaged approximately $1,500. **Duration:** 1 year.
Eligibility Requirements: This program is open to 1) U.S. citizens who reside in the mid-Atlantic region (defined as the District of Columbia and the states of Delaware, Maryland, New Jersey, North Carolina, Pennsylvania, Virginia, and West Virginia); and 2) British subjects who were born in Scotland. Applicants must be enrolled full time as a junior, senior, or graduate student at a college or university in the United States or Scotland. The proposed course of study must contribute to their intellectual development and economic independence. Special attention is given to applicants whose study relates to Scottish history or culture. They must be able to demonstrate their Scottish descent and must submit a statement of their plans and goals. Financial need is considered in the selection process. **Deadline for Receipt:** April of each year.

1920 ■ SWEDISH WOMEN'S EDUCATION ASSOCIATION INTERNATIONAL-SOUTH FLORIDA CHAPTER

c/o Yerti Nelson, Scholarship Committee
3759 Mykonos Court
Boca Raton, FL 33486
Tel: (561)997-2050
Fax: (561)997-8010
E-mail: florida@swea.org
Web Site: http://www.chapters-swea.org/florida
To provide financial assistance to Florida residents interested in studying in Sweden or an area related to Swedish studies.
Title of Award: South Florida SWEA Scholarship **Area, Field, or Subject:** Art; Art industries and trade; Crafts; Design; Environmental conservation; Environmental science; Foreign languages; General studies/Field of study not specified; Literature; Music; Swedish studies **Level of Education for which Award is Granted:** Graduate, Professional, Undergraduate **Number Awarded:** 1 each year. **Funds Available:** The stipend is $3,000.
Eligibility Requirements: This program is open to all residents of Florida interested in participating in an exchange program in Sweden. Applicants may also propose to study in the United States, if the studies specifically emphasize Sweden and Swedish aspects, including 1) Swedish language; 2) Swedish culture or traditions; 3) environmental science; 4) a health care program promoting better health for women and children; or 5) handicraft, art, glass art, music, literature, or design. Study proposals must be well-defined in time and content. Along with their application, they must submit a transcript from college, university, or vocational school; curriculum vitae; project proposal, describing the planned studies, length of studies, and goals; financial statement; and letter of recommendation from an instructor. **Deadline for Receipt:** January of each year. **Additional Information:** Within 3 months after the end of studies or the project, the recipient must report to the scholarship committee or, if possible, accept an invitation to an organization meeting to share the experience.

Jewish Studies

1921 ■ JEWISH FEDERATION OF DELAWARE

Attn: Jewish Fund for the Future
100 West Tenth Street, Suite 301
Wilmington, DE 19801-1628
Tel: (302)427-2100
Fax: (302)427-2438
E-mail: gina.kozicki@shalomdelaware.org
Web Site: http://www.shalomdelaware.org
To provide financial assistance to Jewish undergraduates from Delaware studying in Israel or Jewish studies in the United States and to Jewish students from outside the United States studying in Delaware.
Title of Award: Joseph and Marion Greenbaum Scholarship Fund **Area, Field, or Subject:** General studies/Field of study not specified; Jewish studies; Religion **Level of Education for which Award is Granted:** Undergraduate **Number Awarded:** Varies each year. **Funds Available:** The stipend is normally $2,500 per year for study in Israel; $625 per year for graduates of Gratz Hebrew High School; or $83 per credit for Jewish studies or for foreign students in Delaware. **Duration:** 1 year.
Eligibility Requirements: This program is open to (in order of priority) 1) Jewish residents of Delaware who wish to attend a college in Israel as an

undergraduate; 2) Jewish residents of Delaware who wish to major or minor in Jewish studies at a college or university in the United States; 3) graduates of Delaware Gratz Hebrew High School or other full-day Jewish high school in Delaware who are enrolled or planning to enroll in an undergraduate college program in the United States; and 4) Jewish students from Israel or other foreign country who wish to work on an undergraduate degree at a college or university in Delaware. Residents of adjacent communities (Elkton, Maryland or the Pennsylvania towns of Avondale, Chadds Ford, Kennett Square, Landenberg, Lincoln University, or Westchester) are also eligible. Applicants must submit a brief essay on what they have learned or hope to learn during the proposed course of study and what they hope to be able to carry with them throughout their lifetime as a result of the courses. Selection is based on the essay, GPA, references, volunteer and community activity, and information about the study program abroad or the courses the applicant plans to take. Financial need is considered only if there are more applicants than available funds or if the applicant is seeking funds beyond the amount of the current guideline award; lack of financial need does not disqualify any applicant. **Deadline for Receipt:** July of each year for study during the fall semester or winter session; November of each year for spring semester or summer session. **Additional Information:** Recipients are required to participate in either the United Jewish Communities Campus Campaign or the Jewish Federation of Delaware's annual campaign.

1922 ■ JEWISH FEDERATION OF GREATER HARTFORD, INC.

Attn: Endowment Foundation
333 Bloomfield Avenue
West Hartford, CT 06117
Tel: (860)523-7460
Fax: (860)231-0576
E-mail: grants@jcfhartford.org
Web Site: http://www.jcfhartford.org
To provide financial assistance for college to students in Connecticut interested in Jewish education.
Title of Award: Hebrew Ladies Sheltering Home Scholarships **Area, Field, or Subject:** Education, Religious; Jewish studies; Religion **Level of Education for which Award is Granted:** Undergraduate **Number Awarded:** 2 to 3 each year. **Funds Available:** The stipend is $1,000. **Duration:** 1 year.
Eligibility Requirements: This program is open to Jewish residents of Connecticut who are graduating high school seniors. Applicants must be interested in working on a degree in Jewish education. U.S. citizenship is required. Selection is based on academic record and financial need. **Deadline for Receipt:** April of each year.

1923 ■ MEMORIAL FOUNDATION FOR JEWISH CULTURE

50 Broadway, 34th Floor
New York, NY 10004
Tel: (212)425-6606
Fax: (212)425-6602
E-mail: office@mfjc.org
Web Site: http://www.mfjc.org
To assist well-qualified individuals to train for careers in a field related to Jewish community service.
Title of Award: International Scholarship Program for Community Service **Area, Field, or Subject:** Education; Jewish studies; Religion; Social work **Level of Education for which Award is Granted:** Graduate, Undergraduate **Funds Available:** The amount of the grant varies, depending on the country in which the student will be trained and other considerations. **Duration:** 1 year; may be renewed.
Eligibility Requirements: The scholarship is open to any individual, regardless of country of origin, who is presently receiving or plans to undertake training in his/her chosen field at a recognized yeshiva, teacher training seminary, school of social work, university, or other educational institution. Applicants must be interested in pursuing professional training for careers in Jewish education, Jewish social service, the rabbinate, or as religious functionaries (e.g., shohatim, mohalim) in Diaspora Jewish communities in need of such personnel. Students planning to serve in the United States, Canada, or Israel are not eligible. **Deadline for Receipt:** November of each year. **Additional Information:** Recipients must agree

to serve for at least 2 to 3 years in a Jewish-deprived Diaspora community where their skills are needed after completing their training.

Latin American Studies

1924 ■ LIBRARY OF CONGRESS

Attn: John W. Kluge Center
101 Independence Avenue, S.E.,
Washington, DC 20540-4860
Tel: (202)707-3302
Fax: (202)707-3595
E-mail: scholarly@loc.gov
Web Site: http://www.loc.gov/loc/kluge/kluge-kislak-short_term.html
To provide funding to scholars at all levels interested in conducting short-term research using the Jay Kislak Collection at the Library of Congress.
Title of Award: Kislak Short Term Fellowship Opportunities in American Studies **Area, Field, or Subject:** Latin American studies **Level of Education for which Award is Granted:** Graduate, Professional, Postdoctoral, Undergraduate **Number Awarded:** At least 2 each year. **Funds Available:** The stipend is $4,000 per month. **Duration:** Up to 4 months.
Eligibility Requirements: This program is open to scholars worldwide interested in conducting research at the Library of Congress. Applicants must be planning to use the Jay Kislak Collection for research related to the discovery, contact, and colonial periods in Florida, the Caribbean, and Mesoamerica. They may be independent scholars, undergraduate or graduate students, or college or university faculty. **Deadline for Receipt:** January or August of each year.

Near and Middle East Studies

1925 ■ NATIONAL SECURITY AGENCY

Attn: Office of Recruitment and Staffing (Roberts)
9800 Savage Road, Suite 6779
P.O. Box 1661, Suite 6779
Fort Meade, MD 20755-6779
Tel: (410)854-4725; (866)672-4473
Web Site: http://www.nsa.gov/careers/students_4.cfm
To provide financial assistance to college juniors interested in preparing for a career with the National Security Agency (NSA) as an intelligence analyst.
Title of Award: Pat Roberts Intelligence Scholars Program for Intelligence Analysts **Area, Field, or Subject:** Asian studies; Banking; Finance; Foreign languages; Geography; Information science and technology; International affairs and relations; Library and archival sciences; Near Eastern studies; South Asian studies; Telecommunications systems **Level of Education for which Award is Granted:** Four Year College **Number Awarded:** Varies each year. **Funds Available:** The stipend is $25,000 per year. After graduation, recipients have an employment obligation to NSA equal to 1.5 times the length of educational support provided. **Duration:** 1 year (the senior year of college).
Eligibility Requirements: This program is open to college juniors whose academic program includes 1 of the following areas of emphasis: 1) regional studies (Middle East or south, east, or central Asia); 2) topical studies (terrorism, proliferation or related sciences, international banking and finance, or telecommunications and information systems networks); or 3) disciplines (intelligence analysis, philosophy, or international relations; familiarity with foreign languages, particularly Arabic, Chinese, Dari, Farsi, Hindi, Korean, Pashto, Urdu, or a central Asian language is desirable; highly qualified applicants studying social network analysis, library science, or geographic information systems may also be considered). Applicants must be enrolled full time with a GPA of 3.0 or higher. Along with their application, they must submit a 1-page essay describing how the proposed program of study will improve their ability to analyze information and to think and write critically. U.S. citizenship and eligibility to obtain a high-level security clearance are required **Deadline for Receipt:** October of each year. **Additional Information:** After graduation, participants enter NSA's Intelligence Analysis Development Program as a full-time employee.

1926 ■ NATIONAL SECURITY AGENCY

Attn: Office of Recruitment and Staffing (Stokes)
9800 Savage Road, Suite 6779

P.O. Box 1661, Suite 6779
Fort Meade, MD 20755-6779
Tel: (410)854-4725; (866)672-4473
Web Site: http://www.nsa.gov/careers/students_4.cfm
To provide minority and other high school seniors and college sophomores with scholarship/loans and work experience at the National Security Agency (NSA).

Title of Award: Stokes Educational Scholarship Program **Area, Field, or Subject:** Asian studies; Computer and information sciences; Engineering, Computer; Engineering, Electrical; Finance; Foreign languages; International affairs and relations; Mathematics and mathematical sciences; Near Eastern studies; South Asian studies **Level of Education for which Award is Granted:** Undergraduate **Number Awarded:** Varies each year. **Funds Available:** Participants receive college tuition for up to 4 years, reimbursement for books and certain fees, a year-round salary, and a housing allowance and travel reimbursement during summer employment if the distance between the agency and school exceeds 75 miles. Following graduation, participants must work for the agency for 1 and a half times their length of study, usually 5 years. Students who leave agency employment earlier must repay the tuition cost. **Duration:** Up to 4 years, followed by employment at the agency for 5 years.

Eligibility Requirements: This program is open to graduating high school seniors, particularly minorities, who 1) are planning a college major in electrical or computer engineering, computer science, international affairs, international finance, mathematics, area studies (Middle East or south, east, or central Asia), foreign languages (recent language interests included Arabic, Chinese, Farsi, and Korean); 2) have minimum scores of 1600 on the SAT (1100 on critical reading and mathematics, 500 in writing) or 25 on the ACT; 3) have a GPA of 3.0 or higher; 4) are U.S. citizens; and 5) demonstrate leadership abilities. Also eligible are college sophomores who are U.S. citizens, have a GPA of 3.0 or higher, and are majoring in the eligible fields. Applicants must include a 1-page essay on why they want to have a career with the NSA. **Deadline for Receipt:** November of each year. **Additional Information:** Participants must attend classes full time and work at the agency during the summer in jobs tailored to their course of study. They must maintain at least a 3.0 GPA. This program, established in 1986, was formerly known as the National Security Agency Undergraduate Training Program.

1927 ■ U.S. AIR FORCE
Attn: Headquarters AFROTC/RRUE
Enlisted Commissioning Section
551 East Maxwell Boulevard
Maxwell AFB, AL 36112-5917
Tel: (334)953-2091; (866)423-7682
Fax: (334)953-6167
E-mail: enlisted@afrotc.com
Web Site: http://www.afoats.af.mil/AFROTC/EnlistedComm/AECP.asp
To allow selected enlisted Air Force personnel to earn a bachelor's degree in approved majors by providing financial assistance for full-time college study.

Title of Award: Airman Education and Commissioning Program **Area, Field, or Subject:** African studies; Asian studies; Computer and information sciences; Engineering; Foreign languages; Mathematics and mathematical sciences; Meteorology; Near Eastern studies; Nursing; Physics; Russian studies **Level of Education for which Award is Granted:** Undergraduate **Number Awarded:** Approximately 60 each year. **Funds Available:** While participating in this program, cadets remain on active duty in the Air Force and receive their regular salary and benefits. They also receive payment of tuition and fees up to $15,000 per year and an annual textbook allowance of $600. **Duration:** 1 to 3 years, until completion of a bachelor's degree.

Eligibility Requirements: Eligible to participate in this program are enlisted members of the Air Force who have been accepted at a university or college (or approved crosstown institution) that is associated with AFROTC and that offers an approved major. The majors currently supported are computer science, all ABET-accredited engineering fields (not engineering technology), foreign area studies (limited to Middle East, Africa, Asia, Russia/Eurasia), foreign languages (limited to Arabic, Armenian, Azeri, Chinese, French, Georgian, Hebrew, Hindi, Indonesian, Kazakh, Pashto, Persian Farsi, Russian, Swahili, and Turkish), mathematics, meteorology, nursing, and physics. Applicants must have completed at least 1 year of time-in-service and 1 year of time-on-station. They must

have scores on the Air Force Officer Qualifying Test of at least 15 on the verbal and 10 on the quantitative and be able to pass the Air Force ROTC Physical Fitness Test. Normally they should have completed at least 30 semester hours of college study with a GPA of 2.75 or higher. They must be younger than 31 years of age or otherwise able to be commissioned before they become 35 years of age. **Deadline for Receipt:** February of each year. **Additional Information:** While attending college, participants in this program attend ROTC classes at their college or university. Upon completing their degree, they are commissioned to serve in the Air Force in their area of specialization with an active-duty service commitment of at least 4 years. Further information is available from base education service officers or an Air Force ROTC unit. This program does not provide for undergraduate flying training.

South Asian Studies

1928 ■ NATIONAL SECURITY AGENCY
Attn: Office of Recruitment and Staffing (Roberts)
9800 Savage Road, Suite 6779
P.O. Box 1661, Suite 6779
Fort Meade, MD 20755-6779
Tel: (410)854-4725; (866)672-4473
Web Site: http://www.nsa.gov/careers/students_4.cfm
To provide financial assistance to college juniors interested in preparing for a career with the National Security Agency (NSA) as an intelligence analyst.

Title of Award: Pat Roberts Intelligence Scholars Program for Intelligence Analysts **Area, Field, or Subject:** Asian studies; Banking; Finance; Foreign languages; Geography; Information science and technology; International affairs and relations; Library and archival sciences; Near Eastern studies; South Asian studies; Telecommunications systems **Level of Education for which Award is Granted:** Four Year College **Number Awarded:** Varies each year. **Funds Available:** The stipend is $25,000 per year. After graduation, recipients have an employment obligation to NSA equal to 1.5 times the length of educational support provided. **Duration:** 1 year (the senior year of college).

Eligibility Requirements: This program is open to college juniors whose academic program includes 1 of the following areas of emphasis: 1) regional studies (Middle East or south, east, or central Asia); 2) topical studies (terrorism, proliferation or related sciences, international banking and finance, or telecommunications and information systems networks); or 3) disciplines (intelligence analysis, philosophy, or international relations; familiarity with foreign languages, particularly Arabic, Chinese, Dari, Farsi, Hindi, Korean, Pashto, Urdu, or a central Asian language is desirable; highly qualified applicants studying social network analysis, library science, or geographic information systems may also be considered). Applicants must be enrolled full time with a GPA of 3.0 or higher. Along with their application, they must submit a 1-page essay describing how the proposed program of study will improve their ability to analyze information and to think and write critically. U.S. citizenship and eligibility to obtain a high-level security clearance are required **Deadline for Receipt:** October of each year. **Additional Information:** After graduation, participants enter NSA's Intelligence Analysis Development Program as a full-time employee.

1929 ■ NATIONAL SECURITY AGENCY
Attn: Office of Recruitment and Staffing (Stokes)
9800 Savage Road, Suite 6779
P.O. Box 1661, Suite 6779
Fort Meade, MD 20755-6779
Tel: (410)854-4725; (866)672-4473
Web Site: http://www.nsa.gov/careers/students_4.cfm
To provide minority and other high school seniors and college sophomores with scholarship/loans and work experience at the National Security Agency (NSA).

Title of Award: Stokes Educational Scholarship Program **Area, Field, or Subject:** Asian studies; Computer and information sciences; Engineering, Computer; Engineering, Electrical; Finance; Foreign languages; International affairs and relations; Mathematics and mathematical sciences; Near Eastern studies; South Asian studies **Level of Education for which Award is Granted:** Undergraduate **Number Awarded:** Varies each year. **Funds Available:** Participants receive college tuition for up to 4 years, reimbursement for books and certain fees, a year-round salary, and a housing allowance and travel reimbursement during summer employment if the distance between the agency and school exceeds 75 miles. Following graduation, participants must work for the agency for 1 and a half times their length of study, usually 5 years. Students who leave agency employment earlier must repay the tuition cost. **Duration:** Up to 4 years, followed by employment at the agency for 5 years.

Eligibility Requirements: This program is open to graduating high school seniors, particularly minorities, who 1) are planning a college major in electrical or computer engineering, computer science, international affairs, international finance, mathematics, area studies (Middle East or south, east, or central Asia), foreign languages (recent language interests included Arabic, Chinese, Farsi, and Korean); 2) have minimum scores of 1600 on the SAT (1100 on critical reading and mathematics, 500 in writing) or 25 on the ACT; 3) have a GPA of 3.0 or higher; 4) are U.S. citizens; and 5) demonstrate leadership abilities. Also eligible are college sophomores who are U.S. citizens, have a GPA of 3.0 or higher, and are majoring in the eligible fields. Applicants must include a 1-page essay on why they want to have a career with the NSA. **Deadline for Receipt:** November of each year. **Additional Information:** Participants must attend classes full time and work at the agency during the summer in jobs tailored to their course of study. They must maintain at least a 3.0 GPA. This program, established in 1986, was formerly known as the National Security Agency Undergraduate Training Program.

Women's Studies

1930 ■ TEXAS FEDERATION OF BUSINESS AND PROFESSIONAL WOMEN'S FOUNDATION, INC.
Attn: TFBPW Foundation
803 Forest Ridge Drive, Suite 207
Bedford, TX 76022
Tel: (817)283-0862
Fax: (817)283-0872
E-mail: bpwtx@swbell.net
Web Site: http://www.bpwtx.org/foundation.asp
To provide financial assistance to women in Texas who are preparing to enter selected professions.
Title of Award: Hermine Dalkowitz Tobolowsky Scholarship **Area, Field, or Subject:** History; Law; Political science; Public administration; Women's studies **Level of Education for which Award is Granted:** Graduate, Undergraduate **Number Awarded:** 1 or more each year. **Funds Available:** A stipend is awarded (amount not specified). **Duration:** 1 year.
Eligibility Requirements: This program is open to women in Texas who are interested in attending school to prepare for a career in law, public service, government, political science, or women's history. Applicants must have completed at least 2 semesters of study at an accredited college or university in Texas, have a GPA of 3.0 or higher, and be U.S. citizens. Selection is based on academic achievement and financial need. **Deadline for Receipt:** April of each year. **Additional Information:** This program was established in 1995.

General

1931 ■ ASSOCIATION OF INDEPENDENT COLLEGES AND UNIVERSITIES OF PENNSYLVANIA
101 North Front Street
Harrisburg, PA 17101-1405
Tel: (717)232-8649
Fax: (717)233-8574
E-mail: info@aicup.org
Web Site: http://www.aicup.org
To provide financial assistance to women and minority students at member institutions of the Association of Independent Colleges and Universities of Pennsylvania (AICUP) who are majoring in designated fields of engineering.
Title of Award: Michael Baker Corporation Scholarship Program for Diversity in Engineering **Area, Field, or Subject:** Engineering, Architectural; Engineering, Civil; Environmental science **Level of Education for which Award is Granted:** Four Year College **Number Awarded:** 1 each year. **Funds Available:** The stipend is $1,000 per year. **Duration:** 1 year; may be renewed 1 additional year if the recipient maintains appropriate academic standards.
Eligibility Requirements: This program is open to full-time undergraduate students at designated AICUP colleges and universities who are women and/or members of the following minority groups: American Indians, Alaska Natives, Asians, Blacks/African Americans, Hispanics/Latinos, Native Hawaiians, or Pacific Islanders. Applicants must be juniors majoring in architectural, civil, or environmental engineering with a GPA of 3.0 or higher. Along with their application, they must submit an essay on what they believe will be the greatest challenge facing the engineering profession over the next decade, and why. **Deadline for Receipt:** April of each year. **Additional Information:** This program, sponsored by the Michael Baker Corporation, is available at the following AICUP colleges and universities: Bucknell University, Carnegie Mellon University, Drexel University, Gannon University, Geneva College, Grove City College, Lafayette College, Lehigh University, Messiah College, Swarthmore College, Villanova University, Widener University, and Wilkes University.

1932 ■ COMMUNITY FOUNDATION OF GREATER JACKSON
525 East Capitol Street, Suite 5B
Jackson, MS 39201
Tel: (601)974-6044
Fax: (601)974-6045
E-mail: info@cfgreaterjackson.org
Web Site: http://www.cfgreaterjackson.org
To provide financial assistance to undergraduate students in Mississippi who are preparing for a career in the field of public works.
Title of Award: APWA Scholarship Fund **Area, Field, or Subject:** Biological and clinical sciences; Chemistry; Engineering, Civil; Engineering, Electrical; Environmental science; Public administration **Level of Education for which Award is Granted:** Four Year College **Number Awarded:** 2 each year. **Funds Available:** The stipend is $1,000. **Duration:** 1 year.
Eligibility Requirements: This program is open to full-time juniors and seniors at public universities in Mississippi who are preparing to enter the field of public works. Applicants must have graduated from a high school

in Mississippi. Eligible majors include civil engineering, electrical engineering, environmental engineering, public administration, biology, or chemistry. Selection is based on merit and need. **Deadline for Receipt:** April of each year. **Additional Information:** This program, established in 2000, is sponsored by the Mississippi chapter of the American Public Works Association (APWA).

1933 ■ CONSULTING ENGINEERS AND LAND SURVEYORS OF CALIFORNIA
Attn: Communications Director
1303 J Street, Suite 450
Sacramento, CA 95814
Tel: (916)441-7991
Fax: (916)441-6312
E-mail: staff@celsoc.org
Web Site: http://www.celsoc.org
To provide financial assistance to students working on a graduate degree at an approved engineering program in California.
Title of Award: Consulting Engineers and Land Surveyors of California Graduate Scholarships **Area, Field, or Subject:** Engineering, Civil; Environmental science **Level of Education for which Award is Granted:** Four Year College, Graduate **Number Awarded:** Varies each year. Recently, 2 of these scholarships were awarded: 1 at $5,000 and 1 at $1,000. **Funds Available:** The stipend is $5,000 or $1,000. **Duration:** 1 year; recipients may reapply for 1 additional year.
Eligibility Requirements: This program is open to U.S. citizens who are working full time on a graduate degree in an ABET-approved civil engineering (including environmental, geotechnical, structural, transportation, etc.) program in California. Applicants must be entering or continuing a graduate program to qualify; students graduating this academic year are not eligible. They must have a GPA of 3.0 or higher; to be considered for some scholarships, they must have a GPA in engineering and land surveying courses of 3.5 or higher and an overall GPA of 3.2 or higher. Along with their application, they must submit an essay, approximately 500 words in length, on "What is a consulting engineer or land surveyor and why should you consider it as a career?" Selection is based on GPA (28 points); the essay (25 points); work experience (20 points); recommendations (17 points); and college activities (10 points). Financial need is not considered in the selection process. **Deadline for Receipt:** January of each year.

1934 ■ HANSCOM OFFICERS' WIVES' CLUB
Attn: Scholarship Chair
P.O. Box 557
Bedford, MA 01730
Tel: (781)275-1251
E-mail: scholarship@hanscomowd.org
Web Site: http://www.hanscomowc.org
To provide financial assistance to children of military personnel and veterans in New England who are interested in studying aviation in college.
Title of Award: Brian Sweeney Memorial Award **Area, Field, or Subject:** Aviation; Engineering, Aerospace/Aeronautical/Astronautical; Engineering, Civil; Environmental science; Meteorology; Protective services **Level of Education for which Award is Granted:** Undergraduate **Number**

Awarded: 1 each year. **Funds Available:** The stipend is $2,000. **Duration:** 1 year; nonrenewable.
Eligibility Requirements: This program is open to college-bound high school seniors living in New England who are dependents of active-duty, retired, or deceased military members of any branch of service. Also eligible are dependents of military recruiters working in the New York area and students living elsewhere but whose military sponsor is stationed at Hanscom Air Force Base. Applicants must demonstrate qualities of responsibility, leadership, scholastics, citizenship, and diversity of interest. They must have a valid military identification card and be planning to work on a college degree in a field related to aviation (including civil, aeronautical, and environmental engineering; maintenance; management; aviation safety and security; and meteorology). Along with their application, they must submit a 2-page essay on their educational goals, how their educational experience will help prepare them to pursue future goals, and how they intend to apply their education to better their community. **Deadline for Receipt:** March of each year. **Additional Information:** This program was established to honor a victim of an airplane crash on September 11, 2001. It is sponsored by the Paul Revere Chapter of the Air Force Association.

1935 ■ HISPANIC SCHOLARSHIP FUND INSTITUTE

1001 Connecticut Avenue, N.W., Suite 632
Washington, DC 20036
Tel: (202)296-0009
Fax: (202)296-3633
E-mail: info@hsfi.org
Web Site: http://www.hsfi.org/scholarships/energy.asp
To provide financial assistance to Hispanic undergraduate students majoring in designated business, engineering, and science fields related to the U.S. Department of Energy (DOE) goals of environmental restoration and waste management.
Title of Award: Environmental Management Scholarship **Area, Field, or Subject:** Business administration; Chemistry; Computer and information sciences; Engineering, Agricultural; Engineering, Civil; Engineering, Electrical; Engineering, Industrial; Engineering, Mechanical; Engineering, Metallurgical; Engineering, Petroleum; Environmental science; Epidemiology; Geology; Hydrology; Management; Mathematics and mathematical sciences; Physics; Radiology; Toxicology **Level of Education for which Award is Granted:** Undergraduate **Number Awarded:** Varies each year. **Funds Available:** The stipend is $3,000 per year for 4-year university students or $2,000 per year for community college students. **Duration:** 1 year.
Eligibility Requirements: This program is open to U.S. citizens and permanent residents of Hispanic background who have completed at least 12 undergraduate credits with a GPA of 3.0 or higher. Applicants must be interested in preparing for a career supportive of the DOE goals of environmental restoration and waste management. Eligible academic majors are in the fields of business (management and system analysis), engineering (agricultural, chemical, civil, electrical, environmental, industrial, mechanical, metallurgical, nuclear, and petroleum), and science (applied math/physics, chemistry, computer science, ecology, environmental, epidemiology, geology, health physics, hydrology, radiochemistry, radio-ecology, and toxicology). Along with their application, they must submit a 2-page essay on 1) how their academic major, interests, and career goals correspond to environmental restoration and waste management issues; and 2) how their Hispanic background and family upbringing have influenced their academic and personal goals. Selection is based on the essay, academic record, academic plans and career goals, financial need, commitment to DOE's goal of environmental restoration and waste management, and a letter of recommendation. **Deadline for Receipt:** March of each year. **Additional Information:** This program, which began in 1990, is sponsored by DOE's Office of Environmental Management. Recipients must enroll full time at a college or university in the United States.

1936 ■ HISPANIC SCHOLARSHIP FUND INSTITUTE

1001 Connecticut Avenue, N.W., Suite 632
Washington, DC 20036
Tel: (202)296-0009
Fax: (202)296-3633
E-mail: info@hsfi.org
Web Site: http://www.hsfi.org/scholarships/generation.asp

To provide financial assistance to Hispanic and other students majoring in designated business, engineering, social science, and science fields who are interested in employment with the U.S. Department of Energy (DOE).
Title of Award: Next Generation of Public Servants Scholarship **Area, Field, or Subject:** Accounting; Biological and clinical sciences; Business administration; Computer and information sciences; Engineering; Environmental science; Finance; Geology; Information science and technology; Management; Mathematics and mathematical sciences; Physics; Political science; Psychology; Sociology **Level of Education for which Award is Granted:** Undergraduate **Number Awarded:** Varies each year. **Funds Available:** The stipend is $3,000 per year. **Duration:** 1 year; may be renewed up to 2 additional years if the recipient maintains full-time enrollment and a GPA of 2.8 or higher.
Eligibility Requirements: This program is open to U.S. citizens enrolled full time as sophomores with a GPA of 2.8 or higher. Applicants must be interested in preparing for a career with the DOE in an energy-related field. Eligible academic majors are in the fields of business (accounting, business administration, finance, and management), engineering (biomedical, chemical, civil, computer, electrical, environmental, industrial, materials, mechanical, metallurgical, nuclear, and petroleum), social science (economics, organizational psychology, political science, and sociology), and science (biological sciences, computer science, geology, information technology, mathematics, microbiology, and physics). They must be willing to participate in co-ops with the DOE. Along with their application, they must submit a 2-page essay on why a career in public service interests them, how their academic major connects with their stated DOE career goal, why the DOE should invest in them through this program, and how they believe the DOE will benefit from this investment. Selection is based on academic achievement, financial need, demonstrated commitment to public service, and interest in federal employment with the DOE. **Deadline for Receipt:** February of each year. **Additional Information:** This program, sponsored by DOE's Office of Economic Impact and Diversity, is administered by the Hispanic Scholarship Fund Institute as part of its effort to increase Hispanic participation in federal service.

1937 ■ NEW ENGLAND WATER WORKS ASSOCIATION

125 Hopping Brook
Holliston, MA 01746
Tel: (508)893-7979
Fax: (508)893-9898
Web Site: http://www.newwa.org
To provide financial assistance to undergraduate or graduate students from New England interested in working on a degree in civil or environmental engineering or in business management.
Title of Award: Francis X. Crowley Scholarship **Area, Field, or Subject:** Business administration; Engineering, Civil; Environmental science; Management **Level of Education for which Award is Granted:** Graduate, Undergraduate **Funds Available:** The stipend is $3,000. **Duration:** 1 year.
Eligibility Requirements: This program is open to members and student members of the New England section of the American Water Works Association or the New England Water Works Association. Applicants must be high school seniors, currently-enrolled college students, or graduate students. They must be majoring or planning to major in civil or environmental engineering or in business management. Along with their application, they must submit a 100-word essay on why they have chosen their field of study and if it will improve the environment, public health, or the water industry. Financial need is also considered in the selection process. **Deadline for Receipt:** July of each year. **Additional Information:** Information is also available from Thomas J. MacElhaney, Scholarship Committee Chair, National Concrete Tanks, P.O. Box 1431, Concord, MA 01742, (617) 512-0203, Fax: (978) 418-9156, E-mail: Tmacelhaney@concretetank.com.

1938 ■ NEW ENGLAND WATER WORKS ASSOCIATION

125 Hopping Brook
Holliston, MA 01746
Tel: (508)893-7979
Fax: (508)893-9898
Web Site: http://www.newwa.org
To provide financial assistance to undergraduate or graduate students from New England interested in working on a degree in civil or environmental engineering.

Title of Award: Elson T. Killam Memorial Scholarship **Area, Field, or Subject:** Engineering, Civil; Environmental science **Level of Education for which Award is Granted:** Graduate, Undergraduate **Funds Available:** The stipend is $1,500. **Duration:** 1 year.

Eligibility Requirements: This program is open to members and student members of the New England section of the American Water Works Association or the New England Water Works Association. Applicants must be high school seniors, currently-enrolled college students, or graduate students. They must be majoring or planning to major in civil or environmental engineering. Along with their application, they must submit a 100-word essay on why they have chosen their field of study and if it will improve the environment, public health, or the water industry. Financial need is also considered in the selection process. **Deadline for Receipt:** July of each year. **Additional Information:** Information is also available from Thomas J. MacElhaney, Scholarship Committee Chair, National Concrete Tanks, P.O. Box 1431, Concord, MA 01742, (617) 512-0203, Fax: (978) 418-9156, E-mail: Tmacelhaney@concretetank.com.

1939 ■ NEW ENGLAND WATER WORKS ASSOCIATION

125 Hopping Brook
Holliston, MA 01746
Tel: (508)893-7979
Fax: (508)893-9898
Web Site: http://www.newwa.org
To provide financial assistance to undergraduate or graduate students from New England interested in working on a degree in civil or environmental engineering, business, or a related science field.

Title of Award: Joseph Murphy Scholarship **Area, Field, or Subject:** Business administration; Engineering, Civil; Environmental science; Science **Level of Education for which Award is Granted:** Graduate, Undergraduate **Funds Available:** The stipend is $1,500. **Duration:** 1 year.

Eligibility Requirements: This program is open to members and student members of the New England section of the American Water Works Association or the New England Water Works Association. Applicants must be high school seniors, currently-enrolled college students, or graduate students. They must be majoring or planning to major in civil or environmental engineering, business, or a related science field. Along with their application, they must submit a 100-word essay on why they have chosen their field of study and if it will improve the environment, public health, or the water industry. Financial need is also considered in the selection process. **Deadline for Receipt:** July of each year. **Additional Information:** Information is also available from Thomas J. MacElhaney, Scholarship Committee Chair, National Concrete Tanks, P.O. Box 1431, Concord, MA 01742, (617) 512-0203, Fax: (978) 418-9156, E-mail: Tmacelhaney@concretetank.com.

1940 ■ ROCKY MOUNTAIN COAL MINING INSTITUTE

Attn: Executive Director
8057 South Yukon Way
Littleton, CO 80128-5510
Tel: (303)948-3300
Fax: (303)948-1132
E-mail: mail@rmcmi.org
Web Site: http://www.rmcmi.org
To provide financial assistance to college students from Rocky Mountain states who are preparing for a career in the mining industry.

Title of Award: Rocky Mountain Coal Mining Institute Scholarships **Area, Field, or Subject:** Business; Engineering, Electrical; Engineering, Geological; Engineering, Mechanical; Engineering, Metallurgical; Engineering, Mining and Mineral; Environmental science; Geology; Metallurgy; Mining **Level of Education for which Award is Granted:** Four Year College **Number Awarded:** 8 each year (1 from each of the participating states). **Funds Available:** The stipend is $2,000 per year. Funds are disbursed to the recipient's institution to be used as a tuition credit. during the junior, senior, and/or fifth year of undergraduate study. **Duration:** 2 years; renewable, if the recipient continues in school as a full-time student in good academic standing.

Eligibility Requirements: This program is open to full-time sophomores or juniors in college who are U.S. citizens and residents of Arizona, Colorado, Montana, New Mexico, North Dakota, Texas, Utah, or Wyoming. Applicants must be working on a degree in engineering (e.g., electrical, environmental, geological, mechanical, metallurgical, mining) or

in a mining-related field (e.g., geology, mineral processing, metallurgy). They may be attending school in 1 of those states or another school approved by the sponsor (e.g., University of Missouri at Rolla, South Dakota School of Mines). Preference is given to students who are particularly interested in western coal as a career. Interviews are required. **Deadline for Receipt:** January of each year.

1941 ■ SIEMENS FOUNDATION

170 Wood Avenue South
Iselin, NJ 08830
877-822-5233
Fax: (732)603-5890
E-mail: foundation@sc.siemens.com
Web Site: http://www.siemens-foundation.org/scholarship
To recognize and reward outstanding high school seniors who have undertaken individual or team research projects in science, mathematics, and technology (or in combinations of those disciplines).

Title of Award: Siemens Westinghouse Competition Awards **Area, Field, or Subject:** Astronomy and astronomical sciences; Atmospheric science; Biochemistry; Biological and clinical sciences; Chemistry; Computer and information sciences; Earth sciences; Engineering, Civil; Engineering, Electrical; Engineering, Mechanical; Environmental science; Genetics; Geosciences; Materials research/science; Mathematics and mathematical sciences; Nutrition; Physics; Writing **Level of Education for which Award is Granted:** Undergraduate **Number Awarded:** In the initial round of judging, up to 300 regional semifinalists (up to 50 in each region) are selected. Of those, 60 are chosen as regional finalists (5 individuals and 5 teams in each of the 6 regions). Then 12 regional winners (1 individual and 1 team) are selected in the regional competitions, and they become the national finalists. **Funds Available:** At the regional level, finalists receive $1,000 scholarships, both as individuals and members of teams. Individual regional winners receive $3,000 scholarships. Winning regional teams receive $6,000 scholarships to be divided among the team members. Those regional winners then receive additional scholarships as national finalists. In the national competition. first-place winners receive an additional $100,000 scholarship, second place an additional $50,000 scholarship, third place an additional $40,000 scholarship, fourth place an additional $30,000 scholarship, fifth place an additional $20,000 scholarship, and sixth place an additional $10,000 scholarship. Those national awards are provided both to individuals and to teams to be divided equally among team members. Scholarship money is sent directly to the recipient's college or university to cover undergraduate and/or graduate educational expenses. Schools with regional finalists receive a $2,000 award to be used to support science, mathematics, and technology programs in their schools. **Duration:** The competition is held annually.

Eligibility Requirements: This program is open to high school seniors who are legal or permanent U.S. residents. They must be enrolled in a high school in the United States, Puerto Rico, Guam, Virgin Islands, American Samoa, Wake and Midway Islands, or the Marianas. U.S. high school students enrolled in a Department of Defense dependents school, an accredited overseas American or international school, a foreign school as an exchange student, or a foreign school because their parent(s) live and work abroad are also eligible. Students being home-schooled qualify if they obtain the endorsement of the school district official responsible for such programs. Research projects may be submitted in mathematics and the biological and physical sciences, or involve combinations of disciplines, such as astrophysics, biochemistry, bioengineering, biology, biophysics, botany, chemistry, computer science, civil engineering, earth and atmospheric science engineering, electrical engineering, environmental sciences, fluid dynamics, genetics, geology, materials science, mathematics, mechanical engineering, nutritional science, physics, toxicology, and virology. Both individual and team projects (2 or 3 members) may be entered. All team members must meet the eligibility requirements. Team projects may include seniors, but that is not a requirement. Competition entrants must submit a detailed report on their research project, including a description of the purpose of the research, rationale for the research, pertinent scientific literature, methodology, results, discussion, and conclusion. All projects must be endorsed by a sponsoring high school (except home-schooled students, who obtain their endorsement from the district or state home-school official). Each project must have a project advisor or mentor who is a member of the instructional staff or a person approved by the endorsing high school. There are 3 judging phases to the competition. An initial review panel selects outstanding research projects from 6 different regions of the country. The students submitting these projects are identified as regional semifinalists. Out of those, the highest-rated projects from each region are selected and the students who submitted them are recognized as regional finalists. For the next phase, the regional finalists are offered all-expense paid trips to the regional competition on the campus of a regional university partner, where their projects are reviewed by a panel of judges appointed by the host institution. Regional finalists are required to prepare a poster display of their research project, make an oral presentation about the research and research findings, and respond to questions from the judges. The top-rated individual and the top-rated team project in each region are selected as regional winners to represent the region in the national competition as national finalists. At that competition, the national finalists again display their projects, make oral presentations, and respond to judges' questions. At each phase, selection is based on clarity of expression, comprehensiveness, creativity, field knowledge, future work, interpretation, literature review, presentation, scientific importance, and validity. **Deadline for Receipt:** September of each year. **Additional Information:** The program is offered by Siemens Foundation, in partnership with the College Board. Information is available from the College Board at (703) 707-8999, E-mail: spro@collegeboard.org. Students submitting the projects with the highest evaluations become part of a registry that is circulated to colleges and universities nationwide. To continue receiving scholarships, winners must attend an accredited academic institution on a full-time basis.

1942 ■ SOCIETY OF AMERICAN MILITARY ENGINEERS-BOSTON POST

c/o John M. Gerstenlauer
Perini Corporation
73 Mt. Wayte Avenue
Framingham, MA 01701-9160
Tel: (508)628-2442
Fax: (508)628-2537
Web Site: http://www.sameboston.org
To provide financial assistance to residents of New England majoring in a college program related to construction.
Title of Award: Boston Post Scholarships **Area, Field, or Subject:** Architecture; Construction; Engineering; Engineering, Civil; Environmental science **Level of Education for which Award is Granted:** Undergraduate **Number Awarded:** Approximately 25 each year. **Funds Available:** The stipend is approximately $2,000 per year. **Duration:** 1 year.
Eligibility Requirements: This program is open to residents of New England who are currently enrolled in an accepted engineering or architecture program, preferably in civil engineering, environmental engineering, architecture, or other construction-related program. Applicants must have completed at least 1 academic year and have at least 1 year remaining. Preference is given to applicants enrolled in ROTC (preferably not a recipient of an ROTC scholarship) or interested in or having prior U.S. military service. U.S. citizenship is required. Interested students are invited to submit an application form, transcripts, documentation of financial need, and a personal letter describing their qualifications and needs. An interview is required. Selection is based on academic achievements, financial need, extracurricular activities, and the interview.
Deadline for Receipt: February of each year.

1943 ■ U.S. AIR FORCE

Attn: Headquarters AFROTC/RRUC
551 East Maxwell Boulevard
Maxwell AFB, AL 36112-5917
Tel: (334)953-2091; (866)423-7682
Fax: (334)953-6167
Web Site: http://www.afrotc.com/scholarships/incolschol/expressSchol.php
To provide financial assistance to students who are interested in joining Air Force ROTC and majoring in critical Air Force officer fields in college.
Title of Award: Air Force ROTC Express Scholarships **Area, Field, or Subject:** Atmospheric science; Engineering, Aerospace/Aeronautical/Astronautical; Engineering, Civil; Engineering, Computer; Engineering, Electrical; Engineering, Mechanical; Environmental science; Meteorology **Level of Education for which Award is Granted:** Undergraduate **Funds Available:** Awards are type 2 AFROTC scholarships that provide for payment of tuition and fees, to a maximum of $15,000 per year, plus an an-

nual book allowance of $600. All recipients are also awarded a tax-free monthly subsistence allowance that is $250 for freshmen, $300 for sophomores, $350 for juniors, and $400 for seniors. **Duration:** 3 and a half years, until completion of a bachelor's degree.
Eligibility Requirements: This program is open to U.S. citizens who are completing at least their first year of college and are working on a degree in fields that may change annually but are of critical interest to the Air Force. Applicants must have a GPA of 2.5 or higher and meet all other academic and physical requirements for participation in AFROTC. At the time of their Air Force commissioning, they may be no more than 31 years of age. They must be able to pass the Air Force Officer Qualifying Test (AFOQT) and the Air Force ROTC Physical Fitness Test. years as active-duty Air Force officers following graduation from college. **Additional Information:** Recently, freshmen were eligible if they were majoring in computer, electrical, or environmental engineering. Sophomores and juniors were eligible if they were majoring in those fields, meteorology and atmospheric sciences, or in the following engineering disciplines: aeronautical, aerospace, astronautical, civil, or mechanical. Recipients must also complete 4 years of aerospace studies courses at 1 of the 144 colleges and universities that have an Air Force ROTC unit on campus or 1 of the approximately 900 colleges that have cross-enrollment agreements with those institutions. They must also attend a 4-week summer training camp at an Air Force base, usually between their sophomore and junior years. Following completion of their bachelor's degree, scholarship recipients earn a commission as a second lieutenant in the Air Force and serve at least 4 years.

1944 ■ U.S. AIR FORCE

Attn: Headquarters AFROTC/RRUC
551 East Maxwell Boulevard
Maxwell AFB, AL 36112-5917
Tel: (334)953-2091; (866)423-7682
Fax: (334)953-6167
Web Site: http://www.afrotc.com/scholarships/hsschol/types.php
To provide financial assistance to high school seniors or graduates who are interested in joining Air Force ROTC in college and are willing to serve as Air Force officers following completion of their bachelor's degree.
Title of Award: Air Force ROTC High School Scholarships **Area, Field, or Subject:** Architecture; Chemistry; Computer and information sciences; Engineering, Aerospace/Aeronautical/Astronautical; Engineering, Architectural; Engineering, Civil; Engineering, Computer; Engineering, Electrical; Engineering, Mechanical; Environmental science; General studies/Field of study not specified; Mathematics and mathematical sciences; Meteorology; Operations research; Physics **Level of Education for which Award is Granted:** Four Year College **Number Awarded:** Approximately 2,000 each year. **Funds Available:** Type 1 scholarships provide payment of full tuition and most laboratory fees, as well as $600 for books. Type 2 scholarships pay the same benefits except tuition is capped at $15,000 per year; students who attend an institution where tuition exceeds $15,000 must pay the difference. Type 7 scholarships pay full tuition and most laboratory fees, but students must attend a college or university where the tuition is less than $9,000 per year or a public college or university where they qualify for the in-state tuition rate; they may not attend an institution with higher tuition and pay the difference. Approximately 5% of scholarship offers are for Type 1, approximately 20% are for Type 2, and approximately 75% for type 7. All recipients are also awarded a tax-free subsistence allowance for 10 months of each year that is $250 per month as a freshman, $300 per month as a sophomore, $350 per month as a junior, and $400 per month as a senior. **Duration:** 4 years.
Eligibility Requirements: This program is open to high school seniors who are U.S. citizens at least 17 of age and have been accepted at a college or university with an Air Force ROTC unit on campus or a college with a cross-enrollment agreement with such a college. Applicants must have a cumulative GPA of 3.0 or higher and an ACT composite score of 24 or higher or an SAT score of 1100 (mathematics and verbal portion only) or higher. At the time of their commissioning in the Air Force, they must be no more than 31 years of age. They must agree to serve for at least 4 years as active-duty Air Force officers following graduation from college. **Deadline for Receipt:** November of each year. **Additional Information:** Recently, approximately 70% of these scholarships were offered to students planning to major in the science and technical fields of architecture, chemistry, computer science, engineering (aeronautical,

aerospace, astronautical, architectural, civil, computer, electrical, environmental, or mechanical), mathematics, meteorology and atmospheric sciences, operations research, or physics. Approximately 30% were offered to students in all other fields. While scholarship recipients can major in any subject, they must enroll in 4 years of aerospace studies courses at 1 of the 144 colleges and universities that have an Air Force ROTC unit on campus; students may also attend nearly 900 other colleges that have cross-enrollment agreements with the institutions that have an Air Force ROTC unit on campus. Recipients must attend a 4-week summer training camp at an Air Force base, usually between their sophomore and junior years. Most cadets incur a 4-year active-duty commitment. Pilots incur a 10-year active-duty service commitment after successfully completing Specialized Undergraduate Pilot Training and navigators incur a 6-year commitment after successfully completing Specialized Undergraduate Navigator Training. The minimum service obligation for intelligence and Air Battle Management career fields is 5 years.

1945 ■ U.S. AIR FORCE

Attn: Headquarters AFROTC/RRUC
551 East Maxwell Boulevard
Maxwell AFB, AL 36112-5917
Tel: (334)953-2091; (866)423-7682
Fax: (334)953-6167
Web Site: http://www.afrotc.com/scholarships/incolschol/incolProgram.php
To provide financial assistance to undergraduate students who are willing to join Air Force ROTC in college and serve as Air Force officers following completion of their bachelor's degree.

Title of Award: Air Force ROTC In-College Scholarship Program **Area, Field, or Subject:** Architecture; Chemistry; Computer and information sciences; Engineering; Engineering, Aerospace/Aeronautical/Astronautical; Engineering, Architectural; Engineering, Civil; Engineering, Computer; Engineering, Electrical; Engineering, Mechanical; Environmental science; General studies/Field of study not specified; Mathematics and mathematical sciences; Meteorology; Operations research; Physics **Level of Education for which Award is Granted:** Undergraduate **Number Awarded:** Varies each year. **Funds Available:** Cadets selected in Phase 1 are awarded type 2 AFROTC scholarships that provide for payment of tuition and fees, to a maximum of $15,000 per year. A limited number of cadets selected in Phase 2 are also awarded type 2 AFROTC scholarships, but most are awarded type 3 AFROTC scholarships with tuition capped at $9,000 per year. Cadets selected in Phase 3 are awarded type 6 AFROTC scholarships with tuition capped at $3,000 per year. All recipients are also awarded a book allowance of $600 and a tax-free subsistence allowance for 10 months of each year that is $300 per month during the sophomore year, $350 during the junior year, and $400 during the senior year. **Duration:** 3 years for students selected as freshmen or 2 years for students selected as sophomores.
Eligibility Requirements: This program is open to U.S. citizens enrolled as freshmen or sophomores at 1 of the 144 colleges and universities that have an Air Force ROTC unit on campus. Applicants must have a cumulative GPA of 2.5 or higher and be able to pass the Air Force Officer Qualifying Test and the Air Force ROTC Physical Fitness Test. At the time of commissioning, they may be no more than 31 years of age. They must agree to serve for at least 4 years as active-duty Air Force officers following graduation from college. Phase 1 is open to students enrolled in the Air Force ROTC program who do not currently have a scholarship but now wish to apply. Phase 2 is open to Phase 1 nonselects and students not enrolled in Air Force ROTC. Phase 3 is open only to Phase 2 nonselects. Recently, the program gave preference to students majoring in the science and technical fields of architecture, chemistry, computer science, engineering (aeronautical, aerospace, astronautical, architectural, civil, computer, electrical, environmental, or mechanical), mathematics, meteorology and atmospheric sciences, operations research, or physics. **Deadline for Receipt:** January of each year. **Additional Information:** While scholarship recipients can major in any subject, they must complete 4 years of aerospace studies courses at 1 of the 144 colleges or universities that have an Air Force ROTC unit on campus. Recipients must also attend a 4-week summer training camp at an Air Force base, usually between their sophomore and junior years; 2-year scholarship awardees attend in the summer after their junior year. Current military personnel are eligible for early release from active duty in order to enter the Air Force

ROTC program. Following completion of their bachelor's degree, scholarship recipients earn a commission as a second lieutenant in the Air Force and serve at least 4 years.

1946 ■ U.S. AIR FORCE

Attn: Headquarters AFROTC/RRUE
Enlisted Commissioning Section
551 East Maxwell Boulevard
Maxwell AFB, AL 36112-5917
Tel: (334)953-2091; (866)423-7682
Fax: (334)953-6167
E-mail: enlisted@afrotc.com
Web Site: http://www.afoats.af.mil/AFROTC/EnlistedComm/ASCP.asp
To allow selected enlisted Air Force personnel to earn a bachelor's degree in approved majors by providing financial assistance for full-time college study.

Title of Award: Airman Scholarship and Commissioning Program **Area, Field, or Subject:** Architecture; Atmospheric science; Chemistry; Computer and information sciences; Engineering; Engineering, Aerospace/Aeronautical/Astronautical; Engineering, Architectural; Engineering, Civil; Engineering, Computer; Engineering, Electrical; Engineering, Mechanical; Environmental science; General studies/Field of study not specified; Mathematics and mathematical sciences; Meteorology; Operations research; Physics **Level of Education for which Award is Granted:** Undergraduate **Number Awarded:** Varies each year. **Funds Available:** Awards are type 2 AFROTC scholarships that provide for payment of tuition and fees, to a maximum of $15,000 per year, plus an annual book allowance of $600. All recipients are also awarded a tax-free subsistence allowance for 10 months of each year that is $300 per month during their sophomore year, $350 during their junior year, and $400 during their senior year. **Duration:** 2 to 4 years, until completion of a bachelor's degree.
Eligibility Requirements: This program is open to active-duty enlisted members of the Air Force who have completed at least 1 year of continuous active duty and at least 1 year on station. Applicants normally must have completed at least 24 semester hours of graded college credit with a cumulative college GPA of 2.5 or higher. If they have not completed 24 hours of graded college credit, they must have an ACT score of 24 or higher or an SAT combined verbal and mathematics score of 1100 or higher. They must also have scores on the Air Force Officer Qualifying Test (AFOQT) of 15 or more on the verbal scale and 10 or more on the quantitative scale and be able to pass the Air Force ROTC Physical Fitness Test. Applicants must have been accepted at a college or university (including crosstown schools) offering the AFROTC 4-year program. When they complete the program and receive their commission, they may not be 31 years of age or older. U.S. citizenship is required. Recently, awards were presented according to the following priorities: 1) computer, electrical, and environmental engineering; 2) aeronautical, aerospace, architectural, astronautical, civil, and mechanical engineering and meteorology and atmospheric sciences; 3) all other ABET-accredited engineering majors, architecture, chemistry, computer science, mathematics, operations research, and physics; 4) all other majors. **Deadline for Receipt:** October of each year. **Additional Information:** Selectees separate from the active-duty Air Force, join an AFROTC detachment, and become full-time students. Upon completing their degree, they are commissioned as officers and returned to active duty in the Air Force with a 4-year service obligation. Further information is available from base education service officers or an Air Force ROTC unit.

1947 ■ U.S. AIR FORCE

Attn: Headquarters AFROTC/RRUE
Enlisted Commissioning Section
551 East Maxwell Boulevard
Maxwell AFB, AL 36112-5917
Tel: (334)953-2091; (866)423-7682
Fax: (334)953-6167
E-mail: enlisted@afrotc.com
Web Site: http://www.afoats.af.mil/AFROTC/EnlistedComm/POC-ERP.asp
To allow selected enlisted Air Force personnel to earn a baccalaureate degree by providing financial assistance for full-time college study.
Title of Award: Professional Officer Course Early Release Program **Area, Field, or Subject:** Architecture; Atmospheric science; Chemistry;

Computer and information sciences; Engineering; Engineering, Aerospace/Aeronautical/Astronautical; Engineering, Architectural; Engineering, Civil; Engineering, Computer; Engineering, Electrical; Engineering, Mechanical; Environmental science; General studies/Field of study not specified; Mathematics and mathematical sciences; Meteorology; Operations research; Physics **Level of Education for which Award is Granted:** Undergraduate **Number Awarded:** Varies each year. **Funds Available:** Participants receive a stipend for 10 months of the year that is $350 per month during the first year and $400 per month during the second year. Scholarship recipients earn the Professional Officer Course Incentive of $3,000 per year for tuition and $600 per year for books. **Duration:** 2 years (no more and no less).

Eligibility Requirements: Eligible to participate in this program are enlisted members of the Air Force under the age of 30 (or otherwise able to be commissioned before becoming 35 years of age) who have completed at least 1 year on continuous active duty, have served on station for at least 1 year, and have no more than 2 years remaining to complete their initial baccalaureate degree. Scholarship applicants must be younger than 31 years of age when they graduate and earn their commission. All applicants must have been accepted at a college or university offering the AFROTC 4-year program and must have a cumulative college GPA of 2.5 or higher. Their Air Force Officer Qualifying Test (AFOQT) scores must be at least 15 on the verbal and 10 on the quantitative. Applicants who have not completed 24 units of college work must have an ACT composite score of 24 or higher or an SAT combined verbal and mathematics score of 1100 or higher. U.S. citizenship is required. Recently, awards were presented according to the following priorities: 1) computer, electrical, and environmental engineering; 2) aeronautical, aerospace, architectural, astronautical, civil, and mechanical engineering and meteorology and atmospheric sciences; 3) all other ABET-accredited engineering majors, architecture, chemistry, computer science, mathematics, operations research, and physics; 4) all other majors. **Deadline for Receipt:** October of each year. **Additional Information:** Upon completing their degree, selectees are commissioned as officers in the Air Force with a 4-year service obligation. Further information is available from base education service officers or an Air Force ROTC unit.

Conservation

1948 ■ AIR & WASTE MANAGEMENT ASSOCIATION-CONNECTICUT CHAPTER

Attn: Ray Yarmac, Secretary
Sci-Tech, Inc.
185 Silas Deane Highway
Wethersfield, CT 06109
Tel: (860)257-0767
E-mail: ryarmac@sce-techinc.com
Web Site: http://www.awma-nes.org/connecticut_chapter.htm
To provide financial assistance to residents of Connecticut who are interested in studying fields related to air and waste management in college.

Title of Award: Connecticut Chapter Scholarship **Area, Field, or Subject:** Air pollution; Engineering; Environmental conservation; Environmental science; Science **Level of Education for which Award is Granted:** Undergraduate **Number Awarded:** 1 each year. **Funds Available:** The stipend is $1,000. **Duration:** 1 year; recipients may reapply.

Eligibility Requirements: This program is open to 1) seniors graduating from high schools in Connecticut who plan to enroll full time in college, and 2) Connecticut residents already enrolled full time in college. Applicants must be interested in working on a degree in science or engineering leading to careers in the environmental field, especially air pollution control or waste management. Selection is based on their proposed plan of study, transcripts, work experience, and volunteer and extracurricular activities; financial need is not considered. **Deadline for Receipt:** April of each year.

1949 ■ ALABAMA SPACE GRANT CONSORTIUM

c/o University of Alabama in Huntsville
Materials Science Building, Room 205
Huntsville, AL 35899
Tel: (256)824-6800

Fax: (256)824-6061
E-mail: reasonj@uah.edu
Web Site: http://www.uah.edu/ASGC
To provide financial assistance to undergraduate students at universities participating in the Alabama Space Grant Consortium who wish to prepare for a career as a teacher of science or mathematics.

Title of Award: Teacher Education Scholarship Program of the Alabama Space Grant Consortium **Area, Field, or Subject:** Aerospace sciences; Earth sciences; Education; Environmental conservation; Environmental science; Geosciences; Mathematics and mathematical sciences; Science; Space and planetary sciences **Level of Education for which Award is Granted:** Undergraduate **Number Awarded:** Varies each year; recently, 10 of these scholarships were awarded. **Funds Available:** The stipend is $1,000 per year. **Duration:** 1 year; nonrenewable.

Eligibility Requirements: This program is open to students enrolled in or accepted for enrollment as full-time undergraduates at universities in Alabama participating in the consortium. Applicants must intend to enter the teacher certification program and teach in a pre-college setting. Priority is given to those majoring in science, mathematics, or earth/space/environmental science. Applicants should have a GPA of 3.0 or higher and must be U.S. citizens. Members of underrepresented groups in science and mathematics (minorities and women) are especially encouraged to apply. Along with their application, they must submit a 1- to 2-page statement on the reasons for their desire to enter the teaching profession, specifically the fields of science or mathematics education. **Deadline for Receipt:** February of each year. **Additional Information:** The member universities are University of Alabama in Huntsville, Alabama A&M University, University of Alabama, University of Alabama at Birmingham, University of South Alabama, Tuskegee University, and Auburn University. Funding for this program is provided by NASA.

1950 ■ AMERICAN CHEMICAL SOCIETY

Attn: Department of Diversity Programs
1155 16th Street, N.W.
Washington, DC 20036
Tel: (202)872-6250
Free: 800-227-5558
Fax: (202)776-8003
E-mail: scholars@acs.org
Web Site: http://www.chemistry.org/scholars
To provide financial assistance to underrepresented minority students with a strong interest in chemistry and a desire to prepare for a career in a chemically-related science.

Title of Award: American Chemical Society Scholars Program **Area, Field, or Subject:** Biochemistry; Chemistry; Engineering, Chemical; Environmental conservation; Environmental science; Materials research/science; Toxicology **Level of Education for which Award is Granted:** Undergraduate **Number Awarded:** Approximately 100 new awards are granted each year. **Funds Available:** The maximum stipend is $2,500 for the freshman year in college or $3,000 per year for sophomores, juniors, and seniors. **Duration:** 1 year; may be renewed.

Eligibility Requirements: This program is open to 1) college-bound high school seniors; 2) college freshmen, sophomores, and juniors enrolled full time at an accredited college or university; 3) community college graduates and transfer students who plan to study for a bachelor's degree; and 4) community college freshmen. Applicants must be African American, Hispanic/Latino, or American Indian. They must be majoring or planning to major in chemistry, biochemistry, chemical engineering, or other chemically-related fields, such as environmental science, materials science, or toxicology, and planning to prepare for a career in the chemical sciences or chemical technology. Students planning careers in medicine or pharmacy are not eligible. U.S. citizenship or permanent resident status is required. Selection is based on academic merit (GPA of 3.0 or higher) and financial need. **Deadline for Receipt:** February of each year. **Additional Information:** This program was established in 1994.

1951 ■ AMERICAN INDIAN SCIENCE AND ENGINEERING SOCIETY

Attn: Scholarship Coordinator
2305 Renard, S.E., Suite 200
P.O. Box 9828
Albuquerque, NM 87119-9828
Tel: (505)765-1052
Fax: (505)765-5608

E-mail: shirley@aises.org

Web Site: http://www.aises.org/highered/scholarships

To provide financial assistance and summer work experience to members of the American Indian Science and Engineering Society (AISES) who are working on an undergraduate degree in engineering or science related to water resources or environmental fields.

Title of Award: Henry Rodriguez Reclamation Scholarship **Area, Field, or Subject:** Engineering; Environmental conservation; Environmental science; Science; Water resources **Level of Education for which Award is Granted:** Undergraduate **Funds Available:** The stipend is $5,000 per year. **Duration:** 1 year; may be renewed up to 3 additional years.

Eligibility Requirements: This program is open to AISES members who are full-time undergraduate students in engineering or science related to water resources or environmental fields. Applicants must have a GPA of 2.5 or higher and be U.S. citizens or permanent residents. Non-Indians may apply, but all applicants must submit an essay on their first-hand knowledge of Indian tribal culture, their interest in engineering or environmental studies, how that interest relates to water resource issues and needs and concerns of Indian tribes, and how they will contribute their knowledge or professional experience to a Native American community. **Deadline for Receipt:** June of each year. **Additional Information:** This program, established in 2001, is funded by the U.S. Bureau of Reclamation and the National Water Research Institute and administered by AISES. Recipients must agree to serve an 8- to 10-week paid internship with the Bureau during the summer at a regional or area office located within the 17 western states served by the Bureau, at its Washington, D.C. headquarters, or at its Denver Technical Service Center.

1952 ■ AMERICAN NUCLEAR SOCIETY

Attn: Scholarship Coordinator

555 North Kensington Avenue

La Grange Park, IL 60526-5592

Tel: (708)352-6611

Fax: (708)352-0499

E-mail: outreach@ans.org

Web Site: http://www.ans.org/honors/scholarships

To provide financial assistance to undergraduate students who are working on a degree in engineering or science that is associated with decommissioning, decontamination, or environmental restoration aspects of nuclear power.

Title of Award: Decommissioning, Decontamination and Reutilization Scholarship **Area, Field, or Subject:** Engineering, Nuclear; Environmental conservation; Environmental science; Nuclear science **Level of Education for which Award is Granted:** Four Year College **Number Awarded:** 1 each year. **Funds Available:** The stipend is $2,000. **Duration:** 1 year; nonrenewable

Eligibility Requirements: This program is open to students entering their junior or senior year in an engineering or science program at an accredited institution in the United States. The program must be associated with 1) decommissioning or decontamination of nuclear facilities; 2) management or characterization of nuclear waste; or 3) restoration of the environment. Applicants must be U.S. citizens and able to demonstrate academic achievement. Along with their application, they must submit a brief essay discussing the importance of an aspect of decommissioning, decontamination, and reutilization to the future of the nuclear field. **Deadline for Receipt:** January of each year. **Additional Information:** This program is offered by the Decommissioning, Decontamination and Reutilization (DD&R) Division of the ANS. Recipients must agree to join the ANS and designate the DD&R Division as 1 of their professional divisions. They must commit to participating in DD&R Division activities by attending the annual and winter meetings of the ANS and serving as a student representative at the DD&R executive committee meetings at both ANS meetings.

1953 ■ AMERICAN NUCLEAR SOCIETY

Attn: Scholarship Coordinator

555 North Kensington Avenue

La Grange Park, IL 60526-5592

Tel: (708)352-6611

Fax: (708)352-0499

E-mail: outreach@ans.org

Web Site: http://www.ans.org/honors/scholarships

To provide financial assistance to upper-division students who are interested in preparing for a career dealing with the environmental aspects of nuclear science or nuclear engineering.

Title of Award: Charles (Tommy) Thomas Memorial Scholarship **Area, Field, or Subject:** Engineering, Nuclear; Environmental conservation; Environmental science; Nuclear science **Level of Education for which Award is Granted:** Four Year College **Number Awarded:** 1 each year. **Funds Available:** The stipend is $2,000. **Duration:** 1 year; nonrenewable.

Eligibility Requirements: This program is open to students entering their junior or senior year in nuclear science, nuclear engineering, or a nuclear-related field at an accredited institution in the United States. Applicants must be interested in preparing for a career dealing with the environmental aspects of nuclear science or nuclear engineering. They must be U.S. citizens or permanent residents and able to demonstrate academic achievement. **Deadline for Receipt:** January of each year. **Additional Information:** This program is offered by the Environmental Sciences Division of the ANS. It was formerly known as the Environmental Sciences Division Scholarship.

1954 ■ AMERICAN PLANNING ASSOCIATION

Attn: Planning and the Black Community Division

122 South Michigan Avenue, Suite 1600

Chicago, IL 60603-6107

Tel: (312)431-9100

Fax: (312)431-9985

E-mail: info_pbcd@planning.org

Web Site: http://www.planning.org/blackcommunity/scholarship.htm

To provide financial assistance to African American undergraduate students interested in majoring in planning or a related field.

Title of Award: Planning and the Black Community Division Scholarship **Area, Field, or Subject:** Environmental conservation; Environmental science; Geography; Public administration; Transportation; Urban affairs/design/planning **Level of Education for which Award is Granted:** Four Year College **Number Awarded:** 1 each year. **Funds Available:** The stipend is $2,500. **Duration:** 1 year.

Eligibility Requirements: This program is open to full-time African American undergraduate students entering their junior or senior year. Applicants must be majoring in planning or a related field (e.g., geography, environmental sciences, public administration, transportation, or urban studies) with a GPA of 3.0 or higher. They must submit a 2-page personal statement on the importance of urban planning to the African American community and how they see themselves making a contribution to the urban planning profession. U.S. citizenship is required. **Deadline for Receipt:** October of each year. **Additional Information:** Information is also available from Sigmund Shipp, Hunter College, Department of Urban Affairs and Planning, 695 Park Avenue, New York, NY 10021.

1955 ■ AMERICAN SOCIETY OF SAFETY ENGINEERS

Attn: ASSE Foundation

1800 East Oakton Street

Des Plaines, IL 60018

Tel: (847)768-3441

Fax: (847)296-9220

E-mail: mrosario@asse.org

Web Site: http://www.asse.org

To provide financial assistance to undergraduate student members of the American Society of Safety Engineers (ASSE).

Title of Award: America Responds Memorial Scholarship **Area, Field, or Subject:** Engineering; Environmental conservation; Environmental science; Fires and fire prevention; Industrial hygiene; Occupational safety and health; Protective services **Level of Education for which Award is Granted:** Four Year College **Number Awarded:** 1 each year. **Funds Available:** The stipend is $1,000 per year. **Duration:** 1 year; nonrenewable.

Eligibility Requirements: This program is open to ASSE student members who are majoring in occupational safety and health or a closely-related field (e.g., safety engineering, safety management, systems safety, environmental science, industrial hygiene, ergonomics, fire science). Applicants must be full-time students who have completed at least 60 semester hours with a GPA of 3.0 or higher. As part of the selection process, they must submit 2 essays of 300 words or less: 1) why they are seeking a degree in safety, a brief description of their current activities, and how those relate to their career goals and objectives; and 2) why they should be awarded this scholarship (including career goals and financial need). **Deadline for Receipt:** November of each year.

1956 ■ AMERICAN SOCIETY OF SAFETY ENGINEERS

Attn: ASSE Foundation
1800 East Oakton Street
Des Plaines, IL 60018
Tel: (847)768-3441
Fax: (847)296-9220
E-mail: mrosario@asse.org
Web Site: http://www.asse.org
To provide financial assistance to undergraduate student members of the American Society of Safety Engineers (ASSE), particularly those interested in construction safety.
Title of Award: Bechtel Foundation Scholarship for Safety and Health **Area, Field, or Subject:** Construction; Engineering; Environmental conservation; Environmental science; Fires and fire prevention; Industrial hygiene; Occupational safety and health; Protective services **Level of Education for which Award is Granted:** Four Year College **Number Awarded:** 1 each year. **Funds Available:** The stipend is $3,000 per year. **Duration:** 1 year; nonrenewable.
Eligibility Requirements: This program is open to ASSE student members who are majoring in occupational safety and health or a closely-related field (e.g., safety engineering, safety management, systems safety, environmental science, industrial hygiene, ergonomics, fire science) with an emphasis on construction safety. Applicants must be full-time students who have completed at least 60 semester hours with a GPA of 3.0 or higher. As part of the selection process, they must submit 2 essays of 300 words or less: 1) why they are seeking a degree in safety, a brief description of their current activities, and how those relate to their career goals and objectives; and 2) why they should be awarded this scholarship (including career goals and financial need). **Deadline for Receipt:** November of each year. **Additional Information:** Funding for this program is provided by Bechtel Foundation.

1957 ■ AMERICAN SOCIETY OF SAFETY ENGINEERS

Attn: ASSE Foundation
1800 East Oakton Street
Des Plaines, IL 60018
Tel: (847)768-3441
Fax: (847)296-9220
E-mail: mrosario@asse.org
Web Site: http://www.asse.org
To provide financial assistance to undergraduate and graduate student members of the American Society of Safety Engineers (ASSE) from designated western states.
Title of Award: Scott Dominguez-Craters of the Moon Chapter Scholarship **Area, Field, or Subject:** Engineering; Environmental conservation; Environmental science; Fires and fire prevention; Industrial hygiene; Occupational safety and health; Protective services **Level of Education for which Award is Granted:** Four Year College, Graduate **Number Awarded:** 1 each year. **Funds Available:** The stipend is $1,000 per year. **Duration:** 1 year; nonrenewable.
Eligibility Requirements: This program is open to ASSE student members who are majoring in occupational safety and health or a closely-related field (e.g., safety engineering, safety management, systems safety, environmental science, industrial hygiene, ergonomics, fire science). First priority is given to residents within the service area of Craters of the Moon Chapter in Idaho; second priority is given to residents of ASSE Region II (Arizona, Colorado, Idaho, Montana, Nevada, New Mexico, Utah, and Wyoming). Special consideration is also given to 1) employees of a sponsoring organization or their dependents; 2) students who are serving their country through active duty in the armed forces or are honorably discharged; 3) former members of the Boy Scouts, Girl Scouts, FFA, or 4-H; 4) recipients of awards from service organizations; and 5) students who have provided volunteer service to an ASSE chapter in a leadership role. Undergraduates must have completed at least 60 semester hours with a GPA of 3.0 or higher. Graduate students must have completed at least 9 semester hours with a GPA of 3.5 or higher and have had a GPA of 3.0 or higher as an undergraduate. As part of the selection process, all applicants must submit 2 essays of 300 words or less: 1) why they are seeking a degree in safety, a brief description of their current

activities, and how those relate to their career goals and objectives; and 2) why they should be awarded this scholarship (including career goals and financial need). **Deadline for Receipt:** November of each year.

1958 ■ AMERICAN SOCIETY OF SAFETY ENGINEERS

Attn: ASSE Foundation
1800 East Oakton Street
Des Plaines, IL 60018
Tel: (847)768-3441
Fax: (847)296-9220
E-mail: mrosario@asse.org
Web Site: http://www.asse.org
To provide financial assistance to undergraduate and graduate student members of the American Society of Safety Engineers (ASSE) from designated western states.
Title of Award: Gold Country Section and Region II Scholarship **Area, Field, or Subject:** Engineering; Environmental conservation; Environmental science; Fires and fire prevention; Industrial hygiene; Occupational safety and health; Protective services **Level of Education for which Award is Granted:** Four Year College, Graduate **Number Awarded:** 1 each year. **Funds Available:** The stipend is $1,000 per year. **Duration:** 1 year; nonrenewable.
Eligibility Requirements: This program is open to ASSE student members who are majoring in occupational safety and health or a closely-related field (e.g., safety engineering, safety management, systems safety, environmental science, industrial hygiene, ergonomics, fire science). Priority is given to residents of ASSE Region II (Arizona, Colorado, Idaho, Montana, Nevada, New Mexico, Utah, and Wyoming). Undergraduates must be full-time students who have completed at least 60 semester hours with a GPA of 3.0 or higher. Graduate students must also be enrolled full time, have completed at least 9 semester hours with a GPA of 3.5 or higher, and have had a GPA of 3.0 or higher as an undergraduate. As part of the selection process, all applicants must submit 2 essays of 300 words or less: 1) why they are seeking a degree in safety, a brief description of their current activities, and how those relate to their career goals and objectives; and 2) why they should be awarded this scholarship (including career goals and financial need). **Deadline for Receipt:** November of each year.

1959 ■ AMERICAN SOCIETY OF SAFETY ENGINEERS

Attn: ASSE Foundation
1800 East Oakton Street
Des Plaines, IL 60018
Tel: (847)768-3441
Fax: (847)296-9220
E-mail: mrosario@asse.org
Web Site: http://www.asse.org
To provide financial assistance to undergraduate student members of the American Society of Safety Engineers (ASSE) from designated southeastern states.
Title of Award: Region IV/Edwin P. Granberry, Jr. Scholarship **Area, Field, or Subject:** Engineering; Environmental conservation; Environmental science; Fires and fire prevention; Industrial hygiene; Occupational safety and health; Protective services **Level of Education for which Award is Granted:** Four Year College **Number Awarded:** 1 each year. **Funds Available:** The stipend is $1,000 per year. **Duration:** 1 year; nonrenewable.
Eligibility Requirements: This program is open to ASSE student members who are majoring in occupational safety and health or a closely-related field (e.g., safety engineering, safety management, systems safety, environmental science, industrial hygiene, ergonomics, fire science). Applicants must be residents of ASSE Region IV (Louisiana, Alabama, Mississippi, Georgia, Florida, Puerto Rico, and the U.S. Virgin Islands), although they may be attending school elsewhere. They must be full-time students who have completed at least 60 semester hours with a GPA of 3.0 or higher. As part of the selection process, they must submit 2 essays of 300 words or less: 1) why they are seeking a degree in safety, a brief description of their current activities, and how those relate to their

career goals and objectives; and 2) why they should be awarded this scholarship (including career goals and financial need). **Deadline for Receipt:** November of each year.

1960 ■ AMERICAN SOCIETY OF SAFETY ENGINEERS

Attn: ASSE Foundation
1800 East Oakton Street
Des Plaines, IL 60018
Tel: (847)768-3441
Fax: (847)296-9220
E-mail: mrosario@asse.org
Web Site: http://www.asse.org

To provide financial assistance to upper-division and graduate students at colleges and universities in New England who are members or family of members of the American Society of Safety Engineers (ASSE).

Title of Award: Greater Boston Chapter Leadership Award **Area, Field, or Subject:** Engineering; Environmental conservation; Environmental science; Fires and fire prevention; Industrial hygiene; Occupational safety and health; Protective services **Level of Education for which Award is Granted:** Four Year College, Graduate **Number Awarded:** 1 each year. **Funds Available:** The stipend is $1,000 per year. **Duration:** 1 year; may be renewed.

Eligibility Requirements: This program is open to undergraduate and graduate students who are working on a degree in occupational safety and health or a closely-related field (e.g., safety engineering, safety management, systems safety, environmental science, industrial hygiene, ergonomics, fire science). Applicants must be 1) a member of an ASSE chapter in New England; 2) the spouse or child of an ASSE chapter member in New England; or 3) a member of an ASSE student section in New England. Undergraduates must be full-time students who have completed at least 60 semester hours with a GPA of 3.0 or higher. Graduate students must also be enrolled full time, have completed at least 9 semester hours with a GPA of 3.5 or higher, and have had a GPA of 3.0 or higher as an undergraduate. As part of the selection process, all applicants must submit 2 essays of 300 words or less: 1) why they are seeking a degree in safety, a brief description of their current activities, and how those relate to their career goals and objectives; and 2) why they should be awarded this scholarship (including career goals and financial need). **Deadline for Receipt:** November of each year.

1961 ■ AMERICAN SOCIETY OF SAFETY ENGINEERS

Attn: ASSE Foundation
1800 East Oakton Street
Des Plaines, IL 60018
Tel: (847)768-3441
Fax: (847)296-9220
E-mail: mrosario@asse.org
Web Site: http://www.asse.org

To provide financial assistance to undergraduate students majoring in fields related to occupational safety and health.

Title of Award: Gulf Coast Past Presidents Scholarship **Area, Field, or Subject:** Engineering; Environmental conservation; Environmental science; Fires and fire prevention; Industrial hygiene; Occupational safety and health; Protective services **Level of Education for which Award is Granted:** Four Year College **Number Awarded:** 1 each year. **Funds Available:** The stipend is $1,000 per year. **Duration:** 1 year; nonrenewable.

Eligibility Requirements: This program is open to undergraduate students who are majoring in occupational safety and health or a closely-related field (e.g., safety engineering, safety management, systems safety, environmental science, industrial hygiene, ergonomics, fire science). Although the program is sponsored by the Gulf Coast (Texas) chapter of the American Society of Safety Engineers (ASSE), there are no geographical restrictions on eligibility. Applicants must be full- or part-time students who have completed at least 60 semester hours with a GPA of 3.0 or higher. Part-time students must be ASSE members. As part of the selection process, all applicants must submit 2 essays of 300 words or less: 1) why they are seeking a degree in safety, a brief description of their current activities, and how those relate to their career goals and objec-

tives; and 2) why they should be awarded this scholarship (including career goals and financial need). **Deadline for Receipt:** November of each year.

1962 ■ AMERICAN SOCIETY OF SAFETY ENGINEERS

Attn: ASSE Foundation
1800 East Oakton Street
Des Plaines, IL 60018
Tel: (847)768-3441
Fax: (847)296-9220
E-mail: mrosario@asse.org
Web Site: http://www.asse.org

To provide financial assistance to upper-division student members of the American Society of Safety Engineers (ASSE).

Title of Award: Liberty Mutual Scholarship **Area, Field, or Subject:** Engineering; Environmental conservation; Environmental science; Fires and fire prevention; Industrial hygiene; Occupational safety and health; Protective services **Level of Education for which Award is Granted:** Four Year College **Number Awarded:** 1 each year. **Funds Available:** The stipend is $3,000 per year. **Duration:** 1 year; nonrenewable.

Eligibility Requirements: This program is open to ASSE student members who are majoring in occupational safety and health or a closely-related field (e.g., safety engineering, safety management, systems safety, environmental science, industrial hygiene, ergonomics, fire science). Applicants must be full-time students who have completed at least 60 semester hours with a GPA of 3.0 or higher. As part of the selection process, they must submit 2 essays of 300 words or less: 1) why they are seeking a degree in safety, a brief description of their current activities, and how those relate to their career goals and objectives; and 2) why they should be awarded this scholarship (including career goals and financial need). **Deadline for Receipt:** November of each year. **Additional Information:** This program is supported by Liberty Mutual.

1963 ■ AMERICAN SOCIETY OF SAFETY ENGINEERS

Attn: ASSE Foundation
1800 East Oakton Street
Des Plaines, IL 60018
Tel: (847)768-3441
Fax: (847)296-9220
E-mail: mrosario@asse.org
Web Site: http://www.asse.org

To provide financial assistance to upper-division student members of the American Society of Safety Engineers (ASSE).

Title of Award: Marsh Risk Consulting Scholarship **Area, Field, or Subject:** Engineering; Environmental conservation; Environmental science; Fires and fire prevention; Industrial hygiene; Occupational safety and health; Protective services **Level of Education for which Award is Granted:** Four Year College **Number Awarded:** 1 each year. **Funds Available:** The stipend is $5,000 per year. **Duration:** 1 year; nonrenewable.

Eligibility Requirements: This program is open to ASSE student members who are majoring in occupational safety and health or a closely-related field (e.g., safety engineering, safety management, systems safety, environmental science, industrial hygiene, ergonomics, fire science). Applicants must be full-time students who have completed at least 60 semester hours with a GPA of 3.0 or higher. As part of the selection process, they must submit 2 essays of 300 words or less: 1) why they are seeking a degree in safety, a brief description of their current activities, and how those relate to their career goals and objectives; and 2) why they should be awarded this scholarship (including career goals and financial need). **Deadline for Receipt:** November of each year. **Additional Information:** Funding for this program is provided by Marsh Risk Consulting.

1964 ■ AMERICAN SOCIETY OF SAFETY ENGINEERS

Attn: ASSE Foundation
1800 East Oakton Street
Des Plaines, IL 60018
Tel: (847)768-3441
Fax: (847)296-9220
E-mail: mrosario@asse.org
Web Site: http://www.asse.org

To provide financial assistance to undergraduate student members of the American Society of Safety Engineers (ASSE).

Title of Award: Marcella Thompson Distinguished Service Award Scholarship **Area, Field, or Subject:** Engineering; Environmental conservation; Environmental science; Fires and fire prevention; Industrial hygiene; Occupational safety and health; Protective services **Level of Education for which Award is Granted:** Four Year College **Number Awarded:** 1 each year. **Funds Available:** The stipend is $2,000 per year. **Duration:** 1 year; nonrenewable.

Eligibility Requirements: This program is open to ASSE student members who are majoring in occupational safety and health or a closely-related field (e.g., safety engineering, safety management, systems safety, environmental science, industrial hygiene, ergonomics, fire science). Applicants must be full-time students who have completed at least 60 semester hours with a GPA of 3.0 or higher. As part of the selection process, they must submit 2 essays of 300 words or less: 1) why they are seeking a degree in safety, a brief description of their current activities, and how those relate to their career goals and objectives; and 2) why they should be awarded this scholarship (including career goals and financial need). **Deadline for Receipt:** November of each year.

1965 ■ AMERICAN SOCIETY OF SAFETY ENGINEERS

Attn: ASSE Foundation
1800 East Oakton Street
Des Plaines, IL 60018
Tel: (847)768-3441
Fax: (847)296-9220
E-mail: mrosario@asse.org
Web Site: http://www.asse.org

To provide financial assistance to minority undergraduate student members of the American Society of Safety Engineers (ASSE).

Title of Award: UPS Diversity Scholarships **Area, Field, or Subject:** Engineering; Environmental conservation; Environmental science; Fires and fire prevention; Industrial hygiene; Occupational safety and health; Protective services **Level of Education for which Award is Granted:** Four Year College **Number Awarded:** Varies each year; recently, 2 of these scholarships at $5,250 each were awarded. **Funds Available:** Stipends range from $4,000 to $6,000 per year. **Duration:** 1 year; nonrenewable.

Eligibility Requirements: This program is open to ASSE student members who are enrolled in a 4-year degree program in occupational safety and health or a closely-related field (e.g., safety engineering, safety management, systems safety, environmental science, industrial hygiene, ergonomics, fire science). Applicants must be U.S. citizens and members of a minority ethnic or racial group. They must be full-time students who have completed at least 60 semester hours with a GPA of 3.0 or higher. As part of the selection process, they must submit 2 essays of 300 words or less: 1) why they are seeking a degree in safety, a brief description of their current activities, and how those relate to their career goals and objectives; and 2) why they should be awarded this scholarship (including career goals and financial need). **Deadline for Receipt:** November of each year. **Additional Information:** Funding for this program is provided by the UPS Foundation.

1966 ■ AMERICAN SOCIETY OF SAFETY ENGINEERS

Attn: ASSE Foundation
1800 East Oakton Street
Des Plaines, IL 60018
Tel: (847)768-3441
Fax: (847)296-9220
E-mail: mrosario@asse.org
Web Site: http://www.asse.org

To provide financial assistance to undergraduate student members of the American Society of Safety Engineers (ASSE).

Title of Award: UPS Scholarships **Area, Field, or Subject:** Engineering; Environmental conservation; Environmental science; Fires and fire prevention; Industrial hygiene; Occupational safety and health; Protective services **Level of Education for which Award is Granted:** Four Year College **Number Awarded:** Varies each year; recently, 4 of these scholarships at $5,250 each were awarded. **Funds Available:** Stipends range from $4,000 to $6,000 per year. **Duration:** 1 year; nonrenewable.

Eligibility Requirements: This program is open to ASSE student members who are enrolled in a 4-year degree program in occupational

safety and health or a closely-related field (e.g., safety engineering, safety management, systems safety, environmental science, industrial hygiene, ergonomics, fire science). Applicants must be full-time students who have completed at least 60 semester hours with a GPA of 3.0 or higher. As part of the selection process, they must submit 2 essays of 300 words or less: 1) why they are seeking a degree in safety, a brief description of their current activities, and how those relate to their career goals and objectives; and 2) why they should be awarded this scholarship (including career goals and financial need). **Deadline for Receipt:** November of each year. **Additional Information:** Funding for this program is provided by the UPS Foundation.

1967 ■ AMERICAN SOCIETY OF SAFETY ENGINEERS-COLUMBIA-WILLAMETTE CHAPTER

c/o Melissa Diede, Scholarship Committee Chair
SAIF Corporation Service Center
15333 S.W. Sequoia Parkway
P.O. Box 4777
Portland, OR 97208-4777
Tel: (503)598-5808
Free: 800-848-2372
Fax: (503)968-5353
E-mail: meldie@saif.com
Web Site: http://www.assecwc.org/scholarships.html

To provide financial assistance for college to members of the American Society of Safety Engineers (ASSE) from Washington and Oregon.

Title of Award: Walter G. Thorsell Memorial Scholarship **Area, Field, or Subject:** Environmental conservation; Environmental science; Industrial hygiene; Occupational safety and health; Protective services **Level of Education for which Award is Granted:** Undergraduate **Number Awarded:** 1 each year. **Funds Available:** The stipend is $1,500. **Duration:** 1 year.

Eligibility Requirements: This program is open to residents of Washington and Oregon who have completed at least 1 term of study toward a bachelor's degree in occupational safety, health, or environmental studies. Applicants must be ASSE student members who are able to demonstrate interest and participation in ASSE and other safety activities. U.S. citizenship and a GPA of 2.75 or higher are required. Selection is based on demonstrated interested in preparing for a career in the field of occupational safety, health, and/or environmental science; a statement of interest in the field; contribution to an ASSE student section or professional chapter; and financial need (considered only if all other qualifications are equal). **Deadline for Receipt:** April of each year.

1968 ■ AMERICAN SOCIETY OF SAFETY ENGINEERS-NEW JERSEY CHAPTER

c/o New Jersey State Safety Council
6 Commerce Drive
Cranford, NJ 07016
Tel: (732)269-7683
Web Site: http://www.njasse.org

To provide financial assistance to undergraduate and graduate students in safety engineering or other safety-related majors in New Jersey.

Title of Award: Theodore M. Brickley/Bernice Shickora Scholarship **Area, Field, or Subject:** Environmental conservation; Environmental science; Industrial hygiene; Protective services **Level of Education for which Award is Granted:** Four Year College, Graduate **Number Awarded:** 1 or more each year. **Funds Available:** The stipend is $1,000.

Eligibility Requirements: This program is open to upper-division and graduate students who are residents of New Jersey enrolled at a college or university in the state. Applicants must be majoring in occupational safety, industrial hygiene, environmental science, or a related field; have completed at least 6 credit hours in occupational safety and health (OSH) and at least 12 credit hours in OSH or related courses; have completed at least 18 credit hours in departmental-related courses (physical sciences, mathematics, engineering); and have a GPA of 2.5 or higher overall and 3.0 or higher in OSH courses. Selection is based on GPA; leadership skills as demonstrated by participation in extracurricular activities; involvement in occupational safety, hygiene, and related activities; involvement with professional occupational safety, hygiene, or related organizations; communication skills; awards and honors; and financial need. **Deadline for Receipt:** April of each year.

1969 ■ ASSOCIATION OF CALIFORNIA WATER AGENCIES

Attn: Scholarship Program
910 K Street, Suite 100
Sacramento, CA 95814-3514
Tel: (916)441-4545
Fax: (916)325-4849
E-mail: lavonnew@acwa.com
Web Site: http://www.acwa.com/news_info/scholarships
To provide financial assistance to upper-division students in California who are majoring in water resources-related fields of study.

Title of Award: Association of California Water Agencies Scholarships **Area, Field, or Subject:** Agricultural sciences; Engineering; Environmental conservation; Environmental science; Public administration; Water resources **Level of Education for which Award is Granted:** Four Year College **Number Awarded:** At least 6 each year. **Funds Available:** The stipend is $1,500. Funds are paid directly to the recipient's school. **Duration:** 1 year.

Eligibility Requirements: This program is open to California residents attending selected colleges and universities in the state. Applicants must be full-time students in their junior or senior year at the time of the award and majoring in a field related to or identified with water resources, including engineering, agricultural and/or urban water supply, environmental sciences, or public administration. Along with their application, they must submit 2-page essay on key water-related issues they would address if given the opportunity, why they have chosen a career in the water resources field, and how their educational and career goals relate to a future in California water resources. Selection is based on scholastic achievement, commitment to a career in the field of water resources, and financial need. **Deadline for Receipt:** March of each year. **Additional Information:** Recipients must attend a college or university in California approved by the sponsor.

1970 ■ ASSOCIATION OF CALIFORNIA WATER AGENCIES

Attn: Scholarship Program
910 K Street, Suite 100
Sacramento, CA 95814-3514
Tel: (916)441-4545
Fax: (916)325-4849
E-mail: lavonnew@acwa.com
Web Site: http://www.acwa.com/news_info/scholarships
To provide financial assistance to upper-division students in California who are majoring in water resources-related fields of study.

Title of Award: Clair A. Hill Scholarship **Area, Field, or Subject:** Agricultural sciences; Engineering; Environmental conservation; Environmental science; Public administration; Water resources **Level of Education for which Award is Granted:** Undergraduate **Number Awarded:** 1 each year. **Funds Available:** The stipend is $3,000. Funds are paid directly to the recipient's school. **Duration:** 1 year.

Eligibility Requirements: Applicants must be California residents attending public colleges or universities in the state. They should 1) have completed their sophomore work, 2) be full-time students in their junior or senior year at the time of the award, and 3) be majoring in a field related to or identified with water resources, including engineering, agricultural sciences, urban water supply, environmental sciences, and public administration. Selection is based on scholastic achievement, career plans, and financial need. **Deadline for Receipt:** March of each year. **Additional Information:** This program is administered each year by the current recipient of the Association of California Water Agencies Clair A. Hill Agency Award for Excellence, which is presented annually to a public water agency in recognition of outstanding and innovative water management programs. The winning agency generally selects a student within its service area. Funding is provided by the consulting firm CH2M Hill. Recipients must attend a branch of the University of California or the California State University system on a full-time basis.

1971 ■ ASSOCIATION FOR IRON & STEEL TECHNOLOGY-OHIO VALLEY CHAPTER

c/o Jeff McKain, Scholarship Chair
Xtek, Inc.

11451 Reading Road
Cincinnati, OH 45241
Tel: (513)733-7843; (999)332-XTEK
Fax: (513)733-7939
E-mail: jeff.mckain@xtek.com
Web Site: http://www.aist.org/chapters/ohiovalley_scholarship.htm
To provide financial assistance for college to student members and children of members of the Ohio Valley Chapter of the Association for Iron & Steel Technology (AIST).

Title of Award: Ohio Valley Chapter AIST Scholarships **Area, Field, or Subject:** Biological and clinical sciences; Chemistry; Computer and information sciences; Earth sciences; Engineering; Engineering, Electrical; Engineering, Mechanical; Environmental conservation; Environmental science; Geosciences; Information science and technology; Metallurgy; Physical sciences; Physics **Level of Education for which Award is Granted:** Undergraduate **Number Awarded:** Up to 2 each year. **Funds Available:** The stipend is $1,000 per year. **Duration:** 1 year; may be renewed up to 3 additional years provided the recipient remains enrolled full time and maintains a GPA of 3.0 or higher.

Eligibility Requirements: This program is open to high school seniors and college students who are either 1) children of Ohio Valley Chapter AIST members, or 2) student AIST members. Applicants must be accepted at, planning to attend, or currently enrolled at an accredited college or university with a major in biology, chemistry, computer programming, computer technology, electrical engineering, engineering, engineering technology, environmental engineering, environmental science, information systems technology, mechanical engineering, metallurgy, microbiology, physical science, physics, or other field approved by the scholarship committee. Along with their application, they must submit a 500-word essay on the reasons for their interests and reasons for working on a degree in their field of study, career goals and objectives, and extracurricular activities and their benefits. Selection is based on overall academic achievement (especially in mathematics and science), the essay, and extracurricular activities. **Deadline for Receipt:** February of each year. **Additional Information:** The AIST was formed in 2004 by the merger of the Iron and Steel Society (ISS) and the Association of Iron and Steel Engineers (AISE). This program was established by the former Ohio Valley District Section of AISE. The Ohio Valley Chapter covers Indiana (except for the northwestern portion), all of Kentucky, western Tennessee, and portions of southern Ohio.

1972 ■ ASSOCIATION FOR WOMEN IN SCIENCE-SEATTLE CHAPTER

c/o Fran Solomon, Scholarship Committee Chair
5805 16th Avenue, N.E.
Seattle, WA 98105
Tel: (206)522-6441
E-mail: fran.solomon@metrokc.gov
Web Site: http://www.scn.org/awis/undergraduate_scholarship.htm
To provide financial assistance to women undergraduates from any state majoring in science, mathematics, or engineering at colleges and universities in western Washington.

Title of Award: AWIS Seattle Scholarships **Area, Field, or Subject:** Biochemistry; Biological and clinical sciences; Chemistry; Engineering; Environmental conservation; Environmental science; Geology; Mathematics and mathematical sciences; Pharmaceutical sciences; Physics **Level of Education for which Award is Granted:** Four Year College **Number Awarded:** Varies each year; recently, 11 of these scholarships were awarded. **Funds Available:** Stipends range from $1,000 to $1,500. **Duration:** 1 year.

Eligibility Requirements: This program is open to women from any state entering their junior or senior year at a 4-year college or university in western Washington. Applicants must have a declared major in science (e.g., biological sciences, environmental science, biochemistry, chemistry, pharmacy, geology, computer science, physics), mathematics, or engineering. Along with their application, they must submit essays on the events that led to their choice of a major, their current career plans and long-term goals, and their volunteer and community activities. Financial need is considered in the selection process. At least 1 scholarship is reserved for a woman from a group that is underrepresented in science, mathematics, and engineering careers, including Native American Indians and Alaska Natives, Black/African Americans, Mexican Americans/Chicanas/Latinas, Native Pacific Islanders (Polynesians, Melanesians, and Micronesians), and women with disabilities. **Deadline for Receipt:** March of each year. **Additional Information:** This program includes the following named awards: the Virginia Badger Scholarship, the Angela Paez Memorial Scholarship, and the Fran Solomon Scholarship. Support for the program is provided by several sponsors, including the American Chemical Society, Iota Sigma Pi, Rosetta Inpharmatics, and ZymoGenetics, Inc.

1973 ■ BIG 33 SCHOLARSHIP FOUNDATION

Attn: Scholarship Committee
511 Bridge Street
P.O. Box 213
New Cumberland, PA 17070
Tel: (717)774-3303; 877-PABIG-33
Fax: (717)774-1749
E-mail: info@big33.org
Web Site: http://www.big33.org/scholarships/default.ashx
To provide financial assistance to graduating high school seniors in Ohio and Pennsylvania who plan to study environmental sciences in college.
Title of Award: Waste Management Scholarships **Area, Field, or Subject:** Environmental conservation; Environmental science **Level of Education for which Award is Granted:** Undergraduate **Number Awarded:** 100 each year. **Funds Available:** The stipend is $1,000. **Duration:** 1 year; nonrenewable.
Eligibility Requirements: This program is open to seniors graduating from public and accredited private high schools in Ohio and Pennsylvania who are planning to study an environmental field in college. Applications are available from high school guidance counselors. Selection is based on special talents, leadership, obstacles overcome, academic achievement (at least a 2.0 GPA), community service, unique endeavors, financial need, and a 1-page essay on why they deserve the scholarship and their involvement with preserving the environment. **Deadline for Receipt:** February of each year. **Additional Information:** Funds for this program are provided by Waste Management, Inc.

1974 ■ BROWN AND CALDWELL

Attn: Scholarship Program
201 North Civic Drive, Suite 115
P.O. Box 8045
Walnut Creek, CA 94596
Tel: (925)937-9010
Fax: (925)937-9026
E-mail: scholarships@brwncald.com
Web Site: http://www.brownandcaldwell.com
To provide financial assistance to minority students working on an undergraduate degree in an environmental or engineering field.
Title of Award: Brown and Caldwell Minority Scholarship **Area, Field, or Subject:** Biological and clinical sciences; Engineering, Chemical; Engineering, Civil; Environmental conservation; Environmental science; Geology; Hydrology; Industrial hygiene; Toxicology **Level of Education for which Award is Granted:** Four Year College **Number Awarded:** 1 each year. **Funds Available:** The stipend is $3,000. **Duration:** 1 year.
Eligibility Requirements: This program is open to members of minority groups (African Americans, Hispanics, Asians, Pacific Islanders, Native Americans, and Alaska Natives) who are full-time students in their junior year at an accredited 4-year college or university. Applicants must have a GPA of 3.0 or higher with a declared major in civil, chemical, or environmental engineering or an environmental science (e.g., biology, ecology, geology, hydrogeology, industrial hygiene, toxicology). Along with their application, they must submit an essay (up to 250 words) on why they chose to major in an environmental discipline. They must be U.S. citizens or permanent resident and available to participate in a summer internship at a Brown and Caldwell office. Financial need is not considered in the selection process. **Deadline for Receipt:** February of each year. **Additional Information:** As part of the paid summer internship at a Brown and Caldwell office at 1 of more than 40 cities in the country, the program provides a mentor to guide the intern through the company's information and communications resources.

1975 ■ BROWN AND CALDWELL

Attn: Scholarship Program
201 North Civic Drive, Suite 115
P.O. Box 8045
Walnut Creek, CA 94596

Tel: (925)937-9010
Fax: (925)937-9026
E-mail: scholarships@brwncald.com
Web Site: http://www.brownandcaldwell.com
To provide financial assistance to undergraduate students working on an degree in an environmental or engineering field.
Title of Award: Dr. W. Wesley Eckenfelder Scholarship **Area, Field, or Subject:** Biological and clinical sciences; Engineering, Chemical; Engineering, Civil; Environmental conservation; Environmental science; Geology; Hydrology; Industrial hygiene; Toxicology **Level of Education for which Award is Granted:** Four Year College **Number Awarded:** 1 each year. **Funds Available:** The stipend is $3,000. **Duration:** 1 year.
Eligibility Requirements: This program is open to U.S. citizens and permanent residents enrolled as full-time students in their junior year at an accredited 4-year college or university. Applicants must have a GPA of 3.0 or higher with a declared major in civil, chemical, or environmental engineering or an environmental science (e.g., biology, ecology, geology, hydrogeology, industrial hygiene, toxicology). Along with their application, they must submit an essay (up to 250 words) on why they chose to major in an environmental discipline. Financial need is not considered in the selection process. **Deadline for Receipt:** February of each year. **Additional Information:** This scholarship was first awarded in 1999.

1976 ■ CALIFORNIA ENVIRONMENTAL HEALTH ASSOCIATION

110 South Fairfax, A11-175
Los Angeles, CA 90036
Tel: (323)634-7698
Fax: (323)571-1889
E-mail: support@ceha.org
Web Site: http://www.ceha.org/awards.html
To provide financial assistance to undergraduates in California interested in preparing for a career in the sciences, especially environmental health.
Title of Award: Martin Smilo Undergraduate Scholarship **Area, Field, or Subject:** Environmental conservation; Environmental science; Public health; Science **Level of Education for which Award is Granted:** Four Year College **Number Awarded:** 1 each year. **Funds Available:** The stipend is $2,500. **Duration:** 1 year.
Eligibility Requirements: This program is open to California students who have completed at least 48 semester units of undergraduate study, including at least 12 semester units in science, with a GPA of 3.0 or higher. Applicants must be enrolled full time at an accredited 4-year college or university with an intention to work on a degree and prepare for a career in science. Preference is given to students in environmental health. Along with their application, they must submit a 3-page essay on 1 of 3 assigned topics related to public health and the role of professional organizations. Financial need is not considered in the selection process. **Deadline for Receipt:** February of each year. **Additional Information:** Information is also available from Matt Fore, CEHA Awards Committee, 160 Gibson Drive, Number 17, Hollister, CA 95023, (831) 636-4035, E-mail: matt@sanbenitoco.org.

1977 ■ COMMUNITY FOUNDATION FOR THE FOX VALLEY REGION, INC.

Attn: Scholarships
4455 West Lawrence Street
P.O. Box 563
Appleton, WI 54912-0563
Tel: (920)830-1290
Fax: (920)830-1293
E-mail: cffvr@cffoxvalley.org
Web Site: http://www.cffoxvalley.org/scholarship_fundslist.html
To provide financial assistance to upper-division and graduate students in Wisconsin who are working on a degree related to gardening.
Title of Award: Wisconsin Garden Club Federation Scholarship **Area, Field, or Subject:** Agricultural sciences; Botany; Environmental conservation; Environmental science; Forestry; Horticulture; Landscape architecture and design; Urban affairs/design/planning **Level of Education for which Award is Granted:** Graduate, Four Year College **Number Awarded:** Varies each year; recently, 4 of these scholarships were awarded. **Funds Available:** The stipend is $1,000. **Duration:** 1 year.
Eligibility Requirements: This program is open to college juniors, seniors, and graduate students at colleges and universities in Wisconsin. Applicants must be majoring in horticulture, floriculture, landscape design/

architecture, botany, forestry, agronomy, plant pathology, environmental studies, city planning, land management, or a related field. They must have a 3.0 GPA or higher. **Deadline for Receipt:** February of each year. **Additional Information:** This program is sponsored by the Wisconsin Garden Club Federation. Information is also available from Carolyn A. Craig, WGCF Scholarship Chair, 900 North Shore Drive, New Richmond, WI 54017-9466, (715) 246-6242, E-mail: cacraig@frontiernet.net.

1978 ■ COMMUNITY FOUNDATION OF LOUISVILLE

Attn: Director of Grants
Waterfront Plaza, Suite 1110
325 West Main Street
Louisville, KY 40202-4251
Tel: (502)585-4649
Fax: (502)587-7484
E-mail: info@cflouisville.org
Web Site: http://www.cflouisville.org
To provide financial assistance to women studying fields related to the environment at colleges and universities in Kentucky.

Title of Award: Thaddeus Colson and Isabelle Saalwaechter Fitzpatrick Memorial Scholarship **Area, Field, or Subject:** Agricultural sciences; Biological and clinical sciences; Environmental conservation; Environmental science; Horticulture **Level of Education for which Award is Granted:** Four Year College **Number Awarded:** 1 each year. **Funds Available:** The stipend is $2,000. Funds are paid directly to the college or university. **Duration:** 1 year; nonrenewable.

Eligibility Requirements: This program is open to female residents of Kentucky who are entering their sophomore, junior, or senior year at a 4-year public college or university in the state. Applicants must be majoring in an environmentally related program (e.g., agriculture, biology, horticulture, environmental studies, environmental engineering). They must be enrolled full time with a GPA of 3.0 or higher. Along with their application, they must submit a 200-word essay describing their interest, leadership, volunteer efforts, and work experience in the environmental field; their future plans and goals in the environmental field; and what they hope to accomplish with their college degree. Financial need is also considered in the selection process. **Deadline for Receipt:** February of each year.

1979 ■ CONFERENCE OF MINORITY TRANSPORTATION OFFICIALS-NEW JERSEY CHAPTER

Attn: Scholarship Committee
P.O. Box 22968
Newark, NJ 07101
E-mail: comtonj@mail.comtonj.org
Web Site: http://www.comtonj.org/scholarshipInfo.asp
To provide financial assistance to college students from New Jersey interested in working on a degree in a field related to transportation.

Title of Award: COMTO NJ Scholarships **Area, Field, or Subject:** Environmental conservation; Environmental science; Protective services; Public administration; Transportation; Urban affairs/design/planning **Level of Education for which Award is Granted:** Undergraduate **Number Awarded:** 4 each year: 1 at $1,000 and 3 at $500. **Funds Available:** Stipends are $1,000 or $500. **Duration:** 1 year.

Eligibility Requirements: This program is open to students entering or attending colleges and universities in New Jersey to major in a field related to transportation (e.g., environmental disciplines, public service, safety, transportation, urban planning). Applicants must have a GPA of 3.0 or higher. Along with their application, they must submit a 500-word essay on why they chose a career in transportation. Selection is based on the essay, academic achievement, extracurricular and community activities, and letters of recommendation. **Deadline for Receipt:** April of each year. **Additional Information:** The sponsor is the New Jersey chapter of the Conference of Minority Transportation Officials (COMTO). The national organization was founded in 1971 to promote, strengthen, and expand the roles of minorities in all aspects of transportation. This program includes the Lewis R. Rosser Scholarship, the Paul Smith Scholarship, and the Garrett Morgan Scholarship. Recipients must attend the COMTO NJ Scholarship Gala to accept the award.

1980 ■ DELAWARE HIGHER EDUCATION COMMISSION

Carvel State Office Building
820 North French Street
Wilmington, DE 19801

Tel: (302)577-3240
Free: 800-292-7935
Fax: (302)577-6765
E-mail: dhec@doe.k12.de.us
Web Site: http://www.doe.state.de.us/high-ed/healy.pat.htm
To provide financial assistance to high school seniors and college students in Delaware who are interested in majoring in engineering or environmental sciences at a college in the state.

Title of Award: John P. "Pat" Healy Scholarship **Area, Field, or Subject:** Environmental conservation; Environmental science **Level of Education for which Award is Granted:** Undergraduate **Number Awarded:** 1 or more each year. **Funds Available:** The stipend is $2,000. **Duration:** 1 year; automatically renewed for 3 additional years if a GPA of 3.0 or higher is maintained.

Eligibility Requirements: This program is open to high school seniors and full-time college students in their freshman or sophomore years who are Delaware residents and majoring in either environmental engineering or environmental sciences at a Delaware college. Applicants must submit a 500-word essay on "What would you do to protect the environment?" Selection is based on financial need, academic performance, community or school involvement, and leadership ability. **Deadline for Receipt:** March of each year. **Additional Information:** This program is sponsored by the Delaware Solid Waste Authority.

1981 ■ DEPARTMENT OF AGRICULTURE

Animal and Plant Health Inspection Service
Marketing and Regulatory Programs
4700 River Road, Unit 22
Riverdale, MD 20737-1230
800-762-2738
Web Site: http://www.aphis.usda.gov/ppq
To provide financial assistance and work experience to college students majoring in the agricultural or biological sciences.

Title of Award: PPQ William F. Helms Student Scholarship Program **Area, Field, or Subject:** Agricultural sciences; Biological and clinical sciences; Botany; Entomology; Environmental conservation; Environmental science; Virology **Level of Education for which Award is Granted:** Undergraduate **Number Awarded:** Several each year. **Funds Available:** The stipend is $5,000 per year. **Duration:** 1 year; may be renewed if the recipient maintains a GPA of 2.5 or higher.

Eligibility Requirements: This program is open to college sophomores and juniors who are attending an accredited college or university, are majoring in an agricultural or biological science (such as biology, plant pathology, entomology, virology, bacteriology, mycology, or ecology), are interested in a career in plant protection and quarantine, and are U.S. citizens. To apply, interested students must submit a completed application form, a personal letter describing their career goals and interest in plant protection and quarantine, transcripts, and 3 letters of recommendation. **Deadline for Receipt:** February of each year. **Additional Information:** The U.S. Department of Agriculture's (USDA) Animal and Plant Health Inspection Service (APHIS) is the agency responsible for protecting America's agriculture base; Plant Protection and Quarantine (PPQ) is the program within APHIS that deals with plant health issues. In addition to financial assistance, the Helms Student Scholarship Program also offers tutoring assistance, mentoring, paid work experience during vacation periods, career exploration, and possible employment upon graduation.

1982 ■ DEPARTMENT OF TRANSPORTATION

Federal Highway Administration
Attn: National Highway Institute, HNHI-20
4600 North Fairfax Drive, Suite 800
Arlington, VA 22203-1553
Tel: (703)235-0538
Fax: (703)235-0593
E-mail: transportationedu@fhwa.dot.gov
Web Site: http://www.nhi.fhwa.dot.gov/ddetfp.asp
To provide financial assistance for undergraduate study in transportation-related fields to students at Hispanic Serving Institutions.

Title of Award: Eisenhower Hispanic-Serving Institutions Fellowships **Area, Field, or Subject:** Accounting; Architecture; Business administration; Engineering, Civil; Environmental conservation; Environmental science; Transportation **Level of Education for which Award is Granted:** Four Year College **Number Awarded:** Varies each year; recently, 18 students received support from this program. **Funds Available:** The stipend covers the fellow's full cost of education, including tuition and fees. **Duration:** 1 year.

Eligibility Requirements: These fellowships are intended for students who are enrolled at federally-designated 4-year Hispanic Serving Institutions (HSIs) and who are working on a degree in a transportation-related field (i.e., engineering, accounting, business, architecture, environmental sciences, etc.). Applicants must have entered their junior year, have at least a 3.0 GPA, and have a faculty sponsor. **Deadline for Receipt:** February of each year.

1983 ■ DEPARTMENT OF TRANSPORTATION

Federal Highway Administration
Attn: National Highway Institute, HNHI-20
4600 North Fairfax Drive, Suite 800
Arlington, VA 22203-1553
Tel: (703)235-0538
Fax: (703)235-0593
E-mail: transportationedu@fhwa.dot.gov
Web Site: http://www.nhi.fhwa.dot.gov/ddetfp.asp
To provide financial assistance for undergraduate study in transportation-related fields to students at Historically Black Colleges and Universities.

Title of Award: Eisenhower Historically Black Colleges and Universities Fellowships **Area, Field, or Subject:** Accounting; Architecture; Business administration; Engineering, Civil; Environmental conservation; Environmental science; Transportation **Level of Education for which Award is Granted:** Four Year College **Number Awarded:** Varies each year; recently, 48 students received support from this program. **Funds Available:** The stipend covers the fellow's full cost of education, including tuition and fees. **Duration:** 1 year.

Eligibility Requirements: These fellowships are intended for students who are enrolled at federally-designated 4-year Historically Black Colleges and Universities (HBCUs) and working on a degree in a transportation-related field (i.e., engineering, accounting, business, architecture, environmental sciences, etc.). Applicants must have entered their junior year, have at least a 3.0 GPA, and have a faculty sponsor. **Deadline for Receipt:** February of each year.

1984 ■ ENVIRONMENTAL PROTECTION AGENCY

Attn: National Center for Environmental Research
Ariel Rios Building - 3500
1200 Pennsylvania Avenue, N.W.
Washington, DC 20460
Tel: (202)343-9862
E-mail: barnwell.thomas@epa.gov
Web Site: http://es.epa.gov/ncer/P3
To provide funding to teams of undergraduate and graduate students interested in conducting a research project related to environmental sustainability.

Title of Award: P3 Award Program **Area, Field, or Subject:** Agricultural sciences; Biological and clinical sciences; Chemistry; Energy-related areas; Environmental conservation; Environmental science; Information science and technology; Public health; Transportation; Water resources **Level of Education for which Award is Granted:** Graduate, Undergraduate **Number Awarded:** Varies each year. Recently, 42 Phase I grants were awarded, of which 10 were selected to receive Phase II grants. **Funds Available:** Phase I grants are $10,000. Phase II grants are $75,000. Grants cover all direct and indirect costs; cost-sharing is not required. **Duration:** 1 year for Phase I and 1 additional year for Phase II.

Eligibility Requirements: This competition is open to teams of undergraduate and graduate students at U.S. colleges and universities who are interested in conducting a research project related to the 3 components of sustainability: people, prosperity, and the planet. Projects must address the causes, effects, extent, prevention, reduction, or elimination of air, water, or solid and hazardous waste pollution. Categories include agriculture (e.g., irrigation practices, reduction or elimination of pesticides); materials and chemicals (e.g., materials conservation, green engineering, green chemistry, biotechnology, recovery and reuse of materials); energy (e.g., reduction in air emissions, energy conservation); information technology (e.g., delivery of and access to environmental performance, technical, educational, or public health information related environmental decision making); water (e.g., quality, quantity, conservation, availability, and access); or the built environment

(e.g., environmental benefits through innovative green buildings, transportation, and mobility strategies, and smart growth as it results in reduced vehicle miles traveled or reduces storm water runoff). Student teams, with a faculty advisor (who serves as the principal investigator on the grant), submit designs for Phase I of the competition. Selection of grantees is based on the extent to which the proposed project achieves the outcomes of minimizing the use and generation of hazardous substances; utilizes resources and energy effectively and efficiently; and advances the goals of economic competitiveness, human health, and environmental protection for societal benefit. Recipients of Phase I grants are then invited to apply for additional funding through a Phase I grant. **Deadline for Receipt:** February of each year. **Additional Information:** This program began in 2004. It is supported by a large number of organizations from industry, the nonprofit sector, and the federal government.

1985 ■ FAMILY CAMPERS AND RVERS

c/o Herb and Marie Petersen, National Scholarship Directors
76 Gaymore Road
Port Jefferson Station, NY 11776
E-mail: petersen76@aol.com
Web Site: http://www.fcrv.org/programs/scholarship.html
To provide financial assistance for college to members of the Family Campers and RVers (FCRV) and their dependent children.

Title of Award: FCRV Scholarships **Area, Field, or Subject:** Environmental conservation; Environmental science; General studies/Field of study not specified; Parks and recreation **Level of Education for which Award is Granted:** Undergraduate **Funds Available:** Scholarships range from $500 to $2,000 per year. **Duration:** 1 year; may be renewed upon reapplication.

Eligibility Requirements: Applicants must have been members of FCRV for at least 1 year or be their dependent children and have been accepted in a 2-year or 4-year accredited institution of higher learning. Applications are accepted from the United States and Canada, but those from other countries will be considered within the educational framework of that country. Students currently enrolled in college are given equal consideration with incoming freshmen; high school students or recent graduates should be in the upper 40% of their graduating class and students already in college should have a GPA of 2.7 or higher. Special consideration is given to students majoring in fields related to conservation, ecology, or outdoor activities, although applicants with any major are considered. Awards are based on maturity, leadership, related activities, and goals of the applicant as related to the objectives of FCRV. **Deadline for Receipt:** April of each year. **Additional Information:** Family Campers and RVers was founded as the National Campers and Hikers Association, and these scholarships are awarded by the National Campers and Hikers Association Scholarship, Inc. (NCHA).

1986 ■ FEDERATED GARDEN CLUBS OF CONNECTICUT, INC.

14 Business Park Drive
P.O. Box 854
Branford, CT 06405-0854
Tel: (203)488-5528
Fax: (203)488-5528
E-mail: gardenclubs@ctgardenclubs.org
Web Site: http://www.ctgardenclubs.org/scholarship.html
To provide financial assistance to Connecticut residents who are interested in majoring in horticulture-related fields at a Connecticut college or university.

Title of Award: Federated Garden Clubs of Connecticut Scholarship **Area, Field, or Subject:** Agricultural sciences; Botany; Environmental conservation; Environmental science; Forestry; Horticulture; Landscape architecture and design; Urban affairs/design/planning **Level of Education for which Award is Granted:** Four Year College, Graduate **Number Awarded:** Varies each year, depending upon the availability of funds. **Funds Available:** Stipends are generally about $1,000 each. Funds are sent to the recipient's school in 2 equal installments. **Duration:** 1 year.

Eligibility Requirements: Applicants must be legal residents of Connecticut who are studying at a college or university in the state in horticulture, floriculture, landscape design, conservation, forestry, botany, agronomy, plant pathology, environmental control, city planning, land management, or related subjects. They must be entering their junior or senior year of college or be a graduate student, have a GPA of 3.0 or higher, and be able to demonstrate financial need. **Deadline for Receipt:** June of each year. **Additional Information:** Information is also available from the Connecticut State Scholarship Chair, Mary Gray, 18 Long Hill Farm Road, Guilford, CT 06437, (203) 458-2784.

1987 ■ HOPI TRIBE
Attn: Office of Education
P.O. Box 123
Kykotsmovi, AZ 86039
Tel: (928)734-3533
Free: 800-762-9630
Fax: (928)734-9575
E-mail: IPolingyumptewa@hopi.nsn.us
Web Site: http://www.hopi.nsn.us/education_htgsp.asp
To encourage Hopi students to get an undergraduate or graduate degree in an area of interest to the Hopi Tribe.
Title of Award: Hopi Tribal Priority Scholarship **Area, Field, or Subject:** Business administration; Education; Engineering; Environmental conservation; Environmental science; Health care services; Law; Medicine **Level of Education for which Award is Granted:** Four Year College, Graduate **Number Awarded:** Varies each year. **Funds Available:** The stipend covers all educational expenses. **Duration:** 1 year; may be renewed.
Eligibility Requirements: This program is open to enrolled members of the Hopi Tribe. They must be college juniors, seniors, or graduate students whose degree is in a subject area that is of priority interest to the Hopi Tribe. Those areas are law, natural resources, education, medicine, health, engineering, or business. This is a highly competitive scholarship. Selection is based on academic merit and the likelihood that the applicants will use their training and expertise for tribal goals and objectives. **Deadline for Receipt:** July of each year. **Additional Information:** Recipients must attend school on a full-time basis.

1988 ■ KENTUCKY ENVIRONMENTAL AND PUBLIC PROTECTION CABINET
Attn: Department for Environmental Protection
14 Reilly Road
Frankfort, KY 40601
Tel: (502)564-2150
Fax: (502)564-4245
E-mail: dep@ky.gov
Web Site: http://www.dep.ky.gov/default.htm
To provide financial assistance to undergraduate and graduate students in Kentucky interested in working for the state's Environmental and Public Protection Cabinet following graduation.
Title of Award: Kentucky Environmental and Public Protection Cabinet Scholarship Program **Area, Field, or Subject:** Environmental conservation; Environmental science **Level of Education for which Award is Granted:** Four Year College, Graduate **Number Awarded:** Varies each year. **Funds Available:** The award covers the average costs of in-state tuition, fees, books, room, and board. Recipients are required to work for the department for 6 months for each semester of scholarship support. If they fail to meet that service requirement, they must repay all funds received with an interest rate of 12%. **Duration:** 1 year; may be renewed.
Eligibility Requirements: This program is open to juniors, seniors, and graduate students working on a degree at a Kentucky university considered to be of critical need to the sponsoring department. Applicants must be willing to work for that department following graduation. They must submit a 500-word essay that describes their career goals, understanding of the environment, and motivation to pursue the scholarship. Selection is based on GPA, the essay, letters of recommendation, and evidence of leadership; financial need is not considered. **Deadline for Receipt:** February of each year. **Additional Information:** This program began in 1991. Information is also available from the Kentucky Water Resources Research Institute, University of Kentucky, 233 Mining and Minerals Building, Rose Street, Lexington, KY 40506-0107, (859) 257-1299, Fax: (859) 323-1049, E-mail: kipp@pop.uky.edu. Recipients must enroll full time.

1989 ■ MAINE COMMUNITY FOUNDATION
Attn: Program Director
245 Main Street
Ellsworth, ME 04605

Tel: (207)667-9735; 877-700-6800
Fax: (207)667-0447
E-mail: info@mainecf.org
Web Site: http://www.mainecf.org/html/scholarships/index.html
To provide financial assistance to Maine students interested in the study of outdoor/nature writing.
Title of Award: R.V. "Gadabout" Gaddis Charitable Fund **Area, Field, or Subject:** Environmental conservation; Environmental science; Parks and recreation; Writing **Level of Education for which Award is Granted:** Four Year College **Number Awarded:** 2 each year. **Funds Available:** The stipend is $1,000 per year. **Duration:** 1 year.
Eligibility Requirements: This program is open to residents of Maine who are college juniors or seniors studying outdoor writing or a related environmental field. Applicants must include a writing sample, up to 10 pages in length, that demonstrates their skill at writing about the "outdoors," including outdoor sports, environmental concerns, and natural history topics. **Deadline for Receipt:** March of each year. **Additional Information:** This program began in 1995.

1990 ■ NATIONAL FFA ORGANIZATION
Attn: Scholarship Office
6060 FFA Drive
P.O. Box 68960
Indianapolis, IN 46268-0960
Tel: (317)802-4321
Fax: (317)802-5321
E-mail: scholarships@ffa.org
Web Site: http://www.ffa.org
To provide financial assistance to FFA members from Florida and Georgia who are interested in studying fields related to agriculture in college.
Title of Award: Chevron Corporation Scholarships **Area, Field, or Subject:** Agricultural sciences; Communications; Education; Environmental conservation; Environmental science; Natural resources; Wildlife conservation, management, and science **Level of Education for which Award is Granted:** Undergraduate **Number Awarded:** 2 each year. **Funds Available:** The stipend is $1,000. Funds are paid directly to the recipient. **Duration:** 1 year; nonrenewable.
Eligibility Requirements: This program is open to members who are graduating high school seniors planning to enroll full time in college. Applicants must be residents of Florida or Georgia planning to work on a 2-year or 4-year degree in agricultural communications and education, environmental engineering, environmental science, natural resource management, wildlife management, or public service and administration in agriculture. Preference is given to those who have shown outstanding leadership. Selection is based on academic achievement (10 points for GPA, 10 points for SAT or ACT score, 10 points for class rank), leadership in FFA activities (30 points), leadership in community activities (10 points), and participation in the Supervised Agricultural Experience (SAE) program (30 points). U.S. citizenship is required. **Deadline for Receipt:** February of each year. **Additional Information:** Funding for these scholarships is provided by ChevronTexaco Corporation.

1991 ■ NATIONAL FFA ORGANIZATION
Attn: Scholarship Office
6060 FFA Drive
P.O. Box 68960
Indianapolis, IN 46268-0960
Tel: (317)802-4321
Fax: (317)802-5321
E-mail: scholarships@ffa.org
Web Site: http://www.ffa.org
To provide financial assistance to FFA members who are interested in studying conservation at a college or university.
Title of Award: Georgia M. Hellberg Memorial Scholarships **Area, Field, or Subject:** Environmental conservation; Environmental science; Soil science; Water resources **Level of Education for which Award is Granted:** Four Year College **Number Awarded:** Approximately 4 each year. **Funds Available:** The stipend is $5,000. Funds are paid directly to the recipient. **Duration:** 1 year; nonrenewable.
Eligibility Requirements: This program is open to members who are graduating high school seniors planning to enroll full time in college. Applicants must be interested in working on a 4-year degree in soil and water conservation or a subject that could lead to employment in those

areas. Selection is based on academic achievement (10 points for GPA, 10 points for SAT or ACT score, 10 points for class rank), leadership in FFA activities (30 points), leadership in community activities (10 points), and participation in the Supervised Agricultural Experience (SAE) program (30 points). U.S. citizenship is required. **Deadline for Receipt:** February of each year.

1992 ■ NATIONAL FFA ORGANIZATION

Attn: Scholarship Office
6060 FFA Drive
P.O. Box 68960
Indianapolis, IN 46268-0960
Tel: (317)802-4321
Fax: (317)802-5321
E-mail: scholarships@ffa.org
Web Site: http://www.ffa.org

To provide financial assistance to FFA members who wish to study agriculture and related fields in college.

Title of Award: National FFA Scholarships for Undergraduates in the Sciences **Area, Field, or Subject:** Agricultural sciences; Animal science and behavior; Dairy science; Engineering, Agricultural; Environmental conservation; Environmental science; Equine studies; Food science and technology; Horticulture; Natural resources; Technology **Level of Education for which Award is Granted:** Undergraduate **Number Awarded:** Varies; generally, a total of approximately 1,000 scholarships are awarded annually by the association. **Funds Available:** Stipends vary, but most are at least $1,000. **Duration:** 1 year or more.

Eligibility Requirements: This program is open to current and former members of the organization who are working or planning to work full time on a degree in fields related to agriculture; this includes: agricultural mechanics and engineering, agricultural technology, animal science, conservation, dairy science, equine science, floriculture, food science, horticulture, irrigation, lawn and landscaping, and natural resources. For most of the scholarships, applicants must be high school seniors; others are open to students currently enrolled in college. The program includes a large number of designated scholarships that specify the locations where the members must live, the schools they must attend, the fields of study they must pursue, or other requirements. Some consider family income in the selection process, but most do not. Selection is based on academic achievement (10 points for GPA, 10 points for SAT or ACT score, 10 points for class rank), leadership in FFA activities (30 points), leadership in community activities (10 points), and participation in the Supervised Agricultural Experience (SAE) program (30 points). U.S. citizenship is required. **Deadline for Receipt:** February of each year. **Additional Information:** Funding for these scholarships is provided by many different corporate sponsors.

1993 ■ NATIONAL FFA ORGANIZATION

Attn: Scholarship Office
6060 FFA Drive
P.O. Box 68960
Indianapolis, IN 46268-0960
Tel: (317)802-4321
Fax: (317)802-5321
E-mail: scholarships@ffa.org
Web Site: http://www.ffa.org

To provide financial assistance to FFA members who are interested in working on a college degree in fields related to natural resources.

Title of Award: National Rifle Association of America Scholarships **Area, Field, or Subject:** Environmental conservation; Environmental science; Natural resources; Wildlife conservation, management, and science **Level of Education for which Award is Granted:** Four Year College **Number Awarded:** 5 each year. **Funds Available:** The stipend is $1,000. Funds are paid directly to the recipient. **Duration:** 1 year; nonrenewable.

Eligibility Requirements: This program is open to members who are graduating high school seniors planning to enroll full time in college. Applicants must be members of the National Rifle Association (NRA). They may be interested in working on a 4-year degree in any area, but preference is given to those majoring in conservation, natural resources, or wildlife management. Selection is based on academic achievement (10 points for GPA, 10 points for SAT or ACT score, 10 points for class rank), leadership in FFA activities (30 points), leadership in community activities (10 points), and participation in the Supervised Agricultural Experience

(SAE) program (30 points). U.S. citizenship is required. **Deadline for Receipt:** February of each year. **Additional Information:** Funding for these scholarships is provided by the National Rifle Association.

1994 ■ NATIONAL FFA ORGANIZATION

Attn: Scholarship Office
6060 FFA Drive
P.O. Box 68960
Indianapolis, IN 46268-0960
Tel: (317)802-4321
Fax: (317)802-5321
E-mail: scholarships@ffa.org
Web Site: http://www.ffa.org

To provide financial assistance to FFA members interested in studying agriculture or conservation in college.

Title of Award: National Wild Turkey Federation Scholarships **Area, Field, or Subject:** Agricultural sciences; Environmental conservation; Environmental science; Natural resources; Wildlife conservation, management, and science **Level of Education for which Award is Granted:** Undergraduate **Number Awarded:** 1 each year. **Funds Available:** The stipend is $5,000. Funds are paid directly to the recipient. **Duration:** 1 year; nonrenewable.

Eligibility Requirements: This program is open to members who are graduating high school seniors planning to enroll full time in college. Applicants must have a GPA of 3.0 or higher and be planning to attend a 2-year or 4-year college or university to major in natural resources, wildlife management, or agriculture. They must support the preservation of the hunting tradition, demonstrate a commitment to conservation, actively participate in the hunting sports, have strong leadership skills, be able to demonstrate financial need, and have work or volunteer experience in the hunting sports. Selection is based on academic achievement (10 points for GPA, 10 points for SAT or ACT score, 10 points for class rank), leadership in FFA activities (30 points), leadership in community activities (10 points), and participation in the Supervised Agricultural Experience (SAE) program (30 points). U.S. citizenship is required. **Deadline for Receipt:** February of each year. **Additional Information:** Funding for these scholarships is provided by the National Wild Turkey Federation.

1995 ■ NATIONAL INVENTORS HALL OF FAME

Attn: Collegiate Inventors Competition
221 South Broadway Street
Akron, OH 44308-1595
Tel: (330)849-6887
E-mail: collegiate@invent.org
Web Site: http://www.invent.org/collegiate

To recognize and reward outstanding inventions by college or university students in the fields of science, engineering, and technology.

Title of Award: Collegiate Inventors Competition **Area, Field, or Subject:** Biological and clinical sciences; Chemistry; Computer and information sciences; Engineering; Environmental conservation; Environmental science; Inventors; Mathematics and mathematical sciences; Medicine; Physics; Science; Technology; Veterinary science and medicine **Level of Education for which Award is Granted:** Graduate, Postdoctoral, Undergraduate **Number Awarded:** 15 semifinalists are selected each year; of those, 3 individuals or teams win prizes. **Funds Available:** Finalists receive an all-expense paid trip to Washington, D.C. to participate in a final round of judging and in the awards dinner and presentation. The Grand Prize winner or team receives $25,000. Other prizes are $10,000 for an undergraduate winner or team and $15,000 for a graduate winner or team. Academic advisors of the winning entries each receive a $3,000 cash prize. Awards are unrestricted cash gifts, not scholarships or grants. **Duration:** The competition is held annually.

Eligibility Requirements: This competition is open to undergraduate and graduate students who are (or have been) enrolled full time at least part of the 12-month period prior to entry in a college or university in the United States. Entries may also be submitted by teams, up to 4 members, of whom at least 1 must meet the full-time requirement and all others must have been enrolled at least half time sometime during the preceding 24-month period. Applicants must submit a description of their invention, including a patent search and summary of current literature that describes the state of the art and identifies the originality of the invention; test data demonstrating that the idea, invention, or design is workable; the societal, economic, and environmental benefits of the invention; and supplemental material that may include photos, slides, disks, videotapes, and even samples. Entries must be original ideas and the work of a student or team and a university advisor; the invention should be reproducible and may not have been 1) made available to the public as a commercial product or process, or 2) patented or published more than 1 year prior to the date of submission for this competition. Entries are first reviewed by a committee of judges that selects the finalists. The committee is comprised of mathematicians, engineers, biologists, chemists, environmentalists, physicists, computer specialists, members of the medical and veterinary profession, and specialists in invention and development of technology. Entries are judged on the basis of originality, inventiveness, potential value to society (socially, environmentally, and economically), and range or scope of use. **Deadline for Receipt:** May of each year. **Additional Information:** This program is co-sponsored by Abbott Laboratories and the United States Patent and Trademark Office. It was established in 1990 as the BFGoodrich Collegiate Inventors Program.

1996 ■ NEW JERSEY UTILITIES ASSOCIATION

50 West State Street, Suite 1117
Trenton, NJ 08608
Tel: (609)392-1000
Fax: (609)396-4231
Web Site: http://www.njua.org
To provide financial assistance to minority, female, and disabled high school seniors in New Jersey interested in majoring in selected subjects in college.
Title of Award: New Jersey Utilities Association Scholarships **Area, Field, or Subject:** Accounting; Biological and clinical sciences; Business administration; Chemistry; Engineering; Environmental conservation; Environmental science **Level of Education for which Award is Granted:** Undergraduate **Number Awarded:** 2 each year. **Funds Available:** The stipend is $1,500 per year. **Duration:** 4 years.
Eligibility Requirements: Eligible to apply for this scholarship are women, minorities (Black, Hispanic, American Indian/Alaska Native, or Asian American/Pacific Islander), and persons with disabilities who are high school seniors in New Jersey. They must be able to demonstrate financial need, be planning to enroll on a full-time basis at an institute of higher education, and be planning to work on a bachelor's degree in engineering, environmental science, chemistry, biology, business administration, or accounting. Children of employees of any New Jersey Utilities Association-member company are ineligible. Selection is based on overall academic excellence and demonstrated financial need. **Deadline for Receipt:** March of each year.

1997 ■ NORTH CENTRAL TEXAS COUNCIL OF GOVERNMENTS

Attn: Transportation Department
616 Six Flags Drive, Centerpoint Two
P.O. Box 5888
Arlington, TX 76005-5888
Tel: (817)695-9242
Fax: (817)640-7806
Web Site: http://www.nctcog.org/trans/admin/fellowship
To provide financial assistance to ethnic minorities, women, and economically disadvantaged persons who are interested in obtaining an undergraduate or graduate degree and work experience in a transportation-related field in Texas.
Title of Award: Transportation Fellowship Program **Area, Field, or Subject:** Engineering, Civil; Environmental conservation; Environmental science; Geography; Law; Management; Transportation; Urban affairs/design/planning **Level of Education for which Award is Granted:** Graduate, Undergraduate **Funds Available:** The stipend is $2,000. **Duration:** 1 year; may be renewed if the recipient maintains a GPA of 3.0 or higher.
Eligibility Requirements: This program is open to ethnic minorities (African Americans, Hispanics, American Indians, Alaskan Natives, Asians, and Pacific Islanders), women, and those who are economically disadvantaged. Only U.S. citizens or permanent residents may apply. They must attend or be willing to attend a college or university within the 16-county North Central Texas region as an undergraduate or graduate student. Applicants must have a GPA of 2.5 or higher. They may be enrolled full or part time, but they must be majoring in a designated transportation-related field: transportation planning, transportation or civil engineering, urban and regional planning, transportation/environmental

sciences, transportation law, urban or spatial geography, logistics, geographic information systems, or transportation management. Selection is based on financial need, interest in a professional career in transportation, and the ability to complete the program. **Deadline for Receipt:** March of each year. **Additional Information:** These fellowships are financed by the Federal Highway Administration, Federal Transit Administration, and the Texas Department of Transportation, in conjunction with local governments in north central Texas. An important part of the fellowship is an internship with a local agency (city or county), school, or transportation agency.

1998 ■ OAK RIDGE INSTITUTE FOR SCIENCE AND EDUCATION

Attn: Global Change Education Program
120 Badger Avenue, M.S. 36
P.O. Box 117
Oak Ridge, TN 37831-0117
Tel: (865)576-9655
E-mail: mary.kinney@orau.gov
Web Site: http://www.atmos.anl.gov/GCEP
To provide undergraduate students with an opportunity to conduct research during the summer on global change.
Title of Award: Global Change Summer Undergraduate Research Experience (SURE) **Area, Field, or Subject:** Atmospheric science; Earth sciences; Environmental conservation; Environmental science; Geosciences **Level of Education for which Award is Granted:** Undergraduate **Number Awarded:** 20 to 30 each year. **Funds Available:** Participants receive a weekly stipend of $475 and support for travel and housing. **Duration:** 10 to 12 weeks during the summer. Successful participants are expected to reapply for a second year of research with their mentors.
Eligibility Requirements: This program is open to undergraduates in their sophomore and junior years, although outstanding freshman and senior applicants are also considered. Applicants must be proposing to conduct research in a program area within the Department of Energy's Office of Biological and Environmental Research (DOE-BER): the atmospheric science program, the environmental meteorology program, the atmospheric radiation measurement program, the terrestrial carbon processes effort, the program for ecosystem research, and studies carried out under the direction of the National Institute for Global Environmental Change. Minority and female students are particularly encouraged to apply. U.S. citizenship is required. **Deadline for Receipt:** February of each year. **Additional Information:** This program, funded by DOE-BER, began in summer 1999. The first 2 weeks are spent in an orientation and focus session at a participating university. For the remaining 10 weeks, students conduct mentored research at 1 of the national laboratories or universities conducting BER-supported global change research.

1999 ■ OAK RIDGE INSTITUTE FOR SCIENCE AND EDUCATION

Attn: Science and Engineering Education
P.O. Box 117
Oak Ridge, TN 37831-0117
Tel: (865)576-9279
Fax: (865)241-5220
E-mail: coxre@orau.gov
Web Site: http://www.orau.gov/orise.htm
To provide financial assistance and research experience to undergraduate students at minority serving institutions who are majoring in scientific fields of interest to the National Oceanic and Atmospheric Administration (NOAA).
Title of Award: National Oceanic and Atmospheric Administration Educational Partnership Program with Minority Serving Institutions Undergraduate Scholarships **Area, Field, or Subject:** Atmospheric science; Biological and clinical sciences; Cartography/Surveying; Chemistry; Computer and information sciences; Engineering; Environmental conservation; Environmental science; Geography; Mathematics and mathematical sciences; Meteorology; Photogrammetry; Physical sciences; Physics **Level of Education for which Award is Granted:** Four Year College **Number Awarded:** 10 each year. **Funds Available:** This program provides payment of tuition and fees (to a maximum of $4,000 per year) and a stipend during the internship of $650 per week. **Duration:** 1 academic year and 2 summers.
Eligibility Requirements: This program is open to juniors and seniors at minority serving institutions, including Hispanic Serving Institutions (HSIs), Historically Black Colleges and Universities (HBCUs), and Tribal Colleges

and Universities (TCUs). Applicants must be majoring in atmospheric science, biology, cartography, chemistry, computer science, engineering, environmental science, geodesy, geography, marine science, mathematics, meteorology, photogrammetry, physical science, physics, or remote sensing. They must also be interested in participating in a research internship at a NOAA site. U.S. citizenship is required. **Deadline for Receipt:** January of each year. **Additional Information:** This program is funded by NOAA through an interagency agreement with the U.S. Department of Energy and administered by Oak Ridge Institute for Science and Education (ORISE).

2000 ■ OREGON STUDENT ASSISTANCE COMMISSION

Attn: Grants and Scholarships Division
1500 Valley River Drive, Suite 100
Eugene, OR 97401-2146
Tel: (541)687-7395
Free: 800-452-8807
Fax: (541)687-7419
E-mail: awardinfo@mercury.osac.state.or.us
Web Site: http://www.osac.state.or.us
To provide financial assistance for college to Eagle Scouts in Oregon interested in studying fields related to wildlife management.
Title of Award: Royden M. Bodley Scholarship **Area, Field, or Subject:** Environmental conservation; Environmental science; Forestry; Wildlife conservation, management, and science **Level of Education for which Award is Granted:** Undergraduate **Number Awarded:** Varies each year; recently, 5 of these scholarships were awarded. **Funds Available:** The stipend is at least $1,400. **Duration:** 1 year.
Eligibility Requirements: This program is open to graduates of high schools in the Boy Scouts of America Cascade Pacific Council. Applicants must have achieved the Eagle rank in Oregon and be attending or planning to attend college in the state. They must be interested in majoring in forestry, wildlife, environment, or a related field. **Deadline for Receipt:** February of each year. **Additional Information:** This program is administered by the Oregon Student Assistance Commission (OSAC) with funds provided by the Oregon Community Foundation, 1221 S.W. Yamhill, Suite 100, Portland, OR 97205, (503) 227-6846, Fax: (503) 274-7771.

2001 ■ PENNSYLVANIA ENERGY CONSORTIUM

Attn: PENCON Foundation
90 Lawton Lane
Milton, PA 17847-9756
Tel: (570)542-5602
E-mail: mwirth@csiu.org
Web Site: http://www.pencon.org
To recognize and reward, with college scholarships, seniors at high schools in Pennsylvania who submit outstanding science or environmental projects.
Title of Award: PENCON Foundation Scholarship **Area, Field, or Subject:** Environmental conservation; Environmental science; Science **Level of Education for which Award is Granted:** Undergraduate **Number Awarded:** Varies each year. Recently, 9 of these scholarships were awarded: 1 at $1,500 per year, 2 at $1,000 per year, 4 at $750 per year, and 2 at $500 per year. **Funds Available:** Stipends range from $500 to $1,500 per year. **Duration:** 1 year; may be renewed up to 3 additional years.
Eligibility Requirements: This competition is open to seniors graduating from high schools that are members of the Pennsylvania Energy Consortium (PENCON). Applicants must have a GPA of 2.0 or higher and be planning to attend an institution of postsecondary education or training. They must submit an abstract of a scientific or environmental project they have conducted, including its goals and objectives, the activities it entailed, what they learned from it, and its significance for them and for others. Selection is based on the merit and quality of the project, the content and quality of an autobiographical essay, initiative and commitment to school and community service activities, academic achievement, recommendations, and financial need. **Deadline for Receipt:** Letters of intent must be submitted by November of each year. Completed projects are due in February.

2002 ■ ROCKY MOUNTAIN ELK FOUNDATION

Attn: Maggie Engler
2291 West Broadway

P.O. Box 8249
Missoula, MT 59807-8249
Tel: (406)523-4500
Free: 800-CALL
Fax: (406)523-4550
E-mail: mengler@rmef.org
Web Site: http://www.rmef.org/pages/scholar.html
To provide financial assistance to upper-division students who are majoring in wildlife studies.
Title of Award: Wildlife Leadership Awards **Area, Field, or Subject:** Environmental conservation; Environmental science; Wildlife conservation, management, and science **Level of Education for which Award is Granted:** Four Year College **Number Awarded:** 10 each year. **Funds Available:** The stipend is $2,000. In addition, recipients are given an engraved plaque and a 1-year membership in the foundation. **Duration:** 1 year; nonrenewable.
Eligibility Requirements: This program is open to students enrolled in a recognized wildlife program at a 4-year college or university in the United States or Canada. Applicants must be juniors or seniors, have at least 1 semester or 2 quarters remaining in their degree program, and be scheduled to enroll as full-time students the following fall semester/quarter. Previous recipients of this award are ineligible. Selection is based on hobbies and leisure activities (5 points), leadership activities (25 points), employment experience (5 points), a 300-word essay on how wildlife fits into specified federal laws (15 points), a 300-word essay on what they believe to be the most important conservation issues facing North American during the next 10 years (20 points), a 250-word essay on the role of hunting in conservation (15 points), and a 100-word statement on their career goals and objectives (5 points). **Deadline for Receipt:** February of each year. **Additional Information:** This program was established in 1990.

2003 ■ ROCKY MOUNTAIN WATER ENVIRONMENT ASSOCIATION

c/o Ray Kemp
City of Fort Collins Water Reclamation
3036 Environmental Drive
Fort Collins, CO 80525
Tel: (970)221-6900
Fax: (970)221-6970
E-mail: rkemp@fcgov.com
Web Site: http://www.rmwea.org
To provide financial assistance to students in Colorado, New Mexico, and Wyoming, including members of the Rocky Mountain Water Environment Association (RMWEA) and their dependents, who are interested in studying a water environment field in college.
Title of Award: Bill Martin Memorial Scholarship **Area, Field, or Subject:** Biological and clinical sciences; Environmental conservation; Environmental science; Water resources **Level of Education for which Award is Granted:** Undergraduate **Number Awarded:** 2 each year: 1 from each category of applicant. **Funds Available:** The stipend is $1,000. Recipients are also entitled to a 1-year complimentary student or associate membership in the RMWEA. **Duration:** 1 year.
Eligibility Requirements: This program is open to 1) members of the RMWEA and their dependents who are enrolled at a 2- or 4-year college or university and working on a degree related to the water environment profession (e.g., biology, environmental science, engineering with a strong emphasis in wastewater treatment, water pollution control, environmental protection); and 2) high school seniors planning to enroll at a 2- or 4-year college or university to prepare for a career in the water environmental field. Along with their application, they must submit an essay of 200 to 300 words on their interest in the environment and how this interest influences their career goals. Selection is based on that essay (25%), relevance of the course of study to the water environment profession (35%), letters of recommendation (20%), and GPA (20%). **Deadline for Receipt:** April of each year. **Additional Information:** This program was established in 2002.

2004 ■ SIEMENS FOUNDATION

170 Wood Avenue South
Iselin, NJ 08830
877-822-5233
Fax: (732)603-5890
E-mail: foundation@sc.siemens.com

Web Site: http://www.siemens-foundation.org/awards

To recognize and reward high school students with exceptional scores on the Advanced Placement (AP) examinations in mathematics and the sciences.

Title of Award: Siemens Awards for Advanced Placement **Area, Field, or Subject:** Biological and clinical sciences; Chemistry; Computer and information sciences; Environmental conservation; Environmental science; Mathematics and mathematical sciences; Physics; Statistics **Level of Education for which Award is Granted:** Professional, Undergraduate **Number Awarded:** 24 regional scholarships (2 females and 2 males in each of the 6 regions), 2 national scholarships (1 female and 1 male), 12 high school awards (in each region, 1 to a school for improvement in the number and percentage of students taking AP examinations, 1 to an urban school for providing access to AP mathematics and science to minorities), and 18 teacher awards (in each region, 2 for commitment to students and the AP program, 1 for teaching minorities) are awarded each year. **Funds Available:** Regional scholarships are $3,000; national winners receive additional $5,000 scholarships. Awards to teachers and to schools are $1,000. **Duration:** The awards are presented annually.

Eligibility Requirements: All students in U.S. high schools are eligible to be considered for these awards (including home-schooled students and those in U.S. territories). Each fall, the College Board identifies the male and female seniors in each of its regions who have earned the highest number of scores on 7 AP exams: biology, calculus BC, chemistry, computer science AB, environmental science, physics C (physics C: mechanics and physics C: electricity each count as half), and statistics. Males and females are considered separately. Regional winners receive all-expense paid trips to Washington, D.C., where national winners are announced. The program also recognizes and rewards monetarily 1) schools that have shown the greatest improvement in the number and percentage of students taking AP examinations in biology, calculus, chemistry, computer science, environmental science, physics, and statistics in the past year; and 2) non-magnet urban schools that provide access to AP mathematics and science to a significant number of underrepresented minority students. In addition, teachers are rewarded for their commitment to students and the AP program. Additional teachers are recognized because they have successfully taught AP mathematics and/or science to underrepresented minority students in non-magnet urban schools. **Deadline for Receipt:** There is no application or nomination process for these awards. The College Board identifies the students, teachers, and high schools for the Siemens Foundation. **Additional Information:** Information from the College Board is available at (703) 707-8999.

2005 ■ SOCIETY OF AMERICAN MILITARY ENGINEERS-WASHINGTON DC POST

c/o Al O'Konski, Scholarship Committee Chair
URS Corporation
2020 K Street, N.W., Suite 300
Washington, DC 20006-1806
Tel: (202)872-0277
Fax: (202)872-0282
E-mail: Al_O'Konski@urscorp.com
Web Site: http://www.samedcpost.org/scholarship.html

To provide financial assistance to students interested in majoring in engineering, architecture, or environmental sciences.

Title of Award: Washington DC Post Scholarships **Area, Field, or Subject:** Architecture; Engineering; Environmental conservation; Environmental science **Level of Education for which Award is Granted:** Undergraduate **Number Awarded:** Varies each year; recently, 8 of these scholarships were awarded. **Funds Available:** The current stipend is $1,200. Funds are paid to the recipient's school after college enrollment is confirmed. **Duration:** 1 year.

Eligibility Requirements: This program is open to students who are enrolled full time at an accredited university as rising freshmen, sophomores, or juniors, are U.S. citizens, are of good character, and are majoring in engineering, architecture, or environmental science. Applicants must submit a 2-page narrative addressing the following topics: their academic performance, academic and professional goals, financial need, extracurricular activities, a summary of previous military service (if any), and a statement of why they should be considered for the award. Preference is given to applicants in the Washington, D.C. area. **Deadline for Receipt:** January of each year. **Additional Information:** This

program includes the following named scholarships: the Paul Brott Scholarship, the Linda McCarthy Scholarship, the T-Bird/RPI Environmental Scholarship, and the Ronald Hubbard Scholarship.

2006 ■ SOCIETY FOR MINING, METALLURGY, AND EXPLORATION, INC.

Attn: Student Center
8307 Shaffer Parkway
Littleton, CO 80127-4102
Tel: (303)973-9550
Free: 800-763-3132
Fax: (303)973-3845
E-mail: sme@smenet.org
Web Site: http://www.smenet.org/education/students/sme_scholarships.cfm

To provide financial assistance to upper-division student members of the Society for Mining, Metallurgy, and Exploration (SME) who are majoring in fields that will develop their skills related to mining and the environment.

Title of Award: Environmental Division Scholarship **Area, Field, or Subject:** Economics; Engineering, Mining and Mineral; Environmental conservation; Environmental science; Geology; Metallurgy **Level of Education for which Award is Granted:** Four Year College **Number Awarded:** 1 or more each year. **Funds Available:** A total of $2,000 is awarded each year. **Duration:** 1 year.

Eligibility Requirements: Applicants must 1) be majoring in a field related to the minerals industry (e.g., geology, minerals engineering, mining engineering, or mineral economics) at a 4-year college or university, 2) have completed at least their sophomore year in college, 3) be a U.S. citizen, and 4) be a student member of the society. They must be of good character, be of sound health, have demonstrated scholastic aptitude (GPA of 3.0 or higher), and be able to demonstrate financial need. Candidates for these scholarships must be working on an undergraduate degree related to mining and the environment with a faculty advisor who has special interests in an environmentally-oriented program. **Deadline for Receipt:** October of each year.

2007 ■ SOIL AND WATER CONSERVATION SOCIETY

Attn: Scholarships
945 S.W. Ankeny Road
Ankeny, IA 50021-9764
Tel: (515)289-2331
Free: 800-THE
Fax: (515)289-1227
E-mail: swcs@swcs.org
Web Site: http://www.swcs.org/en/scholarships

To provide financial assistance to members of the Soil and Water Conservation Society (SWCS) who are currently employed and wish to improve their technical or administrative competence.

Title of Award: Donald A. Williams Soil Conservation Scholarships **Area, Field, or Subject:** Environmental conservation; Environmental science; Soil science; Water resources **Level of Education for which Award is Granted:** Undergraduate **Number Awarded:** 1 each year. **Funds Available:** The stipend is $1,500. **Duration:** 1 year.

Eligibility Requirements: This program is open to undergraduate members of the society who have completed at least 1 year of full-time employment in a natural resource conservation job with a federal, state, or local government agency, organization, or business firm. Applicants must be currently employed and able to show reasonable financial need. Selection is based on demonstrated integrity, ability, competence in work, and skills gained through training or experience. **Deadline for Receipt:** February of each year. **Additional Information:** Recipients are not required to work on a degree.

2008 ■ SOUTH CAROLINA SPACE GRANT CONSORTIUM

c/o College of Charleston
Department of Geology and Environmental Sciences
66 George Street
Charleston, SC 29424
Tel: (843)953-5463
Fax: (843)953-5446
E-mail: scozzarot@cofc.edu
Web Site: http://www.cofc.edu/~scsgrant/scholar/overview.html

To provide financial assistance to upper-division and graduate students in South Carolina who are preparing for a career as a science and mathematics teacher.

Title of Award: South Carolina Space Grant Consortium Pre-Service Teacher Scholarships **Area, Field, or Subject:** Aerospace sciences; Astronomy and astronomical sciences; Education; Engineering; Engineering, Aerospace/Aeronautical/Astronautical; Environmental conservation; Environmental science; Science; Space and planetary sciences **Level of Education for which Award is Granted:** Four Year College, Graduate **Number Awarded:** Varies each year. **Funds Available:** The stipend is $2,000. Funds may be used for such expenses as 1) partial payment of tuition; 2) travel and registration for attending science and mathematics education workshops or conferences for the purpose of professional development; 3) purchase of supplies for student teaching activities; or 4) other supportive activities that lead to successful professional development and graduation as an educator in South Carolina. **Duration:** 1 year.

Eligibility Requirements: This program is open to juniors, seniors, and graduate students at member institutions of the South Carolina Space Grant Consortium. Applicants must be working on a teaching certificate in science, mathematics, or engineering. Their areas of interest may include, but are not limited to, the basic sciences, astronomy, science education, planetary science, environmental studies, or engineering. U.S. citizenship is required. Selection is based on academic qualifications of the applicant; 2 letters of recommendation; a description of past activities, current interests, and future plans concerning a space science or aerospace-related field; a sample lesson plan using curriculum materials available from the U.S. National Aeronautics and Space Administration (NASA); and faculty sponsorship. Women, minorities, and persons with disabilities are encouraged to apply. **Deadline for Receipt:** January of each year. **Additional Information:** Members of the consortium are Benedict College, The Citadel, College of Charleston, Clemson University, Coastal Carolina University, Furman University, University of South Carolina, Wofford College, South Carolina State University, The Medical University of South Carolina, and University of the Virgin Islands. This program is funded by NASA.

2009 ■ SOUTH DAKOTA SPACE GRANT CONSORTIUM

Attn: Deputy Director and Outreach Coordinator
South Dakota School of Mines and Technology
Mineral Industries Building, Room 228
501 East St. Joseph Street
Rapid City, SD 57701-3995
Tel: (605)394-1975
Fax: (605)394-5360
E-mail: Thomas.Durkin@sdsmt.edu
Web Site: http://www.sdsmt.edu/space

To provide funding to undergraduate and graduate students for space-related activities in South Dakota.

Title of Award: South Dakota Space Grant Consortium Graduate Fellowships and Undergraduate Scholarships **Area, Field, or Subject:** Aerospace sciences; Earth sciences; Engineering, Aerospace/Aeronautical/Astronautical; Environmental conservation; Environmental science; Geology; Geosciences; Mathematics and mathematical sciences; Space and planetary sciences; Technology **Level of Education for which Award is Granted:** Graduate, Undergraduate **Number Awarded:** Varies each year. Approximately $70,000 is available for this program annually. **Funds Available:** Stipends range from $1,000 to $7,500. **Duration:** 1 academic year, semester, or summer.

Eligibility Requirements: This program is open to undergraduate and graduate students at member and affiliated institutions of the South Dakota Space Grant Consortium. Applicants must be interested in 1) earth- and space-science related educational and research projects in fields relevant to the goals of the U.S. National Aeronautics and Space Administration (NASA); or 2) eventual employment with NASA or in a NASA-related career field in science, technology, engineering, and mathematics (STEM) education. Activities may include student research and educational efforts in remote sensing, GIS, global and regional geoscience, environmental science, and K-12 educational outreach; exposure to NASA-relevant projects; and internship experiences at various NASA centers and the Earth Resources Observation and Science (EROS) Center in Sioux Falls. U.S. citizenship is required. Women, members of underrepresented groups (African Americans, Hispanics, Pacific Islanders, Asian Americans, Native Americans, and persons with disabilities), and Tribal College students are specifically encouraged to apply. Selection is based on academic qualifications of the application (preference is given to students with a GPA of 3.0 or higher), quality of the application and its career goal statement, and assessment of the applicant's motivation toward an earth science, aerospace, or engineering career or research. **Deadline for Receipt:** January of each year. **Additional Information:** Member institutions include South Dakota School of Mines and Technology, South Dakota State University, and Augustana College. Educational affiliates include Black Hills State University, the University of South Dakota, Dakota State University, Lower Brule Community College, Oglala Lakota College, Sinte Gleska University, and Lake Area Technical Institute.

2010 ■ SURFRIDER FOUNDATION

Attn: Pratte Scholarship
P.O. Box 6010
San Clemente, CA 92674-6010
Tel: (949)492-8170
Fax: (949)492-8142
E-mail: prattescholarship@surfrider.org
Web Site: http://www.surfrider.org

To provide financial assistance to members of the Surfrider Foundation working on an undergraduate or graduate degree in an environmental field.

Title of Award: Thomas Pratte Memorial Scholarships **Area, Field, or Subject:** Environmental conservation; Environmental science; Marine biology; Natural resources; Oceanography; Public administration; Urban affairs/design/planning **Level of Education for which Award is Granted:** Four Year College, Graduate **Number Awarded:** 3 each year: 1 for a student at each academic level. **Funds Available:** The stipend is $2,000 for an undergraduate, $3,000 for a master's degree student, and $5,000 for a doctoral student. **Duration:** 1 year.

Eligibility Requirements: This program is open to members of the foundation working on an undergraduate, master's, or doctoral degree in a field consistent with the foundation's mission, including (but not limited to) oceanography, marine affairs, environmental sciences, public policy, community planning, or natural resources. Applicants must be enrolled at an accredited college or university in the United States or Puerto Rico as an upper-division or graduate student. Undergraduates must have a GPA of 3.4 or higher and graduate students 3.6 or higher. Along with their application, they must submit 1) a personal statement describing their career goals, volunteer activities, work, or summer plans as they pertain to the coastal environmental issues relevant to the foundation and its mission; and 2) a description of their current research and how it relates to the foundation's stated mission and environmental programs. Financial need is not considered in the selection process. **Deadline for Receipt:** March of each year. **Additional Information:** This foundation, established in 1984 by a group of surfers, is a nonprofit environmental grassroots organization dedicated to the protection and preservation of the world's waves, oceans, and beaches. It currently has 50,000 members with 60 chapters in 22 states.

2011 ■ SWEDISH WOMEN'S EDUCATION ASSOCIATION INTERNATIONAL-SOUTH FLORIDA CHAPTER

c/o Yerti Nelson, Scholarship Committee
3759 Mykonos Court
Boca Raton, FL 33486
Tel: (561)997-2050
Fax: (561)997-8010
E-mail: florida@swea.org
Web Site: http://www.chapters-swea.org/florida

To provide financial assistance to Florida residents interested in studying in Sweden or an area related to Swedish studies.

Title of Award: South Florida SWEA Scholarship **Area, Field, or Subject:** Art; Art industries and trade; Crafts; Design; Environmental conservation; Environmental science; Foreign languages; General studies/Field of study not specified; Literature; Music; Swedish studies **Level of Education for which Award is Granted:** Graduate, Professional, Undergraduate **Number Awarded:** 1 each year. **Funds Available:** The stipend is $3,000.

Eligibility Requirements: This program is open to all residents of Florida interested in participating in an exchange program in Sweden. Applicants may also propose to study in the United States, if the studies specifically emphasize Sweden and Swedish aspects, including 1) Swedish language; 2) Swedish culture or traditions; 3) environmental science; 4) a health care program promoting better health for women and children; or 5) handicraft, art, glass art, music, literature, or design. Study proposals must be well-defined in time and content. Along with their application, they must submit a transcript from college, university, or vocational school; curriculum vitae; project proposal, describing the planned studies, length of studies, and goals; financial statement; and letter of recommendation from an instructor. **Deadline for Receipt:** January of each year. **Additional Information:** Within 3 months after the end of studies or the project, the recipient must report to the scholarship committee or, if possible, accept an invitation to an organization meeting to share the experience.

2012 ■ HARRY S. TRUMAN SCHOLARSHIP FOUNDATION

Attn: Executive Secretary
712 Jackson Place, N.W.
Washington, DC 20006
Tel: (202)395-4831
Fax: (202)395-6995
E-mail: office@truman.gov
Web Site: http://www.truman.gov
To provide grants-for-service for graduate school to current college juniors who are interested in preparing for a career in public service.
Title of Award: Harry S. Truman Scholarship Program **Area, Field, or Subject:** Agricultural sciences; Biological and clinical sciences; Economics; Education; Engineering; Environmental conservation; Environmental science; History; International affairs and relations; Law; Physical sciences; Political science; Public administration; Public health; Public service; Social sciences; Technology **Level of Education for which Award is Granted:** Four Year College, Graduate **Number Awarded:** 70 to 75 each year: a) 1 "state" scholarship is available to a qualified resident nominee in each of the 50 states, the District of Columbia, Puerto Rico, and the Islands (Guam, the Virgin Islands, American Samoa, and the Commonwealth of the Northern Mariana Islands); and b) up to 25 at-large scholars. **Funds Available:** The program provides up to $30,000, including up to $15,000 for the first year of graduate study and up to $15,000 for the final year of graduate study. **Duration:** Support is provided for the first and last year of graduate study.
Eligibility Requirements: Students must be nominated to be considered for this program. Nominees must be full-time students with junior standing at a 4-year institution, committed to a career in government or public service, in the upper quarter of their class, and U.S. citizens or nationals. Each participating institution may nominate up to 4 candidates (and up to 3 additional students who completed their first 2 years at a community college); community colleges and other 2-year institutions may nominate former students who are enrolled as full-time students with junior-level academic standing at accredited 4-year institutions. Selection is based on extent and quality of community service and government involvement, academic performance, leadership record, suitability of the nominee's proposed program of study for a career in public service, and writing and analytical skills. Priority is given to candidates who plan to enroll in a graduate program that specifically trains them for a career in public service, including government at any level, uniformed services, public interest organizations, nongovernmental research and/or educational organizations, public and private schools, and public service oriented nonprofit organizations. The fields of study may include agriculture, biology, engineering, environmental management, physical and social sciences, and technology policy, as well as such traditional fields as economics, education, government, history, international relations, law, nonprofit management, political science, public administration, public health, and public policy. Interviews are required. **Deadline for Receipt:** February of each year. **Additional Information:** Recipients may attend graduate school in the United States or in foreign countries. Scholars are required to work in public service for 3 of the 7 years following completion of a graduate degree program funded by this program. Scholars who do not meet this service requirement, or who fail to provide timely proof to the foundation of such employment, will be required to repay funds received, along with interest.

2013 ■ MORRIS K. UDALL FOUNDATION

130 South Scott Avenue
Tucson, AZ 85701-1922
Tel: (520)670-5529

Fax: (520)670-5530
Web Site: http://www.udall.gov/scholarship
To provide financial assistance to 1) college sophomores and juniors who intend to prepare for a career in environmental public policy and 2) Native American and Alaska Native students who intend to prepare for a career in health care or tribal public policy.
Title of Award: Morris K. Udall Scholarships **Area, Field, or Subject:** Business administration; Economics; Education; Environmental conservation; Environmental science; Health care services; Native American studies; Natural resources; Political science; Public administration; Public health; Urban affairs/design/planning **Level of Education for which Award is Granted:** Undergraduate **Number Awarded:** Approximately 80 scholarships and 50 honorable mentions are awarded each year. **Funds Available:** The maximum stipend for scholarship winners is $5,000 per year. Funds are to be used for tuition, fees, books, and room and board. Honorable mention stipends are $350. **Duration:** 1 year; recipients nominated as sophomores may be renominated in their junior year.
Eligibility Requirements: Each 2-year and 4-year college and university in the United States and its possessions may nominate up to 6 sophomores or juniors from either or both categories of this program: 1) students who intend to prepare for a career in environmental public policy, and 2) Native American and Alaska Native students who intend to prepare for a career in health care or tribal public policy. For the first category, the program seeks future leaders across a wide spectrum of environmental fields, such as policy, engineering, science, education, urban planning and renewal, business, health, justice, and economics. For the second category, the program seeks future Native American and Alaska Native leaders in public and community health care, tribal government, and public policy affecting Native American communities, including land and resource management, economic development, and education. Nominees must be U.S. citizens, nationals, or permanent residents with a GPA of 3.0 or higher. Along with their application, they must submit an 800-word essay discussing a significant public speech, legislative act, or public policy statement by former Congressman Morris K. Udall and its impact on their field of study, interests, and career goals. Selection is based on demonstrated commitment to 1) environmental issues through substantial commitment to and participation in 1 or more of the following: campus activities, research, community service, or public service; or 2) tribal public policy or Native American health through substantial contributions to and participation in 1 or more of the following: campus activities, tribal involvement, community or public service, or research; a course of study and proposed career likely to lead to position where nominee can make significant contributions to the shaping of environmental, tribal public policy, or Native American health care issues, whether through scientific advances, public or political service, or community action; and leadership, character, desire to make a difference, and general well-roundedness. **Deadline for Receipt:** Faculty representatives must submit their nominations by early March of each year.

2014 ■ U.S. MARINE CORPS

Manpower and Reserve Affairs (MMEA-85)
3280 Russell Road
Quantico, VA 22134-5103
Tel: (703)784-9264
Fax: (703)784-9843
Web Site: http://www.usmc.mil
To allow selected noncommissioned Marine Corps officers to earn a bachelor's degree in selected fields by pursuing full-time college study while continuing to receive their regular pay and allowances.
Title of Award: Marine Corps Staff Noncommissioned Officers Degree Completion Program **Area, Field, or Subject:** Accounting; Business administration; Education; Environmental conservation; Environmental science; Finance; Management; Music; Protective services; Psychology **Level of Education for which Award is Granted:** Undergraduate **Number Awarded:** Varies each year; recently, 5 Marines were selected to participate in this program. **Funds Available:** Noncommissioned officers selected to participate in this program receive their regular Marine Corps pay while attending a college or university on a full-time basis. Tuition, matriculation fees, and other expenses (such as books) must be paid by the recipient through personal funds, in-service Montgomery GI Bill benefits, student loans, or other non-Marine Corps means. **Duration:** Up to the equivalent of 2 academic years.

Eligibility Requirements: Eligible to participate in this program are regular active-duty Marines, especially in the grades of staff sergeant and gunnery sergeant. Applicants must have completed at least 2 years of postsecondary study and have been accepted by an accredited degree-granting college or university in a program offered to all matriculating students; enrollment in a multiple major program designed for adults returning to school does not qualify. The program recently was limited to the following majors: accounting, business administration with an emphasis on accounting or financial management, education, environmental safety, environmental health management, hazardous material and waste control, music, occupational safety, psychology, safety education, safety management, and waste control. **Deadline for Receipt:** April of each year. **Additional Information:** Applicants must agree to extend/reenlist for a period of 4 years beyond completion of this program.

2015 ■ U.S. NAVY

Attn: Naval Medical Education
Code OG3
8901 Wisconsin Avenue, 16th Floor, Tower 1
Bethesda, MD 20889-5611
Tel: (301)319-4520
E-mail: mscipp@nmetc.med.navy.mil
Web Site: http://nshs.med.navy.mil/mscipp/mscipp.htm
To provide funding to Navy and Marine enlisted personnel who wish to earn an undergraduate or graduate degree in selected health care specialties while continuing to receive their regular pay and allowances.
Title of Award: Medical Service Corps Inservice Procurement Program (MSC-IPP) **Area, Field, or Subject:** Entomology; Environmental conservation; Environmental science; Health care services; Industrial hygiene; Medical assisting; Pharmaceutical sciences **Level of Education for which Award is Granted:** Four Year College, Graduate **Number Awarded:** Varies each year. Recently, 36 of these positions were available: 20 in health care administration, 10 in physician assistant, 2 in pharmacy, 2 in environmental health, 1 in industrial hygiene, and 1 in entomology. **Funds Available:** Participants receive payment of tuition, mandatory fees, a book allowance, and full pay and allowances for their enlisted pay grade. They are eligible for advancement while in college. **Duration:** 24 to 48 months of full-time, year-round study, until completion of a relevant degree.
Eligibility Requirements: This program is open to enlisted personnel who are serving on active duty in pay grades E-5 through E-9 of the U.S. Navy, U.S. Marine Corps, Naval Reserve (including the Training and Administration of the Reserve Program), and the Marine Corps Reserve (including the Active Reserve Program). Applicants must be interested in working on a degree to become commissioned in the following medical specialties: health care administration, physician assistant, pharmacy, environmental health, industrial hygiene, or entomology. If they plan to work on a graduate degree, they must have scores of at least 900 on the GRE or 470 on the GMAT; if they plan to work on a bachelor's or physician assistant degree, they must have scores of at least 1000 on the SAT (including 460 on the mathematics portion) or 42 on the ACT. They must be U.S. citizens who can be commissioned before they reach their 42nd birthday. **Deadline for Receipt:** August of each year. **Additional Information:** Following graduation, participants are commissioned in the Medical Service Corps and attend Officer Indoctrination School.

2016 ■ VIRGINIA DAUGHTERS OF THE AMERICAN REVOLUTION

c/o Catherine Rafferty, Scholarship Chair
10101 Sanders Court
Great Falls, VA 22066-2526
Web Site: http://www.vadar.org/vadarscholarships.htm
To provide financial assistance to high school seniors in Virginia who wish to study designated fields in college.
Title of Award: Virginia DAR Scholarships **Area, Field, or Subject:** Environmental conservation; Environmental science; Forestry; Genealogy; History, American; Home Economics; Medicine; Science **Level of Education for which Award is Granted:** Undergraduate **Number Awarded:** 2 each year: 1 at $1,000 and 1 at $500. **Funds Available:** Stipends are $1,000 or $500. **Duration:** 1 year.
Eligibility Requirements: This program is open to seniors graduating from high schools in Virginia who plan to attend a Virginia college or university. Applicants must be planning to work on a degree in the field of science, medicine, conservation, ecology, forestry, home arts, genealogi-

cal research, or American history. Along with their application, they must submit a 1,000-word letter giving their reasons for interest in the scholarship, a transcript of grades, a letter of recommendation from a teacher in their chosen field, and documentation of financial need. **Deadline for Receipt:** January of each year.

2017 ■ VIRGINIA SPACE GRANT CONSORTIUM

Attn: Fellowship Coordinator
Old Dominion University Peninsula Center
600 Butler Farm Road
Hampton, VA 23666
Tel: (757)766-5210
Fax: (757)766-5205
E-mail: vsgc@odu.edu
Web Site: http://www.vsgc.odu.edu/Menu3_1_1.htm
To provide financial assistance for college or graduate school to students in Virginia planning a career as science, mathematics, or technology educators.
Title of Award: Virginia Space Grant Teacher Education Scholarship Program **Area, Field, or Subject:** Aerospace sciences; Earth sciences; Education; Environmental conservation; Environmental science; Geosciences; Mathematics and mathematical sciences; Science; Space and planetary sciences; Technology **Level of Education for which Award is Granted:** Four Year College, Master's **Number Awarded:** Approximately 10 each year. **Funds Available:** The maximum stipend is $1,000. **Duration:** 1 year; nonrenewable.
Eligibility Requirements: This program is open to full-time undergraduate students at the Virginia Space Grant Consortium (VSGC) colleges and universities in a track that will qualify them to teach in a pre-college setting. Priority is given to those majoring in technology education, mathematics, or science, particularly earth, space, or environmental science. Applicants may apply while seniors in high school or sophomores in a community college, with the award contingent on their enrollment at a VSGC college and entrance into a teacher certification program. They must submit a statement of academic goals and plan of study, explaining their reasons for desiring to enter the teaching profession, specifically the fields of science, mathematics, or technology education. Students currently enrolled in a VSGC college can apply when they declare their intent to enter the teacher certification program. Students enrolled in a master of education degree program leading to teacher certification in eligible fields are also eligible to apply. Applicants must be U.S. citizens with a GPA of 3.0 or higher. Since an important purpose of this program is to increase the participation of underrepresented minorities, women, and persons with disabilities in science, mathematics, and technology education, the VSGC especially encourages applications from those students. **Deadline for Receipt:** February of each year. **Additional Information:** The VSGC institutions are College of William and Mary, Hampton University, Old Dominion University, the University of Virginia, and Virginia Polytechnic Institute and State University. This program is funded by the U.S. National Aeronautics and Space Administration (NASA).

2018 ■ IZAAK WALTON LEAGUE OF AMERICA-MINNESOTA DIVISION

Attn: Scholarship Committee
555 Park Street, Suite 140
St. Paul, MN 55103-2110
Tel: (651)221-0215
E-mail: ikes@minnesotaikes.org
Web Site: http://www.minnesotaikes.org
To provide financial assistance to Minnesota residents who are studying an environmental field in college.
Title of Award: Minnesota Division Scholarship **Area, Field, or Subject:** Education; Environmental conservation; Environmental law; Environmental science; Wildlife conservation, management, and science **Level of Education for which Award is Granted:** Undergraduate **Number Awarded:** 1 or more each year. **Funds Available:** The stipend is $1,000 per year. **Duration:** 1 year; may be renewed.
Eligibility Requirements: This program is open to residents of Minnesota who are in at least their second year of college. Applicants must be majoring in environmental education, environmental law, wildlife management, or some other conservation-oriented program. They must be U.S. citizens and able to demonstrate financial need. Along with their application, they must submit a 1-page essay on their belief in conservation and

what the future holds for them (including their educational plans and career goals), a transcript, a description of their program of study, and 2 letters of recommendation. An interview may be requested. **Deadline for Receipt:** May of each year.

2019 ■ WILDLIFE SOCIETY-FLORIDA CHAPTER

c/o Maria Zondervan, Scholarship Committee Chair
St. Johns River Water Management District
975 Keller Road
Altamonte Springs, FL 32714-1618
Tel: (407)659-4872
E-mail: mzondervan@sjrwmd.com
Web Site: http://fltws.org
To provide financial assistance to upper-division students working on a degree in wildlife ecology and/or management at a Florida college.
Title of Award: Florida Chapter of the Wildlife Society Scholarship **Area, Field, or Subject:** Environmental conservation; Environmental science; Wildlife conservation, management, and science **Level of Education for which Award is Granted:** Four Year College **Number Awarded:** 1 each year. **Funds Available:** The stipend is $1,000. **Duration:** 1 year.
Eligibility Requirements: This program is open to students entering their junior or senior year at a 4-year college or university in Florida. Applicants must be interested in preparing for a career in wildlife ecology and/or management. They must have a GPA of 2.5 or higher. Along with their application, they must submit a letter describing their professional goals and financial need. Selection is based on goals as expressed in the letter, extracurricular activities, demonstrated leadership, professional potential, and financial need. **Deadline for Receipt:** November of each year. **Additional Information:** This program, established in 1998, is jointly sponsored by the Florida chapter of The Wildlife Society, the Florida chapter of the National Wild Turkey Federation, and the Florida Wildlife Federation.

Ecology

2020 ■ MINNESOTA TRAPPERS ASSOCIATION

c/o Deb Offerdahl
230 Second Street S.E.
Milaca, MN 56353
Tel: (320)982-1385
Web Site: http://www.mntrappers.com
To provide financial assistance for college to members of the Minnesota Trappers Association (MTA) and to other students working on a degree in a field related to natural resources.
Title of Award: Minnesota Trappers Association Scholarships **Area, Field, or Subject:** Agricultural sciences; Engineering, Agricultural; Forestry; General studies/Field of study not specified; Natural resources; Veterinary science and medicine; Wildlife conservation, management, and science; Zoology **Level of Education for which Award is Granted:** Undergraduate **Number Awarded:** 7 each year: 1 at $2,000, 2 at $1,000, 1 at $600 (the Russ Cumberland Scholarship), and 3 at $500. **Funds Available:** Stipends range from $500 to $2,000. **Duration:** 1 year.
Eligibility Requirements: This program is open to 1) MTA members working on an undergraduate degree in any field; and 2) other undergraduates working on a degree in agricultural engineering, agricultural science, forestry, natural resources, veterinary medicine, wildlife biology, or zoology. Applicants must be entering or enrolled in a 2- or 4-year program at an accredited college or university and have a college GPA of 2.5 or higher (entering freshmen must submit a transcript of their first term of college work before funds are released). **Deadline for Receipt:** June of each year. **Additional Information:** This program includes the Russ Cumberland Scholarship. Information is also available from Todd Roggenkamp, 28952 438th Lane, Palasade, MN 56373, (218) 768-2597.

2021 ■ NATIONAL FFA ORGANIZATION

Attn: Scholarship Office
6060 FFA Drive
P.O. Box 68960
Indianapolis, IN 46268-0960
Tel: (317)802-4321
Fax: (317)802-5321
E-mail: scholarships@ffa.org

Web Site: http://www.ffa.org
To provide financial assistance to FFA members from Florida and Georgia who are interested in studying fields related to agriculture in college.
Title of Award: Chevron Corporation Scholarships **Area, Field, or Subject:** Agricultural sciences; Communications; Education; Environmental conservation; Environmental science; Natural resources; Wildlife conservation, management, and science **Level of Education for which Award is Granted:** Undergraduate **Number Awarded:** 2 each year. **Funds Available:** The stipend is $1,000. Funds are paid directly to the recipient. **Duration:** 1 year; nonrenewable.
Eligibility Requirements: This program is open to members who are graduating high school seniors planning to enroll full time in college. Applicants must be residents of Florida or Georgia planning to work on a 2-year or 4-year degree in agricultural communications and education, environmental engineering, environmental science, natural resource management, wildlife management, or public service and administration in agriculture. Preference is given to those who have shown outstanding leadership. Selection is based on academic achievement (10 points for GPA, 10 points for SAT or ACT score, 10 points for class rank), leadership in FFA activities (30 points), leadership in community activities (10 points), and participation in the Supervised Agricultural Experience (SAE) program (30 points). U.S. citizenship is required. **Deadline for Receipt:** February of each year. **Additional Information:** Funding for these scholarships is provided by ChevronTexaco Corporation.

2022 ■ NATIONAL FFA ORGANIZATION

Attn: Scholarship Office
6060 FFA Drive
P.O. Box 68960
Indianapolis, IN 46268-0960
Tel: (317)802-4321
Fax: (317)802-5321
E-mail: scholarships@ffa.org
Web Site: http://www.ffa.org
To provide financial assistance to FFA members who are interested in working on a college degree in fields related to natural resources.
Title of Award: National Rifle Association of America Scholarships **Area, Field, or Subject:** Environmental conservation; Environmental science; Natural resources; Wildlife conservation, management, and science **Level of Education for which Award is Granted:** Four Year College **Number Awarded:** 5 each year. **Funds Available:** The stipend is $1,000. Funds are paid directly to the recipient. **Duration:** 1 year; nonrenewable.
Eligibility Requirements: This program is open to members who are graduating high school seniors planning to enroll full time in college. Applicants must be members of the National Rifle Association (NRA). They may be interested in working on a 4-year degree in any area, but preference is given to those majoring in conservation, natural resources, or wildlife management. Selection is based on academic achievement (10 points for GPA, 10 points for SAT or ACT score, 10 points for class rank), leadership in FFA activities (30 points), leadership in community activities (10 points), and participation in the Supervised Agricultural Experience (SAE) program (30 points). U.S. citizenship is required. **Deadline for Receipt:** February of each year. **Additional Information:** Funding for these scholarships is provided by the National Rifle Association.

2023 ■ NATIONAL FFA ORGANIZATION

Attn: Scholarship Office
6060 FFA Drive
P.O. Box 68960
Indianapolis, IN 46268-0960
Tel: (317)802-4321
Fax: (317)802-5321
E-mail: scholarships@ffa.org
Web Site: http://www.ffa.org
To provide financial assistance to FFA members interested in studying agriculture or conservation in college.
Title of Award: National Wild Turkey Federation Scholarships **Area, Field, or Subject:** Agricultural sciences; Environmental conservation; Environmental science; Natural resources; Wildlife conservation, management, and science **Level of Education for which Award is Granted:** Undergraduate **Number Awarded:** 1 each year. **Funds Available:** The stipend is $5,000. Funds are paid directly to the recipient. **Duration:** 1 year; nonrenewable.

Eligibility Requirements: This program is open to members who are graduating high school seniors planning to enroll full time in college. Applicants must have a GPA of 3.0 or higher and be planning to attend a 2-year or 4-year college or university to major in natural resources, wildlife management, or agriculture. They must support the preservation of the hunting tradition, demonstrate a commitment to conservation, actively participate in the hunting sports, have strong leadership skills, be able to demonstrate financial need, and have work or volunteer experience in the hunting sports. Selection is based on academic achievement (10 points for GPA, 10 points for SAT or ACT score, 10 points for class rank), leadership in FFA activities (30 points), leadership in community activities (10 points), and participation in the Supervised Agricultural Experience (SAE) program (30 points). U.S. citizenship is required. **Deadline for Receipt:** February of each year. **Additional Information:** Funding for these scholarships is provided by the National Wild Turkey Federation.

2024 ■ NATIONAL FFA ORGANIZATION

Attn: Scholarship Office
6060 FFA Drive
P.O. Box 68960
Indianapolis, IN 46268-0960
Tel: (317)802-4321
Fax: (317)802-5321
E-mail: scholarships@ffa.org
Web Site: http://www.ffa.org
To provide financial assistance to FFA members interested in studying agriculture in college.

Title of Award: Purina Mills/Land O'Lakes Purina Feeds Dealer Scholarships **Area, Field, or Subject:** Agricultural sciences; Animal science and behavior; Equine studies; Veterinary science and medicine; Wildlife conservation, management, and science **Level of Education for which Award is Granted:** Four Year College **Number Awarded:** Varies each year, depending on the number of participating Purina dealers. **Funds Available:** The stipend is $1,000 per year. Funds are paid directly to the recipient. **Duration:** 1 year; nonrenewable.

Eligibility Requirements: This program is open to members who are graduating high school seniors planning to enroll full time in college. Applicants must be interested in working on a 4-year college degree in agriculture. Preference is given to applicants displaying an interest in animal nutrition, aquaculture, animal science, equine science, wildlife management, or specialty animals. Selection is based on academic achievement (10 points for GPA, 10 points for SAT or ACT score, 10 points for class rank), leadership in FFA activities (30 points), leadership in community activities (10 points), and participation in the Supervised Agricultural Experience (SAE) program (30 points). U.S. citizenship is required. **Deadline for Receipt:** February of each year. **Additional Information:** Funding for these scholarships is provided by Purina Mills, LLC.

2025 ■ OREGON STUDENT ASSISTANCE COMMISSION

Attn: Grants and Scholarships Division
1500 Valley River Drive, Suite 100
Eugene, OR 97401-2146
Tel: (541)687-7395
Free: 800-452-8807
Fax: (541)687-7419
E-mail: awardinfo@mercury.osac.state.or.us
Web Site: http://www.osac.state.or.us
To provide financial assistance for college to Eagle Scouts in Oregon interested in studying fields related to wildlife management.

Title of Award: Royden M. Bodley Scholarship **Area, Field, or Subject:** Environmental conservation; Environmental science; Forestry; Wildlife conservation, management, and science **Level of Education for which Award is Granted:** Undergraduate **Number Awarded:** Varies each year; recently, 5 of these scholarships were awarded. **Funds Available:** The stipend is at least $1,400. **Duration:** 1 year.

Eligibility Requirements: This program is open to graduates of high schools in the Boy Scouts of America Cascade Pacific Council. Applicants must have achieved the Eagle rank in Oregon and be attending or planning to attend college in the state. They must be interested in majoring in forestry, wildlife, environment, or a related field. **Deadline for Receipt:** February of each year. **Additional Information:** This program is administered by the Oregon Student Assistance Commission (OSAC) with

funds provided by the Oregon Community Foundation, 1221 S.W. Yamhill, Suite 100, Portland, OR 97205, (503) 227-6846, Fax: (503) 274-7771.

2026 ■ ROCKY MOUNTAIN ELK FOUNDATION

Attn: Maggie Engler
2291 West Broadway
P.O. Box 8249
Missoula, MT 59807-8249
Tel: (406)523-4500
Free: 800-CALL
Fax: (406)523-4550
E-mail: mengler@rmef.org
Web Site: http://www.rmef.org/pages/scholar.html
To provide financial assistance to upper-division students who are majoring in wildlife studies.

Title of Award: Wildlife Leadership Awards **Area, Field, or Subject:** Environmental conservation; Environmental science; Wildlife conservation, management, and science **Level of Education for which Award is Granted:** Four Year College **Number Awarded:** 10 each year. **Funds Available:** The stipend is $2,000. In addition, recipients are given an engraved plaque and a 1-year membership in the foundation. **Duration:** 1 year; nonrenewable.

Eligibility Requirements: This program is open to students enrolled in a recognized wildlife program at a 4-year college or university in the United States or Canada. Applicants must be juniors or seniors, have at least 1 semester or 2 quarters remaining in their degree program, and be scheduled to enroll as full-time students the following fall semester/ quarter. Previous recipients of this award are ineligible. Selection is based on hobbies and leisure activities (5 points), leadership activities (25 points), employment experience (5 points), a 300-word essay on how wildlife fits into specified federal laws (15 points), a 300-word essay on what they believe to be the most important conservation issues facing North American during the next 10 years (20 points), a 250-word essay on the role of hunting in conservation (15 points), and a 100-word statement on their career goals and objectives (5 points). **Deadline for Receipt:** February of each year. **Additional Information:** This program was established in 1990.

2027 ■ IZAAK WALTON LEAGUE OF AMERICA-MINNESOTA DIVISION

Attn: Scholarship Committee
555 Park Street, Suite 140
St. Paul, MN 55103-2110
Tel: (651)221-0215
E-mail: ikes@minnesotaikes.org
Web Site: http://www.minnesotaikes.org
To provide financial assistance to Minnesota residents who are studying an environmental field in college.

Title of Award: Minnesota Division Scholarship **Area, Field, or Subject:** Education; Environmental conservation; Environmental law; Environmental science; Wildlife conservation, management, and science **Level of Education for which Award is Granted:** Undergraduate **Number Awarded:** 1 or more each year. **Funds Available:** The stipend is $1,000 per year. **Duration:** 1 year; may be renewed.

Eligibility Requirements: This program is open to residents of Minnesota who are in at least their second year of college. Applicants must be majoring in environmental education, environmental law, wildlife management, or some other conservation-oriented program. They must be U.S. citizens and able to demonstrate financial need. Along with their application, they must submit a 1-page essay on their belief in conservation and what the future holds for them (including their educational plans and career goals), a transcript, a description of their program of study, and 2 letters of recommendation. An interview may be requested. **Deadline for Receipt:** May of each year.

2028 ■ WILDLIFE SOCIETY-FLORIDA CHAPTER

c/o Maria Zondervan, Scholarship Committee Chair
St. Johns River Water Management District
975 Keller Road
Altamonte Springs, FL 32714-1618
Tel: (407)659-4872
E-mail: mzondervan@sjrwmd.com
Web Site: http://fltws.org

To provide financial assistance to upper-division students working on a degree in wildlife ecology and/or management at a Florida college.
Title of Award: Florida Chapter of the Wildlife Society Scholarship **Area, Field, or Subject:** Environmental conservation; Environmental science; Wildlife conservation, management, and science **Level of Education for which Award is Granted:** Four Year College **Number Awarded:** 1 each year. **Funds Available:** The stipend is $1,000. **Duration:** 1 year.
Eligibility Requirements: This program is open to students entering their junior or senior year at a 4-year college or university in Florida. Applicants must be interested in preparing for a career in wildlife ecology and/or management. They must have a GPA of 2.5 or higher. Along with their application, they must submit a letter describing their professional goals and financial need. Selection is based on goals as expressed in the letter, extracurricular activities, demonstrated leadership, professional potential, and financial need. **Deadline for Receipt:** November of each year. **Additional Information:** This program, established in 1998, is jointly sponsored by the Florida chapter of The Wildlife Society, the Florida chapter of the National Wild Turkey Federation, and the Florida Wildlife Federation.

General

2029 ■ AMERICAN LEGION

Attn: Americanism and Children & Youth Division
P.O. Box 1055
Indianapolis, IN 46206-1055
Tel: (317)630-1249
Fax: (317)630-1223
E-mail: acy@legion.org
Web Site: http://www.legion.org
To recognize and reward high school students who participate in an oratorical contest on a theme related to the U.S. constitution.
Title of Award: American Legion National High School Oratorical Contest **Area, Field, or Subject:** General studies/Field of study not specified; Patriotism; Speech, Debate, and Forensics **Level of Education for which Award is Granted:** Undergraduate **Number Awarded:** 3 national winners; hundreds of sectional, regional, and departmental winners. **Funds Available:** Scholarship awards are presented to the 3 finalists in the national contest: $18,000 to the first-place winner; $16,000 to the second-place winner; and $14,000 to the third-place winner. Each Department (state) winner who participates in the first round of the national contest receives a $1,500 scholarship; each first-round winner who advances to and participates in the second round, but does not advance to the final round, receives an additional $1,500 scholarship. **Duration:** The competition is held annually.
Eligibility Requirements: This program is open to U.S. citizens under the age of 20 who are currently enrolled in junior high or high school (grades 9-12). Students enter the contest through their Department (state) American Legion (many of these departments offer scholarships to participants in their state, in addition to the scholarships offered through the national program; check with your state department for further information). Each department then chooses 1 contestant to enter the regional contest. Regional winners compete in sectional contests; sectional winners compete on the national level. In all competitions, participants are evaluated on both the content and presentation of their prepared and extemporaneous speeches, which must deal with some aspect of the American Constitution or principles of government under the Constitution. **Deadline for Receipt:** The dates of departmental competitions vary; check with your local American Legion post. The national competition is generally held in April. **Additional Information:** The National Organization of the American Legion pays the travel costs of Department winners and their chaperones as they progress in national competition. Scholarships may be used to attend any accredited college or university in the United States. All contestants must be accompanied by a chaperone.

2030 ■ CALIFORNIA STATE UNIVERSITY

Office of the Chancellor
Attn: Lori Redfearn, Vice President
401 Golden Shore, Sixth Floor
Long Beach, CA 90802-4210
Tel: (562)951-4815
E-mail: lredfearn@calstate.edu
Web Site: http://www.calstate.edu/foundation/scholarship.shtml

To provide financial assistance to students majoring in humanities at campuses of the California State University (CSU) system.
Title of Award: Angelina Aliberti Ruggie and Lawrence L. Ruggie Scholarships **Area, Field, or Subject:** Humanities **Level of Education for which Award is Granted:** Four Year College **Number Awarded:** 10 each year, rotated among the 23 CSU campuses. **Funds Available:** The stipend is $1,000 per year. **Duration:** 1 year.
Eligibility Requirements: This program is open to students enrolled at CSU campuses who are majoring in the humanities, including law and social work but excluding military sciences.

2031 ■ CANADIAN INSTITUTE OF UKRAINIAN STUDIES

c/o University of Alberta
450 Athabasca Hall
Edmonton, AB, Canada T6G 2E8
E-mail: cius@ualberta.ca
Web Site: http://www.ualberta.ca/CIUS/cius-grants.htm
To provide financial assistance to Canadian undergraduate students majoring in a field related to Ukrainian or Ukrainian Canadian studies.
Title of Award: Leo J. Krysa Family Undergraduate Scholarship **Area, Field, or Subject:** Canadian studies; Education; European studies; Humanities; Social sciences; Ukrainian studies **Level of Education for which Award is Granted:** Four Year College **Number Awarded:** 1 each year. **Funds Available:** The maximum stipend is $C3,500. **Duration:** 8 months; nonrenewable.
Eligibility Requirements: This program is open to Canadian citizens and permanent residents who are entering the final year of study for an undergraduate degree at a college or university in Canada. Applicants' programs must emphasize Ukrainian and/or Ukrainian Canadian studies, through a combination of Ukrainian and east European or Canadian courses in education, history, humanities, or the social sciences. Selection is based on overall academic record, performance in Ukrainian-content courses, a working sample, and community involvement. **Deadline for Receipt:** February of each year. **Additional Information:** Recipients may attend any Canadian university.

2032 ■ CHINESE HISTORICAL SOCIETY OF SOUTHERN CALIFORNIA

Attn: Scholarship Chair
415 Bernard Street
P.O. Box 862647
Los Angeles, CA 90086-2647
Tel: (323)222-0856
E-mail: chssc@chssc.org
Web Site: http://www.chssc.org
To provide financial assistance to students from any state who who attending college in southern California and interested in majoring in Chinese American studies.
Title of Award: CHSSC Scholarship **Area, Field, or Subject:** Asian studies; Humanities; Social sciences **Level of Education for which Award is Granted:** Graduate, Undergraduate **Number Awarded:** 1 each year. **Funds Available:** The stipend is $1,000. **Duration:** 1 year.
Eligibility Requirements: This program is open to undergraduate and graduate students from any state who are attending an accredited college or university in southern California on a full-time basis, have earned at

least a 3.0 GPA, and are have an academic interest related to Chinese American studies in the humanities or social sciences. Applicants must submit a 300- to 500-word essay in English on the importance to them of Chinese American studies; a statement of additional factors, such as financial need, family circumstances, employment history, and campus and community activities that may advance their application; transcripts; and an optional letter of recommendation. **Deadline for Receipt:** March of each year. **Additional Information:** This program began in 1992. Information is also available from Susie Ling, E-mail: shling@pasadena.edu.

2033 ■ DALLAS FOUNDATION

Attn: Scholarship Administrator
900 Jackson Street, Suite 150
Dallas, TX 75202
Tel: (214)741-9898
Fax: (214)741-9848
E-mail: cmcnally@dallasfoundation.org
Web Site: http://www.dallasfoundation.org/gs_schFundProfiles.cfm
To provide financial assistance to adult students and high school seniors in Texas interested in studying the humanities in college.
Title of Award: Chuck Fulgham Scholarship **Area, Field, or Subject:** General studies/Field of study not specified; Humanities **Level of Education for which Award is Granted:** Undergraduate **Number Awarded:** 1 or more each year. **Funds Available:** The maximum stipend is $2,500. Funds are paid directly to the recipient's school. **Duration:** 1 year; nonrenewable.
Eligibility Requirements: This program is open to 1) adult graduates of a literacy program who need financial assistance to attend a regionally-accredited college or university, and 2) high school seniors who have not been successful in high school by traditional academic standards (must have a GPA below 3.0) but who have a genuine interest in literature and humanities and show promise for achievement in college. Applicants must be Texas residents and able to demonstrate financial need; preference is given to applicants from the Dallas area and to applicants who have participated in sports activities. **Deadline for Receipt:** March of each year. **Additional Information:** This program was established in 1999.

2034 ■ FINANCE AUTHORITY OF MAINE

Attn: Education Finance Programs
5 Community Drive
P.O. Box 949
Augusta, ME 04332-0949
Tel: (207)623-3263
Free: 800-228-3734
Fax: (207)623-0095
E-mail: info@famemaine.com
Web Site: http://www.famemaine.com/html/education/fameprogs.html
To provide scholarship/loans to high school seniors, college students, and graduate students in Maine who are interested in preparing for a career as a teacher.
Title of Award: Educators for Maine Program **Area, Field, or Subject:** Child development; Education; Speech and language pathology/audiology **Level of Education for which Award is Granted:** Graduate, Undergraduate **Funds Available:** Full-time undergraduate students receive $3,000 per academic year; postbaccalaureate students receive $2,000 per academic year. This is a scholarship/loan program. Recipients may receive 1 year of loan forgiveness by completing 1 year of full-time teaching in a Maine public or private elementary or secondary school. The repayment option can be accelerated to 2 years of loan forgiveness for each year of teaching if the service is conducted in an educator shortage area or underserved subject area. If the loan recipient does not meet the service obligation, the total amount borrowed must be repaid at 9% interest; undergraduate borrowers must complete repayment within 10 years of graduation or withdrawal from school; postbaccalaureate students must complete repayment within 5 years of graduation or withdrawal from school. **Duration:** 1 year; may be renewed up to 3 additional years if the recipient remains a Maine resident and maintains a cumulative GPA of 2.5 or higher.
Eligibility Requirements: This program is open to 1) high school seniors planning to attend college to prepare for a career in education; 2) currently-enrolled college students; and 3) postbaccalaureate students who are enrolled or planning to enroll in a program leading to certification

as a teacher, speech pathologist, or child care provider. Applicants must be residents of Maine with a GPA of 3.0 or higher. Selection is based on academic achievement, activities, community service, and an essay; financial need is not considered. Preference is given to applicants planning to teach a shortage subject. **Deadline for Receipt:** March of each year. **Additional Information:** These scholarship/loans may be used at any accredited postsecondary institution offering certificate, 2-year, 4-year, or graduate programs that lead to an associate, baccalaureate, master's, or doctoral degree. This program was formerly known as Teachers for Maine. Undergraduate recipients must attend school on a full-time basis, but postbaccalaureate students and teachers are not required to enroll as full-time students.

2035 ■ FOUNDATION FOR AMATEUR RADIO, INC.

Attn: Scholarship Committee
P.O. Box 831
Riverdale, MD 20738
E-mail: aa3of@arrl.net
Web Site: http://www.amateurradio-far.org/scholarships.php
To provide funding to licensed radio amateurs who are interested in studying humanities or the social sciences in college.
Title of Award: Kevin Barry Perdue Memorial Scholarship **Area, Field, or Subject:** Humanities; Social sciences **Level of Education for which Award is Granted:** Undergraduate **Number Awarded:** 1 each year. **Funds Available:** The stipend is $2,000. **Duration:** 1 year.
Eligibility Requirements: Applicants must have at least a technician class license and intend to pursue a course of study in the liberal arts, humanities, or social sciences. They must intend to earn a bachelor's degree from a U.S. college or university. **Deadline for Receipt:** Requests for applications must be submitted by April of each year. **Additional Information:** Recipients must attend an accredited school (university, college, or technical institute) on a full-time basis.

2036 ■ HARVEST EDUCATION FOUNDATION

P.O. Box 100
Romeo, MI 48065-0100
Tel: (586)752-6066
Web Site: http://www.marvac.org/harvestapp.html
To provide financial assistance for college to Michigan residents interested in preparing for a career in the manufactured homes, recreational vehicles, or campground industries.
Title of Award: HARVEST Scholarships **Area, Field, or Subject:** Design; Engineering; Management; Marketing and distribution; Personnel administration/human resources **Level of Education for which Award is Granted:** Undergraduate **Number Awarded:** 1 or more each year. **Funds Available:** A stipend is awarded (amount not specified). **Duration:** 1 year; may be renewed.
Eligibility Requirements: This program is open to Michigan students enrolled or planning to enroll at an accredited college or university to prepare for a career in the manufactured homes, recreational vehicles, or campground industries. Fields of study may include engineering, marketing, management, service, design, human resources, or any other discipline that will serve the needs of the industries. Applicants must submit an essay of 200 to 300 words on their career goals and why they feel they deserve this scholarship. Selection is based on merit and/or financial need. **Deadline for Receipt:** March of each year. **Additional Information:** The HARVEST Education Foundation is a joint venture of the Michigan Manufactured Housing Association and the Michigan Association of Recreation Vehicles and Campgrounds, both at 2222 Association Drive, Okemos, MI 48864-5978, (517) 349-3300, E-mail: michhome@michhome.org and marvac@marvac.org.

2037 ■ KENTUCKY BAPTIST CONVENTION

Attn: Brotherhood Department
10701 Shelbyville Road
P.O. Box 43433
Louisville, KY 40253-0433
Tel: (502)245-4101; 888-254-5720
Web Site: http://www.kybaptist.org
To recognize and reward, with college scholarships, high school senior members of the Kentucky Baptist Convention who deliver outstanding speeches on their participation in On Mission Youth.
Title of Award: Young Statesman Scholarship **Area, Field, or Subject:** General studies/Field of study not specified; Speech, Debate, and

Forensics **Level of Education for which Award is Granted:** Undergraduate **Number Awarded:** 1 each year. **Funds Available:** The stipend is $1,000 per year. **Duration:** 1 year; may be renewed up to 3 additional years provided the recipient remains enrolled in college and supplies written evidence that they continue to be leaders in living an On Mission lifestyle, in missions efforts, and in spiritual development.

Eligibility Requirements: This program is open to seniors at public, private, and home schools who are actively living an On Mission lifestyle and involved in mission education at their local Kentucky Baptist Convention affiliated-church. Applicants must give a 6- to 8-minute speech on an On Mission topic. Selection is based on topic choice (5 points), evidence of research (15 points), development of ideas (50 points), presentation and delivery (20 points), and conclusion (10 points).

2038 ■ LOWE'S COMPANIES, INC.
Attn: Scholarship Program
P.O. Box 1111
North Wilkesboro, NC 28656
Tel: (336)658-4104
Free: 800-44-LOWES
Web Site: http://www.lowes.com/scholarships
To provide financial assistance to students at selected community and technical colleges who are preparing for a career in a business or technical field related to Lowe's stores.

Title of Award: Lowe's Educational Scholarship Program **Area, Field, or Subject:** Business; Construction; Drafting; Electronics; Heating, air conditioning, and refrigeration; Horticulture **Level of Education for which Award is Granted:** Two Year College, Vocational/Occupational **Number Awarded:** Varies each year; since the program was established, more than 150 of these scholarships have been awarded. **Funds Available:** Stipends are $2,000 for full-time students, $1,000 for three-quarter time students, or $800 for half-time students. **Duration:** 1 year; may be renewed if the recipient qualifies for employment at Lowe's.

Eligibility Requirements: This program is open to students who are at least 18 years of age and currently enrolled in a community or technical college that is cooperating with Lowe's stores. Applicants must intend to prepare for a career in an approved discipline within the business division (business management, business administration) or vocational/technical division (air conditioning, heating and refrigeration, construction, electrical or electronics, industrial maintenance, machining, mechanical drafting and design, plumbing, carpentry, or horticulture) of Lowe's. They must have completed at least 1 semester with a GPA of 2.0 or higher. Applications are accepted from current Lowe's employees, but students working for another major retailer are not eligible. **Additional Information:** This program was established in 1999. Currently, 32 community and technical colleges are participating in the program. For a list, contact Lowe's.

2039 ■ MARYLAND ASSOCIATION OF PRIVATE COLLEGES AND CAREER SCHOOLS
Attn: Scholarship Committee
3100 Dunglow Road
Baltimore, MD 21222
Tel: (410)282-4012
Fax: (410)282-4133
E-mail: mdapcs@yahoo.com
Web Site: http://www.mapccs.org/scholarships.html
To provide financial assistance to students interested in attending selected private career schools in Maryland.

Title of Award: Maryland Association of Private Colleges and Career Schools Scholarships **Area, Field, or Subject:** Broadcasting; Cosmetology; Drafting; Health care services; Mechanics and repairs; Medicine, Holistic/alternative; Secretarial sciences **Level of Education for which Award is Granted:** Vocational/Occupational **Number Awarded:** Varies each year; since the program was established in 1983, more than $3 million in scholarships have been awarded. **Funds Available:** Individual awards range from $500 to more than $5,000. The H.R. Leslie Scholarship is $1,000. Funds must be applied for full or partial payment of tuition. Recently, a total of $164,000 was awarded. **Duration:** 1 year.

Eligibility Requirements: This program is open to high school seniors and graduates who are interested in attending a participating private career school in Maryland. Applicants should be interested in working on a degree in such business or technical areas as cosmetology, barbering, diesel mechanics, automotive technology, massage therapy, allied health,

secretarial sciences, or drafting. The H.R. Leslie Scholarship is open to any student who applies to a member school. Selection is based on GPA, involvement in school and community activities, recommendations from school officials, desire, and potential to succeed in their career field. Financial need is not considered in the selection process. **Deadline for Receipt:** March of each year. **Additional Information:** The participating schools are All State Career School (Baltimore) American Beauty Academy (Wheaton), Americare School of Allied Health (Silver Spring), Avara's Academy of Hair Design (Baltimore), Baltimore School of Massage, Baltimore Studio of Hair Design, Bladensburg Barber School (Bladensburg), Broadcasting Institute of Maryland (Baltimore), Diesel Institute of America (Grantsville), Frederick School of Cosmetology (Frederick), Hair Academy (New Carrollton), Holistic Massage Training Institute (Baltimore), International Beauty School (Bel Air), Lincoln Technical Institute (Columbia), Medix School (Towson), Savage Neon (Baltimore), and Von Lee School of Aesthetics (Pikesville). Scholarships can be used only to attend the schools listed above.

2040 ■ MISSISSIPPI OFFICE OF STUDENT FINANCIAL AID
3825 Ridgewood Road
Jackson, MS 39211-6453
Tel: (601)432-6997
Free: 800-327-2980
Fax: (601)432-6527
E-mail: sfa@ihl.state.ms.us
Web Site: http://www.ihl.state.ms.us/financialaid/hcp.html
To provide scholarship/loans to Mississippi residents who are majoring in a critical health care field in college.

Title of Award: Mississippi Health Care Professions Loan/Scholarship Program **Area, Field, or Subject:** Health care services; Occupational therapy; Physical therapy; Psychology; Speech and language pathology/audiology **Level of Education for which Award is Granted:** Four Year College, Graduate **Number Awarded:** Varies each year, depending on the availability of funds; awards are granted on a first-come, first-served basis. **Funds Available:** Under this program, $1,500 is awarded per year to undergraduate students and $3,000 per year to graduate students. This is a scholarship/loan program. Obligation can be discharged on the basis of 1 year's service in the health profession at a state-operated health institution in Mississippi for 1 year's scholarship/loan award. In the event the recipient fails to fulfill the service obligation, repayment of principal and interest is required. **Duration:** Up to 2 years for undergraduates and for graduate students in physical therapy; 1 year for graduate students in occupational therapy.

Eligibility Requirements: This program is open to Mississippi residents who are enrolled as a junior, senior, or graduate student in an approved training program in the state of Mississippi. Approved programs of study currently include speech pathology and psychology on the undergraduate level and occupational therapy and physical therapy on the graduate level. Selection is based on cumulative GPA. The highest priority is given to renewal students. **Deadline for Receipt:** March of each year. **Additional Information:** State health institutions include the following: Mississippi State Hospital, Ellisville State School, East Mississippi State Hospital, Mississippi Children's Rehabilitation Center, North Mississippi Retardation Center, Hudspeth Retardation Center, South Mississippi Retardation Center, University of Mississippi Hospital, Boswell Retardation Center, State Board of Health, Department of Mental Health, and health care facilities under the Department of Corrections.

2041 ■ NATIONAL AMBUCS, INC.
Attn: Scholarship Coordinator
P.O. Box 5127
High Point, NC 27262
Tel: (336)852-0052
Fax: (336)852-6830
E-mail: ambucs@ambucs.org
Web Site: http://www.ambucs.org
To provide financial assistance to undergraduate and graduate students who are interested in preparing for a career serving disabled citizens in various fields of clinical therapy.

Title of Award: AMBUCS Scholarships for Therapists **Area, Field, or Subject:** Occupational therapy; Physical therapy; Rehabilitation, Physical/Psychological; Speech and language pathology/audiology **Level of Education for which Award is Granted:** Four Year College, Graduate

Number Awarded: Approximately 400 each year, with a total value of $225,000. **Funds Available:** Most of these awards range from $500 to $1,500 per year; 1 scholarship of $6,000 for 2 years is also awarded. Funds are paid directly to the recipient's school. **Duration:** 1 year.
Eligibility Requirements: This program is open to U.S. citizens who have been accepted at the upper-division or graduate level in an accredited program that qualifies the students for clinical practice in occupational therapy, physical therapy, speech language pathology, or hearing audiology. Programs for therapy assistants are not included. Applicants must submit college transcripts for the last 3 semesters, a 500-word essay on their interest in therapy as a career, and a statement of family financial circumstances. Selection is based on financial need, commitment to local community, demonstrated academic accomplishment, character for compassion and integrity, and career objectives. **Deadline for Receipt:** April of each year. **Additional Information:** This program was established in 1955; since then, the association has awarded more than $5 million for more than 9,900 scholarships.

2042 ■ OPTIMIST INTERNATIONAL

Attn: Programs Department
4494 Lindell Boulevard
St. Louis, MO 63108
Tel: (314)371-6000
Free: 800-500-8130
Fax: (314)371-6006
E-mail: programs@optimist.org
Web Site: http://www.optimist.org
To recognize and reward outstanding presentations made by hearing impaired high school students.

Title of Award: Optimist International Communication Contest for the Deaf and Hard of Hearing **Area, Field, or Subject:** General studies/Field of study not specified; Speech, Debate, and Forensics **Level of Education for which Award is Granted:** Undergraduate **Number Awarded:** Nearly 300 Optimist International clubs participate in this program each year. Each participating district offers 1 scholarship; some districts may offer a second award with separate competitions for signing and oral competitors, or for male and female entrants. **Funds Available:** Each district winner receives a $1,500 college scholarship, payable to an educational institution of the recipient's choice, subject to the approval of Optimist International. **Duration:** The competition is held annually.
Eligibility Requirements: This program is open to young people up to and including grade 12 in the United States and Canada, to CEGEP in Quebec, and to grade 13 in the Caribbean. Applicants must be identified by a qualified audiologist as deaf or hard of hearing with a hearing loss of 40 decibels or more. They are invited to make a presentation (using oral communication, sign language, or a combination of both) from 4 to 5 minutes on a topic that changes annually; a recent topic was "My Future is Bright because..." Competition is first conducted at the level of individual clubs, with winners advancing to zone and then district competitions. Selection is based on material organization (40 points), delivery and presentation (30 points), and overall effectiveness (30 points). **Deadline for Receipt:** Each club sets its own deadline. The district deadline is the end of September of each year. **Additional Information:** Entry information is available only from local Optimist Clubs.

2043 ■ OPTIMIST INTERNATIONAL

Attn: Programs Department
4494 Lindell Boulevard
St. Louis, MO 63108
Tel: (314)371-6000
Free: 800-500-8130
Fax: (314)371-6009
E-mail: programs@optimist.org
Web Site: http://www.optimist.org
To recognize and reward outstanding orators at the high school or younger level.

Title of Award: Optimist International Oratorical Contest **Area, Field, or Subject:** General studies/Field of study not specified; Speech, Debate, and Forensics **Level of Education for which Award is Granted:** Undergraduate **Number Awarded:** Each year, more than $150,000 is awarded in scholarships. **Funds Available:** Each district awards either 2 scholarships of $1,500 (1 for a boy and 1 for a girl) or (if the district chooses to have a combined gender contest) a first-place scholarship of

$1,500, a second-place scholarship of $1,000, and a third-place scholarship of $500. **Duration:** The competition is held annually.
Eligibility Requirements: All students in public, private, or parochial elementary, junior high, and senior high schools in the United States, Canada, or the Caribbean who are under 16 years of age may enter. All contestants must prepare their own orations of 4 to 5 minutes, but they may receive advice and make minor changes or improvements in the oration at any time. Each year a different subject is selected for the orations; a recent topic was "My Future in Bright because..." The orations may be delivered in a language other than English if that language is an official language of the country in which the sponsoring club is located. Selection is based on poise (20 points), content of speech (35 points), delivery and presentation (35 points), and overall effectiveness (10 points). Competition is first conducted at the level of individual clubs, with winners advancing to zone and then district competitions. At the discretion of the district, boys may compete against boys and girls against girls in separate contests. **Deadline for Receipt:** Each local club sets its own deadline. The district deadline is the end of June. **Additional Information:** This competition was first held in 1928. Nearly 2,000 Optimist International local clubs participate in the program each year. Entry information is available only from local Optimist Clubs.

2044 ■ SOUTHERN BAPTIST CONVENTION

North American Mission Board
Attn: Youth Mission Education
4200 North Point Parkway
Alpharetta, GA 30022-4176
Tel: (770)410-6489
Fax: (770)410-6082
E-mail: ahuesing@namb.net
Web Site: http://www.studentz.com/challengers
To recognize and reward outstanding orators in the Southern Baptist Convention's Challengers Speak Out Contest.

Title of Award: Challengers National Mission Speak Out Contest **Area, Field, or Subject:** General studies/Field of study not specified; Religion; Speech, Debate, and Forensics **Level of Education for which Award is Granted:** Undergraduate **Number Awarded:** 2 each year. **Funds Available:** At the national level, first place is a $1,000 scholarship plus $800 for a mission project/trip of the winner's choice. Second place is a $500 scholarship. **Duration:** The competition is held annually.
Eligibility Requirements: This competition is open to male members of Southern Baptist churches who are participating in a Challengers group as high school sophomores, juniors, or seniors. Challengers can represent their state in this national speech competition. They must prepare a speech, from 5 to 7 minutes in length, on 1 of the following topics: why I should be a mission volunteer; what mission involvement means to me; discovering my gifts for mission service; me, a missionary; the cooperative program: supporting missions around the world; encountering God through Bible study; or what Challengers means to me. Selection is based on content (50 points), composition (25 points), and delivery (25 points). **Additional Information:** The winner also serves as a page at the Southern Baptist Convention and has the opportunity to present his speech at the Challengers Rally.

Architecture

2045 ■ ALABAMA CONCRETE INDUSTRIES ASSOCIATION

Attn: President
660 Adams Avenue, Suite 188
Montgomery, AL 36104
Tel: (334)265-0501
Free: 800-732-9118
Fax: (334)265-2250
E-mail: jsorrell@alconcrete.org
Web Site: http://www.alconcrete.org/scholarships
To provide financial assistance to students majoring in architecture, building sciences, or engineering in Alabama.

Title of Award: Alabama Concrete Industries Association Scholarships **Area, Field, or Subject:** Architecture; Construction; Engineering **Level of Education for which Award is Granted:** Four Year College **Number Awarded:** 2 each year. **Funds Available:** A stipend is awarded (amount not specified). **Duration:** 1 year.

Eligibility Requirements: This program is open to students completing their junior year at colleges and universities in Alabama. Applicants must be enrolled in an accredited program in architecture, engineering, or building sciences. Selection is based on academic and extracurricular activity record. **Additional Information:** This program was established in 1993.

2046 ■ AMERICAN NURSERY AND LANDSCAPE ASSOCIATION

Attn: Horticultural Research Institute
1000 Vermont Avenue N.W., Suite 300
Washington, DC 20005-4914
Tel: (202)789-2900
Fax: (202)789-1893
E-mail: hriresearch@anla.org
Web Site: http://www.anla.org/research/scholarships/index.htm
To provide financial assistance to residents of Maryland, Virginia, and West Virginia working on an undergraduate or graduate degree in landscape architecture or horticulture.
Title of Award: Carville M. Akehurst Memorial Scholarship **Area, Field, or Subject:** Horticulture; Landscape architecture and design **Level of Education for which Award is Granted:** Graduate, Undergraduate **Number Awarded:** 1 each year. **Funds Available:** The stipend is $2,000. **Duration:** 1 year; may be renewed.
Eligibility Requirements: This program is open to students enrolled full time in a landscape or horticulture undergraduate or graduate program at an accredited 2-year or 4-year college or university. Applicants must be residents of Maryland, Virginia, or West Virginia, although they are not required to attend an institution within those states. They must be enrolled as a junior in a 4-year program or a senior in a 2-year program and have a minimum GPA of 2.7 overall and 3.0 in their major. Preference is given to applicants who plan to work within the nursery industry, including nursery operations; landscape architecture, design, construction, or maintenance; interiorscape; horticultural distribution; or retail garden center. **Deadline for Receipt:** March of each year. **Additional Information:** This program was established in 2002 by the Mid-Atlantic Nursery Trade Show, Inc.

2047 ■ AMERICAN NURSERY AND LANDSCAPE ASSOCIATION

Attn: Horticultural Research Institute
1000 Vermont Avenue N.W., Suite 300
Washington, DC 20005-4914
Tel: (202)789-2900
Fax: (202)789-1893
E-mail: hriresearch@anla.org
Web Site: http://www.anla.org/research/Scholarships/TandPBigelow.htm
To provide financial support to residents of New England interested in working on an undergraduate or graduate degree in landscape architecture or horticulture.
Title of Award: Timothy Bigelow and Palmer W. Bigelow, Jr. Scholarships **Area, Field, or Subject:** Horticulture; Landscape architecture and design **Level of Education for which Award is Granted:** Graduate, Undergraduate **Number Awarded:** Up to 3 each year. **Funds Available:** The stipend is $2,500. **Duration:** 1 year; nonrenewable.
Eligibility Requirements: This program is open to full-time students enrolled in an accredited landscape or horticulture program in 1) the final year of a 2-year curriculum, 2) the third year of a 4-year curriculum, or 3) a graduate program. Applicants must have a minimum GPA of 2.25 as undergraduates or 3.0 as graduate students. They must be a resident of 1 of the 6 New England states, although attendance at an institution within those states is not required. Preference is given to applicants who plan to work in an aspect of the nursery industry, including a business of their own, and to applicants who demonstrate financial need. **Deadline for Receipt:** March of each year. **Additional Information:** This program was created in 1988.

2048 ■ AMERICAN NURSERY AND LANDSCAPE ASSOCIATION

Attn: Horticultural Research Institute
1000 Vermont Avenue N.W., Suite 300
Washington, DC 20005-4914
Tel: (202)789-2900
Fax: (202)789-1893
E-mail: hriresearch@anla.org
Web Site: http://www.anla.org/research/scholarships/index.htm

To provide financial assistance to students working on an undergraduate or graduate degree in landscape architecture or horticulture.
Title of Award: Spring Meadow Nursery Scholarship **Area, Field, or Subject:** Agricultural sciences; Horticulture; Landscape architecture and design **Level of Education for which Award is Granted:** Graduate, Undergraduate **Number Awarded:** 1 each year. **Funds Available:** The stipend is $2,000. **Duration:** 1 year; may be renewed.
Eligibility Requirements: This program is open to students enrolled full time in a landscape or horticulture undergraduate or graduate program at an accredited 2-year or 4-year college or university. Students enrolled in a vocational agriculture program are also eligible. Applicants must have a minimum GPA of 2.25 overall and 2.7 in their major. Preference is given to applicants who plan to work within the nursery industry, including nursery operations; landscape architecture, design, construction, or maintenance; interiorscape; horticultural distribution; or retail garden center. **Deadline for Receipt:** March of each year. **Additional Information:** This program was established in 1999.

2049 ■ AMERICAN NURSERY AND LANDSCAPE ASSOCIATION

Attn: Horticultural Research Institute
1000 Vermont Avenue N.W., Suite 300
Washington, DC 20005-4914
Tel: (202)789-2900
Fax: (202)789-1893
E-mail: hriresearch@anla.org
Web Site: http://www.anla.org/research/scholarships/index.htm
To provide financial assistance to undergraduate and graduate students working on a degree in landscape architecture or horticulture at colleges and universities in California.
Title of Award: Usrey Family Scholarship **Area, Field, or Subject:** Agricultural sciences; Horticulture; Landscape architecture and design **Level of Education for which Award is Granted:** Graduate, Undergraduate **Number Awarded:** 1 each year. **Funds Available:** The stipend is $2,000. **Duration:** 1 year; may be renewed.
Eligibility Requirements: This program is open to students enrolled full time in a landscape or horticulture undergraduate or graduate program at an accredited 2-year or 4-year college or university in California. Students enrolled in a vocational agriculture program are also eligible. Applicants must have a minimum GPA of 2.25 overall and 2.7 in their major. California state residency is not required. Preference is given to applicants who plan to work within the nursery industry, including nursery operations; landscape architecture, design, construction, or maintenance; interiorscape; horticultural distribution; or retail garden center. **Deadline for Receipt:** March of each year.

2050 ■ AMERICAN SOCIETY OF ENGINEERS OF INDIAN ORIGIN

c/o Ramu Ramamurthy, Scholarship Committee Chair
47790 Pavillon Road
Canton, MI 48188
Tel: (248)226-6895
Fax: (248)226-7166
E-mail: awards@aseimichigan.org
Web Site: http://www.aseio.org
To provide financial assistance to undergraduate students of Indian origin (from India) who are majoring in architecture, engineering, or related areas.
Title of Award: ASEI Undergraduate Scholarships **Area, Field, or Subject:** Architecture; Computer and information sciences; Engineering **Level of Education for which Award is Granted:** Undergraduate **Number Awarded:** Several each year. **Funds Available:** The stipend is $1,000. **Duration:** 1 year.
Eligibility Requirements: This program is open to undergraduate students of Indian origin (by birth, ancestry, or relation). They must be enrolled full time at an accredited college or university in the United States and majoring in engineering, architecture, computer science, or allied science with a GPA of 3.2 or higher. Selection is based on demonstrated ability, academic achievement (including GPA, honors, and awards), career objectives, faculty recommendations, involvement in science fair and campus activities, and industrial exposure (including part-time work and internships). **Deadline for Receipt:** June of each year.

2051 ■ AQUATROLS CORPORATION

1273 Imperial Way
Paulsboro, NJ 08066

Tel: (856)537-6003
Free: 800-257-7797
Fax: (856)537-6018
E-mail: essay.contest@aquatrols.com
Web Site: http://www.aquatrols.com
To recognize and reward, with college scholarships, students whose parents are employed in a turf or landscape management capacity and who submit outstanding essays on a related subject.
Title of Award: Aquatrols Essay Contest **Area, Field, or Subject:** Landscape architecture and design; Turfgrass management; Water resources; Writing **Level of Education for which Award is Granted:** Undergraduate **Number Awarded:** 2 each year. **Funds Available:** First prize is a $2,000 scholarship and second prize is a $1,000 scholarship. **Duration:** The contest is held annually.
Eligibility Requirements: This competition is open to children of employees in a turf or landscape management capacity. Applicants must be enrolled or planning to enroll in an undergraduate program. They must submit an original essay of 1,500 to 2,000 words on a topic that changes annually; recently, students were invited to write on "The role of surfactants in enhancing water use and/or irrigation efficiency." Essays should be original, compelling, well-organized, readable, persuasive, and creative. Technical accuracy, composition skills, and adherence to contest rules are also considered. **Deadline for Receipt:** February of each year.

2052 ■ ASSOCIATED GENERAL CONTRACTORS OF MINNESOTA

Capitol Office Building
525 Park Street, Suite 110
St. Paul, MN 55103-2186
Tel: (651)632-8929
Free: 800-552-7670
Fax: (651)632-8928
E-mail: jsanem@agcmn.org
Web Site: http://www.agcmn.org
To provide financial assistance to students in Minnesota preparing for a career in the construction industry.
Title of Award: Associated General Contractors of Minnesota Scholarships **Area, Field, or Subject:** Architecture; Construction; Engineering, Civil; Engineering, Electrical; Heating, air conditioning, and refrigeration **Level of Education for which Award is Granted:** Undergraduate **Number Awarded:** Varies each year. Recently, 14 of these scholarships were awarded: 2 at $2,500, 2 at $2,000, 3 at $1,000, and 7 at $750. **Funds Available:** Stipends range from $750 to $2,500. **Duration:** 1 year.
Eligibility Requirements: This program is open to students enrolled in construction programs at colleges and universities in Minnesota. Fields of study include, but are not limited to, architecture, civil engineering, construction management, electrical engineering, and HVAC systems services. Applicants must submit a personal statement that includes information on their work-related experience, involvement in student or community organizations, honors or awards they have received, their financial situation, and other appropriate information. Selection is based on academic standing(20%), career objectives(20%), financial need (20%), personal information (20%), and overall application clarity (20%). **Deadline for Receipt:** May of each year.

2053 ■ ASSOCIATION OF INDEPENDENT COLLEGES AND UNIVERSITIES OF PENNSYLVANIA

101 North Front Street
Harrisburg, PA 17101-1405
Tel: (717)232-8649
Fax: (717)233-8574
E-mail: info@aicup.org
Web Site: http://www.aicup.org
To provide financial assistance to women and minority students at member institutions of the Association of Independent Colleges and Universities of Pennsylvania (AICUP) who are majoring in designated fields of engineering.
Title of Award: Michael Baker Corporation Scholarship Program for Diversity in Engineering **Area, Field, or Subject:** Engineering, Architectural; Engineering, Civil; Environmental science **Level of Education for which Award is Granted:** Four Year College **Number Awarded:** 1 each year. **Funds Available:** The stipend is $1,000 per year. **Duration:** 1 year; may be renewed 1 additional year if the recipient maintains appropriate academic standards.

Eligibility Requirements: This program is open to full-time undergraduate students at designated AICUP colleges and universities who are women and/or members of the following minority groups: American Indians, Alaska Natives, Asians, Blacks/African Americans, Hispanics/Latinos, Native Hawaiians, or Pacific Islanders. Applicants must be juniors majoring in architectural, civil, or environmental engineering with a GPA of 3.0 or higher. Along with their application, they must submit an essay on what they believe will be the greatest challenge facing the engineering profession over the next decade, and why. **Deadline for Receipt:** April of each year. **Additional Information:** This program, sponsored by the Michael Baker Corporation, is available at the following AICUP colleges and universities: Bucknell University, Carnegie Mellon University, Drexel University, Gannon University, Geneva College, Grove City College, Lafayette College, Lehigh University, Messiah College, Swarthmore College, Villanova University, Widener University, and Wilkes University.

2054 ■ ASSOCIATION OF THE WALL AND CEILING INDUSTRY

Attn: Foundation of the Wall and Ceiling Industry
803 West Broad Street, Suite 600
Falls Church, VA 22046
Tel: (703)538-1615
Fax: (703)534-8307
Web Site: http://www.awci.org/thefoundation.shtml
To provide financial assistance for undergraduate or graduate study in disciplines related to the wall and ceiling industry to employees of firms that are members of the Association of the Wall and Ceiling Industries-International (AWCI) and their dependents.
Title of Award: Foundation of the Wall and Ceiling Industry Scholarships **Area, Field, or Subject:** Architecture; Construction; Engineering **Level of Education for which Award is Granted:** Graduate, Undergraduate **Number Awarded:** 1 each year. **Funds Available:** The stipend is $10,000. **Duration:** 1 year.
Eligibility Requirements: This program is open to employees of AWCI member companies and their dependents. Applicants must be working on or planning to work on, as a full-time student, postsecondary education in the field of construction management, engineering, or architecture. They must have a GPA of 3.0 or higher during their last 2 semesters of study. Students in graduate schools, technical schools, associate degree programs, and 4-year colleges and universities are all eligible.

2055 ■ ASSOCIATION FOR WOMEN IN ARCHITECTURE

Attn: Scholarship Chair
22815 Frampton Avenue
Torrance, CA 90501-5034
Tel: (310)534-8466
Fax: (310)257-6885
E-mail: scholarship@awa-la.org
Web Site: http://www.awa-la.org/scholarships.php
To provide financial assistance to women undergraduates in California who are interested in careers in architecture.
Title of Award: Association for Women in Architecture Scholarships **Area, Field, or Subject:** Architecture; Engineering; Engineering, Civil; Engineering, Electrical; Engineering, Mechanical; Graphic art and design; Illustrators and illustrations; Interior design; Landscape architecture and design; Urban affairs/design/planning **Level of Education for which Award is Granted:** Undergraduate **Number Awarded:** 3 each year: 1 at $2,500, 1 at $1,500, and 1 at $1,000. **Funds Available:** Stipends are $2,500, $1,500, or $1,000. **Duration:** 1 year.
Eligibility Requirements: Eligible to apply are women students who have completed at least 1 full year of study in any of the following fields: architecture; civil, structural, mechanical, or electrical engineering as related to architecture; landscape architecture; urban and land planning; interior design; architectural rendering and illustration; or environmental design. They must be residents of California or attending school in California. Interviews are required for semifinalists. Selection is based on grades, a personal statement, financial need, recommendations, and the quality and organization of materials submitted. **Deadline for Receipt:** April of each year.

2056 ■ BEZEK-DURST-SEISER ARCHITECTS AND PLANNERS

Attn: Scholarship Program
3330 C Street, Suite 200
Anchorage, AK 99503

Tel: (907)562-6076
Fax: (907)562-6635
E-mail: bds@bdsak.com
Web Site: http://www.bdsak.com
To provide financial assistance to Alaska Native high school seniors interested in studying architecture, planning, or interior design in college.
Title of Award: Bezek-Durst-Seiser Scholarship Program **Area, Field, or Subject:** Architecture; Interior design; Urban affairs/design/planning **Level of Education for which Award is Granted:** Undergraduate **Number Awarded:** 1 each year. **Funds Available:** The stipend is $1,500 per year. **Duration:** 1 year; may be renewed.
Eligibility Requirements: This program is open to seniors graduating from high schools in Alaska who are Natives accepted into an architecture, planning, or interior design program. Applications must be submitted through a school district or native corporation; direct applications from students are not accepted. Each school district and native corporation in the state may submit 2 applications. Students must include essays on what they are like, the school activities and interests that interest them, why they have chosen their career field, what they have done to prepare themselves to enter that field, why they chose the university or college they plan to attend, and if they plan to return to Alaska after college. **Deadline for Receipt:** April of each year. **Additional Information:** Recipients are also offered paid internships at the Bezek-Durst-Seiser office in Anchorage during summer breaks.

2057 ■ BUILDERS ASSOCIATION OF MINNESOTA

Attn: Minnesota Building Industry Foundation
570 Asbury Street, Suite 301
St. Paul, MN 55104
Tel: (651)646-7959
Free: 800-654-7783
Fax: (651)646-2860
Web Site: http://www.mbif.org/scholarship/cfm
To provide financial assistance to high school seniors in Minnesota who are interested in preparing for a career in a field related to construction.
Title of Award: Building Industry Scholarship Program **Area, Field, or Subject:** Architecture; Construction **Level of Education for which Award is Granted:** Undergraduate **Number Awarded:** 9 each year. **Funds Available:** The stipend is $1,000. **Duration:** 1 year; nonrenewable.
Eligibility Requirements: This program is open to seniors graduating from high schools in Minnesota who are interested in continuing their education. Applicants must be interested in a program in carpentry, woodworking, residential design, architectural drafting, or residential construction management. Along with their application, they must include a list of classes they have already taken in the construction area where they are seeking further training, information on their work background, a current transcript, their attendance record, and a letter of recommendation from an instructor or counselor. **Deadline for Receipt:** April of each year. **Additional Information:** This program includes the Harold E. Swanson Scholarship Program and the Chad Woxland Wausau Homes Scholarship Program.

2058 ■ CALIFORNIA DEPARTMENT OF TRANSPORTATION

Attn: Division of Engineering Services
MS 9 5/2J
P.O. Box 168041
Sacramento, CA 95816-8041
Tel: (916)227-8126
E-mail: karen_bailey@dot.ca.gov
Web Site: http://www.dot.ca.gov/hq/esc/scholarships
To provide financial assistance to high school seniors in California who plan to study engineering or architecture at a college or university in the state.
Title of Award: Division of Engineering Services Engineering/Architectural Scholarship **Area, Field, or Subject:** Architecture; Engineering **Level of Education for which Award is Granted:** Undergraduate **Number Awarded:** At least 1 each year. **Funds Available:** The stipend is $1,000. **Duration:** 1 year.
Eligibility Requirements: This program is open to seniors graduating from high schools in California and planning to enroll in an engineering or architectural program at a community college, state college, or university in the state. Applicants must submit 1) a 100-word personal statement on

their college and career plans and how they believe they can make a contribution to Caltrans; 2) a 500-word essay on how they would improve California's current transportation system; 3) a list of community and school activities; 4) information on work and/or volunteer experience; and 4) letters of recommendation. **Deadline for Receipt:** March **Additional Information:** This program is jointly sponsored by the California Department of Transportation (Caltrans) Division of Engineering Services and the California Transportation Foundation (CTF).

2059 ■ COLORADO READY MIXED CONCRETE ASSOCIATION/ COLORADO ROCK PRODUCTS ASSOCIATION

Attn: Scholarship Fund
6855 South Havana Street, Suite 540
Centennial, CO 80112
Tel: (303)290-0303
Fax: (303)290-8008
E-mail: pschauer@crmca.org
Web Site: http://www.crmca.org/scholarships/default.php
To provide financial assistance to upper-division students from Colorado who are preparing for a career in areas of interest to the Colorado Ready Mixed Concrete Association (CRMCA) and the Colorado Rock Products Association (CRPA).
Title of Award: CRMCA/CRPA Scholarships **Area, Field, or Subject:** Architecture; Business; Construction; Engineering; Engineering, Materials; Materials research/science **Level of Education for which Award is Granted:** Four Year College **Number Awarded:** 4 each year. **Funds Available:** The stipend is $1,000. Funds are paid directly to the student's institution. **Duration:** 1 year.
Eligibility Requirements: This program is open to full-time juniors and seniors at colleges and universities in Colorado who have a GPA of 3.0 or higher. Applicants must be preparing for a career in such fields as aggregate extraction, building construction, road building, municipal utility construction, building design, heavy equipment design, materials research or application, or other fields associated with the use of aggregates or concrete. Preference is given to students whose home residence is Colorado, have graduated from a high school in Colorado, and have a parent employed in concrete or aggregate production industries or associated or auxiliary industries. Along with their application, they must submit a brief resume of their current activities and work experience, 3 letters of character reference, and a 1-page statement on their plans for the future and career. Financial need is not considered in the selection process. **Deadline for Receipt:** July of each year.

2060 ■ COMMUNITY FOUNDATION FOR THE FOX VALLEY REGION, INC.

Attn: Scholarships
4455 West Lawrence Street
P.O. Box 563
Appleton, WI 54912-0563
Tel: (920)830-1290
Fax: (920)830-1293
E-mail: cffvr@cffoxvalley.org
Web Site: http://www.cffoxvalley.org/scholarship_fundslist.html
To provide financial assistance to upper-division and graduate students in Wisconsin who are working on a degree related to gardening.
Title of Award: Wisconsin Garden Club Federation Scholarship **Area, Field, or Subject:** Agricultural sciences; Botany; Environmental conservation; Environmental science; Forestry; Horticulture; Landscape architecture and design; Urban affairs/design/planning **Level of Education for which Award is Granted:** Graduate, Four Year College **Number Awarded:** Varies each year; recently, 4 of these scholarships were awarded. **Funds Available:** The stipend is $1,000. **Duration:** 1 year.
Eligibility Requirements: This program is open to college juniors, seniors, and graduate students at colleges and universities in Wisconsin. Applicants must be majoring in horticulture, floriculture, landscape design/architecture, botany, forestry, agronomy, plant pathology, environmental studies, city planning, land management, or a related field. They must have a 3.0 GPA or higher. **Deadline for Receipt:** February of each year. **Additional Information:** This program is sponsored by the Wisconsin Garden Club Federation. Information is also available from Carolyn A.

Craig, WGCF Scholarship Chair, 900 North Shore Drive, New Richmond, WI 54017-9466, (715) 246-6242, E-mail: cacraig@frontiernet.net.

2061 ■ CONNECTICUT ASSOCIATION OF SCHOOLS

Attn: Executive Director
30 Realty Drive
Cheshire, CT 06410
Tel: (203)250-1111
Fax: (203)250-1345
E-mail: msavage@casciac.org
Web Site: http://www.casciac.org

To provide financial assistance to high school seniors in Connecticut who plan to study the arts in college.

Title of Award: Bruce Eagleson Memorial Scholarship Awards **Area, Field, or Subject:** Architecture; Dance; Design; Music; Performing arts; Visual arts **Level of Education for which Award is Granted:** Undergraduate **Number Awarded:** 3 each year: 1 at $10,000 and 2 at $5,000. **Funds Available:** Stipends are $10,000 or $5,000. **Duration:** 1 year.

Eligibility Requirements: This program is open to seniors graduating from high schools in Connecticut who plan to enroll in college to study the arts, including (but not limited to) visual arts, music, theater, dance, design, and architecture. Applicants must be able to demonstrate 1) considerable experience in the arts as evidenced by involvement in shows, exhibits, performances, video productions, or similar activities; 2) involvement in service to peers and/or community through artistic or other activities; and 3) financial need. Along with their application, they must submit a 250-word statement on what led them to their decision to prepare for a career in the arts. **Deadline for Receipt:** March of each year. **Additional Information:** This program is sponsored by Westfield Corporation in honor of its former East Coast Vice-President of Management who was killed while working for the company at the World Trade Center on September 11, 2001.

2062 ■ CONNECTICUT BUILDING CONGRESS

Attn: Scholarship Fund
2600 Dixwell Avenue, Suite 7
Hamden, CT 06514-1800
Tel: (203)281-3183
Fax: (203)281-8932
E-mail: info@cbc-ct.org
Web Site: http://www.cbc-ct.org/secondpage_folder/member.html

To provide financial assistance to high school seniors in Connecticut who are interested in studying a field related to the construction industry in college.

Title of Award: Connecticut Building Congress Scholarships **Area, Field, or Subject:** Architecture; Cartography/Surveying; Construction; Engineering; Management; Urban affairs/design/planning **Level of Education for which Award is Granted:** Undergraduate **Number Awarded:** Varies each year. **Funds Available:** Stipends range from $500 to $2,000 per year. **Duration:** Up to 4 years.

Eligibility Requirements: This program is open to graduating seniors at high schools in Connecticut. Applicants must be interested in attending a 2- or 4-year college or university to major in a field related to construction (e.g., architecture, engineering, construction management, surveying, planning, drafting). They must submit an essay (up to 500 words) that explains how their planned studies will relate to a career in the construction industry. Selection is based on academic merit, extracurricular activities, potential, and financial need. **Deadline for Receipt:** February of each year.

2063 ■ CONNECTICUT CHAPTER OF THE AMERICAN PLANNING ASSOCIATION

c/o Alan L. Weiner, Member Services Committee
City Planner, City of Bristol
111 North Main Street
Bristol, CT 06010
Tel: (860)584-6225
Fax: (860)584-3838
E-mail: alanweiner@ci.bristol.ct.us
Web Site: http://www.ccapa.org

To provide financial assistance to undergraduate students in planning or architecture at schools in New England and New York.

Title of Award: Sam Pine Scholarship **Area, Field, or Subject:** Architecture; Urban affairs/design/planning **Level of Education for which**

Award is Granted: Undergraduate **Number Awarded:** 1 each year. **Funds Available:** The stipend is $2,000. **Duration:** 1 year.

Eligibility Requirements: This program is open to undergraduate students in planning, architecture, or a related field. Applicants must attend a college or university in New England or New York. Selection is based, first, on financial need and then on academic record. **Additional Information:** This program was established in 1997.

2064 ■ CONSTRUCTION SPECIFICATIONS INSTITUTE-DC METROPOLITAN CHAPTER

c/o Dave Metzger, Academic Affairs Committee Chair
Heller & Metzger PC
11 Dupont Circle, N.W., Suite 601
Washington, DC 20036
Tel: (202)364-2222
Fax: (202)234-5502
E-mail: davem@hellerandmetzger.com
Web Site: http://www.csidcmetro.org/warner_fund.html

To provide financial assistance to members of student chapters of the Construction Specifications Institute (CSI) at colleges and universities in the Washington, D.C. metropolitan area.

Title of Award: Franklyn E. Warner Student Fellowship for Balanced Achievement **Area, Field, or Subject:** Architecture; Construction; Engineering **Level of Education for which Award is Granted:** Four Year College **Number Awarded:** 1 each year. **Funds Available:** A stipend is awarded (amount not specified). **Duration:** 1 year.

Eligibility Requirements: This program is open to CSI student members at schools in the Washington, D.C. metropolitan area who are rising seniors or graduating seniors. Applicants must be majoring in architecture, engineering, or construction management. Along with their application, they must submit an essay of 500 to 750 words that demonstrates their understanding of the balanced relationships among the aesthetic, functional, technical, and managerial aspects of the built environment. Selection is based on the essay, potential as future leader in the design and construction industry, and letters of recommendation demonstrating the applicant's skills and abilities across a balanced and diversified range of professional areas. **Deadline for Receipt:** January of each year. **Additional Information:** This program was established in 2003.

2065 ■ CONSTRUCTION SPECIFICATIONS INSTITUTE-GRAND RAPIDS CHAPTER

c/o Lynn J. DePeal, Academic Affairs Committee Chair
IR SSC Michigan
2556 Albert Drive, S.E.
Grand Rapids, MI 49506
Tel: (616)285-8009
Fax: (616)285-8009
E-mail: lynn_depeal@irco.com
Web Site: http://www.csigrandrapids.org

To provide financial assistance to students at colleges and universities in Michigan who are preparing for a career in the construction industry.

Title of Award: Grand Rapids Chapter CSI Scholarship **Area, Field, or Subject:** Architecture; Construction; Engineering; Engineering, Electrical; Engineering, Mechanical **Level of Education for which Award is Granted:** Undergraduate **Number Awarded:** 1 or more each year. **Funds Available:** Stipends up to $1,500 are available. **Duration:** 1 year.

Eligibility Requirements: This program is open to students enrolled at an accredited college, university, or trade school in Michigan. Applicants must be working on a degree in a field directly related to the construction industry, including architecture, engineering (electrical, mechanical, construction), management technology, and facilities maintenance. Along with their application, they must submit brief essays about 1) the kinds of activities they participate in and enjoy, and the people who participate in those activities with them; 2) how they see their career in the construction-related industry and what they think they can offer the industry; and 3) their financial need and desire for assistance. Selection is based on scholastic ability, references, overall impression of the applicant as presented in the essays, and how the applicant will benefit from receiving this scholarship. Preference is given to applicants who are members of the Construction Specifics Institute (CSI) or related to a member. **Deadline for Receipt:** April of each year.

2066 ■ CONSTRUCTION SPECIFICATIONS INSTITUTE-MAINE CHAPTER

c/o James Beaulieu, Academic Affairs Committee Chair
Ledgewood Construction
27 Main Street
South Portland, ME 04106
Tel: (207)767-1866
Fax: (207)767-1869
Web Site: http://www.mecsi.org
To provide financial assistance to Maine residents preparing for a career in a field related to construction technology at a public university in the state.
Title of Award: Advancement of Construction Technology Scholarship **Area, Field, or Subject:** Architecture; Engineering **Level of Education for which Award is Granted:** Undergraduate **Number Awarded:** 1 each year. **Funds Available:** The stipend is at least $1,000. **Duration:** 1 year.
Eligibility Requirements: This program is open to residents of Maine who have completed at least 1 year of study at a campus of the University of Maine system. Applicants must be preparing for a career in architectural or engineering technology. They must be able to demonstrate active involvement in a career or industry organization or association.

2067 ■ CONSTRUCTION SPECIFICATIONS INSTITUTE-RICHMOND CHAPTER

Attn: Richmond CSI Scholarship Fund Foundation
9016 Peaks Road
Ashland, VA 23005
Tel: (804)307-3282
Fax: (804)752-2670
E-mail: csirichmond@wans.net
Web Site: http://www.richmondcsi.org/scholarship.shtml
To provide financial assistance to undergraduate students in Virginia who are preparing for a construction-related career.
Title of Award: Norman F. Jacobs, Jr. Scholarship **Area, Field, or Subject:** Architecture; Construction; Engineering; Engineering, Civil; Engineering, Electrical; Engineering, Mechanical **Level of Education for which Award is Granted:** Four Year College **Number Awarded:** Up to 2 each year. **Funds Available:** The stipend is at least $1,000. Funds are sent directly to the recipient's institution. **Duration:** 1 year.
Eligibility Requirements: Eligible to apply are students who are enrolled full time at an accredited Virginia college or university and majoring in architecture, construction, or a construction-related field of engineering (civil, structural, mechanical, electrical). Applicants must have completed 1 year of a 2-year program or 2 full years of a 4- or 5-year bachelor's degree program. They must have a GPA of 2.5 or higher and be able to demonstrate financial need. **Deadline for Receipt:** April of each year.

2068 ■ DEPARTMENT OF TRANSPORTATION

Federal Highway Administration
Attn: National Highway Institute, HNHI-20
4600 North Fairfax Drive, Suite 800
Arlington, VA 22203-1553
Tel: (703)235-0538
Fax: (703)235-0593
E-mail: transportationedu@fhwa.dot.gov
Web Site: http://www.nhi.fhwa.dot.gov/ddetfp.asp
To provide financial assistance for undergraduate study in transportation-related fields to students at Hispanic Serving Institutions.
Title of Award: Eisenhower Hispanic-Serving Institutions Fellowships **Area, Field, or Subject:** Accounting; Architecture; Business administration; Engineering, Civil; Environmental conservation; Environmental science; Transportation **Level of Education for which Award is Granted:** Four Year College **Number Awarded:** Varies each year; recently, 18 students received support from this program. **Funds Available:** The stipend covers the fellow's full cost of education, including tuition and fees. **Duration:** 1 year.
Eligibility Requirements: These fellowships are intended for students who are enrolled at federally-designated 4-year Hispanic Serving Institutions (HSIs) and who are working on a degree in a transportation-related field (i.e., engineering, accounting, business, architecture, environmental

sciences, etc.). Applicants must have entered their junior year, have at least a 3.0 GPA, and have a faculty sponsor. **Deadline for Receipt:** February of each year.

2069 ■ DEPARTMENT OF TRANSPORTATION

Federal Highway Administration
Attn: National Highway Institute, HNHI-20
4600 North Fairfax Drive, Suite 800
Arlington, VA 22203-1553
Tel: (703)235-0538
Fax: (703)235-0593
E-mail: transportationedu@fhwa.dot.gov
Web Site: http://www.nhi.fhwa.dot.gov/ddetfp.asp
To provide financial assistance for undergraduate study in transportation-related fields to students at Historically Black Colleges and Universities.
Title of Award: Eisenhower Historically Black Colleges and Universities Fellowships **Area, Field, or Subject:** Accounting; Architecture; Business administration; Engineering, Civil; Environmental conservation; Environmental science; Transportation **Level of Education for which Award is Granted:** Four Year College **Number Awarded:** Varies each year; recently, 48 students received support from this program. **Funds Available:** The stipend covers the fellow's full cost of education, including tuition and fees. **Duration:** 1 year.
Eligibility Requirements: These fellowships are intended for students who are enrolled at federally-designated 4-year Historically Black Colleges and Universities (HBCUs) and working on a degree in a transportation-related field (i.e., engineering, accounting, business, architecture, environmental sciences, etc.). Applicants must have entered their junior year, have at least a 3.0 GPA, and have a faculty sponsor. **Deadline for Receipt:** February of each year.

2070 ■ FEDERATED GARDEN CLUBS OF CONNECTICUT, INC.

14 Business Park Drive
P.O. Box 854
Branford, CT 06405-0854
Tel: (203)488-5528
Fax: (203)488-5528
E-mail: gardenclubs@ctgardenclubs.org
Web Site: http://www.ctgardenclubs.org/scholarship.html
To provide financial assistance to Connecticut residents who are interested in majoring in horticulture-related fields at a Connecticut college or university.
Title of Award: Federated Garden Clubs of Connecticut Scholarship **Area, Field, or Subject:** Agricultural sciences; Botany; Environmental conservation; Environmental science; Forestry; Horticulture; Landscape architecture and design; Urban affairs/design/planning **Level of Education for which Award is Granted:** Four Year College, Graduate **Number Awarded:** Varies each year, depending upon the availability of funds. **Funds Available:** Stipends are generally about $1,000 each. Funds are sent to the recipient's school in 2 equal installments. **Duration:** 1 year.
Eligibility Requirements: Applicants must be legal residents of Connecticut who are studying at a college or university in the state in horticulture, floriculture, landscape design, conservation, forestry, botany, agronomy, plant pathology, environmental control, city planning, land management, or related subjects. They must be entering their junior or senior year of college or be a graduate student, have a GPA of 3.0 or higher, and be able to demonstrate financial need. **Deadline for Receipt:** June of each year. **Additional Information:** Information is also available from the Connecticut State Scholarship Chair, Mary Gray, 18 Long Hill Farm Road, Guilford, CT 06437, (203) 458-2784.

2071 ■ FLORIDA NURSERYMEN, GROWERS AND LANDSCAPE ASSOCIATION-ACTION CHAPTER

Attn: Gina Mazzie-Forbrick, Scholarship Committee Chair
ForemostCo, Inc.
1751 Williams Road
Winter Garden, FL 34787-9162
Tel: (407)877-8876
Fax: (407)877-8684
E-mail: gina@foremostco.com
To provide financial assistance to students in Florida interested in preparing for a career in horticulture.
Title of Award: FNGLA Action Chapter Scholarship **Area, Field, or Subject:** Horticulture; Landscape architecture and design; Turfgrass

management **Level of Education for which Award is Granted:** Undergraduate **Number Awarded:** 1 or more each year. A total of $4,000 is available through this program each year. **Funds Available:** Stipends range from $500 to $1,500. **Duration:** 1 year.
Eligibility Requirements: Applicants must have been accepted by or be currently enrolled in a Florida junior college, college, or university. They may be attending school full or part time, but they must be majoring in 1 of the following subjects: environmental horticulture, landscaping, landscape architecture, turf management, or a related field. All applicants must have at least a 2.75 GPA. Selection is based on academic record, work experience, awards received, letters of recommendation, and an essay (300 words) on the applicant's career plans. **Deadline for Receipt:** June of each year.

2072 ■ FOUNDATION FOR AMATEUR RADIO, INC.

Attn: Scholarship Committee
P.O. Box 831
Riverdale, MD 20738
E-mail: aa3of@arrl.net
Web Site: http://www.amateurradio-far.org/scholarships.php
To provide funding to licensed radio amateurs from selected states who are interested in studying selected subjects in college.
Title of Award: Nanticoke Amateur Radio Club Scholarship **Area, Field, or Subject:** Architecture; Electronics; Engineering; Science **Level of Education for which Award is Granted:** Undergraduate **Number Awarded:** 1 each year. **Funds Available:** The stipend is $1,000. **Duration:** 1 year.
Eligibility Requirements: This program is open to college students who have an amateur radio license with HF privileges and are interested in majoring in architecture, engineering, electronics, science, or a related field at an institution of higher learning in the United States. They must be residents of Delaware, Maryland, Virginia, or the District of Columbia. **Deadline for Receipt:** Requests for applications must be submitted by April of each year. **Additional Information:** Recipients must attend an accredited school (university, college, or technical institute) on a full-time basis.

2073 ■ HAWAI'I COMMUNITY FOUNDATION

Attn: Scholarship Department
1164 Bishop Street, Suite 800
Honolulu, HI 96813
Tel: (808)566-5570; 888-731-3863
Fax: (808)521-6286
E-mail: scholarships@hcf-hawaii.org
Web Site: http://www.hawaiicommunityfoundation.org/scholar/scholar.php
To provide financial assistance to Hawaii residents who are interested in preparing for a career that will fill gaps in the local job market.
Title of Award: Hawai'i Community Foundation Community Scholarship Fund **Area, Field, or Subject:** Architecture; Art; Education; Humanities; Social sciences **Level of Education for which Award is Granted:** Graduate, Undergraduate **Number Awarded:** Varies each year; recently, 97 of these scholarships were awarded. **Funds Available:** The amount awarded varies; recently, stipends averaged $1,000. **Duration:** 1 year.
Eligibility Requirements: This program is open to students in Hawaii who show potential for filling a community need; demonstrate accomplishment, motivation, initiative, and vision; are residents of the state of Hawaii; intend to return to, or stay in, Hawaii to work; are able to demonstrate financial need; are interested in attending an accredited 2- or 4-year college or university as a full-time student at either the undergraduate or graduate level; plan to major in the arts, architecture, education, humanities, or social science; and are able to demonstrate academic achievement (GPA of 3.0 or higher). **Deadline for Receipt:** February of each year. **Additional Information:** Recipients may attend school in Hawaii or on the mainland. This fund was established in 1947.

2074 ■ HISPANIC CONTRACTORS OF COLORADO

1114 West Seventh Avenue, Suite 210
Denver, CO 80204
Tel: (303)893-3893
Fax: (303)893-2877
Web Site: http://www.hispanic-contractors.org/html/scholarships.htm
To provide financial assistance for college to Hispanic residents of Colorado who are interested in preparing for a career in the construction industry.

Title of Award: Hispanic Contractors of Colorado Scholarships **Area, Field, or Subject:** Architecture; Construction; Engineering; Heating, air conditioning, and refrigeration **Level of Education for which Award is Granted:** Undergraduate **Number Awarded:** 1 or more each year. **Funds Available:** A stipend is awarded (amount not specified). **Duration:** 1 year.
Eligibility Requirements: This program is open to residents of Colorado of Hispanic heritage who have been accepted at or are attending an accredited college, university, or technical school. Applicants must have a cumulative GPA of 2.5 or higher and a declared major or certificate interest in a construction-related field (e.g., architecture, construction management, construction technology, engineering, HVAC certificate). Students in a 4-year college or university program must be juniors or above. Selection is based on a statement on career goals and why the applicant has chosen a career in construction, academic achievement, 2 letters of recommendation, community service and/or extracurricular activities, and financial need. **Deadline for Receipt:** March of each year.

2075 ■ HOME BUILDERS ASSOCIATION OF ILLINOIS

112 West Edwards Street
Springfield, IL 62704
Tel: (217)753-3963
Fax: (217)753-3811
Web Site: http://www.hbai.org/Student/index.asp
To recognize and reward, with funds for continuing education, students in Illinois who are preparing for a career in the building industry.
Title of Award: Home Builders Association of Illinois Student of the Year Scholarships **Area, Field, or Subject:** Architecture; Construction **Level of Education for which Award is Granted:** Undergraduate **Number Awarded:** 3 each year. **Funds Available:** Awards are $2,000 for first place, $1,500 for second place, and $1,000 for third place. Funds are paid to the student's school to be used for continuing education. If the recipients is not remaining in school, they may use the award for certified graduate builder or remodeler courses offered through the home builders association. **Duration:** Awards are offered annually.
Eligibility Requirements: This program is open to students enrolled in a building trades or architecture program at a high school, university, community college, or technical school in Illinois. Students must be nominated by a local affiliate of the Home Builders Association of Illinois. They must have a "C+" average or higher. Selection is based on academics, involvement with the building industry, leadership and extracurricular activities, community involvement, and awards and honor.

2076 ■ ILLUMINATING ENGINEERING SOCIETY OF NORTH AMERICA-GOLDEN GATE SECTION

c/o Phil Hall
1514 Gibbons Drive
Alameda, CA 94501
Tel: (510)208-5005
Fax: (510)864-8511
E-mail: mrcatisbac@aol.com
Web Site: http://www.iesgg.org
To provide financial assistance to undergraduate or graduate students interested in studying or conducting research in lighting.
Title of Award: Robert W. Thunen Memorial Scholarships **Area, Field, or Subject:** Architecture; Engineering, Electrical; Filmmaking; Interior design; Lighting science; Radio and television **Level of Education for which Award is Granted:** Four Year College, Graduate **Number Awarded:** At least 2 each year. **Funds Available:** The stipend is $2,500. **Duration:** 1 year.
Eligibility Requirements: Applicants must be enrolled full time as an upper-division or graduate student at an accredited 4-year educational institution in northern California, northern Nevada, Oregon, or Washington and be studying architecture, electrical engineering, film/TV, lighting design, theater, or vision with an emphasis on lighting. Undergraduate students must be proposing course work related to potential employment in the lighting field. Graduate students must be proposing to conduct a research project that will further the lighting field or industry. Financial

need is not considered in the selection process. **Deadline for Receipt:** March of each year. **Additional Information:** This program was established in 1986.

2077 ■ NATIONAL ASSOCIATION OF WOMEN IN CONSTRUCTION-BUFFALO CHAPTER 172

c/o Susan Zipp
Siemens Building Technologies
85 Northpointe Parkway, Suite 8
Amherst, NY 14228-1886
Tel: (716)568-0983
Web Site: http://buffalonawic.tripod.com/pr02.htm

To provide financial assistance to residents of New York attending college in the state to prepare for a career in construction.

Title of Award: Buffalo Chapter NAWIC Scholarship **Area, Field, or Subject:** Architecture; Construction; Design; Drafting; Engineering **Level of Education for which Award is Granted:** Undergraduate **Number Awarded:** 1 each year. **Funds Available:** The stipend is $1,000. **Duration:** 1 year.

Eligibility Requirements: This program is open to residents of New York entering the second, third, or fourth year at a 2- or 4-year college or university in the state. Applicants must be majoring in a construction-related program of study (e.g., architecture, construction technology, drafting and design, engineering, estimating). U.S. citizenship is required. **Deadline for Receipt:** June of each year.

2078 ■ NATIONAL ASSOCIATION OF WOMEN IN CONSTRUCTION-GREATER OMAHA CHAPTER 116

Attn: Scholarship Committee
8712 West Dodge Road, Suite 200
Omaha, NE 68114
E-mail: nawicomaha@yahoo.com
Web Site: http://www.geocities.com/nawicomaha

To provide financial assistance to students in Nebraska who are preparing for a career in construction.

Title of Award: Greater Omaha Chapter NAWIC Scholarship **Area, Field, or Subject:** Architecture; Construction; Engineering **Level of Education for which Award is Granted:** Undergraduate **Number Awarded:** 1 or more each year. **Funds Available:** A stipend is awarded (amount not specified). **Duration:** 1 year.

Eligibility Requirements: This program is open to graduating high school seniors and current college students in Nebraska. Applicants must be preparing for a career in the construction industry (e.g., architecture, engineering, construction management). They must have a GPA of 2.75 or higher and be enrolled or planning to enroll full time. **Deadline for Receipt:** March of each year.

2079 ■ NATIONAL ASSOCIATION OF WOMEN IN CONSTRUCTION-MAINE CHAPTER 276

P.O. Box 366
Hallowell, ME 04347
Tel: (207)623-4683
E-mail: nawicmaine@aol.com
Web Site: http://www.nawicmaine.org

To provide financial assistance to Maine residents who are working on a college degree in a field related to construction.

Title of Award: Maine Chapter 276 Scholarships **Area, Field, or Subject:** Architecture; Business; Construction; Engineering, Civil; Welding **Level of Education for which Award is Granted:** Undergraduate **Number Awarded:** Varies each year; recently, 7 of these scholarships were awarded. **Funds Available:** Stipends range from $500 to $1,000. **Duration:** 1 year.

Eligibility Requirements: This program is open to residents of Maine who are enrolled in a postsecondary educational program. Applicants must be preparing for a career in construction, including carpentry, civil engineering, architecture, welding, electrical, plumbing, or construction management. Along with their application, they must submit a 50-word statement on why they have chosen a career in construction. Selection is based on academic achievement and financial need. **Deadline for**

Receipt: April of each year. **Additional Information:** Information is also available from Joyce Newman, 3 Hillcrest Street, Hallowell, ME 04347.

2080 ■ NATIONAL ASSOCIATION OF WOMEN IN CONSTRUCTION-METROPOLITAN DENVER CHAPTER 112

c/o Laruie Mullane
P.O. Box 40208
Denver, CO 80204-0204
Tel: (303)571-5377

To provide financial assistance to high school seniors in Colorado who are interested in preparing for a career in construction.

Title of Award: Vona J. Wagner Memorial Scholarship **Area, Field, or Subject:** Architecture; Construction; Engineering **Level of Education for which Award is Granted:** Undergraduate **Number Awarded:** Varies; generally, 3 to 4 each year. **Funds Available:** The stipend is $1,000. Money is not paid at the time of the award but only on a reimbursement basis after the recipient submits proof of enrollment at a Colorado institution and receipts for tuition, books, laboratory fees, and other school expenses; living expenses are not reimbursable. **Duration:** 1 year; nonrenewable.

Eligibility Requirements: This program is open to high school seniors who have applied to or been admitted to a college, university, or trade school in Colorado. Applicants must be interested in studying field related to construction (e.g., architecture, engineering, construction management) in college and planning to work on a bachelor's degree or certificate of completion. They must have a GPA of 2.5 or higher. Financial need is considered but it not an absolute requirement. **Deadline for Receipt:** March of each year.

2081 ■ NATIONAL ASSOCIATION OF WOMEN IN CONSTRUCTION-NASHVILLE CHAPTER 16

Attn: Scholarship Fund
P.O. Box 22246
Nashville, TN 37202-2246
E-mail: info@nawicnashville.com
Web Site: http://www.nawicnashville.com

To provide financial assistance to residents of Tennessee working on an undergraduate degree in a construction-related field.

Title of Award: Cordie Hughes Scholarship **Area, Field, or Subject:** Architecture; Construction; Engineering **Level of Education for which Award is Granted:** Undergraduate **Number Awarded:** Varies each year; recently, a total of $2,000 was available for this program. **Funds Available:** A stipend is awarded (amount not specified). **Duration:** 1 year.

Eligibility Requirements: This program is open to residents of Tennessee attending a college or university in Alabama, Georgia, or Tennessee. Applicants must be working on a degree in a field related to construction (e.g., architecture, engineering, construction management). They must have a GPA of 2.8 or higher and be able to demonstrate financial need. Priority is given to applicants entering their junior or senior year at a 4-year institution. If no student at a 4-year school qualifies, students at 2-year colleges are considered.

2082 ■ NATIONAL ASSOCIATION OF WOMEN IN CONSTRUCTION-SAN ANTONIO CHAPTER 11

c/o Deborah L. Schievelbein, Scholarship Chair
405 North St. Mary's Street, Suite 150
San Antonio, TX 78205
Tel: (210)476-0400
E-mail: dbdrumm@world-net.net
Web Site: http://www.nawicsat.org

To provide financial assistance to students in Texas working on an undergraduate degree in a construction-related field.

Title of Award: San Antonio Chapter NAWIC Scholarship **Area, Field, or Subject:** Architecture; Construction; Engineering **Level of Education for which Award is Granted:** Undergraduate **Number Awarded:** 1 or more each year. **Funds Available:** A stipend is awarded (amount not specified). Funds are paid directly to the recipient's college or university. **Duration:** 1 year; may be renewed.

Eligibility Requirements: This program is open to full-time students who are residents of Texas and undergraduates attending a college or university in the state. Applicants must be majoring in a field related to construction (e.g., architecture, engineering, construction management). They must have a GPA of 3.0 or higher. Previous recipient are given priority in the selection process. **Deadline for Receipt:** January of each year.

2083 ■ NATIONAL FEDERATION OF THE BLIND

c/o Peggy Elliott, Scholarship Committee Chair
805 Fifth Avenue
Grinnell, IA 50112
Tel: (641)236-3366
Web Site: http://www.nfb.org/sch_intro.htm

To provide financial assistance for college or graduate school to blind students studying or planning to study law, medicine, engineering, architecture, or the natural sciences.

Title of Award: Howard Brown Rickard Scholarships **Area, Field, or Subject:** Architecture; Engineering; Law; Medicine; Natural sciences **Level of Education for which Award is Granted:** Graduate, Undergraduate **Number Awarded:** 1 each year. **Funds Available:** The stipend is $3,000. **Duration:** 1 year; recipients may resubmit applications up to 2 additional years.

Eligibility Requirements: This program is open to legally blind students who are enrolled in or planning to enroll in a full-time undergraduate or graduate course of study. Applicants must be studying or planning to study law, medicine, engineering, architecture, or the natural sciences. Selection is based on academic excellence, service to the community, and financial need. **Deadline for Receipt:** March of each year. **Additional Information:** Scholarships are awarded at the federation convention in July. Recipients attend the convention at federation expense; that funding is in addition to the scholarship grant.

2084 ■ NATIONAL FFA ORGANIZATION

Attn: Scholarship Office
6060 FFA Drive
P.O. Box 68960
Indianapolis, IN 46268-0960
Tel: (317)802-4321
Fax: (317)802-5321
E-mail: scholarships@ffa.org
Web Site: http://www.ffa.org

To provide financial assistance to FFA members interested in studying agriculture, horticulture, or landscaping in college.

Title of Award: Irrigation Association Education Foundation Scholarship **Area, Field, or Subject:** Agricultural sciences; Horticulture; Landscape architecture and design **Level of Education for which Award is Granted:** Four Year College **Number Awarded:** 1 each year. **Funds Available:** The stipend is $1,000 per year. Funds are paid directly to the recipient. **Duration:** 1 year; nonrenewable.

Eligibility Requirements: This program is open to members who are graduating high school seniors planning to enroll full time in college. Applicants must be interested in working on a 4-year college degree in agriculture, horticulture, or landscaping. They must be in the top 10% of their class and an interest in irrigation that is confirmed by their advisor. Selection is based on academic achievement (10 points for GPA, 10 points for SAT or ACT score, 10 points for class rank), leadership in FFA activities (30 points), leadership in community activities (10 points), and participation in the Supervised Agricultural Experience (SAE) program (30 points). U.S. citizenship is required. **Deadline for Receipt:** February of each year. **Additional Information:** Funding for this scholarship is provided by the Irrigation Association Education Foundation.

2085 ■ NATIONAL FFA ORGANIZATION

Attn: Scholarship Office
6060 FFA Drive
P.O. Box 68960
Indianapolis, IN 46268-0960
Tel: (317)802-4321
Fax: (317)802-5321
E-mail: scholarships@ffa.org
Web Site: http://www.ffa.org

To provide financial assistance to FFA members who wish to study agricultural journalism and related fields in college.

Title of Award: National FFA Scholarships for Undergraduates in the Humanities **Area, Field, or Subject:** Agricultural sciences; Communications; Horticulture; Landscape architecture and design **Level of Education for which Award is Granted:** Undergraduate **Number Awarded:** Varies; generally, a total of approximately 1,000 scholarships are awarded

annually by the association. **Funds Available:** Stipends vary, but most are at least $1,000. **Duration:** 1 year or more.

Eligibility Requirements: This program is open to current and former members of the organization who are working or planning to work full time on a degree in fields related to agricultural journalism and communications, floriculture, and landscape design. For most of the scholarships, applicants must be high school seniors; others are open to students currently enrolled in college. The program includes a large number of designated scholarships that specify the locations where the members must live, the schools they must attend, the fields of study they must pursue, or other requirements. Some consider family income in the selection process, but most do not. Selection is based on academic achievement (10 points for GPA, 10 points for SAT or ACT score, 10 points for class rank), leadership in FFA activities (30 points), leadership in community activities (10 points), and participation in the Supervised Agricultural Experience (SAE) program (30 points). U.S. citizenship is required. **Deadline for Receipt:** February of each year. **Additional Information:** Funding for these scholarships is provided by many different corporate sponsors.

2086 ■ NATIONAL FFA ORGANIZATION

Attn: Scholarship Office
6060 FFA Drive
P.O. Box 68960
Indianapolis, IN 46268-0960
Tel: (317)802-4321
Fax: (317)802-5321
E-mail: scholarships@ffa.org
Web Site: http://www.ffa.org

To provide financial assistance to FFA members interested in studying a field related to the landscape industry in college.

Title of Award: PLANET Scholarships **Area, Field, or Subject:** Horticulture; Landscape architecture and design **Level of Education for which Award is Granted:** Undergraduate **Number Awarded:** 2 each year: 1 to a high school senior and 1 to a current college student. **Funds Available:** The stipend is $1,500 per year. Funds are paid directly to the recipient. **Duration:** 1 year; nonrenewable.

Eligibility Requirements: This program is open to members who are either high school seniors or already enrolled full time in college. Applicants must be working on or planning to work on a 2-year or 4-year degree in a field directly related to the landscape industry. Selection is based on academic achievement (10 points for GPA, 10 points for SAT or ACT score, 10 points for class rank), leadership in FFA activities (30 points), leadership in community activities (10 points), and participation in the Supervised Agricultural Experience (SAE) program (30 points). U.S. citizenship is required. **Deadline for Receipt:** February of each year. **Additional Information:** Funding for this scholarship is provided by the Professional Landcare Network (PLANET), formed in 2005 as the result of a merger between the Associated Landscape Contractors of America (ALCA) and the Professional Lawn Care Association of America (PLCAA).

2087 ■ NATIONAL FFA ORGANIZATION

Attn: Scholarship Office
6060 FFA Drive
P.O. Box 68960
Indianapolis, IN 46268-0960
Tel: (317)802-4321
Fax: (317)802-5321
E-mail: scholarships@ffa.org
Web Site: http://www.ffa.org

To provide financial assistance to FFA members interested in studying designated agricultural specialties in college.

Title of Award: Spraying Systems Company TeeJet Spray Products Scholarship **Area, Field, or Subject:** Agricultural sciences; Engineering, Agricultural; Horticulture; Landscape architecture and design; Turfgrass management **Level of Education for which Award is Granted:** Four Year College **Number Awarded:** 1 each year. **Funds Available:** The stipend is $1,000 per year. Funds are paid directly to the recipient. **Duration:** 1 year; nonrenewable.

Eligibility Requirements: This program is open to members who are graduating high school seniors planning to enroll full time in college. Applicants must be interested in working on a 4-year college degree in agronomy, agricultural engineering/mechanization, landscape/turfgrass management, or horticulture. Selection is based on academic achievement (10 points for GPA, 10 points for SAT or ACT score, 10 points for class rank), leadership in FFA activities (30 points), leadership in community activities (10 points), and participation in the Supervised Agricultural Experience (SAE) program (30 points). U.S. citizenship is required. **Deadline for Receipt:** February of each year. **Additional Information:** Funding for this scholarship is provided by Spraying Systems Company, manufacturer of TeeJet brand spray products.

2088 ■ NATIONAL HOUSING ENDOWMENT

1201 15th Street, N.W.
Washington, DC 20005
Tel: (202)266-8483
Free: 800-368-5242
Fax: (202)266-8177
E-mail: nhe@nahb.com
Web Site: http://www.nationalhousingendowment.com/Scholarships.htm
To provide financial assistance to undergraduate students interested in preparing for a career in the building industry (particularly as a manager).
Title of Award: Centex Homes Build Your Future Scholarship **Area, Field, or Subject:** Architecture; Construction; Engineering, Civil **Level of Education for which Award is Granted:** Undergraduate **Number Awarded:** Varies each year; recently, 18 of these scholarships were awarded. **Funds Available:** Stipends range from $500 to $2,000. Funds are made payable to the recipient and sent to the recipient's school. **Duration:** 1 year; may be renewed.
Eligibility Requirements: This program is open to full-time undergraduate students working on a degree in a housing-related program, such as construction management, residential building, construction technology, civil engineering, architecture, or a trade specialty. Applicants must have at least a 2.5 GPA in all courses and at least a 3.0 GPA in core curriculum classes. Preference is given to applicants who would be unable to afford college without financial assistance and to applicants who demonstrate their interest in residential construction through 1 or more of the following activities: 1) experience/internships in the industry; 2) membership and participation in service organizations and activities related to the building industry; and 3) membership in a student chapter of the National Association of Home Builders. Along with their application, they must submit an essay on their reasons for becoming a professional in the housing industry and their career goals. Selection is based on financial need, career goals, academic achievement, employment history, extracurricular activities, and letters of recommendation. **Deadline for Receipt:** March of each year. **Additional Information:** The National Housing Endowment is the philanthropic arm of the National Association of Home Builders. Centex Homes established this scholarship in 1999.

2089 ■ NATIONAL HOUSING ENDOWMENT

1201 15th Street, N.W.
Washington, DC 20005
Tel: (202)266-8483
Free: 800-368-5242
Fax: (202)266-8177
E-mail: nhe@nahb.com
Web Site: http://www.nationalhousingendowment.com/Scholarships.htm
To provide financial assistance to undergraduate students, especially women, interested in preparing for a career in the building industry.
Title of Award: NAHB Women's Council Strategies for Success Scholarship **Area, Field, or Subject:** Architecture; Construction; Engineering, Civil **Level of Education for which Award is Granted:** Undergraduate **Number Awarded:** Varies each year; recently, 2 of these scholarships were awarded. **Funds Available:** The stipend is $2,000. Funds are made payable to the recipient and sent to the recipient's school. **Duration:** 1 year; may be renewed.
Eligibility Requirements: This program is open to high school seniors and current undergraduates who are enrolled or planning to enroll full time at a 2- or 4-year college or university or vocational program. Applicants must be working on or planning to work on a degree in a housing-related program, such as construction management, building, construction technology, civil engineering, architecture, or a trade specialty. They must have at least a 2.5 GPA in all courses and at least a 3.0 GPA in core curriculum classes. Preference is given to 1) women; 2) applicants who would be unable to afford college without financial assistance; and 3) scholarship who are current members (or will be members in the upcoming

semester) of a student chapter of the National Association of Home Builders (NAHB). Along with their application, they must submit an essay on their reasons for becoming a professional in the housing industry and their career goals. Selection is based on financial need, career goals, academic achievement, employment history, extracurricular activities, and letters of recommendation. **Deadline for Receipt:** March of each year. **Additional Information:** The National Housing Endowment is the philanthropic arm of the National Association of Home Builders (NAHB). Its women's council established this scholarship in 2001.

2090 ■ PROFESSIONAL LANDCARE NETWORK

Attn: ALCA Educational Foundation
950 Herndon Parkway, Suite 450
Herndon, VA 20170
Tel: (703)736-9666
Free: 800-395-ALCA
Fax: (703)736-9668
E-mail: scholarship@landcarenetwork.org
Web Site: http://www.landcarenetwork.org/cms/programs/foundation.html
To provide financial assistance to students at colleges and universities that have a connection to the Professional Landcare Network (PLANET).
Title of Award: ALCA Educational Foundation Scholarships **Area, Field, or Subject:** Horticulture; Landscape architecture and design **Level of Education for which Award is Granted:** Undergraduate **Number Awarded:** Varies each year. Recently, 37 of these scholarships were awarded: 1 at $2,500, 1 at $1,500, 34 at $1,000, and 1 at $500. **Funds Available:** Stipends range from $500 to $2,500. **Duration:** 1 year.
Eligibility Requirements: This program is open to students at colleges and universities that 1) have an accredited PLANET landscape contracting curriculum, 2) have a PLANET student chapter, and/or 3) participate in PLANET student career days activities. Applicants must provide information on awards, honors, and scholarships received in high school or college; high school, college, and community activities related to horticulture; PLANET events attended; work experience; and brief essays on what they have learned about financial management as part of their education that will help them in their career, how their landscape industry related curriculum has helped them in achieving their career goals, the kind of training and work experience they will complete to attain their goals, their plan to attain more leadership and human relations skills, their reasons for desiring the scholarship, their career objectives as they relate to the field of landscape contracting and horticulture, and where they see their career 5 years after graduation. **Deadline for Receipt:** January of each year. **Additional Information:** PLANET was formed in 2005 as the result of a merger between the Associated Landscape Contractors of America (ALCA) and the Professional Lawn Care Association of America (PLCAA). It offers the following named scholarships: the Akerman Family Scholarship, Theodore W. Brickman Jr. Scholarship, Chapel Valley/Reeve Family Scholarship, Damgaard Family Landscape Contracting Scholarship, Davey Tree Expert Company-Commercial Grounds Management Division Scholarship, John Deere Green Industry Scholarship, Gachina Family Scholarship, Parley Glover Memorial Scholarship, Glowacki Family Scholarship, Gravely Landscape Maintenance Scholarship, Groundmasters Scholarship, Leonard Harris Memorial Scholarship, Hunt Family Scholarship, Hunter Industries Scholarship, Husqvarna Forest & Garden Scholarship, Ron and Sally Kujawa Scholarship, Tom and Carol Lied Scholarship, Shirley B. Mangum Family Scholarship, Vito Mariani, Sr. Scholarship, Marjorie and B.E. Minor Scholarship, Moore Landscapes Scholarship, William F. and Mary B. Murdy Scholarship, Richard J. Ott Family Scholarship, Stihl Landscape Contracting Scholarship, Thornton Landscape/Doesburg Family Scholarship, Toro Company/Exmark Scholarship, and Trugreen Landcare Scholarship.

2091 ■ SOCIETY OF AMERICAN MILITARY ENGINEERS-ARKANSAS POST

P.O. Box 867
Little Rock, AR 72203-0867
Web Site: http://www.same.org/arkansas
To provide financial assistance to Arkansas high school seniors interested in studying architecture or engineering in college.
Title of Award: Arkansas Post Scholarships **Area, Field, or Subject:** Architecture; Engineering **Level of Education for which Award is Granted:** Undergraduate **Number Awarded:** 4 each year: 2 at $1,000 and 2 at $500. **Funds Available:** Stipends are $1,000 or $500. **Duration:** 1 year.

Eligibility Requirements: This program is open to seniors graduating from high schools in Arkansas. Applicants must be interested in studying architecture or engineering in college. **Additional Information:** Information is also available from Mike Callahan, Second Vice President, Cromwell Architects Engineers, (501) 372-2900, ext. 177, E-mail: macallahan@cromwell.com.

2092 ■ SOCIETY OF AMERICAN MILITARY ENGINEERS-BALTIMORE POST

c/o Al-Nisa Montague Aduwu
McDonough Bolyard Peck, Inc.
10440 Little Patuxent Parkway, Suite 530
Columbia, MD 21044
Tel: (410)715-9462
E-mail: aaduwu@mbpce.com
Web Site: http://www.same-balt.org/Scholarship/scholarship_home.htm
To provide financial assistance to high school seniors who plan to attend a college or university in the Baltimore area and major in engineering, architecture, or a related science.
Title of Award: Baltimore Post 4-Year Scholarships **Area, Field, or Subject:** Architecture; Engineering; Science **Level of Education for which Award is Granted:** Four Year College **Number Awarded:** 1 or more each year. **Funds Available:** The stipend is $2,000 per year. **Duration:** 4 years.
Eligibility Requirements: This program is open to high school seniors who plan to attend a designated university in the Baltimore area and major in engineering, architecture, or a related science. Applicants must plan to enroll on a full-time basis; be Maryland residents and U.S. citizens, and have a GPA of 3.0 or higher. Extracurricular activities and financial need are also considered in the selection process. **Deadline for Receipt:** September of each year. **Additional Information:** Recipients must enroll as full-time students at the following colleges and universities in the Baltimore area: Johns Hopkins University; Loyola College; University of Maryland, College Park; University of Maryland, Baltimore County; or Morgan State University. Other schools may also be designated annually.

2093 ■ SOCIETY OF AMERICAN MILITARY ENGINEERS-BOSTON POST

c/o John M. Gerstenlauer
Perini Corporation
73 Mt. Wayte Avenue
Framingham, MA 01701-9160
Tel: (508)628-2442
Fax: (508)628-2537
Web Site: http://www.sameboston.org
To provide financial assistance to residents of New England majoring in a college program related to construction.
Title of Award: Boston Post Scholarships **Area, Field, or Subject:** Architecture; Construction; Engineering; Engineering, Civil; Environmental science **Level of Education for which Award is Granted:** Undergraduate **Number Awarded:** Approximately 25 each year. **Funds Available:** The stipend is approximately $2,000 per year. **Duration:** 1 year.
Eligibility Requirements: This program is open to residents of New England who are currently enrolled in an accepted engineering or architecture program, preferably in civil engineering, environmental engineering, architecture, or other construction-related program. Applicants must have completed at least 1 academic year and have at least 1 year remaining. Preference is given to applicants enrolled in ROTC (preferably not a recipient of an ROTC scholarship) or interested in or having prior U.S. military service. U.S. citizenship is required. Interested students are invited to submit an application form, transcripts, documentation of financial need, and a personal letter describing their qualifications and needs. An interview is required. Selection is based on academic achievements, financial need, extracurricular activities, and the interview. **Deadline for Receipt:** February of each year.

2094 ■ SOCIETY OF AMERICAN MILITARY ENGINEERS-GUAM POST

c/o Lt. Titania B. Cross
PSC 455. Box 175
FPO, AP 96540-2200
Tel: (671)339-3820
Fax: (671)339-4955

E-mail: crosstb@pwcguam.navy.mil
Web Site: http://www.same.org/guam
To provide financial assistance to residents of Guam who are interested in majoring in engineering or architecture in college.
Title of Award: Charlie Corn Scholarships **Area, Field, or Subject:** Architecture; Engineering **Level of Education for which Award is Granted:** Undergraduate **Number Awarded:** Varies each year. **Funds Available:** The stipend is $1,000 per year for high school seniors, $2,000 per year for students already in college, or $500 per year for students at Guam Community College. **Duration:** 1 year; may be renewed if the recipient maintains full-time enrollment and a GPA of 3.0 or higher.
Eligibility Requirements: This program is open to residents of Guam and the islands within the geographic area known as Micronesia. Applicants must be 1) high school seniors planning to attend their first year of college to work on a bachelor's degree in engineering or architecture; 2) upper-division students working on a bachelor's degree in engineering or architecture at an accredited college or university; and 3) students planning to attend Guam Community College to work on a 2-year engineering technology degree. They must demonstrate a sincere interest in returning to Guam or Micronesia after graduation to begin a professional career. Selection is based on that interest as well as scholastic achievement, aptitude, attitude, character, and financial need. **Deadline for Receipt:** May of each year.

2095 ■ SOCIETY OF AMERICAN MILITARY ENGINEERS-HONOLULU POST

Attn: LCDR Dustin Hamacher, Scholarship Committee Chair
USCG Naval Engineering Unit Honolulu
Sand Island Road
Honolulu, HI 96819-4398
Tel: (808)843-3871
Web Site: http://www.same.org/honolulu
To provide financial assistance to high school seniors from Hawaii who are interested in attending college to work on a degree in engineering or architecture.
Title of Award: Honolulu Post Scholarships **Area, Field, or Subject:** Architecture; Engineering **Level of Education for which Award is Granted:** Undergraduate **Number Awarded:** 2 each year. **Funds Available:** The stipend is $2,500. **Duration:** 1 year.
Eligibility Requirements: This program is open to seniors graduating from high schools in Hawaii who plan to work full time on an undergraduate degree in engineering or architecture at an accredited college or university. Applicants must be U.S. citizens with a GPA of 3.0 or higher. Military affiliation or experience (i.e., ROTC, member or dependent of a member of the Society of Military Engineers (SAME), military dependent, Junior ROTC) is not required but is given preference. Applicants must submit a transcript; a resume of work experience, academic activities, and extracurricular accomplishments; and an essay (1 page) written around an architecture or engineering theme and its impact on society and the nation's defense or homeland security. **Deadline for Receipt:** March of each year.

2096 ■ SOCIETY OF AMERICAN MILITARY ENGINEERS-NEW JERSEY POST

c/o John Booth
CTSC
P.O. Box 60
Fort Monmouth, NJ 07703
Tel: (732)544-0995
E-mail: john.booth@mail1.monmouth.army.mil
Web Site: http://www.same.org/newjersey
To provide financial assistance to students in New Jersey working on an undergraduate degree in architecture, engineering, or a related field.
Title of Award: New Jersey Post SAME Scholarship **Area, Field, or Subject:** Architecture; Engineering **Level of Education for which Award is Granted:** Undergraduate **Number Awarded:** 1 each year. **Funds Available:** The stipend is $1,000. **Duration:** 1 year.
Eligibility Requirements: This program is open to undergraduate students working on a degree in architecture, engineering, or a related field. Candidates must be nominated by a member of the New Jersey Post of the Society of American Military Engineers (SAME). Selection is based on school and community activities, educational goals, academics, recommendations, and employment. **Deadline for Receipt:** March of each year.

2097 ■ SOCIETY OF AMERICAN MILITARY ENGINEERS-VIRGINIA PENINSULA POST

c/o Jeffrey B. Merz, Scholarship Chair
HQ ACC/CEP
129 Andrews Street, Suite 102
Langley AFB, VA 23665-2769
Tel: (757)764-6579
E-mail: jeffrey.merz@langley.af.mil

To provide financial assistance to students at universities in Virginia and dependents of members of the Virginia Peninsula Post of the Society of American Military Engineers (SAME) who have a commitment to future military service and are majoring in engineering or architecture.

Title of Award: Virginia Peninsula Post Scholarship **Area, Field, or Subject:** Architecture; Engineering **Level of Education for which Award is Granted:** Four Year College **Number Awarded:** 3 each year. **Funds Available:** The stipend is $1,000 and 1-year's membership in the society. **Duration:** 1 year.

Eligibility Requirements: This program is open to students enrolled in an engineering or architecture program at the sophomore level or above. Applicants must be 1) attending a college or university in Virginia, or 2) the dependent of a SAME Virginia Peninsula Post member attending anywhere. They must have demonstrated commitment to future military service by enrolling in an ROTC program, a commissioning program, or an extended enlistment. Selection is based on financial need, academic standing, and involvement in university and community programs. **Deadline for Receipt:** March of each year.

2098 ■ SOCIETY OF AMERICAN MILITARY ENGINEERS-WASHINGTON DC POST

c/o Al O'Konski, Scholarship Committee Chair
URS Corporation
2020 K Street, N.W., Suite 300
Washington, DC 20006-1806
Tel: (202)872-0277
Fax: (202)872-0282
E-mail: Al_O'Konski@urscorp.com
Web Site: http://www.samedcpost.org/scholarship.html

To provide financial assistance to students interested in majoring in engineering, architecture, or environmental sciences.

Title of Award: Washington DC Post Scholarships **Area, Field, or Subject:** Architecture; Engineering; Environmental conservation; Environmental science **Level of Education for which Award is Granted:** Undergraduate **Number Awarded:** Varies each year; recently, 8 of these scholarships were awarded. **Funds Available:** The current stipend is $1,200. Funds are paid to the recipient's school after college enrollment is confirmed. **Duration:** 1 year.

Eligibility Requirements: This program is open to students who are enrolled full time at an accredited university as rising freshmen, sophomores, or juniors, are U.S. citizens, are of good character, and are majoring in engineering, architecture, or environmental science. Applicants must submit a 2-page narrative addressing the following topics: their academic performance, academic and professional goals, financial need, extracurricular activities, a summary of previous military service (if any), and a statement of why they should be considered for the award. Preference is given to applicants in the Washington, D.C. area. **Deadline for Receipt:** January of each year. **Additional Information:** This program includes the following named scholarships: the Paul Brott Scholarship, the Linda McCarthy Scholarship, the T-Bird/RPI Environmental Scholarship, and the Ronald Hubbard Scholarship.

2099 ■ TREE RESEARCH AND EDUCATION ENDOWMENT FUND

Attn: Executive Director
711 East Roosevelt Road
Wheaton, IL 60187
Tel: (630)221-8127
Fax: (630)690-0702
E-mail: treefund@treefund.org
Web Site: http://www.treefund.org/grants/Grants.aspx

To provide financial assistance to undergraduate and technical school students interested in preparing for a career in commercial arboriculture.

Title of Award: Robert Felix Memorial Scholarship **Area, Field, or Subject:** Agricultural sciences; Entomology; Horticulture; Landscape architecture and design; Soil science **Level of Education for which**

Award is Granted: Undergraduate **Number Awarded:** 4 each year. **Funds Available:** The stipend is $3,000. **Duration:** 1 year.

Eligibility Requirements: This program is open to student members of the International Society of Arboriculture who are entering the second year of a 2-year program or the third or fourth year of a 4-year program. Applicants must be preparing for a career in commercial arboriculture. They must have a GPA of 3.0 or higher. Along with their application, they must submit a 1,000-word essay describing their reasons for pursuing their chosen career, their goals and objectives, and why they should be chosen for this scholarship. Financial need is not considered in the selection process. **Deadline for Receipt:** April of each year. **Additional Information:** The Tree Research and Education Endowment (TREE) Fund was established in 2002 as the result of a merger of the International Society of Arboriculture Research Trust (established in 1976) and the National Arborist Foundation (established in 1985). Fields of study often considered appropriate for a career in commercial arboriculture include agriculture, entomology, horticulture, landscape architecture, or soils science.

2100 ■ U.S. AIR FORCE

Attn: Headquarters AFROTC/RRUC
551 East Maxwell Boulevard
Maxwell AFB, AL 36112-5917
Tel: (334)953-2091; (866)423-7682
Fax: (334)953-6167
Web Site: http://www.afrotc.com/scholarships/hsschol/types.php

To provide financial assistance to high school seniors or graduates who are interested in joining Air Force ROTC in college and are willing to serve as Air Force officers following completion of their bachelor's degree.

Title of Award: Air Force ROTC High School Scholarships **Area, Field, or Subject:** Architecture; Chemistry; Computer and information sciences; Engineering, Aerospace/Aeronautical/Astronautical; Engineering, Architectural; Engineering, Civil; Engineering, Computer; Engineering, Electrical; Engineering, Mechanical; Environmental science; General studies/Field of study not specified; Mathematics and mathematical sciences; Meteorology; Operations research; Physics **Level of Education for which Award is Granted:** Four Year College **Number Awarded:** Approximately 2,000 each year. **Funds Available:** Type 1 scholarships provide payment of full tuition and most laboratory fees, as well as $600 for books. Type 2 scholarships pay the same benefits except tuition is capped at $15,000 per year; students who attend an institution where tuition exceeds $15,000 must pay the difference. Type 7 scholarships pay full tuition and most laboratory fees, but students must attend a college or university where the tuition is less than $9,000 per year or a public college or university where they qualify for the in-state tuition rate; they may not attend an institution with higher tuition and pay the difference. Approximately 5% of scholarship offers are for Type 1, approximately 20% are for Type 2, and approximately 75% are for type 7. All recipients are also awarded a tax-free subsistence allowance for 10 months of each year that is $250 per month as a freshman, $300 per month as a sophomore, $350 per month as a junior, and $400 per month as a senior. **Duration:** 4 years.

Eligibility Requirements: This program is open to high school seniors who are U.S. citizens at least 17 of age and have been accepted at a college or university with an Air Force ROTC unit on campus or a college with a cross-enrollment agreement with such a college. Applicants must have a cumulative GPA of 3.0 or higher and an ACT composite score of 24 or higher or an SAT score of 1100 (mathematics and verbal portion only) or higher. At the time of their commissioning in the Air Force, they must be no more than 31 years of age. They must agree to serve for at least 4 years as active-duty Air Force officers following graduation from college. **Deadline for Receipt:** November of each year. **Additional Information:** Recently, approximately 70% of these scholarships were offered to students planning to major in the science and technical fields of architecture, chemistry, computer science, engineering (aeronautical, aerospace, astronautical, architectural, civil, computer, electrical, environmental, or mechanical), mathematics, meteorology and atmospheric sciences, operations research, or physics. Approximately 30% were offered to students in all other fields. While scholarship recipients can major in any subject, they must enroll in 4 years of aerospace studies courses at 1 of the 144 colleges and universities that have an Air Force ROTC unit on campus; students may also attend nearly 900 other colleges that have cross-enrollment agreements with the institutions that have an Air Force ROTC unit on campus. Recipients must attend a 4-week summer training camp at an Air Force base, usually between their sophomore and junior years. Most cadets incur a 4-year active-duty commitment. Pilots incur a 10-year active-duty service commitment after successfully completing Specialized Undergraduate Pilot Training and navigators incur a 6-year commitment after successfully completing Specialized Undergraduate Navigator Training. The minimum service obligation for intelligence and Air Battle Management career fields is 5 years.

2101 ■ U.S. AIR FORCE

Attn: Headquarters AFROTC/RRUC
551 East Maxwell Boulevard
Maxwell AFB, AL 36112-5917
Tel: (334)953-2091; (866)423-7682
Fax: (334)953-6167
Web Site: http://www.afrotc.com/scholarships/incolschol/incolProgram.php
To provide financial assistance to undergraduate students who are willing to join Air Force ROTC in college and serve as Air Force officers following completion of their bachelor's degree.

Title of Award: Air Force ROTC In-College Scholarship Program **Area, Field, or Subject:** Architecture; Chemistry; Computer and information sciences; Engineering, Aerospace/Aeronautical/Astronautical; Engineering, Architectural; Engineering, Civil; Engineering, Computer; Engineering, Electrical; Engineering, Mechanical; Environmental science; General studies/Field of study not specified; Mathematics and mathematical sciences; Meteorology; Operations research; Physics **Level of Education for which Award is Granted:** Undergraduate **Number Awarded:** Varies each year. **Funds Available:** Cadets selected in Phase 1 are awarded type 2 AFROTC scholarships that provide for payment of tuition and fees, to a maximum of $15,000 per year. A limited number of cadets selected in Phase 2 are also awarded type 2 AFROTC scholarships, but most are awarded type 3 AFROTC scholarships with tuition capped at $9,000 per year. Cadets selected in Phase 3 are awarded type 6 AFROTC scholarships with tuition capped at $3,000 per year. All recipients are also awarded a book allowance of $600 and a tax-free subsistence allowance for 10 months of each year that is $300 per month during the sophomore year, $350 during the junior year, and $400 during the senior year. **Duration:** 3 years for students selected as freshmen or 2 years for students selected as sophomores.
Eligibility Requirements: This program is open to U.S. citizens enrolled as freshmen or sophomores at 1 of the 144 colleges and universities that have an Air Force ROTC unit on campus. Applicants must have a cumulative GPA of 2.5 or higher and be able to pass the Air Force Officer Qualifying Test and the Air Force ROTC Physical Fitness Test. At the time of commissioning, they may be no more than 31 years of age. They must agree to serve for at least 4 years as active-duty Air Force officers following graduation from college. Phase 1 is open to students enrolled in the Air Force ROTC program who do not currently have a scholarship but now wish to apply. Phase 2 is open to Phase 1 nonselects and students not enrolled in Air Force ROTC. Phase 3 is open only to Phase 2 nonselects. Recently, the program gave preference to students majoring in the science and technical fields of architecture, chemistry, computer science, engineering (aeronautical, aerospace, astronautical, architectural, civil, computer, electrical, environmental, or mechanical), mathematics, meteorology and atmospheric sciences, operations research, or physics. **Deadline for Receipt:** January of each year. **Additional Information:** While scholarship recipients can major in any subject, they must complete 4 years of aerospace studies courses at 1 of the 144 colleges or universities that have an Air Force ROTC unit on campus. Recipients must also attend a 4-week summer training camp at an Air Force base, usually between their sophomore and junior years; 2-year scholarship awardees attend in the summer after their junior year. Current military personnel are eligible for early release from active duty in order to enter the Air Force ROTC program. Following completion of their bachelor's degree, scholarship recipients earn a commission as a second lieutenant in the Air Force and serve at least 4 years.

2102 ■ U.S. AIR FORCE

Attn: Headquarters AFROTC/RRUE
Enlisted Commissioning Section
551 East Maxwell Boulevard
Maxwell AFB, AL 36112-5917

Tel: (334)953-2091; (866)423-7682
Fax: (334)953-6167
E-mail: enlisted@afrotc.com
Web Site: http://www.afoats.af.mil/AFROTC/EnlistedComm/ASCP.asp
To allow selected enlisted Air Force personnel to earn a bachelor's degree in approved majors by providing financial assistance for full-time college study.

Title of Award: Airman Scholarship and Commissioning Program **Area, Field, or Subject:** Architecture; Atmospheric science; Chemistry; Computer and information sciences; Engineering; Engineering, Aerospace/Aeronautical/Astronautical; Engineering, Architectural; Engineering, Civil; Engineering, Computer; Engineering, Electrical; Engineering, Mechanical; Environmental science; General studies/Field of study not specified; Mathematics and mathematical sciences; Meteorology; Operations research; Physics **Level of Education for which Award is Granted:** Undergraduate **Number Awarded:** Varies each year. **Funds Available:** Awards are type 2 AFROTC scholarships that provide for payment of tuition and fees, to a maximum of $15,000 per year, plus an annual book allowance of $600. All recipients are also awarded a tax-free subsistence allowance for 10 months of each year that is $300 per month during their sophomore year, $350 during their junior year, and $400 during their senior year. **Duration:** 2 to 4 years, until completion of a bachelor's degree.
Eligibility Requirements: This program is open to active-duty enlisted members of the Air Force who have completed at least 1 year of continuous active duty and at least 1 year on station. Applicants normally must have completed at least 24 semester hours of graded college credit with a cumulative college GPA of 2.5 or higher. If they have not completed 24 hours of graded college credit, they must have an ACT score of 24 or higher or an SAT combined verbal and mathematics score of 1100 or higher. They must also have scores on the Air Force Officer Qualifying Test (AFOQT) of 15 or more on the verbal scale and 10 or more on the quantitative scale and be able to pass the Air Force ROTC Physical Fitness Test. Applicants must have been accepted at a college or university (including crosstown schools) offering the AFROTC 4-year program. When they complete the program and receive their commission, they may not be 31 years of age or older. U.S. citizenship is required. Recently, awards were presented according to the following priorities: 1) computer, electrical, and environmental engineering; 2) aeronautical, aerospace, architectural, astronautical, civil, and mechanical engineering and meteorology and atmospheric sciences; 3) all other ABET-accredited engineering majors, architecture, chemistry, computer science, mathematics, operations research, and physics; 4) all other majors. **Deadline for Receipt:** October of each year. **Additional Information:** Selectees separate from the active-duty Air Force, join an AFROTC detachment, and become full-time students. Upon completing their degree, they are commissioned as officers and returned to active duty in the Air Force with a 4-year service obligation. Further information is available from base education service officers or an Air Force ROTC unit.

2103 ■ U.S. AIR FORCE

Attn: Headquarters AFROTC/RRUE
Enlisted Commissioning Section
551 East Maxwell Boulevard
Maxwell AFB, AL 36112-5917
Tel: (334)953-2091; (866)423-7682
Fax: (334)953-6167
E-mail: enlisted@afrotc.com
Web Site: http://www.afoats.af.mil/AFROTC/EnlistedComm/POC-ERP.asp
To allow selected enlisted Air Force personnel to earn a baccalaureate degree by providing financial assistance for full-time college study.

Title of Award: Professional Officer Course Early Release Program **Area, Field, or Subject:** Architecture; Atmospheric science; Chemistry; Computer and information sciences; Engineering; Engineering, Aerospace/Aeronautical/Astronautical; Engineering, Architectural; Engineering, Civil; Engineering, Computer; Engineering, Electrical; Engineering, Mechanical; Environmental science; General studies/Field of study not specified; Mathematics and mathematical sciences; Meteorology; Operations research; Physics **Level of Education for which Award is Granted:** Undergraduate **Number Awarded:** Varies each year. **Funds Available:** Participants receive a stipend for 10 months of the year that is $350 per month during the first year and $400 per month during the second year. Scholarship recipients earn the Professional Officer Course Incentive of $3,000 per year for tuition and $600 per year for books. **Duration:** 2 years (no more and no less).

Eligibility Requirements: Eligible to participate in this program are enlisted members of the Air Force under the age of 30 (or otherwise able to be commissioned before becoming 35 years of age) who have completed at least 1 year on continuous active duty, have served on station for at least 1 year, and have no more than 2 years remaining to complete their initial baccalaureate degree. Scholarship applicants must be younger than 31 years of age when they graduate and earn their commission. All applicants must have been accepted at a college or university offering the AFROTC 4-year program and must have a cumulative college GPA of 2.5 or higher. Their Air Force Officer Qualifying Test (AFOQT) scores must be at least 15 on the verbal and 10 on the quantitative. Applicants who have not completed 24 units of college work must have an ACT composite score of 24 or higher or an SAT combined verbal and mathematics score of 1100 or higher. U.S. citizenship is required. Recently, awards were presented according to the following priorities: 1) computer, electrical, and environmental engineering; 2) aeronautical, aerospace, architectural, astronautical, civil, and mechanical engineering and meteorology and atmospheric sciences; 3) all other ABET-accredited engineering majors, architecture, chemistry, computer science, mathematics, operations research, and physics; 4) all other majors. **Deadline for Receipt:** October of each year. **Additional Information:** Upon completing their degree, selectees are commissioned as officers in the Air Force with a 4-year service obligation. Further information is available from base education service officers or an Air Force ROTC unit.

2104 ■ U.S. NAVY

Attn: Commander, Naval Service Training Command
250 Dallas Street, Suite A
Pensacola, FL 32508-5268
Tel: (850)452-9563
Fax: (850)452-2486
E-mail: PNSC-STA21@navy.mil
Web Site: http://www.navy.com/careers/officerplanner/enlistedtoofficer
To allow outstanding enlisted Navy personnel to complete a bachelor's degree and receive a commission in the Civil Engineer Corps (CEC).
Title of Award: Civil Engineer Corps Option of the Seaman to Admiral-21 Program **Area, Field, or Subject:** Architecture; Engineering; Engineering, Civil; Engineering, Electrical; Engineering, Mechanical **Level of Education for which Award is Granted:** Four Year College **Number Awarded:** Varies each year. **Funds Available:** Awardees continue to receive their regular Navy pay and allowances while they attend college on a full-time basis. They also receive reimbursement for tuition, fees, and books up to $10,000 per year. If base housing is available, they are eligible to live there. Participants are not eligible to receive benefits under the Navy's Tuition Assistance Program (TA), the Montgomery GI Bill (MGIB), Navy College Fund, or the Veterans Educational Assistance Program (VEAP). **Duration:** Selectees are supported for up to 36 months of full-time, year-round study or completion of a bachelor's degree, as long as they maintain a GPA of 3.0 or higher.
Eligibility Requirements: This program is open to U.S. citizens who are currently serving on active duty in the Navy as enlisted personnel of occupational field 13 (Seabees). Applicants must have completed at least 4 years of active duty, of which at least 3 years were in an other than formal training environment. They must be high school graduates (or GED recipients) who are able to complete requirements for a professional Accreditation Board for Engineering and Technology (ABET) engineering degree or National Architectural Accrediting Board (NAAB) architectural degree within 36 months or less. Preferred specialties are for civil, electrical, and mechanical engineering. When applicants complete their degree requirements, they must be younger than 35 years of age. Within the past 3 years, they must have taken the SAT test (and achieved scores of at least 500 on the mathematics section and 500 on the verbal or critical reading section) or the ACT test (and achieved a score of 41 or higher, including at least 21 on the mathematics portion and 20 on the English portion). **Deadline for Receipt:** July of each year. **Additional Information:** This program was established in 2001 as a replacement for the Civil Engineer Corps Enlisted Commissioning Program (CECECP). Upon acceptance into the program, selectees attend the Naval Science Institute (NSI) in Newport, Rhode Island for an 8-week program in the fundamental core concepts of being a naval officer (navigation, engineering, weapons,

military history and justice, etc.). They then enter a college or university with an NROTC unit that is designated for the CEC and pursue full-time study for a bachelor's degree. They become members of and drill with the NROTC unit. When they complete their degree, they are commissioned as ensigns in the United States Naval Reserve and assigned to initial training as an officer in the CEC. After commissioning, 5 years of active service are required.

2105 ■ U.S. NAVY

Attn: Navy Personnel Command
5722 Integrity Drive
Millington, TN 38055-5057
Tel: (901)874-4034; (866)CEC-NAVY
Fax: (901)874-2681
E-mail: p4413d@persnet.navy.mil
Web Site: http://www.cec.navy.mil/scholarships.html
To provide financial assistance to undergraduate and graduate students in architecture and engineering who are interested in serving in the Navy's Civil Engineer Corps (CEC) following graduation.
Title of Award: Civil Engineer Corps Scholarships **Area, Field, or Subject:** Architecture; Engineering, Civil; Engineering, Electrical; Engineering, Mechanical; Engineering, Ocean **Level of Education for which Award is Granted:** Master's, Undergraduate **Number Awarded:** Varies each year. **Funds Available:** Students accepted as undergraduates receive E-3 pay (approximately $2,000 per month), allowance, and benefits; after completing 12 months of the program or being referred to other specified programs, they may be advanced to E-4 or E-5 levels. Graduate students receive payment of tuition and fees plus full officers' salary and allowances. **Duration:** Up to 24 months for the Exceptional Student Program, up to 12 months for the Collegiate Program, and up to 18 months (6 months of undergraduate school plus 12 months of graduate school) for the Graduate Program.
Eligibility Requirements: This program is open to undergraduate and master's degree students who are U.S. citizens between 19 and 35 years of age. Applicants must be enrolled in an engineering program accredited by the Accreditation Board for Engineering and Technology (ABET) or an architecture program accredited by the National Architectural Accrediting Board (NAAB) with a GPA of 3.0 or higher. Eligible majors include civil engineering, electrical engineering, mechanical engineering, ocean engineering, or architecture. For the Exceptional Student Program, they must apply at the end of their sophomore year. For the Collegiate Program, they must apply at the end of their junior year. For the Graduate Program, they must apply upon acceptance to an accredited graduate school and when they are within 6 months of completing a bachelor's degree in engineering. Preference is given to applicants who have engineering or architecture work experience and registration as a Professional Engineer (P.E.) or Engineer-in-Training (EIT). Students majoring in mathematics, physics, non-engineering programs, and engineering or architectural technology are not eligible. Applicants must also be able to meet the Navy's physical fitness requirements. **Additional Information:** While in college, selectees have no uniforms, drills, or military duties. After graduation with a bachelor's or master's degree, they enter the Navy and attend 13 weeks at Officer Candidate School (OCS) in Pensacola, Florida, followed by 15 weeks at Civil Engineer Corps Officers School (CECOS) in Port Hueneme, California. They then serve 4 years in the CEC, rotating among public works, contract management, and the Naval Construction Force (Seabees).

2106 ■ VERMONT STUDENT ASSISTANCE CORPORATION

Champlain Mill
Attn: Scholarship Programs
P.O. Box 2000
Winooski, VT 05404-2601
Tel: (802)654-3798; 888-253-4819
Fax: (802)654-3765
E-mail: info@vsac.org
Web Site: http://www.vsac.org
To provide financial assistance to residents of Vermont who are interested in working on an undergraduate or graduate degree in a field related to design.
Title of Award: Alfred T. Granger Student Art Fund **Area, Field, or Subject:** Architecture; Art; Engineering, Architectural; Graphic art and design; Interior design; Lighting science **Level of Education for which**

Award is Granted: Graduate, Undergraduate **Number Awarded:** 2 graduate scholarships and 4 undergraduate scholarships are awarded each year. **Funds Available:** The stipend is $5,000 per year for graduate students or $2,500 per year for undergraduates. **Duration:** 1 year; recipients may reapply.

Eligibility Requirements: This program is open to residents of Vermont who are graduating high school seniors, high school graduates, or GED recipients. Applicants must be interested in attending an accredited postsecondary institution to work on a degree in architecture, interior design, fine arts, architectural engineering, mechanical drawing, or lighting design. Selection is based on academic achievement, a portfolio, letters of recommendation, required essays, and financial need. **Deadline for Receipt:** May of each year.

2107 ■ WESTERN INTERSTATE COMMISSION FOR HIGHER EDUCATION

Attn: Student Exchange Programs
3035 Center Green Drive
P.O. Box 9752
Boulder, CO 80301-9752
Tel: (303)541-0210
Fax: (303)541-0291
E-mail: info-sep@wiche.edu
Web Site: http://www.wiche.edu/sep/psep

To underwrite some of the cost of out-of-state professional schooling for students in selected western states.

Title of Award: Professional Student Exchange Program **Area, Field, or Subject:** Architecture; Dentistry; Library and archival sciences; Medical assisting; Medicine; Medicine, Osteopathic; Nursing; Occupational therapy; Optometry; Pharmaceutical sciences; Physical therapy; Podiatry; Public health; Veterinary science and medicine **Level of Education for which Award is Granted:** Graduate, Undergraduate **Number Awarded:** Varies each year. **Funds Available:** The assistance consists of reduced levels of tuition, usually resident tuition in public institutions or reduced standard tuition at private schools. The home state pays a support fee to the admitting school to help cover the cost of the recipient's education. **Duration:** 1 year; may be renewed.

Eligibility Requirements: This program is open to residents of 13 western states who are interested in pursuing professional study at selected out-of-state institutions, usually because those fields of study are not available in their home states. The eligible programs, and the states whose residents are eligible, presently include: 1) architecture (master's degree), for residents of Wyoming, to study at designated institutions in Arizona, California, Colorado, Idaho, Montana, New Mexico, Oregon, Utah, or Washington); 2) dentistry, for residents of Alaska, Arizona, Hawaii, Montana, New Mexico, North Dakota, and Wyoming, to study at designated institutions in Arizona, California, Colorado, Nevada, Oregon, or Washington; 3) library studies (master's degree), for residents of New Mexico and Wyoming, to study at designated institutions in Arizona, California, Hawaii, or Washington; 4) medicine, for residents of Montana and Wyoming, to study at designated institutions in Arizona, California, Colorado, Hawaii, Nevada, New Mexico, North Dakota, Oregon, or Utah; 5) nursing (graduate degree), for residents of Wyoming, to study at designated institutions in California, Hawaii, North Dakota, or Oregon; 6) occupational therapy (bachelors' or master's degree), for residents of Alaska, Arizona, Hawaii, Montana, and Wyoming, to study at designated institutions in Arizona, California, Idaho, New Mexico, North Dakota, Oregon, Utah, or Washington; 7) optometry, for residents of Alaska, Arizona, Colorado, Hawaii, Idaho, Montana, Nevada, New Mexico, North Dakota, Utah, Washington, and Wyoming, to study at designated institutions in California or Oregon; 8) osteopathic medicine, for residents of Arizona, Montana, New Mexico, Washington, and Wyoming, to study at designated institutions in Arizona or California; 9) pharmacy, for residents of Alaska, Hawaii, and Nevada, to study at designated institutions in Arizona, California, Colorado, Idaho, Montana, New Mexico, North Dakota, Oregon, Utah, Washington, or Wyoming; 10) physical therapy (master's or doctoral degree), for residents of Alaska, Hawaii, and Wyoming, to study at designated institutions in Arizona, California, Colorado, Idaho, Montana, New Mexico, North Dakota, Oregon, Utah, or Washington; 11) physician assistant, for residents of Alaska, Arizona, Nevada, and Wyoming, to study at designated institutions in Arizona, California, Colorado, Idaho, Oregon, Utah, or Washington; 12) podiatry, for residents of Alaska, Montana, New Mexico, Utah, and Wyoming, to

study at a designated institution in California; 13) public health, for residents of Montana and New Mexico, to study at designated institutions in California, Colorado, or Washington; and 14) veterinary medicine, for residents of Arizona, Hawaii, Montana, Nevada, New Mexico, North Dakota, Utah, and Wyoming, to study at designated institutions in California, Colorado, Oregon, or Washington. The financial status of the applicants is not considered. Interested students must apply for admission and for PSEP assistance directly from the institution of their choice. They must be certified by their state of residence to become an exchange student and be seeking enrollment at the first professional degree level. **Deadline for Receipt:** In most states, the deadline for receiving completed applications for certification is in October. After obtaining certification, students must still apply to the school of their choice, which also sets its own deadline.

2108 ■ WISCONSIN FOUNDATION FOR INDEPENDENT COLLEGES, INC.

Attn: Program Manager
735 North Water Street, Suite 600
Milwaukee, WI 53202-4100
Tel: (414)273-5980
Fax: (414)273-5995
E-mail: wfic@wficweb.org
Web Site: http://www.wficweb.org/scholar.html

To provide financial assistance to students majoring in selected fields at member institutions of the Wisconsin Foundation for Independent Colleges (WFIC).

Title of Award: Sentry Insurance Foundation Scholarships **Area, Field, or Subject:** Architecture; Business administration; Design; Economics; Information science and technology; Interior design; Mathematics and mathematical sciences **Level of Education for which Award is Granted:** Four Year College **Number Awarded:** 20 each year: 1 at each of the participating schools. **Funds Available:** The stipend is $1,000. **Duration:** 1 year.

Eligibility Requirements: This program is open to student enrolled or planning to enroll at WFIC member colleges and universities. Applicants must have a declared major in 1 of the following fields: business, economics, mathematics, management information systems, industrial design, communication design, or interior architecture and design. They must have a GPA of 3.3 or higher; entering freshmen must rank in the top 25% of their high school class. Financial need is considered in the selection process. **Deadline for Receipt:** Each participating college sets its own deadline. **Additional Information:** The WFIC member schools are Alverno College, Beloit College, Cardinal Stritch University, Carroll College, Carthage College, Concordia University of Wisconsin, Edgewood College, Lakeland College, Lawrence University, Marian College, Marquette University, Milwaukee Institute of Art & Design, Milwaukee School of Engineering, Mount Mary College, Northland College, Ripon College, St. Norbert College, Silver Lake College, Viterbo University, and Wisconsin Lutheran College. This program is supported by the Sentry Insurance Foundation.

2109 ■ WISCONSIN SPACE GRANT CONSORTIUM

c/o University of Wisconsin at Green Bay
Department of Natural and Applied Sciences
2420 Nicolet Drive
Green Bay, WI 54311-7001
Tel: (920)465-2108
Fax: (920)465-2376
E-mail: wsgc@uwgb.edu
Web Site: http://www.uwgb.edu/wsgc/students/us.asp

To provide financial assistance to undergraduate students at colleges and universities participating in the Wisconsin Space Grant Consortium (WSGC).

Title of Award: Wisconsin Space Grant Consortium Undergraduate Scholarships **Area, Field, or Subject:** Aerospace sciences; Architecture; Business administration; Engineering; Engineering, Aerospace/ Aeronautical/Astronautical; Law; Medicine; Nursing; Science; Space and planetary sciences **Level of Education for which Award is Granted:** Undergraduate **Number Awarded:** Varies each year; recently, 26 of these scholarships were awarded. **Funds Available:** Stipends up to $1,500 per year are available. **Duration:** 1 academic year.

Eligibility Requirements: This program is open to undergraduate students enrolled at universities participating in the WSGC. Applicants must be U.S. citizens; be working full time on a bachelor's degree in space science, aerospace, or interdisciplinary space studies (including, but not limited to, engineering, the sciences, architecture, law, business, nursing, and medicine); and have a GPA of 3.0 or higher. The consortium especially encourages applications from underrepresented minorities, women, and students with disabilities. Selection is based on academic performance and space-related promise. **Deadline for Receipt:** February of each year. **Additional Information:** Funding for this program is provided by the U.S. National Aeronautics and Space Administration (NASA). The schools participating in the consortium include the University of Wisconsin campuses at Fox Valley, Green Bay, La Crosse, Madison, Milwaukee, Oshkosh, Parkside, Superior, and Whitewater; Alverno College; Marquette University; College of the Menominee Nation; Carroll College; Lawrence University; Milwaukee School of Engineering; Ripon College; Medical College of Wisconsin; Western Wisconsin Technical College; and Wisconsin Lutheran College.

2110 ■ WORLDSTUDIO FOUNDATION

200 Varick Street, Suite 507
New York, NY 10014
Tel: (212)366-1317
Fax: (212)807-0024
E-mail: scholarshipcoordinator@worldstudio.org
Web Site: http://www.worldstudio.org/schol/index.html
To provide financial assistance to undergraduate and graduate students, especially minorities, who wish to study fine or commercial arts, design, or architecture.
Title of Award: Worldstudio Foundation Scholarships **Area, Field, or Subject:** Advertising; Architecture; Art; Art industries and trade; Crafts; Design; Fashion design; Filmmaking; Graphic art and design; Interior design; Landscape architecture and design; Photography; Urban affairs/design/planning **Level of Education for which Award is Granted:** Graduate, Undergraduate **Number Awarded:** Varies each year; recently, 24 scholarships and 7 honorable mentions were awarded. **Funds Available:** Basic scholarships range from $1,000 to $2,000, but awards between $3,000 and $5,000 are also presented at the discretion of the jury. Honorable mentions are $100. Funds are paid directly to the recipient's school. **Duration:** 1 academic year. Recipients may reapply.
Eligibility Requirements: This program is open to undergraduate and graduate students who are currently enrolled or planning to enroll at an accredited college or university and major in 1 of the following areas: advertising (art direction only), architecture, crafts, environmental graphics, fashion design, film/video (direction or cinematography only), film/theater design (including set, lighting, and costume design), fine arts, furniture design, graphic design, industrial/product design, interior design, landscape architecture, new media, photography, surface/textile design, or urban planning. Although not required, minority status is a significant factor in the selection process. International students may apply if they are enrolled at a U.S. college or university. Applicants must have a GPA of 2.0 or higher. Along with their application, they must submit a 600-word statement of purpose that includes a brief autobiography, an explanation of how their experiences have influenced their creative work and/or their career plans, and how they see themselves contributing to the community at large in the future. Selection is based on that statement, the quality of submitted work, financial need, minority status, and academic record.
Deadline for Receipt: March of each year. **Additional Information:** The foundation encourages the scholarship recipients to focus on ways that their work can address issues of social and environmental responsibility. This program includes the following named awards: the Sherry and Gary Baker Award, the Bobolink Foundation Award, the Bombay Sapphire Awards, the Richard and Jean Coyne Family Foundation Awards, the David A. Dechman Foundation Awards, the Philip and Edina Jennison Award, the Kraus Family Foundation Awards, the Dena McKelvey Award, the New York Design Center Award, the Rudin Foundation Awards, the Starr Foundation Awards, and the John F. Wright III Award.

Classical Studies

2111 ■ AMERICAN PHILOLOGICAL ASSOCIATION

Attn: Executive Director
University of Pennsylvania

292 Logan Hall
249 South 36th Street
Philadelphia, PA 19104-6304
Tel: (215)898-4975
Fax: (215)573-7874
E-mail: apaclassics@sas.upenn.edu
Web Site: http://www.apaclassics.org/Administration/Comm/cmsform.html
To prepare minority undergraduates during the summer for advanced work in the classics.
Title of Award: American Philological Association Minority Scholarship **Area, Field, or Subject:** Classical studies **Level of Education for which Award is Granted:** Four Year College **Number Awarded:** 1 each year. **Funds Available:** The maximum award is $3,000. **Duration:** 1 summer.
Eligibility Requirements: Eligible to apply are minority (African American, Hispanic American, Asian American, and Native American) undergraduate students who wish to engage in summer study as preparation for graduate work in the classics. Applicants may propose participation in summer programs in Italy, Greece, Egypt, or other classical centers; language training at institutions in the United States or Canada; or other relevant courses of study. Selection is based on academic qualifications, especially in classics; demonstrated ability in at least 1 classical language; quality of the proposal for study with respect to preparation for a career in classics; and financial need. Applications must be endorsed by a member of the American Philological Association (APA).
Deadline for Receipt: February of each year. **Additional Information:** Information is also available from Professor Erwin F. Cook, Trinity University, Department of Classical Studies, 715 Stadium Drive, Box 39, San Antonio, TX 78212-7200, (210) 999-7841, Fax: (210) 999-8008, E-mail: ecook@trinity.edu.

2112 ■ CLASSICAL ASSOCIATION OF THE MIDDLE WEST AND SOUTH

c/o Eleanor Winsor Leach
Indiana University
Department of Classical Studies
547 Ballantine Hall
Bloomington, IN 47405
Tel: (812)855-4129
E-mail: leach@indiana.edu
Web Site: http://www.camws.org/awards/MAScollege.html
To provide financial assistance to undergraduate students majoring in classics at a college or university in the area of the Classical Association of the Middle West and South (CAMWS).
Title of Award: Manson A. Stewart Scholarships **Area, Field, or Subject:** Classical studies; Foreign languages **Level of Education for which Award is Granted:** Undergraduate **Number Awarded:** Varies each year; recently, 6 of these scholarships were awarded. **Funds Available:** The award is $1,000. **Duration:** 1 year.
Eligibility Requirements: This program is open to undergraduate students who are majoring in classics at the sophomore or junior level at a college or university in the geographic area served by the association. Candidates must be nominated by the chair of their department or program; students then fill out an application and send it along with transcripts and letters of recommendation from 2 members of the association. Nominees are expected to take at least 2 courses in Latin or Greek during the junior or senior year in which the scholarship is held. **Deadline for Receipt:** February of each year.

2113 ■ CLASSICAL ASSOCIATION OF NEW ENGLAND

c/o Allen M. Ware
University of Connecticut
Department of History
Box U-103
Storrs, CT 06269-2103
Tel: (860)486-3722
Fax: (860)486-0641
E-mail: ward@uconnvm.uconn.edu
Web Site: http://www.caneweb.org
To provide financial assistance to upper-division and graduate students in New England who are working on certification as a teacher of Latin or Greek.
Title of Award: CANE Certification Scholarship **Area, Field, or Subject:** Classical studies; Education, Secondary; Foreign languages **Level of Education for which Award is Granted:** Four Year College, Master's

Number Awarded: 1 each year. **Funds Available:** The stipend is $1,500. Funds are intended to cover tuition and fees. **Duration:** 1 year or summer session.

Eligibility Requirements: This program is open to junior and senior undergraduates at colleges and universities in New England and to holders of a master's degree. Applicants must be preparing for secondary school certification as a teacher of Latin or Greek or both in a New England state. Full-time, part-time, and summer programs qualify. Along with their application, they must submit 2 letters of recommendation from college classicists, a letter attesting to their ability to communicate and work with young people and inspire them to high levels of achievement, a 1,000-word personal statement explaining why they are preparing for a career as a secondary school classicist, high school and college transcripts, and a description of their program and the expenses involved. **Deadline for Receipt:** February of each year.

2114 ■ MARYLAND HIGHER EDUCATION COMMISSION

Attn: Office of Student Financial Assistance
839 Bestgate Road, Suite 400
Annapolis, MD 21401-3013
Tel: (410)260-4545
Free: 800-974-1024
Fax: (410)974-5376
E-mail: osfamail@mhec.state.md.us
Web Site: http://www.mhec.state.md.us/financialAid/
ProgramDescriptions/prog_scm.asp
To provide scholarship/loans to Maryland residents who wish to prepare for a teaching career.

Title of Award: Sharon Christa McAuliffe Memorial Teacher Education Award **Area, Field, or Subject:** Chemistry; Classical studies; Computer and information sciences; Earth sciences; Education; Education, English as a second language; Education, Special; Education, Vocational-technical; Foreign languages; Geosciences; Health care services; Hearing and deafness; Mathematics and mathematical sciences; Physical sciences; Physics; Space and planetary sciences; Visual impairment **Level of Education for which Award is Granted:** Master's, Professional, Undergraduate **Number Awarded:** Varies each year. **Funds Available:** The amount of the award is based on the recipient's enrollment and housing status, to a maximum of $17,000 per year. The total amount of all state awards may not exceed the cost of attendance as determined by the school's financial aid office or $17,800, whichever is less. Following graduation, recipients must teach at a Maryland public school for 1 year for each year of financial aid received under this program. If they fail to meet that service obligation, they must repay all funds they received with interest. They must begin the service obligation within 12 months of graduation. **Duration:** 1 year; may be renewed for 1 additional year if the recipient maintains satisfactory academic progress with a cumulative GPA of 3.0 or higher and enrollment at a 2-year or 4-year Maryland college or university in an approved teacher education program.

Eligibility Requirements: This program is open to Maryland residents who are college students with at least 60 semester credit hours completed, college graduates, and teachers in a non-critical shortage area. Applicants must have a GPA of 3.0 or higher and plan to teach in a field identified as a critical shortage area. Selection is based on cumulative GPA, applicable work or volunteer experience, quality of academic background in certification field, and a writing sample. **Deadline for Receipt:** December of each year. **Additional Information:** Recently, the eligible critical shortage areas were business education, chemistry, computer science, earth and space science, English for speakers of other languages, family and consumer sciences, German, health occupations, Latin, mathematics, physical science, physics, Spanish, special education (generic infant-grade 3, generic grades 1-8, generic grades 6-adult, hearing impaired, severely and profoundly handicapped, visually impaired), and technology education.

2115 ■ OHIO CLASSICAL CONFERENCE

c/o Amy J. Sawan, Scholarship Committee
Medina Senior High School
777 East Union Street
Medina, OH 44256
Tel: (330)636-3200
E-mail: LIAMOT@aol.com
Web Site: http://dept.kent.edu/mcls/classics/occ

To provide financial assistance to Ohio residents preparing for a career as a Latin teacher.

Title of Award: Ohio Classical Conference Scholarship for Prospective Latin Teachers **Area, Field, or Subject:** Classical studies; Education, Elementary; Education, Secondary; Foreign languages **Level of Education for which Award is Granted:** Undergraduate **Number Awarded:** 1 each year. **Funds Available:** The stipend is $1,500. **Duration:** 1 year; nonrenewable.

Eligibility Requirements: This program is open to residents of Ohio enrolled at least at the sophomore level at a college or university in the United States. Applicants must be taking courses leading to a career in the teaching of Latin at the K-12 level in a public, private, or parochial school. They must submit college transcripts, 2 letters of recommendation (including 1 from a member of their classics department), a prospectus of courses completed and to be taken as part of the program, and a 1-page statement of their academic goals and reasons for applying for the scholarship. **Deadline for Receipt:** March of each year.

2116 ■ OHIO CLASSICAL CONFERENCE

c/o Amy J. Sawan, Scholarship Committee
Medina Senior High School
777 East Union Street
Medina, OH 44256
Tel: (330)636-3200
E-mail: LIAMOT@aol.com
Web Site: http://dept.kent.edu/mcls/classics/occ
To provide financial assistance to Ohio high school seniors planning to study Latin in college.

Title of Award: Ohio Classical Conference Scholarship for the Study of Latin **Area, Field, or Subject:** Classical studies; Foreign languages **Level of Education for which Award is Granted:** Undergraduate **Number Awarded:** 1 each year. **Funds Available:** The stipend is $1,500. **Duration:** 1 year; nonrenewable.

Eligibility Requirements: This program is open to seniors graduating from high schools in Ohio and entering a college or university in the United States. Applicants must be planning to study Latin, although they do not need to major in Latin or classics. They must submit an official high school transcript, 2 letters of recommendation (including 1 from their high school Latin teacher), and a 1-page statement on their reasons for studying Latin or the classics. **Deadline for Receipt:** March of each year.

2117 ■ SOUTH CAROLINA STUDENT LOAN CORPORATION

Interstate Center
16 Berryhill Road, Suite 210
P.O. Box 21487
Columbia, SC 29221-1487
Tel: (803)798-0916
Free: 800-347-2752
Fax: (803)772-9410
Web Site: http://www.slc.sc.edu
To provide scholarship/loans to students in South Carolina who wish to teach certain subjects or in certain geographic areas.

Title of Award: South Carolina Teacher Loan Program **Area, Field, or Subject:** Agricultural sciences; Classical studies; Consumer affairs; Dance; Education, Elementary; Education, Music; Education, Special; English language and literature; Foreign languages; Library and archival sciences; Mathematics and mathematical sciences; Science; Speech and language pathology/audiology; Technology **Level of Education for which Award is Granted:** Graduate, Undergraduate **Number Awarded:** Varies each year. **Funds Available:** Freshmen and sophomores may borrow up to $2,500 per academic year; juniors, seniors, and graduate students may borrow up to $5,000 per academic year. This is a scholarship/loan program; loans are forgivable at the rate of 20% or $3,000, whichever is greater, for each full year of teaching in an area (either geographic or subject) of critical need; for students who teach in both critical subject and geographic areas, the rate of cancellation is 33% or $5,000, whichever is greater, per year. Borrowers who fail to teach in either a critical subject or geographic area must repay the loan at an annual interest rate that varies (currently, 5.37%) but is capped at 10.25%. **Duration:** 1 year; may be renewed for a total of 5 years of undergraduate and 5 years of graduate study.

Eligibility Requirements: Eligible to apply are residents of South Carolina who are planning to teach in certain critical geographic areas of the state, or to teach in critical subject areas. Entering freshmen must have ranked in the top 40% of their high school class and have an ACT or SAT score greater than the South Carolina average (recently 986 on the SAT or 19.3 on the ACT); enrolled undergraduates or entering graduate students must have at least a 2.75 cumulative GPA; graduate students who have completed at least 1 term must have a GPA of 3.5 or better. Undergraduate students at South Carolina colleges must have taken and passed the Education Entrance Exam; students at institutions outside South Carolina must have completed the necessary prerequisites required at that institution. Only U.S. citizens may apply. **Deadline for Receipt:** May of each year. **Additional Information:** Recently, the critical subject areas include mathematics, science (biology, chemistry, physics, and general science), media specialist, special education, industrial technology, foreign languages (Spanish, French, Latin, and German), family and consumer science, art, music, business education, English and language arts, dance, speech and drama/theater, and agriculture. For a list of critical geographic area, contact the sponsor.

2118 ■ TEXAS CLASSICAL ASSOCIATION

c/o Andrew Riggsby, Scholarship Committee Chair
University of Texas at Austin
Waggener 123
Austin, TX 78712-1181
Tel: (512)471-5742
E-mail: ariggsby@utxvms.cc.utexas.edu
Web Site: http://www.txclassics.org/schol.htm
To provide financial assistance to high school seniors in Texas who plan to study Latin or Greek in college.

Title of Award: TSJCL Lourania Miller Scholarship **Area, Field, or Subject:** Classical studies; Foreign languages **Level of Education for which Award is Granted:** Undergraduate **Number Awarded:** 1 each year. **Funds Available:** The stipend is $1,000. **Duration:** 1 year.

Eligibility Requirements: This program is open to residents of Texas who have been active members of the Texas Classical Association (TCA) for at least 2 years. Applicants must be graduating from high school and planning to continue their study of Latin and Greek during their freshman year in college. Enrollment in Latin cannot be at a beginning level. Courses in classical civilization are not accepted. **Deadline for Receipt:** June of each year. **Additional Information:** This program is offered jointly by the Texas State Junior Classical League (TSJCL) and TCA.

2119 ■ TEXAS CLASSICAL ASSOCIATION

c/o Andrew Riggsby, Scholarship Committee Chair
University of Texas at Austin
Waggener 123
Austin, TX 78712-1181
Tel: (512)471-5742
E-mail: ariggsby@utxvms.cc.utexas.edu
Web Site: http://www.txclassics.org/schol.htm
To provide financial assistance to high school seniors in Texas who plan to study Latin or Greek in college.

Title of Award: TSJCL Gareth Morgan Scholarship **Area, Field, or Subject:** Classical studies; Foreign languages **Level of Education for which Award is Granted:** Undergraduate **Number Awarded:** 1 each year. **Funds Available:** The stipend is $1,000. **Duration:** 1 year.

Eligibility Requirements: This program is open to residents of Texas who have been active members of the Texas Classical Association (TCA) for at least 2 years. Applicants must be graduating from high school and planning to continue their study of Latin and Greek during their freshman year in college. Enrollment in Latin cannot be at a beginning level. Courses in classical civilization are not accepted. **Deadline for Receipt:** June of each year. **Additional Information:** This program is offered jointly by the Texas State Junior Classical League (TSJCL) and TCA.

Creative Arts

2120 ■ ACADEMY OF TELEVISION ARTS & SCIENCES FOUNDATION

Attn: Education Department
5220 Lankershim Boulevard
North Hollywood, CA 91601-3109
Tel: (818)754-2830

Fax: (818)761-ATAS
E-mail: collegeawards@emmys.org
Web Site: http://www.emmys.tv/foundation/index.php
To provide financial assistance to upper-division and graduate students interested in working on a project in a field related to children's media.

Title of Award: Fred Rogers Memorial Scholarship **Area, Field, or Subject:** Art, Caricatures and cartoons; Child development; Education, Early childhood; Filmmaking; Music; Psychology; Radio and television **Level of Education for which Award is Granted:** Four Year College, Graduate **Number Awarded:** 1 each year. **Funds Available:** The stipend is $10,000. **Duration:** 1 year.

Eligibility Requirements: This program is open to upper-division and graduate students interested in preparing for a career in children's media. Applicants must be able to demonstrate a commitment, either through course work or experience, to any combination of at least 2 of the following fields: early childhood education, child development, child psychology, film or television production, music, or animation. They may apply for support for any of the following areas: research on the relationship between children's media and learning or children's use of media and personal growth; development of program concepts or extended development of creative elements of an existing concept (e.g., design of puppets, scripts, storyboards, characters, music); professional internship in an organization that is relevant to the applicant's goal for use of the award. **Deadline for Receipt:** January of each year. **Additional Information:** This scholarship, first awarded in 2005, is supported by Ernst & Young.

2121 ■ AMERICAN CERAMIC SOCIETY

Attn: Electronics Division
735 Ceramic Place, Suite 100
Westerville, OH 43081
Tel: (614)890-4700
Fax: (614)899-6109
E-mail: info@ceramics.org
Web Site: http://www.ceramics.org
To provide financial assistance to undergraduate students in a field related to ceramic science.

Title of Award: Dr. Lewis C. Hoffman Scholarship **Area, Field, or Subject:** Crafts; Engineering, Materials; Materials research/science **Level of Education for which Award is Granted:** Four Year College **Number Awarded:** 1 each year. **Funds Available:** The stipend is $2,000. **Duration:** 1 year.

Eligibility Requirements: This program is open to juniors enrolled in a program related to ceramics/materials science and engineering. Applicants must submit a 500-word essay on a topic that changes annually; recently, the topic was "Electronic Ceramics in Clean Energy Technologies." Selection is based on the essay, extracurricular activities, a letter of recommendation from a faculty advisor, PSAT/SAT/ACT scores, and GPA (cumulative and in science courses). **Deadline for Receipt:** March of each year. **Additional Information:** Further information is also available from the Chair of the Awards and Scholarships Committee, Amit Goyal, Oak Ridge National Laboratory, Metals and Ceramics Division, Superconducting Materials Research, Oak Ridge, TN 37831-6116, (865) 574-1587, Fax: (865) 574-7659, E-mail: goyala@ornl.gov.

2122 ■ AMERICAN CERAMIC SOCIETY-NEW ENGLAND SECTION

c/o Lou Trostel, Counselor
Ceramics Concepts
P.O. Box 199
Princeton, MA 01541
Tel: (978)464-2469
Fax: (978)464-2755
E-mail: ljtjr@worldnet.att.net
Web Site: http://www.ceramics.org
To provide financial assistance to residents of the New England states who are working on a college degree in ceramics.

Title of Award: New England Section Scholarship **Area, Field, or Subject:** Crafts; Engineering, Materials **Level of Education for which Award is Granted:** Undergraduate **Number Awarded:** 1 or more each year. **Funds Available:** The stipend is $1,000. **Duration:** 1 year.

Eligibility Requirements: This program is open to undergraduates from New England who are working on a degree in ceramics in an accredited program in the United States.

2123 ■ AMERICAN INDIAN ARTS COUNCIL, INC.

Attn: Scholarship Committee
725 Preston Forest Shopping Center, Suite B
Dallas, TX 75230
Tel: (214)891-9640
Fax: (214)891-0221
E-mail: aiac@flash.net
To provide financial assistance to American Indian undergraduates or graduate students planning a career in the arts or arts administration.
Title of Award: American Indian Arts Council Scholarship Program **Area, Field, or Subject:** Art; Creative writing; Management; Performing arts; Visual arts **Level of Education for which Award is Granted:** Graduate, Undergraduate **Number Awarded:** Varies each year. **Funds Available:** Stipends range from $250 to $1,000 per semester. **Duration:** 1 semester; may be renewed if the recipient maintains a GPA of 2.5 or higher.
Eligibility Requirements: This program is open to American Indian undergraduate and graduate students who are preparing for a career in fine arts, visual and performing arts, communication arts, creative writing, or arts administration or management. Applicants must be currently enrolled in and attending a fully-accredited college or university. They must provide official tribal documentation verifying American Indian heritage and have a GPA of 2.5 or higher. Applicants majoring in the visual or performing arts (including writing) must submit slides, photographs, videotapes, audio tapes, or other examples of their work. Letters of recommendation are required. Awards are based on either merit or merit and financial need. If the applicants wish to be considered for a need-based award, a letter from their financial aid office is required to verify financial need. **Deadline for Receipt:** September of each year for the fall semester; March of each year for the spring semester. **Additional Information:** This program was established in 1993.

2124 ■ AMERICAN LEGION AUXILIARY

Attn: Department of Maryland
1589 Sulphur Spring Road, Suite 105
Baltimore, MD 21227
Tel: (410)242-9519
Fax: (410)242-9553
E-mail: anna@alamd.org
To provide financial assistance for college to the daughters of veterans who are Maryland residents and wish to study arts, sciences, business, public administration, education, or a medical field.
Title of Award: Maryland Legion Auxiliary Children and Youth Fund Scholarship **Area, Field, or Subject:** Art; Business administration; Education; Medicine; Public administration; Science **Level of Education for which Award is Granted:** Undergraduate **Number Awarded:** 1 each year. **Funds Available:** The stipend is $2,000. **Duration:** 1 year; may be renewed up to 3 additional years.
Eligibility Requirements: Eligible for this scholarship are Maryland senior high girls with veteran parents who wish to study arts, sciences, business, public administration, education, or a medical field other than nursing at a college or university in the state. Preference is given to children of members of the American Legion or American Legion Auxiliary. Selection is based on character (30%), Americanism (20%), leadership (10%), scholarship (20%), and financial need (20%). **Deadline for Receipt:** April of each year.

2125 ■ ARMED FORCES COMMUNICATIONS AND ELECTRONICS ASSOCIATION

Attn: AFCEA Educational Foundation
4400 Fair Lakes Court
Fairfax, VA 22033-3899
Tel: (703)631-6149
Free: 800-336-4583
Fax: (703)631-4693
E-mail: scholarship@afcea.org
Web Site: http://www.afcea.org/education/scholarships/undergraduate/graphicdes.asp
To provide financial assistance to students who are working on an undergraduate or graduate degree in computer graphic design.

Title of Award: Computer Graphic Design Scholarships **Area, Field, or Subject:** Computer and information sciences; Graphic art and design; Internet design and development **Level of Education for which Award is Granted:** Four Year College, Graduate **Number Awarded:** 1 or more each year. **Funds Available:** The stipend is $2,000. **Duration:** 1 year; may be renewed.
Eligibility Requirements: This program is open to full-time students who are enrolled at an accredited college or university in the United States at least as a sophomore. Applicants must be U.S. citizens working on an undergraduate or graduate degree in computer graphic design or a related field. They must submit a sample of digital graphic artwork for intranets and internets, especially web-based graphics. Along with the artwork, include a textual statement of 100 to 200 words that describes the image submitted, how it was created, and what specific intent or purpose it represents. Selection is based on artistic creativity, mastery of web technology, a statement of career goals, school and community activities, and financial need. **Deadline for Receipt:** October of each year.

2126 ■ ASIAN AMERICAN JOURNALISTS ASSOCIATION

Attn: Student Programs Coordinator
1182 Market Street, Suite 320
San Francisco, CA 94102
Tel: (415)346-2051
Fax: (415)346-6343
E-mail: brandons@aaja.org
Web Site: http://www.aaja.org/programs/for_students/scholarships
To provide financial assistance to student members of the Asian American Journalists Association (AAJA) interested in careers in broadcast, photo, or print journalism.
Title of Award: Cox Foundation Scholarships **Area, Field, or Subject:** Communications; Graphic art and design; Journalism; Photography, Journalistic **Level of Education for which Award is Granted:** Graduate, Undergraduate **Number Awarded:** Varies each year. **Funds Available:** The stipend is $2,500. **Duration:** 1 year; may be renewed.
Eligibility Requirements: This program is open to AAJA members who are high school seniors or college students (graduate or undergraduate) enrolled full time in accredited institutions. Applicants must submit a 500-word essay on their involvement or interest in the Asian American community and how, if they are awarded this scholarship, they would contribute to the field of journalism and/or media issues involving the Asian American and Pacific Islander community. Selection is based on scholastic ability, commitment to journalism, sensitivity to Asian American and Pacific Islander issues as demonstrated by community involvement, journalistic ability, and financial need. **Deadline for Receipt:** April of each year. **Additional Information:** This program is supported by the Cox Foundation.

2127 ■ ASSOCIATION OF AMERICAN EDITORIAL CARTOONISTS

Attn: Locher Award Contest
3899 North Front Street
Harrisburg, PA 17101
Tel: (717)703-3069
Fax: (717)703-3001
Web Site: http://aaeconline.org/aaecweb/LocherEntry.cfm
To recognize and reward outstanding student editorial cartoonists.
Title of Award: John Locher Memorial Award **Area, Field, or Subject:** Art, Caricatures and cartoons **Level of Education for which Award is Granted:** Undergraduate **Number Awarded:** 1 each year. **Funds Available:** Winners receive an all-expense paid trip to the Association of American Editorial Cartoonists' convention. **Duration:** The competition is held annually.
Eligibility Requirements: This competition is open to undergraduate student editorial cartoonists only; no professionals can enter. Candidates must be between the ages of 17 and 25 years. They may reside in the United States, Canada, or Mexico. Entrants are invited to submit photocopied examples of their work as published in their college or university newspaper. Comic strips may not be submitted, unless the format lends itself to an editorial statement. **Deadline for Receipt:** March

of each year. **Additional Information:** This award was established in 1986. Entries are not returned. The entry fee is $10.

2128 ■ ASSOCIATION FOR WOMEN IN ARCHITECTURE
Attn: Scholarship Chair
22815 Frampton Avenue
Torrance, CA 90501-5034
Tel: (310)534-8466
Fax: (310)257-6885
E-mail: scholarship@awa-la.org
Web Site: http://www.awa-la.org/scholarships.php
To provide financial assistance to women undergraduates in California who are interested in careers in architecture.
Title of Award: Association for Women in Architecture Scholarships **Area, Field, or Subject:** Architecture; Engineering; Engineering, Civil; Engineering, Electrical; Engineering, Mechanical; Graphic art and design; Illustrators and illustrations; Interior design; Landscape architecture and design; Urban affairs/design/planning **Level of Education for which Award is Granted:** Undergraduate **Number Awarded:** 3 each year: 1 at $2,500, 1 at $1,500, and 1 at $1,000. **Funds Available:** Stipends are $2,500, $1,500, or $1,000. **Duration:** 1 year.
Eligibility Requirements: Eligible to apply are women students who have completed at least 1 full year of study in any of the following fields: architecture; civil, structural, mechanical, or electrical engineering as related to architecture; landscape architecture; urban and land planning; interior design; architectural rendering and illustration; or environmental design. They must be residents of California or attending school in California. Interviews are required for semifinalists. Selection is based on grades, a personal statement, financial need, recommendations, and the quality and organization of materials submitted. **Deadline for Receipt:** April of each year.

2129 ■ ALEXANDER GRAHAM BELL ASSOCIATION FOR THE DEAF
Attn: Financial Aid Coordinator
3417 Volta Place, N.W.
Washington, DC 20007-2778
Tel: (202)337-5220
Fax: (202)337-8314
E-mail: financialaid@agbell.org
Web Site: http://www.agbell.org/
DesktopDefault.aspx?p=College_Scholarship_Awards
To provide financial aid to hearing impaired students who are participating in extracurricular activities in arts and sciences.
Title of Award: Arts and Sciences Awards **Area, Field, or Subject:** Art; Performing arts; Science **Level of Education for which Award is Granted:** Undergraduate **Number Awarded:** Varies each year. **Funds Available:** The amount of the award varies, depending upon the cost of the program in which the recipient is enrolled. **Duration:** 1 year; may be renewed upon reapplication.
Eligibility Requirements: Applicants must be diagnosed as having a moderate to profound hearing loss (55 dB or greater loss in the better ear in the speech frequencies of 500, 1000, and 2000 Hz) and must use speech, residual hearing, and/or speechreading as their primary form of communication. They must be between 6 and 19 years of age and enrolled in an art or science program as an extracurricular activity during after-school time, summer, or weekends. Recreational summer camps, sports camps or sports, and travel and study abroad programs that do not have an explicit arts or science focus are not eligible. **Deadline for Receipt:** Applications must be requested between December and February of each year and submitted by May of each year.

2130 ■ BEZEK-DURST-SEISER ARCHITECTS AND PLANNERS
Attn: Scholarship Program
3330 C Street, Suite 200
Anchorage, AK 99503
Tel: (907)562-6076
Fax: (907)562-6635
E-mail: bds@bdsak.com
Web Site: http://www.bdsak.com
To provide financial assistance to Alaska Native high school seniors interested in studying architecture, planning, or interior design in college.
Title of Award: Bezek-Durst-Seiser Scholarship Program **Area, Field, or Subject:** Architecture; Interior design; Urban affairs/design/planning

Level of Education for which Award is Granted: Undergraduate **Number Awarded:** 1 each year. **Funds Available:** The stipend is $1,500 per year. **Duration:** 1 year; may be renewed.
Eligibility Requirements: This program is open to seniors graduating from high schools in Alaska who are Natives accepted into an architecture, planning, or interior design program. Applications must be submitted through a school district or native corporation; direct applications from students are not accepted. Each school district and native corporation in the state may submit 2 applications. Students must include essays on what they are like, the school activities and interests that interest them, why they have chosen their career field, what they have done to prepare themselves to enter that field, why they chose the university or college they plan to attend, and if they plan to return to Alaska after college.
Deadline for Receipt: April of each year. **Additional Information:** Recipients are also offered paid internships at the Bezek-Durst-Seiser office in Anchorage during summer breaks.

2131 ■ BIG 33 SCHOLARSHIP FOUNDATION
Attn: Scholarship Committee
511 Bridge Street
P.O. Box 213
New Cumberland, PA 17070
Tel: (717)774-3303; 877-PABIG-33
Fax: (717)774-1749
E-mail: info@big33.org
Web Site: http://www.big33.org/scholarships/default.ashx
To provide financial assistance and work experience to graduating high school seniors in Ohio and Pennsylvania who plan to study graphic arts in college.
Title of Award: Waveland Direct Printing and Publishing Scholarship **Area, Field, or Subject:** Graphic art and design **Level of Education for which Award is Granted:** Undergraduate **Number Awarded:** 1 each year. **Funds Available:** The stipend is $1,000. **Duration:** 1 year; nonrenewable.
Eligibility Requirements: This program is open to seniors graduating from public and accredited private high schools in Ohio and Pennsylvania who are planning to study graphic arts as related to printing and publishing technology in college. Applications are available from high school guidance counselors. Selection is based on special talents, leadership, obstacles overcome, academic achievement (at least a 2.0 GPA), community service, unique endeavors, financial need, and a 1-page essay on why the applicant deserves the scholarship. **Deadline for Receipt:** February of each year. **Additional Information:** Funds for this program are provided by Waveline Direct, Inc., which also provides an internship at their facility in Mechanicsburg, Pennsylvania

2132 ■ CALIFORNIA ALLIANCE FOR ARTS EDUCATION
495 East Colorado Boulevard
Pasadena, CA 91101
Tel: (626)578-9315
Fax: (626)578-9894
E-mail: eyaa@artsed411.org
Web Site: http://www.artsed411.org/projects/eya.stm
To provide financial assistance to outstanding high school seniors in California who are interested in training to become professional performing artists.
Title of Award: Emerging Young Artist Awards **Area, Field, or Subject:** Art; Dance; Illustrators and illustrations; Music; Painting; Performing arts; Playwriting; Sculpture; Visual arts **Level of Education for which Award is Granted:** Four Year College **Number Awarded:** 12 each year: 4 winners (1 in each category) and 8 runners-up (2 in each category). **Funds Available:** The stipend is $5,000 per year for the winners (for a total of $20,000) and 1-time awards of $1,000 for the runners-up. **Duration:** The winners receive a 4-year scholarship.
Eligibility Requirements: High school seniors in California are eligible to apply in 1 or more of the following categories: dance, music, theater, or visual arts (including painting, drawing, illustration, and sculpture). Applicants must be planning to enter a 4-year institution or accredited professional training program in 1 of those areas. They must be able to demonstrate financial need. Students who apply in the areas of dance, music, and theater must submit a performance work sample. If they advance to the semifinals and finals, they are requested to demonstrate ability with a live performance. **Deadline for Receipt:** January of each

year. **Additional Information:** There is a $10 application fee. Awards are not given in non-performance areas (e.g., music composition, technical theater, or choreography).

2133 ■ CALIFORNIA STATE FAIR

Attn: Friends of the Fair Scholarship Program
1600 Exposition Boulevard
P.O. Box 15649
Sacramento, CA 95852
Tel: (916)274-5969
E-mail: wross@calexpo.com
Web Site: http://www.bigfun.org
To provide financial assistance to residents of California who are studying the arts in college.
Title of Award: California State Fair Arts Scholarships **Area, Field, or Subject:** Cinema; Dance; Filmmaking; Music; Performing arts; Visual arts **Level of Education for which Award is Granted:** Undergraduate **Number Awarded:** 2 each year: 1 at $1,500 and 1 at $500. **Funds Available:** Stipends are $1,500 or $500. **Duration:** 1 year.
Eligibility Requirements: This program is open to residents of California currently working on an undergraduate degree at a college or university in the state. Applicants must be studying the arts, including visual arts, dance, music, film, etc. They must have a GPA of 3.0 or higher. Along with their application, they must submit a 2-page essay on why they are pursuing their desired career and life goals. Selection is based on personal commitment, goals established for their chosen field, leadership potential, and civic accomplishments. **Deadline for Receipt:** March of each year. **Additional Information:** The Friends of the Fair Scholarship Program was established in 1993.

2134 ■ CHICKASAW FOUNDATION

P.O. Box 1726
Ada, OK 74821-1726
Tel: (580)421-9030
Fax: (580)421-9031
Web Site: http://www.cflink.org
To provide financial assistance to members of the Chickasaw Nation who are majoring in fields of interest to ComputerCraft Corporation.
Title of Award: ComputerCraft Corporation Scholarship **Area, Field, or Subject:** Biological and clinical sciences; Engineering, Computer; General studies/Field of study not specified; Graphic art and design; International affairs and relations **Level of Education for which Award is Granted:** Undergraduate **Number Awarded:** 1 each year. **Funds Available:** The stipend is $1,500 per year. **Duration:** 1 year.
Eligibility Requirements: This program is open to Chickasaw students who are currently enrolled full time as an undergraduate student. The sponsor recruits computer engineers, graphic designers, biologists, conference managers, and international trade specialists. Preference may be given to those majors, but all fields of study are eligible. Applicants must have a GPA of 2.5 or higher. Along with their application, they must submit high school or college transcripts, 2 letters of recommendation, a copy of their Certificate of Degree of Indian Blood, a copy of their Chickasaw Nation citizenship card, and a 1-page essay on their long-term goals and plans for achieving them. Financial need is not considered in the selection process. **Deadline for Receipt:** May of each year.

2135 ■ CLAYFOLK

Attn: Scholarship Committee
P.O. Box 274
Talent, OR 97540
To provide financial assistance to ceramic art students in California and Oregon who are interested in pursuing upper-division college courses, workshops at accredited institutions, and study at foreign institutions.
Title of Award: Ellice T. Johnston Scholarship for the Ceramic Arts **Area, Field, or Subject:** Art; Crafts; Design; Sculpture **Level of Education for which Award is Granted:** Four Year College **Funds Available:** The stipend is $1,500. Funds are provided directly to the recipient. **Duration:** 1 year; may be renewed.
Eligibility Requirements: Applicants must be residents of Oregon or northern California and have completed 2 years of college or the equivalent level of art education; this may include sculpture, drawing, design; and the study of aesthetics or technical ceramics. They must be looking for funding to further their education in upper-division college or

art school courses, workshops at accredited institutions, or study abroad at accredited institutions. Applications are considered only after the following supporting documents are received: a portfolio of work (8 to 12 slides and/or photographs), a brief statement about their work and how they plan to use the award, 2 letters of recommendation, a recent academic transcript, a copy of the College Scholarship Service Financial Aid Form (FAF) or a 1040 tax form from the previous year, and a self-addressed stamped envelope to use in returning the portfolio. Financial need is considered in the selection process. **Deadline for Receipt:** June of each year.

2136 ■ COOK INLET REGION, INC.

Attn: CIRI Foundation
2600 Cordova Street, Suite 206
Anchorage, AK 99503
Tel: (907)263-5582
Free: 800-764-3382
Fax: (907)263-5588
E-mail: tcf@ciri.com
Web Site: http://www.thecirifoundation.org/scholarship.html
To provide financial assistance for undergraduate or graduate studies in selected liberal arts to Alaska Natives who are original enrollees to Cook Inlet Region, Inc. (CIRI) and their lineal descendants.
Title of Award: Lawrence Matson Memorial Endowment Fund Scholarships **Area, Field, or Subject:** Art; Communications; Education; Law; Linguistics; Social sciences **Level of Education for which Award is Granted:** Four Year College, Graduate **Number Awarded:** Varies each year; recently, 1 of these scholarships (at $7,000 per year) was awarded. **Funds Available:** The stipend is $9,000 per year, $7,000 per year, or $2,000 per semester, depending on GPA. **Duration:** 1 year (2 semesters).
Eligibility Requirements: This program is open to Alaska Native enrollees to CIRI under the Alaska Native Claims Settlement Act (ANCSA) of 1971 and their lineal descendants. There are no Alaska residency requirements or age limitations. Applicants must be accepted or enrolled full time in a 4-year undergraduate or a graduate degree program in the following liberal arts fields: language, education, social sciences, arts, communications, or law. They must have a GPA of 2.5 or higher. Selection is based on academic achievement, rigor of course work or degree program, quality of a statement of purpose, student financial contribution, financial need, grade level, previous work performance, education and community activities, letters of recommendation, seriousness of purpose, and practicality of educational and professional goals. **Deadline for Receipt:** May of each year. **Additional Information:** This fund was established in 1989. Recipients must attend school on a full-time basis.

2137 ■ DELTA SIGMA THETA SORORITY, INC.

1707 New Hampshire Avenue, N.W.
Washington, DC 20009
Tel: (202)986-2400
Fax: (202)986-2513
E-mail: dstemail@deltasigmatheta.org
Web Site: http://www.deltasigmatheta.org
To provide financial assistance to members of Delta Sigma Theta who are interested in careers in the performing or creative arts.
Title of Award: Myra Davis Hemmings Scholarship **Area, Field, or Subject:** Art; Performing arts **Level of Education for which Award is Granted:** Undergraduate **Number Awarded:** 1 each year. **Funds Available:** The amount awarded varies, depending upon the recipient's financial need. Funds must be used for tuition or school expenses only. **Duration:** 1 year; may be renewed.
Eligibility Requirements: Applicants must be active, dues-paying members of Delta Sigma Theta and majoring in the performing or the creative arts. They must submit transcripts of all college records. Selection is based on meritorious achievement. **Deadline for Receipt:** March of each year.

2138 ■ DREW UNIVERSITY

Attn: Office of International and Off-Campus Programs
Brothers College Room 115
36 Madison Avenue
Madison, NJ 07940-4036
Tel: (973)408-3438
Fax: (973)408-3768

E-mail: intlprog@drew.edu
Web Site: http://depts.drew.edu/offcamp/non-DrewScholarships.htm
To provide financial assistance to students from any college who wish to participate in the off-campus programs in the United States or abroad sponsored by Drew University.
Title of Award: Drew University Off Campus Programs Scholarships **Area, Field, or Subject:** Art; British studies; English language and literature; European studies; General studies/Field of study not specified; Performing arts; Political science **Level of Education for which Award is Granted:** Undergraduate **Number Awarded:** Varies each year. **Funds Available:** Grants up to $3,000 per semester are available to be applied to the cost of the programs. **Duration:** 1 semester.
Eligibility Requirements: Students from any American college or university who have been accepted to participate in 1 of the off-campus programs sponsored by Drew University may apply for financial aid if the university's financial aid office determines that they meet the standards of financial need. Applicants for semester programs must be entering their junior or senior year and have a GPA of 2.7 or higher. **Deadline for Receipt:** April of each year for the fall semester; November of each year for the spring semester. **Additional Information:** The programs available recently included a Washington semester on American politics, a semester on the United Nations in New York, a New York semester on contemporary art and culture, a semester on the new Europe, a program in Eritrea on developing countries, and a London semester on British politics, history, drama, or literature.

2139 ■ ELECTRONIC DOCUMENT SYSTEMS FOUNDATION
Attn: EDSF Scholarship Awards
24238 Hawthorne Boulevard
Torrance, CA 90505-6505
Tel: (310)541-1481
Fax: (310)541-4803
Web Site: http://www.edsf.org/scholarships.cfm
To provide financial assistance to college juniors, seniors, and graduate students interested in working with electronic documents as a career.
Title of Award: Wayne Alexander Memorial Scholarship **Area, Field, or Subject:** Computer and information sciences; Graphic art and design; Internet design and development; Marketing and distribution; Printing trades and industries; Telecommunications systems **Level of Education for which Award is Granted:** Four Year College, Graduate **Number Awarded:** 1 each year. **Funds Available:** The stipend is $2,000. **Duration:** 1 year.
Eligibility Requirements: This program is open to juniors, seniors, and graduate students who are working full time on a degree in the field of document communication, including marketing, graphic communication and arts, e-commerce, imaging science, printing, web authoring, electronic publishing, computer science, or telecommunications. Priority consideration is given to students at the University of Central Florida. Applicants must submit a statement of their career goals in the field of document communications, an essay on a topic related to their view of the future of the document management and production industry, a list of current professional and college extracurricular activities and achievements, college transcripts (GPA of 3.0 or higher), samples of their creative work, and 2 letters of recommendation. Financial need is not considered. **Deadline for Receipt:** May of each year. **Additional Information:** This program is sponsored by AXIS Inc.

2140 ■ ELECTRONIC DOCUMENT SYSTEMS FOUNDATION
Attn: EDSF Scholarship Awards
24238 Hawthorne Boulevard
Torrance, CA 90505-6505
Tel: (310)541-1481
Fax: (310)541-4803
Web Site: http://www.edsf.org/scholarships.cfm
To provide financial assistance to college juniors, seniors, and graduate students interested in working with electronic documents as a career.
Title of Award: EDSF Board of Directors Scholarships **Area, Field, or Subject:** Computer and information sciences; Graphic art and design; Internet design and development; Marketing and distribution; Printing trades and industries; Telecommunications systems **Level of Education for which Award is Granted:** Four Year College, Graduate **Number Awarded:** 20 each year. **Funds Available:** The stipend is $2,000. **Duration:** 1 year.

Eligibility Requirements: This program is open to juniors, seniors, and graduate students who are working full time on a degree in the field of document communication, including marketing, graphic communication and arts, e-commerce, imaging science, printing, web authoring, electronic publishing, computer science, or telecommunications. Applicants must submit a statement of their career goals in the field of document communications, an essay on a topic related to their view of the future of the document management and production industry, a list of current professional and college extracurricular activities and achievements, college transcripts (GPA of 3.0 or higher), samples of their creative work, and 2 letters of recommendation. Financial need is not considered. **Deadline for Receipt:** May of each year.

2141 ■ ELECTRONIC DOCUMENT SYSTEMS FOUNDATION
Attn: EDSF Scholarship Awards
24238 Hawthorne Boulevard
Torrance, CA 90505-6505
Tel: (310)541-1481
Fax: (310)541-4803
Web Site: http://www.edsf.org/scholarships.cfm
To provide financial assistance to students in technical schools and community colleges who are interested in working with electronic documents as a career.
Title of Award: EDSF Board of Directors Technical and Community College Scholarship **Area, Field, or Subject:** Computer and information sciences; Graphic art and design; Internet design and development; Marketing and distribution; Printing trades and industries; Telecommunications systems **Level of Education for which Award is Granted:** Two Year College, Vocational/Occupational **Number Awarded:** 5 each year. **Funds Available:** The stipend is $1,000. **Duration:** 1 year.
Eligibility Requirements: This program is open to first- and second-year students at technical and trade schools and community colleges. Applicants must be working on a degree in the field of electronic document communication, including marketing, graphic communication and arts, e-commerce, imaging science, printing, web authoring, electronic publishing, computer science, or telecommunications. They must submit a 1-page essay on 1 of the following topics: 1) a definition of their career goals in the field of document management and communications; 2) a recent technological change and how it has or will affect the document communication industry; or 3) a definition of the document communication industry. Selection is based on the essay, extracurricular activities and achievements, high school transcripts (GPA of 3.0 or higher), samples of creative work, and 2 letters of recommendation. Financial need is not considered. **Deadline for Receipt:** May of each year.

2142 ■ ELECTRONIC DOCUMENT SYSTEMS FOUNDATION
Attn: EDSF Scholarship Awards
24238 Hawthorne Boulevard
Torrance, CA 90505-6505
Tel: (310)541-1481
Fax: (310)541-4803
Web Site: http://www.edsf.org/scholarships.cfm
To provide financial assistance to upper-division and graduate students interested in working with electronic documents as a career.
Title of Award: David Hoods Memorial Scholarship **Area, Field, or Subject:** Computer and information sciences; Graphic art and design; Internet design and development; Marketing and distribution; Printing trades and industries; Public relations; Telecommunications systems **Level of Education for which Award is Granted:** Four Year College, Graduate **Number Awarded:** 1 each year. **Funds Available:** The stipend is $2,000. **Duration:** 1 year.
Eligibility Requirements: This program is open to full-time juniors, seniors, and graduate students who demonstrate a strong interest in working with electronic documents as a career (including graphic communications, document management, document content, and/or document distribution). Special consideration is given to students interested in marketing and public relations. Applicants must submit a statement of their career goals in the field of document communications, an essay on a topic related to their view of the future of the document management and production industry, a list of current professional and college extracurricular activities and achievements, college transcripts (GPA of 3.0 or higher), samples of their creative work, and 2 letters of recommendation. Financial need is not considered. **Deadline for Receipt:** May of each year.

2143 ■ ELECTRONIC DOCUMENT SYSTEMS FOUNDATION

Attn: EDSF Scholarship Awards
24238 Hawthorne Boulevard
Torrance, CA 90505-6505
Tel: (310)541-1481
Fax: (310)541-4803
Web Site: http://www.edsf.org/scholarships.cfm
To provide financial assistance to college juniors, seniors, and graduate students interested in working with electronic documents as a career.

Title of Award: John A. Lopiano Scholarship **Area, Field, or Subject:** Computer and information sciences; Graphic art and design; Internet design and development; Marketing and distribution; Printing trades and industries; Telecommunications systems **Level of Education for which Award is Granted:** Four Year College, Graduate **Number Awarded:** 1 each year. **Funds Available:** The stipend is $2,000. **Duration:** 1 year.
Eligibility Requirements: This program is open to juniors, seniors, and graduate students who are working full time on a degree in the field of document communication, including marketing, graphic communication and arts, e-commerce, imaging science, printing, web authoring, electronic publishing, computer science, or telecommunications. Priority consideration is given to students who work in or whose family member has worked or currently works in a segment of the high volume transaction output (HVTO) industry. Applicants must submit a statement of their career goals in the field of document communications, an essay on a topic related to their view of the future of the document management and production industry, a list of current professional and college extracurricular activities and achievements, college transcripts (GPA of 3.0 or higher), samples of their creative work, and 2 letters of recommendation. Financial need is not considered. **Deadline for Receipt:** May of each year. **Additional Information:** This program is sponsored by COPI/OutputLinks.

2144 ■ ELECTRONIC DOCUMENT SYSTEMS FOUNDATION

Attn: EDSF Scholarship Awards
24238 Hawthorne Boulevard
Torrance, CA 90505-6505
Tel: (310)541-1481
Fax: (310)541-4803
Web Site: http://www.edsf.org/scholarships.cfm
To provide financial assistance to upper-division and graduate students in Canada who are interested in working with electronic documents as a career.

Title of Award: Xplor Canada Scholarship **Area, Field, or Subject:** Computer and information sciences; Graphic art and design; Internet design and development; Printing trades and industries **Level of Education for which Award is Granted:** Four Year College, Graduate **Number Awarded:** 1 each year. **Funds Available:** The stipend is $C2,000. **Duration:** 1 year.
Eligibility Requirements: This program is open to third-year, fourth-year, and advanced-degree students who are working full time on a degree in the field of electronic documents, including content and design, print technologies, graphic communications, or computer science. Applicants must be Canadian citizens or landed immigrants and living in Canada, but they may be attending a course of study outside of Canada. They must submit a statement of their career goals in the field of document/communication systems, an essay on a topic related to their view of the future of the document management and production industry, a list of current professional and college extracurricular activities and achievements, college transcripts (GPA of 3.0 or higher), samples of their creative work, and 2 letters of recommendation. Financial need is not considered. **Deadline for Receipt:** May of each year. **Additional Information:** This program is sponsored by Xplor Canada.

2145 ■ ENGLISH-SPEAKING UNION OF THE UNITED STATES-WASHINGTON DC AREA BRANCH

1604 New Hampshire Avenue, N.W.
Washington, DC 20009
Tel: (202)234-4602
Fax: (202)234-4639
E-mail: esuwdc@msn.com
Web Site: http://www.esuwdc.org/fellowships.html
To provide funding to residents of the metropolitan Washington area who are interested in conducting research or other projects anywhere in the world on a topic that relates to the English-speaking tradition.

Title of Award: Helen Gladstone Williams Scholarships **Area, Field, or Subject:** Art; General studies/Field of study not specified; History; Philosophy **Level of Education for which Award is Granted:** Graduate, Professional, Postdoctoral, Undergraduate **Number Awarded:** 1 or more each year. **Funds Available:** The grant ranges up to $5,000.
Eligibility Requirements: This program is open to permanent residents of the Washington, D.C. metropolitan area who have at least a bachelor's degree. Applicants must be interested in conducting a project, either independently or in conjunction with an accredited institution, on a subject that relates to English-speaking traditions in locales other than, or in addition to, the United States. They must submit a 2-page summary that describes the course of study to be undertaken and discusses how it would advance the objectives of the sponsoring organization, a brief resume of academic and employment experience, and 3 letters of support. Applicants who do not have a diploma at the bachelor's level or above must also submit a transcript from an accredited institution of higher learning that indicates progress toward a degree to be bestowed in the near future. Projects should focus primarily on endeavors that shed light on history, philosophy, the arts, or other aspects of culture. Selection is based on the significance of the project in relation to the field(s) it seeks to address, the project's relevance to the aims and values of the sponsoring organization, the credentials of the applicant, and the likelihood that the project will be completed successfully and on schedule. **Deadline for Receipt:** March of each year.

2146 ■ FASHION GROUP INTERNATIONAL OF WASHINGTON

Attn: Julie Caine Brooks, Scholarship Chair
P.O. Box 1288
Great Falls, VA 22066
To provide financial assistance for college or graduate school to residents of Maryland, Virginia, and Washington, D. C. interested in preparing for a career in fashion or a fashion-related field.

Title of Award: Washington Fashion Group International Scholarship **Area, Field, or Subject:** Fashion design; Interior design; Journalism; Marketing and distribution; Photography; Textile science **Level of Education for which Award is Granted:** Graduate, Undergraduate **Number Awarded:** 1 each year. **Funds Available:** The maximum stipend is $5,000. **Duration:** 1 year; nonrenewable
Eligibility Requirements: This program is open to residents of Washington, D.C. and all cities and counties in Maryland and Virginia. Applicants must be graduating high school seniors or current undergraduate or graduate students enrolled in a fashion or fashion-related degree program (commercial arts, textiles and clothing design, interior design, journalism, merchandising, or photography). They must submit a 200-word personal statement on their career goals and motivation for entering a fashion-related career. Selection is based on that statement, academic achievement, creative ability, related work activity (paid or unpaid), extracurricular activities and awards, and 3 letters of reference. Finalists are interviewed and asked to submit portfolio material of their work. **Deadline for Receipt:** April of each year.

2147 ■ FOUNDATION FOR THE CAROLINAS

Attn: Senior Vice President, Scholarships
217 South Tryon Street
P.O. Box 34769
Charlotte, NC 28234-4769
Tel: (704)973-4535
Free: 800-973-7244
Fax: (704)973-4935
E-mail: jseymour@fftc.org
Web Site: http://www.fftc.org/scholarships
To provide financial assistance to college students from North Carolina who are interested in the arts.

Title of Award: Spirit Square Center for Arts and Education Scholarship **Area, Field, or Subject:** Art; Performing arts **Level of Education for which Award is Granted:** Undergraduate **Number Awarded:** 1 or more each year. **Funds Available:** Stipends range up to $4,000 per year; Funds are paid directly to the recipient's school to be used for tuition, required fees, books, and supplies. **Duration:** 1 year; may be renewed.
Eligibility Requirements: This program is open to college juniors and seniors who can demonstrate an interest and career potential in the arts. Along with their application, they must submit a 1- to 2-page statement expressing their reasons for applying for the scholarship, their interest in

the arts, and their educational and career goals in the arts. Selection is based on academic achievement (preferably a GPA of 3.0 or higher) school and community involvement, personal achievements, and commitment to and demonstrated potential for a career in the arts. Preference is given to residents of Mecklenburg and surrounding counties in North Carolina attending colleges and universities in that state. **Deadline for Receipt:** February of each year.

2148 ■ FRAMELINE

Attn: Film and Video Completion Fund
145 Ninth Street, Suite 300
San Francisco, CA 94103
Tel: (415)703-8650
Fax: (415)861-1404
E-mail: info@frameline.org
Web Site: http://www.frameline.org/fund
To provide funding to lesbian and gay film/video artists.
Title of Award: Horizons/Frameline Film and Video Completion Fund **Area, Field, or Subject:** Filmmaking; Homosexuality **Level of Education for which Award is Granted:** Graduate, Professional, Undergraduate **Number Awarded:** Varies each year; recently, 4 of these grants were awarded. **Funds Available:** Grants range from $3,000 to $5,000.
Eligibility Requirements: This program is open to lesbian and gay artists who are in the last stages of the production of documentary, educational, animated, or experimental projects about or of interest to lesbians, gay men, bisexuals, and transgender people and their communities. Applicants may be independent artists, students, producers, or nonprofit corporations. They must be interested in completion or post-production work, including subtitling or conversion from video to film (or vice versa). In particular, women and people of color are encouraged to apply. Selection is based on financial need, the contribution the grant will make to completing the project, assurances that the project will be completed, and the statement the project makes about lesbian, gay, bisexual, and transgender people and/or issues of concern to them and their communities. Grants are not awarded for script development, research, pre-production, or production work. **Deadline for Receipt:** October of each year.

2149 ■ FRIENDS-IN-ART

c/o Harvey Miller
402 East French Broad Street
Brevard, NC 28712-3410
Tel: (828)862-3412
E-mail: hhmiller@citcom.net
To provide financial assistance to blind students who are majoring or planning to major in fields related to the arts.
Title of Award: Friends-in-Art Scholarship **Area, Field, or Subject:** Art; Creative writing; Music; Playwriting **Level of Education for which Award is Granted:** Undergraduate **Number Awarded:** 1 each year. **Funds Available:** The stipend is $1,000. **Duration:** 1 year.
Eligibility Requirements: This program is open to blind and visually impaired high school seniors and college students who are majoring or planning to major in music, art, drama, or creative writing. Required submissions are a recording of 2 contrasting pieces for music students; 10 slides of their work for art students; a recording of 1 dramatic and 1 comic scene for drama students; and a varied selection of their writing for creative writing students. Selection is based on achievement, talent, and excellence in the arts. **Deadline for Receipt:** April of each year. **Additional Information:** This program began in 1999.

2150 ■ HANDWEAVERS GUILD OF AMERICA, INC.

Attn: Scholarship Chair
1255 Buford Highway, Suite 211
Suwanee, GA 30024
Tel: (678)730-0010
Fax: (678)730-0836
E-mail: hga@weavespindye.org
Web Site: http://www.weavespindye.org
To provide financial assistance to undergraduate and graduate students working on a degree in the field of fiber arts.
Title of Award: Dendel Scholarships **Area, Field, or Subject:** Art conservation; History; Textile science **Level of Education for which Award is Granted:** Graduate, Undergraduate **Number Awarded:** Varies;

more than $4,000 is available for this program each year. **Funds Available:** The amount of the award depends on the availability of funds. Recipients may use the funds for tuition, materials (e.g., film for photographs), or travel. **Duration:** 1 year.
Eligibility Requirements: This program is open to undergraduate and graduate students enrolled in accredited colleges and universities in the United States, its possessions, and Canada. Applicants must be working on a degree in the field of fiber arts, including training for research, textile history, and conservation. Along with their application, they must submit 1) an essay on their study goals and how those fit into their future plans, and 2) 5 to 16 slides of their work. Selection is based on artistic and technical merit; financial need is not considered. **Deadline for Receipt:** March of each year.

2151 ■ HANDWEAVERS GUILD OF AMERICA, INC.

Attn: Scholarship Chair
1255 Buford Highway, Suite 211
Suwanee, GA 30024
Tel: (678)730-0010
Fax: (678)730-0836
E-mail: hga@weavespindye.org
Web Site: http://www.weavespindye.org
To provide financial assistance to undergraduate and graduate students working on a degree in the field of fiber arts.
Title of Award: HGA Scholarships **Area, Field, or Subject:** Art conservation; History; Textile science **Level of Education for which Award is Granted:** Graduate, Undergraduate **Number Awarded:** Varies; more than $4,000 is available for this program each year. **Funds Available:** The amount of the award depends on the availability of funds. Use of funds is restricted to tuition. **Duration:** 1 year.
Eligibility Requirements: This program is open to undergraduate and graduate students enrolled in accredited colleges and universities in the United States, its possessions, and Canada. Applicants must be working on a degree in the field of fiber arts, including training for research, textile history, and conservation. Along with their application, they must submit 1) an essay on their study goals and how they fit into their future plans, and 2) 5 to 16 slides of their work. Selection is based on artistic and technical merit; financial need is not considered. **Deadline for Receipt:** March of each year.

2152 ■ HAWAI'I COMMUNITY FOUNDATION

Attn: Scholarship Department
1164 Bishop Street, Suite 800
Honolulu, HI 96813
Tel: (808)566-5570; 888-731-3863
Fax: (808)521-6286
E-mail: scholarships@hcf-hawaii.org
Web Site: http://www.hawaiicommunityfoundation.org/scholar/scholar.php
To provide financial assistance to Hawaii residents who are interested in preparing for a career in the graphic arts.
Title of Award: American Institute of Graphic Arts (AIGA) Honolulu Chapter Scholarship Fund **Area, Field, or Subject:** Graphic art and design **Level of Education for which Award is Granted:** Undergraduate **Number Awarded:** Varies each year. **Funds Available:** A stipend is awarded (amount not specified). **Duration:** 1 year.
Eligibility Requirements: This program is open to Hawaii residents who are interested in majoring in graphic design, visual communication, or commercial arts, including print production. Applicants must be able to demonstrate academic achievement (GPA of 2.7 or higher), good moral character, and financial need. **Deadline for Receipt:** February of each year. **Additional Information:** Recipients may attend college in Hawaii or on the mainland.

2153 ■ HAWAI'I COMMUNITY FOUNDATION

Attn: Scholarship Department
1164 Bishop Street, Suite 800
Honolulu, HI 96813
Tel: (808)566-5570; 888-731-3863
Fax: (808)521-6286
E-mail: scholarships@hcf-hawaii.org
Web Site: http://www.hawaiicommunityfoundation.org/scholar/scholar.php
To provide financial assistance to residents of Hawaii who are interested in working on a degree in art.

Title of Award: Laheenae Rebecca Hart Gay Scholarship **Area, Field, or Subject:** Art **Level of Education for which Award is Granted:** Graduate, Undergraduate **Number Awarded:** Varies each year; recently, 1 of these scholarships was awarded. **Funds Available:** The amount of the award depends on the availability of funds and the need of the recipient; recently, stipends averaged $1,500. **Duration:** 1 year.
Eligibility Requirements: This program is open to residents of Hawaii who are planning to study art (not video, film, performing arts, or the culinary arts) as full-time students on the undergraduate or graduate level. Applicants must be able to demonstrate academic achievement (GPA of 2.7 or higher), good moral character, and financial need. **Deadline for Receipt:** February of each year. **Additional Information:** Recipients may attend college in Hawaii or on the mainland.

2154 ■ HAWAI'I COMMUNITY FOUNDATION

Attn: Scholarship Department
1164 Bishop Street, Suite 800
Honolulu, HI 96813
Tel: (808)566-5570; 888-731-3863
Fax: (808)521-6286
E-mail: scholarships@hcf-hawaii.org
Web Site: http://www.hawaiicommunityfoundation.org/scholar/scholar.php
To provide financial assistance to Hawaii residents who are interested in preparing for a career that will fill gaps in the local job market.
Title of Award: Hawai'i Community Foundation Community Scholarship Fund **Area, Field, or Subject:** Architecture; Art; Education; Humanities; Social sciences **Level of Education for which Award is Granted:** Graduate, Undergraduate **Number Awarded:** Varies each year; recently, 97 of these scholarships were awarded. **Funds Available:** The amount awarded varies; recently, stipends averaged $1,000. **Duration:** 1 year.
Eligibility Requirements: This program is open to students in Hawaii who show potential for filling a community need; demonstrate accomplishment, motivation, initiative, and vision; are residents of the state of Hawaii; intend to return to, or stay in, Hawaii to work; are able to demonstrate financial need; are interested in attending an accredited 2- or 4-year college or university as a full-time student at either the undergraduate or graduate level; plan to major in the arts, architecture, education, humanities, or social science; and are able to demonstrate academic achievement (GPA of 3.0 or higher). **Deadline for Receipt:** February of each year. **Additional Information:** Recipients may attend school in Hawaii or on the mainland. This fund was established in 1947.

2155 ■ HAWAI'I COMMUNITY FOUNDATION

Attn: Scholarship Department
1164 Bishop Street, Suite 800
Honolulu, HI 96813
Tel: (808)566-5570; 888-731-3863
Fax: (808)521-6286
E-mail: scholarships@hcf-hawaii.org
Web Site: http://www.hawaiicommunityfoundation.org/scholar/scholar.php
To provide financial assistance to residents of Hawaii who are interested in working on a degree in fine art.
Title of Award: Esther Kanagawa Memorial Art Scholarship **Area, Field, or Subject:** Crafts; Painting; Photography; Sculpture **Level of Education for which Award is Granted:** Graduate, Undergraduate **Number Awarded:** Varies each year; recently, 1 of these scholarships was awarded. **Funds Available:** The amount of the award depends on the availability of funds and the need of the recipient; recently, stipends averaged $1,000. **Duration:** 1 year.
Eligibility Requirements: This program is open to residents of Hawaii who are planning to study fine art (drawing, painting, sculpture, ceramics, or photography) as full-time students on the undergraduate or graduate level. Students majoring in video, film, performing arts, or the culinary arts are not eligible. Applicants must be able to demonstrate academic achievement (GPA of 2.7 or higher), good moral character, and financial need. **Deadline for Receipt:** February of each year. **Additional Information:** Recipients may attend college in Hawaii or on the mainland.

2156 ■ HAWAI'I COMMUNITY FOUNDATION

Attn: Scholarship Department
1164 Bishop Street, Suite 800
Honolulu, HI 96813
Tel: (808)566-5570; 888-731-3863

Fax: (808)521-6286
E-mail: scholarships@hcf-hawaii.org
Web Site: http://www.hawaiicommunityfoundation.org/scholar/scholar.php
To provide financial assistance to Hawaii residents who are interested in preparing for a career in the arts.
Title of Award: PHG Foundation Scholarship **Area, Field, or Subject:** Art; Art industries and trade; Crafts **Level of Education for which Award is Granted:** Graduate, Undergraduate **Number Awarded:** Varies each year; recently, 5 of these scholarships were awarded. **Funds Available:** The amounts of the awards depend on the availability of funds and the need of the recipient; recently, stipends averaged $1,000. **Duration:** 1 year.
Eligibility Requirements: This program is open to Hawaii residents who are interested in majoring in art or arts and crafts (not video, film, culinary arts, or the performing arts). They may be studying full or part time, on the undergraduate or graduate school level. They must be able to demonstrate academic achievement (GPA of 2.7 or higher), good moral character, and financial need. In addition to filling out the standard application form, applicants must write a short statement indicating their reasons for attending college, their planned course of study, and their career goals. **Deadline for Receipt:** February of each year. **Additional Information:** Recipients may attend college in Hawaii or on the mainland. This scholarship was established by a foundation created by the Pacific Handcrafters Guild (PHG), P.O. Box 602, Waimanalo, HI 98795, (808) 948-3890.

2157 ■ HISPANIC SCHOLARSHIP FUND

Attn: Selection Committee
55 Second Street, Suite 1500
San Francisco, CA 94105
Tel: (415)808-2350; 877-HSF-INFO
Fax: (415)808-2302
E-mail: college1@hsf.net
Web Site: http://www.hsf.net/scholarship/programs/mcnamara.php
To provide funding to Hispanic undergraduate and graduate students interested in beginning and completing an art project.
Title of Award: McNamara Family Creative Arts Project Grants **Area, Field, or Subject:** Communications; Creative writing; Filmmaking; Performing arts **Level of Education for which Award is Granted:** Graduate, Undergraduate **Number Awarded:** 1 or more each year. **Funds Available:** Grants range from $5,000 to $20,000. **Duration:** These are 1-time grants.
Eligibility Requirements: This program is open to U.S. citizens, permanent residents, and visitors with a passport stamped I-551. Applicants must be of Hispanic heritage and working full time on an undergraduate or graduate degree at an accredited college or university in the United States, Puerto Rico, or the U.S. Virgin Islands. They must have completed at least 12 undergraduate units with a GPA of 3.0 or higher and be majoring in the arts, including (but not limited to) media, film, performing arts, communications, and writing. Along with their application, they must submit a 3-page concept paper describing the art project for which they are seeking funding, a portfolio of their work, and 600-word essays on 1) how their Hispanic heritage, family upbringing, and/or role models have influenced their personal long-term goals; 2) how they contribute to their community and what they have learned from their experiences; and 3) an academic challenge they have faced and how they have overcome it. Selection is based on those submissions, academic record, plans and career goals, community service, and financial need. **Deadline for Receipt:** May of each year. **Additional Information:** This program is offered by the Hispanic Scholarship Fund (HSF) in partnership with the McNamara Family Foundation.

2158 ■ ILLUMINATING ENGINEERING SOCIETY OF NORTH AMERICA-GOLDEN GATE SECTION

c/o Phil Hall
1514 Gibbons Drive
Alameda, CA 94501
Tel: (510)208-5005
Fax: (510)864-8511
E-mail: mrcatisbac@aol.com
Web Site: http://www.iesgg.org
To provide financial assistance to undergraduate or graduate students interested in studying or conducting research in lighting.

Title of Award: Robert W. Thunen Memorial Scholarships **Area, Field, or Subject:** Architecture; Engineering, Electrical; Filmmaking; Interior design; Lighting science; Radio and television **Level of Education for which Award is Granted:** Four Year College, Graduate **Number Awarded:** At least 2 each year. **Funds Available:** The stipend is $2,500. **Duration:** 1 year.
Eligibility Requirements: Applicants must be enrolled full time as an upper-division or graduate student at an accredited 4-year educational institution in northern California, northern Nevada, Oregon, or Washington and be studying architecture, electrical engineering, film/TV, lighting design, theater, or vision with an emphasis on lighting. Undergraduate students must be proposing course work related to potential employment in the lighting field. Graduate students must be proposing to conduct a research project that will further the lighting field or industry. Financial need is not considered in the selection process. **Deadline for Receipt:** March of each year. **Additional Information:** This program was established in 1986.

2159 ■ IMPERIAL POLK ADVERTISING FEDERATION
Attn: Scholarship Program
P.O. Box 24201
Lakeland, FL 33802-4201
Tel: (863)858-3736
Fax: (863)858-3736
Web Site: http://www.polkadfed.com
To provide financial assistance to undergraduate students majoring in fields related to advertising at Florida colleges.
Title of Award: William E. Gregory Scholarship **Area, Field, or Subject:** Advertising; Communications; Graphic art and design; Marketing and distribution **Level of Education for which Award is Granted:** Undergraduate **Number Awarded:** 1 or more each year. **Funds Available:** A total of $2,000 is available for this program each year. **Duration:** 1 year; nonrenewable.
Eligibility Requirements: This program is open to full-time undergraduate students at universities, colleges, and technical schools in Florida. Applicants must be working on a degree in advertising, communications, graphic design, or marketing. They must have a GPA of 3.0 or higher. Along with their application, they must submit 1) a 500-word essay describing their future professional and educational goals; and 2) a project they have recently completed for a class or internship. Financial need is not considered in the selection process. **Deadline for Receipt:** November of each year. **Additional Information:** Information is also available from Samantha Hocker, Scholarship Chair, (863) 701-7789, E-mail: shocker@keisercollege.edu.

2160 ■ INTERNATIONAL CINEMATOGRAPHERS GUILD
Attn: Scholarships
7755 Sunset Boulevard
Los Angeles, CA 90046
Tel: (323)876-0160
Fax: (323)876-6383
Web Site: http://www.cameraguild.com
To provide financial assistance to children and grandchildren of members of the International Cinematographers Guild (ICG) interested in working on an undergraduate or graduate degree in cinematography.
Title of Award: William Hines Scholarship in Cinematography **Area, Field, or Subject:** Filmmaking **Level of Education for which Award is Granted:** Graduate, Undergraduate **Number Awarded:** 1 each year. **Funds Available:** The stipend is $1,000. **Duration:** 1 year.
Eligibility Requirements: This program is open to high school seniors and students in a postsecondary educational program who are the children or grandchildren of ICG members in good standing. Applicants must be interested in working full time on an undergraduate or graduate degree in cinematography. Along with their application, they must submit a 2-page essay on what they care about, their passion, and how those things relate to their academic, extracurricular, or employment life. They may also submit a second optional essay on other matters they want the selection committee to consider, such as their financial need or special circumstances. **Deadline for Receipt:** January of each year.

2161 ■ INTERNATIONAL FOODSERVICE EDITORIAL COUNCIL
P.O. Box 491
Hyde Park, NY 12538

Tel: (845)229-6973
Fax: (845)229-6993
E-mail: ifec@aol.com
Web Site: http://www.ifec-is-us.com
To provide financial assistance to undergraduate or graduate students who are interested in preparing for a career in communications in the food service industry.
Title of Award: IFEC Scholarships **Area, Field, or Subject:** Communications; Creative writing; Culinary arts; English language and literature; Food science and technology; Food service careers; Graphic art and design; Hotel, institutional, and restaurant management; Journalism; Management; Marketing and distribution; Nutrition; Photography; Photography, Journalistic; Public relations **Level of Education for which Award is Granted:** Master's, Undergraduate **Number Awarded:** Varies each year; recently, 5 of these scholarships were awarded. **Funds Available:** The stipend is $3,000 per year. **Duration:** 1 year.
Eligibility Requirements: This program is open to currently-enrolled college students who are working on an associate, bachelor's, or master's degree. They must be enrolled full time and planning on a career in editorial, public relations, photography, food styling, or a related aspect of communications in the food service industry. The following food service majors are considered appropriate for this program: culinary arts; hospitality management; hotel, restaurant, and institutional management; dietetics; food science and technology; and nutrition. Applicable communications areas include journalism, English, mass communications, public relations, marketing, broadcast journalism, creative writing, graphic arts, and photography. Selection is based on academic record, character references, and demonstrated financial need. **Deadline for Receipt:** March of each year.

2162 ■ JUNIOR ACHIEVEMENT
Attn: Scholarships Coordinator
One Education Way
Colorado Springs, CO 80906-4477
Tel: (719)540-6255; 888-4JA-ALUM
Fax: (719)540-6175
E-mail: scholarships@ja.org
Web Site: http://www.ja.org/programs/programs_schol_dis.shtml
To provide financial assistance to high school seniors who participated in the Junior Achievement (JA) program and are interested in majoring in business or the fine arts in college.
Title of Award: Walt Disney Company Foundation Scholarship **Area, Field, or Subject:** Art; Business administration **Level of Education for which Award is Granted:** Four Year College **Number Awarded:** 1 each year. **Funds Available:** This scholarship provides full payment of tuition at the college or university of the recipient's choice plus a stipend of $200 cash per year for incidental fees. **Duration:** 4 years, provided the recipient maintains grades satisfactory to the college or university.
Eligibility Requirements: This program is open to graduating high school seniors who have participated in the JA Company Program or JA Economics. Applicants must have an exceptional record of academic achievement and extracurricular activities. They must be interested in majoring in business administration or the fine arts in college. Letters of recommendation are required. **Deadline for Receipt:** January of each year. **Additional Information:** This scholarship, first awarded in 1979, is sponsored by the Walt Disney Company Foundation. Recipients must attend a 4-year college or university.

2163 ■ KNIGHT RIDDER, INC.
Attn: Office of Diversity
50 West San Fernando Street, Suite 1200
San Jose, CA 95113
Tel: (408)938-7734
Fax: (408)938-7755
Web Site: http://www.knightridder.com/career/internships.html
To provide financial assistance and work experience to minority high school seniors who are interested in going to college to prepare for a career in journalism.
Title of Award: Knight Ridder Minority Scholars Program **Area, Field, or Subject:** Advertising; Graphic art and design; Information science and technology; Journalism; Marketing and distribution; Photography, Journalistic **Level of Education for which Award is Granted:** Undergraduate **Number Awarded:** Up to 5 each year: 2 for news, 2 for busi-

ness, and 1 for either. **Funds Available:** The stipend is $5,000 per year for the freshman and sophomore year and $15,000 per year for the junior and senior year. **Duration:** 1 year; may be renewed for up to 3 additional years, if the recipient maintains a GPA of 3.0 or higher and satisfactory performance on internships. **Eligibility Requirements:** This program is open to minority seniors graduating from high schools in areas served by Knight Ridder. Applicants must be interested in attending college to prepare for a career in the newspaper industry. They first apply to their local Knight Ridder newspaper and compete for local scholarships; selected winners are then nominated for this award. Both "news" and "business" students are eligible. **Additional Information:** Recipients are offered an internship opportunity at a Knight Ridder newspaper during the summer. News scholars work in the newsroom, writing and editing stories, taking photographs, crafting illustrations, and designing news pages. Business scholars complete internships in advertising, marketing, information technology, circulation, and other areas essential to the industry. At the end of the sophomore year, recipients must agree to work at a Knight Ridder newspaper for 1 year after graduation.

2164 ■ KNIGHT RIDDER NEWSPAPERS-WASHINGTON BUREAU

Attn: Anthony Pugh
700 12th Street, N.W., Suite 1000
Washington, DC 20005-3994
Tel: (202)383-6013
Fax: (202)383-3738
E-mail: tpugh@krwashington.com
Web Site: http://www.krwashington.com
To provide financial assistance to minority high school seniors from the Washington, D.C. area who are interested in attending college to prepare for a career in the newspaper industry.
Title of Award: Washington Bureau Minority Scholarships **Area, Field, or Subject:** Advertising; Business administration; Computer and information sciences; Graphic art and design; Journalism; Photography, Journalistic **Level of Education for which Award is Granted:** Undergraduate **Number Awarded:** 2 each year. **Funds Available:** The stipend is $1,000. **Duration:** 1 year.
Eligibility Requirements: This program is open to minority seniors graduating from high schools in the metropolitan area of Washington, D.C. Applicants must be able to demonstrate an interest in journalism, but they are not required to have been school newspaper reporters or editors. They may be photographers, graphic artists, computer experts, delivery workers with an interest in circulation, or business and advertising staff members. Along with their application, they must submit a transcript of grades (with a GPA of 3.0 or higher), SAT/ACT scores, 2 letters of recommendation, a list of journalism or business experience, information on extracurricular activities, up to 5 samples of work with bylines (for journalism applicants), and a 500-word essay on why they want to prepare for a career in journalism or communication business. **Deadline for Receipt:** January of each year. **Additional Information:** The recipients of these scholarships are entered into competition for the Knight Ridder Minority Scholarship Program of $40,000 over 4 years.

2165 ■ LADIES AUXILIARY TO THE VETERANS OF FOREIGN WARS

c/o National Headquarters
406 West 34th Street
Kansas City, MO 64111
Tel: (816)561-8655
Fax: (816)931-4753
E-mail: info@ladiesauxvfw.com
Web Site: http://www.ladiesauxvfw.com
To recognize and reward high school students who submit outstanding works of art on patriotic themes.
Title of Award: Young American Creative Patriotic Art Scholarships **Area, Field, or Subject:** Art; Patriotism **Level of Education for which Award is Granted:** Undergraduate **Number Awarded:** 3 national winners are selected each year. **Funds Available:** National awards are $10,000 for first prize, $5,000 for second prize, and $2,500 for third prize. Funds must be used for continued art education or for art supplies.
Eligibility Requirements: Any student who is a U.S. citizen in grades 9-12 may enter. Home-schooled students are eligible; foreign exchange students are not. Entrants may submit art on paper or canvas using water color, pencil, pastel, charcoal, tempera, crayon, acrylic, pen-and-ink, or

oil. Digital art may be submitted, but it must be on paper or canvas. Competitions are held in individual Veterans of Foreign Wars (VFW) Auxiliaries, then at department, and finally national levels. Students must be sponsored by an Auxiliary; they must attend school in the same state as the sponsoring Auxiliary. Entries are judged on the originality of concept, presentation, and patriotism expressed; content, how it relates to patriotism, and clarity of ideas; design technique; total impact of work; and uniqueness. **Deadline for Receipt:** March of each year. **Additional Information:** First prize also includes an all-expense paid trip to the annual VFW Auxiliary National Community Service Conference and display of the art on the cover of the National *Ladies Auxiliary VFW Magazine* and on the Auxiliary web site. Second- and third-place winners are featured in the magazine and on the web site. National winners may not compete again.

2166 ■ MAINE COMMUNITY FOUNDATION

Attn: Program Director
245 Main Street
Ellsworth, ME 04605
Tel: (207)667-9735; 877-700-6800
Fax: (207)667-0447
E-mail: info@mainecf.org
Web Site: http://www.mainecf.org/html/scholarships/index.html
To provide financial assistance to Maine residents who are interested in participating in an educational program outside of the traditional school environment.
Title of Award: Daniel Cardillo Charitable Fund **Area, Field, or Subject:** Art; Athletics; General studies/Field of study not specified **Level of Education for which Award is Granted:** Undergraduate **Number Awarded:** 1 or more each year. **Funds Available:** A stipend is paid (amount not specified). **Duration:** Recipients must use the funds within 12 months of the grant or forfeit the award.
Eligibility Requirements: This program is open to young residents of Maine who are interested in pursuing their artistic, academic, athletic, and vocational or "life's passion" outside of the traditional school environment (e.g., experiential education, tuition for summer programs or studies, special athletic instruction). Applicants must 1) have a demonstrated compassion for others (through school and community involvement); 2) clearly demonstrate a commitment to their "passion," (through participation in lessons, performances, competitions, or volunteerism) and a clear vision of their goals; and 3) be able to demonstrate financial need. Along with their application, they must submit an essay (up to 500 words) telling about themselves, their "passion," where they think it might take them, and how they feel their life exemplifies the qualities, characteristics, and values demonstrated by Dan Cardillo's life. **Deadline for Receipt:** April of each year. **Additional Information:** This program was established in 1999.

2167 ■ MINNESOTA HIGHER EDUCATION SERVICES OFFICE

1450 Energy Park Drive, Suite 350
St. Paul, MN 55108-5227
Tel: (651)642-0567
Free: 800-657-3866
Fax: (651)642-0675
E-mail: info@heso.state.mn.us
Web Site: http://www.mheso.state.mn.us
To provide financial assistance for college to outstanding high school seniors or graduates in Minnesota.
Title of Award: Minnesota Academic Excellence Scholarship **Area, Field, or Subject:** Art; Creative writing; English language and literature; Linguistics; Mathematics and mathematical sciences; Science; Social sciences **Level of Education for which Award is Granted:** Undergraduate **Number Awarded:** Varies each year. **Funds Available:** Scholarships at public institutions cover the cost of full-time attendance; scholarships at private institutions cover an amount equal to the lesser of the actual tuition and fees charged by the institution or the tuition and fees in comparable public institutions. **Duration:** 1 year; may be renewed up to 3 additional years.
Eligibility Requirements: This program is open to Minnesota residents who have demonstrated outstanding ability, achievement, and potential in English, creative writing, fine arts, foreign language, mathematics, science, or social science. Applicants must have been admitted as full-time students at a branch of the University of Minnesota, a Minnesota state

university, or a private, baccalaureate degree-granting college or university in Minnesota. **Additional Information:** This program was established by the Minnesota Legislature in 1991. Funds for this program come from the sale of special collegiate license plates.

2168 ■ NEW YORK STATE ARCHIVES
Attn: Coordinator of Educational Programs
Cultural Education Center, Suite 9B52
Albany, NY 12230
Tel: (518)474-6926
E-mail: jdaniels@mail.nysed.gov
Web Site: http://www.archives.nysed.gov/a/grantsawards/
ga_student_sraguidelines.shtml
To recognize and reward outstanding historical research conducted by students in grades 4 through 12 in New York State.
Title of Award: New York State Archives Student Research Award **Area, Field, or Subject:** Creative writing; History, American; Playwriting; Writing **Level of Education for which Award is Granted:** Undergraduate **Number Awarded:** 3 each year: 1 in each grade level category. **Funds Available:** The award in each category consists of a certificate and a cash prize. **Duration:** The competition is held annually.
Eligibility Requirements: This is a statewide competition open to students in New York in 3 categories: grades 4-5, grades 6-8, and grades 9-12. Individual students and groups of students (including entire classes) may be nominated. All nominations for the award must be made by a teacher or administrator in the school attended by the entrants. Research projects prepared for other competitions (e.g., History Day) are eligible if they meet other relevant criteria, especially the use of historical records. An annotated bibliography is required for all entries. A substantial portion of the research must be based on historical records from archives, museums, historical societies, libraries, local governments, community organizations, businesses, families, and/or individuals. The product of the student research may be any of the following: research paper; exhibit; audiovisual production; performance; proposal for designation of historic marker, property, or district; or web sites, PowerPoint presentations, and other computer-based entries. Oral history interviews are not eligible for this award program. **Deadline for Receipt:** May of each year. **Additional Information:** This program began in 1990.

2169 ■ NEW YORK STATE LEGION PRESS ASSOCIATION
c/o Scholarship Chairman
American Legion (NYSLPA)
P.O. Box 650
East Aurora, NY 14052
To provide financial assistance to the children of members of the American Legion or American Legion Auxiliary in New York who are interested in careers in communications.
Title of Award: New York State Legion Press Association Scholarship **Area, Field, or Subject:** Communications; Graphic art and design; Journalism; Public relations **Level of Education for which Award is Granted:** Four Year College **Number Awarded:** 1 each year. **Funds Available:** The stipend is $1,000. **Duration:** 1 year.
Eligibility Requirements: This program is open to New York residents who are the children of members of the American Legion or American Legion Auxiliary, or members of the Sons of the American Legion, or junior members of the American Legion Auxiliary, or graduates of the New York Boys State or Girls State. Applicants must be entering or attending an accredited 4-year college or university, working on a degree in communications (including public relations, journalism, reprographics, newspaper design or management, or other related fields acceptable to the scholarship committee). Along with their application, they must submit a 500-word essay on why they chose the field of communications as a future vocation. Financial need and class standing are not considered. **Deadline for Receipt:** May of each year.

2170 ■ OREGON STUDENT ASSISTANCE COMMISSION
Attn: Grants and Scholarships Division
1500 Valley River Drive, Suite 100
Eugene, OR 97401-2146
Tel: (541)687-7395
Free: 800-452-8807
Fax: (541)687-7419
E-mail: awardinfo@mercury.osac.state.or.us

Web Site: http://www.osac.state.or.us
To provide financial assistance to students in Oregon interested in preparing for a career in a fashion-related field.
Title of Award: Fashion Group International of Portland Scholarship **Area, Field, or Subject:** Fashion design **Level of Education for which Award is Granted:** Undergraduate **Number Awarded:** Varies each year; recently, 5 of these scholarships were awarded. **Funds Available:** The stipend is at least $1,500. **Duration:** 1 year.
Eligibility Requirements: This program is open to residents of Oregon preparing for a career in a fashion-related field. Applicants must be enrolled at a college or university in California, Idaho, Oregon, or Washington as a sophomore or higher with a cumulative GPA of 3.0 or higher. Semifinalists are interviewed by the sponsor. **Deadline for Receipt:** February of each year. **Additional Information:** This program is sponsored by Fashion Group International of Portland.

2171 ■ POETRY MAGAZINE
Attn: Poetry Foundation
1030 North Clark Street
Chicago, IL 60610-5412
Tel: (312)787-7070
Fax: (312)787-6650
E-mail: mail@poetryfoundation.org
Web Site: http://www.poetryfoundation.org/foundation/
prizes_fellowship.html
To provide financial assistance to undergraduate and graduate students who are studying poetry.
Title of Award: Ruth Lilly Poetry Fellowships **Area, Field, or Subject:** Creative writing; English language and literature; Poetry **Level of Education for which Award is Granted:** Graduate, Undergraduate **Number Awarded:** 2 each year. **Funds Available:** The stipend is $15,000 per year. **Duration:** 1 year.
Eligibility Requirements: This program is open to undergraduate and graduate students in creative writing or English who have not yet received a master's or doctoral degree. Program directors and department chairs at colleges and universities in the United States are invited to nominate 1 student-poet from their program. Candidates must be younger than 31 years of age and may not have published a book of poems. Nominations must be accompanied by samples of the candidate's poetry. **Deadline for Receipt:** April of each year. **Additional Information:** This program began in 1989.

2172 ■ PRINCESS GRACE AWARDS
Attn: Executive Director
150 East 58th Street, 25th Floor
New York, NY 10155
Tel: (212)317-1470
Fax: (212)317-1473
E-mail: pgfusa@pgfusa.com
Web Site: http://www.pgfusa.com/awards/film/index.html
To provide funding to students in a film program who are working on their undergraduate or graduate thesis project.
Title of Award: Film Scholarships **Area, Field, or Subject:** Filmmaking **Level of Education for which Award is Granted:** Four Year College, Graduate **Number Awarded:** Varies each year. Recently, 8 of the grants were awarded: 4 to undergraduates and 4 to graduate students. **Funds Available:** Stipends range from $5,000 to $25,000. **Duration:** Up to 1 year.
Eligibility Requirements: Each year, the foundation invites accredited film programs to nominate students who are working on their senior thesis or graduate thesis project. For a list of schools invited to participate in this program, write to the sponsor. Applicants must be nominated by the dean/chair of the film department; individuals may not submit an application independently. Nominees should be younger than 30 years of age and in their second to last year of study. They must have already completed 1 film. Nominees are invited to submit an application, an autobiography, an essay, a portfolio, and references. **Deadline for Receipt:** May of each year. **Additional Information:** This program includes the Cary Grant Film Award and the John H. Johnson Film Award.

2173 ■ PRINCESS GRACE AWARDS
Attn: Executive Director
150 East 58th Street, 25th Floor
New York, NY 10155

Tel: (212)317-1470
Fax: (212)317-1473
E-mail: pgfusa@pgfusa.com
Web Site: http://www.pgfusa.com/awards/theater/index.html
To provide financial support to students and professionals interested in acting, directing, and scenic, lighting, sound, and costume design.
Title of Award: Theater Awards **Area, Field, or Subject:** Fashion design; Lighting science; Performing arts **Level of Education for which Award is Granted:** Four Year College, Master's, Professional **Number Awarded:** Varies each year. Recently, 6 of these grants were awarded: 2 as scholarships, 2 as apprenticeships, and 2 as fellowships. **Funds Available:** Grants range from $5,000 to $25,000. Companies receiving apprenticeships and fellowships are entitled to additional support equal to 15-20% of the award to be used for general operating expenses. **Duration:** Up to 1 year.
Eligibility Requirements: Nominations for these grants are invited from the artistic directors of theater companies and the deans and department chairs of professional schools of theater. Nominees may be actors, directors, or designers (costume, scenic, sound, and lighting). Grants are available as 1) scholarships for tuition for the last year of professional training at a nonprofit school in the United States; 2) apprenticeships for salary assistance for individual artists who are "learning the trade" under the supervision of a skilled staff person or mentor; and 3) fellowships for salary assistance for individual artists who are "advanced" members of a company and are ready to assume significant production responsibilities on 1 or more mainstage production(s). Professional companies must employ professional artistic and management staff, have been in continuous operation as a professional company for at least 3 years, provide a total of 20 weeks of research and performance for the current and previous 3 years, and have demonstrated the ability to raise public and other private funds. Artists must have been with the company for less than 5 years. All nominees must be U.S. citizens or permanent residents. Individuals may not submit an application independently. **Deadline for Receipt:** March of each year. **Additional Information:** This program includes the following named awards: the Robert and Gloria Hausman Theater Award, the Faberge Theater Award, the Gant Gaither Theater Award, the George C. Wolfe Theater Award, the Pierre Cardin Theater Award, and the Grace Le Vine Theater Award.

2174 ■ RHODE ISLAND FOUNDATION

Attn: Scholarship Coordinator
One Union Station
Providence, RI 02903
Tel: (401)274-4564
Fax: (401)331-8085
E-mail: libbym@rifoundation.org
Web Site: http://www.rifoundation.org
To provide financial assistance to residents of Rhode Island who are enrolled in college to prepare for a career in advertising.
Title of Award: J.D. Edsal Advertising Scholarship **Area, Field, or Subject:** Advertising; Broadcasting; Filmmaking; Graphic art and design; Marketing and distribution; Public relations; Radio and television **Level of Education for which Award is Granted:** Undergraduate **Number Awarded:** 2 each year. **Funds Available:** The stipend is $1,500. **Duration:** 1 year.
Eligibility Requirements: This program is open to residents of Rhode Island who are enrolled full time as undergraduates at the sophomore level or above. Applicants must be preparing for a career in advertising and majoring in a related field (e.g., broadcast production, graphic design, interactive film, marketing, public relations, television, or video). Along with their application, they must submit an essay (up to 300 words) on the impact they would like to have on the advertising industry. Financial need is also considered in the selection process. **Deadline for Receipt:** April of each year.

2175 ■ RHODE ISLAND FOUNDATION

Attn: Scholarship Coordinator
One Union Station
Providence, RI 02903
Tel: (401)274-4564
Fax: (401)331-8085
E-mail: libbym@rifoundation.org
Web Site: http://www.rifoundation.org

To provide financial assistance to college students studying a field related to jewelry.
Title of Award: MJSA Education Foundation Jewelry Scholarship **Area, Field, or Subject:** Crafts **Level of Education for which Award is Granted:** Undergraduate **Number Awarded:** Varies each year; recently, 5 of these scholarships were awarded. **Funds Available:** Stipends range from $500 to $2,000 per year. **Duration:** 1 year; may be renewed for up to 3 additional years if the recipient maintains good academic standing.
Eligibility Requirements: This program is open to students in colleges, universities, and postsecondary nonprofit technical schools in the United States. Applicants must be studying tool making, design, metals fabrication, or other field related to jewelry. Along with their application, they must submit an essay (up to 300 words), in which they describe their program of study, how far along they are towards completion, their reason for choosing the program, and their professional goal. Selection is based on course of study, career objectives, samples of work (if appropriate), jewelry industry experience, academic achievement, recommendations, and financial need. **Deadline for Receipt:** May of each year. **Additional Information:** The MJSA Education Foundation is a nonprofit educational branch of the Manufacturing Jewelers and Suppliers of America, Inc. Its scholarship fund consists of 6 endowment funds that are managed by the Rhode Island Foundation, but a connection to Rhode Island is not required for eligibility for these scholarships.

2176 ■ RHODE ISLAND FOUNDATION

Attn: Scholarship Coordinator
One Union Station
Providence, RI 02903
Tel: (401)274-4564
Fax: (401)331-8085
E-mail: libbym@rifoundation.org
Web Site: http://www.rifoundation.org
To provide financial assistance to Rhode Island students of color interested in preparing for a career in communications.
Title of Award: RDW Group, Inc. Minority Scholarship for Communications **Area, Field, or Subject:** Advertising; Art; Communications; Filmmaking; Graphic art and design **Level of Education for which Award is Granted:** Graduate, Undergraduate **Number Awarded:** 1 each year. **Funds Available:** The stipend is $2,000. **Duration:** 1 year; nonrenewable.
Eligibility Requirements: This program is open to minority undergraduate and graduate students who are Rhode Island residents. Applicants must intend to major in communications (including computer graphics, art, cinematography, or other fields that would prepare them for a career in advertising). They must be able to demonstrate financial need and a commitment to a career in communications. Along with their application, they must submit an essay (up to 300 words) on the impact they would like to have on the communications field. **Deadline for Receipt:** April of each year. **Additional Information:** This program is sponsored by the RDW Group, Inc.

2177 ■ SERVICE EMPLOYEES INTERNATIONAL UNION

Attn: Education Department
1313 L Street, N.W.
Washington, DC 20005
Tel: (202)898-3326
Free: 800-448-SEIU
Fax: (202)898-3348
Web Site: http://www.seiu.org/mbe/scholarships/moefoner.cfm
To provide financial assistance to members and children of members of the Service Employees International Union (SEIU) who are interested in studying the visual or performing arts in college.
Title of Award: Moe Foner Scholarship Program for Visual and Performing Arts **Area, Field, or Subject:** Art; Performing arts **Level of Education for which Award is Granted:** Undergraduate **Number Awarded:** 1 each year. **Funds Available:** The stipend is $5,000. **Duration:** 1 year; nonrenewable.
Eligibility Requirements: This program is open to members of an SEIU local or affiliated union and their children. Applicants must be working on or planning to work on a degree or training program in the visual or performing arts at a 2-year or 4-year college or university, community college, technical or trade school, or an alternate course of study or training in an arts-related field. Along with their application, they must submit a

200-word essay describing what the labor movement has meant to them and their family; a 200-word essay describing their educational and career goals in the visual or performing arts (including how they plan to use this education to improve the lives of working families and work for economic and social justice); a high school transcript; and either 1) an essay of 500 words or less identifying a workplace issue and how they would use visual and performing arts to reflect the stories and struggles of working people, or 2) 6 copies of their creative work, showing how they would interpret the theme of working people and their struggles through the visual or performing arts. Selection is based on originality, clarity, and commitment to social and economic justice in the workplace. **Deadline for Receipt:** February of each year. **Additional Information:** This program is administered by Scholarship Program Administrators, Inc., 1201 Eighth Avenue South, P.O. Box 23737, Nashville, TN 27202-3737, (615) 320-3149, Fax: (615) 320-3151, E-mail: info@spaprog.com.

2178 ■ SOUTH CAROLINA COMMISSION ON HIGHER EDUCATION

Attn: Director of Student Services
1333 Main Street, Suite 200
Columbia, SC 29201
Tel: (803)737-2260; 877-349-7183
Fax: (803)737-2297
E-mail: dbrown@che.sc.gov
Web Site: http://www.che.sc.gov
To provide scholarship/loans to teachers in South Carolina who wish to improve their content knowledge and degree programs.
Title of Award: South Carolina Teaching Scholarship Grants Program **Area, Field, or Subject:** Art; Dance; Economics; Education; Education, Early childhood; Education, Elementary; Education, Music; Education, Secondary; Education, Special; Geography; History; Linguistics; Mathematics and mathematical sciences; Music; Political science; Science **Level of Education for which Award is Granted:** Graduate, Professional, Undergraduate **Number Awarded:** Varies each year. **Funds Available:** The stipend is $1,000 per fiscal year. This is a scholarship/loan program. Recipients must sign a commitment to teach in South Carolina public schools for at least 1 year following completion of the scholarship grant year and agree to refund the scholarship amount if the 1-year teaching commitment is not honored. **Duration:** 1 year; may be renewed if recipients maintain a GPA of 3.0 or higher. They may receive up to 3 grants in a 5-year period.
Eligibility Requirements: This program is open to residents of South Carolina who have a professional teaching certificate and are under contract as a teacher in a public school in the state. Applicants must be 1) accepted as a degree-seeking graduate student in the teaching field at the master's level and enrolled at an eligible institution in the state; or 2) enrolled for graduate or undergraduate courses in their current teaching field or in a teaching field in which they wish to add on certification. Proposed fields of study must relate to core content areas of English, reading or language arts, mathematics, science, foreign languages, civics and government, economics, arts (advanced fine arts, art, dance, drama, music, and speech), history, or geography; early childhood, elementary education, middle level education, secondary education, and special education also qualify. Priority is given to classroom teachers (not administrators, counselors, media specialists, or other support personnel) whose teaching specialties are critical need subject areas. Continuing graduate students must have a GPA of 3.0 or higher. U.S. citizenship or permanent resident status is required. **Deadline for Receipt:** December of each year for second summer session and fall semester; June of each year for spring semester and first summer session. **Additional Information:** This program was established in 2001.

2179 ■ SOUTH CAROLINA STATE DEPARTMENT OF EDUCATION

1429 Senate Street, Room 1010A
Columbia, SC 29201
Tel: (803)734-8485
E-mail: sspade@sde.state.sc.us
Web Site: http://www.myscschools.com/offices/ombudsman/arscholarship
To recognize and reward high school seniors in South Carolina who participate in a competition in art, creative writing, drama, or music.
Title of Award: Archibald Rutledge Scholarship Program **Area, Field, or Subject:** Art; Creative writing; Graphic art and design; Music composition; Painting; Playwriting; Poetry; Visual arts; Writing **Level of Education for which Award is Granted:** Undergraduate **Number Awarded:** 4 each

year: 1 in each of the 4 categories. **Funds Available:** The award consists of a $4,000 scholarship, to be used for tuition, room, board, and instructional resource expenses. **Duration:** 1 year.
Eligibility Requirements: This program is open to U.S. citizens who have attended South Carolina public high schools for at least 2 years, are currently seniors, and are planning to attend a South Carolina college or university. Applicants compete by submitting samples of their work in 1 of 4 areas: 1) visual arts, limited to 2-dimensional work such as drawing and painting media, printmaking, and collage; no 3-dimensional works, photographs, or computer-generated images are accepted; 2) creative writing, as a sonnet, lyric, or narrative poem, up to 1 page; 3) drama, a 1-act play with a performing time of 20 to 45 minutes; or 4) music, a composition of 3 to 5 minutes for solo or small ensemble, vocal or instrumental, in any appropriate style. In addition to the work, they must submit a process folio that contains documentation of the planning and development of the project and a 1-page reflection statement addressing the intent of the work and comparing the final product with the original concept. A panel of professionals in the field selects up to 10 finalists, based on originality, creativity, and the correlation and implications of the process folio for the final composition. Finalists must attend the scholarship competition, where they present a portfolio of a number of selected works as specified by the judges. **Deadline for Receipt:** February of each year.

2180 ■ SWEDISH WOMEN'S EDUCATION ASSOCIATION INTERNATIONAL-SOUTH FLORIDA CHAPTER

c/o Yerti Nelson, Scholarship Committee
3759 Mykonos Court
Boca Raton, FL 33486
Tel: (561)997-2050
Fax: (561)997-8010
E-mail: florida@swea.org
Web Site: http://www.chapters-swea.org/florida
To provide financial assistance to Florida residents interested in studying in Sweden or an area related to Swedish studies.
Title of Award: South Florida SWEA Scholarship **Area, Field, or Subject:** Art; Art industries and trade; Crafts; Design; Environmental conservation; Environmental science; Foreign languages; General studies/Field of study not specified; Literature; Music; Swedish studies **Level of Education for which Award is Granted:** Graduate, Professional, Undergraduate **Number Awarded:** 1 each year. **Funds Available:** The stipend is $3,000.
Eligibility Requirements: This program is open to all residents of Florida interested in participating in an exchange program in Sweden. Applicants may also propose to study in the United States, if the studies specifically emphasize Sweden and Swedish aspects, including 1) Swedish language; 2) Swedish culture or traditions; 3) environmental science; 4) a health care program promoting better health for women and children; or 5) handicraft, art, glass art, music, literature, or design. Study proposals must be well-defined in time and content. Along with their application, they must submit a transcript from college, university, or vocational school; curriculum vitae; project proposal, describing the planned studies, length of studies, and goals; financial statement; and letter of recommendation from an instructor. **Deadline for Receipt:** January of each year. **Additional Information:** Within 3 months after the end of studies or the project, the recipient must report to the scholarship committee or, if possible, accept an invitation to an organization meeting to share the experience.

2181 ■ VERMONT STUDENT ASSISTANCE CORPORATION

Champlain Mill
Attn: Scholarship Programs
P.O. Box 2000
Winooski, VT 05404-2601
Tel: (802)654-3798; 888-253-4819
Fax: (802)654-3765
E-mail: info@vsac.org
Web Site: http://www.vsac.org
To provide financial assistance to residents of Vermont who are interested in working on an undergraduate or graduate degree in a field related to design.
Title of Award: Alfred T. Granger Student Art Fund **Area, Field, or Subject:** Architecture; Art; Engineering, Architectural; Graphic art and design; Interior design; Lighting science **Level of Education for which

Award is Granted: Graduate, Undergraduate **Number Awarded:** 2 graduate scholarships and 4 undergraduate scholarships are awarded each year. **Funds Available:** The stipend is $5,000 per year for graduate students or $2,500 per year for undergraduates. **Duration:** 1 year; recipients may reapply.

Eligibility Requirements: This program is open to residents of Vermont who are graduating high school seniors, high school graduates, or GED recipients. Applicants must be interested in attending an accredited postsecondary institution to work on a degree in architecture, interior design, fine arts, architectural engineering, mechanical drawing, or lighting design. Selection is based on academic achievement, a portfolio, letters of recommendation, required essays, and financial need. **Deadline**

for Receipt: May of each year.

2182 ■ VERMONT STUDENT ASSISTANCE CORPORATION

Champlain Mill
Attn: Scholarship Programs
P.O. Box 2000
Winooski, VT 05404-2601
Tel: (802)654-3798; 888-253-4819
Fax: (802)654-3765
E-mail: info@vsac.org
Web Site: http://www.vsac.org
To provide financial assistance to residents of Vermont who are interested in majoring in arts or crafts in college.
Title of Award: Vermont Hand Crafters Artisanship Scholarships **Area, Field, or Subject:** Art industries and trade; Crafts; Visual arts **Level of Education for which Award is Granted:** Undergraduate **Number Awarded:** Varies each year; recently, 5 of these scholarships were awarded. **Funds Available:** Stipends range from $500 to $1,000. **Duration:** 1 year.

Eligibility Requirements: This scholarship is available to high school seniors, high school graduates, and currently-enrolled college students in Vermont who are enrolled or planning to enroll at least half time in a postsecondary degree program in the visual arts (particularly arts and crafts). Applicants must have been residents of Vermont for at least 2 years. Selection is based on financial need, academic achievement, a portfolio, a letter of recommendation, required essays, and a personal interview (if necessary). **Deadline for Receipt:** June of each year.

2183 ■ VESALIUS TRUST FOR VISUAL COMMUNICATIONS IN THE HEALTH SCIENCES

Attn: Wendy Hiller Gee, Student Grants and Scholarships
Krames-West Coast
1100 Grundy Lane
San Bruno, CA 94066
Tel: (650)244-4320
E-mail: wendy.hillergee@krames.com
Web Site: http://www.vesaliustrust.org/scholarships.html
To provide funding to students working on a research project in biocommunications.
Title of Award: Vesalius Trust Student Research Grants **Area, Field, or Subject:** Communications; Illustrators and illustrations; Medicine **Level of Education for which Award is Granted:** Graduate, Undergraduate **Number Awarded:** Varies each year. Recently, 19 of these grants were awarded, including 1 designated as the Alan Cole Scholarship and 5 designated as the Vesalian Scholarships. **Funds Available:** Grant amounts vary each year. **Duration:** 1 year.

Eligibility Requirements: This program is open to undergraduate and graduate students who have completed at least 1 year of a biocommunications program in medical illustrating. Applicants must be interested in conducting a research project under the guidance of a faculty preceptor. Selection is based on the background and education of the applicant (20%); an evaluation by the preceptor of the student's ability to complete the project and its potential contributions (10%); the project concept and subject matter (30%); project design (20%); and production plan (20%). **Deadline for Receipt:** November of each year. **Additional Information:**

The top-ranked applicant receives the Alan Cole Scholarship. Other recipients whose projects show evidence of significant merit are designated Vesalian Scholarships.

2184 ■ VSA ARTS

Attn: VOA Awards
P.O. Box 33699
Washington, DC 20033-3699
Tel: (202)628-2800
Free: 800-933-8721
Fax: (202)737-0725
E-mail: voa@vsarts.org
Web Site: http://www.vsarts.org/x267.xml
To recognize and reward young artists with disabilities.
Title of Award: VSA arts/Volkswagen Art Awards **Area, Field, or Subject:** Art; Graphic art and design; Painting; Photography **Level of Education for which Award is Granted:** Graduate, Undergraduate **Number Awarded:** A total of 15 cash prizes are awarded each year: 1 grand prize, 1 first prize, 1 second prize, and 12 awards of excellence. **Funds Available:** The grand prize is $20,000, first prize is $10,000, second prize is $6,000, and awards of excellence are $2,000. **Duration:** The competition is held annually.

Eligibility Requirements: This program is open to artists between 16 and 25 years of age who have a physical, cognitive, or mental disability. Applicants are invited to submit artwork that they have created in the last 3 years on a theme that changes annually. Recently, the theme was "Shifting Gears," in which artists were invited to reflect on a pivotal moment or event in their life that led them to a greater understanding of themselves in relation to their art and/or their disability. Both representational and abstract art may be submitted. Eligible media include paintings and drawings (oil, watercolor, acrylic, pencil, or charcoal), fine art prints (lithographs, etching, intaglio, or woodcuts), photography, computer generated prints, and 2-dimensional mixed media. Up to 5 slides may be submitted, along with a 400-word essay covering their artistic background and answers to questions on when they started creating artwork, what motivated them to begin, the techniques and media they use, the role their art plays in living with their disability, how their disability affects their artwork, a significant experience during their education where the arts played an important part, and when the arts were most effective in their education. **Deadline for Receipt:** July of each year. **Additional Information:** This program, which began in 2002, is sponsored by Volkswagen of America, Inc.

2185 ■ WESTERN ART ASSOCIATION

Attn: Foundation
13730 Loumont Street
Whittier, CA 90601
To provide financial assistance for art school to female high school seniors whose art demonstrates a "congruence with the art of Grandma Moses."
Title of Award: Grandma Moses GTI Scholarship **Area, Field, or Subject:** Art **Level of Education for which Award is Granted:** Undergraduate **Number Awarded:** 1 each year. **Funds Available:** The stipend is $3,000 per year. **Duration:** 1 year; may be renewed up to 3 additional years.

Eligibility Requirements: This program is open to female graduating high school seniors. Applicants must be planning to study art in a college, university, or specialized school of art. Preference is given to applicants from the western United States. Candidates must submit samples of their artwork; selection is based on the extent to which their work "manifests a congruence with the work of the famed folk artist, Grandma Moses." Financial need is not considered. **Deadline for Receipt:** March of each year. **Additional Information:** Requests for applications should be accompanied by a self-addressed stamped envelope, the student's e-mail address, and the source where they found the scholarship information.

2186 ■ WISCONSIN FOUNDATION FOR INDEPENDENT COLLEGES, INC.

Attn: College-to-Work Program
735 North Water Street, Suite 600
Milwaukee, WI 53202-4100
Tel: (414)273-5980
Fax: (414)273-5995

E-mail: wfic@wficweb.org
Web Site: http://www.wficweb.org/work.html
To provide financial assistance and work experience to minority students majoring in fields related to the fashion industry at member institutions of the Wisconsin Foundation for Independent Colleges (WFIC).

Title of Award: Jockey International College-to-Work Program **Area, Field, or Subject:** Art; Computer and information sciences; Fashion design; Finance; Graphic art and design; Marketing and distribution **Level of Education for which Award is Granted:** Four Year College **Number Awarded:** 1 each year. **Funds Available:** The stipend is $1,500 for the scholarship; the internship is paid hourly. **Duration:** 1 year for the scholarship; 10 weeks for the internship.

Eligibility Requirements: This program is open to minority students who are full-time juniors and seniors at WFIC member colleges or universities. Applicants may be majoring in any liberal arts field, but they must be preparing for or considering a career in art, computer science/MIS, fashion design, fashion merchandising, finance, graphic design, human resources, international business, or marketing. They must be interested in an internship at Jockey International in Kenosha, Wisconsin. Along with their application, they must submit a 1-page essay that includes why they are applying for the internship, why they have selected their major and what interests them about it, why they are attending their chosen college or university, and their future career objectives. **Deadline for Receipt:** February of each year. **Additional Information:** The WFIC member schools are Alverno College, Beloit College, Cardinal Stritch University, Carroll College, Carthage College, Concordia University of Wisconsin, Edgewood College, Lakeland College, Lawrence University, Marian College, Marquette University, Milwaukee Institute of Art & Design, Milwaukee School of Engineering, Mount Mary College, Northland College, Ripon College, St. Norbert College, Silver Lake College, Viterbo University, and Wisconsin Lutheran College. This program is sponsored by Jockey International, Inc.

2187 ■ WISCONSIN FOUNDATION FOR INDEPENDENT COLLEGES, INC.
Attn: College-to-Work Program
735 North Water Street, Suite 600
Milwaukee, WI 53202-4100
Tel: (414)273-5980
Fax: (414)273-5995
E-mail: wfic@wficweb.org
Web Site: http://www.wficweb.org/work.html
To provide financial assistance and work experience to students majoring in fields related to communications at member institutions of the Wisconsin Foundation for Independent Colleges (WFIC).

Title of Award: Manitowoc American Red Cross College-to-Work Program **Area, Field, or Subject:** Communications; English language and literature; General studies/Field of study not specified; Graphic art and design; Public relations **Level of Education for which Award is Granted:** Four Year College **Number Awarded:** 1 each year. **Funds Available:** The stipends are $3,500 for the scholarship and $1,500 for the internship. **Duration:** 1 year for the scholarship; 10 weeks for the internship.

Eligibility Requirements: This program is open to full-time sophomores, juniors, and seniors at private colleges and universities in Wisconsin. Applicants must be interested in an internship at the Manitowoc/Calumet County Chapter of the American Red Cross in Manitowoc. Preference is given to 1) students attending Lakeland College or Silver Lake College; 2) residents of Manitowoc County attending another WFIC member institution; and 3) students majoring in communications, English, graphic design, or public relations. Along with their application, they must submit a 1-page essay that includes why they are applying for the internship, why they have selected their major and what interests them about it, why they are attending their chosen college or university, and their future career objectives. **Deadline for Receipt:** February of each year. **Additional Information:** The other WFIC schools are Alverno College, Beloit College, Cardinal Stritch University, Carroll College, Carthage College, Concordia University of Wisconsin, Edgewood College, Lawrence University, Marian College, Marquette University, Milwaukee Institute of Art & Design, Milwaukee School of Engineering, Mount Mary College, Northland College, Ripon College, St. Norbert College, Viterbo University, and Wisconsin Lutheran College. This program is sponsored by the Manitowoc/Calumet County Chapter of the American Red Cross. The

WFIC's College-to-Work Program includes a number of other financial assistance and work experience programs aimed at eligible students interested in majoring in fields related to communications, journalism, media, and related fields, including the Post-Crescent College-to-Work Program and Reporter College-to-Work Program.

2188 ■ WISCONSIN FOUNDATION FOR INDEPENDENT COLLEGES, INC.
Attn: Program Manager
735 North Water Street, Suite 600
Milwaukee, WI 53202-4100
Tel: (414)273-5980
Fax: (414)273-5995
E-mail: wfic@wficweb.org
Web Site: http://www.wficweb.org/scholar.html
To provide financial assistance to students majoring in selected fields at member institutions of the Wisconsin Foundation for Independent Colleges (WFIC).

Title of Award: Sentry Insurance Foundation Scholarships **Area, Field, or Subject:** Architecture; Business administration; Design; Economics; Information science and technology; Interior design; Mathematics and mathematical sciences **Level of Education for which Award is Granted:** Four Year College **Number Awarded:** 20 each year: 1 at each of the participating schools. **Funds Available:** The stipend is $1,000. **Duration:** 1 year.

Eligibility Requirements: This program is open to student enrolled or planning to enroll at WFIC member colleges and universities. Applicants must have a declared major in 1 of the following fields: business, economics, mathematics, management information systems, industrial design, communication design, or interior architecture and design. They must have a GPA of 3.3 or higher; entering freshmen must rank in the top 25% of their high school class. Financial need is considered in the selection process. **Deadline for Receipt:** Each participating college sets its own deadline. **Additional Information:** The WFIC member schools are Alverno College, Beloit College, Cardinal Stritch University, Carroll College, Carthage College, Concordia University of Wisconsin, Edgewood College, Lakeland College, Lawrence University, Marian College, Marquette University, Milwaukee Institute of Art & Design, Milwaukee School of Engineering, Mount Mary College, Northland College, Ripon College, St. Norbert College, Silver Lake College, Viterbo University, and Wisconsin Lutheran College. This program is supported by the Sentry Insurance Foundation.

2189 ■ WOMEN IN FILM/DALLAS
Attn: Scholarship Grant Fund
2600 Stemmons Freeway, Suite 117
Dallas, TX 75207
Tel: (214)954-4488
Fax: (214)954-0004
E-mail: scholarships@wifdallas.org
Web Site: http://www.wifdallas.org/scholarships.asp
To provide financial assistance to women residents of Texas who are studying or planning to study film and video in college.

Title of Award: Women in Film/Dallas College/University Student Tuition Scholarship **Area, Field, or Subject:** Filmmaking **Level of Education for which Award is Granted:** Undergraduate **Number Awarded:** 1 each year. **Funds Available:** The stipend is $1,500. **Duration:** 1 year.

Eligibility Requirements: This program is open to women who are 1) residents of Texas majoring or with a primary field of study in film or video at an accredited college or university in the north Texas area; or 2) graduating high school seniors who are planning to enroll at an accredited college or university in Texas with a major or primary field of study in film and video. Applicants must have consistently maintained a GPA of 3.0 or higher. Along with their application, they must submit a 3-page essay on what they plan to do with their film or video degree, 2 letters of recommendation, a letter from the college or university verifying their enrollment, and an official college or high school transcript. Financial need is not considered in the selection process. **Deadline for Receipt:** August of each year.

2190 ■ WOMEN'S JEWELRY ASSOCIATION
Attn: Scholarship Committee
373 B Route 46 West, Building E, Suite 215
Fairfield, NJ 07004

Tel: (973)575-7190
Fax: (973)575-1445
E-mail: info@womensjewelry.org
Web Site: http://www.womensjewelry.org/scholarships.html
To provide financial assistance for college to women who are interested in careers in jewelry.
Title of Award: Women's Jewelry Association Scholarship **Area, Field, or Subject:** Business administration; Crafts; Finance; Marketing and distribution; Metallurgy **Level of Education for which Award is Granted:** Undergraduate **Number Awarded:** Varies each year. Recently, 12 of these scholarships were awarded: 1 at $5,000, 2 at $3,000, 1 at $2,500, 1 at $1,500 and 7 at $1,000. **Funds Available:** Stipends range from $500 to $5,000 per year. **Duration:** 1 year.
Eligibility Requirements: Women who are enrolled in a jewelry-related curriculum at an institution of higher learning located anywhere in the United States are eligible to apply. Eligible fields of study range from design to gemological analysis and include metalsmithing, finance, business, and marketing. Applicants must submit 2 letters of recommendation, a short essay explaining why they wish to prepare for a career in jewelry/toolmaking and their aspirations for the future, 3 slides showing examples of their work, and a list of 3 courses related to jewelry that have been most important to them. Financial need is considered in the selection process. **Deadline for Receipt:** April of each year. **Additional Information:** This program includes the June Herman Scholarship of $5,000, awarded for the first time in 2001.

2191 ■ WORLDSTUDIO FOUNDATION

200 Varick Street, Suite 507
New York, NY 10014
Tel: (212)366-1317
Fax: (212)807-0024
E-mail: scholarshipcoordinator@worldstudio.org
Web Site: http://www.worldstudio.org/schol/index.html
To provide financial support for college or graduate school to art students of Native American heritage.
Title of Award: Worldstudio Foundation Indigenous Peoples Award **Area, Field, or Subject:** Art; Art industries and trade; Crafts; Native American studies **Level of Education for which Award is Granted:** Graduate, Undergraduate **Number Awarded:** 1 or more each year. **Funds Available:** The stipend ranges from $1,000 to $2,000. **Duration:** 1 academic year. Recipients may reapply.
Eligibility Requirements: This program is open to art students affiliated with Native American, Alaska Native/Inuit, or other indigenous tribes of the Americas. Applicants must be interested in maintaining traditional art, designs, or crafts. They must be undergraduate or graduate students at an accredited college or university in the United States with a GPA of 2.0 or higher. Selection is based on the quality of submitted work, a written statement of purpose, financial need, and academic record. **Deadline for Receipt:** March of each year.

2192 ■ WORLDSTUDIO FOUNDATION

200 Varick Street, Suite 507
New York, NY 10014
Tel: (212)366-1317
Fax: (212)807-0024
E-mail: scholarshipcoordinator@worldstudio.org
Web Site: http://www.worldstudio.org/schol/index.html
To provide financial assistance to undergraduate and graduate students, especially minorities, who wish to study fine or commercial arts, design, or architecture.
Title of Award: Worldstudio Foundation Scholarships **Area, Field, or Subject:** Advertising; Architecture; Art; Art industries and trade; Crafts; Design; Fashion design; Filmmaking; Graphic art and design; Interior design; Landscape architecture and design; Photography; Urban affairs/design/planning **Level of Education for which Award is Granted:** Graduate, Undergraduate **Number Awarded:** Varies each year; recently, 24 scholarships and 7 honorable mentions were awarded. **Funds Available:** Basic scholarships range from $1,000 to $2,000, but awards between $3,000 and $5,000 are also presented at the discretion of the jury. Honorable mentions are $100. Funds are paid directly to the recipient's school. **Duration:** 1 academic year. Recipients may reapply.
Eligibility Requirements: This program is open to undergraduate and graduate students who are currently enrolled or planning to enroll at an

accredited college or university and major in 1 of the following areas: advertising (art direction only), architecture, crafts, environmental graphics, fashion design, film/video (direction or cinematography only), film/theater design (including set, lighting, and costume design), fine arts, furniture design, graphic design, industrial/product design, interior design, landscape architecture, new media, photography, surface/textile design, or urban planning. Although not required, minority status is a significant factor in the selection process. International students may apply if they are enrolled at a U.S. college or university. Applicants must have a GPA of 2.0 or higher. Along with their application, they must submit a 600-word statement of purpose that includes a brief autobiography, an explanation of how their experiences have influenced their creative work and/or their career plans, and how they see themselves contributing to the community at large in the future. Selection is based on that statement, the quality of submitted work, financial need, minority status, and academic record. **Deadline for Receipt:** March of each year. **Additional Information:** The foundation encourages the scholarship recipients to focus on ways that their work can address issues of social and environmental responsibility. This program includes the following named awards: the Sherry and Gary Baker Award, the Bobolink Foundation Award, the Bombay Sapphire Awards, the Richard and Jean Coyne Family Foundation Awards, the David A. Dechman Foundation Awards, the Philip and Edina Jennison Award, the Kraus Family Foundation Awards, the Dena McKelvey Award, the New York Design Center Award, the Rudin Foundation Awards, the Starr Foundation Awards, and the John F. Wright III Award.

2193 ■ WORLDSTUDIO FOUNDATION

200 Varick Street, Suite 507
New York, NY 10014
Tel: (212)366-1317
Fax: (212)807-0024
E-mail: scholarshipcoordinator@worldstudio.org
Web Site: http://www.worldstudio.org/schol/index.html
To provide financial assistance to members of disadvantaged and ethnic minority groups who wish to study illustration, animation, or cartooning in college.
Title of Award: Worldstudio Foundation Special Animation and Illustration Scholarships **Area, Field, or Subject:** Art, Caricatures and cartoons; Illustrators and illustrations **Level of Education for which Award is Granted:** Undergraduate **Number Awarded:** 25 each year. **Funds Available:** The stipend is $1,500. Funds are paid directly to the recipient's school. **Duration:** 1 academic year. Recipients may reapply.
Eligibility Requirements: This program is open to members of disadvantaged or minority groups who are currently enrolled or planning to enroll in an accredited college or university in the United States. Applicants must be majoring or planning to major in illustration, animation, or cartooning. They must submit their most recent college or high school transcripts, documentation of financial need, a portfolio of their work, and a 600-word statement of purpose that includes a brief autobiography and how they plan to contribute to the community. International students are also eligible. Selection is based on the quality of submitted work, the strength of the written statement of purpose, financial need, and academic record. **Deadline for Receipt:** March of each year. **Additional Information:** This program was established in 2002 with funding from the W.K. Kellogg Foundation.

Language and Literature

2194 ■ ACADEMY OF APPLIED SCIENCE

Attn: JSHS National Office
24 Warren Street
Concord, NH 03301
Tel: (603)228-4520
Fax: (603)228-4730
E-mail: phampton@jshs.org
Web Site: http://www.jshs.org
To recognize and reward outstanding participants in the Army, Navy, and Air Force Junior Science and Humanities Symposia (JSHS).
Title of Award: JSHS Scholarships **Area, Field, or Subject:** Engineering; Mathematics and mathematical sciences; Science; Writing **Level of Education for which Award is Granted:** Undergraduate **Number Awarded:** Scholarships are awarded to 3 regional winners in each of the

48 regional symposia, to 6 first-place finalists in the national symposium, to 6 second-place national finalists, and to 6 third-place national finalists. Teacher awards are presented to 48 teachers, 1 in each of the regions. **Funds Available:** At each regional symposium, 5 finalists receive all-expense paid trips to the national symposium, the first and second place winners are invited to present their research investigation at the national symposium, and scholarships of $1,500, $1,000, and $500, are awarded. In the national competition, first-place finalists receive $16,000 scholarships, second-place finalists receive $6,000 scholarships, and third-place finalists receive $2,000 scholarships (all national scholarships are in addition to the regional scholarships). Top finalists are also awarded an all-expense paid trip to the International Youth Science Forum, held in London. The outstanding teacher in each region receives a $500 award. **Duration:** This competition is held annually. National scholarships are paid over a period of 4 years provided the recipients enroll full time and maintain a GPA of at least 3.0. **Eligibility Requirements:** This program is open to students in grades 9-12, enrolled in public, private, or home schools, who have completed an original research investigation in the sciences, engineering, or mathematics. Investigations reporting on experimental, field, observational, or applied research are eligible. Students present their findings at a regional symposium, held on a university campus in their area. At each regional symposium, selected paper presenters are chosen to receive scholarships. From each of the 48 regional symposia, 5 students are selected to attend the national JSHS, where 1 of them presents his or her research paper in competition for further awards. **Additional Information:** The JSHS program was established by the Army in 1958 and since 1963 has been administered by the Academy of Applied Science. Since 1995, funding has also been provided by the Office of Naval Research and the Air Force Office of Scientific Research.

2195 ■ AIR FORCE SERVICES AGENCY

Attn: HQ AFSVA/SVICO
10100 Reunion Place, Suite 501
San Antonio, TX 78216-4138
Tel: (210)652-6312
Free: 800-443-4834
Fax: (210)652-7041
E-mail: svi@agency.afsv.af.mil
Web Site: http://www-p.afsv.af.mil/Clubs/Scholarship.htm
To recognize and reward, with college scholarships, Air Force Club members and their families who submit outstanding essays.
Title of Award: Air Force Services Club Membership Scholarship Program **Area, Field, or Subject:** General studies/Field of study not specified; Writing **Level of Education for which Award is Granted:** Graduate, Undergraduate **Number Awarded:** 6 each year. **Funds Available:** Awards are scholarships of $6,000 for first place, $5,500 for second place, $4,500 for third place, $3,500 for fourth place, $3,000 for fifth place, and $2,500 for sixth place. **Duration:** The competition is held annually.
Eligibility Requirements: This program is open to Air Force Club members and their spouses, children, and stepchildren who have been accepted by or are enrolled at an accredited college or university. Grandchildren are eligible if they are a dependent of the club member. Applicants may be undergraduate or graduate students enrolled full or part time. They must submit an essay of up to 500 words on a topic that changes annually; a recent topic was "My Hero, and Why." Applicants must also include a 1-page summary of their long-term career and life goals and previous accomplishments, including civic, athletic, and academic awards. **Deadline for Receipt:** Entries must be submitted to the member's base services commander or division chief by July of each year. **Additional Information:** This competition, first held in 1997, is sponsored by Chase Bank and MasterCard.

2196 ■ AKADEMOS, INC.

Attn: TextbookX.com
25 Van Zant Street, Suite 1A-2
Norwalk, CT 06855-1727
Tel: (203)866-0190
Fax: (203)866-0199
Web Site: http://www.textbookx.com/scholarship
To recognize and reward undergraduate and graduate students who submit outstanding essays on a topic that changes annually.
Title of Award: TextbookX.com Scholarship Program **Area, Field, or Subject:** General studies/Field of study not specified; Writing **Level of**

Education for which Award is Granted: Graduate, Undergraduate **Number Awarded:** 3 each semester: 1 grand prize and 2 runners-up. **Funds Available:** The grand prize is $2,000 and runner-up prizes are $250 gift certificates for the sponsor. Prizes are paid directly to the winners. **Duration:** The competition is held annually.
Eligibility Requirements: This competition is open to undergraduate and graduate students enrolled at an accredited college or university in the United States. Applicants must be legal residents of the United States or international students with valid visas. They must submit an essay, from 250 to 750 words in length, on a topic that changes each semester. Recently, the topic was "How, if at all, would American society change if the current legal right to abortion is either severely restricted or eliminated?" Essays must be the original work of the applicant and must reference a book that has influenced the response to the essay. **Deadline for Receipt:** April of each year for spring; October of each year for fall. **Additional Information:** This competition began in 2002.

2197 ■ ALABAMA BANKERS ASSOCIATION

Attn: Scholarship Applications
534 Adams Avenue
Montgomery, AL 36104
Tel: (334)834-1890
Free: 800-239-5521
Fax: (334)834-4443
E-mail: info@alabamabankers.org
Web Site: http://www.alabamabankers.org
To recognize and reward, with college scholarships, high school seniors in Alabama who submit outstanding essays on personal finance.
Title of Award: Alabama Young Bankers Essay Scholarship **Area, Field, or Subject:** Finance; Writing **Level of Education for which Award is Granted:** Undergraduate **Number Awarded:** 1 each year. **Funds Available:** The award is a $1,000 college scholarship. **Duration:** The award is presented annually.
Eligibility Requirements: This program is open to seniors graduating from high schools in Alabama who can demonstrate knowledge of good money management skills. Applicants must submit a 3-page essay on a topic that changes annually but relates to personal finance; a recent topic was, "Three Things Every High School Graduate Should Know About Personal Finance." Selection is based on comprehension (20%), organization (20%), conclusions (20%), creativity (20%), and writing (20%). **Deadline for Receipt:** February of each year.

2198 ■ AMERICAN FEDERATION OF TELEVISION AND RADIO ARTISTS

Attn: AFTRA/Heller Memorial Foundation, Inc.
260 Madison Avenue, Seventh Floor
New York, NY 10016
Tel: (212)532-0800
Fax: (212)532-2242
E-mail: info@aftra.com
Web Site: http://www.aftra.org/benefits/scholarship.htm
To provide financial assistance to undergraduate and graduate students who are members or the dependent children of members of the American Federation of Television and Radio Artists (AFTRA).
Title of Award: AFTRA/Heller Memorial Foundation Scholarships **Area, Field, or Subject:** Communications; General studies/Field of study not specified; Industrial and labor relations; Journalism; Performing arts **Level of Education for which Award is Granted:** Graduate, Undergraduate **Number Awarded:** 12 to 15 each year. **Funds Available:** Stipends up to $2,500 per year are available. **Duration:** 1 year; nonrenewable.
Eligibility Requirements: This program is open to AFTRA members and the dependent children of AFTRA members (or deceased members) in good standing for at least 5 years. Applicants may be interested in working on a bachelor's or advanced degree in any field, including broadcast journalism and labor relations, or professional training in the performing arts. Selection is based on academic achievement and financial need. **Deadline for Receipt:** April of each year.

2199 ■ AMERICAN FIRE SPRINKLER ASSOCIATION

9696 Skillman Street, Suite 300
Dallas, TX 75243-8264
Tel: (214)349-5965
Fax: (214)343-8898

E-mail: afsainfo@firesprinkler.org
Web Site: http://www.afsascholarship.org
To recognize and reward, with college scholarships, high school seniors who write outstanding essays on fire sprinklers.

Title of Award: AFSA Annual Essay Scholarship Contest **Area, Field, or Subject:** General studies/Field of study not specified; Writing **Level of Education for which Award is Granted:** Undergraduate **Number Awarded:** 7 regional winners are selected each year; from among those, 3 are selected as national winners **Funds Available:** Each regional winner receives a $1,000 scholarship. From among those winners, the national first prize is an additional $3,000 scholarship, second prize an additional $2,000 scholarship, and third prize an additional $1,000 scholarship. Funds are paid directly to the recipients' educational institutions. The school of each winning student receives an additional $500 for its general fund. **Duration:** The competition is held annually.

Eligibility Requirements: This competition is open to seniors at high schools in the United States. Home-schooled students are eligible if their course of study is equivalent to that of a senior in high school. Applicants must submit an essay of 700 to 1,000 words on a topic that varies annually but relates to fire sprinklers. Recently, students were invited to write about a successful fire sprinkler activation in their town, area, or state. Entries must be submitted through an online process. Selection is based on 1) content; 2) accuracy; 3) creativity and originality; and 4) spelling, grammar, and punctuation. Competitions are first held at the regional level. **Deadline for Receipt:** January of each year. **Additional Information:** This competition was first held in 1996.

2200 ■ AMERICAN FIRE SPRINKLER ASSOCIATION-CAROLINAS CHAPTER

c/o Tom Strange, Sr., Chair
Sunland Fire Protection, Inc.
P.O. Box 277
Jamestown, NC 27282
Tel: (336)886-7027
Fax: (336)886-7024
E-mail: tom.strange@sunlandfire.com
Web Site: http://www.sprinklernet.com/chapters/carolinas/index.html
To recognize and reward, with college scholarships, high school seniors in North Carolina who write outstanding essays on fire sprinklers.

Title of Award: William C. Klutz Scholarship Contest **Area, Field, or Subject:** General studies/Field of study not specified; Writing **Level of Education for which Award is Granted:** Undergraduate **Number Awarded:** 3 each year. **Funds Available:** Prizes are scholarships of $2,000 for first place, $1,500 for second, and $1,000 for third. **Duration:** The contest is held annually.

Eligibility Requirements: This competition is open to seniors at high schools in North Carolina. Home-schooled students are eligible if their course of study is equivalent to that of a senior in high school. Applicants must submit an essay of 700 to 1,000 words on a topic that varies annually but relates to fire sprinklers. Recently, students were invited to write about a successful fire sprinkler activation in their town, area, or state. Entries must be submitted through an online process. Selection is based on 1) content; 2) accuracy; 3) creativity and originality; and 4) spelling, grammar, and punctuation. Competitions are first held at the regional level. **Deadline for Receipt:** December of each year.

2201 ■ AMERICAN FOUNDATION FOR THE BLIND

Attn: Scholarship Committee
11 Penn Plaza, Suite 300
New York, NY 10001
Tel: (212)502-7661
Free: 800-AFB-LINE
Fax: (212)502-7771
E-mail: afbinfo@afb.net
Web Site: http://www.afb.org/scholarships.asp
To provide financial assistance to legally blind undergraduate women who are studying literature or music.

Title of Award: R.L. Gillette Scholarships **Area, Field, or Subject:** Literature; Music **Level of Education for which Award is Granted:** Four Year College **Number Awarded:** 2 each year. **Funds Available:** The stipend is $1,000. **Duration:** 1 academic year.

Eligibility Requirements: This program is open to women who are legally blind, U.S. citizens, and enrolled in a 4-year baccalaureate degree

program in literature or music. Along with their application, they must submit an essay that includes the field of study they are pursuing and why they have chosen it; their educational and personal goals; their work experience; any extracurricular activities with which they have been involved, including those in school, religious organizations, and the community; and how they intend to use scholarship monies that may be awarded. They must also submit a sample performance tape (not to exceed 30 minutes) or a creative writing sample. **Deadline for Receipt:** April of each year.

2202 ■ AMERICAN LEGION

Attn: Department of Pennsylvania
Attn: Scholarship Secretary
P.O. Box 2324
Harrisburg, PA 17105-2324
Tel: (717)730-9100
Fax: (717)975-2836
E-mail: hq@pa-legion.com
Web Site: http://www.pa-legion.com/essay.shtml
To recognize and reward high school students in Pennsylvania who submit outstanding essays on a patriotic topic.

Title of Award: Pennsylvania Legion State High School Essay Contest **Area, Field, or Subject:** General studies/Field of study not specified; Patriotism; Writing **Level of Education for which Award is Granted:** Undergraduate **Number Awarded:** 3 state winners are selected each year. **Funds Available:** At the state level, the first-place winner receives a $3,500 scholarship, second a $3,000 scholarship, and third a $2,500 scholarship. If winners choose not to attend college, prizes are $300 for first place, $200 for second, and $200 for third. Local posts, counties, districts, and sections also offer awards. **Duration:** The competition is held annually.

Eligibility Requirements: This program is open to students who are currently enrolled in grades 9-12 in a Pennsylvania public, parochial, private, or home school. Applicants must submit an essay, from 600 to 1,000 words, on a topic that changes annually but relates to a patriotic theme; a recent topic was "America-Sweet Land of Liberty." Competitions are held at the level of local American Legion post, county, district, inter-district, sectional, and then state. Selection is based on proper English structure, accuracy, extent of information, and originality. **Deadline for Receipt:** Applications must be submitted to the local American Legion post by February of each year.

2203 ■ AMERICAN MUSEUM OF NATURAL HISTORY

Attn: National Center for Science Literacy
Central Park West at 79th Street
New York, NY 10024-5192
Tel: (212)496-3498
E-mail: yna@amnh.org
Web Site: http://www.amnh.org/nationalcenter/youngnaturalistawards
To recognize and reward high school students who develop outstanding science projects.

Title of Award: Young Naturalist Awards **Area, Field, or Subject:** Science; Writing **Level of Education for which Award is Granted:** Undergraduate **Number Awarded:** 12 awards are presented each year: 2 for each grade level. **Funds Available:** This program provides scholarships of $2,500 for grade 12, $2,000 for grade 11, $1,500 for grade 10, $1,000 for grade 9, $750 for grade 8, or $500 for grade 7 **Duration:** Awards are presented annually.

Eligibility Requirements: This program is open to students in grades 7-12 currently enrolled in a public, private, parochial, or home school in the United States, Canada, the U.S. territories, or U.S.-sponsored schools abroad. Applicants are invited to submit reports of observation-based projects on a scientific theme that is the same every year: "Scientific Discovery Begins with Expeditions." Entries must be between 500 and 2,000 words for grades 7 and 8, between 750 and 2,500 words for grades 9 and 10, or between 1,000 and 3,000 words for grades 11 and 12. Students may include original drawings, photographs, timelines, maps, or graphs to support their writing. Entries are judged by grade level. Selection is based on focus of investigation (15 points), procedure (20 points), analysis and interpretation (20 points), documentation of research materials (15 points), personal voice (10 points), clarity and style (10 points), and use of visuals (10 points). **Deadline for Receipt:** January of each year. **Additional Information:** This program is sponsored by JPMorgan

Chase Foundation. The authors of the winning essays also receive a trip to New York City, a tour of the American Museum of Natural History, publishing opportunities, and a chance to meet with scientists from the museum.

2204 ■ AMERICAN PSYCHOLOGICAL ASSOCIATION

Attn: Education Directorate
750 First Street, N.E.
Washington, DC 20002-4242
Tel: (202)572-3013
Fax: (202)336-5962
E-mail: eleary@apa.org
Web Site: http://www.apa.org/ed/topss/apftopsscholar.html
To recognize and reward, with college scholarships, high school students who submit outstanding research papers on psychology.
Title of Award: APF/APA TOPSS Scholars Competition **Area, Field, or Subject:** Psychology; Writing **Level of Education for which Award is Granted:** Undergraduate **Number Awarded:** 3 each year. **Funds Available:** The award is $1,000. **Duration:** The competition is held annually.
Eligibility Requirements: This competition is open to high school students who have been enrolled or are currently enrolled in a psychology course. Candidates must be sponsored by a member of the American Psychological Association (APA) Teachers of Psychology in Secondary Schools (TOPSS). They must submit a paper, up to 3,000 words in length, on an assigned topic relating to psychology. Selection is based on the literature review (10 points per item) and research proposal (10 points per item). **Deadline for Receipt:** February of each year. **Additional Information:** This program is cosponsored by the American Psychological Foundation (APF).

2205 ■ AMERICAN RADIO RELAY LEAGUE

Attn: ARRL Foundation
225 Main Street
Newington, CT 06111
Tel: (860)594-0397
Fax: (860)594-0259
E-mail: foundation@arrl.org
Web Site: http://www.arrl.org/arrlf/scholgen.html
To provide financial assistance to licensed radio amateurs, particularly from designated midwestern states, who are interested in working on an undergraduate degree, particularly in journalism or the sciences.
Title of Award: PHD ARA Scholarship **Area, Field, or Subject:** Computer and information sciences; Engineering; General studies/Field of study not specified; Journalism **Level of Education for which Award is Granted:** Undergraduate **Number Awarded:** 1 each year. **Funds Available:** The stipend is $1,000. **Duration:** 1 year.
Eligibility Requirements: This program is open to licensed radio amateurs of any class who are pursuing postsecondary education. Preference is given to 1) residents of Iowa, Kansas, Missouri, and Nebraska; 2) students majoring in journalism, computer science, or electronic engineering; and 3) children of deceased radio amateurs. Applicants must submit an essay on the role amateur radio has played in their lives and provide documentation of financial need. **Deadline for Receipt:** January of each year.

2206 ■ AQUATROLS CORPORATION

1273 Imperial Way
Paulsboro, NJ 08066
Tel: (856)537-6003
Free: 800-257-7797
Fax: (856)537-6018
E-mail: essay.contest@aquatrols.com
Web Site: http://www.aquatrols.com
To recognize and reward, with college scholarships, students whose parents are employed in a turf or landscape management capacity and who submit outstanding essays on a related subject.
Title of Award: Aquatrols Essay Contest **Area, Field, or Subject:** Landscape architecture and design; Turfgrass management; Water resources; Writing **Level of Education for which Award is Granted:** Undergraduate **Number Awarded:** 2 each year. **Funds Available:** First prize is a $2,000 scholarship and second prize is a $1,000 scholarship. **Duration:** The contest is held annually.
Eligibility Requirements: This competition is open to children of employees in a turf or landscape management capacity. Applicants must

be enrolled or planning to enroll in an undergraduate program. They must submit an original essay of 1,500 to 2,000 words on a topic that changes annually; recently, students were invited to write on "The role of surfactants in enhancing water use and/or irrigation efficiency." Essays should be original, compelling, well-organized, readable, persuasive, and creative. Technical accuracy, composition skills, and adherence to contest rules are also considered. **Deadline for Receipt:** February of each year.

2207 ■ ARAB AMERICAN INSTITUTE FOUNDATION

Attn: Scholarship Administrator
1600 K Street, N.W., Suite 601
Washington, DC 20006
Tel: (202)429-9210
Fax: (202)429-9214
E-mail: aaif@aaiusa.org
Web Site: http://www.aaiusa.org/foundation/154/student-resource-center
To provide financial assistance to Arab American students interested in working on an undergraduate or graduate degree in journalism.
Title of Award: Al Muammar Scholarships for Journalism **Area, Field, or Subject:** Communications; Journalism **Level of Education for which Award is Granted:** Graduate, Undergraduate **Number Awarded:** Up to 4 each year. **Funds Available:** The stipend is $5,000. **Duration:** 1 year.
Eligibility Requirements: This program is open to U.S. citizens and permanent residents of Arab descent who are enrolled full time at an accredited college or university in the United States. Applicants must be undergraduates or college seniors admitted to a graduate program. They must have a GPA of 3.3 or higher and a demonstrated commitment to the field of print or broadcast journalism. Selection is based on sensitivity to Arab American issues, demonstrated community involvement, initiative in social advocacy and civic empowerment, journalistic ability, academic ability, commitment to the field of journalism, and financial need. **Deadline for Receipt:** February of each year. **Additional Information:** These scholarships were first awarded in 2006.

2208 ■ ARIZONA STATE UNIVERSITY

Attn: Center for Meteorite Studies
P.O. Box 871404
Tempe, AZ 85287-1404
Tel: (602)965-6511
E-mail: meteorites@asu.edu
Web Site: http://meteorites.asu.edu/nininger
To recognize and reward outstanding student papers dealing with aspects of meteoritic investigation.
Title of Award: Dr. and Mrs. H.H. Nininger Meteorite Award **Area, Field, or Subject:** Physical sciences; Writing **Level of Education for which Award is Granted:** Graduate, Undergraduate **Number Awarded:** 1 each year. **Funds Available:** The prize is $2,500. **Duration:** The competition is held annually.
Eligibility Requirements: This competition is open to both undergraduate and graduate students. They are invited to submit a paper (under 10,000 words) reflecting an aspect of meteoritic investigation. Research topics may include (but are not limited to) physical and chemical properties of meteorites, origin of meteoritic material, and cratering. Observational, experimental, statistical, or theoretical investigations are allowed. Students must be the first author of the paper, but they do not have to be the sole author. Papers must have been written, submitted, or published during the first 10 and a half months of the calendar year. They must cover original research conducted by the student. **Deadline for Receipt:** November of each year. **Additional Information:** Entries not awarded the prize may be resubmitted in the original or a revised form as long as the author is a student at an American college or university.

2209 ■ ASIAN AMERICAN JOURNALISTS ASSOCIATION

Attn: Student Programs Coordinator
1182 Market Street, Suite 320
San Francisco, CA 94102
Tel: (415)346-2051
Fax: (415)346-6343
E-mail: brandons@aaja.org
Web Site: http://www.aaja.org/programs/for_students/scholarships
To provide financial assistance to student members of the Asian American Journalists Association (AAJA) interested in careers in broadcast, photo, or print journalism.

Title of Award: Cox Foundation Scholarships **Area, Field, or Subject:** Communications; Graphic art and design; Journalism; Photography, Journalistic **Level of Education for which Award is Granted:** Graduate, Undergraduate **Number Awarded:** Varies each year. **Funds Available:** The stipend is $2,500. **Duration:** 1 year; may be renewed.

Eligibility Requirements: This program is open to AAJA members who are high school seniors or college students (graduate or undergraduate) enrolled full time in accredited institutions. Applicants must submit a 500-word essay on their involvement or interest in the Asian American community and how, if they are awarded this scholarship, they would contribute to the field of journalism and/or media issues involving the Asian American and Pacific Islander community. Selection is based on scholastic ability, commitment to journalism, sensitivity to Asian American and Pacific Islander issues as demonstrated by community involvement, journalistic ability, and financial need. **Deadline for Receipt:** April of each year. **Additional Information:** This program is supported by the Cox Foundation.

2210 ■ ASIAN AMERICAN JOURNALISTS ASSOCIATION

Attn: Student Programs Coordinator
1182 Market Street, Suite 320
San Francisco, CA 94102
Tel: (415)346-2051
Fax: (415)346-6343
E-mail: brandons@aaja.org
Web Site: http://www.aaja.org/programs/for_students/scholarships
To provide financial assistance to graduating high school seniors who are members of the Asian American Journalists Association (AAJA) and interested in majoring in journalism in college.

Title of Award: Mary Moy Quan Ing Memorial Scholarship **Area, Field, or Subject:** Journalism **Level of Education for which Award is Granted:** Undergraduate **Number Awarded:** 1 each year. **Funds Available:** The stipend is $2,000. **Duration:** 1 year.

Eligibility Requirements: This program is open to graduating high school seniors who are AAJA members enrolling in college to study journalism. Applicants must submit a 500-word essay on their involvement or interest in the Asian American community and how, if they are awarded this scholarship, they would contribute to the field of journalism and/or media issues involving the Asian Pacific American and Pacific Islander community. Selection is based on scholastic ability, commitment to journalism, sensitivity to Asian American and Pacific Islander issues as demonstrated by community involvement, journalistic ability, and financial need. **Deadline for Receipt:** April of each year.

2211 ■ ASIAN AMERICAN JOURNALISTS ASSOCIATION

Attn: Student Programs Coordinator
1182 Market Street, Suite 320
San Francisco, CA 94102
Tel: (415)346-2051
Fax: (415)346-6343
E-mail: brandons@aaja.org
Web Site: http://www.aaja.org/programs/for_students/scholarships
To provide financial assistance and summer work experience in print journalism to members of the Asian American Journalists Association (AAJA) who are undergraduate or graduate students.

Title of Award: S.I. Newhouse Foundation Scholarships **Area, Field, or Subject:** Journalism **Level of Education for which Award is Granted:** Graduate, Undergraduate **Number Awarded:** Varies each year; recently, 7 of these scholarships (2 at $5,000, 3 at $4,000, 1 at $2,000, and 1 at $1,000) were awarded. **Funds Available:** Stipends are $5,000, $3,000, or $1,000 per year. **Duration:** 4 years for a graduating high school senior; 1 year for current undergraduate or graduate students.

Eligibility Requirements: This program is open to all students but especially welcomes applications from historically underrepresented Asian Pacific American groups, including southeast Asians (Vietnamese, Cambodians, and Hmong), south Asians, and Pacific Islanders. Applicants may be graduating high school seniors who declare journalism as a major or undergraduate or graduate students working on a degree in journalism and a career in print journalism. AAJA membership is required. Along with their application, they must submit a 500-word essay on their involvement or interest in the Asian American community and how, if they are awarded this scholarship, they would contribute to the field of journalism and/or media issues involving the Asian American and Pacific Islander com-

munity. Selection is based on scholastic ability, commitment to journalism, sensitivity to Asian American and Pacific Islander issues as demonstrated by community involvement, journalistic ability, and financial need. **Deadline for Receipt:** April of each year. **Additional Information:** This program began in 1994; it is funded by Newhouse News Service and administered by AAJA. Recipients are also eligible for summer internships with a Newhouse publication.

2212 ■ ASIAN AMERICAN JOURNALISTS ASSOCIATION

Attn: Student Programs Coordinator
1182 Market Street, Suite 320
San Francisco, CA 94102
Tel: (415)346-2051
Fax: (415)346-6343
E-mail: brandons@aaja.org
Web Site: http://www.aaja.org/programs/for_students/scholarships
To provide financial assistance to male Asian American students who are members of the Asian American Journalists Association (AAJA) and interested in a career in broadcast journalism.

Title of Award: Minoru Yasui Memorial Scholarship Award **Area, Field, or Subject:** Communications; Journalism **Level of Education for which Award is Granted:** Graduate, Undergraduate **Number Awarded:** 1 each year. **Funds Available:** The stipend is $2,000. **Duration:** 1 year.

Eligibility Requirements: This program is open to Asian American male high school seniors, undergraduates, or graduate students enrolled full time at an accredited college or university in a broadcast journalism program. Applicants must be AAJA members. Along with their application, they must submit a 500-word essay on their involvement or interest in the Asian American community and how, if they are awarded this scholarship, they would contribute to the field of journalism and/or media issues involving the Asian American and Pacific Islander community. Selection is based on scholastic ability, commitment to journalism, sensitivity to Asian American and Pacific Islander issues as demonstrated by community involvement, journalistic ability, and financial need. **Deadline for Receipt:** April of each year. **Additional Information:** This scholarship honors Minoru Yasui, a civil rights advocate and attorney who was 1 of 3 Nisei to challenge the internment of Japanese Americans during World War II.

2213 ■ ASIAN AMERICAN JOURNALISTS ASSOCIATION-PHILADELPHIA CHAPTER

c/o Murali Balaji
950 West Basin Road
New Castle, DE 19720
Tel: (302)324-2553
E-mail: aajaphilly@yahoo.com
Web Site: http://chapters.aaja.org/Philadelphia
To provide financial assistance to members of the Asian American Journalists Association (AAJA) in the Delaware Valley area who are studying or planning to study journalism in college.

Title of Award: Future Building Initiative Scholarships **Area, Field, or Subject:** Journalism **Level of Education for which Award is Granted:** Undergraduate **Number Awarded:** 4 each year. **Funds Available:** A stipend is awarded (amount not specified). **Duration:** 1 year.

Eligibility Requirements: This program is open to AAJA members enrolled in high schools or colleges in the tri-state area of Pennsylvania, New Jersey, and Delaware. Applicants must have a GPA of 3.0 or higher and a stated interest in journalism. They must have demonstrated leadership and initiative by starting an AAJA student chapter at their high school or college. Along with their application, they must submit a letter of intent stating their interest in journalism and the benefits they see in being involved in AAJA, a letter of recommendation, and an unofficial copy of their transcript. **Deadline for Receipt:** January of each year.

2214 ■ ASIAN AMERICAN JOURNALISTS ASSOCIATION-PORTLAND CHAPTER

c/o Tracy Jan
The Oregonian
Metro East News Bureau
295 N.E. Second Street
Gresham, OR 97030
Tel: (503)294-5970
E-mail: tracyjan@news.oregonian.com
Web Site: http://chapters.aaja.org/Portland/scholar.html

To provide financial assistance to undergraduate and graduate journalism students in Oregon and southwestern Washington area who have been involved in the Asian American community.

Title of Award: Portland Chapter AAJA Scholarships **Area, Field, or Subject:** Communications; Journalism; Photography, Journalistic **Level of Education for which Award is Granted:** Graduate, Undergraduate **Number Awarded:** 1 each year. **Funds Available:** Stipends up to $2,000 are available. **Duration:** 1 year.

Eligibility Requirements: This program is open to high school seniors, undergraduates, and graduate students who live or attend school in Oregon or the Vancouver, Washington area. Applicants must be enrolled or planning to enroll full time in a journalism program and be able to demonstrate involvement in the Asian American community. Along with their application, they must submit an essay (up to 750 words) on how they became interested in journalism or how they see themselves contributing to the Asian American community. They must also submit work samples (print: up to 3 articles; radio: up to 3 different stories on standard audio tapes; television: up to 3 different stories on a VHS tape; photojournalism: a portfolio of up to 15 entries). Selection is based on scholastic ability, commitment to journalism, sensitivity to Asian American issues as demonstrated by community involvement, journalistic ability, and financial need. **Deadline for Receipt:** March of each year.

2215 ■ ASIAN AMERICAN JOURNALISTS ASSOCIATION-TEXAS CHAPTER

c/o Julie Tam, Scholarship Chair
KLTV-TV ABC 7
105 West Ferguson
P.O. Box 957
Tyler, TX 75710
Tel: (903)597-5588
Fax: (903)510-7847
E-mail: julie@julietam.com
Web Site: http://chapters.aaja.org/Texas/schol.html

To provide financial assistance to members of the Asian American Journalists Association (AAJA) in Texas who are working on an undergraduate or graduate degree in journalism.

Title of Award: Texas Chapter Scholarships **Area, Field, or Subject:** Communications; Journalism; Photography, Journalistic **Level of Education for which Award is Granted:** Graduate, Undergraduate **Number Awarded:** 2 each year. **Funds Available:** The stipend is $1,000 per year. **Duration:** 1 year.

Eligibility Requirements: This program is open to graduating high school seniors, undergraduates, and graduate students who are either Texas residents or planning to attend an accredited college or university in Texas. Applicants must be AAJA members. Along with their application, they must submit a 250-word autobiography that explains why they are interested in a career in journalism, a 500-word essay on the role of ethnic diversity in news coverage (both for the subjects of the news events and also the journalists involved), their most recent official transcript, a statement of financial need, 2 letters of recommendation, and a resume. Work samples to be submitted are 2 legible clips from print journalism students; 3 to 5 prints or slides with captions or descriptions from print photojournalism students; 2 VHS taped excerpts with corresponding scripts from television broadcast students; 2 edited VHS excepts from television photojournalism students; 3 taped cassette excerpts with corresponding scripts from radio broadcast students; or 3 legible online articles from web journalism students. Selection is based on commitment to the field of journalism, awareness of Asian American issues, journalistic ability, scholastic ability, and financial need. **Deadline for Receipt:** April of each year.

2216 ■ ASSOCIATED PRESS TELEVISION/RADIO ASSOCIATION OF CALIFORNIA AND NEVADA

c/o Roberta Gonzales
CBS 5 TV
855 Battery Street
San Francisco, CA 94111
Tel: (415)362-5550
E-mail: gonzales@kpix.cbs.com
Web Site: http://www.aptra.org

To provide financial assistance to students at colleges and universities in California and Nevada who are interested in broadcast journalism careers.

Title of Award: Kathryn Dettman Memorial Journalism Scholarship Award **Area, Field, or Subject:** Communications; Journalism **Level of Education for which Award is Granted:** Undergraduate **Number Awarded:** 1 each year. **Funds Available:** The stipend is $1,500 per year. **Duration:** 1 year.

Eligibility Requirements: This program is open to students at colleges and universities in California and Nevada. Applicants must have a broadcast journalism career objective. Selection is based on a 500-word essay on why the students wish to pursue broadcast journalism; another 500-word essay on their honors, awards, and broadcast experience; 3 letters of recommendation; and a statement of how they are financing their education. **Deadline for Receipt:** December of each year.

2217 ■ ASSOCIATED PRESS TELEVISION/RADIO ASSOCIATION OF CALIFORNIA AND NEVADA

c/o Roberta Gonzales
CBS 5 TV
855 Battery Street
San Francisco, CA 94111
Tel: (415)362-5550
E-mail: gonzales@kpix.cbs.com
Web Site: http://www.aptra.org

To provide financial assistance to students at colleges and universities in California and Nevada who are interested in broadcast journalism careers.

Title of Award: Clete Roberts Memorial Journalism Scholarship Award **Area, Field, or Subject:** Communications; Journalism **Level of Education for which Award is Granted:** Undergraduate **Number Awarded:** 2 each year. **Funds Available:** The stipend is $1,500 per year. **Duration:** 1 year.

Eligibility Requirements: This program is open to students at colleges and universities in California and Nevada. Applicants must have a broadcast journalism career objective. Selection is based on a 500-word essay on why the students wish to pursue broadcast journalism; another 500-word essay on their honors, awards, and broadcast experience; 3 letters of recommendation; and a statement of how they are financing their education. **Deadline for Receipt:** December of each year.

2218 ■ BILOXI SUN HERALD

Attn: Scholarship Committee
P.O. Box 4567
Biloxi, MS 39535-4567
Tel: (228)896-2365
Fax: (228)896-2151
Web Site: http://www.sunherald.com

To provide financial assistance to minority high school students in Mississippi who are interested in attending college to prepare for a career in the newspaper industry.

Title of Award: Biloxi Sun Herald Minority Scholarship Program **Area, Field, or Subject:** Business administration; Journalism **Level of Education for which Award is Granted:** Undergraduate **Number Awarded:** 1 each year. **Funds Available:** The stipend is $1,000. **Duration:** 1 year.

Eligibility Requirements: This program is open to minority high school seniors graduating from high schools in Mississippi. They must be interested in attending college to prepare for a career in the news or business aspects of the newspaper industry. Along with their application, they must submit a 500-word essay on why they want to prepare for a career in the newspaper industry. Selection is based on the essay, 2 letters of recommendation, a transcript of grades (including SAT/ACT scores), journalism or business experience, and extracurricular activities. **Deadline for Receipt:** January of each year. **Additional Information:** The recipients of these scholarships are automatically entered into competition for the Knight Ridder Minority Scholarship Program of $40,000 over 4 years.

2219 ■ CALIFORNIA CHICANO NEWS MEDIA ASSOCIATION

c/o University of Southern California
Annenberg School of Journalism
300 South Grand Avenue, Suite 3950
Los Angeles, CA 90071
Tel: (213)437-4408
Fax: (213)437-4423
E-mail: ccnmainfo@ccnma.org

Web Site: http://www.ccnma.org

To provide financial assistance to Latino students in California interested in preparing for a career in journalism.

Title of Award: Joel Garcia Memorial Scholarships **Area, Field, or Subject:** Journalism; Photography, Journalistic **Level of Education for which Award is Granted:** Undergraduate **Number Awarded:** Varies each year; recently, 13 of these scholarships were awarded. **Funds Available:** Stipends range from $500 to $2,000. **Duration:** 1 year.

Eligibility Requirements: This program is open to high school seniors and college students of Latino descent who are California residents or students from other states attending a college or university in California. Applicants may major in any field, but they must enroll full time and be able to prove a sincere interest in preparing for a career in journalism. They must submit 1) an essay of 300 to 500 words explaining their family background, including any hardships they have experienced, and what they believe is the role of Latino journalists in the news media; 2) samples of their journalism-related work (e.g., newspaper articles, photographs, or TV or radio audition tapes); 3) transcripts; and 4) letters of reference. Finalists are interviewed. Selection is based on academic achievement, commitment to the journalism field, awareness of the community in which they live, and financial need. **Deadline for Receipt:** March of each year. **Additional Information:** This program includes the Los Angeles Times/ Frank del Olmo Scholarships.

2220 ■ CALIFORNIA LABOR FEDERATION, AFL-CIO

Attn: Education Committee
600 Grand Avenue, Suite 410
Oakland, CA 94610-3561
Tel: (510)663-4024
Fax: (510)663-4099
E-mail: scholarships@calaborfed.org
Web Site: http://www.calaborfed.org/Scholarship.htm

To recognize and reward, with college scholarships, graduating high school seniors in California who submit outstanding essays on topics related to labor unions.

Title of Award: California Labor Federation Scholarships **Area, Field, or Subject:** General studies/Field of study not specified; Industrial and labor relations; Writing **Level of Education for which Award is Granted:** Undergraduate **Number Awarded:** Varies each year; recently, 22 of these awards were presented. **Funds Available:** The award is a $2,000 scholarship. **Duration:** The competition is held annually.

Eligibility Requirements: This competition is open to graduating high school students in public, private, or parochial schools in California who plan to enroll in an accredited college or technical school. Applicants must write an essay of up to 1,000 words on topics that change annually; recently, students were invited to write on an important event in the history of California's unions, why it was important when it happened, and what impact it has on working people in California today. Essays are submitted to high school principals who forward them for judging. **Deadline for Receipt:** April of each year. **Additional Information:** This program is administered by the University of California's Center for Labor Research and Education, 2521 Channing Way, Berkeley, CA 94720-5555, (510) 642-0323, Fax: (510) 642-6432, E-mail: osmer@uclink4.berkeley.edu.

2221 ■ JORGE MAS CANOSA FREEDOM FOUNDATION

c/o Cuban American National Foundation
1312 S.W. 27th Avenue
P.O. Box 440069
Miami, FL 33144-9926
Tel: (305)592-7768
Fax: (305)592-7889
Web Site: http://www.canf.org

To provide financial assistance to students of Cuban descent who are working on an undergraduate or graduate degree in selected subject areas.

Title of Award: Mas Family Scholarship Program **Area, Field, or Subject:** Business administration; Communications; Economics; Engineering; International affairs and relations; Journalism **Level of Education for which Award is Granted:** Graduate, Undergraduate **Funds Available:** The amount of the award depends on the cost of tuition at the recipient's selected institution, on the family's situation, and on the amount of funds received from other sources. The amount of the yearly award cannot exceed $10,000. Full scholarships are not awarded to students who will be receiving full tuition scholarships and/or stipendiary support from other sources. **Duration:** 1 year; recipients may reapply and are given preference over other candidates.

Eligibility Requirements: This program is open to students who are direct descendants of those who left Cuba or were born in Cuba themselves. Applicants must be or have been in the top 10% of their high school graduating class and have be able to meet federal standards of financial need. At least 1 parent or 2 grandparents must have been born in Cuba. Both undergraduate and graduate students may apply, provided they are majoring in 1 of the following subjects: engineering, business, international relations, economics, communications, or journalism. Selection is based on academic performance, leadership qualities, financial need, potential to contribute to the advancement of a free society, and likelihood of succeeding in their chosen field. Finalists may be interviewed. **Deadline for Receipt:** March of each year. **Additional Information:** This program was previously offered by the Cuban American National Foundation.

2222 ■ WILLA CATHER PIONEER MEMORIAL AND EDUCATIONAL FOUNDATION

Attn: Scholarship Program
413 North Webster
Red Cloud, NE 68970
Tel: (402)746-2653
Fax: (402)746-2652
Web Site: http://www.willacather.org/scholarship.htm

To provide financial assistance to female graduates of Nebraska high schools who are or will be majoring in English at an accredited college or university.

Title of Award: Norma Ross Walter Scholarship Program **Area, Field, or Subject:** English language and literature; Literature **Level of Education for which Award is Granted:** Undergraduate **Number Awarded:** 1 each year. **Funds Available:** The stipend is $1,000. **Duration:** 1 year; nonrenewable.

Eligibility Requirements: This program is open to women who have graduated or plan to graduate from a Nebraska high school and enter a college or university as a first-year student. Applicants must plan to continue their education as English majors (journalism is not acceptable). Along with their application, they must submit a 1,500-word essay on several of the short stories or a novel written by Willa Cather. Selection is based on intellectual promise, creativity, and character. **Deadline for Receipt:** January of each year.

2223 ■ CHELA FINANCIAL USA, INC.

388 Market Street, 12th Floor
San Francisco, CA 94111
Tel: (415)283-2800; (866)34-CHELA
Fax: (415)283-2888
E-mail: scholarships@chelafin.org
Web Site: http://www.chelastudentloans.org/Scholarships/ Scholarships.asp

To recognize and reward (with scholarships) college-bound high school seniors who submit outstanding essays on borrowing and money management.

Title of Award: Gateway to Success Scholarships **Area, Field, or Subject:** General studies/Field of study not specified; Writing **Level of Education for which Award is Granted:** Undergraduate **Number Awarded:** 10 each year. **Funds Available:** The award is a $5,000 scholarship. **Duration:** Awards are presented annually.

Eligibility Requirements: This competition is open to high school seniors who have a GPA of 2.0 or higher and are planning to attend an accredited U.S. 2-year or 4-year at least half time. Applicants must complete an essay, up to 300 words, on "How I am Financing My College Education." They do not need to have a student loan to qualify, but their essays should focus on how responsible borrowing and money management are helping them pay for college and meet their life goals. Other requirements include U.S. citizenship or permanent resident status and possession of a valid E-mail address. Essays are evaluated on the basis of appropriateness to overall theme (30%), persuasiveness (30%), quality of writing

(20%), and creativity (20%). **Deadline for Receipt:** April of each year. **Additional Information:** This competition was first held in 2003.

2224 ■ CHELA FINANCIAL USA, INC.

388 Market Street, 12th Floor
San Francisco, CA 94111
Tel: (415)283-2800; (866)34-CHELA
Fax: (415)283-2888
E-mail: info@deresource.org
Web Site: http://www.chelastudentloans.org/Scholarships/
Scholarships.asp
To recognize and reward (with scholarships) undergraduate and graduate students enrolled in a distance education program.
Title of Award: Go the Distance Scholarships **Area, Field, or Subject:** General studies/Field of study not specified; Writing **Level of Education for which Award is Granted:** Graduate, Undergraduate **Number Awarded:** 30 each year: 15 undergraduates (3 each for freshmen, sophomores, juniors, seniors, and fifth-year students) and 15 graduate students (3 in each year of graduate school). **Funds Available:** The award is a $5,000 scholarship. **Duration:** Awards are presented annually.
Eligibility Requirements: This competition is open to undergraduate and graduate students enrolled in a distance education program. Applicants must complete an essay, up to 300 words, on "My Challenges in Financing a Distance Degree." The essay should focus on challenges they have faced in covering the cost of their distance education responsibly and how they will do that while achieving their goals. They do not need to have a student loan to qualify. Essays are evaluated on the basis of appropriateness to overall theme (30%), persuasiveness (30%), quality of writing (20%), and creativity (20%). **Deadline for Receipt:** April of each year. **Additional Information:** This competition was first held in 2004.

2225 ■ CHELA FINANCIAL USA, INC.

388 Market Street, 12th Floor
San Francisco, CA 94111
Tel: (415)283-2800; (866)34-CHELA
Fax: (415)283-2888
E-mail: scholarships@chelafin.org
Web Site: http://www.chelastudentloans.org
To recognize and reward (with scholarships) undergraduate and graduate students who submit outstanding essays on borrowing and money management.
Title of Award: Money Matters Scholarships **Area, Field, or Subject:** Finance; Writing **Level of Education for which Award is Granted:** Graduate, Undergraduate **Number Awarded:** 15 each year. **Funds Available:** The award is a $5,000 scholarship. **Duration:** Awards are presented annually.
Eligibility Requirements: This competition is open to undergraduate and graduate students who have a GPA of 2.0 or higher. Applicants must complete an essay, up to 300 words, on "How I am Financing My College Education." They do not need to have a student loan to qualify, but their essays should focus on how responsible borrowing and money management are helping them pay for college and meet their life goals. Essays are evaluated on the basis of appropriateness to overall theme (30%), persuasiveness (30%), quality of writing (20%), and creativity (20%). U.S. citizenship or permanent resident status is required. **Deadline for Receipt:** October of each year.

2226 ■ CHRISTIAN LIFE RESOURCES

Attn: WELS Lutherans for Life
Scholarship Review Committee
2949 North Mayfair Road, Suite 309
Milwaukee, WI 53222-4304
Tel: (414)774-1331
Fax: (414)774-1360
Web Site: http://www.christianliferesources.com
To provide financial assistance to Lutheran high school seniors in Wisconsin who are interested in studying life-related issues in college.
Title of Award: WELS Lutherans for Life Scholarship Program **Area, Field, or Subject:** Biological and clinical sciences; Education, Special; Engineering, Biomedical; Journalism; Law; Medicine; Physical therapy; Political science; Psychology; Social work **Level of Education for which Award is Granted:** Four Year College **Number Awarded:** Varies each year; recently, 9 of these scholarships were awarded. **Funds Available:** Stipends up to $1,000 are available. **Duration:** 1 year.

Eligibility Requirements: This program is open to high school seniors who are active members of the Wisconsin Evangelical Lutheran Synod (WELS) or an affiliated church. Applicants must be planning to go to a 4-year school to prepare for a secular career in which pro-life values will be demonstrated. Acceptable fields include medicine, biotechnology/biological engineering, medical research/genetics, law/politics, journalism/media, psychology, physical therapy, social services, or special education. They must have a GPA of 3.25 or higher. Along with their application, they must submit essays on 1) the field of study they plan to enter and how it relates to pro-life issues; 2) why the scholarship should be awarded to them, including their future goals; and 3) how they have demonstrated a Christian, pro-life attitude in their life. **Deadline for Receipt:** February of each year. **Additional Information:** WELS Lutherans for Life was formerly a ministry of the Wisconsin Evangelical Lutheran Synod.

2227 ■ COMMUNITIES FOUNDATION OF TEXAS

Attn: Scholarship Department
5500 Caruth Haven Lane
Dallas, TX 75225-8146
Tel: (214)750-4222
Fax: (214)750-4210
E-mail: grants@cftexas.org
Web Site: http://www.cftexas.org
To provide financial assistance to upper-division and graduate students who are working on a degree in journalism and have an interest in aviation.
Title of Award: George E. Haddaway Scholarship **Area, Field, or Subject:** Aviation; Communications; Journalism **Level of Education for which Award is Granted:** Four Year College, Graduate **Number Awarded:** 1 each year. **Funds Available:** The stipend is $2,500 per year. **Duration:** 1 year; nonrenewable.
Eligibility Requirements: This program is open to college juniors, seniors, and graduate students who can demonstrate interest in aviation by such activities as 1) current or former membership in the aviation program of a college or university, the Boy or Girl Scouts of America, the Civil Air Patrol, or a similar organization; or 2) pursuit or completion of the requirements for an aircraft license. Applicants must be working on a baccalaureate or advanced degree in print or electronic journalism and have completed at least 52 hours of college course work with a GPA of 2.75 or higher. They must be able to demonstrate financial need. Along with their application, they must submit an essay (200 to 500 words) describing their interest in aviation and how they might combine that interest with a career in journalism. U.S. citizenship is required. **Deadline for Receipt:** March of each year.

2228 ■ COMMUNITY FOUNDATION FOR GREATER ATLANTA, INC.

50 Hurt Plaza, Suite 449
Atlanta, GA 30303
Tel: (404)688-5525
Fax: (404)688-3060
E-mail: vweekes@atlcf.org
Web Site: http://www.atlcf.org/GrantsScholarships/Scholarships/
RonAutry.aspx
To provide financial assistance to Georgia residents who are majoring in journalism at a 4-year college or university.
Title of Award: Ron Autry Scholarship **Area, Field, or Subject:** Advertising; Journalism; Personnel administration/human resources **Level of Education for which Award is Granted:** Four Year College **Number Awarded:** 1 each year. **Funds Available:** The maximum stipend is $2,000 per year. **Duration:** 1 year.
Eligibility Requirements: This program is open to legal residents of Georgia who are enrolled as a junior or senior at a college or university and preparing for a career in journalism or the newspaper industry (news, advertising, circulation, or human resources). Applicants must be enrolled full time, have a GPA of 2.0 or higher and be able to demonstrate financial need. Along with their application, they must submit a 500-word essay on a topic that changes annually; recently, applicants were invited to write on the topic: "What has been the impact of the Jayson Blair scandal on Black journalists and what should be done to avoid plagiarism?" **Deadline for Receipt:** March of each year. **Additional Information:** This program is sponsored by the Atlanta Association of Black Journalists (AABJ), P.O. Box 54128, Atlanta, GA 30308, (404) 508-4612. Applications may be submitted to the Community Foundation for Greater Atlanta or directly to

the AABJ. The recipient is selected by the AABJ.

2229 ■ CONNECTICUT SPORTS WRITERS ALLIANCE

c/o Manchester Journal Inquirer
P.O. Box 70
Unionville, CT 06085
Tel: (203)789-5651
E-mail: mail@ctsportswriters.org
Web Site: http://www.ctsportswriters.org
To provide financial assistance to high school seniors in Connecticut who are interested in preparing for a career as a sports journalist.
Title of Award: Bohdan "Bo" Kolinsky Memorial Scholarship **Area, Field, or Subject:** Sports writing **Level of Education for which Award is Granted:** Four Year College **Number Awarded:** 1 each year. **Funds Available:** The stipend is $1,000. **Duration:** 1 year; may be renewed.
Eligibility Requirements: This program is open to seniors graduating from high schools in Connecticut who are interested in attending a 4-year college or university to study sports journalism. Applicants must submit a resume showing good academic standing, involvement in journalism, extracurricular involvement, and awards; a 1-page essay on why they wish to prepare for a career in print journalism; a letter of recommendation; and 3 samples of their writing published in a daily or weekly newspaper, a magazine, or a school publication. Selection is based on promise as a journalist and ability to complete college-level academic work. **Deadline for Receipt:** January of each year.

2230 ■ COOK INLET REGION, INC.

Attn: CIRI Foundation
2600 Cordova Street, Suite 206
Anchorage, AK 99503
Tel: (907)263-5582
Free: 800-764-3382
Fax: (907)263-5588
E-mail: tcf@ciri.com
Web Site: http://www.thecirifoundation.org/scholarship.html
To provide financial assistance for undergraduate or graduate studies in the literary, performing, and visual arts to Alaska Natives who are original enrollees to Cook Inlet Region, Inc. (CIRI) and their lineal descendants.
Title of Award: Susie Qimmiqsak Bevins Endowment Scholarship Fund **Area, Field, or Subject:** Literature; Performing arts; Visual arts; Writing **Level of Education for which Award is Granted:** Graduate, Undergraduate **Number Awarded:** Varies each year; recently, 1 of these scholarships (at $2,000 per semester) was awarded. **Funds Available:** The stipend is $2,000 per semester. **Duration:** 1 semester; recipients may reapply.
Eligibility Requirements: This program is open to Alaska Native enrollees to CIRI under the Alaska Native Claims Settlement Act (ANCSA) of 1971 and their lineal descendants. There are no Alaska residency requirements or age limitations. Applicants must be accepted or enrolled full time in a 2-year, 4-year, or graduate degree program in the literary, visual, or performing arts. Selection is based on academic achievement, rigor of course work or degree program, quality of a statement of purpose, student financial contribution, financial need, grade level, previous work performance, education and community activities, letters of recommendation, seriousness of purpose, and practicality of educational and professional goals. **Deadline for Receipt:** May of each year. **Additional Information:** This program was established in 1990. Recipients must attend school on a full-time basis.

2231 ■ DELAWARE HIGHER EDUCATION COMMISSION

Carvel State Office Building
820 North French Street
Wilmington, DE 19801
Tel: (302)577-3240
Free: 800-292-7935
Fax: (302)577-6765
E-mail: dhec@doe.k12.de.us
Web Site: http://www.doe.state.de.us/high-ed/essay.htm
To recognize and reward, with college scholarships, Delaware high school seniors who submit outstanding essays on a topic of historical significance.
Title of Award: Delaware Legislative Essay Scholarships **Area, Field, or Subject:** General studies/Field of study not specified; Writing **Level of**

Education for which Award is Granted: Undergraduate **Number Awarded:** 65 each year: 1 in each of the 21 senatorial districts and 41 representative districts plus 3 statewide winners. **Funds Available:** Legislative district awards are $750. Statewide winners receive $7,500 for first, $3,750 for second, and $2,250 for third. **Duration:** 1 year; nonrenewable.
Eligibility Requirements: This program is open to seniors graduating from high schools in Delaware who plan to enroll full time in an accredited college or university. Applicants must submit an essay of 500 to 2,000 words on a topic that changes annually. U.S. citizenship or permanent resident status is required. Students first compete within their state senatorial and representative legislative district. **Deadline for Receipt:** November of each year.

2232 ■ DELAWARE HIGHER EDUCATION COMMISSION

Carvel State Office Building
820 North French Street
Wilmington, DE 19801
Tel: (302)577-3240
Free: 800-292-7935
Fax: (302)577-6765
E-mail: dhec@doe.k12.de.us
Web Site: http://www.doe.state.de.us/high-ed/christa.htm
To provide scholarship/loans for teacher training to Delaware residents with outstanding academic records.
Title of Award: Christa McAuliffe Teacher Scholarship/Loan **Area, Field, or Subject:** Counseling/Guidance; Education; Education, Bilingual and cross-cultural; Education, English as a second language; Education, Special; English language and literature; Library and archival sciences; Linguistics; Mathematics and mathematical sciences; Reading; Technology **Level of Education for which Award is Granted:** Undergraduate **Number Awarded:** Up to 50 each year. **Funds Available:** Funds up to the cost of tuition, fees, and other direct educational expenses are provided. This is a scholarship/loan program; if the recipient performs required service at a school in Delaware, the loan is forgiven at the rate of 1 year of assistance for each year of service. **Duration:** 1 year; may be renewed for up to 3 additional years.
Eligibility Requirements: This program is open to Delaware residents who are enrolled or accepted for enrollment at a Delaware college or university in a program leading to teacher qualification. Preference is given to applicants planning to teach in an area of critical need. High school seniors must rank in the top half of their class and have a combined score of at least 1570 on the SAT; applicants who are already enrolled in college must have a cumulative GPA of 2.75 or higher. Selection is based on academic achievement. U.S. citizenship or permanent resident status is required. **Deadline for Receipt:** March of each year.
Additional Information: The areas of critical need recently included bilingual education, business education, English, foreign languages, English to speakers of other languages, mathematics, reading, science, school librarianship, special education, and technology education.

2233 ■ DELTA SIGMA THETA SORORITY, INC.

1707 New Hampshire Avenue, N.W.
Washington, DC 20009
Tel: (202)986-2400
Fax: (202)986-2513
E-mail: dstemail@deltasigmatheta.org
Web Site: http://www.deltasigmatheta.org
To provide financial assistance to members of Delta Sigma Theta who are interested in preparing for a career in journalism or another area of communications.
Title of Award: Julia Bumry Jones Scholarship Program **Area, Field, or Subject:** Communications; Journalism **Level of Education for which Award is Granted:** Four Year College, Graduate **Funds Available:** The stipends range from $1,000 to $2,000. The funds may be used to cover tuition, fees, and living expenses. **Duration:** 1 year; may be renewed up to 2 additional years.
Eligibility Requirements: Applicants must be college seniors or graduate students who are interested in preparing for a career in journalism or another area of communications and who are active, dues-paying members of Delta Sigma Theta. **Deadline for Receipt:** March of each year. **Additional Information:** Winners may also receive financial assistance from other sources. Confirmation of registration must be received before stipends are paid.

2234 ■ DETROIT FREE PRESS
Attn: High School Journalism Directors
600 West Fort Street
Detroit, MI 48226
Tel: (313)222-6428
Free: 800-678-6400
Fax: (313)222-8874
E-mail: highschools@freepress.com
Web Site: http://www.freep.com
To provide financial assistance for college to minority high school seniors in the circulation area of the *Detroit Free Press* who are interested in a career in journalism or newspaper business operations.
Title of Award: Detroit Free Press Minority Scholarships **Area, Field, or Subject:** Business administration; Communications; Journalism **Level of Education for which Award is Granted:** Four Year College **Number Awarded:** 3 each year, of whom at least 2 are nominated for the national scholarships. **Funds Available:** The stipend is $1,000. **Duration:** 1 year.
Eligibility Requirements: This program is open to minority high school seniors in Michigan, the greater Toledo metropolitan area, and the greater Windsor metropolitan area. Applicants must be planning to attend a 4-year college or university to major in journalism, communications, or a related field. They must be interested in preparing for a career in journalism or newspaper business operations. Along with their application, they must submit 2 letters of recommendation, a transcript of grades, SAT/ACT scores, up to 5 samples of work with bylines (for journalism applicants), and an essay on "Why Journalism or the Newspaper Business is the Life for Me." **Deadline for Receipt:** January of each year. **Additional Information:** The recipients of these scholarships may be entered into competition for the Knight Ridder Minority Scholarship Program of $40,000 over 4 years.

2235 ■ DOW JONES NEWSPAPER FUND
P.O. Box 300
Princeton, NJ 08543-0300
Tel: (609)452-2820
Fax: (609)520-5804
E-mail: newsfund@wsj.dowjones.com
Web Site: http://DJNewspaperFund.dowjones.com/fund/
cs_internships.asp
To provide work experience and financial assistance to minority college students who are interested in careers in journalism.
Title of Award: Business Reporting Intern Program for Minority College Sophomores and Juniors **Area, Field, or Subject:** Journalism **Level of Education for which Award is Granted:** Undergraduate **Number Awarded:** Up to 12 each year. **Funds Available:** Interns receive a salary of $350 per week during the summer and a $1,000 scholarship at the successful completion of the program. **Duration:** 10 weeks for the summer internship; 1 year for the scholarship.
Eligibility Requirements: This program is open to college sophomores and juniors who are U.S. citizens interested in careers in journalism and participating in a summer internship at a daily newspaper as a business reporter. Applicants must be members of a minority group (African American, Hispanic, Asian American, Pacific Islander, American Indian, or Alaskan Native) enrolled as full-time students. They must submit a resume, 3 to 5 recently-published clips, an list of courses with grades, and a 500-word essay. **Deadline for Receipt:** October of each year.

2236 ■ DOW JONES NEWSPAPER FUND
P.O. Box 300
Princeton, NJ 08543-0300
Tel: (609)452-2820
Fax: (609)520-5804
E-mail: newsfund@wsj.dowjones.com
Web Site: http://DJNewspaperFund.dowjones.com/fund/
cs_internships.asp
To provide financial assistance and work experience to undergraduate and graduate students interested in preparing for a career in journalism.
Title of Award: Newspaper Copy Editing Program for College Juniors, Seniors and Graduate Students **Area, Field, or Subject:** Journalism **Level of Education for which Award is Granted:** Four Year College, Graduate **Number Awarded:** Up to 100 each year. **Funds Available:** Interns receive a salary of $350 per week during the summer and a $1,000 scholarship at the successful completion of the program. **Duration:** 10 weeks for the summer internship; 1 year for the scholarship.

Eligibility Requirements: College juniors, college seniors, and graduate students are eligible to apply for the internship if they are full-time students interested in a career in journalism. Along with their application, they must submit a resume, a list of courses with grades, and a 500-word essay. Interns returning to undergraduate or graduate studies receive a scholarship. U.S. citizenship or permanent resident status is required. College professors and instructors and former full-time professional journalists are ineligible. **Deadline for Receipt:** October of each year. **Additional Information:** Interns attend a 2-week editing residency and then work as copy editors on a daily newspaper. Residencies have been held at Temple University, Florida Southern College, University of Missouri at Columbia, San Jose State University, Pennsylvania State University, University of North Carolina at Chapel Hill, and University of Texas at Austin.

2237 ■ DOW JONES NEWSPAPER FUND
P.O. Box 300
Princeton, NJ 08543-0300
Tel: (609)452-2820
Fax: (609)520-5804
E-mail: newsfund@wsj.dowjones.com
Web Site: http://DJNewspaperFund.dowjones.com/fund/
cs_internships.asp
To provide financial assistance and work experience to undergraduate and graduate students interested in preparing for a career in sports reporting.
Title of Award: Sports Copy Editing Program for College Juniors, Seniors and Graduate Students **Area, Field, or Subject:** Sports writing **Level of Education for which Award is Granted:** Four Year College, Graduate **Number Awarded:** Varies each year. **Funds Available:** Interns receive a salary of $350 per week during the summer and a $1,000 scholarship at the successful completion of the program. **Duration:** 10 weeks for the summer internship; 1 year for the scholarship.
Eligibility Requirements: College juniors, college seniors, and graduate students are eligible to apply for the internship if they are full-time students interested in a career in sports journalism. Along with their application, they must submit a resume, a list of courses with grades, and a 500-word essay. Interns returning to undergraduate or graduate studies receive a scholarship. U.S. citizenship or permanent resident status is required. College professors and instructors and former full-time professional journalists are ineligible. **Deadline for Receipt:** October of each year. **Additional Information:** Interns attend a 2-week editing residency and then work as sports copy editors on a daily newspaper. Recently, the residency was held at the University of Nebraska.

2238 ■ DOW JONES NEWSPAPER FUND
P.O. Box 300
Princeton, NJ 08543-0300
Tel: (609)452-2820
Fax: (609)520-5804
E-mail: newsfund@wsf.dowjones.com
Web Site: http://DJNewspaperFund.dowjones.com/fund/
hss_writing_competition.asp
To recognize and reward outstanding participants in journalism workshops for minority high school students.
Title of Award: Summer Workshops Writing Competition for Minority High School Students **Area, Field, or Subject:** Journalism **Level of Education for which Award is Granted:** Undergraduate **Number Awarded:** 8 each year. **Funds Available:** The award is a college scholarship of $1,000. **Duration:** Workshops normally last 2 weeks during the summer. Scholarships are for 1 year and may be renewed for 1 additional year if the recipient maintains a GPA of 2.5 or higher and an interest in journalism.
Eligibility Requirements: Each summer, workshops on college campuses around the country allow minority high school students to experience work on a professional-quality publication. Students are taught to write, report, design, and layout a newspaper on topics relevant to youth. The director of each workshop nominates 1 student who submits an article from the workshop newspaper and an essay on why he/she wants to pursue journalism as a career. The students whose articles and essay are judged most outstanding receive these college scholarships. **Additional Information:** Recently, workshops were held on college campuses in Alabama, Arizona, Arkansas, California, Florida, Illinois, Kentucky, Massachusetts, Minnesota, Mississippi, Missouri, New Jersey,

New York, Ohio, Oklahoma, Pennsylvania, South Dakota, Texas, Virginia, Washington, and Wisconsin. For the name and address of the director of each workshop, contact the Newspaper Fund.

2239 ■ DREW UNIVERSITY

Attn: Office of International and Off-Campus Programs
Brothers College Room 115
36 Madison Avenue
Madison, NJ 07940-4036
Tel: (973)408-3438
Fax: (973)408-3768
E-mail: intlprog@drew.edu
Web Site: http://depts.drew.edu/offcamp/non-DrewScholarships.htm
To provide financial assistance to students from any college who wish to participate in the off-campus programs in the United States or abroad sponsored by Drew University.

Title of Award: Drew University Off Campus Programs Scholarships **Area, Field, or Subject:** Art; British studies; English language and literature; European studies; General studies/Field of study not specified; Performing arts; Political science **Level of Education for which Award is Granted:** Undergraduate **Number Awarded:** Varies each year. **Funds Available:** Grants up to $3,000 per semester are available to be applied to the cost of the programs. **Duration:** 1 semester.

Eligibility Requirements: Students from any American college or university who have been accepted to participate in 1 of the off-campus programs sponsored by Drew University may apply for financial aid if the university's financial aid office determines that they meet the standards of financial need. Applicants for semester programs must be entering their junior or senior year and have a GPA of 2.7 or higher. **Deadline for Receipt:** April of each year for the fall semester; November of each year for the spring semester. **Additional Information:** The programs available recently included a Washington semester on American politics, a semester on the United Nations in New York, a New York semester on contemporary art and culture, a semester on the new Europe, a program in Eritrea on developing countries, and a London semester on British politics, history, drama, or literature.

2240 ■ EVANGELICAL PRESS ASSOCIATION

Attn: Scholarships
P.O. Box 28129
Crystal, MN 55428
Tel: (763)535-4793
Fax: (763)535-4794
E-mail: director@epassoc.org
Web Site: http://www.epassoc.org/scholarships.html
To provide financial assistance to upper-division and graduate students interested in preparing for a career in Christian journalism.

Title of Award: Evangelical Press Association Scholarships **Area, Field, or Subject:** Communications; Journalism; Religion **Level of Education for which Award is Granted:** Four Year College, Graduate **Number Awarded:** Several each year. **Funds Available:** Stipends range from $500 to $2,000. **Duration:** 1 year.

Eligibility Requirements: This program is open to entering juniors, seniors, and graduate students who have at least 1 years of full-time study remaining. Applicants must be majoring or minoring in journalism or communications, preferably with an interest in the field of Christian journalism. They must be enrolled at an accredited Christian or secular college or university in the United States or Canada with a GPA of 3.0 or higher. Along with their application, they must submit a biographical sketch that includes their birth date, hometown, family, and something about the factors that shaped their interest in Christian journalism; a copy of their academic record; references from their pastor and from an instructor; samples of published writing from church or school publications; and an original essay (from 500 to 700 words) on the state of journalism today. **Deadline for Receipt:** March of each year. **Additional Information:** This program includes the Mel Larson Memorial Scholarship.

2241 ■ FASHION GROUP INTERNATIONAL OF WASHINGTON

Attn: Julie Caine Brooks, Scholarship Chair
P.O. Box 1288
Great Falls, VA 22066
To provide financial assistance for college or graduate school to residents of Maryland, Virginia, and Washington, D. C. interested in preparing for a career in fashion or a fashion-related field.

Title of Award: Washington Fashion Group International Scholarship **Area, Field, or Subject:** Fashion design; Interior design; Journalism; Marketing and distribution; Photography; Textile science **Level of Education for which Award is Granted:** Graduate, Undergraduate **Number Awarded:** 1 each year. **Funds Available:** The maximum stipend is $5,000. **Duration:** 1 year; nonrenewable

Eligibility Requirements: This program is open to residents of Washington, D.C. and all cities and counties in Maryland and Virginia. Applicants must be graduating high school seniors or current undergraduate or graduate students enrolled in a fashion or fashion-related degree program (commercial arts, textiles and clothing design, interior design, journalism, merchandising, or photography). They must submit a 200-word personal statement on their career goals and motivation for entering a fashion-related career. Selection is based on that statement, academic achievement, creative ability, related work activity (paid or unpaid), extracurricular activities and awards, and 3 letters of reference. Finalists are interviewed and asked to submit portfolio material of their work. **Deadline for Receipt:** April of each year.

2242 ■ FISHER COMMUNICATIONS

Attn: Minority Scholarship
100 Fourth Avenue North, Suite 510
Seattle, WA 98109
Tel: (206)404-7000
Fax: (206)404-6037
E-mail: Info@fsci.com
Web Site: http://www.fsci.com/x100.xml
To provide financial assistance to minority college students in selected states who are interested in preparing for a career in broadcasting, marketing, or journalism.

Title of Award: Fisher Broadcasting Scholarships for Minorities **Area, Field, or Subject:** Broadcasting; Journalism; Marketing and distribution **Level of Education for which Award is Granted:** Undergraduate **Number Awarded:** Varies; a total of $10,000 is available for this program each year. **Funds Available:** A stipend is awarded (amount not specified). **Duration:** 1 year; recipients may reapply.

Eligibility Requirements: This program is open to students of non-white origin who are U.S. citizens, have a GPA of 2.5 or higher, and are at least sophomores enrolled in 1) a broadcasting, marketing, or journalism curriculum leading to a bachelor's degree at an accredited 4-year college or university; 2) a broadcast curriculum at an accredited community college, transferable to a 4-year baccalaureate degree program; or 3) a broadcast curriculum at an accredited vocational/technical school. Applicants must be either 1) residents of Washington, Oregon, Idaho, or Montana; or 2) attending a school in those states. They must submit an essay that explains their financial need, education and career goals, and school activities; a copy of their college transcript; and 2 letters of recommendation. Selection is based on need, academic achievement, and personal qualities. **Deadline for Receipt:** April of each year. **Additional Information:** This program began in 1987.

2243 ■ FLEET RESERVE ASSOCIATION

Attn: Americanism Essay Contest
125 North West Street
Alexandria, VA 22314-2754
Tel: (703)683-1400
Free: 800-372-1924
Fax: (703)549-6610
E-mail: fra@fra.org
Web Site: http://www.fra.org/Content/fra/AboutFRA/EssayContest/default.htm
To recognize and reward outstanding high school student essays on Americanism.

Title of Award: Fleet Reserve Association Americanism Essay Contest **Area, Field, or Subject:** Patriotism; Writing **Level of Education for which Award is Granted:** Undergraduate **Number Awarded:** 1 Grand Prize and 18 grade-level prizes (3 for each grade from 7 through 12) are offered on the national level. Many smaller prizes are awarded on the local and regional levels. **Funds Available:** The Grand National Prize is a $15,000 U.S. savings bond. For each grade level, first place is a $5,000 U.S. savings bond, second place is a $3,000 U.S. savings bond, and third place is a $2,000 U.S. savings bond. Additional prizes are awarded to students winning at local branch and regional levels of competition. **Duration:** The competition is held annually.

Eligibility Requirements: Any student, grade 7-12, may enter this contest. The contest is not restricted to children of the Fleet Reserve Association (FRA) or its Ladies Auxiliary. However, each entrant must be sponsored by an FRA member, branch, or Ladies Auxiliary unit. Essays must be on the annual theme (recently: "What My Vote Will Mean to Me") and cannot exceed 350 words. Students may submit only 1 entry per year. Essays are first graded on the FRA branch level and the top essays from each branch are forwarded to the regional level. From there, the top essays in each region are sent to the national level to be graded. **Deadline for Receipt:** November of each year.

2244 ■ FLORIDA STATE ASSOCIATION OF SUPERVISORS OF ELECTIONS

c/o David H. Stafford
Escambia County Supervisor of Elections
213 Palafox Place, Suite 4
P.O. Box 12601
Pensacola, FL 32591-2601
Tel: (850)595-3900
Fax: (850)595-3914
E-mail: soe@escambiavotes.com
Web Site: http://www.gotvflorida.com/scholarship.htm
To provide financial assistance to Florida residents who are interested in majoring in business, political science, or communications in college.
Title of Award: Florida State Association of Supervisors of Elections Scholarship **Area, Field, or Subject:** Business administration; Communications; Journalism; Political science; Public administration **Level of Education for which Award is Granted:** Four Year College **Number Awarded:** 3 each year. **Funds Available:** The stipend is $1,200 per year. **Duration:** 1 year; recipients may reapply.
Eligibility Requirements: This program is open to residents of Florida who have completed 2 years of undergraduate study and are enrolled or planning to enroll full time at a 4-year college or university in the state. Applicants must be majoring in business administration, political science/public administration, or journalism/mass communications and have a GPA of 2.0 or higher. They must be U.S. citizens registered to vote in Florida. Along with their application, they must submit 2 letters of recommendation, a resume of high school and/or college activities, and documentation of financial need. Applications should be submitted to the student's county Supervisor of Elections. Each county's supervisor will review the applications received and select 1 finalist to be sent to the association for consideration. **Deadline for Receipt:** March of each year. **Additional Information:** This program includes the following named scholarships: the Joe Oldmixon Scholarship, the Jimmy Whitehouse Scholarship, and the Dorothy Walker Ruggles Scholarship.

2245 ■ FOUNDATION FOR AMATEUR RADIO, INC.

Attn: Scholarship Committee
P.O. Box 831
Riverdale, MD 20738
E-mail: aa3of@arrl.net
Web Site: http://www.amateurradio-far.org/scholarships.php
To provide funding to licensed radio amateurs who are interested in earning a bachelor's degree, particularly in the field of journalism.
Title of Award: Ralph V. "Andy" Anderson-K0NL, Scholarship **Area, Field, or Subject:** General studies/Field of study not specified; Journalism **Level of Education for which Award is Granted:** Undergraduate **Number Awarded:** 1 each year. **Funds Available:** The stipend is $1,000. **Duration:** 1 year.
Eligibility Requirements: This program is open to residents of the United States and its territories who have an amateur radio license of at least general class. Applicants must be working on a bachelor's degree. There is no restriction on the course of study, but preference is given to applicants majoring in journalism. **Deadline for Receipt:** Requests for applications must be submitted by April of each year. **Additional Information:** Recipients must attend an accredited school (university, college, or technical institute) on a full-time basis.

2246 ■ GEORGIA PRESS EDUCATIONAL FOUNDATION, INC.

Attn: Member Services
3066 Mercer University Drive, Suite 200
Atlanta, GA 30341-4137
Tel: (770)454-6776
Fax: (770)454-6778
E-mail: mail@gapress.org
Web Site: http://www.gapress.org/scholar_intern.html
To provide financial assistance to high school seniors and college students in Georgia who are interested in preparing for a career in journalism.
Title of Award: Georgia Press Educational Foundation Scholarships **Area, Field, or Subject:** Journalism **Level of Education for which Award is Granted:** Undergraduate **Number Awarded:** Varies each year. Recently, 15 of these scholarships were awarded: 3 at $2,000, 1 at $1,500, and 11 at $1,000. **Funds Available:** Stipends range from $1,000 to $2,000. **Duration:** 1 year.
Eligibility Requirements: This program is open to high school seniors and currently-enrolled college students in Georgia. They must be U.S. citizens or permanent residents, have been legal residents of Georgia for at least 3 years or be the children of parents who have been legal residents of Georgia for at least 2 years, have had prior newspaper experience, and be recommended by a high school counselor, college professor, or member of the Georgia Press Educational Foundation. Selection is based on academic record, standardized test scores, career plans, and financial need. **Deadline for Receipt:** January of each year. **Additional Information:** Among the scholarships offered through this program are the Morris Newspaper Corporation Scholarship, established in 1987 by Charles Morris of the Morris Newspaper Corporation in Savannah, and the Durwood McAlister Scholarship, established in 1992 by *The Atlanta Journal*. Recipients of scholarships of $1,000 or more are required to intern for at least 4 weeks with a Georgia newspaper.

2247 ■ HAWAI'I COMMUNITY FOUNDATION

Attn: Scholarship Department
1164 Bishop Street, Suite 800
Honolulu, HI 96813
Tel: (808)566-5570; 888-731-3863
Fax: (808)521-6286
E-mail: scholarships@hcf-hawaii.org
Web Site: http://www.hawaiicommunityfoundation.org/scholar/scholar.php
To provide financial assistance to Hawaii residents who are interested in preparing for a career in journalism.
Title of Award: Edward Payson and Bernice Pi'ilani Irwin Scholarship **Area, Field, or Subject:** Communications; Journalism **Level of Education for which Award is Granted:** Four Year College, Graduate **Number Awarded:** Varies each year; recently, 24 of these scholarships were awarded. **Funds Available:** The amounts of the awards depend on the availability of funds and the need of the recipient; recently, stipends averaged $1,840. **Duration:** 1 year.
Eligibility Requirements: This program is open to Hawaii residents who are studying journalism or communications as college juniors, seniors, or graduate students. They must be able to demonstrate academic achievement (GPA of 2.7 or higher), good moral character, and financial need. In addition to filling out the standard application form, applicants must write a short statement indicating their reasons for attending college, their planned course of study, their career goals, and why they have chosen to major in journalism. **Deadline for Receipt:** February of each year. **Additional Information:** Recipients may attend college in Hawaii or on the mainland.

2248 ■ HEALTHCARE FINANCIAL MANAGEMENT ASSOCIATION-CONNECTICUT CHAPTER

Attn: Scholarship Committee Chair
110 Barnes Road
P.O. Box 90
Wallingford, CT 06492-0090
Tel: (203)949-6383
Fax: (203)949-6331
E-mail: jagorin@mmm.com
Web Site: http://www.cthfma.org
To recognize and reward, with scholarships, undergraduate and graduate students in fields related to health care financial management at colleges and universities in Connecticut who submit outstanding essays on topics in the field.
Title of Award: Connecticut Chapter HFMA Scholarships **Area, Field, or Subject:** Accounting; Business administration; Finance; Health care services; Information science and technology; Nursing; Writing **Level of**

Education for which Award is Granted: Graduate, Undergraduate **Number Awarded:** 2 each year: 1 for an undergraduate and 1 for a graduate student. **Funds Available:** The winner receives a $2,000 fellowship, membership in the Connecticut chapter of HFMA, a 1-year subscription to *Healthcare Financial Management,* and waiver of chapter program fees for 1 year. **Duration:** 1 year.

Eligibility Requirements: This competition is open to undergraduate and graduate students at colleges and universities in Connecticut, children of members of the Connecticut chapter of the Healthcare Financial Management Association (HFMA) attending a school outside of Connecticut, and residents of Connecticut commuting to a college or university in a state that borders Connecticut. Applicants must be enrolled in a business, finance, accounting, or information systems program and have an interest in health care or be enrolled in a nursing or allied health program. They must submit an essay, up to 5 pages, on a topic that changes annually; recently, applicants were allowed to choose among the new Medicare prescription drug coverage and its impact on providers and beneficiaries, the impact of the "baby boomer" segment of the U.S. population on the health care system, the impact of health care spending accounts on employers and individuals, or the voluntary and required reporting of clinical and operational data by health care providers. Finalists may be interviewed. **Deadline for Receipt:** March of each year.

2249 ■ INSTITUTE OF ELECTRICAL AND ELECTRONICS ENGINEERS

c/o Gene Stuffle
Idaho State University
College of Engineering
833 South Eighth Avenue
Pocatello, ID 83209-8060
Tel: (208)282-2902
E-mail: gene.stuffle@isu.edu
Web Site: http://www.coe.isu.edu/ieee/wescon
To provide financial assistance for college to high school authors of outstanding papers on electronics.

Title of Award: Bruce Angwin Memorial Scholarships **Area, Field, or Subject:** Electronics; Engineering; Writing **Level of Education for which Award is Granted:** Four Year College **Number Awarded:** 2 scholarships are awarded each year. **Funds Available:** The first prize is $5,000 and second prize is $3,000; funds are sent directly to the winners' engineering schools of choice after they have started college classes with a defined major in electronics or a related field. Winners also receive transportation and 1 night's accommodations at the Wescon Electronics Show and Convention, held in alternating years in the San Francisco and Los Angeles areas. **Duration:** The competition is held annually.

Eligibility Requirements: This competition is open to students who are juniors in high school planning to attend 4-year colleges and major in electronics engineering or associated fields. They must be attending high school in Region 6 of the Institute of Electrical and Electronics Engineers, which covers the states of Alaska, Arizona, California, Hawaii, Idaho, Montana, Nevada, New Mexico, Oregon, Utah, and Washington. The competition requires entrants to write a 500- to 600-word essay explaining the importance of electronics technology, the future of electronics in the United States, what electronics will offer to the next generation, how the students plan to prepare for a career in electronics, how they will contribute, and how they and others will benefit. **Deadline for Receipt:** April of each year. **Additional Information:** This program began in 1986 to honor the 7 astronauts who lost their lives aboard Space Shuttle Challenger. Originally named the Wescon Scholarships, its current name was adopted in 2004.

2250 ■ INTERNATIONAL COMMUNICATIONS INDUSTRIES ASSOCIATION, INC.

Attn: Director of Strategic Initiatives
11242 Waples Mill Road, Suite 200
Fairfax, VA 22030
Tel: (703)273-7200
Free: 800-659-7469
Fax: (703)278-8082
E-mail: dwilbert@infocomm.org
Web Site: http://www.infocomm.org/Foundation/Scholarships/College.cfm
To provide financial assistance to college students in their final year of study who are interested in preparing for a career in the audiovisual industry.

Title of Award: International Communications Industries Association College Scholarships **Area, Field, or Subject:** Electronics; Information science and technology; Journalism; Telecommunications systems **Level of Education for which Award is Granted:** Graduate, Undergraduate **Number Awarded:** Varies each year; recently, 7 of these scholarships were awarded. **Funds Available:** The stipend is $2,500. **Duration:** 1 year.

Eligibility Requirements: This program is open to 1) college juniors completing their bachelor's degree in the following year; 2) college seniors who plan to enter graduate school; and 3) students in their final year of study for an associate degree. Applicants must have a GPA of 2.75 or higher in a program of audio, visual, audiovisual, electronics, telecommunications, technical theater, data networking, software development, or information technology. Students in other programs, such as journalism, may be eligible if they can demonstrate a relationship to career goals in the audiovisual industry. Along with their application, they must submit essays on why they are applying for this scholarship, why they are interested in the audiovisual industry, and their professional plans following graduation. Minority and women candidates are especially encouraged to apply. Selection is based on the essays, presentation of the application, GPA, work experience, and letters of recommendation. **Deadline for Receipt:** April of each year. **Additional Information:** Recipients are required to work during the summer as paid interns with a manufacturer, dealer, designer, or other firm that is a member of the International Communications Industries Association.

2251 ■ INTERNATIONAL COMMUNICATIONS INDUSTRIES ASSOCIATION, INC.

Attn: Director of Strategic Initiatives
11242 Waples Mill Road, Suite 200
Fairfax, VA 22030
Tel: (703)273-7200
Free: 800-659-7469
Fax: (703)278-8082
E-mail: dwilbert@infocomm.org
Web Site: http://www.infocomm.org/Foundation/Scholarships
To provide financial assistance for college to dependents of members of the International Communications Industries Association (ICIA) interested in preparing for a career in the audiovisual industry.

Title of Award: Scholarships for Dependents of ICIA Members **Area, Field, or Subject:** Electronics; Information science and technology; Journalism; Telecommunications systems **Level of Education for which Award is Granted:** Undergraduate **Number Awarded:** Varies each year; recently, 3 of these scholarships were awarded. **Funds Available:** The stipend is $1,500. **Duration:** 1 year.

Eligibility Requirements: This program is open to graduating high school seniors and current college students who are the children, stepchildren, and spouses of employees at ICIA member companies. Applicants must have a GPA of 2.75 or higher and be majoring or planning to major in audio, visual, audiovisual, electronics, telecommunications, technical theater, data networking, software development, or information technology. Students in other programs, such as journalism, may be eligible if they can demonstrate a relationship to career goals in the audiovisual industry. Along with their application, they must submit 1) an essay of 150 to 200 words on the career path they see themselves pursuing in the next 5 years and why, and 2) an essay of 250 to 300 words on the experience or person that most influenced them in selecting the audiovisual industry as their career of choice. Minority and women candidates are especially encouraged to apply. Selection is based on the essays, presentation of the application, GPA, work experience, and letters of recommendation. **Deadline for Receipt:** April of each year.

2252 ■ INTERNATIONAL FOODSERVICE EDITORIAL COUNCIL

P.O. Box 491
Hyde Park, NY 12538
Tel: (845)229-6973
Fax: (845)229-6993
E-mail: ifec@aol.com
Web Site: http://www.ifec-is-us.com
To provide financial assistance to undergraduate or graduate students who are interested in preparing for a career in communications in the food service industry.

Title of Award: IFEC Scholarships **Area, Field, or Subject:** Communications; Creative writing; Culinary arts; English language and literature;

Food science and technology; Food service careers; Graphic art and design; Hotel, institutional, and restaurant management; Journalism; Management; Marketing and distribution; Nutrition; Photography; Photography, Journalistic; Public relations **Level of Education for which Award is Granted:** Master's, Undergraduate **Number Awarded:** Varies each year; recently, 5 of these scholarships were awarded. **Funds Available:** The stipend is $3,000 per year. **Duration:** 1 year.

Eligibility Requirements: This program is open to currently-enrolled college students who are working on an associate, bachelor's, or master's degree. They must be enrolled full time and planning on a career in editorial, public relations, photography, food styling, or a related aspect of communications in the food service industry. The following food service majors are considered appropriate for this program: culinary arts; hospitality management; hotel, restaurant, and institutional management; dietetics; food science and technology; and nutrition. Applicable communications areas include journalism, English, mass communications, public relations, marketing, broadcast journalism, creative writing, graphic arts, and photography. Selection is based on academic record, character references, and demonstrated financial need. **Deadline for Receipt:** March of each year.

2253 ■ IOWA FEDERATION OF LABOR, AFL-CIO

Attn: Scholarship Program
2000 Walker Street, Suite A
Des Moines, IA 50317-5290
Tel: (515)262-9571
Free: 800-372-4817
Fax: (515)262-9573
E-mail: ifl@iowaaflcio.org
Web Site: http://www.iowaaflcio.org
To recognize and reward outstanding essays on a labor-related topic written by high school seniors in Iowa.
Title of Award: Iowa Federation of Labor Scholarships **Area, Field, or Subject:** History, American; Industrial and labor relations; Writing **Level of Education for which Award is Granted:** Undergraduate **Number Awarded:** 3 each year. **Funds Available:** First prize is $1,500, second prize is $1,000, and third prize is $500. Funds may be used as a scholarship at the college or university of the recipient's choice. **Duration:** The competition is held annually.
Eligibility Requirements: This competition is open to all seniors in accredited high schools in Iowa (public, private, and parochial). Students must write an essay (from 500 to 750 words) on the history of the labor movement in the United States. It is recommended that competitors read *A History of the Labor Movement in the United States* before writing the essay. **Deadline for Receipt:** March of each year.

2254 ■ KAPLAN, INC.

Attn: Pre-College
1440 Broadway, Ninth Floor
New York, NY 10018
Tel: (212)997-5886
Free: 800-KAP-TEST
Web Site: http://www.kaptest.com/oneoff/essay/index.jhtml
To recognize and reward, with college scholarships, high school students who write outstanding essays on topics related to their personal development and growth.
Title of Award: Kaplan/Newsweek "My Turn" Essay Competition **Area, Field, or Subject:** General studies/Field of study not specified; Writing **Level of Education for which Award is Granted:** Undergraduate **Number Awarded:** 10 each year: 1 first-prize winner, 1 second-prize winner, and 8 third-prize winners. **Funds Available:** First prize is $5,000, second $2,000, and third $1,000. All funds are to be used for future educational needs. **Duration:** The competition is held annually.
Eligibility Requirements: This program is open to U.S. high school students planning to attend college after graduation. Applicants must write an essay of 500 to 1,000 words on a topic of their choice that is similar in format to the weekly "My Turn" column in *Newsweek* magazine, in which a member of the public shares an opinion, experience, or personal feeling. Judges look for direct personal experiences and observations with a fresh, original, engaging, moving, and thought-provoking point of view that appeals to a national readership. Selection is based on 1) effectiveness, insightfulness, creativity, and completeness; 2) organization and development of the ideas expressed, with clear and appropriate examples to sup-

port them; and 3) consistency in the use of language, variety in sentence structure and range of vocabulary, and use of proper grammar, spelling, and punctuation. **Deadline for Receipt:** February of each year. **Additional Information:** This competition is co-sponsored by Kaplan and *Newsweek* Magazine.

2255 ■ KNIGHT RIDDER, INC.

Attn: Office of Diversity
50 West San Fernando Street, Suite 1200
San Jose, CA 95113
Tel: (408)938-7734
Fax: (408)938-7755
Web Site: http://www.kri.com/career/internships.html
To provide financial assistance and work experience to students at selected Historically Black Colleges and Universities (HBCUs) who are studying advertising, business, or journalism.
Title of Award: Knight Ridder HBCU Scholarships **Area, Field, or Subject:** Advertising; Business administration; Journalism **Level of Education for which Award is Granted:** Four Year College **Number Awarded:** Varies each year. **Funds Available:** The stipend is $2,500 per year. Recipients also work as an intern at a Knight Ridder newspaper during the summer after their junior year and receive a salary according to the newspaper's normal scale. **Duration:** 1 year; may be renewed for 1 additional year, if the recipient maintains a GPA of 3.0 or higher.
Eligibility Requirements: This program is open to students at selected HBCUs who are entering their junior year. Applicants must be majoring in advertising, business, or journalism. **Additional Information:** The participating HBCUs are Howard University, Florida A&M University, Morehouse College, and Spelman College. Further information is available from the placement office at those institutions.

2256 ■ KNIGHT RIDDER, INC.

Attn: Office of Diversity
50 West San Fernando Street, Suite 1200
San Jose, CA 95113
Tel: (408)938-7734
Fax: (408)938-7755
Web Site: http://www.knightridder.com/career/internships.html
To provide financial assistance and work experience to minority high school seniors who are interested in going to college to prepare for a career in journalism.
Title of Award: Knight Ridder Minority Scholars Program **Area, Field, or Subject:** Advertising; Graphic art and design; Information science and technology; Journalism; Marketing and distribution; Photography, Journalistic **Level of Education for which Award is Granted:** Undergraduate **Number Awarded:** Up to 5 each year: 2 for news, 2 for business, and 1 for either. **Funds Available:** The stipend is $5,000 per year for the freshman and sophomore year and $15,000 per year for the junior and senior year. **Duration:** 1 year; may be renewed for up to 3 additional years, if the recipient maintains a GPA of 3.0 or higher and satisfactory performance on internships.
Eligibility Requirements: This program is open to minority seniors graduating from high schools in areas served by Knight Ridder. Applicants must be interested in attending college to prepare for a career in the newspaper industry. They first apply to their local Knight Ridder newspaper and compete for local scholarships; selected winners are then nominated for this award. Both "news" and "business" students are eligible. **Additional Information:** Recipients are offered an internship opportunity at a Knight Ridder newspaper during the summer. News scholars work in the newsroom, writing and editing stories, taking photographs, crafting illustrations, and designing news pages. Business scholars complete internships in advertising, marketing, information technology, circulation, and other areas essential to the industry. At the end of the sophomore year, recipients must agree to work at a Knight Ridder newspaper for 1 year after graduation.

2257 ■ KNIGHT RIDDER NEWSPAPERS-WASHINGTON BUREAU

Attn: Anthony Pugh
700 12th Street, N.W., Suite 1000
Washington, DC 20005-3994
Tel: (202)383-6013
Fax: (202)383-3738
E-mail: tpugh@krwashington.com

Web Site: http://www.krwashington.com
To provide financial assistance to minority high school seniors from the Washington, D.C. area who are interested in attending college to prepare for a career in the newspaper industry.
Title of Award: Washington Bureau Minority Scholarships **Area, Field, or Subject:** Advertising; Business administration; Computer and information sciences; Graphic art and design; Journalism; Photography, Journalistic **Level of Education for which Award is Granted:** Undergraduate **Number Awarded:** 2 each year. **Funds Available:** The stipend is $1,000. **Duration:** 1 year.
Eligibility Requirements: This program is open to minority seniors graduating from high schools in the metropolitan area of Washington, D.C. Applicants must be able to demonstrate an interest in journalism, but they are not required to have been school newspaper reporters or editors. They may be photographers, graphic artists, computer experts, delivery workers with an interest in circulation, or business and advertising staff members. Along with their application, they must submit a transcript of grades (with a GPA of 3.0 or higher), SAT/ACT scores, 2 letters of recommendation, a list of journalism or business experience, information on extracurricular activities, up to 5 samples of work with bylines (for journalism applicants), and a 500-word essay on why they want to prepare for a career in journalism or communication business. **Deadline for Receipt:** January of each year. **Additional Information:** The recipients of these scholarships are entered into competition for the Knight Ridder Minority Scholarship Program of $40,000 over 4 years.

2258 ■ GILDER LEHRMAN INSTITUTE OF AMERICAN HISTORY
Attn: Prize in American History
19 West 44th Street, Suite 500
New York, NY 10036
Tel: (646)366-9666
Fax: (646)366-9669
E-mail: info@gilderlehrman.org
Web Site: http://www.gilderlehrman.org
To recognize and reward high school students who write outstanding essays on topics related to U.S. history.
Title of Award: Gilder Lehrman Prize in American History **Area, Field, or Subject:** History, American; Writing **Level of Education for which Award is Granted:** Undergraduate **Number Awarded:** 3 cash prizes are awarded each year. **Funds Available:** First prize is $5,000, second $3,000, and third $1,000. **Duration:** The competition is held annually.
Eligibility Requirements: This competition is open to students at high schools in the United States. Candidates submit essays on topics related to American history to the *Concord Review*. The editors of that journal then select 10 outstanding essays on U.S. history and refer them to the sponsors of this competition. **Additional Information:** This competition began in 2000. Information on the *Concord Review* is available from its Editor, 730 Boston Post Road, Suite 24, Sudbury, MA 01776, (800) 331-5007, E-mail: fitzhugh@tcr.org.

2259 ■ LUSO-AMERICAN EDUCATION FOUNDATION
Attn: Administrative Director
7080 Donlon Way, Suite 202
P.O. Box 2967
Dublin, CA 94568
Tel: (925)828-3883
Fax: (925)828-3883
Web Site: http://www.luso-american.org/laef
To provide financial assistance to undergraduate students with a Portuguese connection in California who are interested in studying writing.
Title of Award: Mericia C. Gonsalves Literary Scholarship **Area, Field, or Subject:** Writing **Level of Education for which Award is Granted:** Four Year College **Number Awarded:** 1 each year. **Funds Available:** The stipend is $1,000. **Duration:** 1 year; nonrenewable.
Eligibility Requirements: Applicants must meet at least 1 of the following requirements: 1) be of Portuguese descent; 2) be planning to enroll in a Portuguese class in college; or 3) be a member of an organization whose scholarships are administered by the Luso-American Education Foundation. All applicants must be California residents younger than 21 years of age, have graduated from an accredited high school by the summer of the year of the award, have a GPA of 3.0 or higher, be enrolled or planning to enroll at a 4-year college or university, and have demonstrated talent and interest in the written creative arts. Selection is based on

promise of success in college, financial need, qualities of leadership, vocational promise, and sincerity of purpose. **Deadline for Receipt:** February of each year.

2260 ■ MAINE COMMUNITY FOUNDATION
Attn: Program Director
245 Main Street
Ellsworth, ME 04605
Tel: (207)667-9735; 877-700-6800
Fax: (207)667-0447
E-mail: info@mainecf.org
Web Site: http://www.mainecf.org/html/scholarships/index.html
To provide financial assistance to Maine students interested in the study of outdoor/nature writing.
Title of Award: R.V. "Gadabout" Gaddis Charitable Fund **Area, Field, or Subject:** Environmental conservation; Environmental science; Parks and recreation; Writing **Level of Education for which Award is Granted:** Four Year College **Number Awarded:** 2 each year. **Funds Available:** The stipend is $1,000 per year. **Duration:** 1 year.
Eligibility Requirements: This program is open to residents of Maine who are college juniors or seniors studying outdoor writing or a related environmental field. Applicants must include a writing sample, up to 10 pages in length, that demonstrates their skill at writing about the "outdoors," including outdoor sports, environmental concerns, and natural history topics. **Deadline for Receipt:** March of each year. **Additional Information:** This program began in 1995.

2261 ■ MAINE COMMUNITY FOUNDATION
Attn: Program Director
245 Main Street
Ellsworth, ME 04605
Tel: (207)667-9735; 877-700-6800
Fax: (207)667-0447
E-mail: info@mainecf.org
Web Site: http://www.mainecf.org/html/scholarships/index.html
To provide financial assistance to Maine residents who are interested in studying journalism in college.
Title of Award: Guy P. Gannett Scholarship Fund **Area, Field, or Subject:** Communications; Journalism **Level of Education for which Award is Granted:** Graduate, Undergraduate **Number Awarded:** 1 or more each year. **Funds Available:** A stipend is paid (amount not specified). **Duration:** 1 year; may be renewed.
Eligibility Requirements: This program is open to graduates of Maine high schools (public and private) and to Maine residents who were schooled at home during their last year of secondary education. Applicants must be attending either an undergraduate (including a trade school or a technical institute program) or a graduate program at an accredited postsecondary institution in the United States. They must be majoring in journalism or a related field, including all forms of print, broadcast, or electronic media. Selection is based on academic achievement, financial need, and a demonstrated interest in a career in a form of journalism. Preference is given to renewal applicants. **Deadline for Receipt:** April of each year. **Additional Information:** This program was established in 2000.

2262 ■ MEL FISHER MARITIME HERITAGE SOCIETY AND MUSEUM
Attn: Curator, Department of Education
200 Greene Street
Key West, FL 33040
Tel: (305)294-2633
Fax: (305)294-5671
Web Site: http://www.melfisher.org/deoaward.htm
To recognize and reward, with funding for college or graduate school, women who submit outstanding essays on the oceans.
Title of Award: Dolores E. Fisher Award **Area, Field, or Subject:** Marine biology; Oceanography; Writing **Level of Education for which Award is Granted:** Graduate, Undergraduate **Number Awarded:** 1 each year. **Funds Available:** The award is $1,000. **Duration:** The award is presented annually.
Eligibility Requirements: This competition is open to women between 16 and 30 years of age. Candidates must submit a 1,000-word essay on how they hope to make a difference in the world through their passion for the oceans, their career goals, and how this award will help them achieve

those goals. They must also include 3 letters of recommendation and a brief statement on the personality characteristic they value most in themselves and why. If they are currently enrolled in school, they must identify their program, but school enrollment is not required. **Deadline for Receipt:** March of each year.

2263 ■ MINNESOTA HIGHER EDUCATION SERVICES OFFICE

1450 Energy Park Drive, Suite 350
St. Paul, MN 55108-5227
Tel: (651)642-0567
Free: 800-657-3866
Fax: (651)642-0675
E-mail: info@heso.state.mn.us
Web Site: http://www.mheso.state.mn.us
To provide financial assistance for college to outstanding high school seniors or graduates in Minnesota.

Title of Award: Minnesota Academic Excellence Scholarship **Area, Field, or Subject:** Art; Creative writing; English language and literature; Linguistics; Mathematics and mathematical sciences; Science; Social sciences **Level of Education for which Award is Granted:** Undergraduate **Number Awarded:** Varies each year. **Funds Available:** Scholarships at public institutions cover the cost of full-time attendance; scholarships at private institutions cover an amount equal to the lesser of the actual tuition and fees charged by the institution or the tuition and fees in comparable public institutions. **Duration:** 1 year; may be renewed up to 3 additional years.

Eligibility Requirements: This program is open to Minnesota residents who have demonstrated outstanding ability, achievement, and potential in English, creative writing, fine arts, foreign language, mathematics, science, or social science. Applicants must have been admitted as full-time students at a branch of the University of Minnesota, a Minnesota state university, or a private, baccalaureate degree-granting college or university in Minnesota. **Additional Information:** This program was established by the Minnesota Legislature in 1991. Funds for this program come from the sale of special collegiate license plates.

2264 ■ NATIONAL AGRICULTURAL AVIATION ASSOCIATION

Attn: Women of the NAAA
1005 E Street, S.E.
Washington, DC 20003-2947
Tel: (202)546-5722
Fax: (202)546-5726
E-mail: information@agaviation.org
Web Site: http://www.agaviation.org/scholarship.htm
To recognize and reward outstanding student essays on agricultural aviation.

Title of Award: Women's National Agricultural Aviation Association Scholarship Essay Contest **Area, Field, or Subject:** Agricultural sciences; Aviation; General studies/Field of study not specified; Writing **Level of Education for which Award is Granted:** Undergraduate **Number Awarded:** 2 each year. **Funds Available:** First prize is $2,000; second prize is $1,000. **Duration:** The competition is held annually.

Eligibility Requirements: This competition is open to the children, grandchildren, sons-in-law, daughters-in-law, or spouses of any National Agricultural Aviation Association operator, pilot member, retired operator, or pilot who maintains an active membership in the association. The contest is also open to the children, grandchildren, sons-in-law, daughters-in-law, or spouses of an allied industry member. Entrants must be high school seniors, high school graduates, or college students. They may be of any age pursuing any area of education beyond high school. They are invited to submit an essay, up to 1,500 words, on a theme related to agricultural aviation that changes annually; recently, the topic was "Agricultural Aviation's Contribution to the World's Food Supply." A photograph of the entrant and a short biography should accompany the submission. Essays are judged on theme, development, clarity, and originality. **Deadline for Receipt:** August of each year.

2265 ■ NATIONAL ASSOCIATION OF NEGRO BUSINESS AND PROFESSIONAL WOMEN'S CLUBS

Attn: Scholarship Committee
1806 New Hampshire Avenue, N.W.
Washington, DC 20009-3208
Tel: (202)483-4206

Fax: (202)462-7253
E-mail: nanbpwc@aol.com
Web Site: http://www.nanbpwc.org/ScholarshipApplications.asp
To provide financial assistance to African American women studying journalism, economics, or a related field in college.

Title of Award: Dr. Julianne Malveaux Scholarship **Area, Field, or Subject:** Economics; Journalism **Level of Education for which Award is Granted:** Undergraduate **Number Awarded:** 1 or more each year. **Funds Available:** The stipend is $1,000. **Duration:** 1 year.

Eligibility Requirements: This program is open to African American women enrolled in an accredited college or university as a sophomore or junior. Applicants must have a GPA of 3.0 or higher and be majoring in journalism, economics, or a related field. **Deadline for Receipt:** February of each year.

2266 ■ NATIONAL DAIRY PROMOTION AND RESEARCH BOARD

c/o Dairy Management Inc.
10255 West Higgins Road, Suite 900
Rosemont, IL 60018-5616
Tel: (847)803-2000
Fax: (847)803-2077
E-mail: marykateg@rosedmi.com
Web Site: http://www.dairycheckoff.com/DairyCheckoff/about/scholarship.htm
To provide financial assistance to undergraduate students in fields related to the dairy industry.

Title of Award: NDPRB Undergraduate Scholarship Program **Area, Field, or Subject:** Business administration; Communications; Dairy science; Economics; Education; Food science and technology; Journalism; Marketing and distribution; Nutrition; Public relations **Level of Education for which Award is Granted:** Four Year College **Number Awarded:** 20 each year: the James H. Loper Jr. Memorial Scholarship at $2,500 and 19 other scholarships at $1,500. **Funds Available:** Stipends are $2,500 or $1,500. **Duration:** 1 year; may be renewed.

Eligibility Requirements: This program is open to sophomores, juniors, and seniors enrolled in college and university programs that emphasize dairy. Eligible majors include agricultural education, business, communications and/or public relations, economics, food science, journalism, marketing, and nutrition. Fields related to production (e.g., animal science) are not eligible. Selection is based on academic performance; interest in a career in dairy; involvement in extracurricular activities, especially those relating to dairy; and evidence of leadership ability, initiative, character, and integrity. The applicant who is judged most outstanding is awarded the James H. Loper Jr. Memorial Scholarship. **Deadline for Receipt:** May of each year. **Additional Information:** Dairy Management Inc. manages this program on behalf of the National Dairy Promotion and Research Board (NDPRB).

2267 ■ NATIONAL FFA ORGANIZATION

Attn: Scholarship Office
6060 FFA Drive
P.O. Box 68960
Indianapolis, IN 46268-0960
Tel: (317)802-4321
Fax: (317)802-5321
E-mail: scholarships@ffa.org
Web Site: http://www.ffa.org
To provide financial assistance to FFA members interested in studying fields related to communications in college.

Title of Award: Progressive Farmer Magazine Scholarships **Area, Field, or Subject:** Advertising; Agricultural sciences; Communications; Journalism **Level of Education for which Award is Granted:** Four Year College **Number Awarded:** 1 each year. **Funds Available:** The stipend is $1,000 per year. Funds are paid directly to the recipient. **Duration:** 1 year; nonrenewable.

Eligibility Requirements: This program is open to members who are graduating high school seniors planning to enroll full time in college. Applicants must be interested in working on a 4-year degree in communications, journalism, or advertising. Selection is based on academic achievement (10 points for GPA, 10 points for SAT or ACT score, 10 points for class rank), leadership in FFA activities (30 points), leadership in community activities (10 points), and participation in the Supervised Agricultural Experience (SAE) program (30 points). U.S. citizenship is required. **Deadline for Receipt:** February of each year. **Additional Information:** Funding for these scholarships is provided by *Progressive Farmer Magazine*.

2268 ■ NATIONAL FFA ORGANIZATION

Attn: Scholarship Office
6060 FFA Drive
P.O. Box 68960
Indianapolis, IN 46268-0960
Tel: (317)802-4321
Fax: (317)802-5321
E-mail: scholarships@ffa.org
Web Site: http://www.ffa.org

To provide financial assistance to FFA members who are interested in studying journalism in college.

Title of Award: Vance Publishing Corporation Scholarship **Area, Field, or Subject:** Agricultural sciences; Communications; Journalism **Level of Education for which Award is Granted:** Four Year College **Number Awarded:** 1 each year. **Funds Available:** The stipend is $1,000. Funds are paid directly to the recipient. **Duration:** 1 year; nonrenewable.

Eligibility Requirements: This program is open to members who are graduating high school seniors planning to enroll full time in college. Applicants must be interested in working on a 4-year degree with a preference for agricultural journalism. Selection is based on academic achievement (10 points for GPA, 10 points for SAT or ACT score, 10 points for class rank), leadership in FFA activities (30 points), leadership in community activities (10 points), and participation in the Supervised Agricultural Experience (SAE) program (30 points). U.S. citizenship is required. **Deadline for Receipt:** February of each year. **Additional Information:** Funding for this scholarship is provided by Vance Publishing Corporation.

2269 ■ NATIONAL PRESS CLUB

Attn: General Manager's Office
529 14th Street, N.W.
Washington, DC 20045
Tel: (202)662-7532
E-mail: jbooze@press.org
Web Site: http://www.press.org/programs/aboutscholarship.cfm

To provide funding to minority high school seniors interested in preparing for a journalism career in college.

Title of Award: Ellen Masin Persina Scholarship **Area, Field, or Subject:** Journalism **Level of Education for which Award is Granted:** Undergraduate **Number Awarded:** 1 or more each year. **Funds Available:** The stipend is $5,000 per year. **Duration:** 4 years.

Eligibility Requirements: This program is open to minority high school seniors who have been accepted to college and plan to prepare for a career in journalism. Applicants must 1) demonstrate an ongoing interest in journalism through work in high school and/or other media; 2) submit a 1-page essay on why they want to prepare for a career in journalism; and 3) have a GPA of 2.75 or higher in high school. Financial need is considered in the selection process. **Deadline for Receipt:** February of each year. **Additional Information:** The program began in 1991. In the past, the Press Club has drawn on the Washington Association of Black Journalists and Youth Connections (a nationwide organization that produces free papers written by high school students).

2270 ■ NATIONAL SCHOLASTIC PRESS ASSOCIATION

2221 University Avenue, S.E., Suite 121
Minneapolis, MN 55414
Tel: (612)625-8335
Fax: (612)626-0720
E-mail: info@studentpress.org
Web Site: http://www.studentpress.org/nspa/contests.html

To recognize and reward outstanding high school journalists.

Title of Award: NSPA Journalism Honor Roll Award **Area, Field, or Subject:** Journalism **Level of Education for which Award is Granted:** Undergraduate **Number Awarded:** 1 each year. **Funds Available:** The award is a $1,000 scholarship. **Duration:** The competition is held annually.

Eligibility Requirements: This program is open to high school seniors who have earned a GPA of 3.75 or higher and have worked in student media for 1 or more years. The publication on which the student works

must have a current membership in the National Scholastic Press Association (NSPA). Candidates must be nominated by their teacher. The nominee judged most outstanding receives this award. Selection is based on cumulative GPA, publication experience (including years on staff, positions held, and workshops/conventions attended), college plans, and an essay of 500 words or less that explains "Why I'm choosing a career in journalism." **Deadline for Receipt:** February of each year.

2271 ■ NATIONAL SCHOLASTIC PRESS ASSOCIATION

2221 University Avenue, S.E., Suite 121
Minneapolis, MN 55414
Tel: (612)625-8335
Fax: (612)626-0720
E-mail: info@studentpress.org
Web Site: http://www.studentpress.org/nspa/contests.html

To provide financial assistance for college to high school journalists.

Title of Award: Wally Wikoff Scholarship for Editorial Leadership **Area, Field, or Subject:** Journalism **Level of Education for which Award is Granted:** Undergraduate **Number Awarded:** 1 each year. **Funds Available:** The stipend is $1,000. **Duration:** 1 year.

Eligibility Requirements: This program is open to high school seniors who have worked on the staff of a student newspaper that is a member of the National Scholastic Press Association (NSPA). Applicants must have a GPA of 3.5 or higher and must submit 3 published editorials and a brief recommendation from the program's adviser. **Deadline for Receipt:** February of each year. **Additional Information:** This scholarship, first presented in 1998, is jointly sponsored by NSPA and the ECI Scholarship Foundation of Educational Communications Inc., publisher of *Who's Who Among American High School Students*.

2272 ■ NEBRASKA PRESS ASSOCIATION FOUNDATION

845 S Street
Lincoln, NE 68508
Tel: (402)476-2851
Free: 800-369-2850
Fax: (402)476-2942
E-mail: nebpress@nebpress.com
Web Site: http://www.nebpress.com

To provide financial assistance to high school seniors in Nebraska who are interested in preparing for a career in print journalism.

Title of Award: Nebraska Press Association Foundation Scholarships **Area, Field, or Subject:** Advertising; Journalism; Photography, Journalistic **Level of Education for which Award is Granted:** Undergraduate **Funds Available:** The stipend is $1,250. **Duration:** 1 year.

Eligibility Requirements: This program is open to high school seniors in Nebraska who are interested in attending a college or university in the state and majoring in print journalism. Preference is given to students with specific interests in news, editorial, photography, circulation, production, or advertising. Applicants must submit information on their academic accomplishments, reasons for applying for this scholarship (including their career plans), and family financial situation. **Deadline for Receipt:** February of each year.

2273 ■ NEW JERSEY VIETNAM VETERANS' MEMORIAL

Attn: Scholarship Committee
1 Memorial Lane
P.O. Box 648
Holmdel, NJ 07733
Tel: (732)335-0033
Fax: (732)335-1107
Web Site: http://www.njvvmf.org

To recognize and reward, with college scholarships, New Jersey high school seniors who have visited the New Jersey Vietnam Veterans' Memorial and written an essay about the experience.

Title of Award: New Jersey Vietnam Veterans' Memorial Scholarships **Area, Field, or Subject:** General studies/Field of study not specified; Writing **Level of Education for which Award is Granted:** Undergraduate **Number Awarded:** 2 each year. **Funds Available:** The award is a $2,500 scholarship. **Duration:** The awards are granted annually.

Eligibility Requirements: This program is open to seniors graduating from high schools in New Jersey who have visited the New Jersey Vietnam Veterans' Memorial. Applicants must submit an essay of 250 to 300 words in which they reflect upon their visit. They must submit proof of acceptance to a college or trade school, but letters of recommendation and transcripts are not required. **Deadline for Receipt:** April of each year. **Additional Information:** These awards were first presented in 2004.

2274 ■ NEW YORK STATE ARCHIVES

Attn: Coordinator of Educational Programs
Cultural Education Center, Suite 9B52
Albany, NY 12230
Tel: (518)474-6926
E-mail: jdaniels@mail.nysed.gov
Web Site: http://www.archives.nysed.gov/a/grantsawards/ ga_student_sraguidelines.shtml
To recognize and reward outstanding historical research conducted by students in grades 4 through 12 in New York State.
Title of Award: New York State Archives Student Research Award **Area, Field, or Subject:** Creative writing; History, American; Playwriting; Writing **Level of Education for which Award is Granted:** Undergraduate **Number Awarded:** 3 each year: 1 in each grade level category. **Funds Available:** The award in each category consists of a certificate and a cash prize. **Duration:** The competition is held annually.
Eligibility Requirements: This is a statewide competition open to students in New York in 3 categories: grades 4-5, grades 6-8, and grades 9-12. Individual students and groups of students (including entire classes) may be nominated. All nominations for the award must be made by a teacher or administrator in the school attended by the entrants. Research projects prepared for other competitions (e.g., History Day) are eligible if they meet other relevant criteria, especially the use of historical records. An annotated bibliography is required for all entries. A substantial portion of the research must be based on historical records from archives, museums, historical societies, libraries, local governments, community organizations, businesses, families, and/or individuals. The product of the student research may be any of the following: research paper; exhibit; audiovisual production; performance; proposal for designation of historic marker, property, or district; or web sites, PowerPoint presentations, and other computer-based entries. Oral history interviews are not eligible for this award program. **Deadline for Receipt:** May of each year. **Additional Information:** This program began in 1990.

2275 ■ NEW YORK STATE LEGION PRESS ASSOCIATION

c/o Scholarship Chairman
American Legion (NYSLPA)
P.O. Box 650
East Aurora, NY 14052
To provide financial assistance to the children of members of the American Legion or American Legion Auxiliary in New York who are interested in careers in communications.
Title of Award: New York State Legion Press Association Scholarship **Area, Field, or Subject:** Communications; Graphic art and design; Journalism; Public relations **Level of Education for which Award is Granted:** Four Year College **Number Awarded:** 1 each year. **Funds Available:** The stipend is $1,000. **Duration:** 1 year.
Eligibility Requirements: This program is open to New York residents who are the children of members of the American Legion or American Legion Auxiliary, or members of the Sons of the American Legion, or junior members of the American Legion Auxiliary, or graduates of the New York Boys State or Girls State. Applicants must be entering or attending an accredited 4-year college or university, working on a degree in communications (including public relations, journalism, reprographics, newspaper design or management, or other related fields acceptable to the scholarship committee). Along with their application, they must submit a 500-word essay on why they chose the field of communications as a future vocation. Financial need and class standing are not considered. **Deadline for Receipt:** May of each year.

2276 ■ OAK RIDGE INSTITUTE FOR SCIENCE AND EDUCATION

Attn: Science and Engineering Education
P.O. Box 117
Oak Ridge, TN 37831-0117
Tel: (865)576-8239
Fax: (865)241-5219
E-mail: igrid.gregory@orau.gov
Web Site: http://www.orau.gov/orise.htm

To provide financial assistance and summer research experience to undergraduate students who are working on a degree in a field of interest to the Department of Homeland Security (DHS).
Title of Award: Department of Homeland Security Undergraduate Scholarships **Area, Field, or Subject:** Agricultural sciences; Biological and clinical sciences; Communications; Computer and information sciences; Engineering; Information science and technology; Mathematics and mathematical sciences; Physical sciences; Psychology; Public administration; Religion; Social sciences; Writing **Level of Education for which Award is Granted:** Undergraduate **Number Awarded:** Approximately 50 each year. **Funds Available:** This program provides a stipend of $1,000 per month during the academic year and $5,000 for the internship plus full payment of tuition and mandatory fees. **Duration:** 2 academic years plus 10 weeks during the intervening summer.
Eligibility Requirements: This program is open to 1) full-time students who are in their second year of college attendance as of the application deadline; and 2) part-time students who have completed at least 45 but no more than 60 semester hours as of the application deadline. Applicants must be majoring in the agricultural sciences, biological and life sciences, computer and information sciences, engineering, mathematics, physical sciences, psychology, social sciences, or selected humanities (religious studies, cultural studies, public policy, advocacy, communications, or science writing). They must have a GPA of 3.3 or higher. Along with their application, they must submit 2 statements on 1) their educational and professional goals, the kinds of research they are interested in conducting, specific questions that interest them, and how they became interested in them; and 2) how they think their interests, talents, and initiative would contribute to make the homeland safer and secure. Selection is based on those statements, academic record, references, and SAT or ACT scores. As part of their program, they must be interested in participating in summer research and development activities at a DHS-designated facility. U.S. citizenship is required. **Deadline for Receipt:** January of each year. **Additional Information:** This program, established in 2003, is funded by DHS and administered by Oak Ridge Institute for Science and Education (ORISE). Recipients must enroll full time.

2277 ■ OKLAHOMA STATE REGENTS FOR HIGHER EDUCATION

Attn: Director of Scholarship and Grant Programs
655 Research Parkway, Suite 200
P.O. Box 108850
Oklahoma City, OK 73101-8850
Tel: (405)225-9239
Free: 800-858-1840
Fax: (405)225-9230
E-mail: studentinfo@osrhe.edu
Web Site: http://www.okhighered.org/student-center/financial-aid/future-teach.shtml
To provide forgivable loans to Oklahoma residents who are interested in teaching (particularly in teacher shortage fields) in Oklahoma.
Title of Award: Oklahoma Future Teachers Scholarship Program **Area, Field, or Subject:** Education; Education, Special; English language and literature; Linguistics; Mathematics and mathematical sciences; Science **Level of Education for which Award is Granted:** Graduate, Undergraduate **Number Awarded:** Varies each year; recently, 136 students received support through this program. **Funds Available:** Full-time students receive up to $1,500 per year if they have completed 60 hours or more or up to $1,000 if they have completed fewer than 60 hours; part-time students receive up to $750 per year if they have completed 60 hours or more or up to $500 per year if they have completed fewer than 60 hours. Funds are paid directly to the institution on the student's behalf. This is a forgivable loan program; recipients must agree to teach in Oklahoma public schools for 3 years following graduation and licensure. **Duration:** 1 year; may be renewable for up to 3 additional years as long as the recipient maintains a GPA of 2.5 or higher.
Eligibility Requirements: Candidates for this program must be nominated by institutions of higher education in Oklahoma. Nominees may be high school seniors, high school graduates, or currently-enrolled undergraduate or graduate students. They must 1) rank in the top 15% of their high school graduating class; 2) have an ACT or SAT score ranking in the top 15% for high school graduates of the same year; 3) have been admitted into a professional education program at an accredited Oklahoma institution of higher education; or 4) have achieved an undergraduate record of outstanding success as defined by the institution.

Both part-time and full-time students are eligible, but preference is given to full-time students. Applicants must be interested in teaching in critical shortage areas in the state upon graduation. These areas change periodically but recently have included special education, mathematics, science, English, and foreign languages. **Deadline for Receipt:** September of each year.

2278 ■ OPTIMIST INTERNATIONAL

Attn: Programs Department
4494 Lindell Boulevard
St. Louis, MO 63108
Tel: (314)371-6000
Free: 800-500-8130
Fax: (314)371-6009
E-mail: programs@optimist.org
Web Site: http://www.optimist.org
To recognize and reward, with college scholarships, outstanding essays by high school students on a topic that changes annually.
Title of Award: Optimist International Essay Contest **Area, Field, or Subject:** General studies/Field of study not specified; Writing **Level of Education for which Award is Granted:** Undergraduate **Number Awarded:** 3 international winners are selected each year. A total of $44,000 in scholarships is awarded annually. **Funds Available:** The international first-place winner receives $5,000, second $3,000, and third $2,000. Funds are to be used to pay college costs. District winners are awarded a $650 college scholarship. **Duration:** The competition is held annually.
Eligibility Requirements: This competition is open to high school students in the United States, the Caribbean, or Canada who are younger than 19 years of age. Applicants are invited to write an essay of 400 to 500 words on a topic that changes each year; a recent topic was "I'm Unique because..." They compete on the local club, district, and national/international levels. Essays may be written in the official language of the area where the club is located (English, Spanish, or French). Selection is based on material organization (40 points); vocabulary and style (30 points); grammar, punctuation, and spelling (20 points); neatness (5 points); and adherence to contest rules (5 points). **Deadline for Receipt:** Essays must be submitted to local clubs by the end of February of each year. The district deadline is in April. **Additional Information:** This competition was first held in 1983. More than 1,200 Optimist International local clubs participate in the program each year. Entry information is available only from local Optimist Clubs.

2279 ■ ORDER SONS OF ITALY IN AMERICA

Attn: Sons of Italy Foundation
219 E Street, N.E.
Washington, DC 20002
Tel: (202)547-5106
Fax: (202)546-8168
E-mail: scholarships@osia.org
Web Site: http://www.osia.org/public/scholarships/grants.asp
To provide financial assistance for college to high school seniors of Italian descent who write about the principles of liberty, freedom, and equality in the United States.
Title of Award: Henry Salvatori Scholarship **Area, Field, or Subject:** General studies/Field of study not specified; Patriotism; Writing **Level of Education for which Award is Granted:** Four Year College **Number Awarded:** 1 each year. **Funds Available:** The stipend is $25,000. **Duration:** 1 year; nonrenewable.
Eligibility Requirements: Eligible are U.S. citizens of Italian descent who are high school seniors planning to enroll as full-time students in an undergraduate program at an accredited 4-year college or university. Applications must be accompanied by essays, from 750 to 1,000 words, on the relevance to the United States today of the Declaration of Independence, the Constitution, or the Bill of Rights and the meaning of those documents to the principles of liberty, freedom, and equality in the 21st century. The scholarship is presented to a student who has demonstrated exceptional leadership, distinguished scholarship, and an understanding of the principles for which the country was founded. **Deadline for**

Receipt: February of each year. **Additional Information:** Applications must be accompanied by a $25 processing fee.

2280 ■ OREGON ASSOCIATION OF BROADCASTERS

Attn: Scholarship Committee
7150 S.W. Hampton Street, Suite 214
Portland, OR 97223-8366
Tel: (503)443-2299
Fax: (503)443-2488
E-mail: theoab@theoab.org
Web Site: http://www.theoab.org/eduopps_foundation.htm
To provide financial assistance to students in Oregon who are interested in majoring in broadcast-related fields in college.
Title of Award: Oregon Association of Broadcasters Scholarships **Area, Field, or Subject:** Broadcasting; Communications; Journalism **Level of Education for which Award is Granted:** Undergraduate **Number Awarded:** 6 each year: 2 to graduating high school seniors and 4 to students currently enrolled in 2- or 4-year college broadcast programs. **Funds Available:** The stipend is $1,000. **Duration:** 1 year.
Eligibility Requirements: This program is open to Oregon residents who are either enrolled or accepted for enrollment at a 2- or 4-year public or private college or university in the state. Applicants must be planning to enroll or be currently enrolled in a full-time undergraduate course of study, majoring in broadcast journalism, production, management, or another broadcast-related field. They must be graduating high school seniors, first- or second-year students in a 2-year program, or sophomores, juniors, or seniors in a 4-year program. Preference is given to applicants with at least a 3.0 cumulative GPA and demonstrated academic and/or professional experience in broadcasting or other electronic-media fields. Along with their application, students must submit an essay that explains their reasons for choosing a broadcast major and includes any broadcast activities in which they have participated, their first job preference after college, their 10-year goals, any other scholarships they have received, and any academic honors they have received. Financial need is not considered in the selection process. **Deadline for Receipt:** February of each year.

2281 ■ OREGON STUDENT ASSISTANCE COMMISSION

Attn: Grants and Scholarships Division
1500 Valley River Drive, Suite 100
Eugene, OR 97401-2146
Tel: (541)687-7395
Free: 800-452-8807
Fax: (541)687-7419
E-mail: awardinfo@mercury.osac.state.or.us
Web Site: http://www.osac.state.or.us
To recognize and reward high school seniors in Oregon who submit essays on the proper use of credit.
Title of Award: Oregon Collectors Association Bob Hasson Memorial Scholarship **Area, Field, or Subject:** General studies/Field of study not specified; Writing **Level of Education for which Award is Granted:** Undergraduate **Number Awarded:** 3 each year. **Funds Available:** Awards are $3,000 for first place, $2,500 for second place, or $1,500 for third place. Funds must be used for tuition and other educational expenses at a college or vocational school in Oregon. **Duration:** The award, presented annually, may not be renewed.
Eligibility Requirements: This program is open to seniors graduating from high schools in Oregon who submit a 3- to 4-page essay entitled "The Proper Use of Credit in the 21st Century." Children and grandchildren of owners and officers of collection agencies registered in Oregon are not eligible. **Deadline for Receipt:** February of each year.

2282 ■ OREGON STUDENT ASSISTANCE COMMISSION

Attn: Grants and Scholarships Division
1500 Valley River Drive, Suite 100
Eugene, OR 97401-2146
Tel: (541)687-7395
Free: 800-452-8807
Fax: (541)687-7419
E-mail: awardinfo@mercury.osac.state.or.us
Web Site: http://www.osac.state.or.us
To provide financial assistance to students in Oregon interested in majoring in journalism.

Title of Award: Jackson Foundation Journalism Scholarship **Area, Field, or Subject:** Journalism **Level of Education for which Award is Granted:** Undergraduate **Number Awarded:** Varies each year; recently, 7 of these scholarships were awarded. **Funds Available:** Stipend amounts vary; recently, they were at least $1,429. **Duration:** 1 year; may be renewed.

Eligibility Requirements: This program is open to graduates of Oregon high schools who are studying or planning to study journalism at a college or university in the state. **Deadline for Receipt:** February of each year. **Additional Information:** This program is administered by the Oregon Student Assistance Commission (OSAC) with funds provided by the Oregon Community Foundation, 1221 S.W. Yamhill, Suite 100, Portland, OR 97205, (503) 227-6846, Fax: (503) 274-7771.

2283 ■ PHILADELPHIA NEWSPAPERS, INC.
Attn: Ivan Sample
400 North Broad Street
P.O. Box 8263
Philadelphia, PA 19101
Tel: (215)854-2429
Fax; (215)854-2578
E-mail: isample@phillynews.com
Web Site: http://www.philly.com/mld/philly/living/education
To provide financial assistance to minority high school seniors from the circulation area of Philadelphia Newspapers Inc. (PNI) who are interested in a career in journalism or communications.
Title of Award: PNI Knight Ridder Minority Scholars Program **Area, Field, or Subject:** Communications; Journalism **Level of Education for which Award is Granted:** Undergraduate **Number Awarded:** 3 each year. **Funds Available:** The stipend is $1,000. **Duration:** 1 year; nonrenewable.

Eligibility Requirements: This program is open to minority seniors graduating from high schools in the service area of the PNI newspapers (the *Philadelphia Inquirer* and the *Philadelphia Daily News*) in Delaware, New Jersey, and Pennsylvania. Applicants must be interested in majoring in journalism in college. Along with their application, they must submit 2 letters of recommendation, transcripts of grades, SAT or ACT scores, up to 5 samples of work with bylines, and an essay on why they want to prepare for a career in the journalism or communication business. **Deadline for Receipt:** January of each year. **Additional Information:** The recipients of these scholarships are automatically entered into competition for the Knight Ridder Minority Scholarship Program of $40,000 over 4 years.

2284 ■ POETRY MAGAZINE
Attn: Poetry Foundation
1030 North Clark Street
Chicago, IL 60610-5412
Tel: (312)787-7070
Fax: (312)787-6650
E-mail: mail@poetryfoundation.org
Web Site: http://www.poetryfoundation.org/foundation/prizes_fellowship.html
To provide financial assistance to undergraduate and graduate students who are studying poetry.
Title of Award: Ruth Lilly Poetry Fellowships **Area, Field, or Subject:** Creative writing; English language and literature; Poetry **Level of Education for which Award is Granted:** Graduate, Undergraduate **Number Awarded:** 2 each year. **Funds Available:** The stipend is $15,000 per year. **Duration:** 1 year.

Eligibility Requirements: This program is open to undergraduate and graduate students in creative writing or English who have not yet received a master's or doctoral degree. Program directors and department chairs at colleges and universities in the United States are invited to nominate 1 student-poet from their program. Candidates must be younger than 31 years of age and may not have published a book of poems. Nominations must be accompanied by samples of the candidate's poetry. **Deadline for Receipt:** April of each year. **Additional Information:** This program began in 1989.

2285 ■ PRESS CLUB OF NEW ORLEANS
Attn: Scholarship Committee
203 Carondelet Street, Suite 415
New Orleans, LA 70130

Tel: (504)523-1010
E-mail: pressclubneworleans@cox.net
Web Site: http://www.pressclubneworleans.org
To provide financial assistance to students in Louisiana who will be majoring in journalism.
Title of Award: Press Club of New Orleans Journalism Scholarship Program **Area, Field, or Subject:** Communications; Journalism **Level of Education for which Award is Granted:** Undergraduate **Number Awarded:** 1 or more each year. **Funds Available:** A total of $5,000 is awarded each year. **Duration:** 1 year.

Eligibility Requirements: This program is open to Louisiana residents who will be enrolled in university-level print or broadcast journalism programs during the upcoming academic year. Applicants must submit 1) a brief (1 to 3 pages) written statement outlining their course of study, career goals, and financial need, and 2) examples of their published work, including newspaper stories, tapes, columns, and/or editorials. **Deadline for Receipt:** April of each year. **Additional Information:** Recipients may attend school in any state.

2286 ■ REACHING COMMON GROUND
c/o Institute for Christian and Jewish Studies
1316 Park Avenue
Baltimore, MD 21217
Tel: (410)523-7227
Fax: (410)523-0636
E-mail: essay@reachingcommonground.com
Web Site: http://
To recognize and reward students who submit outstanding essays on interfaith dialogue between Christians and Jews.
Title of Award: Reaching Common Ground Essay Contest **Area, Field, or Subject:** Religion; Writing **Level of Education for which Award is Granted:** Undergraduate **Number Awarded:** 27 each year: 1 first prize, 1 second prize, 10 third prizes, and 15 fourth prizes. **Funds Available:** Prizes are $25,000 for first, $10,000 for second, $5,000 for third, and $1,000 for fourth. **Duration:** The competition is held annually.

Eligibility Requirements: This program is open to all students between 16 and 22 years of age in the United States. Applicants must submit an essay, up to 2,500 words in length, on 1 of 3 assigned topics. The topics involve faith and the Bible, history, or current events and stress the common ground between Christians and Jews. Selection is based on ability to represent accurately multiple points of view (35%), range and depth of knowledge as demonstrated in the essay (30%), creativity (20%), and literary merit (15%). **Deadline for Receipt:** July of each year. **Additional Information:** This program was established in 2004. From among the winners, 12 are selected to be fellows at the Institute for Christian and Jewish Studies and participate in 2 weekend retreats on interfaith learning.

2287 ■ SCHOOL BAND AND ORCHESTRA MAGAZINE
Attn: Student Scholarships
21 Highland Circle, Suite 1
Needham, MA 02494
Tel: (781)453-9310
Free: 800-964-5150
Fax: (781)453-9389
Web Site: http://www.sbomagazine.com/Essay
To recognize and reward, with college scholarships, elementary and high school students who submit outstanding essays on playing a musical instrument.
Title of Award: Annual Music Student Scholarships **Area, Field, or Subject:** Music; Writing **Level of Education for which Award is Granted:** Undergraduate **Number Awarded:** 10 each year: 5 to students in grades 4-8 and 5 to students in grades 9-12. **Funds Available:** The award is a $1,000 college scholarship. **Duration:** The competition is held annually.

Eligibility Requirements: This competition is open to public and private school students in grades 4 through 12. Applicants must submit an essay of up to 250 words on "How Playing a Musical Instrument Made Me a Better Student." **Deadline for Receipt:** December of each year.

2288 ■ SIEMENS FOUNDATION
170 Wood Avenue South
Iselin, NJ 08830

877-822-5233
Fax: (732)603-5890
E-mail: foundation@sc.siemens.com
Web Site: http://www.siemens-foundation.org/scholarship
To recognize and reward outstanding high school seniors who have undertaken individual or team research projects in science, mathematics, and technology (or in combinations of those disciplines).

Title of Award: Siemens Westinghouse Competition Awards **Area, Field, or Subject:** Astronomy and astronomical sciences; Atmospheric science; Biochemistry; Biological and clinical sciences; Chemistry; Computer and information sciences; Earth sciences; Engineering, Civil; Engineering, Electrical; Engineering, Mechanical; Environmental science; Genetics; Geosciences; Materials research/science; Mathematics and mathematical sciences; Nutrition; Physics; Writing **Level of Education for which Award is Granted:** Undergraduate **Number Awarded:** In the initial round of judging, up to 300 regional semifinalists (up to 50 in each region) are selected. Of those, 60 are chosen as regional finalists (5 individuals and 5 teams in each of the 6 regions). Then 12 regional winners (1 individual and 1 team) are selected in the regional competitions, and they become the national finalists. **Funds Available:** At the regional level, finalists receive $1,000 scholarships, both as individuals and members of teams. Individual regional winners receive $3,000 scholarships. Winning regional teams receive $6,000 scholarships to be divided among the team members. Those regional winners then receive additional scholarships as national finalists. In the national competition, first-place winners receive an additional $100,000 scholarship, second place an additional $50,000 scholarship, third place an additional $40,000 scholarship, fourth place an additional $30,000 scholarship, fifth place an additional $20,000 scholarship, and sixth place an additional $10,000 scholarship. Those national awards are provided both to individuals and to teams to be divided equally among team members. Scholarship money is sent directly to the recipient's college or university to cover undergraduate and/or graduate educational expenses. Schools with regional finalists receive a $2,000 award to be used to support science, mathematics, and technology programs in their schools. **Duration:** The competition is held annually.

Eligibility Requirements: This program is open to high school seniors who are legal or permanent U.S. residents. They must be enrolled in a high school in the United States, Puerto Rico, Guam, Virgin Islands, American Samoa, Wake and Midway Islands, or the Marianas. U.S. high school students enrolled in a Department of Defense dependents school, an accredited overseas American or international school, a foreign school as an exchange student, or a foreign school because their parent(s) live and work abroad are also eligible. Students being home-schooled qualify if they obtain the endorsement of the school district official responsible for such programs. Research projects may be submitted in mathematics and the biological and physical sciences, or involve combinations of disciplines, such as astrophysics, biochemistry, bioengineering, biology, biophysics, botany, chemistry, computer science, civil engineering, earth and atmospheric science engineering, electrical engineering, environmental sciences, fluid dynamics, genetics, geology, materials science, mathematics, mechanical engineering, nutritional science, physics, toxicology, and virology. Both individual and team projects (2 or 3 members) may be entered. All team members must meet the eligibility requirements. Team projects may include seniors, but that is not a requirement. Competition entrants must submit a detailed report on their research project, including a description of the purpose of the research, rationale for the research, pertinent scientific literature, methodology, results, discussion, and conclusion. All projects must be endorsed by a sponsoring high school (except home-schooled students, who obtain their endorsement from the district or state home-school official). Each project must have a project advisor or mentor who is a member of the instructional staff or a person approved by the endorsing high school. There are 3 judging phases to the competition. An initial review panel selects outstanding research projects from 6 different regions of the country. The students submitting these projects are identified as regional semifinalists. Out of those, the highest-rated projects from each region are selected and the students who submitted them are recognized as regional finalists. For the next phase, the regional finalists are offered all-expense paid trips to the regional competition on the campus of a regional university partner, where their projects are reviewed by a panel of judges appointed by the host institution. Regional finalists are required to prepare a poster display of their research project, make an oral presentation about the research and research findings, and respond to questions from the

judges. The top-rated individual and the top-rated team project in each region are selected as regional winners to represent the region in the national competition as national finalists. At that competition, the national finalists again display their projects, make oral presentations, and respond to judges' questions. At each phase, selection is based on clarity of expression, comprehensiveness, creativity, field knowledge, future work, interpretation, literature review, presentation, scientific importance, and validity. **Deadline for Receipt:** September of each year. **Additional Information:** The program is offered by Siemens Foundation, in partnership with the College Board. Information is available from the College Board at (703) 707-8999, E-mail: spro@collegeboard.org. Students submitting the projects with the highest evaluations become part of a registry that is circulated to colleges and universities nationwide. To continue receiving scholarships, winners must attend an accredited academic institution on a full-time basis.

2289 ■ ANDRE SOBEL RIVER OF LIFE FOUNDATION
Attn: Awards
8899 Beverly Boulevard, Suite 111
Los Angeles, CA 90048
Tel: (310)276-7111
Fax: (310)276-0244
E-mail: info@andreriveroflife.org
Web Site: http://www.andreriveroflife.org
To recognize and reward young cancer survivors who submit outstanding essays on their illness.

Title of Award: Andre Sobel Award **Area, Field, or Subject:** Writing **Level of Education for which Award is Granted:** Undergraduate **Number Awarded:** 5 cash prizes are awarded each year. **Funds Available:** First prize is $5,000. Other cash prizes are awarded to second- through fifth-place winners. **Duration:** The competition is held annually.

Eligibility Requirements: This competition is open to cancer survivors under 21 years of age. Applicants are allowed to define themselves as a survivor; not medical definition or certain amount of time is required. They must submit an essay, up to 1,500 words in length, on a topic that changes annually but relates to their illness. Recently, applicants were invited to write on "The Letter I Would Like to Have Received From My Best Friend During My Illness." **Deadline for Receipt:** June of each year. **Additional Information:** These awards were first presented in 2000.

2290 ■ SOUTH CAROLINA STATE DEPARTMENT OF EDUCATION
1429 Senate Street, Room 1010A
Columbia, SC 29201
Tel: (803)734-8485
E-mail: sspade@sde.state.sc.us
Web Site: http://www.myscschools.com/offices/ombudsman/arscholarship
To recognize and reward high school seniors in South Carolina who participate in a competition in art, creative writing, drama, or music.

Title of Award: Archibald Rutledge Scholarship Program **Area, Field, or Subject:** Art; Creative writing; Graphic art and design; Music composition; Painting; Playwriting; Poetry; Visual arts; Writing **Level of Education for which Award is Granted:** Undergraduate **Number Awarded:** 4 each year: 1 in each of the 4 categories. **Funds Available:** The award consists of a $4,000 scholarship, to be used for tuition, room, board, and instructional resource expenses. **Duration:** 1 year.

Eligibility Requirements: This program is open to U.S. citizens who have attended South Carolina public high schools for at least 2 years, are currently seniors, and are planning to attend a South Carolina college or university. Applicants compete by submitting samples of their work in 1 of 4 areas: 1) visual arts, limited to 2-dimensional work such as drawing and painting media, printmaking, and collage; no 3-dimensional works, photographs, or computer-generated images are accepted; 2) creative writing, as a sonnet, lyric, or narrative poem, up to 1 page; 3) drama, a 1-act play with a performing time of 20 to 45 minutes; or 4) music, a composition of 3 to 5 minutes for solo or small ensemble, vocal or instrumental, in any appropriate style. In addition to the work, they must submit a process folio that contains documentation of the planning and development of the project and a 1-page reflection statement addressing the intent of the work and comparing the final product with the original concept. A panel of professionals in the field selects up to 10 finalists, based on originality, creativity, and the correlation and implications of the process folio for the final composition. Finalists must attend the scholarship competition, where they present a portfolio of a number of selected works as specified by the judges. **Deadline for Receipt:** February of each year.

2291 ■ SOUTH CAROLINA STUDENT LOAN CORPORATION

Interstate Center
16 Berryhill Road, Suite 210
P.O. Box 21487
Columbia, SC 29221-1487
Tel: (803)798-0916
Free: 800-347-2752
Fax: (803)772-9410
Web Site: http://www.slc.sc.edu

To provide scholarship/loans to students in South Carolina who wish to teach certain subjects or in certain geographic areas.
Title of Award: South Carolina Teacher Loan Program **Area, Field, or Subject:** Agricultural sciences; Classical studies; Consumer affairs; Dance; Education, Elementary; Education, Music; Education, Special; English language and literature; Foreign languages; Library and archival sciences; Mathematics and mathematical sciences; Science; Speech and language pathology/audiology; Technology **Level of Education for which Award is Granted:** Graduate, Undergraduate **Number Awarded:** Varies each year. **Funds Available:** Freshmen and sophomores may borrow up to $2,500 per academic year; juniors, seniors, and graduate students may borrow up to $5,000 per academic year. This is a scholarship/loan program; loans are forgivable at the rate of 20% or $3,000, whichever is greater, for each full year of teaching in an area (either geographic or subject) of critical need; for students who teach in both critical subject and geographic areas, the rate of cancellation is 33% or $5,000, whichever is greater, per year. Borrowers who fail to teach in either a critical subject or geographic area must repay the loan at an annual interest rate that varies (currently, 5.37%) but is capped at 10.25%. **Duration:** 1 year; may be renewed for a total of 5 years of undergraduate and 5 years of graduate study.
Eligibility Requirements: Eligible to apply are residents of South Carolina who are planning to teach in certain critical geographic areas of the state, or to teach in critical subject areas. Entering freshmen must have ranked in the top 40% of their high school class and have an ACT or SAT score greater than the South Carolina average (recently 986 on the SAT or 19.3 on the ACT); enrolled undergraduates or entering graduate students must have at least a 2.75 cumulative GPA; graduate students who have completed at least 1 term must have a GPA of 3.5 or better. Undergraduate students at South Carolina colleges must have taken and passed the Education Entrance Exam; students at institutions outside South Carolina must have completed the necessary prerequisites required at that institution. Only U.S. citizens may apply. **Deadline for Receipt:** May of each year. **Additional Information:** Recently, the critical subject areas include mathematics, science (biology, chemistry, physics, and general science), media specialist, special education, industrial technology, foreign languages (Spanish, French, Latin, and German), family and consumer science, art, music, business education, English and language arts, dance, speech and drama/theater, and agriculture. For a list of critical geographic area, contact the sponsor.

2292 ■ SOUTH CAROLINA VOCATIONAL REHABILITATION DEPARTMENT

Attn: Lucerne Iseman, Assistant Commissioner
1410 Boston Avenue
P.O. Box 15
West Columbia, SC 29171-0015
Tel: (803)896-6833; (866)247-8354
E-mail: info@scvrd.state.sc.us
Web Site: http://www.scvrd.net/g_journal_contest.html

To recognize and reward, with college scholarships, high school students in South Carolina who submit outstanding newspaper articles on topics related to employment of people with disabilities.
Title of Award: South Carolina Vocational Rehabilitation Department Journalism Contest **Area, Field, or Subject:** Journalism; Writing **Level of Education for which Award is Granted:** Undergraduate **Number Awarded:** 1 each year. **Funds Available:** The winner receives full payment of tuition and fees at a South Carolina state-supported institution. Some schools include room and board as part of tuition and fees. **Duration:** 4 years, provided the recipient maintains general scholastic and conduct standards.

Eligibility Requirements: This competition is open to South Carolina residents between 16 and 19 years of age enrolled as juniors or seniors in high school or otherwise qualified to begin postsecondary education no later than 2 years after the contest. Applicants are not required to have a disability, but they must submit a newspaper article, up to 3 pages in length, on a topic that changes annually but relates to employment of people with disabilities. A recent topic was "Workers with Disabilities: Ready for Tomorrow's Jobs Today." Articles should use correct grammar and sentence structure and follow standard journalistic practice of the 5 Ws (who, what, where, when, and why). **Deadline for Receipt:** January of each year. **Additional Information:** This competition is sponsored by the South Carolina Governor's Committee on Employment of People with Disabilities.

2293 ■ STUDENT PRESS LAW CENTER

Attn: Executive Director
1101 Wilson Boulevard, Suite 1100
Arlington, VA 22209-2211
Tel: (703)807-1904
E-mail: splc@splc.org
Web Site: http://www.splc.org/csjaward.asp

To recognize and reward secondary school student journalists and school officials who have supported the First Amendment.
Title of Award: Courage in Student Journalism Awards **Area, Field, or Subject:** Intellectual freedom; Journalism **Level of Education for which Award is Granted:** Professional, Undergraduate **Number Awarded:** 2 each year: 1 student and 1 school official. **Funds Available:** The winners in each category (student and administrator) receive a $5,000 award. **Duration:** The award is presented annually.

Eligibility Requirements: This program is open to deserving middle and high school student journalists and school officials who have stood up in support of the First Amendment. Student applicants must have shown determination, despite difficulty and resistance, in exercising their First Amendment press rights. School administrator applicants must have demonstrated support, under difficult circumstances, for the First Amendment press rights of their school's student media. Entrants should submit a written description (up to 600 words) of how their case meets the entry criteria, along with 2 letters of support and supporting materials or press clippings. **Deadline for Receipt:** June of each year. **Additional Information:** This program, which began in 1998, is sponsored by The Newseum, the National Scholastic Press Association, and the Student Press Law Center.

2294 ■ STUDENT PRESS LAW CENTER

Attn: Executive Director
1101 Wilson Boulevard, Suite 1100
Arlington, VA 22209-2211
Tel: (703)807-1904
E-mail: splc@splc.org
Web Site: http://www.splc.org/legalfellow.asp

To provide financial assistance and work experience to undergraduate and graduate students interested in news writing and media law.
Title of Award: Scripps Howard Foundation Journalism Internships **Area, Field, or Subject:** Journalism; Law **Level of Education for which Award is Granted:** Graduate, Undergraduate **Number Awarded:** The number of internships varies each year; up to 2 scholarships are awarded to undergraduate summer interns. **Funds Available:** Full-time interns during the fall and spring receive a stipend of $3,000. Full-time interns during the summer receive a stipend of $2,300. The scholarship stipend is $600. **Duration:** 1 semester or summer for the internships; 1 year for the scholarship.

Eligibility Requirements: This program is open to undergraduate and graduate students who have experience in news writing and an interest in media law. Applicants must be interested in working at the Student Press Law Center during the summer, fall, or spring. Summer interns who are undergraduates on the staff of a student publication that is a member of the Associated Collegiate Press are also eligible to apply for a scholarship for the academic year following their internship. Selection of scholarship recipients is based on journalism experience, writing ability, and commitment to freedom of the press. **Deadline for Receipt:** Students are encouraged to submit applications for summer internships by January of each year, for fall internships by May of each year, and for spring internships by October of each year. **Additional Information:** This program, which began in 2002, is sponsored by the Scripps Howard Foundation. Interns research, write, and help edit the *Report,* the publication of the Student Press Law Center that chronicles student press cases and controversies from around the country. They also participate in issue-oriented seminars organized by the Center and the Reporters Committee for Freedom of the Press. Further information on the scholarships is available from the Associated Collegiate Press, 2221 University Avenue, S.E., Minneapolis, MN 55414, (612) 625-8335.

2295 ■ SWEDISH WOMEN'S EDUCATION ASSOCIATION INTERNATIONAL-SOUTH FLORIDA CHAPTER

c/o Yerti Nelson, Scholarship Committee
3759 Mykonos Court
Boca Raton, FL 33486
Tel: (561)997-2050
Fax: (561)997-8010
E-mail: florida@swea.org
Web Site: http://www.chapters-swea.org/florida

To provide financial assistance to Florida residents interested in studying in Sweden or an area related to Swedish studies.

Title of Award: South Florida SWEA Scholarship **Area, Field, or Subject:** Art; Art industries and trade; Crafts; Design; Environmental conservation; Environmental science; Foreign languages; General studies/Field of study not specified; Literature; Music; Swedish studies **Level of Education for which Award is Granted:** Graduate, Professional, Undergraduate **Number Awarded:** 1 each year. **Funds Available:** The stipend is $3,000.

Eligibility Requirements: This program is open to all residents of Florida interested in participating in an exchange program in Sweden. Applicants may also propose to study in the United States, if the studies specifically emphasize Sweden and Swedish aspects, including 1) Swedish language; 2) Swedish culture or traditions; 3) environmental science; 4) a health care program promoting better health for women and children; or 5) handicraft, art, glass art, music, literature, or design. Study proposals must be well-defined in time and content. Along with their application, they must submit a transcript from college, university, or vocational school; curriculum vitae; project proposal, describing the planned studies, length of studies, and goals; financial statement; and letter of recommendation from an instructor. **Deadline for Receipt:** January of each year. **Additional Information:** Within 3 months after the end of studies or the project, the recipient must report to the scholarship committee or, if possible, accept an invitation to an organization meeting to share the experience.

2296 ■ UNITED DAUGHTERS OF THE CONFEDERACY

Attn: Education Director
328 North Boulevard
Richmond, VA 23220-4057
Tel: (804)355-1636
Fax: (804)353-1396
E-mail: hqudc@rcn.com
Web Site: http://www.hqudc.org/scholarships/scholarships.html

To provide financial assistance to lineal descendants of Confederate veterans in certain southern states who are interested in majoring in southern history or literature.

Title of Award: Helen James Brewer Scholarship **Area, Field, or Subject:** English language and literature; History, American; Literature; United States studies **Level of Education for which Award is Granted:** Undergraduate **Number Awarded:** 1 each year. **Funds Available:** The amount of this scholarship depends on the availability of funds. **Duration:** 1 year; may be renewed.

Eligibility Requirements: Eligible to apply for these scholarships are lineal descendants of worthy Confederates or collateral descendants who are current or former members of the Children of the Confederacy or current members of the United Daughters of the Confederacy. Applicants must intend to study English or southern history and literature and must submit a family financial report and certified proof of the Confederate record of 1 ancestor, with the company and regiment in which he served. They must have at least a 3.0 GPA in high school. Residency in Alabama, Florida, Georgia, South Carolina, Tennessee, or Virginia is required. **Deadline for Receipt:** March of each year. **Additional Information:** Information is also available from Mrs. Robert C. Kraus, Second Vice President General, 239 Deerfield Lane, Franklin, NC 28734-0112. Members of the same family may not hold scholarships simultaneously,

and only 1 application per family will be accepted within any 1 year. All requests for applications must be accompanied by a self-addressed stamped envelope.

2297 ■ U.S. COAST GUARD CHIEF PETTY OFFICERS ASSOCIATION

Attn: CCCAF Scholarship Committee
5520-G Hempstead Way
Springfield, VA 22151-4009
Tel: (703)941-0395
Fax: (703)941-0397
E-mail: cgcpoa@aol.com
Web Site: http://www.uscgcpoa.org/0-main/scholarships/scholarships.htm

To recognize and reward, with college scholarships, children of members or deceased members of the U.S. Coast Guard Chief Petty Officers Association (CPOA) or the Coast Guard Enlisted Association (CGEA) who submit outstanding essays.

Title of Award: Captain Caliendo College Assistance Fund Scholarship **Area, Field, or Subject:** General studies/Field of study not specified; Writing **Level of Education for which Award is Granted:** Undergraduate **Number Awarded:** 1 each year. **Funds Available:** The award is a $3,500 scholarship. **Duration:** The competition is held annually.

Eligibility Requirements: This competition is open to children of members or deceased members of the CPOA or CGEA who are attending or planning to attend a college, university, or vocational school. Applicants may not be older than 24 years of age (the age limit does not apply to disabled children). They must submit an essay, up to 500 words, on a topic that changes annually; a recent topic was "What impact does the Patriot Act make on you and your community?" The author of the essay judged most outstanding receives this scholarship. **Deadline for Receipt:** February of each year.

2298 ■ UNIVERSITY OF TEXAS AT AUSTIN

Attn: Office of Community Relations
P.O. Box N
Austin, TX 78713-8914
Tel: (512)232-7599
Fax: (512)232-4848
E-mail: deb_duval@mail.utexas.edu
Web Site: http://www.utexas.edu/world/barbarajordan

To recognize and reward, with college scholarships, high school students in Texas who submit outstanding essays on topics related to African Americans in the state.

Title of Award: Barbara Jordan Historical Essay Competition **Area, Field, or Subject:** General studies/Field of study not specified; Writing **Level of Education for which Award is Granted:** Undergraduate **Number Awarded:** 3 prizes are awarded each year. **Funds Available:** In the state finals, first prize is $2,500, second $1,500, and third $1,000. Prizes are scholarships that may be used at any institution of the winner's choice. **Duration:** The competition is held annually.

Eligibility Requirements: This competition is open to high school students in grades 9-12 in Texas. Applicants must submit an essay, from 1,500 to 2,500 words in length on a topic that changes annually; recently, students were invited to write on "The African American in Texas: Past and Present." Competitions are first held in 10 regions in the state, with 3 regional winners advancing to the state finals. **Deadline for Receipt:** March of each year. **Additional Information:** The winning essays are submitted to the Texas State Historical Association for consideration for publication in its student journal, *Texas Historian.*

2299 ■ VETERANS OF FOREIGN WARS OF THE UNITED STATES

VFW Building
406 West 34th Street
Kansas City, MO 64111
Tel: (816)968-1117
Fax: (816)968-1149
E-mail: KHarmer@vfw.org
Web Site: http://www.vfw.org

To recognize and reward, with college scholarships, outstanding high school students in a national broadcast scriptwriting competition dealing with freedom and democracy.

Title of Award: Voice of Democracy Scholarship Program **Area, Field, or Subject:** General studies/Field of study not specified; Patriotism; Writing

Level of Education for which Award is Granted: Undergraduate **Number Awarded:** Recently, a total of 54 of these scholarships were awarded. In addition to the 5 top winners, other scholarships included 2 at $5,000, 1 at $4,000, 1 at $3,500, 2 at $3,000, 2 at $2,500, 9 at $2,000, 7 at $1,500, and 25 at $1,000. **Funds Available:** A total of $145,000 in national scholarships is awarded each year; first place is $25,000, second $16,000, third $10,000, fourth $7,000, and fifth $5,000. Other state winners receive scholarships that may vary each year but range from $1,000 to $5,000. Winners in each state also receive an all-expense paid trip to Washington, D.C. for the national competition. **Duration:** The competition is held annually.

Eligibility Requirements: This competition is open to students in grades 9-12 at high schools and home schools in the United States, its territories and possessions, and U.S. military and civilian dependent overseas schools. Contestants prepare a script, from 3 to 5 minutes in length, on a topic chosen annually but related to freedom and democracy; a recent theme was "How I Demonstrate My Freedom." Students record the script themselves on audiocassette and submit it for sponsorship by a local post or auxiliary of the Veterans of Foreign Wars (VFW). Scripts must reflect the entrant's own original thinking. Selection is based on delivery (35 points), content (35 points), and originality (30 points). **Deadline for Receipt:** October of each year. **Additional Information:** The first-place award is designated the T.C. Selman Memorial Scholarship Award. The second-place award is designated the Charles Kuralt Memorial Scholarship Award.

2300 ■ VIRGINIA COALITION OF POLICY AND DEPUTY SHERIFFS

Attn: Scholarship Competition
10500 Sager Avenue, Suite C
Fairfax, VA 22030
Web Site: http://www.virginiacops.org/programs/Scholar/Scholarship.htm
To recognize and reward, with college scholarships, high school seniors in Virginia who submit outstanding essays on law enforcement.

Title of Award: VCOPS College Scholarship Program **Area, Field, or Subject:** General studies/Field of study not specified; Writing **Level of Education for which Award is Granted:** Undergraduate **Number Awarded:** 3 winners are selected each year. **Funds Available:** The award is a $1,000 scholarship. Funds are paid directly to the winners' college or university account. **Duration:** The competition is held annually.

Eligibility Requirements: This program is open to college-bound seniors graduating from high schools in Virginia. Applicants must submit an essay, up to 1,500 words in length, on Virginia law enforcement and the general theme, "Virginia Law Enforcement: A Commitment to Community." They must also include a 150-word statement on their plans for college. **Deadline for Receipt:** April of each year.

2301 ■ ELIE WIESEL FOUNDATION FOR HUMANITY

Attn: Program Coordinator
529 Fifth Avenue, Suite 1802
New York, NY 10017
Tel: (212)490-7777
Fax: (212)490-6006
E-mail: info@eliewieselfoundation.org
Web Site: http://www.eliewieselfoundation.org
To recognize and reward outstanding student essays on a topic related to ethics.

Title of Award: Elie Wiesel Prize in Ethics **Area, Field, or Subject:** Ethics and bioethics; Writing **Level of Education for which Award is Granted:** Four Year College **Number Awarded:** 5 prizes each year: a first, second, and third prize as well as 2 honorable mentions. **Funds Available:** First prize is $5,000, second prize is $2,500, third prize is $1,500, and each honorable mention is $500. **Duration:** The competition is held annually.

Eligibility Requirements: Eligible to compete are full-time juniors and seniors at accredited colleges and universities in the United States. Essays must be submitted by the college or university, each of which may submit only 3 student works. Essays must be between 3,000 and 4,000 words in length and on a theme of the student's choice that involves ethical choices. Readers look for adherence to design format, carefully proofread essays, well thought-out essays that do not stray from the topic, depth of feeling and genuine grappling with a moral dilemma, originality and imagination, eloquence of writing style, and intensity and unity in the essay. **Deadline for Receipt:** December of each year.

2302 ■ WISCONSIN FOUNDATION FOR INDEPENDENT COLLEGES, INC.

Attn: College-to-Work Program
735 North Water Street, Suite 600
Milwaukee, WI 53202-4100
Tel: (414)273-5980
Fax: (414)273-5995
E-mail: wfic@wficweb.org
Web Site: http://www.wficweb.org/work.html
To provide financial assistance and work experience to students majoring in fields related to communications at member institutions of the Wisconsin Foundation for Independent Colleges (WFIC).

Title of Award: Manitowoc American Red Cross College-to-Work Program **Area, Field, or Subject:** Communications; English language and literature; General studies/Field of study not specified; Graphic art and design; Public relations **Level of Education for which Award is Granted:** Four Year College **Number Awarded:** 1 each year. **Funds Available:** The stipends are $3,500 for the scholarship and $1,500 for the internship. **Duration:** 1 year for the scholarship; 10 weeks for the internship.

Eligibility Requirements: This program is open to full-time sophomores, juniors, and seniors at private colleges and universities in Wisconsin. Applicants must be interested in an internship at the Manitowoc/Calumet County Chapter of the American Red Cross in Manitowoc. Preference is given to 1) students attending Lakeland College or Silver Lake College; 2) residents of Manitowoc County attending another WFIC member institution; and 3) students majoring in communications, English, graphic design, or public relations. Along with their application, they must submit a 1-page essay that includes why they are applying for the internship, why they have selected their major and what interests them about it, why they are attending their chosen college or university, and their future career objectives. **Deadline for Receipt:** February of each year. **Additional Information:** The other WFIC schools are Alverno College, Beloit College, Cardinal Stritch University, Carroll College, Carthage College, Concordia University of Wisconsin, Edgewood College, Lawrence University, Marian College, Marquette University, Milwaukee Institute of Art & Design, Milwaukee School of Engineering, Mount Mary College, Northland College, Ripon College, St. Norbert College, Viterbo University, and Wisconsin Lutheran College. This program is sponsored by the Manitowoc/Calumet County Chapter of the American Red Cross. The WFIC's College-to-Work Program includes a number of other financial assistance and work experience programs aimed at eligible students interested in majoring in fields related to communications, journalism, media, and related fields, including the Post-Crescent College-to-Work Program and Reporter College-to-Work Program.

Music

2303 ■ AMERICAN INDIAN ARTS COUNCIL, INC.

Attn: Scholarship Committee
725 Preston Forest Shopping Center, Suite B
Dallas, TX 75230
Tel: (214)891-9640
Fax: (214)891-0221
E-mail: aiac@flash.net
To provide financial assistance to American Indian undergraduates or graduate students planning a career in the arts or arts administration.

Title of Award: American Indian Arts Council Scholarship Program **Area, Field, or Subject:** Art; Creative writing; Management; Performing arts; Visual arts **Level of Education for which Award is Granted:** Graduate, Undergraduate **Number Awarded:** Varies each year. **Funds Available:** Stipends range from $250 to $1,000 per semester. **Duration:** 1 semester; may be renewed if the recipient maintains a GPA of 2.5 or higher.

Eligibility Requirements: This program is open to American Indian undergraduate and graduate students who are preparing for a career in fine arts, visual and performing arts, communication arts, creative writing, or arts administration or management. Applicants must be currently enrolled in and attending a fully-accredited college or university. They must provide official tribal documentation verifying American Indian heritage and have a GPA of 2.5 or higher. Applicants majoring in the visual or performing arts (including writing) must submit slides, photographs, videotapes, audio tapes, or other examples of their work. Letters of recommendation are required. Awards are based on either merit or merit and financial need. If the applicants wish to be considered for a need-based award, a letter from their financial aid office is required to verify financial need. **Deadline for Receipt:** September of each year for the fall semester; March of each year for the spring semester. **Additional Information:** This program was established in 1993.

2304 ■ CALIFORNIA ALLIANCE FOR ARTS EDUCATION

495 East Colorado Boulevard
Pasadena, CA 91101
Tel: (626)578-9315
Fax: (626)578-9894
E-mail: eyaa@artsed411.org
Web Site: http://www.artsed411.org/projects/eya.stm
To provide financial assistance to outstanding high school seniors in California who are interested in training to become professional performing artists.

Title of Award: Emerging Young Artist Awards **Area, Field, or Subject:** Art; Dance; Illustrators and illustrations; Music; Painting; Performing arts; Playwriting; Sculpture; Visual arts **Level of Education for which Award is Granted:** Four Year College **Number Awarded:** 12 each year: 4 winners (1 in each category) and 8 runners-up (2 in each category). **Funds Available:** The stipend is $5,000 per year for the winners (for a total of $20,000) and 1-time awards of $1,000 for the runners-up. **Duration:** The winners receive a 4-year scholarship.

Eligibility Requirements: High school seniors in California are eligible to apply in 1 or more of the following categories: dance, music, theater, or visual arts (including painting, drawing, illustration, and sculpture). Applicants must be planning to enter a 4-year institution or accredited professional training program in 1 of those areas. They must be able to demonstrate financial need. Students who apply in the areas of dance, music, and theater must submit a performance work sample. If they advance to the semifinals and finals, they are requested to demonstrate ability with a live performance. **Deadline for Receipt:** January of each year. **Additional Information:** There is a $10 application fee. Awards are not given in non-performance areas (e.g., music composition, technical theater, or choreography).

2305 ■ CALIFORNIA STATE FAIR

Attn: Friends of the Fair Scholarship Program
1600 Exposition Boulevard
P.O. Box 15649
Sacramento, CA 95852
Tel: (916)274-5969
E-mail: wross@calexpo.com
Web Site: http://www.bigfun.org
To provide financial assistance to residents of California who are studying the arts in college.

Title of Award: California State Fair Arts Scholarships **Area, Field, or Subject:** Cinema; Dance; Filmmaking; Music; Performing arts; Visual arts **Level of Education for which Award is Granted:** Undergraduate **Number Awarded:** 2 each year: 1 at $1,500 and 1 at $500. **Funds Available:** Stipends are $1,500 or $500. **Duration:** 1 year.

Eligibility Requirements: This program is open to residents of California currently working on an undergraduate degree at a college or university in the state. Applicants must be studying the arts, including visual arts, dance, music, film, etc. They must have a GPA of 3.0 or higher. Along with their application, they must submit a 2-page essay on why they are pursuing their desired career and life goals. Selection is based on personal commitment, goals established for their chosen field, leadership potential, and civic accomplishments. **Deadline for Receipt:** March of each year. **Additional Information:** The Friends of the Fair Scholarship Program was established in 1993.

2306 ■ CONNECTICUT ASSOCIATION OF SCHOOLS

Attn: Executive Director
30 Realty Drive
Cheshire, CT 06410
Tel: (203)250-1111
Fax: (203)250-1345
E-mail: msavage@casciac.org
Web Site: http://www.casciac.org

To provide financial assistance to high school seniors in Connecticut who plan to study the arts in college.

Title of Award: Bruce Eagleson Memorial Scholarship Awards **Area, Field, or Subject:** Architecture; Dance; Design; Music; Performing arts; Visual arts **Level of Education for which Award is Granted:** Undergraduate **Number Awarded:** 3 each year: 1 at $10,000 and 2 at $5,000. **Funds Available:** Stipends are $10,000 or $5,000. **Duration:** 1 year.

Eligibility Requirements: This program is open to seniors graduating from high schools in Connecticut who plan to enroll in college to study the arts, including (but not limited to) visual arts, music, theater, dance, design, and architecture. Applicants must be able to demonstrate 1) considerable experience in the arts as evidenced by involvement in shows, exhibits, performances, video productions, or similar activities; 2) involvement in service to peers and/or community through artistic or other activities; and 3) financial need. Along with their application, they must submit a 250-word statement on what led them to their decision to prepare for a career in the arts. **Deadline for Receipt:** March of each year. **Additional Information:** This program is sponsored by Westfield Corporation in honor of its former East Coast Vice-President of Management who was killed while working for the company at the World Trade Center on September 11, 2001.

2307 ■ COOK INLET REGION, INC.

Attn: CIRI Foundation
2600 Cordova Street, Suite 206
Anchorage, AK 99503
Tel: (907)263-5582
Free: 800-764-3382
Fax: (907)263-5588
E-mail: tcf@ciri.com
Web Site: http://www.thecirifoundation.org/scholarship.html
To provide financial assistance for undergraduate or graduate studies in the literary, performing, and visual arts to Alaska Natives who are original enrollees to Cook Inlet Region, Inc. (CIRI) and their lineal descendants.

Title of Award: Susie Qimmiqsak Bevins Endowment Scholarship Fund **Area, Field, or Subject:** Literature; Performing arts; Visual arts; Writing **Level of Education for which Award is Granted:** Graduate, Undergraduate **Number Awarded:** Varies each year; recently, 1 of these scholarships (at $2,000 per semester) was awarded. **Funds Available:** The stipend is $2,000 per semester. **Duration:** 1 semester; recipients may reapply.

Eligibility Requirements: This program is open to Alaska Native enrollees to CIRI under the Alaska Native Claims Settlement Act (ANCSA) of 1971 and their lineal descendants. There are no Alaska residency requirements or age limitations. Applicants must be accepted or enrolled full time in a 2-year, 4-year, or graduate degree program in the literary, visual, or performing arts. Selection is based on academic achievement, rigor of course work or degree program, quality of a statement of purpose, student financial contribution, financial need, grade level, previous work performance, education and community activities, letters of recommendation, seriousness of purpose, and practicality of educational and professional goals. **Deadline for Receipt:** May of each year. **Additional Information:** This program was established in 1990. Recipients must attend school on a full-time basis.

2308 ■ MARYLAND HIGHER EDUCATION COMMISSION

Attn: Office of Student Financial Assistance
839 Bestgate Road, Suite 400
Annapolis, MD 21401-3013
Tel: (410)260-4569
Free: 800-974-1024
Fax: (410)974-5376
E-mail: osfamail@mhec.state.md.us
Web Site: http://www.mhec.state.md.us/financialAid/
ProgramDescriptions/prog_ds.asp
To provide financial assistance for college to outstanding high school juniors in Maryland.

Title of Award: Maryland Distinguished Scholar Awards **Area, Field, or Subject:** Dance; General studies/Field of study not specified; Music; Music, Vocal; Visual arts **Level of Education for which Award is Granted:** Undergraduate **Number Awarded:** 350 each year. **Funds Available:** The stipend is $3,000 per year. The total amount of all state awards may not exceed the cost of attendance as determined by the school's financial aid office or $17,800, whichever is less. **Duration:** 1 year; may be renewed up to 3 additional years if the recipient maintains at least a 3.0 GPA and remains enrolled full time at an eligible Maryland institution.

Eligibility Requirements: Eligible to apply are outstanding high school juniors in Maryland who intend to work on an undergraduate degree on a full-time basis at an accredited college, university, or private career school in the state. Students may qualify in 1 of 3 ways: 1) superior academic achievement, in which finalists are selected on the basis of GPA (minimum 3.7) and scores on PSAT, SAT, or ACT exams; 2) National Achievement Scholarship and National Merit Scholarship programs, in which finalists automatically receive these scholarships if they enroll in eligible Maryland institutions; and 3) superior talent in the arts, in which finalists are selected in statewide auditions or portfolio evaluations in visual art, instrumental music, vocal music, dance, or drama. Financial need is not considered. **Deadline for Receipt:** Applications in the academic achievement category must be submitted in February of each year; nominations in the talent category must be submitted in April of each year.

2309 ■ NATIONAL ASSOCIATION FOR THE ADVANCEMENT OF COLORED PEOPLE

Attn: ACT-SO Director
4805 Mt. Hope Drive
Baltimore, MD 21215
Tel: (410)580-5650
E-mail: ACTSO@naacpnet.org
Web Site: http://www.naacp.org/programs/actso/actso_index.html
To recognize and reward outstanding African American high school students who distinguish themselves in the Afro-Academic, Cultural, Technological and Scientific Olympics (ACT-SO) program.

Title of Award: Afro-Academic, Cultural, Technological and Scientific Olympics (ACT-SO) **Area, Field, or Subject:** Art; Business administration; Humanities; Performing arts; Science; Visual arts **Level of Education for which Award is Granted:** Undergraduate **Number Awarded:** 75 each year: 3 in each of 25 categories. **Funds Available:** In each category, the first-prize winner receives a gold medal and a $2,000 scholarship, the second-prize winner receives a silver medal and a $1,500 scholarship, and the third-prize winner receives a bronze medal and a $1,000 scholarship. **Duration:** The competition has been held annually since 1977.

Eligibility Requirements: This competition is open to high school students (grades 9-12) of African descent who are U.S. citizens and amateurs in the category in which they wish to participate. Competitions are held in 25 categories in 5 general areas: humanities (music composition, original essay, playwriting, and poetry), sciences (architecture, biology, chemistry, computer science, mathematics, physics/electronics, physics/energy, and physics/general), performing arts (dance, dramatics, music instrumental/classical, music instrumental/contemporary, music vocal/classical, music vocal/contemporary, and oratory), visual arts (drawing, painting, photography, sculpture, and filmmaking/video), and business (entrepreneurship). Competition is first conducted by local chapters of the NAACP; winners in each event at the local level then compete at the national level. **Deadline for Receipt:** Local competitions usually take place between March and May. The national finals are held each year in July.

2310 ■ SOUTH CAROLINA STATE DEPARTMENT OF EDUCATION

1429 Senate Street, Room 1010A
Columbia, SC 29201
Tel: (803)734-8485
E-mail: sspade@sde.state.sc.us
Web Site: http://www.myscschools.com/offices/ombudsman/arscholarship
To recognize and reward high school seniors in South Carolina who participate in a competition in art, creative writing, drama, or music.

Title of Award: Archibald Rutledge Scholarship Program **Area, Field, or Subject:** Art; Creative writing; Graphic art and design; Music composition; Painting; Playwriting; Poetry; Visual arts; Writing **Level of Education for which Award is Granted:** Undergraduate **Number Awarded:** 4 each year: 1 in each of the 4 categories. **Funds Available:** The award consists of a $4,000 scholarship, to be used for tuition, room, board, and instructional resource expenses. **Duration:** 1 year.

Eligibility Requirements: This program is open to U.S. citizens who have attended South Carolina public high schools for at least 2 years, are currently seniors, and are planning to attend a South Carolina college or university. Applicants compete by submitting samples of their work in 1 of 4 areas: 1) visual arts, limited to 2-dimensional work such as drawing and painting media, printmaking, and collage; no 3-dimensional works, photographs, or computer-generated images are accepted; 2) creative writing, as a sonnet, lyric, or narrative poem, up to 1 page; 3) drama, a 1-act play with a performing time of 20 to 45 minutes; or 4) music, a composition of 3 to 5 minutes for solo or small ensemble, vocal or instrumental, in any appropriate style. In addition to the work, they must submit a process folio that contains documentation of the planning and development of the project and a 1-page reflection statement addressing the intent of the work and comparing the final product with the original concept. A panel of professionals in the field selects up to 10 finalists, based on originality, creativity, and the correlation and implications of the process folio for the final composition. Finalists must attend the scholarship competition, where they present a portfolio of a number of selected works as specified by the judges. **Deadline for Receipt:** February of each year.

2311 ■ VERMONT STUDENT ASSISTANCE CORPORATION

Champlain Mill
Attn: Scholarship Programs
P.O. Box 2000
Winooski, VT 05404-2601
Tel: (802)654-3798; 888-253-4819
Fax: (802)654-3765
E-mail: info@vsac.org
Web Site: http://www.vsac.org
To provide financial assistance to residents of Vermont who are interested in majoring in arts or crafts in college.

Title of Award: Vermont Hand Crafters Artisanship Scholarships **Area, Field, or Subject:** Art industries and trade; Crafts; Visual arts **Level of Education for which Award is Granted:** Undergraduate **Number Awarded:** Varies each year; recently, 5 of these scholarships were awarded. **Funds Available:** Stipends range from $500 to $1,000. **Duration:** 1 year.

Eligibility Requirements: This scholarship is available to high school seniors, high school graduates, and currently-enrolled college students in Vermont who are enrolled or planning to enroll at least half time in a postsecondary degree program in the visual arts (particularly arts and crafts). Applicants must have been residents of Vermont for at least 2 years. Selection is based on financial need, academic achievement, a portfolio, a letter of recommendation, required essays, and a personal interview (if necessary). **Deadline for Receipt:** June of each year.

Performing Arts

2312 ■ ACADEMY OF TELEVISION ARTS & SCIENCES FOUNDATION

Attn: Education Department
5220 Lankershim Boulevard
North Hollywood, CA 91601-3109
Tel: (818)754-2830
Fax: (818)761-ATAS
E-mail: collegeawards@emmys.org
Web Site: http://www.emmys.tv/foundation/index.php
To provide financial assistance to upper-division and graduate students interested in working on a project in a field related to children's media.

Title of Award: Fred Rogers Memorial Scholarship **Area, Field, or Subject:** Art, Caricatures and cartoons; Child development; Education, Early childhood; Filmmaking; Music; Psychology; Radio and television **Level of Education for which Award is Granted:** Four Year College, Graduate **Number Awarded:** 1 each year. **Funds Available:** The stipend is $10,000. **Duration:** 1 year.

Eligibility Requirements: This program is open to upper-division and graduate students interested in preparing for a career in children's media. Applicants must be able to demonstrate a commitment, either through course work or experience, to any combination of at least 2 of the following fields: early childhood education, child development, child psychology, film or television production, music, or animation. They may apply for support for any of the following areas: research on the relationship between children's media and learning or children's use of media and personal growth; development of program concepts or extended development of creative elements of an existing concept (e.g., design of puppets, scripts, storyboards, characters, music); professional internship in an organization that is relevant to the applicant's goal for use of the award. **Deadline for Receipt:** January of each year. **Additional Information:** This scholarship, first awarded in 2005, is supported by Ernst & Young.

2313 ■ ALEXANDER CHRISTIAN FOUNDATION OF INDIANA
312 East Main Street, Suite B
P.O. Box 246
Greenfield, IN 46140-0246
Tel: (317)467-1223
Web Site: http://www.acfindiana.org
To provide financial assistance to members of the Christian Church or Church of Christ (Independent) in Indiana who are preparing for a church-related vocation.
Title of Award: Alexander Christian Foundation of Indiana Scholarships **Area, Field, or Subject:** Education, Religious; Music; Religion **Level of Education for which Award is Granted:** Graduate, Undergraduate **Number Awarded:** Varies each year. **Funds Available:** Stipends range from $1,200 to $2,000 per year. **Duration:** 1 year; may be renewed.
Eligibility Requirements: This program is open to members of the Christian Church or Church of Christ (Independent) in Indiana who are candidates for a church-related vocation or currently working full time on an appropriate undergraduate or graduate degree. Applicants must be attending or planning to attend a college or seminary affiliated with the Christian Churches/Churches of Christ. Students at Christian colleges must have a GPA of 3.0 or higher. Along with their application, they must submit an essay of 500 to 1,000 words on "Why I Desire to Serve Christ in a Church-Related Vocation." Selection is based on that essay, evaluations of the applicant's character and motivation by their home church minister and an elder of their church, and transcripts. **Deadline for Receipt:** February of each year. **Additional Information:** This program was established in 1964. Church-related vocations include preaching ministry, youth ministry, missions ministry, music ministry, counseling ministry, and education ministry.

2314 ■ AMERICAN FOUNDATION FOR THE BLIND
Attn: Scholarship Committee
11 Penn Plaza, Suite 300
New York, NY 10001
Tel: (212)502-7661
Free: 800-AFB-LINE
Fax: (212)502-7771
E-mail: afbinfo@afb.net
Web Site: http://www.afb.org/scholarships.asp
To provide financial assistance to legally blind undergraduate or graduate women who are studying religious or classical music.
Title of Award: Gladys C. Anderson Memorial Scholarship **Area, Field, or Subject:** Music; Music, Classical; Religion **Level of Education for which Award is Granted:** Graduate, Undergraduate **Number Awarded:** 1 each year. **Funds Available:** The stipend is $1,000. **Duration:** 1 academic year.
Eligibility Requirements: This program is open to legally blind women who are U.S. citizens and have been accepted in an accredited undergraduate or graduate program in religious or classical music. Along with their application, they must submit an essay that includes the field of study they are pursuing and why they have chosen it; their educational and personal goals; their work experience; any extracurricular activities with which they have been involved, including those in school, religious organizations, and the community; and how they intend to use scholarship monies that may be awarded. They must also submit a sample performance tape (a voice or instrumental selection). **Deadline for Receipt:** April of each year.

2315 ■ AMERICAN FOUNDATION FOR THE BLIND
Attn: Scholarship Committee
11 Penn Plaza, Suite 300
New York, NY 10001
Tel: (212)502-7661
Free: 800-AFB-LINE
Fax: (212)502-7771
E-mail: afbinfo@afb.net

Web Site: http://www.afb.org/scholarships.asp
To provide financial assistance to legally blind undergraduate women who are studying literature or music.
Title of Award: R.L. Gillette Scholarships **Area, Field, or Subject:** Literature; Music **Level of Education for which Award is Granted:** Four Year College **Number Awarded:** 2 each year. **Funds Available:** The stipend is $1,000. **Duration:** 1 academic year.
Eligibility Requirements: This program is open to women who are legally blind, U.S. citizens, and enrolled in a 4-year baccalaureate degree program in literature or music. Along with their application, they must submit an essay that includes the field of study they are pursuing and why they have chosen it; their educational and personal goals; their work experience; any extracurricular activities with which they have been involved, including those in school, religious organizations, and the community; and how they intend to use scholarship monies that may be awarded. They must also submit a sample performance tape (not to exceed 30 minutes) or a creative writing sample. **Deadline for Receipt:** April of each year.

2316 ■ AMERICAN GUILD OF ORGANISTS-GREATER BRIDGEPORT CHAPTER
c/o K. Bryan Kirk
1700 Broadbridge Avenue, A32
Stratford, CT 06614
Tel: (203)377-5240
E-mail: kbkirkorg@aol.com
To provide financial assistance to undergraduate students interested in preparing for a career in organ performance and church music.
Title of Award: M. Louise Miller Scholarship **Area, Field, or Subject:** Music; Religion **Level of Education for which Award is Granted:** Undergraduate **Number Awarded:** 1 each year. **Funds Available:** The stipend is $1,000. **Duration:** 1 year.
Eligibility Requirements: This program is open to undergraduates enrolled or planning to enroll at a college, university, or conservatory in the United States. Applicants must be preparing for a career in organ performance and church music. They must submit a short essay and a recording of 2 standard organ pieces. **Deadline for Receipt:** February of each year. **Additional Information:** This program was established in 1998.

2317 ■ AMERICAN LEGION
Attn: Department of Kansas
1314 S.W. Topeka Boulevard
Topeka, KS 66612-1886
Tel: (785)232-9315
Fax: (785)232-1399
Web Site: http://www.ksamlegion.org/programs.htm
To provide financial assistance to students of music at institutions in Kansas.
Title of Award: Kansas American Legion Music Scholarship **Area, Field, or Subject:** Music **Level of Education for which Award is Granted:** Undergraduate **Number Awarded:** 1 each year. **Funds Available:** The stipend is $1,000. **Duration:** 1 year.
Eligibility Requirements: This program is open to residents of Kansas who are high school seniors or college freshmen or sophomores. Applicants must be studying or planning to major or minor in music at an approved college, university, or community college in Kansas. **Deadline for Receipt:** February of each year.

2318 ■ AMERICAN SOCIETY OF COMPOSERS, AUTHORS AND PUBLISHERS
Attn: ASCAP Foundation
ASCAP Building
One Lincoln Plaza
New York, NY 10023
Tel: (212)621-6320
Fax: (212)621-6236
E-mail: ascapfoundation@ascap.com
Web Site: http://www.ascapfoundation.org/gould-info.html
To recognize and reward outstanding young American composers.
Title of Award: Morton Gould Young Composer Awards **Area, Field, or Subject:** Music composition **Level of Education for which Award is Granted:** Graduate, Undergraduate **Number Awarded:** Varies each year;

recently, 21 students received these awards. **Funds Available:** The winners share cash awards of more than $30,000. **Duration:** The award is presented annually.

Eligibility Requirements: Applicants must be U.S. citizens, permanent residents, or enrolled students with proper visas who are younger than 30 years of age, including students in grades K-12, undergraduates, and graduate students. Original music of any style is considered. However, works that have earned awards or prizes in other national competitions are ineligible, as are arrangements. To compete, each applicant must submit a completed application form, 1 reproduction of a manuscript or score, biographical information, a list of compositions to date, and 2 professional recommendations. Only 1 composition per composer may be submitted. A cassette tape or CD of the composition may be included. So that music materials may be returned, each entry must be accompanied by a self-addressed envelope with sufficient postage. **Deadline for Receipt:** February of each year. **Additional Information:** Morton Gould was president of the American Society of Composers, Authors and Publishers. This program was established in 1979. The awards include the Leo Kaplan Award.

2319 ■ BROADCAST MUSIC INC.

Attn: BMI Foundation
320 West 57th Street
New York, NY 10019-3790
Tel: (212)830-2537
Fax: (212)246-2163
E-mail: classical@bmi.com
Web Site: http://www.bmifoundation.org/pages/SComposer.asp
To recognize and reward outstanding student composers from the Western Hemisphere.

Title of Award: BMI Student Composer Awards **Area, Field, or Subject:** Music; Music composition **Level of Education for which Award is Granted:** Graduate, Undergraduate **Number Awarded:** Varies each year; recently, 8 of these awards were presented. A total of $20,000 in prizes is awarded each year. **Funds Available:** Prizes range from $500 to $5,000. **Duration:** The competition is held annually.

Eligibility Requirements: This competition is open to citizens of countries in North, Central, or South America, the Caribbean Island nations, or the Hawaiian Islands who are younger than 26 years of age. Applicants must be enrolled in accredited public, private, or parochial secondary schools, enrolled in accredited colleges or conservatories of music, or engaged in the private study of music with recognized and established teachers (other than a relative). Any composer having won the award 3 times previously is not eligible to enter the contest again. Compositions may be for vocal, instrumental, electronic, or any combination of those. There are no limitations on medium, instrumentation, or length of the work. Manuscripts may be submitted either on usual score paper or reproduced by a generally accepted reproduction process. Electronic music and recordings of graphic works that cannot adequately be presented in score may be submitted on cassette or CD. Selection is based on evidence of creative talent. Academic finesse is considered, but that is secondary to vital musicality and clarity of expression of the composer's work. Judges consider 1) formal content of the composition; 2) melodic, harmonic, and rhythmic idioms, but only in terms of their consistency and suitability for the intent of the particular composition; 3) instrumentation, orchestration, and vocal writing; and 4) age of the composer (if 2 compositions are of equal merit, preference is given to the younger contestant). **Deadline for Receipt:** February of each year. **Additional Information:** This program began in 1951. The score judged "most outstanding" in the competition receives the William Schuman Prize, named in honor of the chairman of this competition for 40 years. The 2 youngest winners receive awards designated the Carlos Surinach Prizes.

2320 ■ BROADCAST MUSIC INC.

Attn: BMI Foundation
320 West 57th Street
New York, NY 10019-3790
Tel: (212)830-2520
Fax: (212)246-2163
E-mail: LennonScholarship@bmifoundation.org
Web Site: http://www.bmifoundation.org/pages/JLennon.asp
To recognize and reward outstanding student composers.

Title of Award: John Lennon Scholarship **Area, Field, or Subject:** Music composition **Level of Education for which Award is Granted:** Undergraduate **Number Awarded:** 3 each year: 1 at $10,000 and 2 at $5,000. **Funds Available:** Prizes are $10,000 or $5,000. **Duration:** The competition is held annually.

Eligibility Requirements: This competition is open to musicians between 15 and 24 years of age who are 1) current students or graduates of 50 selected colleges, universities, or schools of music, or 2) participating through a local collegiate chapter of the National Association for Music Education at their school. Applicants may not have had any musical work commercially recorded or distributed or have been a prior winner in this competition. They must submit (on audio cassette or CD with a typed copy of the lyrics) an original song with lyrics and accompanied by any instrumentation. Both lyrics and music must be original and not based on any prior work. **Deadline for Receipt:** January of each year. **Additional Information:** This program was established in 1997 by Yoko Ono in conjunction with Gibson Musical Instruments and the BMI Foundation. For a list of the selected organizations, contact BMI.

2321 ■ BROADCAST MUSIC INC.

Attn: BMI Foundation
320 West 57th Street
New York, NY 10019-3790
Tel: (212)830-2537
Fax: (212)246-2163
E-mail: info@bmifoundation.org
Web Site: http://www.bmifoundation.org/pages/peermusic.asp
To recognize and reward students at colleges and universities in selected states who submit outstanding songs or instrumental works in a Latin genre.

Title of Award: peermusic Latin Scholarship **Area, Field, or Subject:** Music composition **Level of Education for which Award is Granted:** Graduate, Undergraduate **Number Awarded:** 1 each year. **Funds Available:** The award is $5,000. **Duration:** The award is presented annually.

Eligibility Requirements: This competition is open to students between 16 and 24 years of age enrolled at colleges and universities in California, Florida, Illinois, Massachusetts, New York, Puerto Rico, or Texas. Applicants may not have had any musical work commercially recorded or distributed. They must submit an original song or instrumental work in a Latin genre. The entry must be submitted on audio cassette or CD, accompanied by 3 typed copies of the lyric. **Deadline for Receipt:** January of each year. **Additional Information:** This award, first presented in 2003, is sponsored by peermusic Companies.

2322 ■ CALIFORNIA ALLIANCE FOR ARTS EDUCATION

495 East Colorado Boulevard
Pasadena, CA 91101
Tel: (626)578-9315
Fax: (626)578-9894
E-mail: eyaa@artsed411.org
Web Site: http://www.artsed411.org/projects/eya.stm
To provide financial assistance to outstanding high school seniors in California who are interested in training to become professional performing artists.

Title of Award: Emerging Young Artist Awards **Area, Field, or Subject:** Art; Dance; Illustrators and illustrations; Music; Painting; Performing arts; Playwriting; Sculpture; Visual arts **Level of Education for which Award is Granted:** Four Year College **Number Awarded:** 12 each year: 4 winners (1 in each category) and 8 runners-up (2 in each category). **Funds Available:** The stipend is $5,000 per year for the winners (for a total of $20,000) and 1-time awards of $1,000 for the runners-up. **Duration:** The winners receive a 4-year scholarship.

Eligibility Requirements: High school seniors in California are eligible to apply in 1 or more of the following categories: dance, music, theater, or visual arts (including painting, drawing, illustration, and sculpture). Applicants must be planning to enter a 4-year institution or accredited professional training program in 1 of those areas. They must be able to demonstrate financial need. Students who apply in the areas of dance, music, and theater must submit a performance work sample. If they advance to the semifinals and finals, they are requested to demonstrate ability with a live performance. **Deadline for Receipt:** January of each year. **Additional Information:** There is a $10 application fee. Awards are not given in non-performance areas (e.g., music composition, technical theater, or choreography).

2323 ■ CALIFORNIA STATE FAIR

Attn: Friends of the Fair Scholarship Program
1600 Exposition Boulevard
P.O. Box 15649
Sacramento, CA 95852
Tel: (916)274-5969
E-mail: wross@calexpo.com
Web Site: http://www.bigfun.org
To provide financial assistance to residents of California who are studying the arts in college.
Title of Award: California State Fair Arts Scholarships **Area, Field, or Subject:** Cinema; Dance; Filmmaking; Music; Performing arts; Visual arts **Level of Education for which Award is Granted:** Undergraduate **Number Awarded:** 2 each year: 1 at $1,500 and 1 at $500. **Funds Available:** Stipends are $1,500 or $500. **Duration:** 1 year.
Eligibility Requirements: This program is open to residents of California currently working on an undergraduate degree at a college or university in the state. Applicants must be studying the arts, including visual arts, dance, music, film, etc. They must have a GPA of 3.0 or higher. Along with their application, they must submit a 2-page essay on why they are pursuing their desired career and life goals. Selection is based on personal commitment, goals established for their chosen field, leadership potential, and civic accomplishments. **Deadline for Receipt:** March of each year. **Additional Information:** The Friends of the Fair Scholarship Program was established in 1993.

2324 ■ CHRISTIAN FELLOWSHIP OF ART MUSIC COMPOSERS

c/o Mark Hijleh
Houghton College
Greatbatch School of Music
Houghton, NY 14744
Tel: (585)567-9424
E-mail: cfamc@cfamc.org
Web Site: http://www.cfamc.org
To provide financial assistance to Christian composers interested in studying art music composition.
Title of Award: Christian Fellowship of Art Music Composers Scholarship **Area, Field, or Subject:** Music; Music composition; Religion **Level of Education for which Award is Granted:** Undergraduate **Number Awarded:** 1 each year. **Funds Available:** The stipend is $1,000; funds are sent directly to the educational institution or summer festival designated by the recipient. **Duration:** 1 academic year or 1 summer; nonrenewable.
Eligibility Requirements: This program is open to Christian student composers who enrolled in a program of art music composition study in a preparatory music program, a collegiate music program, or an approved summer music program. Applicants must submit 2 letters of recommendation, a brief Christian testimony, a brief essay on how their compositional activities and Christian life are related, a curriculum vitae, a detailed explanation of how the award will be used, and 1 or 2 scores of art music composed for voice, instruments, and/or electronic media. **Deadline for Receipt:** October of each year. **Additional Information:** This program began in 1998. Applicants automatically become student composer members for 1 year in the Christian Fellowship of Art Music Composers.

2325 ■ CLAN SCOTT SOCIETY, INC.

P.O. Box 13021
Austin, TX 78711-3021
To provide financial assistance to individuals under the age of 19 who are interested in study or training in the Scottish performing arts.
Title of Award: Clan Scott Society Scholarship **Area, Field, or Subject:** Dance; Music; Scottish studies **Level of Education for which Award is Granted:** Undergraduate **Number Awarded:** Varies each year. **Funds Available:** The amount awarded depends upon the needs of the recipient and the funds available. Funds are paid directly to the individual or organization providing the training or education to the scholarship recipient. **Duration:** Up to 1 year.
Eligibility Requirements: This program is open to children, aged 18 or younger, who need financial assistance to support their education, training, or development in the Scottish performing arts. For the purposes of this program, these arts are defined as the traditional music or dance of Scotland as typically performed in competition at Scottish games and gatherings (including, but not restricted to, Scottish bagpipes, drumming,

fiddle, harp, and Highland dance). Preference is given to members of the society and to their families. All applications must be submitted in writing and identify the applicant's name, the Scottish performing art for which the scholarship will be used, the person or organization providing the training or education, the dates or time period during which the training will occur, the cost of the training or education, and a brief explanation of why the applicant deserves the scholarship. **Deadline for Receipt:** Applications may be submitted at any time.

2326 ■ COLBURN-PLEDGE MUSIC SCHOLARSHIP FOUNDATION

Attn: Secretary
6322 Cornplanter
San Antonio, TX 78209
To provide financial assistance to pre-college and college students who are Texas residents and interested in studying classical music.
Title of Award: Colburn-Pledge Music Scholarship **Area, Field, or Subject:** Music, Classical; Music, Viola; Music, Violin **Level of Education for which Award is Granted:** Undergraduate **Funds Available:** Stipends range up to $2,000. **Duration:** 1 year.
Eligibility Requirements: Applicants must be 1) residents of Texas, 2) studying a string instrument (violin, viola, cello, bass) in classical music with the intention of becoming a professional musician, and 3) less than high school age, currently in high school, or currently in college. Financial need must be demonstrated, but selection is based primarily on musical talent. **Deadline for Receipt:** April of each year. **Additional Information:** Recipients may attend college, music schools, or music camps in Texas or in any other state.

2327 ■ COMMUNITY FOUNDATION FOR GREATER ATLANTA, INC.

50 Hurt Plaza, Suite 449
Atlanta, GA 30303
Tel: (404)688-5525
Fax: (404)688-3060
E-mail: vweekes@atlcf.org
Web Site: http://www.atlcf.org/GrantsScholarships/Scholarships/Smyth.aspx
To provide financial assistance for college to high school seniors, especially those from designated states.
Title of Award: James M. and Virginia M. Smyth Scholarship Fund **Area, Field, or Subject:** General studies/Field of study not specified; Music; Religion; Social work **Level of Education for which Award is Granted:** Undergraduate **Number Awarded:** Varies each year. **Funds Available:** Stipends range up to $2,500. **Duration:** 1 year; recipients may reapply.
Eligibility Requirements: This program is open to graduating high school seniors, with special consideration given to residents of Georgia, Illinois, Mississippi, Missouri, Oklahoma, Tennessee, and Texas. Applicants must have a GPA of 3.0 or higher and be interested in attending a college, university, or community college to work on a degree in the arts and sciences, human services, music, or ministry. They must be able to demonstrate financial need and a commitment to community service through school, community, or religious organizations. Adults returning to school to increase employability are also eligible. **Deadline for Receipt:** March of each year.

2328 ■ COMMUNITY FOUNDATION OF MIDDLE TENNESSEE

Attn: Scholarship Committee
3833 Cleghorn Avenue, Suite 400
Nashville, TN 37215-2519
Tel: (615)321-4939; 888-540-5200
Fax: (615)327-2746
E-mail: mail@cfmt.org
Web Site: http://www.cfmt.org/scholarship_info.htm
To provide financial assistance to African American upper-division and graduate students from Tennessee who are working on a degree in music.
Title of Award: John W. Work III Memorial Foundation Scholarship **Area, Field, or Subject:** Music **Level of Education for which Award is Granted:** Four Year College, Graduate **Number Awarded:** 1 or more each year. **Funds Available:** Stipends range from $500 to $2,500 per year. Funds are paid to the recipient's school and must be used for tuition, fees, books, supplies, room, board, or miscellaneous expenses. **Duration:** 1 year.
Eligibility Requirements: This program is open to African American residents of Tennessee enrolled as juniors, seniors, or graduate students

at an accredited college, university, or institute. Applicants must be working on a degree in music and have a GPA of 3.0 or higher. Selection is based on demonstrated potential for excellence in music, academic record, standardized test scores, extracurricular activities, work experience, community involvement, recommendations, and financial need. **Deadline for Receipt:** March of each year.

2329 ■ CONGRESSIONAL BLACK CAUCUS FOUNDATION, INC.

Attn: Director, Educational Programs
1720 Massachusetts Avenue, N.W.
Washington, DC 20036
Tel: (202)263-2836
Free: 800-784-2577
Fax: (202)775-0773
E-mail: spouses@cbcfinc.org
Web Site: http://www.cbcfinc.org
To provide financial assistance to minority and other undergraduate and graduate students who reside in a Congressional district represented by an African American and are interested in studying the performing arts in college.
Title of Award: CBC Spouses Performing Arts Scholarship **Area, Field, or Subject:** Business; Music; Performing arts **Level of Education for which Award is Granted:** Graduate, Undergraduate **Number Awarded:** 10 each year. **Funds Available:** The stipend is $3,000. **Duration:** 1 year. **Eligibility Requirements:** This program is open to 1) minority and other graduating high school seniors planning to attend an accredited institution of higher education and 2) currently-enrolled full-time undergraduate, graduate, and doctoral students in good academic standing with a GPA of 2.5 or higher. Applicants must reside or attend school in a Congressional district represented by a member of the Congressional Black Caucus (CBC). They must be interested in preparing for a career in the performing arts, music, or a related field in the entertainment industry. Along with their application, they must submit a videotape of their performance and a 500-word personal statement on 1) the field of study they intend to pursue and why they have chosen that field; 2) their interests, involvement in school activities, community and public service, hobbies, special talents, sports, and other highlight areas; and 3) any other experiences, skills, or qualifications they feel should be considered. They must also be able to document financial need. **Deadline for Receipt:** April of each year. **Additional Information:** This program, established in 2000, is sponsored by Heineken USA.

2330 ■ CONNECTICUT ASSOCIATION OF SCHOOLS

Attn: Executive Director
30 Realty Drive
Cheshire, CT 06410
Tel: (203)250-1111
Fax: (203)250-1345
E-mail: msavage@casciac.org
Web Site: http://www.casciac.org
To provide financial assistance to high school seniors in Connecticut who plan to study the arts in college.
Title of Award: Bruce Eagleson Memorial Scholarship Awards **Area, Field, or Subject:** Architecture; Dance; Design; Music; Performing arts; Visual arts **Level of Education for which Award is Granted:** Undergraduate **Number Awarded:** 3 each year: 1 at $10,000 and 2 at $5,000. **Funds Available:** Stipends are $10,000 or $5,000. **Duration:** 1 year. **Eligibility Requirements:** This program is open to seniors graduating from high schools in Connecticut who plan to enroll in college to study the arts, including (but not limited to) visual arts, music, theater, dance, design, and architecture. Applicants must be able to demonstrate 1) considerable experience in the arts as evidenced by involvement in shows, exhibits, performances, video productions, or similar activities; 2) involvement in service to peers and/or community through artistic or other activities; and 3) financial need. Along with their application, they must submit a 250-word statement on what led them to their decision to prepare for a career in the arts. **Deadline for Receipt:** March of each year. **Additional Information:** This program is sponsored by Westfield

Corporation in honor of its former East Coast Vice-President of Management who was killed while working for the company at the World Trade Center on September 11, 2001.

2331 ■ THE FELLOWSHIP OF UNITED METHODISTS IN MUSIC AND WORSHIP ARTS-FLORIDA CHAPTER

c/o Luke Nash
5836-4 Queen Elizabeth Way
Fort Myers, FL 33907
E-mail: bigluke@peganet.com
Web Site: http://www.floridafellowship.org/scholarship.htm
To provide financial assistance to undergraduate students majoring in music who are members of a United Methodist Church in Florida.
Title of Award: Grant K. Pulen Scholarship **Area, Field, or Subject:** Music **Level of Education for which Award is Granted:** Undergraduate **Number Awarded:** 1 each year. **Funds Available:** The stipend is $1,500 per year. **Duration:** 1 year; may be renewed. **Eligibility Requirements:** This program is open to high school seniors and current undergraduate students who are majoring in music. Applicants must have been a member of a United Methodist church in the Florida Conference for at least 1 year prior to applying. Preference is given to applicants currently active in religious and music activities in churches, schools, or other organizations. Selection is based on health, emotional stability, Christian character, talent, leadership ability, promise of future usefulness to the Methodist church, transcripts, 3 letters of recommendation, and financial need. **Deadline for Receipt:** May of each year.

2332 ■ FORT COLLINS SYMPHONY ORCHESTRA

Attn: Young Artist Competition
214 South College Avenue
P.O. Box 1963
Fort Collins, CO 80522
Tel: (970)482-4823
Fax: (970)482-4858
E-mail: note@fcsymphony.org
Web Site: http://www.fcsymphony.org/youngartist.shtml
To recognize and reward outstanding young pianists and instrumentalists.
Title of Award: Fort Collins Symphony Orchestra Senior Concerto Competition **Area, Field, or Subject:** Music; Music, Piano **Level of Education for which Award is Granted:** Graduate, Undergraduate **Number Awarded:** 10 semifinalists and 3 finalists are chosen each year; all 3 finalists receive a prize. **Funds Available:** The first-place winner receives the Adeline Rosenberg Memorial Prize of $6,000. Second prize is $4,000. The awards are cash prizes only. **Duration:** The competition is held annually. **Eligibility Requirements:** Applicants must be students 25 years of age or younger and submit cassette tapes of a standard, readily available solo concerto or similar work played from memory. Based on the tapes, semifinalists are invited to Fort Collins for a second round in March. From the semifinalists, finalists are chosen for the third round of performances in April. **Deadline for Receipt:** January of each year. **Additional Information:** The competition is for piano in even-numbered years and instruments in odd-numbered years. The entry fee is $50. Requests for applications must be accompanied by a self-addressed stamped envelope.

2333 ■ FRIDAY MORNING MUSIC CLUB, INC.

Attn: FMMC Foundation
2233 Wisconsin Avenue, N.W., Suite 326
Washington, DC 20007-4126
Tel: (202)333-2075
Web Site: http://www.fmmc.org/johansen
To recognize and reward outstanding young string players.
Title of Award: Johansen International Competition for Young String Players **Area, Field, or Subject:** Music, Viola; Music, Violin **Level of Education for which Award is Granted:** Undergraduate **Number Awarded:** 3 first prizes (1 each for violin, viola, and cello) are awarded in each competition. The number of other prizes varies; recently, those included 2 second prizes, 2 third prizes, an honorable mention, and an award for best performance of the commissioned piece for violin players and 1 honorable mention for cello players. **Funds Available:** First prize in each category is $10,000. Other prizes vary in each competition.

Recently, violin players received second prizes of $7,000, third prizes of $5,000, honorable mention of $750, and best performance on the commissioned piece $500. No other awards were presented to viola players. Honorable mentioned for cello was $750. **Duration:** The competition is held triennially (2006, 2009, etc.).

Eligibility Requirements: This competition is open to young string players (13 through 17 years of age). Applicants must submit an audiocassette or CD with 1) 5 minutes or less of an unaccompanied sonata, partita, or suite of J.S. Bach; 2) 12 minutes or less of a sonata from the classical, romantic, impressionist, or contemporary period; and 3) 13 minutes or less of a concerto or major work for soloist or orchestra by a composer other than Bach. Based on those recordings, semifinalists are invited to compete in Washington, D.C. They must be prepared to play any selection from their preliminary repertoire as well as a new work commissioned for this competition and sent to them prior to the semifinals. Finalists are selected from those auditions and compete the following day. All repertoire must be performed from memory. Separate awards are presented for violin, viola, and cello. **Deadline for Receipt:** December of the year prior to the competition. **Additional Information:** The first-prize winners also appear in solo recitals. This competition was established in 1997. Information is also available from Alice Berman, P.O. Box 500, Kensington, MD 20895, (301) 946-9531, There is a nonrefundable $50 application fee.

2334 ■ FRIENDS-IN-ART

c/o Harvey Miller
402 East French Broad Street
Brevard, NC 28712-3410
Tel: (828)862-3412
E-mail: hhmiller@citcom.net

To provide financial assistance to blind students who are majoring or planning to major in fields related to the arts.

Title of Award: Friends-in-Art Scholarship **Area, Field, or Subject:** Art; Creative writing; Music; Playwriting **Level of Education for which Award is Granted:** Undergraduate **Number Awarded:** 1 each year. **Funds Available:** The stipend is $1,000. **Duration:** 1 year.

Eligibility Requirements: This program is open to blind and visually impaired high school seniors and college students who are majoring or planning to major in music, art, drama, or creative writing. Required submissions are a recording of 2 contrasting pieces for music students; 10 slides of their work for art students; a recording of 1 dramatic and 1 comic scene for drama students; and a varied selection of their writing for creative writing students. Selection is based on achievement, talent, and excellence in the arts. **Deadline for Receipt:** April of each year. **Additional Information:** This program began in 1999.

2335 ■ HANSCOM OFFICERS' WIVES' CLUB

Attn: Scholarship Chair
P.O. Box 557
Bedford, MA 01730
Tel: (781)275-1251
E-mail: scholarship@hanscomowd.org
Web Site: http://www.hanscomowc.org

To provide financial assistance to children of military personnel and veterans in New England who are interested in studying music in college.

Title of Award: Air Force Band of Liberty Musical Excellence Scholarship **Area, Field, or Subject:** Music; Music, Vocal **Level of Education for which Award is Granted:** Undergraduate **Number Awarded:** 1 each year. **Funds Available:** A stipend is awarded (amount not specified). **Duration:** 1 year; nonrenewable.

Eligibility Requirements: This program is open to college-bound high school seniors living in New England who are dependents of active-duty, retired, or deceased military members of any branch of service. Also eligible are dependents of military recruiters working in the New York area and students living elsewhere but whose military sponsor is stationed at Hanscom Air Force Base. Applicants must be able to demonstrate musical accomplishment. although they do not necessarily have to major in music in college. Musical categories include brass, woodwind, mallet percussion, voice, jazz or classical guitar, or piano. Along with their application, they must submit a 2-page essay on their educational goals, how their educational experience will help prepare them to pursue future goals, and how they intend to apply their education to better their community. On the basis of application material, 3 finalists are selected and asked to submit a

recent solo recording of their playing or singing. **Deadline for Receipt:** March of each year. **Additional Information:** Information is also available from MSGT Malcolm Ranney, Air Force Band of Liberty, 25 Chennault Street, Hanscom AFB, MA 01731-1612.

2336 ■ HAWAI'I COMMUNITY FOUNDATION

Attn: Scholarship Department
1164 Bishop Street, Suite 800
Honolulu, HI 96813
Tel: (808)566-5570; 888-731-3863
Fax: (808)521-6286
E-mail: scholarships@hcf-hawaii.org
Web Site: http://www.hawaiicommunityfoundation.org/scholar/scholar.php

To provide financial assistance to residents of Hawaii who are interested in preparing for a career in classical music.

Title of Award: Doris and Clarence Glick Classical Music Scholarship Fund **Area, Field, or Subject:** Music; Music, Classical **Level of Education for which Award is Granted:** Graduate, Undergraduate **Number Awarded:** Varies each year; recently, 8 of these scholarships were awarded. **Funds Available:** The amount of the award depends on the availability of funds and the need of the recipient; recently, stipends averaged $1,000. **Duration:** 1 year.

Eligibility Requirements: This program is open to residents of Hawaii who are planning to study music (with an emphasis on classical music) as full-time students on the undergraduate or graduate level. Applicants must be able to demonstrate academic achievement (GPA of 2.7 or higher), good moral character, and financial need. In addition to filling out the standard application form, they must write a short statement indicating their reasons for attending college, their planned course of study, their career goals, and their program of study as it relates to classical music. **Deadline for Receipt:** February of each year. **Additional Information:** Recipients may attend college in Hawaii or on the mainland. This program was established in 1996.

2337 ■ ILLINOIS STUDENT ASSISTANCE COMMISSION

Attn: Scholarship and Grant Services
1755 Lake Cook Road
Deerfield, IL 60015-5209
Tel: (847)948-8550
Free: 800-899-ISAC
Fax: (847)831-8549
E-mail: collegezone@isac.org
Web Site: http://www.collegezone.com

To provide scholarship/loans to college students in Illinois who are interested in training or retraining for a teaching career in academic shortage areas.

Title of Award: Illinois Future Teacher Corps Program **Area, Field, or Subject:** Education; Education, Bilingual and cross-cultural; Education, Early childhood; Education, Elementary; Education, Music; Education, Physical; Education, Secondary; Education, Special; Hearing and deafness; Visual impairment **Level of Education for which Award is Granted:** Four Year College **Number Awarded:** Varies each year, depending on the availability of funds. **Funds Available:** This program pays tuition and fees, room and board, or a commuter allowance at academic institutions in Illinois. The maximum award is $5,000 or $10,000 (and may even be increased by an additional $5,000), depending on the teaching commitment the recipient makes. Funds are paid directly to the school. This is a scholarship/loan program. Recipients must agree to teach in an Illinois public, private, or parochial preschool, elementary school, or secondary school for 1 year for each full year of assistance received. The teaching obligation must be completed within 5 years of completion of the degree or certificate program for which the scholarship was awarded. That time period may be extended if the recipient serves in the U.S. armed forces, enrolls full time in a graduate program related to teaching, becomes temporarily disabled, is unable to find employment as a teacher, or takes additional courses on at least a half-time basis to teach in a specialized teacher shortage discipline. Recipients who fail to honor this work obligation must repay the award with interest. **Duration:** 1 year; may be renewed.

Eligibility Requirements: This program is open to Illinois residents who are enrolled at the junior level or higher at an institution of higher education in the state. Applicants must be planning to prepare for a career as a preschool, elementary, or secondary school teacher. Preference is given to students working on a degree in designated teacher shortage disciplines, making a commitment to teach at a hard-to-staff school, and/or planning to teach minority students. Recently, the teacher shortage disciplines included behavior disordered, bilingual teacher (K-12), cross categorical (seeking certification in 2 or more areas of special education), general special education (including blind and deaf specialties and early childhood special education), learning disabled, mathematics (K-12), music (K-12), physical education (K-12), reading and English language arts (K-12), and speech and language impaired. Preference is given to renewal applicants. Selection is based on cumulative GPA, expected family contribution, and minority student status. **Deadline for Receipt:** Priority consideration is given to applications submitted by February of each year. **Additional Information:** This program was formerly known as the David A. DeBolt Teacher Shortage Scholarship Program.

2338 ■ KANSAS-NEBRASKA CONVENTION OF SOUTHERN BAPTISTS

Attn: Kansas-Nebraska Southern Baptist Foundation
5410 S.W. Seventh Street
Topeka, KS 66606-2398
Tel: (785)273-4880
Free: 800-984-9092
Fax: (785)273-4992
E-mail: pdavis@kncsb.org
Web Site: http://kncsb.org

To provide financial assistance to Southern Baptists from Kansas and Nebraska who are interested in preparing for a career as a church musician.
Title of Award: Ed VanLandingham Music Scholarship **Area, Field, or Subject:** Music; Religion **Level of Education for which Award is Granted:** Undergraduate **Number Awarded:** 1 or more each year. **Funds Available:** A stipend is awarded (amount not specified). **Duration:** 1 year. **Eligibility Requirements:** This program is open to members of churches in the Kansas-Nebraska Convention of Southern Baptists who are attending or planning to attend a college or university. Applicants must have declared church music as their vocation. **Deadline for Receipt:** May of each year.

2339 ■ KOSCIUSZKO FOUNDATION

Attn: Director of Cultural Events
15 East 65th Street
New York, NY 10021-6595
Tel: (212)734-2130
Free: 800-287-9956
Fax: (212)628-4552
E-mail: culture@thekf.org
Web Site: http://www.thekf.org/MUChopin.html

To recognize and reward outstanding pianists.
Title of Award: Kosciuszko Foundation Chopin Piano Competition **Area, Field, or Subject:** Music, Piano **Level of Education for which Award is Granted:** Undergraduate **Number Awarded:** 3 national prizes are awarded each year. **Funds Available:** The preliminary competitions provide small cash prizes and round-trip airfare to the national finals. In the national competitions, first place is $5,000, second place $2,500, and third place $1,500. **Duration:** The competition is held annually; the preliminaries are held in March and the national finals in April.
Eligibility Requirements: The competition is open to U.S. citizens, permanent residents of the United States, and international full-time students with valid student visas; all entrants must be between 16 and 22 years of age. Contestants prepare a program of 60 to 75 minutes encompassing a selection of works by Chopin, a mazurka by Szymanowski, a major work by J.S. Bach, a complete classical (Beethoven, Haydn, Mozart or Schubert) sonata, a major 19th-century work by a composer other than Chopin, and a substantial work by an American, Polish, or Polish American composer written after 1950; jurors choose works from the program for the auditions. Preliminary competitions take place in Chicago and New York; winners advance to the national competitions in New York. **Deadline for Receipt:** February of each year. **Additional Information:** This competition was established in 1949. The first-prize

winner also performs at concerts arranged by the Kosciuszko Foundation in the United States and Poland. Applications must be accompanied by a nonrefundable fee of $35.

2340 ■ KOSCIUSZKO FOUNDATION

Attn: Director of Cultural Events
15 East 65th Street
New York, NY 10021-6595
Tel: (212)734-2130
Free: 800-287-9956
Fax: (212)628-4552
E-mail: culture@thekf.org
Web Site: http://www.thekf.org/MUViolin.html

To recognize and reward outstanding violinists.
Title of Award: Kosciuszko Foundation Wieniawski Violin Competition **Area, Field, or Subject:** Music, Violin **Level of Education for which Award is Granted:** Undergraduate **Number Awarded:** 3 national prizes are awarded each year. **Funds Available:** First place is $5,000, second $2,500, and third $1,500. **Duration:** The competition is held annually, in April.
Eligibility Requirements: The competition is open to U.S. citizens, permanent residents of the United States, and international full-time students with valid student visas; all entrants must be between 16 and 22 years of age. Contestants prepare a program of 60 to 75 minutes encompassing a concerto by Wieniawski or Szymanowski, the first 2 movements of a Bach sonata, a sonata by Beethoven or Mozart, a virtuostic 19th-century work, a Paganini caprice, and a substantial work by an American, Polish, or Polish American composer written after 1950. They must submit an audition CD of approximately 15 minutes with selections from their program. Based on those CDs, finalists are invited to the competition in New York. **Deadline for Receipt:** March of each year. **Additional Information:** Applications must be accompanied by a nonrefundable fee of $35.

2341 ■ KOSCIUSZKO FOUNDATION

Attn: Director of Cultural Events
15 East 65th Street
New York, NY 10021-6595
Tel: (212)734-2130
Free: 800-287-9956
Fax: (212)628-4552
E-mail: culture@thekf.org
Web Site: http://www.thekf.org/MUvoice.html

To recognize and reward outstanding singers.
Title of Award: Marcella Sembrich Voice Competition **Area, Field, or Subject:** Music, Vocal **Level of Education for which Award is Granted:** Graduate, Professional, Undergraduate **Number Awarded:** 3 prizes are awarded each year of the competition. **Funds Available:** The first-prize winner receives a $1,000 cash scholarship; round-trip airfare from New York City to Warsaw, accommodations, and meals in Poland to perform in the International Moniuszko Competition; a recital at the Moniuszko Festival in Poland; and an invitation to perform at the Sembrich Memorial Association in Lake George, New York. Second and third prizes are $750 and $500, respectively. **Duration:** The competition is held triennially, in March.
Eligibility Requirements: The competition is open to U.S. citizens, permanent residents of the United States, and international full-time students with valid student visas; all entrants must be between 18 and 35 years of age and preparing for professional singing careers. They must submit an audio cassette recording of a proposed program if they are selected for the competition; the program must include a Baroque or Classical aria, an aria by Giuseppe Verdi, a Polish song, a 19th-century Romantic opera aria, a contemporary American aria or song, and an aria by Stanislaw Moniuszko. **Deadline for Receipt:** December of the years prior to the competitions, which are held in 2007, 2010, etc. **Additional Information:** Applications must be accompanied by a nonrefundable fee of $35.

2342 ■ LUSO-AMERICAN EDUCATION FOUNDATION

Attn: Administrative Director
7080 Donlon Way, Suite 202
P.O. Box 2967
Dublin, CA 94568

Tel: (925)828-3883

Fax: (925)828-3883

Web Site: http://www.luso-american.org/laef/scholarships.html

To provide financial assistance for undergraduate study to members of the Luso-American Fraternal Federation who are musically oriented.

Title of Award: Antonio Toledo Memorial Scholarships **Area, Field, or Subject:** Music **Level of Education for which Award is Granted:** Undergraduate **Number Awarded:** Varies each year; recently, 7 of these scholarships were awarded. **Funds Available:** A stipend is provided (amount not specified). **Duration:** 1 year; renewable.

Eligibility Requirements: This program is open to members of the federation who are high school seniors with a GPA of 3.0 or higher. Applicants should be interested in studying music. Preference is given to residents of the Chino/Ontario area of California. **Deadline for Receipt:** February of each year. **Additional Information:** Membership in the Luso-American Fraternal Federation is limited to people who hold Luso-American Life Insurance policies or annuities.

2343 ■ MAINE COMMUNITY FOUNDATION

Attn: Program Director

245 Main Street

Ellsworth, ME 04605

Tel: (207)667-9735; 877-700-6800

Fax: (207)667-0447

E-mail: info@mainecf.org

Web Site: http://www.mainecf.org/html/scholarships/index.html

To provide financial assistance to Maine residents interested in working pursuing classical voice training.

Title of Award: Lee Patterson Scholarship for Classical Voice Training **Area, Field, or Subject:** Music, Vocal **Level of Education for which Award is Granted:** Undergraduate **Number Awarded:** Varies each year.

Funds Available: A stipend is awarded (amount not specified).

Eligibility Requirements: This program is open to residents of Maine who are at least 14 years of age. Preference is given to residents of Hancock and Washington countries. Applicants must be interested in pursuing classical voice training (opera, operettas, and art song literature composed between 1600 and 1920) with a certified voice teacher. Financial need is considered in the selection process. **Deadline for Receipt:** March of each year. **Additional Information:** This program was established in 2001. Information is also available from Lee Patterson, P.O. Box 200, Mount Desert, ME 04660. Recipients must agree to sing with the Gilbert and Sullivan Society of Hancock County in all activities, staged and concert, during the term of their scholarship.

2344 ■ MARYLAND HIGHER EDUCATION COMMISSION

Attn: Office of Student Financial Assistance

839 Bestgate Road, Suite 400

Annapolis, MD 21401-3013

Tel: (410)260-4569

Free: 800-974-1024

Fax: (410)974-5376

E-mail: osfamail@mhec.state.md.us

Web Site: http://www.mhec.state.md.us/financialAid/ProgramDescriptions/prog_ds.asp

To provide financial assistance for college to outstanding high school juniors in Maryland.

Title of Award: Maryland Distinguished Scholar Awards **Area, Field, or Subject:** Dance; General studies/Field of study not specified; Music; Music, Vocal; Visual arts **Level of Education for which Award is Granted:** Undergraduate **Number Awarded:** 350 each year. **Funds Available:** The stipend is $3,000 per year. The total amount of all state awards may not exceed the cost of attendance as determined by the school's financial aid office or $17,800, whichever is less. **Duration:** 1 year; may be renewed up to 3 additional years if the recipient maintains at least a 3.0 GPA and remains enrolled full time at an eligible Maryland institution.

Eligibility Requirements: Eligible to apply are outstanding high school juniors in Maryland who intend to work on an undergraduate degree on a full-time basis at an accredited college, university, or private career school in the state. Students may qualify in 1 of 3 ways: 1) superior academic achievement, in which finalists are selected on the basis of GPA (minimum 3.7) and scores on PSAT, SAT, or ACT exams; 2) National Achievement Scholarship and National Merit Scholarship programs, in which finalists automatically receive these scholarships if they enroll in eligible Maryland institutions; and 3) superior talent in the arts, in which finalists are selected in statewide auditions or portfolio evaluations in visual art, instrumental music, vocal music, dance, or drama. Financial need is not considered. **Deadline for Receipt:** Applications in the academic achievement category must be submitted in February of each year; nominations in the talent category must be submitted in April of each year.

2345 ■ NATIONAL FEDERATION OF MUSIC CLUBS

1336 North Delaware Street

Indianapolis, IN 46202-2481

Tel: (317)638-4003

Fax: (317)638-0503

E-mail: info@nfmc-music.org

Web Site: http://www.nfmc-music.org/Competitions/Biennial%20Student%20Aud./suppstudentaud.ht m

To recognize and reward outstanding young singers who are members of the National Federation of Music Clubs (NFMC).

Title of Award: Hazel Heffner Becchina Award **Area, Field, or Subject:** Music, Vocal **Level of Education for which Award is Granted:** Graduate, Professional, Undergraduate, Other **Number Awarded:** 2 every other year: 1 to a woman and 1 to a man. **Funds Available:** The prize is $1,500. Funds must be used for continued study. **Duration:** The competition is held biennially, in odd-numbered years.

Eligibility Requirements: This award is presented to singers between 18 and 26 years of age. Men and women are judged separately. Membership in the federation and U.S. citizenship are required. Candidates for the NFMC Biennial Student Audition Awards competition are automatically considered for this award; no separation application is necessary. **Deadline for Receipt:** January of odd-numbered years. **Additional Information:** Applications and further information on these awards are available from Mrs. Robert Carroll, 17583 North 1090 East Road, Pontiac, IL 61764-9801, E-mail: scarroll@frontiernet.net; information on all federation scholarships and awards is available from Chair, Competitions and Awards Board, Dr. George R. Keck, 421 Cherry Street, Arkadelphia, AR 71923-5116, E-mail: keckg@obu.edu. The entry fee is $30.

2346 ■ NATIONAL FEDERATION OF MUSIC CLUBS

1336 North Delaware Street

Indianapolis, IN 46202-2481

Tel: (317)638-4003

Fax: (317)638-0503

E-mail: info@nfmc-music.org

Web Site: http://www.nfmc-music.org/Competitions/Annual%20Senior/annual_senior_div.htm

To provide financial assistance for undergraduate education to members of the National Federation of Music Clubs (NFMC) whose careers have been delayed or interrupted as a result of their service in the U.S. armed forces.

Title of Award: Anne M. Gannett Award for Veterans **Area, Field, or Subject:** Music **Level of Education for which Award is Granted:** Undergraduate **Number Awarded:** 1 each year. **Funds Available:** The stipend is $1,250. **Duration:** 1 year.

Eligibility Requirements: Eligible to apply are undergraduate students who are majoring in music and whose musical careers were interrupted by military service. Student membership in the federation and U.S. citizenship are required. **Deadline for Receipt:** February of each year. **Additional Information:** Applications and further information are also available from Doris Whinery, 4200 East Cedar Lane Road, Noble, OK 73068, E-mail: idwhinery@aol.com; information on all federation scholarships and awards is available from Chair, Competitions and Awards Board, Dr. George R. Keck, 421 Cherry Street, Arkadelphia, AR 71923-5116, E-mail: keckg@obu.edu.

2347 ■ NATIONAL FEDERATION OF MUSIC CLUBS

1336 North Delaware Street

Indianapolis, IN 46202-2481

Tel: (317)638-4003

Fax: (317)638-0503

E-mail: info@nfmc-music.org

Web Site: http://www.nfmc-music.org/Competitions/Biennial%20Student%20Aud./suppstudentaud.ht m

To recognize and reward outstanding young singers who are members of the National Federation of Music Clubs (NFMC).

Title of Award: Irene S. Muir Award **Area, Field, or Subject:** Music, Vocal **Level of Education for which Award is Granted:** Graduate, Professional, Undergraduate, Other **Number Awarded:** 2 every other year: 1 to a woman and 1 to a man. **Funds Available:** The prize is $1,000. Funds must be used for continued study. **Duration:** The competition is held biennially, in odd-numbered years.

Eligibility Requirements: This award is presented to singers between 18 and 26 years of age. Men and women are judged separately. Membership in the federation and U.S. citizenship are required. Candidates for the NFMC Biennial Student Audition Awards competition are automatically considered for this award; no separation application is necessary.

Deadline for Receipt: January of odd-numbered years. **Additional Information:** Applications and further information on these awards are available from Mrs. Robert Carroll, 17583 North 1090 East Road, Pontiac, IL 61764-9801, E-mail: scarroll@frontiernet.net; information on all federation scholarships and awards is available from Chair, Competitions and Awards Board, Dr. George R. Keck, 421 Cherry Street, Arkadelphia, AR 71923-5116, E-mail: keckg@obu.edu. The entry fee is $30.

2348 ■ NATIONAL FEDERATION OF MUSIC CLUBS

1336 North Delaware Street
Indianapolis, IN 46202-2481
Tel: (317)638-4003
Fax: (317)638-0503
E-mail: info@nfmc-music.org
Web Site: http://www.nfmc-music.org/Competitions/
Bien%20Student%20Spec/BienStudentSpecial.ht m

To recognize and reward outstanding young composers who are members of the National Federation of Music Clubs.

Title of Award: Lynn Freeman Olson Composition Award **Area, Field, or Subject:** Music composition **Level of Education for which Award is Granted:** Graduate, Undergraduate **Number Awarded:** 3 every other year: 1 in each of the divisions. **Funds Available:** The award is $1,500 for the advanced division, $1,000 for the high school division, or $500 for the intermediate division. Funds must be used for further music study.

Eligibility Requirements: This competition is open to keyboard composers in the advanced division (high school graduate through 25 years of age), the high school division (grades 10-12), or the intermediate division (grades 7 through 9). Applicants may be citizens of any country, but they must be members of either the junior or student division of the federation. They may not previously have published any works for the purpose of general public use or sales. Compositions must be written within the skill levels of early elementary through intermediate levels of piano study.

Deadline for Receipt: February of odd-numbered years. **Additional Information:** Further information on this award is also available from James Schnars, 28 Evonaire Circle, Belleair FL 33756-1602; information on all federation scholarships and awards is available from Chair, Competitions and Awards Board, Dr. George R. Keck, 421 Cherry Street, Arkadelphia, AR 71923-5116, E-mail: keckg@obu.edu.

2349 ■ NATIONAL FEDERATION OF MUSIC CLUBS

1336 North Delaware Street
Indianapolis, IN 46202-2481
Tel: (317)638-4003
Fax: (317)638-0503
E-mail: info@nfmc-music.org
Web Site: http://www.nfmc-music.org/Competitions/Annual%20Student/
annual_student.htm

To recognize and reward outstanding young composers who are members of the National Federation of Music Clubs.

Title of Award: Marion Richter American Music Composition Award **Area, Field, or Subject:** Music composition **Level of Education for which Award is Granted:** Four Year College **Number Awarded:** 1 each year. **Funds Available:** The stipend is $1,250. **Duration:** The competition is held annually.

Eligibility Requirements: This program is open to members of the federation who are college juniors, seniors, or graduate students and U.S. citizens. Applicants must be between 18 and 26 years of age and majoring in composition. They must submit an original composition up to the equivalent of 4 engraved manuscript pages. Solo/ensemble arrangements and ensemble settings of standard works are not eligible. **Deadline for**

Receipt: February of each year. **Additional Information:** Applications and further information are available from Wilmot Irish, 600 Warren Road, Apartment 3-2A, Ithaca, NY 14850; information on all federation scholarships and awards is available from Chair, Competitions and Awards Board, Dr. George R. Keck, 421 Cherry Street, Arkadelphia, AR 71923-5116, E-mail: keckg@obu.edu. The entry fee is $10.

2350 ■ NATIONAL FEDERATION OF MUSIC CLUBS

1336 North Delaware Street
Indianapolis, IN 46202-2481
Tel: (317)638-4003
Fax: (317)638-0503
E-mail: info@nfmc-music.org
Web Site: http://www.nfmc-music.org/Competitions/Annual%20Junior/
annual_junior.htm

To recognize and reward outstanding young musicians who are members of the National Federation of Music Clubs (NFMC).

Title of Award: Stillman-Kelley Awards **Area, Field, or Subject:** Music **Level of Education for which Award is Granted:** Undergraduate **Number Awarded:** 2 each year. **Funds Available:** Awards, to be used for further study, are $1,000 for first place and $500 for second place.

Eligibility Requirements: Eligible are instrumentalists who are younger than 17 years of age, U.S. citizens, and junior members of the federation. Applicants must present a program of 15 to 20 minutes, performed from memory, on their selected solo instrument. Awards are rotated by NFMC region, with northeastern and southeastern in even-numbered years and central and western in odd-numbered years. **Deadline for Receipt:** January of each year. **Additional Information:** Information on these awards is also available from Mr. Stillman Kelly, 415 Sussex Circle, Vacaville, CA 95687, E-mail: slkmusic@aol.com; information on all federation scholarships and awards is available from Chair, Competitions and Awards Board, Dr. George R. Keck, 421 Cherry Street, Arkadelphia, AR 71923-5116, E-mail: keckg@obu.edu.

2351 ■ NATIONAL FEDERATION OF MUSIC CLUBS

1336 North Delaware Street
Indianapolis, IN 46202-2481
Tel: (317)638-4003
Fax: (317)638-0503
E-mail: info@nfmc-music.org
Web Site: http://www.nfmc-music.org/Competitions/Annual%20Student/
annual_student.htm

To provide financial assistance to college student members of the National Federation of Music Clubs (NFMC) who are majoring in music education.

Title of Award: Gretchen E. Van Roy Music Education Scholarship **Area, Field, or Subject:** Education, Music **Level of Education for which Award is Granted:** Four Year College **Number Awarded:** 1 each year. **Funds Available:** The stipend is $1,000. **Duration:** 1 year.

Eligibility Requirements: Applicants must be college juniors majoring in music education at a college or university. U.S. citizenship and membership in the student division of the federation are required. **Deadline for Receipt:** February of each year. **Additional Information:** Information on this award is also available from Mrs. Ralph Suggs, 606 East Ridge Village Drive, Miami, FL 33157, E-mail: rose331s@aol.com; information on all federation scholarships and awards is available from Chair, Competitions and Awards Board, Dr. George R. Keck, 421 Cherry Street, Arkadelphia, AR 71923-5116, E-mail: keckg@obu.edu.

2352 ■ NATIONAL FEDERATION OF MUSIC CLUBS

1336 North Delaware Street
Indianapolis, IN 46202-2481
Tel: (317)638-4003
Fax: (317)638-0503
E-mail: info@nfmc-music.org
Web Site: http://www.nfmc-music.org/Competitions/
Biennial%20Student%20Aud./suppstudentaud.ht m

To recognize and reward outstanding young singers who are members of the National Federation of Music Clubs (NFMC).

Title of Award: Virginia Peace Mackey-Althouse Voice Award **Area, Field, or Subject:** Music, Vocal **Level of Education for which Award is Granted:** Graduate, Professional, Undergraduate, Other **Number Awarded:** 2 every other year: 1 to a woman and 1 to a man. **Funds Avail-**

able: The prize is $1,200. Funds must be used for continued study. Duration: The competition is held biennially, in odd-numbered years.

Eligibility Requirements: This award is presented to singers between 18 and 26 years of age. Membership in the federation and U.S. citizenship are required. Candidates for the NFMC Biennial Student Audition Awards competition are automatically considered for this award; no separation application is necessary. Deadline for Receipt: January of odd-numbered years. Additional Information: Applications and further information on these awards are available from Mrs. Robert Carroll, 17583 North 1090 East Road, Pontiac, IL 61764-9801, E-mail: scarroll@frontiernet.net; information on all federation scholarships and awards is available from Chair, Competitions and Awards Board, Dr. George R. Keck, 421 Cherry Street, Arkadelphia, AR 71923-5116, E-mail: keckg@obu.edu. The entry fee is $30.

2353 ■ NATIONAL FEDERATION OF MUSIC CLUBS

1336 North Delaware Street
Indianapolis, IN 46202-2481
Tel: (317)638-4003
Fax: (317)638-0503
E-mail: info@nfmc-music.org
Web Site: http://www.nfmc-music.org/Competitions/Annual%20Senior/annual_senior_div.htm
To provide financial assistance for undergraduate education to members of the National Federation of Music Clubs (NFMC) whose careers have been delayed or interrupted as a result of their service in the U.S. armed forces.

Title of Award: Lucille Parrish Ward Veteran's Award Area, Field, or Subject: Music Level of Education for which Award is Granted: Undergraduate Number Awarded: 1 each year. Funds Available: The award is $2,000. Duration: 1 year; may be renewed if the recipient maintains a GPA of 3.0 or higher.

Eligibility Requirements: Eligible to apply are undergraduate students who are majoring in music and whose musical careers were interrupted by service in the armed forces. Veterans who served overseas receive preference. Student membership in the federation and U.S. citizenship are required. Deadline for Receipt: February of each year. Additional Information: Applications and further information are also available from Mrs. Stephen L. Johnston, 4015 Devon Street S.E., Huntsville, AL 35802-1017; information on all federation scholarships and awards is available from Chair, Competitions and Awards Board, Dr. George R. Keck, 421 Cherry Street, Arkadelphia, AR 71923-5116, E-mail: keckg@obu.edu.

2354 ■ NATIONAL RELIGIOUS MUSIC WEEK ALLIANCE

201 Dayton Street
Hamilton, OH 45011
Tel: (513)884-1500
Fax: (513)884-1999
E-mail: musicweek@aol.com
Web Site: http://www.religiousmusicweek.com/scholar.html
To provide financial assistance to students enrolled in a college music program leading to a career in the ministry of music.

Title of Award: National Religious Music Week Alliance Scholarships Area, Field, or Subject: Music; Religion Level of Education for which Award is Granted: Undergraduate Number Awarded: 2 each year. Funds Available: The stipend is $2,500. Duration: 1 year.

Eligibility Requirements: This program is open to students enrolled in a college or university and majoring in music. Applicants must be interested in preparing for a career in church music. Along with their application, they must submit a brief essay on their plans for continuing their education and their goals following graduation. Selection is based on the essay, grade transcripts, 2 letters of recommendation, scholastic distinctions and honors, and involvement in church, school, or community activities. Financial need is not considered. Deadline for Receipt: March of each year. Additional Information: These scholarships were first awarded in 2004.

2355 ■ PRINCESS GRACE AWARDS

Attn: Grants Coordinator
150 East 58th Street, 25th Floor
New York, NY 10155
Tel: (212)317-1470
Fax: (212)317-1473

E-mail: pgfusa@pgfusa.com
Web Site: http://www.pgfusa.com/awards/dance/index.html
To provide financial support for college to students interested in dance.

Title of Award: Dance Scholarships Area, Field, or Subject: Dance Level of Education for which Award is Granted: Undergraduate Number Awarded: Varies each year. Funds Available: Stipends range from $5,000 to $25,000, depending upon tuition. No other expenses (e.g., room and board, materials, books, costumes) may be included. Duration: Up to 1 year.

Eligibility Requirements: This program is open to students who have completed at least 1 year of training at a professional, nonprofit school of dance in the United States and are seeking support for tuition. Candidates must be nominated by the dean or chair of the dance department; only 1 student may be nominated per institution. Individuals may not submit an application independently. Nominees are invited to send an application, an autobiography, an essay, a portfolio, and references. All nominees must be U.S. citizens or permanent residents. Selection is based on the candidates' past artistic merit, the significance of the award to their current artistic development, and the potential for future excellence and impact in the field. Deadline for Receipt: April of each year.

2356 ■ DONNA REED FOUNDATION FOR THE PERFORMING ARTS

1305 Broadway
Denison, IA 51442
Tel: (712)263-3334
Free: 800-336-4692
Fax: (712)263-8026
E-mail: info@donnareed.org
Web Site: http://www.donnareed.org
To provide financial assistance to high school seniors interested in studying the performing arts in college.

Title of Award: Donna Reed Performing Arts Scholarships Area, Field, or Subject: Music; Music, Vocal; Performing arts Level of Education for which Award is Granted: Undergraduate Number Awarded: 9 each year: in each of the 3 divisions, 1 national winner and 2 other finalists receive awards. In addition, each of the 9 national finalists receive free tuition and all expenses to participate in the Donna Reed Festival and Workshops for the Performing Arts. Another 3 scholarships (1 in each division) are awarded to Iowa residents, and another 3 scholarships (1 in each division) are awarded to residents of Crawford County, Iowa. Funds Available: National winners receive $1,000 per year and finalists receive $500. Funds may be used for an accredited postsecondary or approved program of study of the recipient's choice. Iowa winners receive $1,000 scholarships and Crawford County winners receive $500 scholarships. Duration: Scholarships for national winners are for 4 years. Scholarships for other winners are for 1 year.

Eligibility Requirements: This program is open to high school seniors who wish to pursue an education or a career in 1 of the following 3 performing arts: acting, vocal (classical, jazz, popular), or musical theater. Applicants must graduate or have graduated from high school during the period between September prior to applying and August after applying. They must submit audio or videotapes; based on those tapes, finalists are invited to a live competition in June at the Donna Reed Festival and Workshops for the Performing Arts in Denison, Iowa. Selection is based on talent. Grades and financial need are not considered. U.S. citizenship or permanent resident status is required. Separate award are presented to residents of Iowa and to residents of Crawford County, Iowa. Deadline for Receipt: February of each year. Additional Information: The widower and friends of the actress Donna Reed established this foundation in 1987, the year after her death. It is based in, and the workshops are held in, Denison, Iowa, Donna Reed's birthplace. A $40 application fee is required for the first discipline category the applicant enters; additional entries require an additional $30 fee. Fees may be waived in cases of financial need.

2357 ■ RHODE ISLAND FOUNDATION

Attn: Scholarship Coordinator
One Union Station
Providence, RI 02903
Tel: (401)274-4564
Fax: (401)331-8085
E-mail: libbym@rifoundation.org
Web Site: http://www.rifoundation.org

To provide financial assistance to students in Rhode Island who demonstrate ability in playing the organ or other keyboard instrument and to church organists.

Title of Award: Bach Organ and Keyboard Music Scholarship **Area, Field, or Subject:** Music; Music, Piano; Religion **Level of Education for which Award is Granted:** Undergraduate **Number Awarded:** Up to 3 each year. **Funds Available:** Stipends range from $300 to $1,000.

Eligibility Requirements: This program is open to music majors specializing in organ or piano in pursuit of a college degree. Applicants must be Rhode Island residents and church organists who are members of the American Guild of Organists (AGO). They must submit a letter of reference from their organ/keyboard teacher or church official and an essay (up to 300 words) on what they hope they will be doing in their professional life 10 years from now. Financial need is considered in the selection process. **Deadline for Receipt:** June of each year.

2358 ■ SCHOLARSHIP ADMINISTRATIVE SERVICES, INC.
Attn: DSA Program
2000 Rock Street, Suite 3
Mountain View, CA 94043

To provide financial assistance to students preparing for a career as a dancer at a college, university, or other institution.

Title of Award: Dance Society of America Scholarships **Area, Field, or Subject:** Dance **Level of Education for which Award is Granted:** Undergraduate **Number Awarded:** Up to 20 each year. **Funds Available:** The stipend is $5,000 per year. **Duration:** 1 year; nonrenewable.

Eligibility Requirements: This program is open to students enrolled or planning to enrolled in a dance program at a college, university, or other recognized school of dance. Applicants must have a record of successful participation in dance competitions at the youth and high school level. They must submit a letter of recommendation from a dance instructor with whom they previously studied and a 500-word essay on what inspired them to become a dancer. Financial need is not considered in the selection process. **Deadline for Receipt:** April of each year. **Additional Information:** This program is sponsored by the Dance Society of America (DSA) and administered by Scholarship Administrative Services, Inc. DSA was established in 2005 to encourage more American students to consider a career as a dancer. Requests for applications should be accompanied by a self-addressed stamped envelope, the student's e-mail address, and the source where they found the scholarship information.

2359 ■ SCHOOL BAND AND ORCHESTRA MAGAZINE
Attn: Student Scholarships
21 Highland Circle, Suite 1
Needham, MA 02494
Tel: (781)453-9310
Free: 800-964-5150
Fax: (781)453-9389
Web Site: http://www.sbomagazine.com/Essay

To recognize and reward, with college scholarships, elementary and high school students who submit outstanding essays on playing a musical instrument.

Title of Award: Annual Music Student Scholarships **Area, Field, or Subject:** Music; Writing **Level of Education for which Award is Granted:** Undergraduate **Number Awarded:** 10 each year: 5 to students in grades 4-8 and 5 to students in grades 9-12. **Funds Available:** The award is a $1,000 college scholarship. **Duration:** The competition is held annually.

Eligibility Requirements: This competition is open to public and private school students in grades 4 through 12. Applicants must submit an essay of up to 250 words on "How Playing a Musical Instrument Made Me a Better Student." **Deadline for Receipt:** December of each year.

2360 ■ SIGMA ALPHA IOTA PHILANTHROPIES, INC.
One Tunnel Road
Asheville, NC 28805
Tel: (828)251-0606
Fax: (828)251-0644
E-mail: philonline@sai-national.org
Web Site: http://www.sai-national.org/phil/philmustech.html

To provide financial assistance for college to members of Sigma Alpha Iota (an organization of women musicians).

Title of Award: Dorothy Cooke Whinery Music Business/Technology Scholarship **Area, Field, or Subject:** Business; Business administration;

Management; Marketing and distribution; Music; Performing arts; Technology **Level of Education for which Award is Granted:** Four Year College **Number Awarded:** 1 each year. **Funds Available:** The stipend is $2,000. **Duration:** 1 year.

Eligibility Requirements: This program is open to members of the organization entering their junior or senior year of college. Applicants must be working on a degree in the field of music business or music technology, including music marketing, music business administration, entertainment industry, commercial music, recording and production, music management, or other related fields. They must have a GPA of 3.0 or higher. Along with their application, they must submit a statement of purpose that includes their career goals. **Deadline for Receipt:** March of each year. **Additional Information:** This program was established in 2003. There is a $25 nonrefundable application fee.

2361 ■ SIGMA ALPHA IOTA PHILANTHROPIES, INC.
One Tunnel Road
Asheville, NC 28805
Tel: (828)251-0606
Fax: (828)251-0644
E-mail: philonline@sai-national.org
Web Site: http://www.sai-national.org/phil/philsch3.html

To provide financial assistance to members of Sigma Alpha Iota (an organization of women musicians) who are interested in working on an undergraduate or graduate degree in jazz performance.

Title of Award: Jazz Performance Awards **Area, Field, or Subject:** Music, Jazz **Level of Education for which Award is Granted:** Graduate, Undergraduate **Number Awarded:** 2 every 3 years. **Funds Available:** Stipends are $2,000 for the winner or $1,500 for the runner-up. **Duration:** 1 year.

Eligibility Requirements: This program is open to members of the organization who are enrolled in an undergraduate or graduate degree program in jazz performance or studies. Applicants must be younger than 32 years of age. Along with their application, they must submit a CD recording of a performance "set" of 30 to 45 minutes. **Deadline for Receipt:** March of the year of the awards (2009, 2012, etc.). **Additional Information:** There is a $25 nonrefundable application fee.

2362 ■ SIGMA ALPHA IOTA PHILANTHROPIES, INC.
One Tunnel Road
Asheville, NC 28805
Tel: (828)251-0606
Fax: (828)251-0644
E-mail: philonline@sai-national.org
Web Site: http://www.sai-national.org/phil/philsch1.html

To provide financial assistance to members of Sigma Alpha Iota (an organization of women musicians) who are interested in working on an undergraduate degree in jazz studies.

Title of Award: Jazz Studies Scholarship **Area, Field, or Subject:** Music, Jazz **Level of Education for which Award is Granted:** Undergraduate **Number Awarded:** 1 each year. **Funds Available:** The stipend is $1,500. **Duration:** 1 year.

Eligibility Requirements: This program is open to members of the organization who are enrolled in a university jazz studies program. Applicants must submit a 500-word essay on their career plans and professional goals in jazz studies and why they feel they are deserving of this scholarship. **Deadline for Receipt:** March of each year. **Additional Information:** There is a $25 nonrefundable application fee.

2363 ■ SIGMA ALPHA IOTA PHILANTHROPIES, INC.
One Tunnel Road
Asheville, NC 28805
Tel: (828)251-0606
Fax: (828)251-0644
E-mail: philonline@sai-national.org
Web Site: http://www.sai-national.org/phil/philhazl.html

To provide loans for educational purposes to members of Sigma Alpha Iota (an organization of women musicians).

Title of Award: Hazel E. Ritchey Loans **Area, Field, or Subject:** Music **Level of Education for which Award is Granted:** Graduate, Undergraduate **Number Awarded:** Varies each year. **Funds Available:** The maximum loans are $2,500. The interest rate is 5% and must be paid while the recipient is still in school. Repayment of principal begins immediately upon graduation and must be completed within 2 year. **Duration:** 1 year; may be renewed for 2 additional years while the recipient is in school and has begun payment of interest.

Eligibility Requirements: Members of the organization may apply if they are enrolled as graduate or undergraduate students. They may be seeking funds to support education leading to an undergraduate or graduate degree in music, to purchase a new musical instrument, for study at a summer musical festival in the United States or abroad, or for special applied music lessons or coaching. **Deadline for Receipt:** Applications may be submitted at any time. **Additional Information:** This program was established in 1927.

2364 ■ SIGMA ALPHA IOTA PHILANTHROPIES, INC.

One Tunnel Road
Asheville, NC 28805
Tel: (828)251-0606
Fax: (828)251-0644
E-mail: philonline@sai-national.org
Web Site: http://www.sai-national.org/phil/philsumr.html
To provide financial assistance for summer study in music, in the United States or abroad, to members of Sigma Alpha Iota (an organization of women musicians).

Title of Award: Sigma Alpha Iota Regional Summer Music Scholarships **Area, Field, or Subject:** Music **Level of Education for which Award is Granted:** Graduate, Undergraduate **Number Awarded:** 5 each year: 1 from each region of Sigma Alpha Iota. **Funds Available:** The stipend is $1,000. **Duration:** Summer months.

Eligibility Requirements: Undergraduate and graduate student members of the organization may apply if they are planning to study at a summer music program in the United States or abroad. Applicants must submit a complete resume (including musical studies and activities, academic GPA, community service record, and record of participation in Sigma Alpha Iota), supporting materials (recital and concert programs, reviews, repertoire list, etc.), a statement of why they chose this program and how it will aid their musical growth, a full brochure of information on the program (including cost and payment due dates), a copy of the completed summer school application and acceptance letter (when available), and a letter of recommendation from their major teacher. **Deadline for Receipt:** March of each year. **Additional Information:** Applications must be accompanied by a nonrefundable fee of $25.

2365 ■ SIGMA ALPHA IOTA PHILANTHROPIES, INC.

One Tunnel Road
Asheville, NC 28805
Tel: (828)251-0606
Fax: (828)251-0644
E-mail: philonline@sai-national.org
Web Site: http://www.sai-national.org/phil/philsch1.html
To provide financial assistance for college or graduate school to members of Sigma Alpha Iota (an organization of women musicians) who have a disability and are working on a degree in music.

Title of Award: Sigma Alpha Iota Special Needs Scholarship **Area, Field, or Subject:** Music; Musicology **Level of Education for which Award is Granted:** Graduate, Undergraduate **Number Awarded:** 1 each year. **Funds Available:** The stipend is $1,000. **Duration:** 1 year.

Eligibility Requirements: This program is open to members of the organization who have a sensory or physical impairment. Applicants must be enrolled in a graduate or undergraduate degree program in music. Performance majors must submit a video or DVD of their work; non-performance majors must submit evidence of work in their area of specialization, such as composition, musicology, or research. **Deadline for Receipt:** March of each year. **Additional Information:** There is a $25 nonrefundable application fee.

2366 ■ SIGMA ALPHA IOTA PHILANTHROPIES, INC.

One Tunnel Road
Asheville, NC 28805
Tel: (828)251-0606
Fax: (828)251-0644
E-mail: philonline@sai-national.org
Web Site: http://www.sai-national.org/phil/philsch1.html
To provide financial assistance for college to members of Sigma Alpha Iota (an organization of women musicians).

Title of Award: Sigma Alpha Iota Undergraduate Scholarships **Area, Field, or Subject:** Music **Level of Education for which Award is Granted:** Undergraduate **Number Awarded:** 15 each year: 3 at $2,000 and 12 at $1,500. **Funds Available:** Stipends are $2,000 or $1,500. **Duration:** 1 year.

Eligibility Requirements: This program is open to members of the organization in the first 3 years of undergraduate study. Candidates must be nominated by their chapter and their chapter adviser must submit a letter of recommendation. Selection is based on financial need, musical ability, scholarship, potential leadership, and contribution to campus and community life. **Deadline for Receipt:** March of each year.

2367 ■ SOUTH CAROLINA COMMISSION ON HIGHER EDUCATION

Attn: Director of Student Services
1333 Main Street, Suite 200
Columbia, SC 29201
Tel: (803)737-2260; 877-349-7183
Fax: (803)737-2297
E-mail: dbrown@che.sc.gov
Web Site: http://www.che.sc.gov
To provide scholarship/loans to teachers in South Carolina who wish to improve their content knowledge and degree programs.

Title of Award: South Carolina Teaching Scholarship Grants Program **Area, Field, or Subject:** Art; Dance; Economics; Education; Education, Early childhood; Education, Elementary; Education, Music; Education, Secondary; Education, Special; Geography; History; Linguistics; Mathematics and mathematical sciences; Music; Political science; Science **Level of Education for which Award is Granted:** Graduate, Professional, Undergraduate **Number Awarded:** Varies each year. **Funds Available:** The stipend is $1,000 per fiscal year. This is a scholarship/loan program. Recipients must sign a commitment to teach in South Carolina public schools for at least 1 year following completion of the scholarship grant year and agree to refund the scholarship amount if the 1-year teaching commitment is not honored. **Duration:** 1 year; may be renewed if recipients maintain a GPA of 3.0 or higher. They may receive up to 3 grants in a 5-year period.

Eligibility Requirements: This program is open to residents of South Carolina who have a professional teaching certificate and are under contract as a teacher in a public school in the state. Applicants must be 1) accepted as a degree-seeking graduate student in the teaching field at the master's level and enrolled at an eligible institution in the state; or 2) enrolled for graduate or undergraduate courses in their current teaching field or in a teaching field in which they wish to add on certification. Proposed fields of study must relate to core content areas of English, reading or language arts, mathematics, science, foreign languages, civics and government, economics, arts (advanced fine arts, art, dance, drama, music, and speech), history, or geography; early childhood, elementary education, middle level education, secondary education, and special education also qualify. Priority is given to classroom teachers (not administrators, counselors, media specialists, or other support personnel) whose teaching specialties are critical need subject areas. Continuing graduate students must have a GPA of 3.0 or higher. U.S. citizenship or permanent resident status is required. **Deadline for Receipt:** December of each year for second summer session and fall semester; June of each year for spring semester and first summer session. **Additional Information:** This program was established in 2001.

2368 ■ SOUTH CAROLINA STATE DEPARTMENT OF EDUCATION

1429 Senate Street, Room 1010A
Columbia, SC 29201
Tel: (803)734-8485
E-mail: sspade@sde.state.sc.us
Web Site: http://www.myscschools.com/offices/ombudsman/arscholarship
To recognize and reward high school seniors in South Carolina who participate in a competition in art, creative writing, drama, or music.

Title of Award: Archibald Rutledge Scholarship Program **Area, Field, or Subject:** Art; Creative writing; Graphic art and design; Music composition; Painting; Playwriting; Poetry; Visual arts; Writing **Level of Education for which Award is Granted:** Undergraduate **Number Awarded:** 4 each year: 1 in each of the 4 categories. **Funds Available:** The award consists of a $4,000 scholarship, to be used for tuition, room, board, and instructional resource expenses. **Duration:** 1 year.

Eligibility Requirements: This program is open to U.S. citizens who have attended South Carolina public high schools for at least 2 years, are currently seniors, and are planning to attend a South Carolina college or university. Applicants compete by submitting samples of their work in 1 of 4 areas: 1) visual arts, limited to 2-dimensional work such as drawing and painting media, printmaking, and collage; no 3-dimensional works, photographs, or computer-generated images are accepted; 2) creative writing, as a sonnet, lyric, or narrative poem, up to 1 page; 3) drama, a 1-act play with a performing time of 20 to 45 minutes; or 4) music, a composition of 3 to 5 minutes for solo or small ensemble, vocal or instrumental, in any appropriate style. In addition to the work, they must submit a process folio that contains documentation of the planning and development of the project and a 1-page reflection statement addressing the intent of the work and comparing the final product with the original concept. A panel of professionals in the field selects up to 10 finalists, based on originality, creativity, and the correlation and implications of the process folio for the final composition. Finalists must attend the scholarship competition, where they present a portfolio of a number of selected works as specified by the judges. **Deadline for Receipt:** February of each year.

2369 ■ SOUTH CAROLINA STUDENT LOAN CORPORATION

Interstate Center
16 Berryhill Road, Suite 210
P.O. Box 21487
Columbia, SC 29221-1487
Tel: (803)798-0916
Free: 800-347-2752
Fax: (803)772-9410
Web Site: http://www.slc.sc.edu
To provide scholarship/loans to students in South Carolina who wish to teach certain subjects or in certain geographic areas.
Title of Award: South Carolina Teacher Loan Program **Area, Field, or Subject:** Agricultural sciences; Classical studies; Consumer affairs; Dance; Education, Elementary; Education, Music; Education, Special; English language and literature; Foreign languages; Library and archival sciences; Mathematics and mathematical sciences; Science; Speech and language pathology/audiology; Technology **Level of Education for which Award is Granted:** Graduate, Undergraduate **Number Awarded:** Varies each year. **Funds Available:** Freshmen and sophomores may borrow up to $2,500 per academic year; juniors, seniors, and graduate students may borrow up to $5,000 per academic year. This is a scholarship/loan program; loans are forgivable at the rate of 20% or $3,000, whichever is greater, for each full year of teaching in an area (either geographic or subject) of critical need; for students who teach in both critical subject and geographic areas, the rate of cancellation is 33% or $5,000, whichever is greater, per year. Borrowers who fail to teach in either a critical subject or geographic area must repay the loan at an annual interest rate that varies (currently, 5.37%) but is capped at 10.25%. **Duration:** 1 year; may be renewed for a total of 5 years of undergraduate and 5 years of graduate study.
Eligibility Requirements: Eligible to apply are residents of South Carolina who are planning to teach in certain critical geographic areas of the state, or to teach in critical subject areas. Entering freshmen must have ranked in the top 40% of their high school class and have an ACT or SAT score greater than the South Carolina average (recently 986 on the SAT or 19.3 on the ACT); enrolled undergraduates or entering graduate students must have at least a 2.75 cumulative GPA; graduate students who have completed at least 1 term must have a GPA of 3.5 or better. Undergraduate students at South Carolina colleges must have taken and passed the Education Entrance Exam; students at institutions outside South Carolina must have completed the necessary prerequisites required at that institution. Only U.S. citizens may apply. **Deadline for Receipt:** May of each year. **Additional Information:** Recently, the critical subject areas include mathematics, science (biology, chemistry, physics, and general science), media specialist, special education, industrial technology, foreign languages (Spanish, French, Latin, and German), family and consumer science, art, music, business education, English and language arts, dance, speech and drama/theater, and agriculture. For a list of critical geographic area, contact the sponsor.

2370 ■ JULIUS & ESTHER STULBERG COMPETITION, INC.

359 South Kalamazoo Mall, Suite 14
Kalamazoo, MI 49007
Tel: (269)343-2776

Fax: (269)343-2797
E-mail: Stulbergcomp@yahoo.com
Web Site: http://www.stulberg.org
To recognize and reward outstanding young string musicians.
Title of Award: Julius & Esther Stulberg International String Competition **Area, Field, or Subject:** Music, Viola; Music, Violin **Level of Education for which Award is Granted:** Undergraduate **Number Awarded:** 4 cash prizes are awarded each year. **Funds Available:** First place is the Stulberg Burdick-Thorne Gold Medal of $5,000 and a solo performance award. Second place is $4,000 and a solo recital at the Fontana Chamber Arts Summer Festival. Third place is $3,000 and a performance with the Kalamazoo Junior Symphony Society. The Bach Award is $500. Funds are to be used for the musical training and education of the winners. **Duration:** The competition is held annually, in March.
Eligibility Requirements: This competition is open to string players 19 years of age or younger who are studying violin, viola, cello, or double bass. Applicants must submit a CD of a performance from the standard solo repertoire (up to 20 minutes in length). The CD must include required selections by Bach for selection of the Bach Award. On the basis of the tapes, judges select 12 finalists to come to Kalamazoo to compete. **Deadline for Receipt:** December of each year. **Additional Information:** This competition was organized in 1975 as a memorial to Julius Stulberg, director of the Kalamazoo Junior Symphony for 31 years and professor of music at Western Michigan University for 27 years. The application fee is $75.

2371 ■ SWEDISH WOMEN'S EDUCATION ASSOCIATION INTERNATIONAL-SOUTH FLORIDA CHAPTER

c/o Yerti Nelson, Scholarship Committee
3759 Mykonos Court
Boca Raton, FL 33486
Tel: (561)997-2050
Fax: (561)997-8010
E-mail: florida@swea.org
Web Site: http://www.chapters-swea.org/florida
To provide financial assistance to Florida residents interested in studying in Sweden or an area related to Swedish studies.
Title of Award: South Florida SWEA Scholarship **Area, Field, or Subject:** Art; Art industries and trade; Crafts; Design; Environmental conservation; Environmental science; Foreign languages; General studies/Field of study not specified; Literature; Music; Swedish studies **Level of Education for which Award is Granted:** Graduate, Professional, Undergraduate **Number Awarded:** 1 each year. **Funds Available:** The stipend is $3,000.
Eligibility Requirements: This program is open to all residents of Florida interested in participating in an exchange program in Sweden. Applicants may also propose to study in the United States, if the studies specifically emphasize Sweden and Swedish aspects, including 1) Swedish language; 2) Swedish culture or traditions; 3) environmental science; 4) a health care program promoting better health for women and children; or 5) handicraft, art, glass art, music, literature, or design. Study proposals must be well-defined in time and content. Along with their application, they must submit a transcript from college, university, or vocational school; curriculum vitae; project proposal, describing the planned studies, length of studies, and goals; financial statement; and letter of recommendation from an instructor. **Deadline for Receipt:** January of each year. **Additional Information:** Within 3 months after the end of studies or the project, the recipient must report to the scholarship committee or, if possible, accept an invitation to an organization meeting to share the experience.

2372 ■ U.S. MARINE CORPS

Manpower and Reserve Affairs (MMEA-85)
3280 Russell Road
Quantico, VA 22134-5103
Tel: (703)784-9264
Fax: (703)784-9843
Web Site: http://www.usmc.mil
To allow selected noncommissioned Marine Corps officers to earn a bachelor's degree in selected fields by pursuing full-time college study while continuing to receive their regular pay and allowances.
Title of Award: Marine Corps Staff Noncommissioned Officers Degree Completion Program **Area, Field, or Subject:** Accounting; Business administration; Education; Environmental conservation; Environmental

science; Finance; Management; Music; Protective services; Psychology **Level of Education for which Award is Granted:** Undergraduate **Number Awarded:** Varies each year; recently, 5 Marines were selected to participate in this program. **Funds Available:** Noncommissioned officers selected to participate in this program receive their regular Marine Corps pay while attending a college or university on a full-time basis. Tuition, matriculation fees, and other expenses (such as books) must be paid by the recipient through personal funds, in-service Montgomery GI Bill benefits, student loans, or other non-Marine Corps means. **Duration:** Up to the equivalent of 2 academic years.

Eligibility Requirements: Eligible to participate in this program are regular active-duty Marines, especially in the grades of staff sergeant and gunnery sergeant. Applicants must have completed at least 2 years of postsecondary study and have been accepted by an accredited degree-granting college or university in a program offered to all matriculating students; enrollment in a multiple major program designed for adults returning to school does not qualify. The program recently was limited to the following majors: accounting, business administration with an emphasis on accounting or financial management, education, environmental safety, environmental health management, hazardous material and waste control, music, occupational safety, psychology, safety education, safety management, and waste control. **Deadline for Receipt:** April of each year. **Additional Information:** Applicants must agree to extend/reenlist for a period of 4 years beyond completion of this program.

2373 ■ VERMONT STUDENT ASSISTANCE CORPORATION
Champlain Mill
Attn: Scholarship Programs
P.O. Box 2000
Winooski, VT 05404-2601
Tel: (802)654-3798; 888-253-4819
Fax: (802)654-3765
E-mail: info@vsac.org
Web Site: http://www.vsac.org
To provide financial assistance to residents of Vermont who are interested in working on a college degree in music.
Title of Award: Lee A. Lyman Memorial Music Scholarship **Area, Field, or Subject:** Music **Level of Education for which Award is Granted:** Undergraduate **Number Awarded:** 4 each year. **Funds Available:** The stipend is $1,000. **Duration:** 1 year; recipients may reapply.
Eligibility Requirements: This scholarship is available to the residents of Vermont who are seniors in high school, high school graduates, or currently enrolled in college. Applicants must be enrolled or planning to enroll in a postsecondary degree program in music. Selection is based on participation in music-related activities, performances, groups, etc.; academic achievement; required essays; letters of recommendation; and financial need. **Deadline for Receipt:** May of each year. **Additional Information:** This program was established in 1995.

2374 ■ VSA ARTS
Attn: Education Office
1300 Connecticut Avenue, N.W., Suite 700
Washington, DC 20036
Tel: (202)628-2800
Free: 800-933-8721
Fax: (202)737-0725
E-mail: soloists@vsarts.org
Web Site: http://www.vsarts.org/x22.xml
To recognize and reward performing musicians who are physically or mentally challenged.
Title of Award: VSA arts Young Soloists Award **Area, Field, or Subject:** Music; Music, Classical; Music, Jazz; Music, Vocal **Level of Education for which Award is Granted:** Graduate, Undergraduate **Number Awarded:** 2 each year. **Funds Available:** A monetary award is presented (amount not specified). **Duration:** The competition is held annually.
Eligibility Requirements: Contestants must be vocalists or instrumentalists under 25 years of age who have a disability. Applicants may be performers in any type of music, including country, classical, jazz, rap, rock, bluegrass, or ethnic. They are required to submit an audition tape and a 1-page biography that describes why they should be selected to receive this award. Tapes are evaluated on the basis of technique, tone, intonation, rhythm, and interpretation. **Deadline for Receipt:** October of each year. **Additional Information:** Applications must first be submitted

to the respective state organization of Very Special arts (VSA). This program was formerly known as the Panasonic Young Soloists Award.

2375 ■ WATTS CHARITY ASSOCIATION, INC.
6245 Bristol Parkway, Suite 224
Culver City, CA 90230
Tel: (323)671-0394
Fax: (323)778-2613
E-mail: wattscharity@yahoo.com
Web Site: http://4watts.tripod.com/id5.html
To provide financial assistance to upper-division college students working on a degree in classical music.
Title of Award: Leonardo Watts Scholarship **Area, Field, or Subject:** Music, Classical; Music, Vocal **Level of Education for which Award is Granted:** Four Year College **Number Awarded:** 1 each year. **Funds Available:** A stipend is awarded (amount not specified). **Duration:** 1 year.
Eligibility Requirements: This program is open to U.S. citizens of African American descent who are enrolled full time as a college or university junior. Applicants must be studying classical music, including voice and/or instrumental. They must have a GPA of 3.0 or higher, be between 17 and 24 years of age, and be able to demonstrate that they intend to continue their education for at least 2 years. Along with their application, they must submit 1) a 1-paragraph statement on why they should be awarded a Watts Foundation scholarship, and 2) a 1- to 2-page essay on a specific type of cancer, based either on how it has impacted their life or on researched information. **Deadline for Receipt:** May of each year. **Additional Information:** Royce R. Watts, Sr. established the Watts Charity Association after he learned he had cancer in 2001.

2376 ■ WOMEN MARINES ASSOCIATION
P.O. Box 8405
Falls Church, VA 22041-8405
E-mail: wma@womenmarines.org
Web Site: http://www.womenmarines.org/scholarships.php
To provide financial assistance for college or graduate school to students sponsored by members of the Women Marines Association (WMA).
Title of Award: Women Marines Association Scholarship Program **Area, Field, or Subject:** General studies/Field of study not specified; Music **Level of Education for which Award is Granted:** Graduate, Undergraduate **Number Awarded:** Varies each year. **Funds Available:** The stipend is $1,500. **Duration:** 1 year.
Eligibility Requirements: Applicants must be sponsored by a WMA member and fall into 1 of the following categories: 1) have served or are serving in the U.S. Marine Corps, regular or Reserve; 2) are a direct descendant by blood, legal adoption, or stepchild of a Marine on active duty or who has served honorably in the U.S. Marine Corps, regular or Reserve; 3) are a sibling or a descendant of a sibling by blood, legal adoption, or stepchild of a Marine on active duty or who has served honorably in the U.S. Marine Corps, regular or Reserve; or 4) have completed 2 years in a Marine Corps JROTC program. No WMA member is allowed to sponsor more than 1 applicant per year. High school applicants must have maintained at least a "B+" average for their sophomore, junior, and first semester of their senior year of high school and must have a combined mathematics and verbal ACT score of at least 25 or a combined mathematics and critical reading SAT score of at least 1100. Graduate students are also eligible. **Deadline for Receipt:** March of each year. **Additional Information:** Information is also available from the WMA Scholarship Chair, Roberta Eaton, 18 Maple Court, New Hyde Park, NY 11040-3105, E-mail: Roeaton@aol.com. This program includes the following named scholarships: the WMA Memorial Scholarships, the Lily H. Gridley Memorial Scholarships, the Ethyl and Armin Wiebke Memorial Scholarship, and the LaRue A. Ditmore Music Scholarships. Applicants must know a WMA member; the WMA will not supply listings of the names or addresses of chapters or individual members.

Philosophy

2377 ■ ENGLISH-SPEAKING UNION OF THE UNITED STATES-WASHINGTON DC AREA BRANCH
1604 New Hampshire Avenue, N.W.
Washington, DC 20009
Tel: (202)234-4602
Fax: (202)234-4639
E-mail: esuwdc@msn.com

Web Site: http://www.esuwdc.org/fellowships.html

To provide funding to residents of the metropolitan Washington area who are interested in conducting research or other projects anywhere in the world on a topic that relates to the English-speaking tradition.

Title of Award: Helen Gladstone Williams Scholarships **Area, Field, or Subject:** Art; General studies/Field of study not specified; History; Philosophy **Level of Education for which Award is Granted:** Graduate, Professional, Postdoctoral, Undergraduate **Number Awarded:** 1 or more each year. **Funds Available:** The grant ranges up to $5,000.

Eligibility Requirements: This program is open to permanent residents of the Washington, D.C. metropolitan area who have at least a bachelor's degree. Applicants must be interested in conducting a project, either independently or in conjunction with an accredited institution, on a subject that relates to English-speaking traditions in locales other than, or in addition to, the United States. They must submit a 2-page summary that describes the course of study to be undertaken and discusses how it would advance the objectives of the sponsoring organization, a brief resume of academic and employment experience, and 3 letters of support. Applicants who do not have a diploma at the bachelor's level or above must also submit a transcript from an accredited institution of higher learning that indicates progress toward a degree to be bestowed in the near future. Projects should focus primarily on endeavors that shed light on history, philosophy, the arts, or other aspects of culture. Selection is based on the significance of the project in relation to the field(s) it seeks to address, the project's relevance to the aims and values of the sponsoring organization, the credentials of the applicant, and the likelihood that the project will be completed successfully and on schedule. **Deadline for Receipt:** March of each year.

2378 ■ HAWAI'I COMMUNITY FOUNDATION

Attn: Scholarship Department
1164 Bishop Street, Suite 800

Honolulu, HI 96813
Tel: (808)566-5570; 888-731-3863
Fax: (808)521-6286
E-mail: scholarships@hcf-hawaii.org
Web Site: http://www.hawaiicommunityfoundation.org/scholar/scholar.php

To provide financial assistance to residents of Hawaii for undergraduate or graduate studies in fields related to achieving world cooperation and international understanding.

Title of Award: Marion Maccarrell Scott Scholarship **Area, Field, or Subject:** Anthropology; Economics; Geography; History; International affairs and relations; Law; Peace studies; Philosophy; Political science; Psychology; Sociology **Level of Education for which Award is Granted:** Graduate, Undergraduate **Number Awarded:** Varies each year; recently, 258 of these scholarships were awarded. **Funds Available:** The amounts of the awards depend on the availability of funds and the need of the recipient; recently, stipends averaged $1,749. **Duration:** 1 year.

Eligibility Requirements: This program is open to graduates of public high schools in Hawaii. They must plan to attend school as full-time students (on the undergraduate or graduate level) on the mainland, majoring in history, government, political science, anthropology, economics, geography, international relations, law, psychology, philosophy, or sociology. They must be residents of the state of Hawaii, able to demonstrate financial need, interested in attending an accredited 2- or 4-year college or university, and able to demonstrate academic achievement (GPA of 2.8 or higher). Along with their application, they must submit an essay on their commitment to world peace that includes their learning experiences (courses, clubs, community activities, or travel) related to achieving world peace and international understanding and explaining how their experiences have enhanced their ability to achieve those goals. **Deadline for Receipt:** February of each year.

General

2379 ■ ALABAMA SPACE GRANT CONSORTIUM

c/o University of Alabama in Huntsville
Materials Science Building, Room 205
Huntsville, AL 35899
Tel: (256)824-6800
Fax: (256)824-6061
E-mail: reasonj@uah.edu
Web Site: http://www.uah.edu/ASGC
To provide financial assistance to undergraduate students at universities participating in the Alabama Space Grant Consortium who wish to prepare for a career as a teacher of science or mathematics.
Title of Award: Teacher Education Scholarship Program of the Alabama Space Grant Consortium **Area, Field, or Subject:** Aerospace sciences; Earth sciences; Education; Environmental conservation; Environmental science; Geosciences; Mathematics and mathematical sciences; Science; Space and planetary sciences **Level of Education for which Award is Granted:** Undergraduate **Number Awarded:** Varies each year; recently, 10 of these scholarships were awarded. **Funds Available:** The stipend is $1,000 per year. **Duration:** 1 year; nonrenewable.
Eligibility Requirements: This program is open to students enrolled in or accepted for enrollment as full-time undergraduates at universities in Alabama participating in the consortium. Applicants must intend to enter the teacher certification program and teach in a pre-college setting. Priority is given to those majoring in science, mathematics, or earth/space/environmental science. Applicants should have a GPA of 3.0 or higher and must be U.S. citizens. Members of underrepresented groups in science and mathematics (minorities and women) are especially encouraged to apply. Along with their application, they must submit a 1- to 2-page statement on the reasons for their desire to enter the teaching profession, specifically the fields of science or mathematics education. **Deadline for Receipt:** February of each year. **Additional Information:** The member universities are University of Alabama in Huntsville, Alabama A&M University, University of Alabama, University of Alabama at Birmingham, University of South Alabama, Tuskegee University, and Auburn University. Funding for this program is provided by NASA.

2380 ■ ALABAMA SPACE GRANT CONSORTIUM

c/o University of Alabama in Huntsville
Materials Science Building, Room 205
Huntsville, AL 35899
Tel: (256)824-6800
Fax: (256)824-6061
E-mail: reasonj@uah.edu
Web Site: http://www.uah.edu/ASGC
To provide financial assistance to undergraduates who are studying the space sciences at universities participating in the Alabama Space Grant Consortium (ASGC).
Title of Award: Undergraduate Scholarship Program of the Alabama Space Grant Consortium **Area, Field, or Subject:** Aerospace sciences; Behavioral sciences; Biological and clinical sciences; Business administration; Communications; Computer and information sciences; Economics; Education; Engineering, Aerospace/Aeronautical/Astronautical; International affairs and relations; Law; Natural sciences; Physical sci-

ences; Public administration; Sociology; Space and planetary sciences **Level of Education for which Award is Granted:** Four Year College **Number Awarded:** Varies each year; recently, 32 of these scholarships were awarded. **Funds Available:** The stipend is $1,000 per year. **Duration:** 1 year; may be renewed 1 additional year.
Eligibility Requirements: This program is open to full-time students entering their junior or senior year at universities participating in the ASGC. Applicants must be studying in a field related to space, including the physical, natural, and biological sciences; engineering, education; economics; business; sociology; behavioral sciences; computer science; communications; law; international affairs; and public administration. They must be U.S. citizens and have a GPA of 3.0 or higher. Individuals from underrepresented groups (African Americans, Hispanic, American Indians, Pacific Islanders, Asian Americans, and women) are especially encouraged to apply. Interested students should submit a completed application with a career goal statement, personal references, a brief resume, and transcripts. Selection is based on 1) academic qualifications, 2) quality of the career goal statement, and 3) assessment of the applicant's motivation for a career in aerospace. **Deadline for Receipt:** February of each year. **Additional Information:** The member universities are University of Alabama in Huntsville, Alabama A&M University, University of Alabama, University of Alabama at Birmingham, University of South Alabama, Tuskegee University, and Auburn University. Funding for this program is provided by NASA.

2381 ■ AMERICAN COUNCIL OF THE BLIND

Attn: Coordinator, Scholarship Program
1155 15th Street, N.W., Suite 1004
Washington, DC 20005
Tel: (202)467-5081
Free: 800-424-8666
Fax: (202)467-5085
E-mail: info@acb.org
Web Site: http://www.acb.org
To provide financial assistance to blind students who are working on an undergraduate or graduate degree in science at an accredited college or university.
Title of Award: Dr. S. Bradley Burson Memorial Scholarship **Area, Field, or Subject:** Biological and clinical sciences; Chemistry; Engineering; Physics **Level of Education for which Award is Granted:** Graduate, Undergraduate **Number Awarded:** 1 each year. **Funds Available:** The stipend is $1,000. In addition, the winner receives a Kurzweil-1000 Reading System. **Duration:** 1 year.
Eligibility Requirements: This program is open to legally blind undergraduate or graduate students majoring in the "hard" sciences (i.e., biology, chemistry, physics, and engineering, but not computer science) in college. They must be U.S. citizens. In addition to letters of recommendation and copies of academic transcripts, applications must include an autobiographical sketch. A cumulative GPA of 3.3 or higher is generally required. Selection is based on demonstrated academic record, involvement in extracurricular and civic activities, and academic objectives. The severity of the applicant's visual impairment and his/her study methods are also taken into account. **Deadline for Receipt:** February of each year. **Additional Information:** Scholarship winners are expected to be present at the council's annual conference; the council will cover all reasonable

expenses connected with convention attendance.

2382 ■ AMERICAN FOUNDATION FOR THE BLIND
Attn: Scholarship Committee
11 Penn Plaza, Suite 300
New York, NY 10001
Tel: (212)502-7661
Free: 800-AFB-LINE
Fax: (212)502-7771
E-mail: afbinfo@afb.net
Web Site: http://www.afb.org/scholarships.asp
To provide financial assistance to visually impaired students who wish to work on a graduate or undergraduate degree in engineering or computer, physical, or life sciences.

Title of Award: Paul and Ellen Ruckes Scholarship **Area, Field, or Subject:** Biological and clinical sciences; Computer and information sciences; Engineering; Physical sciences **Level of Education for which Award is Granted:** Graduate, Undergraduate **Number Awarded:** 1 each year. **Funds Available:** The stipend is $1,000. **Duration:** 1 year.

Eligibility Requirements: This program is open to visually impaired undergraduate or graduate students who are U.S. citizens working on a degree in engineering or the computer, physical, or life sciences. Legal blindness is not required. Along with their application, they must submit an essay that includes the field of study they are pursuing and why they have chosen it; their educational and personal goals; their work experience; any extracurricular activities with which they have been involved, including those in school, religious organizations, and the community; and how they intend to use scholarship monies that may be awarded. **Deadline for Receipt:** April of each year.

2383 ■ AMERICAN INDIAN SCIENCE AND ENGINEERING SOCIETY
Attn: Scholarship Coordinator
2305 Renard, S.E., Suite 200
P.O. Box 9828
Albuquerque, NM 87119-9828
Tel: (505)765-1052
Fax: (505)765-5608
E-mail: shirley@aises.org
Web Site: http://www.aises.org/highered/scholarships
To provide financial assistance to members of the American Indian Science and Engineering Society who are majoring in designated fields as undergraduate or graduate students.

Title of Award: A.T. Anderson Memorial Scholarship Program **Area, Field, or Subject:** Engineering; Mathematics and mathematical sciences; Medicine; Natural resources; Physical sciences; Science **Level of Education for which Award is Granted:** Graduate, Undergraduate **Number Awarded:** Varies; generally, 200 or more each year, depending upon the availability of funds from corporate and other sponsors. **Funds Available:** The annual stipend is $1,000 for undergraduates or $2,000 for graduate students. **Duration:** 1 year; nonrenewable.

Eligibility Requirements: This program is open to members of the society who can furnish proof of tribal enrollment or Certificate of Degree of Indian Blood. Applicants must be full-time students at the undergraduate or graduate school level attending an accredited 4-year college or university or a 2-year college leading to an academic degree in engineering, mathematics, medicine, natural resources, physical science, or the sciences. They must submit a 500-word essay that demonstrates their interest in and motivation to continue higher education, an understanding of the importance of college and a commitment to completion, their educational and/or career goals, and a commitment to learning and giving back to the community. Selection is based on the essay, academic achievement (GPA of 2.0 or higher), leadership potential, and commitment to helping other American Indians. Financial need is not considered. **Deadline for Receipt:** June of each year. **Additional Information:** This program was launched in 1983 in memory of A.T. Anderson, a Mohawk and a chemical engineer who worked with Albert Einstein. Anderson was 1 of the society's founders and was the society's first executive director. The program includes the following named awards: the Al Qoyawayma Award for an applicant who is majoring in science or engineering and also has a strong interest in the arts, the Norbert S. Hill, Jr. Leadership Award, the Polingaysi Qoyawayma Award for an applicant who is working on a teaching degree in order to teach mathematics or science in a Native community or an advanced degree for personal improvement or teaching

at the college level, and the Robert W. Brocksbank Scholarship.

2384 ■ AMERICAN INDIAN SCIENCE AND ENGINEERING SOCIETY
Attn: Scholarship Coordinator
2305 Renard, S.E., Suite 200
P.O. Box 9828
Albuquerque, NM 87119-9828
Tel: (505)765-1052
Fax: (505)765-5608
E-mail: shirley@aises.org
Web Site: http://www.aises.org/highered/scholarships
To provide financial assistance for college to outstanding American Indian high school seniors from designated states who are members of American Indian Science and Engineering Society (AISES).

Title of Award: Burlington Northern Santa Fe Foundation Scholarship **Area, Field, or Subject:** Business administration; Engineering; Mathematics and mathematical sciences; Medicine; Natural resources; Physical sciences; Science; Technology **Level of Education for which Award is Granted:** Four Year College **Number Awarded:** 5 new awards are made each year. **Funds Available:** The stipend is $2,500 per year. **Duration:** 4 years or until completion of a baccalaureate degree, whichever occurs first.

Eligibility Requirements: This program is open to AISES members who are high school seniors planning to attend an accredited 4-year college or university and major in business, engineering, mathematics, medicine, natural resources, physical science, science, or technology. Applicants must submit 1) proof of tribal enrollment or a Certificate of Degree of Indian Blood; 2) evidence of residence in the service area of the Burlington Northern and Santa Fe Corporation (Arizona, California, Colorado, Kansas, Minnesota, Montana, New Mexico, North Dakota, Oklahoma, Oregon, South Dakota, and Washington); 3) a statement of financial need; 4) a 500-word essay on why they chose their particular field of study, their career aspirations, an evaluation of past scholastic performance, obstacles faced as a student, and involvement in and commitment to tribal community life; and 5) high school transcripts showing a GPA of 2.0 or higher. **Deadline for Receipt:** April of each year. **Additional Information:** This program is funded by the Burlington Northern Santa Fe Foundation and administered by AISES.

2385 ■ AMERICAN SOCIETY FOR ENGINEERING EDUCATION
Attn: SMART Defense Scholarship Program
1818 N Street, N.W., Suite 600
Washington, DC 20036-2479
Tel: (202)331-3516
Fax: (202)265-8504
E-mail: smart@asee.org
Web Site: http://www.asee.org/resources/fellowships/smart/index.cfm
To provide scholarship/loans to upper-division and graduate students in areas of science, mathematics, and engineering that are of interest to the U.S. Department of Defense.

Title of Award: Science, Mathematics, and Research for Transformation (SMART) Defense Scholarship Program **Area, Field, or Subject:** Architecture, Naval; Behavioral sciences; Biological and clinical sciences; Chemistry; Computer and information sciences; Earth sciences; Engineering, Aerospace/Aeronautical/Astronautical; Engineering, Chemical; Engineering, Civil; Engineering, Electrical; Engineering, Materials; Engineering, Mechanical; Engineering, Ocean; Geosciences; Materials research/science; Mathematics and mathematical sciences; Oceanography; Physics **Level of Education for which Award is Granted:** Four Year College, Graduate **Number Awarded:** Varies each year; recently, 36 of these scholarships were awarded. **Funds Available:** The program provides full payment of tuition, fees, room, board, and other normal educational expenses at the recipient's institution. A book allowance of $1,000 per year is also provided. This is a scholarship/loan program; recipients must agree to serve as a civilian employee of the Department of Defense in a science and engineering position. If they fail to fulfill that service obligation, they must reimburse the federal government for all funds they received. **Duration:** Up to 24 months.

Eligibility Requirements: This program is open to upper-division and graduate students working on an undergraduate or graduate degree in any of the following fields: aeronautical and astronautical engineering; biosciences; chemical engineering; chemistry; civil engineering; cognitive, neural, and behavioral sciences; computer and computational sciences;

electrical engineering; geosciences, including terrain, water, and air; materials science and engineering; mathematics; mechanical engineering; naval architecture and ocean engineering; oceanography; or physics. Applicants must be U.S. citizens who have a GPA of 3.0 or higher. Selection is based on academic records, personal statements, letters of recommendation, and GRE scores. **Deadline for Receipt:** March of each year. **Additional Information:** This program, established in 2005, is sponsored by the Army Research Laboratory, the Air Force Office of Scientific Research, the Office of Naval Research, the Air Force Research Laboratory, the Defense Advanced Research Projects Agency, the Defense Information Systems Agency, and the Defense Threat Reduction Agency.

2386 ■ APPALACHIAN COLLEGE ASSOCIATION

Attn: Director of Programs
210 Center Street
Berea, KY 40403
Tel: (859)986-4584
Fax: (859)986-9549
E-mail: kathrynb@acaweb.org
Web Site: http://www.acaweb.org

To provide financial assistance to upper-division students majoring in biology, chemistry, or mathematics at colleges and universities that are members of the Appalachian College Association (ACA) who plan to become teachers.

Title of Award: Robert Noyce Scholarships **Area, Field, or Subject:** Biological and clinical sciences; Chemistry; Education; Mathematics and mathematical sciences **Level of Education for which Award is Granted:** Four Year College **Number Awarded:** 12 each year. **Funds Available:** The stipend is $7,500 per year. Recipients must be willing to sign a promissory note with a commitment to teach in a high-need middle or high school for 2 years for every year of the scholarship. **Duration:** 1 year; may be renewed 1 additional year.

Eligibility Requirements: This program is open to full-time students entering their junior or senior year at ACA member institutions with a major in biology, chemistry, or mathematics and plans to earn a teaching license. Applicants must have a GPA of 3.0 or higher and be able to document financial need. Along with their application, they must submit a 500-word essay describing their interest in becoming a 6-12 teacher; their commitment to the Appalachian region, including the impact they hope to have as a teacher; and actual and planned progress toward becoming certified. U.S. citizenship is required. Preference is given to graduates of high schools in the Appalachian region and to applicants who express a desire to teach in a high-need middle or high school, especially schools in central Appalachia. **Deadline for Receipt:** March of each year. **Additional Information:** Funding for this program is provided by the National Science Foundation. The ACA includes member institutions in Kentucky (Alice Lloyd College, Berea College, Campbellsville University, University of the Cumberlands, Kentucky Christian University, Lindsey Wilson College, Pikeville College, and Union College), North Carolina (Brevard College, Lees-McRae College, Mars Hill College, Montreat College, and Warren Wilson College), Tennessee (Bryan College, Carson-Newman College, King College, Lee University, Lincoln Memorial University, Maryville College, Milligan College, Tennessee Wesleyan College, Tusculum College, and University of the South), Virginia (Bluefield College, Emery & Henry College, Ferrum College, and Virginia Intermont College), and West Virginia (Alderson-Broaddus College, Bethany College, Davis & Elkins College, Ohio Valley University, University of Charleston, West Virginia Wesleyan College, and Wheeling Jesuit University).

2387 ■ ARKANSAS DEPARTMENT OF HIGHER EDUCATION

Attn: Financial Aid Division
114 East Capitol Avenue
Little Rock, AR 72201-3818
Tel: (501)371-2050
Free: 800-54-STUDY
Fax: (501)371-2001
E-mail: finaid@adhe.arknet.edu
Web Site: http://www.starark.com

To provide scholarship/loans to college students in Arkansas who are interested in preparing for a teaching career in an approved subject or geographic shortage area.

Title of Award: Arkansas State Teacher Assistance Resource (STAR) Program **Area, Field, or Subject:** Biological and clinical sciences;

Chemistry; Earth sciences; Education; Education, Secondary; Education, Special; Geosciences; Linguistics; Mathematics and mathematical sciences; Physical sciences; Physics **Level of Education for which Award is Granted:** Master's, Undergraduate **Number Awarded:** Varies each year; recently, 42 of these scholarship/loans were approved. **Funds Available:** The award is $3,000 per year for students who agree to teach in either a geographic teacher shortage area or a subject teacher shortage area. For students who agree to teach in both a geographic shortage area and a subject shortage area, the award is $6,000 per year. This is a scholarship/loan program. Recipients must teach in an Arkansas geographic or subject shortage area for 1 year for each year of support they receive. If they fail to complete that teaching obligation, they must repay all funds received. **Duration:** 1 year; may be renewed for 1 additional year if the recipient is enrolled in a 4-year teacher education program or 2 additional years if enrolled in a 5-year teacher education program. Renewal requires that the recipient maintain a GPA of 2.75 or higher and complete 24 semester hours as an undergraduate or 18 semester hours as a graduate student.

Eligibility Requirements: This program is open to Arkansas residents who are full-time students enrolled 1) at a 4-year public or private college or university in the state with an approved teacher education program; 2) in an associate of arts in teaching program; or 3) in an master of arts in teaching program. Applicants must have a GPA of 2.75 or higher and be entering their sophomore, junior, or senior year (or be in a master's degree program). They must be willing to teach in a public school located in a geographic area of Arkansas designated as having a critical shortage of teachers or in a subject matter area designated as having a critical shortage of teachers. Applicants must have completed their freshman year at an accredited Arkansas public or private college or university in a major field of study leading to secondary teacher certification in 1 of the shortage areas. U.S. citizenship is required. **Deadline for Receipt:** May of each year. **Additional Information:** This program was established in 2004 as a replacement for the former Arkansas Emergency Secondary Education Loan Program. Recently, the subject areas designated as having a critical shortage of teachers were foreign language, mathematics, chemistry, physics, biology, physical science, earth science, and special education. For a list of geographic areas of Arkansas that are designated as having a critical shortage of teachers, contact the Department of Higher Education. The State Teacher Assistance Resource (STAR) program also provides that teachers who received federal student loans may have those loans repaid 1) at the rate of $3,000 per year if they teach a subject area in Arkansas that is designated as a shortage area or if they teach in a geographic area of the state with a shortage of teachers, or 2) at the rate of $6,000 per year if they teach a shortage subject area in a shortage geographic area. Students may not, however, participate in both the scholarship/loan program and the federal loan repayment program.

2388 ■ ARKANSAS DEPARTMENT OF WORKFORCE EDUCATION

Luther Hardin Building
Three Capitol Mall, Room 207
Little Rock, AR 72201-1083
Tel: (501)682-1500
Fax: (501)682-1509
Web Site: http://dwe.arkansas.gov/LoanForgiveness/atcslfp.htm

To provide forgivable loans to residents of Arkansas who are interested in pursuing technical education and working in the state.

Title of Award: Arkansas Technical Careers Student Loan Forgiveness Program **Area, Field, or Subject:** Biological and clinical sciences; Computer and information sciences; Engineering; Engineering, Biomedical; Engineering, Computer; Engineering, Electrical; Engineering, Industrial; Health care services; Physical sciences **Level of Education for which Award is Granted:** Undergraduate **Number Awarded:** Varies each year. **Funds Available:** The maximum loan is $2,500 per year. Loans are forgiven if the recipient works full time in the high demand technical field in Arkansas. Each year's loan may be forgiven with 1 year of full-time employment. Loan recipients who do not graduate from the program or work full time in the field in Arkansas must repay the loan in full. **Duration:** Up to 4 years.

Eligibility Requirements: This program is open to residents of Arkansas who are U.S. citizens or permanent residents admitted to an approved program resulting in a diploma, certificate, or degree in a high demand technical field. Applicants must indicate their intention to work in Arkansas in the field for which they receive the training. **Deadline for Receipt:** Applications must be submitted within 6 months of the completion of the program of study. **Additional Information:** The Arkansas General Assembly established this program in 1999. Recently, the designated career fields related to advanced manufacturing (including engineering and engineering technology, industrial electronics installers and repairers, machinist and machine technologies, and tool and die maker and technologist); computer and information technology (including computer engineering, computer and information sciences, electrical and electronic engineering and related technology, electromechanical instrumentation and maintenance technology, and computer installer and repairer); and biomedical and biotechnology (including biological and life sciences, physical sciences, science technologies, health professions and related sciences, bioengineering and biomedical engineering, and biomedical engineering technology and technician).

2389 ■ ASSOCIATION FOR IRON & STEEL TECHNOLOGY-OHIO VALLEY CHAPTER

c/o Jeff McKain, Scholarship Chair
Xtek, Inc.
11451 Reading Road
Cincinnati, OH 45241
Tel: (513)733-7843; (999)332-XTEK
Fax: (513)733-7939
E-mail: jeff.mckain@xtek.com
Web Site: http://www.aist.org/chapters/ohiovalley_scholarship.htm
To provide financial assistance for college to student members and children of members of the Ohio Valley Chapter of the Association for Iron & Steel Technology (AIST).

Title of Award: Ohio Valley Chapter AIST Scholarships **Area, Field, or Subject:** Biological and clinical sciences; Chemistry; Computer and information sciences; Earth sciences; Engineering; Engineering, Electrical; Engineering, Mechanical; Environmental conservation; Environmental science; Geosciences; Information science and technology; Metallurgy; Physical sciences; Physics **Level of Education for which Award is Granted:** Undergraduate **Number Awarded:** Up to 2 each year. **Funds Available:** The stipend is $1,000 per year. **Duration:** 1 year; may be renewed up to 3 additional years provided the recipient remains enrolled full time and maintains a GPA of 3.0 or higher.

Eligibility Requirements: This program is open to high school seniors and college students who are either 1) children of Ohio Valley Chapter AIST members, or 2) student AIST members. Applicants must be accepted at, planning to attend, or currently enrolled at an accredited college or university with a major in biology, chemistry, computer programming, computer technology, electrical engineering, engineering, engineering technology, environmental engineering, environmental science, information systems technology, mechanical engineering, metallurgy, microbiology, physical science, physics, or other field approved by the scholarship committee. Along with their application, they must submit a 500-word essay on the reasons for their interests and reasons for working on a degree in their field of study, career goals and objectives, and extracurricular activities and their benefits. Selection is based on overall academic achievement (especially in mathematics and science), the essay, and extracurricular activities. **Deadline for Receipt:** February of each year. **Additional Information:** The AIST was formed in 2004 by the merger of the Iron and Steel Society (ISS) and the Association of Iron and Steel Engineers (AISE). This program was established by the former Ohio Valley District Section of AISE. The Ohio Valley Chapter covers Indiana (except for the northwestern portion), all of Kentucky, western Tennessee, and portions of southern Ohio.

2390 ■ ASSOCIATION FOR WOMEN GEOSCIENTISTS

Attn: AWG Foundation
P.O. Box 30645
Lincoln, NE 68503-0645
E-mail: awgscholarship@yahoo.com
Web Site: http://www.awg.org/eas/minority.html
To provide financial assistance to minority women who are interested in working on an undergraduate degree in the geosciences.

Title of Award: Association for Women Geoscientists Minority Scholarship **Area, Field, or Subject:** Chemistry; Earth sciences; Education; Geology; Geosciences; Hydrology; Meteorology; Oceanography **Level of Education for which Award is Granted:** Undergraduate **Number Awarded:** 1 or more each year. **Funds Available:** A total of $5,000 is available for this program each year. **Duration:** 1 year; may be renewed.

Eligibility Requirements: This program is open to women who are African American, Hispanic, or Native American (including Eskimo, Hawaiian, Samoan, or American Indian). Applicants must be full-time students working on, or planning to work on, an undergraduate degree in the geosciences (including geology, geophysics, geochemistry, hydrology, meteorology, physical oceanography, planetary geology, or earth science education). They must submit a 500-word essay on why they have chosen to major in the geosciences and their career goals, 2 letters of recommendation, high school and/or college transcripts, and SAT or ACT scores. Financial need is not considered in the selection process. **Deadline for Receipt:** May of each year. **Additional Information:** This program, first offered in 2004, is supported by ExxonMobil Foundation.

2391 ■ ASSOCIATION FOR WOMEN GEOSCIENTISTS

Attn: AWG Foundation
P.O. Box 30645
Lincoln, NE 68503-0645
E-mail: awgscholarship@yahoo.com
Web Site: http://www.awg.org/members/po_scholarships.html
To provide financial assistance to minority women working on an undergraduate or graduate degree in the geosciences in the Potomac Bay region.

Title of Award: William Rucker Greenwood Scholarship **Area, Field, or Subject:** Earth sciences; Geology; Geosciences **Level of Education for which Award is Granted:** Graduate, Undergraduate **Number Awarded:** 1 each year. **Funds Available:** The stipend is $1,000. The recipient also is granted a 1-year membership in the Association for Women Geoscientists (AWG). **Duration:** 1 year.

Eligibility Requirements: This program is open to minority women who are currently enrolled as full-time undergraduate or graduate geoscience majors in an accredited, degree-granting college or university in Delaware, the District of Columbia, Maryland, Virginia, or West Virginia. Selection is based on the applicant's 1) participation in geoscience or earth science educational activities, and 2) potential for leadership as a future geoscience professional. **Deadline for Receipt:** April of each year. **Additional Information:** This program is sponsored by the AWG Potomac Area Chapter. Information is also available from Laurel M. Bybell, U.S. Geological Survey, 926 National Center, Reston, VA 20192.

2392 ■ ASSOCIATION FOR WOMEN GEOSCIENTISTS

Attn: AWG Foundation
P.O. Box 30645
Lincoln, NE 68503-0645
E-mail: awgscholarship@yahoo.com
Web Site: http://www.awg.org/eas/ekdale.html
To provide financial assistance for a summer field camp to women majoring in geoscience at a college or university in Utah.

Title of Award: Susan Ekdale Memorial Scholarship **Area, Field, or Subject:** Earth sciences; Geosciences **Level of Education for which Award is Granted:** Undergraduate **Number Awarded:** 1 each year. **Funds Available:** The stipend is $1,000. Funds must be used to help pay field camp expenses. **Duration:** Summer months.

Eligibility Requirements: This program is open to women majoring in geoscience at a college or university in Utah who must attend a summer field camp as part of their graduation requirements. Women geoscience students from Utah attending college in other states are also eligible. Applicants must submit a 1- to 2-page essay in which they describe their personal and academic highlights, their plans for applying their geoscience education to their future work or education, their reasons for applying for the scholarship, and what they, as women, can contribute to the geosciences. Selection is based on merit and need. **Deadline for Receipt:** March of each year. **Additional Information:** This program is sponsored by the Salt Lake chapter of the Association for Women Geoscientists. Information is also available from the Ekdale Scholarship Co-chair, Janae Wallace Boyer, P.O. Box 146100, Salt Lake City, UT 84114, (801) 537-3387.

2393 ■ ASSOCIATION FOR WOMEN IN SCIENCE-SEATTLE CHAPTER

c/o Fran Solomon, Scholarship Committee Chair
5805 16th Avenue, N.E.
Seattle, WA 98105
Tel: (206)522-6441

E-mail: fran.solomon@metrokc.gov

Web Site: http://www.scn.org/awis/undergraduate_scholarship.htm

To provide financial assistance to women undergraduates from any state majoring in science, mathematics, or engineering at colleges and universities in western Washington.

Title of Award: AWIS Seattle Scholarships **Area, Field, or Subject:** Biochemistry; Biological and clinical sciences; Chemistry; Engineering; Environmental conservation; Environmental science; Geology; Mathematics and mathematical sciences; Pharmaceutical sciences; Physics **Level of Education for which Award is Granted:** Four Year College **Number Awarded:** Varies each year; recently, 11 of these scholarships were awarded. **Funds Available:** Stipends range from $1,000 to $1,500. **Duration:** 1 year.

Eligibility Requirements: This program is open to women from any state entering their junior or senior year at a 4-year college or university in western Washington. Applicants must have a declared major in science (e.g., biological sciences, environmental science, biochemistry, chemistry, pharmacy, geology, computer science, physics), mathematics, or engineering. Along with their application, they must submit essays on the events that led to their choice of a major, their current career plans and long-term goals, and their volunteer and community activities. Financial need is considered in the selection process. At least 1 scholarship is reserved for a woman from a group that is underrepresented in science, mathematics, and engineering careers, including Native American Indians and Alaska Natives, Black/African Americans, Mexican Americans/ Chicanas/Latinas, Native Pacific Islanders (Polynesians, Melanesians, and Micronesians), and women with disabilities. **Deadline for Receipt:** March of each year. **Additional Information:** This program includes the following named awards: the Virginia Badger Scholarship, the Angela Paez Memorial Scholarship, and the Fran Solomon Scholarship. Support for the program is provided by several sponsors, including the American Chemical Society, Iota Sigma Pi, Rosetta Inpharmatics, and ZymoGenetics, Inc.

2394 ■ BETA BETA BETA

c/o National Secretary-Treasurer

University of North Alabama

UNA Box 5079

Florence, AL 35632

E-mail: tribeta@una.edu

Web Site: http://www.tri-beta.org/bbbawards.html

To provide funding to undergraduate members of Beta Beta Beta (a national honor society in biology) who are interested in conducting research projects in biology.

Title of Award: Beta Beta Beta Foundation Research Scholarships **Area, Field, or Subject:** Biological and clinical sciences **Level of Education for which Award is Granted:** Undergraduate **Number Awarded:** 1 or more each year. **Funds Available:** The amount granted varies, depending upon the scope of the funded project. **Duration:** 1 year.

Eligibility Requirements: This program is open to undergraduate members of the society who are interested in conducting research projects in biology. Applicants must describe their research project and present a proposed budget. **Deadline for Receipt:** September of each year. **Additional Information:** This program was established in 1994.

2395 ■ BROWN AND CALDWELL

Attn: Scholarship Program

201 North Civic Drive, Suite 115

P.O. Box 8045

Walnut Creek, CA 94596

Tel: (925)937-9010

Fax: (925)937-9026

E-mail: scholarships@brwncald.com

Web Site: http://www.brownandcaldwell.com

To provide financial assistance to minority students working on an undergraduate degree in an environmental or engineering field.

Title of Award: Brown and Caldwell Minority Scholarship **Area, Field, or Subject:** Biological and clinical sciences; Engineering, Chemical; Engineering, Civil; Environmental conservation; Environmental science; Geology; Hydrology; Industrial hygiene; Toxicology **Level of Education for which Award is Granted:** Four Year College **Number Awarded:** 1 each year. **Funds Available:** The stipend is $3,000. **Duration:** 1 year.

Eligibility Requirements: This program is open to members of minority groups (African Americans, Hispanics, Asians, Pacific Islanders, Native Americans, and Alaska Natives) who are full-time students in their junior year at an accredited 4-year college or university. Applicants must have a GPA of 3.0 or higher with a declared major in civil, chemical, or environmental engineering or an environmental science (e.g., biology, ecology, geology, hydrogeology, industrial hygiene, toxicology). Along with their application, they must submit an essay (up to 250 words) on why they chose to major in an environmental discipline. They must be U.S. citizens or permanent resident and available to participate in a summer internship at a Brown and Caldwell office. Financial need is not considered in the selection process. **Deadline for Receipt:** February of each year. **Additional Information:** As part of the paid summer internship at a Brown and Caldwell office at 1 of more than 40 cities in the country, the program provides a mentor to guide the intern through the company's information and communications resources.

2396 ■ BROWN AND CALDWELL

Attn: Scholarship Program

201 North Civic Drive, Suite 115

P.O. Box 8045

Walnut Creek, CA 94596

Tel: (925)937-9010

Fax: (925)937-9026

E-mail: scholarships@brwncald.com

Web Site: http://www.brownandcaldwell.com

To provide financial assistance to undergraduate students working on an degree in an environmental or engineering field.

Title of Award: Dr. W. Wesley Eckenfelder Scholarship **Area, Field, or Subject:** Biological and clinical sciences; Engineering, Chemical; Engineering, Civil; Environmental conservation; Environmental science; Geology; Hydrology; Industrial hygiene; Toxicology **Level of Education for which Award is Granted:** Four Year College **Number Awarded:** 1 each year. **Funds Available:** The stipend is $3,000. **Duration:** 1 year.

Eligibility Requirements: This program is open to U.S. citizens and permanent residents enrolled as full-time students in their junior year at an accredited 4-year college or university. Applicants must have a GPA of 3.0 or higher with a declared major in civil, chemical, or environmental engineering or an environmental science (e.g., biology, ecology, geology, hydrogeology, industrial hygiene, toxicology). Along with their application, they must submit an essay (up to 250 words) on why they chose to major in an environmental discipline. Financial need is not considered in the selection process. **Deadline for Receipt:** February of each year. **Additional Information:** This scholarship was first awarded in 1999.

2397 ■ BUSINESS AND PROFESSIONAL WOMEN OF VIRGINIA

Attn: Virginia BPW Foundation

P.O. Box 4842

McLean, VA 22103-4842

Web Site: http://www.bpwva.org/Foundation.shtml

To provide financial assistance to women in Virginia who are interested in working on a bachelor's or advanced degree in science or technology.

Title of Award: Women in Science and Technology Scholarship **Area, Field, or Subject:** Actuarial science; Biological and clinical sciences; Chemistry; Computer and information sciences; Dentistry; Engineering; Engineering, Biomedical; Insurance and insurance-related fields; Mathematics and mathematical sciences; Medicine; Physics; Science; Technology **Level of Education for which Award is Granted:** Graduate, Undergraduate **Number Awarded:** At least 1 each year. **Funds Available:** Stipends range from $500 to $1,000 per year, depending on the need of the recipient; funds may be used for tuition, fees, books, transportation, living expenses, and dependent care. **Duration:** 1 year; recipients may reapply (but prior recipients are not given priority).

Eligibility Requirements: This program is open to women who are at least 18 years of age, U.S. citizens, Virginia residents, accepted at or currently studying at a Virginia college or university, and working on a bachelor's, master's, or doctoral degree in 1 of the following fields: actuarial science, biology, bioengineering, chemistry, computer science, dentistry, engineering, mathematics, medicine, physics, or a similar scientific or technical field. Applicants must have a definite plan to use their education in a scientific or technical profession. They must be able to demonstrate financial need. **Deadline for Receipt:** March of each year. **Additional Information:** Recipients must complete their studies within 2 years.

2398 ■ CHICKASAW FOUNDATION
P.O. Box 1726
Ada, OK 74821-1726
Tel: (580)421-9030
Fax: (580)421-9031
Web Site: http://www.cflink.org
To provide financial assistance to members of the Chickasaw Nation who are majoring in fields of interest to ComputerCraft Corporation.
Title of Award: ComputerCraft Corporation Scholarship **Area, Field, or Subject:** Biological and clinical sciences; Engineering, Computer; General studies/Field of study not specified; Graphic art and design; International affairs and relations **Level of Education for which Award is Granted:** Undergraduate **Number Awarded:** 1 each year. **Funds Available:** The stipend is $1,500 per year. **Duration:** 1 year.
Eligibility Requirements: This program is open to Chickasaw students who are currently enrolled full time as an undergraduate student. The sponsor recruits computer engineers, graphic designers, biologists, conference managers, and international trade specialists. Preference may be given to those majors, but all fields of study are eligible. Applicants must have a GPA of 2.5 or higher. Along with their application, they must submit high school or college transcripts, 2 letters of recommendation, a copy of their Certificate of Degree of Indian Blood, a copy of their Chickasaw Nation citizenship card, and a 1-page essay on their long-term goals and plans for achieving them. Financial need is not considered in the selection process. **Deadline for Receipt:** May of each year.

2399 ■ CHRISTIAN LIFE RESOURCES
Attn: WELS Lutherans for Life
Scholarship Review Committee
2949 North Mayfair Road, Suite 309
Milwaukee, WI 53222-4304
Tel: (414)774-1331
Fax: (414)774-1360
Web Site: http://www.christianliferesources.com
To provide financial assistance to Lutheran high school seniors in Wisconsin who are interested in studying life-related issues in college.
Title of Award: WELS Lutherans for Life Scholarship Program **Area, Field, or Subject:** Biological and clinical sciences; Education, Special; Engineering, Biomedical; Journalism; Law; Medicine; Physical therapy; Political science; Psychology; Social work **Level of Education for which Award is Granted:** Four Year College **Number Awarded:** Varies each year; recently, 9 of these scholarships were awarded. **Funds Available:** Stipends up to $1,000 are available. **Duration:** 1 year.
Eligibility Requirements: This program is open to high school seniors who are active members of the Wisconsin Evangelical Lutheran Synod (WELS) or an affiliated church. Applicants must be planning to go to a 4-year school to prepare for a secular career in which pro-life values will be demonstrated. Acceptable fields include medicine, biotechnology/biological engineering, medical research/genetics, law/politics, journalism/media, psychology, physical therapy, social services, or special education. They must have a GPA of 3.25 or higher. Along with their application, they must submit essays on 1) the field of study they plan to enter and how it relates to pro-life issues; 2) why the scholarship should be awarded to them, including their future goals; and 3) how they have demonstrated a Christian, pro-life attitude in their life. **Deadline for Receipt:** February of each year. **Additional Information:** WELS Lutherans for Life was formerly a ministry of the Wisconsin Evangelical Lutheran Synod.

2400 ■ COMMUNITY FOUNDATION OF GREATER JACKSON
525 East Capitol Street, Suite 5B
Jackson, MS 39201
Tel: (601)974-6044
Fax: (601)974-6045
E-mail: info@cfgreaterjackson.org
Web Site: http://www.cfgreaterjackson.org
To provide financial assistance to undergraduate students in Mississippi who are preparing for a career in the field of public works.
Title of Award: APWA Scholarship Fund **Area, Field, or Subject:** Biological and clinical sciences; Chemistry; Engineering, Civil; Engineer-

ing, Electrical; Environmental science; Public administration **Level of Education for which Award is Granted:** Four Year College **Number Awarded:** 2 each year. **Funds Available:** The stipend is $1,000. **Duration:** 1 year.
Eligibility Requirements: This program is open to full-time juniors and seniors at public universities in Mississippi who are preparing to enter the field of public works. Applicants must have graduated from a high school in Mississippi. Eligible majors include civil engineering, electrical engineering, environmental engineering, public administration, biology, or chemistry. Selection is based on merit and need. **Deadline for Receipt:** April of each year. **Additional Information:** This program, established in 2000, is sponsored by the Mississippi chapter of the American Public Works Association (APWA).

2401 ■ CONGRESSIONAL BLACK CAUCUS FOUNDATION, INC.
Attn: Director, Educational Programs
1720 Massachusetts Avenue, N.W.
Washington, DC 20036
Tel: (202)263-2836
Free: 800-784-2577
Fax: (202)775-0773
E-mail: spouses@cbcfinc.org
Web Site: http://www.cbcfinc.org
To provide financial assistance to minority and other undergraduate and graduate students who reside in a Congressional district represented by an African American and are interested in preparing for a health-related career.
Title of Award: Cheerios Brand Health Initiative Scholarship **Area, Field, or Subject:** Biological and clinical sciences; Chemistry; Education, Physical; Engineering; Food service careers; Health care services; Medicine; Nursing **Level of Education for which Award is Granted:** Graduate, Undergraduate **Number Awarded:** Varies each year. **Funds Available:** A stipend is awarded (amount not specified). **Duration:** 1 year.
Eligibility Requirements: This program is open to 1) minority and other graduating high school seniors planning to attend an accredited institution of higher education and 2) currently-enrolled full-time undergraduate, graduate, and doctoral students in good academic standing with a GPA of 2.5 or higher. Applicants must reside or attend school in a Congressional district represented by a member of the Congressional Black Caucus. They must be interested in preparing for a career in a medical, food services, or other health-related field, including pre-medicine, nursing, chemistry, biology, physical education, and engineering. Along with their application, they must submit a 500-word personal statement on 1) the field of study they intend to pursue and why they have chosen that field; 2) their interests, involvement in school activities, community and public service, hobbies, special talents, sports, and other highlight areas; and 3) any other experiences, skills, or qualifications they feel should be considered. They must also be able to document financial need. **Deadline for Receipt:** April of each year. **Additional Information:** The program was established in 1998 with support from General Mills, Inc.

2402 ■ FLORIDA SEA GRANT COLLEGE PROGRAM
Attn: Director
University of Florida
Building 803 McCarty Drive
P.O. Box 110400
Gainesville, FL 32611-0400
Tel: (352)392-5870
Fax: (352)392-5113
Web Site: http://www.flseagrant.org/students/scholarships/index.htm
To provide financial assistance to undergraduate or graduate students working on a degree in a marine science-related field at any Florida university that participates in the Florida Sea Grant College Program.
Title of Award: Aylesworth Foundation for the Advancement of Marine Science Scholarships **Area, Field, or Subject:** Biological and clinical sciences; Economics; Engineering; Food science and technology; Marine biology **Level of Education for which Award is Granted:** Graduate, Undergraduate **Number Awarded:** Generally, 4 or more each year. **Funds Available:** The maximum stipend awarded is 65% of the annual official university or college cost of attendance or $4,000, whichever is less. **Duration:** 1 year; renewable until the recipient completes the degree.
Eligibility Requirements: Eligible to be nominated by their department chair are undergraduate or graduate students who are working on a

degree in an academic discipline that has direct application in marine science (ranging from biology and engineering to economics and food science) at a university or college in Florida that participates in the Florida Sea Grant College Program. Financial need is the principal factor used in the selection process, although academic record, leadership, and personal character are also considered. Florida residents are given preference. **Deadline for Receipt:** November of each year. **Additional Information:** The Florida Sea Grant College Program, established in 1986, operates as a partnership between the Florida Board of Education and the U.S. National Oceanic and Atmospheric Administration. The participating institutions are Florida A&M University, Florida Gulf Coast University, Florida Atlantic University, Florida Institute of Technology, Florida International University, Florida State University, Harbor Branch Oceanographic Institution, Mote Marine Laboratory, New College of Florida, Nova Southeastern University, University of Central Florida, University of Florida, University of Miami, University of North Florida, University of South Florida, and University of West Florida. These scholarships are sponsored by the Aylesworth Foundation for the Advancement of Marine Science, the Southeastern Fisheries Association, and the Florida Sea Grant College Program.

2403 ■ BARRY M. GOLDWATER SCHOLARSHIP AND EXCELLENCE IN EDUCATION FOUNDATION

Springfield Corporate Center
6225 Brandon Avenue, Suite 315
Springfield, VA 22150-2519
Tel: (703)756-6012
Fax: (703)756-6015
E-mail: goldh2o@vacoxmail.com
Web Site: http://www.act.org/goldwater
To provide financial assistance to outstanding college students planning careers in mathematics, engineering, or the natural sciences.

Title of Award: Barry M. Goldwater Scholarships **Area, Field, or Subject:** Engineering; Mathematics and mathematical sciences; Natural sciences **Level of Education for which Award is Granted:** Undergraduate **Number Awarded:** Up to 300 each year. **Funds Available:** Scholarships cover the cost of tuition, fees, books, and room and board up to a maximum of $7,500 per year. **Duration:** Students who receive scholarships as juniors are eligible for 2 years of support or until they complete their baccalaureate degree; students who receive scholarships as seniors are eligible for 1 year of support or until they complete their baccalaureate degree.

Eligibility Requirements: Eligible to be nominated are full-time students enrolled as sophomores or juniors who are in the top quarter of their class and majoring in the natural sciences, mathematics, or engineering with a GPA of at least 3.0. Students intending to enter medical school are eligible if they plan a career in research rather than private practice. Status as a U.S. citizen, national, or resident alien is also required. Students must be nominated by their institutions; 4-year colleges and universities may nominate up to 4 current sophomores or juniors and 2-year colleges may nominate up to 2 sophomores. Applicants must submit a 2-page essay on a significant issue or problem in their field of study that is of particular interest to them. Selection is based on academic performance and demonstrated potential for and commitment to a career in mathematics, engineering, or the natural sciences. **Deadline for Receipt:** Institutions set their own deadlines; they must submit nominations to the foundation by January of each year. **Additional Information:** This program was authorized by the U.S. Congress in 1986. Information is also available from the Goldwater Scholarship Review Committee, 2201 North Dodge Street, P.O. Box 4030, Iowa City, IA 52243-4030.

2404 ■ HISPANIC SCHOLARSHIP FUND INSTITUTE

1001 Connecticut Avenue, N.W., Suite 632
Washington, DC 20036
Tel: (202)296-0009
Fax: (202)296-3633
E-mail: info@hsfi.org
Web Site: http://www.hsfi.org/scholarships/generation.asp
To provide financial assistance to Hispanic and other students majoring in designated business, engineering, social science, and science fields who are interested in employment with the U.S. Department of Energy (DOE).

Title of Award: Next Generation of Public Servants Scholarship **Area, Field, or Subject:** Accounting; Biological and clinical sciences; Business

administration; Computer and information sciences; Engineering; Environmental science; Finance; Geology; Information science and technology; Management; Mathematics and mathematical sciences; Physics; Political science; Psychology; Sociology **Level of Education for which Award is Granted:** Undergraduate **Number Awarded:** Varies each year. **Funds Available:** The stipend is $3,000 per year. **Duration:** 1 year; may be renewed up to 2 additional years if the recipient maintains full-time enrollment and a GPA of 2.8 or higher.

Eligibility Requirements: This program is open to U.S. citizens enrolled full time as sophomores with a GPA of 2.8 or higher. Applicants must be interested in preparing for a career with the DOE in an energy-related field. Eligible academic majors are in the fields of business (accounting, business administration, finance, and management), engineering (biomedical, chemical, civil, computer, electrical, environmental, industrial, materials, mechanical, metallurgical, nuclear, and petroleum), social science (economics, organizational psychology, political science, and sociology), and science (biological sciences, computer science, geology, information technology, mathematics, microbiology, and physics). They must be willing to participate in co-ops with the DOE. Along with their application, they must submit a 2-page essay on why a career in public service interests them, how their academic major connects with their stated DOE career goal, why the DOE should invest in them through this program, and how they believe the DOE will benefit from this investment. Selection is based on academic achievement, financial need, demonstrated commitment to public service, and interest in federal employment with the DOE. **Deadline for Receipt:** February of each year. **Additional Information:** This program, sponsored by DOE's Office of Economic Impact and Diversity, is administered by the Hispanic Scholarship Fund Institute as part of its effort to increase Hispanic participation in federal service.

2405 ■ IOWA SPACE GRANT CONSORTIUM

Attn: Director
Iowa State University
2271 Howe Hall, Room 2365
Ames, IA 50011-2271
Tel: (515)294-3106
Free: 800-854-1667
Fax: (515)294-3361
E-mail: isgc@iastate.edu
Web Site: http://www.ia.spacegrant.org
To provide financial assistance to undergraduate and graduate students majoring in science, technology, engineering, or mathematics (STEM) disciplines at member institutions of the Iowa Space Grant Consortium (ISGC).

Title of Award: Iowa Space Grant Scholarship Program **Area, Field, or Subject:** Aerospace sciences; Biological and clinical sciences; Engineering, Aerospace/Aeronautical/Astronautical; Mathematics and mathematical sciences; Science; Space and planetary sciences; Technology **Level of Education for which Award is Granted:** Four Year College, Graduate **Number Awarded:** Approximately 16 each year. **Funds Available:** The stipend is $6,000. **Duration:** 1 year.

Eligibility Requirements: This program is open to U.S. citizens enrolled full time as undergraduate or graduate students at ISGC member institutions. Applicants must be majoring in a STEM discipline of interest to the National Aeronautics and Space Administration. They must be interested in working on the base research program at their institution. Students from underrepresented groups (women, minorities, and persons with disabilities) are especially encouraged to apply. **Deadline for Receipt:** March of each year. **Additional Information:** Member institutions of ISGC, and their base programs, include Drake University (molecular biology and space life sciences), Iowa State University (the Spacecraft Systems and Operations Laboratory), the University of Iowa (the Operator Performance Laboratory), and the University of Northern Iowa (student research program on Iowa's lakes and wetlands). Funding for this program is provided by NASA.

2406 ■ KANSAS WILDSCAPE FOUNDATION, INC.

1 Riverfront Plaza, Suite 311
Lawrence, KS 66044
Tel: (785)843-9453; (866)455-6377
Fax: (785)843-6379
E-mail: wildscape@sunflower.com

Web Site: http://www.kansaswildscape.org

To provide financial assistance to high school seniors in Kansas who plan to attend a college or university in the state to major in natural resources or photography.

Title of Award: Steve Harper Memorial Scholarship **Area, Field, or Subject:** Natural resources; Photography **Level of Education for which Award is Granted:** Four Year College **Number Awarded:** 1 each year. **Funds Available:** The stipend is $1,000. **Duration:** 1 year.

Eligibility Requirements: This program is open to seniors graduating from high schools and planning to attend a 4-year college or university in the state. Applicants must be planning to study photography or natural resources. Selection is based on past or current involvement in the natural resources or photography area, strength of application, academic performance, and financial need. **Deadline for Receipt:** April of each year. **Additional Information:** This program was established following the death in 2000 of Steve Harper, a photojournalism instructor at Wichita State University and outdoor writer and photographer for the *Wichita Eagle*.

2407 ■ KOSTER INSURANCE AGENCY

Attn: Scholarship
500 Victory Road
Quincy, MA 02171
Tel: (617)770-9889
Free: 800-457-5599
Fax: (617)479-0860
E-mail: Scholarship@kosterins.com
Web Site: http://www.kosterweb.com/about/scholarship_main.php

To provide financial assistance to undergraduate students working on a degree in a health-related field.

Title of Award: Koster Insurance Health Careers Scholarship Program **Area, Field, or Subject:** Biological and clinical sciences; Chemistry; Dentistry; Health care services; Nursing; Occupational therapy; Optometry; Pharmaceutical sciences; Physical therapy; Physiology; Public health; Social work **Level of Education for which Award is Granted:** Undergraduate **Number Awarded:** 5 each year. **Funds Available:** The stipend is $3,000 per year. **Duration:** 1 year; may be renewed 1 additional year.

Eligibility Requirements: This program is open to full-time undergraduates entering their second-to-last or final year of study in a health-related field, including (but not limited to) pre-medicine, nursing, public and community health, physical therapy, occupational therapy, pharmacy, biology, chemistry, physiology, social work, dentistry, and optometry. Applicants must have a GPA of 3.0 or higher and be able to demonstrate financial need. Along with their application, they must submit a 1-page essay describing their personal goals, including their reasons for preparing for a career in health care. Selection is based on motivation to pursue a career in health care, academic excellence, dedication to community service, and financial need. **Deadline for Receipt:** April of each year. **Additional Information:** This program began in 2001.

2408 ■ CLARE BOOTHE LUCE FUND

c/o Henry Luce Foundation, Inc.
111 West 50th Street, Suite 4601
New York, NY 10020
Tel: (212)489-7700
Fax: (212)581-9541
E-mail: jdaniels@hluce.org
Web Site: http://www.hluce.org

To provide funding to women interested in studying science or engineering at the undergraduate level at designated universities.

Title of Award: Clare Boothe Luce Scholarships in Science and Engineering **Area, Field, or Subject:** Biological and clinical sciences; Chemistry; Computer and information sciences; Engineering; Engineering, Aerospace/Aeronautical/Astronautical; Engineering, Civil; Engineering, Electrical; Engineering, Mechanical; Engineering, Nuclear; Mathematics and mathematical sciences; Meteorology; Physics **Level of Education for which Award is Granted:** Undergraduate **Number Awarded:** Varies; since the program began, more than 800 of these scholarships have been awarded. **Funds Available:** The amount awarded is established individually by each of the participating institutions. The stipends are intended to augment rather than replace any existing institutional support in these fields. Each stipend is calculated to include the cost of room and board as well as tuition and other fees or expenses. **Duration:** 2 years; in certain special circumstances, awards for the full 4 years of undergraduate study may be offered.

Eligibility Requirements: This program is open to female undergraduate students (particularly juniors and seniors) majoring in biology, chemistry, computer science, engineering (aeronautical, civil, electrical, mechanical, nuclear, and others), mathematics, meteorology, and physics. Applicants must be U.S. citizens attending 1 of the 12 designated colleges and universities affiliated with this program; periodically, other institutions are invited to participate. Premedical science majors are ineligible for this competition. The participating institutions select the recipients without regard to race, age, religion, ethnic background, or need. All awards are made on the basis of merit. **Deadline for Receipt:** Varies; check with the participating institutions for their current schedule. **Additional Information:** The participating institutions are Boston University, Colby College, Creighton University, Fordham University, Georgetown University, Marymount University, Mount Holyoke College, St. John's University, Santa Clara University, Seton Hall University, Trinity College, and University of Notre Dame.

2409 ■ MAINE SPACE GRANT CONSORTIUM

Attn: Executive Director
87 Winthrop Street, Suite 200
Augusta, ME 04330
Tel: (207)622-4688; 877-397-7223
Fax: (207)622-4548
E-mail: shehata@msgc.org
Web Site: http://www.msgc.org/education_students.asp

To provide funding to undergraduate and graduate students at colleges and universities in Maine interested in working on projects related to space.

Title of Award: Maine Space Grant Consortium Scholarship and Fellowship Program **Area, Field, or Subject:** Aerospace sciences; Biological and clinical sciences; Computer and information sciences; Earth sciences; Engineering, Aerospace/Aeronautical/Astronautical; Geosciences; Physical sciences; Social sciences; Space and planetary sciences; Technology **Level of Education for which Award is Granted:** Graduate, Undergraduate **Number Awarded:** Varies each year. **Funds Available:** Stipends are $2,500 for undergraduates or $5,000 for graduate students. **Duration:** 1 year.

Eligibility Requirements: This program is open to U.S. citizens who are enrolled on a full-time basis in an undergraduate or graduate program at a 2- or 4-year college or university in Maine, including those not members of the Maine Space Grant Consortium. Applicants must be proposing to conduct a project on a topic of interest to the U.S. National Aeronautics and Space Administration (NASA) in biological, earth, physical, social, or space science; human exploration and development of space; or other related science, technology, computer, or engineering fields. Undergraduates must have a GPA of 3.0 or higher; graduate students must have a GPA of 3.2 or higher. Proposals may involve conducting research at their home institution, traveling to conduct research and/or to present finished project work at a NASA field center, or facilitating technology transfer from NASA to their institution and industry in Maine. Applications are especially encouraged from women, minorities, and persons with disabilities. Selection is based on the relevance of the project to NASA's mission and its strategic enterprises, collaboration with researchers at NASA space flight centers, qualifications of the student, technical content and quality of the proposal, and recommendation from a faculty member. **Deadline for Receipt:** May or October of each year. **Additional Information:** This program is funded by NASA.

2410 ■ MAINE SPACE GRANT CONSORTIUM

Attn: Executive Director
87 Winthrop Street, Suite 200
Augusta, ME 04330
Tel: (207)622-4688; 877-397-7223
Fax: (207)622-4548
E-mail: shehata@msgc.org
Web Site: http://www.msgc.org/education_students.asp

To provide funding to undergraduate and graduate students at member institutions of the Maine Space Grant Consortium (MSGC) interested in working on projects related to space.

Title of Award: MSGC Undergraduate and Graduate Research Fellowships **Area, Field, or Subject:** Aerospace sciences; Biological and clinical sciences; Earth sciences; Engineering, Aerospace/Aeronautical/ Astronautical; Geosciences; Physical sciences; Space and planetary sciences **Level of Education for which Award is Granted:** Graduate, Undergraduate **Number Awarded:** Varies each year. **Funds Available:** Stipends vary at participating institutions, ranging from $2,500 to $5,000 per year for undergraduates and from $5,000 to $15,000 per year for graduate students. **Duration:** 1 year; may be renewed.

Eligibility Requirements: This program is open to U.S. citizens who are enrolled on a full-time basis in an undergraduate or graduate program at a MSGC member institution. Applicants must be proposing to conduct a project on a topic of interest to the U.S. National Aeronautics and Space Administration (NASA) in aerospace technology, biological and physical research, space science, earth science, human exploration and development of space, and other related science or engineering fields. They may be proposing to conduct research at their home institution, spend time conducting research at a NASA flight center, facilitate the development of a liaison between researchers at their home institution and a NASA center, or facilitate technology transfer from their home institution to industry. Selection is based on the relevance of the proposed research project to NASA's mission. Applications are especially encouraged from women and minorities. **Deadline for Receipt:** Each participating institution sets its own deadline. **Additional Information:** The member institutions are the University of Maine, the University of Southern Maine, the University of New England, and Maine Maritime Academy. This program is funded by NASA.

2411 ■ MARYLAND HIGHER EDUCATION COMMISSION
Attn: Office of Student Financial Assistance
839 Bestgate Road, Suite 400
Annapolis, MD 21401-3013
Tel: (410)260-4545
Free: 800-974-1024
Fax: (410)974-5376
E-mail: osfamail@mhec.state.md.us
Web Site: http://www.mhec.state.md.us/financialAid/
ProgramDescriptions/prog_scm.asp
To provide scholarship/loans to Maryland residents who wish to prepare for a teaching career.
Title of Award: Sharon Christa McAuliffe Memorial Teacher Education Award **Area, Field, or Subject:** Chemistry; Classical studies; Computer and information sciences; Earth sciences; Education; Education, English as a second language; Education, Special; Education, Vocational-technical; Foreign languages; Geosciences; Health care services; Hearing and deafness; Mathematics and mathematical sciences; Physical sciences; Physics; Space and planetary sciences; Visual impairment **Level of Education for which Award is Granted:** Master's, Professional, Undergraduate **Number Awarded:** Varies each year. **Funds Available:** The amount of the award is based on the recipient's enrollment and housing status, to a maximum of $17,000 per year. The total amount of all state awards may not exceed the cost of attendance as determined by the school's financial aid office or $17,800, whichever is less. Following graduation, recipients must teach at a Maryland public school for 1 year for each year of financial aid received under this program. If they fail to meet that service obligation, they must repay all funds they received with interest. They must begin the service obligation within 12 months of graduation. **Duration:** 1 year; may be renewed for 1 additional year if the recipient maintains satisfactory academic progress with a cumulative GPA of 3.0 or higher and enrollment at a 2-year or 4-year Maryland college or university in an approved teacher education program.
Eligibility Requirements: This program is open to Maryland residents who are college students with at least 60 semester credit hours completed, college graduates, and teachers in a non-critical shortage area. Applicants must have a GPA of 3.0 or higher and plan to teach in a field identified as a critical shortage area. Selection is based on cumulative GPA, applicable work or volunteer experience, quality of academic background in certification field, and a writing sample. **Deadline for Receipt:** December of each year. **Additional Information:** Recently, the eligible critical shortage areas were business education, chemistry, computer science, earth and space science, English for speakers of other languages, family and consumer sciences, German, health occupations, Latin, mathematics, physical science, physics, Spanish, special education

(generic infant-grade 3, generic grades 1-8, generic grades 6-adult, hearing impaired, severely and profoundly handicapped, visually impaired), and technology education.

2412 ■ MARYLAND SPACE GRANT CONSORTIUM
c/o Johns Hopkins University
203 Bloomberg Center for Physics and Astronomy
3400 North Charles Street
Baltimore, MD 21218-2686
Tel: (410)516-7351
Fax: (410)516-4109
E-mail: info@mdspacegrant.org
Web Site: http://www.mdspacegrant.org/scholars_about.html
To provide financial assistance to undergraduates who are interested in studying space-related fields at selected universities in Maryland that are members of the Maryland Space Grant Consortium.
Title of Award: Maryland Space Scholars Program **Area, Field, or Subject:** Aerospace sciences; Astronomy and astronomical sciences; Biological and clinical sciences; Chemistry; Computer and information sciences; Engineering; Geology; Mathematics and mathematical sciences; Physics; Space and planetary sciences **Level of Education for which Award is Granted:** Undergraduate **Number Awarded:** Varies each year; recently 16 of these scholarships were awarded (2 at Johns Hopkins University, 5 at Morgan State University, 2 at Hagerstown Community College, 2 at Towson University, and 5 at the University of Maryland at College Park). **Funds Available:** Scholars receive partial payment of tuition at the participating university they attend. **Duration:** 1 year; may be renewed if the recipient maintains a GPA of 3.0 or higher.
Eligibility Requirements: This program is open to residents of Maryland and graduates of Maryland high schools who are enrolled full time at a member institution. Applicants must be interested in preparing for a career in mathematics, science, engineering, technology, or a space-related field. They must be majoring in a relevant field, including (but not limited to) astronomy, the biological and life sciences, chemistry, computer science, engineering, geological sciences, or physics. U.S. citizenship is required. Along with their application, they must submit an essay of 200 to 500 words on how this scholarship will help them meet their educational and financial goals. This program is a component of the U.S. National Aeronautics and Space Administration (NASA) Space Grant program, which encourages participation by women, underrepresented minorities, and persons with disabilities. **Deadline for Receipt:** August of each year. **Additional Information:** The participating universities are Hagerstown Community College, Johns Hopkins University, Morgan State University, Towson University, the University of Maryland at College Park, and Washington College. Funding for this program is provided by NASA.

2413 ■ MEL FISHER MARITIME HERITAGE SOCIETY AND MUSEUM
Attn: Curator, Department of Education
200 Greene Street
Key West, FL 33040
Tel: (305)294-2633
Fax: (305)294-5671
Web Site: http://www.melfisher.org/deoaward.htm
To recognize and reward, with funding for college or graduate school, women who submit outstanding essays on the oceans.
Title of Award: Dolores E. Fisher Award **Area, Field, or Subject:** Marine biology; Oceanography; Writing **Level of Education for which Award is Granted:** Graduate, Undergraduate **Number Awarded:** 1 each year. **Funds Available:** The award is $1,000. **Duration:** The award is presented annually.
Eligibility Requirements: This competition is open to women between 16 and 30 years of age. Candidates must submit a 1,000-word essay on how they hope to make a difference in the world through their passion for the oceans, their career goals, and how this award will help them achieve those goals. They must also include 3 letters of recommendation and a brief statement on the personality characteristic they value most in themselves and why. If they are currently enrolled in school, they must identify their program, but school enrollment is not required. **Deadline for Receipt:** March of each year.

2414 ■ MINNESOTA SPACE GRANT CONSORTIUM
c/o University of Minnesota
Department of Aerospace Engineering and Mechanics

107 Akerman Hall
110 Union Street S.E.
Minneapolis, MN 55455
Tel: (612)626-9295
Fax: (612)626-1558
E-mail: mnsgc@aem.umn.edu
Web Site: http://www.aem.umn.edu/msgc/Scholarships/sf.shtml
To provide financial assistance for space-related studies to undergraduate and graduate students in Minnesota.

Title of Award: Minnesota Space Grant Consortium Scholarships and Fellowships **Area, Field, or Subject:** Earth sciences; Engineering; Life sciences; Physical sciences; Social sciences **Level of Education for which Award is Granted:** Graduate, Undergraduate **Number Awarded:** 8 to 12 undergraduate scholarships and 2 to 3 graduate fellowships are awarded each year. **Funds Available:** This program awards approximately $125,000 in undergraduate scholarships and graduate fellowships each year. The amounts of the awards are set by each of the participating institutions, which augment funding from this program with institutional resources. **Duration:** 1 year; renewable.

Eligibility Requirements: This program is open to graduate and undergraduate full-time students at institutions that are affiliates of the Minnesota Space Grant Consortium. U.S. citizenship and a GPA of 3.2 or higher are required. Eligible fields of study include the physical sciences (astronomy, astrophysics, chemistry, computer science, mathematics, physics, planetary geoscience, and planetary science), life sciences (biology, biochemistry, botany, health science/nutrition, medicine, molecular/cellular biology, and zoology), social sciences (anthropology, architecture, art, economics, education, history, philosophy, political science/public policy, and psychology), earth sciences (atmospheric science, climatology/meteorology, environmental science, geography, geology, geophysics, and oceanography), and engineering (agricultural, aeronautical, aerospace, architectural, bioengineering, chemical, civil, computer, electrical, electronic, environmental, industrial, materials science, mechanical, mining, nuclear, petroleum, engineering science, and engineering mechanics). The Minnesota Space Grant Consortium is a component of the U.S. National Aeronautics and Space Administration (NASA) Space Grant program, which encourages participation by women, underrepresented minorities, and persons with disabilities. **Deadline for Receipt:** March of each year. **Additional Information:** This program is funded by NASA. The member institutions are: Augsburg College, Bethel College, Bemidji State University, College of St. Catherine, Carleton College, Concordia College, Fond du Lac Community College, Itasca Community College, Leech Lake Tribal College, Macalaster College, Normandale Community College, Southwest State University, University of Minnesota at Duluth, University of Minnesota at Twin Cities, and University of St. Thomas.

2415 ■ MONTANA SPACE GRANT CONSORTIUM
c/o Montana State University
416 Cobleigh Hall
P.O. Box 173835
Bozeman, MT 59717-3835
Tel: (406)994-4223
Fax: (406)994-4452
E-mail: msgc@montana.edu
Web Site: http://spacegrant.montana.edu/Text/ScholarProgram.html
To provide financial assistance to students in Montana who are interested in working on an undergraduate degree in the space sciences and/or engineering.

Title of Award: Montana Space Grant Consortium Undergraduate Scholarships **Area, Field, or Subject:** Aerospace sciences; Astronomy and astronomical sciences; Biological and clinical sciences; Chemistry; Computer and information sciences; Engineering, Aerospace/Aeronautical/Astronautical; Engineering, Chemical; Engineering, Civil; Engineering, Electrical; Engineering, Mechanical; Geology; Physics; Space and planetary sciences **Level of Education for which Award is Granted:** Undergraduate **Number Awarded:** Varies each year; recently, 23 of these scholarships were awarded. **Funds Available:** The stipend is $1,000 per year. **Duration:** 1 year; may be renewed.

Eligibility Requirements: This program is open to full-time undergraduate students at member institutions of the Montana Space Grant Consortium (MSGC) majoring in fields related to space sciences and engineering. Those fields include, but are not limited to, astronomy,

biological and life sciences, chemical engineering, chemistry, civil engineering, computer sciences, electrical engineering, geological sciences, mathematics, mechanical engineering, and physics. Priority is given to students who have been involved in aerospace-related research. U.S. citizenship is required. The MSGC is a component of the U.S. National Aeronautics and Space Administration (NASA) Space Grant program, which encourages participation by women, underrepresented minorities, and persons with disabilities. **Deadline for Receipt:** March of each year. **Additional Information:** The MSGC member institutions are Blackfeet Community College, Carroll College, Chief Dull Knife College, Fort Belknap College, Fort Peck Community College, Little Big Horn College, Montana State University at Billings, Montana State University at Bozeman, Montana State University Northern, Montana Tech, Rocky Mountain College, Salish Kootenai College, Stone Child College, University of Great Falls, University of Montana, and University of Montana Western. Funding for this program is provided by NASA.

2416 ■ NATIONAL CONSORTIUM FOR GRADUATE DEGREES FOR MINORITIES IN ENGINEERING AND SCIENCE (GEM)
P.O. Box 537
Notre Dame, IN 46556
Tel: (574)631-7771
Fax: (574)287-1486
E-mail: gem.1@nd.edu
Web Site: http://www.gemfellowship.org
To provide financial assistance and summer work experience to underrepresented minority students interested in obtaining a Ph.D. degree in the life sciences, mathematics, or physical sciences.

Title of Award: GEM Ph.D. Science Fellowship Program **Area, Field, or Subject:** Biological and clinical sciences; Chemistry; Computer and information sciences; Earth sciences; Geosciences; Mathematics and mathematical sciences; Natural sciences; Physics **Level of Education for which Award is Granted:** Four Year College, Doctorate **Number Awarded:** Varies each year; recently, 40 of these fellowships were awarded. **Funds Available:** The stipend is $14,000 per year, plus tuition and fees. In addition, there is a summer internship program that provides a salary and reimbursement for travel expenses to and from the summer work site. The total value of the award is between $60,000 and $100,000, depending upon academic status at the time of application, summer employer, and graduate school attended. **Duration:** 3 to 5 years for the fellowship; 12 weeks during at least 1 summer for the internship. Fellows selected as juniors or seniors intern each summer until entrance to graduate school; fellows selected after college graduation intern at least 1 summer.

Eligibility Requirements: This program is open to U.S. citizens who are members of ethnic groups underrepresented in the natural sciences: Native Americans, African Americans, Latinos, Puerto Ricans, and other Hispanic Americans. Applicants must be juniors, seniors, or recent baccalaureate graduates in the life sciences, mathematics, or physical sciences (chemistry, computer science, earth sciences, and physics) with an academic record that indicates the ability to pursue doctoral studies (including a GPA of 3.0 or higher). **Deadline for Receipt:** October of each year. **Additional Information:** This program is valid only at 1 of 95 participating GEM member universities; write to GEM for a list. The fellowship award is designed to support the student in the first year of the doctoral program without working. Subsequent years are subsidized by the respective university and will usually include either a teaching or research assistantship. Recipients must participate in the GEM summer internship; failure to agree to accept the internship cancels the fellowship. Recipients must enroll in the same scientific discipline as their undergraduate major.

2417 ■ NATIONAL FEDERATION OF THE BLIND
c/o Peggy Elliott, Scholarship Committee Chair
805 Fifth Avenue
Grinnell, IA 50112
Tel: (641)236-3366
Web Site: http://www.nfb.org/sch_intro.htm
To provide financial assistance for college or graduate school to blind students studying or planning to study law, medicine, engineering, architecture, or the natural sciences.

Title of Award: Howard Brown Rickard Scholarships **Area, Field, or Subject:** Architecture; Engineering; Law; Medicine; Natural sciences

Level of Education for which Award is Granted: Graduate, Undergraduate **Number Awarded:** 1 each year. **Funds Available:** The stipend is $3,000. **Duration:** 1 year; recipients may resubmit applications up to 2 additional years.

Eligibility Requirements: This program is open to legally blind students who are enrolled in or planning to enroll in a full-time undergraduate or graduate course of study. Applicants must be studying or planning to study law, medicine, engineering, architecture, or the natural sciences. Selection is based on academic excellence, service to the community, and financial need. **Deadline for Receipt:** March of each year. **Additional Information:** Scholarships are awarded at the federation convention in July. Recipients attend the convention at federation expense; that funding is in addition to the scholarship grant.

2418 ■ NATIONAL FFA ORGANIZATION

Attn: Scholarship Office
6060 FFA Drive
P.O. Box 68960
Indianapolis, IN 46268-0960
Tel: (317)802-4321
Fax: (317)802-5321
E-mail: scholarships@ffa.org
Web Site: http://www.ffa.org
To provide financial assistance to FFA members who are interested in majoring in natural resources in college.

Title of Award: Federal Cartridge Company Scholarship **Area, Field, or Subject:** Natural resources **Level of Education for which Award is Granted:** Four Year College **Number Awarded:** 1 each year. **Funds Available:** The stipend is $1,000. Funds are paid directly to the recipient. **Duration:** 1 year; nonrenewable.

Eligibility Requirements: This program is open to members who are graduating high school seniors planning to enroll full time in college. Applicants must be interested in working on a 4-year degree in natural resources. Selection is based on academic achievement (10 points for GPA, 10 points for SAT or ACT score, 10 points for class rank), leadership in FFA activities (30 points), leadership in community activities (10 points), and participation in the Supervised Agricultural Experience (SAE) program (30 points). U.S. citizenship is required. **Deadline for Receipt:** February of each year. **Additional Information:** Funding for this scholarship is provided by Federal Cartridge Company.

2419 ■ NATIONAL FFA ORGANIZATION

Attn: Scholarship Office
6060 FFA Drive
P.O. Box 68960
Indianapolis, IN 46268-0960
Tel: (317)802-4321
Fax: (317)802-5321
E-mail: scholarships@ffa.org
Web Site: http://www.ffa.org
To provide financial assistance to FFA members who are interested in studying conservation at a college or university.

Title of Award: Georgia M. Hellberg Memorial Scholarships **Area, Field, or Subject:** Environmental conservation; Environmental science; Soil science; Water resources **Level of Education for which Award is Granted:** Four Year College **Number Awarded:** Approximately 4 each year. **Funds Available:** The stipend is $5,000. Funds are paid directly to the recipient. **Duration:** 1 year; nonrenewable.

Eligibility Requirements: This program is open to members who are graduating high school seniors planning to enroll full time in college. Applicants must be interested in working on a 4-year degree in soil and water conservation or a subject that could lead to employment in those areas. Selection is based on academic achievement (10 points for GPA, 10 points for SAT or ACT score, 10 points for class rank), leadership in FFA activities (30 points), leadership in community activities (10 points), and participation in the Supervised Agricultural Experience (SAE) program (30 points). U.S. citizenship is required. **Deadline for Receipt:** February of each year.

2420 ■ NATIONAL FFA ORGANIZATION

Attn: Scholarship Office
6060 FFA Drive
P.O. Box 68960
Indianapolis, IN 46268-0960

Tel: (317)802-4321
Fax: (317)802-5321
E-mail: scholarships@ffa.org
Web Site: http://www.ffa.org
To provide financial assistance to FFA members who are interested in working on a college degree in fields related to natural resources.

Title of Award: National Rifle Association of America Scholarships **Area, Field, or Subject:** Environmental conservation; Environmental science; Natural resources; Wildlife conservation, management, and science **Level of Education for which Award is Granted:** Four Year College **Number Awarded:** 5 each year. **Funds Available:** The stipend is $1,000. Funds are paid directly to the recipient. **Duration:** 1 year; nonrenewable.

Eligibility Requirements: This program is open to members who are graduating high school seniors planning to enroll full time in college. Applicants must be members of the National Rifle Association (NRA). They may be interested in working on a 4-year degree in any area, but preference is given to those majoring in conservation, natural resources, or wildlife management. Selection is based on academic achievement (10 points for GPA, 10 points for SAT or ACT score, 10 points for class rank), leadership in FFA activities (30 points), leadership in community activities (10 points), and participation in the Supervised Agricultural Experience (SAE) program (30 points). U.S. citizenship is required. **Deadline for Receipt:** February of each year. **Additional Information:** Funding for these scholarships is provided by the National Rifle Association.

2421 ■ NATIONAL INVENTORS HALL OF FAME

Attn: Collegiate Inventors Competition
221 South Broadway Street
Akron, OH 44308-1595
Tel: (330)849-6887
E-mail: collegiate@invent.org
Web Site: http://www.invent.org/collegiate
To recognize and reward outstanding inventions by college or university students in the fields of science, engineering, and technology.

Title of Award: Collegiate Inventors Competition **Area, Field, or Subject:** Biological and clinical sciences; Chemistry; Computer and information sciences; Engineering; Environmental conservation; Environmental science; Inventors; Mathematics and mathematical sciences; Medicine; Physics; Science; Technology; Veterinary science and medicine **Level of Education for which Award is Granted:** Graduate, Postdoctoral, Undergraduate **Number Awarded:** 15 semifinalists are selected each year; of those, 3 individuals or teams win prizes. **Funds Available:** Finalists receive an all-expense paid trip to Washington, D.C. to participate in a final round of judging and in the awards dinner and presentation. The Grand Prize winner or team receives $25,000. Other prizes are $10,000 for an undergraduate winner or team and $15,000 for a graduate winner or team. Academic advisors of the winning entries each receive a $3,000 cash prize. Awards are unrestricted cash gifts, not scholarships or grants. **Duration:** The competition is held annually.

Eligibility Requirements: This competition is open to undergraduate and graduate students who are (or have been) enrolled full time at least part of the 12-month period prior to entry in a college or university in the United States. Entries may also be submitted by teams, up to 4 members, of whom at least 1 must meet the full-time requirement and all others must have been enrolled at least half time sometime during the preceding 24-month period. Applicants must submit a description of their invention, including a patent search and summary of current literature that describes the state of the art and identifies the originality of the invention; test data demonstrating that the idea, invention, or design is workable; the societal, economic, and environmental benefits of the invention; and supplemental material that may include photos, slides, disks, videotapes, and even samples. Entries must be original ideas and the work of a student or team and a university advisor; the invention should be reproducible and may not have been 1) made available to the public as a commercial product or process, or 2) patented or published more than 1 year prior to the date of submission for this competition. Entries are first reviewed by a committee of judges that selects the finalists. The committee is comprised of mathematicians, engineers, biologists, chemists, environmentalists, physicists, computer specialists, members of the medical and veterinary profession, and specialists in invention and development of technology. Entries are judged on the basis of originality, inventiveness, potential value to society (socially, environmentally, and economically), and range or scope of use. **Deadline for Receipt:** May of each year. **Additional**

Information: This program is co-sponsored by Abbott Laboratories and the United States Patent and Trademark Office. It was established in 1990 as the BFGoodrich Collegiate Inventors Program.

2422 ■ NATIONAL SOCIETY OF BLACK ENGINEERS

Attn: Programs Department
1454 Duke Street
Alexandria, VA 22314
Tel: (703)549-2207
Fax: (703)683-5312
E-mail: scholarships@nsbe.org
Web Site: http://www.nsbe.org/programs/schol_jnj.php
To provide financial assistance to members of the National Society of Black Engineers (NSBE) who are majoring in designated engineering fields.
Title of Award: Johnson & Johnson NSBE Corporate Scholarship Program **Area, Field, or Subject:** Biological and clinical sciences; Chemistry; Computer and information sciences; Engineering, Biomedical; Engineering, Chemical; Engineering, Computer; Engineering, Electrical; Engineering, Industrial; Engineering, Materials; Engineering, Mechanical; Logistics **Level of Education for which Award is Granted:** Four Year College **Number Awarded:** 13 each year: 1 national award and 12 regional awards (2 in each NSBE region). **Funds Available:** The national stipend is $2,000; the regional stipends are $1,500. **Duration:** 1 year.
Eligibility Requirements: This program is open to members of the society who are entering their junior or senior year in college and majoring in biology, chemistry, computer science, operations/logistics, or the following fields of engineering: biomedical, chemical, computer, electrical, industrial, material, or mechanical. Applicants must have a GPA of 3.2 or higher and a demonstrated interest in employment with Johnson & Johnson. Along with their application, they must submit a resume and official transcript. **Deadline for Receipt:** January of each year.

2423 ■ NEBRASKA ACADEMY OF SCIENCES

c/o University of Nebraska
302 Morrill Hall
14th and U Streets
P.O. Box 880339
Lincoln, NE 68588-0339
Tel: (402)472-2644
E-mail: nebacad@unl.edu
Web Site: http://www.neacadsci.org/Info/coll_scholarship.htm
To provide financial assistance to upper-division students majoring in science at colleges and universities in Nebraska.
Title of Award: C. Bertrand and Marian Othmer Scultz Collegiate Scholarship **Area, Field, or Subject:** Biological and clinical sciences; Chemistry; Geology; Physics **Level of Education for which Award is Granted:** Four Year College **Number Awarded:** 1 each year. **Funds Available:** The stipend is $3,000 per year. **Duration:** 1 year; may be renewed 1 additional year.
Eligibility Requirements: This program is open to student entering their junior or senior year at 4-year colleges and universities in Nebraska. Applicants must have a declared major in a natural science discipline (chemistry, physics, biology, or geology). They must be preparing for a career in a science-related industry, science teaching, or scientific research. A member of the Nebraska Academy of Sciences must provide a letter of nomination. **Deadline for Receipt:** January of each year. **Additional Information:** This scholarship was first awarded in 2006.

2424 ■ NEW HAMPSHIRE SPACE GRANT CONSORTIUM

c/o University of New Hampshire
Institute for the Study of Earth, Oceans, and Space
Morse Hall
39 College Road
Durham, NH 03824-3525
Tel: (603)862-0094
Fax: (603)862-1915
E-mail: nhspacegrant@unh.edu
Web Site: http://www.nhsgc.sr.unh.edu
To provide financial assistance to students at member institutions of the New Hampshire Space Grant Consortium (NHSGC) who are interested in participating in space-related activities.
Title of Award: New Hampshire Space Grant Consortium Project Support **Area, Field, or Subject:** Aerospace sciences; Astronomy and astronomi-

cal sciences; Atmospheric science; Biological and clinical sciences; Computer and information sciences; Earth sciences; Engineering, Aerospace/Aeronautical/Astronautical; Geosciences; Oceanography; Physics; Space and planetary sciences **Level of Education for which Award is Granted:** Graduate, Undergraduate **Number Awarded:** Varies each year. **Funds Available:** The amount of the award depends on the nature of the project. **Duration:** From 1 quarter to 1 year.
Eligibility Requirements: This program is open to students at member institutions of the NHSGC. Applicants must be studying space physics, astrophysics, astronomy, or aspects of computer science, engineering, earth sciences, ocean sciences, atmospheric sciences, or life sciences that utilize space technology and/or adopt a planetary view of the global environment. U.S. citizenship is required. The New Hampshire Space Grant Consortium is a component of the U.S. National Aeronautics and Space Administration (NASA) Space Grant program, which encourages participation by women, underrepresented minorities, and persons with disabilities. **Deadline for Receipt:** Each participating college or university sets its own deadline. **Additional Information:** This program is funded by NASA. Currently, projects operating through this program include space grant fellowships at the University of New Hampshire, Agnes M. Lindsay Trust/NASA Challenge Scholars Initiative at the New Hampshire Community Technical College System, Presidential Scholars Research Assistantships at Dartmouth College, and Women in Science Internships at Dartmouth.

2425 ■ NEW JERSEY UTILITIES ASSOCIATION

50 West State Street, Suite 1117
Trenton, NJ 08608
Tel: (609)392-1000
Fax: (609)396-4231
Web Site: http://www.njua.org
To provide financial assistance to minority, female, and disabled high school seniors in New Jersey interested in majoring in selected subjects in college.
Title of Award: New Jersey Utilities Association Scholarships **Area, Field, or Subject:** Accounting; Biological and clinical sciences; Business administration; Chemistry; Engineering; Environmental conservation; Environmental science **Level of Education for which Award is Granted:** Undergraduate **Number Awarded:** 2 each year. **Funds Available:** The stipend is $1,500 per year. **Duration:** 4 years.
Eligibility Requirements: Eligible to apply for this scholarship are women, minorities (Black, Hispanic, American Indian/Alaska Native, or Asian American/Pacific Islander), and persons with disabilities who are high school seniors in New Jersey. They must be able to demonstrate financial need, be planning to enroll on a full-time basis at an institute of higher education, and be planning to work on a bachelor's degree in engineering, environmental science, chemistry, biology, business administration, or accounting. Children of employees of any New Jersey Utilities Association-member company are ineligible. Selection is based on overall academic excellence and demonstrated financial need. **Deadline for Receipt:** March of each year.

2426 ■ OAK RIDGE INSTITUTE FOR SCIENCE AND EDUCATION

Attn: Global Change Education Program
120 Badger Avenue, M.S. 36
P.O. Box 117
Oak Ridge, TN 37831-0117
Tel: (865)576-9655
E-mail: mary.kinney@orau.gov
Web Site: http://www.atmos.anl.gov/GCEP
To provide undergraduate students with an opportunity to conduct research during the summer on global change.
Title of Award: Global Change Summer Undergraduate Research Experience (SURE) **Area, Field, or Subject:** Atmospheric science; Earth sciences; Environmental conservation; Environmental science; Geosciences **Level of Education for which Award is Granted:** Undergraduate **Number Awarded:** 20 to 30 each year. **Funds Available:** Participants receive a weekly stipend of $475 and support for travel and housing. **Duration:** 10 to 12 weeks during the summer. Successful participants are expected to reapply for a second year of research with their mentors.
Eligibility Requirements: This program is open to undergraduates in their sophomore and junior years, although outstanding freshman and senior applicants are also considered. Applicants must be proposing to

conduct research in a program area within the Department of Energy's Office of Biological and Environmental Research (DOE-BER): the atmospheric science program, the environmental meteorology program, the atmospheric radiation measurement program, the terrestrial carbon processes effort, the program for ecosystem research, and studies carried out under the direction of the National Institute for Global Environmental Change. Minority and female students are particularly encouraged to apply. U.S. citizenship is required. **Deadline for Receipt:** February of each year. **Additional Information:** This program, funded by DOE-BER, began in summer 1999. The first 2 weeks are spent in an orientation and focus session at a participating university. For the remaining 10 weeks, students conduct mentored research at 1 of the national laboratories or universities conducting BER-supported global change research.

2427 ■ OAK RIDGE INSTITUTE FOR SCIENCE AND EDUCATION

Attn: Science and Engineering Education
P.O. Box 117
Oak Ridge, TN 37831-0117
Tel: (865)576-9279
Fax: (865)241-5220
E-mail: coxre@orau.gov
Web Site: http://www.orau.gov/orise.htm

To provide financial assistance and research experience to undergraduate students at minority serving institutions who are majoring in scientific fields of interest to the National Oceanic and Atmospheric Administration (NOAA).

Title of Award: National Oceanic and Atmospheric Administration Educational Partnership Program with Minority Serving Institutions Undergraduate Scholarships **Area, Field, or Subject:** Atmospheric science; Biological and clinical sciences; Cartography/Surveying; Chemistry; Computer and information sciences; Engineering; Environmental conservation; Environmental science; Geography; Mathematics and mathematical sciences; Meteorology; Photogrammetry; Physical sciences; Physics **Level of Education for which Award is Granted:** Four Year College **Number Awarded:** 10 each year. **Funds Available:** This program provides payment of tuition and fees (to a maximum of $4,000 per year) and a stipend during the internship of $650 per week. **Duration:** 1 academic year and 2 summers.

Eligibility Requirements: This program is open to juniors and seniors at minority serving institutions, including Hispanic Serving Institutions (HSIs), Historically Black Colleges and Universities (HBCUs), and Tribal Colleges and Universities (TCUs). Applicants must be majoring in atmospheric science, biology, cartography, chemistry, computer science, engineering, environmental science, geodesy, geography, marine science, mathematics, meteorology, photogrammetry, physical science, physics, or remote sensing. They must also be interested in participating in a research internship at a NOAA site. U.S. citizenship is required. **Deadline for Receipt:** January of each year. **Additional Information:** This program is funded by NOAA through an interagency agreement with the U.S. Department of Energy and administered by Oak Ridge Institute for Science and Education (ORISE).

2428 ■ OHIO SPACE GRANT CONSORTIUM

c/o Ohio Aerospace Institute
22800 Cedar Point Road
Cleveland, OH 44142
Tel: (440)962-3032
Free: 800-828-OSGC
Fax: (440)962-3057
E-mail: osgc@oai.org
Web Site: http://www.osgc.org/Scholarship.html

To provide financial assistance to students in their junior year at selected universities in Ohio who wish to working on a bachelor's degree in an aerospace-related field.

Title of Award: Ohio Space Grant Consortium Junior Scholarships **Area, Field, or Subject:** Astronomy and astronomical sciences; Biological and clinical sciences; Chemistry; Computer and information sciences; Engineering, Aerospace/Aeronautical/Astronautical; Engineering, Chemical; Engineering, Civil; Engineering, Computer; Engineering, Electrical; Engineering, Industrial; Engineering, Materials; Engineering, Mechanical; Engineering, Petroleum; Geography; Geology; Materials research/science; Mathematics and mathematical sciences; Physics; Space and planetary sciences **Level of Education for which Award is Granted:**

Four Year College **Number Awarded:** Varies each year; recently, 20 of these scholarships were awarded. **Funds Available:** The stipend is $2,000. **Duration:** 1 year; recipients may apply for a senior scholarship if they maintain satisfactory academic performance and good progress on their research project.

Eligibility Requirements: These scholarships are available to U.S. citizens who expect to complete within 2 years the requirements for a bachelor of science degree in an aerospace-related discipline (aeronautical engineering, aerospace engineering, astronomy, biology, chemical engineering, chemistry, civil engineering, computer engineering and science, control engineering, electrical engineering, engineering mechanics, geography, geology, industrial engineering, manufacturing engineering, materials science and engineering, mathematics, mechanical engineering, petroleum engineering, physics, and systems engineering). Applicants must be attending a member university of the Ohio Space Grant Consortium (OSGC) or another participating university. They must propose and initiate a research project on campus under the guidance of a faculty member. Along with their application, they must submit a 1-page personal objective statement that discusses their career goals and anticipated benefits to be derived from this program. Women, underrepresented minorities, and persons with disabilities are particularly encouraged to apply. **Deadline for Receipt:** February of each year. **Additional Information:** These scholarships are funded through the National Space Grant College and Fellowship Program administered by the National Aeronautics and Space Administration (NASA), with matching funds provided by the member universities, the Ohio Aerospace Institute, and private industry. The OSGC member universities include the University of Akron, Case Western Reserve University, Central State University, University of Cincinnati, Cleveland State University, University of Dayton, Ohio State University, Ohio University, University of Toledo, Wilberforce University, and Wright State University. Other participating universities are Cedarville University, Marietta College (petroleum engineering), Miami University (manufacturing engineering), Ohio Northern University (mechanical engineering), and Youngstown State University (mechanical and industrial engineering). Recipients are required to attend the annual spring research symposium sponsored by the OSGC and present a poster on their research project.

2429 ■ PENNSYLVANIA SPACE GRANT CONSORTIUM

c/o Pennsylvania State University
2217 Earth-Engineering Sciences Building
University Park, PA 16802
Tel: (814)863-7687
Fax: (814)863-8286
E-mail: spacegrant@psu.edu
Web Site: http://www.psu.edu/spacegrant/highered/scholar.html

To provide financial assistance for space-related study to undergraduate students at universities affiliated with the Pennsylvania Space Grant Consortium.

Title of Award: Pennsylvania Space Grant Consortium Scholarships **Area, Field, or Subject:** Aerospace sciences; Biological and clinical sciences; Earth sciences; Engineering, Aerospace/Aeronautical/Astronautical; Geosciences; Physical sciences; Space and planetary sciences **Level of Education for which Award is Granted:** Undergraduate **Number Awarded:** Varies each year. **Funds Available:** The stipend is set by each participating university. At Pennsylvania State University, for instance, it is $4,000 per year. **Duration:** 1 year.

Eligibility Requirements: This program is open to full-time undergraduate students at participating universities. Applicants must be studying a field that does, or can, promote a strategic enterprise of the U.S. National Aeronautics and Space Administration (NASA): aerospace technology, earth science, human exploration and development of space, biological and physical research, or space science. U.S. citizenship is required. Students from underrepresented groups (women, minorities, rural populations, and those with disabilities) are especially encouraged to apply. **Deadline for Receipt:** Each participating university sets its own deadline. **Additional Information:** Participating institutions include California University of Pennsylvania, Carnegie Mellon University, Clarion University, Lincoln University, Pennsylvania State University, University of Pittsburgh, Susquehanna University, Lincoln University, Temple University, West Chester University, and Pennsylvania State University at Abington. At Pennsylvania State University, the award is designated as the Sylvia Stein Memorial Space Grant Scholarship. This program is sponsored by the

U.S. National Aeronautics and Space Administration (NASA).

2430 ■ ROCKY MOUNTAIN WATER ENVIRONMENT ASSOCIATION
c/o Ray Kemp
City of Fort Collins Water Reclamation
3036 Environmental Drive
Fort Collins, CO 80525
Tel: (970)221-6900
Fax: (970)221-6970
E-mail: rkemp@fcgov.com
Web Site: http://www.rmwea.org

To provide financial assistance to students in Colorado, New Mexico, and Wyoming, including members of the Rocky Mountain Water Environment Association (RMWEA) and their dependents, who are interested in studying a water environment field in college.

Title of Award: Bill Martin Memorial Scholarship **Area, Field, or Subject:** Biological and clinical sciences; Environmental conservation; Environmental science; Water resources **Level of Education for which Award is Granted:** Undergraduate **Number Awarded:** 2 each year: 1 from each category of applicant. **Funds Available:** The stipend is $1,000. Recipients are also entitled to a 1-year complimentary student or associate membership in the RMWEA. **Duration:** 1 year.
Eligibility Requirements: This program is open to 1) members of the RMWEA and their dependents who are enrolled at a 2- or 4-year college or university and working on a degree related to the water environment profession (e.g., biology, environmental science, engineering with a strong emphasis in wastewater treatment, water pollution control, environmental protection); and 2) high school seniors planning to enroll at a 2- or 4-year college or university to prepare for a career in the water environmental field. Along with their application, they must submit an essay of 200 to 300 words on their interest in the environment and how this interest influences their career goals. Selection is based on that essay (25%), relevance of the course of study to the water environment profession (35%), letters of recommendation (20%), and GPA (20%). **Deadline for Receipt:** April of each year. **Additional Information:** This program was established in 2002.

2431 ■ SEALASKA CORPORATION
Attn: Sealaska Heritage Institute
One Sealaska Plaza, Suite 301
Juneau, AK 99801-1249
Tel: (907)586-9166; 888-311-4992
Fax: (907)586-9293
E-mail: scholarship@sealaska.com
Web Site: http://www.sealaskaheritage.org/programs/
university_scholarships.htm

To provide financial assistance for undergraduate or graduate study to Native Alaskans who have a connection to Sealaska Corporation and are majoring in designated fields.

Title of Award: Sealaska Heritage Institute 7(i) Scholarships **Area, Field, or Subject:** Business administration; Chemistry; Engineering, Chemical; Health care services; Mathematics and mathematical sciences; Natural resources; Physics **Level of Education for which Award is Granted:** Graduate, Undergraduate **Number Awarded:** Varies each year. **Funds Available:** The amount of the award depends on the availability of funds, the number of qualified applicants, class standing, and cumulative GPA. **Duration:** 1 year; may be renewed up to 5 years for a bachelor's degree, up to 3 years for a master's degree, up to 2 years for a doctorate, or up to 3 years for vocational study. The maximum total support is limited to 9 years. Renewal depends on recipients' maintaining full-time enrollment and a GPA of 2.5 or higher.
Eligibility Requirements: This program is open to 1) Alaska Natives who are enrolled to Sealaska Corporation, and 2) Native lineal descendants of Alaska Natives enrolled to Sealaska Corporation, whether or not the applicant owns Sealaska Corporation stock. Applicants must be enrolled or accepted for enrollment as full-time undergraduate or graduate students. Along with their application, they must submit 2 essays: 1) their personal history and educational goals, and 2) their expected contributions to the Alaska Native or Native American community. Financial need is also considered in the selection process. The following areas of study qualify for these awards: natural resources (environmental sciences, engineering, conservation biology, environmental law, fisheries, geology, marine science/biology, forestry, wildlife management, and mining technology);

business administration (accounting, finance, marketing, international business, international commerce and trade, management of information systems, human resources management, economics, computer information systems, and industrial management); and other special fields (cadastral surveys, chemistry, equipment/machinery operators, industrial safety specialists, health specialists, plastics engineers, trade specialists, physics, mathematics, and marine trades and occupations). **Deadline for Receipt:** February of each year. **Additional Information:** Funding for this program is provided from Alaska Native Claims Settlement Act (ANSCA) Section 7(i) revenue sharing provisions. Sealaska sponsors a number of other scholarships, including the Cape Fox Scholarships and the Sealaska Heritage Institute Scholarships.

2432 ■ SIEMENS FOUNDATION
170 Wood Avenue South
Iselin, NJ 08830
877-822-5233
Fax: (732)603-5890
E-mail: foundation@sc.siemens.com
Web Site: http://www.siemens-foundation.org/awards

To recognize and reward high school students with exceptional scores on the Advanced Placement (AP) examinations in mathematics and the sciences.

Title of Award: Siemens Awards for Advanced Placement **Area, Field, or Subject:** Biological and clinical sciences; Chemistry; Computer and information sciences; Environmental conservation; Environmental science; Mathematics and mathematical sciences; Physics; Statistics **Level of Education for which Award is Granted:** Professional, Undergraduate **Number Awarded:** 24 regional scholarships (2 females and 2 males in each of the 6 regions), 2 national scholarships (1 female and 1 male), 12 high school awards (in each region, 1 to a school for improvement in the number and percentage of students taking AP examinations, 1 to an urban school for providing access to AP mathematics and science to minorities), and 18 teacher awards (in each region, 2 for commitment to students and the AP program, 1 for teaching minorities) are awarded each year. **Funds Available:** Regional scholarships are $3,000; national winners receive additional $5,000 scholarships. Awards to teachers and to schools are $1,000. **Duration:** The awards are presented annually.
Eligibility Requirements: All students in U.S. high schools are eligible to be considered for these awards (including home-schooled students and those in U.S. territories). Each fall, the College Board identifies the male and female seniors in each of its regions who have earned the highest number of scores on 7 AP exams: biology, calculus BC, chemistry, computer science AB, environmental science, physics C (physics C: mechanics and physics C: electricity each count as half), and statistics. Males and females are considered separately. Regional winners receive all-expense paid trips to Washington, D.C., where national winners are announced. The program also recognizes and rewards monetarily 1) schools that have shown the greatest improvement in the number and percentage of students taking AP examinations in biology, calculus, chemistry, computer science, environmental science, physics, and statistics in the past year; and 2) non-magnet urban schools that provide access to AP mathematics and science to a significant number of underrepresented minority students. In addition, teachers are rewarded for their commitment to students and the AP program. Additional teachers are recognized because they have successfully taught AP mathematics and/or science to underrepresented minority students in non-magnet urban schools. **Deadline for Receipt:** There is no application or nomination process for these awards. The College Board identifies the students, teachers, and high schools for the Siemens Foundation. **Additional Information:** Information from the College Board is available at (703) 707-8999.

2433 ■ SIEMENS FOUNDATION
170 Wood Avenue South
Iselin, NJ 08830
877-822-5233
Fax: (732)603-5890
E-mail: foundation@sc.siemens.com
Web Site: http://www.siemens-foundation.org/scholarship

To recognize and reward outstanding high school seniors who have undertaken individual or team research projects in science, mathematics, and technology (or in combinations of those disciplines).

Title of Award: Siemens Westinghouse Competition Awards **Area, Field, or Subject:** Astronomy and astronomical sciences; Atmospheric science; Biochemistry; Biological and clinical sciences; Chemistry; Computer and information sciences; Earth sciences; Engineering, Civil; Engineering, Electrical; Engineering, Mechanical; Environmental science; Genetics; Geosciences; Materials research/science; Mathematics and mathematical sciences; Nutrition; Physics; Writing **Level of Education for which Award is Granted:** Undergraduate **Number Awarded:** In the initial round of judging, up to 300 regional semifinalists (up to 50 in each region) are selected. Of those, 60 are chosen as regional finalists (5 individuals and 5 teams in each of the 6 regions). Then 12 regional winners (1 individual and 1 team) are selected in the regional competitions, and they become the national finalists. **Funds Available:** At the regional level, finalists receive $1,000 scholarships, both as individuals and members of teams. Individual regional winners receive $3,000 scholarships. Winning regional teams receive $6,000 scholarships to be divided among the team members. Those regional winners then receive additional scholarships as national finalists. In the national competition, first-place winners receive an additional $100,000 scholarship, second place an additional $50,000 scholarship, third place an additional $40,000 scholarship, fourth place an additional $30,000 scholarship, fifth place an additional $20,000 scholarship, and sixth place an additional $10,000 scholarship. Those national awards are provided both to individuals and to teams to be divided equally among team members. Scholarship money is sent directly to the recipient's college or university to cover undergraduate and/or graduate educational expenses. Schools with regional finalists receive a $2,000 award to be used to support science, mathematics, and technology programs in their schools. **Duration:** The competition is held annually. **Eligibility Requirements:** This program is open to high school seniors who are legal or permanent U.S. residents. They must be enrolled in a high school in the United States, Puerto Rico, Guam, Virgin Islands, American Samoa, Wake and Midway Islands, or the Marianas. U.S. high school students enrolled in a Department of Defense dependents school, an accredited overseas American or international school, a foreign school as an exchange student, or a foreign school because their parent(s) live and work abroad are also eligible. Students being home-schooled qualify if they obtain the endorsement of the school district official responsible for such programs. Research projects may be submitted in mathematics and the biological and physical sciences, or involve combinations of disciplines, such as astrophysics, biochemistry, bioengineering, biology, biophysics, botany, chemistry, computer science, civil engineering, earth and atmospheric science engineering, electrical engineering, environmental sciences, fluid dynamics, genetics, geology, materials science, mathematics, mechanical engineering, nutritional science, physics, toxicology, and virology. Both individual and team projects (2 or 3 members) may be entered. All team members must meet the eligibility requirements. Team projects may include seniors, but that is not a requirement. Competition entrants must submit a detailed report on their research project, including a description of the purpose of the research, rationale for the research, pertinent scientific literature, methodology, results, discussion, and conclusion. All projects must be endorsed by a sponsoring high school (except home-schooled students, who obtain their endorsement from the district or state home-school official). Each project must have a project advisor or mentor who is a member of the instructional staff or a person approved by the endorsing high school. There are 3 judging phases to the competition. An initial review panel selects outstanding research projects from 6 different regions of the country. The students submitting these projects are identified as regional semifinalists. Out of those, the highest-rated projects from each region are selected and the students who submitted them are recognized as regional finalists. For the next phase, the regional finalists are offered all-expense paid trips to the regional competition on the campus of a regional university partner, where their projects are reviewed by a panel of judges appointed by the host institution. Regional finalists are required to prepare a poster display of their research project, make an oral presentation about the research and research findings, and respond to questions from the judges. The top-rated individual and the top-rated team project in each region are selected as regional winners to represent the region in the national competition as national finalists. At that competition, the national finalists again display their projects, make oral presentations, and respond to judges' questions. At each phase, selection is based on clarity of expression, comprehensiveness, creativity, field knowledge, future work,

interpretation, literature review, presentation, scientific importance, and validity. **Deadline for Receipt:** September of each year. **Additional Information:** The program is offered by Siemens Foundation, in partnership with the College Board. Information is available from the College Board at (703) 707-8999, E-mail: spro@collegeboard.org. Students submitting the projects with the highest evaluations become part of a registry that is circulated to colleges and universities nationwide. To continue receiving scholarships, winners must attend an accredited academic institution on a full-time basis.

2434 ■ SOCIETY OF AMERICAN MILITARY ENGINEERS-ANCHORAGE POST
P.O. Box 6149
Elmendorf AFB, AK 99506-6149
E-mail: william_kontess@urscorp.com
Web Site: http://www.sameanchorage.org/h_about/scholinfo.html
To provide financial assistance to upper-division students from Alaska who are majoring in engineering or the natural sciences.
Title of Award: BG Benjamin B. Talley Scholarship **Area, Field, or Subject:** Engineering; Natural sciences **Level of Education for which Award is Granted:** Four Year College **Number Awarded:** Varies; recently, 6 were awarded. **Funds Available:** Varies; generally, stipends are $3,000, $2,000, or $1,000. **Duration:** 1 year.
Eligibility Requirements: Eligible to apply for this funding are juniors and seniors who are majoring in engineering or the natural sciences. Applicants must be U.S. citizens and either Alaska residents or attending school in Alaska. They must be 1) a member of the sponsoring organization, 2) the dependent of a member, 3) a member of the armed forces on active duty in Alaska, or 4) a dependent of a member of the armed forces on active duty in Alaska. Their GPA must be 2.5 or higher. Selection is based on academic achievement, participation in school and community activities, an essay on career goals (100 to 250 words), and work/family activities. Financial need is not considered in the selection process. **Deadline for Receipt:** November of each year. **Additional Information:** This program was established in 1997. Information is also available from Bruce Steely, Dihthaad Global Services, 10223 Stewart Drive, Eagle River, AK 99507, (907) 223-6339, Fax: (907) 694-3241, E-mail: Dihthaad_2@hotmail.com.

2435 ■ SOCIETY FOR INTEGRATIVE AND COMPARATIVE BIOLOGY
1313 Dolley Madison Boulevard, Suite 402
McLean, VA 22101
Tel: (703)790-1745
Free: 800-955-1236
Fax: (703)790-2672
E-mail: sicb@BurkInc.com
Web Site: http://sicb.org/grants/hyman
To provide financial assistance to students interested in taking courses or conducting research at a biological field station anywhere in the world.
Title of Award: Libbie N. Hyman Memorial Scholarship **Area, Field, or Subject:** Biological and clinical sciences **Level of Education for which Award is Granted:** Four Year College, Graduate **Number Awarded:** 1 each year. **Funds Available:** The stipend is $1,000.
Eligibility Requirements: This program is open to advanced undergraduates and first- and second-year graduate students. Applicants must be interested in taking courses or conducting research on invertebrates at a marine, freshwater, or terrestrial field station anywhere in the world. **Deadline for Receipt:** March of each year. **Additional Information:** Information is also available from Isidro Bosch, SUNY Geneseo, Department of Biology, Geneseo, NY 14454, (585) 245-5303, Fax: (585) 245-5007, E-mail: bosch@geneseo.edu.

2436 ■ SOIL AND WATER CONSERVATION SOCIETY
Attn: Scholarships
945 S.W. Ankeny Road
Ankeny, IA 50021-9764
Tel: (515)289-2331
Free: 800-THE
Fax: (515)289-1227
E-mail: swcs@swcs.org
Web Site: http://www.swcs.org/en/scholarships
To provide financial assistance to members of the Soil and Water Conservation Society (SWCS) who are currently employed and wish to improve their technical or administrative competence.

Title of Award: Donald A. Williams Soil Conservation Scholarships **Area, Field, or Subject:** Environmental conservation; Environmental science; Soil science; Water resources **Level of Education for which Award is Granted:** Undergraduate **Number Awarded:** 1 each year. **Funds Available:** The stipend is $1,500. **Duration:** 1 year.

Eligibility Requirements: This program is open to undergraduate members of the society who have completed at least 1 year of full-time employment in a natural resource conservation job with a federal, state, or local government agency, organization, or business firm. Applicants must be currently employed and able to show reasonable financial need. Selection is based on demonstrated integrity, ability, competence in work, and skills gained through training or experience. **Deadline for Receipt:** February of each year. **Additional Information:** Recipients are not required to work on a degree.

2437 ■ SOUTH CAROLINA SPACE GRANT CONSORTIUM

c/o College of Charleston
Department of Geology and Environmental Sciences
66 George Street
Charleston, SC 29424
Tel: (843)953-5463
Fax: (843)953-5446
E-mail: scozzarot@cofc.edu
Web Site: http://www.cofc.edu/~scsgrant/scholar/overview.html
To provide financial assistance to outstanding science students in South Carolina.

Title of Award: Kathryn D. Sullivan Science and Engineering Fellowship **Area, Field, or Subject:** Engineering; Natural sciences **Level of Education for which Award is Granted:** Four Year College **Number Awarded:** 1 each year. **Funds Available:** The stipend is $7,000 per year. **Duration:** 1 year.

Eligibility Requirements: This program is open to students entering their senior year at a college or university in South Carolina or at the University of the Virgin Islands. Applicants must be studying natural science or engineering. Selection is based on academic qualifications of the applicant; 2 letters of recommendation; a description of past activities, current interests, and future plans concerning natural science-related and engineering-related studies; and faculty sponsorship. U.S. citizenship is required. **Deadline for Receipt:** January of each year. **Additional Information:** This program is funded by the National Aeronautics and Space Administration (NASA) through its Space Grant program and the National Oceanic and Atmospheric Administration (NOAA) through its Sea Grant program.

2438 ■ SOUTH DAKOTA SPACE GRANT CONSORTIUM

Attn: Deputy Director and Outreach Coordinator
South Dakota School of Mines and Technology
Mineral Industries Building, Room 228
501 East St. Joseph Street
Rapid City, SD 57701-3995
Tel: (605)394-1975
Fax: (605)394-5360
E-mail: Thomas.Durkin@sdsmt.edu
Web Site: http://www.sdsmt.edu/space
To provide funding to undergraduate and graduate students for space-related activities in South Dakota.

Title of Award: South Dakota Space Grant Consortium Graduate Fellowships and Undergraduate Scholarships **Area, Field, or Subject:** Aerospace sciences; Earth sciences; Engineering, Aerospace/Aeronautical/Astronautical; Environmental conservation; Environmental science; Geology; Geosciences; Mathematics and mathematical sciences; Space and planetary sciences; Technology **Level of Education for which Award is Granted:** Graduate, Undergraduate **Number Awarded:** Varies each year. Approximately $70,000 is available for this program annually. **Funds Available:** Stipends range from $1,000 to $7,500. **Duration:** 1 academic year, semester, or summer.

Eligibility Requirements: This program is open to undergraduate and graduate students at member and affiliated institutions of the South Dakota Space Grant Consortium. Applicants must be interested in 1) earth- and space-science related educational and research projects in fields relevant to the goals of the U.S. National Aeronautics and Space Administration (NASA); or 2) eventual employment with NASA or in a NASA-related career field in science, technology, engineering, and

mathematics (STEM) education. Activities may include student research and educational efforts in remote sensing, GIS, global and regional geoscience, environmental science, and K-12 educational outreach; exposure to NASA-relevant projects; and internship experiences at various NASA centers and the Earth Resources Observation and Science (EROS) Center in Sioux Falls. U.S. citizenship is required. Women, members of underrepresented groups (African Americans, Hispanics, Pacific Islanders, Asian Americans, Native Americans, and persons with disabilities), and Tribal College students are specifically encouraged to apply. Selection is based on academic qualifications of the application (preference is given to students with a GPA of 3.0 or higher), quality of the application and its career goal statement, and assessment of the applicant's motivation toward an earth science, aerospace, or engineering career or research. **Deadline for Receipt:** January of each year. **Additional Information:** Member institutions include South Dakota School of Mines and Technology, South Dakota State University, and Augustana College. Educational affiliates include Black Hills State University, the University of South Dakota, Dakota State University, Lower Brule Community College, Oglala Lakota College, Sinte Gleska University, and Lake Area Technical Institute.

2439 ■ SURFRIDER FOUNDATION

Attn: Pratte Scholarship
P.O. Box 6010
San Clemente, CA 92674-6010
Tel: (949)492-8170
Fax: (949)492-8142
E-mail: prattescholarship@surfrider.org
Web Site: http://www.surfrider.org
To provide financial assistance to members of the Surfrider Foundation working on an undergraduate or graduate degree in an environmental field.

Title of Award: Thomas Pratte Memorial Scholarships **Area, Field, or Subject:** Environmental conservation; Environmental science; Marine biology; Natural resources; Oceanography; Public administration; Urban affairs/design/planning **Level of Education for which Award is Granted:** Four Year College, Graduate **Number Awarded:** 3 each year: 1 for a student at each academic level. **Funds Available:** The stipend is $2,000 for an undergraduate, $3,000 for a master's degree student, and $5,000 for a doctoral student. **Duration:** 1 year.

Eligibility Requirements: This program is open to members of the foundation working on an undergraduate, master's, or doctoral degree in a field consistent with the foundation's mission, including (but not limited to) oceanography, marine affairs, environmental sciences, public policy, community planning, or natural resources. Applicants must be enrolled at an accredited college or university in the United States or Puerto Rico as an upper-division or graduate student. Undergraduates must have a GPA of 3.4 or higher and graduate students 3.6 or higher. Along with their application, they must submit 1) a personal statement describing their career goals, volunteer activities, work, or summer plans as they pertain to the coastal environmental issues relevant to the foundation and its mission; and 2) a description of their current research and how it relates to the foundation's stated mission and environmental programs. Financial need is not considered in the selection process. **Deadline for Receipt:** March of each year. **Additional Information:** This foundation, established in 1984 by a group of surfers, is a nonprofit environmental grassroots organization dedicated to the protection and preservation of the world's waves, oceans, and beaches. It currently has 50,000 members with 60 chapters in 22 states.

2440 ■ TEXAS SPACE GRANT CONSORTIUM

Attn: Administrative Assistant
3925 West Braker Lane, Suite 200
Austin, TX 78759
Tel: (512)471-3583
Free: 800-248-8742
Fax: (512)471-3585
E-mail: scholarships@tsgc.utexas.edu
Web Site: http://www.tsgc.utexas.edu/grants
To provide financial assistance to upper-division and medical students at Texas universities working on degrees in the fields of space science and engineering.

Title of Award: Columbia Crew Memorial Undergraduate Scholarships **Area, Field, or Subject:** Aerospace sciences; Biological and clinical sciences; Chemistry; Engineering, Aerospace/Aeronautical/Astronautical; Engineering, Chemical; Engineering, Electrical; Engineering, Industrial; Engineering, Mechanical; Geology; Mathematics and mathematical sciences; Physics; Space and planetary sciences **Level of Education for which Award is Granted:** Doctorate, Undergraduate **Number Awarded:** Varies each year; recently, 29 of these scholarships were awarded. **Funds Available:** The stipend is $1,000. **Duration:** 1 year; nonrenewable.

Eligibility Requirements: Applicants must be U.S. citizens, eligible for financial assistance, and registered for full-time study at a participating college or university. Applicants must be a sophomore at a 2-year institution, a junior or senior at a 4-year institution, or a first- or second-year student at a medical school. Supported fields of study have included aerospace engineering, biology, chemical engineering, chemistry, electrical engineering, geology, industrial engineering, mathematics, mechanical engineering, and physics. The program encourages participation by members of groups underrepresented in science and engineering (persons with disabilities, women, African Americans, Hispanic Americans, Native Americans, and Pacific Islanders). Selection is based on excellence in academics, participation in space education projects, participation in research projects, and exhibited leadership qualities. **Deadline for Receipt:** March of each year. **Additional Information:** In 2003, the Texas Space Grant Consortium renamed its undergraduate scholarship program in honor of the 7 Space Shuttle Columbia astronauts. The participating universities are Baylor University, Lamar University, Prairie View A&M University, Rice University, San Jacinto College, Southern Methodist University, Sul Ross State University, Texas A&M University (including Kingsville and Corpus Christi campuses), Texas Christian University, Texas Southern University, Texas Tech University, Trinity University, University of Houston (including Clear Lake and Downtown campuses), University of Texas at Arlington, University of Texas at Austin, University of Texas at Dallas, University of Texas at El Paso, University of Texas at San Antonio, and University of Texas/Pan American. This program is funded by the National Aeronautics and Space Administration (NASA).

2441 ■ MORRIS K. UDALL FOUNDATION

130 South Scott Avenue
Tucson, AZ 85701-1922
Tel: (520)670-5529
Fax: (520)670-5530
Web Site: http://www.udall.gov/scholarship
To provide financial assistance to 1) college sophomores and juniors who intend to prepare for a career in environmental public policy and 2) Native American and Alaska Native students who intend to prepare for a career in health care or tribal public policy.

Title of Award: Morris K. Udall Scholarships **Area, Field, or Subject:** Business administration; Economics; Education; Environmental conservation; Environmental science; Health care services; Native American studies; Natural resources; Political science; Public administration; Public health; Urban affairs/design/planning **Level of Education for which Award is Granted:** Undergraduate **Number Awarded:** Approximately 80 scholarships and 50 honorable mentions are awarded each year. **Funds Available:** The maximum stipend for scholarship winners is $5,000 per year. Funds are to be used for tuition, fees, books, and room and board. Honorable mention stipends are $350. **Duration:** 1 year; recipients nominated as sophomores may be renominated in their junior year.

Eligibility Requirements: Each 2-year and 4-year college and university in the United States and its possessions may nominate up to 6 sophomores or juniors from either or both categories of this program: 1) students who intend to prepare for a career in environmental public policy, and 2) Native American and Alaska Native students who intend to prepare for a career in health care or tribal public policy. For the first category, the program seeks future leaders across a wide spectrum of environmental fields, such as policy, engineering, science, education, urban planning and renewal, business, health, justice, and economics. For the second category, the program seeks future Native American and Alaska Native leaders in public and community health care, tribal government, and public policy affecting Native American communities, including land and resource management, economic development, and education. Nominees must be U.S. citizens, nationals, or permanent residents with a GPA of 3.0 or higher. Along with their application, they must submit an 800-word essay discussing a significant public speech, legislative act, or public policy statement by former Congressman Morris K. Udall and its impact on their

field of study, interests, and career goals. Selection is based on demonstrated commitment to 1) environmental issues through substantial commitment to and participation in 1 or more of the following: campus activities, research, community service, or public service; or 2) tribal public policy or Native American health through substantial contributions to and participation in 1 or more of the following: campus activities, tribal involvement, community or public service, or research; a course of study and proposed career likely to lead to position where nominee can make significant contributions to the shaping of environmental, tribal public policy, or Native American health care issues, whether through scientific advances, public or political service, or community action; and leadership, character, desire to make a difference, and general well-roundedness. **Deadline for Receipt:** Faculty representatives must submit their nominations by early March of each year.

2442 ■ U.S. NAVY

Attn: Naval Medical Education
Code OG3
8901 Wisconsin Avenue, 16th Floor, Tower 1
Bethesda, MD 20889-5611
Tel: (301)319-4520
E-mail: mscipp@nmetc.med.navy.mil
Web Site: http://nshs.med.navy.mil/mscipp/mscipp.htm
To provide funding to Navy and Marine enlisted personnel who wish to earn an undergraduate or graduate degree in selected health care specialties while continuing to receive their regular pay and allowances.

Title of Award: Medical Service Corps Inservice Procurement Program (MSC-IPP) **Area, Field, or Subject:** Entomology; Environmental conservation; Environmental science; Health care services; Industrial hygiene; Medical assisting; Pharmaceutical sciences **Level of Education for which Award is Granted:** Four Year College, Graduate **Number Awarded:** Varies each year. Recently, 36 of these positions were available: 20 in health care administration, 10 in physician assistant, 2 in pharmacy, 2 in environmental health, 1 in industrial hygiene, and 1 in entomology. **Funds Available:** Participants receive payment of tuition, mandatory fees, a book allowance, and full pay and allowances for their enlisted pay grade. They are eligible for advancement while in college. **Duration:** 24 to 48 months of full-time, year-round study, until completion of a relevant degree.

Eligibility Requirements: This program is open to enlisted personnel who are serving on active duty in pay grades E-5 through E-9 of the U.S. Navy, U.S. Marine Corps, Naval Reserve (including the Training and Administration of the Reserve Program), and the Marine Corps Reserve (including the Active Reserve Program). Applicants must be interested in working on a degree to become commissioned in the following medical specialties: health care administration, physician assistant, pharmacy, environmental health, industrial hygiene, or entomology. If they plan to work on a graduate degree, they must have scores of at least 900 on the GRE or 470 on the GMAT; if they plan to work on a bachelor's or physician assistant degree, they must have scores of at least 1000 on the SAT (including 460 on the mathematics portion) or 42 on the ACT. They must be U.S. citizens who can be commissioned before they reach their 42nd birthday. **Deadline for Receipt:** August of each year. **Additional Information:** Following graduation, participants are commissioned in the Medical Service Corps and attend Officer Indoctrination School.

2443 ■ VIRGINIA SPACE GRANT CONSORTIUM

Attn: Fellowship Coordinator
Old Dominion University Peninsula Center
600 Butler Farm Road
Hampton, VA 23666
Tel: (757)766-5210
Fax: (757)766-5205
E-mail: vsgc@odu.edu
Web Site: http://www.vsgc.odu.edu/Menu3_1_1.htm
To provide financial assistance for college or graduate school to students in Virginia planning a career as science, mathematics, or technology educators.

Title of Award: Virginia Space Grant Teacher Education Scholarship Program **Area, Field, or Subject:** Aerospace sciences; Earth sciences; Education; Environmental conservation; Environmental science; Geosciences; Mathematics and mathematical sciences; Science; Space and planetary sciences; Technology **Level of Education for which**

Award is Granted: Four Year College, Master's **Number Awarded:** Approximately 10 each year. **Funds Available:** The maximum stipend is $1,000. **Duration:** 1 year; nonrenewable.

Eligibility Requirements: This program is open to full-time undergraduate students at the Virginia Space Grant Consortium (VSGC) colleges and universities in a track that will qualify them to teach in a pre-college setting. Priority is given to those majoring in technology education, mathematics, or science, particularly earth, space, or environmental science. Applicants may apply while seniors in high school or sophomores in a community college, with the award contingent on their enrollment at a VSGC college and entrance into a teacher certification program. They must submit a statement of academic goals and plan of study, explaining their reasons for desiring to enter the teaching profession, specifically the fields of science, mathematics, or technology education. Students currently enrolled in a VSGC college can apply when they declare their intent to enter the teacher certification program. Students enrolled in a master of education degree program leading to teacher certification in eligible fields are also eligible to apply. Applicants must be U.S. citizens with a GPA of 3.0 or higher. Since an important purpose of this program is to increase the participation of underrepresented minorities, women, and persons with disabilities in science, mathematics, and technology education, the VSGC especially encourages applications from those students. **Deadline for Receipt:** February of each year. **Additional Information:** The VSGC institutions are College of William and Mary, Hampton University, Old Dominion University, the University of Virginia, and Virginia Polytechnic Institute and State University. This program is funded by the U.S. National Aeronautics and Space Administration (NASA).

Agriculture

2444 ■ AMERICAN BRAHMAN BREEDERS ASSOCIATION
Attn: Youth Activities Director
3003 South Loop West, Suite 140
Houston, TX 77054
Tel: (713)349-0854
Fax: (713)349-9795
E-mail: abba@brahman.org
Web Site: http://www.brahman.org
To provide financial assistance to members of the American Junior Brahman Association (AJBA) interested in attending college to prepare for an agriculture-oriented career.

Title of Award: Ladies of the ABBA Scholarships **Area, Field, or Subject:** Agricultural sciences **Level of Education for which Award is Granted:** Undergraduate **Number Awarded:** Varies each year; recently, 6 of these scholarships were awarded **Funds Available:** Scholarships range from $500 to $1,000.

Eligibility Requirements: Applicants must be active members of the AJBA, the youth division of the American Brahman Breeders Association (ABBA), who are graduating high school seniors and planning to prepare for an agriculture-oriented career. Applications must be accompanied by a record of 4-H, FFA, and FHA involvement; a record of AJBA involvement; a list of leadership roles and citizenship activities; a summary of other interests and activities (music, athletics, church, work, hobbies, etc.); and a brief essay on why the applicant selected agriculture as a field of study. **Deadline for Receipt:** April of each year.

2445 ■ AMERICAN NURSERY AND LANDSCAPE ASSOCIATION
Attn: Horticultural Research Institute
1000 Vermont Avenue N.W., Suite 300
Washington, DC 20005-4914
Tel: (202)789-2900
Fax: (202)789-1893
E-mail: hriresearch@anla.org
Web Site: http://www.anla.org/research/scholarships/index.htm
To provide financial assistance to students working on an undergraduate or graduate degree in landscape architecture or horticulture.

Title of Award: Spring Meadow Nursery Scholarship **Area, Field, or Subject:** Agricultural sciences; Horticulture; Landscape architecture and design **Level of Education for which Award is Granted:** Graduate, Undergraduate **Number Awarded:** 1 each year. **Funds Available:** The stipend is $2,000. **Duration:** 1 year; may be renewed.

Eligibility Requirements: This program is open to students enrolled full time in a landscape or horticulture undergraduate or graduate program at an accredited 2-year or 4-year college or university. Students enrolled in a vocational agriculture program are also eligible. Applicants must have a minimum GPA of 2.25 overall and 2.7 in their major. Preference is given to applicants who plan to work within the nursery industry, including nursery operations; landscape architecture, design, construction, or maintenance; interiorscape; horticultural distribution; or retail garden center. **Deadline for Receipt:** March of each year. **Additional Information:** This program was established in 1999.

2446 ■ AMERICAN NURSERY AND LANDSCAPE ASSOCIATION
Attn: Horticultural Research Institute
1000 Vermont Avenue N.W., Suite 300
Washington, DC 20005-4914
Tel: (202)789-2900
Fax: (202)789-1893
E-mail: hriresearch@anla.org
Web Site: http://www.anla.org/research/scholarships/index.htm
To provide financial assistance to undergraduate and graduate students working on a degree in landscape architecture or horticulture at colleges and universities in California.

Title of Award: Usrey Family Scholarship **Area, Field, or Subject:** Agricultural sciences; Horticulture; Landscape architecture and design **Level of Education for which Award is Granted:** Graduate, Undergraduate **Number Awarded:** 1 each year. **Funds Available:** The stipend is $2,000. **Duration:** 1 year; may be renewed.

Eligibility Requirements: This program is open to students enrolled full time in a landscape or horticulture undergraduate or graduate program at an accredited 2-year or 4-year college or university in California. Students enrolled in a vocational agriculture program are also eligible. Applicants must have a minimum GPA of 2.25 overall and 2.7 in their major. California state residency is not required. Preference is given to applicants who plan to work within the nursery industry, including nursery operations; landscape architecture, design, construction, or maintenance; interiorscape; horticultural distribution; or retail garden center. **Deadline for Receipt:** March of each year.

2447 ■ AMERICAN SOCIETY OF AGRICULTURAL AND BIOLOGICAL ENGINEERS
Attn: ASABE Foundation
2950 Niles Road
St. Joseph, MI 49085-9659
Tel: (269)429-0300
Fax: (269)429-3852
E-mail: hq@asabe.org
Web Site: http://www.asabe.org/membership/students/grant1.html
To provide financial assistance to undergraduate student members of the American Society of Agricultural and Biological Engineers (ASABE).

Title of Award: William J. and Marijane E. Adams, Jr. Agricultural Engineering Scholarship **Area, Field, or Subject:** Biological and clinical sciences; Engineering, Agricultural **Level of Education for which Award is Granted:** Undergraduate **Number Awarded:** 1 each year. **Funds Available:** The stipend is $1,000. Funds must be used for tuition, fees, books, and on-campus room and board. **Duration:** 1 year.

Eligibility Requirements: This program is open to undergraduate students who have a declared major in biological or agricultural engineering (must be accredited by ABET or CEAB), are student members of the society, are in at least the second year of college, have at least 1 year of undergraduate study remaining, have a GPA of 2.5 or higher, can demonstrate financial need, and have a special interest in agricultural machinery product design and development. Interested applicants should submit a personal letter (up to 2 pages long) stating how the money will be used, outlining their financial need, and describing their interest in the design and development of new agricultural machinery products. **Deadline for Receipt:** March of each year.

2448 ■ AMERICAN SOCIETY OF AGRICULTURAL AND BIOLOGICAL ENGINEERS
Attn: ASABE Foundation
2950 Niles Road
St. Joseph, MI 49085-9659
Tel: (269)429-0300
Fax: (269)429-3852
E-mail: hq@asabe.org

Web Site: http://www.asabe.org/membership/students/foundation.html
To provide financial assistance to undergraduate student members of the American Society of Agricultural Engineers (ASAE).

Title of Award: ASABE Foundation Scholarship **Area, Field, or Subject:** Biological and clinical sciences; Engineering, Agricultural **Level of Education for which Award is Granted:** Undergraduate **Number Awarded:** 1 each year. **Funds Available:** The stipend is $1,000. Funds must be used for tuition, fees, books, and on-campus room and board. **Duration:** 1 year.

Eligibility Requirements: This program is open to undergraduate students who have a declared major in biological or agricultural engineering (must be accredited by ABET or CEAB), are student members of the society, are in at least the second year of college, have at least 1 year of undergraduate student remaining, have a GPA of 2.5 or higher, can demonstrate financial need, and can verify that graduation from their degree program assures eligibility for the Professional Engineer (PE) licensing examination. Interested applicants should submit a personal letter (up to 2 pages long) stating how the money will be used and presenting proof that their degree program assures eligibility for the PE licensing examination. **Deadline for Receipt:** March of each year. **Additional Information:** This scholarship was first awarded in 2002.

2449 ■ AMERICAN SOCIETY OF AGRICULTURAL AND BIOLOGICAL ENGINEERS
Attn: ASABE Foundation
2950 Niles Road
St. Joseph, MI 49085-9659
Tel: (269)429-0300
Fax: (269)429-3852
E-mail: hq@asabe.org
Web Site: http://www.asabe.org/membership/students/engscholar.html
To recognize and reward student members of the American Society of Agricultural Engineers (ASAE) who participate in a competition to select the best student of the year.

Title of Award: ASABE Student Engineer of the Year Scholarship **Area, Field, or Subject:** Biological and clinical sciences; Engineering, Agricultural **Level of Education for which Award is Granted:** Undergraduate **Number Awarded:** 1 each year. **Funds Available:** The award is a $1,000 scholarship. **Duration:** The competition is held annually.

Eligibility Requirements: This program is open to biological and agricultural engineering students at colleges and universities in Canada and the United States. Applicants must have completed at least 1 year of undergraduate study with a GPA of 3.0 or higher, have at least 1 year remaining, and be members of the society. Selection is based on: scholarship, with special consideration given to students who demonstrate improvement in academic work from freshman to sophomore to junior years (20 points); character and personal development, including participation in non-university activities and service to others (10 points); student membership in the society and active participation in a student branch organization (25 points); participation in other school activities (15 points); leadership qualities, creativity, initiative, and responsibility (25 points); and level of financial self-support provided by the student (5 points). In addition, the judges consider the candidate's paper, up to 500 words, on "My Goals in the Engineering Profession." **Deadline for Receipt:** March of each year. **Additional Information:** This scholarship was first awarded in 1997

2450 ■ AMERICAN SOCIETY OF AGRICULTURAL AND BIOLOGICAL ENGINEERS
Attn: ASABE Foundation
2950 Niles Road
St. Joseph, MI 49085-9659
Tel: (269)429-0300
Fax: (269)429-3852
E-mail: hq@asabe.org
Web Site: http://www.asabe.org/membership/merriam.html
To provide financial assistance to undergraduate student members of the American Society of Agricultural Engineers (ASAE) interested in soil and water issues.

Title of Award: John L. and Sarah G. Merriam Scholarship **Area, Field, or Subject:** Biological and clinical sciences; Engineering, Agricultural; Soil science; Water resources **Level of Education for which Award is Granted:** Undergraduate **Number Awarded:** 1 each year. **Funds Available:** The stipend is $1,000. **Duration:** 1 year.

Eligibility Requirements: This program is open to undergraduate students who have a declared major in biological or agricultural engineering (must be accredited by ABET or CEAB), are student members of the society, are in at least the second year of college, have a GPA of 2.5 or higher, have at least 1 year of undergraduate study remaining, and have a special interest in soil and water issues. Interested applicants should submit a personal letter (up to 2 pages long) explaining why they have selected the soil and water discipline as the focus of their degree. Financial need is not considered in the selection process. **Deadline for Receipt:** March of each year. **Additional Information:** This scholarship was first awarded in 2001.

2451 ■ ASSOCIATION OF CALIFORNIA WATER AGENCIES
Attn: Scholarship Program
910 K Street, Suite 100
Sacramento, CA 95814-3514
Tel: (916)441-4545
Fax: (916)325-4849
E-mail: lavonnew@acwa.com
Web Site: http://www.acwa.com/news_info/scholarships
To provide financial assistance to upper-division students in California who are majoring in water resources-related fields of study.

Title of Award: Association of California Water Agencies Scholarships **Area, Field, or Subject:** Agricultural sciences; Engineering; Environmental conservation; Environmental science; Public administration; Water resources **Level of Education for which Award is Granted:** Four Year College **Number Awarded:** At least 6 each year. **Funds Available:** The stipend is $1,500. Funds are paid directly to the recipient's school. **Duration:** 1 year.

Eligibility Requirements: This program is open to California residents attending selected colleges and universities in the state. Applicants must be full-time students in their junior or senior year at the time of the award and majoring in a field related to or identified with water resources, including engineering, agricultural and/or urban water supply, environmental sciences, or public administration. Along with their application, they must submit 2-page essay on key water-related issues they would address if given the opportunity, why they have chosen a career in the water resources field, and how their educational and career goals relate to a future in California water resources. Selection is based on scholastic achievement, commitment to a career in the field of water resources, and financial need. **Deadline for Receipt:** March of each year. **Additional Information:** Recipients must attend a college or university in California approved by the sponsor.

2452 ■ ASSOCIATION OF CALIFORNIA WATER AGENCIES
Attn: Scholarship Program
910 K Street, Suite 100
Sacramento, CA 95814-3514
Tel: (916)441-4545
Fax: (916)325-4849
E-mail: lavonnew@acwa.com
Web Site: http://www.acwa.com/news_info/scholarships
To provide financial assistance to upper-division students in California who are majoring in water resources-related fields of study.

Title of Award: Clair A. Hill Scholarship **Area, Field, or Subject:** Agricultural sciences; Engineering; Environmental conservation; Environmental science; Public administration; Water resources **Level of Education for which Award is Granted:** Undergraduate **Number Awarded:** 1 each year. **Funds Available:** The stipend is $3,000. Funds are paid directly to the recipient's school. **Duration:** 1 year.

Eligibility Requirements: Applicants must be California residents attending public colleges or universities in the state. They should 1) have completed their sophomore work, 2) be full-time students in their junior or senior year at the time of the award, and 3) be majoring in a field related to or identified with water resources, including engineering, agricultural sciences, urban water supply, environmental sciences, and public administration. Selection is based on scholastic achievement, career plans, and financial need. **Deadline for Receipt:** March of each year. **Additional Information:** This program is administered each year by the current recipient of the Association of California Water Agencies Clair A. Hill Agency Award for Excellence, which is presented annually to a public water agency in recognition of outstanding and innovative water management programs. The winning agency generally selects a student within its service area. Funding is provided by the consulting firm CH2M Hill. Recipients must attend a branch of the University of California or the California State University system on a full-time basis.

2453 ■ AYRSHIRE BREEDERS' ASSOCIATION

1224 Alton Darby Creek Road, Suite B
Columbus, OH 43228
Tel: (614)335-0020
Fax: (614)335-0023
E-mail: info@usayrshire.com
Web Site: http://www.usayrshire.com
To provide financial assistance to members of the Ayrshire Breeders' Association who are interested in studying agriculture in college.
Title of Award: National Ayrshire Youth Scholarship **Area, Field, or Subject:** Agricultural sciences **Level of Education for which Award is Granted:** Undergraduate **Number Awarded:** 2 each year: 1 at $2,500 and 1 at $1,000. **Funds Available:** Stipends are $2,500 or $1,000. **Duration:** 1 year; nonrenewable.
Eligibility Requirements: This program is open to high school seniors and students currently enrolled in a 2-year or 4-year college or university. Applicants must have been a junior member in good standing with the association for at least the past 5 years. They must be majoring or planning to major in a field related to agriculture. Along with their application, they must submit a description of their involvement in Ayrshire activities on the local, state, and/or national level; a description of their involvement in 4-H and/or FFA activities on the local, state, and/or national level; a description of their involvement in school, church, and community activities; a summary of their career goals and aspirations related to their major area of study; a copy of their high school transcript; a copy of their acceptance into a postsecondary program; and 3 letters of recommendation. **Deadline for Receipt:** February of each year.

2454 ■ CALIFORNIA STATE FAIR

Attn: Friends of the Fair Scholarship Program
1600 Exposition Boulevard
P.O. Box 15649
Sacramento, CA 95852
Tel: (916)274-5969
E-mail: wross@calexpo.com
Web Site: http://www.bigfun.org
To provide financial assistance to high school students in California who plan to attend a 4-year college or university in the state to study agriculture.
Title of Award: California State Fair Agricultural College Scholarships for High School Students **Area, Field, or Subject:** Agricultural sciences **Level of Education for which Award is Granted:** Four Year College **Number Awarded:** 2 each year: 1 at $1,500 and 1 at $500. **Funds Available:** Stipends are $1,500 or $500. **Duration:** 1 year.
Eligibility Requirements: This program is open to juniors and seniors currently enrolled at high schools in California. Applicants must be planning to attend a 4-year college or university in the state to major in agriculture. They must have a GPA of 3.0 or higher. Along with their application, they must submit a 2-page essay on why they are pursuing their desired career and life goals. Selection is based on personal commitment, goals established for their chosen field, leadership potential, and civic accomplishments. **Deadline for Receipt:** March of each year. **Additional Information:** The Friends of the Fair Scholarship Program was established in 1993.

2455 ■ CALIFORNIA STATE FAIR

Attn: Friends of the Fair Scholarship Program
1600 Exposition Boulevard
P.O. Box 15649
Sacramento, CA 95852
Tel: (916)274-5969
E-mail: wross@calexpo.com
Web Site: http://www.bigfun.org
To provide financial assistance to high school students in California who plan to attend a community college in the state to study agriculture.
Title of Award: California State Fair Agricultural Community College Scholarships for High School Students **Area, Field, or Subject:** Agricultural sciences **Level of Education for which Award is Granted:** Two Year College **Number Awarded:** 2 each year: 1 at $1,000 and 1 at $500. **Funds Available:** Stipends are $1,000 or $500. **Duration:** 1 year.

Eligibility Requirements: This program is open to juniors and seniors currently enrolled at high schools in California. Applicants must be planning to attend a community college in the state to major in agriculture. They must have a GPA of 3.0 or higher. Along with their application, they must submit a 2-page essay on why they are pursuing their desired career and life goals. Selection is based on personal commitment, goals established for their chosen **Deadline for Receipt:** March of each year. **Additional Information:** The Friends of the Fair Scholarship Program was established in 1993.

2456 ■ CALIFORNIA STATE FAIR

Attn: Friends of the Fair Scholarship Program
1600 Exposition Boulevard
P.O. Box 15649
Sacramento, CA 95852
Tel: (916)274-5969
E-mail: wross@calexpo.com
Web Site: http://www.bigfun.org
To provide financial assistance to community college students in California who are studying agriculture.
Title of Award: California State Fair Community College Scholarships in Agriculture **Area, Field, or Subject:** Agricultural sciences **Level of Education for which Award is Granted:** Two Year College **Number Awarded:** 2 each year: 1 at $1,000 and 1 at $500. **Funds Available:** Stipends are $1,000 or $500. **Duration:** 1 year.
Eligibility Requirements: This program is open to students currently enrolled at community colleges in California. Applicants must have completed at least 12 units of undergraduate course work in agricultural classes. They must have a GPA of 3.0 or higher. Along with their application, they must submit a 2-page essay on why they are pursuing their desired career and life goals. Selection is based on personal commitment, goals established for their chosen field, leadership potential, and civic accomplishments. **Deadline for Receipt:** March of each year. **Additional Information:** The Friends of the Fair Scholarship Program was established in 1993.

2457 ■ CALIFORNIA STATE FAIR

Attn: Friends of the Fair Scholarship Program
1600 Exposition Boulevard
P.O. Box 15649
Sacramento, CA 95852
Tel: (916)274-5969
E-mail: wross@calexpo.com
Web Site: http://www.bigfun.org
To provide financial assistance to undergraduate and graduate students in California who are studying agriculture.
Title of Award: California State Fair Undergraduate and Graduate Scholarships in Agriculture **Area, Field, or Subject:** Agricultural sciences **Level of Education for which Award is Granted:** Four Year College, Graduate **Number Awarded:** 2 each year: 1 at $1,500 and 1 at $500. **Funds Available:** Stipends are $1,500 or $500. **Duration:** 1 year.
Eligibility Requirements: This program is open to undergraduate and graduate students currently enrolled at 4-year colleges and university in California. Applicants must have completed at least 12 units of course work in agricultural classes. They must have a GPA of 3.0 or higher. Along with their application, they must submit a 2-page essay on why they are pursuing their desired career and life goals. Selection is based on personal commitment, goals established for their chosen field, leadership potential, and civic accomplishments. **Deadline for Receipt:** March of each year. **Additional Information:** The Friends of the Fair Scholarship Program was established in 1993.

2458 ■ CALIFORNIA STATE FAIR

Attn: Friends of the Fair Scholarship Program
1600 Exposition Boulevard
P.O. Box 15649
Sacramento, CA 95852
Tel: (916)274-5969
E-mail: wross@calexpo.com
Web Site: http://www.bigfun.org
To provide financial assistance for college to residents of California who are interested in majoring in designated fields or preparing for a career in the Fair industry.

Title of Award: Eddie G. Cole Memorial Scholarships **Area, Field, or Subject:** Agricultural sciences; Education, Physical; Equine studies **Level of Education for which Award is Granted:** Undergraduate **Number Awarded:** 2 each year: 1 at $1,000 and 1 at $500. **Funds Available:** Stipends are $1,000 or $500. **Duration:** 1 year.

Eligibility Requirements: This program is open to residents of California currently working on an undergraduate degree at a college or university in the state. Applicants be 1) majoring in physical education, agriculture, or equine studies; or 2) preparing for a career in the Fair industry. They must have a GPA of 3.0 or higher. Along with their application, they must submit a 2-page essay on why they are pursuing their desired career and life goals. Selection is based on personal commitment, goals established for their chosen field, leadership potential, and civic accomplishments. **Deadline for Receipt:** March of each year. **Additional Information:** The Friends of the Fair Scholarship Program was established in 1993.

2459 ■ COLORADO WEED MANAGEMENT ASSOCIATION

Attn: Scholarship Program
P.O. Box 1910
Granby, CO 80446-1910
Tel: (970)887-1228
Fax: (970)887-1229
E-mail: cwma@rkymtnhi.com
Web Site: http://www.cwma.org/scholarship.htm
To provide financial assistance to high school seniors and college students in Colorado who are interested in weed management.

Title of Award: Colorado Weed Management Association Scholarship **Area, Field, or Subject:** Agricultural sciences; Botany; Natural resources **Level of Education for which Award is Granted:** Undergraduate **Number Awarded:** 1 each year. **Funds Available:** A stipend is awarded (amount not specified). **Duration:** 1 year; nonrenewable.

Eligibility Requirements: This program is open to high school seniors and college students who have demonstrated an interest in weed management and are planning to major in agriculture, natural resource management, botany, range management, or a related field. Applicants must be attending or planning to attend a 2-year college or 4-year college or university in Colorado. Along with their application, they must submit an essay, up to 3 pages in length, on the topic, "The Threat of Noxious Weeds Is..." High school seniors must have a GPA of 2.5 or higher; college freshmen must have a cumulative GPA of 2.0 or higher; college sophomores, juniors, and seniors must have a GPA of 2.5 or higher. Financial need is also considered in the selection process. **Deadline for Receipt:** March of each year.

2460 ■ COMMUNITY FOUNDATION FOR THE FOX VALLEY REGION, INC.

Attn: Scholarships
4455 West Lawrence Street
P.O. Box 563
Appleton, WI 54912-0563
Tel: (920)830-1290
Fax: (920)830-1293
E-mail: cffvr@cffoxvalley.org
Web Site: http://www.cffoxvalley.org/scholarship_fundslist.html
To provide financial assistance to upper-division and graduate students in Wisconsin who are working on a degree related to gardening.

Title of Award: Wisconsin Garden Club Federation Scholarship **Area, Field, or Subject:** Agricultural sciences; Botany; Environmental conservation; Environmental science; Forestry; Horticulture; Landscape architecture and design; Urban affairs/design/planning **Level of Education for which Award is Granted:** Graduate, Four Year College **Number Awarded:** Varies each year; recently, 4 of these scholarships were awarded. **Funds Available:** The stipend is $1,000. **Duration:** 1 year.

Eligibility Requirements: This program is open to college juniors, seniors, and graduate students at colleges and universities in Wisconsin. Applicants must be majoring in horticulture, floriculture, landscape design/architecture, botany, forestry, agronomy, plant pathology, environmental studies, city planning, land management, or a related field. They must have a 3.0 GPA or higher. **Deadline for Receipt:** February of each year. **Additional Information:** This program is sponsored by the Wisconsin Garden Club Federation. Information is also available from Carolyn A. Craig, WGCF Scholarship Chair, 900 North Shore Drive, New Richmond, WI 54017-9466, (715) 246-6242, E-mail: cacraig@frontiernet.net.

2461 ■ COMMUNITY FOUNDATION OF LOUISVILLE

Attn: Director of Grants
Waterfront Plaza, Suite 1110
325 West Main Street
Louisville, KY 40202-4251
Tel: (502)585-4649
Fax: (502)587-7484
E-mail: info@cflouisville.org
Web Site: http://www.cflouisville.org
To provide financial assistance to women studying fields related to the environment at colleges and universities in Kentucky.

Title of Award: Thaddeus Colson and Isabelle Saalwaechter Fitzpatrick Memorial Scholarship **Area, Field, or Subject:** Agricultural sciences; Biological and clinical sciences; Environmental conservation; Environmental science; Horticulture **Level of Education for which Award is Granted:** Four Year College **Number Awarded:** 1 each year. **Funds Available:** The stipend is $2,000. Funds are paid directly to the college or university. **Duration:** 1 year; nonrenewable.

Eligibility Requirements: This program is open to female residents of Kentucky who are entering their sophomore, junior, or senior year at a 4-year public college or university in the state. Applicants must be majoring in an environmentally related program (e.g., agriculture, biology, horticulture, environmental studies, environmental engineering). They must be enrolled full time with a GPA of 3.0 or higher. Along with their application, they must submit a 200-word essay describing their interest, leadership, volunteer efforts, and work experience in the environmental field; their future plans and goals in the environmental field; and what they hope to accomplish with their college degree. Financial need is also considered in the selection process. **Deadline for Receipt:** February of each year.

2462 ■ COMMUNITY FOUNDATION OF NEW JERSEY

Attn: Scholarship Services
Knox Hill Road
P.O. Box 338
Morristown, NJ 07963-0338
Tel: (973)267-5533
Free: 800-659-5533
Fax: (973)267-2903
E-mail: fkrueger@cfnj.org
Web Site: http://www.cfnj.org
To provide financial assistance to residents of New Jersey who are working on an undergraduate or graduate degree in agriculture.

Title of Award: Stephen A. Johnston Memorial Scholarships **Area, Field, or Subject:** Agricultural sciences **Level of Education for which Award is Granted:** Graduate, Undergraduate **Number Awarded:** 2 each year. **Funds Available:** The stipend is $1,000 per year. Funds are made payable jointly to the recipients and their educational institution. **Duration:** 1 year; recipients may reapply if they maintain a GPA of at least 3.0.

Eligibility Requirements: This program is open to New Jersey residents enrolled as a sophomore, junior, senior, or graduate student at a college or university in the United States. Applicants must be interested in preparing for a career in agriculture with an emphasis on production agriculture. Preference is given to students majoring in plant pathology and to students who have worked or will work with the Rutgers Agricultural Research and Extension Center. **Deadline for Receipt:** April of each year.

2463 ■ COMMUNITY FOUNDATION OF NEW JERSEY

Attn: Donor Services
Knox Hill Road
P.O. Box 338
Morristown, NJ 07963-0338
Tel: (973)267-5533
Fax: (973)267-2903
E-mail: Cangeleri@cfnj.org
Web Site: http://www.cfnj.org
To provide financial assistance to college and graduate students from New Jersey who are preparing for a career in vegetable crop production or a related field.

Title of Award: Stephen A. Johnston Memorial Scholarships **Area, Field, or Subject:** Agricultural sciences **Level of Education for which Award is Granted:** Graduate, Undergraduate **Number Awarded:** 2 each year. **Funds Available:** The stipend is $1,000 per year. Funds are paid jointly to the recipient and the educational institution. **Duration:** 1 year; recipients may reapply if they maintain a "B" average.

Eligibility Requirements: This program is open to residents of New Jersey who are college sophomores, juniors, seniors, and graduate students at accredited colleges and universities in the United States. Applicants must have an interest in vegetable crop production or a related field. Preference is given to students majoring in plant pathology and to students who have worked or will work with the Rutgers Agricultural Research and Extension Center (RAREC). Along with their application, they must submit a 1-page statement of their career goals and the reasons for those goals. Selection is based on academic performance, extracurricular activities, work experience, and financial need. **Deadline for Receipt:** September of each year.

2464 ■ BILLY CONSALO MEMORIAL AGRICULTURAL SCHOLARSHIP FUND

c/o Dottie Kargman, Trustee
1485 Catawba Avenue
Newfield, NJ 08344
Tel: (856)697-0581
Fax: (856)697-1594
To provide financial assistance to high school seniors in New Jersey who are interested in studying agriculture in college.

Title of Award: Billy Consalo Memorial Agricultural Scholarship **Area, Field, or Subject:** Agricultural sciences **Level of Education for which Award is Granted:** Undergraduate **Number Awarded:** 1 each year. **Funds Available:** The stipend is $2,500. **Duration:** 1 year.

Eligibility Requirements: This program is open to seniors graduating from high schools in New Jersey who have a "C" average or higher. Applicants must be planning to attend a college, university, technical school, or other institute of higher education to study agriculture or a related field. They must submit a letter explaining why they are interested in agriculture, a transcript, 3 letters of recommendation, and information on their financial need. **Deadline for Receipt:** April of each year.

2465 ■ DEPARTMENT OF AGRICULTURE

Animal and Plant Health Inspection Service
Marketing and Regulatory Programs
4700 River Road, Unit 22
Riverdale, MD 20737-1230
800-762-2738
Web Site: http://www.aphis.usda.gov/ppq
To provide financial assistance and work experience to college students majoring in the agricultural or biological sciences.

Title of Award: PPQ William F. Helms Student Scholarship Program **Area, Field, or Subject:** Agricultural sciences; Biological and clinical sciences; Botany; Entomology; Environmental conservation; Environmental science; Virology **Level of Education for which Award is Granted:** Undergraduate **Number Awarded:** Several each year. **Funds Available:** The stipend is $5,000 per year. **Duration:** 1 year; may be renewed if the recipient maintains a GPA of 2.5 or higher.

Eligibility Requirements: This program is open to college sophomores and juniors who are attending an accredited college or university, are majoring in an agricultural or biological science (such as biology, plant pathology, entomology, virology, bacteriology, mycology, or ecology), are interested in a career in plant protection and quarantine, and are U.S. citizens. To apply, interested students must submit a completed application form, a personal letter describing their career goals and interest in plant protection and quarantine, transcripts, and 3 letters of recommendation. **Deadline for Receipt:** February of each year. **Additional Information:** The U.S. Department of Agriculture's (USDA) Animal and Plant Health Inspection Service (APHIS) is the agency responsible for protecting America's agriculture base; Plant Protection and Quarantine (PPQ) is the program within APHIS that deals with plant health issues. In addition to financial assistance, the Helms Student Scholarship Program also offers tutoring assistance, mentoring, paid work experience during vacation periods, career exploration, and possible employment upon graduation.

2466 ■ ENVIRONMENTAL PROTECTION AGENCY

Attn: National Center for Environmental Research
Ariel Rios Building - 3500
1200 Pennsylvania Avenue, N.W.
Washington, DC 20460

Tel: (202)343-9862
E-mail: barnwell.thomas@epa.gov
Web Site: http://es.epa.gov/ncer/P3
To provide funding to teams of undergraduate and graduate students interested in conducting a research project related to environmental sustainability.

Title of Award: P3 Award Program **Area, Field, or Subject:** Agricultural sciences; Biological and clinical sciences; Chemistry; Energy-related areas; Environmental conservation; Environmental science; Information science and technology; Public health; Transportation; Water resources **Level of Education for which Award is Granted:** Graduate, Undergraduate **Number Awarded:** Varies each year. Recently, 42 Phase I grants were awarded, of which 10 were selected to receive Phase II grants. **Funds Available:** Phase I grants are $10,000. Phase II grants are $75,000. Grants cover all direct and indirect costs; cost-sharing is not required. **Duration:** 1 year for Phase I and 1 additional year for Phase II.

Eligibility Requirements: This competition is open to teams of undergraduate and graduate students at U.S. colleges and universities who are interested in conducting a research project related to the 3 components of sustainability: people, prosperity, and the planet. Projects must address the causes, effects, extent, prevention, reduction, or elimination of air, water, or solid and hazardous waste pollution. Categories include agriculture (e.g., irrigation practices, reduction or elimination of pesticides); materials and chemicals (e.g., materials conservation, green engineering, green chemistry, biotechnology, recovery and reuse of materials); energy (e.g., reduction in air emissions, energy conservation); information technology (e.g., delivery of and access to environmental performance, technical, educational, or public health information related environmental decision making); water (e.g., quality, quantity, conservation, availability, and access); or the built environment (e.g., environmental benefits through innovative green buildings, transportation, and mobility strategies, and smart growth as it results in reduced vehicle miles traveled or reduces storm water runoff). Student teams, with a faculty advisor (who serves as the principal investigator on the grant), submit designs for Phase I of the competition. Selection of grantees is based on the extent to which the proposed project achieves the outcomes of minimizing the use and generation of hazardous substances; utilizes resources and energy effectively and efficiently; and advances the goals of economic competitiveness, human health, and environmental protection for societal benefit. Recipients of Phase I grants are then invited to apply for additional funding through a Phase I grant. **Deadline for Receipt:** February of each year. **Additional Information:** This program began in 2004. It is supported by a large number of organizations from industry, the nonprofit sector, and the federal government.

2467 ■ FEDERATED GARDEN CLUBS OF CONNECTICUT, INC.

14 Business Park Drive
P.O. Box 854
Branford, CT 06405-0854
Tel: (203)488-5528
Fax: (203)488-5528
E-mail: gardenclubs@ctgardenclubs.org
Web Site: http://www.ctgardenclubs.org/scholarship.html
To provide financial assistance to Connecticut residents who are interested in majoring in horticulture-related fields at a Connecticut college or university.

Title of Award: Federated Garden Clubs of Connecticut Scholarship **Area, Field, or Subject:** Agricultural sciences; Botany; Environmental conservation; Environmental science; Forestry; Horticulture; Landscape architecture and design; Urban affairs/design/planning **Level of Education for which Award is Granted:** Four Year College, Graduate **Number Awarded:** Varies each year, depending upon the availability of funds. **Funds Available:** Stipends are generally about $1,000 each. Funds are sent to the recipient's school in 2 equal installments. **Duration:** 1 year.

Eligibility Requirements: Applicants must be legal residents of Connecticut who are studying at a college or university in the state in horticulture, floriculture, landscape design, conservation, forestry, botany, agronomy, plant pathology, environmental control, city planning, land management, or related subjects. They must be entering their junior or senior year of college or be a graduate student, have a GPA of 3.0 or higher, and be able to demonstrate financial need. **Deadline for Receipt:** June of each year. **Additional Information:** Information is also available from the Connecticut State Scholarship Chair, Mary Gray, 18 Long Hill Farm Road, Guilford, CT 06437, (203) 458-2784.

2468 ■ FIRST PIONEER FARM CREDIT, ACA

Attn: Scholarships
174 South Road
Enfield, CT 06082
Tel: (860)741-4380
Fax: (860)253-5565
E-mail: info@firstpioneer.com
Web Site: http://www.firstpioneer.com

To provide financial assistance for college to residents of designated northeastern states, especially stockholders of First Pioneer Farm Credit. **Title of Award:** First Pioneer Farm Credit Scholarships **Area, Field, or Subject:** Agricultural sciences; General studies/Field of study not specified **Level of Education for which Award is Granted:** Undergraduate **Number Awarded:** 15 each year. **Funds Available:** The stipend is $1,000. Funds are paid directly to the student to be used for tuition, room and board, books, and other academic charges. **Duration:** 1 year; nonrenewable.

Eligibility Requirements: This program is open to residents of Massachusetts, Connecticut, Rhode Island, New Jersey, and portions of New York and New Hampshire. Applicants must be either 1) an individual eligible to own voting stock in First Pioneer Farm Credit or the child of such an individual; or 2) a college student working on a degree in an applied agricultural field regardless of their parents' membership status. Eligibility to own voting stock is limited to U.S. citizens and permanent residents who own agricultural land or are engaged in harvesting, production, processing, or marketing of agricultural products. Students in that category may be majoring in any field, but preference is given to the study of agriculture or closely-related areas. Applicants in both categories may be high school seniors, attending college, or in the work force and working on or planning to work on an associate, bachelor's, or graduate degree. They must submit a 200-word essay on why they wish to prepare for a career in agriculture or in their chosen field. Selection is based on the essay, extracurricular activities (including job responsibilities on the home farm), and interest in agriculture **Deadline for Receipt:** April **Additional Information:** Recipients are given priority for an internship with the sponsor in the summer following their junior year.

2469 ■ HAWAI'I COMMUNITY FOUNDATION

Attn: Scholarship Department
1164 Bishop Street, Suite 800
Honolulu, HI 96813
Tel: (808)566-5570; 888-731-3863
Fax: (808)521-6286
E-mail: scholarships@hcf-hawaii.org
Web Site: http://www.hawaiicommunityfoundation.org/scholar/scholar.php

To provide financial assistance to residents of designated sections of Hawaii who are interested in going to college to prepare for a career in agriculture, medicine, science, or nursing. **Title of Award:** Dan and Pauline Lutkenhouse Tropical Botanical Garden Scholarship **Area, Field, or Subject:** Agricultural sciences; Medicine; Nursing; Science **Level of Education for which Award is Granted:** Graduate, Undergraduate **Number Awarded:** Varies each year; recently, 2 of these scholarships were awarded. **Funds Available:** The amount of the award depends on the availability of funds and the need of the recipient; recently, stipends averaged $1,000. **Duration:** 1 year.

Eligibility Requirements: This program is open to residents of the Hilo Coast and the Hamakua Coast, north of the Wailuku River, who are interested in attending college as full-time undergraduate or graduate students. Applicants must be majoring or planning to major in agriculture, medicine, nursing, or science. They must be able to demonstrate academic achievement (GPA of 2.7 or higher), good moral character, and financial need. In addition to filling out the standard application form, applicants must write a short statement indicating their reasons for attending college, their planned course of study, and their career goals. **Deadline for Receipt:** February of each year. **Additional Information:** Recipients may attend college in Hawaii or on the mainland.

2470 ■ HISPANIC SCHOLARSHIP FUND INSTITUTE

1001 Connecticut Avenue, N.W., Suite 632
Washington, DC 20036

Tel: (202)296-0009
Fax: (202)296-3633
E-mail: info@hsfi.org
Web Site: http://www.hsfi.org/scholarships/energy.asp

To provide financial assistance to Hispanic undergraduate students majoring in designated business, engineering, and science fields related to the U.S. Department of Energy (DOE) goals of environmental restoration and waste management.

Title of Award: Environmental Management Scholarship **Area, Field, or Subject:** Business administration; Chemistry; Computer and information sciences; Engineering, Agricultural; Engineering, Civil; Engineering, Electrical; Engineering, Industrial; Engineering, Mechanical; Engineering, Metallurgical; Engineering, Petroleum; Environmental science; Epidemiology; Geology; Hydrology; Management; Mathematics and mathematical sciences; Physics; Radiology; Toxicology **Level of Education for which Award is Granted:** Undergraduate **Number Awarded:** Varies each year. **Funds Available:** The stipend is $3,000 per year for 4-year university students or $2,000 per year for community college students. **Duration:** 1 year.

Eligibility Requirements: This program is open to U.S. citizens and permanent residents of Hispanic background who have completed at least 12 undergraduate credits with a GPA of 3.0 or higher. Applicants must be interested in preparing for a career supportive of the DOE goals of environmental restoration and waste management. Eligible academic majors are in the fields of business (management and system analysis), engineering (agricultural, chemical, civil, electrical, environmental, industrial, mechanical, metallurgical, nuclear, and petroleum), and science (applied math/physics, chemistry, computer science, ecology, environmental, epidemiology, geology, health physics, hydrology, radiochemistry, radio-ecology, and toxicology). Along with their application, they must submit a 2-page essay on 1) how their academic major, interests, and career goals correspond to environmental restoration and waste management issues; and 2) how their Hispanic background and family upbringing have influenced their academic and personal goals. Selection is based on the essay, academic record, academic plans and career goals, financial need, commitment to DOE's goal of environmental restoration and waste management, and a letter of recommendation. **Deadline for Receipt:** March of each year. **Additional Information:** This program, which began in 1990, is sponsored by DOE's Office of Environmental Management. Recipients must enroll full time at a college or university in the United States.

2471 ■ IOWA FOUNDATION FOR AGRICULTURAL ADVANCEMENT

Attn: Department IFFAA/Iowa State Fair
P.O. Box 57130
Des Moines, IA 50317-0003
800-545-FAIR
E-mail: saleofchampions@yahoo.com
Web Site: http://www.iowastatefair.org/saleofchamps

To provide financial assistance for college to Iowa high school seniors interested in majoring in animal science or livestock-related fields. **Title of Award:** IFFAA Scholarships **Area, Field, or Subject:** Agricultural sciences; Animal science and behavior **Level of Education for which Award is Granted:** Undergraduate **Number Awarded:** Varies each year. Recently, 74 scholarships (with a value of $77,00) and 64 performance and carcass awards (with a value of $11,500) were presented. **Funds Available:** Stipends range from $500 to $2,500. **Duration:** 1 year; nonrenewable.

Eligibility Requirements: This program is open to students who will be entering an Iowa 2- or 4-year postsecondary institution in the following fall. Applicants must be residents of Iowa, active in 4-H or FFA livestock projects, and planning to major in animal science or a field in agriculture or home economics that is related to the animal industry. Selection is based on level of 4-H or FFA involvement in livestock project work, livestock exhibition, and/or judging (50%); scholarship (15%); leadership and activities (25%); and curriculum and career plans (10%). The program also includes performance and carcass awards in which animals are selected on the basis of visual appraisal and then evaluated in a carcass contest for economically important traits, such as loin eye or rib eye area, tenth rib fat, and average daily gain. **Deadline for Receipt:** May of each year. **Additional Information:** Information is also available from county 4-H offices in Iowa and local FFA advisors. Winners are announced at the Iowa State Fair's annual 4-H/FFA "Sale of Champions" in August, sponsored by the Iowa Foundation for Agricultural Advancement (IFFAA). The IFFAA was established in 1988 and began offering scholarships in 1990.

2472 ■ MAINE COMMUNITY FOUNDATION

Attn: Program Director
245 Main Street
Ellsworth, ME 04605
Tel: (207)667-9735; 877-700-6800
Fax: (207)667-0447
E-mail: info@mainecf.org
Web Site: http://www.mainecf.org/html/scholarships/index.html
To provide financial assistance to FFA members from Maine who are interested in preparing for a career in agriculture.
Title of Award: Ronald P. Guerrette FFA Scholarship Fund **Area, Field, or Subject:** Agricultural sciences **Level of Education for which Award is Granted:** Undergraduate **Number Awarded:** 3 each year. **Funds Available:** A stipend is paid (amount not specified). **Duration:** 1 year.
Eligibility Requirements: This program is open to residents of Maine who are enrolled or planning to enroll in a course of study to prepare for a career in farming and agriculture. Current FFA membership is required. Priority is given first to students from Caribou High School, then to residents of Aroostook County, and then to residents of the state of Maine. Financial need is considered in the selection process. **Deadline for Receipt:** February of each year. **Additional Information:** This program began in 1998.

2473 ■ MINNESOTA TRAPPERS ASSOCIATION

c/o Deb Offerdahl
230 Second Street S.E.
Milaca, MN 56353
Tel: (320)982-1385
Web Site: http://www.mntrappers.com
To provide financial assistance for college to members of the Minnesota Trappers Association (MTA) and to other students working on a degree in a field related to natural resources.
Title of Award: Minnesota Trappers Association Scholarships **Area, Field, or Subject:** Agricultural sciences; Engineering, Agricultural; Forestry; General studies/Field of study not specified; Natural resources; Veterinary science and medicine; Wildlife conservation, management, and science; Zoology **Level of Education for which Award is Granted:** Undergraduate **Number Awarded:** 7 each year: 1 at $2,000, 2 at $1,000, 1 at $600 (the Russ Cumberland Scholarship), and 3 at $500. **Funds Available:** Stipends range from $500 to $2,000. **Duration:** 1 year.
Eligibility Requirements: This program is open to 1) MTA members working on an undergraduate degree in any field; and 2) other undergraduates working on a degree in agricultural engineering, agricultural science, forestry, natural resources, veterinary medicine, wildlife biology, or zoology. Applicants must be entering or enrolled in a 2- or 4-year program at an accredited college or university and have a college GPA of 2.5 or higher (entering freshmen must submit a transcript of their first term of college work before funds are released). **Deadline for Receipt:** June of each year. **Additional Information:** This program includes the Russ Cumberland Scholarship. Information is also available from Todd Roggenkamp, 28952 438th Lane, Palasade, MN 56373, (218) 768-2597.

2474 ■ NATIONAL AGRICULTURAL AVIATION ASSOCIATION

Attn: Women of the NAAA
1005 E Street, S.E.
Washington, DC 20003-2947
Tel: (202)546-5722
Fax: (202)546-5726
E-mail: information@agaviation.org
Web Site: http://www.agaviation.org/scholarship.htm
To recognize and reward outstanding student essays on agricultural aviation.
Title of Award: Women's National Agricultural Aviation Association Scholarship Essay Contest **Area, Field, or Subject:** Agricultural sciences; Aviation; General studies/Field of study not specified; Writing **Level of Education for which Award is Granted:** Undergraduate **Number Awarded:** 2 each year. **Funds Available:** First prize is $2,000; second prize is $1,000. **Duration:** The competition is held annually.
Eligibility Requirements: This competition is open to the children, grandchildren, sons-in-law, daughters-in-law, or spouses of any National

Agricultural Aviation Association operator, pilot member, retired operator, or pilot who maintains an active membership in the association. The contest is also open to the children, grandchildren, sons-in-law, daughters-in-law, or spouses of an allied industry member. Entrants must be high school seniors, high school graduates, or college students. They may be of any age pursuing any area of education beyond high school. They are invited to submit an essay, up to 1,500 words, on a theme related to agricultural aviation that changes annually; recently, the topic was "Agricultural Aviation's Contribution to the World's Food Supply." A photograph of the entrant and a short biography should accompany the submission. Essays are judged on theme, development, clarity, and originality. **Deadline for Receipt:** August of each year.

2475 ■ NATIONAL FFA ORGANIZATION

Attn: Scholarship Office
6060 FFA Drive
P.O. Box 68960
Indianapolis, IN 46268-0960
Tel: (317)802-4321
Fax: (317)802-5321
E-mail: scholarships@ffa.org
Web Site: http://www.ffa.org
To provide financial assistance to FFA members currently studying agriculture in college.
Title of Award: Accelerated Genetics Scholarships **Area, Field, or Subject:** Agricultural sciences **Level of Education for which Award is Granted:** Undergraduate **Number Awarded:** 2 each year. **Funds Available:** The stipend is $1,000 per year. Funds are paid directly to the recipient. **Duration:** 1 year; nonrenewable.
Eligibility Requirements: This program is open to members currently enrolled full time in college and working on a 2-year or 4-year degree in agriculture. Applicants, or their parents, must be purchasing semen or farm products from an authorized Accelerated Genetics representative. They must live on a family-owned farm. Selection is based on academic achievement (10 points for GPA, 10 points for SAT or ACT score, 10 points for class rank), leadership in FFA activities (30 points), leadership in community activities (10 points), and participation in the Supervised Agricultural Experience (SAE) program (30 points). U.S. citizenship is required. **Deadline for Receipt:** February of each year. **Additional Information:** Funding for these scholarships is provided by Accelerated Genetics.

2476 ■ NATIONAL FFA ORGANIZATION

Attn: Scholarship Office
6060 FFA Drive
P.O. Box 68960
Indianapolis, IN 46268-0960
Tel: (317)802-4321
Fax: (317)802-5321
E-mail: scholarships@ffa.org
Web Site: http://www.ffa.org
To provide financial assistance to FFA members studying agriculture in college.
Title of Award: AGCO Corporation Scholarships **Area, Field, or Subject:** Agricultural sciences **Level of Education for which Award is Granted:** Four Year College **Number Awarded:** 4 each year. **Funds Available:** The stipend is $2,400. Funds are paid directly to the recipient. **Duration:** 1 year; nonrenewable.
Eligibility Requirements: This program is open to members who are working full time on a 4-year college degree in agriculture. Selection is based on academic achievement (10 points for GPA, 10 points for SAT or ACT score, 10 points for class rank), leadership in FFA activities (30 points), leadership in community activities (10 points), and participation in the Supervised Agricultural Experience (SAE) program (30 points). U.S. citizenship is required. **Deadline for Receipt:** February of each year. **Additional Information:** Funding for these scholarships is provided by AGCO Corporation.

2477 ■ NATIONAL FFA ORGANIZATION

Attn: Scholarship Office
6060 FFA Drive
P.O. Box 68960
Indianapolis, IN 46268-0960

Tel: (317)802-4321
Fax: (317)802-5321
E-mail: scholarships@ffa.org
Web Site: http://www.ffa.org
To provide financial assistance to FFA members interested in studying agriculture in college.
Title of Award: AGDATA Scholarships **Area, Field, or Subject:** Agricultural sciences **Level of Education for which Award is Granted:** Undergraduate **Number Awarded:** 4 each year: 2 to high school seniors and 2 to current college students. **Funds Available:** The stipend is $2,500 per year. Funds are paid directly to the recipient. **Duration:** 1 year; nonrenewable.
Eligibility Requirements: This program is open to members who are either high school seniors or already enrolled full time in college. Applicants must be working on or planning to work on a 2-year or 4-year degree in an area of agriculture. Selection is based on academic achievement (10 points for GPA, 10 points for SAT or ACT score, 10 points for class rank), leadership in FFA activities (30 points), leadership in community activities (10 points), and participation in the Supervised Agricultural Experience (SAE) program (30 points). Financial need is also considered. U.S. citizenship is required. **Deadline for Receipt:** February of each year. **Additional Information:** Funding for this scholarship is provided by AGDATA Inc.

2478 ■ NATIONAL FFA ORGANIZATION
Attn: Scholarship Office
6060 FFA Drive
P.O. Box 68960
Indianapolis, IN 46268-0960
Tel: (317)802-4321
Fax: (317)802-5321
E-mail: scholarships@ffa.org
Web Site: http://www.ffa.org
To provide financial assistance to FFA members interested in studying an agricultural field in college.
Title of Award: Agrium U.S. Scholarships **Area, Field, or Subject:** Agribusiness; Agricultural sciences; Engineering, Agricultural; Soil science **Level of Education for which Award is Granted:** Four Year College **Number Awarded:** 5 each year. **Funds Available:** The stipend is $1,000. Funds are paid directly to the recipient. **Duration:** 1 year; nonrenewable.
Eligibility Requirements: This program is open to members who are graduating high school seniors planning to enroll full time in a 4-year college. Applicants must be planning to prepare for a career in agricultural sales, marketing, engineering, agronomy, crop science, or soil science. They must have a GPA of 3.0 or higher and be residents of the U.S. mainland. Selection is based on academic achievement (10 points for GPA, 10 points for SAT or ACT score, 10 points for class rank), leadership in FFA activities (30 points), leadership in community activities (10 points), and participation in the Supervised Agricultural Experience (SAE) program (30 points). U.S. citizenship is required. **Deadline for Receipt:** February of each year. **Additional Information:** Funding for this scholarship is provided by Agrium U.S. Inc. of Denver.

2479 ■ NATIONAL FFA ORGANIZATION
Attn: Scholarship Office
6060 FFA Drive
P.O. Box 68960
Indianapolis, IN 46268-0960
Tel: (317)802-4321
Fax: (317)802-5321
E-mail: scholarships@ffa.org
Web Site: http://www.ffa.org
To provide financial assistance to male FFA members who are interested in studying agriculture in college.
Title of Award: Alpha Gamma Rho Educational Foundation Scholarship **Area, Field, or Subject:** Agricultural sciences **Level of Education for which Award is Granted:** Four Year College **Number Awarded:** 1 each year. **Funds Available:** The stipend is $1,000. Funds are paid directly to the recipient. **Duration:** 1 year; nonrenewable.
Eligibility Requirements: This program is open to members who are graduating high school seniors planning to enroll full time in college to work on a 4-year degree in agriculture. Applicants must be males planning to attend a university with an Alpha Gamma Rho chapter. Selection is

based on academic achievement (10 points for GPA, 10 points for SAT or ACT score, 10 points for class rank), leadership in FFA activities (30 points), leadership in community activities (10 points), and participation in the Supervised Agricultural Experience (SAE) program (30 points). U.S. citizenship is required. **Deadline for Receipt:** February of each year. **Additional Information:** Funding for this scholarship is provided by the Alpha Gamma Rho Educational Foundation.

2480 ■ NATIONAL FFA ORGANIZATION
Attn: Scholarship Office
6060 FFA Drive
P.O. Box 68960
Indianapolis, IN 46268-0960
Tel: (317)802-4321
Fax: (317)802-5321
E-mail: scholarships@ffa.org
Web Site: http://www.ffa.org
To provide financial assistance to FFA members who are interested in studying agriculture in college.
Title of Award: Archer Daniels Midland Company High School Scholarships **Area, Field, or Subject:** Agricultural sciences **Level of Education for which Award is Granted:** Undergraduate **Number Awarded:** 80 each year. **Funds Available:** The stipend is $1,000. Funds are paid directly to the recipient. **Duration:** 1 year; nonrenewable.
Eligibility Requirements: This program is open to members who are graduating high school seniors planning to enroll full time in college. Applicants must be interested in working on a 4-year degree in agriculture. Selection is based on academic achievement (10 points for GPA, 10 points for SAT or ACT score, 10 points for class rank), leadership in FFA activities (30 points), leadership in community activities (10 points), and participation in the Supervised Agricultural Experience (SAE) program (30 points). U.S. citizenship is required. **Deadline for Receipt:** February of each year. **Additional Information:** Funding for this scholarship is provided by Archer Daniels Midland Company of Decatur, Illinois.

2481 ■ NATIONAL FFA ORGANIZATION
Attn: Scholarship Office
6060 FFA Drive
P.O. Box 68960
Indianapolis, IN 46268-0960
Tel: (317)802-4321
Fax: (317)802-5321
E-mail: scholarships@ffa.org
Web Site: http://www.ffa.org
To provide financial assistance for college to FFA members from designated states.
Title of Award: Arysta LifeScience North America Scholarship **Area, Field, or Subject:** Agricultural sciences **Level of Education for which Award is Granted:** Undergraduate **Number Awarded:** 1 each year. **Funds Available:** The stipend is $5,350 per year. Funds are paid directly to the recipient. **Duration:** 1 year; nonrenewable.
Eligibility Requirements: This program is open to members from California, Illinois, Iowa, Kansas, New Mexico, North Dakota, Oregon, South Dakota, or Washington. Applicants must be high school seniors or college students working or planning to work full time on a degree in agriculture. They must have a GPA of 3.0 or higher. Selection is based on academic achievement (10 points for GPA, 10 points for SAT or ACT score, 10 points for class rank), leadership in FFA activities (30 points), leadership in community activities (10 points), and participation in the Supervised Agricultural Experience (SAE) program (30 points). U.S. citizenship is required. **Deadline for Receipt:** February of each year. **Additional Information:** This program is sponsored by Arysta LifeScience North America.

2482 ■ NATIONAL FFA ORGANIZATION
Attn: Scholarship Office
6060 FFA Drive
P.O. Box 68960
Indianapolis, IN 46268-0960
Tel: (317)802-4321
Fax: (317)802-5321
E-mail: scholarships@ffa.org
Web Site: http://www.ffa.org

To provide financial assistance to FFA members from Oklahoma and from designated counties in Arkansas, Kansas, Missouri, and Texas who are interested in studying agriculture in college.

Title of Award: Atwoods Stores Scholarships **Area, Field, or Subject:** Agricultural sciences **Level of Education for which Award is Granted:** Four Year College **Number Awarded:** 1 each year. **Funds Available:** The stipend is $1,000 per year. Funds are paid directly to the recipient. **Duration:** 1 year; nonrenewable.

Eligibility Requirements: This program is open to members who are graduating high school seniors planning to enroll full time in college. Applicants must be planning to work on a 4-year college degree in agriculture at an accredited institution in Arkansas, Kansas, Missouri, Oklahoma, or Texas. Arkansas residents are eligible if they are from 1 of the following 4 counties: Crawford, Logan, Scott, or Sebastian. Kansas residents are eligible if they are from 1 of the following 4 counties: Butler, Cowley, Sedgwick, or Sumner. Missouri residents are eligible if they are from 1 of the following 5 counties: Barton, Dade, Jasper, Lawrence, or Newton. Oklahoma residents from all counties are eligible. Texas residents are eligible if they are from 1 of the following 6 counties: Archer, Baylor, Clay, Wichita, Wilbarger, or Young. Selection is based on academic achievement (10 points for GPA, 10 points for SAT or ACT score, 10 points for class rank), leadership in FFA activities (30 points), leadership in community activities (10 points), and participation in the Supervised Agricultural Experience (SAE) program (30 points). U.S. citizenship is required. **Deadline for Receipt:** February of each year. **Additional Information:** Funding for these scholarships is provided by Atwoods Stores.

2483 ■ NATIONAL FFA ORGANIZATION

Attn: Scholarship Office
6060 FFA Drive
P.O. Box 68960
Indianapolis, IN 46268-0960
Tel: (317)802-4321
Fax: (317)802-5321
E-mail: scholarships@ffa.org
Web Site: http://www.ffa.org

To provide financial assistance to FFA members who are interested in studying agricultural science or engineering in college.

Title of Award: BASF Plant Systems Scholarships **Area, Field, or Subject:** Agricultural sciences; Engineering, Agricultural **Level of Education for which Award is Granted:** Four Year College **Number Awarded:** 3 each year. **Funds Available:** The stipend is $1,000. Funds are paid directly to the recipient. **Duration:** 1 year; nonrenewable.

Eligibility Requirements: This program is open to members who are graduating high school seniors planning to enroll full time in college. Applicants must be interested in working on a 4-year degree in agricultural science or engineering. They must have a GPA of 3.2 or higher and rank in the upper 30% of their class. Selection is based on academic achievement (10 points for GPA, 10 points for SAT or ACT score, 10 points for class rank), leadership in FFA activities (30 points), leadership in community activities (10 points), and participation in the Supervised Agricultural Experience (SAE) program (30 points). Financial need is also considered. U.S. citizenship is required. **Deadline for Receipt:** February of each year. **Additional Information:** Funding for these scholarships is provided by BASF Plant Sciences LLC.

2484 ■ NATIONAL FFA ORGANIZATION

Attn: Scholarship Office
6060 FFA Drive
P.O. Box 68960
Indianapolis, IN 46268-0960
Tel: (317)802-4321
Fax: (317)802-5321
E-mail: scholarships@ffa.org
Web Site: http://www.ffa.org

To provide financial assistance to FFA members from Nebraska who are interested in studying science or agriculture in college.

Title of Award: Walter and Ruby Behlen Memorial Scholarship **Area, Field, or Subject:** Agricultural sciences; Science **Level of Education for which Award is Granted:** Undergraduate **Number Awarded:** 1 each year. **Funds Available:** The stipend is $1,000. Funds are paid directly to the recipient. **Duration:** 1 year; nonrenewable.

Eligibility Requirements: This program is open to members who are graduating high school seniors planning to enroll full time in college. Applicants must be residents of Nebraska who are interested in working on a 2- or 4-year college degree in an agriculture or science area. Selection is based on academic achievement (10 points for GPA, 10 points for SAT or ACT score, 10 points for class rank), leadership in FFA activities (30 points), leadership in community activities (10 points), and participation in the Supervised Agricultural Experience (SAE) program (30 points). U.S. citizenship is required. **Deadline for Receipt:** February of each year. **Additional Information:** Funding for this scholarship is provided by Behlen Manufacturing Company.

2485 ■ NATIONAL FFA ORGANIZATION

Attn: Scholarship Office
6060 FFA Drive
P.O. Box 68960
Indianapolis, IN 46268-0960
Tel: (317)802-4321
Fax: (317)802-5321
E-mail: scholarships@ffa.org
Web Site: http://www.ffa.org

To provide financial assistance for the study of agriculture or agribusiness in college to FFA members from Alabama, Florida, and Georgia.

Title of Award: Birdsong Peanuts Scholarship **Area, Field, or Subject:** Agribusiness; Agricultural sciences **Level of Education for which Award is Granted:** Four Year College, Professional **Number Awarded:** 1 each year. **Funds Available:** The stipend is $1,000 per year. Funds are paid directly to the recipient. **Duration:** 1 year; nonrenewable.

Eligibility Requirements: This program is open to members who are graduating high school seniors planning to enroll full time in college. Applicants must be residents of Georgia, Florida, or Alabama who are planning to work on a 4-year degree in agriculture or agribusiness. They must be either peanut producers or from a peanut-producing family. Selection is based on academic achievement (10 points for GPA, 10 points for SAT or ACT score, 10 points for class rank), leadership in FFA activities (30 points), leadership in community activities (10 points), and participation in the Supervised Agricultural Experience (SAE) program (30 points). U.S. citizenship is required. **Deadline for Receipt:** February of each year. **Additional Information:** Funding for this scholarship is provided by Birdsong Peanuts.

2486 ■ NATIONAL FFA ORGANIZATION

Attn: Scholarship Office
6060 FFA Drive
P.O. Box 68960
Indianapolis, IN 46268-0960
Tel: (317)802-4321
Fax: (317)802-5321
E-mail: scholarships@ffa.org
Web Site: http://www.ffa.org

To provide financial assistance for college to FFA members who have served as an officer of the organization.

Title of Award: James C. Borel FFA Leaders Scholarship **Area, Field, or Subject:** Agricultural sciences **Level of Education for which Award is Granted:** Four Year College **Number Awarded:** 1 or more each year. **Funds Available:** The stipend is $1,000 per year. Funds are paid directly to the recipient. **Duration:** 1 year; nonrenewable.

Eligibility Requirements: This program is open to members who are either graduating high school seniors planning to enroll full time in college or students already enrolled in college on a full-time basis. Applicants must have served as a chapter, state, or national FFA officer. They must be working on or planning to work on a 4-year degree in agriculture and have a GPA of 3.5 or higher. Preference is given to students who have demonstrated exemplary leadership skills in their home, school, and community. Selection is based on academic achievement (10 points for GPA, 10 points for SAT or ACT score, 10 points for class rank), leadership in FFA activities (30 points), leadership in community activities (10 points), and participation in the Supervised Agricultural Experience (SAE) program (30 points). U.S. citizenship is required. **Deadline for Receipt:** February of each year.

2487 ■ NATIONAL FFA ORGANIZATION

Attn: Scholarship Office
6060 FFA Drive

P.O. Box 68960
Indianapolis, IN 46268-0960
Tel: (317)802-4321
Fax: (317)802-5321
E-mail: scholarships@ffa.org
Web Site: http://www.ffa.org
To provide financial assistance to FFA members who are interested in studying agricultural engineering in college.
Title of Award: Bridgestone/Firestone Trust Fund-Firestone Agricultural Tire Company Scholarships **Area, Field, or Subject:** Engineering, Agricultural; General studies/Field of study not specified **Level of Education for which Award is Granted:** Four Year College **Number Awarded:** 5 each year. **Funds Available:** The stipend is $2,500. Funds are paid directly to the recipient. **Duration:** 1 year; nonrenewable.
Eligibility Requirements: This program is open to members who are either graduating high school seniors planning to enroll in college or students already enrolled full time in college. Applicants must be interested in working on a 4-year degree with a preferred major in agricultural engineering. They must submit a parent financial analysis and obtain a certified Firestone dealer's signature on their application. Selection is based on academic achievement (10 points for GPA, 10 points for SAT or ACT score, 10 points for class rank), leadership in FFA activities (30 points), leadership in community activities (10 points), and participation in the Supervised Agricultural Experience (SAE) program (30 points). U.S. citizenship is required. **Deadline for Receipt:** February of each year. **Additional Information:** Funding for these scholarships is provided by the Bridgestone/Firestone Trust Fund and Firestone Agricultural Tire Company.

2488 ■ NATIONAL FFA ORGANIZATION

Attn: Scholarship Office
6060 FFA Drive
P.O. Box 68960
Indianapolis, IN 46268-0960
Tel: (317)802-4321
Fax: (317)802-5321
E-mail: scholarships@ffa.org
Web Site: http://www.ffa.org
To provide financial assistance to FFA members with disabilities who are interested in studying agriculture in college.
Title of Award: Building Rural Initiative for Disabled through Group Effort (B.R.I.D.G.E.) Endowment Fund Scholarships **Area, Field, or Subject:** Agricultural sciences **Level of Education for which Award is Granted:** Undergraduate **Number Awarded:** 1 or more each year. **Funds Available:** The stipend is $5,000. **Duration:** 1 year; nonrenewable.
Eligibility Requirements: This program is open to members with physical disabilities who are graduating high school seniors planning to enroll full time in college. Applicants must be interested in working on a 2-year or 4-year degree in agriculture. Selection is based on academic achievement (10 points for GPA, 10 points for SAT or ACT score, 10 points for class rank), leadership in FFA activities (30 points), leadership in community activities (10 points), and participation in the Supervised Agricultural Experience (SAE) program (30 points). U.S. citizenship is required. **Deadline for Receipt:** February of each year. **Additional Information:** This program is supported by the Dr. Scholl Foundation, Outdoor Advertising Association of America, and many caring individuals.

2489 ■ NATIONAL FFA ORGANIZATION

Attn: Scholarship Office
6060 FFA Drive
P.O. Box 68960
Indianapolis, IN 46268-0960
Tel: (317)802-4321
Fax: (317)802-5321
E-mail: scholarships@ffa.org
Web Site: http://www.ffa.org
To provide financial assistance to FFA members from designated states who are interested in studying agriculture or food science in college.
Title of Award: Bunge North America Scholarship **Area, Field, or Subject:** Agricultural sciences; Food science and technology **Level of Education for which Award is Granted:** Four Year College **Number Awarded:** 1 each year. **Funds Available:** The stipend is $2,000. Funds are paid directly to the recipient. **Duration:** 1 year; nonrenewable.

Eligibility Requirements: This program is open to members who are graduating high school seniors planning to enroll full time in college. Applicants must be residents of Alabama, Arkansas, California, Illinois, Indiana, Iowa, Kansas, Kentucky, Louisiana, Minnesota, Mississippi, Missouri, Nebraska, Ohio, Rhode Island, Tennessee, or Texas and interested in working on a 4-year degree in agriculture or food science. They must have a GPA of 3.0 or higher and be able to demonstrate active community involvement and strong leadership skills. Selection is based on academic achievement (10 points for GPA, 10 points for SAT or ACT score, 10 points for class rank), leadership in FFA activities (30 points), leadership in community activities (10 points), and participation in the Supervised Agricultural Experience (SAE) program (30 points). U.S. citizenship is required. **Deadline for Receipt:** February of each year. **Additional Information:** Funding for this scholarship is provided by Bunge North America, Inc. of St. Louis.

2490 ■ NATIONAL FFA ORGANIZATION

Attn: Scholarship Office
6060 FFA Drive
P.O. Box 68960
Indianapolis, IN 46268-0960
Tel: (317)802-4321
Fax: (317)802-5321
E-mail: scholarships@ffa.org
Web Site: http://www.ffa.org
To provide financial assistance for the study of agriculture in college to FFA members.
Title of Award: Burley Tobacco Growers Cooperative Association Scholarship **Area, Field, or Subject:** Agricultural sciences **Level of Education for which Award is Granted:** Four Year College **Number Awarded:** 1 each year. **Funds Available:** The stipend is $1,000 per year. Funds are paid directly to the recipient. **Duration:** 1 year; nonrenewable.
Eligibility Requirements: This program is open to members who are graduating high school seniors planning to enroll or currently enrolled full time in college. Applicants must have a GPA of 2.5 or higher and be planning to work on a 4-year degree with an agricultural major. They must be from a tobacco-producing family and must include a statement of interest in the tobacco industry in their application. Selection is based on academic achievement (10 points for GPA, 10 points for SAT or ACT score, 10 points for class rank), leadership in FFA activities (30 points), leadership in community activities (10 points), and participation in the Supervised Agricultural Experience (SAE) program (30 points). U.S. citizenship is required. **Deadline for Receipt:** February of each year. **Additional Information:** Funding for this scholarship is provided by the Burley Tobacco Growers Cooperative Association of Lexington, Kentucky.

2491 ■ NATIONAL FFA ORGANIZATION

Attn: Scholarship Office
6060 FFA Drive
P.O. Box 68960
Indianapolis, IN 46268-0960
Tel: (317)802-4321
Fax: (317)802-5321
E-mail: scholarships@ffa.org
Web Site: http://www.ffa.org
To provide financial assistance to FFA members from selected states interested in studying field related to agribusiness in college.
Title of Award: Burlington Northern Santa Fe Corporation Scholarships **Area, Field, or Subject:** Agribusiness; Agriculture, Economic aspects; Finance; Marketing and distribution **Level of Education for which Award is Granted:** Four Year College **Number Awarded:** 10 each year: 1 from each of the eligible states. **Funds Available:** The stipend is $1,250 per year. Funds are paid directly to the recipient. **Duration:** 1 year; may be renewed up to 3 additional years provided the recipient maintains a GPA of 3.0 or higher.
Eligibility Requirements: This program is open to members who are graduating high school seniors planning to enroll full time in college. Applicants must be residents of California, Illinois, Iowa, Kansas, Minnesota, Montana, Nebraska, North Dakota, South Dakota, or Texas planning to work on a 4-year degree in the following areas of agriculture: business management, finance, economics, sales, and marketing. They must have a GPA of 3.0 or higher. Selection is based on academic achievement (10 points for GPA, 10 points for SAT or ACT score, 10 points for class rank),

leadership in FFA activities (30 points), leadership in community activities (10 points), and participation in the Supervised Agricultural Experience (SAE) program (30 points). U.S. citizenship is required. **Deadline for Receipt:** February of each year. **Additional Information:** Funding for these scholarships is provided by the Burlington Northern Santa Fe Foundation.

2492 ■ NATIONAL FFA ORGANIZATION
Attn: Scholarship Office
6060 FFA Drive
P.O. Box 68960
Indianapolis, IN 46268-0960
Tel: (317)802-4321
Fax: (317)802-5321
E-mail: scholarships@ffa.org
Web Site: http://www.ffa.org
To provide financial assistance to FFA members from Oregon who are Native Americans interested in studying agriculture in college.
Title of Award: Carl Casale Honorary Scholarship **Area, Field, or Subject:** Agricultural sciences **Level of Education for which Award is Granted:** Undergraduate **Number Awarded:** 1 each year. **Funds Available:** The stipend is $2,000. Funds are paid directly to the recipient. **Duration:** 1 year; nonrenewable.
Eligibility Requirements: This program is open to members who are Native Americans and graduating high school seniors planning to enroll full time in college. Applicants must be residents of Oregon interested in studying agriculture. They must have a GPA of 3.0 or higher. Selection is based on academic achievement (10 points for GPA, 10 points for SAT or ACT score, 10 points for class rank), leadership in FFA activities (30 points), leadership in community activities (10 points), and participation in the Supervised Agricultural Experience (SAE) program (30 points). U.S. citizenship is required. **Deadline for Receipt:** February of each year.

2493 ■ NATIONAL FFA ORGANIZATION
Attn: Scholarship Office
6060 FFA Drive
P.O. Box 68960
Indianapolis, IN 46268-0960
Tel: (317)802-4321
Fax: (317)802-5321
E-mail: scholarships@ffa.org
Web Site: http://www.ffa.org
To provide financial assistance to FFA members from selected states interested in studying agriculture or agribusiness in college.
Title of Award: Casey's General Stores Scholarships **Area, Field, or Subject:** Agribusiness; Agricultural sciences **Level of Education for which Award is Granted:** Undergraduate **Number Awarded:** 3 each year. **Funds Available:** The stipend is $1,000 per year. Funds are paid directly to the recipient. **Duration:** 1 year; nonrenewable.
Eligibility Requirements: This program is open to members who are graduating high school seniors planning to enroll full time in college. Applicants must be residents of Illinois, Indiana, Iowa, Kansas, Minnesota, Missouri, Nebraska, South Dakota, or Wisconsin planning to work on a 2-year or 4-year college degree in agriculture or agribusiness. Selection is based on financial need, leadership, and academic achievement. **Deadline for Receipt:** February of each year. **Additional Information:** Funding for these scholarships is provided by Casey's General Stores, Inc.

2494 ■ NATIONAL FFA ORGANIZATION
Attn: Scholarship Office
6060 FFA Drive
P.O. Box 68960
Indianapolis, IN 46268-0960
Tel: (317)802-4321
Fax: (317)802-5321
E-mail: scholarships@ffa.org
Web Site: http://www.ffa.org
To provide financial assistance to FFA members from Florida and Georgia who are interested in studying fields related to agriculture in college.
Title of Award: Chevron Corporation Scholarships **Area, Field, or Subject:** Agricultural sciences; Communications; Education; Environmental conservation; Environmental science; Natural resources; Wildlife conservation, management, and science **Level of Education for which Award is Granted:** Undergraduate **Number Awarded:** 2 each year. **Funds Available:** The stipend is $1,000. Funds are paid directly to the recipient. **Duration:** 1 year; nonrenewable.
Eligibility Requirements: This program is open to members who are graduating high school seniors planning to enroll full time in college. Applicants must be residents of Florida or Georgia planning to work on a 2-year or 4-year degree in agricultural communications and education, environmental engineering, environmental science, natural resource management, wildlife management, or public service and administration in agriculture. Preference is given to those who have shown outstanding leadership. Selection is based on academic achievement (10 points for GPA, 10 points for SAT or ACT score, 10 points for class rank), leadership in FFA activities (30 points), leadership in community activities (10 points), and participation in the Supervised Agricultural Experience (SAE) program (30 points). U.S. citizenship is required. **Deadline for Receipt:** February of each year. **Additional Information:** Funding for these scholarships is provided by ChevronTexaco Corporation.

2495 ■ NATIONAL FFA ORGANIZATION
Attn: Scholarship Office
6060 FFA Drive
P.O. Box 68960
Indianapolis, IN 46268-0960
Tel: (317)802-4321
Fax: (317)802-5321
E-mail: scholarships@ffa.org
Web Site: http://www.ffa.org
To provide financial assistance to FFA members interested in studying agribusiness or management in college.
Title of Award: Chicago Mercantile Exchange Scholarships **Area, Field, or Subject:** Agribusiness; Agriculture, Economic aspects; Management **Level of Education for which Award is Granted:** Four Year College **Number Awarded:** 1 each year. **Funds Available:** The stipend is $1,000 per year. Funds are paid directly to the recipient. **Duration:** 1 year; nonrenewable.
Eligibility Requirements: This program is open to members who are graduating high school seniors planning to enroll full time in college. Applicants must be interested in working on a 4-year degree in agribusiness, including such majors as agricultural economics or agricultural business management. Special consideration is given to students whose family's livelihood is connected to the commodity brokerage business. Selection is based on academic achievement (10 points for GPA, 10 points for SAT or ACT score, 10 points for class rank), leadership in FFA activities (30 points), leadership in community activities (10 points), and participation in the Supervised Agricultural Experience (SAE) program (30 points). U.S. citizenship is required. **Deadline for Receipt:** February of each year. **Additional Information:** Funding for this scholarship is provided by the Chicago Mercantile Exchange.

2496 ■ NATIONAL FFA ORGANIZATION
Attn: Scholarship Office
6060 FFA Drive
P.O. Box 68960
Indianapolis, IN 46268-0960
Tel: (317)802-4321
Fax: (317)802-5321
E-mail: scholarships@ffa.org
Web Site: http://www.ffa.org
To provide financial assistance to FFA members from Nebraska who are interested in studying agriculture in college.
Title of Award: Chief Industries Scholarships **Area, Field, or Subject:** Agricultural sciences **Level of Education for which Award is Granted:** Four Year College **Number Awarded:** 1 each year. **Funds Available:** The stipend is $1,000. Funds are paid directly to the recipient. **Duration:** 1 year; nonrenewable.
Eligibility Requirements: This program is open to members who are graduating high school seniors planning to enroll full time in college. Applicants must be residents of Nebraska interested in working on a 4-year degree in agriculture at a college in the state. Selection is based on academic achievement (10 points for GPA, 10 points for SAT or ACT score, 10 points for class rank), leadership in FFA activities (30 points), leadership in community activities (10 points), and participation in the

Supervised Agricultural Experience (SAE) program (30 points). U.S. citizenship is required. **Deadline for Receipt:** February of each year. **Additional Information:** Funding for these scholarships is provided by Chief Industries, Inc.

2497 ■ NATIONAL FFA ORGANIZATION

Attn: Scholarship Office
6060 FFA Drive
P.O. Box 68960
Indianapolis, IN 46268-0960
Tel: (317)802-4321
Fax: (317)802-5321
E-mail: scholarships@ffa.org
Web Site: http://www.ffa.org
To provide financial assistance to FFA members from Illinois interested in studying agriculture in college.

Title of Award: ClawEl Scholarships **Area, Field, or Subject:** Agricultural sciences **Level of Education for which Award is Granted:** Undergraduate **Number Awarded:** 2 each year. **Funds Available:** The stipend is $1,250 per year. Funds are paid directly to the recipient. **Duration:** 1 year; nonrenewable.

Eligibility Requirements: This program is open to members who are graduating high school seniors in Illinois and planning to enroll full time in college. Applicants must have a GPA of 2.5 or higher and be interested in working on a 2- or 4-year degree in agriculture. Selection is based on academic achievement (10 points for GPA, 10 points for SAT or ACT score, 10 points for class rank), leadership in FFA activities (30 points), leadership in community activities (10 points), and participation in the Supervised Agricultural Experience (SAE) program (30 points). U.S. citizenship is required. **Deadline for Receipt:** February of each year. **Additional Information:** Funding for these scholarships is provided by ClawEl Specialty Products.

2498 ■ NATIONAL FFA ORGANIZATION

Attn: Scholarship Office
6060 FFA Drive
P.O. Box 68960
Indianapolis, IN 46268-0960
Tel: (317)802-4321
Fax: (317)802-5321
E-mail: scholarships@ffa.org
Web Site: http://www.ffa.org
To provide financial assistance to high school students from farm families who plan to study agriculture in college.

Title of Award: Commitment to Agriculture Scholarship Program **Area, Field, or Subject:** Agricultural sciences **Level of Education for which Award is Granted:** Undergraduate **Number Awarded:** 100 each year. **Funds Available:** The stipend is $1,500. **Duration:** 1 year; nonrenewable.

Eligibility Requirements: This program is open to high school seniors whose families are actively engaged in production agriculture. Applicants must be planning to study an agricultural field in college on a full-time basis and prepare for a career in agriculture. They must have an ACT composite score of 18 or higher or an SAT combined verbal and math score of 850 or higher. As part of the application process, they must submit an essay on the importance of innovation to U.S. agriculture. If they are a member of FFA, they must also include a statement from their advisor evaluating their involvement in FFA activities and indicating special circumstances, such as financial need, that should be considered. If they are not FFA members, they must provide documentation of other school, community, leadership, and work activities. **Deadline for Receipt:** February of each year. **Additional Information:** This program, established in 1999, is funded by Monsanto Company (using pretrial settlement funds received in seed patent infringement cases) and the National Association of Farm Broadcasters.

2499 ■ NATIONAL FFA ORGANIZATION

Attn: Scholarship Office
6060 FFA Drive
P.O. Box 68960
Indianapolis, IN 46268-0960
Tel: (317)802-4321
Fax: (317)802-5321

E-mail: scholarships@ffa.org
Web Site: http://www.ffa.org
To provide financial assistance to FFA members interested in studying dairy science in college.

Title of Award: Hoard's Dairyman Scholarship **Area, Field, or Subject:** Agricultural sciences; Communications; Dairy science **Level of Education for which Award is Granted:** Four Year College **Number Awarded:** 1 each year. **Funds Available:** The stipend is $1,000 per year. Funds are paid directly to the recipient. **Duration:** 1 year; nonrenewable.

Eligibility Requirements: This program is open to members who are graduating high school seniors planning to enroll full time in college. Applicants must be interested in working on a 4-year degree in dairy science. Preference is given to applicants with agricultural journalism experience. Selection is based on academic achievement (10 points for GPA, 10 points for SAT or ACT score, 10 points for class rank), leadership in FFA activities (30 points), leadership in community activities (10 points), and participation in the Supervised Agricultural Experience (SAE) program (30 points). U.S. citizenship is required. **Deadline for Receipt:** February of each year. **Additional Information:** Funding for this scholarship is provided by W.D. Hoard & Sons Company, publisher of *Hoard's Dairyman.*

2500 ■ NATIONAL FFA ORGANIZATION

Attn: Scholarship Office
6060 FFA Drive
P.O. Box 68960
Indianapolis, IN 46268-0960
Tel: (317)802-4321
Fax: (317)802-5321
E-mail: scholarships@ffa.org
Web Site: http://www.ffa.org
To provide financial assistance to FFA members from selected states interested in studying agriculture in college.

Title of Award: Delta and Pine Land Company Scholarship **Area, Field, or Subject:** Agricultural sciences **Level of Education for which Award is Granted:** Four Year College **Number Awarded:** 4 each year. **Funds Available:** The stipend is $1,250 per year. Funds are paid directly to the recipient. **Duration:** 1 year; nonrenewable.

Eligibility Requirements: This program is open to members who are high school seniors or college students enrolled or planning to enroll full time at a 4-year college or university and work on a degree in any field of agriculture. Applicants must be a resident of Georgia, Mississippi, North Carolina, South Carolina, or Texas. Preference is given to students whose families are involved in the cotton industry. Selection is based on academic achievement (10 points for GPA, 10 points for SAT or ACT score, 10 points for class rank), leadership in FFA activities (30 points), leadership in community activities (10 points), and participation in the Supervised Agricultural Experience (SAE) program (30 points). U.S. citizenship is required. **Deadline for Receipt:** February of each year. **Additional Information:** Funding for this scholarship is provided by Delta and Pine Land Company.

2501 ■ NATIONAL FFA ORGANIZATION

Attn: Scholarship Office
6060 FFA Drive
P.O. Box 68960
Indianapolis, IN 46268-0960
Tel: (317)802-4321
Fax: (317)802-5321
E-mail: scholarships@ffa.org
Web Site: http://www.ffa.org
To provide financial assistance to FFA members from Minnesota and Nebraska who are interested in studying agriculture in college.

Title of Award: DTN Scholarships **Area, Field, or Subject:** Agricultural sciences **Level of Education for which Award is Granted:** Four Year College **Number Awarded:** 2 each year: 1 to a resident of each state. **Funds Available:** The stipend is $2,000. Funds are paid directly to the recipient. **Duration:** 1 year; nonrenewable.

Eligibility Requirements: This program is open to members who are graduating high school seniors planning to enroll or college students currently enrolled full time. Applicants must be residents of Minnesota or Nebraska working on or planning to work on a 4-year degree in agriculture. Selection is based on academic achievement (10 points for

GPA, 10 points for SAT or ACT score, 10 points for class rank), leadership in FFA activities (30 points), leadership in community activities (10 points), and participation in the Supervised Agricultural Experience (SAE) program (30 points). U.S. citizenship is required. **Deadline for Receipt:** February of each year. **Additional Information:** Funding for these scholarships is provided by DTN.

2502 ■ NATIONAL FFA ORGANIZATION

Attn: Scholarship Office
6060 FFA Drive
P.O. Box 68960
Indianapolis, IN 46268-0960
Tel: (317)802-4321
Fax: (317)802-5321
E-mail: scholarships@ffa.org
Web Site: http://www.ffa.org
To provide financial assistance to FFA members from Nebraska who are interested in studying agriculture in college.

Title of Award: Virgil Eihusen Foundation Scholarships **Area, Field, or Subject:** Agricultural sciences **Level of Education for which Award is Granted:** Undergraduate **Number Awarded:** 1 each year. **Funds Available:** The stipend is $1,400. Funds are paid directly to the recipient. **Duration:** 1 year; nonrenewable.
Eligibility Requirements: This program is open to members who are either graduating high school seniors planning to enroll full time in college or students already enrolled in college on a full-time basis. Applicants must be residents of Nebraska working on or planning to work on a 2-year or 4-year degree in agriculture. Selection is based on academic achievement (10 points for GPA, 10 points for SAT or ACT score, 10 points for class rank), leadership in FFA activities (30 points), leadership in community activities (10 points), and participation in the Supervised Agricultural Experience (SAE) program (30 points). U.S. citizenship is required. **Deadline for Receipt:** February of each year. **Additional Information:** Funding for these scholarships is provided by the MFS/YORK/STORMOR division of Global Industries, Inc. of Grand Island, Nebraska.

2503 ■ NATIONAL FFA ORGANIZATION

Attn: Scholarship Office
6060 FFA Drive
P.O. Box 68960
Indianapolis, IN 46268-0960
Tel: (317)802-4321
Fax: (317)802-5321
E-mail: scholarships@ffa.org
Web Site: http://www.ffa.org
To provide financial assistance to FFA members from family farms interested in studying agriculture in college.

Title of Award: FarmAid Scholarships **Area, Field, or Subject:** Agricultural sciences **Level of Education for which Award is Granted:** Four Year College **Number Awarded:** Approximately 4 each year. **Funds Available:** The stipend is $1,500 for the freshman year, $1,000 for the sophomore year, and $500 for the junior year. Funds are paid directly to the recipient. **Duration:** 3 years, provided the recipient maintains a GPA of 2.0 or higher.
Eligibility Requirements: This program is open to members who are graduating high school seniors planning to enroll full time in college. Applicants must be from family-owned farms and must be planning to work on a 4-year degree in agriculture. Selection is based on academic achievement (10 points for GPA, 10 points for SAT or ACT score, 10 points for class rank), leadership in FFA activities (30 points), leadership in community activities (10 points), and participation in the Supervised Agricultural Experience (SAE) program (30 points). Financial need is also considered. U.S. citizenship is required. **Deadline for Receipt:** February of each year. **Additional Information:** FarmAid has established a $300,000 FFA scholarship endowment, with the income to be used for scholarships.

2504 ■ NATIONAL FFA ORGANIZATION

Attn: Scholarship Office
6060 FFA Drive
P.O. Box 68960
Indianapolis, IN 46268-0960

Tel: (317)802-4321
Fax: (317)802-5321
E-mail: scholarships@ffa.org
Web Site: http://www.ffa.org
To provide financial assistance to FFA members from selected states who are interested in studying agriculture at a 4-year institution.

Title of Award: Farmers Mutual Hail Insurance Company of Iowa Scholarships **Area, Field, or Subject:** Agricultural sciences **Level of Education for which Award is Granted:** Four Year College **Number Awarded:** 15 each year: 1 from each of the specified states. **Funds Available:** The stipend is $1,000. Funds are paid directly to the recipient. **Duration:** 1 year; nonrenewable.
Eligibility Requirements: This program is open to members who are graduating high school seniors planning to enroll or students already enrolled full time in college. Applicants must be interested in working on a 4-year degree in agriculture and be residents of 1 of the following states: Arkansas, Colorado, Illinois, Indiana, Iowa, Kansas, Michigan, Minnesota, Missouri, Nebraska, North Dakota, Ohio, Oklahoma, South Dakota, or Wisconsin. Selection is based on academic achievement (10 points for GPA, 10 points for SAT or ACT score, 10 points for class rank), leadership in FFA activities (30 points), leadership in community activities (10 points), and participation in the Supervised Agricultural Experience (SAE) program (30 points). U.S. citizenship is required. **Deadline for Receipt:** February of each year. **Additional Information:** Funding for these scholarships is provided by Farmers Mutual Hail Insurance Company of Iowa.

2505 ■ NATIONAL FFA ORGANIZATION

Attn: Scholarship Office
6060 FFA Drive
P.O. Box 68960
Indianapolis, IN 46268-0960
Tel: (317)802-4321
Fax: (317)802-5321
E-mail: scholarships@ffa.org
Web Site: http://www.ffa.org
To provide financial assistance to FFA members from designated states who are interested in studying agricultural business management.

Title of Award: Fastline Publications Scholarships **Area, Field, or Subject:** Agricultural sciences; Business administration; Management **Level of Education for which Award is Granted:** Undergraduate **Number Awarded:** 27 each year: 17 to students at 4-year colleges and universities (1 each to residents of Illinois, Indiana, Iowa, Kansas, Kentucky, Michigan, Minnesota, Missouri, Nebraska, Ohio, Oklahoma, Tennessee, and Wisconsin; 1 to a resident of North or South Carolina; 1 to a resident of Arkansas or Louisiana; 1 to a resident of New York or Pennsylvania; and 1 to a resident of Alabama, Florida, or Georgia); and 10 to students at 2-year colleges and vocational schools (1 each to residents of Kansas, Kentucky, Missouri, Ohio, Oklahoma, and Texas; 1 to a resident of North or South Carolina; 1 to a resident of Arkansas or Louisiana; 1 to a resident of New York or Pennsylvania; and 1 to a resident of Alabama, Florida, or Georgia). **Funds Available:** The stipend is $1,000 per year. Funds are paid directly to the recipient. **Duration:** 1 year; nonrenewable.
Eligibility Requirements: This program is open to members who are graduating high school seniors planning to enroll full time in college. Applicants must be interested in working on a degree in agricultural business management and demonstrate interest in managing a farm. They must be planning to enroll at a 4-year college or university and be a resident of 22 designated states, or enroll at a 2-year college or vocational school and be a resident of 15 designated states. Selection is based on academic achievement (10 points for GPA, 10 points for SAT or ACT score, 10 points for class rank), leadership in FFA activities (30 points), leadership in community activities (10 points), and participation in the Supervised Agricultural Experience (SAE) program (30 points). U.S. citizenship is required. **Deadline for Receipt:** February of each year. **Additional Information:** Funding for these scholarships is provided by Fastline Publications.

2506 ■ NATIONAL FFA ORGANIZATION

Attn: Scholarship Office
6060 FFA Drive
P.O. Box 68960
Indianapolis, IN 46268-0960

Tel: (317)802-4321
Fax: (317)802-5321
E-mail: scholarships@ffa.org
Web Site: http://www.ffa.org
To provide financial assistance to FFA members from specified states interested in studying agriculture in college.

Title of Award: Fontanelle Hybrid Seed Company Scholarships **Area, Field, or Subject:** Agricultural sciences **Level of Education for which Award is Granted:** Four Year College **Number Awarded:** 4 each year: 1 to a student from each of the eligible states. **Funds Available:** The stipend is $1,000 per year. Funds are paid directly to the recipient. **Duration:** 1 year; nonrenewable.
Eligibility Requirements: This program is open to members who are graduating high school seniors or current college students. Applicants must be residents of Iowa, Kansas, Missouri, or Nebraska and working on or planning to work on a 4-year degree in agriculture at a college or university in their home state. Selection is based on academic achievement (10 points for GPA, 10 points for SAT or ACT score, 10 points for class rank), leadership in FFA activities (30 points), leadership in community activities (10 points), and participation in the Supervised Agricultural Experience (SAE) program (30 points). U.S. citizenship is required. **Deadline for Receipt:** February of each year. **Additional Information:** Funding for these scholarships is provided by Fontanelle Hybrid Seed Company.

2507 ■ NATIONAL FFA ORGANIZATION
Attn: Scholarship Office
6060 FFA Drive
P.O. Box 68960
Indianapolis, IN 46268-0960
Tel: (317)802-4321
Fax: (317)802-5321
E-mail: scholarships@ffa.org
Web Site: http://www.ffa.org
To provide financial assistance to FFA members who are interested in studying agriculture in college.

Title of Award: Garst Seed Company Scholarship **Area, Field, or Subject:** Agribusiness; Agricultural sciences; Communications; Education; Marketing and distribution **Level of Education for which Award is Granted:** Four Year College **Number Awarded:** 25 each year: 10 to students with any agricultural major, 5 to students majoring in agricultural communications or education, and 10 to students in agricultural marketing, merchandising, or sales. **Funds Available:** The stipend is $1,000. Funds are paid directly to the recipient. **Duration:** 1 year; nonrenewable.
Eligibility Requirements: This program is open to members who are graduating high school seniors planning to enroll or students currently enrolled full time in college. Applicants must be interested in working on a 4-year college degree in agriculture; in agricultural communications or education; or in agricultural marketing, merchandising, or sales. Selection is based on academic achievement (10 points for GPA, 10 points for SAT or ACT score, 10 points for class rank), leadership in FFA activities (30 points), leadership in community activities (10 points), and participation in the Supervised Agricultural Experience (SAE) program (30 points). U.S. citizenship is required. **Deadline for Receipt:** February of each year. **Additional Information:** Funding for this scholarship is provided by Garst Seed Company.

2508 ■ NATIONAL FFA ORGANIZATION
Attn: Scholarship Office
6060 FFA Drive
P.O. Box 68960
Indianapolis, IN 46268-0960
Tel: (317)802-4321
Fax: (317)802-5321
E-mail: scholarships@ffa.org
Web Site: http://www.ffa.org
To provide financial assistance to FFA members from Indiana interested in studying agriculture at a university in the state.

Title of Award: Indiana Farmers Mutual Insurance Group Scholarship **Area, Field, or Subject:** Agricultural sciences **Level of Education for which Award is Granted:** Four Year College **Number Awarded:** 1 each year. **Funds Available:** The stipend is $1,000 per year. Funds are paid directly to the recipient. **Duration:** 1 year; nonrenewable.

Eligibility Requirements: This program is open to members who are graduating high school seniors or students already enrolled in college. Applicants must be residents of Indiana and planning to full time work on a 4-year degree in agriculture at a university in the state. Selection is based on academic achievement (10 points for GPA, 10 points for SAT or ACT score, 10 points for class rank), leadership in FFA activities (30 points), leadership in community activities (10 points), and participation in the Supervised Agricultural Experience (SAE) program (30 points). U.S. citizenship is required. **Deadline for Receipt:** February of each year. **Additional Information:** Funding for this scholarship is provided by Indiana Farmers Mutual Insurance Group.

2509 ■ NATIONAL FFA ORGANIZATION
Attn: Scholarship Office
6060 FFA Drive
P.O. Box 68960
Indianapolis, IN 46268-0960
Tel: (317)802-4321
Fax: (317)802-5321
E-mail: scholarships@ffa.org
Web Site: http://www.ffa.org
To provide financial assistance to FFA members interested in studying agriculture, horticulture, or landscaping in college.

Title of Award: Irrigation Association Education Foundation Scholarship **Area, Field, or Subject:** Agricultural sciences; Horticulture; Landscape architecture and design **Level of Education for which Award is Granted:** Four Year College **Number Awarded:** 1 each year. **Funds Available:** The stipend is $1,000 per year. Funds are paid directly to the recipient. **Duration:** 1 year; nonrenewable.
Eligibility Requirements: This program is open to members who are graduating high school seniors planning to enroll full time in college. Applicants must be interested in working on a 4-year college degree in agriculture, horticulture, or landscaping. They must be in the top 10% of their class and an interest in irrigation that is confirmed by their advisor. Selection is based on academic achievement (10 points for GPA, 10 points for SAT or ACT score, 10 points for class rank), leadership in FFA activities (30 points), leadership in community activities (10 points), and participation in the Supervised Agricultural Experience (SAE) program (30 points). U.S. citizenship is required. **Deadline for Receipt:** February of each year. **Additional Information:** Funding for this scholarship is provided by the Irrigation Association Education Foundation.

2510 ■ NATIONAL FFA ORGANIZATION
Attn: Scholarship Office
6060 FFA Drive
P.O. Box 68960
Indianapolis, IN 46268-0960
Tel: (317)802-4321
Fax: (317)802-5321
E-mail: scholarships@ffa.org
Web Site: http://www.ffa.org
To provide financial assistance to FFA members, including those from specified communities, interested in studying agriculture in college.

Title of Award: Kraft Foods Scholarships **Area, Field, or Subject:** Agricultural sciences **Level of Education for which Award is Granted:** Four Year College **Number Awarded:** 15 each year: 4 to applicants from the designated communities and 11 selected from any state that has a Kraft facility. **Funds Available:** The stipend is $1,000 per year. Funds are paid directly to the recipient. **Duration:** 1 year; nonrenewable.
Eligibility Requirements: This program is open to members who are either graduating high school seniors planning to enroll full time in college or students already enrolled in college on a full-time basis. Applicants must be working on or planning to work on a 4-year degree in agriculture. They must have a GPA of 3.0 or higher and be in the 75th percentile of their class. The program includes awards designated for applicants from Lowville, New York (Lowville Central FFA), Champaign, Illinois (Rantoul and Monticello FFA), Tulare, California (Tulare Western FFA), and Waupaca, Wisconsin (Waupace-Fre FFA). Selection is based on academic achievement (10 points for GPA, 10 points for SAT or ACT score, 10 points for class rank), leadership in FFA activities (30 points), leadership in community activities (10 points), and participation in the Supervised Agricultural Experience (SAE) program (30 points). U.S. citizenship is required. **Deadline for Receipt:** February of each year. **Ad-**

ditional Information: This program is sponsored by Kraft Foods, Inc.

2511 ■ NATIONAL FFA ORGANIZATION

Attn: Scholarship Office
6060 FFA Drive
P.O. Box 68960
Indianapolis, IN 46268-0960
Tel: (317)802-4321
Fax: (317)802-5321
E-mail: scholarships@ffa.org
Web Site: http://www.ffa.org
To provide financial assistance to FFA members from California, Idaho, or Arizona interested in studying agriculture in college.
Title of Award: FFA Charles P. Lake Rain for Rent Scholarship **Area, Field, or Subject:** Agricultural sciences; Soil science; Water resources **Level of Education for which Award is Granted:** Four Year College **Number Awarded:** 1 each year. **Funds Available:** The stipend is $1,000 per year. Funds are paid directly to the recipient. **Duration:** 1 year; nonrenewable.
Eligibility Requirements: This program is open to members who have completed the freshman year of a 4-year degree program with a major in agriculture. Preference is given to students who are specializing in irrigation and soil technology. Applicants must 1) be residents of Arizona, California, or Idaho; 2) have a GPA of 3.0 or higher; and 3) include the parent financial analysis. Selection is based on scholastic achievement, leadership skills, and financial need. **Deadline for Receipt:** February of each year. **Additional Information:** Funding for these scholarships is provided by Rain for Rent. Recipients must be willing to provide a picture for publicity purposes and visit the Rain for Rent facilities for an orientation.

2512 ■ NATIONAL FFA ORGANIZATION

Attn: Scholarship Office
6060 FFA Drive
P.O. Box 68960
Indianapolis, IN 46268-0960
Tel: (317)802-4321
Fax: (317)802-5321
E-mail: scholarships@ffa.org
Web Site: http://www.ffa.org
To provide financial assistance to FFA members from Minnesota interested in studying food-related fields at a college or university in the state.
Title of Award: Malt-O-Meal Company Scholarship **Area, Field, or Subject:** Agricultural sciences; Business administration; Food science and technology **Level of Education for which Award is Granted:** Undergraduate **Number Awarded:** 2 each year. **Funds Available:** The stipend is $1,000 per year. Funds are paid directly to the recipient. **Duration:** 1 year; nonrenewable.
Eligibility Requirements: This program is open to members who are graduating high school seniors planning to enroll full time in college. Applicants must be residents of Minnesota interested in working on a 2- or 4-year degree in agriculture, food science, food technology, or business at a college or university in the state. Selection is based on academic achievement (10 points for GPA, 10 points for SAT or ACT score, 10 points for class rank), leadership in FFA activities (30 points), leadership in community activities (10 points), and participation in the Supervised Agricultural Experience (SAE) program (30 points). U.S. citizenship is required. **Deadline for Receipt:** February of each year. **Additional Information:** Funding for this scholarship is provided by Malt-O-Meal Company.

2513 ■ NATIONAL FFA ORGANIZATION

Attn: Scholarship Office
6060 FFA Drive
P.O. Box 68960
Indianapolis, IN 46268-0960
Tel: (317)802-4321
Fax: (317)802-5321
E-mail: scholarships@ffa.org
Web Site: http://www.ffa.org
To provide financial assistance to FFA members who are interested in majoring in agricultural and forest production in college.

Title of Award: Manistique Papers Scholarships **Area, Field, or Subject:** Agricultural sciences; Forestry **Level of Education for which Award is Granted:** Undergraduate **Number Awarded:** 2 each year. **Funds Available:** The stipend is $1,000. Funds are paid directly to the recipient. **Duration:** 1 year; nonrenewable.
Eligibility Requirements: This program is open to members who are either graduating high school seniors planning to enroll full time in college or students already enrolled in college on a full-time basis. Applicants must be working on or planning to work on a 2-year or 4-year degree in agricultural and forest production. Selection is based on academic achievement (10 points for GPA, 10 points for SAT or ACT score, 10 points for class rank), leadership in FFA activities (30 points), leadership in community activities (10 points), and participation in the Supervised Agricultural Experience (SAE) program (30 points). U.S. citizenship is required. **Deadline for Receipt:** February of each year. **Additional Information:** Funding for these scholarships is provided by Manistique Papers, Inc. of Manistique, Michigan.

2514 ■ NATIONAL FFA ORGANIZATION

Attn: Scholarship Office
6060 FFA Drive
P.O. Box 68960
Indianapolis, IN 46268-0960
Tel: (317)802-4321
Fax: (317)802-5321
E-mail: scholarships@ffa.org
Web Site: http://www.ffa.org
To provide financial assistance to FFA members from designated states who are interested in studying agriculture or agribusiness in college.
Title of Award: MetLife Foundation Scholarships **Area, Field, or Subject:** Agribusiness; Agricultural sciences **Level of Education for which Award is Granted:** Four Year College **Number Awarded:** 10 each year; no more than 1 student from each state may receive a scholarship. **Funds Available:** The stipend is $2,000. Funds are paid directly to the recipient. **Duration:** 1 year; nonrenewable.
Eligibility Requirements: This program is open to members who are graduating high school seniors planning to enroll full time in college. Applicants must be residents of Arkansas, California, Florida, Idaho, Illinois, Indiana, Iowa, Minnesota, Mississippi, Missouri, Nebraska, North Dakota, Ohio, South Dakota, Texas, or Washington and interested in working on a 4-year degree in agriculture or agribusiness. Selection is based on academic achievement (10 points for GPA, 10 points for SAT or ACT score, 10 points for class rank), leadership in FFA activities (30 points), leadership in community activities (10 points), and participation in the Supervised Agricultural Experience (SAE) program (30 points). U.S. citizenship is required. **Deadline for Receipt:** February of each year. **Additional Information:** Funding for these scholarships is provided by the MetLife Foundation.

2515 ■ NATIONAL FFA ORGANIZATION

Attn: Scholarship Office
6060 FFA Drive
P.O. Box 68960
Indianapolis, IN 46268-0960
Tel: (317)802-4321
Fax: (317)802-5321
E-mail: scholarships@ffa.org
Web Site: http://www.ffa.org
To provide financial assistance to FFA members from selected states who are interested in studying agriculture or agribusiness in college.
Title of Award: Mid-States Wool Growers Cooperative Association Scholarship **Area, Field, or Subject:** Agribusiness; Agricultural sciences; Business **Level of Education for which Award is Granted:** Four Year College **Number Awarded:** 1 each year. **Funds Available:** The stipend is $1,000. Funds are paid directly to the recipient. **Duration:** 1 year; nonrenewable.
Eligibility Requirements: This program is open to members who are graduating high school seniors planning to enroll full time in college. Applicants must be residents of Illinois, Indiana, Iowa, Kansas, Kentucky, Michigan, Minnesota, Missouri, Nebraska, North Carolina, North Dakota, Ohio, Oklahoma, Pennsylvania, South Dakota, Virginia, or Wisconsin interested in working on a 4-year degree in agriculture or agribusiness. They must be sheep producers or from a family of sheep producers with

an operation of 20 or more ewes; advisors must confirm this sheep involvement. Selection is based on academic achievement (10 points for GPA, 10 points for SAT or ACT score, 10 points for class rank), leadership in FFA activities (30 points), leadership in community activities (10 points), and participation in the Supervised Agricultural Experience (SAE) program (30 points). U.S. citizenship is required. **Deadline for Receipt:** February of each year. **Additional Information:** Funding for this scholarship is provided by the Mid-States Wool Growers Cooperative Association.

2516 ■ NATIONAL FFA ORGANIZATION

Attn: Scholarship Office
6060 FFA Drive
P.O. Box 68960
Indianapolis, IN 46268-0960
Tel: (317)802-4321
Fax: (317)802-5321
E-mail: scholarships@ffa.org
Web Site: http://www.ffa.org
To provide financial assistance to FFA members interested in studying agriculture in college and then returning to the farm.
Title of Award: Montgomery Gentry/Sony Music Scholarship **Area, Field, or Subject:** Agricultural sciences **Level of Education for which Award is Granted:** Undergraduate **Number Awarded:** 3 each year. **Funds Available:** The stipend is $2,000 per year. Funds are paid directly to the recipient. **Duration:** 1 year; nonrenewable.
Eligibility Requirements: This program is open to members who are either graduating high school seniors planning to enroll full time in college or students already enrolled in college on a full-time basis. Applicants must be working on or planning to work on a 2-year or 4-year degree in agriculture. They must be from a family farm and have plans to return to the farm. Completion of the parent financial analysis section of the application is required. Selection is based on academic achievement (10 points for GPA, 10 points for SAT or ACT score, 10 points for class rank), leadership in FFA activities (30 points), leadership in community activities (10 points), and participation in the Supervised Agricultural Experience (SAE) program (30 points). U.S. citizenship is required. **Deadline for Receipt:** February of each year. **Additional Information:** Eddie Montgomery and Troy Gentry, the Academy of Country Music's Top New Duo or Group award winner in 1999, provide this scholarship to encourage young people to return to the farm and continue the family farm's legacy.

2517 ■ NATIONAL FFA ORGANIZATION

Attn: Scholarship Office
6060 FFA Drive
P.O. Box 68960
Indianapolis, IN 46268-0960
Tel: (317)802-4321
Fax: (317)802-5321
E-mail: scholarships@ffa.org
Web Site: http://www.ffa.org
To provide financial assistance to FFA members who are interested in studying agriculture in college.
Title of Award: NAPA Auto Parts Scholarships **Area, Field, or Subject:** Agricultural sciences **Level of Education for which Award is Granted:** Undergraduate **Number Awarded:** 15 each year; 1 in each of NAPA's 9 divisional territories and 6 at large. **Funds Available:** The stipend is $1,000. Funds are paid directly to the recipient. **Duration:** 1 year; nonrenewable.
Eligibility Requirements: This program is open to members who are graduating high school seniors planning to work full time on a 2-year or 4-year degree in agriculture. Preference is given to students interested in a career in the agricultural parts/aftermarket. Selection is based on academic achievement (10 points for GPA, 10 points for SAT or ACT score, 10 points for class rank), leadership in FFA activities (30 points), leadership in community activities (10 points), and participation in the Supervised Agricultural Experience (SAE) program (30 points). U.S. citizenship is required. **Deadline for Receipt:** February of each year. **Additional Information:** Funding for these scholarships is provided by NAPA Auto Parts.

2518 ■ NATIONAL FFA ORGANIZATION

Attn: Scholarship Office
6060 FFA Drive

P.O. Box 68960
Indianapolis, IN 46268-0960
Tel: (317)802-4321
Fax: (317)802-5321
E-mail: scholarships@ffa.org
Web Site: http://www.ffa.org
To provide financial assistance to FFA members who wish to study agriculture or agribusiness at 4-year land grant colleges in designated states.
Title of Award: National By-Products Foundation Scholarships **Area, Field, or Subject:** Agribusiness; Agricultural sciences **Level of Education for which Award is Granted:** Four Year College **Number Awarded:** 1 each year. **Funds Available:** The stipend is $2,000 per year. Funds are paid directly to the recipient. **Duration:** 1 year; nonrenewable.
Eligibility Requirements: This program is open to members who are graduating high school seniors planning to enroll full time in college. Applicants must be interested in working on a 4-year degree in agriculture or agribusiness at a land grant college in Colorado, Illinois, Indiana, Iowa, Kansas, Nebraska, or Wisconsin. Selection is based on academic achievement (10 points for GPA, 10 points for SAT or ACT score, 10 points for class rank), leadership in FFA activities (30 points), leadership in community activities (10 points), and participation in the Supervised Agricultural Experience (SAE) program (30 points). U.S. citizenship is required. **Deadline for Receipt:** February of each year. **Additional Information:** Funding for these scholarships is provided by National By-Products, Inc.

2519 ■ NATIONAL FFA ORGANIZATION

Attn: Scholarship Office
6060 FFA Drive
P.O. Box 68960
Indianapolis, IN 46268-0960
Tel: (317)802-4321
Fax: (317)802-5321
E-mail: scholarships@ffa.org
Web Site: http://www.ffa.org
To provide financial assistance to FFA members who wish to study agricultural journalism and related fields in college.
Title of Award: National FFA Scholarships for Undergraduates in the Humanities **Area, Field, or Subject:** Agricultural sciences; Communications; Horticulture; Landscape architecture and design **Level of Education for which Award is Granted:** Undergraduate **Number Awarded:** Varies; generally, a total of approximately 1,000 scholarships are awarded annually by the association. **Funds Available:** Stipends vary, but most are at least $1,000. **Duration:** 1 year or more.
Eligibility Requirements: This program is open to current and former members of the organization who are working or planning to work full time on a degree in fields related to agricultural journalism and communications, floriculture, and landscape design. For most of the scholarships, applicants must be high school seniors; others are open to students currently enrolled in college. The program includes a large number of designated scholarships that specify the locations where the members must live, the schools they must attend, the fields of study they must pursue, or other requirements. Some consider family income in the selection process, but most do not. Selection is based on academic achievement (10 points for GPA, 10 points for SAT or ACT score, 10 points for class rank), leadership in FFA activities (30 points), leadership in community activities (10 points), and participation in the Supervised Agricultural Experience (SAE) program (30 points). U.S. citizenship is required. **Deadline for Receipt:** February of each year. **Additional Information:** Funding for these scholarships is provided by many different corporate sponsors.

2520 ■ NATIONAL FFA ORGANIZATION

Attn: Scholarship Office
6060 FFA Drive
P.O. Box 68960
Indianapolis, IN 46268-0960
Tel: (317)802-4321
Fax: (317)802-5321
E-mail: scholarships@ffa.org
Web Site: http://www.ffa.org

To provide financial assistance to FFA members who wish to study agriculture and related fields in college.
Title of Award: National FFA Scholarships for Undergraduates in the Sciences **Area, Field, or Subject:** Agricultural sciences; Animal science and behavior; Dairy science; Engineering, Agricultural; Environmental conservation; Environmental science; Equine studies; Food science and technology; Horticulture; Natural resources; Technology **Level of Education for which Award is Granted:** Undergraduate **Number Awarded:** Varies; generally, a total of approximately 1,000 scholarships are awarded annually by the association. **Funds Available:** Stipends vary, but most are at least $1,000. **Duration:** 1 year or more.
Eligibility Requirements: This program is open to current and former members of the organization who are working or planning to work full time on a degree in fields related to agriculture; this includes: agricultural mechanics and engineering, agricultural technology, animal science, conservation, dairy science, equine science, floriculture, food science, horticulture, irrigation, lawn and landscaping, and natural resources. For most of the scholarships, applicants must be high school seniors; others are open to students currently enrolled in college. The program includes a large number of designated scholarships that specify the locations where the members must live, the schools they must attend, the fields of study they must pursue, or other requirements. Some consider family income in the selection process, but most do not. Selection is based on academic achievement (10 points for GPA, 10 points for SAT or ACT score, 10 points for class rank), leadership in FFA activities (30 points), leadership in community activities (10 points), and participation in the Supervised Agricultural Experience (SAE) program (30 points). U.S. citizenship is required. **Deadline for Receipt:** February of each year. **Additional Information:** Funding for these scholarships is provided by many different corporate sponsors.

2521 ■ NATIONAL FFA ORGANIZATION
Attn: Scholarship Office
6060 FFA Drive
P.O. Box 68960
Indianapolis, IN 46268-0960
Tel: (317)802-4321
Fax: (317)802-5321
E-mail: scholarships@ffa.org
Web Site: http://www.ffa.org
To provide financial assistance to FFA members who wish to study agribusiness and related fields in college.
Title of Award: National FFA Scholarships for Undergraduates in the Social Sciences **Area, Field, or Subject:** Agribusiness; Agriculture, Economic aspects; Education; Finance; Marketing and distribution **Level of Education for which Award is Granted:** Undergraduate **Number Awarded:** Varies; generally, a total of approximately 1,000 scholarships are awarded annually by the association. **Funds Available:** Stipends vary, but most are at least $1,000. **Duration:** 1 year or more.
Eligibility Requirements: This program is open to current and former members of the organization who are working or planning to work full time on a degree in fields related to business and the social sciences; this includes: agribusiness, agricultural economics, agricultural education, agricultural finance, and agricultural marketing. For most of the scholarships, applicants must be high school seniors; others are open to students currently enrolled in college. The program includes a large number of designated scholarships that specify the locations where the members must live, the schools they must attend, the fields of study they must pursue, or other requirements. Some consider family income in the selection process, but most do not. Selection is based on academic achievement (10 points for GPA, 10 points for SAT or ACT score, 10 points for class rank), leadership in FFA activities (30 points), leadership in community activities (10 points), and participation in the Supervised Agricultural Experience (SAE) program (30 points). U.S. citizenship is required. **Deadline for Receipt:** February of each year. **Additional Information:** Funding for these scholarships is provided by many different corporate sponsors.

2522 ■ NATIONAL FFA ORGANIZATION
Attn: Scholarship Office
6060 FFA Drive
P.O. Box 68960
Indianapolis, IN 46268-0960

Tel: (317)802-4321
Fax: (317)802-5321
E-mail: scholarships@ffa.org
Web Site: http://www.ffa.org
To provide financial assistance to FFA members who are interested in studying agriculture in college.
Title of Award: National Pork Board Scholarships **Area, Field, or Subject:** Agricultural sciences **Level of Education for which Award is Granted:** Four Year College **Number Awarded:** 5 each year. **Funds Available:** The stipend is $1,000. Funds are paid directly to the recipient. **Duration:** 1 year; nonrenewable.
Eligibility Requirements: This program is open to members who are graduating high school seniors planning to enroll or college students currently enrolled full time. Applicants must be working on or planning to work on a 4-year degree in agriculture. They must be from a swine producing family or involved in swine production with at least 50% of family income earned from that activity. Selection is based on academic achievement (10 points for GPA, 10 points for SAT or ACT score, 10 points for class rank), leadership in FFA activities (30 points), leadership in community activities (10 points), and participation in the Supervised Agricultural Experience (SAE) program (30 points). U.S. citizenship is required. **Deadline for Receipt:** February of each year. **Additional Information:** Funding for these scholarships is provided by the National Pork Producers Council and the National Pork Board.

2523 ■ NATIONAL FFA ORGANIZATION
Attn: Scholarship Office
6060 FFA Drive
P.O. Box 68960
Indianapolis, IN 46268-0960
Tel: (317)802-4321
Fax: (317)802-5321
E-mail: scholarships@ffa.org
Web Site: http://www.ffa.org
To provide financial assistance to FFA members interested in studying agriculture or conservation in college.
Title of Award: National Wild Turkey Federation Scholarships **Area, Field, or Subject:** Agricultural sciences; Environmental conservation; Environmental science; Natural resources; Wildlife conservation, management, and science **Level of Education for which Award is Granted:** Undergraduate **Number Awarded:** 1 each year. **Funds Available:** The stipend is $5,000. Funds are paid directly to the recipient. **Duration:** 1 year; nonrenewable.
Eligibility Requirements: This program is open to members who are graduating high school seniors planning to enroll full time in college. Applicants must have a GPA of 3.0 or higher and be planning to attend a 2-year or 4-year college or university to major in natural resources, wildlife management, or agriculture. They must support the preservation of the hunting tradition, demonstrate a commitment to conservation, actively participate in the hunting sports, have strong leadership skills, be able to demonstrate financial need, and have work or volunteer experience in the hunting sports. Selection is based on academic achievement (10 points for GPA, 10 points for SAT or ACT score, 10 points for class rank), leadership in FFA activities (30 points), leadership in community activities (10 points), and participation in the Supervised Agricultural Experience (SAE) program (30 points). U.S. citizenship is required. **Deadline for Receipt:** February of each year. **Additional Information:** Funding for these scholarships is provided by the National Wild Turkey Federation.

2524 ■ NATIONAL FFA ORGANIZATION
Attn: Scholarship Office
6060 FFA Drive
P.O. Box 68960
Indianapolis, IN 46268-0960
Tel: (317)802-4321
Fax: (317)802-5321
E-mail: scholarships@ffa.org
Web Site: http://www.ffa.org
To provide financial assistance to FFA members interested in studying agriculture in college.
Title of Award: Nationwide Foundation Scholarships **Area, Field, or Subject:** Agricultural sciences **Level of Education for which Award is Granted:** Undergraduate **Number Awarded:** 3 each year. **Funds Avail-

able: The stipend is $1,000 per year. Funds are paid directly to the recipient. **Duration:** 1 year; nonrenewable.

Eligibility Requirements: This program is open to members who are graduating high school seniors planning to enroll and college students currently enrolled full time. Applicants must be working on or planning to work on a 2-year or 4-year degree in a field related to agriculture. Selection is based on academic achievement (10 points for GPA, 10 points for SAT or ACT score, 10 points for class rank), leadership in FFA activities (30 points), leadership in community activities (10 points), and participation in the Supervised Agricultural Experience (SAE) program (30 points). U.S. citizenship is required. **Deadline for Receipt:** February of each year.
Additional Information: Funding for these scholarships is provided by the Nationwide Foundation.

2525 ■ NATIONAL FFA ORGANIZATION

Attn: Scholarship Office
6060 FFA Drive
P.O. Box 68960
Indianapolis, IN 46268-0960
Tel: (317)802-4321
Fax: (317)802-5321
E-mail: scholarships@ffa.org
Web Site: http://www.ffa.org
To provide financial assistance to FFA members from designated states interested in studying a field related to agriculture in college.
Title of Award: NC Hybrids Scholarships **Area, Field, or Subject:** Agribusiness; Agricultural sciences **Level of Education for which Award is Granted:** Undergraduate **Number Awarded:** 2 each year. **Funds Available:** The stipend is $1,000. Funds are paid directly to the recipient. **Duration:** 1 year; nonrenewable.
Eligibility Requirements: This program is open to members who are graduating high school seniors planning to enroll full time in college. Applicants must be residents of Colorado, Illinois, Iowa, Kansas, Minnesota, Missouri, Nebraska, New Mexico, New York, Oklahoma, South Dakota, or Texas and interested in working on a 2- or 4-year degree in agronomy, crop production, or agribusiness. Their family must earn at least 50% of its income from production agriculture, with preference to corn, grain sorghum, or soybeans. Selection is based on academic achievement (10 points for GPA, 10 points for SAT or ACT score, 10 points for class rank), leadership in FFA activities (30 points), leadership in community activities (10 points), and participation in the Supervised Agricultural Experience (SAE) program (30 points). Financial need is also considered. U.S. citizenship is required. **Deadline for Receipt:** February of each year. **Additional Information:** Funding for these scholarships is provided by NC+ Hybrids of Lincoln, Nebraska.

2526 ■ NATIONAL FFA ORGANIZATION

Attn: Scholarship Office
6060 FFA Drive
P.O. Box 68960
Indianapolis, IN 46268-0960
Tel: (317)802-4321
Fax: (317)802-5321
E-mail: scholarships@ffa.org
Web Site: http://www.ffa.org
To provide financial assistance for the study of agriculture in college to FFA members with a connection to a Farmland System cooperative.
Title of Award: Kenneth and Ellen Nielsen Cooperative Scholarships **Area, Field, or Subject:** Agricultural sciences **Level of Education for which Award is Granted:** Four Year College **Number Awarded:** 1 or more each year. **Funds Available:** The stipend is $1,000. Funds are paid directly to the recipient. **Duration:** 1 year; nonrenewable.
Eligibility Requirements: This program is open to members who are graduating high school seniors or current college students working or planning to work full time on a 4-year degree in agriculture. Applicants or their parents must be members of a Farmland System cooperative or have a direct livestock producer membership in Farmland. Selection is based on academic achievement (10 points for GPA, 10 points for SAT or ACT score, 10 points for class rank), leadership in FFA activities (30 points), leadership in community activities (10 points), and participation in

the Supervised Agricultural Experience (SAE) program (30 points). U.S. citizenship is required. **Deadline for Receipt:** February of each year.

2527 ■ NATIONAL FFA ORGANIZATION

Attn: Scholarship Office
6060 FFA Drive
P.O. Box 68960
Indianapolis, IN 46268-0960
Tel: (317)802-4321
Fax: (317)802-5321
E-mail: scholarships@ffa.org
Web Site: http://www.ffa.org
To provide financial assistance to current or former FFA members who are interested in studying a field related to agriculture at a college or university in designated states.
Title of Award: Norfolk Southern Foundation Scholarships **Area, Field, or Subject:** Agribusiness; Agricultural sciences; Communications; Education; Engineering, Agricultural; Finance; Forestry; Management; Marketing and distribution **Level of Education for which Award is Granted:** Four Year College **Number Awarded:** 3 each year. **Funds Available:** The stipend is $1,000. Funds are paid directly to the recipient. **Duration:** 1 year; nonrenewable.
Eligibility Requirements: This program is open to members who are either graduating high school seniors planning to enroll in college or students already enrolled in college. Applicants must be interested in working full time on a 4-year degree in agricultural and forestry production, communication, education, engineering, finance, management, marketing, merchandising, sales, or agricultural science. They must be planning to attend a college or university in Alabama, Delaware, Georgia, Illinois, Indiana, Louisiana, Maryland, Michigan, Missouri, New York, North Carolina, Ohio, Pennsylvania, South Carolina, Tennessee, or Virginia. Selection is based on academic achievement (10 points for GPA, 10 points for SAT or ACT score, 10 points for class rank), leadership in FFA activities (30 points), leadership in community activities (10 points), and participation in the Supervised Agricultural Experience (SAE) program (30 points). U.S. citizenship is required. **Deadline for Receipt:** February of each year. **Additional Information:** Funding for these scholarships is provided by the Norfolk Southern Foundation.

2528 ■ NATIONAL FFA ORGANIZATION

Attn: Scholarship Office
6060 FFA Drive
P.O. Box 68960
Indianapolis, IN 46268-0960
Tel: (317)802-4321
Fax: (317)802-5321
E-mail: scholarships@ffa.org
Web Site: http://www.ffa.org
To provide financial assistance to FFA members who are interested in studying agriculture or related fields in college.
Title of Award: Olds Garden Seed Scholarship **Area, Field, or Subject:** Agricultural sciences **Level of Education for which Award is Granted:** Undergraduate **Number Awarded:** 1 each year. **Funds Available:** The stipend is $1,000. Funds are paid directly to the recipient. **Duration:** 1 year; nonrenewable.
Eligibility Requirements: This program is open to members who are graduating high school seniors planning to enroll full time in college or college students already enrolled. Applicants must be interested in working on a degree in an agriculture-related major. They must have a GPA of 3.0 or higher and work-related experience on a farm or in a farm store, co-op, garden center, greenhouse, or nursery. Selection is based on academic achievement (10 points for GPA, 10 points for SAT or ACT score, 10 points for class rank), leadership in FFA activities (30 points), leadership in community activities (10 points), and participation in the Supervised Agricultural Experience (SAE) program (30 points). Financial need is also considered. U.S. citizenship is required. **Deadline for Receipt:** February of each year. **Additional Information:** Funding for this program is provided by Olds Garden Seed.

2529 ■ NATIONAL FFA ORGANIZATION

Attn: Scholarship Office
6060 FFA Drive
P.O. Box 68960
Indianapolis, IN 46268-0960

Tel: (317)802-4321
Fax: (317)802-5321
E-mail: scholarships@ffa.org
Web Site: http://www.ffa.org
To provide financial assistance to FFA members who are interested in studying agriculture, especially agricultural communications, at a 4-year institution.

Title of Award: Primedia Business Magazines & Media Scholarship **Area, Field, or Subject:** Agricultural sciences; Communications **Level of Education for which Award is Granted:** Four Year College **Number Awarded:** 1 each year. **Funds Available:** The stipend is $1,000. Funds are paid directly to the recipient. **Duration:** 1 year; nonrenewable.
Eligibility Requirements: This program is open to members who are graduating high school seniors planning to enroll full time in college. Applicants must be interested in working on a 4-year degree in an agricultural-related major, preferably agricultural journalism or agricultural communications. They must live on a family-owned farm and at least 50% of their family income must come from production agriculture. Selection is based on academic achievement (10 points for GPA, 10 points for SAT or ACT score, 10 points for class rank), leadership in FFA activities (30 points), leadership in community activities (10 points), and participation in the Supervised Agricultural Experience (SAE) program (30 points). Financial need is also considered. U.S. citizenship is required. **Deadline for Receipt:** February of each year. **Additional Information:** Funding for this scholarship is provided by Primedia Business Magazines & Media.

2530 ■ NATIONAL FFA ORGANIZATION
Attn: Scholarship Office
6060 FFA Drive
P.O. Box 68960
Indianapolis, IN 46268-0960
Tel: (317)802-4321
Fax: (317)802-5321
E-mail: scholarships@ffa.org
Web Site: http://www.ffa.org
To provide financial assistance to FFA members interested in studying fields related to communications in college.

Title of Award: Progressive Farmer Magazine Scholarships **Area, Field, or Subject:** Advertising; Agricultural sciences; Communications; Journalism **Level of Education for which Award is Granted:** Four Year College **Number Awarded:** 1 each year. **Funds Available:** The stipend is $1,000 per year. Funds are paid directly to the recipient. **Duration:** 1 year; nonrenewable.
Eligibility Requirements: This program is open to members who are graduating high school seniors planning to enroll full time in college. Applicants must be interested in working on a 4-year degree in communications, journalism, or advertising. Selection is based on academic achievement (10 points for GPA, 10 points for SAT or ACT score, 10 points for class rank), leadership in FFA activities (30 points), leadership in community activities (10 points), and participation in the Supervised Agricultural Experience (SAE) program (30 points). U.S. citizenship is required. **Deadline for Receipt:** February of each year. **Additional Information:** Funding for these scholarships is provided by *Progressive Farmer Magazine.*

2531 ■ NATIONAL FFA ORGANIZATION
Attn: Scholarship Office
6060 FFA Drive
P.O. Box 68960
Indianapolis, IN 46268-0960
Tel: (317)802-4321
Fax: (317)802-5321
E-mail: scholarships@ffa.org
Web Site: http://www.ffa.org
To provide financial assistance to FFA members interested in studying agriculture in college.

Title of Award: Purina Mills/Land O'Lakes Purina Feeds Dealer Scholarships **Area, Field, or Subject:** Agricultural sciences; Animal science and behavior; Equine studies; Veterinary science and medicine; Wildlife conservation, management, and science **Level of Education for which Award is Granted:** Four Year College **Number Awarded:** Varies each year, depending on the number of participating Purina dealers. **Funds Available:** The stipend is $1,000 per year. Funds are paid directly to the recipient. **Duration:** 1 year; nonrenewable.

Eligibility Requirements: This program is open to members who are graduating high school seniors planning to enroll full time in college. Applicants must be interested in working on a 4-year college degree in agriculture. Preference is given to applicants displaying an interest in animal nutrition, aquaculture, animal science, equine science, wildlife management, or specialty animals. Selection is based on academic achievement (10 points for GPA, 10 points for SAT or ACT score, 10 points for class rank), leadership in FFA activities (30 points), leadership in community activities (10 points), and participation in the Supervised Agricultural Experience (SAE) program (30 points). U.S. citizenship is required. **Deadline for Receipt:** February of each year. **Additional Information:** Funding for these scholarships is provided by Purina Mills, LLC.

2532 ■ NATIONAL FFA ORGANIZATION
Attn: Scholarship Office
6060 FFA Drive
P.O. Box 68960
Indianapolis, IN 46268-0960
Tel: (317)802-4321
Fax: (317)802-5321
E-mail: scholarships@ffa.org
Web Site: http://www.ffa.org
To provide financial assistance to FFA members who are interested in studying fields related to agriculture or agribusiness in college.

Title of Award: Rabo AgriFinance Scholarships **Area, Field, or Subject:** Agribusiness; Agricultural sciences; Agriculture, Economic aspects; Animal science and behavior; Computer and information sciences; Management **Level of Education for which Award is Granted:** Undergraduate **Number Awarded:** 3 each year. **Funds Available:** The stipend is $1,000 per year. Funds are paid directly to the recipient. **Duration:** 1 year; nonrenewable.
Eligibility Requirements: This program is open to members who are graduating high school seniors planning to enroll full time in college. Applicants must be interested in working on a 2- or 4-year degree in agronomy and crop science, farm and ranch management, livestock management, agricultural economics, agricultural power and equipment, or computer systems in agriculture. They must have a GPA of 30 or higher and rank in the upper 50% of their class. Selection is based on academic achievement (10 points for GPA, 10 points for SAT or ACT score, 10 points for class rank), leadership in FFA activities (30 points), leadership in community activities (10 points), and participation in the Supervised Agricultural Experience (SAE) program (30 points). U.S. citizenship is required. **Deadline for Receipt:** February of each year. **Additional Information:** Funding for this program is provided by Rabo AgriFinance.

2533 ■ NATIONAL FFA ORGANIZATION
Attn: Scholarship Office
6060 FFA Drive
P.O. Box 68960
Indianapolis, IN 46268-0960
Tel: (317)802-4321
Fax: (317)802-5321
E-mail: scholarships@ffa.org
Web Site: http://www.ffa.org
To provide financial assistance FFA members from designated states interested in studying an agricultural field in college.

Title of Award: Royster-Clark Scholarship **Area, Field, or Subject:** Agricultural sciences; Soil science **Level of Education for which Award is Granted:** Four Year College **Number Awarded:** 11 each year. **Funds Available:** The stipend is $1,000 per year. Funds are paid directly to the recipient. **Duration:** 1 year; nonrenewable.
Eligibility Requirements: This program is open to members who are graduating high school seniors planning to enroll full time in college. Applicants must be residents of Alabama, Delaware, Florida, Georgia, Illinois, Indiana, Kentucky, Maryland, Michigan, Mississippi, Missouri, North Carolina, Ohio, South Carolina, Tennessee, Virginia, West Virginia, or Wisconsin and interested in working on a 4-year college degree in agriculture with an emphasis on soils, crop production, or agronomy. Preference is given to students with outstanding leadership activities and work-related experience. Selection is based on academic achievement (10 points for GPA, 10 points for SAT or ACT score, 10 points for class rank), leadership in FFA activities (30 points), leadership in community

activities (10 points), and participation in the Supervised Agricultural Experience (SAE) program (30 points). U.S. citizenship is required. **Deadline for Receipt:** February of each year. **Additional Information:** Funding for this scholarship is provided by Royster-Clark, Inc.

2534 ■ NATIONAL FFA ORGANIZATION
Attn: Scholarship Office
6060 FFA Drive
P.O. Box 68960
Indianapolis, IN 46268-0960
Tel: (317)802-4321
Fax: (317)802-5321
E-mail: scholarships@ffa.org
Web Site: http://www.ffa.org
To provide financial assistance to FFA members, especially those from designated states, interested in studying agriculture in college.
Title of Award: Seneca Foods Corporation Scholarship **Area, Field, or Subject:** Agricultural sciences **Level of Education for which Award is Granted:** Four Year College **Number Awarded:** 5 each year. **Funds Available:** The stipend is $1,000 per year. Funds are paid directly to the recipient. **Duration:** 1 year; nonrenewable.
Eligibility Requirements: This program is open to members who are either graduating high school seniors planning to enroll in college or students already enrolled in college. Applicants must be interested in working full time on a 4-year degree in agriculture. They must have a GPA of 2.0 or higher. Preference is given to residents of Idaho, Illinois, Minnesota, Washington, and Wisconsin, and if 1) the applicant or a member of the applicant's family is employed in the vegetable processing industry; 2) the applicant's family produces vegetables for processing (caning or freezing); or 3) the applicant has related work experience in vegetable processing. Selection Selection is based on academic achievement (10 points for GPA, 10 points for SAT or ACT score, 10 points for class rank), leadership in FFA activities (30 points), leadership in community activities (10 points), and participation in the Supervised Agricultural Experience (SAE) program (30 points). U.S. citizenship is required. **Deadline for Receipt:** February of each year. **Additional Information:** Funding for this scholarship is provided by Seneca Foods Corporation of Vienna, Virginia.

2535 ■ NATIONAL FFA ORGANIZATION
Attn: Scholarship Office
6060 FFA Drive
P.O. Box 68960
Indianapolis, IN 46268-0960
Tel: (317)802-4321
Fax: (317)802-5321
E-mail: scholarships@ffa.org
Web Site: http://www.ffa.org
To provide financial assistance to FFA members who are studying a field related to communications, business, or education in college.
Title of Award: Solutions Inc. Results Through Creative Marketing Scholarships **Area, Field, or Subject:** Agribusiness; Agricultural sciences; Communications; Education; Marketing and distribution **Level of Education for which Award is Granted:** Four Year College **Number Awarded:** 3 each year. **Funds Available:** The stipend is $1,000 per year. Funds are paid directly to the recipient. **Duration:** 1 year; nonrenewable.
Eligibility Requirements: This program is open to members currently enrolled full time in college and working on a 4-year degree in agricultural communications, marketing, merchandising, sales, or as an education specialist. Applicants must have a GPA of 3.0 or higher. Selection is based on academic achievement (10 points for GPA, 10 points for SAT or ACT score, 10 points for class rank), leadership in FFA activities (30 points), leadership in community activities (10 points), and participation in the Supervised Agricultural Experience (SAE) program (30 points). U.S. citizenship is required. **Deadline for Receipt:** February of each year. **Additional Information:** This program is sponsored by the creative marketing firm Solutions Inc. Results Through Creative Marketing.

2536 ■ NATIONAL FFA ORGANIZATION
Attn: Scholarship Office
6060 FFA Drive
P.O. Box 68960
Indianapolis, IN 46268-0960
Tel: (317)802-4321

Fax: (317)802-5321
E-mail: scholarships@ffa.org
Web Site: http://www.ffa.org
To provide financial assistance to FFA members from Iowa and Michigan interested in studying agriculture in college.
Title of Award: Earl R. Sorensen Memorial Scholarships **Area, Field, or Subject:** Agricultural sciences **Level of Education for which Award is Granted:** Four Year College **Number Awarded:** 2 each year. **Funds Available:** The stipend is $1,000 per year. Funds are paid directly to the recipient. **Duration:** 1 year; nonrenewable.
Eligibility Requirements: This program is open to members who are graduating high school seniors, residents of Iowa or Michigan, and planning to work full time on a 4-year degree in agriculture. Selection is based on academic achievement (10 points for GPA, 10 points for SAT or ACT score, 10 points for class rank), leadership in FFA activities (30 points), leadership in community activities (10 points), and participation in the Supervised Agricultural Experience (SAE) program (30 points). U.S. citizenship is required. **Deadline for Receipt:** February of each year. **Additional Information:** These scholarships are funded by H.D. Hudson Manufacturing Company.

2537 ■ NATIONAL FFA ORGANIZATION
Attn: Scholarship Office
6060 FFA Drive
P.O. Box 68960
Indianapolis, IN 46268-0960
Tel: (317)802-4321
Fax: (317)802-5321
E-mail: scholarships@ffa.org
Web Site: http://www.ffa.org
To provide financial assistance to FFA members interested in studying designated agricultural specialties in college.
Title of Award: Spraying Systems Company TeeJet Spray Products Scholarship **Area, Field, or Subject:** Agricultural sciences; Engineering, Agricultural; Horticulture; Landscape architecture and design; Turfgrass management **Level of Education for which Award is Granted:** Four Year College **Number Awarded:** 1 each year. **Funds Available:** The stipend is $1,000 per year. Funds are paid directly to the recipient. **Duration:** 1 year; nonrenewable.
Eligibility Requirements: This program is open to members who are graduating high school seniors planning to enroll full time in college. Applicants must be interested in working on a 4-year college degree in agronomy, agricultural engineering/mechanization, landscape/turfgrass management, or horticulture. Selection is based on academic achievement (10 points for GPA, 10 points for SAT or ACT score, 10 points for class rank), leadership in FFA activities (30 points), leadership in community activities (10 points), and participation in the Supervised Agricultural Experience (SAE) program (30 points). U.S. citizenship is required. **Deadline for Receipt:** February of each year. **Additional Information:** Funding for this scholarship is provided by Spraying Systems Company, manufacturer of TeeJet brand spray products.

2538 ■ NATIONAL FFA ORGANIZATION
Attn: Scholarship Office
6060 FFA Drive
P.O. Box 68960
Indianapolis, IN 46268-0960
Tel: (317)802-4321
Fax: (317)802-5321
E-mail: scholarships@ffa.org
Web Site: http://www.ffa.org
To provide financial assistance to FFA members interested in studying irrigation in college.
Title of Award: Toro Agricultural Irrigation Scholarship **Area, Field, or Subject:** Agricultural sciences; Water resources **Level of Education for which Award is Granted:** Four Year College **Number Awarded:** 1 each year. **Funds Available:** The stipend is $1,000 per year. Funds are paid directly to the recipient. **Duration:** 1 year; nonrenewable.
Eligibility Requirements: This program is open to members who are either graduating high school seniors planning to enroll in college or students already enrolled in college. Applicants must be interested in working full time on a 4-year degree with a focus on irrigation, as confirmed by their advisor. They must have a GPA of 3.0 or higher. Selec-

tion is based on academic achievement (10 points for GPA, 10 points for SAT or ACT score, 10 points for class rank), leadership in FFA activities (30 points), leadership in community activities (10 points), and participation in the Supervised Agricultural Experience (SAE) program (30 points). U.S. citizenship is required. **Deadline for Receipt:** February of each year. **Additional Information:** Funding for this scholarship is provided by Toro Agricultural Irrigation.

2539 ■ NATIONAL FFA ORGANIZATION
Attn: Scholarship Office
6060 FFA Drive
P.O. Box 68960
Indianapolis, IN 46268-0960
Tel: (317)802-4321
Fax: (317)802-5321
E-mail: scholarships@ffa.org
Web Site: http://www.ffa.org
To provide financial assistance to FFA members from designated states interested in working on a college degree in agriculture, especially agricultural engineering or technology.
Title of Award: Toyota Motor Sales, U.S.A. Scholarships **Area, Field, or Subject:** Agricultural sciences; Engineering, Agricultural; General studies/Field of study not specified **Level of Education for which Award is Granted:** Four Year College **Number Awarded:** 10 each year. **Funds Available:** The stipend is $2,500 per year. Funds are paid directly to the recipient. **Duration:** 1 year; nonrenewable.
Eligibility Requirements: This program is open to members who are graduating high school seniors or current college students. Applicants must be residents of Alabama, California, Indiana, Kentucky, Michigan, Missouri, Texas, or West Virginia, and planning to work full time on a 4-year degree. They may study any area of agriculture, but preference is given to agricultural engineering or agricultural science/technology majors. Their application must include the parent financial analysis section. Selection is based on academic achievement (10 points for GPA, 10 points for SAT or ACT score, 10 points for class rank), leadership in FFA activities (30 points), leadership in community activities (10 points), and participation in the Supervised Agricultural Experience (SAE) program (30 points). If those criteria are equal, the applicants with the greatest financial need are selected. U.S. citizenship is required. **Deadline for Receipt:** February of each year. **Additional Information:** Funds for this scholarship are provided by Toyota Motor Sales, U.S.A., Inc. Winners must allow Toyota Motor Sales, U.S.A., Inc. to publicize or advertise scholarship winners' names or likenesses and those of their families.

2540 ■ NATIONAL FFA ORGANIZATION
Attn: Scholarship Office
6060 FFA Drive
P.O. Box 68960
Indianapolis, IN 46268-0960
Tel: (317)802-4321
Fax: (317)802-5321
E-mail: scholarships@ffa.org
Web Site: http://www.ffa.org
To provide financial assistance to FFA members from specified states interested in studying agriculture in college.
Title of Award: Tractor Supply Company Scholarship **Area, Field, or Subject:** Agricultural sciences **Level of Education for which Award is Granted:** Four Year College **Number Awarded:** 1 or more each year. **Funds Available:** The stipend is $3,000. Funds are paid directly to the recipient. **Duration:** 1 year; nonrenewable.
Eligibility Requirements: This program is open to members who are graduating high school seniors planning to enroll full time in college. Applicants must be residents of Alabama, Arkansas, Florida, Illinois, Indiana, Iowa, Kansas, Kentucky, Maryland, Michigan, Minnesota, Mississippi, Missouri, Montana, Nebraska, New York, North Carolina, North Dakota, Ohio, Oklahoma, Pennsylvania, South Carolina, South Dakota, Tennessee, Texas, Virginia, or Wisconsin. They must be interested in working on a 4-year degree in agriculture. Selection is based on academic achievement (10 points for GPA, 10 points for SAT or ACT score, 10 points for class rank), leadership in FFA activities (30 points), leadership in community activities (10 points), and participation in the Supervised Agricultural Experience (SAE) program (30 points). Financial need is also considered. U.S. citizenship is required. **Deadline for Receipt:** February

of each year. **Additional Information:** Funding for this scholarship is provided by Tractor Supply Company of Nashville, Tennessee. Recipients must be willing to allow Tractor Supply Company to use photographs of themselves and their families for company advertising.

2541 ■ NATIONAL FFA ORGANIZATION
Attn: Scholarship Office
6060 FFA Drive
P.O. Box 68960
Indianapolis, IN 46268-0960
Tel: (317)802-4321
Fax: (317)802-5321
E-mail: scholarships@ffa.org
Web Site: http://www.ffa.org
To provide financial assistance to FFA members who are interested in studying fields related to agriculture, business, engineering, or nursing in college.
Title of Award: Tyson Foods Scholarships **Area, Field, or Subject:** Agribusiness; Agricultural sciences; Business; Business administration; Engineering; Food science and technology; Management; Nursing; Packaging **Level of Education for which Award is Granted:** Undergraduate **Number Awarded:** 10 each year. **Funds Available:** The stipend is $1,000. Funds are paid directly to the recipient. **Duration:** 1 year; nonrenewable.
Eligibility Requirements: This program is open to members who are either high school seniors or already enrolled full time in college. Applicants must be working on or planning to work on a 2-year or 4-year degree in agriculture, food science, food technology, supply chain management, product development, product development, product packaging, nursing, engineering, or business. They must reside in a community in which a Tyson Foods processing facility is located. Selection is based on academic achievement (10 points for GPA, 10 points for SAT or ACT score, 10 points for class rank), leadership in FFA activities (30 points), leadership in community activities (10 points), and participation in the Supervised Agricultural Experience (SAE) program (30 points). U.S. citizenship is required. **Deadline for Receipt:** February of each year. **Additional Information:** Funding for these scholarships is provided by Tyson Foods, Inc.

2542 ■ NATIONAL FFA ORGANIZATION
Attn: Scholarship Office
6060 FFA Drive
P.O. Box 68960
Indianapolis, IN 46268-0960
Tel: (317)802-4321
Fax: (317)802-5321
E-mail: scholarships@ffa.org
Web Site: http://www.ffa.org
To provide financial assistance to FFA members currently studying agriculture in college.
Title of Award: United Agri Products Scholarships **Area, Field, or Subject:** Agricultural sciences **Level of Education for which Award is Granted:** Four Year College **Number Awarded:** 10 each year. **Funds Available:** The stipend is $1,300 per year. Funds are paid directly to the recipient. **Duration:** 1 year; nonrenewable.
Eligibility Requirements: This program is open to members currently enrolled full time in college and working on a 4-year degree in agriculture. Applicants must have a GPA of 3.0 or higher and be able to demonstrate financial need. Selection is based on academic achievement (10 points for GPA, 10 points for SAT or ACT score, 10 points for class rank), leadership in FFA activities (30 points), leadership in community activities (10 points), and participation in the Supervised Agricultural Experience (SAE) program (30 points). U.S. citizenship is required. **Deadline for Receipt:** February of each year. **Additional Information:** Funding for these scholarships is provided by United Agri Products.

2543 ■ NATIONAL FFA ORGANIZATION
Attn: Scholarship Office
6060 FFA Drive
P.O. Box 68960
Indianapolis, IN 46268-0960
Tel: (317)802-4321
Fax: (317)802-5321

E-mail: scholarships@ffa.org
Web Site: http://www.ffa.org
To provide financial assistance to FFA members who are interested in studying journalism in college.
Title of Award: Vance Publishing Corporation Scholarship **Area, Field, or Subject:** Agricultural sciences; Communications; Journalism **Level of Education for which Award is Granted:** Four Year College **Number Awarded:** 1 each year. **Funds Available:** The stipend is $1,000. Funds are paid directly to the recipient. **Duration:** 1 year; nonrenewable.
Eligibility Requirements: This program is open to members who are graduating high school seniors planning to enroll full time in college. Applicants must be interested in working on a 4-year degree with a preference for agricultural journalism. Selection is based on academic achievement (10 points for GPA, 10 points for SAT or ACT score, 10 points for class rank), leadership in FFA activities (30 points), leadership in community activities (10 points), and participation in the Supervised Agricultural Experience (SAE) program (30 points). U.S. citizenship is required. **Deadline for Receipt:** February of each year. **Additional Information:** Funding for this scholarship is provided by Vance Publishing Corporation.

2544 ■ NATIONAL FFA ORGANIZATION

Attn: Scholarship Office
6060 FFA Drive
P.O. Box 68960
Indianapolis, IN 46268-0960
Tel: (317)802-4321
Fax: (317)802-5321
E-mail: scholarships@ffa.org
Web Site: http://www.ffa.org
To provide financial assistance to minority FFA members who are interested in studying agriculture in college.
Title of Award: Booker T. Washington Scholarships **Area, Field, or Subject:** Agricultural sciences **Level of Education for which Award is Granted:** Four Year College **Number Awarded:** 4 each year: 1 at $10,000 and 3 at $5,000. **Funds Available:** Scholarships are either $10,000 or $5,000. Funds are paid directly to the recipient. **Duration:** 1 year; nonrenewable.
Eligibility Requirements: This program is open to members who are graduating high school seniors planning to enroll full time in college. Applicants must be members of a minority ethnic group (African American, Asian American, Pacific Islander, Hispanic, Alaska Native, or American Indian) planning to work on a 4-year degree in agriculture. Selection is based on academic achievement (10 points for GPA, 10 points for SAT or ACT score, 10 points for class rank), leadership in FFA activities (30 points), leadership in community activities (10 points), and participation in the Supervised Agricultural Experience (SAE) program (30 points). U.S. citizenship is required. **Deadline for Receipt:** February of each year.

2545 ■ NATIONAL FFA ORGANIZATION

Attn: Scholarship Office
6060 FFA Drive
P.O. Box 68960
Indianapolis, IN 46268-0960
Tel: (317)802-4321
Fax: (317)802-5321
E-mail: scholarships@ffa.org
Web Site: http://www.ffa.org
To provide financial assistance to FFA members from designated states who are interested in studying a field related to agriculture in college.
Title of Award: Wilbur-Ellis Company Scholarships **Area, Field, or Subject:** Agribusiness; Agricultural sciences; Agriculture, Economic aspects; Animal science and behavior; Biochemistry; Business administration; Computer and information sciences; Entomology; Finance; Forestry; Genetics; Horticulture; Management; Marketing and distribution; Poultry science; Soil science **Level of Education for which Award is Granted:** Four Year College **Number Awarded:** 13 each year: 1 at $5,000, 2 at $2,000, and 10 at $1,000. **Funds Available:** Stipends are $5,000, $2,000, or $1,000 per year. Funds are paid directly to the recipient. **Duration:** 1 year; nonrenewable.
Eligibility Requirements: This program is open to members who are graduating high school seniors planning to enroll or college students currently enrolled full time. Applicants must be residents of the following

states: Arizona, California, Idaho, Indiana, Michigan, Minnesota, Montana, New Mexico, North Dakota, Ohio, Oregon, South Dakota, Texas, Utah, Washington, Wisconsin, or Wyoming. They must be planning to work on a 4-year degree in agricultural production, forest management, agronomy and crop science, animal nutrition, farm and ranch management, horticulture, nursery and landscape management, plant science, poultry science, general agriculture, business management, economics, international agriculture, finance, sales and marketing, biochemistry, biotechnology, computer systems in agriculture, entomology, plant breeding and genetics, plant pathology, range science, or soil science. Their combined SAT score must be 1000 or higher and their GPA must be 3.0 or higher. Selection is based on academic achievement (10 points for GPA, 10 points for SAT or ACT score, 10 points for class rank), leadership in FFA activities (30 points), leadership in community activities (10 points), and participation in the Supervised Agricultural Experience (SAE) program (30 points). Financial need is also considered in the selection process. U.S. citizenship is required. **Deadline for Receipt:** February of each year. **Additional Information:** Funding for this scholarship is provided by the agriculture division of the Wilbur-Ellis Company.

2546 ■ NATIONAL FFA ORGANIZATION

Attn: Scholarship Office
6060 FFA Drive
P.O. Box 68960
Indianapolis, IN 46268-0960
Tel: (317)802-4321
Fax: (317)802-5321
E-mail: scholarships@ffa.org
Web Site: http://www.ffa.org
To provide financial assistance to FFA members who are interested in studying agricultural mechanics or engineering in college.
Title of Award: WIX Filters Scholarships **Area, Field, or Subject:** Agricultural sciences; Engineering, Agricultural; Technology **Level of Education for which Award is Granted:** Undergraduate **Number Awarded:** 4 each year. **Funds Available:** The stipend is $1,000. Funds are paid directly to the recipient. **Duration:** 1 year; nonrenewable.
Eligibility Requirements: This program is open to members who are graduating high school seniors planning to enroll full time in college. Applicants must be interested in working on a 2-year or 4-year degree in agricultural mechanics or agricultural engineering. Selection is based on academic achievement (10 points for GPA, 10 points for SAT or ACT score, 10 points for class rank), leadership in FFA activities (30 points), leadership in community activities (10 points), and participation in the Supervised Agricultural Experience (SAE) program (30 points). U.S. citizenship is required. **Deadline for Receipt:** February of each year. **Additional Information:** Funding for these scholarships is provided by WIX Filters.

2547 ■ NATIONAL FFA ORGANIZATION

Attn: Scholarship Office
6060 FFA Drive
P.O. Box 68960
Indianapolis, IN 46268-0960
Tel: (317)802-4321
Fax: (317)802-5321
E-mail: scholarships@ffa.org
Web Site: http://www.ffa.org
To provide financial assistance to FFA members who are interested in studying agriculture in college.
Title of Award: Woodstream Corporation Scholarships **Area, Field, or Subject:** Agricultural sciences **Level of Education for which Award is Granted:** Undergraduate **Number Awarded:** 1 each year. **Funds Available:** The stipend is $1,000. Funds are paid directly to the recipient. **Duration:** 1 year; nonrenewable.
Eligibility Requirements: This program is open to members who are graduating high school seniors planning to enroll or college students currently enrolled full time. Applicants must be interested in working on a 2-year or 4-year degree in agriculture. Selection is based on academic achievement (10 points for GPA, 10 points for SAT or ACT score, 10 points for class rank), leadership in FFA activities (30 points), leadership in community activities (10 points), and participation in the Supervised Agricultural Experience (SAE) program (30 points). U.S. citizenship is required. **Deadline for Receipt:** February of each year. **Additional**

Information: Funding for this scholarship is provided by the Woodstream Corporation.

2548 ■ NATIONAL FFA ORGANIZATION

Attn: Scholarship Office
6060 FFA Drive
P.O. Box 68960
Indianapolis, IN 46268-0960
Tel: (317)802-4321
Fax: (317)802-5321
E-mail: scholarships@ffa.org
Web Site: http://www.ffa.org
To provide financial assistance to FFA members from selected states who are interested in majoring in agriculture in college.
Title of Award: Stephen M. Yoder Foundation/American Soybean Association Scholarships **Area, Field, or Subject:** Agricultural sciences **Level of Education for which Award is Granted:** Four Year College **Number Awarded:** 2 each year. **Funds Available:** The stipend is $1,000. Funds are paid directly to the recipient. **Duration:** 1 year; nonrenewable. **Eligibility Requirements:** This program is open to members who are either graduating high school seniors planning to enroll in college or students already enrolled in college. Applicants must be interested in working full time on a 4-year degree in agriculture at an accredited institution. They must be residents of Alabama, Arkansas, Delaware, Florida, Georgia, Illinois, Indiana, Iowa, Kansas, Kentucky, Louisiana, Maryland, Michigan, Minnesota, Mississippi, Missouri, Nebraska, New Jersey, North Carolina, North Dakota, Ohio, Oklahoma, Pennsylvania, South Carolina, South Dakota, Tennessee, Texas, Virginia, or Wisconsin. Selection is based on academic achievement (10 points for GPA, 10 points for SAT or ACT score, 10 points for class rank), leadership in FFA activities (30 points), leadership in community activities (10 points), and participation in the Supervised Agricultural Experience (SAE) program (30 points). U.S. citizenship is required. **Deadline for Receipt:** February of each year. **Additional Information:** Funding for these scholarships is provided by the Stephen M. Yoder Foundation and the American Soybean Association.

2549 ■ NATIONAL POULTRY AND FOOD DISTRIBUTORS ASSOCIATION

Attn: NPFDA Scholarship Foundation
958 McEver Road Extension, Unit B-8
Gainesville, GA 30504
Tel: (770)535-9901; 877-845-1545
Fax: (770)535-7385
E-mail: info@npfda.org
Web Site: http://www.npfda.org
To provide financial assistance to students enrolled in fields related to the poultry and food industries.
Title of Award: NPFDA Scholarships **Area, Field, or Subject:** Agriculture, Economic aspects; Food science and technology; Nutrition; Poultry science **Level of Education for which Award is Granted:** Four Year College **Number Awarded:** 4 each year. **Funds Available:** Stipends range from $1,500 to $2,000. **Duration:** 1 year. **Eligibility Requirements:** This program is open to full-time students entering their junior or senior year of college. Applicants must be studying poultry science, food science, agricultural economics or marketing, nutrition, or another area related to the poultry industry. Along with their application, they must submit a 1-page narrative on their goals and ambitions and their transcripts. Selection is based on academic excellence, past and current involvement in poultry and food-related activities, and professional objectives. **Deadline for Receipt:** May of each year. **Additional Information:** The National Poultry and Food Distributors Association (NPFDA) established its Scholarship Foundation in 1979. The following named scholarships are included in the program: the Albin S. Johnson Memorial Scholarship, the William Manson Family Memorial Scholarship, and the Alfred Schwartz Memorial Scholarship.

2550 ■ NEBRASKA FARM BUREAU

Attn: Young Farmers & Ranchers
5225 South 16th Street
P.O. Box 80299
Lincoln, NE 68501
Tel: (402)421-4750
Fax: (402)421-4432

E-mail: cathyd@nefb.org
Web Site: http://www.nefb.org/yfr/default.aspx
To provide financial assistance to members of the Nebraska Farm Bureau who plan to study agriculture in college.
Title of Award: Greater Horizon Scholarship **Area, Field, or Subject:** Agricultural sciences **Level of Education for which Award is Granted:** Undergraduate **Number Awarded:** 1 each year. **Funds Available:** The stipend is $1,000. **Duration:** 1 year. **Eligibility Requirements:** This program is open to residents of Nebraska who belong to a member family of a county farm bureau of have their own membership. Applicants must be between 18 and 35 years of age and planning to enroll full time in a college or university agricultural program. Along with their application, they must submit a brief statement on what they wish to do 1 year following college graduation and their long-range goals over the next 5 to 10 years. Financial need is also considered in the selection process. **Deadline for Receipt:** February of each year.

2551 ■ NORTHWEST FARM CREDIT SERVICES

Attn: Marketing Department
P.O. Box 2515
Spokane, WA 99220
Tel: (509)340-5207
Free: 800-743-2125
Fax: 800-255-1789
E-mail: farm-credit@accountlist.com
Web Site: http://www.farm-credit.com
To provide financial assistance for college to residents of designated northwestern states who are customers or children of customers of Northwest Farm Credit Services.
Title of Award: Farm Credit Scholarship Program **Area, Field, or Subject:** Agricultural sciences; General studies/Field of study not specified **Level of Education for which Award is Granted:** Undergraduate **Number Awarded:** 32 each year. From each of the 4 states, 6 high school seniors and 2 college students are awarded scholarships. **Funds Available:** The stipend is $1,000. **Duration:** 1 year; nonrenewable. **Eligibility Requirements:** This program is open to 1) high school seniors who are children of customers and planning to attend an institution of higher education, and 2) college juniors and seniors who are customers. Applicants must be residents of Idaho, Montana, Oregon, or Washington. All academic majors are eligible, but preference is given to students who are preparing for a career related to agriculture. Along with their application, they must submit a 250-word essay describing their plans for higher education, how they will benefit from that education, and how the scholarship will help them financially. Selection is based on the essay (15 points), scholastic performance (5 points), leadership (10 points), and participation in extracurricular activities (10 points). **Deadline for Receipt:** March of each year.

2552 ■ OAK RIDGE INSTITUTE FOR SCIENCE AND EDUCATION

Attn: Science and Engineering Education
P.O. Box 117
Oak Ridge, TN 37831-0117
Tel: (865)576-8239
Fax: (865)241-5219
E-mail: igrid.gregory@orau.gov
Web Site: http://www.orau.gov/orise.htm
To provide financial assistance and summer research experience to undergraduate students who are working on a degree in a field of interest to the Department of Homeland Security (DHS).
Title of Award: Department of Homeland Security Undergraduate Scholarships **Area, Field, or Subject:** Agricultural sciences; Biological and clinical sciences; Communications; Computer and information sciences; Engineering; Information science and technology; Mathematics and mathematical sciences; Physical sciences; Psychology; Public administration; Religion; Social sciences; Writing **Level of Education for which Award is Granted:** Undergraduate **Number Awarded:** Approximately 50 each year. **Funds Available:** This program provides a stipend of $1,000 per month during the academic year and $5,000 for the internship plus full payment of tuition and mandatory fees. **Duration:** 2 academic years plus 10 weeks during the intervening summer. **Eligibility Requirements:** This program is open to 1) full-time students who are in their second year of college attendance as of the application deadline; and 2) part-time students who have completed at least 45 but

no more than 60 semester hours as of the application deadline. Applicants must be majoring in the agricultural sciences, biological and life sciences, computer and information sciences, engineering, mathematics, physical sciences, psychology, social sciences, or selected humanities (religious studies, cultural studies, public policy, advocacy, communications, or science writing). They must have a GPA of 3.3 or higher. Along with their application, they must submit 2 statements on 1) their educational and professional goals, the kinds of research they are interested in conducting, specific questions that interest them, and how they became interested in them; and 2) how they think their interests, talents, and initiative would contribute to make the homeland safer and secure. Selection is based on those statements, academic record, references, and SAT or ACT scores. As part of their program, they must be interested in participating in summer research and development activities at a DHS-designated facility. U.S. citizenship is required. **Deadline for Receipt:** January of each year. **Additional Information:** This program, established in 2003, is funded by DHS and administered by Oak Ridge Institute for Science and Education (ORISE). Recipients must enroll full time.

2553 ■ OAK RIDGE INSTITUTE FOR SCIENCE AND EDUCATION
Attn: Science and Engineering Education
P.O. Box 117
Oak Ridge, TN 37831-0117
Tel: (865)241-8240
Fax: (865)241-5219
E-mail: hollingsscholarship@orau.gov
Web Site: http://www.orau.gov/orise.htm
To provide financial assistance and summer research experience to upper-division students who are working on a degree in a field of interest to the National Oceanic and Atmospheric Administration (NOAA).
Title of Award: Ernest F. Hollings Scholarship Program **Area, Field, or Subject:** Agricultural sciences; Behavioral sciences; Biological and clinical sciences; Computer and information sciences; Education; Engineering; Information science and technology; Mathematics and mathematical sciences; Physical sciences; Social sciences **Level of Education for which Award is Granted:** Four Year College **Number Awarded:** Approximately 100 each year. **Funds Available:** This program provides a stipend of $8,000 per academic year and $650 per week during the internship, a housing subsidy and limited travel reimbursement for round-trip transportation to the internship site, and travel expenses to the scholarship program conference at the completion of the internship. **Duration:** 2 academic years plus 10 weeks during the intervening summer.
Eligibility Requirements: This program is open to full-time students entering their junior year at an accredited college or university in the United States or its territories. Applicants must be majoring in a discipline related to oceanic and atmospheric science, research, technology, and education, and supportive of the purposes of NOAA's programs and mission (e.g., biological, life, and agricultural sciences; computer and information sciences; engineering; mathematics; physical sciences; social and behavioral sciences; or teacher education). They must have a GPA of 3.0 or higher. As part of their program, they must be interested in participating in summer research and development activities at NOAA headquarters (Silver Spring, Maryland) or field centers. U.S. citizenship is required. **Deadline for Receipt:** May of each year. **Additional Information:** This program, established in 2005, is funded by NOAA and administered by Oak Ridge Institute for Science and Education (ORISE).

2554 ■ SCHOLARSHIP ADMINISTRATIVE SERVICES, INC.
Attn: ALfA Program
2000 Rock Street, Suite 3
Mountain View, CA 94043
To provide financial assistance to undergraduate and graduate students working on a degree in a field related to agriculture.
Title of Award: AgLife for America Scholarships **Area, Field, or Subject:** Agricultural sciences **Level of Education for which Award is Granted:** Graduate, Undergraduate **Number Awarded:** Up to 20 each year. **Funds Available:** The stipend is $5,000 per year. **Duration:** 1 year; may be renewed 1 additional year if the recipient maintains full-time enrollment and a GPA of 3.0 or higher.
Eligibility Requirements: This program is open to full-time students working on or planning to work on an undergraduate or graduate degree in an agriculture-related field. Applicants must have a GPA of 3.0 or higher and be able to demonstrate a record of involvement in extracurricular and

work activities related to agriculture. Along with their application, they must submit a 1,000-word essay on their educational and career goals, why they believe agriculture is essential to America, and why they have decided to prepare for a career in agriculture. Financial need is not considered in the selection process. **Deadline for Receipt:** April of each year. **Additional Information:** This program is sponsored by AgLife for America (ALfA) and administered by Scholarship Administrative Services, Inc. ALfA was established in 2003 to encourage more American students to consider remaining on the farm. Requests for applications should be accompanied by a self-addressed stamped envelope, the student's e-mail address, and the source where they found the scholarship information.

2555 ■ SOUTH CAROLINA STUDENT LOAN CORPORATION
Interstate Center
16 Berryhill Road, Suite 210
P.O. Box 21487
Columbia, SC 29221-1487
Tel: (803)798-0916
Free: 800-347-2752
Fax: (803)772-9410
Web Site: http://www.slc.sc.edu
To provide scholarship/loans to students in South Carolina who wish to teach certain subjects or in certain geographic areas.
Title of Award: South Carolina Teacher Loan Program **Area, Field, or Subject:** Agricultural sciences; Classical studies; Consumer affairs; Dance; Education, Elementary; Education, Music; Education, Special; English language and literature; Foreign languages; Library and archival sciences; Mathematics and mathematical sciences; Science; Speech and language pathology/audiology; Technology **Level of Education for which Award is Granted:** Graduate, Undergraduate **Number Awarded:** Varies each year. **Funds Available:** Freshmen and sophomores may borrow up to $2,500 per academic year; juniors, seniors, and graduate students may borrow up to $5,000 per academic year. This is a scholarship/loan program; loans are forgivable at the rate of 20% or $3,000, whichever is greater, for each full year of teaching in an area (either geographic or subject) of critical need; for students who teach in both critical subject and geographic areas, the rate of cancellation is 33% or $5,000, whichever is greater, per year. Borrowers who fail to teach in either a critical subject or geographic area must repay the loan at an annual interest rate that varies (currently, 5.37%) but is capped at 10.25%. **Duration:** 1 year; may be renewed for a total of 5 years of undergraduate and 5 years of graduate study.
Eligibility Requirements: Eligible to apply are residents of South Carolina who are planning to teach in certain critical geographic areas of the state, or to teach in critical subject areas. Entering freshmen must have ranked in the top 40% of their high school class and have an ACT or SAT score greater than the South Carolina average (recently 986 on the SAT or 19.3 on the ACT); enrolled undergraduates or entering graduate students must have at least a 2.75 cumulative GPA; graduate students who have completed at least 1 term must have a GPA of 3.5 or better. Undergraduate students at South Carolina colleges must have taken and passed the Education Entrance Exam; students at institutions outside South Carolina must have completed the necessary prerequisites required at that institution. Only U.S. citizens may apply. **Deadline for Receipt:** May of each year. **Additional Information:** Recently, the critical subject areas include mathematics, science (biology, chemistry, physics, and general science), media specialist, special education, industrial technology, foreign languages (Spanish, French, Latin, and German), family and consumer science, art, music, business education, English and language arts, dance, speech and drama/theater, and agriculture. For a list of critical geographic area, contact the sponsor.

2556 ■ TEXAS 4-H YOUTH DEVELOPMENT FOUNDATION
Attn: Executive Director
Texas A&M University
7606 Eastmark Drive, Suite 101
College Station, TX 77843-2473
Tel: (979)845-1213
Fax: (979)845-6495
E-mail: texas4-hscholarships@tamu.edu
Web Site: http://texas4-h.tamu.edu/scholarships
To provide financial assistance to high school seniors who have been active in Texas 4-H activities in spite of unforeseen obstacles related to their medical/health, family, and/or educational situation.

Title of Award: Texas 4-H Youth Development Foundation Courageous Heart Scholarships **Area, Field, or Subject:** Agricultural sciences; General studies/Field of study not specified **Level of Education for which Award is Granted:** Undergraduate **Number Awarded:** The foundation awards approximately 170 scholarships, worth more than $1.2 million, for all of its programs each year. **Funds Available:** Stipends range from $1,500 to $10,000, depending on the contributions from various donors. **Duration:** 1 year.
Eligibility Requirements: This program is open to graduating seniors at high schools in Texas who have been actively participating in 4-H and plan to attend a college, university, or accredited technical school in the state. Candidates must be nominated by a community leader, such as county extension agent, education, elected official, religious leader, or 4-H community volunteer or leader. Nominees must have passed all sections of the TAAS, THEA, and/or TAKS test and be able to demonstrate financial need. They must be able to present documentation and testimonials to 1 of the following life obstacles: 1) medical or health conditions such as major surgeries with lasting effects, cancer and/or other diseases, long-term illnesses, or physical disabilities; 2) family situations, such as death of a family member, family housing, parental employment, or income obstacles; or 3) educational obstacles, including dyslexia or other learning disabilities. Some scholarships require a major in agriculture; others are unrestricted. **Deadline for Receipt:** Nominations must be submitted directly to the Texas 4-H Youth Development Foundation office by March of each year. **Additional Information:** Students who apply to the Texas FFA Association or the Texas chapter of Family, Career and Community Leaders of America (FCCLA) for a scholarship will have their 4-H application voided.

2557 ■ TREE RESEARCH AND EDUCATION ENDOWMENT FUND

Attn: Executive Director
711 East Roosevelt Road
Wheaton, IL 60187
Tel: (630)221-8127
Fax: (630)690-0702
E-mail: treefund@treefund.org
Web Site: http://www.treefund.org/grants/Grants.aspx
To provide financial assistance to undergraduate and technical school students interested in preparing for a career in commercial arboriculture.
Title of Award: Robert Felix Memorial Scholarship **Area, Field, or Subject:** Agricultural sciences; Entomology; Horticulture; Landscape architecture and design; Soil science **Level of Education for which Award is Granted:** Undergraduate **Number Awarded:** 4 each year. **Funds Available:** The stipend is $3,000. **Duration:** 1 year.
Eligibility Requirements: This program is open to student members of the International Society of Arboriculture who are entering the second year of a 2-year program or the third or fourth year of a 4-year program. Applicants must be preparing for a career in commercial arboriculture. They must have a GPA of 3.0 or higher. Along with their application, they must submit a 1,000-word essay describing their reasons for pursuing their chosen career, their goals and objectives, and why they should be chosen for this scholarship. Financial need is not considered in the selection process. **Deadline for Receipt:** April of each year. **Additional Information:** The Tree Research and Education Endowment (TREE) Fund was established in 2002 as the result of a merger of the International Society of Arboriculture Research Trust (established in 1976) and the National Arborist Foundation (established in 1985). Fields of study often considered appropriate for a career in commercial arboriculture include agriculture, entomology, horticulture, landscape architecture, or soils science.

2558 ■ HARRY S. TRUMAN SCHOLARSHIP FOUNDATION

Attn: Executive Secretary
712 Jackson Place, N.W.
Washington, DC 20006
Tel: (202)395-4831
Fax: (202)395-6995
E-mail: office@truman.gov
Web Site: http://www.truman.gov
To provide grants-for-service for graduate school to current college juniors who are interested in preparing for a career in public service.
Title of Award: Harry S. Truman Scholarship Program **Area, Field, or Subject:** Agricultural sciences; Biological and clinical sciences; Econom-ics; Education; Engineering; Environmental conservation; Environmental science; History; International affairs and relations; Law; Physical sciences; Political science; Public administration; Public health; Public service; Social sciences; Technology **Level of Education for which Award is Granted:** Four Year College, Graduate **Number Awarded:** 70 to 75 each year: a) 1 "state" scholarship is available to a qualified resident nominee in each of the 50 states, the District of Columbia, Puerto Rico, and the Islands (Guam, the Virgin Islands, American Samoa, and the Commonwealth of the Northern Mariana Islands); and b) up to 25 at-large scholars. **Funds Available:** The program provides up to $30,000, including up to $15,000 for the first year of graduate study and up to $15,000 for the final year of graduate study. **Duration:** Support is provided for the first and last year of graduate study.
Eligibility Requirements: Students must be nominated to be considered for this program. Nominees must be full-time students with junior standing at a 4-year institution, committed to a career in government or public service, in the upper quarter of their class, and U.S. citizens or nationals. Each participating institution may nominate up to 4 candidates (and up to 3 additional students who completed their first 2 years at a community college); community colleges and other 2-year institutions may nominate former students who are enrolled as full-time students with junior-level academic standing at accredited 4-year institutions. Selection is based on extent and quality of community service and government involvement, academic performance, leadership record, suitability of the nominee's proposed program of study for a career in public service, and writing and analytical skills. Priority is given to candidates who plan to enroll in a graduate program that specifically trains them for a career in public service, including government at any level, uniformed services, public interest organizations, nongovernmental research and/or educational organizations, public and private schools, and public service oriented nonprofit organizations. The fields of study may include agriculture, biology, engineering, environmental management, physical and social sciences, and technology policy, as well as such traditional fields as economics, education, government, history, international relations, law, nonprofit management, political science, public administration, public health, and public policy. Interviews are required. **Deadline for Receipt:** February of each year. **Additional Information:** Recipients may attend graduate school in the United States or in foreign countries. Scholars are required to work in public service for 3 of the 7 years following completion of a graduate degree program funded by this program. Scholars who do not meet this service requirement, or who fail to provide timely proof to the foundation of such employment, will be required to repay funds received, along with interest.

2559 ■ UTAH GOLF ASSOCIATION

Attn: Scholarship Committee
9121 South 150 West, Suite D
P.O. Box 5601
Sandy, UT 84091-5601
Tel: (801)563-0400
Fax: (801)563-0632
Web Site: http://www.uga.org/awards/scholarship/index.html
To provide financial assistance for college or graduate school to students in Utah who have been active in golf.
Title of Award: Utah Golf Association Scholarships **Area, Field, or Subject:** Agricultural sciences; General studies/Field of study not specified; Turfgrass management **Level of Education for which Award is Granted:** Graduate, Undergraduate **Number Awarded:** At least 3 each year. **Funds Available:** The stipend is $1,200. **Duration:** 1 year.
Eligibility Requirements: This program is open to students enrolled or planning to enroll at a postsecondary institution in Utah. Preference is given to applicants already in college or working on an advanced degree. At least 1 scholarship is reserved for a student interested in preparing for a career in agronomy, turf grass management, or as a golf course superintendent. Applicants have been involved in golf, but skill is not considered. They must describe their long-range educational and occupational goals and objectives, what they like about golf, and their background, interested, and future plans in golf. Selection is based on educational experience, achievements, GPA, test scores, goals, and objectives (25%); leadership, extracurricular activities, work experience,

volunteerism, and character (25%); golf affiliation and interest (25%); and financial need (25%). **Deadline for Receipt:** April of each year.

2560 ■ VERMONT STUDENT ASSISTANCE CORPORATION
Champlain Mill
Attn: Scholarship Programs
P.O. Box 2000
Winooski, VT 05404-2601
Tel: (802)654-3798; 888-253-4819
Fax: (802)654-3765
E-mail: info@vsac.org
Web Site: http://www.vsac.org
To provide financial assistance to residents of Vermont who are interested in majoring in an agriculture-related field in college.
Title of Award: Vermont Feed Dealers and Manufacturers Association Scholarship **Area, Field, or Subject:** Agribusiness; Agricultural sciences; Animal science and behavior; Botany; Equine studies; Forestry; Horticulture; Soil science; Veterinary science and medicine **Level of Education for which Award is Granted:** Undergraduate **Number Awarded:** Varies each year; recently, 6 of these scholarships were awarded. **Funds Available:** The maximum stipend is $3,000. **Duration:** 1 year; recipients may reapply.
Eligibility Requirements: This scholarship is available to high school seniors, high school graduates, and currently-enrolled college students in Vermont who are enrolled or planning to enroll in a postsecondary degree program in agriculture, including but not limited to animal sciences, equine studies, agribusiness, plant and soil science, forestry, horticulture, and veterinary medicine or technology. Selection is based on a letter of recommendation and required essays. **Deadline for Receipt:** June of each year.

Animal Sciences

2561 ■ CALIFORNIA STATE FAIR
Attn: Friends of the Fair Scholarship Program
1600 Exposition Boulevard
P.O. Box 15649
Sacramento, CA 95852
Tel: (916)274-5969
E-mail: wross@calexpo.com
Web Site: http://www.bigfun.org
To provide financial assistance for college to residents of California who are interested in majoring in designated fields or preparing for a career in the Fair industry.
Title of Award: Eddie G. Cole Memorial Scholarships **Area, Field, or Subject:** Agricultural sciences; Education, Physical; Equine studies **Level of Education for which Award is Granted:** Undergraduate **Number Awarded:** 2 each year: 1 at $1,000 and 1 at $500. **Funds Available:** Stipends are $1,000 or $500. **Duration:** 1 year.
Eligibility Requirements: This program is open to residents of California currently working on an undergraduate degree at a college or university in the state. Applicants be 1) majoring in physical education, agriculture, or equine studies; or 2) preparing for a career in the Fair industry. They must have a GPA of 3.0 or higher. Along with their application, they must submit a 2-page essay on why they are pursuing their desired career and life goals. Selection is based on personal commitment, goals established for their chosen field, leadership potential, and civic accomplishments. **Deadline for Receipt:** March of each year. **Additional Information:** The Friends of the Fair Scholarship Program was established in 1993.

2562 ■ DEAF FRIENDS INTERNATIONAL
P.O. Box 13192
Hamilton, OH 45013
Tel: (513)896-5075
Fax: (513)896-5075
E-mail: dfa@workersforjesus.com
Web Site: http://www.workersforjesus.com/dfi/dfi_grants.htm
To provide funding to individuals and groups in any country to meet the needs of deaf people.
Title of Award: DFI Care Program **Area, Field, or Subject:** Equine studies; General studies/Field of study not specified **Level of Education for which Award is Granted:** Graduate, Undergraduate, Other **Number**

Awarded: Varies each year. **Funds Available:** The amount of the grant depends on the need of the recipient and the availability of funds.
Eligibility Requirements: This program is open to individuals and groups seeking assistance to help deaf children and adults around the world. The assistance that can be offered includes scholarships for undergraduate or graduate study, hearing aids, disaster relief, TTYs and other special equipment, school supplies, expenses related to the adoption of deaf children, and medical needs. Requests must come from teachers, school officials, doctors, social agency personnel, missionaries, or church leaders. They must be submitted on official stationery.

2563 ■ HARRY ALAN GREGG FOUNDATION
One Verney Drive
Greenfield, NH 03047
Tel: (603)547-3311
Fax: (603)547-6212
E-mail: hag@cmf.org
Web Site: http://www.crotchedmountain.org
To provide financial assistance to children and adults in New Hampshire who have physical, emotional, or intellectual disabilities.
Title of Award: Harry Alan Gregg Foundation Grants **Area, Field, or Subject:** Equine studies; General studies/Field of study not specified **Level of Education for which Award is Granted:** Undergraduate, Other **Number Awarded:** More than 300 each year. **Funds Available:** Most grants range from $100 to $1,000, but they may be larger. **Duration:** Recipients may receive a maximum of 4 grants (no more than 2 in any year).
Eligibility Requirements: This program is open to New Hampshire residents of all ages who have physical, intellectual, or emotional disabilities. Funds may be requested for broad purposes but must specifically benefit the applicant. Examples of acceptable purposes include, but are not limited to: the costs of nonreimbursed medical, dental, vision, hearing, or therapy treatments; special equipment, services, or supplies; modifications to living area, workplace, or vehicle; respite services for the recipient or care givers; recreational functions, such as camperships or other activities; and vocational, educational, or driver training tuition assistance. Selection is based on demonstrated need for a product of service, the applicant's financial circumstances, and the ability of the foundation to help improve the quality of life of a grant recipient. **Deadline for Receipt:** Applications may be submitted at any time. **Additional Information:** This foundation was established in 1989. If a request is not funded, applicants may reapply 6 months later for the same or a different purpose.

2564 ■ IOWA FOUNDATION FOR AGRICULTURAL ADVANCEMENT
Attn: Department IFFAA/Iowa State Fair
P.O. Box 57130
Des Moines, IA 50317-0003
800-545-FAIR
E-mail: saleofchampions@yahoo.com
Web Site: http://www.iowastatefair.org/saleofchamps
To provide financial assistance for college to Iowa high school seniors interested in majoring in animal science or livestock-related fields.
Title of Award: IFFAA Scholarships **Area, Field, or Subject:** Agricultural sciences; Animal science and behavior **Level of Education for which Award is Granted:** Undergraduate **Number Awarded:** Varies each year. Recently, 74 scholarships (with a value of $77,00) and 64 performance and carcass awards (with a value of $11,500) were presented. **Funds Available:** Stipends range from $500 to $2,500. **Duration:** 1 year; nonrenewable.
Eligibility Requirements: This program is open to students who will be entering an Iowa 2- or 4-year postsecondary institution in the following fall. Applicants must be residents of Iowa, active in 4-H or FFA livestock projects, and planning to major in animal science or a field in agriculture or home economics that is related to the animal industry. Selection is based on level of 4-H or FFA involvement in livestock project work, livestock exhibition, and/or judging (50%); scholarship (15%); leadership and activities (25%); and curriculum and career plans (10%). The program also includes performance and carcass awards in which animals are selected on the basis of visual appraisal and then evaluated in a carcass contest for economically important traits, such as loin eye or rib eye area, tenth rib fat, and average daily gain. **Deadline for Receipt:** May of each year. **Additional Information:** Information is also available from county

4-H offices in Iowa and local FFA advisors. Winners are announced at the Iowa State Fair's annual 4-H/FFA "Sale of Champions" in August, sponsored by the Iowa Foundation for Agricultural Advancement (IFFAA). The IFFAA was established in 1988 and began offering scholarships in 1990.

2565 ■ LIONS CLUBS INTERNATIONAL

Attn: Program Development Department
300 22nd Street
Oak Brook, IL 60523-8842
Tel: (630)571-5466
Fax: (630)571-1692
E-mail: executiveservices@lionsclubs.org
Web Site: http://www.lionsclubs.org/EN/content/
vision_services_aids.shtml
To provide college scholarships and other assistance to blind people.

Title of Award: Lions Clubs Support Services for the Blind and Visually Impaired **Area, Field, or Subject:** Equine studies; General studies/Field of study not specified **Level of Education for which Award is Granted:** Graduate, Undergraduate, Other **Funds Available:** The amount of this assistance varies.

Eligibility Requirements: These programs are open to blind people and others involved in service to the blind. Applicants may be seeking support for the following activities: scholarships for the blind and visually impaired, medical research, assistive technology grants, independent mobility, transportation, reading materials and aids, audio products, Braille products, and other aids. **Additional Information:** Support is provided by local clubs of Lions Clubs International. Requests send to the international office are referred to the appropriate district governor. If any of the clubs within the district conduct programs for which the applicant might be considered, the governor will advise the particular club to contact the applicant. No funds are available from the office of Lions Clubs International.

2566 ■ NATIONAL FFA ORGANIZATION

Attn: Scholarship Office
6060 FFA Drive
P.O. Box 68960
Indianapolis, IN 46268-0960
Tel: (317)802-4321
Fax: (317)802-5321
E-mail: scholarships@ffa.org
Web Site: http://www.ffa.org
To provide financial assistance to FFA members who are interested in studying animal science or a related field in college.

Title of Award: Bayer Animal Health Scholarship **Area, Field, or Subject:** Animal science and behavior; Equine studies; Veterinary science and medicine **Level of Education for which Award is Granted:** Four Year College **Number Awarded:** 5 each year. **Funds Available:** The stipend is $1,000 per year. Funds are paid directly to the recipient. **Duration:** 1 year; nonrenewable.

Eligibility Requirements: This program is open to members who are graduating high school seniors planning to enroll full time in college. Applicants must be interested in working on a 4-year degree in animal or pre-veterinary science, equine science, animal nutrition, or animal pathology. They must have a GPA of 3.0 or higher. Selection is based on academic achievement (10 points for GPA, 10 points for SAT or ACT score, 10 points for class rank), leadership in FFA activities (30 points), leadership in community activities (10 points), and participation in the Supervised Agricultural Experience (SAE) program (30 points). U.S. citizenship is required. **Deadline for Receipt:** February of each year. **Additional Information:** Funding for this program is provided by Bayer Animal Health.

2567 ■ NATIONAL FFA ORGANIZATION

Attn: Scholarship Office
6060 FFA Drive
P.O. Box 68960
Indianapolis, IN 46268-0960
Tel: (317)802-4321
Fax: (317)802-5321
E-mail: scholarships@ffa.org
Web Site: http://www.ffa.org

To provide financial assistance to FFA members interested in studying animal or dairy science in college.

Title of Award: Church & Dwight Company Scholarship **Area, Field, or Subject:** Animal science and behavior; Dairy science **Level of Education for which Award is Granted:** Four Year College **Number Awarded:** 2 each year: 1 to a high school senior and 1 to a college student. **Funds Available:** The stipend is $1,000 per year. Funds are paid directly to the recipient. **Duration:** 1 year; nonrenewable.

Eligibility Requirements: This program is open to members who are graduating high school seniors planning to enroll or students currently enrolled full time in college. Applicants must be studying or planning to study dairy or animal science at a 4-year institution. Preference is given to students with a demonstrated interest in a dairy-related career. Selection is based on academic achievement (10 points for GPA, 10 points for SAT or ACT score, 10 points for class rank), leadership in FFA activities (30 points), leadership in community activities (10 points), and participation in the Supervised Agricultural Experience (SAE) program (30 points). U.S. citizenship is required. **Deadline for Receipt:** February of each year. **Additional Information:** Funding for this scholarship is provided by Church & Dwight Company, Inc.

2568 ■ NATIONAL FFA ORGANIZATION

Attn: Scholarship Office
6060 FFA Drive
P.O. Box 68960
Indianapolis, IN 46268-0960
Tel: (317)802-4321
Fax: (317)802-5321
E-mail: scholarships@ffa.org
Web Site: http://www.ffa.org
To provide financial assistance to FFA members who are interested in studying animal science, dairy science, or nutrition in college.

Title of Award: Cooperative Resources International Scholarships **Area, Field, or Subject:** Animal science and behavior; Dairy science; Nutrition **Level of Education for which Award is Granted:** Four Year College **Number Awarded:** 2 each year. **Funds Available:** The stipend is $1,000. Funds are paid directly to the recipient. **Duration:** 1 year; nonrenewable.

Eligibility Requirements: This program is open to members who are graduating high school seniors planning to enroll or students already enrolled full time in college. Applicants must be interested in working on a 4-year degree in animal science, dairy science, or nutrition. Selection is based on academic achievement (10 points for GPA, 10 points for SAT or ACT score, 10 points for class rank), leadership in FFA activities (30 points), leadership in community activities (10 points), and participation in the Supervised Agricultural Experience (SAE) program (30 points). U.S. citizenship is required. **Deadline for Receipt:** February of each year. **Additional Information:** Funding for these scholarships is provided by Cooperative Resources International.

2569 ■ NATIONAL FFA ORGANIZATION

Attn: Scholarship Office
6060 FFA Drive
P.O. Box 68960
Indianapolis, IN 46268-0960
Tel: (317)802-4321
Fax: (317)802-5321
E-mail: scholarships@ffa.org
Web Site: http://www.ffa.org

To provide financial assistance to FFA members from selected states who are interested in studying animal science in college.

Title of Award: Lextron Scholarship **Area, Field, or Subject:** Animal science and behavior **Level of Education for which Award is Granted:** Four Year College **Number Awarded:** 1 each year. **Funds Available:** The stipend is $1,000. Funds are paid directly to the recipient. **Duration:** 1 year; nonrenewable.

Eligibility Requirements: This program is open to members who are graduating high school seniors planning to enroll full time in college. Applicants must be residents of Alabama, Arizona, Arkansas, California, Colorado, Florida, Georgia, Idaho, Iowa, Kansas, Louisiana, Minnesota, Mississippi, Missouri, Montana, Nebraska, Nevada, New Mexico, North Dakota, Oklahoma, Oregon, South Dakota, Texas, Utah, Washington, or Wyoming interested in working on a 4-year degree in animal science. Selection is based on academic achievement (10 points for GPA, 10 points for SAT or ACT score, 10 points for class rank), leadership in FFA activities (30 points), leadership in community activities (10 points), and participation in the Supervised Agricultural Experience (SAE) program (30 points). U.S. citizenship is required. **Deadline for Receipt:** February of each year. **Additional Information:** Funding for this scholarship is provided by Lextron, Inc.

2570 ■ NATIONAL FFA ORGANIZATION
Attn: Scholarship Office
6060 FFA Drive
P.O. Box 68960
Indianapolis, IN 46268-0960
Tel: (317)802-4321
Fax: (317)802-5321
E-mail: scholarships@ffa.org
Web Site: http://www.ffa.org
To provide financial assistance to FFA members who wish to study agriculture and related fields in college.
Title of Award: National FFA Scholarships for Undergraduates in the Sciences **Area, Field, or Subject:** Agricultural sciences; Animal science and behavior; Dairy science; Engineering, Agricultural; Environmental conservation; Environmental science; Equine studies; Food science and technology; Horticulture; Natural resources; Technology **Level of Education for which Award is Granted:** Undergraduate **Number Awarded:** Varies; generally, a total of approximately 1,000 scholarships are awarded annually by the association. **Funds Available:** Stipends vary, but most are at least $1,000. **Duration:** 1 year or more.
Eligibility Requirements: This program is open to current and former members of the organization who are working or planning to work full time on a degree in fields related to agriculture; this includes: agricultural mechanics and engineering, agricultural technology, animal science, conservation, dairy science, equine science, floriculture, food science, horticulture, irrigation, lawn and landscaping, and natural resources. For most of the scholarships, applicants must be high school seniors; others are open to students currently enrolled in college. The program includes a large number of designated scholarships that specify the locations where the members must live, the schools they must attend, the fields of study they must pursue, or other requirements. Some consider family income in the selection process, but most do not. Selection is based on academic achievement (10 points for GPA, 10 points for SAT or ACT score, 10 points for class rank), leadership in FFA activities (30 points), leadership in community activities (10 points), and participation in the Supervised Agricultural Experience (SAE) program (30 points). U.S. citizenship is required. **Deadline for Receipt:** February of each year. **Additional Information:** Funding for these scholarships is provided by many different corporate sponsors.

2571 ■ NATIONAL FFA ORGANIZATION
Attn: Scholarship Office
6060 FFA Drive
P.O. Box 68960
Indianapolis, IN 46268-0960
Tel: (317)802-4321
Fax: (317)802-5321
E-mail: scholarships@ffa.org
Web Site: http://www.ffa.org
To provide financial assistance to FFA members interested in studying dairy science in college.
Title of Award: NMC Scholarship **Area, Field, or Subject:** Animal science and behavior; Dairy science; Veterinary science and medicine **Level of Education for which Award is Granted:** Undergraduate **Number Awarded:** 1 each year. **Funds Available:** The stipend is $1,000 per year. Funds are paid directly to the recipient. **Duration:** 1 year; nonrenewable.
Eligibility Requirements: This program is open to members who are either graduating high school seniors planning to enroll full time in college or students already enrolled in college on a full-time basis. Applicants must be working on or planning to work on a 2-year or 4-year degree in dairy science, animal science, or pre-veterinary science. They must have a dairy background or be planning to prepare for a career related to dairy. Selection is based on academic achievement (10 points for GPA, 10 points for SAT or ACT score, 10 points for class rank), leadership in FFA activities (30 points), leadership in community activities (10 points), and participation in the Supervised Agricultural Experience (SAE) program (30

points). U.S. citizenship is required. **Deadline for Receipt:** February of each year. **Additional Information:** Funding for this scholarship is provided by NMC (formerly the National Mastitis Council).

2572 ■ NATIONAL FFA ORGANIZATION
Attn: Scholarship Office
6060 FFA Drive
P.O. Box 68960
Indianapolis, IN 46268-0960
Tel: (317)802-4321
Fax: (317)802-5321
E-mail: scholarships@ffa.org
Web Site: http://www.ffa.org
To provide financial assistance to FFA members who are interested in studying agribusiness or animal science in college.
Title of Award: Pfizer Animal Health Scholarships **Area, Field, or Subject:** Agribusiness; Animal science and behavior **Level of Education for which Award is Granted:** Four Year College **Number Awarded:** 1 or more each year. **Funds Available:** The stipend is $1,250. Funds are paid directly to the recipient. **Duration:** 1 year; nonrenewable.
Eligibility Requirements: This program is open to members who are graduating high school seniors planning to enroll full time in college. Applicants must be interested in working on a 4-year degree in agribusiness or animal science. Selection is based on academic achievement (10 points for GPA, 10 points for SAT or ACT score, 10 points for class rank), leadership in FFA activities (30 points), leadership in community activities (10 points), and participation in the Supervised Agricultural Experience (SAE) program (30 points). U.S. citizenship is required. **Deadline for Receipt:** February of each year. **Additional Information:** Funding for these scholarships is provided by Pfizer Animal Health.

2573 ■ NATIONAL FFA ORGANIZATION
Attn: Scholarship Office
6060 FFA Drive
P.O. Box 68960
Indianapolis, IN 46268-0960
Tel: (317)802-4321
Fax: (317)802-5321
E-mail: scholarships@ffa.org
Web Site: http://www.ffa.org
To provide financial assistance to FFA members interested in studying agriculture in college.
Title of Award: Purina Mills/Land O'Lakes Purina Feeds Dealer Scholarships **Area, Field, or Subject:** Agricultural sciences; Animal science and behavior; Equine studies; Veterinary science and medicine; Wildlife conservation, management, and science **Level of Education for which Award is Granted:** Four Year College **Number Awarded:** Varies each year, depending on the number of participating Purina dealers. **Funds Available:** The stipend is $1,000 per year. Funds are paid directly to the recipient. **Duration:** 1 year; nonrenewable.
Eligibility Requirements: This program is open to members who are graduating high school seniors planning to enroll full time in college. Applicants must be interested in working on a 4-year college degree in agriculture. Preference is given to applicants displaying an interest in animal nutrition, aquaculture, animal science, equine science, wildlife management, or specialty animals. Selection is based on academic achievement (10 points for GPA, 10 points for SAT or ACT score, 10 points for class rank), leadership in FFA activities (30 points), leadership in community activities (10 points), and participation in the Supervised Agricultural Experience (SAE) program (30 points). U.S. citizenship is required. **Deadline for Receipt:** February of each year. **Additional Information:** Funding for these scholarships is provided by Purina Mills, LLC.

2574 ■ NATIONAL FFA ORGANIZATION
Attn: Scholarship Office
6060 FFA Drive
P.O. Box 68960
Indianapolis, IN 46268-0960
Tel: (317)802-4321
Fax: (317)802-5321
E-mail: scholarships@ffa.org
Web Site: http://www.ffa.org

To provide financial assistance to FFA members who are interested in studying fields related to agriculture or agribusiness in college.

Title of Award: Rabo AgriFinance Scholarships **Area, Field, or Subject:** Agribusiness; Agricultural sciences; Agriculture, Economic aspects; Animal science and behavior; Computer and information sciences; Management **Level of Education for which Award is Granted:** Undergraduate **Number Awarded:** 3 each year. **Funds Available:** The stipend is $1,000 per year. Funds are paid directly to the recipient. **Duration:** 1 year; nonrenewable.

Eligibility Requirements: This program is open to members who are graduating high school seniors planning to enroll full time in college. Applicants must be interested in working on a 2- or 4-year degree in agronomy and crop science, farm and ranch management, livestock management, agricultural economics, agricultural power and equipment, or computer systems in agriculture. They must have a GPA of 30 or higher and rank in the upper 50% of their class. Selection is based on academic achievement (10 points for GPA, 10 points for SAT or ACT score, 10 points for class rank), leadership in FFA activities (30 points), leadership in community activities (10 points), and participation in the Supervised Agricultural Experience (SAE) program (30 points). U.S. citizenship is required. **Deadline for Receipt:** February of each year. **Additional Information:** Funding for this program is provided by Rabo AgriFinance.

2575 ■ NATIONAL FFA ORGANIZATION

Attn: Scholarship Office
6060 FFA Drive
P.O. Box 68960
Indianapolis, IN 46268-0960
Tel: (317)802-4321
Fax: (317)802-5321
E-mail: scholarships@ffa.org
Web Site: http://www.ffa.org
To provide financial assistance to FFA members who are interested in studying animal science in college.

Title of Award: Retriever Dog Food Scholarships **Area, Field, or Subject:** Animal science and behavior **Level of Education for which Award is Granted:** Four Year College **Number Awarded:** 3 each year. **Funds Available:** The stipend is $1,000. Funds are paid directly to the recipient. **Duration:** 1 year; nonrenewable.

Eligibility Requirements: This program is open to members who are graduating high school seniors planning to enroll and college students currently enrolled full time. Applicants must be working on or planning to work on a degree in animal science. Selection is based on academic achievement (10 points for GPA, 10 points for SAT or ACT score, 10 points for class rank), leadership in FFA activities (30 points), leadership in community activities (10 points), and participation in the Supervised Agricultural Experience (SAE) program (30 points). U.S. citizenship is required. **Deadline for Receipt:** February of each year. **Additional Information:** Funding for these scholarships is provided by Doane Pet Care Company, manufacturer of Retriever Dog Food.

2576 ■ NATIONAL FFA ORGANIZATION

Attn: Scholarship Office
6060 FFA Drive
P.O. Box 68960
Indianapolis, IN 46268-0960
Tel: (317)802-4321
Fax: (317)802-5321
E-mail: scholarships@ffa.org
Web Site: http://www.ffa.org
To provide financial assistance for college to FFA members from Idaho who have a dairy background.

Title of Award: United Dairymen of Idaho Scholarships **Area, Field, or Subject:** Animal science and behavior; Dairy science; Veterinary science and medicine **Level of Education for which Award is Granted:** Undergraduate **Number Awarded:** 3 each year. **Funds Available:** The stipend is $1,600 per year. Funds are paid directly to the recipient. **Duration:** 1 year; nonrenewable.

Eligibility Requirements: This program is open to members who are graduating high school seniors planning to enroll full time in college. Applicants must be residents of Idaho who live or work on a dairy farm. They must be interested in working on a 2- or 4-year degree in dairy science, dairy-related crop sciences, large animal nutrition, or large animal

veterinarian. Selection is based on academic achievement (10 points for GPA, 10 points for SAT or ACT score, 10 points for class rank), leadership in FFA activities (30 points), leadership in community activities (10 points), and participation in the Supervised Agricultural Experience (SAE) program (30 points). U.S. citizenship is required. **Deadline for Receipt:** February of each year. **Additional Information:** Funding for these scholarships is provided by United Dairymen of Idaho.

2577 ■ NATIONAL FFA ORGANIZATION

Attn: Scholarship Office
6060 FFA Drive
P.O. Box 68960
Indianapolis, IN 46268-0960
Tel: (317)802-4321
Fax: (317)802-5321
E-mail: scholarships@ffa.org
Web Site: http://www.ffa.org
To provide financial assistance to FFA members from designated states who are interested in studying a field related to agriculture in college.

Title of Award: Wilbur-Ellis Company Scholarships **Area, Field, or Subject:** Agribusiness; Agricultural sciences; Agriculture, Economic aspects; Animal science and behavior; Biochemistry; Business administration; Computer and information sciences; Entomology; Finance; Forestry; Genetics; Horticulture; Management; Marketing and distribution; Poultry science; Soil science **Level of Education for which Award is Granted:** Four Year College **Number Awarded:** 13 each year: 1 at $5,000, 2 at $2,000, and 10 at $1,000. **Funds Available:** Stipends are $5,000, $2,000, or $1,000 per year. Funds are paid directly to the recipient. **Duration:** 1 year; nonrenewable.

Eligibility Requirements: This program is open to members who are graduating high school seniors planning to enroll or college students currently enrolled full time. Applicants must be residents of the following states: Arizona, California, Idaho, Indiana, Michigan, Minnesota, Montana, New Mexico, North Dakota, Ohio, Oregon, South Dakota, Texas, Utah, Washington, Wisconsin, or Wyoming. They must be planning to work on a 4-year degree in agricultural production, forest management, agronomy and crop science, animal nutrition, farm and ranch management, horticulture, nursery and landscape management, plant science, poultry science, general agriculture, business management, economics, international agriculture, finance, sales and marketing, biochemistry, biotechnology, computer systems in agriculture, entomology, plant breeding and genetics, plant pathology, range science, or soil science. Their combined SAT score must be 1000 or higher and their GPA must be 3.0 or higher. Selection is based on academic achievement (10 points for GPA, 10 points for SAT or ACT score, 10 points for class rank), leadership in FFA activities (30 points), leadership in community activities (10 points), and participation in the Supervised Agricultural Experience (SAE) program (30 points). Financial need is also considered in the selection process. U.S. citizenship is required. **Deadline for Receipt:** February of each year. **Additional Information:** Funding for this scholarship is provided by the agriculture division of the Wilbur-Ellis Company.

2578 ■ OPPORTUNITIES FOR THE BLIND, INC.

Attn: Grant Committee
P.O. Box 98
Fairplay, MD 21733
Tel: (240)420-6500
E-mail: OppBlind@yahoo.com
Web Site: http://www.opportunitiesfortheblind.org
To provide funding to blind people interested in improving their employment situation.

Title of Award: Opportunities for the Blind Grants **Area, Field, or Subject:** Equine studies; General studies/Field of study not specified **Level of Education for which Award is Granted:** Undergraduate, Other **Number Awarded:** Varies each year. **Funds Available:** Grants normally range from $3,000 to $5,000, and may go as high as $10,000. **Duration:** This is a 1-time award.

Eligibility Requirements: This program is open to legally blind U.S. citizens. Applicants must be seeking funding for the following categories: scholarships and training, job-related service, special equipment, or self-employment projects. Preference is given to applicants who are preparing for careers in fields where the blind are not typically found. **Deadline for Receipt:** February, May, August, or October of each year. **Additional**

Information: This program was established in 1981.

2579 ■ TRAVELERS PROTECTIVE ASSOCIATION OF AMERICA

Attn: TPA Scholarship Trust for the Deaf and Near Deaf
3755 Lindell Boulevard
St. Louis, MO 63108-3476
Tel: (314)371-0533
Fax: (314)371-0537
E-mail: support@tpahq.org
Web Site: http://www.travelersprotectiveasn.com/deaf_scholarships.htm
To provide assistance to deaf and hearing impaired persons. to obtain additional education, mechanical devices, specialized medical treatment, or other treatments.
Title of Award: Scholarship Trust for the Deaf and Near Deaf **Area, Field, or Subject:** Equine studies; General studies/Field of study not specified **Level of Education for which Award is Granted:** Undergraduate, Other **Number Awarded:** Varies each year; since the trust was established, it has distributed more than $1.1 million to more than 2,400 recipients. **Funds Available:** The grant depends on the need of the recipient. **Duration:** 1 year; recipients may reapply.
Eligibility Requirements: This assistance is available to U.S. residents who are deaf or hearing impaired. Applicants must be able to demonstrate that they will benefit from special programs, services, or other activities for the deaf, but that they are unable to provide the necessary funds. **Deadline for Receipt:** February of each year. **Additional Information:** This fund was established in 1975. Support has been provided to children as young as 2 months and to adults as old as 82 years. Funds have been used for mechanical devices, tuition at schools that specialize in educating the deaf (e.g., Gallaudet University, Rochester Institute of Technology, Central Institute for the Deaf), note takers and interpreters in classes in regular schools that do not provide those services to the deaf, speech and language therapy (especially for those who have had the Cochlear Implant), medical or other specialized treatments, and computer programs that assist deaf and their families learn and apply skills presented in the classroom.

2580 ■ VERMONT STUDENT ASSISTANCE CORPORATION

Champlain Mill
Attn: Scholarship Programs
P.O. Box 2000
Winooski, VT 05404-2601
Tel: (802)654-3798; 888-253-4819
Fax: (802)654-3765
E-mail: info@vsac.org
Web Site: http://www.vsac.org
To provide financial assistance to residents of Vermont who are interested in majoring in a veterinary field in college or graduate school.
Title of Award: Gail Richardson Scholarship **Area, Field, or Subject:** Animal science and behavior; Veterinary science and medicine **Level of Education for which Award is Granted:** Doctorate, Undergraduate **Number Awarded:** 1 each year. **Funds Available:** The stipend is $1,000. **Duration:** 1 year.
Eligibility Requirements: This program is open to residents of Vermont who are graduating high school seniors, high school graduates, or GED recipients. Applicants must be interested in attending an accredited postsecondary institution to work on a degree in veterinary medicine, veterinary technology, animal science, or a related field. Selection is based on academic achievement (GPA of 2.5 or higher), required essays, letters of recommendation, and financial need. **Deadline for Receipt:** April of each year. **Additional Information:** The Vermont Student Assistance Corporation Board of Directors established this scholarship in 2001 to honor a former member.

2581 ■ VERMONT STUDENT ASSISTANCE CORPORATION

Champlain Mill
Attn: Scholarship Programs
P.O. Box 2000
Winooski, VT 05404-2601
Tel: (802)654-3798; 888-253-4819
Fax: (802)654-3765
E-mail: info@vsac.org
Web Site: http://www.vsac.org

To provide financial assistance to residents of Vermont who are interested in majoring in an agriculture-related field in college.
Title of Award: Vermont Feed Dealers and Manufacturers Association Scholarship **Area, Field, or Subject:** Agribusiness; Agricultural sciences; Animal science and behavior; Botany; Equine studies; Forestry; Horticulture; Soil science; Veterinary science and medicine **Level of Education for which Award is Granted:** Undergraduate **Number Awarded:** Varies each year; recently, 6 of these scholarships were awarded. **Funds Available:** The maximum stipend is $3,000. **Duration:** 1 year; recipients may reapply.
Eligibility Requirements: This scholarship is available to high school seniors, high school graduates, and currently-enrolled college students in Vermont who are enrolled or planning to enroll in a postsecondary degree program in agriculture, including but not limited to animal sciences, equine studies, agribusiness, plant and soil science, forestry, horticulture, and veterinary medicine or technology. Selection is based on a letter of recommendation and required essays. **Deadline for Receipt:** June of each year.

Forestry

2582 ■ COMMUNITY FOUNDATION FOR THE FOX VALLEY REGION, INC.

Attn: Scholarships
4455 West Lawrence Street
P.O. Box 563
Appleton, WI 54912-0563
Tel: (920)830-1290
Fax: (920)830-1293
E-mail: cffvr@cffoxvalley.org
Web Site: http://www.cffoxvalley.org/scholarship_fundslist.html
To provide financial assistance to upper-division and graduate students in Wisconsin who are working on a degree related to gardening.
Title of Award: Wisconsin Garden Club Federation Scholarship **Area, Field, or Subject:** Agricultural sciences; Botany; Environmental conservation; Environmental science; Forestry; Horticulture; Landscape architecture and design; Urban affairs/design/planning **Level of Education for which Award is Granted:** Graduate, Four Year College **Number Awarded:** Varies each year; recently, 4 of these scholarships were awarded. **Funds Available:** The stipend is $1,000. **Duration:** 1 year.
Eligibility Requirements: This program is open to college juniors, seniors, and graduate students at colleges and universities in Wisconsin. Applicants must be majoring in horticulture, floriculture, landscape design/architecture, botany, forestry, agronomy, plant pathology, environmental studies, city planning, land management, or a related field. They must have a 3.0 GPA or higher. **Deadline for Receipt:** February of each year. **Additional Information:** This program is sponsored by the Wisconsin Garden Club Federation. Information is also available from Carolyn A. Craig, WGCF Scholarship Chair, 900 North Shore Drive, New Richmond, WI 54017 9466, (715) 246-6242, E-mail: cacraig@frontiernet.net.

2583 ■ FEDERATED GARDEN CLUBS OF CONNECTICUT, INC.

14 Business Park Drive
P.O. Box 854
Branford, CT 06405-0854
Tel: (203)488-5528
Fax: (203)488-5528
E-mail: gardenclubs@ctgardenclubs.org
Web Site: http://www.ctgardenclubs.org/scholarship.html
To provide financial assistance to Connecticut residents who are interested in majoring in horticulture-related fields at a Connecticut college or university.
Title of Award: Federated Garden Clubs of Connecticut Scholarship **Area, Field, or Subject:** Agricultural sciences; Botany; Environmental conservation; Environmental science; Forestry; Horticulture; Landscape architecture and design; Urban affairs/design/planning **Level of Education for which Award is Granted:** Four Year College, Graduate **Number Awarded:** Varies each year, depending upon the availability of funds. **Funds Available:** Stipends are generally about $1,000 each. Funds are sent to the recipient's school in 2 equal installments. **Duration:** 1 year.
Eligibility Requirements: Applicants must be legal residents of Connecticut who are studying at a college or university in the state in

horticulture, floriculture, landscape design, conservation, forestry, botany, agronomy, plant pathology, environmental control, city planning, land management, or related subjects. They must be entering their junior or senior year of college or be a graduate student, have a GPA of 3.0 or higher, and be able to demonstrate financial need. **Deadline for Receipt:** June of each year. **Additional Information:** Information is also available from the Connecticut State Scholarship Chair, Mary Gray, 18 Long Hill Farm Road, Guilford, CT 06437, (203) 458-2784.

2584 ■ MINNESOTA TRAPPERS ASSOCIATION
c/o Deb Offerdahl
230 Second Street S.E.
Milaca, MN 56353
Tel: (320)982-1385
Web Site: http://www.mntrappers.com
To provide financial assistance for college to members of the Minnesota Trappers Association (MTA) and to other students working on a degree in a field related to natural resources.
Title of Award: Minnesota Trappers Association Scholarships **Area, Field, or Subject:** Agricultural sciences; Engineering, Agricultural; Forestry; General studies/Field of study not specified; Natural resources; Veterinary science and medicine; Wildlife conservation, management, and science; Zoology **Level of Education for which Award is Granted:** Undergraduate **Number Awarded:** 7 each year: 1 at $2,000, 2 at $1,000, 1 at $600 (the Russ Cumberland Scholarship), and 3 at $500. **Funds Available:** Stipends range from $500 to $2,000. **Duration:** 1 year.
Eligibility Requirements: This program is open to 1) MTA members working on an undergraduate degree in any field; and 2) other undergraduates working on a degree in agricultural engineering, agricultural science, forestry, natural resources, veterinary medicine, wildlife biology, or zoology. Applicants must be entering or enrolled in a 2- or 4-year program at an accredited college or university and have a college GPA of 2.5 or higher (entering freshmen must submit a transcript of their first term of college work before funds are released). **Deadline for Receipt:** June of each year. **Additional Information:** This program includes the Russ Cumberland Scholarship. Information is also available from Todd Roggenkamp, 28952 438th Lane, Palasade, MN 56373, (218) 768-2597.

2585 ■ NATIONAL FFA ORGANIZATION
Attn: Scholarship Office
6060 FFA Drive
P.O. Box 68960
Indianapolis, IN 46268-0960
Tel: (317)802-4321
Fax: (317)802-5321
E-mail: scholarships@ffa.org
Web Site: http://www.ffa.org
To provide financial assistance to FFA members who are interested in majoring in agricultural and forest production in college.
Title of Award: Manistique Papers Scholarships **Area, Field, or Subject:** Agricultural sciences; Forestry **Level of Education for which Award is Granted:** Undergraduate **Number Awarded:** 2 each year. **Funds Available:** The stipend is $1,000. Funds are paid directly to the recipient. **Duration:** 1 year; nonrenewable.
Eligibility Requirements: This program is open to members who are either graduating high school seniors planning to enroll full time in college or students already enrolled in college on a full-time basis. Applicants must be working on or planning to work on a 2-year or 4-year degree in agricultural and forest production. Selection is based on academic achievement (10 points for GPA, 10 points for SAT or ACT score, 10 points for class rank), leadership in FFA activities (30 points), leadership in community activities (10 points), and participation in the Supervised Agricultural Experience (SAE) program (30 points). U.S. citizenship is required. **Deadline for Receipt:** February of each year. **Additional Information:** Funding for these scholarships is provided by Manistique Papers, Inc. of Manistique, Michigan.

2586 ■ NATIONAL FFA ORGANIZATION
Attn: Scholarship Office
6060 FFA Drive
P.O. Box 68960
Indianapolis, IN 46268-0960
Tel: (317)802-4321

Fax: (317)802-5321
E-mail: scholarships@ffa.org
Web Site: http://www.ffa.org
To provide financial assistance to current or former FFA members who are interested in studying a field related to agriculture at a college or university in designated states.
Title of Award: Norfolk Southern Foundation Scholarships **Area, Field, or Subject:** Agribusiness; Agricultural sciences; Communications; Education; Engineering, Agricultural; Finance; Forestry; Management; Marketing and distribution **Level of Education for which Award is Granted:** Four Year College **Number Awarded:** 3 each year. **Funds Available:** The stipend is $1,000. Funds are paid directly to the recipient. **Duration:** 1 year; nonrenewable.
Eligibility Requirements: This program is open to members who are either graduating high school seniors planning to enroll in college or students already enrolled in college. Applicants must be interested in working full time on a 4-year degree in agricultural and forestry production, communication, education, engineering, finance, management, marketing, merchandising, sales, or agricultural science. They must be planning to attend a college or university in Alabama, Delaware, Georgia, Illinois, Indiana, Louisiana, Maryland, Michigan, Missouri, New York, North Carolina, Ohio, Pennsylvania, South Carolina, Tennessee, or Virginia. Selection is based on academic achievement (10 points for GPA, 10 points for SAT or ACT score, 10 points for class rank), leadership in FFA activities (30 points), leadership in community activities (10 points), and participation in the Supervised Agricultural Experience (SAE) program (30 points). U.S. citizenship is required. **Deadline for Receipt:** February of each year. **Additional Information:** Funding for these scholarships is provided by the Norfolk Southern Foundation.

2587 ■ NATIONAL FFA ORGANIZATION
Attn: Scholarship Office
6060 FFA Drive
P.O. Box 68960
Indianapolis, IN 46268-0960
Tel: (317)802-4321
Fax: (317)802-5321
E-mail: scholarships@ffa.org
Web Site: http://www.ffa.org
To provide financial assistance to FFA members from designated states who are interested in studying a field related to agriculture in college.
Title of Award: Wilbur-Ellis Company Scholarships **Area, Field, or Subject:** Agribusiness; Agricultural sciences; Agriculture, Economic aspects; Animal science and behavior; Biochemistry; Business administration; Computer and information sciences; Entomology; Finance; Forestry; Genetics; Horticulture; Management; Marketing and distribution; Poultry science; Soil science **Level of Education for which Award is Granted:** Four Year College **Number Awarded:** 13 each year: 1 at $5,000, 2 at $2,000, and 10 at $1,000. **Funds Available:** Stipends are $5,000, $2,000, or $1,000 per year. Funds are paid directly to the recipient. **Duration:** 1 year; nonrenewable.
Eligibility Requirements: This program is open to members who are graduating high school seniors planning to enroll or college students currently enrolled full time. Applicants must be residents of the following states: Arizona, California, Idaho, Indiana, Michigan, Minnesota, Montana, New Mexico, North Dakota, Ohio, Oregon, South Dakota, Texas, Utah, Washington, Wisconsin, or Wyoming. They must be planning to work on a 4-year degree in agricultural production, forest management, agronomy and crop science, animal nutrition, farm and ranch management, horticulture, nursery and landscape management, plant science, poultry science, general agriculture, business management, economics, international agriculture, finance, sales and marketing, biochemistry, biotechnology, computer systems in agriculture, entomology, plant breeding and genetics, plant pathology, range science, or soil science. Their combined SAT score must be 1000 or higher and their GPA must be 3.0 or higher. Selection is based on academic achievement (10 points for GPA, 10 points for SAT or ACT score, 10 points for class rank), leadership in FFA activities (30 points), leadership in community activities (10 points), and participation in the Supervised Agricultural Experience (SAE) program (30 points). Financial need is also considered in the selection process. U.S. citizenship is required. **Deadline for Receipt:** February of each year. **Additional Information:** Funding for this scholarship is provided by the agriculture division of the Wilbur-Ellis Company.

2588 ■ OREGON STUDENT ASSISTANCE COMMISSION

Attn: Grants and Scholarships Division
1500 Valley River Drive, Suite 100
Eugene, OR 97401-2146
Tel: (541)687-7395
Free: 800-452-8807
Fax: (541)687-7419
E-mail: awardinfo@mercury.osac.state.or.us
Web Site: http://www.osac.state.or.us
To provide financial assistance for college to Eagle Scouts in Oregon interested in studying fields related to wildlife management.
Title of Award: Royden M. Bodley Scholarship **Area, Field, or Subject:** Environmental conservation; Environmental science; Forestry; Wildlife conservation, management, and science **Level of Education for which Award is Granted:** Undergraduate **Number Awarded:** Varies each year; recently, 5 of these scholarships were awarded. **Funds Available:** The stipend is at least $1,400. **Duration:** 1 year.
Eligibility Requirements: This program is open to graduates of high schools in the Boy Scouts of America Cascade Pacific Council. Applicants must have achieved the Eagle rank in Oregon and be attending or planning to attend college in the state. They must be interested in majoring in forestry, wildlife, environment, or a related field. **Deadline for Receipt:** February of each year. **Additional Information:** This program is administered by the Oregon Student Assistance Commission (OSAC) with funds provided by the Oregon Community Foundation, 1221 S.W. Yamhill, Suite 100, Portland, OR 97205, (503) 227-6846, Fax: (503) 274-7771.

2589 ■ VERMONT STUDENT ASSISTANCE CORPORATION

Champlain Mill
Attn: Scholarship Programs
P.O. Box 2000
Winooski, VT 05404-2601
Tel: (802)654-3798; 888-253-4819
Fax: (802)654-3765
E-mail: info@vsac.org
Web Site: http://www.vsac.org
To provide financial assistance to residents of Vermont who are interested in majoring in an agriculture-related field in college.
Title of Award: Vermont Feed Dealers and Manufacturers Association Scholarship **Area, Field, or Subject:** Agribusiness; Agricultural sciences; Animal science and behavior; Botany; Equine studies; Forestry; Horticulture; Soil science; Veterinary science and medicine **Level of Education for which Award is Granted:** Undergraduate **Number Awarded:** Varies each year; recently, 6 of these scholarships were awarded. **Funds Available:** The maximum stipend is $3,000. **Duration:** 1 year; recipients may reapply.
Eligibility Requirements: This scholarship is available to high school seniors, high school graduates, and currently-enrolled college students in Vermont who are enrolled or planning to enroll in a postsecondary degree program in agriculture, including but not limited to animal sciences, equine studies, agribusiness, plant and soil science, forestry, horticulture, and veterinary medicine or technology. Selection is based on a letter of recommendation and required essays. **Deadline for Receipt:** June of each year.

2590 ■ VIRGINIA DAUGHTERS OF THE AMERICAN REVOLUTION

c/o Catherine Rafferty, Scholarship Chair
10101 Sanders Court
Great Falls, VA 22066-2526
Web Site: http://www.vadar.org/vadarscholarships.htm
To provide financial assistance to high school seniors in Virginia who wish to study designated fields in college.
Title of Award: Virginia DAR Scholarships **Area, Field, or Subject:** Environmental conservation; Environmental science; Forestry; Genealogy; History, American; Home Economics; Medicine; Science **Level of Education for which Award is Granted:** Undergraduate **Number Awarded:** 2 each year: 1 at $1,000 and 1 at $500. **Funds Available:** Stipends are $1,000 or $500. **Duration:** 1 year.
Eligibility Requirements: This program is open to seniors graduating from high schools in Virginia who plan to attend a Virginia college or university. Applicants must be planning to work on a degree in the field of science, medicine, conservation, ecology, forestry, home arts, genealogical research, or American history. Along with their application, they must submit a 1,000-word letter giving their reasons for interest in the scholar-

ship, a transcript of grades, a letter of recommendation from a teacher in their chosen field, and documentation of financial need. **Deadline for Receipt:** January of each year.

Horticulture

2591 ■ AMERICAN FLORAL ENDOWMENT

P.O. Box 945
Edwardsville, IL 62025
Tel: (618)692-0045
Fax: (618)692-4045
E-mail: afe@endowment.org
Web Site: http://www.endowment.org/ball3.htm
To provide financial assistance and work experience to students working on an undergraduate degree in floriculture.
Title of Award: Vic and Margaret Ball Internship **Area, Field, or Subject:** Horticulture **Level of Education for which Award is Granted:** Undergraduate **Number Awarded:** 1 or more each year. **Funds Available:** Employers must agree to pay a fair market wage for the geographic area and position. In addition, students receive a grant of $6,000 for a 6-month internship, $4,000 for a 4-month internship, or $1,500 for a 3-month summer internship. **Duration:** 6 months, 4 months, or 3 summer months.
Eligibility Requirements: This program is open to U.S. citizens who are currently enrolled full time in a 2-year or 4-year college or university in the United States in a floriculture or environmental horticulture program. Applicants must be maintaining satisfactory progress in a degree or certificate program and a GPA of "C" or better. They must be interested in gaining additional training by interning at a commercial production greenhouse or nursery of sufficient size to support a well-rounded internship program away from their home and school community. **Deadline for Receipt:** February or October of each year. **Additional Information:** This program was established in 1992.

2592 ■ AMERICAN FLORAL ENDOWMENT

P.O. Box 945
Edwardsville, IL 62025
Tel: (618)692-0045
Fax: (618)692-4045
E-mail: afe@endowment.org
Web Site: http://www.endowment.org/mosmiller2.htm
To provide financial assistance and work experience to students working on an undergraduate degree in floriculture or business.
Title of Award: Mosmiller Scholar Program **Area, Field, or Subject:** Business administration; Horticulture **Level of Education for which Award is Granted:** Undergraduate **Number Awarded:** 1 or more each year. **Funds Available:** Employers must agree to pay a fair market wage for the geographic area and position. In addition, students receive a grant of $2,000 following completion of the internship. **Duration:** Internships are for 10 to 16 weeks. Preference is given to fall or spring internships, but summer internships are allowed if the location can provide valuable experience.
Eligibility Requirements: This program is open to U.S. citizens who are currently enrolled full time in a 2-year or 4-year college or university in the United States in a floriculture, environmental horticulture, or business program. Applicants must be maintaining satisfactory progress in a degree or certificate program and a GPA of "C" or better. They must be interested in interning at a wholesale, retail, or allied trade company located in the United States away from their home and school. Following completion of the internship, they receive a grant for continued study. **Deadline for Receipt:** February or October of each year. **Additional Information:** This program was established in 1975.

2593 ■ AMERICAN NURSERY AND LANDSCAPE ASSOCIATION

Attn: Horticultural Research Institute
1000 Vermont Avenue N.W., Suite 300
Washington, DC 20005-4914
Tel: (202)789-2900
Fax: (202)789-1893
E-mail: hriresearch@anla.org
Web Site: http://www.anla.org/research/scholarships/index.htm

To provide financial assistance to residents of Maryland, Virginia, and West Virginia working on an undergraduate or graduate degree in landscape architecture or horticulture.

Title of Award: Carville M. Akehurst Memorial Scholarship **Area, Field, or Subject:** Horticulture; Landscape architecture and design **Level of Education for which Award is Granted:** Graduate, Undergraduate **Number Awarded:** 1 each year. **Funds Available:** The stipend is $2,000. **Duration:** 1 year; may be renewed.

Eligibility Requirements: This program is open to students enrolled full time in a landscape or horticulture undergraduate or graduate program at an accredited 2-year or 4-year college or university. Applicants must be residents of Maryland, Virginia, or West Virginia, although they are not required to attend an institution within those states. They must be enrolled as a junior in a 4-year program or a senior in a 2-year program and have a minimum GPA of 2.7 overall and 3.0 in their major. Preference is given to applicants who plan to work within the nursery industry, including nursery operations; landscape architecture, design, construction, or maintenance; interiorscape; horticultural distribution; or retail garden center. **Deadline for Receipt:** March of each year. **Additional Information:** This program was established in 2002 by the Mid-Atlantic Nursery Trade Show, Inc.

2594 ■ AMERICAN NURSERY AND LANDSCAPE ASSOCIATION

Attn: Horticultural Research Institute
1000 Vermont Avenue N.W., Suite 300
Washington, DC 20005-4914
Tel: (202)789-2900
Fax: (202)789-1893
E-mail: hriresearch@anla.org
Web Site: http://www.anla.org/research/Scholarships/TandPBigelow.htm

To provide financial support to residents of New England interested in working on an undergraduate or graduate degree in landscape architecture or horticulture.

Title of Award: Timothy Bigelow and Palmer W. Bigelow, Jr. Scholarships **Area, Field, or Subject:** Horticulture; Landscape architecture and design **Level of Education for which Award is Granted:** Graduate, Undergraduate **Number Awarded:** Up to 3 each year. **Funds Available:** The stipend is $2,500. **Duration:** 1 year; nonrenewable.

Eligibility Requirements: This program is open to full-time students enrolled in an accredited landscape or horticulture program in 1) the final year of a 2-year curriculum, 2) the third year of a 4-year curriculum, or 3) a graduate program. Applicants must have a minimum GPA of 2.25 as undergraduates or 3.0 as graduate students. They must be a resident of 1 of the 6 New England states, although attendance at an institution within those states is not required. Preference is given to applicants who plan to work in an aspect of the nursery industry, including a business of their own, and to applicants who demonstrate financial need. **Deadline for Receipt:** March of each year. **Additional Information:** This program was created in 1988.

2595 ■ AMERICAN NURSERY AND LANDSCAPE ASSOCIATION

Attn: Horticultural Research Institute
1000 Vermont Avenue N.W., Suite 300
Washington, DC 20005-4914
Tel: (202)789-2900
Fax: (202)789-1893
E-mail: hriresearch@anla.org
Web Site: http://www.anla.org/research/scholarships/index.htm

To provide financial assistance to students working on an undergraduate or graduate degree in landscape architecture or horticulture.

Title of Award: Spring Meadow Nursery Scholarship **Area, Field, or Subject:** Agricultural sciences; Horticulture; Landscape architecture and design **Level of Education for which Award is Granted:** Graduate, Undergraduate **Number Awarded:** 1 each year. **Funds Available:** The stipend is $2,000. **Duration:** 1 year; may be renewed.

Eligibility Requirements: This program is open to students enrolled full time in a landscape or horticulture undergraduate or graduate program at an accredited 2-year or 4-year college or university. Students enrolled in a vocational agriculture program are also eligible. Applicants must have a minimum GPA of 2.25 overall and 2.7 in their major. Preference is given to applicants who plan to work within the nursery industry, including nursery operations; landscape architecture, design, construction, or maintenance; interiorscape; horticultural distribution; or retail garden center. **Deadline**

for Receipt: March of each year. **Additional Information:** This program was established in 1999.

2596 ■ AMERICAN NURSERY AND LANDSCAPE ASSOCIATION

Attn: Horticultural Research Institute
1000 Vermont Avenue N.W., Suite 300
Washington, DC 20005-4914
Tel: (202)789-2900
Fax: (202)789-1893
E-mail: hriresearch@anla.org
Web Site: http://www.anla.org/research/scholarships/index.htm

To provide financial assistance to undergraduate and graduate students working on a degree in landscape architecture or horticulture at colleges and universities in California.

Title of Award: Usrey Family Scholarship **Area, Field, or Subject:** Agricultural sciences; Horticulture; Landscape architecture and design **Level of Education for which Award is Granted:** Graduate, Undergraduate **Number Awarded:** 1 each year. **Funds Available:** The stipend is $2,000. **Duration:** 1 year; may be renewed.

Eligibility Requirements: This program is open to students enrolled full time in a landscape or horticulture undergraduate or graduate program at an accredited 2-year or 4-year college or university in California. Students enrolled in a vocational agriculture program are also eligible. Applicants must have a minimum GPA of 2.25 overall and 2.7 in their major. California state residency is not required. Preference is given to applicants who plan to work within the nursery industry, including nursery operations; landscape architecture, design, construction, or maintenance; interiorscape; horticultural distribution; or retail garden center. **Deadline for Receipt:** March of each year.

2597 ■ COLORADO WEED MANAGEMENT ASSOCIATION

Attn: Scholarship Program
P.O. Box 1910
Granby, CO 80446-1910
Tel: (970)887-1228
Fax: (970)887-1229
E-mail: cwma@rkymtnhi.com
Web Site: http://www.cwma.org/scholarship.htm

To provide financial assistance to high school seniors and college students in Colorado who are interested in weed management.

Title of Award: Colorado Weed Management Association Scholarship **Area, Field, or Subject:** Agricultural sciences; Botany; Natural resources **Level of Education for which Award is Granted:** Undergraduate **Number Awarded:** 1 each year. **Funds Available:** A stipend is awarded (amount not specified). **Duration:** 1 year; nonrenewable.

Eligibility Requirements: This program is open to high school seniors and college students who have demonstrated an interest in weed management and are planning to major in agriculture, natural resource management, botany, range management, or a related field. Applicants must be attending or planning to attend a 2-year college or 4-year college or university in Colorado. Along with their application, they must submit an essay, up to 3 pages in length, on the topic, "The Threat of Noxious Weeds Is..." High school seniors must have a GPA of 2.5 or higher; college freshmen must have a cumulative GPA of 2.0 or higher; college sophomores, juniors, and seniors must have a GPA of 2.5 or higher. Financial need is also considered in the selection process. **Deadline for Receipt:** March of each year.

2598 ■ COMMUNITY FOUNDATION FOR THE FOX VALLEY REGION, INC.

Attn: Scholarships
4455 West Lawrence Street
P.O. Box 563
Appleton, WI 54912-0563
Tel: (920)830-1290
Fax: (920)830-1293
E-mail: cffvr@cffoxvalley.org
Web Site: http://www.cffoxvalley.org/scholarship_fundslist.html

To provide financial assistance to upper-division and graduate students in Wisconsin who are working on a degree related to gardening.

Title of Award: Wisconsin Garden Club Federation Scholarship **Area, Field, or Subject:** Agricultural sciences; Botany; Environmental conservation; Environmental science; Forestry; Horticulture; Landscape architecture and design; Urban affairs/design/planning **Level of Education for which Award is Granted:** Graduate, Four Year College **Number Awarded:** Varies each year; recently, 4 of these scholarships were awarded. **Funds Available:** The stipend is $1,000. **Duration:** 1 year. **Eligibility Requirements:** This program is open to college juniors, seniors, and graduate students at colleges and universities in Wisconsin. Applicants must be majoring in horticulture, floriculture, landscape design/architecture, botany, forestry, agronomy, plant pathology, environmental studies, city planning, land management, or a related field. They must have a 3.0 GPA or higher. **Deadline for Receipt:** February of each year. **Additional Information:** This program is sponsored by the Wisconsin Garden Club Federation. Information is also available from Carolyn A. Craig, WGCF Scholarship Chair, 900 North Shore Drive, New Richmond, WI 54017-9466, (715) 246-6242, E-mail: cacraig@frontiernet.net.

2599 ■ COMMUNITY FOUNDATION OF LOUISVILLE

Attn: Director of Grants
Waterfront Plaza, Suite 1110
325 West Main Street
Louisville, KY 40202-4251
Tel: (502)585-4649
Fax: (502)587-7484
E-mail: info@cflouisville.org
Web Site: http://www.cflouisville.org
To provide financial assistance to women studying fields related to the environment at colleges and universities in Kentucky.
Title of Award: Thaddeus Colson and Isabelle Saalwaechter Fitzpatrick Memorial Scholarship **Area, Field, or Subject:** Agricultural sciences; Biological and clinical sciences; Environmental conservation; Environmental science; Horticulture **Level of Education for which Award is Granted:** Four Year College **Number Awarded:** 1 each year. **Funds Available:** The stipend is $2,000. Funds are paid directly to the college or university. **Duration:** 1 year; nonrenewable.
Eligibility Requirements: This program is open to female residents of Kentucky who are entering their sophomore, junior, or senior year at a 4-year public college or university in the state. Applicants must be majoring in an environmentally related program (e.g., agriculture, biology, horticulture, environmental studies, environmental engineering). They must be enrolled full time with a GPA of 3.0 or higher. Along with their application, they must submit a 200-word essay describing their interest, leadership, volunteer efforts, and work experience in the environmental field; their future plans and goals in the environmental field; and what they hope to accomplish with their college degree. Financial need is also considered in the selection process. **Deadline for Receipt:** February of each year.

2600 ■ DEPARTMENT OF AGRICULTURE

Animal and Plant Health Inspection Service
Marketing and Regulatory Programs
4700 River Road, Unit 22
Riverdale, MD 20737 1230
800-762-2738
Web Site: http://www.aphis.usda.gov/ppq
To provide financial assistance and work experience to college students majoring in the agricultural or biological sciences.
Title of Award: PPQ William F. Helms Student Scholarship Program **Area, Field, or Subject:** Agricultural sciences; Biological and clinical sciences; Botany; Entomology; Environmental conservation; Environmental science; Virology **Level of Education for which Award is Granted:** Undergraduate **Number Awarded:** Several each year. **Funds Available:** The stipend is $5,000 per year. **Duration:** 1 year; may be renewed if the recipient maintains a GPA of 2.5 or higher.
Eligibility Requirements: This program is open to college sophomores and juniors who are attending an accredited college or university, are majoring in an agricultural or biological science (such as biology, plant pathology, entomology, virology, bacteriology, mycology, or ecology), are interested in a career in plant protection and quarantine, and are U.S. citizens. To apply, interested students must submit a completed application form, a personal letter describing their career goals and interest in plant protection and quarantine, transcripts, and 3 letters of recommendation. **Deadline for Receipt:** February of each year. **Additional Information:** The U.S. Department of Agriculture's (USDA) Animal and Plant Health Inspection Service (APHIS) is the agency responsible for protect-

ing America's agriculture base; Plant Protection and Quarantine (PPQ) is the program within APHIS that deals with plant health issues. In addition to financial assistance, the Helms Student Scholarship Program also offers tutoring assistance, mentoring, paid work experience during vacation periods, career exploration, and possible employment upon graduation.

2601 ■ FEDERATED GARDEN CLUBS OF CONNECTICUT, INC.

14 Business Park Drive
P.O. Box 854
Branford, CT 06405-0854
Tel: (203)488-5528
Fax: (203)488-5528
E-mail: gardenclubs@ctgardenclubs.org
Web Site: http://www.ctgardenclubs.org/scholarship.html
To provide financial assistance to Connecticut residents who are interested in majoring in horticulture-related fields at a Connecticut college or university.
Title of Award: Federated Garden Clubs of Connecticut Scholarship **Area, Field, or Subject:** Agricultural sciences; Botany; Environmental conservation; Environmental science; Forestry; Horticulture; Landscape architecture and design; Urban affairs/design/planning **Level of Education for which Award is Granted:** Four Year College, Graduate **Number Awarded:** Varies each year, depending upon the availability of funds. **Funds Available:** Stipends are generally about $1,000 each. Funds are sent to the recipient's school in 2 equal installments. **Duration:** 1 year. **Eligibility Requirements:** Applicants must be legal residents of Connecticut who are studying at a college or university in the state in horticulture, floriculture, landscape design, conservation, forestry, botany, agronomy, plant pathology, environmental control, city planning, land management, or related subjects. They must be entering their junior or senior year of college or be a graduate student, have a GPA of 3.0 or higher, and be able to demonstrate financial need. **Deadline for Receipt:** June of each year. **Additional Information:** Information is also available from the Connecticut State Scholarship Chair, Mary Gray, 18 Long Hill Farm Road, Guilford, CT 06437, (203) 458-2784.

2602 ■ FLORIDA NURSERYMEN, GROWERS AND LANDSCAPE ASSOCIATION-ACTION CHAPTER

Attn: Gina Mazzie-Forbrick, Scholarship Committee Chair
ForemostCo, Inc.
1751 Williams Road
Winter Garden, FL 34787-9162
Tel: (407)877-8876
Fax: (407)877-8684
E-mail: gina@foremostco.com
To provide financial assistance to students in Florida interested in preparing for a career in horticulture.
Title of Award: FNGLA Action Chapter Scholarship **Area, Field, or Subject:** Horticulture; Landscape architecture and design; Turfgrass management **Level of Education for which Award is Granted:** Undergraduate **Number Awarded:** 1 or more each year. A total of $4,000 is available through this program each year. **Funds Available:** Stipends range from $500 to $1,500. **Duration:** 1 year.
Eligibility Requirements: Applicants must have been accepted by or be currently enrolled in a Florida junior college, college, or university. They may be attending school full or part time, but they must be majoring in 1 of the following subjects: environmental horticulture, landscaping, landscape architecture, turf management, or a related field. All applicants must have at least a 2.75 GPA. Selection is based on academic record, work experience, awards received, letters of recommendation, and an essay (300 words) on the applicant's career plans. **Deadline for Receipt:** June of each year.

2603 ■ KENTUCKY TURFGRASS COUNCIL

c/o David Williams, Executive Secretary
University of Kentucky
Plant and Soil Science Department
N-222 Agriculture Science Center North
Lexington, KY 40546-0091
Tel: (859)257-2715
Fax: (859)323-1952
E-mail: dwilliam@uky.edu

Web Site: http://www.uky.edu/Agriculture/ukturf/KTC2002/
scholarships.htm
To provide financial assistance to students majoring in turfgrass science
at colleges and universities in Kentucky.
Title of Award: Kentucky Turfgrass Council College Scholarships **Area,
Field, or Subject:** Horticulture; Turfgrass management **Level of Education for which Award is Granted:** Undergraduate **Number Awarded:** 1
or more each year. **Funds Available:** A stipend is awarded (amount not
specified). **Duration:** 1 year.
Eligibility Requirements: This program is open to students who are
enrolled full time at Kentucky universities and majoring in turfgrass science or horticulture. Applicants must submit 2 letters of recommendation,
an official copy of their university transcripts, a copy of their resume, and 2
paragraphs on 1) their plans after graduation and 2) why they believe they
deserve this scholarship. All qualified candidates are interviewed.
Deadline for Receipt: October of each year. **Additional Information:**
Information is also available from Gary Duvarado, Scholarship Committee
Chair, P.O. Box 323, Bardstown, KY 40004, E-mail: garyd67@hotmail.
com.

2604 ■ LOWE'S COMPANIES, INC.

Attn: Scholarship Program
P.O. Box 1111
North Wilkesboro, NC 28656
Tel: (336)658-4104
Free: 800-44-LOWES
Web Site: http://www.lowes.com/scholarships
To provide financial assistance to students at selected community and
technical colleges who are preparing for a career in a business or techni-
cal field related to Lowe's stores.
Title of Award: Lowe's Educational Scholarship Program **Area, Field, or
Subject:** Business; Construction; Drafting; Electronics; Heating, air
conditioning, and refrigeration; Horticulture **Level of Education for which
Award is Granted:** Two Year College, Vocational/Occupational **Number
Awarded:** Varies each year; since the program was established, more
than 150 of these scholarships have been awarded. **Funds Available:**
Stipends are $2,000 for full-time students, $1,000 for three-quarter time
students, or $800 for half-time students. **Duration:** 1 year; may be
renewed if the recipient qualifies for employment at Lowe's.
Eligibility Requirements: This program is open to students who are at
least 18 years of age and currently enrolled in a community or technical
college that is cooperating with Lowe's stores. Applicants must intend to
prepare for a career in an approved discipline within the business division
(business management, business administration) or vocational/technical
division (air conditioning, heating and refrigeration, construction, electrical
or electronics, industrial maintenance, machining, mechanical drafting and
design, plumbing, carpentry, or horticulture) of Lowe's. They must have
completed at least 1 semester with a GPA of 2.0 or higher. Applications
are accepted from current Lowe's employees, but students working for
another major retailer are not eligible. **Additional Information:** This
program was established in 1999. Currently, 32 community and technical
colleges are participating in the program. For a list, contact Lowe's.

2605 ■ NATIONAL FFA ORGANIZATION

Attn: Scholarship Office
6060 FFA Drive
P.O. Box 68960
Indianapolis, IN 46268-0960
Tel: (317)802-4321
Fax: (317)802-5321
E-mail: scholarships@ffa.org
Web Site: http://www.ffa.org
To provide financial assistance to FFA members interested in studying
agriculture, horticulture, or landscaping in college.
Title of Award: Irrigation Association Education Foundation Scholarship
Area, Field, or Subject: Agricultural sciences; Horticulture; Landscape
architecture and design **Level of Education for which Award is
Granted:** Four Year College **Number Awarded:** 1 each year. **Funds
Available:** The stipend is $1,000 per year. Funds are paid directly to the
recipient. **Duration:** 1 year; nonrenewable.
Eligibility Requirements: This program is open to members who are
graduating high school seniors planning to enroll full time in college. Applicants must be interested in working on a 4-year college degree in

agriculture, horticulture, or landscaping. They must be in the top 10% of
their class and an interest in irrigation that is confirmed by their advisor.
Selection is based on academic achievement (10 points for GPA, 10
points for SAT or ACT score, 10 points for class rank), leadership in FFA
activities (30 points), leadership in community activities (10 points), and
participation in the Supervised Agricultural Experience (SAE) program (30
points). U.S. citizenship is required. **Deadline for Receipt:** February of
each year. **Additional Information:** Funding for this scholarship is
provided by the Irrigation Association Education Foundation.

2606 ■ NATIONAL FFA ORGANIZATION

Attn: Scholarship Office
6060 FFA Drive
P.O. Box 68960
Indianapolis, IN 46268-0960
Tel: (317)802-4321
Fax: (317)802-5321
E-mail: scholarships@ffa.org
Web Site: http://www.ffa.org
To provide financial assistance to FFA members who wish to study
agricultural journalism and related fields in college.
Title of Award: National FFA Scholarships for Undergraduates in the
Humanities **Area, Field, or Subject:** Agricultural sciences; Communica-
tions; Horticulture; Landscape architecture and design **Level of Educa-
tion for which Award is Granted:** Undergraduate **Number Awarded:**
Varies; generally, a total of approximately 1,000 scholarships are awarded
annually by the association. **Funds Available:** Stipends vary, but most
are at least $1,000. **Duration:** 1 year or more.
Eligibility Requirements: This program is open to current and former
members of the organization who are working or planning to work full time
on a degree in fields related to agricultural journalism and communications, floriculture, and landscape design. For most of the scholarships, applicants must be high school seniors; others are open to students currently enrolled in college. The program includes a large number of
designated scholarships that specify the locations where the members
must live, the schools they must attend, the fields of study they must
pursue, or other requirements. Some consider family income in the selection process, but most do not. Selection is based on academic achievement (10 points for GPA, 10 points for SAT or ACT score, 10 points for
class rank), leadership in FFA activities (30 points), leadership in community activities (10 points), and participation in the Supervised
Agricultural Experience (SAE) program (30 points). U.S. citizenship is
required. **Deadline for Receipt:** February of each year. **Additional
Information:** Funding for these scholarships is provided by many different
corporate sponsors.

2607 ■ NATIONAL FFA ORGANIZATION

Attn: Scholarship Office
6060 FFA Drive
P.O. Box 68960
Indianapolis, IN 46268-0960
Tel: (317)802-4321
Fax: (317)802-5321
E-mail: scholarships@ffa.org
Web Site: http://www.ffa.org
To provide financial assistance to FFA members who wish to study
agriculture and related fields in college.
Title of Award: National FFA Scholarships for Undergraduates in the Sci-
ences **Area, Field, or Subject:** Agricultural sciences; Animal science and
behavior; Dairy science; Engineering, Agricultural; Environmental
conservation; Environmental science; Equine studies; Food science and
technology; Horticulture; Natural resources; Technology **Level of Education for which Award is Granted:** Undergraduate **Number Awarded:**
Varies; generally, a total of approximately 1,000 scholarships are awarded
annually by the association. **Funds Available:** Stipends vary, but most
are at least $1,000. **Duration:** 1 year or more.
Eligibility Requirements: This program is open to current and former
members of the organization who are working or planning to work full time
on a degree in fields related to agriculture; this includes: agricultural
mechanics and engineering, agricultural technology, animal science,
conservation, dairy science, equine science, floriculture, food science,
horticulture, irrigation, lawn and landscaping, and natural resources. For
most of the scholarships, applicants must be high school seniors; others

are open to students currently enrolled in college. The program includes a large number of designated scholarships that specify the locations where the members must live, the schools they must attend, the fields of study they must pursue, or other requirements. Some consider family income in the selection process, but most do not. Selection is based on academic achievement (10 points for GPA, 10 points for SAT or ACT score, 10 points for class rank), leadership in FFA activities (30 points), leadership in community activities (10 points), and participation in the Supervised Agricultural Experience (SAE) program (30 points). U.S. citizenship is required. **Deadline for Receipt:** February of each year. **Additional Information:** Funding for these scholarships is provided by many different corporate sponsors.

2608 ■ NATIONAL FFA ORGANIZATION

Attn: Scholarship Office
6060 FFA Drive
P.O. Box 68960
Indianapolis, IN 46268-0960
Tel: (317)802-4321
Fax: (317)802-5321
E-mail: scholarships@ffa.org
Web Site: http://www.ffa.org
To provide financial assistance to FFA members interested in studying a field related to the landscape industry in college.
Title of Award: PLANET Scholarships **Area, Field, or Subject:** Horticulture; Landscape architecture and design **Level of Education for which Award is Granted:** Undergraduate **Number Awarded:** 2 each year: 1 to a high school senior and 1 to a current college student. **Funds Available:** The stipend is $1,500 per year. Funds are paid directly to the recipient. **Duration:** 1 year; nonrenewable.
Eligibility Requirements: This program is open to members who are either high school seniors or already enrolled full time in college. Applicants must be working on or planning to work on a 2-year or 4-year degree in a field directly related to the landscape industry. Selection is based on academic achievement (10 points for GPA, 10 points for SAT or ACT score, 10 points for class rank), leadership in FFA activities (30 points), leadership in community activities (10 points), and participation in the Supervised Agricultural Experience (SAE) program (30 points). U.S. citizenship is required. **Deadline for Receipt:** February of each year. **Additional Information:** Funding for this scholarship is provided by the Professional Landcare Network (PLANET), formed in 2005 as the result of a merger between the Associated Landscape Contractors of America (ALCA) and the Professional Lawn Care Association of America (PLCAA).

2609 ■ NATIONAL FFA ORGANIZATION

Attn: Scholarship Office
6060 FFA Drive
P.O. Box 68960
Indianapolis, IN 46268-0960
Tel: (317)802-4321
Fax: (317)802 5321
E-mail: scholarships@ffa.org
Web Site: http://www.ffa.org
To provide financial assistance to FFA members interested in studying designated agricultural specialties in college.
Title of Award: Spraying Systems Company TeeJet Spray Products Scholarship **Area, Field, or Subject:** Agricultural sciences; Engineering, Agricultural; Horticulture; Landscape architecture and design; Turfgrass management **Level of Education for which Award is Granted:** Four Year College **Number Awarded:** 1 each year. **Funds Available:** The stipend is $1,000 per year. Funds are paid directly to the recipient. **Duration:** 1 year; nonrenewable.
Eligibility Requirements: This program is open to members who are graduating high school seniors planning to enroll full time in college. Applicants must be interested in working on a 4-year college degree in agronomy, agricultural engineering/mechanization, landscape/turfgrass management, or horticulture. Selection is based on academic achievement (10 points for GPA, 10 points for SAT or ACT score, 10 points for class rank), leadership in FFA activities (30 points), leadership in community activities (10 points), and participation in the Supervised Agricultural Experience (SAE) program (30 points). U.S. citizenship is required. **Deadline for Receipt:** February of each year. **Additional Information:** Funding for this scholarship is provided by Spraying

Systems Company, manufacturer of TeeJet brand spray products.

2610 ■ NATIONAL FFA ORGANIZATION

Attn: Scholarship Office
6060 FFA Drive
P.O. Box 68960
Indianapolis, IN 46268-0960
Tel: (317)802-4321
Fax: (317)802-5321
E-mail: scholarships@ffa.org
Web Site: http://www.ffa.org
To provide financial assistance to FFA members from designated states who are interested in studying a field related to agriculture in college.
Title of Award: Wilbur-Ellis Company Scholarships **Area, Field, or Subject:** Agribusiness; Agricultural sciences; Agriculture, Economic aspects; Animal science and behavior; Biochemistry; Business administration; Computer and information sciences; Entomology; Finance; Forestry; Genetics; Horticulture; Management; Marketing and distribution; Poultry science; Soil science **Level of Education for which Award is Granted:** Four Year College **Number Awarded:** 13 each year: 1 at $5,000, 2 at $2,000, and 10 at $1,000. **Funds Available:** Stipends are $5,000, $2,000, or $1,000 per year. Funds are paid directly to the recipient. **Duration:** 1 year; nonrenewable.
Eligibility Requirements: This program is open to members who are graduating high school seniors planning to enroll or college students currently enrolled full time. Applicants must be residents of the following states: Arizona, California, Idaho, Indiana, Michigan, Minnesota, Montana, New Mexico, North Dakota, Ohio, Oregon, South Dakota, Texas, Utah, Washington, Wisconsin, or Wyoming. They must be planning to work on a 4-year degree in agricultural production, forest management, agronomy and crop science, animal nutrition, farm and ranch management, horticulture, nursery and landscape management, plant science, poultry science, general agriculture, business management, economics, international agriculture, finance, sales and marketing, biochemistry, biotechnology, computer systems in agriculture, entomology, plant breeding and genetics, plant pathology, range science, or soil science. Their combined SAT score must be 1000 or higher and their GPA must be 3.0 or higher. Selection is based on academic achievement (10 points for GPA, 10 points for SAT or ACT score, 10 points for class rank), leadership in FFA activities (30 points), leadership in community activities (10 points), and participation in the Supervised Agricultural Experience (SAE) program (30 points). Financial need is also considered in the selection process. U.S. citizenship is required. **Deadline for Receipt:** February of each year. **Additional Information:** Funding for this scholarship is provided by the agriculture division of the Wilbur-Ellis Company.

2611 ■ PROFESSIONAL LANDCARE NETWORK

Attn: ALCA Educational Foundation
950 Herndon Parkway, Suite 450
Herndon, VA 20170
Tel: (703)736-9666
Free: 800-395-ALCA
Fax: (703)736-9668
E-mail: scholarship@landcarenetwork.org
Web Site: http://www.landcarenetwork.org/cms/programs/foundation.html
To provide financial assistance to students at colleges and universities that have a connection to the Professional Landcare Network (PLANET).
Title of Award: ALCA Educational Foundation Scholarships **Area, Field, or Subject:** Horticulture; Landscape architecture and design **Level of Education for which Award is Granted:** Undergraduate **Number Awarded:** Varies each year. Recently, 37 of these scholarships were awarded: 1 at $2,500, 1 at $1,500, 34 at $1,000, and 1 at $500. **Funds Available:** Stipends range from $500 to $2,500. **Duration:** 1 year.
Eligibility Requirements: This program is open to students at colleges and universities that 1) have an accredited PLANET landscape contracting curriculum, 2) have a PLANET student chapter, and/or 3) participate in PLANET student career days activities. Applicants must provide information on awards, honors, and scholarships received in high school or college; high school, college, and community activities related to horticulture; PLANET events attended; work experience; and brief essays on what they have learned about financial management as part of their education that will help them in their career, how their landscape industry related curriculum has helped them in achieving their career goals, the kind of

training and work experience they will complete to attain their goals, their plan to attain more leadership and human relations skills, their reasons for desiring the scholarship, their career objectives as they relate to the field of landscape contracting and horticulture, and where they see their career 5 years after graduation. **Deadline for Receipt:** January of each year. **Additional Information:** PLANET was formed in 2005 as the result of a merger between the Associated Landscape Contractors of America (ALCA) and the Professional Lawn Care Association of America (PLCAA). It offers the following named scholarships: the Akerman Family Scholarship, Theodore W. Brickman Jr. Scholarship, Chapel Valley/Reeve Family Scholarship, Damgaard Family Landscape Contracting Scholarship, Davey Tree Expert Company-Commercial Grounds Management Division Scholarship, John Deere Green Industry Scholarship, Gachina Family Scholarship, Parley Glover Memorial Scholarship, Glowacki Family Scholarship, Gravely Landscape Maintenance Scholarship, Groundmasters Scholarship, Leonard Harris Memorial Scholarship, Hunt Family Scholarship, Hunter Industries Scholarship, Husqvarna Forest & Garden Scholarship, Ron and Sally Kujawa Scholarship, Tom and Carol Lied Scholarship, Shirley B. Mangum Family Scholarship, Vito Mariani, Sr. Scholarship, Marjorie and B.E. Minor Scholarship, Moore Landscapes Scholarship, William F. and Mary B. Murdy Scholarship, Richard J. Ott Family Scholarship, Stihl Landscape Contracting Scholarship, Thornton Landscape/Doesburg Family Scholarship, Toro Company/Exmark Scholarship, and Trugreen Landcare Scholarship.

2612 ■ JOSEPH SHINODA MEMORIAL SCHOLARSHIP FOUNDATION INC.

Attn: Executive Secretary
234 Via La Paz
San Luis Obispo, CA 93401
Tel: (805)544-0717
E-mail: info@shinodascholarship.org
Web Site: http://www.shinodascholarship.org
To provide financial assistance to undergraduates working on a degree in floriculture.

Title of Award: Joseph Shinoda Memorial Scholarship **Area, Field, or Subject:** Horticulture **Level of Education for which Award is Granted:** Undergraduate **Number Awarded:** Approximately 6 each year. Since the foundation was established, it has awarded more than $644,000 to 579 floriculture students. **Funds Available:** Stipends range from $1,500 to $3,500. **Duration:** 1 year.
Eligibility Requirements: This program is open to undergraduates entering their sophomore, junior, or senior year at an accredited college or university in the United States. Applicants must be majoring in a degree program related to floriculture (production, distribution, research, or retail) and be planning to work in a phase of commercial floriculture after graduation. Financial need is considered in the selection process. **Deadline for Receipt:** March of each year. **Additional Information:** These scholarships were first awarded in 1965. Information is also available from Virginia R. Walter, Horticulture and Crop Science Department, California Polytechnic State University, San Luis Obispo, CA 93407.

2613 ■ TREE RESEARCH AND EDUCATION ENDOWMENT FUND

Attn: Executive Director
711 East Roosevelt Road
Wheaton, IL 60187

Tel: (630)221-8127
Fax: (630)690-0702
E-mail: treefund@treefund.org
Web Site: http://www.treefund.org/grants/Grants.aspx
To provide financial assistance to undergraduate and technical school students interested in preparing for a career in commercial arboriculture.
Title of Award: Robert Felix Memorial Scholarship **Area, Field, or Subject:** Agricultural sciences; Entomology; Horticulture; Landscape architecture and design; Soil science **Level of Education for which Award is Granted:** Undergraduate **Number Awarded:** 4 each year. **Funds Available:** The stipend is $3,000. **Duration:** 1 year.
Eligibility Requirements: This program is open to student members of the International Society of Arboriculture who are entering the second year of a 2-year program or the third or fourth year of a 4-year program. Applicants must be preparing for a career in commercial arboriculture. They must have a GPA of 3.0 or higher. Along with their application, they must submit a 1,000-word essay describing their reasons for pursuing their chosen career, their goals and objectives, and why they should be chosen for this scholarship. Financial need is not considered in the selection process. **Deadline for Receipt:** April of each year. **Additional Information:** The Tree Research and Education Endowment (TREE) Fund was established in 2002 as the result of a merger of the International Society of Arboriculture Research Trust (established in 1976) and the National Arborist Foundation (established in 1985). Fields of study often considered appropriate for a career in commercial arboriculture include agriculture, entomology, horticulture, landscape architecture, or soils science.

2614 ■ VERMONT STUDENT ASSISTANCE CORPORATION

Champlain Mill
Attn: Scholarship Programs
P.O. Box 2000
Winooski, VT 05404-2601
Tel: (802)654-3798; 888-253-4819
Fax: (802)654-3765
E-mail: info@vsac.org
Web Site: http://www.vsac.org
To provide financial assistance to residents of Vermont who are interested in majoring in an agriculture-related field in college.
Title of Award: Vermont Feed Dealers and Manufacturers Association Scholarship **Area, Field, or Subject:** Agribusiness; Agricultural sciences; Animal science and behavior; Botany; Equine studies; Forestry; Horticulture; Soil science; Veterinary science and medicine **Level of Education for which Award is Granted:** Undergraduate **Number Awarded:** Varies each year; recently, 6 of these scholarships were awarded. **Funds Available:** The maximum stipend is $3,000. **Duration:** 1 year; recipients may reapply.
Eligibility Requirements: This scholarship is available to high school seniors, high school graduates, and currently-enrolled college students in Vermont who are enrolled or planning to enroll in a postsecondary degree program in agriculture, including but not limited to animal sciences, equine studies, agribusiness, plant and soil science, forestry, horticulture, and veterinary medicine or technology. Selection is based on a letter of recommendation and required essays. **Deadline for Receipt:** June of each year.

General

2615 ■ ALASKA COMMISSION ON POSTSECONDARY EDUCATION
Attn: AlaskAdvantage Programs
3030 Vintage Boulevard
Juneau, AK 99801-7109
Tel: (907)465-6779; (866)427-5683
Fax: (907)465-5316
E-mail: customer_service@acpe.ak.us
Web Site: http://alaskaadvantage.state.ak.us/page/276
To provide financial assistance to Alaska residents who attend college in the state to prepare for a career in designated fields with a workforce shortage.
Title of Award: AlaskAdvantage Educational Grants **Area, Field, or Subject:** Education; Health care services; Social work **Level of Education for which Award is Granted:** Undergraduate **Number Awarded:** Varies each year; students with the greatest financial need are awarded support until funds are exhausted. **Funds Available:** Grants range from $500 to $2,000 per year, depending on the need of the recipient. **Duration:** 1 year; may be renewed as long as the recipient remains enrolled at least half time, makes satisfactory academic progress, and continues to meet residency and financial need requirements.
Eligibility Requirements: This program is open to residents of Alaska who have been admitted to an undergraduate degree or vocational certificate program at a qualifying institution in the state. Applicants must be planning to work on a degree or certificate in a field that the state has designated as a workforce shortage area; currently, those are allied health sciences, community or social service, and teaching. They must be able to demonstrate financial need and SAT or ACT scores in the top quartile. U.S. citizenship or permanent resident status is required. **Deadline for Receipt:** April of each year.

2616 ■ ALASKA NATIVE TRIBAL HEALTH CONSORTIUM
Attn: Education and Development
4000 Ambassador Drive, Suite 114
Anchorage, AK 99508
Tel: (907)729-1917
Free: 800-684-8361
Fax: (907)729-1335
Web Site: http://www.anthc.org/jt/int
To provide financial assistance for college or graduate school to Natives and American Indians who are residents of Alaska interested in a career in health care.
Title of Award: ANTHC Scholarships **Area, Field, or Subject:** Health care services **Level of Education for which Award is Granted:** Graduate, Undergraduate **Number Awarded:** 10 each year: 5 for undergraduate students and 5 for graduate students. **Funds Available:** The stipend is $5,000 per year. **Duration:** 1 year; may be renewed if they maintain a minimum GPA of 2.0 for undergraduates or 3.0 for graduate students.
Eligibility Requirements: This program is open to Alaska Natives and American Indians who are undergraduates or graduate students interested in preparing for a career in the field of health care. Applicants must be residents of Alaska enrolled full time. Along with their application, they must submit a resume, 3 letters of recommendation, documentation of financial need, and a 1-page personal statement that covers their

personal and educational history, accomplishments, educational and career goals, involvement in the Native community, and how this scholarship and degree program correspond with their career goals. **Deadline for Receipt:** February of each year.

2617 ■ ALPHA MU TAU FRATERNITY
c/o American Society for Clinical Laboratory Science
6701 Democracy Boulevard, Suite 300
Bethesda, MD 20817
Tel: (301)657-2768
Fax: (301)657-2909
E-mail: ascls@ascls.org
Web Site: http://www.ascls.org/leadership/awards/amt.asp
To provide financial assistance for undergraduate studies to members of Alpha Mu Tau, a national fraternity for professionals in the clinical laboratory sciences.
Title of Award: Alpha Mu Tau Undergraduate Scholarships **Area, Field, or Subject:** Medical technology **Level of Education for which Award is Granted:** Undergraduate **Number Awarded:** Several each year. **Funds Available:** The stipend is $1,500. **Duration:** 1 year.
Eligibility Requirements: Applicants must be U.S. citizens or permanent residents, members of Alpha Mu Tau, and accepted into or currently enrolled in an undergraduate program in clinical laboratory science, including cytotechnology, histotechnology, clinical laboratory science/medical technology, and clinical laboratory technician/medical laboratory technician. Applicants must be entering their last year of study. Along with their application, they must submit a 500-word statement describing their interest and reasons for preparing for a career in clinical laboratory science. Financial need is also considered in the selection process. **Deadline for Receipt:** March of each year. **Additional Information:** Information is also available from Joe Briden, Alpha Mu Tau Fraternity Scholarship Coordinator, 7809 South 21st Drive, Phoenix, AZ 85041-7736, E-mail: alphamutaujoe@yahoo.com

2618 ■ ALPHA MU TAU FRATERNITY
c/o American Society for Clinical Laboratory Science
6701 Democracy Boulevard, Suite 300
Bethesda, MD 20817
Tel: (301)657-2768
Fax: (301)657-2909
E-mail: ascls@ascls.org
Web Site: http://www.ascls.org/leadership/awards/e_and_r.asp
To provide financial assistance for undergraduate studies to members of Alpha Mu Tau, a national laboratory fraternity.
Title of Award: ASCLS Education and Research Fund Undergraduate Scholarships **Area, Field, or Subject:** Medical technology **Level of Education for which Award is Granted:** Undergraduate **Number Awarded:** 1 or more each year. **Funds Available:** The stipend is $1,500. **Duration:** 1 year.
Eligibility Requirements: Applicants must be U.S. citizens or permanent residents, members of Alpha Mu Tau, and accepted into or currently enrolled in a program in clinical laboratory science, including clinical laboratory science/medical technology and clinical laboratory technician/medical laboratory technician for undergraduates. Applicants must be entering their last year of study. **Deadline for Receipt:** March of each

year. **Additional Information:** Funding for this program is provided by the Education and Research Fund of the American Society for Clinical Laboratory Science (ASCLS). Information is also available from Carol Lee Shearer, 3024 Tamarak Drive, Manhattan, KS 66503, E-mail: Carol_Shearer@dadebehring.com.

2619 ■ ALPHA MU TAU FRATERNITY

c/o American Society for Clinical Laboratory Science
6701 Democracy Boulevard, Suite 300
Bethesda, MD 20817
Tel: (301)657-2768
Fax: (301)657-2909
E-mail: ascls@ascls.org
Web Site: http://www.ascls.org/leadership/awards/amt.asp
To provide financial assistance for undergraduate or graduate studies to members of Alpha Mu Tau, a national fraternity for professionals in the clinical laboratory sciences.
Title of Award: Ruth M. French Graduate or Undergraduate Scholarship **Area, Field, or Subject:** Medical technology **Level of Education for which Award is Granted:** Graduate, Undergraduate **Number Awarded:** 1 each year. **Funds Available:** The stipend is $3,000. **Duration:** 1 year.
Eligibility Requirements: Applicants must be U.S. citizens or permanent residents, members of Alpha Mu Tau, and accepted into or currently enrolled in a program in clinical laboratory science, including clinical laboratory education or management programs for graduate students and clinical laboratory science/medical technology and clinical laboratory technician/medical laboratory technician for undergraduates. Undergraduate applicants must be entering their last year of study. Along with their application, they must submit a 500-word statement describing their interest and reasons for preparing for a career in clinical laboratory science. Financial need is also considered in the selection process. **Deadline for Receipt:** March of each year. **Additional Information:** Information is also available from Joe Briden, Alpha Mu Tau Fraternity Scholarship Coordinator, 7809 South 21st Drive, Phoenix, AZ 85041-7736, E-mail: alphamutaujoe@yahoo.com.

2620 ■ ALPHA MU TAU FRATERNITY

c/o American Society for Clinical Laboratory Science
6701 Democracy Boulevard, Suite 300
Bethesda, MD 20817
Tel: (301)657-2768
Fax: (301)657-2909
E-mail: ascls@ascls.org
Web Site: http://www.ascls.org/leadership/awards/amt.asp
To provide financial assistance for undergraduate studies to members of Alpha Mu Tau, a national fraternity for professionals in the clinical laboratory sciences.
Title of Award: Dorothy Morrison Undergraduate Scholarship **Area, Field, or Subject:** Medical technology **Level of Education for which Award is Granted:** Undergraduate **Number Awarded:** 1 each year. **Funds Available:** The stipend is $2,000. **Duration:** 1 year.
Eligibility Requirements: Applicants must be U.S. citizens or permanent residents, members of Alpha Mu Tau, and accepted into or currently enrolled in a program in clinical laboratory science, including clinical laboratory science/medical technology and clinical laboratory technician/medical laboratory technician for undergraduates. They must be entering their last year of study. Along with their application, they must submit a 500-word statement describing their interest and reasons for preparing for a career in clinical laboratory science. Financial need is also considered in the selection process. **Deadline for Receipt:** March of each year. **Additional Information:** Information is also available from Joe Briden, Alpha Mu Tau Fraternity Scholarship Coordinator, 7809 South 21st Drive, Phoenix, AZ 85041-7736, E-mail: alphamutaujoe@yahoo.com.

2621 ■ AMERICAN ACADEMY OF PHYSICIAN ASSISTANTS

Attn: Veterans Caucus
950 North Washington Street
Alexandria, VA 22314-1552
Tel: (703)836-2272
Fax: (703)684-1924
E-mail: aapa@aapa.org
Web Site: http://www.veteranscaucus.org

To provide financial assistance to veterans and Reserve component personnel who are studying to become physician assistants.
Title of Award: AAPA Veteran's Caucus Scholarships **Area, Field, or Subject:** Medical assisting **Level of Education for which Award is Granted:** Graduate, Undergraduate **Number Awarded:** Varies each year. Recently, 15 of these scholarships were awarded: 1 at $2,000, 2 at $1,500, and 12 at $1,250. **Funds Available:** Stipends are $2,000, $1,500, or $1,250. **Duration:** 1 year.
Eligibility Requirements: This program is open to U.S. citizens who are currently enrolled in a physician assistant program. The program must be approved by the Commission on Accreditation of Allied Health Education. Applicants must be honorably discharged members of a uniformed service of the United States or an active member of the Guard or Reserve of a uniformed service of the United States. Selection is based on military honors and awards received, civic and college honors and awards received, professional memberships and activities, and GPA. An electronic copy of the applicant's DD Form 214 must accompany the application. **Deadline for Receipt:** February of each year. **Additional Information:** This program includes the following named scholarships: the Donna Jones Moritsugu Memorial Awards, the SSGT Craig Ivory Memorial Scholarships, the Order of St. Lazarus/Green Cross Project Award, the Andrea Long Memorial Scholarships, the Society of Air Force Physician Assistants Scholarship, the Society of Army Physician Assistants Scholarship, the Naval Association of Physician Assistants Scholarship, the Major Jessie and Sharon Edwards Scholarship (established in 2004), the John M. Dwyer Memorial Scholarship (established in 2004), and the Vicki Moritsugu Memorial Scholarship (established in 2004). Information is also available from Sharon Hanley, P.O. Box 362, Danville, PA 17821-0362, (570) 271-6692, (800) 271-6692, Fax: (570) 271-5850, E-mail: skhanley@ptd.net.

2622 ■ AMERICAN ACADEMY OF PHYSICIAN ASSISTANTS

Attn: African Heritage Caucus
950 North Washington Street
Alexandria, VA 22314-1552
Tel: (703)835-2272
Fax: (703)684-1924
E-mail: ahcscholarship2005@verizon.net
Web Site: http://www.aapa.org/caucus/scholar.html
To provide financial assistance to student members of the African Heritage Caucus within the American Academy of Physician Assistants (AAPA).
Title of Award: African Heritage Caucus Scholarships **Area, Field, or Subject:** Medical assisting **Level of Education for which Award is Granted:** Graduate, Undergraduate **Number Awarded:** 1 or more each year. **Funds Available:** A stipend is awarded (amount not specified). **Duration:** 1 year.
Eligibility Requirements: Applicants for these scholarships must be members of both the AAPA and its African Heritage Caucus enrolled in an accredited physician assistant program. Their application must 1) list the volunteer activities in which they participate and that contribute to their community or profession, and 2) discuss how they will address the increasing disparities in health care access and treatment for minorities in their clinic setting. Selection is based on academic progress, financial need, community and/or professional activities, and knowledge of health care issues and the physician assistant's role. **Deadline for Receipt:** February of each year. **Additional Information:** Information is also available from Katherine Lewis, AHC Scholarship Committee Chair, 16 Stebbins Avenue, Staten Island, NY 10310.

2623 ■ AMERICAN ACADEMY OF PHYSICIAN ASSISTANTS

Attn: Veterans Caucus
950 North Washington Street
Alexandria, VA 22314-1552
Tel: (703)836-2272
Fax: (703)684-1924
E-mail: aapa@aapa.org
Web Site: http://www.veteranscaucus.org
To provide financial assistance to children of veterans of the Army Special Forces who are studying to become physician assistants.
Title of Award: Chan-Padgett Special Forces Memorial Scholarship **Area, Field, or Subject:** Medical assisting **Level of Education for which Award is Granted:** Graduate, Undergraduate **Number Awarded:** 1 each year. **Funds Available:** The stipend is $1,250. **Duration:** 1 year.

Eligibility Requirements: This program is open to U.S. citizens who are currently enrolled in a physician assistant program. The program must be approved by the Commission on Accreditation of Allied Health Education. Applicants must be children of honorably discharged members of the Army Special Forces. Selection is based on military honors and awards received, civic and college honors and awards received, professional memberships and activities, and GPA. An electronic copy of the sponsor's DD Form 214 must accompany the application. **Deadline for Receipt:** February of each year. **Additional Information:** This program was established in 2002. Information is also available from Sharon Hanley, P.O. Box 362, Danville, PA 17821-0362, (570) 271-6692, (800) 271-6692, Fax: (570) 271-5850, E-mail: skhanley@ptd.net.

2624 ■ AMERICAN ACADEMY OF PHYSICIAN ASSISTANTS

Attn: Physician Assistants for Latino Health
950 North Washington Street
Alexandria, VA 22314-1552
800-596-7494
Fax: (703)684-1924
E-mail: palh@aapa.org
Web Site: http://www.palh.org/PALH_Scholarship.html
To provide financial assistance to student members of the Physician Assistants for Latino Health (PALH) within the American Academy of Physician Assistants (AAPA).
Title of Award: PALH Scholarships **Area, Field, or Subject:** Medical assisting **Level of Education for which Award is Granted:** Graduate, Undergraduate **Number Awarded:** 2 each year. **Funds Available:** A stipend is awarded; amount not specified. **Duration:** 1 year.
Eligibility Requirements: This program is open to students who are members of both the AAPA and its PALH caucus enrolled in a physician assistant program. Applicants must be able to demonstrate leadership in the Latino community or an interest in Latino health issues. They must have a GPA of 3.0 or higher. Along with their application, they must submit a statement on their personal background, pertinent experiences working with underserved Latino communities, future goals and expectations upon completing their physician assistant program, and why they should be considered for a PALH scholarship. Financial need is not considered in the selection process. **Deadline for Receipt:** March of each year.

2625 ■ AMERICAN ACADEMY OF PHYSICIAN ASSISTANTS

Attn: Physician Assistant Foundation
950 North Washington Street
Alexandria, VA 22314-1552
Tel: (703)519-5686
Fax: (703)684-1924
E-mail: aapa@aapa.org
Web Site: http://www.aapa.org/paf/pafprog.html
To provide financial assistance to student members of the American Academy of Physician Assistants (AAPA).
Title of Award: Physician Assistant Foundation Scholarships **Area, Field, or Subject:** Medical assisting **Level of Education for which Award is Granted:** Graduate, Undergraduate **Number Awarded:** Varies each year; recently, 35 of these scholarships were awarded. **Funds Available:** Stipends are $5,000, $3,000, or $2,000. **Duration:** 1 year; nonrenewable.
Eligibility Requirements: This program is open to AAPA student members attending a physician assistant program accredited by the Commission on Accreditation of Allied Health Education Programs. Applicants must have entered the professional phase of the program. Selection is based on financial need, academic achievement, extracurricular activities, and future goals. **Deadline for Receipt:** January of each year. **Additional Information:** This program, established in 1989, is sponsored by the following firms: AstraZeneca Pharmaceuticals, Eli Lilly and Company, GlaxoSmithKline, McNeil Consumer and Specialty Pharmaceuticals, Pfizer Inc., Procter and Gamble Pharmaceuticals, Purdue Pharma, Roche Pharmaceuticals, and Wyeth Pharmaceuticals.

2626 ■ AMERICAN CHEMICAL SOCIETY

Attn: Department of Diversity Programs
1155 16th Street, N.W.
Washington, DC 20036
Tel: (202)872-6250
Free: 800-227-5558
Fax: (202)776-8003

E-mail: scholars@acs.org
Web Site: http://www.chemistry.org/scholars
To provide financial assistance to underrepresented minority students with a strong interest in chemistry and a desire to prepare for a career in a chemically-related science.
Title of Award: American Chemical Society Scholars Program **Area, Field, or Subject:** Biochemistry; Chemistry; Engineering, Chemical; Environmental conservation; Environmental science; Materials research/science; Toxicology **Level of Education for which Award is Granted:** Undergraduate **Number Awarded:** Approximately 100 new awards are granted each year. **Funds Available:** The maximum stipend is $2,500 for the freshman year in college or $3,000 per year for sophomores, juniors, and seniors. **Duration:** 1 year; may be renewed.
Eligibility Requirements: This program is open to 1) college-bound high school seniors; 2) college freshmen, sophomores, and juniors enrolled full time at an accredited college or university; 3) community college graduates and transfer students who plan to study for a bachelor's degree; and 4) community college freshmen. Applicants must be African American, Hispanic/Latino, or American Indian. They must be majoring or planning to major in chemistry, biochemistry, chemical engineering, or other chemically-related fields, such as environmental science, materials science, or toxicology, and planning to prepare for a career in the chemical sciences or chemical technology. Students planning careers in medicine or pharmacy are not eligible. U.S. citizenship or permanent resident status is required. Selection is based on academic merit (GPA of 3.0 or higher) and financial need. **Deadline for Receipt:** February of each year. **Additional Information:** This program was established in 1994.

2627 ■ AMERICAN COLLEGE OF MEDICAL PRACTICE EXECUTIVES

Attn: ACMPE Scholarship Fund Inc.
104 Inverness Terrace East
Englewood, CO 80112-5306
Tel: (303)799-1111; 877-ASK-MGMA
Fax: (303)643-4439
E-mail: acmpe@mgma.com
Web Site: http://www.mgma.com/academics/scholar.cfm
To provide financial assistance to practitioners in medical practice management interested in pursuing professional development through undergraduate or graduate education.
Title of Award: ACMPE Leaders Scholarships **Area, Field, or Subject:** Business administration; Health care services; Management; Public health **Level of Education for which Award is Granted:** Graduate, Professional, Undergraduate **Number Awarded:** 4 each year. **Funds Available:** The stipend is $3,000. Funds are paid directly to the recipient's college or university. **Duration:** 1 year.
Eligibility Requirements: This program is open to professionals working on an undergraduate or graduate degree in a program relevant to medical practice management, including public health, business administration, health care administration, or other related areas. Students working on a degree in medicine, physical therapy, nursing, or other clinically-related professions are not eligible. Applicants must submit a letter describing their career goals and objectives relevant to medical practice management; a resume; 2 reference letters commenting on their performance, character, potential to succeed, and need for scholarship support; and either documentation indicating acceptance into an undergraduate or graduate program or academic transcripts indicating undergraduate or graduate work completed to date. **Deadline for Receipt:** April of each year. **Additional Information:** This program is managed by Scholarship Program Administrators, Inc. 1201 Eighth Avenue South, P.O. Box 23737, Nashville, TN 27202-3737, (615) 320-3149, (800) 310-4053, Fax: (615) 320-3151, E-mail: info@spaprog.com. It was established to honor past presidents of the American College of Medical Practice Executives (ACMPE), Ernest S. Moscatello, Edgar J. Saux, Charles Wallace, Robert W. "Win" Baker, the Medical Group Management Association (MGMA) Academic Practice Assembly (APA), the MGMA Anesthesia Administration Assembly (AAA), and the MGMA Integrated Health Care Organizations Society (IHOS).

2628 ■ AMERICAN COLLEGE OF MEDICAL PRACTICE EXECUTIVES

Attn: ACMPE Scholarship Fund Inc.
104 Inverness Terrace East
Englewood, CO 80112-5306
Tel: (303)799-1111; 877-ASK-MGMA

Fax: (303)643-4439

E-mail: acmpe@mgma.com

Web Site: http://www.mgma.com/academics/scholar.cfm

To provide financial assistance to undergraduate and graduate students who are interested in preparing for a career in medical group management.

Title of Award: Richard L. Davis/Barbara B. Watson National Scholarship **Area, Field, or Subject:** Business administration; Health care services; Management; Public health **Level of Education for which Award is Granted:** Graduate, Undergraduate **Number Awarded:** 1 each year. **Funds Available:** The stipend is $1,500. Funds are paid directly to the recipient's college or university. **Duration:** 1 year.

Eligibility Requirements: This program is open to full-time students working on an undergraduate or graduate degree in a program relevant to medical practice management, including public health, business administration, health care administration, or other related areas. Students working on a degree in medicine, physical therapy, nursing, or other clinically-related professions are not eligible. Applicants must submit a letter describing their career goals and objectives relevant to medical practice management; a resume; 3 reference letters commenting on their performance, character, potential to succeed, and need for scholarship support; and either documentation indicating acceptance into an undergraduate or graduate college or university or academic transcripts indicating undergraduate or graduate work completed to date. **Deadline for Receipt:** April of each year. **Additional Information:** This program is managed by Scholarship Program Administrators, Inc. 1201 Eighth Avenue South, P.O. Box 23737, Nashville, TN 27202-3737, (615) 320-3149, (800) 310-4053, Fax: (615) 320-3151, E-mail: info@spaprog.com.

2629 ■ AMERICAN COLLEGE OF MEDICAL PRACTICE EXECUTIVES

Attn: ACMPE Scholarship Fund Inc.

104 Inverness Terrace East

Englewood, CO 80112-5306

Tel: (303)799-1111; 877-ASK-MGMA

Fax: (303)643-4439

E-mail: acmpe@mgma.com

Web Site: http://www.mgma.com/academics/scholar.cfm

To provide financial assistance to individuals currently employed in medical group management who wish to pursue professional development on the undergraduate or graduate level.

Title of Award: Richard L. Davis Managers Scholarship **Area, Field, or Subject:** Business administration; Health care services; Management; Public health **Level of Education for which Award is Granted:** Graduate, Professional, Undergraduate **Number Awarded:** 1 each year. **Funds Available:** The stipend is $1,500. Funds are paid directly to the recipient's college or university. **Duration:** 1 year.

Eligibility Requirements: This program is open to medical group management professionals who want to pursue professional development through undergraduate or graduate education in a program relevant to medical practice management, including public health, business administration, health care administration, or other related areas. Professionals interested in studying medicine, physical therapy, nursing, or other clinically-related professions are not eligible. Applicants must submit a letter describing their career goals and objectives relevant to medical practice management; a resume; 3 reference letters commenting on their performance, character, potential to succeed, and need for scholarship support; and either documentation indicating acceptance into an undergraduate or graduate college or university or academic transcripts indicating undergraduate or graduate work completed to date. **Deadline for Receipt:** April of each year. **Additional Information:** This program is managed by Scholarship Program Administrators, Inc. 1201 Eighth Avenue South, P.O. Box 23737, Nashville, TN 27202-3737, (615) 320-3149, (800) 310-4053, Fax: (615) 320-3151, E-mail: info@spaprog.com.

2630 ■ AMERICAN COLLEGE OF MEDICAL PRACTICE EXECUTIVES

Attn: ACMPE Scholarship Fund Inc.

104 Inverness Terrace East

Englewood, CO 80112-5306

Tel: (303)799-1111; 877-ASK-MGMA

Fax: (303)643-4439

E-mail: acmpe@mgma.com

Web Site: http://www.mgma.com/academics/scholar.cfm

To provide financial assistance to undergraduate or graduate students who are interested in preparing for a career in medical group management.

Title of Award: Harry J. Harwick Scholarships **Area, Field, or Subject:** Business administration; Health care services; Management; Public health **Level of Education for which Award is Granted:** Graduate, Undergraduate **Number Awarded:** 2 each year. **Funds Available:** The stipend is $5,000. Funds are paid directly to the recipient's college or university. **Duration:** 1 year.

Eligibility Requirements: Eligible are 1) graduate students enrolled in a program accredited by the Accrediting Commission on Education for Health Services Administration and 2) undergraduate students enrolled in a program that is a member of the Association of University Programs in Health Administration. Applicants must be working on a degree in a program relevant to medical practice management, including public health, business administration, health care administration, or other related areas. Students working on a degree in medicine, physical therapy, nursing, or other clinically-related professions are not eligible. Along with their application, they must submit a letter describing their career goals and objectives relevant to medical practice management; a resume; 3 reference letters commenting on their performance, character, potential to succeed, and need for scholarship support; and either documentation indicating acceptance into an undergraduate or graduate college or university or academic transcripts indicating undergraduate or graduate work completed to date. **Deadline for Receipt:** April of each year. **Additional Information:** This program is managed by Scholarship Program Administrators, Inc. 1201 Eighth Avenue South, P.O. Box 23737, Nashville, TN 27202-3737, (615) 320-3149, (800) 310-4053, Fax: (615) 320-3151, E-mail: info@spaprog.com.

2631 ■ AMERICAN COLLEGE OF MEDICAL PRACTICE EXECUTIVES

Attn: ACMPE Scholarship Fund Inc.

104 Inverness Terrace East

Englewood, CO 80112-5306

Tel: (303)799-1111; 877-ASK-MGMA

Fax: (303)643-4439

E-mail: acmpe@mgma.com

Web Site: http://www.mgma.com/academics/scholar.cfm

To provide financial assistance to undergraduate or graduate women in Georgia who are working on a degree in health care or health care administration.

Title of Award: Constance L. Lloyd Scholarship **Area, Field, or Subject:** Business administration; Health care services; Management; Public health **Level of Education for which Award is Granted:** Graduate, Undergraduate **Number Awarded:** 1 each year. **Funds Available:** The stipend is $2,500. Funds are paid directly to the recipient's college or university. **Duration:** 1 year.

Eligibility Requirements: This program is open to women enrolled at the undergraduate or graduate level at an accredited college or university in Georgia who are working on either an administrative or clinically-related degree in the health care field. Students working on a degree in medicine, physical therapy, nursing, or other clinically-related professions are not eligible. Applicants must submit a letter describing their career goals and objectives relevant to medical practice management; a resume; 3 reference letters commenting on their performance, character, potential to succeed, and need for scholarship support; and either documentation indicating acceptance into an undergraduate or graduate program or academic transcripts indicating undergraduate or graduate work completed to date. **Deadline for Receipt:** April of each year. **Additional Information:** This program, established in 1993, is managed by Scholarship Program Administrators, Inc. 1201 Eighth Avenue South, P.O. Box 23737, Nashville, TN 27202-3737, (615) 320-3149, (800) 310-4053, Fax: (615) 320-3151, E-mail: info@spaprog.com.

2632 ■ AMERICAN COLLEGE OF MEDICAL PRACTICE EXECUTIVES

Attn: ACMPE Scholarship Fund Inc.

104 Inverness Terrace East

Englewood, CO 80112-5306

Tel: (303)799-1111; 877-ASK-MGMA

Fax: (303)643-4439

E-mail: acmpe@mgma.com

Web Site: http://www.mgma.com/academics/scholar.cfm

To provide financial assistance to members of the Medical Group Management Association (MGMA) Midwest Section who are interested in undergraduate or graduate education.

Title of Award: MGMA Midwest Section Scholarships **Area, Field, or Subject:** Business administration; Health care services; Management; Public health **Level of Education for which Award is Granted:** Graduate, Professional, Undergraduate **Number Awarded:** 1 each year. **Funds Available:** The stipend is $2,000. Funds are paid directly to the recipient's college or university. **Duration:** 1 year.

Eligibility Requirements: Eligible to apply are individuals resident in the MGMA Midwest Section (Illinois, Indiana, Iowa, Michigan, Minnesota, Nebraska, North Dakota, Ohio, South Dakota, and Wisconsin) who wish to work on an undergraduate or graduate degree in medical practice management, including public health, business administration, health care administration, or other related areas. Students working on a degree in medicine, physical therapy, nursing, or other clinically-related professions are not eligible. Applicants must submit a letter describing their career goals and objectives relevant to medical practice management; a resume; 3 reference letters commenting on their performance, character, potential to succeed, and need for scholarship support; and either documentation indicating acceptance into an undergraduate or graduate college or university or academic transcripts indicating undergraduate or graduate work completed to date. **Deadline for Receipt:** April of each year. **Additional Information:** This program is managed by Scholarship Program Administrators, Inc. 1201 Eighth Avenue South, P.O. Box 23737, Nashville, TN 27202-3737, (615) 320-3149, (800) 310-4053, Fax: (615) 320-3151, E-mail: info@spaprog.com.

2633 ■ AMERICAN COLLEGE OF MEDICAL PRACTICE EXECUTIVES

Attn: ACMPE Scholarship Fund Inc.
104 Inverness Terrace East
Englewood, CO 80112-5306
Tel: (303)799-1111; 877-ASK-MGMA
Fax: (303)643-4439
E-mail: acmpe@mgma.com
Web Site: http://www.mgma.com/academics/scholar.cfm

To provide financial assistance to members of the Medical Group Management Association (MGMA) Western Section who are interested in undergraduate or graduate education.

Title of Award: MGMA Western Section Scholarships **Area, Field, or Subject:** Business administration; Health care services; Management; Public health **Level of Education for which Award is Granted:** Graduate, Professional, Undergraduate **Number Awarded:** 1 each year. **Funds Available:** The stipend is $2,000. Funds are paid directly to the recipient's college or university. **Duration:** 1 year.

Eligibility Requirements: Eligible to apply are individuals who reside in and have been members of the MGMA Western Section (Alaska, Arizona, California, Colorado, Hawaii, Idaho, Montana, Nevada, New Mexico, Oregon, Utah, Washington, and Wyoming) for at least 2 years. Applicants must wish to work on an undergraduate or graduate degree in medical practice management, including public health, business administration, health care administration, or other related areas. Students working on a degree in medicine, physical therapy, nursing, or other clinically-related professions are not eligible. Applicants must submit a letter describing their career goals and objectives relevant to medical practice management; a resume; 3 reference letters commenting on their performance, character, potential to succeed, and need for scholarship support; and either documentation indicating acceptance into an undergraduate or graduate college or university or academic transcripts indicating undergraduate or graduate work completed to date. **Deadline for Receipt:** April of each year. **Additional Information:** This program is managed by Scholarship Program Administrators, Inc. 1201 Eighth Avenue South, P.O. Box 23737, Nashville, TN 27202-3737, (615) 320-3149, (800) 310-4053, Fax: (615) 320-3151, E-mail: info@spaprog.com.

2634 ■ AMERICAN COLLEGE OF MEDICAL PRACTICE EXECUTIVES

Attn: ACMPE Scholarship Fund Inc.
104 Inverness Terrace East
Englewood, CO 80112-5306
Tel: (303)799-1111; 877-ASK-MGMA
Fax: (303)643-4439
E-mail: acmpe@mgma.com
Web Site: http://www.mgma.com/academics/scholar.cfm

To provide financial assistance to residents of Ohio and West Virginia who are working on an undergraduate or graduate degree in health care management related to hematology or oncology.

Title of Award: Oncology Practice Alliance Scholarship **Area, Field, or Subject:** Business administration; Health care services; Management; Oncology; Public health **Level of Education for which Award is Granted:** Graduate, Undergraduate **Number Awarded:** 1 each year. **Funds Available:** The stipend is at least $1,000. Funds are paid directly to the recipient's college or university. **Duration:** 1 year.

Eligibility Requirements: This program is open to full-time students working on an undergraduate or graduate degree in a program relevant to medical practice management (e.g., public health, business administration, health care administration) with a specialty in oncology or hematology. Students working on a degree in medicine, physical therapy, nursing, or other clinically-related professions are not eligible. Applicants must have been residents of Ohio or West Virginia for at least 12 months prior to applying. They must submit a letter describing their career goals and objectives relevant to medical practice management; a resume; 3 reference letters commenting on their performance, character, potential to succeed, and need for scholarship support; and either documentation indicating acceptance into an undergraduate or graduate program or academic transcripts indicating undergraduate or graduate work completed to date. **Deadline for Receipt:** April of each year. **Additional Information:** This program is managed by Scholarship Program Administrators, Inc. 1201 Eighth Avenue South, P.O. Box 23737, Nashville, TN 27202-3737, (615) 320-3149, (800) 310-4053, Fax: (615) 320-3151, E-mail: info@spaprog.com.

2635 ■ AMERICAN COLLEGE OF NURSE-MIDWIVES

Attn: ACNM Foundation, Inc.
8403 Coleville Road, Suite 1550
Silver Spring, MD 20915
Tel: (240)485-1850
Fax: (240)485-1818
Web Site: http://www.midwife.org/
support.cfm?CFID=2021597&CFTOKEN=50504296

To provide financial assistance for midwifery education to student members of the American College of Nurse-Midwives (ACNM).

Title of Award: Basic Midwifery Scholarships **Area, Field, or Subject:** Midwifery **Level of Education for which Award is Granted:** Master's, Undergraduate **Number Awarded:** Varies each year; recently, 4 of these scholarships were awarded. **Funds Available:** The stipend is $3,000. **Duration:** 1 year.

Eligibility Requirements: This program is open to ACNM members who are currently enrolled in an accredited basic midwife education program and have successfully completed 1 academic or clinical semester/quarter or clinical module. Applicants must submit a 150-word essay on their midwifery career plans and a 100-word essay on their intended future participation in the local, regional, and/or national activities of the ACNM. Selection is based on leadership potential, financial need, academic history, and potential for future professional contribution to the organization. **Deadline for Receipt:** March of each year. **Additional Information:** This program includes the following named scholarships: the A.C.N.M. Foundation Memorial Scholarship, the TUMS Calcium for Life Scholarship (presented by GlaxoSmithKline), the Edith B. Wonnell CNM Scholarship, and the Margaret Edmundson Scholarship.

2636 ■ AMERICAN COLLEGE OF NURSE-MIDWIVES

Attn: ACNM Foundation, Inc.
8403 Coleville Road, Suite 1550
Silver Spring, MD 20915
Tel: (240)485-1850
Fax: (240)485-1818
Web Site: http://www.midwife.org/
support.cfm?CFID=2021597&CFTOKEN=50504296

To provide financial assistance for midwifery education to student members of color of the American College of Nurse-Midwives (ACNM).

Title of Award: Watson Midwives of Color Scholarship **Area, Field, or Subject:** Midwifery **Level of Education for which Award is Granted:** Master's, Undergraduate **Number Awarded:** Varies each year; recently, 2 of these scholarships were awarded. **Funds Available:** The stipend is $3,000. **Duration:** 1 year.

Eligibility Requirements: This program is open to ACNM members of color who are currently enrolled in an accredited basic midwife education program and have successfully completed 1 academic or clinical semester/quarter or clinical module. Applicants must submit a 150-word essay on their midwifery career plans and a 100-word essay on their intended future participation in the local, regional, and/or national activities of the ACNM. Selection is based on leadership potential, financial need, academic history, and potential for future professional contribution to the organization. **Deadline for Receipt:** March of each year.

2637 ■ AMERICAN HEALTH INFORMATION MANAGEMENT ASSOCIATION

Attn: Foundation of Research and Education
233 North Michigan Avenue, Suite 2150
Chicago, IL 60601-5806
Tel: (312)233-1168
Fax: (312)233-1090
E-mail: fore@ahima.org
Web Site: http://www.ahima.org/fore/programs.asp
To provide financial assistance to minority members of the American Health Information Management Association (AHIMA) who are interested in working on an undergraduate or graduate degree in health information administration or technology.
Title of Award: FORE Diversity Scholarships **Area, Field, or Subject:** Health care services; Information science and technology; Management; Technology **Level of Education for which Award is Granted:** Graduate, Undergraduate **Number Awarded:** Varies each year. Recently, 5 of these scholarships were awarded: 4 to undergraduates and 1 to a graduate student. **Funds Available:** Stipends range from $1,000 to $5,000. **Duration:** 1 year; nonrenewable.
Eligibility Requirements: This program is open to AHIMA members who are enrolled in a health information administration or health information technology program accredited by the Commission on Accreditation of Allied Health Education Programs. Applicants must be minorities, be working on an undergraduate or graduate degree on at least a half-time basis, and have a GPA of 3.0 or higher. U.S. citizenship is required. Selection is based (in order of importance) on GPA and academic achievement, volunteer and work experience, commitment to the health information management profession, suitability to the health information management profession, quality and suitability of references provided, and clarity of application. **Deadline for Receipt:** May of each year.

2638 ■ AMERICAN HEALTH INFORMATION MANAGEMENT ASSOCIATION

Attn: Foundation of Research and Education
233 North Michigan Avenue, Suite 2150
Chicago, IL 60601-5806
Tel: (312)233-1168
Fax: (312)233-1090
E-mail: fore@ahima.org
Web Site: http://www.ahima.org/fore/programs.asp
To provide financial assistance to members of the American Health Information Management Association (AHIMA) who are interested in working on an undergraduate degree in health information administration or technology.
Title of Award: FORE Undergraduate Merit Scholarships **Area, Field, or Subject:** Health care services; Information science and technology; Management; Technology **Level of Education for which Award is Granted:** Undergraduate **Number Awarded:** Varies each year; recently, 41 of these scholarships were awarded. **Funds Available:** Stipends range from $1,000 to $5,000. **Duration:** 1 year; nonrenewable.
Eligibility Requirements: This program is open to AHIMA members who are enrolled in a health information administration or health information technology program accredited by the Commission on Accreditation of Allied Health Education Programs. Applicants must be working on a degree on at least a half-time basis and have a GPA of 3.0 or higher. U.S. citizenship is required. Selection is based (in order of importance) on GPA and academic achievement, volunteer and work experience, commitment to the health information management profession, suitability to the health information management profession, quality and suitability of references provided, and clarity of application. **Deadline for Receipt:** May of each year. **Additional Information:** This program includes the following named scholarships (not all of which may be offered each year): the David A. Cohen Scholarship (established in 2004), the Jimmy Gamble Memorial Scholarship (established in 2001 and sponsored by 3M Health Information

Systems), the Sanfra L. Key Memorial Scholarship (established in 2003 and sponsored by Healthcare Contract Resources), the Lucretia Spears Scholarship (established in 1998), the Julia LeBlond Memorial Undergraduate Scholarships (sponsored by St. Anthony Publishing/Medicode, Ingenix Companies), the Rita Finnegan Memorial Scholarship (established in 2001 and sponsored by MC Strategies, Inc.), the Annie Blaylock Memorial Scholarship (established in 2002), the Connie Marshall Memorial Scholarship (established in 2004 and sponsored by MedQuist Inc.), the Bright Future Scholarship (sponsored by previous Merit Scholarship recipients), the PricewaterhouseCoopers Scholarship, the Smart Corporation Scholarships, the Aspen Systems Corporation Scholarship, the Care Communications, Inc. Scholarship, the Siemens Medical Solutions Scholarship, and the Precyse Solutions, Inc. Scholarship.

2639 ■ AMERICAN HEALTH INFORMATION MANAGEMENT ASSOCIATION

Attn: Foundation of Research and Education
233 North Michigan Avenue, Suite 2150
Chicago, IL 60601-5806
Tel: (312)233-1168
Fax: (312)233-1090
E-mail: fore@ahima.org
Web Site: http://www.ahima.org/fore/programs.asp
To provide educational loans to undergraduate members of the American Health Information Management Association (AHIMA) who are interested in majoring in health information administration or technology.
Title of Award: FORE Undergraduate Student Loans **Area, Field, or Subject:** Health care services; Information science and technology; Management; Technology **Level of Education for which Award is Granted:** Undergraduate **Number Awarded:** Several each year. **Funds Available:** Loans are provided up to $1,000 for coding specialist programs, up to $2,000 for technology programs, and up to $5,000 for management programs. Repayment at 8% interest must be completed within 3 years after graduation. **Duration:** 1 year; may be renewed.
Eligibility Requirements: This program is open to 1) undergraduate students who are accepted for enrollment in a program for health information administration or health information technology that is approved by the Commission on Accreditation of Allied Health Education Programs or 2) students enrolled in a coding specialist program affiliated with a regionally accredited college or university. Applicants must be U.S. citizens making satisfactory progress toward a degree or certificate. Selection is based on demonstrated need and ability to repay a loan. **Deadline for Receipt:** May of each year.

2640 ■ AMERICAN HEALTH INFORMATION MANAGEMENT ASSOCIATION

Attn: Foundation of Research and Education
233 North Michigan Avenue, Suite 2150
Chicago, IL 60601-5806
Tel: (312)233-1168
Fax: (312)233-1090
E-mail: fore@ahima.org
Web Site: http://www.ahima.org/fore/programs.asp
To provide financial assistance to members of the American Health Information Management Association (AHIMA) from Colorado who are interested in working on an undergraduate or graduate degree in health information administration or technology.
Title of Award: Viola M. Griffin Memorial Scholarship **Area, Field, or Subject:** Health care services; Information science and technology; Management; Technology **Level of Education for which Award is Granted:** Graduate, Undergraduate **Number Awarded:** 1 each year. **Funds Available:** The stipend ranges from $1,000 to $5,000. **Duration:** 1 year; nonrenewable.
Eligibility Requirements: This program is open to AHIMA members who are residents of Colorado and enrolled in a health information administration or health information technology program accredited by the Commission on Accreditation of Allied Health Education Programs. Applicants must be working on an undergraduate or graduate degree on at least a half-time basis and have a GPA of 3.0 or higher. U.S. citizenship is required. Selection is based on (in order of importance) GPA and academic achievement, volunteer and work experience, commitment to the health information management profession, suitability to the health information management profession, quality and suitability of references

provided, and clarity of application. **Deadline for Receipt:** May of each year. **Additional Information:** Funding for this program, established in 2003, is provided by Craig Hospital.

2641 ■ AMERICAN HEALTH INFORMATION MANAGEMENT ASSOCIATION

Attn: Foundation of Research and Education
233 North Michigan Avenue, Suite 2150
Chicago, IL 60601-5806
Tel: (312)233-1168
Fax: (312)233-1090
E-mail: fore@ahima.org
Web Site: http://www.ahima.org/fore/programs.asp
To provide financial assistance to members of the American Health Information Management Association (AHIMA) who are single parents interested in working on an undergraduate or graduate degree in health information administration or technology.

Title of Award: Redi-Tag Corporation Scholarship **Area, Field, or Subject:** Health care services; Information science and technology; Management; Technology **Level of Education for which Award is Granted:** Graduate, Undergraduate **Number Awarded:** 1 each year. **Funds Available:** The stipend ranges from $1,000 to $5,000. **Duration:** 1 year; nonrenewable.
Eligibility Requirements: This program is open to AHIMA members who are single parents enrolled in a health information administration or health information technology program accredited by the Commission on Accreditation of Allied Health Education Programs. Applicants must be working on an undergraduate or graduate degree on at least a half-time basis and have a GPA of 3.0 or higher. U.S. citizenship is required. Selection is based on (in order of importance) GPA and academic achievement, volunteer and work experience, commitment to the health information management profession, suitability to the health information management profession, quality and suitability of references provided, and clarity of application. **Deadline for Receipt:** May of each year. **Additional Information:** Funding for this program is provided by the Redi-Tag Corporation.

2642 ■ AMERICAN HEALTH INFORMATION MANAGEMENT ASSOCIATION

Attn: Foundation of Research and Education
233 North Michigan Avenue, Suite 2150
Chicago, IL 60601-5806
Tel: (312)233-1168
Fax: (312)233-1090
E-mail: fore@ahima.org
Web Site: http://www.ahima.org/fore/programs.asp
To provide financial assistance to African American members of the American Health Information Management Association (AHIMA) who are interested in working on an undergraduate or graduate degree in health information administration or technology.

Title of Award: Esther Mayo Sherard Scholarship **Area, Field, or Subject:** Health care services; Information science and technology; Management; Technology **Level of Education for which Award is Granted:** Graduate, Undergraduate **Number Awarded:** 1 each year. **Funds Available:** The stipend ranges from $1,000 to $5,000. **Duration:** 1 year; nonrenewable.
Eligibility Requirements: This program is open to AHIMA members who are African Americans enrolled in a health information administration or health information technology program accredited by the Commission on Accreditation of Allied Health Education Programs. Applicants must be working on an undergraduate or graduate degree on at least a half-time basis and have a GPA of 3.0 or higher. U.S. citizenship is required. Selection is based (in order of importance) on GPA and academic achievement, volunteer and work experience, commitment to the health information management profession, suitability to the health information management profession, quality and suitability of references provided, and clarity of application. **Deadline for Receipt:** May of each year. **Additional Information:** This program was established in 2000 by the Esther Mayo Sherard Foundation.

2643 ■ AMERICAN INDIAN SCIENCE AND ENGINEERING SOCIETY

Attn: Scholarship Coordinator
2305 Renard, S.E., Suite 200
P.O. Box 9828
Albuquerque, NM 87119-9828

Tel: (505)765-1052
Fax: (505)765-5608
E-mail: shirley@aises.org
Web Site: http://www.aises.org/highered/scholarships
To provide financial assistance to members of the American Indian Science and Engineering Society who are majoring in designated fields as undergraduate or graduate students.

Title of Award: A.T. Anderson Memorial Scholarship Program **Area, Field, or Subject:** Engineering; Mathematics and mathematical sciences; Medicine; Natural resources; Physical sciences; Science **Level of Education for which Award is Granted:** Graduate, Undergraduate **Number Awarded:** Varies; generally, 200 or more each year, depending upon the availability of funds from corporate and other sponsors. **Funds Available:** The annual stipend is $1,000 for undergraduates or $2,000 for graduate students. **Duration:** 1 year; nonrenewable.
Eligibility Requirements: This program is open to members of the society who can furnish proof of tribal enrollment or Certificate of Degree of Indian Blood. Applicants must be full-time students at the undergraduate or graduate school level attending an accredited 4-year college or university or a 2-year college leading to an academic degree in engineering, mathematics, medicine, natural resources, physical science, or the sciences. They must submit a 500-word essay that demonstrates their interest in and motivation to continue higher education, an understanding of the importance of college and a commitment to completion, their educational and/or career goals, and a commitment to learning and giving back to the community. Selection is based on the essay, academic achievement (GPA of 2.0 or higher), leadership potential, and commitment to helping other American Indians. Financial need is not considered. **Deadline for Receipt:** June of each year. **Additional Information:** This program was launched in 1983 in memory of A.T. Anderson, a Mohawk and a chemical engineer who worked with Albert Einstein. Anderson was 1 of the society's founders and was the society's first executive director. The program includes the following named awards: the Al Qoyawayma Award for an applicant who is majoring in science or engineering and also has a strong interest in the arts, the Norbert S. Hill, Jr. Leadership Award, the Polingaysi Qoyawayma Award for an applicant who is working on a teaching degree in order to teach mathematics or science in a Native community or an advanced degree for personal improvement or teaching at the college level, and the Robert W. Brocksbank Scholarship.

2644 ■ AMERICAN INDIAN SCIENCE AND ENGINEERING SOCIETY

Attn: Scholarship Coordinator
2305 Renard, S.E., Suite 200
P.O. Box 9828
Albuquerque, NM 87119-9828
Tel: (505)765-1052
Fax: (505)765-5608
E-mail: shirley@aises.org
Web Site: http://www.aises.org/highered/scholarships
To provide financial assistance for college to outstanding American Indian high school seniors from designated states who are members of American Indian Science and Engineering Society (AISES).

Title of Award: Burlington Northern Santa Fe Foundation Scholarship **Area, Field, or Subject:** Business administration; Engineering; Mathematics and mathematical sciences; Medicine; Natural resources; Physical sciences; Science; Technology **Level of Education for which Award is Granted:** Four Year College **Number Awarded:** 5 new awards are made each year. **Funds Available:** The stipend is $2,500 per year. **Duration:** 4 years or until completion of a baccalaureate degree, whichever occurs first.
Eligibility Requirements: This program is open to AISES members who are high school seniors planning to attend an accredited 4-year college or university and major in business, engineering, mathematics, medicine, natural resources, physical science, science, or technology. Applicants must submit 1) proof of tribal enrollment or a Certificate of Degree of Indian Blood; 2) evidence of residence in the service area of the Burlington Northern and Santa Fe Corporation (Arizona, California, Colorado, Kansas, Minnesota, Montana, New Mexico, North Dakota, Oklahoma, Oregon, South Dakota, and Washington); 3) a statement of financial need; 4) a 500-word essay on why they chose their particular field of study, their career aspirations, an evaluation of past scholastic performance, obstacles faced as a student, and involvement in and commitment to tribal community life; and 5) high school transcripts showing a

GPA of 2.0 or higher. **Deadline for Receipt:** April of each year. **Additional Information:** This program is funded by the Burlington Northern Santa Fe Foundation and administered by AISES.

2645 ■ AMERICAN LEGION AUXILIARY

Attn: Department of Maryland
1589 Sulphur Spring Road, Suite 105
Baltimore, MD 21227
Tel: (410)242-9519
Fax: (410)242-9553
E-mail: anna@alamd.org
To provide financial assistance for college to the daughters of veterans who are Maryland residents and wish to study arts, sciences, business, public administration, education, or a medical field.
Title of Award: Maryland Legion Auxiliary Children and Youth Fund Scholarship **Area, Field, or Subject:** Art; Business administration; Education; Medicine; Public administration; Science **Level of Education for which Award is Granted:** Undergraduate **Number Awarded:** 1 each year. **Funds Available:** The stipend is $2,000. **Duration:** 1 year; may be renewed up to 3 additional years.
Eligibility Requirements: Eligible for this scholarship are Maryland senior high girls with veteran parents who wish to study arts, sciences, business, public administration, education, or a medical field other than nursing at a college or university in the state. Preference is given to children of members of the American Legion or American Legion Auxiliary. Selection is based on character (30%), Americanism (20%), leadership (10%), scholarship (20%), and financial need (20%). **Deadline for Receipt:** April of each year.

2646 ■ AMERICAN LEGION AUXILIARY

Attn: Department of New York
112 State Street, Suite 1310
Albany, NY 12207
Tel: (518)463-1162
Free: 800-421-6348
Fax: (518)449-5406
E-mail: alanyhdqtrs@worldnet.att.net
Web Site: http://www.deptny.org/Scholarships.htm
To provide financial assistance to descendants of wartime veterans in New York who are interested in preparing for a career in the medical field.
Title of Award: New York Legion Auxiliary Past Presidents Parley Student Scholarship in Medical Field **Area, Field, or Subject:** Medicine **Level of Education for which Award is Granted:** Undergraduate **Number Awarded:** 1 each year. **Funds Available:** The stipend is $1,000. **Duration:** 1 year.
Eligibility Requirements: This program is open to residents of New York who are the children, grandchildren, or great grandchildren of veterans (living or deceased) of World War I, World War II, the Korean Conflict, the Vietnam War, Grenada/Lebanon, Panama, or the Persian Gulf. Applicants must be high school seniors or graduates younger than 20 years of age. They must be interested in attending an accredited college or university to prepare for a career in a medical field. Along with their application, they must submit a 500-word essay on "Why I Selected the Medical Field." Selection is based on character (30%), Americanism (20%), leadership (10%), scholarship (20%), and financial need (20%). **Deadline for Receipt:** March of each year.

2647 ■ AMERICAN SOCIETY FOR CLINICAL LABORATORY SCIENCE

Attn: Coordinating Council
6701 Democracy Boulevard, Suite 300
Bethesda, MD 20817
Tel: (301)657-2768
Fax: (301)657-2909
E-mail: ascls@ascls.org
Web Site: http://www.ascls.org/education/index.asp
To provide financial assistance to students enrolled in an associate degree program in clinical laboratory technology.
Title of Award: Dade Behring Medical Technician Scholarships **Area, Field, or Subject:** Medical technology **Level of Education for which Award is Granted:** Two Year College **Number Awarded:** 50 each year. **Funds Available:** The stipend is $1,000. **Duration:** 1 year.
Eligibility Requirements: This program is open to students entering the second year of an NAACLS accredited associate degree program in clini-

cal laboratory technology or medical laboratory technology. Applicants must have a GPA of 2.5 or higher. Along with their application, they must submit a transcript of grades, 2 letters of recommendation, a statement explaining why they chose this field, and documentation of financial need. **Deadline for Receipt:** July of each year. **Additional Information:** This program, established in 2004, is sponsored by Dade Behring Inc., a producer of clinical diagnostic products and systems. Information is also available from Joe Briden, 7809 South 21st Drive, Phoenix, AZ 85041-7736.

2648 ■ AMERICAN SOCIETY FOR CLINICAL LABORATORY SCIENCE

Attn: Forum for Concerns of Minorities
6701 Democracy Boulevard, Suite 300
Bethesda, MD 20817
Tel: (301)657-2768
Fax: (301)657-2909
E-mail: ascls@ascls.org
Web Site: http://www.ascls.org/leadership/awards/fcm.asp
To provide financial assistance to minority students in clinical laboratory scientist and clinical laboratory technician programs.
Title of Award: Forum for Concerns of Minorities Scholarships **Area, Field, or Subject:** Medical technology **Level of Education for which Award is Granted:** Undergraduate **Number Awarded:** 2 each year: 1 to a CLS/MT student and 1 to a CLT/MLT student. **Funds Available:** Stipends depend on the need of the recipients and the availability of funds. **Duration:** 1 year.
Eligibility Requirements: This program is open to minority students who are enrolled in a program in clinical laboratory science, including clinical laboratory science/medical technology (CLS/MT) and clinical laboratory technician/medical laboratory technician (CLT/MLT). Applicants must be able to demonstrate financial need. Membership in the American Society for Clinical Laboratory Science is encouraged but not required. **Deadline for Receipt:** March of each year. **Additional Information:** Information is also available from Ruby Howard, 5207 Griffith Road, Gaithersburg, MD 20882, E-mail: rmhowa@aol.com.

2649 ■ AMERICAN SOCIETY FOR CLINICAL LABORATORY SCIENCE-OHIO

c/o Sondra Sutherland, Scholarship Chair
Jefferson Community College
4000 Sunset Boulevard
Steubenville, OH 43952
Tel: (740)264-5591
Fax: (740)264-9504
E-mail: ssutherlan@jcc.edu
Web Site: http://www.oscls.org
To provide financial assistance to college students in Ohio who are interested in preparing for a career in clinical laboratory science.
Title of Award: Stella Griffin Memorial Scholarship **Area, Field, or Subject:** Medical technology **Level of Education for which Award is Granted:** Undergraduate **Number Awarded:** 1 each year. **Funds Available:** The stipend is $1,000. Funds are paid directly to the recipient. **Duration:** 1 year; recipients may reapply.
Eligibility Requirements: This program is open to Ohio residents who are enrolled in the clinical laboratory science curriculum of an Ohio college or school of medical technology. They must have at least a 2.5 GPA, be in need of financial assistance, and have the following personal characteristics: an inquiring mind, an aptitude for science, initiative, adaptability to people and situations, patience, consideration for and an interest in others, a sense of responsibility, honesty, and integrity. **Deadline for Receipt:** March of each year. **Additional Information:** The sponsor was formerly the Ohio Society for Clinical Laboratory Science.

2650 ■ AMERICAN SOCIETY FOR CLINICAL PATHOLOGY

Attn: Associate Member Section
2100 West Harrison Street
Chicago, IL 60612-3798
Tel: (312)738-1336
Free: 800-621-4142
Fax: (312)738-1619
E-mail: info@ascp.org
Web Site: http://www.ascp.org

To provide funding to students enrolled in programs related to clinical laboratory science.

Title of Award: ASCP Student Scholarships **Area, Field, or Subject:** Medical technology; Science **Level of Education for which Award is Granted:** Four Year College **Number Awarded:** Varies each year. Recently, 40 of these scholarships were awarded: 3 for CT students, 3 for HTL students, 10 for MLT students, and 24 for MT students. **Funds Available:** The stipend is $1,000. **Duration:** 1 year.

Eligibility Requirements: This program is open to students enrolled in a NAACLS or CAAHEP accredited college/university program as a cytotechnologist (CT), histologic technician (HT), histotechnologist (HTL), medical laboratory technician (MLT), or medical technologist (MT). Applicants must be in the final clinical year of education and either U.S. citizens or permanent residents. HT applicants have no minimum GPA requirement, but other applicants must have a GPA of 3.0 or higher. Selection is based on academic achievement, leadership abilities, professional goals, and community activities. **Deadline for Receipt:** November of each year. **Additional Information:** This program was established in 1992.

2651 ■ AMERICAN SOCIETY FOR CLINICAL PATHOLOGY

Attn: Dale Behring Student Scholarships
2100 West Harrison Street
Chicago, IL 60612-3798
Tel: (312)738-1336
Free: 800-621-4142
Fax: (312)738-1619
E-mail: info@ascp.org
Web Site: http://www.ascp.org

To provide funding to upper-division students enrolled in a medical technologist program.

Title of Award: Emil von Behring Medical Technologist Student Scholarships **Area, Field, or Subject:** Medical technology **Level of Education for which Award is Granted:** Four Year College **Number Awarded:** 34 each year. **Funds Available:** The stipend is $2,500. **Duration:** 1 year.

Eligibility Requirements: This program is open to students enrolled in the third or fourth year of an NAACLS-accredited medical technologist program. Applicants must be U.S. citizens with a GPA of 2.5 or higher. Along with their application, they must submit a 500-word essay on their professional goals and what makes them among the best students in the nation. Financial need is not considered in the selection process. **Deadline for Receipt:** October of each year. **Additional Information:** This program, established in 2004, is sponsored by Dade Behring Inc., a producer of clinical diagnostic products and systems.

2652 ■ AMERICAN SOCIETY OF EXTRA-CORPOREAL TECHNOLOGY, INC.

Attn: AmSECT Foundation
2209 Dickens Road
P.O. Box 11086
Richmond, VA 23230-1086
Tel: (804)565-6363
Fax: (804)282-0090
E-mail: AmSECT@amsect.org
Web Site: http://www.amsect.org/scholarships/scholarships_grants.html

To provide financial assistance to student members of the American Society of Extra-Corporeal Technology (AmSECT) who are enrolled in a perfusion training program.

Title of Award: AmSECT Presidential Scholarship **Area, Field, or Subject:** Medical technology **Level of Education for which Award is Granted:** Undergraduate **Number Awarded:** 1 each year. **Funds Available:** The stipend is $1,000 per year. **Duration:** 1 year.

Eligibility Requirements: This program is open to student members of the society who are enrolled in (or accepted at) an accredited perfusion training program. Applicants must have completed at least one quarter of the required course work and have at least a 2.75 GPA. They must submit 250-word essays on how they would improve AmSECT and how they could improve the perfusion profession. Financial need is not considered

in the selection process. **Deadline for Receipt:** November of each year. **Additional Information:** Funds for this program are provided by Terumo Cardiovascular Systems.

2653 ■ AMERICAN SOCIETY OF EXTRA-CORPOREAL TECHNOLOGY, INC.

Attn: AmSECT Foundation
2209 Dickens Road
P.O. Box 11086
Richmond, VA 23230-1086
Tel: (804)565-6363
Fax: (804)282-0090
E-mail: AmSECT@amsect.org
Web Site: http://www.amsect.org/scholarships/scholarships_grants.html

To provide financial assistance to student members of the American Society of Extra-Corporeal Technology (AmSECT) who are enrolled in a perfusion training program.

Title of Award: AmSECT Scholarship **Area, Field, or Subject:** Medical technology **Level of Education for which Award is Granted:** Undergraduate **Number Awarded:** 1 each year. **Funds Available:** The stipend is $1,000 per year. **Duration:** 1 year.

Eligibility Requirements: This program is open to student members of the society who are enrolled in (or accepted at) an accredited perfusion training program. Applicants must have completed at least one quarter of the required course work and have at least a 2.75 GPA. They must submit 250-word essays on how they would improve AmSECT and how they could improve the perfusion profession. Financial need is not considered in the selection process. **Deadline for Receipt:** November of each year.

2654 ■ AMERICAN SOCIETY OF EXTRA-CORPOREAL TECHNOLOGY, INC.

Attn: AmSECT Foundation
2209 Dickens Road
P.O. Box 11086
Richmond, VA 23230-1086
Tel: (804)565-6363
Fax: (804)282-0090
E-mail: AmSECT@amsect.org
Web Site: http://www.amsect.org/scholarships/scholarships_grants.html

To provide financial assistance to student members of the American Society of Extra-Corporeal Technology (AmSECT) who are enrolled in a perfusion training program.

Title of Award: Becky Cole Boswell Memorial Scholarship **Area, Field, or Subject:** Medical technology **Level of Education for which Award is Granted:** Undergraduate **Number Awarded:** 1 each year. **Funds Available:** The stipend is $1,000 per year. **Duration:** 1 year.

Eligibility Requirements: This program is open to student members of the society who are enrolled in (or accepted at) an accredited perfusion training program. Applicants must have completed at least one quarter of the required course work and have at least a 2.75 GPA. They must submit 250-word essays on how they would improve AmSECT and how they could improve the perfusion profession. Financial need is not considered in the selection process. **Deadline for Receipt:** November of each year.

2655 ■ AMERICAN SOCIETY OF EXTRA-CORPOREAL TECHNOLOGY, INC.

Attn: AmSECT Foundation
2209 Dickens Road
P.O. Box 11086
Richmond, VA 23230-1086
Tel: (804)565-6363
Fax: (804)282-0090
E-mail: AmSECT@amsect.org
Web Site: http://www.amsect.org/scholarships/scholarships_grants.html

To provide financial assistance to student members of the American Society of Extra-Corporeal Technology (AmSECT) who are enrolled in a perfusion training program.

Title of Award: Michael Dunaway Scholarship **Area, Field, or Subject:** Medical technology **Level of Education for which Award is Granted:** Undergraduate **Number Awarded:** 1 each year. **Funds Available:** The stipend is $1,000 per year. **Duration:** 1 year.

Eligibility Requirements: This program is open to student members of the society who are enrolled in (or accepted at) an accredited perfusion training program. Applicants must have completed at least one quarter of the required course work and have at least a 2.75 GPA. They must submit 250-word essays on how they would improve AmSECT and how they could improve the perfusion profession. Financial need is not considered in the selection process. **Deadline for Receipt:** November of each year.

2656 ■ AMERICAN SOCIETY OF PODIATRIC MEDICAL ASSISTANTS

Attn: Executive Office
2124 South Austin Boulevard
Cicero, IL 60804
Tel: (708)863-6303; 888-88-ASPMA
E-mail: aspmaex@aol.com
Web Site: http://www.aspma.org
To provide financial assistance to podiatry college students.
Title of Award: Zelda Walling Vicha Memorial Trust Fund **Area, Field, or Subject:** Podiatry **Level of Education for which Award is Granted:** Four Year College, Doctorate **Number Awarded:** 2 each year. **Funds Available:** The stipend is $1,500. **Duration:** 1 year.
Eligibility Requirements: Applicants must be fourth-year podiatry students who have at least a 3.2 GPA, are in good academic standing, have demonstrated leadership ability, and can demonstrate financial need. **Deadline for Receipt:** May of each year. **Additional Information:** Information is also available from the Scholarship Chair, Janet B. Grace, E-mail: Janetgpmac@aol.com.

2657 ■ AMERICAN SOCIETY FOR QUALITY

Attn: Biomedical Division
600 North Plankinton Avenue
P.O. Box 3005
Milwaukee, WI 53201-3005
Tel: (414)272-8575
Free: 800-248-1946
Fax: (414)272-1734
E-mail: cs@asqu.org
Web Site: http://www.asq.org/biomed/scholarship/index.html
To provide financial assistance to undergraduate and graduate students working on a degree in a field related to quality in the biomedical community.
Title of Award: William J. Feingold Scholarship **Area, Field, or Subject:** Biomedical sciences; Engineering, Biomedical **Level of Education for which Award is Granted:** Four Year College, Graduate **Number Awarded:** 1 or more each year. **Funds Available:** The stipend is $5,000 per year. **Duration:** 1 year; may be renewed 1 additional year.
Eligibility Requirements: This program is open to students who have completed at least 2 years of study in a program that involves the use of quality principles, concepts, and technologies in the biomedical community. Applicants must have a GPA of 3.0 or higher. Along with their application, they must submit essays on 1) their career objectives and how they relate to quality issues within the biomedical community; and 2) why quality systems are important in the biomedical community. Graduate students are eligible, but preference is given to undergraduates. Priority is given to students who 1) are enrolled in a technical or scientific course of study; 2) have a demonstrated contribution or participation in activities related to quality in the biomedical community; and 3) have a higher GPA or more compelling essay. **Deadline for Receipt:** April of each year. **Additional Information:** This program was approved in 2004. Information is also available from Hal Greenberg, 6 Coe Road, Framingham, MA 01701.

2658 ■ AMERICAN SOCIETY OF RADIOLOGIC TECHNOLOGISTS

Attn: ASRT Education and Research Foundation
15000 Central Avenue, S.E.
Albuquerque, NM 87123-3917
Tel: (505)298-4500
Free: 800-444-2778
Fax: (505)298-5063
E-mail: foundation@asrt.org
Web Site: http://www.asrt.org
To provide financial assistance to students enrolled in entry-level radiologic sciences programs.
Title of Award: Jerman-Cahoon Student Scholarship **Area, Field, or Subject:** Radiology **Level of Education for which Award is Granted:** Undergraduate **Number Awarded:** Varies each year; recently, 5 of these scholarships were awarded. **Funds Available:** The stipend is $2,500. **Duration:** 1 year; may be renewed for 1 additional year.

Eligibility Requirements: This program is open to U.S. citizens, nationals, and permanent residents who are enrolled in an entry-level radiologic sciences program. Applicants must have a GPA in radiologic sciences core courses of 3.0 or higher and be able to demonstrate financial need. They may not have a previous degree or certificate in the radiologic sciences. Along with their application, they must submit an essay of 450 to 500 words on their reason for entering the radiologic sciences, career goals, and financial need. **Deadline for Receipt:** January of each year.

2659 ■ AMERICAN SOCIETY OF RADIOLOGIC TECHNOLOGISTS

Attn: ASRT Education and Research Foundation
15000 Central Avenue, S.E.
Albuquerque, NM 87123-3917
Tel: (505)298-4500
Free: 800-444-2778
Fax: (505)298-5063
E-mail: foundation@asrt.org
Web Site: http://www.asrt.org
To provide financial assistance to minority students enrolled in entry-level radiologic sciences programs.
Title of Award: Royce Osborn Minority Student Scholarships **Area, Field, or Subject:** Radiology **Level of Education for which Award is Granted:** Undergraduate **Number Awarded:** 5 each year. **Funds Available:** The stipend is $4,000. **Duration:** 1 year; may be renewed for 1 additional year.
Eligibility Requirements: This program is open to African Americans, Native Americans (including American Indians, Eskimos, Hawaiians, and Samoans), Hispanic Americans, Asian Americans, and Pacific Islanders who are enrolled in an entry-level radiologic sciences program. Applicants must have a GPA in radiologic sciences core courses of 3.0 or higher and be able to demonstrate financial need. They may not have a previous degree or certificate in the radiologic sciences. Along with their application, they must submit an essay of 450 to 500 words on their reason for entering the radiologic sciences, career goals, and financial need. Only U.S. citizens, nationals, and permanent residents are eligible. **Deadline for Receipt:** January of each year.

2660 ■ AMERICAN SOCIETY OF RADIOLOGIC TECHNOLOGISTS

Attn: ASRT Education and Research Foundation
15000 Central Avenue, S.E.
Albuquerque, NM 87123-3917
Tel: (505)298-4500
Free: 800-444-2778
Fax: (505)298-5063
E-mail: foundation@asrt.org
Web Site: http://www.asrt.org
To provide financial assistance to members of the American Society of Radiologic Technologists (ASRT) who are interested in continuing their education.
Title of Award: Siemens Scholar Award Program **Area, Field, or Subject:** Radiology **Level of Education for which Award is Granted:** Graduate, Professional, Undergraduate **Number Awarded:** Varies each year; recently, 1 of these scholarships was awarded. **Funds Available:** The stipend is $3,000. **Duration:** 1 year; may be renewed for 1 additional year.
Eligibility Requirements: This program is open to licensed radiologic technologists who are current members of ASRT and have worked in the radiologic sciences profession for at least 1 year during the past 5 years in a clinical or didactic setting. Applicants must have applied to 1) an accredited certificate program related to the radiologic sciences, or 2) a course of study at the associate, baccalaureate, master's, or doctoral level intended to further their career. Along with their application, they must submit an essay of 750 words or less that covers their professional, educational, and career goals and how this scholarship will help them achieve those goals. Financial need is considered in the selection process. **Deadline for Receipt:** January of each year. **Additional Information:** This program is supported by the Oncology Care Group of Siemens Medical Solutions USA, Inc.

2661 ■ AMERICAN SOCIETY OF RADIOLOGIC TECHNOLOGISTS

Attn: ASRT Education and Research Foundation
15000 Central Avenue, S.E.
Albuquerque, NM 87123-3917
Tel: (505)298-4500

Free: 800-444-2778
Fax: (505)298-5063
E-mail: foundation@asrt.org
Web Site: http://www.asrt.org
To provide financial assistance to members of the American Society of Radiologic Technologists (ASRT) who are interested in continuing their education.
Title of Award: Isadore N. Stern Scholarships **Area, Field, or Subject:** Radiology **Level of Education for which Award is Granted:** Graduate, Professional, Undergraduate **Number Awarded:** Varies each year; recently, 9 of these scholarships were awarded. **Funds Available:** The stipend is $1,000. **Duration:** 1 year; may be renewed for 1 additional year.
Eligibility Requirements: This program is open to licensed radiologic technologists who are current members of ASRT and have worked in the radiologic sciences profession for at least 1 year during the past 5 years in a clinical or didactic setting. Applicants must have applied to 1) an accredited certificate program related to the radiologic sciences, or 2) a course of study at the associate, baccalaureate, master's, or doctoral level intended to further their career. Along with their application, they must submit an essay of 750 words or less that covers their professional, educational, and career goals and how this scholarship will help them achieve those goals. Financial need is considered in the selection process. **Deadline for Receipt:** January of each year. **Additional Information:** This program is supported by E-Z-EM Inc.

2662 ■ AMERICAN SOCIETY OF RADIOLOGIC TECHNOLOGISTS

Attn: ASRT Education and Research Foundation
15000 Central Avenue, S.E.
Albuquerque, NM 87123-3917
Tel: (505)298-4500
Free: 800-444-2778
Fax: (505)298-5063
E-mail: foundation@asrt.org
Web Site: http://www.asrt.org
To provide financial assistance to students enrolled in entry-level radiation therapy programs.
Title of Award: Varian Radiation Therapy Scholarships **Area, Field, or Subject:** Radiology **Level of Education for which Award is Granted:** Undergraduate **Number Awarded:** Varies each year; recently, 11 of these scholarships were awarded. **Funds Available:** The stipend is $5,000. **Duration:** 1 year; may be renewed for 1 additional year.
Eligibility Requirements: This program is open to U.S. citizens, nationals, and permanent residents who are enrolled in an entry-level radiation therapy program. Applicants must have a GPA in radiologic sciences core courses of 3.0 or higher and be able to demonstrate financial need. They may not have a previous degree or certificate in radiation therapy. Along with their application, they must submit an essay of 450 to 500 words on their reason for entering the radiologic sciences, career goals, and financial need. **Deadline for Receipt:** January of each year. **Additional Information:** Support for this program is provided by Varian Medical Systems.

2663 ■ ARKANSAS DEPARTMENT OF WORKFORCE EDUCATION

Luther Hardin Building
Three Capitol Mall, Room 207
Little Rock, AR 72201-1083
Tel: (501)682-1500
Fax: (501)682-1509
Web Site: http://dwe.arkansas.gov/LoanForgiveness/atcslfp.htm
To provide forgivable loans to residents of Arkansas who are interested in pursuing technical education and working in the state.
Title of Award: Arkansas Technical Careers Student Loan Forgiveness Program **Area, Field, or Subject:** Biological and clinical sciences; Computer and information sciences; Engineering; Engineering, Biomedical; Engineering, Computer; Engineering, Electrical; Engineering, Industrial; Health care services; Physical sciences **Level of Education for which Award is Granted:** Undergraduate **Number Awarded:** Varies each year. **Funds Available:** The maximum loan is $2,500 per year. Loans are forgiven if the recipient works full time in the high demand technical field in Arkansas. Each year's loan may be forgiven with 1 year of full-time employment. Loan recipients who do not graduate from the program or work full time in the field in Arkansas must repay the loan in full. **Duration:** Up to 4 years.

Eligibility Requirements: This program is open to residents of Arkansas who are U.S. citizens or permanent residents admitted to an approved program resulting in a diploma, certificate, or degree in a high demand technical field. Applicants must indicate their intention to work in Arkansas in the field for which they receive the training. **Deadline for Receipt:** Applications must be submitted within 6 months of the completion of the program of study. **Additional Information:** The Arkansas General Assembly established this program in 1999. Recently, the designated career fields related to advanced manufacturing (including engineering and engineering technology, industrial electronics installers and repairers, machinist and machine technologies, and tool and die maker and technologist); computer and information technology (including computer engineering, computer and information sciences, electrical and electronic engineering and related technology, electromechanical instrumentation and maintenance technology, and computer installer and repairer); and biomedical and biotechnology (including biological and life sciences, physical sciences, science technologies, health professions and related sciences, bioengineering and biomedical engineering, and biomedical engineering technology and technician).

2664 ■ BOYS & GIRLS CLUBS OF GREATER SAN DIEGO

Attn: Scholarships
4635 Clairemont Mesa Boulevard
San Diego, CA 92117
Tel: (619)298-3520; (866)SD-YOUTH
Fax: (619)298-3615
Web Site: http://www.sdyouth.org/scholarships.htm
To provide financial assistance to graduating male high school seniors who plan to study designated fields in college.
Title of Award: Spence Reese Scholarships **Area, Field, or Subject:** Engineering; Law; Medicine; Political science **Level of Education for which Award is Granted:** Undergraduate **Number Awarded:** 4 each year: 1 in each of the designated fields. **Funds Available:** The stipend is $2,000 per year. **Duration:** 4 years.
Eligibility Requirements: Applicants must be graduating male high school seniors planning to study law, medicine, engineering, or political science in college. They may live anywhere in the United States, but must attend an interview in San Diego, California. Selection is based on academic standing, potential for good citizenship, academic ability, and financial need. **Deadline for Receipt:** April of each year. **Additional Information:** Travel expenses for the interview are reimbursed by the sponsor. A $10 processing fee must accompany all applications.

2665 ■ BROWN AND CALDWELL

Attn: Scholarship Program
201 North Civic Drive, Suite 115
P.O. Box 8045
Walnut Creek, CA 94596
Tel: (925)937-9010
Fax: (925)937-9026
E-mail: scholarships@brwncald.com
Web Site: http://www.brownandcaldwell.com
To provide financial assistance to minority students working on an undergraduate degree in an environmental or engineering field.
Title of Award: Brown and Caldwell Minority Scholarship **Area, Field, or Subject:** Biological and clinical sciences; Engineering, Chemical; Engineering, Civil; Environmental conservation; Environmental science; Geology; Hydrology; Industrial hygiene; Toxicology **Level of Education for which Award is Granted:** Four Year College **Number Awarded:** 1 each year. **Funds Available:** The stipend is $3,000. **Duration:** 1 year.
Eligibility Requirements: This program is open to members of minority groups (African Americans, Hispanics, Asians, Pacific Islanders, Native Americans, and Alaska Natives) who are full-time students in their junior year at an accredited 4-year college or university. Applicants must have a GPA of 3.0 or higher with a declared major in civil, chemical, or environmental engineering or an environmental science (e.g., biology, ecology, geology, hydrogeology, industrial hygiene, toxicology). Along with their application, they must submit an essay (up to 250 words) on why they chose to major in an environmental discipline. They must be U.S. citizens or permanent resident and available to participate in a summer internship at a Brown and Caldwell office. Financial need is not considered in the selection process. **Deadline for Receipt:** February of each year. **Additional Information:** As part of the paid summer internship

at a Brown and Caldwell office at 1 of more than 40 cities in the country, the program provides a mentor to guide the intern through the company's information and communications resources.

2666 ■ BROWN AND CALDWELL

Attn: Scholarship Program
201 North Civic Drive, Suite 115
P.O. Box 8045
Walnut Creek, CA 94596
Tel: (925)937-9010
Fax: (925)937-9026
E-mail: scholarships@brwncald.com
Web Site: http://www.brownandcaldwell.com
To provide financial assistance to undergraduate students working on an degree in an environmental or engineering field.
Title of Award: Dr. W. Wesley Eckenfelder Scholarship **Area, Field, or Subject:** Biological and clinical sciences; Engineering, Chemical; Engineering, Civil; Environmental conservation; Environmental science; Geology; Hydrology; Industrial hygiene; Toxicology **Level of Education for which Award is Granted:** Four Year College **Number Awarded:** 1 each year. **Funds Available:** The stipend is $3,000. **Duration:** 1 year.
Eligibility Requirements: This program is open to U.S. citizens and permanent residents enrolled as full-time students in their junior year at an accredited 4-year college or university. Applicants must have a GPA of 3.0 or higher with a declared major in civil, chemical, or environmental engineering or an environmental science (e.g., biology, ecology, geology, hydrogeology, industrial hygiene, toxicology). Along with their application, they must submit an essay (up to 250 words) on why they chose to major in an environmental discipline. Financial need is not considered in the selection process. **Deadline for Receipt:** February of each year. **Additional Information:** This scholarship was first awarded in 1999.

2667 ■ BUSINESS AND PROFESSIONAL WOMEN OF VIRGINIA

Attn: Virginia BPW Foundation
P.O. Box 4842
McLean, VA 22103-4842
Web Site: http://www.bpwva.org/Foundation.shtml
To provide financial assistance to mature women in Virginia who are interested in upgrading their skills or education at a college, law school, or medical school in the state.
Title of Award: Buena M. Chesshir Memorial Women's Educational Scholarship **Area, Field, or Subject:** General studies/Field of study not specified; Law; Medicine **Level of Education for which Award is Granted:** Graduate, Professional, Undergraduate **Number Awarded:** 1 or more each year. **Funds Available:** Stipends range from $100 to $1,000 per year; funds may be used for tuition, fees, books, transportation, living expenses, and dependent care. **Duration:** Recipients must complete their course of study within 2 years.
Eligibility Requirements: This program is open to women who are residents of Virginia, U.S. citizens, and at least 25 years of age. Applicants must have been accepted into an accredited program or course of study at a Virginia institution, have a definite plan to use their training to improve their chances for upward mobility in the work force, and be graduating within 2 years. Undergraduate applicants may by majoring in any field, but graduate student applicants must be working on a degree in law or medicine. Selection is based on demonstrated financial need and defined career goals. **Deadline for Receipt:** March of each year.

2668 ■ CALIFORNIA ACADEMY OF PHYSICIAN ASSISTANTS

3100 West Warner Avenue, Suite 3
Santa Ana, CA 92704
Tel: (714)427-0321
Fax: (714)427-0324
E-mail: capa@capanet.org
Web Site: http://www.capanet.org/capa_scholarships.cfm
To provide financial assistance to student members of the California Academy of Physician Assistants (CAPA) enrolled in physician assistant programs in California.
Title of Award: CAPA Community Outreach Scholarship **Area, Field, or Subject:** Medical assisting **Level of Education for which Award is Granted:** Undergraduate **Number Awarded:** 1 each year. **Funds Available:** The stipend is $1,000. **Duration:** 1 year.
Eligibility Requirements: This program is open to student members of CAPA enrolled in primary care physician assistant programs in California.

Applicants must have demonstrated community outreach and other philanthropic activities as a student.

2669 ■ CALIFORNIA ACADEMY OF PHYSICIAN ASSISTANTS

3100 West Warner Avenue, Suite 3
Santa Ana, CA 92704
Tel: (714)427-0321
Fax: (714)427-0324
E-mail: capa@capanet.org
Web Site: http://www.capanet.org/capa_scholarships.cfm
To provide financial assistance to student members of the California Academy of Physician Assistants (CAPA) enrolled in physician assistant programs in California.
Title of Award: Ray Dale Memorial Scholarship **Area, Field, or Subject:** Medical assisting **Level of Education for which Award is Granted:** Undergraduate **Number Awarded:** 1 each year. **Funds Available:** The stipend is $1,000. **Duration:** 1 year.
Eligibility Requirements: This program is open to student members of CAPA enrolled in primary care physician assistant programs in California.

2670 ■ CALIFORNIA ACADEMY OF PHYSICIAN ASSISTANTS

3100 West Warner Avenue, Suite 3
Santa Ana, CA 92704
Tel: (714)427-0321
Fax: (714)427-0324
E-mail: capa@capanet.org
Web Site: http://www.capanet.org/capa_scholarships.cfm
To provide financial assistance to minority student members of the California Academy of Physician Assistants (CAPA) enrolled in physician assistant programs in California.
Title of Award: Ruth Webb Minority Scholarship **Area, Field, or Subject:** Medical assisting **Level of Education for which Award is Granted:** Undergraduate **Number Awarded:** 1 each year. **Funds Available:** The stipend is $1,000. **Duration:** 1 year.
Eligibility Requirements: This program is open to student members of CAPA enrolled in primary care physician assistant programs in California. Applicants must be members of a minority group.

2671 ■ CALIFORNIA RURAL INDIAN HEALTH BOARD, INC.

Attn: Administrative Services Department
4400 Auburn Boulevard, Second Floor
Sacramento, CA 95841
Tel: (916)929-9761
Free: 800-274-4288
Fax: (916)929-7246
E-mail: shelley.whitebear@ihs.gov
Web Site: http://www.crihb.org/scholarship.htm
To provide financial assistance to California Indians working on an undergraduate or graduate degree in a health-related field.
Title of Award: Phillip R. Lee Scholarship **Area, Field, or Subject:** Health care services **Level of Education for which Award is Granted:** Graduate, Undergraduate **Number Awarded:** Varies; a total of $25,000 is available to this program each year. **Funds Available:** Stipends range from $300 to $2,500. **Duration:** 1 year; may be renewed as long as the recipient maintains a GPA of 3.0 or higher.
Eligibility Requirements: This program is open to California Indians who have completed at least 1 semester of undergraduate or graduate study at an accredited college or vocational program. Applicants must be enrolled in a health or related field of study and have a GPA of 3.0 or higher. They must submit tribal certification from their tribe or the U.S. Bureau of Indian Affairs. Financial need is considered in the selection process. **Deadline for Receipt:** February or June of each year.

2672 ■ CLINICAL LABORATORY MANAGEMENT ASSOCIATION-MAINE CHAPTER

c/o Sonia E. Russell, Scholarship Chair
DCPA
337 State Street
Bangor, ME 04401
Tel: (207)942-6759
Fax: (207)942-2613
E-mail: srussell@mint.net
Web Site: http://www.melabs.org/clma/scholarship.htm

To provide financial assistance to residents of Maine working on a degree in laboratory medicine.

Title of Award: Maine Chapter CLMA Undergraduate Scholarships **Area, Field, or Subject:** Medical technology **Level of Education for which Award is Granted:** Undergraduate **Number Awarded:** 3 each year. **Funds Available:** The stipend is $1,000. **Duration:** 1 year.

Eligibility Requirements: This program is open to Maine residents who are preparing for a career as a medical technologist, medical laboratory technician, histotechnologist, cytologist, or clinical laboratory scientist. Applicants must submit a brief essay describing why they have chosen their field of study and why they are applying for this scholarship. Selection is based on academic performance, character, commitment to laboratory medicine, and financial need. **Deadline for Receipt:** May of each year.

2673 ■ COMMUNITY FOUNDATION FOR GREATER ATLANTA, INC.

50 Hurt Plaza, Suite 449
Atlanta, GA 30303
Tel: (404)688-5525
Fax: (404)688-3060
E-mail: vweekes@atlcf.org
Web Site: http://www.atlcf.org/GrantsScholarships/Scholarships/SteveDearduff.aspx

To provide financial assistance to Georgia residents who are working on an undergraduate or graduate degree, especially in medicine or social work.

Title of Award: Steve Dearduff Scholarship **Area, Field, or Subject:** General studies/Field of study not specified; Medicine; Social work **Level of Education for which Award is Granted:** Graduate, Undergraduate **Number Awarded:** Varies each year; recently, 7 of these scholarships were awarded. **Funds Available:** Stipends range up to $2,500 per year. **Duration:** 1 year; recipients may reapply.

Eligibility Requirements: This program is open to legal residents of Georgia who are enrolled in or accepted at an accredited institution of higher learning on the undergraduate or graduate school level. Applicants must be able to demonstrate a history of outstanding community service and potential for success in their chosen field. They must have a GPA of 2.0 or higher. Preference is given to candidates entering the fields of medicine (research or clinical practice) or social work. **Deadline for Receipt:** March of each year.

2674 ■ CONGRESSIONAL BLACK CAUCUS FOUNDATION, INC.

Attn: Director, Educational Programs
1720 Massachusetts Avenue, N.W.
Washington, DC 20036
Tel: (202)263-2836
Free: 800-784-2577
Fax: (202)775-0773
E-mail: spouses@cbcfinc.org
Web Site: http://www.cbcfinc.org

To provide financial assistance to high school seniors and undergraduate students interested in preparing for a career of service to the African American community in medicine or science.

Title of Award: Vivien Thomas Scholarship for Medicine and Science **Area, Field, or Subject:** Medicine; Science **Level of Education for which Award is Granted:** Undergraduate **Number Awarded:** 10 every 4 years. **Funds Available:** The stipend is $10,000 per year. **Duration:** 1 year; may be renewed up to 3 additional years.

Eligibility Requirements: This program is open to high school seniors and full-time undergraduates with a cumulative GPA of 3.0 or higher. Applicants must be working on or planning to work on a degree in medicine or science. They must be U.S. citizens or legal residents able to demonstrate financial need. Along with their application, they must submit 2 essays on the following topics: 1) their interest in medicine and science, the career they want to pursue upon completing their college education, how this scholarship will make a difference for their college career, and the qualities they posses to ensure that they reach their goals; and 2) why it is important for persons of African heritage to prepare for a career in medicine and science, and the contributions that persons of African heritage have made in the fields of medicine and science. **Deadline for Receipt:** May of the year of the award; these scholarships will next be

offered in 2007. **Additional Information:** This program, established in 2003, is sponsored by GlaxoSmithKline.

2675 ■ CONNECTICUT DEPARTMENT OF HIGHER EDUCATION

Attn: Education and Employment Information Center
61 Woodland Street
Hartford, CT 06105-2326
Tel: (860)947-1846
Free: 800-842-0229
Fax: (860)947-1311
E-mail: setig@ctdhe.org
Web Site: http://www.ctdhe.org/SFA/sfa.htm

To provide financial assistance to undergraduate and graduate students in Connecticut who are preparing for a career as a special education teacher.

Title of Award: Connecticut Special Education Teacher Incentive Grant **Area, Field, or Subject:** Education, Special; Hearing and deafness; Visual impairment **Level of Education for which Award is Granted:** Four Year College, Graduate **Number Awarded:** Varies each year. **Funds Available:** The stipend is $5,000 per year for full-time study or $2,000 per year for part-time graduate study. **Duration:** 1 year.

Eligibility Requirements: This program is open to full-time juniors and seniors and full- or part-time graduate students who are residents of Connecticut. Applicants must be enrolled in 1) special education teacher preparation programs at selected universities in Connecticut; or 2) out-of-state teacher preparation programs seeking cross-endorsement for teaching "low-incidence student" areas. They must be nominated by the dean of education at their school and have a stated intent to teach in a Connecticut public school, an approved private special education facility, or a Regional Educational Service Center. Priority is given to minority (African American, Hispanic/Latino, Asian American, and Native American) and bilingual students and to Connecticut residents enrolled in an approved out-of-state program. **Deadline for Receipt:** August of each year. **Additional Information:** The approved in-state programs are at Central Connecticut State University, Fairfield University, Saint Joseph College, Southern Connecticut State University, University of Connecticut, and University of Hartford. The programs for students seeking cross-endorsement certification for teaching students who are blind and partially-sighted or visually impaired are at Hunter College of CUNY (New York, New York), Dominican College (Orangeburg, New York), Teachers College of Columbia University (New York, New York), and University of Northern Colorado (Greeley, Colorado). The programs for students seeking cross-endorsement certification for teaching students who are deaf or hearing-impaired are at Hunter College, Teachers College, Clarke School for the Deaf at Smith College (Northampton, Massachusetts), and Boston University (Boston, Massachusetts).

2676 ■ COOK INLET REGION, INC.

Attn: CIRI Foundation
2600 Cordova Street, Suite 206
Anchorage, AK 99503
Tel: (907)263-5582
Free: 800-764-3382
Fax: (907)263-5588
E-mail: tcf@ciri.com
Web Site: http://www.thecirifoundation.org/scholarship.html

To provide financial assistance for undergraduate or graduate studies in selected fields to Alaska Natives who are original enrollees to Cook Inlet Region, Inc. (CIRI) and their lineal descendants.

Title of Award: CIRI Foundation Special Excellence Scholarships **Area, Field, or Subject:** Business administration; Education; Engineering; General studies/Field of study not specified; Health care services; Mathematics and mathematical sciences; Science **Level of Education for which Award is Granted:** Four Year College, Graduate **Number Awarded:** 1 or more each year. **Funds Available:** The stipend is $18,000 per year. **Duration:** 1 year; may be renewed.

Eligibility Requirements: This program is open to Alaska Native enrollees to CIRI under the Alaska Native Claims Settlement Act (ANCSA) of 1971 and their lineal descendants. There are no Alaska residency requirements or age limitations. Applicants must be accepted or enrolled full time in a 4-year undergraduate or a graduate degree program. They must have a GPA of 3.7 or higher. Preference is given to students working on a degree in business, education, mathematics, sciences, health services, or engineering. Selection is based on academic achievement, rigor of course work or degree program, quality of a statement of purpose, student financial contribution, financial need, grade level, previous work performance, education and community activities, letters of recommendation, seriousness of purpose, and practicality of educational and professional goals. **Deadline for Receipt:** May of each year. **Additional Information:** This program was established in 1997. Recipients must enroll in school on a full-time basis.

2677 ■ COOK INLET REGION, INC.

Attn: CIRI Foundation
2600 Cordova Street, Suite 206
Anchorage, AK 99503
Tel: (907)263-5582
Free: 800-764-3382
Fax: (907)263-5588
E-mail: tcf@ciri.com
Web Site: http://www.thecirifoundation.org/scholarship.html
To provide financial assistance for undergraduate or graduate studies in health and other areas to Alaska Natives who are original enrollees to Cook Inlet Region, Inc. (CIRI) and their lineal descendants.
Title of Award: Roy M. Huhndorf Endowment Scholarship Fund **Area, Field, or Subject:** General studies/Field of study not specified; Health care services **Level of Education for which Award is Granted:** Four Year College, Graduate **Number Awarded:** Varies each year; recently, 2 of these scholarships (at $2,000 per semester) were awarded. **Funds Available:** The stipend is $9,000 per year, $7,000 per year, or $2,000 per semester, depending on GPA. **Duration:** 1 year (2 semesters).
Eligibility Requirements: This program is open to Alaska Native enrollees to CIRI under the Alaska Native Claims Settlement Act (ANCSA) of 1971 and their lineal descendants. There are no Alaska residency requirements or age limitations. Applicants must be accepted or enrolled full time in a 4-year undergraduate or a graduate degree program. They must be working on a degree in health science and have a GPA of 2.5 or higher. Selection is based on academic achievement, rigor of course work or degree program, quality of a statement of purpose, student financial contribution, financial need, grade level, previous work performance, education and community activities, letters of recommendation, seriousness of purpose, and practicality of educational and professional goals. **Deadline for Receipt:** May of each year. **Additional Information:** This program was established in 1995. Recipients must attend school on a full-time basis.

2678 ■ DELAWARE VOLUNTEER FIREMEN'S ASSOCIATION

Attn: Executive Secretary
122A South Bradford Street
P.O. Box 1849
Dover, DE 19903-1849
Tel: (302)734-9390; 877-455-3832
Fax: (302)734-9404
E-mail: exsec@dvfassn.com
Web Site: http://www.dvfassn.com/html/schol.htm
To provide financial assistance for college to Delaware residents or members of fire departments or auxiliaries in the state.
Title of Award: Delaware Volunteer Firemen's Association Scholarship **Area, Field, or Subject:** Engineering; Fires and fire prevention; Medical technology **Level of Education for which Award is Granted:** Professional, Undergraduate **Number Awarded:** Varies each year; recently, 11 of these scholarships were awarded. **Funds Available:** The maximum stipend is $2,500. **Duration:** 1 year.
Eligibility Requirements: This program is open to 1) Delaware residents or 2) active members (for at least 1 year) of a fire department or auxiliary that is a member in good standing of the Delaware Volunteer Firemen's Association or DVFA Ladies Auxiliary. Applicants must have been accepted into an accredited fire service technology, medical technology, engineering, or related certificate, diploma, or degree program. Along with their application, they must submit 3 letters of recommendation, college and fire school transcripts, and a 250-word statement that covers their reasons for applying for financial assistance, why their course of study will be useful, and their career goals and objectives. **Deadline for Receipt:** March of each year. **Additional Information:** Information is also available from the DVFA Scholarship Committee, Delaware State Fire School, 1461 Chestnut Grove Road, Dover, DE 19904-1545, (302) 376-6393.

2679 ■ DELTA SIGMA THETA SORORITY, INC.-PROVIDENCE ALUMNAE CHAPTER

Attn: Financial Awards Review Committee
P.O. Box 40175
Providence, RI 02904-0175
Web Site: http://www.dstprovidencealumnae.com
To provide financial assistance to African American female high school seniors from Rhode Island who are either physically challenged or planning to prepare for a health-related career.
Title of Award: Hernandez-Lopes Award **Area, Field, or Subject:** General studies/Field of study not specified; Health care services **Level of Education for which Award is Granted:** Undergraduate **Number Awarded:** 1 or more each year. **Funds Available:** A stipend is awarded (amount not specified). **Duration:** 1 year.
Eligibility Requirements: This program is open to college-bound African American women who are seniors graduating from high schools in Rhode Island. Applicants must be either 1) physically challenged, or 2) preparing for a career in a health-related field. They must submit a current official transcript, letter of recommendation, documentation of financial need, and an essay describing their career goals, community service activities, educational accomplishments, and personal interests and talents. **Deadline for Receipt:** February of each year.

2680 ■ DEPARTMENT OF AGRICULTURE

Attn: Animal and Plant Health Inspection Service
Human Resources/Employment
4700 River Road, Unit 106
Riverdale, MD 20737-1230
Tel: (301)734-5596
Free: 800-762-2738
Web Site: http://www.aphis.usda.gov/mrpbs/scholarship_info.html
To provide scholarship/loans and work experience to undergraduate and graduate students interested in preparing for a career in veterinary medicine and biomedical sciences.
Title of Award: Saul T. Wilson, Jr. Scholarship **Area, Field, or Subject:** Biomedical sciences; Veterinary science and medicine **Level of Education for which Award is Granted:** Four Year College, Doctorate **Number Awarded:** 1 or more each year. **Funds Available:** The maximum stipend is $5,000 per year for undergraduates or $10,000 per year for graduate students. Funds must be used for tuition, books, tutors, and laboratory fees. During summers and school breaks, scholars receive paid employment as a veterinary student trainee with APHIS at a salary that ranges from $9 to $13 per hour, depending on the student's qualifications. After 640 hours of study-related work with APHIS in the career experience program and graduation with a D.V.M. degree, and at the option of APHIS, the student must become a full-time employee for at least 1 calendar year for each school year of support from this scholarship. If scholarship recipients refuse to accept an APHIS offer of employment, they must reimburse the agency for all financial assistance received. If recipients fail to serve the entire length of the mandatory APHIS employment period, they must reimburse APHIS a prorated share of scholarship funds used. **Duration:** 1 year; may be renewed.
Eligibility Requirements: This program is open to U.S. citizens enrolled in an accredited college or university in the United States as a full-time student. Undergraduates must have completed at least 2-years of a 4-year preveterinary medicine or other biomedical science program. Graduate students must have completed not more than 1 year of study in veterinary medicine. All applicants must submit a 500-word essay on why they should receive this scholarship and what contributions they would make to veterinary services of the Animal and Plant Health Inspection Service (APHIS). A preference is given to veterans of the U.S. armed forces. Financial need is not considered in the selection process. **Deadline for Receipt:** February of each year.

2681 ■ DEVON HEALTH SERVICES, INC.

Attn: Devon Scholars Committee
1100 First Avenue, Suite 100
King of Prussia, PA 19406
Tel: (610)265-8000
Free: 800-431-CARE
Fax: (610)768-4509
E-mail: jgrant@devonhealth.com

Web Site: http://www.devonhealth.com/pages/corp_headquarters/devonscholars/default.htm
To provide financial assistance to high school seniors interested in attending college to prepare for a career in the health care industry.
Title of Award: Devon Scholars Program **Area, Field, or Subject:** Health care services **Level of Education for which Award is Granted:** Undergraduate **Number Awarded:** 3 each year. **Funds Available:** Stipends are $2,500 for first place, $1,000 for second, and $500 for third. **Duration:** 1 year.
Eligibility Requirements: This program is open to seniors graduating from high schools anywhere in the United States with a GPA of 3.0 or higher. Applicants must be interested in attending college full time to prepare for a career in the health care industry. Along with their application, they must submit an essay of 800 to 1,500 words on why they are interested in preparing for a career in health-related studies, the health-related field in which they are interested, current issues in the health care marketplace, and how they plan to make a difference. Selection is based on that essay, financial need and resources available to the student, references, community and school activities, and academic performance. **Deadline for Receipt:** April of each year.

2682 ■ HAWAI'I COMMUNITY FOUNDATION

Attn: Scholarship Department
1164 Bishop Street, Suite 800
Honolulu, HI 96813
Tel: (808)566-5570; 888-731-3863
Fax: (808)521-6286
E-mail: scholarships@hcf-hawaii.org
Web Site: http://www.hawaiicommunityfoundation.org/scholar/scholar.php
To provide financial assistance to residents in selected areas of Hawaii who are interested in preparing for a career in the health field.
Title of Award: Aiea General Hospital Association Scholarships **Area, Field, or Subject:** Health care services **Level of Education for which Award is Granted:** Graduate, Undergraduate **Number Awarded:** Varies each year; recently, 23 of these scholarships were awarded. **Funds Available:** The amounts of the awards depend on the availability of funds and the need of the recipient; recently, stipends averaged $1,000. **Duration:** 1 year.
Eligibility Requirements: This program is open to Hawaii residents in designated areas of Leeward O'ahu who are interested in studying a health-related field as full-time students (on the undergraduate or graduate school level). They must be able to demonstrate academic achievement (GPA of 2.7 or higher), good moral character, and financial need. In addition to filling out the standard application form, they must write a short statement indicating their reasons for attending college, their planned course of study, and their career goals. **Deadline for Receipt:** February of each year. **Additional Information:** Recipients may attend college in Hawaii or on the mainland. This program was established in 1985 with the remaining assets of Aiea General Hospital after it closed its doors in 1983.

2683 ■ HAWAI'I COMMUNITY FOUNDATION

Attn: Scholarship Department
1164 Bishop Street, Suite 800
Honolulu, HI 96813
Tel: (808)566-5570; 888-731-3863
Fax: (808)521-6286
E-mail: scholarships@hcf-hawaii.org
Web Site: http://www.hawaiicommunityfoundation.org/scholar/scholar.php
To provide financial assistance to Hawaii residents who are interested in studying gerontology on the undergraduate or graduate school level.
Title of Award: Edward J. Doty Scholarship **Area, Field, or Subject:** Gerontology **Level of Education for which Award is Granted:** Graduate, Undergraduate **Number Awarded:** Varies each year; recently, 2 of these scholarships were awarded. **Funds Available:** The amounts of the awards depend on the availability of funds and the need of the recipient; recently, stipends averaged $1,000. **Duration:** 1 year.
Eligibility Requirements: This program is open to college juniors, seniors, and graduate students from Hawaii who are studying gerontology on a full-time basis. Applicants must be able to demonstrate academic achievement (GPA of 2.7 or higher), good moral character, and financial need. In addition to filling out the standard application form, applicants must write a short statement indicating their reasons for attending college, their planned course of study, and their career goals. Also eligible for this

program are 1) dependents of current or former employees of Doty Equities with 1 year of service, and 2) dependents of former employees of Eagle Distributors, Inc. who were in its employ in 1996 and had at least 1 year of service with the company. **Deadline for Receipt:** February of each year. **Additional Information:** Recipients may attend college in Hawaii or on the mainland.

2684 ■ HAWAI'I COMMUNITY FOUNDATION

Attn: Scholarship Department
1164 Bishop Street, Suite 800
Honolulu, HI 96813
Tel: (808)566-5570; 888-731-3863
Fax: (808)521-6286
E-mail: scholarships@hcf-hawaii.org
Web Site: http://www.hawaiicommunityfoundation.org/scholar/scholar.php
To provide financial assistance to Hawaii residents of Filipino ancestry who are interested in preparing for a career in the health field.
Title of Award: Cora Aguda Manayan Fund **Area, Field, or Subject:** Health care services **Level of Education for which Award is Granted:** Graduate, Undergraduate **Number Awarded:** Varies each year; recently, 10 of these scholarships were awarded. **Funds Available:** The amounts of the awards depend on the availability of funds and the need of the recipient; recently, stipends averaged $1,000. **Duration:** 1 year.
Eligibility Requirements: This program is open to Hawaii residents of Filipino ancestry who are interested in studying in Hawaii as full-time students and majoring in a health-related field (on the undergraduate or graduate school level). They must be able to demonstrate academic achievement (GPA of 2.7 or higher), good moral character, and financial need. In addition to filling out the standard application form, they must write a short statement indicating their reasons for attending college, their planned course of study, and their career goals. **Deadline for Receipt:** February of each year.

2685 ■ HAWAI'I COMMUNITY FOUNDATION

Attn: Scholarship Department
1164 Bishop Street, Suite 800
Honolulu, HI 96813
Tel: (808)566-5570; 888-731-3863
Fax: (808)521-6286
E-mail: scholarships@hcf-hawaii.org
Web Site: http://www.hawaiicommunityfoundation.org/scholar/scholar.php
To provide financial assistance to Hawaii residents who are interested in preparing for a career in designated health fields.
Title of Award: Robanna Fund Scholarships **Area, Field, or Subject:** Health care services **Level of Education for which Award is Granted:** Undergraduate **Number Awarded:** Varies each year; recently, 10 of these scholarships were awarded. **Funds Available:** The amounts of the awards depend on the availability of funds and the need of the recipient; recently, stipends averaged $1,000. **Duration:** 1 year.
Eligibility Requirements: This program is open to Hawaii residents who are enrolled as full-time undergraduate students in a health-related field. They must be able to demonstrate academic achievement (GPA of 2.7 or higher), good moral character, and financial need. In addition to filling out the standard application form, applicants must write a short statement indicating their reasons for attending college, their planned course of study, and their career goals. **Deadline for Receipt:** February of each year. **Additional Information:** Recipients may attend college in Hawaii or on the mainland.

2686 ■ HAWAI'I COMMUNITY FOUNDATION

Attn: Scholarship Department
1164 Bishop Street, Suite 800
Honolulu, HI 96813
Tel: (808)566-5570; 888-731-3863
Fax: (808)521-6286
E-mail: scholarships@hcf-hawaii.org
Web Site: http://www.hawaiicommunityfoundation.org/scholar/scholar.php
To provide financial assistance to Hawaii residents of Chinese descent who are interested in studying gerontology on the undergraduate or graduate school level.
Title of Award: Thz Fo Farm Fund **Area, Field, or Subject:** Gerontology **Level of Education for which Award is Granted:** Graduate, Undergraduate **Number Awarded:** Varies each year; recently, 1 of these

scholarships was awarded. **Funds Available:** The amounts of the awards depend on the availability of funds and the need of the recipient; recently, stipends averaged $1,000. **Duration:** 1 year.

Eligibility Requirements: This program is open to high school seniors, high school graduates, and college students in Hawaii who are of Chinese ancestry and are interested in studying gerontology as full-time undergraduate or graduate students. They must be able to demonstrate academic achievement (GPA of 2.7 or higher), good moral character, and financial need. In addition to filling out the standard application form, applicants must write a short statement indicating their reasons for attending college, their planned course of study, and their career goals. **Deadline for Receipt:** February of each year. **Additional Information:** Recipients may attend college in Hawaii or on the mainland.

2687 ■ HAWAI'I COMMUNITY FOUNDATION

Attn: Scholarship Department
1164 Bishop Street, Suite 800
Honolulu, HI 96813
Tel: (808)566-5570; 888-731-3863
Fax: (808)521-6286
E-mail: scholarships@hcf-hawaii.org
Web Site: http://www.hawaiicommunityfoundation.org/scholar/scholar.php
To provide financial assistance to Hawaii residents who are interested in preparing for a career in the health field.

Title of Award: Dr. Hans and Clara Zimmerman Foundation Health Scholarships **Area, Field, or Subject:** Health care services **Level of Education for which Award is Granted:** Four Year College, Graduate **Number Awarded:** Varies each year; recently, 195 of these scholarships were awarded. **Funds Available:** The amounts of the awards depend on the availability of funds and the need of the recipients; recently, stipends averaged $3,065. **Duration:** 1 year.

Eligibility Requirements: This program is open to Hawaii residents who are interested in majoring in a health-related field as full-time students at a college or university in the United States (as juniors, seniors or graduate students). Students planning to major in sports medicine, psychology (unless clinical), and social work are not eligible. Applicants must be able to demonstrate academic achievement (GPA of 3.0 or higher), good moral character, and financial need. In addition to filling out the standard application form, they must write a short statement indicating their reasons for attending college, their planned course of study, and their career goals. **Deadline for Receipt:** February of each year. **Additional Information:** This is 1 of the largest scholarship funds in Hawaii.

2688 ■ HEALTHCARE FINANCIAL MANAGEMENT ASSOCIATION-GEORGIA CHAPTER

c/o Eddie Phillips, Awards Committee Chair
Pershing Yoakley & Associates
Two Ravinia Drive, Suite 200
Atlanta, GA 30346
Tel: (678)441-0645
Fax: (678)441-0637
E-mail: ephillips@pyapc.com
Web Site: http://www.georgiahfma.org/scholarships.asp
To provide financial assistance to members of the Georgia chapter of the Healthcare Financial Management Association (HFMA) who are planning to enter the health care financial management industry.

Title of Award: O.J. Booker Scholarship Award **Area, Field, or Subject:** Finance; Health care services; Management **Level of Education for which Award is Granted:** Master's, Undergraduate **Number Awarded:** 1 each year. **Funds Available:** The stipend is $1,500. **Duration:** 1 year.

Eligibility Requirements: This program is open to student members of the HFMA Georgia chapter who are nominated by a chapter member. Letters of nomination should include the place of employment, degree of program being pursued, and reason for nomination. Nominees must be enrolled full time in a program to prepare for a career in the health care financial management industry. **Additional Information:** This program was established in 1987.

2689 ■ HEALTHCARE FINANCIAL MANAGEMENT ASSOCIATION-INDIANA PRESSLER MEMORIAL CHAPTER

Attn: Sarah Killion, Administrative Assistant
9041 Colgate Street
Indianapolis, IN 46268-1210

Tel: (317)471-8608
Fax: (317)872-0795
E-mail: skillion2@comcast.net
Web Site: http://www.hfma-indiana.org
To provide financial assistance to members of the Healthcare Financial Management Association (HFMA) in Indiana and their families who are interested in attending college to prepare for a career in the health care field.

Title of Award: Indiana Pressler Memorial Chapter HFMA Healthcare Educational Scholarship **Area, Field, or Subject:** Health care services **Level of Education for which Award is Granted:** Undergraduate **Number Awarded:** 1 or more each year. **Funds Available:** The stipend is $1,000. Funds are paid directly to the recipient. **Duration:** 1 year.

Eligibility Requirements: This program is open to HFMA members in Indiana, their spouses, and their children. Applicants must be enrolled or planning to enroll at a postsecondary institution to prepare for a career in a field related to health care. They must have a GPA of 3.0 or higher. Along with their application, they must submit a 500-word essay on how their career objectives relate to the field of health care. **Deadline for Receipt:** February of each year.

2690 ■ HEALTHCARE FINANCIAL MANAGEMENT ASSOCIATION-NEW HAMPSHIRE/VERMONT CHAPTER

c/o Sperry Wilson Kelley
Sperry Small Business Services
220 Vermont Route 132
P.O. Box 237
South Strafford, VT 05070
Tel: (802)765-4556
E-mail: sperrysbs@aol.com
Web Site: http://www.nhvthfma.org
To provide financial assistance to members of the New Hampshire/Vermont chapter of the Healthcare Financial Management Association (HFMA) who are working on a degree in health care financial management.

Title of Award: New Hampshire/Vermont Chapter HFMA Continuing Education Scholarship **Area, Field, or Subject:** Finance; Health care services; Management **Level of Education for which Award is Granted:** Master's, Undergraduate **Number Awarded:** 2 each year. **Funds Available:** The maximum stipend is $1,000. Funds are paid directly to the school. **Duration:** Funding is provided for 1 course; recipients may apply for support for 1 additional course if they earn a GPA of 3.0 or higher for the first course.

Eligibility Requirements: This program is open to chapter members who are enrolled in a bachelor's or master's program at an accredited college or university in the field of health care finance or administration. Applicants must have accumulated at least 40 founders award points. They may only apply for 1 course per college term. Along with their application, they must submit a description of their financial need, the benefit they will receive by attending the course, their desire to further their education, and anything else they feel is important. The program in which they wish to enroll may be located in any state. **Deadline for Receipt:** October or May of each year. **Additional Information:** Information is also available from Thomas Lenkowski, Scholarship Committee Chair, (802) 447-5011, E-mail: link@phin.org.

2691 ■ HEALTHCARE FINANCIAL MANAGEMENT ASSOCIATION-TENNESSEE CHAPTER

c/o Lee Ann Burney, President
Ardent Health Services
One Burton Hills Boulevard, Suite 250
Nashville, TN 37215
Tel: (615)296-3286
Fax: (615)296-6286
E-mail: leeann.burney@ardenthealth.com
Web Site: http://www.tnhfma.org
To provide financial assistance for undergraduate study of healthcare finance to members of the Healthcare Financial Management Association (HMFA) and their families in Tennessee.

Title of Award: Gloria Adams Memorial Scholarship **Area, Field, or Subject:** Finance; Health care services **Level of Education for which Award is Granted:** Undergraduate **Number Awarded:** 1 each year. **Funds Available:** The stipend is $1,000. **Duration:** 1 year.

Eligibility Requirements: This program is open to HFMA members in Tennessee and their children and grandchildren. Applicants must be high school seniors or college students enrolled or planning to enroll as a full-time student at an accredited college, university, or trade school to study healthcare finance or a related field. **Deadline for Receipt:** February or July of each year. **Additional Information:** Information is also available from Deborah Barksdale, Scholarship Committee Chair, BMHCC Physician Development Department, 350 North Humphreys Boulevard, Memphis, TN 38120, E-mail: deborah.barksdale@bmhcc.org.

2692 ■ HEALTHCARE FINANCIAL MANAGEMENT ASSOCIATION-VIRGINIA CHAPTER
c/o Herbert D. Harvey, Scholarship Committee Chair
Obici Health System
2800 Godwin Boulevard
Suffolk, VA 23435
Tel: (757)934-4642
E-mail: hharvey@obici.com
Web Site: http://www.vahfma.org
To provide financial assistance to members of the Virginia chapter of the Healthcare Financial Management Association (HFMA) who are interested in a program of continuing education.
Title of Award: Robert H. Thomas Scholarship Fund **Area, Field, or Subject:** Finance; Health care services **Level of Education for which Award is Granted:** Graduate, Professional, Undergraduate **Number Awarded:** 1 each year. **Funds Available:** The stipend is $1,000. **Duration:** 1 year.
Eligibility Requirements: This program is open to HFMA members in Virginia who are interested in working on an advanced degree, completing a certification program, taking undergraduate courses, or engaging in other educational activities to enhance their career. Selection is based primarily on a 2-page essay that describes their academic goals, how the scholarship will help them achieve those goals, and how they expect their career to be improved. **Deadline for Receipt:** April of each year.

2693 ■ HISPANIC SCHOLARSHIP FUND INSTITUTE
1001 Connecticut Avenue, N.W., Suite 632
Washington, DC 20036
Tel: (202)296-0009
Fax: (202)296-3633
E-mail: info@hsfi.org
Web Site: http://www.hsfi.org/scholarships/energy.asp
To provide financial assistance to Hispanic undergraduate students majoring in designated business, engineering, and science fields related to the U.S. Department of Energy (DOE) goals of environmental restoration and waste management.
Title of Award: Environmental Management Scholarship **Area, Field, or Subject:** Business administration; Chemistry; Computer and information sciences; Engineering, Agricultural; Engineering, Civil; Engineering, Electrical; Engineering, Industrial; Engineering, Mechanical; Engineering, Metallurgical; Engineering, Petroleum; Environmental science; Epidemiology; Geology; Hydrology; Management; Mathematics and mathematical sciences; Physics; Radiology; Toxicology **Level of Education for which Award is Granted:** Undergraduate **Number Awarded:** Varies each year. **Funds Available:** The stipend is $3,000 per year for 4-year university students or $2,000 per year for community college students. **Duration:** 1 year.
Eligibility Requirements: This program is open to U.S. citizens and permanent residents of Hispanic background who have completed at least 12 undergraduate credits with a GPA of 3.0 or higher. Applicants must be interested in preparing for a career supportive of the DOE goals of environmental restoration and waste management. Eligible academic majors are in the fields of business (management and system analysis), engineering (agricultural, chemical, civil, electrical, environmental, industrial, mechanical, metallurgical, nuclear, and petroleum), and science (applied math/physics, chemistry, computer science, ecology, environmental, epidemiology, geology, health physics, hydrology, radiochemistry, radio-ecology, and toxicology). Along with their application, they must submit a 2-page essay on 1) how their academic major, interests, and career goals correspond to environmental restoration and waste management issues; and 2) how their Hispanic background and family upbringing have influenced their academic and personal goals. Selection is based on the essay, academic record, academic plans and career goals, financial

need, commitment to DOE's goal of environmental restoration and waste management, and a letter of recommendation. **Deadline for Receipt:** March of each year. **Additional Information:** This program, which began in 1990, is sponsored by DOE's Office of Environmental Management. Recipients must enroll full time at a college or university in the United States.

2694 ■ HOPI TRIBE
Attn: Office of Education
P.O. Box 123
Kykotsmovi, AZ 86039
Tel: (928)734-3533
Free: 800-762-9630
Fax: (928)734-9575
E-mail: IPolingyumptewa@hopi.nsn.us
Web Site: http://www.hopi.nsn.us/education_htgsp.asp
To encourage Hopi students to get an undergraduate or graduate degree in an area of interest to the Hopi Tribe.
Title of Award: Hopi Tribal Priority Scholarship **Area, Field, or Subject:** Business administration; Education; Engineering; Environmental conservation; Environmental science; Health care services; Law; Medicine **Level of Education for which Award is Granted:** Four Year College, Graduate **Number Awarded:** Varies each year. **Funds Available:** The stipend covers all educational expenses. **Duration:** 1 year; may be renewed.
Eligibility Requirements: This program is open to enrolled members of the Hopi Tribe. They must be college juniors, seniors, or graduate students whose degree is in a subject area that is of priority interest to the Hopi Tribe. Those areas are law, natural resources, education, medicine, health, engineering, or business. This is a highly competitive scholarship. Selection is based on academic merit and the likelihood that the applicants will use their training and expertise for tribal goals and objectives. **Deadline for Receipt:** July of each year. **Additional Information:** Recipients must attend school on a full-time basis.

2695 ■ ILLINOIS STUDENT ASSISTANCE COMMISSION
Attn: Scholarship and Grant Services
1755 Lake Cook Road
Deerfield, IL 60015-5209
Tel: (847)948-8550
Free: 800-899-ISAC
Fax: (847)831-8549
E-mail: collegezone@isac.org
Web Site: http://www.collegezone.com
To provide scholarship/loans to college students in Illinois who are interested in training or retraining for a teaching career in academic shortage areas.
Title of Award: Illinois Future Teacher Corps Program **Area, Field, or Subject:** Education; Education, Bilingual and cross-cultural; Education, Early childhood; Education, Elementary; Education, Music; Education, Physical; Education, Secondary; Education, Special; Hearing and deafness; Visual impairment **Level of Education for which Award is Granted:** Four Year College **Number Awarded:** Varies each year, depending on the availability of funds. **Funds Available:** This program pays tuition and fees, room and board, or a commuter allowance at academic institutions in Illinois. The maximum award is $5,000 or $10,000 (and may even be increased by an additional $5,000), depending on the teaching commitment the recipient makes. Funds are paid directly to the school. This is a scholarship/loan program. Recipients must agree to teach in an Illinois public, private, or parochial preschool, elementary school, or secondary school for 1 year for each full year of assistance received. The teaching obligation must be completed within 5 years of completion of the degree or certificate program for which the scholarship was awarded. That time period may be extended if the recipient serves in the U.S. armed forces, enrolls full time in a graduate program related to teaching, becomes temporarily disabled, is unable to find employment as a teacher, or takes additional courses on at least a half-time basis to teach in a specialized teacher shortage discipline. Recipients who fail to honor this work obligation must repay the award with interest. **Duration:** 1 year; may be renewed.
Eligibility Requirements: This program is open to Illinois residents who are enrolled at the junior level or higher at an institution of higher education in the state. Applicants must be planning to prepare for a career as a

preschool, elementary, or secondary school teacher. Preference is given to students working on a degree in designated teacher shortage disciplines, making a commitment to teach at a hard-to-staff school, and/or planning to teach minority students. Recently, the teacher shortage disciplines included behavior disordered, bilingual teacher (K-12), cross categorical (seeking certification in 2 or more areas of special education), general special education (including blind and deaf specialties and early childhood special education), learning disabled, mathematics (K-12), music (K-12), physical education (K-12), reading and English language arts (K-12), and speech and language impaired. Preference is given to renewal applicants. Selection is based on cumulative GPA, expected family contribution, and minority student status. **Deadline for Receipt:** Priority consideration is given to applications submitted by February of each year. **Additional Information:** This program was formerly known as the David A. DeBolt Teacher Shortage Scholarship Program.

2696 ■ ILLINOIS STUDENT ASSISTANCE COMMISSION

Attn: Scholarship and Grant Services
1755 Lake Cook Road
Deerfield, IL 60015-5209
Tel: (847)948-8550
Free: 800-899-ISAC
Fax: (847)831-8549
E-mail: collegezone@isac.org
Web Site: http://www.collegezone.com
To provide scholarship/loans to students in Illinois who are interested in training or retraining for a career in special education.
Title of Award: Illinois Special Education Teacher Tuition Waiver Program **Area, Field, or Subject:** Disabilities; Education, Special **Level of Education for which Award is Granted:** Four Year College, Graduate, Professional **Number Awarded:** 250 each year. **Funds Available:** This program waives tuition and fees at 12 participating Illinois public 4-year universities. Recipients must agree to teach full time in a special education discipline at an Illinois public, private, or parochial school for 2 of the 5 years immediately following graduation or termination of enrollment. That teaching requirement may be postponed if the recipient serves in the U.S. armed forces, enrolls full time in a graduate or postgraduate program, becomes temporarily disabled, is unable to find employment as a teacher, or withdraws from a course of study leading to a teacher certification in special education but remains enrolled full time in another academic discipline. Participants who fail to fulfill that teaching requirement must repay the entire amount of the tuition waiver prorated to the fraction of the teaching requirement not completed, plus interest at a rate of 5% per year. **Duration:** Up to 4 continuous calendar years.
Eligibility Requirements: Eligible for support under this program are Illinois residents who are enrolled or planning to enroll in an Illinois public institution of higher education to prepare for a career as a public, private, or parochial elementary or secondary school teacher in the state. Applicants must be undergraduate or graduate students seeking certification in an area of special education. They must rank in the upper half of their Illinois high school graduating class. Current teachers who have a valid teaching certificate that is not in the discipline of special education are also eligible. **Deadline for Receipt:** February of each year. **Additional Information:** The participating universities are Chicago State University, Eastern Illinois University, Governors State University, Illinois State University, Northeastern Illinois University, Northern Illinois University, Southern Illinois University at Carbondale, Southern Illinois University at Edwardsville, University of Illinois at Chicago, University of Illinois at Springfield, University of Illinois at Urbana, and Western Illinois University.

2697 ■ INTERNATIONAL FOUNDATION FOR GENDER EDUCATION

Attn: Transgender Scholarship and Education Legacy Fund
P.O. Box 540229
Waltham, MA 02454-0229
Tel: (781)899-2212
Fax: (781)899-5703
E-mail: carrie@tself.org
Web Site: http://www.tself.org
To provide financial assistance to transgender students who are working on an undergraduate or graduate degree in the caring professions.
Title of Award: Transgender Scholarship and Education Legacy Fund Awards **Area, Field, or Subject:** Education; Health care services; Law; Religion; Social work **Level of Education for which Award is Granted:**

Graduate, Undergraduate **Number Awarded:** Varies each year; recently, 4 of these scholarships were awarded. **Funds Available:** Stipends average $2,000. Funds are paid directly to the student. **Duration:** 1 year; nonrenewable.
Eligibility Requirements: This program is open to undergraduate and graduate students who are living full time in a gender or sex role that differs from that assigned to them at birth and who are "out and proud" about their transgender identity. Applicants must be working on a degree in the helping and caring professions, including, but not limited to, social services, health care, religious instruction, education, and the law. They may be of any age or nationality, but they must be attending or planning to attend a college, university, trade school, or technical college in the United States or Canada. Selection is based on affirmation of transgender identity; demonstration of integrity and honesty; participation and leadership in community activities; service as role model, mentor, colleague, or advisor for the transgender communities; and service as transgender role model, mentor, colleague, or advisor to non-transpeople in the helping and caring professions. **Deadline for Receipt:** January of each year. **Additional Information:** This program includes the TSELF Youth Award (for applicants under 22 years of age entering their first or second year of postsecondary education); the TSELF Schools Education Award (for applicants working on a degree in education and teaching); the Lee Frances Heller Memorial Award (for Christian students or applicants who are or will be attending a college, university, or other institution for religious studies); the HIV/AIDS Prevention and Treatment Award (for applicants who have been involved in HIV/AIDS prevention, care, and treatment activities); and the Chicago Gender Society Leadership Award (for applicants who have been involved in community building activities).

2698 ■ KANSAS FEDERATION OF BUSINESS & PROFESSIONAL WOMEN'S CLUBS, INC.

Attn: Kansas BPW Educational Foundation
c/o Diane Smith, Executive Secretary
10418 Haskins
Lenexa, KS 66215-2162
E-mail: desmith@fcbankonline.com
Web Site: http://www.bpwkansas.org/bpw_foundation.htm
To provide financial assistance to residents of Kansas who are preparing for a career in a health profession in the state.
Title of Award: Elsie Borck Health Care Scholarship **Area, Field, or Subject:** Health care services **Level of Education for which Award is Granted:** Four Year College, Graduate **Number Awarded:** 1 or more each year. **Funds Available:** A stipend is awarded (amount not specified). **Duration:** 1 year.
Eligibility Requirements: This program is open to Kansas residents (men and women) who are at least a college junior and preparing to practice in a health profession in the state. Applicants must submit a 3-page personal biography in which they express their career goals, the direction they want to take in the future, their proposed field of study, their reason for selecting that field, the institutions they plan to attend and why, their circumstances for reentering school (if a factor), and what makes them uniquely qualified for this scholarship. They must also be able to document financial need. Applications must be submitted through a local organization of the sponsor. **Deadline for Receipt:** December of each year.

2699 ■ MARYLAND ASSOCIATION OF PRIVATE COLLEGES AND CAREER SCHOOLS

Attn: Scholarship Committee
3100 Dunglow Road
Baltimore, MD 21222
Tel: (410)282-4012
Fax: (410)282-4133
E-mail: mdapcs@yahoo.com
Web Site: http://www.mapccs.org/scholarships.html
To provide financial assistance to students interested in attending selected private career schools in Maryland.
Title of Award: Maryland Association of Private Colleges and Career Schools Scholarships **Area, Field, or Subject:** Broadcasting; Cosmetology; Drafting; Health care services; Mechanics and repairs; Medicine, Holistic/alternative; Secretarial sciences **Level of Education for which Award is Granted:** Vocational/Occupational **Number Awarded:** Varies each year; since the program was established in 1983, more than $3 mil-

lion in scholarships have been awarded. **Funds Available:** Individual awards range from $500 to more than $5,000. The H.R. Leslie Scholarship is $1,000. Funds must be applied for full or partial payment of tuition. Recently, a total of $164,000 was awarded. **Duration:** 1 year.

Eligibility Requirements: This program is open to high school seniors and graduates who are interested in attending a participating private career school in Maryland. Applicants should be interested in working on a degree in such business or technical areas as cosmetology, barbering, diesel mechanics, automotive technology, massage therapy, allied health, secretarial sciences, or drafting. The H.R. Leslie Scholarship is open to any student who applies to a member school. Selection is based on GPA, involvement in school and community activities, recommendations from school officials, desire, and potential to succeed in their career field. Financial need is not considered in the selection process. **Deadline for Receipt:** March of each year. **Additional Information:** The participating schools are All State Career School (Baltimore) American Beauty Academy (Wheaton), Americare School of Allied Health (Silver Spring), Avara's Academy of Hair Design (Baltimore), Baltimore School of Massage, Baltimore Studio of Hair Design, Bladensburg Barber School (Bladensburg), Broadcasting Institute of Maryland (Baltimore), Diesel Institute of America (Grantsville), Frederick School of Cosmetology (Frederick), Hair Academy (New Carrollton), Holistic Massage Training Institute (Baltimore), International Beauty School (Bel Air), Lincoln Technical Institute (Columbia), Medix School (Towson), Savage Neon (Baltimore), and Von Lee School of Aesthetics (Pikesville). Scholarships can be used only to attend the schools listed above.

2700 ■ MARYLAND HIGHER EDUCATION COMMISSION
Attn: Office of Student Financial Assistance
839 Bestgate Road, Suite 400
Annapolis, MD 21401-3013
Tel: (410)260-4574
Free: 800-974-1024
Fax: (410)974-5376
E-mail: osfamail@mhec.state.md.us
Web Site: http://www.mhec.state.md.us/financialAid/ProgramDescriptions/prog_fire.asp

To provide financial assistance for college and graduate school to fire fighters, ambulance, and rescue squad members in Maryland.

Title of Award: Maryland Fire Fighter, Ambulance, and Rescue Squad Member Tuition Reimbursement Program **Area, Field, or Subject:** Fires and fire prevention; Medical technology **Level of Education for which Award is Granted:** Graduate, Professional, Undergraduate **Number Awarded:** Varies each year. **Funds Available:** Awards provide full reimbursement of tuition charges the student has paid. **Duration:** 1 year; may be renewed if the recipient maintains satisfactory academic progress and remains enrolled in an eligible program.

Eligibility Requirements: Eligible for this support are fire fighters, ambulance, and rescue squad members who are enrolled as full-time or part-time undergraduate or graduate students at an accredited institution of higher education in Maryland in a degree or certificate program for fire service technology or emergency medical technology. Applicants must have received at least a grade of "C" in any course required for completion of their program. They must be serving a Maryland community while they are taking college courses. **Deadline for Receipt:** June of each year. **Additional Information:** Recipients must continue to serve a Maryland community for an additional year following completion of the courses.

2701 ■ MARYLAND HIGHER EDUCATION COMMISSION
Attn: Office of Student Financial Assistance
839 Bestgate Road, Suite 400
Annapolis, MD 21401-3013
Tel: (410)260-4545
Free: 800-974-1024
Fax: (410)974-5376
E-mail: osfamail@mhec.state.md.us
Web Site: http://www.mhec.state.md.us/financialAid/ProgramDescriptions/prog_scm.asp

To provide scholarship/loans to Maryland residents who wish to prepare for a teaching career.

Title of Award: Sharon Christa McAuliffe Memorial Teacher Education Award **Area, Field, or Subject:** Chemistry; Classical studies; Computer and information sciences; Earth sciences; Education; Education, English

as a second language; Education, Special; Education, Vocational-technical; Foreign languages; Geosciences; Health care services; Hearing and deafness; Mathematics and mathematical sciences; Physical sciences; Physics; Space and planetary sciences; Visual impairment **Level of Education for which Award is Granted:** Master's, Professional, Undergraduate **Number Awarded:** Varies each year. **Funds Available:** The amount of the award is based on the recipient's enrollment and housing status, to a maximum of $17,000 per year. The total amount of all state awards may not exceed the cost of attendance as determined by the school's financial aid office or $17,800, whichever is less. Following graduation, recipients must teach at a Maryland public school for 1 year for each year of financial aid received under this program. If they fail to meet that service obligation, they must repay all funds they received with interest. They must begin the service obligation within 12 months of graduation. **Duration:** 1 year; may be renewed for 1 additional year if the recipient maintains satisfactory academic progress with a cumulative GPA of 3.0 or higher and enrollment at a 2-year or 4-year Maryland college or university in an approved teacher education program.

Eligibility Requirements: This program is open to Maryland residents who are college students with at least 60 semester credit hours completed, college graduates, and teachers in a non-critical shortage area. Applicants must have a GPA of 3.0 or higher and plan to teach in a field identified as a critical shortage area. Selection is based on cumulative GPA, applicable work or volunteer experience, quality of academic background in certification field, and a writing sample. **Deadline for Receipt:** December of each year. **Additional Information:** Recently, the eligible critical shortage areas were business education, chemistry, computer science, earth and space science, English for speakers of other languages, family and consumer sciences, German, health occupations, Latin, mathematics, physical science, physics, Spanish, special education (generic infant-grade 3, generic grades 1-8, generic grades 6-adult, hearing impaired, severely and profoundly handicapped, visually impaired), and technology education.

2702 ■ MARYLAND STATE GRANGE
Attn: Master
8743 Old Kiln Road
Thurmont, MD 21788-1219
Tel: (301)447-2075
Fax: (301)447-2019
E-mail: rlt-rox@juno.com

To provide financial assistance for college or graduate school to Maryland residents who are either deaf or preparing to work with hearing-impaired people.

Title of Award: Maryland State Grange Deaf Scholarship **Area, Field, or Subject:** Education, Special; General studies/Field of study not specified; Hearing and deafness **Level of Education for which Award is Granted:** Graduate, Undergraduate **Number Awarded:** 1 or more each year. **Funds Available:** A stipend is awarded (amount not specified). **Duration:** 1 year; may be renewed if the recipient maintains a GPA of 3.0 or higher.

Eligibility Requirements: This program is open to residents of Maryland who graduated from a high school in the state and are attending college or graduate school in the state. Applicants must be 1) deaf or hearing impaired, or 2) preparing for a career working with deaf or hearing-impaired people. **Deadline for Receipt:** May of each year. **Additional Information:** Information is also available from Donna D. Wiles, Deaf Activities Director, 5543 Buffalo Road, Mount Airy, MD 21771, (301) 829-0545.

2703 ■ MEDICAL LIBRARY ASSOCIATION
Attn: Professional Development Department
65 East Wacker Place, Suite 1900
Chicago, IL 60601-7298
Tel: (312)419-9094
Fax: (312)419-8950
E-mail: mlapd2@mlahq.org
Web Site: http://www.mlanet.org/awards/grants/lindberg.html

To provide funding to scholars and students interested in conducting research in the field of health sciences librarianship.

Title of Award: Donald A.B. Lindbergh Research Fellowship **Area, Field, or Subject:** Health care services; Library and archival sciences; Medicine **Level of Education for which Award is Granted:** Graduate, Professional, Postdoctoral, Undergraduate **Number Awarded:** 1 each year. **Funds Available:** The grant is $25,000. **Duration:** 1 year.

Eligibility Requirements: This program is open to health sciences librarians, health professionals, researchers, educators, students, and administrators. Applicants must have a bachelor's, master's, or doctoral degree or be enrolled in a program leading to such a degree and demonstrate a commitment to the health sciences. They must be nominated by an institution or organization, such as a board, committee, section, or chapter of the Medical Library Association; graduate school of library and information science; library organization; or scientific academy or society. Proposals must extend the knowledge base of health sciences librarianship or improve the practice of the profession through applied research. Areas of interest include the organization, delivery, use, technology, and impact of information and knowledge on health care access and delivery, consumer use of health information, biomedical research, public health services, or education for the health professions. U.S. citizenship or permanent resident status is required. **Deadline for Receipt:** November of each year. **Additional Information:** This fellowship was first awarded in 2003. The fellowship is not designed to support research for a master's thesis or doctoral dissertation.

2704 ■ MINNESOTA TRAPPERS ASSOCIATION

c/o Deb Offerdahl
230 Second Street S.E.
Milaca, MN 56353
Tel: (320)982-1385
Web Site: http://www.mntrappers.com

To provide financial assistance for college to members of the Minnesota Trappers Association (MTA) and to other students working on a degree in a field related to natural resources.
Title of Award: Minnesota Trappers Association Scholarships **Area, Field, or Subject:** Agricultural sciences; Engineering, Agricultural; Forestry; General studies/Field of study not specified; Natural resources; Veterinary science and medicine; Wildlife conservation, management, and science; Zoology **Level of Education for which Award is Granted:** Undergraduate **Number Awarded:** 7 each year: 1 at $2,000, 2 at $1,000, 1 at $600 (the Russ Cumberland Scholarship), and 3 at $500. **Funds Available:** Stipends range from $500 to $2,000. **Duration:** 1 year.
Eligibility Requirements: This program is open to 1) MTA members working on an undergraduate degree in any field; and 2) other undergraduates working on a degree in agricultural engineering, agricultural science, forestry, natural resources, veterinary medicine, wildlife biology, or zoology. Applicants must be entering or enrolled in a 2- or 4-year program at an accredited college or university and have a college GPA of 2.5 or higher (entering freshmen must submit a transcript of their first term of college work before funds are released). **Deadline for Receipt:** June of each year. **Additional Information:** This program includes the Russ Cumberland Scholarship. Information is also available from Todd Roggenkamp, 28952 438th Lane, Palasade, MN 56373, (218) 768-2597.

2705 ■ MONTANA ACADEMY OF PHYSICIAN ASSISTANTS

c/o Penny Denning
Scholarship/Awards Committee
107 Dilworth
Glendive, MT 59330-2053
E-mail: montanapas@aapa.org
Web Site: http://www.aapa.org/mapa/students.htm

To provide financial assistance to students interested in practicing as physician assistants in Montana.
Title of Award: Montana Academy of Physician Assistants Scholarship **Area, Field, or Subject:** Medical assisting **Level of Education for which Award is Granted:** Undergraduate **Number Awarded:** 1 or more each year. **Funds Available:** A stipend is awarded (amount not specified). **Duration:** 1 year; may be renewed.
Eligibility Requirements: This program is open to students enrolled in an approved physician assistant program. Preference is given to applicants who are residents of Montana, but residents of all states are encouraged to apply. Selection is based on completeness of the application, professionalism (as demonstrated by application materials), supporting recommendation from program director, academic achievement,

financial need, and interest in primary care medicine in Montana. **Deadline for Receipt:** April of each year.

2706 ■ NATIONAL ASSOCIATION OF HEALTH SERVICES EXECUTIVES

Attn: Educational Assistance Program
8630 Fenton Street, Suite 126
Silver Spring, MD 20910
Tel: (202)628-3953
Fax: (301)588-0011
E-mail: NationalHQ@nahse.org
Web Site: http://www.nahse.org

To provide financial assistance to African Americans who are members of the National Association of Health Services Executives (NAHSE) and interested in preparing for a career in health care administration.
Title of Award: National Association of Health Services Executives Scholarship Program **Area, Field, or Subject:** Health care services; Management **Level of Education for which Award is Granted:** Graduate, Undergraduate **Funds Available:** The stipends are $2,500 per year. Funds are sent to the recipient's institution. **Duration:** 1 year.
Eligibility Requirements: This program is open to African Americans who are either enrolled or accepted in an accredited college or university program, working on a bachelor's, master's, or doctoral degree in health care administration. Applicants must have at least a 2.5 GPA (3.0 if graduate students), be members of NAHSE, and be able to demonstrate financial need. To apply, students must submit a completed application, 3 letters of recommendation, a recent resume, a 3-page essay on "the impact of the team concept approach to organizational improvement when restructuring into an urban integrated healthcare network," a copy of their most recent federal income tax return, transcripts from all colleges attended, and 2 photographs. **Deadline for Receipt:** January of each year.

2707 ■ NATIONAL FEDERATION OF THE BLIND

c/o Peggy Elliott, Scholarship Committee Chair
805 Fifth Avenue
Grinnell, IA 50112
Tel: (641)236-3366
Web Site: http://www.nfb.org/sch_intro.htm

To provide financial assistance for college or graduate school to blind students studying or planning to study law, medicine, engineering, architecture, or the natural sciences.
Title of Award: Howard Brown Rickard Scholarships **Area, Field, or Subject:** Architecture; Engineering; Law; Medicine; Natural sciences **Level of Education for which Award is Granted:** Graduate, Undergraduate **Number Awarded:** 1 each year. **Funds Available:** The stipend is $3,000. **Duration:** 1 year; recipients may resubmit applications up to 2 additional years.
Eligibility Requirements: This program is open to legally blind students who are enrolled in or planning to enroll in a full-time undergraduate or graduate course of study. Applicants must be studying or planning to study law, medicine, engineering, architecture, or the natural sciences. Selection is based on academic excellence, service to the community, and financial need. **Deadline for Receipt:** March of each year. **Additional Information:** Scholarships are awarded at the federation convention in July. Recipients attend the convention at federation expense; that funding is in addition to the scholarship grant.

2708 ■ NATIONAL FFA ORGANIZATION

Attn: Scholarship Office
6060 FFA Drive
P.O. Box 68960
Indianapolis, IN 46268-0960
Tel: (317)802-4321
Fax: (317)802-5321
E-mail: scholarships@ffa.org
Web Site: http://www.ffa.org

To provide financial assistance to FFA members who are interested in studying animal science or a related field in college.
Title of Award: Bayer Animal Health Scholarship **Area, Field, or Subject:** Animal science and behavior; Equine studies; Veterinary science and medicine **Level of Education for which Award is Granted:** Four Year College **Number Awarded:** 5 each year. **Funds Available:** The stipend is $1,000 per year. Funds are paid directly to the recipient. **Duration:** 1 year; nonrenewable.

Eligibility Requirements: This program is open to members who are graduating high school seniors planning to enroll full time in college. Applicants must be interested in working on a 4-year degree in animal or pre-veterinary science, equine science, animal nutrition, or animal pathology. They must have a GPA of 3.0 or higher. Selection is based on academic achievement (10 points for GPA, 10 points for SAT or ACT score, 10 points for class rank), leadership in FFA activities (30 points), leadership in community activities (10 points), and participation in the Supervised Agricultural Experience (SAE) program (30 points). U.S. citizenship is required. **Deadline for Receipt:** February of each year. **Additional Information:** Funding for this program is provided by Bayer Animal Health.

2709 ■ NATIONAL FFA ORGANIZATION
Attn: Scholarship Office
6060 FFA Drive
P.O. Box 68960
Indianapolis, IN 46268-0960
Tel: (317)802-4321
Fax: (317)802-5321
E-mail: scholarships@ffa.org
Web Site: http://www.ffa.org
To provide financial assistance to FFA members interested in studying dairy science in college.
Title of Award: NMC Scholarship **Area, Field, or Subject:** Animal science and behavior; Dairy science; Veterinary science and medicine **Level of Education for which Award is Granted:** Undergraduate **Number Awarded:** 1 each year. **Funds Available:** The stipend is $1,000 per year. Funds are paid directly to the recipient. **Duration:** 1 year; nonrenewable.
Eligibility Requirements: This program is open to members who are either graduating high school seniors planning to enroll full time in college or students already enrolled in college on a full-time basis. Applicants must be working on or planning to work on a 2-year or 4-year degree in dairy science, animal science, or pre-veterinary science. They must have a dairy background or be planning to prepare for a career related to dairy. Selection is based on academic achievement (10 points for GPA, 10 points for SAT or ACT score, 10 points for class rank), leadership in FFA activities (30 points), leadership in community activities (10 points), and participation in the Supervised Agricultural Experience (SAE) program (30 points). U.S. citizenship is required. **Deadline for Receipt:** February of each year. **Additional Information:** Funding for this scholarship is provided by NMC (formerly the National Mastitis Council).

2710 ■ NATIONAL FFA ORGANIZATION
Attn: Scholarship Office
6060 FFA Drive
P.O. Box 68960
Indianapolis, IN 46268-0960
Tel: (317)802-4321
Fax: (317)802-5321
E-mail: scholarships@ffa.org
Web Site: http://www.ffa.org
To provide financial assistance to FFA members interested in studying agriculture in college.
Title of Award: Purina Mills/Land O'Lakes Purina Feeds Dealer Scholarships **Area, Field, or Subject:** Agricultural sciences; Animal science and behavior; Equine studies; Veterinary science and medicine; Wildlife conservation, management, and science **Level of Education for which Award is Granted:** Four Year College **Number Awarded:** Varies each year, depending on the number of participating Purina dealers. **Funds Available:** The stipend is $1,000 per year. Funds are paid directly to the recipient. **Duration:** 1 year; nonrenewable.
Eligibility Requirements: This program is open to members who are graduating high school seniors planning to enroll full time in college. Applicants must be interested in working on a 4-year college degree in agriculture. Preference is given to applicants displaying an interest in animal nutrition, aquaculture, animal science, equine science, wildlife management, or specialty animals. Selection is based on academic achievement (10 points for GPA, 10 points for SAT or ACT score, 10 points for class rank), leadership in FFA activities (30 points), leadership in community activities (10 points), and participation in the Supervised Agricultural Experience (SAE) program (30 points). U.S. citizenship is required. **Deadline for Receipt:** February of each year. **Additional**

Information: Funding for these scholarships is provided by Purina Mills, LLC.

2711 ■ NATIONAL FFA ORGANIZATION
Attn: Scholarship Office
6060 FFA Drive
P.O. Box 68960
Indianapolis, IN 46268-0960
Tel: (317)802-4321
Fax: (317)802-5321
E-mail: scholarships@ffa.org
Web Site: http://www.ffa.org
To provide financial assistance for college to FFA members from Idaho who have a dairy background.
Title of Award: United Dairymen of Idaho Scholarships **Area, Field, or Subject:** Animal science and behavior; Dairy science; Veterinary science and medicine **Level of Education for which Award is Granted:** Undergraduate **Number Awarded:** 3 each year. **Funds Available:** The stipend is $1,600 per year. Funds are paid directly to the recipient. **Duration:** 1 year; nonrenewable.
Eligibility Requirements: This program is open to members who are graduating high school seniors planning to enroll full time in college. Applicants must be residents of Idaho who live or work on a dairy farm. They must be interested in working on a 2- or 4-year degree in dairy science, dairy-related crop sciences, large animal nutrition, or large animal veterinarian. Selection is based on academic achievement (10 points for GPA, 10 points for SAT or ACT score, 10 points for class rank), leadership in FFA activities (30 points), leadership in community activities (10 points), and participation in the Supervised Agricultural Experience (SAE) program (30 points). U.S. citizenship is required. **Deadline for Receipt:** February of each year. **Additional Information:** Funding for these scholarships is provided by United Dairymen of Idaho.

2712 ■ NATIONAL FFA ORGANIZATION
Attn: Scholarship Office
6060 FFA Drive
P.O. Box 68960
Indianapolis, IN 46268-0960
Tel: (317)802-4321
Fax: (317)802-5321
E-mail: scholarships@ffa.org
Web Site: http://www.ffa.org
To provide financial assistance to FFA members from designated states who are interested in studying a field related to agriculture in college.
Title of Award: Wilbur-Ellis Company Scholarships **Area, Field, or Subject:** Agribusiness; Agricultural sciences; Agriculture, Economic aspects; Animal science and behavior; Biochemistry; Business administration; Computer and information sciences; Entomology; Finance; Forestry; Genetics; Horticulture; Management; Marketing and distribution; Poultry science; Soil science **Level of Education for which Award is Granted:** Four Year College **Number Awarded:** 13 each year: 1 at $5,000, 2 at $2,000, and 10 at $1,000. **Funds Available:** Stipends are $5,000, $2,000, or $1,000 per year. Funds are paid directly to the recipient. **Duration:** 1 year; nonrenewable.
Eligibility Requirements: This program is open to members who are graduating high school seniors planning to enroll or college students currently enrolled full time. Applicants must be residents of the following states: Arizona, California, Idaho, Indiana, Michigan, Minnesota, Montana, New Mexico, North Dakota, Ohio, Oregon, South Dakota, Texas, Utah, Washington, Wisconsin, or Wyoming. They must be planning to work on a 4-year degree in agricultural production, forest management, agronomy and crop science, animal nutrition, farm and ranch management, horticulture, nursery and landscape management, plant science, poultry science, general agriculture, business management, economics, international agriculture, finance, sales and marketing, biochemistry, biotechnology, computer systems in agriculture, entomology, plant breeding and genetics, plant pathology, range science, or soil science. Their combined SAT score must be 1000 or higher and their GPA must be 3.0 or higher. Selection is based on academic achievement (10 points for GPA, 10 points for SAT or ACT score, 10 points for class rank), leadership in FFA activities (30 points), leadership in community activities (10 points), and participation in the Supervised Agricultural Experience (SAE) program (30 points). Financial need is also considered in the selection process.

U.S. citizenship is required. **Deadline for Receipt:** February of each year.
Additional Information: Funding for this scholarship is provided by the agriculture division of the Wilbur-Ellis Company.

2713 ■ NATIONAL INSTITUTE OF ALLERGY AND INFECTIOUS DISEASES

Attn: Office of Special Populations
6700-B Rockledge Drive, Room 2133
Bethesda, MD 20892-7610
Tel: (301)486-8697
Fax: (301)496-8729
E-mail: mh35c@nih.gov
Web Site: http://www.niaid.nih.gov/ncn/training/minor.htm

To provide funding to principal investigators on grants from the National Institute of Allergy and Infectious Diseases (NIAID) who wish to include underrepresented minority high school and undergraduate students as research assistants on their project.

Title of Award: Richard M. Asofsky Scholars in Research Awards **Area, Field, or Subject:** Biomedical sciences **Level of Education for which Award is Granted:** Four Year College, Postdoctoral **Number Awarded:** Varies each year. **Funds Available:** Supplements for high school students are limited to $3,000 per student in direct costs; students are reimbursed at the rate of $6.25 per hour. Supplements for undergraduates include salary for the student that is consistent with the institution's policies plus up to $200 per month for supplies and travel. from the student's academic institution to the National Institutes of Health (NIH) in Bethesda, Maryland. Graduate students also receive a salary. **Duration:** Student assistants may be recruited to work up to 2 years.
Eligibility Requirements: This program is open to principal investigators who have an active grant from NIAID with at least 2 years or more of support remaining. Applicants must be seeking supplemental funding to hire underrepresented minority students, defined as individuals belonging to a particular ethnic or racial group that the grantee institution has determined to be underrepresented in the biomedical, behavioral, clinical, or social sciences. High school students must have expressed an interest in the health-related sciences and have passed advanced science courses. Undergraduate students must have expressed an interest in biomedical research and a desire to pursue graduate training. The proposed research experience must be an integral part of the approved ongoing grant and have the potential to contribute significantly to the research career development of the student. The program encourages partnerships between NIAID grantees at major universities and local community colleges, tribal colleges, Historically Black Colleges and Universities (HBCUs), Hispanic Serving Institutions (HSIs), and colleges and universities where Native American populations are high. **Additional Information:** This program originated in 1979 as the Introduction to Biomedical Research Program (IBRP). That program was restructured in 2003 to encompass this program and the Intramural NIAID Research Opportunities Program.

2714 ■ NATIONAL INSTITUTE OF GENERAL MEDICAL SCIENCES

Attn: Division of Minority Opportunities in Research
45 Center Drive, Suite 2AS37
Bethesda, MD 20892-6200
Tel: (301)594-3900
Fax: (301)480-2753
E-mail: at21z@nih.gov
Web Site: http://www.nih.gov/nigms

To enable faculty at minority and minority-serving institutions to complete a Ph.D. degree in the biomedical sciences.

Title of Award: Minority Access to Research Careers (MARC) Faculty Predoctoral Fellowships **Area, Field, or Subject:** Behavioral sciences; Biomedical sciences; Mathematics and mathematical sciences **Level of Education for which Award is Granted:** Four Year College, Professional, Doctorate **Funds Available:** The fellowships provide a stipend of $32,820 per year and a supplement that offsets the cost of tuition, fees, and health insurance at a rate of 100% up to $3,000 and 60% of costs above $3,000. An institutional allowance of $2,750 per year is also provided. **Duration:** Up to 5 years.
Eligibility Requirements: This program is open to full-time faculty in a biomedical or behavioral science department (including mathematics) at minority and minority-serving institutions who lack a Ph.D. degree. The institution must be a college or university where the candidate has been

employed for at least 3 years and that has substantial enrollments of students in biomedical and related sciences from minority groups underrepresented in those sciences. The candidate must have been accepted into the doctoral program at a research university, institution, or center with active biomedical and behavioral science research faculties. They must be sponsored by their home institution, which must have granted them a study leave and where they are expected to return after completing their doctoral degree. Only U.S. citizens, nationals, and permanent residents are eligible. **Deadline for Receipt:** April or December of each year.

2715 ■ NATIONAL INSTITUTES OF HEALTH

Attn: Office of Loan Repayment and Scholarship
2 Center Drive, Room 2E24
Bethesda, MD 20892-0230
800-528-7689
Fax: (301)480-5481
E-mail: ugsp@nih.gov
Web Site: http://ugsp.info.nih.gov

To provide loans-for-service for undergraduate education in the life sciences to students from disadvantaged backgrounds.

Title of Award: National Institutes of Health Undergraduate Scholarship Program **Area, Field, or Subject:** Behavioral sciences; Biomedical sciences; Social sciences **Level of Education for which Award is Granted:** Undergraduate **Number Awarded:** 15 each year. **Funds Available:** Stipends are available up to $20,000 per year, to be used for tuition, educational expenses (such as books and lab fees), and qualified living expenses while attending a college or university. Recipients incur a service obligation to work as an employee of the NIH in Bethesda, Maryland for 10 consecutive weeks (during the summer) during the sponsored year and, upon graduation, for 52 weeks for each academic year of scholarship support. The NIH 52-week employment obligation may be deferred if the recipient goes to graduate or medical school. **Duration:** 1 year; may be renewed for up to 3 additional years.
Eligibility Requirements: This program is open to U.S. citizens, nationals, and permanent residents who are enrolled or accepted for enrollment as full-time students at accredited institutions of higher education and committed to careers in biomedical, behavioral, and social science health-related research. Applicants must come from a family that meets federal standards of low income, currently defined as a family with an annual income below $18,620 for a 1-person family, ranging to below $63,140 for families of 8 or more. They must have a GPA of 3.5 or higher or be in the top 5% of their class. Selection is based on commitment to a career in biomedical, behavioral, or social science health-related research as an employee of the National Institutes of Health (NIH); academic achievements; recommendations and evaluations of skills, abilities, and goals; and relevant extracurricular activities. Applicants are ranked according to the following priorities: first, juniors and seniors who have completed 2 years of undergraduate course work including 4 core science courses in biology, chemistry, physics, and calculus; second, other undergraduates who have completed those 4 core science courses; third, freshmen and sophomores at accredited undergraduate institutions; and fourth, high school seniors who have been accepted for enrollment as full-time students at accredited undergraduate institutions. The sponsor especially encourages applications from underrepresented minorities, women, and individuals with disabilities. **Deadline for Receipt:** February of each year.

2716 ■ NATIONAL INVENTORS HALL OF FAME

Attn: Collegiate Inventors Competition
221 South Broadway Street
Akron, OH 44308-1595
Tel: (330)849-6887
E-mail: collegiate@invent.org
Web Site: http://www.invent.org/collegiate

To recognize and reward outstanding inventions by college or university students in the fields of science, engineering, and technology.

Title of Award: Collegiate Inventors Competition **Area, Field, or Subject:** Biological and clinical sciences; Chemistry; Computer and information sciences; Engineering; Environmental conservation; Environmental science; Inventors; Mathematics and mathematical sciences; Medicine; Physics; Science; Technology; Veterinary science and medicine **Level of Education for which Award is Granted:** Graduate, Postdoctoral, Undergraduate **Number Awarded:** 15 semifinalists are selected each year; of those,

3 individuals or teams win prizes. **Funds Available:** Finalists receive an all-expense paid trip to Washington, D.C. to participate in a final round of judging and in the awards dinner and presentation. The Grand Prize winner or team receives $25,000. Other prizes are $10,000 for an undergraduate winner or team and $15,000 for a graduate winner or team. Academic advisors of the winning entries each receive a $3,000 cash prize. Awards are unrestricted cash gifts, not scholarships or grants. **Duration:** The competition is held annually.

Eligibility Requirements: This competition is open to undergraduate and graduate students who are (or have been) enrolled full time at least part of the 12-month period prior to entry in a college or university in the United States. Entries may also be submitted by teams, up to 4 members, of whom at least 1 must meet the full-time requirement and all others must have been enrolled at least half time sometime during the preceding 24-month period. Applicants must submit a description of their invention, including a patent search and summary of current literature that describes the state of the art and identifies the originality of the invention; test data demonstrating that the idea, invention, or design is workable; the societal, economic, and environmental benefits of the invention; and supplemental material that may include photos, slides, disks, videotapes, and even samples. Entries must be original ideas and the work of a student or team and a university advisor; the invention should be reproducible and may not have been 1) made available to the public as a commercial product or process, or 2) patented or published more than 1 year prior to the date of submission for this competition. Entries are first reviewed by a committee of judges that selects the finalists. The committee is comprised of mathematicians, engineers, biologists, chemists, environmentalists, physicists, computer specialists, members of the medical and veterinary profession, and specialists in invention and development of technology. Entries are judged on the basis of originality, inventiveness, potential value to society (socially, environmentally, and economically), and range or scope of use. **Deadline for Receipt:** May of each year. **Additional Information:** This program is co-sponsored by Abbott Laboratories and the United States Patent and Trademark Office. It was established in 1990 as the BFGoodrich Collegiate Inventors Program.

2717 ■ NAVAL RESERVE ASSOCIATION

Attn: Educational Assistance Program
1619 King Street
Alexandria, VA 22314-2793
Tel: (703)548-5800; (866)672-4968
Fax: (866)683-3647
E-mail: admin@navy-reserve.org
Web Site: http://www.navy-reserve.org

To provide financial assistance for college to the children of members of the Naval Reserve Association.

Title of Award: Naval Reserve Association Scholarships **Area, Field, or Subject:** Engineering; General studies/Field of study not specified; Mathematics and mathematical sciences; Medicine **Level of Education for which Award is Granted:** Undergraduate **Number Awarded:** Varies each year; recently, 6 of these scholarships were awarded. **Funds Available:** The amounts of the stipends vary but recently averaged more than $4,000 per year. **Duration:** 1 year.

Eligibility Requirements: This program is open to the children of association members who are enrolled or accepted for enrollment at a college or university as a full-time student. Applicants must be U.S. citizens under 24 years of age. Preference is given to applicants who have demonstrated an interest in the "hard sciences" (e.g., mathematics, medicine, and engineering). **Deadline for Receipt:** April of each year.

2718 ■ NAVY WIVES CLUB OF AMERICA

P.O. Box 54022
Millington, TN 38053-6022
(866)511-NWCA
E-mail: nwca@navywivesclubsofamerica.org
Web Site: http://www.navywivesclubsofamerica.org/nwc/scholarships.htm

To provide financial assistance for college or medical school to the children of naval personnel.

Title of Award: Navy Wives Club of America National Scholarships **Area, Field, or Subject:** Education, Special; General studies/Field of study not specified; Medicine **Level of Education for which Award is Granted:** Doctorate, Undergraduate **Number Awarded:** 41 each year: 6 to freshmen, 18 for renewals, 4 to current undergraduates applying for the first

time, 2 to medical students, 2 to students majoring in special education, and 9 to children of NWCA members. **Funds Available:** The stipend is $1,500. **Duration:** 1 year; may be renewed up to 3 additional years.

Eligibility Requirements: Applicants for these scholarships must be the children (natural born, legally adopted, or stepchildren) of enlisted members of the Navy, Marine Corps, or Coast Guard on active duty, retired with pay, or deceased. Applicants must be attending or planning to attend an accredited college or university. Along with their application, they must submit an essay on their career objectives and the reasons they chose those objectives. Selection is based on academic standing, moral character, and financial need. Some scholarships are reserved for students majoring in special education, medical students, and children of members of Navy Wives Club of American (NWCA). **Deadline for Receipt:** May of each year. **Additional Information:** Information is also available from the NWCA Scholarship Foundation Director, Susan Quinn, 1644A Jana Court, Norfolk, VA 23503. Membership in the NWCA is open to spouses of enlisted personnel serving in the Navy, Marine Corps, Coast Guard, and the active Reserve units of those services; spouses of enlisted personnel who have been honorable discharged, retired, or transferred to the Fleet Reserve on completion of duty; and widows of enlisted personnel in those services.

2719 ■ NEW JERSEY TRANSPLANT ASSOCIATION

841 Mountain Avenue
Springfield, NJ 07081-3437
Tel: (973)912-8119
Fax: (973)912-9056
E-mail: njtascholarship@verizon.net

To provide financial assistance for college to New Jersey high school seniors who have involved in organ transplant activities.

Title of Award: New Jersey Transplant Association Scholarships **Area, Field, or Subject:** General studies/Field of study not specified; Medicine **Level of Education for which Award is Granted:** Undergraduate **Number Awarded:** 3 each year. **Funds Available:** The stipend is $2,000. **Duration:** 1 year.

Eligibility Requirements: This program is open to seniors graduating from high schools in New Jersey and planning to attend college. Applicants must have been active in organ donor awareness, a transplant donor, an immediate family member of a donor, a transplant recipient, or a transplant candidate. They must be in the top 50% of their class. Along with their application, they must submit 3 letters of recommendation, a transcript, SAT or ACT scores, and an essay about organ transplantation. Special consideration is given to applicants planning to prepare for a career in a medical field. **Deadline for Receipt:** March of each year.

2720 ■ NEW MEXICO ELKS ASSOCIATION

Attn: Charitable and Benevolent Trust Commission
c/o Jim Larrabee, Scholarship Committee
302 Ciniza Court
Gallup, NM 87301
Fax: (505)863-3821
E-mail: JimLarrabee@cnetco.com
Web Site: http://www.nmelks.org

To provide financial assistance to high school seniors in New Mexico who are interested in preparing for a career working with people with disabilities.

Title of Award: Ed Harbaugh Memorial Scholarship **Area, Field, or Subject:** Disabilities **Level of Education for which Award is Granted:** Undergraduate **Number Awarded:** 1 or more each year. **Funds Available:** A stipend is awarded, generally either $1,000 or $2,000. **Duration:** 1 year.

Eligibility Requirements: Applicants must be seniors graduating from a high school in New Mexico. They must be interested in majoring in college in the fields of speech or physical therapy, or in any other field that would aid individuals with disabilities. In addition, they must have exhibited outstanding scholastic and leadership ability, including extracurricular and civic activities. High school class rank, GPA, and standardized test scores must be validated by a school official. An endorsement from the local Elks

Lodge is required. Financial need is also considered in the selection process. **Deadline for Receipt:** March of each year.

2721 ■ NORTON SOUTH HEALTH CORPORATION

Attn: Scholarships
P.O. Box 966
Nome, AK 99762
Tel: (907)443-4530
Fax: (907)443-2085
E-mail: info@nortonsoundhealth.org
Web Site: http://www.nortonsoundhealth.org
To provide financial assistance to Native and other residents of Alaska who are interested in working on an undergraduate or graduate degree in a health-related field.
Title of Award: Norton South Health Corporation Scholarships **Area, Field, or Subject:** Health care services **Level of Education for which Award is Granted:** Graduate, Undergraduate **Number Awarded:** Varies each year. **Funds Available:** A stipend is awarded (amount not specified). **Duration:** 1 year; may be renewed if the recipient maintains full-time enrollment and a GPA of 2.5 or higher.
Eligibility Requirements: This program is open to students enrolled in or planning to enrolled in an undergraduate or graduate program in a field of study relevant to employment at Norton Sound Health Corporation (NSHC). Priority is given to applicants in the following order: 1) Native residents of the Bering Straits region of Alaska; 2) Native residents of other regions of Alaska; and 3) non-Native residents of the Bering Straits region. They must submit brief statements on their educational goals and objectives, the activities in which they are currently participating, their community activities, and honors or awards they have received. Financial need is also considered in the selection process. **Deadline for Receipt:** April of each year for fall terms; November of each year for spring terms. **Additional Information:** The Norton Sound Health Corporation was founded in 1970 to serve the health care need of the Inupiat, Yupik, and Siberian Yupik people of the Bering Straits region of northwest Alaska.

2722 ■ OMAHA VOLUNTEERS FOR HANDICAPPED CHILDREN

c/o Lois Carlson
2010 Country Club Avenue
Omaha, NE 68104
Tel: (402)553-0378
To provide financial assistance for college to Nebraska residents who have a physical disability or are preparing for a career related to people with orthopedic impairments or physical disabilities.
Title of Award: Omaha Volunteers for Handicapped Children Scholarships **Area, Field, or Subject:** Disabilities; Education, Special; General studies/Field of study not specified **Level of Education for which Award is Granted:** Undergraduate **Number Awarded:** 5 to 10 each year. **Funds Available:** The stipend is $1,000 per year. **Duration:** 1 year; may be renewed.
Eligibility Requirements: This program is open to residents of Nebraska who are U.S. citizens. First priority applicants must have an orthopedic impairment or physical disability and be 1) high school seniors with a GPA of 2.25 or higher and accepted into the school of their choice or 2) college students making satisfactory progress toward graduation. Second priority applicants must be enrolled in the college of their choice and preparing for a teaching or health-related career of service to people with orthopedic impairments or physical disabilities. All applicants must submit a 250-word essay on their future goals and need for the scholarship. **Deadline for Receipt:** July of each year.

2723 ■ JOANNA F. REED MEDICAL SCHOLARSHIP TRUST

c/o South Alabama Trust Company
227 Belleville Avenue
P.O. Box 469
Brewton, AL 36427-0469
Tel: (251)809-2239
Fax: (251)809-2123
To provide financial assistance to students in Alabama and selected parts of Florida who are working on a pre-med (undergraduate) or medical (graduate) degree at a private university.
Title of Award: Joanna F. Reed Medical Scholarship **Area, Field, or Subject:** Medicine **Level of Education for which Award is Granted:** Doctorate, Undergraduate **Number Awarded:** 1 or more each year. **Funds Available:** The stipend is $7,500. **Duration:** 1 year; may renewed.

Eligibility Requirements: This program is open to men and women who are working on a degree in medicine at a recognized private medical school and to men and women who are working on an undergraduate degree in pre-medicine at a private university. They must be residents of Alabama or northwest Florida (all counties in the state west of the Apalachicola River: Escambia, Santa Rosa, Okaloosa, Walton, Homes, Washington, Bay, Jackson, Calhoun, and Gulf). They may attend school anywhere in the United States. Selection is based on academic performance, recommendations, financial need, motivation, character, ability, and career potential. Special consideration is given to students who wish to become general practitioners or internists. **Deadline for Receipt:** May of each year.

2724 ■ ROCKY MOUNTAIN NASA SPACE GRANT CONSORTIUM

c/o Utah State University
EL Building, Room 302
Logan, UT 84322-4140
Tel: (435)797-3666
Fax: (435)797-3382
E-mail: spacegrant@cc.usu.edu
Web Site: http://spacegrant.usu.edu
To provide financial support to undergraduate students at designated universities in Utah or Colorado who are working on a degree in fields of interest to the National Aeronautics and Space Administration (NASA).
Title of Award: Rocky Mountain NASA Space Grant Consortium Undergraduate Scholarships **Area, Field, or Subject:** Aerospace sciences; Engineering; Engineering, Aerospace/Aeronautical/Astronautical; Medicine; Science; Space and planetary sciences; Technology **Level of Education for which Award is Granted:** Undergraduate **Number Awarded:** Varies each year. **Funds Available:** The amount of the awards depends on the availability of funds. **Duration:** 1 year.
Eligibility Requirements: This program is open to undergraduate students at member institutions of the Rocky Mountain NASA Space Grant Consortium who are studying engineering, science, medicine, or technology. U.S. citizenship is required. Selection is based on academic performance to date and potential for the future, with emphasis on space-related research interests. This program is part of the NASA Space Grant program, which encourages participation by women, underrepresented minorities, and persons with disabilities. **Deadline for Receipt:** June of each year. **Additional Information:** Members of the consortium are Utah State University, the University of Utah, Brigham Young University, Dixie State College, Salt Lake Community College, Shoshone-Bannock School, Snow College, Southern Utah University, the University of Denver, and Weber State University. This program is funded by NASA.

2725 ■ SEALASKA CORPORATION

Attn: Sealaska Heritage Institute
One Sealaska Plaza, Suite 301
Juneau, AK 99801-1249
Tel: (907)586-9166; 888-311-4992
Fax: (907)586-9293
E-mail: scholarship@sealaska.com
Web Site: http://www.sealaskaheritage.org/programs/university_scholarships.htm
To provide financial assistance for undergraduate or graduate study to Native Alaskans who have a connection to Sealaska Corporation and are majoring in designated fields.
Title of Award: Sealaska Heritage Institute 7(i) Scholarships **Area, Field, or Subject:** Business administration; Chemistry; Engineering, Chemical; Health care services; Mathematics and mathematical sciences; Natural resources; Physics **Level of Education for which Award is Granted:** Graduate, Undergraduate **Number Awarded:** Varies each year. **Funds Available:** The amount of the award depends on the availability of funds, the number of qualified applicants, class standing, and cumulative GPA. **Duration:** 1 year; may be renewed up to 5 years for a bachelor's degree, up to 3 years for a master's degree, up to 2 years for a doctorate, or up to 3 years for vocational study. The maximum total support is limited to 9 years. Renewal depends on recipients' maintaining full-time enrollment and a GPA of 2.5 or higher.
Eligibility Requirements: This program is open to 1) Alaska Natives who are enrolled to Sealaska Corporation, and 2) Native lineal descendants of Alaska Natives enrolled to Sealaska Corporation, whether or not the applicant owns Sealaska Corporation stock. Applicants must be enrolled or

accepted for enrollment as full-time undergraduate or graduate students. Along with their application, they must submit 2 essays: 1) their personal history and educational goals, and 2) their expected contributions to the Alaska Native or Native American community. Financial need is also considered in the selection process. The following areas of study qualify for these awards: natural resources (environmental sciences, engineering, conservation biology, environmental law, fisheries, geology, marine science/biology, forestry, wildlife management, and mining technology); business administration (accounting, finance, marketing, international business, international commerce and trade, management of information systems, human resources management, economics, computer information systems, and industrial management); and other special fields (cadastral surveys, chemistry, equipment/machinery operators, industrial safety specialists, health specialists, plastics engineers, trade specialists, physics, mathematics, and marine trades and occupations). **Deadline for Receipt:** February of each year. **Additional Information:** Funding for this program is provided from Alaska Native Claims Settlement Act (ANSCA) Section 7(i) revenue sharing provisions. Sealaska sponsors a number of other scholarships, including the Cape Fox Scholarships and the Sealaska Heritage Institute Scholarships.

2726 ■ SERVICE EMPLOYEES INTERNATIONAL UNION

Attn: Education Department
1313 L Street, N.W.
Washington, DC 20005
Tel: (202)898-3326
Free: 800-448-SEIU
Fax: (202)898-3348
Web Site: http://www.seiu.org/mbe/scholarships/norapiore.cfm
To provide financial assistance for to members and children of members of the Service Employees International Union (SEIU) who plan to major in health-related fields in college.
Title of Award: Nora Piore Scholarship Program **Area, Field, or Subject:** Health care services **Level of Education for which Award is Granted:** Undergraduate **Number Awarded:** Only 1 student may hold this scholarship at a time. It is offered whenever a current recipient completes his or her training. **Funds Available:** The stipend is $4,375 per year. **Duration:** 1 year; may be renewed up to 3 additional years.
Eligibility Requirements: This program is open to members of SEIU working in health care fields and their children. Applicants must be working on or planning to work on a degree or training for an occupation in health care or health care policy. Financial need is considered in the selection process. **Deadline for Receipt:** February of the year when available. **Additional Information:** This program is administered by Scholarship Program Administrators, Inc., 1201 Eighth Avenue South, P.O. Box 23737, Nashville, TN 27202-3737, (615) 320-3149, Fax: (615) 320-3151, E-mail: info@spaprog.com.

2727 ■ SLOVAK CATHOLIC SOKOL

Attn: Membership Memorial Scholarship Fund
205 Madison Street
P.O. Box 899
Passaic, NJ 07055-0899
Tel: (973)777-2605
Free: 800-886-7656
Fax: (973)779-8245
E-mail: sokol205@aol.com
Web Site: http://www.slovakcatholicsokol.org/members/scholarships.htm
To provide financial assistance for college or graduate school to members of the Slovak Catholic Sokol.
Title of Award: Theodore and Mary Jane Rich Scholarships **Area, Field, or Subject:** Medicine **Level of Education for which Award is Granted:** Graduate, Undergraduate **Number Awarded:** 2 each year: 1 for a male and 1 for a female. **Funds Available:** The stipend is $2,500 per year. **Duration:** 1 year; may be renewed 1 additional year.
Eligibility Requirements: This program is open to members of the Slovak Catholic Sokol who have completed at least 1 semester of college and are currently enrolled full time as an undergraduate or graduate student at an accredited college, university, or professional school. Applicants must have been a member for at least 5 years, have at least $3,000 permanent life insurance coverage, and have at least 1 parent who is a member and is of Slovak ancestry. They must be majoring in a medical program. Males and females compete for scholarships separately.

Deadline for Receipt: February of each year. **Additional Information:** Slovak Catholic Sokol was founded as a fraternal benefit society in 1905. It is licensed to operate in the following states: Connecticut, Illinois, Indiana, Massachusetts, Michigan, New Jersey, New York, Ohio, Pennsylvania, and Wisconsin. This program was established in 2003.

2728 ■ SOCIETY OF NUCLEAR MEDICINE

Attn: Committee on Awards
1850 Samuel Morse Drive
Reston, VA 20190-5316
Tel: (703)708-9000
Fax: (703)708-9020
E-mail: grantinfo@snm.org
Web Site: http://www.snm.org
To provide financial support to students seeking training in nuclear medicine technology.
Title of Award: Paul Cole Scholarship Award **Area, Field, or Subject:** Medical technology **Level of Education for which Award is Granted:** Undergraduate **Number Awarded:** Varies each year; recently, 30 of these scholarships were awarded. **Funds Available:** The stipend is $1,000. **Duration:** 1 year.
Eligibility Requirements: This program is open to students in baccalaureate, associate, or certificate programs in nuclear medicine technology. Applicants must have a cumulative GPA of 2.5 or higher. Selection is based on financial need and academic achievement. **Deadline for Receipt:** October of each year.

2729 ■ SOCIETY OF NUCLEAR MEDICINE

Attn: Committee on Awards
1850 Samuel Morse Drive
Reston, VA 20190-5316
Tel: (703)708-9000
Fax: (703)708-9020
E-mail: grantinfo@snm.org
Web Site: http://www.snm.org
To provide financial support to minority students working on an associate or bachelor's degree in nuclear medicine technology.
Title of Award: PDEF Mickey Williams Minority Student Scholarship **Area, Field, or Subject:** Medical technology **Level of Education for which Award is Granted:** Undergraduate **Number Awarded:** 1 each year. **Funds Available:** The stipend is $5,000. **Duration:** 1 year; may be renewed for 1 additional year.
Eligibility Requirements: This program is open to students accepted or enrolled in a baccalaureate or associate degree program in nuclear medicine technology. Applicants must be members of a minority group: African American, Native American (including American Indian, Eskimo, Hawaiian, and Samoan), Hispanic American, Asian American, or Pacific Islander. They must have a cumulative GPA of 2.5 or higher and be able to demonstrate financial need. U.S. citizenship or permanent resident status is required. **Deadline for Receipt:** October of each year. **Additional Information:** This program is supported by corporate sponsors of the Professional Development and Education Fund (PDEF) of the Society of Nuclear Medicine Technologist Section.

2730 ■ TEXAS ASSOCIATION OF CLINICAL LABORATORY SCIENCES

c/o Cindy Martine
1222 Harris Way
Galveston, TX 77555
E-mail: camartin@utmb.edu
Web Site: http://www.tacls.org
To provide financial assistance to undergraduate and graduate students from Texas who are working on a degree in laboratory medicine.
Title of Award: Texas Association of Clinical Laboratory Sciences Scholarships **Area, Field, or Subject:** Medical technology **Level of Education for which Award is Granted:** Graduate, Undergraduate **Number Awarded:** 1 or more each year. **Funds Available:** A stipend is awarded (amount not specified). **Duration:** 1 year.
Eligibility Requirements: This program is open to residents of Texas who are members of the Texas Association of Clinical Laboratory Sciences (TACLS), achieved through membership in the American Society for Clinical Laboratory Science (ASCLS). Applicants must be 1) full-time students enrolled or accepted at an accredited program in clinical labora-

tory technology/medical laboratory technology or clinical laboratory science/medical technology; or 2) full-time graduate students enrolled in a degree plan directly related to laboratory medicine. They must have a GPA of 2.8 or higher. **Deadline for Receipt:** March of each year.

2731 ■ TEXAS HIGHER EDUCATION COORDINATING BOARD

Attn: Grants and Special Programs
1200 East Anderson Lane
P.O. Box 12788, Capitol Station
Austin, TX 78711-2788
Tel: (512)427-6367
Free: 800-242-3062
Fax: (512)427-6127
E-mail: grantinfo@thecb.state.tx.us
Web Site: http://www.collegefortexans.com
To provide financial assistance to residents of Texas who are interested in training as an emergency medical technician (EMT) and working in a rural community in the state.
Title of Award: Texas Rural Emergency Medical Services Scholarship Incentive Program **Area, Field, or Subject:** Medicine **Level of Education for which Award is Granted:** Undergraduate **Number Awarded:** Varies each year. **Funds Available:** This program provides up to $2,000 in matching funds towards the costs of tuition and other expenses associated with EMT, EMT-I, and EMT-P training. **Duration:** 1 year.
Eligibility Requirements: This program is open to Texas residents who are at least 18 years of age and have a high school diploma or GED certificate. Applicants must be interested in obtaining training as an EMT, EMT-I (must already have a license as an EMT), or EMT-P (must already have a license as an EMT-I). Applicants must enter into a contract with a community in a rural country in Texas to provide emergency medical services upon completion of their training for at least 1 year. The community must commit to raising funds to match the amount provided by this program. **Additional Information:** This program is offered in cooperation with the Office of Rural Community Affairs (ORCA), Attn: Texas Health Service Corps, 1700 North Congress, Suite 220, P.O. Box 12877, Austin, TX 78711, (512) 936-6701, (800) 544-2042, Fax: (512) 936-6776, E-mail: orca@orca.state.tx.us.

2732 ■ MORRIS K. UDALL FOUNDATION

130 South Scott Avenue
Tucson, AZ 85701-1922
Tel: (520)670-5529
Fax: (520)670-5530
Web Site: http://www.udall.gov/scholarship
To provide financial assistance to 1) college sophomores and juniors who intend to prepare for a career in environmental public policy and 2) Native American and Alaska Native students who intend to prepare for a career in health care or tribal public policy.
Title of Award: Morris K. Udall Scholarships **Area, Field, or Subject:** Business administration; Economics; Education; Environmental conservation; Environmental science; Health care services; Native American studies; Natural resources; Political science; Public administration; Public health; Urban affairs/design/planning **Level of Education for which Award is Granted:** Undergraduate **Number Awarded:** Approximately 80 scholarships and 50 honorable mentions are awarded each year. **Funds Available:** The maximum stipend for scholarship winners is $5,000 per year. Funds are to be used for tuition, fees, books, and room and board. Honorable mention stipends are $350. **Duration:** 1 year; recipients nominated as sophomores may be renominated in their junior year.
Eligibility Requirements: Each 2-year and 4-year college and university in the United States and its possessions may nominate up to 6 sophomores or juniors from either or both categories of this program: 1) students who intend to prepare for a career in environmental public policy, and 2) Native American and Alaska Native students who intend to prepare for a career in health care or tribal public policy. For the first category, the program seeks future leaders across a wide spectrum of environmental fields, such as policy, engineering, science, education, urban planning and renewal, business, health, justice, and economics. For the second category, the program seeks future Native American and Alaska Native leaders in public and community health care, tribal government, and public policy affecting Native American communities, including land and resource management, economic development, and education. Nominees must be U.S. citizens, nationals, or permanent residents with a GPA of 3.0

or higher. Along with their application, they must submit an 800-word essay discussing a significant public speech, legislative act, or public policy statement by former Congressman Morris K. Udall and its impact on their field of study, interests, and career goals. Selection is based on demonstrated commitment to 1) environmental issues through substantial commitment to and participation in 1 or more of the following: campus activities, research, community service, or public service; or 2) tribal public policy or Native American health through substantial contributions to and participation in 1 or more of the following: campus activities, tribal involvement, community or public service, or research; a course of study and proposed career likely to lead to position where nominee can make significant contributions to the shaping of environmental, tribal public policy, or Native American health care issues, whether through scientific advances, public or political service, or community action; and leadership, character, desire to make a difference, and general well-roundedness. **Deadline for Receipt:** Faculty representatives must submit their nominations by early March of each year.

2733 ■ UNITED DAUGHTERS OF THE CONFEDERACY-VIRGINIA DIVISION

c/o Suzie Snyder, Education Committee Chair
8440 Bradshaw Road
Salem, VA 24153-2246
Tel: (540)384-6884
E-mail: Suzienotes@aol.com
Web Site: http://users.erols.com/va-udc/scholarships.html
To provide financial assistance for undergraduate or graduate study in medicine or engineering to Confederate descendants from Virginia.
Title of Award: Mary Anne Williams Scholarship **Area, Field, or Subject:** Engineering; Medicine **Level of Education for which Award is Granted:** Graduate, Undergraduate **Number Awarded:** This scholarship is offered whenever a prior recipient graduates or is no longer eligible. **Funds Available:** The amount of the stipend depends on the availability of funds. Payment is made directly to the college or university the recipient attends. **Duration:** 1 year; may be renewed up to 3 additional years if the recipient maintains a GPA of 3.0 or higher.
Eligibility Requirements: This program is open to residents of Virginia who are 1) lineal descendants of Confederates, or 2) collateral descendants and also members of the Children of the Confederacy or the United Daughters of the Confederacy. Applicants must be interested in working on an undergraduate or graduate degree in medicine or engineering. They must submit proof of the Confederate military record of at least 1 ancestor, with the company and regiment in which he served. They must also submit a personal letter pledging to make the best possible use of the scholarship; describing their health, social, family, religious, and fraternal connections within the community; and reflecting on what a Southern heritage means to them (using the term "War Between the States" in lieu of "Civil War"). They must have a GPA of 3.0 or higher and be able to demonstrate financial need. **Deadline for Receipt:** May of years in which the scholarship is available. **Additional Information:** Information is also available from Mrs. George W. Bryson, 10103 Rixeyville Road, Culpeper, VA 22701-4422, E-mail: brysdale@aol.com.

2734 ■ VASA ORDER OF AMERICA

Attn: Vice Grand Master
3236 Berkeley Avenue
Cleveland Heights, OH 44118-2055
Tel: (216)371-5141
E-mail: rolf.bergman@sbcglobal.net
Web Site: http://www.vasaorder.com
To provide financial assistance for education in a medical field to members of the Vasa Order of America.
Title of Award: Ellis F. Hillner Award **Area, Field, or Subject:** Medicine **Level of Education for which Award is Granted:** Doctorate, Undergraduate **Number Awarded:** 1 each year. **Funds Available:** The stipend is $2,000. **Duration:** 1 year.
Eligibility Requirements: Applicants must have belonged to the organization for at least 1 year and be attending or planning to attend an accredited institution on a full-time basis for studies in the medical field. Selection is based on a transcript, letters of recommendation from school and local Vasa lodge officials, and an essay of up to 1,000 words on a topic related to Vasa. **Deadline for Receipt:** February of each year. **Additional Information:** Vasa Order of America is a Swedish American

fraternal organization incorporated in 1899.

2735 ■ VERMONT STUDENT ASSISTANCE CORPORATION

Champlain Mill
Attn: Scholarship Programs
P.O. Box 2000
Winooski, VT 05404-2601
Tel: (802)654-3798; 888-253-4819
Fax: (802)654-3765
E-mail: info@vsac.org
Web Site: http://www.vsac.org
To provide financial assistance to residents of Vermont interested in obtaining an undergraduate degree, graduate degree, or certificate in a field related to home health care.

Title of Award: Elizabeth J. Davis Scholarship **Area, Field, or Subject:** Health care services **Level of Education for which Award is Granted:** Graduate, Undergraduate **Number Awarded:** Varies each year; recently, 7 of these scholarships were awarded. **Funds Available:** Stipends range from $1,000 to $3,000 per year. **Duration:** 1 year; may be renewed up to 3 additional years.

Eligibility Requirements: This scholarship is available to the residents of Vermont who are high school seniors, current undergraduate students, and home health care professionals. Applicants must be interested in obtaining a bachelor's degree in a health profession, certification as a home health aide, or (for home health care professionals) an advanced degree. They must be able to demonstrate interest in a career in the home health care field and an intent to work in Vermont for at least 2 years. Selection is based on financial need, required essays, a letter of recommendation, and a personal interview (if necessary). **Deadline for Receipt:** June of each year.

2736 ■ VERMONT STUDENT ASSISTANCE CORPORATION

Champlain Mill
Attn: Scholarship Programs
P.O. Box 2000
Winooski, VT 05404-2601
Tel: (802)654-3798; 888-253-4819
Fax: (802)654-3765
E-mail: info@vsac.org
Web Site: http://www.vsac.org
To provide financial assistance to residents of Vermont who are interested in majoring in a veterinary field in college or graduate school.

Title of Award: Gail Richardson Scholarship **Area, Field, or Subject:** Animal science and behavior; Veterinary science and medicine **Level of Education for which Award is Granted:** Doctorate, Undergraduate **Number Awarded:** 1 each year. **Funds Available:** The stipend is $1,000. **Duration:** 1 year.

Eligibility Requirements: This program is open to residents of Vermont who are graduating high school seniors, high school graduates, or GED recipients. Applicants must be interested in attending an accredited postsecondary institution to work on a degree in veterinary medicine, veterinary technology, animal science, or a related field. Selection is based on academic achievement (GPA of 2.5 or higher), required essays, letters of recommendation, and financial need. **Deadline for Receipt:** April of each year. **Additional Information:** The Vermont Student Assistance Corporation Board of Directors established this scholarship in 2001 to honor a former member.

2737 ■ VERMONT STUDENT ASSISTANCE CORPORATION

Champlain Mill
Attn: Scholarship Programs
P.O. Box 2000
Winooski, VT 05404-2601
Tel: (802)654-3798; 888-253-4819
Fax: (802)654-3765
E-mail: info@vsac.org
Web Site: http://www.vsac.org
To provide financial assistance to residents of Vermont who are interested in majoring in an agriculture-related field in college.

Title of Award: Vermont Feed Dealers and Manufacturers Association Scholarship **Area, Field, or Subject:** Agribusiness; Agricultural sciences; Animal science and behavior; Botany; Equine studies; Forestry; Horticulture; Soil science; Veterinary science and medicine **Level of**

Education for which Award is Granted: Undergraduate **Number Awarded:** Varies each year; recently, 6 of these scholarships were awarded. **Funds Available:** The maximum stipend is $3,000. **Duration:** 1 year; recipients may reapply.

Eligibility Requirements: This scholarship is available to high school seniors, high school graduates, and currently-enrolled college students in Vermont who are enrolled or planning to enroll in a postsecondary degree program in agriculture, including but not limited to animal sciences, equine studies, agribusiness, plant and soil science, forestry, horticulture, and veterinary medicine or technology. Selection is based on a letter of recommendation and required essays. **Deadline for Receipt:** June of each year.

2738 ■ VERMONT STUDENT ASSISTANCE CORPORATION

Champlain Mill
Attn: Scholarship Programs
P.O. Box 2000
Winooski, VT 05404-2601
Tel: (802)654-3798; 888-253-4819
Fax: (802)654-3765
E-mail: info@vsac.org
Web Site: http://www.vsac.org
To provide financial assistance to adults in Vermont who are interested in majoring in a health-related field or human resources in college.

Title of Award: Vermont Healthcare Human Resources Association Scholarship **Area, Field, or Subject:** Health care services; Personnel administration/human resources **Level of Education for which Award is Granted:** Undergraduate **Number Awarded:** 1 or 2 each year. **Funds Available:** The stipend is $1,000. **Duration:** 1 year.

Eligibility Requirements: This scholarship is available to nontraditional-aged students who reside in Vermont and have been accepted to attend an accredited postsecondary school to work on a degree in a health care field and/or human resources. Applicants must intend to work in Vermont for at least 1 year. Selection is based on commitment to employment in Vermont, financial need, a letter of recommendation, an essay, and a resume. **Deadline for Receipt:** April of each year. **Additional Information:** Applications are reviewed and selection is made by the Vermont Healthcare Human Resources Association (formerly the Vermont Hospital Personnel Association) in association with the Vermont Student Assistance Corporation.

2739 ■ VESALIUS TRUST FOR VISUAL COMMUNICATIONS IN THE HEALTH SCIENCES

Attn: Wendy Hiller Gee, Student Grants and Scholarships
Krames-West Coast
1100 Grundy Lane
San Bruno, CA 94066
Tel: (650)244-4320
E-mail: wendy.hillergee@krames.com
Web Site: http://www.vesaliustrust.org/scholarships.html
To provide funding to students working on a research project in biocommunications.

Title of Award: Vesalius Trust Student Research Grants **Area, Field, or Subject:** Communications; Illustrators and illustrations; Medicine **Level of Education for which Award is Granted:** Graduate, Undergraduate **Number Awarded:** Varies each year. Recently, 19 of these grants were awarded, including 1 designated as the Alan Cole Scholarship and 5 designated as the Vesalian Scholarships. **Funds Available:** Grant amounts vary each year. **Duration:** 1 year.

Eligibility Requirements: This program is open to undergraduate and graduate students who have completed at least 1 year of a biocommunications program in medical illustrating. Applicants must be interested in conducting a research project under the guidance of a faculty preceptor. Selection is based on the background and education of the applicant (20%); an evaluation by the preceptor of the student's ability to complete the project and its potential contributions (10%); the project concept and subject matter (30%); project design (20%); and production plan (20%). **Deadline for Receipt:** November of each year. **Additional Information:**

The top-ranked applicant receives the Alan Cole Scholarship. Other recipients whose projects show evidence of significant merit are designated Vesalian Scholarships.

2740 ■ VETERANS OF FOREIGN WARS OF MAINE

c/o Jane Poulin
50 Lisbon Street
Lisbon, ME 04250-6017
Tel: (207)353-4879
To provide financial assistance to children and grandchildren of members of the Veterans of Foreign Wars (VFW) and its Ladies Auxiliary in Maine who are studying a medical field in college.
Title of Award: Past National President Frances Booth Medical Scholarship **Area, Field, or Subject:** Medicine **Level of Education for which Award is Granted:** Undergraduate **Number Awarded:** 1 or more each year. **Funds Available:** The stipend is $1,000 per year. Funds are paid to the school of the recipient's choice. **Duration:** 1 year; may be renewed. **Eligibility Requirements:** This program is open to Maine residents who are the children, grandchildren, stepchildren, or foster children of current or immediate past year members of the VFW or its Ladies Auxiliary in Maine. Applicants must be enrolled at a 2-year or 4-year college, university, or vocational school and majoring in a field related to medicine. **Deadline for Receipt:** March of each year.

2741 ■ VIRGINIA DAUGHTERS OF THE AMERICAN REVOLUTION

c/o Catherine Rafferty, Scholarship Chair
10101 Sanders Court
Great Falls, VA 22066-2526
Web Site: http://www.vadar.org/vadarscholarships.htm
To provide financial assistance to high school seniors in Virginia who wish to study designated fields in college.
Title of Award: Virginia DAR Scholarships **Area, Field, or Subject:** Environmental conservation; Environmental science; Forestry; Genealogy; History, American; Home Economics; Medicine; Science **Level of Education for which Award is Granted:** Undergraduate **Number Awarded:** 2 each year: 1 at $1,000 and 1 at $500. **Funds Available:** Stipends are $1,000 or $500. **Duration:** 1 year.
Eligibility Requirements: This program is open to seniors graduating from high schools in Virginia who plan to attend a Virginia college or university. Applicants must be planning to work on a degree in the field of science, medicine, conservation, ecology, forestry, home arts, genealogical research, or American history. Along with their application, they must submit a 1,000-word letter giving their reasons for interest in the scholarship, a transcript of grades, a letter of recommendation from a teacher in their chosen field, and documentation of financial need. **Deadline for Receipt:** January of each year.

2742 ■ WATTS CHARITY ASSOCIATION, INC.

6245 Bristol Parkway, Suite 224
Culver City, CA 90230
Tel: (323)671-0394
Fax: (323)778-2613
E-mail: wattscharity@yahoo.com
Web Site: http://4watts.tripod.com/id5.html
To provide financial assistance to upper-division college students interested in health, civil rights, or administration.
Title of Award: Royce R. Watts Sr. Scholarship **Area, Field, or Subject:** Business administration; Civil rights; Health care services; Human rights; Medicine; Public administration **Level of Education for which Award is Granted:** Four Year College **Number Awarded:** 1 each year. **Funds Available:** A stipend is awarded (amount not specified). **Duration:** 1 year.
Eligibility Requirements: This program is open to U.S. citizens of African American descent who are enrolled full time as a college or university junior. Applicants must have an interest in health and pre-medicine, community activities and civil rights, or administration. They must have a GPA of 3.0 or higher, be between 17 and 24 years of age, and be able to demonstrate that they intend to continue their education for at least 2 years. Along with their application, they must submit 1) a 1-paragraph statement on why they should be awarded a Watts Foundation scholarship, and 2) a 1- to 2-page essay on a specific type of cancer, based either on how it has impacted their life or on researched information. **Deadline for Receipt:** May of each year. **Additional Information:** Royce R. Watts, Sr. established the Watts Charity Association after he learned he had cancer in 2001.

2743 ■ WISCONSIN SOCIETY FOR CLINICAL LABORATORY SCIENCE

c/o Mary Ann Nelson, Scholarship Fund Secretary
302 Park Avenue
Wausau, WI 54403
Tel: (715)845-3662
E-mail: manelson@dwave.net
Web Site: http://www.wiscls.org/scholarship.htm
To provide financial assistance to high school seniors in Wisconsin planning to enroll in a laboratory medicine program.
Title of Award: Wisconsin Society for Clinical Laboratory Science High School Scholarship **Area, Field, or Subject:** Medical technology **Level of Education for which Award is Granted:** Undergraduate **Number Awarded:** 1 or more each year. **Funds Available:** The stipend is $500 per semester ($1,000 per year). Funds are paid directly to the university. **Duration:** 1 semester; may be renewed up to 7 additional semesters provided the recipient continues to display satisfactory academic progress.
Eligibility Requirements: This program is open to seniors graduating from high schools in Wisconsin. Applicants must be planning to attend college to major in medical technology/clinical laboratory science.

Allied Health

2744 ■ ALASKA COMMISSION ON POSTSECONDARY EDUCATION

Attn: AlaskAdvantage Programs
3030 Vintage Boulevard
Juneau, AK 99801-7109
Tel: (907)465-6779; (866)427-5683
Fax: (907)465-5316
E-mail: customer_service@acpe.ak.us
Web Site: http://alaskaadvantage.state.ak.us/page/256
To provide educational loans to Alaska residents who attend out-of-state professional schools in specified fields through the Professional Student Exchange Program (PSEP) of the Western Interstate Commission for Higher Education (WICHE).
Title of Award: Alaska Professional Student Exchange Loan Program **Area, Field, or Subject:** Dentistry; Medical assisting; Occupational therapy; Optometry; Pharmaceutical sciences; Physical therapy; Podiatry **Level of Education for which Award is Granted:** Undergraduate **Number Awarded:** Varies each year. **Funds Available:** Loans up to the annual support fee are available, to a maximum of $17,200. No origination fee is charged. The interest rate is 6%. **Duration:** 1 year; may be renewed.
Eligibility Requirements: This program is open to residents of Alaska who are attending a professional school in another state as part of the PSEP of WICHE. The fields of study currently available are dentistry, occupational therapy, optometry, physician assistant, podiatry, pharmacy, and physical therapy. In most cases, PSEP students pay resident tuition (or reduced tuition at private institutions) and their home state pays an additional support fee to the institution. Alaska requires PSEP students to pay the tuition and support fee, and provides these loans to enable them to do so.

2745 ■ AMERICAN PHYSICAL THERAPY ASSOCIATION

Attn: Honors and Awards Program
1111 North Fairfax Street
Alexandria, VA 22314-1488
Tel: (703)684-APTA
Free: 800-999-APTA
Fax: (703)684-7343
E-mail: Governce@apta.org
Web Site: http://www.apta.org
To provide financial assistance to students in physical therapist assistant, professional physical therapy education, and post-professional master's degree programs.
Title of Award: Mary McMillan Scholarship Awards **Area, Field, or Subject:** Physical therapy **Level of Education for which Award is Granted:** Master's, Undergraduate **Number Awarded:** Varies each year. **Funds Available:** The stipend is $3,000 for physical therapist assistant students or $5,000 for physical therapist professional education students (including entry-level doctor of physical therapy degree students) and post-professional master's degree students. **Duration:** 1 year.

Eligibility Requirements: This program is open to 1) physical therapist assistant education program students in the final year of study; 2) physical therapist professional education program students (including entry-level doctor of physical therapy degree students) who have completed at least 1 full year of entry-level education; and 3) post-professional master's degree students who have completed at least 1 term in the program and are enrolled at the time. Students must be nominated by the school they are attending. Selection is based on scholastic performance, past productivity, evidence of potential contribution to physical therapy, and service to the American Physical Therapy Association. **Deadline for Receipt:** November of each year.

2746 ■ AMERICAN PHYSICAL THERAPY ASSOCIATION

Attn: Department of Minority/International Affairs
1111 North Fairfax Street
Alexandria, VA 22314-1488
Tel: (703)706-3144
Free: 800-999-APTA
Fax: (703)706-8519
E-mail: min-intl@apta.org
Web Site: http://www.apta.org
To provide financial assistance to minority students who are interested in becoming a physical therapist or physical therapy assistant.
Title of Award: Minority Scholarship Award in Physical Therapy **Area, Field, or Subject:** Physical therapy **Level of Education for which Award is Granted:** Professional, Undergraduate **Number Awarded:** Varies each year; recently, 8 of these awards were granted to physical therapy students and 1 to a physical therapy assistant student. **Funds Available:** The stipend varies; recently, minimum awards were $6,000 for physical therapy students or $3,000 for physical therapy assistant students. **Duration:** 1 year.
Eligibility Requirements: This program is open to U.S. citizens and permanent residents who are members of the following minority groups: African American or Black, Asian, Native Hawaiian or other Pacific Islander, American Indian or Alaska Native, or Hispanic/Latino. Applicants must be in the final year of a professional physical therapy or physical therapy assistant education program. They must submit a personal essay outlining their professional goals and minority service. U.S. citizenship or permanent resident status is required. Selection is based on 1) demonstrated evidence of contributions in the area of minority affairs and services with an emphasis on contributions made while enrolled in a physical therapy program; 2) potential to contribute to the profession of physical therapy; and 3) scholastic achievement. **Deadline for Receipt:** November of each year.

2747 ■ CHRISTIAN LIFE RESOURCES

Attn: WELS Lutherans for Life
Scholarship Review Committee
2949 North Mayfair Road, Suite 309
Milwaukee, WI 53222-4304
Tel: (414)774-1331
Fax: (414)774-1360
Web Site: http://www.christianliferesources.com
To provide financial assistance to Lutheran high school seniors in Wisconsin who are interested in studying life-related issues in college.
Title of Award: WELS Lutherans for Life Scholarship Program **Area, Field, or Subject:** Biological and clinical sciences; Education, Special; Engineering, Biomedical; Journalism; Law; Medicine; Physical therapy; Political science; Psychology; Social work **Level of Education for which Award is Granted:** Four Year College **Number Awarded:** Varies each year; recently, 9 of these scholarships were awarded. **Funds Available:** Stipends up to $1,000 are available. **Duration:** 1 year.
Eligibility Requirements: This program is open to high school seniors who are active members of the Wisconsin Evangelical Lutheran Synod (WELS) or an affiliated church. Applicants must be planning to go to a 4-year school to prepare for a secular career in which pro-life values will be demonstrated. Acceptable fields include medicine, biotechnology/biological engineering, medical research/genetics, law/politics, journalism/media, psychology, physical therapy, social services, or special education. They must have a GPA of 3.25 or higher. Along with their application, they must submit essays on 1) the field of study they plan to enter and how it relates to pro-life issues; 2) why the scholarship should be awarded to them, including their future goals; and 3) how they have demonstrated a

Christian, pro-life attitude in their life. **Deadline for Receipt:** February of each year. **Additional Information:** WELS Lutherans for Life was formerly a ministry of the Wisconsin Evangelical Lutheran Synod.

2748 ■ HAWAI'I COMMUNITY FOUNDATION

Attn: Scholarship Department
1164 Bishop Street, Suite 800
Honolulu, HI 96813
Tel: (808)566-5570; 888-731-3863
Fax: (808)521-6286
E-mail: scholarships@hcf-hawaii.org
Web Site: http://www.hawaiicommunityfoundation.org/scholar/scholar.php
To provide financial assistance to Hawaii residents who are interested in preparing for a career in designated health fields.
Title of Award: Dr. Alvin and Monica Saake Foundation Scholarships **Area, Field, or Subject:** Athletics; Education, Physical; Medicine, Sports; Occupational therapy; Parks and recreation; Physical therapy **Level of Education for which Award is Granted:** Four Year College, Graduate **Number Awarded:** Varies each year; recently, 19 of these scholarships were awarded. **Funds Available:** The amounts of the awards depend on the availability of funds and the need of the recipient; recently, stipends averaged $2,895. **Duration:** 1 year.
Eligibility Requirements: This program is open to Hawaii residents who are enrolled as full-time juniors, seniors, or graduate students. Applicants must be majoring in kinesiology, leisure science, physical education, athletic training, exercise science, sports medicine, physical therapy, or occupational therapy. They must be able to demonstrate academic achievement (GPA of 2.7 or higher), good moral character, and financial need. In addition to filling out the standard application form, applicants must write a short statement indicating their reasons for attending college, their planned course of study, and their career goals. **Deadline for Receipt:** February of each year. **Additional Information:** Recipients may attend college in Hawaii or on the mainland.

2749 ■ HAWAI'I COMMUNITY FOUNDATION

Attn: Scholarship Department
1164 Bishop Street, Suite 800
Honolulu, HI 96813
Tel: (808)566-5570; 888-731-3863
Fax: (808)521-6286
E-mail: scholarships@hcf-hawaii.org
Web Site: http://www.hawaiicommunityfoundation.org/scholar/scholar.php
To provide financial assistance to Hawaii residents who are interested in preparing for a career in physical therapy.
Title of Award: Paulina L. Sorg Scholarships **Area, Field, or Subject:** Physical therapy **Level of Education for which Award is Granted:** Four Year College, Graduate **Number Awarded:** Varies each year; recently, 5 of these scholarships were awarded. **Funds Available:** The amounts of the awards depend on the availability of funds and the need of the recipient; recently, stipends averaged $1,000. **Duration:** 1 year.
Eligibility Requirements: This program is open to Hawaii residents who are studying physical therapy as full-time juniors, seniors, or graduate students. They must be able to demonstrate academic achievement (GPA of 2.7 or higher), good moral character, and financial need. In addition to filling out the standard application form, applicants must write a short statement indicating their reasons for attending college, their planned course of study, and their career goals. **Deadline for Receipt:** February of each year. **Additional Information:** Recipients may attend college in Hawaii or on the mainland.

2750 ■ INDIAN HEALTH SERVICE

Attn: Scholarship Program
801 Thompson Avenue, Suite 120
Rockville, MD 20852
Tel: (301)443-6197
Fax: (301)443-6048
E-mail: bmiller@na.ihs.gov
Web Site: http://www.ihs.gov
To provide financial assistance to Native American students who need compensatory or preprofessional education to qualify for enrollment in a health professions school.
Title of Award: Health Professions Preparatory Scholarship Program **Area, Field, or Subject:** Engineering; Health care services; Medical

technology; Nursing; Nutrition; Pharmaceutical sciences; Physical therapy; Social work **Level of Education for which Award is Granted:** Undergraduate **Number Awarded:** Varies each year. **Funds Available:** Awards provide a payment directly to the school for tuition and required fees; a stipend for living expenses of approximately $1,160 per month for 10 months; a lump sum to cover the costs of books, travel, and other necessary educational expenses; and up to $400 for approved tutorial costs. **Duration:** Up to 2 years of full-time study or up to 4 years of part-time study.

Eligibility Requirements: Applicants must be American Indians or Alaska Natives; be high school graduates or the equivalent; have the capacity to complete a health professions course of study; and be enrolled or accepted for enrollment in a compensatory or preprofessional general education course or curriculum. The qualifying fields of study include pre-medical technology, pre-dietetics, pre-nursing, pre-pharmacy, pre-physical therapy, pre-social work, and pre-engineering. Recipients must intend to serve Indian people upon completion of professional health care education as a health care provider in the discipline for which they are enrolled at the pregraduate level. **Deadline for Receipt:** February of each year.

2751 ■ INDIAN HEALTH SERVICE

Attn: Scholarship Program
801 Thompson Avenue, Suite 120
Rockville, MD 20852
Tel: (301)443-6197
Fax: (301)443-6048
E-mail: bmiller@na.ihs.gov
Web Site: http://www.ihs.gov
To provide loans-for-service to American Indian and Alaska Native students enrolled in health professions and allied health professions programs.
Title of Award: Health Professions Scholarship Program **Area, Field, or Subject:** Counseling/Guidance; Dental hygiene; Dentistry; Health care services; Medical assisting; Medical technology; Medicine; Medicine, Osteopathic; Nursing; Nutrition; Optometry; Pharmaceutical sciences; Physical therapy; Podiatry; Psychology; Public health; Radiology; Respiratory therapy; Social work; **Level of Education for which Award is Granted:** Graduate, Undergraduate **Number Awarded:** Varies each year. **Funds Available:** Awards provide a payment directly to the school for tuition and required fees; a stipend for living expenses of approximately $1,160 per month for 12 months; a lump sum to cover the costs of books, travel, and other necessary educational expenses; and up to $400 for approved tutorial costs. Upon completion of their program of study, recipients are required to provide payback service of 1 year for each year of scholarship support at the Indian Health Service, a tribal health programs, an urban Indian health program, or in private practice in a designated health professional shortage area serving a substantial number of Indians. Recipients who fail to complete their service obligation must repay all funds received (although no interest is charged). **Duration:** 1 year; may be renewed for up to 3 additional years.

Eligibility Requirements: This program is open to American Indians and Alaska Natives who are at least high school graduates and enrolled in a full-time study program leading to a degree in a health-related professions school within the United States. Priority is given to upper-division and graduate students. Qualifying fields of study include chemical dependency counseling (bachelor's or master's degree), clinical psychology (Ph.D. only), coding specialist (certificate), counseling psychology (Ph.D. only), dental hygiene (B.S.), dentistry (D.D.S.), diagnostic radiology technology (certificate, associate, or B.S.), dietitian (B.S.), civil or environmental engineering (B.S.), environmental health (B.S.), health care administration (B.S. or M.S.), health education (B.S. or M.S.), health records (R.H.I.T. or R.H.I.A.), injury prevention specialist (certificate), medical technology (B.S.), allopathic and osteopathic medicine, nursing (A.D.N., B.S.N., or C.R.N.A.), optometry, pharmacy (B.S. or Pharm.D.), physician assistant (B.S.), physical therapy (M.S. or D.P.T.), podiatry (D.P.M.), public health (M.P.H. only), public health nutrition (master's only), social work (master's only), respiratory therapy (associate), and ultrasonography. **Deadline for Receipt:** February of each year.

2752 ■ IOWA PHYSICAL THERAPY ASSOCIATION

Attn: Foundation
1228 Eighth Street, Suite 106
West Des Moines, IA 50265-2624

Tel: (515)222-9838
Fax: (515)222-9839
E-mail: mail@iowaapta.org
Web Site: http://www.iowaapta.org/foundati.htm
To loan money to students enrolled in a physical therapy program in Iowa.
Title of Award: Olive C. Farr Loan Fund **Area, Field, or Subject:** Physical therapy **Level of Education for which Award is Granted:** Undergraduate **Number Awarded:** Up to 4 each year. **Funds Available:** The maximum loan is $1,000 per year. Repayment begins 1 month following non-enrollment or graduation with interest of 10%. Repayment must be completed within 6 months. **Duration:** 1 year; may be renewed 1 additional year.

Eligibility Requirements: This program is open to members of the American Physical Therapy Association (APTA) who are enrolled in an accredited physical therapy program in Iowa. Applicants must be able to demonstrate financial need. **Deadline for Receipt:** June of each year. **Additional Information:** An administrative fee of $25 per year per $1,000 of loan is charged.

2753 ■ KOSTER INSURANCE AGENCY

Attn: Scholarship
500 Victory Road
Quincy, MA 02171
Tel: (617)770-9889
Free: 800-457-5599
Fax: (617)479-0860
E-mail: Scholarship@kosterins.com
Web Site: http://www.kosterweb.com/about/scholarship_main.php
To provide financial assistance to undergraduate students working on a degree in a health-related field.
Title of Award: Koster Insurance Health Careers Scholarship Program **Area, Field, or Subject:** Biological and clinical sciences; Chemistry; Dentistry; Health care services; Nursing; Occupational therapy; Optometry; Pharmaceutical sciences; Physical therapy; Physiology; Public health; Social work **Level of Education for which Award is Granted:** Undergraduate **Number Awarded:** 5 each year. **Funds Available:** The stipend is $3,000 per year. **Duration:** 1 year; may be renewed 1 additional year.

Eligibility Requirements: This program is open to full-time undergraduates entering their second-to-last or final year of study in a health-related field, including (but not limited to) pre-medicine, nursing, public and community health, physical therapy, occupational therapy, pharmacy, biology, chemistry, physiology, social work, dentistry, and optometry. Applicants must have a GPA of 3.0 or higher and be able to demonstrate financial need. Along with their application, they must submit a 1-page essay describing their personal goals, including their reasons for preparing for a career in health care. Selection is based on motivation to pursue a career in health care, academic excellence, dedication to community service, and financial need. **Deadline for Receipt:** April of each year. **Additional Information:** This program began in 2001.

2754 ■ MARYLAND HIGHER EDUCATION COMMISSION

Attn: Office of Student Financial Assistance
839 Bestgate Road, Suite 400
Annapolis, MD 21401-3013
Tel: (410)260-4594
Free: 800-974-1024
Fax: (410)974-5376
E-mail: osfamail@mhec.state.md.us
Web Site: http://www.mhec.state.md.us/financialAid/ProgramDescriptions/prog_devdis.asp
To provide scholarship/loans to students in Maryland who are interested in working on a degree in a designated human services program.
Title of Award: Maryland Developmental Disabilities, Mental Health, Child Welfare, and Juvenile Justice Workforce Tuition Assistance Program **Area, Field, or Subject:** Counseling/Guidance; Criminal justice; Criminology; Disabilities; Education, Special; Gerontology; Law enforcement; Mental health; Nursing; Occupational therapy; Physical therapy; Psychology; Rehabilitation, Physical/Psychological; Social work **Level of Education for which Award is Granted:** Graduate, Undergraduate **Number Awarded:** Varies each year. **Funds Available:** The maximum stipend is $2,000 per year for students attending a 2-year institution or $3,000 per year for students at a 4-year institution. The total amount of all state

awards may not exceed the cost of attendance as determined by the school's financial aid office or $17,800, whichever is less. Recipients must agree to work in a Maryland community-based program that is licensed by the Developmental Disabilities Administration or approved by the Mental Hygiene Administration, or in a residential program that is licensed by the Department of Human Resources or the Department of Juvenile Justice. The service obligation must begin within 6 months of graduation. The total service requirement is 2,000 hours if the award amount is $1,999 or less, 3,000 hours if the award amount is $2,000 to $3,999, or 4,000 hours if the award amount is $4,000 or more. If the service requirement is not completed, the award must be repaid with interest. **Duration:** 1 year; may be renewed if the recipient maintains satisfactory academic progress and remains enrolled in a human services degree program.
Eligibility Requirements: This program is open to high school seniors and full-time and part-time undergraduate and graduate students. Applicants and their parents must be Maryland residents attending a college or university in the state in 1 of the following human services degree programs: aging services, counseling, disability services, mental health, nursing, occupational therapy, physical therapy, psychology, rehabilitation, social work, special education, supported employment, vocational rehabilitation, or any other concentration in the healing arts or a program providing support services to individuals with special needs including child welfare and juvenile justice. Financial need is not considered in the selection process. **Deadline for Receipt:** June of each year.

2755 ■ MARYLAND HIGHER EDUCATION COMMISSION

Attn: Office of Student Financial Assistance
839 Bestgate Road, Suite 400
Annapolis, MD 21401-3013
Tel: (410)260-4574
Free: 800-974-1024
Fax: (410)974-5376
E-mail: osfamail@mhec.state.md.us
Web Site: http://www.mhec.state.md.us/financialAid/
ProgramDescriptions/prog_otpt.asp
To provide scholarship/loans to students in Maryland who are interested in preparing for a career as a physical or occupational therapist or assistant.
Title of Award: Maryland Physical and Occupational Therapists and Assistants Grants **Area, Field, or Subject:** Occupational therapy; Physical therapy **Level of Education for which Award is Granted:** Graduate, Undergraduate **Number Awarded:** Varies each year. **Funds Available:** The stipend is $2,000 per year. The total amount of all state awards may not exceed the cost of attendance as determined by the school's financial aid office or $17,800, whichever is less. This is a scholarship/loan program. Recipients must work 1 year in a Maryland facility that accommodates or provides service to handicapped children for each year the award was received, or the award must be repaid with interest. Employment must begin within 6 months of graduation. **Duration:** 1 year; may be renewed for up to 3 additional years.
Eligibility Requirements: This program is open to Maryland residents who are enrolled or planning to enroll as a full-time undergraduate or graduate student in a 2- or 4-year college or university in Maryland with an approved program of occupational or physical therapy. Applicants must be interested in obtaining licensure as a therapist or therapy assistant. Selection is based on high school or college GPA; financial need is not considered. **Deadline for Receipt:** June of each year.

2756 ■ MISSISSIPPI OFFICE OF STUDENT FINANCIAL AID

3825 Ridgewood Road
Jackson, MS 39211-6453
Tel: (601)432-6997
Free: 800-327-2980
Fax: (601)432-6527
E-mail: sfa@ihl.state.ms.us
Web Site: http://www.ihl.state.ms.us/financialaid/hcp.html
To provide scholarship/loans to Mississippi residents who are majoring in a critical health care field in college.
Title of Award: Mississippi Health Care Professions Loan/Scholarship Program **Area, Field, or Subject:** Health care services; Occupational therapy; Physical therapy; Psychology; Speech and language pathology/audiology **Level of Education for which Award is Granted:** Four Year College, Graduate **Number Awarded:** Varies each year, depending on the availability of funds; awards are granted on a first-come, first-served

basis. **Funds Available:** Under this program, $1,500 is awarded per year to undergraduate students and $3,000 per year to graduate students. This is a scholarship/loan program. Obligation can be discharged on the basis of 1 year's service in the health profession at a state-operated health institution in Mississippi for 1 year's scholarship/loan award. In the event the recipient fails to fulfill the service obligation, repayment of principal and interest is required. **Duration:** Up to 2 years for undergraduates and for graduate students in physical therapy; 1 year for graduate students in occupational therapy.
Eligibility Requirements: This program is open to Mississippi residents who are enrolled as a junior, senior, or graduate student in an approved training program in the state of Mississippi. Approved programs of study currently include speech pathology and psychology on the undergraduate level and occupational therapy and physical therapy on the graduate level. Selection is based on cumulative GPA. The highest priority is given to renewal students. **Deadline for Receipt:** March of each year. **Additional Information:** State health institutions include the following: Mississippi State Hospital, Ellisville State School, East Mississippi State Hospital, Mississippi Children's Rehabilitation Center, North Mississippi Retardation Center, Hudspeth Retardation Center, South Mississippi Retardation Center, University of Mississippi Hospital, Boswell Retardation Center, State Board of Health, Department of Mental Health, and health care facilities under the Department of Corrections.

2757 ■ NATIONAL AMBUCS, INC.

Attn: Scholarship Coordinator
P.O. Box 5127
High Point, NC 27262
Tel: (336)852-0052
Fax: (336)852-6830
E-mail: ambucs@ambucs.org
Web Site: http://www.ambucs.org
To provide financial assistance to undergraduate and graduate students who are interested in preparing for a career serving disabled citizens in various fields of clinical therapy.
Title of Award: AMBUCS Scholarships for Therapists **Area, Field, or Subject:** Occupational therapy; Physical therapy; Rehabilitation, Physical/Psychological; Speech and language pathology/audiology **Level of Education for which Award is Granted:** Four Year College, Graduate **Number Awarded:** Approximately 400 each year, with a total value of $225,000. **Funds Available:** Most of these awards range from $500 to $1,500 per year; 1 scholarship of $6,000 for 2 years is also awarded. Funds are paid directly to the recipient's school. **Duration:** 1 year.
Eligibility Requirements: This program is open to U.S. citizens who have been accepted at the upper-division or graduate level in an accredited program that qualifies the students for clinical practice in occupational therapy, physical therapy, speech language pathology, or hearing audiology. Programs for therapy assistants are not included. Applicants must submit college transcripts for the last 3 semesters, a 500-word essay on their interest in therapy as a career, and a statement of family financial circumstances. Selection is based on financial need, commitment to local community, demonstrated academic accomplishment, character for compassion and integrity, and career objectives. **Deadline for Receipt:** April of each year. **Additional Information:** This program was established in 1955; since then, the association has awarded more than $5 million for more than 9,900 scholarships.

2758 ■ NORTH CAROLINA STATE EDUCATION ASSISTANCE AUTHORITY

Attn: Scholarship and Grant Services
10 T.W. Alexander Drive
P.O. Box 14223
Research Triangle Park, NC 27709-4223
Tel: (919)549-8614
Free: 800-700-1775
Fax: (919)549-8481
E-mail: information@ncseaa.edu
Web Site: http://www.ncseaa.edu
To provide loans and loans-for-service to North Carolina residents who are interested in preparing for a career in health, science, or mathematics.
Title of Award: North Carolina Student Loan Program for Health, Science, and Mathematics **Area, Field, or Subject:** Allied health; Dentistry; Medicine; Nursing; Optometry; Public health; Social work **Level of**

Education for which Award is Granted: Graduate, Undergraduate **Number Awarded:** Varies each year; recently, a total of 497 students were receiving $3,238,569 in support through this program. **Funds Available:** Maximum loans are $3,000 per year for associate degree and certificate programs, $5,000 per year for baccalaureate degree/certificate programs, $6,500 per year for master's degree programs, or $8,500 per year for health/professional doctoral programs. The maximum amount that any student can borrow through this program is $58,000. The interest rate is 4% while the borrowers are attending school and from 10 to 15% after they leave school. Cash repayments must begin 90 days or less after completion of course work and training. Under specified conditions, certain loan recipients in qualifying disciplines may have their loans canceled through service in North Carolina. **Duration:** 1 year; renewable for 1 additional year for diploma, associate, certificate, and master's degree programs, for 2 additional years for baccalaureate degree programs, or for 3 additional years for doctoral programs.
Eligibility Requirements: North Carolina residents are eligible to apply for this program if they have been accepted as full-time students in an accredited associate, baccalaureate, master's, or doctoral program leading to a degree in 1 of the following areas: allied health (including audiology/communications assistant, cytotechnology, dental hygiene, diagnostic medical sonographer, imaging technologist, medical technology, nuclear medicine technologist, occupational therapy/assistant, physician assistant, physical therapy/assistant, radiation therapist, radiography, respiratory therapy, and speech language pathology); clinical psychology (Ph.D. level only); dentistry; dietetics and nutrition (graduate level only); mathematics education; medicine (including chiropractic medicine, emergency medicine, family medicine, geriatrics, internal medicine, obstetrics and gynecology, osteopathic medicine, pediatrics, podiatry, primary care medicine, and psychiatry); nursing (including anesthetist, family nurse practitioner, nursing administration, general nursing, and midwifery); optometry; pharmacy; public health (graduate level only); science education (including biology, chemistry, communications and technologies, computer and information sciences, engineering, and physical science); social work (graduate level only); and veterinary medicine. U.S. citizenship is required. Selection is based on academic progress, financial ability of sureties to repay all loans and accrued interest in case of applicant's default, applicant's willingness to work in underserved areas of the state or in disciplines for which there is a shortage of professionals, applicant's willingness to comply with all program regulations, and financial need. **Deadline for Receipt:** May of each year. **Additional Information:** Recipients may attend a North Carolina postsecondary institution or an eligible out-of-state institution. This program was formerly known as the North Carolina Medical Student Loan Program.

2759 ■ STATE STUDENT ASSISTANCE COMMISSION OF INDIANA
Attn: Grant Division
150 West Market Street, Suite 500
Indianapolis, IN 46204-2811
Tel: (317)232-2350; 888-528-4719
Fax: (317)232-3260
E-mail: special@ssaci.state.in.us
Web Site: http://www.in.gov/ssaci/programs/m-teach.html
To provide scholarship/loans to Black and Hispanic undergraduate students in Indiana interested in preparing for a teaching career and to other residents of the state preparing for a career in special education, occupational therapy, or physical therapy.
Title of Award: Indiana Minority Teacher/Special Education Services Scholarship **Area, Field, or Subject:** Education, Elementary; Education, Secondary; Education, Special; Occupational therapy; Physical therapy **Level of Education for which Award is Granted:** Undergraduate **Number Awarded:** Varies each year. **Funds Available:** Up to $1,000 annually; if students demonstrate financial need, they may receive up to $4,000 annually. For 3 out of the 5 years following graduation, recipients must teach full time in an elementary or secondary school in Indiana or practice as an occupational or physical therapist at a school or rehabilitation facility in the state. If they fail to meet that service requirement, they are required to reimburse the state of Indiana for all funds received. **Duration:** 1 year; may be renewed up to 3 additional years if recipients maintain a 2.0 GPA. They may, however, take up to 6 years to complete the program from the start of receiving the first scholarship.
Eligibility Requirements: This program is open to 1) Black and Hispanic students seeking teacher certification; 2) students seeking special educa-

tion teaching certification; or 3) students seeking occupational or physical therapy certification. Applicants must be Indiana residents and U.S. citizens who are enrolled or accepted for enrollment as full-time students at an academic institution in Indiana. Students who are already enrolled in college must have a GPA of 2.0 or higher. Applicants must be preparing to teach in an accredited elementary or secondary school in Indiana or to work as an occupational or physical therapist at a school or rehabilitation facility. Financial need may be considered, but it is not a requirement. Preference is given to minorities and to students enrolling in college for the first time. **Deadline for Receipt:** Each participating college or university establishes its filing deadline for this program. **Additional Information:** This program was established in 1988 to address the critical shortage of Black and Hispanic teachers in Indiana. An amendment in 1990 added the field of special education, and in 1991 the fields of occupational and physical therapy were added. Participating colleges in Indiana select the recipients. Students must submit their application to the financial aid office of the college they plan to attend (not to the State Student Assistance Commission of Indiana).

2760 ■ U.S. AIR FORCE
Attn: Headquarters AFROTC/RRUC
551 East Maxwell Boulevard
Maxwell AFB, AL 36112-5917
Tel: (334)953-2091; (866)423-7682
Fax: (334)953-6167
Web Site: http://www.afrotc.com/admissions/professional/biomed.php
To provide financial assistance to students who are interested in joining Air Force ROTC in college and preparing for a career as a physical therapist, optometrist, or pharmacist.
Title of Award: Air Force ROTC Biomedical Sciences Corps **Area, Field, or Subject:** Optometry; Pharmaceutical sciences; Physical therapy **Level of Education for which Award is Granted:** Undergraduate **Funds Available:** Awards are type 2 AFROTC scholarships that provide for payment of tuition and fees, to a maximum of $15,000 per year, plus an annual book allowance of $600. All recipients are also awarded a tax-free subsistence allowance for 10 months of each year that is $300 per month during their sophomore year, $350 during their junior year, and $400 during their senior year. **Duration:** 2 or 3 years, provided the recipient maintains a GPA of 2.0 or higher.
Eligibility Requirements: This program is open to U.S. citizens who are freshmen or sophomores in college and interested in a career as a physical therapist, optometrist, or pharmacist. Applicants must have a GPA of 2.0 or higher and meet all other academic and physical requirements for participation in AFROTC. At the time of their Air Force commissioning, they may be no more than 31 years of age. They must agree to serve for at least 4 years as nonline active-duty Air Force officers following graduation from college. **Deadline for Receipt:** June of each year. **Additional Information:** Recipients must also complete 4 years of aerospace studies courses at 1 of the 144 colleges and universities that have an Air Force ROTC unit on campus or 1 of the approximately 900 colleges that have cross-enrollment agreements with those institutions. They must also attend a 4-week summer training camp at an Air Force base, usually between their sophomore and junior years. Following completion of their bachelor's degree, scholarship recipients earn a commission as a second lieutenant in the Air Force and serve at least 4 years.

2761 ■ WESTERN INTERSTATE COMMISSION FOR HIGHER EDUCATION
Attn: Student Exchange Programs
3035 Center Green Drive
P.O. Box 9752
Boulder, CO 80301-9752
Tel: (303)541-0210
Fax: (303)541-0291
E-mail: info-sep@wiche.edu
Web Site: http://www.wiche.edu/sep/psep
To underwrite some of the cost of out-of-state professional schooling for students in selected western states.
Title of Award: Professional Student Exchange Program **Area, Field, or Subject:** Architecture; Dentistry; Library and archival sciences; Medical assisting; Medicine; Medicine, Osteopathic; Nursing; Occupational therapy; Optometry; Pharmaceutical sciences; Physical therapy; Podiatry; Public health; Veterinary science and medicine **Level of Education for**

which Award is Granted: Graduate, Undergraduate **Number Awarded:** Varies each year. **Funds Available:** The assistance consists of reduced levels of tuition, usually resident tuition in public institutions or reduced standard tuition at private schools. The home state pays a support fee to the admitting school to help cover the cost of the recipient's education. **Duration:** 1 year; may be renewed.

Eligibility Requirements: This program is open to residents of 13 western states who are interested in pursuing professional study at selected out-of-state institutions, usually because those fields of study are not available in their home states. The eligible programs, and the states whose residents are eligible, presently include: 1) architecture (master's degree), for residents of Wyoming, to study at designated institutions in Arizona. California, Colorado, Idaho, Montana, New Mexico, Oregon, Utah, or Washington); 2) dentistry, for residents of Alaska, Arizona, Hawaii, Montana, New Mexico, North Dakota, and Wyoming, to study at designated institutions in Arizona, California, Colorado, Nevada, Oregon, or Washington; 3) library studies (master's degree), for residents of New Mexico and Wyoming, to study at designated institutions in Arizona, California, Hawaii, or Washington; 4) medicine, for residents of Montana and Wyoming, to study at designated institutions in Arizona, California, Colorado, Hawaii, Nevada, New Mexico, North Dakota, Oregon, or Utah; 5) nursing (graduate degree), for residents of Wyoming, to study at designated institutions in California, Hawaii, North Dakota, or Oregon; 6) occupational therapy (bachelors' or master's degree), for residents of Alaska, Arizona, Hawaii, Montana, and Wyoming, to study at designated institutions in Arizona, California, Idaho, New Mexico, North Dakota, Oregon, Utah, or Washington; 7) optometry, for residents of Alaska, Arizona, Colorado, Hawaii, Idaho, Montana, Nevada, New Mexico, North Dakota, Utah, Washington, and Wyoming, to study at designated institutions in California or Oregon; 8) osteopathic medicine, for residents of Arizona, Montana, New Mexico, Washington, and Wyoming, to study at designated institutions in Arizona or California; 9) pharmacy, for residents of Alaska, Hawaii, and Nevada, to study at designated institutions in Arizona, California, Colorado, Idaho, Montana, New Mexico, North Dakota, Oregon, Utah, Washington, or Wyoming; 10) physical therapy (master's or doctoral degree), for residents of Alaska, Hawaii, and Wyoming, to study at designated institutions in Arizona, California, Colorado, Idaho, Montana, New Mexico, North Dakota, Oregon, Utah, or Washington; 11) physician assistant, for residents of Alaska, Arizona, Nevada, and Wyoming, to study at designated institutions in Arizona, California, Colorado, Idaho, Oregon, Utah, or Washington; 12) podiatry, for residents of Alaska, Montana, New Mexico, Utah, and Wyoming, to study at a designated institution in California; 13) public health, for residents of Montana and New Mexico, to study at designated institutions in California, Colorado, or Washington; and 14) veterinary medicine, for residents of Arizona, Hawaii, Montana, Nevada, New Mexico, North Dakota, Utah, and Wyoming, to study at designated institutions in California, Colorado, Oregon, or Washington. The financial status of the applicants is not considered. Interested students must apply for admission and for PSEP assistance directly from the institution of their choice. They must be certified by their state of residence to become an exchange student and be seeking enrollment at the first professional degree level. **Deadline for Receipt:** In most states, the deadline for receiving completed applications for certification is in October. After obtaining certification, students must still apply to the school of their choice, which also sets its own deadline.

Chiropractic

2762 ■ AMERICAN COLLEGE OF CHIROPRACTIC ORTHOPEDISTS
c/o Bill Fisher, Scholarship Committee Chair
P.O. Box 424
Delmont, PA 15626
Tel: (724)523-5505
Fax: (724)523-6875
Web Site: http://www.accoweb.org
To provide financial assistance to college students enrolled in their fifth term or later of chiropractic college.
Title of Award: F. Maynard Lipe Scholarship Award **Area, Field, or Subject:** Medicine, Chiropractic; Medicine, Orthopedic **Level of Education for which Award is Granted:** Undergraduate **Number Awarded:** 1 each year. **Funds Available:** The award is $1,000. Funds are sent to the

recipient's school and may be used to pay for tuition (not for books, lab fees, or other ancillary expenses). **Duration:** The award is granted annually.

Eligibility Requirements: This program is open to students who have completed at least 4 terms in an approved college of chiropractic. Applicants must have a GPA of 3.0 or higher and a career objective to specialize in chiropractic orthopedics. Along with their application, they must submit an article from 1,000 to 2,500 words in length on a subject related to chiropractic orthopedics. Selection is based on the excellence of the article. **Deadline for Receipt:** January of each year. **Additional Information:** When possible, the student is a guest at the association's convention.

2763 ■ INTERNATIONAL CHIROPRACTORS ASSOCIATION
1110 North Glebe Road, Suite 1000
Arlington, VA 22201
Tel: (703)528-5000
Free: 800-423-4690
Fax: (703)528-5023
E-mail: chiro@chiropractic.org
Web Site: http://www.chiropractic.org
To provide financial assistance to student members of the International Chiropractors Association (SICA).
Title of Award: Alma Neilsen Perpetual Scholarship **Area, Field, or Subject:** Medicine, Chiropractic **Level of Education for which Award is Granted:** Four Year College **Number Awarded:** Varies each year. **Funds Available:** A stipend is awarded (amount not specified). **Duration:** 1 year.
Eligibility Requirements: This program is open to members of the SICA organization on the campus of a college approved by the International Chiropractors Association (ICA). Applicants must be sophomores, juniors, or seniors and able to demonstrate financial need. They must submit a short statement (100 to 120 words) on their commitment to chiropractic and why this scholarship should be awarded to them. **Deadline for Receipt:** April of each year. **Additional Information:** Approved ICA chiropractic colleges include Cleveland Chiropractic College of Kansas City, Cleveland Chiropractic College of Los Angeles, Life Chiropractic College (Marietta, Georgia), Life Chiropractic College-West (Hayward, California), Logan College of Chiropractic, (Chesterfield, Missouri), Los Angeles College of Chiropractic, New York Chiropractic College (Seneca Falls, New York), Palmer College of Chiropractic (Davenport, Iowa), Palmer College of Chiropractic-West (San Jose, California), and Palmer College of Chiropractic-Florida (Port Orange, Florida). Information is also available from Jackie Ballard, ICAA Scholarship Chair, 815 Jefferson Avenue, Huntington, WV 25704.

Dentistry

2764 ■ ALASKA COMMISSION ON POSTSECONDARY EDUCATION
Attn: AlaskAdvantage Programs
3030 Vintage Boulevard
Juneau, AK 99801-7109
Tel: (907)465-6779; (866)427-5683
Fax: (907)465-5316
E-mail: customer_service@acpe.ak.us
Web Site: http://alaskaadvantage.state.ak.us/page/256
To provide educational loans to Alaska residents who attend out-of-state professional schools in specified fields through the Professional Student Exchange Program (PSEP) of the Western Interstate Commission for Higher Education (WICHE).
Title of Award: Alaska Professional Student Exchange Loan Program **Area, Field, or Subject:** Dentistry; Medical assisting; Occupational therapy; Optometry; Pharmaceutical sciences; Physical therapy; Podiatry **Level of Education for which Award is Granted:** Undergraduate **Number Awarded:** Varies each year. **Funds Available:** Loans up to the annual support fee are available, to a maximum of $17,200. No origination fee is charged. The interest rate is 6%. **Duration:** 1 year; may be renewed.
Eligibility Requirements: This program is open to residents of Alaska who are attending a professional school in another state as part of the PSEP of WICHE. The fields of study currently available are dentistry, occupational therapy, optometry, physician assistant, podiatry, pharmacy, and physical therapy. In most cases, PSEP students pay resident tuition

(or reduced tuition at private institutions) and their home state pays an additional support fee to the institution. Alaska requires PSEP students to pay the tuition and support fee, and provides these loans to enable them to do so.

2765 ■ AMERICAN ASSOCIATION OF WOMEN DENTISTS

330 South Wells Street, Suite 1100
Chicago, IL 60606
Tel: (312)913-9327
Free: 800-920-AAWD
Fax: (312)461-0238
E-mail: info@aawd.org
Web Site: http://www.aawd.org
To provide low-interest loans to promising women dental students.
Title of Award: Gillette Hayden Memorial Foundation Loan Program **Area, Field, or Subject:** Dentistry **Level of Education for which Award is Granted:** Four Year College, Graduate **Number Awarded:** Varies, depending upon available funds; generally ranges from 2 to 6 each year. **Funds Available:** Loans are made up to $2,000. Interest at 5% begins 1 month after graduation. The note is due and payable 13 months after graduation. **Eligibility Requirements:** Eligible to apply are women dental students exhibiting financial need who are juniors, seniors, or graduate students. Selection is based on scholarship, need for assistance, and reasons for and amount of indebtedness already accumulated. **Deadline for Receipt:** July of each year.

2766 ■ AMERICAN DENTAL ASSOCIATION

Attn: ADA Foundation
211 East Chicago Avenue
Chicago, IL 60611
Tel: (312)440-2547
Fax: (312)440-3526
E-mail: adaf@ada.org
Web Site: http://www.ada.org/ada/prod/adaf/prog_scholarship_prog.asp
To provide financial assistance to dental assisting students.
Title of Award: ADA Dental Assisting Scholarships **Area, Field, or Subject:** Dental laboratory technology **Level of Education for which Award is Granted:** Undergraduate **Number Awarded:** 10 each year. **Funds Available:** Stipends range up to $1,000 per year. Funds are to be used to cover school expenses (tuition, fees, books, supplies, living expenses) and are paid in 2 equal installments to the recipient's school. **Duration:** 1 year. **Eligibility Requirements:** Applicants must be U.S. citizens and entering students accepted by a dental assisting program accredited by the Commission on Dental Accreditation. They must have a GPA of 3.0 or higher and be able to demonstrate financial need of at least $1,000. Selection is based on academic achievement, a written summary of personal and professional goals, letters of reference, and financial need. **Deadline for Receipt:** September of each year. **Additional Information:** This program was established in 1991.

2767 ■ AMERICAN DENTAL ASSOCIATION

Attn: ADA Foundation
211 East Chicago Avenue
Chicago, IL 60611
Tel: (312)440-2547
Fax: (312)440-3526
E-mail: adaf@ada.org
Web Site: http://www.ada.org/ada/prod/adaf/prog_scholarship_prog.asp
To provide financial assistance to dental hygiene students.
Title of Award: ADA Dental Hygiene Scholarships **Area, Field, or Subject:** Dental hygiene **Level of Education for which Award is Granted:** Undergraduate **Number Awarded:** 15 each year. **Funds Available:** Stipends range up to $1,000 per year. Funds are to be used to cover school expenses (tuition, fees, books, supplies, living expenses) and are paid in 2 equal installments to the recipient's school. **Duration:** 1 year. **Eligibility Requirements:** Applicants must be U.S. citizens and entering their final year of study at a dental hygiene program accredited by the Commission on Dental Accreditation. They must have a GPA of 3.0 or higher and be able to demonstrate financial need of at least $1,000. Selection is based on academic achievement, a written summary of

personal and professional goals, letters of reference, and financial need. **Deadline for Receipt:** August of each year. **Additional Information:** This program was established in 1991.

2768 ■ AMERICAN DENTAL ASSOCIATION

Attn: ADA Foundation
211 East Chicago Avenue
Chicago, IL 60611
Tel: (312)440-2547
Fax: (312)440-3526
E-mail: adaf@ada.org
Web Site: http://www.ada.org/ada/prod/adaf/prog_scholarship_prog.asp
To provide financial assistance to dental laboratory technology students.
Title of Award: ADA Dental Laboratory Technology Scholarships **Area, Field, or Subject:** Dental laboratory technology **Level of Education for which Award is Granted:** Undergraduate **Number Awarded:** 5 each year. **Funds Available:** Stipends range up to $1,000 per year. Funds are to be used to cover school expenses (tuition, fees, books, supplies, living expenses) and are paid in 2 equal installments to the recipient's school. **Duration:** 1 year. **Eligibility Requirements:** Applicants must be U.S. citizens and entering their final year of study at a dental laboratory technology program accredited by the Commission on Dental Accreditation. They must have a GPA of 3.0 or higher and be able to demonstrate financial need of at least $1,000. Selection is based on academic achievement, a written summary of personal and professional goals, letters of reference, and financial need. **Deadline for Receipt:** August of each year. **Additional Information:** This program, established in 1991, is sponsored by Handler Manufacturing, Inc.

2769 ■ AMERICAN DENTAL EDUCATION ASSOCIATION

Attn: Awards Selection Committee
1400 K Street, N.W., Suite 1100
Washington, DC 20005
Tel: (202)289-7201
Fax: (202)289-7204
E-mail: MorganM@ada.org
Web Site: http://www.adea.org
To provide financial assistance to dental hygiene students who are interested in an academic career.
Title of Award: Oral-B Scholarships for Dental Hygiene Students Pursuing Academic Careers **Area, Field, or Subject:** Dental hygiene **Level of Education for which Award is Granted:** Four Year College, Graduate **Number Awarded:** 2 each year. **Funds Available:** The stipend is $2,500. Funds are applied to tuition and fees. **Duration:** 1 year; nonrenewable. **Eligibility Requirements:** This program is open to students who have graduated from an accredited dental hygiene program with an associate degree or certificate to practice dental hygiene and are currently enrolled in a degree completion program for a bachelor's or graduate degree at an institution that is a member of the American Dental Education Association (ADEA). Applicants must show a commitment to pursuing an academic degree in dental hygiene and be individual ADEA members. Along with their application, they must submit a personal statement that details their experiences, influences, and decision-making that demonstrate a firm commitment to become an allied dental faculty member. Priority is given to qualified candidates enrolled in bachelor's degree completion programs. **Deadline for Receipt:** December of each year. **Additional Information:** Funding for this program is provided by Oral-B Laboratories.

2770 ■ AMERICAN DENTAL HYGIENISTS' ASSOCIATION

Attn: Institute for Oral Health
444 North Michigan Avenue, Suite 3400
Chicago, IL 60611
Tel: (312)440-8918
Free: 800-735-4916
Fax: (312)440-8929
E-mail: institute@adha.net
Web Site: http://www.adha.org/institute/Scholarship/index.htm
To provide financial assistance to undergraduate students who are preparing for careers in dental hygiene and have been active in community service activities.
Title of Award: Cadbury Adams Community Outreach Scholarships **Area, Field, or Subject:** Dental hygiene **Level of Education for which Award**

is Granted: Undergraduate **Number Awarded:** 10 each year. **Funds Available:** Stipends range from $1,000 to $2,000. **Duration:** 1 year.
Eligibility Requirements: This program is open to full-time undergraduate students who are active members of the Student American Dental Hygienists' Association (SADHA) or the American Dental Hygienists' Association (ADHA). Applicants must have a GPA of 3.0 or higher, be able to document financial need of at least $1,500, and have completed at least 1 year in an accredited dental hygiene program in the United States. Along with their application, they must submit 2 essays: 1) a statement that covers their long-term career goals, their intended contribution to the dental hygiene profession, their professional interests, and the manner in which their degree will enhance their professional capacity; and 2) an essay on their commitment to improving oral health through community service and specific examples of community service projects in which they have participated. **Deadline for Receipt:** April of each year. **Additional Information:** This program, established in 2004, is sponsored by Cadbury Adams, maker of Trident Sugarfree Chewing Gum.

2771 ■ AMERICAN DENTAL HYGIENISTS' ASSOCIATION

Attn: Institute for Oral Health
444 North Michigan Avenue, Suite 3400
Chicago, IL 60611
Tel: (312)440-8918
Free: 800-735-4916
Fax: (312)440-8929
E-mail: institute@adha.net
Web Site: http://www.adha.org/institute/Scholarship/index.htm
To provide financial assistance to needy undergraduate students preparing for careers in dental hygiene.
Title of Award: ADHA Institute General Scholarships **Area, Field, or Subject:** Dental hygiene **Level of Education for which Award is Granted:** Undergraduate **Number Awarded:** Varies each year; recently, 20 of these scholarships were awarded. **Funds Available:** Stipends range from $1,000 to $2,000. **Duration:** 1 year.
Eligibility Requirements: This program is open to full-time undergraduate students who are active members of the Student American Dental Hygienists' Association (SADHA) or the American Dental Hygienists' Association (ADHA). Applicants must have a GPA of 3.0 or higher, be able to document financial need of at least $1,500, and have completed at least 1 year in an accredited dental hygiene program in the United States. Along with their application, they must submit a statement that covers their long-term career goals, their intended contribution to the dental hygiene profession, their professional interests, and the manner in which their degree will enhance their professional capacity. **Deadline for Receipt:** April of each year.

2772 ■ AMERICAN DENTAL HYGIENISTS' ASSOCIATION

Attn: Institute for Oral Health
444 North Michigan Avenue, Suite 3400
Chicago, IL 60611
Tel: (312)440-8918
Free: 800-735-4916
Fax: (312)440-8929
E-mail: institute@adha.net
Web Site: http://www.adha.org/institute/Scholarship/index.htm
To provide financial assistance to exceptional undergraduate students preparing for careers in dental hygiene.
Title of Award: ADHA Institute Merit Scholarships **Area, Field, or Subject:** Dental hygiene **Level of Education for which Award is Granted:** Undergraduate **Number Awarded:** Varies each year; the ADHA awards 10% of all general scholarship funds on the basis of academic merit. **Funds Available:** Stipends range from $1,000 to $2,000. **Duration:** 1 year.
Eligibility Requirements: This program is open to full-time undergraduate students who are active members of the Student American Dental Hygienists' Association (SADHA) or the American Dental Hygienists' Association (ADHA). Applicants must have a GPA of 3.0 or higher, be able to demonstrate exceptional academic merit, and have completed at least 1

year in an accredited dental hygiene program in the United States. Financial need is not considered in the selection process. **Deadline for Receipt:** April of each year.

2773 ■ AMERICAN DENTAL HYGIENISTS' ASSOCIATION

Attn: Institute for Oral Health
444 North Michigan Avenue, Suite 3400
Chicago, IL 60611
Tel: (312)440-8918
Free: 800-735-4916
Fax: (312)440-8929
E-mail: institute@adha.net
Web Site: http://www.adha.org/institute/Scholarship/index.htm
To provide financial assistance to students enrolled part time in doctoral, master's, baccalaureate, or certificate/associate programs in dental hygiene.
Title of Award: ADHA Institute Part-Time Scholarship **Area, Field, or Subject:** Dental hygiene **Level of Education for which Award is Granted:** Graduate, Undergraduate **Number Awarded:** 1 each year. **Funds Available:** Stipends range from $1,000 to $2,000. **Duration:** 1 year.
Eligibility Requirements: This program is open to part-time undergraduate and graduate students who are active members of the Student American Dental Hygienists' Association (SADHA) or the American Dental Hygienists' Association (ADHA). Applicants must have a GPA of 3.0 or higher, be able to document financial need of at least $1,500, and have completed at least 1 year in an accredited dental hygiene program in the United States. Along with their application, they must submit a statement that covers their long-term career goals, their intended contribution to the dental hygiene profession, their professional interests, and the manner in which their degree will enhance their professional capacity. **Deadline for Receipt:** April of each year.

2774 ■ AMERICAN DENTAL HYGIENISTS' ASSOCIATION

Attn: Institute for Oral Health
444 North Michigan Avenue, Suite 3400
Chicago, IL 60611
Tel: (312)440-8918
Free: 800-243-2342
Fax: (312)440-8929
E-mail: institute@adha.net
Web Site: http://www.adha.org/institute/Grants/Research/rg-description.htm
To provide funding to dental hygienists and dental hygiene students who are interested in conducting research.
Title of Award: ADHA Institute Research Grant Competition **Area, Field, or Subject:** Dental hygiene **Level of Education for which Award is Granted:** Graduate, Professional, Undergraduate **Number Awarded:** 1 or more each year. **Funds Available:** Grants range from $1,000 to $10,000 for licensed hygienists or from $1,000 to $5,000 for dental hygiene students. **Duration:** 1 year.
Eligibility Requirements: This program is open to licensed dental hygienists and to dental hygiene students, undergraduate or graduate, full-time or part-time. Applicants must be proposing to conduct research related to dental hygiene. They must be active members of the Student American Dental Hygienists' Association (SADHA) or the American Dental Hygienists' Association (ADHA). Priority is given to proposals addressing these topics: access to care/underserved populations, health promotion and disease prevention, alternative practice settings, and oral health public policy. **Deadline for Receipt:** January of each year.

2775 ■ AMERICAN DENTAL HYGIENISTS' ASSOCIATION

Attn: Institute for Oral Health
444 North Michigan Avenue, Suite 3400
Chicago, IL 60611
Tel: (312)440-8918
Free: 800-735-4916
Fax: (312)440-8929
E-mail: institute@adha.net
Web Site: http://www.adha.org/institute/Scholarship/index.htm
To provide financial assistance to minority students and males of any race enrolled in undergraduate programs in dental hygiene.
Title of Award: American Dental Hygienists' Association Institute Minority Scholarships **Area, Field, or Subject:** Dental hygiene **Level of Educa-

tion for which Award is Granted: Undergraduate **Number Awarded:** 2 each year. **Funds Available:** Stipends range from $1,000 to $2,000. **Duration:** 1 year; nonrenewable.

Eligibility Requirements: This program is open to members of groups currently underrepresented in the dental hygiene profession (Native Americans, African Americans, Hispanics, Asians, and males) who are active members of the Student American Dental Hygienists' Association (SADHA) or the American Dental Hygienists' Association (ADHA). Applicants must have a GPA of 3.0 or higher, be able to document financial need of at least $1,500, and have completed at least 1 year of full-time enrollment in an accredited dental hygiene program in the United States. Along with their application, they must submit a statement that covers their long-term career goals, their intended contribution to the dental hygiene profession, their professional interests, and the manner in which their degree will enhance their professional capacity. **Deadline for Receipt:** April of each year.

2776 ■ AMERICAN DENTAL HYGIENISTS' ASSOCIATION

Attn: Institute for Oral Health
444 North Michigan Avenue, Suite 3400
Chicago, IL 60611
Tel: (312)440-8918
Free: 800-735-4916
Fax: (312)440-8929
E-mail: institute@adha.net
Web Site: http://www.adha.org/institute/Scholarship/index.htm
To provide financial assistance to undergraduate students in selected states who are preparing for careers in dental hygiene.

Title of Award: Carol Bauhs Benson Memorial Scholarship **Area, Field, or Subject:** Dental hygiene **Level of Education for which Award is Granted:** Four Year College **Number Awarded:** 1 each year. **Funds Available:** Stipends range from $1,000 to $2,000. **Duration:** 1 year.

Eligibility Requirements: This program is open to full-time undergraduate students who are active members of the Student American Dental Hygienists' Association (SADHA) or the American Dental Hygienists' Association (ADHA). Applicants must have a GPA of 3.0 or higher, be able to document financial need of at least $1,500, and have completed at least 1 year in an accredited dental hygiene program in Minnesota, North Dakota, South Dakota, or Wisconsin. Along with their application, they must submit a statement that covers their long-term career goals, their intended contribution to the dental hygiene profession, their professional interests, and the manner in which their degree will enhance their professional capacity. **Deadline for Receipt:** April of each year.

2777 ■ AMERICAN DENTAL HYGIENISTS' ASSOCIATION

Attn: Institute for Oral Health
444 North Michigan Avenue, Suite 3400
Chicago, IL 60611
Tel: (312)440-8918
Free: 800-735-4916
Fax: (312)440-8929
E-mail: institute@adha.net
Web Site: http://www.adha.org/institute/Scholarship/index.htm
To provide financial assistance to minority students and males of any race enrolled in undergraduate programs in dental hygiene.

Title of Award: Colgate "Bright Smiles, Bright Futures" Minority Scholarships **Area, Field, or Subject:** Dental hygiene **Level of Education for which Award is Granted:** Undergraduate **Number Awarded:** 2 each year. **Funds Available:** Stipends range from $1,000 to $2,000. **Duration:** 1 year; nonrenewable.

Eligibility Requirements: This program is open to members of groups currently underrepresented in the dental hygiene profession (Native Americans, African Americans, Hispanics, Asians, and males) who are active members of the Student American Dental Hygienists' Association (SADHA) or the American Dental Hygienists' Association (ADHA). Applicants must have a GPA of 3.0 or higher, be able to document financial need of at least $1,500, and have completed at least 1 year of full-time enrollment in an accredited dental hygiene program in the United States. Along with their application, they must submit a statement that covers their long-term career goals, their intended contribution to the dental hygiene profession, their professional interests, and the manner in which their degree will enhance their professional capacity. **Deadline for Receipt:** April of each year. **Additional Information:** These scholarships

are sponsored by the Colgate-Palmolive Company.

2778 ■ AMERICAN DENTAL HYGIENISTS' ASSOCIATION

Attn: Institute for Oral Health
444 North Michigan Avenue, Suite 3400
Chicago, IL 60611
Tel: (312)440-8918
Free: 800-735-4916
Fax: (312)440-8929
E-mail: institute@adha.net
Web Site: http://www.adha.org/institute/Scholarship/index.htm
To provide financial assistance to undergraduate students preparing for careers in dental hygiene.

Title of Award: Rebecca Fisk Scholarship **Area, Field, or Subject:** Dental hygiene **Level of Education for which Award is Granted:** Undergraduate **Number Awarded:** 1 each year. **Funds Available:** Stipends range from $1,000 to $2,000. **Duration:** 1 year.

Eligibility Requirements: This program is open to full-time undergraduate students who are active members of the Student American Dental Hygienists' Association (SADHA) or the American Dental Hygienists' Association (ADHA). Applicants must have a GPA of 3.0 or higher, be able to document financial need of at least $1,500, and have completed at least 1 year in an accredited dental hygiene program in the United States. Along with their application, they must submit a statement that covers their long-term career goals, their intended contribution to the dental hygiene profession, their professional interests, and the manner in which their degree will enhance their professional capacity. **Deadline for Receipt:** April of each year.

2779 ■ AMERICAN DENTAL HYGIENISTS' ASSOCIATION

Attn: Institute for Oral Health
444 North Michigan Avenue, Suite 3400
Chicago, IL 60611
Tel: (312)440-8918
Free: 800-735-4916
Fax: (312)440-8929
E-mail: institute@adha.net
Web Site: http://www.adha.org/institute/Scholarship/index.htm
To provide financial assistance to dental hygiene students who are in a bachelor's or graduate degree program and intend to become teachers or educators.

Title of Award: Dr. Alfred C. Fones Scholarship **Area, Field, or Subject:** Dental hygiene **Level of Education for which Award is Granted:** Graduate, Four Year College **Number Awarded:** 1 each year. **Funds Available:** Stipends range from $1,000 to $2,000. **Duration:** 1 year.

Eligibility Requirements: This program is open to dental hygiene students at the baccalaureate, master's, and doctoral level who have completed at least 1 year of study with a GPA of at least 3.0. Applicants must intend to prepare for a career as a dental hygiene teacher or educator. They must be active members of the Student American Dental Hygienists' Association (SADHA) or the American Dental Hygienists' Association (ADHA) and be able to document financial need of at least $1,500. Along year in an accredited dental hygiene program in the United States. Along with their application, they must submit a statement that covers their long-term career goals, their intended contribution to the dental hygiene profession, their professional interests, and the manner in which their degree will enhance their professional capacity. Graduate applicants must also include a description of the research in which they are involved or would like to become involved and a list of past and/or present involvement in professional and/or community activities. **Deadline for Receipt:** April of each year.

2780 ■ AMERICAN DENTAL HYGIENISTS' ASSOCIATION

Attn: Institute for Oral Health
444 North Michigan Avenue, Suite 3400
Chicago, IL 60611
Tel: (312)440-8918
Free: 800-735-4916
Fax: (312)440-8929
E-mail: institute@adha.net
Web Site: http://www.adha.org/institute/Scholarship/index.htm
To provide financial assistance to students enrolled in a baccalaureate dental hygiene program who can demonstrate exceptional academic and clinical performance.

Title of Award: Dr. Harold Hillenbrand Scholarship **Area, Field, or Subject:** Dental hygiene **Level of Education for which Award is Granted:** Four Year College **Number Awarded:** 1 each year. **Funds Available:** Stipends range from $1,000 to $2,000. **Duration:** 1 year.
Eligibility Requirements: This program is open to full-time undergraduate students who are active members of the Student American Dental Hygienists' Association (SADHA) or the American Dental Hygienists' Association (ADHA). Applicants must have a GPA of 3.5 or higher, be able to document financial need of at least $1,500, be able to demonstrate academic excellence and outstanding clinical performance, and have completed at least 1 year in an accredited dental hygiene program in the United States. Along with their application, they must submit a statement that covers their long-term career goals, their intended contribution to the dental hygiene profession, their professional interests, and the manner in which their degree will enhance their professional capacity. **Deadline for Receipt:** April of each year.

2781 ■ AMERICAN DENTAL HYGIENISTS' ASSOCIATION

Attn: Institute for Oral Health
444 North Michigan Avenue, Suite 3400
Chicago, IL 60611
Tel: (312)440-8918
Free: 800-735-4916
Fax: (312)440-8929
E-mail: institute@adha.net
Web Site: http://www.adha.org/institute/Scholarship/index.htm
To provide financial assistance to undergraduate students preparing for careers in dental hygiene.
Title of Award: Marsh Affinity Group Services Scholarship **Area, Field, or Subject:** Dental hygiene **Level of Education for which Award is Granted:** Undergraduate **Number Awarded:** 1 each year. **Funds Available:** Stipends range from $1,000 to $2,000. **Duration:** 1 year.
Eligibility Requirements: This program is open to full-time undergraduate students who are active members of the Student American Dental Hygienists' Association (SADHA) or the American Dental Hygienists' Association (ADHA). Applicants must have a GPA between 3.0 and 3.5, be able to document financial need of at least $1,500, and have completed at least 1 year in an accredited dental hygiene program in the United States. Along with their application, they must submit a statement that covers their long-term career goals, their intended contribution to the dental hygiene profession, their professional interests, and the manner in which their degree will enhance their professional capacity. **Deadline for Receipt:** April of each year. **Additional Information:** This program is sponsored by Marsh Affinity Group Services, a service of Seabury and Smith, Inc.

2782 ■ AMERICAN DENTAL HYGIENISTS' ASSOCIATION

Attn: Institute for Oral Health
444 North Michigan Avenue, Suite 3400
Chicago, IL 60611
Tel: (312)440-8918
Free: 800-735-4916
Fax: (312)440-8929
E-mail: institute@adha.net
Web Site: http://www.adha.org/institute/Scholarship/index.htm
To provide financial assistance to undergraduate students in California preparing for careers in dental hygiene.
Title of Award: Wilma Motley California Merit Scholarship **Area, Field, or Subject:** Dental hygiene **Level of Education for which Award is Granted:** Undergraduate **Number Awarded:** 1 each year. **Funds Available:** Stipends range from $1,000 to $2,000. **Duration:** 1 year.
Eligibility Requirements: This program is open to full-time undergraduate students who are active members of the Student American Dental Hygienists' Association (SADHA) or the American Dental Hygienists' Association (ADHA). Applicants must have a GPA of 3.5 or higher, be able to demonstrate exceptional academic merit, and have completed at least 1 year in an accredited dental hygiene program in California. Financial need is not considered in the selection process. **Deadline for Receipt:** April of each year.

2783 ■ AMERICAN DENTAL HYGIENISTS' ASSOCIATION

Attn: Institute for Oral Health
444 North Michigan Avenue, Suite 3400
Chicago, IL 60611

Tel: (312)440-8918
Free: 800-735-4916
Fax: (312)440-8929
E-mail: institute@adha.net
Web Site: http://www.adha.org/institute/Scholarship/index.htm
To provide financial assistance to undergraduate students who are preparing for careers in dental hygiene and have a 4.0 GPA.
Title of Award: Wilma E. Motley Scholarship **Area, Field, or Subject:** Dental hygiene **Level of Education for which Award is Granted:** Undergraduate **Number Awarded:** 1 each year. **Funds Available:** Stipends range from $1,000 to $2,000. **Duration:** 1 year.
Eligibility Requirements: This program is open to full-time undergraduate students who are active members of the Student American Dental Hygienists' Association (SADHA) or the American Dental Hygienists' Association (ADHA). Applicants must have a GPA of 4.0, be able to document financial need of at least $1,500, and have completed at least 1 year in an accredited dental hygiene program in the United States. Along with their application, they must submit a statement that covers their long-term career goals, their intended contribution to the dental hygiene profession, their professional interests, and the manner in which their degree will enhance their professional capacity. **Deadline for Receipt:** April of each year.

2784 ■ AMERICAN DENTAL HYGIENISTS' ASSOCIATION

Attn: Institute for Oral Health
444 North Michigan Avenue, Suite 3400
Chicago, IL 60611
Tel: (312)440-8918
Free: 800-735-4916
Fax: (312)440-8929
E-mail: institute@adha.net
Web Site: http://www.adha.org/institute/Scholarship/index.htm
To provide financial assistance to students in a baccalaureate or graduate degree program in dental hygiene who demonstrate strong potential in public health or community dental health.
Title of Award: Irene E. Newman Scholarship **Area, Field, or Subject:** Dental hygiene; Public health **Level of Education for which Award is Granted:** Graduate, Four Year College **Number Awarded:** 1 each year. **Funds Available:** Stipends range from $1,000 to $2,000. **Duration:** 1 year.
Eligibility Requirements: This program is open to students who have completed at least 1 year in a dental hygiene program at the baccalaureate, master's, or doctoral level with a GPA of at least 3.0. Applicants must demonstrate strong potential in public health or community dental health. They must be active members of the Student American Dental Hygienists' Association (SADHA) or the American Dental Hygienists' Association (ADHA) and be able to document financial need of at least $1,500. Along with their application, they must submit a statement that covers their long-term career goals, their intended contribution to the dental hygiene profession, their professional interests, and the manner in which their degree will enhance their professional capacity. Graduate applicants must also include a description of the research in which they are involved or would like to become involved and a list of past and/or present involvement in professional and/or community activities, and full-time enrollment. Selection is based on their potential in public health or community dental health. **Deadline for Receipt:** April of each year.

2785 ■ AMERICAN DENTAL HYGIENISTS' ASSOCIATION

Attn: Institute for Oral Health
444 North Michigan Avenue, Suite 3400
Chicago, IL 60611
Tel: (312)440-8918
Free: 800-735-4916
Fax: (312)440-8929
E-mail: institute@adha.net
Web Site: http://www.adha.org/institute/Scholarship/index.htm
To provide financial assistance to baccalaureate students in dental hygiene.
Title of Award: Oral-B Laboratories Dental Hygiene Scholarships **Area, Field, or Subject:** Dental hygiene **Level of Education for which Award is Granted:** Four Year College **Number Awarded:** 2 each year. **Funds Available:** Stipends range from $1,000 to $2,000. **Duration:** 1 year.
Eligibility Requirements: This program is open to full-time undergraduate students who are active members of the Student American Dental

Hygienists' Association (SADHA) or the American Dental Hygienists' Association (ADHA). Applicants must have a GPA of 3.5 or higher, be able to document financial need of at least $1,500, be able to demonstrate academic excellence and outstanding clinical performance, and have completed at least 1 year in an accredited dental hygiene program in the United States. They must be able to demonstrate an intent to encourage professional excellence and scholarship, quality research, and dental hygiene through public and private education. Along with their application, they must submit a statement that covers their long-term career goals, their intended contribution to the dental hygiene profession, their professional interests, and the manner in which their degree will enhance their professional capacity. **Deadline for Receipt:** April of each year. **Additional Information:** Funds for these scholarships are provided by Oral-B Laboratories.

2786 ■ AMERICAN DENTAL HYGIENISTS' ASSOCIATION

Attn: Institute for Oral Health
444 North Michigan Avenue, Suite 3400
Chicago, IL 60611
Tel: (312)440-8918
Free: 800-735-4916
Fax: (312)440-8929
E-mail: institute@adha.net
Web Site: http://www.adha.org/institute/Scholarship/index.htm
To provide financial assistance to undergraduate students preparing for careers in dental hygiene.
Title of Award: Pfizer Inc. Scholarships **Area, Field, or Subject:** Dental hygiene **Level of Education for which Award is Granted:** Undergraduate **Number Awarded:** 5 each year. **Funds Available:** Stipends range from $1,000 to $2,000. **Duration:** 1 year.
Eligibility Requirements: This program is open to full-time undergraduate students who are active members of the Student American Dental Hygienists' Association (SADHA) or the American Dental Hygienists' Association (ADHA). Applicants must have a GPA of 3.5 or higher, be able to document financial need of at least $1,500, and have completed at least 1 year in an accredited dental hygiene program in the United States. Along with their application, they must submit a statement that covers their long-term career goals, their intended contribution to the dental hygiene profession, their professional interests, and the manner in which their degree will enhance their professional capacity. **Deadline for Receipt:** April of each year. **Additional Information:** This program is sponsored by Pfizer Inc.

2787 ■ AMERICAN DENTAL HYGIENISTS' ASSOCIATION

Attn: Institute for Oral Health
444 North Michigan Avenue, Suite 3400
Chicago, IL 60611
Tel: (312)440-8918
Free: 800-735-4916
Fax: (312)440-8929
E-mail: institute@adha.net
Web Site: http://www.adha.org/institute/Scholarship/index.htm
To provide financial assistance to full-time students enrolled in undergraduate programs in dental hygiene who are members of Sigma Phi Alpha.
Title of Award: Sigma Phi Alpha Undergraduate Scholarship Program **Area, Field, or Subject:** Dental hygiene **Level of Education for which Award is Granted:** Undergraduate **Number Awarded:** 1 each year. **Funds Available:** Stipends range from $1,000 to $2,000. **Duration:** 1 year.
Eligibility Requirements: This program is open to full-time undergraduate students who are active members of Sigma Phi Alpha. Applicants must have a GPA of 3.5 or higher, be able to document financial need of at least $1,500, and have completed at least 1 year in an accredited dental hygiene program in the United States. Along with their application, they must submit a statement that covers their long-term career goals, their intended contribution to the dental hygiene profession, their professional interests, and the manner in which their degree will enhance their professional capacity. **Deadline for Receipt:** April of each year.

2788 ■ AMERICAN DENTAL HYGIENISTS' ASSOCIATION

Attn: Institute for Oral Health
444 North Michigan Avenue, Suite 3400
Chicago, IL 60611

Tel: (312)440-8918
Free: 800-735-4916
Fax: (312)440-8929
E-mail: institute@adha.net
Web Site: http://www.adha.org/institute/Scholarship/index.htm
To provide financial assistance to students enrolled in a dental hygiene program who demonstrate exceptional organizational leadership potential.
Title of Award: Margaret E. Swanson Scholarship **Area, Field, or Subject:** Dental hygiene **Level of Education for which Award is Granted:** Graduate, Undergraduate **Number Awarded:** 1 each year. **Funds Available:** Stipends range from $1,000 to $2,000. **Duration:** 1 year.
Eligibility Requirements: This program is open to students who have completed at least 1 year in a certificate/associate, baccalaureate, master's, or doctoral program in dental hygiene with at least a 3.0 GPA. Applicants must be able to demonstrate exceptional organizational leadership potential. They must be active members of the Student American Dental Hygienists' Association (SADHA) or the American Dental Hygienists' Association (ADHA) and be able to document financial need of at least $1,500. Along with their application, they must submit a statement that covers their long-term career goals, their intended contribution to the dental hygiene profession, their professional interests, and the manner in which their degree will enhance their professional capacity. Graduate applicants must also include a description of the research in which they are involved or would like to become involved and a list of past and/or present involvement in professional and/or community activities, and full-time enrollment. Selection is based on their potential in public health or community dental health. **Deadline for Receipt:** April of each year.

2789 ■ AMERICAN DENTAL HYGIENISTS' ASSOCIATION

Attn: Institute for Oral Health
444 North Michigan Avenue, Suite 3400
Chicago, IL 60611
Tel: (312)440-8918
Free: 800-735-4916
Fax: (312)440-8929
E-mail: institute@adha.net
Web Site: http://www.adha.org/institute/Scholarship/index.htm
To provide financial assistance to undergraduate students preparing for careers in dental hygiene.
Title of Award: Esther Wilkins/Lippincott Williams & Wilkins Scholarship **Area, Field, or Subject:** Dental hygiene **Level of Education for which Award is Granted:** Undergraduate **Number Awarded:** 1 each year. **Funds Available:** Stipends range from $1,000 to $2,000. **Duration:** 1 year.
Eligibility Requirements: This program is open to full-time undergraduate students who are active members of the Student American Dental Hygienists' Association (SADHA) or the American Dental Hygienists' Association (ADHA). Applicants must have a GPA of 3.5 or higher, be able to document financial need of at least $1,500, and have completed at least 1 year in an accredited dental hygiene program in the United States. Along with their application, they must submit a statement that covers their long-term career goals, their intended contribution to the dental hygiene profession, their professional interests, and the manner in which their degree will enhance their professional capacity. **Deadline for Receipt:** April of each year. **Additional Information:** This program is sponsored by Lippincott Williams & Wilkins.

2790 ■ H. FLETCHER BROWN TRUST

PNC Bank Delaware
Attn: Donald W. Davis
222 Delaware Avenue, 16th Floor
Wilmington, DE 19899
Tel: (302)429-2827
Fax: (302)429-5658
E-mail: Robbie.testa@pncadvisors.com
To provide financial assistance to residents of Delaware who are interested in studying engineering, chemistry, medicine, dentistry, or law.
Title of Award: H. Fletcher Brown Scholarship **Area, Field, or Subject:** Chemistry; Dentistry; Engineering; Law; Medicine; Medicine, Osteopathic **Level of Education for which Award is Granted:** Graduate, Professional, Undergraduate **Funds Available:** The amount of the scholarship is determined by the scholarship committee and is awarded in installments

over the length of study. **Duration:** 1 year; may be renewed if the recipient maintains a GPA of 2.5 or higher and continues to be worthy of and eligible for the award.

Eligibility Requirements: This program is open to Delaware residents who were born in Delaware, are either high school seniors entering the first year of college or college seniors entering the first year of graduate school, are of good moral character, and need financial assistance from sources outside their family. Applicants must have combined mathematics and verbal SAT scores of 1000 or higher, rank in the upper 20% of their class, and come from a family whose income is less than $75,000. Their proposed fields of study must be engineering, chemistry, medicine (for an M.D. or D.O. degree only), dentistry, or law. Finalists are interviewed. **Deadline for Receipt:** March of each year.

2791 ■ BUSINESS AND PROFESSIONAL WOMEN OF VIRGINIA

Attn: Virginia BPW Foundation
P.O. Box 4842
McLean, VA 22103-4842
Web Site: http://www.bpwva.org/Foundation.shtml
To provide financial assistance to women in Virginia who are interested in working on a bachelor's or advanced degree in science or technology.

Title of Award: Women in Science and Technology Scholarship **Area, Field, or Subject:** Actuarial science; Biological and clinical sciences; Chemistry; Computer and information sciences; Dentistry; Engineering; Engineering, Biomedical; Insurance and insurance-related fields; Mathematics and mathematical sciences; Medicine; Physics; Science; Technology **Level of Education for which Award is Granted:** Graduate, Undergraduate **Number Awarded:** At least 1 each year. **Funds Available:** Stipends range from $500 to $1,000 per year, depending on the need of the recipient; funds may be used for tuition, fees, books, transportation, living expenses, and dependent care. **Duration:** 1 year; recipients may reapply (but prior recipients are not given priority).

Eligibility Requirements: This program is open to women who are at least 18 years of age, U.S. citizens, Virginia residents, accepted at or currently studying at a Virginia college or university, and working on a bachelor's, master's, or doctoral degree in 1 of the following fields: actuarial science, biology, bioengineering, chemistry, computer science, dentistry, engineering, mathematics, medicine, physics, or a similar scientific or technical field. Applicants must have a definite plan to use their education in a scientific or technical profession. They must be able to demonstrate financial need. **Deadline for Receipt:** March of each year. **Additional Information:** Recipients must complete their studies within 2 years.

2792 ■ CANADIAN INSTITUTES OF HEALTH RESEARCH

Attn: Grants and Awards
160 Elgin Street, Ninth Floor
Address Locator 4809A
Ottawa, ON, Canada K1A 0W9
Tel: (613)954-1968; 888-603-4178
Fax: (613)954-1800
E-mail: info@cihr-irsc.gc.ca
Web Site: http://www.cihr-irsc.gc.ca
To provide research funding to undergraduate and graduate students interested in preparing for a career in health-related fields in Canada.

Title of Award: Health Professional Students Research Awards of the Canadian Institutes of Health Research **Area, Field, or Subject:** Dentistry; Medicine; Nursing; Optometry; Pharmaceutical sciences **Level of Education for which Award is Granted:** Graduate, Undergraduate **Number Awarded:** Varies each year. **Funds Available:** The stipend for students registered in a health professional school is $C1,417 per month. The stipend for students enrolled in a combined degree program is $C1,987 per month. **Duration:** Up to 3 months.

Eligibility Requirements: This program is open to 1) undergraduate and graduate students enrolled at Canadian schools offered programs leading to licensure in medicine, dentistry, nursing, physiotherapy, or related fields; and 2) medical students working on a combined degree (e.g., M.D./ M.Sc., M.D./Ph.D.). Applicants must have completed their first year of study and be interested in participating in a health research project. They must be citizens or permanent residents of Canada. **Deadline for Receipt:** February **Additional Information:** The Canadian Institutes of Health Research (CIHR) was formerly the Medical Research Council (MRC) of Canada. This program was formerly designated the Burroughs

Wellcome Fund Student Research Awards.

2793 ■ HAWAI'I COMMUNITY FOUNDATION

Attn: Scholarship Department
1164 Bishop Street, Suite 800
Honolulu, HI 96813
Tel: (808)566-5570; 888-731-3863
Fax: (808)521-6286
E-mail: scholarships@hcf-hawaii.org
Web Site: http://www.hawaiicommunityfoundation.org/scholar/scholar.php
To provide financial assistance to Hawaii residents who are interested in preparing for a career in the dental field.

Title of Award: John Dawe Dental Education Scholarship **Area, Field, or Subject:** Dental hygiene; Dentistry **Level of Education for which Award is Granted:** Graduate, Undergraduate **Number Awarded:** Varies each year; recently, 8 of these scholarships were awarded. **Funds Available:** The amounts of the awards depend on the availability of funds and the need of the recipient; recently, stipends averaged $1,000. **Duration:** 1 year.

Eligibility Requirements: This program is open to Hawaii residents who are interested in full-time study in dentistry, dental hygiene, or dental assisting. They must be able to demonstrate academic achievement (GPA of 2.7 or higher), good moral character, and financial need. In addition to filling out the standard application form, applicants must write a short statement indicating their reasons for attending college, their planned course of study, and their career goals. **Deadline for Receipt:** February of each year. **Additional Information:** Recipients may attend college in Hawaii or on the mainland.

2794 ■ INDIAN HEALTH SERVICE

Attn: Scholarship Program
801 Thompson Avenue, Suite 120
Rockville, MD 20852
Tel: (301)443-6197
Fax: (301)443-6048
E-mail: bmiller@na.ihs.gov
Web Site: http://www.ihs.gov
To provide financial support to American Indian students interested in majoring in pre-medicine or pre-dentistry in college.

Title of Award: Health Professions Pregraduate Scholarship Program **Area, Field, or Subject:** Dentistry; Medicine; Medicine, Osteopathic **Level of Education for which Award is Granted:** Undergraduate **Number Awarded:** Varies each year. **Funds Available:** Awards provide a payment directly to the school for tuition and required fees; a stipend for living expenses of approximately $1,160 per month for 10 months; a lump sum to cover the costs of books, travel, and other necessary educational expenses; and up to $400 for approved tutorial costs. **Duration:** Up to 4 years of full-time study or up to 8 years of part-time study.

Eligibility Requirements: Applicants must be American Indians or Alaska Natives; be high school graduates or the equivalent; have the capacity to complete a health professions course of study; and be enrolled or accepted for enrollment in a baccalaureate degree program to prepare for entry into a school of medicine, osteopathy, or dentistry. Priority is given to students entering their junior or senior year; support is provided to freshmen and sophomores only if remaining funds are available. Selection is based on academic performance, work experience and community background, faculty/employer recommendations, and applicant's reasons for seeking the scholarship. Recipients must intend to serve Indian people upon completion of their professional health care education. **Deadline for Receipt:** February of each year.

2795 ■ INDIAN HEALTH SERVICE

Attn: Scholarship Program
801 Thompson Avenue, Suite 120
Rockville, MD 20852
Tel: (301)443-6197
Fax: (301)443-6048
E-mail: bmiller@na.ihs.gov
Web Site: http://www.ihs.gov
To provide loans-for-service to American Indian and Alaska Native students enrolled in health professions and allied health professions programs.

Title of Award: Health Professions Scholarship Program **Area, Field, or Subject:** Counseling/Guidance; Dental hygiene; Dentistry; Health care services; Medical assisting; Medical technology; Medicine; Medicine, Osteopathic; Nursing; Nutrition; Optometry; Pharmaceutical sciences; Physical therapy; Podiatry; Psychology; Public health; Radiology; Respiratory therapy; Social work; **Level of Education for which Award is Granted:** Graduate, Undergraduate **Number Awarded:** Varies each year. **Funds Available:** Awards provide a payment directly to the school for tuition and required fees; a stipend for living expenses of approximately $1,160 per month for 12 months; a lump sum to cover the costs of books, travel, and other necessary educational expenses; and up to $400 for approved tutorial costs. Upon completion of their program of study, recipients are required to provide payback service of 1 year for each year of scholarship support at the Indian Health Service, a tribal health programs, an urban Indian health program, or in private practice in a designated health professional shortage area serving a substantial number of Indians. Recipients who fail to complete their service obligation must repay all funds received (although no interest is charged). **Duration:** 1 year; may be renewed for up to 3 additional years.

Eligibility Requirements: This program is open to American Indians and Alaska Natives who are at least high school graduates and enrolled in a full-time study program leading to a degree in a health-related professions school within the United States. Priority is given to upper-division and graduate students. Qualifying fields of study include chemical dependency counseling (bachelor's or master's degree), clinical psychology (Ph.D. only), coding specialist (certificate), counseling psychology (Ph.D. only), dental hygiene (B.S.), dentistry (D.D.S.), diagnostic radiology technology (certificate, associate, or B.S.), dietitian (B.S.), civil or environmental engineering (B.S.), environmental health (B.S.), health care administration (B.S. or M.S.), health education (B.S. or M.S.), health records (R.H.I.T. or R.H.I.A.), injury prevention specialist (certificate), medical technology (B.S.), allopathic and osteopathic medicine, nursing (A.D.N., B.S.N., or C.R.N.A), optometry, pharmacy (B.S. or Pharm.D.), physician assistant (B.S.), physical therapy (M.S. or D.P.T.), podiatry (D.P.M.), public health (M.P.H. only), public health nutrition (master's only), social work (master's only), respiratory therapy (associate), and ultrasonography. **Deadline for Receipt:** February of each year.

2796 ■ KOSTER INSURANCE AGENCY

Attn: Scholarship
500 Victory Road
Quincy, MA 02171
Tel: (617)770-9889
Free: 800-457-5599
Fax: (617)479-0860
E-mail: Scholarship@kosterins.com
Web Site: http://www.kosterweb.com/about/scholarship_main.php
To provide financial assistance to undergraduate students working on a degree in a health-related field.
Title of Award: Koster Insurance Health Careers Scholarship Program **Area, Field, or Subject:** Biological and clinical sciences; Chemistry; Dentistry; Health care services; Nursing; Occupational therapy; Optometry; Pharmaceutical sciences; Physical therapy; Physiology; Public health; Social work **Level of Education for which Award is Granted:** Undergraduate **Number Awarded:** 5 each year. **Funds Available:** The stipend is $3,000 per year. **Duration:** 1 year; may be renewed 1 additional year.

Eligibility Requirements: This program is open to full-time undergraduates entering their second-to-last or final year of study in a health-related field, including (but not limited to) pre-medicine, nursing, public and community health, physical therapy, occupational therapy, pharmacy, biology, chemistry, physiology, social work, dentistry, and optometry. Applicants must have a GPA of 3.0 or higher and be able to demonstrate financial need. Along with their application, they must submit a 1-page essay describing their personal goals, including their reasons for preparing for a career in health care. Selection is based on motivation to pursue a career in health care, academic excellence, dedication to community service, and financial need. **Deadline for Receipt:** April of each year. **Additional Information:** This program began in 2001.

2797 ■ PAPA OLA LOKAHI, INC.

Attn: Native Hawaiian Health Scholarship Program
345 Queen Street, Suite 706
Honolulu, HI 96813
Tel: (808)585-8944

Fax: (808)585-8081
E-mail: nhhsp@hawaii.rr.com
Web Site: http://www.nhhsp.org
To provide scholarship/loans to Native Hawaiians for training in the health professions in exchange for service in a federally-designated health professional shortage area (HPSA) or other facility for Native Hawaiians.
Title of Award: Native Hawaiian Health Scholarship Program **Area, Field, or Subject:** Dental hygiene; Dentistry; Family/Marital therapy; Health care services; Medical assisting; Medicine; Medicine, Osteopathic; Midwifery; Nursing; Nursing, Psychiatric; Psychiatry; Psychology; Public health **Level of Education for which Award is Granted:** Graduate, Undergraduate **Number Awarded:** Varies each year, depending upon the funding available. Since the program began, 151 scholars have received support. **Funds Available:** Full coverage of tuition and fees is paid directly to the health professional school. A stipend, current set at $1,157 per month, is paid directly to the scholar. This is a scholarship/loan program. Participants are obligated to provide full-time clinical primary health care services to populations in 1) a Native Hawaiian Health Care System, or 2) an HPSA in Hawaii, medically underserved area (MUA), or another area or facility in Hawaii designated by the U.S. Department of Health and Human Services. Participants owe 1 year of service in the National Health Service Corps for each full or partial year of support received under this program. The minimum service obligation is 2 years. **Duration:** 1 year; may be renewed for up to 3 additional years.

Eligibility Requirements: Applicants must be Native Hawaiians training in allopathic or osteopathic medicine, dentistry, clinical psychology, registered nursing, nurse midwifery, psychiatric nursing, public health/community nursing, social work, dental hygiene, physician assistant, public health, marriage and family therapy, or primary care nurse practitioner. They may be studying in any state. Recipients must agree to serve in a designated health-care facility in Hawaii upon completion of training. First priority is given to former scholars who have completed their previous service obligation and are seeking another year of support. Second priority is given to applicants who appear to have characteristics that increase the probability they will continue to serve underserved Native Hawaiians after the completion of their service obligations. **Deadline for Receipt:** March of each year. **Additional Information:** This program, which began in 1991, is administered by the U.S. Health Resources and Services Administration, Bureau of Health Professions, through a contract with Papa Ola Lokahi, Inc.

2798 ■ MAINE DENTAL ASSOCIATION

Attn: Executive Director
28 Association Drive
P.O. Box 215
Manchester, ME 04351-0215
Tel: (207)622-7900
Free: 800-369-8217
Fax: (207)622-6210
E-mail: info@medental.org
Web Site: http://www.medental.org/resources/student_resources.html
To provide educational loans to dental hygiene students from Maine.
Title of Award: Maine Dental Hygiene Student Loans **Area, Field, or Subject:** Dental hygiene **Level of Education for which Award is Granted:** Undergraduate **Number Awarded:** Varies each year. **Funds Available:** The maximum loan is $1,000 per academic term (semester, trimester, or 2 quarters). The loan aggregate may not exceed $3,000 during a 2-year program of study leading to a degree in dental hygiene, or $5,000 during a 3-year program of study, or $7,000 during a 4-year program of study. The total loan plus interest shall be due and payable 5 years from date of graduation or completion of postgraduate study. The interest rate is 4% while enrolled in dental hygiene school and during the first 6 months following graduation, 8% during the first full year through the fifth year following graduation or 4% during that period if the recipient secures employment in Maine, and 9% on any balance that remains unpaid at the end of 5 years following graduation. **Duration:** 1 term; may be renewed.

Eligibility Requirements: Applicants must have been residents of Maine for at least 5 years and have completed at least 1 semester of study in an accredited dental hygiene program. They must submit an up-to-date transcript of academic records and documentation of financial need.

2799 ■ NORTH CAROLINA STATE EDUCATION ASSISTANCE AUTHORITY

Attn: Scholarship and Grant Services
10 T.W. Alexander Drive
P.O. Box 14223
Research Triangle Park, NC 27709-4223
Tel: (919)549-8614
Free: 800-700-1775
Fax: (919)549-8481
E-mail: information@ncseaa.edu
Web Site: http://www.ncseaa.edu
To provide loans and loans-for-service to North Carolina residents who are interested in preparing for a career in health, science, or mathematics. **Title of Award:** North Carolina Student Loan Program for Health, Science, and Mathematics **Area, Field, or Subject:** Allied health; Dentistry; Medicine; Nursing; Optometry; Public health; Social work **Level of Education for which Award is Granted:** Graduate, Undergraduate **Number Awarded:** Varies each year; recently, a total of 497 students were receiving $3,238,569 in support through this program. **Funds Available:** Maximum loans are $3,000 per year for associate degree and certificate programs, $5,000 per year for baccalaureate degree/certificate programs, $6,500 per year for master's degree programs, or $8,500 per year for health/professional doctoral programs. The maximum amount that any student can borrow through this program is $58,000. The interest rate is 4% while the borrowers are attending school and from 10 to 15% after they leave school. Cash repayments must begin 90 days or less after completion of course work and training. Under specified conditions, certain loan recipients in qualifying disciplines may have their loans canceled through service in North Carolina. **Duration:** 1 year; renewable for 1 additional year for diploma, associate, certificate, and master's degree programs, for 2 additional years for baccalaureate degree programs, or for 3 additional years for doctoral programs. **Eligibility Requirements:** North Carolina residents are eligible to apply for this program if they have been accepted as full-time students in an accredited associate, baccalaureate, master's, or doctoral program leading to a degree in 1 of the following areas: allied health (including audiology/communications assistant, cytotechnology, dental hygiene, diagnostic medical sonographer, imaging technologist, medical technology, nuclear medicine technologist, occupational therapy/assistant, physician assistant, physical therapy/assistant, radiation therapist, radiography, respiratory therapy, and speech language pathology); clinical psychology (Ph.D. level only); dentistry; dietetics and nutrition (graduate level only); mathematics education; medicine (including chiropractic medicine, emergency medicine, family medicine, geriatrics, internal medicine, obstetrics and gynecology, osteopathic medicine, pediatrics, podiatry, primary care medicine, and psychiatry); nursing (including anesthetist, family nurse practitioner, nursing administration, general nursing, and midwifery); optometry; pharmacy; public health (graduate level only); science education (including biology, chemistry, communications and technologies, computer and information sciences, engineering, and physical science); social work (graduate level only); and veterinary medicine. U.S. citizenship is required. Selection is based on academic progress, financial ability of sureties to repay all loans and accrued interest in case of applicant's default, applicant's willingness to work in underserved areas of the state or in disciplines for which there is a shortage of professionals, applicant's willingness to comply with all program regulations, and financial need. **Deadline for Receipt:** May of each year. **Additional Information:** Recipients may attend a North Carolina postsecondary institution or an eligible out-of-state institution. This program was formerly known as the North Carolina Medical Student Loan Program.

2800 ■ TEXAS HIGHER EDUCATION COORDINATING BOARD

Attn: Hinson-Hazlewood College Student Loan Program
1200 East Anderson Lane
P.O. Box 12788, Capitol Station
Austin, TX 78711-2788
Tel: (512)427-6340
Free: 800-242-3062
Fax: (512)427-6423
E-mail: loaninfo@thecb.state.tx.us

Web Site: http://www.hhloans.com
To provide educational loans to students in Texas in health-related degree programs.
Title of Award: Hinson-Hazlewood Health Education Loan Program **Area, Field, or Subject:** Dentistry; Health care services; Medicine; Medicine, Osteopathic; Nursing; Optometry; Pharmaceutical sciences; Podiatry; Public health; Veterinary science and medicine **Level of Education for which Award is Granted:** Four Year College, Graduate **Number Awarded:** Varies each year. **Funds Available:** The maximum annual loan is $12,500 for pharmacy, nursing, allied health, and public health students; or $20,000 for medicine, dentistry, optometry, osteopathy, podiatry, or veterinary medicine students. The origination fee is 3%. After a grace period of 9 months, repayment must be completed within 25 years at a minimum monthly payment of $50. The current interest rate is 5.25% which begins to accrue immediately, even while the student is in school. **Duration:** 1 year; may be renewed up to 3 additional years. The maximum total loan is $50,000 for pharmacy, nursing, allied health, and public health students or $80,000 for medicine, dentistry, optometry, osteopathy, podiatry, or veterinary medicine students. **Eligibility Requirements:** This program is open to students who qualify as Texas residents and meet the academic requirements of a public or private college or university in the state. Applicants must be enrolled at least half time in a course of study leading to 1) a doctoral degree in medicine, dentistry, optometry, osteopathy, podiatry, or veterinary medicine; 2) a bachelor's or master's degree in pharmacy; 3) a graduate or equivalent degree in public health; or 4) an associate, bachelor's, or graduate degree in nursing or allied health fields. They must be able to demonstrate financial need and enroll full time. U.S. citizenship is required. **Additional Information:** Applications must be submitted through the financial aid office at the college or university attended. This program is part of the Hinton-Hazlewood College Student Loan Program (HHCSLP).

2801 ■ VERMONT STUDENT ASSISTANCE CORPORATION

Champlain Mill
Attn: Scholarship Programs
P.O. Box 2000
Winooski, VT 05404-2601
Tel: (802)654-3798; 888-253-4819
Fax: (802)654-3765
E-mail: info@vsac.org
Web Site: http://www.vsac.org
To provide financial assistance to Vermont residents who are studying dental hygiene.
Title of Award: Vermont Dental Hygiene Scholarship **Area, Field, or Subject:** Dental hygiene **Level of Education for which Award is Granted:** Undergraduate **Number Awarded:** 1 or more each year. **Funds Available:** The maximum stipend is $1,000. **Duration:** 1 year; nonrenewable.
Eligibility Requirements: This scholarship is available to residents of Vermont who are currently enrolled in the second year of a dental hygiene program. Selection is based on academic achievement (GPA of 3.0 or higher), letters of recommendation, required essays, and financial need. **Deadline for Receipt:** May of each year.

2802 ■ WASHINGTON DENTAL SERVICE FOUNDATION

Attn: Grant Administrator
P.O. Box 75688
Seattle, WA 98125
Tel: (206)528-2337
Free: 800-572-7835
Fax: (206)528-7373
E-mail: Foundation@DeltaDentalWA.com
Web Site: http://www.DeltaDentalWA.com
To provide financial assistance to members of underrepresented minority groups in Washington who are interested in preparing for a career as a dental hygienist, dental assistant, or laboratory technician.
Title of Award: Washington Dental Service Foundation Scholarships **Area, Field, or Subject:** Dental hygiene; Dental laboratory technology; Medical technology **Level of Education for which Award is Granted:** Two Year College, Vocational/Occupational **Number Awarded:** 1 or more each year. **Funds Available:** Stipends range from $1,000 to $4,000 per year, depending on the need of the recipient. **Duration:** 1 year.

Eligibility Requirements: This program is open to residents of Washington who are African or Black Americans, Native Americans, Alaskan Natives, Hispanics/Latinos, or Pacific Islanders. Applicants must be planning to enroll in an eligible program in dental hygiene, dental assisting, or laboratory technology at a community or technical college in the state. They must be able to demonstrate financial need. Along with their application, they must submit essays of 100 to 300 words on 1) why they are interested in becoming a dental professional; 2) their career goals, how they decided upon those goals, and how completion of their proposed program will help them reach those goals; 3) how they have prepared themselves academically for those chosen program of study; 4) a leadership experience they have had in school, work, athletics, family, church, community, or other area of their life; and 5) how they help or serve others in their family and/or community. **Deadline for Receipt:** September of each year.

2803 ■ WASHINGTON HIGHER EDUCATION COORDINATING BOARD

917 Lakeridge Way
P.O. Box 43430
Olympia, WA 98504-3430
Tel: (360)753-7844
Fax: (360)753-7808
E-mail: kathy.mcvay@hecb.wa.gov
Web Site: http://www.hecb.wa.gov/financialaid/other/health.asp
To provide scholarship/loans for primary care health professional education to students who agree to work in designated areas of Washington.
Title of Award: Washington State Health Professional Scholarship Program **Area, Field, or Subject:** Dental hygiene; Dentistry; Medicine; Medicine, Osteopathic; Midwifery; Nursing; Pharmaceutical sciences **Level of Education for which Award is Granted:** Graduate, Undergraduate **Number Awarded:** Varies each year. **Funds Available:** The stipend is intended to cover eligible expenses: tuition, books, equipment, fees, and room and board. This is a scholarship/loan program. Recipients who fail to complete the course of study are required to repay the amount received, plus a penalty and interest. Scholars who fail to serve in health professional shortage areas in Washington are required to repay the scholarship, with penalty plus interest. The interest rate on the repayments is 8% for the first 4 years and 10% for the fifth year. **Duration:** Up to 5 years.
Eligibility Requirements: Applicants must be enrolled or accepted for enrollment in an accredited program leading to eligibility for licensure in Washington State in a designated health profession. They must agree to practice in Washington for 3 to 5 years following graduation, but they do not need to be Washington residents or to attend an educational institution in the state. Currently, there are no geographic restrictions for registered nurses or practical nurses. For other primary care health professionals (M.D., D.O., N.D., P.A., N.P., C.N.M., L.M.), dental care professionals (D.D.S., R.D.H.), and pharmacists, service must be in designated areas of the state. State correctional facilities, state mental health facilities, community and migrant health centers, and any other facility with more than 40% of its caseload consisting of Medicaid and sliding fee patients also qualify. **Deadline for Receipt:** April of each year.

2804 ■ WASHINGTON STATE DENTAL HYGIENISTS' ASSOCIATION

Attn: Central Offices
P.O. Box 389
Lynnwood, WA 98046
Tel: (425)771-3201
Fax: (425)776-5289
E-mail: wsdha@verizon.net
Web Site: http://www.wsdha.com
To provide financial assistance to members of the Washington State Dental Hygienists' Association (WSDHA).
Title of Award: Lona Hulbush Jacobs Memorial Scholarship **Area, Field, or Subject:** Dental hygiene **Level of Education for which Award is Granted:** Undergraduate **Number Awarded:** 1 each year. **Funds Available:** The stipend is $1,000. **Duration:** 1 year.
Eligibility Requirements: This program is open to WSDHA members in the first year of a dental hygiene program. Applicants must have a GPA of 3.0 or higher and be able to demonstrate financial need. Along with their application, they must submit a brief essay on why they have pursued dental hygiene as a career. **Deadline for Receipt:** April of each year. **Ad-**

ditional Information: This program was established in 1986.

2805 ■ WESTERN INTERSTATE COMMISSION FOR HIGHER EDUCATION

Attn: Student Exchange Programs
3035 Center Green Drive
P.O. Box 9752
Boulder, CO 80301-9752
Tel: (303)541-0210
Fax: (303)541-0291
E-mail: info-sep@wiche.edu
Web Site: http://www.wiche.edu/sep/psep
To underwrite some of the cost of out-of-state professional schooling for students in selected western states.
Title of Award: Professional Student Exchange Program **Area, Field, or Subject:** Architecture; Dentistry; Library and archival sciences; Medical assisting; Medicine; Medicine, Osteopathic; Nursing; Occupational therapy; Optometry; Pharmaceutical sciences; Physical therapy; Podiatry; Public health; Veterinary science and medicine **Level of Education for which Award is Granted:** Graduate, Undergraduate **Number Awarded:** Varies each year. **Funds Available:** The assistance consists of reduced levels of tuition, usually resident tuition in public institutions or reduced standard tuition at private schools. The home state pays a support fee to the admitting school to help cover the cost of the recipient's education. **Duration:** 1 year; may be renewed.
Eligibility Requirements: This program is open to residents of 13 western states who are interested in pursuing professional study at selected out-of-state institutions, usually because those fields of study are not available in their home states. The eligible programs, and the states whose residents are eligible, presently include: 1) architecture (master's degree), for residents of Wyoming, to study at designated institutions in Arizona, California, Colorado, Idaho, Montana, New Mexico, Oregon, Utah, or Washington); 2) dentistry, for residents of Alaska, Arizona, Hawaii, Montana, New Mexico, North Dakota, and Wyoming, to study at designated institutions in Arizona, California, Colorado, Nevada, Oregon, or Washington; 3) library studies (master's degree), for residents of New Mexico and Wyoming, to study at designated institutions in Arizona, California, Hawaii, or Washington; 4) medicine, for residents of Montana and Wyoming, to study at designated institutions in Arizona, California, Colorado, Hawaii, Nevada, New Mexico, North Dakota, Oregon, or Utah; 5) nursing (graduate degree), for residents of Wyoming, to study at designated institutions in California, Hawaii, North Dakota, or Oregon; 6) occupational therapy (bachelors' or master's degree), for residents of Alaska, Arizona, Hawaii, Montana, and Wyoming, to study at designated institutions in Arizona, California, Idaho, New Mexico, North Dakota, Oregon, Utah, or Washington; 7) optometry, for residents of Alaska, Arizona, Colorado, Hawaii, Idaho, Montana, Nevada, New Mexico, North Dakota, Utah, Washington, and Wyoming, to study at designated institutions in California or Oregon; 8) osteopathic medicine, for residents of Arizona, Montana, New Mexico, Washington, and Wyoming, to study at designated institutions in Arizona or California; 9) pharmacy, for residents of Alaska, Hawaii, and Nevada, to study at designated institutions in Arizona, California, Colorado, Idaho, Montana, New Mexico, North Dakota, Oregon, Utah, Washington, or Wyoming; 10) physical therapy (master's or doctoral degree), for residents of Alaska, Hawaii, and Wyoming, to study at designated institutions in Arizona, California, Colorado, Idaho, Montana, New Mexico, North Dakota, Oregon, Utah, or Washington; 11) physician assistant, for residents of Alaska, Arizona, Nevada, and Wyoming, to study at designated institutions in Arizona, California, Colorado, Idaho, Oregon, Utah, or Washington; 12) podiatry, for residents of Alaska, Montana, New Mexico, Utah, and Wyoming, to study at a designated institution in California; 13) public health, for residents of Montana and New Mexico, to study at designated institutions in California, Colorado, or Washington; and 14) veterinary medicine, for residents of Arizona, Hawaii, Montana, Nevada, New Mexico, North Dakota, Utah, and Wyoming, to study at designated institutions in California, Colorado, Oregon, or Washington. The financial status of the applicants is not considered. Interested students must apply for admission and for PSEP assistance directly from the institution of their choice. They must be certified by their state of residence to become an exchange student and be seeking enrollment at the first professional degree level. **Deadline for Receipt:** In most states, the deadline for receiving completed applications for certification is in October. After obtaining

certification, students must still apply to the school of their choice, which also sets its own deadline.

Neurosciences

2806 ■ EPILEPSY FOUNDATION
Attn: Research Department
4351 Garden City Drive
Landover, MD 20785-7223
Tel: (301)459-3700
Free: 800-EFA-1000
Fax: (301)577-2684
E-mail: grants@efa.org
Web Site: http://www.epilepsyfoundation.org/research/grants.cfm
To provide funding to undergraduate and graduate students interested in working on a summer research training project in a field relevant to epilepsy.
Title of Award: Behavioral Sciences Student Fellowships in Epilepsy **Area, Field, or Subject:** Anthropology; Behavioral sciences; Counseling/Guidance; Economics; Epilepsy; Nursing; Political science; Psychology; Rehabilitation, Physical/Psychological; Social work; Sociology **Level of Education for which Award is Granted:** Graduate, Undergraduate **Number Awarded:** Varies each year; recently, 4 of these fellowships were awarded. **Funds Available:** The grant is $3,000. **Duration:** 3 months during the summer.
Eligibility Requirements: This program is open to undergraduate and graduate students in a behavioral science program relevant to epilepsy research or clinical care, including, but not limited to, sociology, social work, psychology, anthropology, nursing, economics, vocational rehabilitation, counseling, and political science. Applicants must be interested in working on an epilepsy research project under the supervision of a qualified mentor. Because the program is designed as a training opportunity, the quality of the training plans and environment are considered in the selection process. Other selection criteria include the quality of the proposed project, the relevance of the proposed work to epilepsy, the applicant's interest in the field of epilepsy, the applicant's qualifications, and the mentor's qualifications, including his or her commitment to the student and the project. U.S. citizenship is not required, but the project must be conducted in the United States. Applications from women, members of minority groups, and people with disabilities are especially encouraged. The program is not intended for students working on a dissertation research project. **Deadline for Receipt:** March of each year. **Additional Information:** This program is supported by the American Epilepsy Society, Abbott Laboratories, Ortho-McNeil Pharmaceutical Corporation, and Pfizer Inc.

Nursing

2807 ■ ACADEMY OF NEONATAL NURSING
2270 Northpoint Parkway
Santa Rosa, CA 95407-7398
Tel: (707)568-2168
Fax: (707)569-0786
Web Site: http://academyonline.org/PDFFiles/
1129223052_ScholarshipAward.pdf
To provide financial assistance to members of the Academy of Neonatal Nursing (ANN) who are working on an undergraduate or graduate degree in neonatal nursing or a related nursing major.
Title of Award: Academy of Neonatal Nursing Scholarship Award **Area, Field, or Subject:** Nursing, Neonatal **Level of Education for which Award is Granted:** Graduate, Professional, Undergraduate **Number Awarded:** 1 or more each year. **Funds Available:** The stipend is $1,000. Funds are paid directly to the recipient and the educational program. **Duration:** 1 year; recipients are not eligible for another scholarship for 5 years.
Eligibility Requirements: This program is open to ANN members who have been in good standing for at least 2 years. Applicants must have at least 2 years of neonatal practice experience with at least 1 of those years completed in the past 18 months. They must be enrolled in a nursing academic degree program or a neonatal graduate program in which they have completed at least 2 degree-required courses with a GPA of 3.0 or

higher. Only professionally-active neonatal nurses are eligible, i.e., currently engaged in a clinical, research, or educational role that contributes directly to the health care of neonates or to the nursing profession and maintaining professional education in neonatal nursing by obtaining 15 contact hours of continuing education a year. Along with their application, they must submit a 200-word essay on why they are pursuing their education and how attainment of this degree will benefit them in their professional role. Financial need is not considered in the selection process. **Deadline for Receipt:** April of each year.

2808 ■ ACADEMY OF NEONATAL NURSING
Attn: Foundation for Neonatal Research and Education
East Holly Avenue, Box 56
Pitman, NJ 08071-0056
Tel: (856)256-2343
Fax: (856)589-7463
E-mail: FNRE@ajj.com
Web Site: http://www.inurse.com/fnre/scholarship.htm
To provide financial assistance to neonatal nurses interested in working on a degree.
Title of Award: Foundation for Neonatal Research and Education Scholarships **Area, Field, or Subject:** Nursing administration; Nursing, Neonatal **Level of Education for which Award is Granted:** Graduate, Professional, Undergraduate **Number Awarded:** The Matthew Hester Scholarship of $1,500 and several scholarships at $1,000 (the exact number depending on the availability of funds) are awarded each year. **Funds Available:** The stipends are $1,500 or $1,000. **Duration:** 1 year.
Eligibility Requirements: Applicants must be professionally active neonatal nurses, engaged in a service, research, or educational role that contributes directly to the health care of neonates or to the neonatal nursing profession. They must be an active member of a professional association dedicated to enhancing neonatal nursing and the care of neonates. Participation in ongoing professional education in neonatal nursing must be demonstrated by at least 10 contact hours in neonatal content over the past 24 months. Qualified nurses must have been admitted to a college or school of higher education to work on 1 of the following: bachelor of science in nursing, master of science in nursing for advanced practice in neonatal nursing, doctoral degree in nursing, or master's or postmaster's degree in nursing administration or business management. They must have a GPA of 3.0 or higher. Along with their application, they must submit a 250-word statement on how they plan to make a significant difference in neonatal nursing practice. Financial need is not considered in the selection process. **Deadline for Receipt:** April of each year. **Additional Information:** The Foundation for Neonatal Research and Education was established in 1992 by the National Association of Neonatal Nurses (NANN), 2270 Northpoint Parkway, Santa Rosa, CA 95407, (707) 568-2168. Originally housed at the NANN office, it moved to its current location in 1998. This program includes the Matthew Hester Memorial Scholarship, sponsored by Anthony J. Jannetti, Inc.

2809 ■ ALABAMA COMMISSION ON HIGHER EDUCATION
Attn: Grants and Scholarships Department
100 North Union Street
P.O. Box 302000
Montgomery, AL 36130-2000
Tel: (334)242-2274
Fax: (334)242-0268
E-mail: wwall@ache.state.al.us
Web Site: http://www.ache.state.al.us/StudentAsst/Programs.htm
To provide scholarship/loans to Alabama residents interested in preparing for a nursing career.
Title of Award: Alabama Nursing Scholarship Program **Area, Field, or Subject:** Nursing **Level of Education for which Award is Granted:** Undergraduate **Funds Available:** The amount awarded varies. This is a scholarship/loan program. Recipients must agree to practice nursing for at least 1 year in Alabama following completion of the nursing program. **Duration:** 1 year; may be renewed.
Eligibility Requirements: This program is open to students who are Alabama residents admitted to nursing programs at institutions in Alabama participating in this program (for a list of those schools, write to the commission). Applications are available from the financial aid offices at the institutions offering this award. **Deadline for Receipt:** Deadline dates vary by institution.

2810 ■ AMERICAN HOLISTIC NURSES' ASSOCIATION

2733 East Lakin Drive
P.O. Box 2130
Flagstaff, AZ 86003-2130
Tel: (928)526-2196
Free: 800-278-AHNA
Fax: (928)526-2752
E-mail: info@ahna.org
Web Site: http://www.ahna.org/edu/assist.html
To provide financial assistance to nurses working on an undergraduate or graduate degree in holistic nursing.
Title of Award: Charlotte McGuire Scholarship Program **Area, Field, or Subject:** Medicine, Holistic/alternative; Nursing **Level of Education for which Award is Granted:** Graduate, Professional, Undergraduate **Number Awarded:** 2 each year: 1 to an undergraduate and 1 to a graduate student. **Funds Available:** The amount awarded varies, depending upon the availability of funds. **Duration:** 1 year.
Eligibility Requirements: This program is open to students who are working on an undergraduate (A.D.N., B.S.N.) or graduate (M.S.N., Ph.D., D.N.Sc.) degree in holistic nursing education. Applicants must have a GPA of 3.0 or higher, have been a member of the American Holistic Nurses' Association (AHNA) for at least 6 months if an undergraduate or 1 year if a graduate student, and have experience in healing and holistic nursing practice. Along with their application, they must submit 1) information on their educational and employment history; 2) a description of their personal interests, hobbies, and activities; 3) documentation of financial need; 4) official transcripts; 5) an essay on how they will integrate the AHNA Philosophy, the Standards of Holistic Nursing Practice, and Core Values of Holistic Nursing into their professional nursing career; and 6) letters from 2 nurses, including 1 AHNA member, who agree to serve as a sponsor. **Deadline for Receipt:** March of each year. **Additional Information:** These scholarships were first offered in 1987.

2811 ■ AMERICAN LEGION

Attn: Department of Massachusetts
State House
24 Beacon Street, Suite 546-2
Boston, MA 02133-1044
Tel: (617)727-2966
Fax: (617)727-2969
To provide financial assistance for nursing education to the children of members of the American Legion in Massachusetts.
Title of Award: Massachusetts Legion Nursing Scholarship **Area, Field, or Subject:** Nursing **Level of Education for which Award is Granted:** Undergraduate **Number Awarded:** 1 each year. **Funds Available:** The stipend is $1,000. Funds are paid directly to the recipient's school. **Duration:** 1 year.
Eligibility Requirements: Eligible to apply are the children and grandchildren of current members in good standing in the American Legion's Department of Massachusetts (or members in good standing at the time of death). Applicants must be under the age of 22, entering their freshman year of college, in financial need, and preparing for a career as a nurse. **Deadline for Receipt:** March of each year.

2812 ■ AMERICAN LEGION AUXILIARY

Attn: Department of California
Veterans War Memorial Building
401 Van Ness Avenue, Room 113
San Francisco, CA 94102-4586
Tel: (415)861-5092
Fax: (415)861-8365
E-mail: calegionaux@calegionaux.org
Web Site: http://www.calegionaux.org/scholarships.html
To provide financial assistance to California residents who are veterans or members of their families and interested in studying nursing.
Title of Award: California Legion Auxiliary Past Presidents' Parley Nursing Scholarships **Area, Field, or Subject:** Nursing **Level of Education for which Award is Granted:** Undergraduate **Number Awarded:** Varies each year. **Funds Available:** Stipends range from $500 to $1,500. **Duration:** 1 year.
Eligibility Requirements: This program is open to California residents who are 1) veterans of World War I, World War II, Korea, Vietnam, Grenada/Lebanon, Panama, or Desert Shield/Desert Storm, or 2) the

spouse, widow(er), or child of such a veteran. Applicants must be entering or continuing students of nursing at an accredited institution of higher learning in California. Financial need is considered in the selection process. **Deadline for Receipt:** April of each year.

2813 ■ AMERICAN LEGION AUXILIARY

Attn: Department of Colorado
7465 East First Avenue, Suite D
Denver, CO 80230
Tel: (303)367-5388
E-mail: ala@coloradolegion.org
To provide financial assistance to wartime veterans and their descendants in Colorado who are interested in preparing for a career in nursing.
Title of Award: Colorado Legion Auxiliary Past President's Parley Nurse's Scholarship **Area, Field, or Subject:** Nursing **Level of Education for which Award is Granted:** Undergraduate **Number Awarded:** Varies each year, depending on the availability of funds. **Funds Available:** The amount of the award depends on the availability of funds. **Duration:** 1 year; nonrenewable.
Eligibility Requirements: This program is open to 1) daughters, sons, spouses, granddaughters, and great-granddaughters of veterans, and 2) veterans who served in the armed forces during eligibility dates for membership in the American Legion. Applicants must be Colorado residents who have been accepted by an accredited school of nursing in the state. As part of the application process, they must submit a 500-word essay on the topic, "Americanism." Selection is based on scholastic ability (25%), financial need (25%), references (13%), a 500-word essay on Americanism (25%), and dedication to chosen field (12%). **Deadline for Receipt:** April of each year.

2814 ■ AMERICAN LEGION AUXILIARY

Attn: Department of Georgia
3035 Mt. Zion Road
Stockbridge, GA 30281-4101
Tel: (678)289-8446
E-mail: amlegaux@bellsouth.net
To provide financial assistance to daughters of veterans in Georgia who are interested in preparing for a career in nursing.
Title of Award: Georgia Legion Auxiliary Past President Parley Nursing Scholarship **Area, Field, or Subject:** Nursing **Level of Education for which Award is Granted:** Undergraduate **Number Awarded:** Varies, depending upon funds available. **Funds Available:** The amount of the award depends on the availability of funds.
Eligibility Requirements: This program is open to George residents who are 1) interested in nursing education and 2) the daughters of veterans. Applicants must be sponsored by a local unit of the American Legion Auxiliary. Selection is based on a statement explaining why they want to become a nurse and why they need a scholarship, a transcript of all high school or college grades, and 4 letters of recommendation (1 from a high school principal or superintendent, 1 from the sponsoring American Legion Auxiliary local unit, and 2 from other responsible people). **Deadline for Receipt:** May of each year.

2815 ■ AMERICAN LEGION AUXILIARY

Attn: Department of Iowa
Education Committee
720 Lyon Street
Des Moines, IA 50309-5457
Tel: (515)282-7987
Fax: (515)282-7583
E-mail: alasectreas@ialegion.org
To provide financial assistance for nursing education to dependents of Iowa veterans and to veterans who are members of the American Legion.
Title of Award: Iowa Legion Auxiliary Past Presidents Scholarship **Area, Field, or Subject:** Nursing **Level of Education for which Award is Granted:** Undergraduate **Number Awarded:** 1 each year. **Funds Available:** The amount of this scholarship depends on the contributions received from past unit, county, district, department, or national presidents. **Duration:** 1 year.
Eligibility Requirements: This program is open to members of the American Legion and the American Legion Auxiliary and the children or grandchildren of veterans of World War I, World War II, Korea, Vietnam, Grenada, Lebanon, Panama, or the Persian Gulf. Applicants must reside

in Iowa and be enrolled or planning to enroll in a nursing program in that state. Selection is based on character, Americanism, activities, and financial need. **Deadline for Receipt:** May of each year.

2816 ■ AMERICAN LEGION AUXILIARY
Attn: Department of Maryland
1589 Sulphur Spring Road, Suite 105
Baltimore, MD 21227
Tel: (410)242-9519
Fax: (410)242-9553
E-mail: anna@alamd.org
To provide financial assistance for nursing education to the female descendants of Maryland veterans.
Title of Award: Maryland Legion Auxiliary Past Presidents' Parley Nursing Scholarship **Area, Field, or Subject:** Nursing **Level of Education for which Award is Granted:** Undergraduate **Number Awarded:** 1 each year. **Funds Available:** The stipend is $2,000. Funds are sent directly to the recipient's school. **Duration:** 1 year; may be renewed for up to 3 additional years if the recipient remains enrolled full time.
Eligibility Requirements: This program is open to Maryland residents who are the daughters, granddaughters, great-granddaughters, step-daughters, step-granddaughters, or step-great-granddaughters of ex-servicewomen (or of ex-servicemen, if there are no qualified descendants of ex-servicewomen). Applicants must be interested in becoming a registered nurse and be able to show financial need. They must submit a 300-word essay on the topic "What a Nursing Career Means to Me." **Deadline for Receipt:** April of each year.

2817 ■ AMERICAN LEGION AUXILIARY
Attn: Department of New Jersey
c/o Lucille M. Miller, Secretary, Treasurer
1540 Kuser Road, Suite A-8
Hamilton, NJ 08619
Tel: (609)581-9580
Fax: (609)581-8429
To provide financial assistance for nursing education to New Jersey residents who are the children or grandchildren of veterans.
Title of Award: New Jersey Legion Auxiliary Past Presidents' Parley Nurses Scholarships **Area, Field, or Subject:** Nursing **Level of Education for which Award is Granted:** Undergraduate **Number Awarded:** Varies each year. **Funds Available:** The amount awarded varies, depending upon the needs of the recipient and the money available. **Duration:** 1 year.
Eligibility Requirements: This program is open to the children and grandchildren of living, deceased, or divorced veterans. Applicants must have been residents of New Jersey for at least 2 years and be graduating high school seniors or the equivalent who plan to study nursing. **Deadline for Receipt:** March of each year.

2818 ■ AMERICAN LEGION AUXILIARY
Attn: Department of Oregon
30450 S.W. Parkway Avenue
P.O. Box 1730
Wilsonville, OR 97070-1730
Tel: (503)682-3162
Fax: (503)685-5008
E-mail: pcalhoun@pcez.com
To provide financial assistance for nursing education to the wives, widows, and children of Oregon veterans.
Title of Award: Oregon Legion Auxiliary Department Nurses Scholarship **Area, Field, or Subject:** Nursing **Level of Education for which Award is Granted:** Undergraduate **Number Awarded:** 1 each year. **Funds Available:** The stipend is $1,500. **Duration:** 1 year; may be renewed.
Eligibility Requirements: Eligible for these scholarships are the wives of veterans with disabilities, the widows of deceased veterans, and the sons and daughters of veterans who are Oregon residents. Applicants must have been accepted by an accredited hospital or university school of nursing in Oregon. Selection is based on ability, aptitude, character, determination, seriousness of purpose, and financial need. **Deadline for Receipt:** May of each year.

2819 ■ AMERICAN NEPHROLOGY NURSES' ASSOCIATION
Attn: ANNA National Office
East Holly Avenue, Box 56
Pitman, NJ 08071-0056

Tel: (856)256-2320; 888-600-2662
Fax: (856)589-7463
E-mail: annascholarships@ajj.com
Web Site: http://www.annanurse.org
To provide financial assistance to members of the American Nephrology Nurses' Association (ANNA) who are interested in working on a baccalaureate or advanced degree in nursing.
Title of Award: Alcavis International Career Mobility Scholarship **Area, Field, or Subject:** Nephrology; Nursing **Level of Education for which Award is Granted:** Four Year College, Graduate, Professional **Number Awarded:** 1 each year. **Funds Available:** The stipend is $2,500. **Duration:** 1 year.
Eligibility Requirements: Applicants must be current association members, have been members for at least 2 years, be currently employed in nephrology nursing, and be accepted or enrolled in a baccalaureate or higher degree program in nursing. Along with their application, they must submit a 250-word essay on their career and education goals that includes how their degree will apply to nephrology nursing, provides a time frame for completing their program, and indicates how the funds will meet their educational needs. **Deadline for Receipt:** October of each year. **Additional Information:** Funds for this scholarship, first awarded in 2006, are supplied by Alcavis International, Inc. Information is also available from Sharon Longton, Awards and Scholarships Chair, (313) 966-2674, E-mail: slongton@dmc.org.

2820 ■ AMERICAN NEPHROLOGY NURSES' ASSOCIATION
Attn: ANNA National Office
East Holly Avenue, Box 56
Pitman, NJ 08071-0056
Tel: (856)256-2320; 888-600-2662
Fax: (856)589-7463
E-mail: annascholarships@ajj.com
Web Site: http://www.annanurse.org
To provide financial assistance to members of the American Nephrology Nurses' Association (ANNA) who are interested in working on a baccalaureate or advanced degree in nursing.
Title of Award: Amgen Career Mobility Scholarship **Area, Field, or Subject:** Nephrology; Nursing **Level of Education for which Award is Granted:** Four Year College, Graduate, Professional **Number Awarded:** 1 each year. **Funds Available:** The stipend is $2,500. **Duration:** 1 year.
Eligibility Requirements: Applicants must be current association members, have been members for at least 2 years, be currently employed in nephrology nursing, and be accepted or enrolled in a baccalaureate or higher degree program in nursing. Along with their application, they must submit a 250-word essay on their career and education goals that includes how their degree will apply to nephrology nursing, provides a time frame for completing their program, and indicates how the funds will meet their educational needs. **Deadline for Receipt:** October of each year. **Additional Information:** Funds for this scholarship, first awarded in 1993, are supplied by Amgen Inc. Information is also available from Sharon Longton, Awards and Scholarships Chair, (313) 966-2674, E-mail: slongton@dmc.org.

2821 ■ AMERICAN NEPHROLOGY NURSES' ASSOCIATION
Attn: ANNA National Office
East Holly Avenue, Box 56
Pitman, NJ 08071-0056
Tel: (856)256-2320; 888-600-2662
Fax: (856)589-7463
E-mail: annascholarships@ajj.com
Web Site: http://www.annanurse.org
To provide financial assistance to members of the American Nephrology Nurses' Association (ANNA) who are interested in working on a baccalaureate or advanced degree in nursing.
Title of Award: ANNA Career Mobility Scholarships **Area, Field, or Subject:** Nephrology; Nursing **Level of Education for which Award is Granted:** Graduate, Professional, Four Year College **Number Awarded:** 5 each year. **Funds Available:** The stipend is $2,000. **Duration:** 1 year.
Eligibility Requirements: Applicants must be current association members, have been members for at least 2 years, be currently employed in nephrology nursing, and be accepted or enrolled in a baccalaureate or higher degree program in nursing. Along with their application, they must submit a 250-word essay on their career and education goals that

includes how their degree will apply to nephrology nursing, provides a time frame for completing their program, and indicates how the funds will meet their educational needs. **Deadline for Receipt:** October of each year. **Additional Information:** These scholarships were first awarded in 1993. Information is also available from Sharon Longton, Awards and Scholarships Chair, (313) 966-2674, E-mail: slongton@dmc.org.

2822 ■ AMERICAN NEPHROLOGY NURSES' ASSOCIATION
Attn: ANNA National Office
East Holly Avenue, Box 56
Pitman, NJ 08071-0056
Tel: (856)256-2320; 888-600-2662
Fax: (856)589-7463
E-mail: annascholarships@ajj.com
Web Site: http://www.annanurse.org
To provide financial assistance to members of the American Nephrology Nurses' Association (ANNA) who are interested in working on a baccalaureate or advanced degree in nursing.
Title of Award: Abbott/Pamela Balzer Career Mobility Scholarship **Area, Field, or Subject:** Nephrology; Nursing **Level of Education for which Award is Granted:** Four Year College, Graduate, Professional **Number Awarded:** 1 each year. **Funds Available:** The stipend is $2,500. **Duration:** 1 year.
Eligibility Requirements: Applicants must be current association members, have been members for at least 2 years, be currently employed in nephrology nursing, and be accepted or enrolled in a baccalaureate or higher degree program in nursing. Along with their application, they must submit a 250-word essay on their career and education goals that includes how their degree will apply to nephrology nursing, provides a time frame for completing their program, and indicates how the funds will meet their educational needs. **Deadline for Receipt:** October of each year. **Additional Information:** Funds for this program, established in 2002, are supplied by Abbott Renal Care Group. Information is also available from Sharon Longton, Awards and Scholarships Chair, (313) 966-2674, E-mail: slongton@dmc.org.

2823 ■ AMERICAN NEPHROLOGY NURSES' ASSOCIATION
Attn: ANNA National Office
East Holly Avenue, Box 56
Pitman, NJ 08071-0056
Tel: (609)256-2320; 888-600-2662
Fax: (856)589-7463
E-mail: annascholarships@ajj.com
Web Site: http://www.annanurse.org
To provide financial assistance to members of the American Nephrology Nurses' Association (ANNA) who are Certified Nephrology Nurses and are interested in working on a baccalaureate or graduate degree in nursing to enhance their nephrology nursing practice.
Title of Award: NNCC Career Mobility Scholarships **Area, Field, or Subject:** Nephrology; Nursing **Level of Education for which Award is Granted:** Four Year College, Graduate, Professional **Number Awarded:** 3 each year. **Funds Available:** The stipend is $2,000. **Duration:** 1 year.
Eligibility Requirements: Applicants must have a current credential as a Certified Nephrology Nurse (CNN) by the Nephrology Nursing Certification Commission (NNCC), be a current full member of the association, have been a member for at least 2 years, be currently employed in nephrology nursing, and be accepted or enrolled in a baccalaureate or higher degree program in nursing. Along with their application, they must submit a 250-word essay on their career and education goals that includes how their degree will apply to nephrology nursing, provides a time frame for completing their program, and indicates how the funds will meet their educational needs. **Deadline for Receipt:** October of each year. **Additional Information:** Funds for this program, established in 1993, are supplied by the NNCC. Information is also available from Sharon Longton, Awards and Scholarships Chair, (313) 966-2674, E-mail: slongton@dmc.org.

2824 ■ AMERICAN NEPHROLOGY NURSES' ASSOCIATION
Attn: ANNA National Office
East Holly Avenue, Box 56
Pitman, NJ 08071-0056
Tel: (856)256-2320; 888-600-2662
Fax: (856)589-7463

E-mail: annascholarships@ajj.com
Web Site: http://www.annanurse.org
To provide financial assistance to members of the American Nephrology Nurses' Association (ANNA) who are interested in working on a baccalaureate or advanced degree in nursing.
Title of Award: Janel Parker Career Mobility Scholarship **Area, Field, or Subject:** Nephrology; Nursing **Level of Education for which Award is Granted:** Graduate, Professional, Four Year College **Number Awarded:** 1 each year. **Funds Available:** The stipend is $2,500. **Duration:** 1 year.
Eligibility Requirements: Applicants must be current association members, have been members for at least 2 years, be currently employed in nephrology nursing, and be accepted or enrolled in a baccalaureate or higher degree program in nursing. Along with their application, they must submit a 250-word essay on their career and education goals that includes how their degree will apply to nephrology nursing, provides a time frame for completing their program, and indicates how the funds will meet their educational needs. **Deadline for Receipt:** October of each year. **Additional Information:** These scholarships, first awarded in 1993, are sponsored by Anthony J. Jannetti, Inc. Information is also available from Sharon Longton, Awards and Scholarships Chair, (313) 966-2674, E-mail: slongton@dmc.org.

2825 ■ AMERICAN NEPHROLOGY NURSES' ASSOCIATION
Attn: ANNA National Office
East Holly Avenue, Box 56
Pitman, NJ 08071-0056
Tel: (856)256-2320; 888-600-2662
Fax: (856)589-7463
E-mail: annascholarships@ajj.com
Web Site: http://www.annanurse.org
To provide financial assistance to members of the American Nephrology Nurses' Association (ANNA) who are interested in working on a baccalaureate or advanced degree in nursing.
Title of Award: Watson Pharma Career Mobility Scholarship **Area, Field, or Subject:** Nephrology; Nursing **Level of Education for which Award is Granted:** Graduate, Professional, Four Year College **Number Awarded:** 1 each year. **Funds Available:** The stipend is $2,500. **Duration:** 1 year.
Eligibility Requirements: Applicants must be current association members, have been members for at least 2 years, be currently employed in nephrology nursing, and be accepted or enrolled in a baccalaureate or higher degree program in nursing. Along with their application, they must submit a 250-word essay on their career and education goals that includes how their degree will apply to nephrology nursing, provides a time frame for completing their program, and indicates how the funds will meet their educational needs. **Deadline for Receipt:** October of each year. **Additional Information:** This scholarship, first awarded in 2003, is sponsored by Watson Pharma, Inc. Information is also available from Sharon Longton, Awards and Scholarships Chair, (313) 966-2674, E-mail: slongton@dmc.org.

2826 ■ AMERICAN RADIO RELAY LEAGUE
Attn: ARRL Foundation
225 Main Street
Newington, CT 06111
Tel: (860)594-0397
Fax: (860)594-0259
E-mail: foundation@arrl.org
Web Site: http://www.arrl.org/arrlf/scholgen.html
To provide financial assistance to licensed radio amateurs who are interested in working on an undergraduate degree.
Title of Award: William R. Goldfarb Memorial Scholarship **Area, Field, or Subject:** Business administration; Computer and information sciences; Engineering; General studies/Field of study not specified; Medicine; Nursing; Science **Level of Education for which Award is Granted:** Undergraduate **Number Awarded:** 1 each year. **Funds Available:** The stipend is at least $10,000. **Duration:** 1 year.
Eligibility Requirements: This program is open to licensed radio amateurs of any class who have applied or been accepted for enrollment at an accredited institution of higher education. Preference is given to students planning to major in computers, medicine, nursing, engineering, science, or a business-related field. Applicants must submit an essay on the role amateur radio has played in their lives and provide documentation

of financial need. **Deadline for Receipt:** January of each year.

2827 ■ ASSOCIATION OF INDEPENDENT COLLEGES AND UNIVERSITIES OF PENNSYLVANIA

101 North Front Street
Harrisburg, PA 17101-1405
Tel: (717)232-8649
Fax: (717)233-8574
E-mail: info@aicup.org
Web Site: http://www.aicup.org
To provide financial assistance to students at member institutions of the Association of Independent Colleges and Universities of Pennsylvania (AICUP) who are enrolled in a nursing or physician assistant program.
Title of Award: McLean Scholarship for Nursing and Physician Assistant Majors **Area, Field, or Subject:** Medical assisting; Nursing **Level of Education for which Award is Granted:** Four Year College **Number Awarded:** Varies each year; recently, 7 of these scholarships were awarded. **Funds Available:** The stipend is $2,500. **Duration:** 1 year.
Eligibility Requirements: This program is open to full-time undergraduate students at AICUP colleges and universities. Applicants must be enrolled in a nursing or physician assistant program and have a GPA of 3.0 or higher. Along with their application, they must submit an essay on how they chose their major, the steps they are taking to ensure that they succeed in their major, what they plan to do after graduation, the volunteer and extracurricular activities in which they participate, and how those activities relate to their major. Selection is based on their GPA (30%), steps taken to ensure success in their major (10%), career goals (10%), volunteer work (25%), relationship of volunteer and extracurricular activities to major (10%), and extent of their leadership activities (15%). Applications must be submitted to the financial aid office at the AICUP college or university that the student attends. **Deadline for Receipt:** April of each year. **Additional Information:** The AICUP includes 83 private colleges and universities in Pennsylvania. For a list of those institutions, contact AICUP.

2828 ■ AUXILIARY TO THE NATIONAL MEDICAL ASSOCIATION

1012 10th Street, N.W.
Washington, DC 20001
Tel: (202)371-9008
Fax: (202)289-ANMA
E-mail: info@anma-online.org
Web Site: http://www.anma-online.org
To provide financial assistance to African American nursing students.
Title of Award: Omega Mason/Maude Bisson Memorial Scholarship **Area, Field, or Subject:** Nursing **Level of Education for which Award is Granted:** Undergraduate **Number Awarded:** 1 each year. **Funds Available:** A stipend is awarded (amount not specified). **Duration:** 1 year.
Eligibility Requirements: Applicants must be African American, be currently enrolled in an accredited nursing school, have earned a GPA of 3.2 or higher, be able to demonstrate financial need, and have a record of community involvement. For 2-year nursing programs, applicants must be second-year students; for 4-year programs, applicants must be entering their third year. In addition to completing a formal application, students must submit a 1-page essay, detailing their educational goals and reasons for requesting this scholarship. The scholarship is awarded to a student nurse in the city where the national convention of the Auxiliary to the National Medical Association (ANMA) is held each year. **Deadline for Receipt:** April of each year.

2829 ■ LUCY C. AYERS FOUNDATION, INC.

The Summit South
300 Centerville Road, Suite 300S
Warwick, RI 02886-0226
To provide financial assistance to nursing students in Rhode Island.
Title of Award: Lucy C. Ayers Scholarships **Area, Field, or Subject:** Nursing **Level of Education for which Award is Granted:** Graduate, Undergraduate **Number Awarded:** 1 or more per year. **Funds Available:** The stipend is $1,000. **Duration:** 1 year.
Eligibility Requirements: This program is open to students enrolled in an accredited Rhode Island nursing program leading to licensure as a registered nurse (R.N.). Applicants may be working on a diploma or an associate, bachelor's, master's, or doctoral degree. They must submit a brief statement describing their reasons for requesting financial aid. **Ad-**

ditional Information: This program was established in 1998 with funds from the sale of the Lucy C. Ayers Residence For Nurses, originally chartered in 1926 as the Lucy C. Ayers Home for Nurses. It had served as a residence for retired or temporarily inactive graduate nurses of Rhode Island Hospital and its school of nursing. The program also provides assistance to graduates of the Rhode Island Hospital School of Nursing who need financial aid for continuing education or other purposes.

2830 ■ BIG 33 SCHOLARSHIP FOUNDATION

Attn: Scholarship Committee
511 Bridge Street
P.O. Box 213
New Cumberland, PA 17070
Tel: (717)774-3303; 877-PABIG-33
Fax: (717)774-1749
E-mail: info@big33.org
Web Site: http://www.big33.org/scholarships/default.ashx
To provide financial assistance to graduating high school seniors in Ohio and Pennsylvania who plan to study nursing in college.
Title of Award: Big 33 Nursing Scholarships **Area, Field, or Subject:** Nursing **Level of Education for which Award is Granted:** Undergraduate **Number Awarded:** Varies each year; recently, 6 of these scholarships were awarded: 2 at $1,600, 2 at $1,500, and 2 at $1,000. **Funds Available:** Stipends range from $1,000 to $1,600. **Duration:** 1 year; nonrenewable.
Eligibility Requirements: This program is open to seniors graduating from public and accredited private high schools in Ohio and Pennsylvania who are planning to attend nursing school. Applications are available from high school guidance counselors. Selection is based on special talents, leadership, obstacles overcome, academic achievement (at least a 2.0 GPA), community service, unique endeavors, financial need, and a 1-page essay on why the applicant wants to become a nurse and deserves the scholarship. **Deadline for Receipt:** February of each year.
Additional Information: Funds for this program are raised by the foundation through its sponsorship of an annual high school All-Star football game.

2831 ■ CALIFORNIA EMERGENCY NURSES ASSOCIATION

3783 West Robinson Avenue
Fresno, CA 93722-4782
E-mail: president@calena.net
Web Site: http://www.calena.net
To provide financial assistance to members of the Emergency Nurses Association (ENA) from California who are interested in working on an advanced degree.
Title of Award: Kelleher Scholarship **Area, Field, or Subject:** Nursing **Level of Education for which Award is Granted:** Graduate, Undergraduate **Number Awarded:** Either 1 at $1,000 or 2 at $500 are awarded each year. **Funds Available:** Stipends are $1,000 or $500. **Duration:** 1 year.
Eligibility Requirements: This program is open to ENA members who have a current California R.N. license and are either enrolled or accepted in an accredited program. Applicants must be working on a baccalaureate or higher degree. They must submit 1) a copy of their curriculum vitae; 2) a letter of intent that includes how the profession of emergency nursing will benefit from their education and a description of their ENA involvement; and 3) proof of enrollment or acceptance at an NLN-accredited school. **Deadline for Receipt:** May of each year.

2832 ■ CANADIAN INSTITUTES OF HEALTH RESEARCH

Attn: Grants and Awards
160 Elgin Street, Ninth Floor
Address Locator 4809A
Ottawa, ON, Canada K1A 0W9
Tel: (613)954-1968; 888-603-4178
Fax: (613)954-1800
E-mail: info@cihr-irsc.gc.ca
Web Site: http://www.cihr-irsc.gc.ca
To provide research funding to undergraduate and graduate students interested in preparing for a career in health-related fields in Canada.
Title of Award: Health Professional Students Research Awards of the Canadian Institutes of Health Research **Area, Field, or Subject:** Dentistry; Medicine; Nursing; Optometry; Pharmaceutical sciences **Level**

of Education for which Award is Granted: Graduate, Undergraduate **Number Awarded:** Varies each year. **Funds Available:** The stipend for students registered in a health professional school is $C1,417 per month. The stipend for students enrolled in a combined degree program is $C1,987 per month. **Duration:** Up to 3 months.

Eligibility Requirements: This program is open to 1) undergraduate and graduate students enrolled at Canadian schools offered programs leading to licensure in medicine, dentistry, nursing, physiotherapy, or related fields; and 2) medical students working on a combined degree (e.g., M.D./M.Sc., M.D./Ph.D.). Applicants must have completed their first year of study and be interested in participating in a health research project. They must be citizens or permanent residents of Canada. **Deadline for Receipt:** February **Additional Information:** The Canadian Institutes of Health Research (CIHR) was formerly the Medical Research Council (MRC) of Canada. This program was formerly designated the Burroughs Wellcome Fund Student Research Awards.

2833 ■ CANADIAN NURSES FOUNDATION

Attn: Study Awards Program
50 Driveway
Ottawa, ON, Canada K2P 1E2
Tel: (613)237-2133
Fax: (613)237-3520
E-mail: info@cnursesfdn.ca
Web Site: http://www.canadiannursesfoundation.com/scholarships.htm
To provide financial assistance to student nurse associates of the Canadian Nurses Foundation (CNF) working on a bachelor's degree.
Title of Award: Birks Family Foundation Award **Area, Field, or Subject:** Nursing **Level of Education for which Award is Granted:** Professional, Undergraduate **Number Awarded:** 1 or more each year. **Funds Available:** The stipend ranges from $C1,000 to $C3,000. **Duration:** 1 year; recipients may reapply.
Eligibility Requirements: This program is open to Canadian citizens and permanent residents who are either 1) entering at least year 2 as a full-time student of a baccalaureate nursing program, or 2) accepted into any year of a post-R.N. program as a full-time student. Applicants must be attending or planning to attend a Canadian college or university. Along with their application, they must submit 200-word essays on 1) how they have demonstrated leadership in the past; 2) their past work and community service experiences and how those prepare them for a career in nursing; and 3) how their educational program will assist them in their future career plans. **Deadline for Receipt:** March of each year. **Additional Information:** Applications must be accompanied by a CNF nurse associates fee of $C35.

2834 ■ CANADIAN NURSES FOUNDATION

Attn: Study Awards Program
50 Driveway
Ottawa, ON, Canada K2P 1E2
Tel: (613)237-2133
Fax: (613)237-3520
E-mail: info@cnursesfdn.ca
Web Site: http://www.canadiannursesfoundation.com/scholarships.htm
To provide financial assistance to student nurse associates of the Canadian Nurses Foundation (CNF) working on a bachelor's degree and intending to work in Canada's north.
Title of Award: Canadian Nurses Foundation Northern Scholarship **Area, Field, or Subject:** Nursing **Level of Education for which Award is Granted:** Professional, Undergraduate **Number Awarded:** 1 each year. **Funds Available:** The stipend ranges from $C1,000 to $C3,000. **Duration:** 1 year; recipients may reapply.
Eligibility Requirements: This program is open to Canadian citizens and permanent residents who are either 1) entering at least year 2 as a full-time student of a baccalaureate nursing program, or 2) accepted into any year of a post-R.N. program as a full-time student. Applicants must be attending or planning to attend a Canadian college or university. They must be intending to practice nursing in Canada's north. Preference is given to nurses who have worked in the north for at least 2 years and/or are of Aboriginal origin. Along with their application, they must submit 200-word essays on 1) how they have demonstrated leadership in the past; 2) their past work and community service experiences and how those prepare them for a career in nursing; and 3) how their educational program will assist them in their future career plans. **Deadline for**

Receipt: March of each year. **Additional Information:** This program was established in 1989. Applications must be accompanied by a CNF nurse associates fee of $C35.

2835 ■ CANADIAN NURSES FOUNDATION

Attn: Study Awards Program
50 Driveway
Ottawa, ON, Canada K2P 1E2
Tel: (613)237-2133
Fax: (613)237-3520
E-mail: info@cnursesfdn.ca
Web Site: http://www.canadiannursesfoundation.com/scholarships.htm
To provide financial assistance to student nurse associates of the Canadian Nurses Foundation (CNF) working on a bachelor's degree.
Title of Award: Eaton Foundation Scholarship **Area, Field, or Subject:** Nursing **Level of Education for which Award is Granted:** Professional, Undergraduate **Number Awarded:** 1 each year. **Funds Available:** The stipend ranges from $C1,000 to $C3,000. **Duration:** 1 year; recipients may reapply.
Eligibility Requirements: This program is open to Canadian citizens and permanent residents who are either 1) entering at least year 2 as a full-time student of a baccalaureate nursing program, or 2) accepted into any year of a post-R.N. program as a full-time student. Applicants must be attending or planning to attend a Canadian college or university. Along with their application, they must submit 200-word essays on 1) how they have demonstrated leadership in the past; 2) their past work and community service experiences and how those prepare them for a career in nursing; and 3) how their educational program will assist them in their future career plans. **Deadline for Receipt:** March of each year. **Additional Information:** Applications must be accompanied by a CNF nurse associates fee of $C35.

2836 ■ CANADIAN NURSES FOUNDATION

Attn: Study Awards Program
50 Driveway
Ottawa, ON, Canada K2P 1E2
Tel: (613)237-2133
Fax: (613)237-3520
E-mail: info@cnursesfdn.ca
Web Site: http://www.canadiannursesfoundation.com/scholarships.htm
To provide financial assistance to student nurse associates of the Canadian Nurses Foundation (CNF) working on a bachelor's degree and intending to work in Canada's north.
Title of Award: Judy Hill Memorial Scholarship **Area, Field, or Subject:** Nursing **Level of Education for which Award is Granted:** Professional, Undergraduate **Number Awarded:** 2 each year. **Funds Available:** The stipend ranges from $C1,000 to $C3,000. **Duration:** 1 year; recipients may reapply.
Eligibility Requirements: This program is open to Canadian citizens and permanent residents who are either 1) entering at least year 2 as a full-time student of a baccalaureate nursing program, or 2) accepted into any year of a post-R.N. program as a full-time student. Applicants must be attending or planning to attend a Canadian college or university. They must be intending to practice nursing in Canada's north. Preference is given to nurses who have worked in the north for at least 2 years. Along with their application, they must submit 200-word essays on 1) how they have demonstrated leadership in the past; 2) their past work and community service experiences and how those prepare them for a career in nursing; and 3) how their educational program will assist them in their future career plans. **Deadline for Receipt:** March of each year. **Additional Information:** Applications must be accompanied by a CNF nurse associates fee of $C35.

2837 ■ CANADIAN NURSES FOUNDATION

Attn: Study Awards Program
50 Driveway
Ottawa, ON, Canada K2P 1E2
Tel: (613)237-2133
Fax: (613)237-3520
E-mail: info@cnursesfdn.ca
Web Site: http://www.canadiannursesfoundation.com/scholarships.htm
To provide financial assistance to student nurse associates of the Canadian Nurses Foundation (CNF) working on a bachelor's degree in operating room or critical care nursing.

Title of Award: Johnson & Johnson Medical Products Award **Area, Field, or Subject:** Nursing **Level of Education for which Award is Granted:** Professional, Undergraduate **Number Awarded:** 1 each year. **Funds Available:** The stipend ranges from $C1,000 to $C3,000. **Duration:** 1 year; recipients may reapply.

Eligibility Requirements: This program is open to Canadian citizens and permanent residents who are either 1) entering at least year 2 as a full-time student of a baccalaureate nursing program, or 2) accepted into any year of a post-R.N. program as a full-time student. Applicants must be attending or planning to attend a Canadian college or university. They must be intending to practice nursing in an operating room or a critical care area. Along with their application, they must submit 200-word essays on 1) how they have demonstrated leadership in the past; 2) their past work and community service experiences and how those prepare them for a career in nursing; and 3) how their educational program will assist them in their future career plans. **Deadline for Receipt:** March of each year. **Additional Information:** This program was established in 1995 by Johnson & Johnson Applications must be accompanied by a CNF nurse associates fee of $C35.

2838 ■ CANADIAN NURSES FOUNDATION
Attn: Study Awards Program
50 Driveway
Ottawa, ON, Canada K2P 1E2
Tel: (613)237-2133
Fax: (613)237-3520
E-mail: info@cnursesfdn.ca
Web Site: http://www.canadiannursesfoundation.com/scholarships.htm
To provide financial assistance to student nurse associates of the Canadian Nurses Foundation (CNF) who are foreign-educated and working on a bachelor's degree.

Title of Award: Tecla Lin and Nelia Laroza Memorial Award **Area, Field, or Subject:** Nursing **Level of Education for which Award is Granted:** Professional, Undergraduate **Number Awarded:** 1 each year. **Funds Available:** The stipend ranges from $C1,000 to $C3,000. **Duration:** 1 year; recipients may reapply.

Eligibility Requirements: This program is open to Canadian citizens and permanent residents who have been accepted into any year of a post-R.N. program as a full-time student. Applicants must have received their prior education at a foreign school and now be planning to attend a Canadian college or university. Along with their application, they must submit 200-word essays on 1) how they have demonstrated leadership in the past; 2) their past work and community service experiences and how those prepare them for a career in nursing; and 3) how their educational program will assist them in their future career plans. **Deadline for Receipt:** March of each year. **Additional Information:** This scholarship was first awarded in 2004. Applications must be accompanied by a CNF nurse associates fee of $C35.

2839 ■ CANADIAN NURSES FOUNDATION
Attn: Study Awards Program
50 Driveway
Ottawa, ON, Canada K2P 1E2
Tel: (613)237-2133
Fax: (613)237-3520
E-mail: info@cnursesfdn.ca
Web Site: http://www.canadiannursesfoundation.com/scholarships.htm
To provide financial assistance to student nurse associates of the Canadian Nurses Foundation (CNF) working on a bachelor's degree in neurosurgical or cancer nursing.

Title of Award: Eleanor J. Martin Award **Area, Field, or Subject:** Nursing; Nursing, Oncological **Level of Education for which Award is Granted:** Professional, Undergraduate **Number Awarded:** 1 each year. **Funds Available:** The stipend ranges from $C1,000 to $C3,000. **Duration:** 1 year; recipients may reapply.

Eligibility Requirements: This program is open to Canadian citizens and permanent residents who are either 1) entering at least year 2 as a full-time student of a baccalaureate nursing program, or 2) accepted into any year of a post-R.N. program as a full-time student. Applicants must be attending or planning to attend a Canadian college or university. They must be studying or demonstrate an interest in neurosurgical or cancer nursing. Along with their application, they must submit 200-word essays on 1) how they have demonstrated leadership in the past; 2) their past

work and community service experiences and how those prepare them for a career in nursing; and 3) how their educational program will assist them in their future career plans. **Deadline for Receipt:** March of each year. **Additional Information:** Applications must be accompanied by a CNF nurse associates fee of $C35.

2840 ■ CANADIAN NURSES FOUNDATION
Attn: Study Awards Program
50 Driveway
Ottawa, ON, Canada K2P 1E2
Tel: (613)237-2133
Fax: (613)237-3520
E-mail: info@cnursesfdn.ca
Web Site: http://www.canadiannursesfoundation.com/scholarships.htm
To provide financial assistance to student nurse associates of the Canadian Nurses Foundation (CNF) from Prince Edward Island who are working on a bachelor's degree.

Title of Award: Dr. Margaret Munro Scholarship **Area, Field, or Subject:** Nursing **Level of Education for which Award is Granted:** Professional, Undergraduate **Number Awarded:** 1 each year. **Funds Available:** The stipend ranges from $C1,000 to $C3,000. **Duration:** 1 year; recipients may reapply.

Eligibility Requirements: This program is open to Canadian citizens and permanent residents who are either 1) entering at least year 2 as a full-time student of a baccalaureate nursing program, or 2) accepted into any year of a post-R.N. program as a full-time student. Applicants must be attending or planning to attend a Canadian college or university. They must be residents of Prince Edward Island. Along with their application, they must submit 200-word essays on 1) how they have demonstrated leadership in the past; 2) their past work and community service experiences and how those prepare them for a career in nursing; and 3) how their educational program will assist them in their future career plans. **Deadline for Receipt:** March of each year. **Additional Information:** This scholarship was first awarded in 2004. Applications must be accompanied by a CNF nurse associates fee of $C35.

2841 ■ CANADIAN NURSES FOUNDATION
Attn: Study Awards Program
50 Driveway
Ottawa, ON, Canada K2P 1E2
Tel: (613)237-2133
Fax: (613)237-3520
E-mail: info@cnursesfdn.ca
Web Site: http://www.canadiannursesfoundation.com/scholarships.htm
To provide financial assistance to student nurse associates of the Canadian Nurses Foundation (CNF) who interested in returning to school to work on a bachelor's degree.

Title of Award: Sharon Nield Memorial Scholarship **Area, Field, or Subject:** Nursing **Level of Education for which Award is Granted:** Professional, Undergraduate **Number Awarded:** 1 each year. **Funds Available:** The stipend ranges from $C1,000 to $C3,000. **Duration:** 1 year; recipients may reapply.

Eligibility Requirements: This program is open to Canadian citizens and permanent residents who have been accepted into any year of a post-R.N. program as a full-time student. Applicants must be planning to attend a Canadian college or university to work on a baccalaureate degree. Along with their application, they must submit 200-word essays on 1) how they have demonstrated leadership in the past; 2) their past work and community service experiences and how those prepare them for a career in nursing; and 3) how their educational program will assist them in their future career plans. **Deadline for Receipt:** March of each year. **Additional Information:** This scholarship was first awarded in 2004. Applications must be accompanied by a CNF nurse associates fee of $C35.

2842 ■ CANADIAN NURSES FOUNDATION
Attn: Study Awards Program
50 Driveway
Ottawa, ON, Canada K2P 1E2
Tel: (613)237-2133
Fax: (613)237-3520
E-mail: info@cnursesfdn.ca
Web Site: http://www.canadiannursesfoundation.com/scholarships.htm

To provide financial assistance to student nurse associates of the Canadian Nurses Foundation (CNF) from Nova Scotia who are working on a bachelor's degree.
Title of Award: Nova Scotia Nurses Scholarship **Area, Field, or Subject:** Nursing **Level of Education for which Award is Granted:** Professional, Undergraduate **Number Awarded:** 1 each year. **Funds Available:** The stipend ranges from $C1,000 to $C3,000. **Duration:** 1 year; recipients may reapply.
Eligibility Requirements: This program is open to Canadian citizens and permanent residents who are either 1) entering at least year 2 as a full-time student of a baccalaureate nursing program, or 2) accepted into any year of a post-R.N. program as a full-time student. Applicants must be attending or planning to attend a Canadian college or university. They must be residents of Nova Scotia. Along with their application, they must submit 200-word essays on 1) how they have demonstrated leadership in the past; 2) their past work and community service experiences and how those prepare them for a career in nursing; and 3) how their educational program will assist them in their future career plans. **Deadline for Receipt:** March of each year. **Additional Information:** This program was established by the Nova Scotia Registered Nurses Foundation in 2003. Applications must be accompanied by a CNF nurse associates fee of $C35.

2843 ■ CANADIAN NURSES FOUNDATION
Attn: Study Awards Program
50 Driveway
Ottawa, ON, Canada K2P 1E2
Tel: (613)237-2133
Fax: (613)237-3520
E-mail: info@cnursesfdn.ca
Web Site: http://www.canadiannursesfoundation.com/scholarships.htm
To provide financial assistance to male student nurse associates of the Canadian Nurses Foundation (CNF) working on a bachelor's degree.
Title of Award: John J. Vanderlee Award for Male Nursing Students **Area, Field, or Subject:** Nursing **Level of Education for which Award is Granted:** Professional, Undergraduate **Number Awarded:** 2 each year. **Funds Available:** The stipend ranges from $C1,000 to $C3,000. **Duration:** 1 year; recipients may reapply.
Eligibility Requirements: This program is open to male Canadian citizens and permanent residents who are either 1) entering at least year 2 as a full-time student of a baccalaureate nursing program, or 2) accepted into any year of a post-R.N. program as a full-time student. Applicants must be attending or planning to attend a Canadian college or university. Along with their application, they must submit 200-word essays on 1) how they have demonstrated leadership in the past; 2) their past work and community service experiences and how those prepare them for a career in nursing; and 3) how their educational program will assist them in their future career plans. **Deadline for Receipt:** March of each year.
Additional Information: Applications must be accompanied by a CNF nurse associates fee of $C35.

2844 ■ CHURCH OF THE BRETHREN
Attn: Association of Brethren Caregivers
1451 Dundee Avenue
Elgin, IL 60120-1694
Tel: (847)742-5100
Free: 800-323-8039
Fax: (847)742-6103
E-mail: abc@brethren.org
Web Site: http://www.brethren.org/abc/scholarship.html
To provide financial assistance to members of the Church of the Brethren working on an undergraduate or graduate degree in nursing.
Title of Award: Association of Brethren Caregivers Nursing Scholarships **Area, Field, or Subject:** Nursing **Level of Education for which Award is Granted:** Graduate, Undergraduate **Number Awarded:** Varies each year. **Funds Available:** The stipend is $2,000 for R.N. and graduate nurse candidates or $1,000 for L.P.N. candidates. **Duration:** 1 year. Recipients are eligible for only 1 scholarship per degree.
Eligibility Requirements: This program is open to students who are members of the Church of the Brethren or employed in a Church of the Brethren agency. Applicants must be enrolled in a L.P.N., R.N., or graduate program in nursing. Along with their application, they must submit 1) a statement describing their reasons for wanting to enter nursing or

continue their nursing education, including something of their aspirations for service in the profession; and 2) a description of how the scholarship will assist them in reaching their educational and career goals. **Deadline for Receipt:** March of each year.

2845 ■ COALITION FOR NURSING CAREERS IN CALIFORNIA
Attn: chooseNursing.com
1800 Harrison Street, 17th Floor
Oakland, CA 94612
Tel: (510)625-7109
Fax: (510)987-1299
Web Site: http://www.choosenursing.com/paying/calfinaid.html
To provide financial assistance to underrepresented and financially disadvantaged students at nursing schools in California.
Title of Award: chooseNursing.com Scholarship Program **Area, Field, or Subject:** Nursing **Level of Education for which Award is Granted:** Undergraduate **Number Awarded:** Varies each year. Recently, 28 of these scholarships were awarded: 11 for bachelor's degree students at $5,000, 2 for associate degree students at $2,500, and 15 for associate degree students at $2,000. **Funds Available:** Stipends are $5,000, $2,500, or $2,000. **Duration:** 1 year.
Eligibility Requirements: This program is open to students enrolled in an accredited associate or bachelor's nursing degree program in California. Applicants must come from an underrepresented and financially disadvantaged (family income may not exceed $50,000 per family member) group. They must have a GPA of 2.5 or higher and may not yet have a R.N. license. Along with their application, they must submit a 500-word essay on what led them to choose a career in nursing, the obstacles or challenges they have faced and overcome to get where they are today, and their professional goals or aspirations for their nursing career. Selection is based on financial need, academic achievement, health care involvement, and enthusiasm or passion for nursing. **Deadline for Receipt:** April of each year. **Additional Information:** This program, first offered in 2002, is sponsored by NurseWeek magazine, chooseNursing.com, and the Coalition for Nursing Careers in California.

2846 ■ CONGRESSIONAL BLACK CAUCUS FOUNDATION, INC.
Attn: Director, Educational Programs
1720 Massachusetts Avenue, N.W.
Washington, DC 20036
Tel: (202)263-2836
Free: 800-784-2577
Fax: (202)775-0773
E-mail: spouses@cbcfinc.org
Web Site: http://www.cbcfinc.org
To provide financial assistance to minority and other undergraduate and graduate students who reside in a Congressional district represented by an African American and are interested in preparing for a health-related career.
Title of Award: Cheerios Brand Health Initiative Scholarship **Area, Field, or Subject:** Biological and clinical sciences; Chemistry; Education, Physical; Engineering; Food service careers; Health care services; Medicine; Nursing **Level of Education for which Award is Granted:** Graduate, Undergraduate **Number Awarded:** Varies each year. **Funds Available:** A stipend is awarded (amount not specified). **Duration:** 1 year.
Eligibility Requirements: This program is open to 1) minority and other graduating high school seniors planning to attend an accredited institution of higher education and 2) currently-enrolled full-time undergraduate, graduate, and doctoral students in good academic standing with a GPA of 2.5 or higher. Applicants must reside or attend school in a Congressional district represented by a member of the Congressional Black Caucus. They must be interested in preparing for a career in a medical, food services, or other health-related field, including pre-medicine, nursing, chemistry, biology, physical education, and engineering. Along with their application, they must submit a 500-word personal statement on 1) the field of study they intend to pursue and why they have chosen that field; 2) their interests, involvement in school activities, community and public service, hobbies, special talents, sports, and other highlight areas; and 3) any other experiences, skills, or qualifications they feel should be considered. They must also be able to document financial need. **Deadline**

for Receipt: April of each year. **Additional Information:** The program was established in 1998 with support from General Mills, Inc.

2847 ■ CONNECTICUT LEAGUE FOR NURSING

Attn: Executive Director
393 Center Street
P.O. Box 365
Wallingford, CT 06492-0365
Tel: (203)265-4248
Fax: (203)265-5311
E-mail: education@ctleaguefornursing.org
Web Site: http://www.ctleaguefornursing.org/scholarships.html
To provide financial assistance to nursing students in Connecticut.
Title of Award: Connecticut League for Nursing Scholarship **Area, Field, or Subject:** Nursing **Level of Education for which Award is Granted:** Graduate, Undergraduate **Number Awarded:** 1 or more each year. **Funds Available:** The stipend depends on the recipient's qualifications and the availability of funds. **Duration:** 1 year.
Eligibility Requirements: This program is open to Connecticut residents who are enrolled in an accredited school of nursing in the state. Baccalaureate applicants must have completed 3 years of a 4-year program; diploma applicants must have completed 1 year of a 2-year program; associate degree applicants must have completed 1 year of a 2-year program; R.N. students in an upper-division B.S.N. program must be entering their senior year; graduate students must have completed 18 credits in an accredited nursing program. Selection is based on scholastic ability, professional potential, and financial need. **Deadline for Receipt:** October of each year.

2848 ■ CONNECTICUT NURSES' FOUNDATION

Attn: Scholarship Committee
377 Research Parkway, Suite 2D
Meriden, CT 06450-7160
Tel: (203)238-1207
Fax: (203)238-3437
E-mail: Amy@ctnurses.org
Web Site: http://www.ctnurses.org
To provide financial assistance to Connecticut residents interested in working on an undergraduate or graduate degree in nursing.
Title of Award: Townsend Scholarship **Area, Field, or Subject:** Nursing **Level of Education for which Award is Granted:** Graduate, Undergraduate **Number Awarded:** 1 or more each year. **Funds Available:** The stipend depends on the qualifications of the recipient and the availability of funds. **Duration:** 1 year.
Eligibility Requirements: This program is open to residents of Connecticut who are entering or enrolled at an accredited school of nursing to work on an associate, bachelor's, master's, or doctoral degree. Selection is based on employment experience; professional, community, and student activities, a statement of professional goals, and financial need. **Deadline for Receipt:** June of each year.

2849 ■ DAUGHTERS OF THE AMERICAN REVOLUTION-COLORADO STATE SOCIETY

c/o Marilyn Fishburn, State Scholarship Chair
1546 West 28th Street
Loveland, CO 80538
E-mail: admin@coloradodar.org
Web Site: http://www.coloradodar.org/scholarships.htm
To provide financial assistance to high school seniors in Colorado who are interested in studying nursing in the state.
Title of Award: Virginia Leyda Roberts Nursing Scholarship **Area, Field, or Subject:** Nursing **Level of Education for which Award is Granted:** Undergraduate **Number Awarded:** 1 each year. **Funds Available:** The stipend is $1,000. Funds are paid directly to the student's school. **Duration:** 1 year; nonrenewable.
Eligibility Requirements: Eligible to apply are graduating high school seniors in Colorado who are 1) American citizens, 2) in the top third of their graduating class, and 3) accepted at 1 of the Colorado colleges offering a B.S.N.: Beth-El College of Nursing, Regis University, Colorado University at Denver, Colorado Health Sciences Center, Metro State University, University of Phoenix, University of Northern Colorado, University of Southern Colorado, or Mesa State College. Applications must include a statement of career interest and goals (up to 500 words), 2

character references, college transcripts, a letter of sponsorship from the Daughters of the American Revolution's Colorado chapter, and a list of scholastic achievements, extracurricular activities, honors, and other significant accomplishments. Selection is based on financial need and academic record. **Deadline for Receipt:** January of each year.

2850 ■ DELAWARE HIGHER EDUCATION COMMISSION

Carvel State Office Building
820 North French Street
Wilmington, DE 19801
Tel: (302)577-3240
Free: 800-292-7935
Fax: (302)577-6765
E-mail: dhec@doe.k12.de.us
Web Site: http://www.doe.state.de.us/high-ed/nursing.htm
To provide scholarship/loans for nursing education to Delaware residents with outstanding academic records.
Title of Award: Delaware Nursing Incentive Program **Area, Field, or Subject:** Nursing **Level of Education for which Award is Granted:** Professional, Undergraduate **Number Awarded:** Up to 50 each year. **Funds Available:** Awards up to the cost of tuition, fees, and other direct educational expenses are available. This is a scholarship/loan program; if the recipient performs required service at a state-owned hospital or clinic in Delaware, the loan is forgiven at the rate of 1 year of service for each year of assistance. Recipients who fail to perform the required service must repay the loan in full. **Duration:** 1 year; may be renewed for up to 3 additional years.
Eligibility Requirements: This program is open to residents of Delaware who are enrolled or planning to enroll full time in an accredited program leading to certification as an R.N. or L.P.N. High school seniors must rank in the upper half of their class and have a cumulative GPA of 2.5 or higher. Current undergraduate students must meet academic requirements of their institution and be enrolled full time. Also eligible are 1) current state employees (they are not required to be Delaware residents and may enroll part time); and 2) registered nurses with 5 or more years of state service (they must be working on a bachelor of science in nursing degree but they may enroll full or part time). U.S. citizenship or permanent resident status is required. **Deadline for Receipt:** March of each year.

2851 ■ EMERGENCY NURSES ASSOCIATION

Attn: ENA Foundation
915 Lee Street
Des Plaines, IL 60016-6569
Tel: (847)460-4100
Free: 800-900-9659
Fax: (847)460-4004
E-mail: foundation@ena.org
Web Site: http://www.ena.org/foundation/grants
To provide financial assistance for baccalaureate study to nurses who are members of the Emergency Nurses Association (ENA).
Title of Award: ENA Foundation Undergraduate Scholarships **Area, Field, or Subject:** Nursing **Level of Education for which Award is Granted:** Professional, Undergraduate **Number Awarded:** 8 each year: 7 at $3,000 and 1 at $5,000. **Funds Available:** Stipends are $5,000 or $3,000. **Duration:** 1 year; nonrenewable.
Eligibility Requirements: This program is open to nurses (R.N., L.P.N., L.V.N.) who are working on a bachelor's degree. Applicants must have been members of the association for at least 12 months. They must submit a 1-page statement on their professional and educational goals and how this scholarship will help them attain those goals. Selection is based on content and clarity of the goal statement (45%), professional association involvement (45%), and GPA (10%). **Deadline for Receipt:** May of each year.

2852 ■ EMERGENCY NURSES ASSOCIATION

Attn: ENA Foundation
915 Lee Street
Des Plaines, IL 60016-6569
Tel: (847)460-4100
Free: 800-900-9659
Fax: (847)460-4004
E-mail: foundation@ena.org

Web Site: http://www.ena.org/foundation/grants

To provide financial assistance to pre-hospital personnel working on an undergraduate degree in nursing.

Title of Award: JEMS/Elsevier Nursing Scholarship **Area, Field, or Subject:** Nursing **Level of Education for which Award is Granted:** Professional, Undergraduate **Number Awarded:** 1 each year. **Funds Available:** The stipend is $5,000. **Duration:** 1 year.

Eligibility Requirements: This program is open to pre-hospital personnel (emergency medical technician or EMT-paramedic) who are going to school to work on an undergraduate nursing degree. Applicants must submit proof of acceptance into an undergraduate nursing program and proof of at least 1 year of pre-hospital work experience. Along with their application, they must submit a 1-page statement on their professional and educational goals and how this scholarship will help them attain those goals. Selection is based on content and clarity of the goal statement (45%), professional involvement (45%), and GPA (10%). **Deadline for Receipt:** May of each year. **Additional Information:** Scholarship winners are also awarded a complimentary 1-year members in the Emergency Nurses Association (ENA). This program is supported by the *Journal of Emergency Medical Services* (JEMS) and its parent company, Elsevier.

The first scholarship was awarded in 2004.

2853 ■ EMERGENCY NURSES ASSOCIATION

Attn: ENA Foundation
915 Lee Street
Des Plaines, IL 60016-6569
Tel: (847)460-4100
Free: 800-900-9659
Fax: (847)460-4004
E-mail: foundation@ena.org
Web Site: http://www.ena.org/foundation/grants

To provide financial assistance for baccalaureate study to nurses who are members of the Emergency Nurses Association (ENA).

Title of Award: Charles Kunz Memorial Undergraduate Scholarship **Area, Field, or Subject:** Nursing **Level of Education for which Award is Granted:** Professional, Undergraduate **Number Awarded:** 1 each year. **Funds Available:** The stipend is $4,000. **Duration:** 1 year; nonrenewable.

Eligibility Requirements: This program is open to nurses (R.N., L.P.N., L.V.N.) who are working on a bachelor's degree. Applicants must have been members of the association for at least 12 months. They must submit a 1-page statement on their professional and educational goals and how this scholarship will help them attain those goals. Selection is based on content and clarity of the goal statement (45%), professional association involvement (45%), and GPA (10%). **Deadline for Receipt:** May of each year.

2854 ■ EMERGENCY NURSES ASSOCIATION

Attn: ENA Foundation
915 Lee Street
Des Plaines, IL 60016-6569
Tel: (847)460-4100
Free: 800-900-9659
Fax: (847)460-4004
E-mail: foundation@ena.org
Web Site: http://www.ena.org/foundation/grants

To provide financial assistance for baccalaureate study to nurses who are members of the Emergency Nurses Association (ENA).

Title of Award: Margaret Miller Memorial Undergraduate Scholarship **Area, Field, or Subject:** Nursing **Level of Education for which Award is Granted:** Professional, Undergraduate **Number Awarded:** 1 each year. **Funds Available:** The stipend is $2,000. **Duration:** 1 year; nonrenewable.

Eligibility Requirements: This program is open to nurses (R.N., L.P.N., L.V.N.) who are working on a bachelor's degree. Applicants must have been members of the association for at least 12 months. They must submit a 1-page statement on their professional and educational goals

and how this scholarship will help them attain those goals. Selection is based on content and clarity of the goal statement (45%), professional association involvement (45%), and GPA (10%). **Deadline for Receipt:** May of each year.

2855 ■ EMERGENCY NURSES ASSOCIATION

Attn: ENA Foundation
915 Lee Street
Des Plaines, IL 60016-6569
Tel: (847)460-4100
Free: 800-900-9659
Fax: (847)460-4004
E-mail: foundation@ena.org
Web Site: http://www.ena.org/foundation/grants

To provide financial assistance to rescue workers working on an undergraduate degree in nursing.

Title of Award: New York State ENA September 11 Scholarship Fund **Area, Field, or Subject:** Nursing **Level of Education for which Award is Granted:** Professional, Undergraduate **Number Awarded:** 1 each year. **Funds Available:** The stipend is $2,000. **Duration:** 1 year.

Eligibility Requirements: This program is open to pre-hospital care providers, fire fighters, and police officers who are going to school to obtain an undergraduate nursing degree. Rescue workers from all states are eligible. Applicants must submit a 1-page statement on their professional and educational goals and how this scholarship will help them attain those goals. Selection is based on content and clarity of the goal statement (45%), professional involvement (45%), and GPA (10%). **Deadline for Receipt:** May of each year. **Additional Information:** Scholarship winners are also awarded a complimentary 1-year members in the Emergency Nurses Association (ENA).

2856 ■ EPILEPSY FOUNDATION

Attn: Research Department
4351 Garden City Drive
Landover, MD 20785-7223
Tel: (301)459-3700
Free: 800-EFA-1000
Fax: (301)577-2684
E-mail: grants@efa.org
Web Site: http://www.epilepsyfoundation.org/research/grants.cfm

To provide funding to undergraduate and graduate students interested in working on a summer research training project in a field relevant to epilepsy.

Title of Award: Behavioral Sciences Student Fellowships in Epilepsy **Area, Field, or Subject:** Anthropology; Behavioral sciences; Counseling/Guidance; Economics; Epilepsy; Nursing; Political science; Psychology; Rehabilitation, Physical/Psychological; Social work; Sociology **Level of Education for which Award is Granted:** Graduate, Undergraduate **Number Awarded:** Varies each year; recently, 4 of these fellowships were awarded. **Funds Available:** The grant is $3,000. **Duration:** 3 months during the summer.

Eligibility Requirements: This program is open to undergraduate and graduate students in a behavioral science program relevant to epilepsy research or clinical care, including, but not limited to, sociology, social work, psychology, anthropology, nursing, economics, vocational rehabilitation, counseling, and political science. Applicants must be interested in working on an epilepsy research project under the supervision of a qualified mentor. Because the program is designed as a training opportunity, the quality of the training plans and environment are considered in the selection process. Other selection criteria include the quality of the proposed project, the relevance of the proposed work to epilepsy, the applicant's interest in the field of epilepsy, the applicant's qualifications, and the mentor's qualifications, including his or her commitment to the student and the project. U.S. citizenship is not required, but the project must be conducted in the United States. Applications from women, members of minority groups, and people with disabilities are especially encouraged. The program is not intended for students working on a dissertation research project. **Deadline for Receipt:** March of each year. **Additional**

Information: This program is supported by the American Epilepsy Society, Abbott Laboratories, Ortho-McNeil Pharmaceutical Corporation, and Pfizer Inc.

2857 ■ GEORGIA STUDENT FINANCE COMMISSION

Attn: Scholarships and Grants Division
2082 East Exchange Place, Suite 200
Tucker, GA 30084-5305
Tel: (770)724-9000
Free: 800-505-GSFC
Fax: (770)724-9089
E-mail: info@mail.gsfc.state.ga.us
Web Site: http://www.gsfc.org/GHEAC/dsp_icapp.cfm
To provide forgivable loans to students at colleges and universities in Georgia who are working on a degree in nursing.
Title of Award: Georgia Intellectual Capital Partnership Program **Area, Field, or Subject:** Nursing **Level of Education for which Award is Granted:** Master's, Undergraduate **Number Awarded:** Varies each year. **Funds Available:** The maximum loan is $7,500. Loans are cancelled at the rate of $2,500 per year for each year that the recipient works in Georgia in a high technology field consistent with their degree. The loan must be repaid by service within 5 years of graduation or in cash with interest over a 10-year period. **Duration:** 1 year.
Eligibility Requirements: This program is open to U.S. citizens and permanent residents working on a bachelor's or master's degree in nursing at a participating college or university in Georgia. Applicants must be willing to work in their field of study at a facility in Georgia after they complete their degree. **Additional Information:** This program was established to provide assistance to students in high technology fields of computer science, web design, and medical transcriptionist. It was recently revised to prepare for the impending nursing shortage.

2858 ■ GEORGIA STUDENT FINANCE COMMISSION

Attn: Scholarships and Grants Division
2082 East Exchange Place, Suite 200
Tucker, GA 30084-5305
Tel: (770)724-9230
Free: 800-505-GSFC
Fax: (770)724-9089
E-mail: info@mail.gsfc.state.ga.us
Web Site: http://www.gsfc.org/gsfa/SCL/dsp_reg_nurse.cfm
To provide forgivable loans to students who are interested in earning a nursing degree at an institution in Georgia and working as a nurse in the state.
Title of Award: Georgia Registered Nurse Service-Cancelable Loan Program **Area, Field, or Subject:** Nursing **Level of Education for which Award is Granted:** Undergraduate **Number Awarded:** Varies each year. **Funds Available:** The maximum loan is $4,500 per academic year. Loans may be cancelled at the rate of $3,000 per year by working for a sponsoring health care facility for up to 3 years. If it is not cancelled within 3 years by service, it must be repaid in cash with interest at a rate that varies up to 10%. **Duration:** 1 year; may be renewed 1 additional year.
Eligibility Requirements: This program is open to students enrolled or planning to enroll in a nursing program at a school in Georgia. Applicants may be entering an R.N. program for the first time or L.P.N.s interested in becoming an R.N. They must be interested in working for a sponsoring health care facility after they receive their R.N. and pass the licensing examination. **Additional Information:** This program, administered by the Georgia Student Finance Commission, was established in 2001 as a partnership involving Darton College, Palmyra Medical Centers, Putney Memorial Hospital (all in Albany) and Archbold Medical Center (in Thomasville). In 2002, it was expanded to Savannah as a partnership involving Armstrong Atlantic State University with sponsorship from Memorial Health University Medical Center and St. Joseph Candler Health System.

2859 ■ GEORGIA STUDENT FINANCE COMMISSION

Attn: Scholarships and Grants Division
2082 East Exchange Place, Suite 200
Tucker, GA 30084-5305
Tel: (770)724-9230
Free: 800-505-GSFC
Fax: (770)724-9089

E-mail: info@mail.gsfc.state.ga.us
Web Site: http://www.gsfc.org/gsfa/SCL/dsp_neg_nurse.cfm
To provide forgivable loans to students who are interested in earning a nursing degree at an institution in northeast Georgia and working as a nurse in the area.
Title of Award: Northeast Georgia Health System Service Cancelable Loans **Area, Field, or Subject:** Nursing **Level of Education for which Award is Granted:** Undergraduate **Number Awarded:** Varies each year. **Funds Available:** The maximum loan is $2,500 for freshmen, $3,500 for sophomores, $4,000 for juniors, or $4,500 for seniors. Loans may be cancelled by working for Northeast Georgia Health System, Inc. **Duration:** 1 year; may be renewed.
Eligibility Requirements: This program is open to students enrolled or planning to enroll in a nursing program at a designated school in northeast Georgia (North Georgia College and State University, Brenau University, Piedmont College, or the Augusta Campus of the Medical College of Georgia). Applicants must be interested in working for Northeast Georgia Health System, Inc. after they receive their R.N. and pass the licensing examination. **Additional Information:** This program is administered by the Georgia Student Finance Authority and financed by Northeast Georgia Health System, Inc.

2860 ■ GOOD SAMARITAN FOUNDATION

5615 Kirby Drive, Suite 308
Houston, TX 77005
Tel: (713)529-4647
Web Site: http://www.gsftx.org/pages/scholar.html
To provide financial assistance to student nurses enrolled in a program in nursing at an accredited university in Texas.
Title of Award: Good Samaritan Foundation Scholarships **Area, Field, or Subject:** Nursing **Level of Education for which Award is Granted:** Graduate, Undergraduate **Number Awarded:** Varies each year. Since the program began, it has awarded more than 10,500 scholarships worth more than $13 million. **Funds Available:** Scholarship awards may be used for clinical education expenses: tuition, fees, books, and some copying and seminars. Undergraduate awards are based on the amount of the tuition fees of that school and its nursing program. Graduate awards are paid on a reimbursement basis up to a pre-determined amount per semester. **Duration:** 1 year.
Eligibility Requirements: This program is open to residents of Texas who have attained the clinical level of their nursing education. Applicants must be enrolled at an institution in Texas in an accredited nursing program at the L.V.N., Diploma, A.D.N., B.S.N., M.S.N., Ph.D., or D.S.N. level. They must be eligible to work in the United States and be planning to work as a nurse in Texas after graduation. Financial need is considered in the selection process. **Deadline for Receipt:** There are no formal deadlines. Completed applications are considered in the order in which they are received and as funds become available. **Additional Information:** This program began in 1951.

2861 ■ HAWAI'I COMMUNITY FOUNDATION

Attn: Scholarship Department
1164 Bishop Street, Suite 800
Honolulu, HI 96813
Tel: (808)566-5570; 888-731-3863
Fax: (808)521-6286
E-mail: scholarships@hcf-hawaii.org
Web Site: http://www.hawaiicommunityfoundation.org/scholar/scholar.php
To provide financial assistance to Hawaii residents of Filipino ancestry who are interested in preparing for a career as a nurse.
Title of Award: Filipino Nurses' Organization of Hawaii Scholarship **Area, Field, or Subject:** Nursing **Level of Education for which Award is Granted:** Graduate, Undergraduate **Number Awarded:** Varies each year. **Funds Available:** The amounts of the awards depend on the availability of funds and the need of the recipient. **Duration:** 1 year.
Eligibility Requirements: This program is open to Hawaii residents of Filipino ancestry who are interested in studying in Hawaii or the mainland as full-time students and majoring in nursing. They must be able to

demonstrate academic achievement (GPA of 2.7 or higher), good moral character, and financial need. **Deadline for Receipt:** February of each year.

2862 ■ HAWAI'I COMMUNITY FOUNDATION

Attn: Scholarship Department
1164 Bishop Street, Suite 800
Honolulu, HI 96813
Tel: (808)566-5570; 888-731-3863
Fax: (808)521-6286
E-mail: scholarships@hcf-hawaii.org
Web Site: http://www.hawaiicommunityfoundation.org/scholar/scholar.php
To provide financial assistance to Hawaii residents who are interested in preparing for a career in nursing.

Title of Award: Hawaii Student Nurses' Association Scholarship **Area, Field, or Subject:** Nursing **Level of Education for which Award is Granted:** Undergraduate **Number Awarded:** Varies each year. **Funds Available:** The amounts of the awards depend on the availability of funds and the need of the recipient. **Duration:** 1 year.
Eligibility Requirements: This program is open to students enrolled in an undergraduate nursing program in Hawaii. Applicants must be residents of the state of Hawaii; be able to demonstrate financial need; be interested in attending an accredited 2- or 4-year college or university as full-time students; and be able to demonstrate academic achievement (3.0 GPA or above). Current and former officers of the Hawaii Student Nurses' Association and the National Student Nurses' Association are ineligible. **Deadline for Receipt:** February of each year. **Additional Information:** This fund was established in 2003.

2863 ■ HAWAI'I COMMUNITY FOUNDATION

Attn: Scholarship Department
1164 Bishop Street, Suite 800
Honolulu, HI 96813
Tel: (808)566-5570; 888-731-3863
Fax; (808)521-6286
E-mail: scholarships@hcf-hawaii.org
Web Site: http://www.hawaiicommunityfoundation.org/scholar/scholar.php
To provide financial assistance to residents of designated sections of Hawaii who are interested in going to college to prepare for a career in agriculture, medicine, science, or nursing.

Title of Award: Dan and Pauline Lutkenhouse Tropical Botanical Garden Scholarship **Area, Field, or Subject:** Agricultural sciences; Medicine; Nursing; Science **Level of Education for which Award is Granted:** Graduate, Undergraduate **Number Awarded:** Varies each year; recently, 2 of these scholarships were awarded. **Funds Available:** The amount of the award depends on the availability of funds and the need of the recipient; recently, stipends averaged $1,000. **Duration:** 1 year.
Eligibility Requirements: This program is open to residents of the Hilo Coast and the Hamakua Coast, north of the Wailuku River, who are interested in attending college as full-time undergraduate or graduate students. Applicants must be majoring or planning to major in agriculture, medicine, nursing, or science. They must be able to demonstrate academic achievement (GPA of 2.7 or higher), good moral character, and financial need. In addition to filling out the standard application form, applicants must write a short statement indicating their reasons for attending college, their planned course of study, and their career goals. **Deadline for Receipt:** February of each year. **Additional Information:** Recipients may attend college in Hawaii or on the mainland.

2864 ■ HEALTHCARE FINANCIAL MANAGEMENT ASSOCIATION-CONNECTICUT CHAPTER

Attn: Scholarship Committee Chair
110 Barnes Road
P.O. Box 90
Wallingford, CT 06492-0090
Tel: (203)949-6383
Fax: (203)949-6331
E-mail: jagorin@mmm.com
Web Site: http://www.cthfma.org
To recognize and reward, with scholarships, undergraduate and graduate students in fields related to health care financial management at colleges and universities in Connecticut who submit outstanding essays on topics in the field.

Title of Award: Connecticut Chapter HFMA Scholarships **Area, Field, or Subject:** Accounting; Business administration; Finance; Health care services; Information science and technology; Nursing; Writing **Level of Education for which Award is Granted:** Graduate, Undergraduate **Number Awarded:** 2 each year: 1 for an undergraduate and 1 for a graduate student. **Funds Available:** The winner receives a $2,000 fellowship, membership in the Connecticut chapter of HFMA, a 1-year subscription to *Healthcare Financial Management*, and waiver of chapter program fees for 1 year. **Duration:** 1 year.
Eligibility Requirements: This competition is open to undergraduate and graduate students at colleges and universities in Connecticut, children of members of the Connecticut chapter of the Healthcare Financial Management Association (HFMA) attending a school outside of Connecticut, and residents of Connecticut commuting to a college or university in a state that borders Connecticut. Applicants must be enrolled in a business, finance, accounting, or information systems program and have an interest in health care or be enrolled in a nursing or allied health program. They must submit an essay, up to 5 pages, on a topic that changes annually; recently, applicants were allowed to choose among the new Medicare prescription drug coverage and its impact on providers and beneficiaries, the impact of the "baby boomer" segment of the U.S. population on the health care system, the impact of health care spending accounts on employers and individuals, or the voluntary and required reporting of clinical and operational data by health care providers. Finalists may be interviewed. **Deadline for Receipt:** March of each year.

2865 ■ HEALTHCARE FINANCIAL MANAGEMENT ASSOCIATION-NEW JERSEY CHAPTER

c/o Richard C. Parker, Executive Director
CBIZ-KA Consulting Services
50 Millstone Road
Building 200, Suite 230
East Windsor, NJ 08520
Tel: (609)918-0990
Fax: (609)918-0930
E-mail: rcparker@cbiz.com
Web Site: http://www.hfmanj.org
To provide financial assistance to members of the New Jersey Chapter of the Healthcare Financial Management Association (HFMA) and their families who are interested in working on a degree related to health care administration.

Title of Award: New Jersey HFMA Member Scholarship **Area, Field, or Subject:** Accounting; Finance; Health care services; Management; Nursing **Level of Education for which Award is Granted:** Master's, Undergraduate **Number Awarded:** Varies each year; recently, the sponsor offered 2 scholarships at $1,500 each. **Funds Available:** A total of $3,000 is available for this program each year. **Duration:** 1 year.
Eligibility Requirements: Applicants must have been a member of the chapter for at least 2 years or the spouse or dependent of a 2-year member. They must be enrolled in an accredited college, university, nursing school, or other allied health professional school. Preference is given to applicants working on a degree in finance, accounting, health care administration, or a field of study related to health care. Along with their application, they must submit an essay describing their educational and professional goals and the role of this scholarship in helping achieve those. Selection is based on the essay, merit, academic achievement, civic and professional activities, course of study, and content of the application. Financial need is not considered. **Deadline for Receipt:** March of each year.

2866 ■ HEALTHCARE INFORMATION AND MANAGEMENT SYSTEMS SOCIETY

Attn: HIMSS Foundation Scholarship Program Coordinator
230 East Ohio Street, Suite 500
Chicago, IL 60611-3269
Tel: (312)664-4467
Fax: (312)664-6143
Web Site: http://www.himss.org/asp/scholarships.asp
To provide financial assistance to student members of the Healthcare Information and Management Systems Society (HIMSS) who are working on an undergraduate or graduate degree in health care informatics or nursing.

Title of Award: Midwest Alliance for Nursing Informatics Scholarship **Area, Field, or Subject:** Health care services; Information science and technology; Nursing **Level of Education for which Award is Granted:** Four Year College, Graduate **Number Awarded:** 1 each year. **Funds Available:** The stipend is $2,500. The award includes an all-expense paid trip to the annual HIMSS conference and exhibition. **Duration:** 1 year; nonrenewable.

Eligibility Requirements: This program is open to student members of the society, although an application for membership, including dues, may accompany the scholarship application. Applicants must be graduate students working on an undergraduate or graduate degree in health care informatics. They must submit a 1-page narrative that describes the integration of informatics in their professional practice, with emphasis on actual work responsibilities and how they would utilize the scholarship. Selection is based on that narrative; student, community, or professional activities in the workplace related to nursing and/or health care informatics; and involvement and participation in health care informatics professional organizations. **Deadline for Receipt:** October of each year. **Additional Information:** This program was established in 2004.

2867 ■ IDAHO STATE BOARD OF EDUCATION
Len B. Jordan Office Building
650 West State Street, Room 307
P.O. Box 83720
Boise, ID 83720-0037
Tel: (208)332-1574
Fax: (208)334-2632
E-mail: board@osbe.state.id.us
Web Site: http://www.idahoboardofed.org/scholarships/loan.asp
To provide scholarship/loans to Idaho students who wish to prepare for a teaching or nursing career in Idaho.
Title of Award: Idaho Education Incentive Loan Forgiveness **Area, Field, or Subject:** Education; Nursing **Level of Education for which Award is Granted:** Undergraduate **Number Awarded:** Approximately 45 each year. **Funds Available:** This is a scholarship/loan program. Loans are forgiven if the recipient pursues a teaching or nursing career within Idaho for at least 2 years. **Duration:** 1 year; renewable.
Eligibility Requirements: Applicants must have graduated from a secondary school in Idaho within the previous 2 years and rank within the upper 15% of their graduating high school class or have earned a cumulative GPA in college of 3.0 or higher. They must enroll as a full-time student at an Idaho public college or university, working on a degree that will qualify them to receive an Idaho teaching certificate or write the licensure examination approved by the Board of Nursing for a registered nurse.

2868 ■ ILLINOIS DEPARTMENT OF PUBLIC HEALTH
Attn: Center for Rural Health
535 West Jefferson Street
Springfield, IL 62761
Tel: (217)782-1624
Fax: (217)782-3987
E-mail: mailus@idph.state.il.us
Web Site: http://www.idph.state.il.us
To provide scholarship/loans to Illinois students preparing for a career as a nurse practitioner, physician assistant, or certified nurse midwife and interested in practicing in areas of the state that have insufficient numbers of primary care providers.
Title of Award: Illinois Allied Health Care Professional Scholarship Program **Area, Field, or Subject:** Medical assisting; Midwifery; Nursing **Level of Education for which Award is Granted:** Undergraduate **Number Awarded:** Approximately 12 each year. **Funds Available:** The stipend is $7,500 per year. This is a scholarship/loan program. Recipients repay scholarships by practicing as nurse practitioners, physician assistants, and certified nurse midwives in areas of Illinois determined by the Illinois Department of Public Health to be designated shortage areas. **Duration:** Students can receive funding for a maximum of 2 years.
Eligibility Requirements: Applicants must be enrolled or accepted for enrollment in a school located in Illinois that is accredited in its field; be preparing to become a nurse practitioner, physician assistant, or certified nurse midwife; be able to demonstrate financial need; and agree to practice full time in a designated shortage area as an allied health care professional for 1 year for each year of scholarship funding received. In addition to a completed application, applicants must submit the following: proof of enrollment or acceptance for admission and a copy of their student aid report. An interview may be required. Preference is given to

applicants demonstrating a commitment to providing primary health care services in designated shortage areas and prior experience with medically underserved populations. **Deadline for Receipt:** June of each year. **Additional Information:** Within 30 days after the student's licensure to practice, or if already licensed in Illinois within 30 days of completing academic training, the recipient must begin repayment of the award by practicing in a designated shortage area in Illinois. The recipient must practice on a full-time basis 1 year for each year scholarship funds were received. The responsibility of securing a suitable practice site to fulfill the obligation lies with the scholarship recipient. Recipients who do not fulfill this obligation are required to reimburse the state 3 times the total amount of the scholarship grant received for each unfulfilled year of obligation plus 7% interest per year on that amount.

2869 ■ ILLINOIS DEPARTMENT OF PUBLIC HEALTH
Attn: Center for Rural Health
535 West Jefferson Street
Springfield, IL 62761
Tel: (217)782-1624
Fax: (217)782-3987
E-mail: mailus@idph.state.il.us
Web Site: http://www.idph.state.il.us
To provide forgivable loans to residents of Illinois who are interested in working on a degree or diploma in nursing.
Title of Award: Illinois Nursing Education Scholarships **Area, Field, or Subject:** Nursing **Level of Education for which Award is Granted:** Graduate, Professional, Undergraduate **Number Awarded:** Varies each year; at least 40% of the scholarships are reserved for students working on a baccalaureate degree, 30% for students working on as associate degree or hospital-based diploma, 20% for students working on a graduate degree in nursing, and 10% for students working on a certificate in practical nursing. **Funds Available:** Students working full time on an associate, bachelor's, or graduate degree at a public college or university receive $4,942 for tuition and fees and $5,943 as a living expense stipend. Students working full time on an associate degree or hospital-based diploma at a community college receive $1,603 for tuition and fees or $5,943 as a living expense stipend. Students in a practical nursing program receive 75% of the average tuition and fees charged at all practical nursing programs and $5,943 as a living expense stipend. Students attending private institutions receive the same amount as students attending public institutions. Awards for part-time students are prorated. Repayment of loans must begin 6 months following withdrawal from school or completion of the degree. Loans are forgiven if the recipient documents either 1) substantially full-time professional nursing practice or full-time post-baccalaureate studies in nursing at an approved institution in Illinois for a number of years equal to the number of years loan funds were received; or 2) substantially half-time professional nursing practice or half-time post-baccalaureate studies in nursing at an approved institution in Illinois for twice the number of years as the number of years loan funds were received. Recipients who fail to perform the service requirement must repay the loans with 7% interest; repayment must be completed within 6 years. **Duration:** Support is available for a total of 2 years for associate degree students, 3 years for hospital-based diploma students, 4 years for baccalaureate degree students, or 1 year for certificate in practical nursing students.
Eligibility Requirements: This program is open to U.S. citizens who have resided in Illinois for at least 1 year. Applicants must be enrolled or accepted for enrollment in an Illinois associate degree in nursing program, hospital-based diploma in nursing program, baccalaureate degree in nursing program, certificate in practical nursing program, or graduate degree in nursing. They must agree to repay the loans in cash or through service. Financial need must be documented. In the selection process, highest priority is given, in order, to applicants 1) with the greatest financial need; 2) studying on a full-time basis; basis; 3) having the fewest number of credit hours remaining; 4) who already have a certificate in practical nursing, a hospital-based diploma in nursing, or an associate degree in nursing and are working on a higher degree; and 5) with the highest cumulative GPA. **Deadline for Receipt:** May of each year.

2870 ■ INDIAN HEALTH SERVICE
Attn: Scholarship Program
801 Thompson Avenue, Suite 120
Rockville, MD 20852

Tel: (301)443-6197
Fax: (301)443-6048
E-mail: bmiller@na.ihs.gov
Web Site: http://www.ihs.gov
To provide financial assistance to Native American students who need compensatory or preprofessional education to qualify for enrollment in a health professions school.
Title of Award: Health Professions Preparatory Scholarship Program **Area, Field, or Subject:** Engineering; Health care services; Medical technology; Nursing; Nutrition; Pharmaceutical sciences; Physical therapy; Social work **Level of Education for which Award is Granted:** Undergraduate **Number Awarded:** Varies each year. **Funds Available:** Awards provide a payment directly to the school for tuition and required fees; a stipend for living expenses of approximately $1,160 per month for 10 months; a lump sum to cover the costs of books, travel, and other necessary educational expenses; and up to $400 for approved tutorial costs. **Duration:** Up to 2 years of full-time study or up to 4 years of part-time study.
Eligibility Requirements: Applicants must be American Indians or Alaska Natives; be high school graduates or the equivalent; have the capacity to complete a health professions course of study; and be enrolled or accepted for enrollment in a compensatory or preprofessional general education course or curriculum. The qualifying fields of study include premedical technology, pre-dietetics, pre-nursing, pre-pharmacy, pre-physical therapy, pre-social work, and pre-engineering. Recipients must intend to serve Indian people upon completion of professional health care education as a health care provider in the discipline for which they are enrolled at the pregraduate level. **Deadline for Receipt:** February of each year.

2871 ■ INDIAN HEALTH SERVICE

Attn: Scholarship Program
801 Thompson Avenue, Suite 120
Rockville, MD 20852
Tel: (301)443-6197
Fax: (301)443-6048
E-mail: bmiller@na.ihs.gov
Web Site: http://www.ihs.gov
To provide loans-for-service to American Indian and Alaska Native students enrolled in health professions and allied health professions programs.
Title of Award: Health Professions Scholarship Program **Area, Field, or Subject:** Counseling/Guidance; Dental hygiene; Dentistry; Health care services; Medical assisting; Medical technology; Medicine; Medicine, Osteopathic; Nursing; Nutrition; Optometry; Pharmaceutical sciences; Physical therapy; Podiatry; Psychology; Public health; Radiology; Respiratory therapy; Social work; **Level of Education for which Award is Granted:** Graduate, Undergraduate **Number Awarded:** Varies each year. **Funds Available:** Awards provide a payment directly to the school for tuition and required fees; a stipend for living expenses of approximately $1,160 per month for 12 months; a lump sum to cover the costs of books, travel, and other necessary educational expenses; and up to $400 for approved tutorial costs. Upon completion of their program of study, recipients are required to provide payback service of 1 year for each year of scholarship support at the Indian Health Service, a tribal health programs, an urban Indian health program, or in private practice in a designated health professional shortage area serving a substantial number of Indians. Recipients who fail to complete their service obligation must repay all funds received (although no interest is charged). **Duration:** 1 year; may be renewed for up to 3 additional years.
Eligibility Requirements: This program is open to American Indians and Alaska Natives who are at least high school graduates and enrolled in a full-time study program leading to a degree in a health-related professions school within the United States. Priority is given to upper-division and graduate students. Qualifying fields of study include chemical dependency counseling (bachelor's or master's degree), clinical psychology (Ph.D. only), coding specialist (certificate), counseling psychology (Ph.D. only), dental hygiene (B.S.), dentistry (D.D.S.), diagnostic radiology technology (certificate, associate, or B.S.), dietitian (B.S.), civil or environmental engineering (B.S.), environmental health (B.S.), health care administration (B.S. or M.S.), health education (B.S. or M.S.), health records (R.H.I.T. or R.H.I.A.), injury prevention specialist (certificate), medical technology (B.S.), allopathic and osteopathic medicine, nursing (A.D.N., B.S.N., or C.R.N.A), optometry, pharmacy (B.S. or Pharm.D.), physician assistant (B.S.),

physical therapy (M.S. or D.P.T.), podiatry (D.P.M.), public health (M.P.H. only), public health nutrition (master's only), social work (master's only), respiratory therapy (associate), and ultrasonography. **Deadline for Receipt:** February of each year.

2872 ■ JAPANESE MEDICAL SOCIETY OF AMERICA, INC.

c/o Yuzuru Anzai, M.D., Scholarship Committee Chair
285 Central Park West, Apartment 3W
New York, NY 10024
Tel: (212)263-8682
Fax: (212)883-5852
E-mail: yuzuru.anzai@med.nyu.edu
Web Site: http://www.jmsa.org
To provide financial assistance to Japanese American nursing school students.
Title of Award: Japanese Medical Society of America Nursing Student Scholarship **Area, Field, or Subject:** Nursing **Level of Education for which Award is Granted:** Undergraduate **Funds Available:** A stipend is awarded (amount not specified). **Duration:** 1 year.
Eligibility Requirements: This program is open to Japanese Americans who are accepted at or currently enrolled in a nursing school in the United States. Applicants must submit a 1-page essay about themselves and how they will be involved in the sponsoring organization's activities. Selection is based on academic excellence, community activities, financial need, and interest in the organization. **Deadline for Receipt:** February of each year.

2873 ■ KAISER PERMANENTE AFRICAN AMERICAN PROFESSIONAL ASSOCIATION

c/o Kaiser Permanente
Waterpark One
2500 Havana Street
Aurora, CO 80014
E-mail: P.J.Ballard@kp.org
To provide financial assistance to undergraduate nursing students who identify with an ethnic minority group.
Title of Award: KPAAPA Bachelor of Science in Nursing Scholarship **Area, Field, or Subject:** Nursing **Level of Education for which Award is Granted:** Undergraduate **Number Awarded:** 1 each year. **Funds Available:** The stipend is $2,000 per year. **Duration:** 1 year.
Eligibility Requirements: This program is open to new and continuing students working or planning to work full time on a B.S.N. degree at an accredited school of nursing. Applicants must have a GPA of 3.0 or higher, although students who have strong leadership skills and community service but a lower GPA are encouraged to apply. Along with their application, they must submit a 1-page essay on their personal philosophy or beliefs about the role of nursing in the health care delivery system, their reason for selecting nursing as a profession, and the importance of having a college degree for nursing. On their application, they must also indicate the ethnic minority group with which they identify and include a photograph. **Deadline for Receipt:** December of each year. **Additional Information:** The photograph and essay of recipients are published in the Black History Month Souvenir Journal of the Kaiser Permanente African American Professional Association (KPAAPA).

2874 ■ KANSAS BOARD OF REGENTS

Attn: Student Financial Aid
1000 S.W. Jackson Street, Suite 520
Topeka, KS 66612-1368
Tel: (785)296-3518
Fax: (785)296-0983
E-mail: dlindeman@ksbor.org
Web Site: http://www.kansasregents.com/financial_aid/nursing.html
To provide scholarship/loans to Kansas residents who are interested in preparing for a nursing career.
Title of Award: Kansas Nursing Service Scholarships **Area, Field, or Subject:** Nursing **Level of Education for which Award is Granted:** Undergraduate **Number Awarded:** Up to 50 for L.P.N. students; up to 200 for R. N. students, of which 100 are reserved for applicants whose sponsors are located in rural counties. **Funds Available:** Stipends are $2,500 per year for students in L.P.N. programs or $3,500 per year for students in R.N. (associate or bachelor's degree) programs. Sponsors pay from $1,000 to one half of the scholarship and the State of Kansas pays the

remaining amount. This is a scholarship/loan program; recipients must work for the sponsor the equivalent of full time for 1 year for each year of scholarship support received. If the recipient changes majors or decides not to work for the sponsor as a nurse, the scholarship becomes a loan, with interest at 5% above the federal PLUS loan rate. **Duration:** 1 year; may be renewed.

Eligibility Requirements: This program is open to students in Kansas who are committed to practicing nursing (L.P.N. or R.N.) in the state. Applicants must be accepted at a Kansas nursing program (pre-nursing students are ineligible). They must locate a sponsor (generally an adult care home, psychiatric hospital, or medical care facility) that is willing to provide up to half of the scholarship and to provide full-time employment to the recipient after licensure. Financial need is considered if there are more applicants than available funding. **Deadline for Receipt:** April of each year. **Additional Information:** There is a $10 application fee.

2875 ■ KENTUCKY COMMUNITY AND TECHNICAL COLLEGE SYSTEM

Attn: Financial Aid
300 North Main Street
Versailles, KY 40383
Tel: (859)256-3100; 877-528-2748
Web Site: http://www.kctcs.edu/student/financialaidscholarships/index.htm
To provide financial assistance to sophomores working on a degree in nursing at an institution within the Kentucky Community and Technical College System (KCTCS).

Title of Award: William Foster Tichenor Tuition Scholarships **Area, Field, or Subject:** Nursing **Level of Education for which Award is Granted:** Two Year College, Vocational/Occupational **Number Awarded:** Varies each year. **Funds Available:** Stipends vary at each participating college but are intended to provide full payment of tuition and required fees. **Duration:** 1 year.

Eligibility Requirements: This program is open to KCTCS students entering their sophomore year with a GPA of 2.5 or higher. Applicants must have completed at least 30 hours of a nursing program and be able to demonstrate financial need. Along with their application, they must submit a 1-page essay on their career choice and personal values. **Deadline for Receipt:** September of each year.

2876 ■ KOSTER INSURANCE AGENCY

Attn: Scholarship
500 Victory Road
Quincy, MA 02171
Tel: (617)770-9889
Free: 800-457-5599
Fax: (617)479-0860
E-mail: Scholarship@kosterins.com
Web Site: http://www.kosterweb.com/about/scholarship_main.php
To provide financial assistance to undergraduate students working on a degree in a health-related field.

Title of Award: Koster Insurance Health Careers Scholarship Program **Area, Field, or Subject:** Biological and clinical sciences; Chemistry; Dentistry; Health care services; Nursing; Occupational therapy; Optometry; Pharmaceutical sciences; Physical therapy; Physiology; Public health; Social work **Level of Education for which Award is Granted:** Undergraduate **Number Awarded:** 5 each year. **Funds Available:** The stipend is $3,000 per year. **Duration:** 1 year; may be renewed 1 additional year.

Eligibility Requirements: This program is open to full-time undergraduates entering their second-to-last or final year of study in a health-related field, including (but not limited to) pre-medicine, nursing, public and community health, physical therapy, occupational therapy, pharmacy, biology, chemistry, physiology, social work, dentistry, and optometry. Applicants must have a GPA of 3.0 or higher and be able to demonstrate financial need. Along with their application, they must submit a 1-page essay describing their personal goals, including their reasons for preparing for a career in health care. Selection is based on motivation to pursue a career in health care, academic excellence, dedication to community service,

and financial need. **Deadline for Receipt:** April of each year. **Additional Information:** This program began in 2001.

2877 ■ PAPA OLA LOKAHI, INC.

Attn: Native Hawaiian Health Scholarship Program
345 Queen Street, Suite 706
Honolulu, HI 96813
Tel: (808)585-8944
Fax: (808)585-8081
E-mail: nhhsp@hawaii.rr.com
Web Site: http://www.nhhsp.org
To provide scholarship/loans to Native Hawaiians for training in the health professions in exchange for service in a federally-designated health professional shortage area (HPSA) or other facility for Native Hawaiians.

Title of Award: Native Hawaiian Health Scholarship Program **Area, Field, or Subject:** Dental hygiene; Dentistry; Family/Marital therapy; Health care services; Medical assisting; Medicine; Medicine, Osteopathic; Midwifery; Nursing; Nursing, Psychiatric; Psychiatry; Psychology; Public health **Level of Education for which Award is Granted:** Graduate, Undergraduate **Number Awarded:** Varies each year, depending upon the funding available. Since the program began, 151 scholars have received support. **Funds Available:** Full coverage of tuition and fees is paid directly to the health professional school. A stipend, current set at $1,157 per month, is paid directly to the scholar. This is a scholarship/loan program. Participants are obligated to provide full-time clinical primary health care services to populations in 1) a Native Hawaiian Health Care System, or 2) an HPSA in Hawaii, medically underserved area (MUA), or another area or facility in Hawaii designated by the U.S. Department of Health and Human Services. Participants owe 1 year of service in the National Health Service Corps for each full or partial year of support received under this program. The minimum service obligation is 2 years. **Duration:** 1 year; may be renewed for up to 3 additional years.

Eligibility Requirements: Applicants must be Native Hawaiians training in allopathic or osteopathic medicine, dentistry, clinical psychology, registered nursing, nurse midwifery, psychiatric nursing, public health/community nursing, social work, dental hygiene, physician assistant, public health, marriage and family therapy, or primary care nurse practitioner. They may be studying in any state. Recipients must agree to serve in a designated health-care facility in Hawaii upon completion of training. First priority is given to former scholars who have completed their previous service obligation and are seeking another year of support. Second priority is given to applicants who appear to have characteristics that increase the probability they will continue to serve underserved Native Hawaiians after the completion of their service obligations. **Deadline for Receipt:** March of each year. **Additional Information:** This program, which began in 1991, is administered by the U.S. Health Resources and Services Administration, Bureau of Health Professions, through a contract with Papa Ola Lokahi, Inc.

2878 ■ MARYLAND HIGHER EDUCATION COMMISSION

Attn: Office of Student Financial Assistance
839 Bestgate Road, Suite 400
Annapolis, MD 21401-3013
Tel: (410)260-4594
Free: 800-974-1024
Fax: (410)974-5376
E-mail: osfamail@mhec.state.md.us
Web Site: http://www.mhec.state.md.us/financialAid/ProgramDescriptions/prog_devdis.asp
To provide scholarship/loans to students in Maryland who are interested in working on a degree in a designated human services program.

Title of Award: Maryland Developmental Disabilities, Mental Health, Child Welfare, and Juvenile Justice Workforce Tuition Assistance Program **Area, Field, or Subject:** Counseling/Guidance; Criminal justice; Criminology; Disabilities; Education, Special; Gerontology; Law enforcement; Mental health; Nursing; Occupational therapy; Physical therapy; Psychology; Rehabilitation, Physical/Psychological; Social work **Level of Education for which Award is Granted:** Graduate, Undergraduate **Number Awarded:** Varies each year. **Funds Available:** The maximum stipend is $2,000 per year for students attending a 2-year institution or $3,000 per year for students at a 4-year institution. The total amount of all state awards may not exceed the cost of attendance as determined by the school's financial aid office or $17,800, whichever is less. Recipients must agree to work in a Maryland community-based program that is licensed by the Developmental Disabilities Administration or approved by the Mental Hygiene Administration, or in a residential program that is licensed by the Department of Human Resources or the Department of Juvenile Justice. The service obligation must begin within 6 months of graduation. The total service requirement is 2,000 hours if the award amount is $1,999 or less, 3,000 hours if the award amount is $2,000 to $3,999, or 4,000 hours if the award amount is $4,000 or more. If the service requirement is not completed, the award must be repaid with interest. **Duration:** 1 year; may be renewed if the recipient maintains satisfactory academic progress and remains enrolled in a human services degree program.

Eligibility Requirements: This program is open to high school seniors and full-time and part-time undergraduate and graduate students. Applicants and their parents must be Maryland residents attending a college or university in the state in 1 of the following human services degree programs: aging services, counseling, disability services, mental health, nursing, occupational therapy, physical therapy, psychology, rehabilitation, social work, special education, supported employment, vocational rehabilitation, or any other concentration in the healing arts or a program providing support services to individuals with special needs including child welfare and juvenile justice. Financial need is not considered in the selection process. **Deadline for Receipt:** June of each year.

2879 ■ MARYLAND HIGHER EDUCATION COMMISSION

Attn: Office of Student Financial Assistance
839 Bestgate Road, Suite 400
Annapolis, MD 21401-3013
Tel: (410)260-4574
Free: 800-974-1024
Fax: (410)974-5376
E-mail: osfamail@mhec.state.md.us
Web Site: http://www.mhec.state.md.us/financialAid/
ProgramDescriptions/prog_nurse.asp
To provide scholarship/loans to college students in Maryland who are interested in preparing for a career as a nurse.

Title of Award: Maryland State Nursing Scholarship and Living Expenses Grants **Area, Field, or Subject:** Nursing **Level of Education for which Award is Granted:** Graduate, Professional, Undergraduate **Number Awarded:** Varies; generally, up to 300 each year. Of the scholarships awarded each year, 10% are reserved for students seeking a graduate degree. **Funds Available:** The stipend for State Nursing Scholarships is for the amount of tuition and mandatory fees, to a maximum of $3,000 per year. The amount of the Living Expenses Grant varies up to $3,000 per year. Recipients enrolled in an accelerated nursing program that requires summer enrollment may receive a maximum annual award of $4,500. The total amount of all state awards may not exceed the cost of attendance as determined by the school's financial aid office or $17,800, whichever is less. Recipients must agree to work as a full-time nurse at an eligible organization in Maryland (licensed hospital, public health agency, nursing home, adult day care center, or home health agency) 1 year for each year of the award. Employment as a nurse at a health maintenance organization (HMO), in a physician's private office, or as an instructor teaching nursing does not meet the service requirement. If they fail to complete that service obligation, they must repay the award with interest. They must begin the service obligation within 6 months of graduation. **Duration:** 1 year; may be renewed for up to 3 additional years if the recipient maintains a GPA of 3.0 or higher, remains enrolled in an eligible program, maintains satisfactory academic progress as defined by their institution, and, if receiving a Living Expenses Grant, continues to demonstrate financial need.

Eligibility Requirements: This program is open to high school seniors and nursing students attending a 2-year or 4-year college or university in Maryland. Applicants must be Maryland residents, be majoring or planning to major in a nursing-related field as a full-time or part-time undergraduate or graduate student, and have a GPA of 3.0 or higher in high school or college. Selection of recipients of State Nursing Scholarships is based on GPA and the type of nursing degree program in which they enroll, not on financial need. Recipients who can also demonstrate financial need are eligible to apply for an additional Living Expenses Grant. **Deadline for Receipt:** Applications must be submitted by June of each year. Students

also applying for the Living Expenses Grant must submit the Free Application for Federal Student Aid (FAFSA) by February of each year.

2880 ■ MARYLAND HIGHER EDUCATION COMMISSION

Attn: Office of Student Financial Assistance
839 Bestgate Road, Suite 400
Annapolis, MD 21401-3013
Tel: (410)260-4546
Free: 800-974-1024
Fax: (410)974-5376
E-mail: osfamail@mhec.state.md.us
Web Site: http://www.mhec.state.md.us/financialAid/
ProgramDescriptions/prog_nonresnurs.asp
To enable residents of states other than Maryland to attend Maryland nursing schools at reduced tuition rates.

Title of Award: Maryland Tuition Reduction for Nonresident Nursing Students **Area, Field, or Subject:** Nursing **Level of Education for which Award is Granted:** Undergraduate **Number Awarded:** Varies each year. **Funds Available:** Recipients are entitled to pay the same tuition as if they were Maryland residents. They must agree to work as a full-time nurse in Maryland in an eligible institution or in a home that provides domiciliary, personal, or nursing care for 2 or more unrelated individuals. They must work for 2 years if they attended a 2-year school, for 4 years if they attended a 4-year school, or repay the scholarship with interest. The service obligation must begin within 12 months of graduation. **Duration:** 1 year; may be renewed for 1 additional year at a 2-year public institution or 3 additional years at a 4-year public institution.

Eligibility Requirements: This program is open to nursing students at Maryland public colleges who are residents of states other than Maryland. Applicants must enroll for at least 6 credits per semester. They are not required to demonstrate financial need. **Deadline for Receipt:** Each participating Maryland school sets its own deadline.

2881 ■ MASSACHUSETTS/RHODE ISLAND LEAGUE FOR NURSING

Attn: Administrative Assistant
One Thompson Square
Charlestown, MA 02129
Tel: (617)242-3009
E-mail: mariln@verizon.net
Web Site: http://www.nln.org/CLWebsites/MARI/scholarship_info.htm
To provide financial assistance to students from Massachusetts or Rhode Island who are enrolled in a registered nursing program or R.N.-B.S.N. program.

Title of Award: MARILN Professional Scholarship Award **Area, Field, or Subject:** Nursing **Level of Education for which Award is Granted:** Professional, Undergraduate **Number Awarded:** 1 each year. **Funds Available:** Funds are paid directly to the recipient's school. **Duration:** 1 year; nonrenewable.

Eligibility Requirements: This program is open to 1) students who have completed 2 semesters (full or part time) of nursing courses in a registered nursing program (A.D.N., diploma, B.S.N), or 2) a registered nurse accepted and enrolled into an R.N.-B.S.N. program at a college or university. Applicants must have resided in Massachusetts or Rhode Island for at least the past 4 years. Selection is based on the applicant's ability to maintain satisfactory academic standing and potential to contribute to the profession of nursing. **Deadline for Receipt:** July of each year. **Additional Information:** Information is also available from Theresa Downey, Scholarship Chair, 294 Essex Street, Lynn, MA 01902, (781) 598-1503, E-mail: terrydowney@aol.com. Requests for applications must be accompanied by a self-addressed stamped envelope.

2882 ■ MASSACHUSETTS/RHODE ISLAND LEAGUE FOR NURSING

Attn: Administrative Assistant
One Thompson Square
Charlestown, MA 02129
Tel: (617)242-3009
E-mail: mariln@verizon.net
Web Site: http://www.nln.org/CLWebsites/MARI/scholarship_info.htm
To provide financial assistance to students from Massachusetts or Rhode Island who are enrolled in a practical nursing program.

Title of Award: MARILN Professional Scholarship for Students Enrolled in Practical Nursing Programs **Area, Field, or Subject:** Nursing **Level of Education for which Award is Granted:** Undergraduate **Number**

Awarded: 1 each year. **Funds Available:** A stipend is awarded (amount not specified). Funds are paid directly to the recipient's school. **Duration:** 1 year; nonrenewable.

Eligibility Requirements: The applicant must have been residents of Massachusetts or Rhode Island for at least 4 years and have completed at least 4 months in a practical nursing program. They must have shown the ability to achieve both academically and clinically in science and nursing courses and the potential to contribute to nursing. Along with their application, they must submit an explanation of how the award will be used to help achieve their stated goals. **Deadline for Receipt:** February of each year. **Additional Information:** Information is also available from Theresa Downey, Scholarship Chair, 294 Essex Street, Lynn, MA 01902, (781) 598-1503, E-mail: terrydowney@aol.com. Requests for applications must be accompanied by a self-addressed stamped envelope.

2883 ■ MISSISSIPPI OFFICE OF STUDENT FINANCIAL AID
3825 Ridgewood Road
Jackson, MS 39211-6453
Tel: (601)432-6997
Free: 800-327-2980
Fax: (601)432-6527
E-mail: sfa@ihl.state.ms.us
Web Site: http://www.ihl.state.ms.us/financialaid/nels-bsn.html
To provide scholarship/loans to Mississippi residents who are interested in working on a bachelor's degree in nursing.
Title of Award: Mississippi Nursing Education Loan/Scholarship Program-BSN **Area, Field, or Subject:** Nursing **Level of Education for which Award is Granted:** Undergraduate **Number Awarded:** Varies each year, depending on the availability of funds; awards are granted on a first-come, first-served basis. **Funds Available:** Scholarship/loans are $4,000 per academic year for up to 2 years or a total of $8,000 (prorated over 3 years for part-time participants). For each year of service in Mississippi as a professional nurse (patient care), 1 year's loan will be forgiven. For nurses who received prorated funding over 3 years, the time of service required is 2 years. In the event the recipient fails to fulfill the service obligation, repayment of principal and interest is required. **Duration:** 1 year; may be renewed up to 1 additional year of full-time study or 2 years of part-time study provided the recipient maintains a GPA of 2.5 or higher each semester.
Eligibility Requirements: This program is open to Mississippi residents working on a B.S.N. degree as a full- or part-time junior or senior at an accredited school of nursing in the state. Applicants must have earned a GPA of 2.5 or higher on all previous college work. They must agree to employment in professional nursing (patient care) in Mississippi. **Deadline for Receipt:** March of each year. **Additional Information:** The service requirement may not be deferred to work on a master's degree.

2884 ■ MISSISSIPPI OFFICE OF STUDENT FINANCIAL AID
3825 Ridgewood Road
Jackson, MS 39211-6453
Tel: (601)432-6997
Free: 800-327-2980
Fax: (601)432-6527
E-mail: sfa@ihl.state.ms.us
Web Site: http://www.ihl.state.ms.us/financialaid/nels-rn-bsn.html
To provide scholarship/loans to registered nurses in Mississippi who are interested in pursing a bachelor's degree.
Title of Award: Mississippi Nursing Education Loan/Scholarship Program-RN to BSN **Area, Field, or Subject:** Nursing **Level of Education for which Award is Granted:** Undergraduate **Number Awarded:** Varies each year, depending on the availability of funds; awards are granted on a first-come, first-served basis. **Funds Available:** Scholarship/loans are $4,000 per academic year for up to 2 years or a total of $8,000 (prorated over 3 years for part-time participants). For each year of service in Mississippi as a professional nurse (patient care) or teacher at an accredited school of nursing, 1 year's loan will be forgiven. For nurses who received prorated funding over 3 years, the time of service required is 2 years. In the event the recipient fails to fulfill the service obligation, repayment of principal and interest is required. **Duration:** 1 year; may be renewed up to 1 additional year of full-time study or 2 years of part-time study provided the recipient maintains a GPA of 2.5 or higher each semester.
Eligibility Requirements: This program is open to residents of Mississippi who have a current nursing license (R.N.). Applicants must be work-

ing on a baccalaureate degree in nursing (B.S.N.) as a full- or part-time student at an accredited school of nursing in Mississippi and have earned a GPA of 2.5 or higher on all previous college work. They must agree to employment in professional nursing (patient care) in Mississippi or teaching at an accredited school of nursing in the state. **Deadline for Receipt:** March of each year.

2885 ■ NATIONAL ASSOCIATION OF HISPANIC NURSES
Attn: National Awards and Scholarship Committee Chair
1501 16th Street, N.W.
Washington, DC 20036
Tel: (202)387-2477
Fax: (202)483-7183
E-mail: info@thehispanicnurses.org
Web Site: http://www.thehispanicnurses.org
To provide financial assistance for nursing education to members of the National Association of Hispanic Nurses (NAHN).
Title of Award: National Association of Hispanic Nurses Scholarships **Area, Field, or Subject:** Nursing **Level of Education for which Award is Granted:** Graduate, Undergraduate **Number Awarded:** Varies each year, depending on the availability of funds. **Funds Available:** The stipend is $1,000. **Duration:** 1 year.
Eligibility Requirements: Eligible are members of the association enrolled in associate, diploma, baccalaureate, graduate, or practical/vocational nursing programs at NLN-accredited schools of nursing. Applicants must submit a 1-page essay that reflects their qualifications and potential for leadership in nursing for the Hispanic community. U.S. citizenship or permanent resident status is required. Selection is based on academic excellence (preferably a GPA of 3.0 or higher), potential for leadership in nursing, and financial need. **Deadline for Receipt:** April of each year.

2886 ■ NATIONAL COALITION OF ETHNIC MINORITY NURSE ASSOCIATIONS
c/o Dr. Betty Smith Williams, President
6101 West Centinela Avenue, Suite 378
Culver City, CA 90230
Tel: (310)258-9515
Fax: (310)258-9513
E-mail: bwilliams@ncemna.org
Web Site: http://www.ncemna.org/scholarships.html
To provide financial assistance to nursing students who are members of constituent organizations of the National Coalition of Ethnic Minority Nurse Associations (NCEMNA) working on a 4-year or master's degree.
Title of Award: Aetna/NCEMNA Scholars Program **Area, Field, or Subject:** Nursing **Level of Education for which Award is Granted:** Master's, Undergraduate **Number Awarded:** 5 each year: 1 nominee from each of the constituent associations. **Funds Available:** The stipend is $2,000. **Duration:** 1 year.
Eligibility Requirements: This program is open to members of the 5 associations that comprise NCEMNA: the Asian American/Pacific Islander Nurses Association, Inc. (AAPINA), the National Alaska Native American Indian Nurses Association, Inc. (NANAINA), the National Association of Hispanic Nurses, Inc. (NAHN), the National Black Nurses Association, Inc. (NBNA), and the Philippine Nurses Association of America, Inc. (PNAA). Applicants must be currently attending or making application to a 4-year or master's degree program in nursing. Along with their application, they must submit a letter of reference, demonstration of leadership and involvement in the ethnic community, and statement of career goals. **Deadline for Receipt:** April of each year. **Additional Information:** This program was established in 2004 with a grant from the Aetna Foundation.

2887 ■ NATIONAL FFA ORGANIZATION
Attn: Scholarship Office
6060 FFA Drive
P.O. Box 68960
Indianapolis, IN 46268-0960
Tel: (317)802-4321
Fax: (317)802-5321
E-mail: scholarships@ffa.org
Web Site: http://www.ffa.org
To provide financial assistance to FFA members who are interested in studying fields related to agriculture, business, engineering, or nursing in college.

Title of Award: Tyson Foods Scholarships **Area, Field, or Subject:** Agribusiness; Agricultural sciences; Business; Business administration; Engineering; Food science and technology; Management; Nursing; Packaging **Level of Education for which Award is Granted:** Undergraduate **Number Awarded:** 10 each year. **Funds Available:** The stipend is $1,000. Funds are paid directly to the recipient. **Duration:** 1 year; nonrenewable.
Eligibility Requirements: This program is open to members who are either high school seniors or already enrolled full time in college. Applicants must be working on or planning to work on a 2-year or 4-year degree in agriculture, food science, food technology, supply chain management, product development, product development, product packaging, nursing, engineering, or business. They must reside in a community in which a Tyson Foods processing facility is located. Selection is based on academic achievement (10 points for GPA, 10 points for SAT or ACT score, 10 points for class rank), leadership in FFA activities (30 points), leadership in community activities (10 points), and participation in the Supervised Agricultural Experience (SAE) program (30 points). U.S. citizenship is required. **Deadline for Receipt:** February of each year. **Additional Information:** Funding for these scholarships is provided by Tyson Foods, Inc.

2888 ■ NATIONAL STUDENT NURSES' ASSOCIATION

Attn: NSNA Foundation
45 Main Street, Suite 606
Brooklyn, NY 11201
Tel: (718)210-0705
Fax: (718)210-0710
E-mail: nsna@nsna.org
Web Site: http://www.nsna.org
To provide financial assistance to disadvantaged minority undergraduate and graduate students who wish to prepare for careers in nursing.
Title of Award: Breakthrough to Nursing Scholarships for Racial/Ethnic Minorities **Area, Field, or Subject:** Nursing **Level of Education for which Award is Granted:** Undergraduate **Number Awarded:** Varies each year. Recently, 13 of these scholarships were awarded: 10 sponsored by the American Association of Critical-Care Nurses and 3 sponsored by the Mayo Clinic. **Funds Available:** Stipends range from $1,000 to $5,000. A total of more than $100,000 is awarded each year by the foundation for all its scholarship programs. **Duration:** 1 year.
Eligibility Requirements: This program is open to students currently enrolled in state-approved schools of nursing or pre-nursing associate degree, baccalaureate, diploma, generic doctorate, or generic master's programs. Graduating high school seniors are not eligible. Support for graduate education is provided only for a first degree in nursing. Applicants must be able to demonstrate that they are from a disadvantaged background, including membership in a racial or ethnic minority underrepresented among registered nurses (American Indian or Alaska Native, Hispanic or Latino, Native Hawaiian or other Pacific Islander, Black or African American, or Asian). Selection is based on academic achievement, financial need, and involvement in student nursing organizations and community health activities. **Deadline for Receipt:** January of each year. **Additional Information:** Applications must be accompanied by a $10 processing fee.

2889 ■ NATIONAL STUDENT NURSES' ASSOCIATION

Attn: NSNA Foundation
45 Main Street, Suite 606
Brooklyn, NY 11201
Tel: (718)210-0705
Fax: (718)210-0710
E-mail: nsna@nsna.org
Web Site: http://www.nsna.org
To provide financial assistance to nurses interested in pursuing additional education.
Title of Award: National Student Nurses' Association Career Mobility Scholarships **Area, Field, or Subject:** Nursing **Level of Education for which Award is Granted:** Master's, Professional, Undergraduate **Number Awarded:** Varies each year. Recently, 3 of these scholarships were awarded: 1 sponsored by Advanstar Medical Economics Nursing Group and 2 sponsored by Anthony J. Jannetti, Inc. **Funds Available:** Stipends range from $1,000 to $5,000. A total of more than $100,000 is awarded each year by the foundation for all its scholarship programs. **Duration:** 1 year.

Eligibility Requirements: This program is open to 1) registered nurses enrolled in programs leading to a baccalaureate or master's degree with a major in nursing or 2) licensed practical/vocational nurses enrolled in programs leading to licensure as a registered nurse. Graduating high school seniors are not eligible. Selection is based on academic achievement, financial need, and involvement in student nursing organizations and community activities related to health care. **Deadline for Receipt:** January of each year. **Additional Information:** Applications must be accompanied by a $10 processing fee.

2890 ■ NATIONAL STUDENT NURSES' ASSOCIATION

Attn: NSNA Foundation
45 Main Street, Suite 606
Brooklyn, NY 11201
Tel: (718)210-0705
Fax: (718)210-0710
E-mail: nsna@nsna.org
Web Site: http://www.nsna.org
To provide financial assistance to nursing or pre-nursing students.
Title of Award: National Student Nurses' Association General Scholarships **Area, Field, or Subject:** Nursing **Level of Education for which Award is Granted:** Graduate, Undergraduate **Number Awarded:** Varies each year. Approximately 30 of these scholarships were awarded recently. **Funds Available:** Stipends range from $1,000 to $5,000. A total of more than $100,000 is awarded each year by the foundation for all its scholarship programs. **Duration:** 1 year.
Eligibility Requirements: This program is open to students currently enrolled in state-approved schools of nursing or pre-nursing associate degree, baccalaureate, diploma, generic doctorate, or generic master's programs. Graduating high school seniors are not eligible. Support for graduate education is provided only for a first degree in nursing. Selection is based on academic achievement, financial need, and involvement in student nursing organizations and community health activities. **Deadline for Receipt:** January of each year. **Additional Information:** This program includes the following named scholarships: the Alice Robinson Memorial Scholarship, the Jeannette Collins Memorial Scholarship, the Cleo Doster Memorial Scholarship, and the Mary Ann Tuft Scholarships. Applications must be accompanied by a $10 processing fee.

2891 ■ NATIONAL STUDENT NURSES' ASSOCIATION

Attn: NSNA Foundation
45 Main Street, Suite 606
Brooklyn, NY 11201
Tel: (718)210-0705
Fax: (718)210-0710
E-mail: nsna@nsna.org
Web Site: http://www.nsna.org
To provide financial assistance to nursing students in designated specialties.
Title of Award: National Student Nurses' Association Specialty Scholarships **Area, Field, or Subject:** Nursing; Nursing, Oncological **Level of Education for which Award is Granted:** Graduate, Undergraduate **Number Awarded:** Varies each year; approximately 16 of these scholarships were awarded recently. **Funds Available:** Stipends range from $1,000 to $5,000. A total of more than $100,000 is awarded each year by the foundation for all its scholarship programs. **Duration:** 1 year.
Eligibility Requirements: This program is open to students currently enrolled in state-approved schools of nursing or pre-nursing associate degree, baccalaureate, diploma, generic doctorate, or generic master's programs. Graduating high school seniors are not eligible. Support for graduate education is provided only for a first degree in nursing. Applicants must designate their intended specialty, which may be anesthesia nursing, critical care, emergency, gerontology, informatics, nephrology, nurse educator, oncology, orthopedic, or perioperative. Selection is based on academic achievement, financial need, and involvement in student nursing organizations and community activities related to health care. **Deadline for Receipt:** January of each year. **Additional Information:** Funding for this program is provided by sponsors from industry who are interested in promoting specialties related to their products. Some scholarships are offered jointly with other nursing organizations, including the American Association of Nurse Anesthetists, the American Nephrology Nurses' Association, the American Organization of Nurse Executives, the Emergency Nurses Association, and the Oncology Nursing Society. Ap-

plications must be accompanied by a $10 processing fee.

2892 ■ NATIONAL STUDENT NURSES' ASSOCIATION

Attn: NSNA Foundation
45 Main Street, Suite 606
Brooklyn, NY 11201
Tel: (718)210-0705
Fax: (718)210-0710
E-mail: nsna@nsna.org
Web Site: http://www.nsna.org
To provide financial assistance to nursing or pre-nursing students at schools in selected geographic locations.
Title of Award: Promise of Nursing Scholarships **Area, Field, or Subject:** Nursing **Level of Education for which Award is Granted:** Graduate, Undergraduate **Number Awarded:** Varies each year. Recently, 154 of these scholarships were awarded: 10 in Dallas/Fort Worth, Texas, 3 in central Florida, 5 in southern Florida, 7 in northern California, 10 in southern California, 7 in Georgia, 7 in Illinois, 15 in Massachusetts, 10 in Michigan, 13 in New Jersey, 21 in New York, 39 in Pennsylvania, and 7 in Tennessee **Funds Available:** Stipends range from $1,000 to $5,000. **Duration:** 1 year.
Eligibility Requirements: This program is open to students currently enrolled in state-approved schools of nursing or pre-nursing associate degree, baccalaureate, diploma, generic doctorate, or generic master's programs. Graduating high school seniors are not eligible. Support for graduate education is provided only for a first degree in nursing. Applicants must be attending school in the Dallas/Fort Worth area of Texas, central or southern Florida, selected areas in northern or southern California, or the states of Georgia, Illinois, Massachusetts, Michigan, New Jersey, New York, Pennsylvania, or Tennessee. Selection is based on academic achievement, financial need, and involvement in student nursing organizations and community health activities. **Deadline for Receipt:** January of each year. **Additional Information:** This program, offered for the first time in 2003, is supported by fundraising events sponsored by Johnson & Johnson. Applications must be accompanied by a $10 processing fee.

2893 ■ NEW ENGLAND NAVY NURSE CORPS ASSOCIATION

c/o Maria K. Carroll, Scholarship Committee
22 William Drive
Middletown, RI 02842-5266
To provide financial assistance to registered nurses (R.N.s) and nursing students working on a bachelor's or master's degree at a college or university in New England.
Title of Award: New England Navy Nurse Corps Association Scholarship **Area, Field, or Subject:** Nursing **Level of Education for which Award is Granted:** Master's, Professional, Undergraduate **Number Awarded:** 1 each year. **Funds Available:** The stipend is $1,000. **Duration:** 1 year.
Eligibility Requirements: This program is open to R.N.s and nursing students in the New England states. Applicants must be working on a bachelor's or master's degree in nursing and have a GPA of 2.3 or higher. They must have completed at least 1 clinical nursing course. Along with their application, they must submit a 500-word essay on why they are qualified for this scholarship, their career goals, and their potential for contribution to the profession. **Deadline for Receipt:** May of each year.

2894 ■ NEW HAMPSHIRE POSTSECONDARY EDUCATION COMMISSION

3 Barrell Court, Suite 300
Concord, NH 03301-8543
Tel: (603)271-2555
Fax: (603)271-2696
E-mail: pedes@pec.state.nh.us
Web Site: http://www.state.nh.us/postsecondary/finwork.html
To provide scholarship/loans to New Hampshire residents who are interested in attending college to prepare for careers in designated professions.
Title of Award: New Hampshire Workforce Incentive Program Forgivable Loans **Area, Field, or Subject:** Chemistry; Education; Education, Special; Linguistics; Mathematics and mathematical sciences; Nursing; Physical sciences; Physics; Science **Level of Education for which Award is Granted:** Graduate, Undergraduate **Number Awarded:** Varies each year. **Funds Available:** The stipend is $500 per semester ($1,000 per year).

This is a scholarship/loan program; recipients must agree to pursue, within New Hampshire, the professional career for which they receive training. Recipients of loans for 1 year have their notes cancelled upon completion of 1 year of full-time service; repayment by service must be completed within 3 years from the date of licensure, certification, or completion of the program. Recipients of loans for more than 1 year have their notes cancelled upon completion of 2 years of full-time service; repayment by service must be completed within 5 years from the date of licensure, certification, or completion of the program. If the note is not cancelled because of service, the recipient must repay the loan within 2 years. **Duration:** 1 year; may be renewed.
Eligibility Requirements: This program is open to residents of New Hampshire who wish to prepare for careers in fields designated by the commission as shortage areas. Currently, the career shortage areas are chemistry, general science, mathematics, physical sciences, physics, special education, world languages, and nursing (L.P.N. through graduate). Applicants must be enrolled as a junior, senior, or graduate student at a college in New Hampshire and must be able to demonstrate financial need. **Deadline for Receipt:** May of each year for fall semester; December of each year for spring semester. **Additional Information:** The time for repayment of the loan, either in cash or through professional service, is extended while the recipient is 1) engaged in a course of study, at least on a half-time basis, at an institution of higher education; 2) serving on active duty as a member of the armed forces of the United States, or as a member of VISTA, the Peace Corps, or AmeriCorps, for a period up to 3 years; 3) temporarily totally disabled for a period up to 3 years; or 4) unable to secure employment because of the need to care for a disabled spouse, child, or parent for a period up to 12 months. The repayment obligation is cancelled if the recipient is unable to work because of a permanent total disability, receives relief under federal bankruptcy laws, or dies. This program went into effect in 1999.

2895 ■ NEW JERSEY HOSPITAL ASSOCIATION

Attn: Health Research and Educational Trust
760 Alexander Road
P.O. Box 1
Princeton, NJ 08543-0001
Tel: (609)275-4224
Fax: (609)452-8097
Web Site: http://www.njha.com/hret/scholarship.aspx
To provide financial assistance to New Jersey residents working on an undergraduate or graduate degree in a health-related field.
Title of Award: Health Research and Educational Trust Scholarships **Area, Field, or Subject:** Health care services; Nursing; Public administration **Level of Education for which Award is Granted:** Graduate, Undergraduate **Number Awarded:** Varies each year; recently, 2 of these scholarships were awarded. **Funds Available:** The stipend is $2,000. **Duration:** 1 year.
Eligibility Requirements: This program is open to residents of New Jersey enrolled in an upper-division or graduate program in hospital or health care administration, public administration, nursing, or other allied health profession. Applicants must have a GPA of 3.0 or higher and be able to demonstrate financial need. Along with their application, they must submit a 2-page essay (on which 50% of the selection is based) describing their academic plans for the future. Minorities and women are especially encouraged to apply. **Deadline for Receipt:** July of each year. **Additional Information:** This program began in 1983.

2896 ■ NIGHTINGALE AWARDS OF PENNSYLVANIA

2090 Linglestown Road, Suite 107
Harrisburg, PA 17110
Tel: (717)909-0350
E-mail: nightingale@pronursingresources.com
Web Site: http://www.nightingaleawards.org/schola.htm
To provide financial assistance to residents of Pennsylvania who are interested in working on an undergraduate or graduate degree in nursing at an institution in the state.
Title of Award: Nightingale Awards of Pennsylvania Scholarship **Area, Field, or Subject:** Nursing **Level of Education for which Award is Granted:** Graduate, Undergraduate **Number Awarded:** 1 or more each year. **Funds Available:** A stipend is awarded (amount not specified). **Duration:** 1 year.
Eligibility Requirements: This program is open to Pennsylvania residents who are enrolled in a program of basic (diploma, A.D., B.S.N.,

L.P.N.) or advanced (master's, doctoral) nursing at an educational institution in the state. Applicants must have a GPA of 3.0 or higher and have completed at least 1 course designated as "nursing." Along with their application, they must submit an essay on their reasons for preparing for a career in nursing. Students who have already completed a diploma or A.D. nursing program are not eligible. Selection is based on academic achievement, leadership potential, community service, and personal commitment. **Deadline for Receipt:** January of each year.

2897 ■ NORTH CAROLINA STATE EDUCATION ASSISTANCE AUTHORITY

Attn: Scholarship and Grant Services
10 T.W. Alexander Drive
P.O. Box 14103
Research Triangle Park, NC 27709-4103
Tel: (919)549-8614
Free: 800-700-1775
Fax: (919)549-8481
E-mail: information@ncseaa.edu
Web Site: http://www.ncseaa.edu
To provide scholarship/loans to students at North Carolina institutions who wish to prepare for a career in nursing.

Title of Award: North Carolina Nurse Education Scholarship Loan Program **Area, Field, or Subject:** Nursing **Level of Education for which Award is Granted:** Undergraduate **Number Awarded:** Varies each year; recently, a total of 1,010 students were receiving $1,062,031 in support through this program. **Funds Available:** The minimum scholarship/loan is $400. The maximum for students enrolled in Associate Degree Nursing (A.D.N.) and practical nurse education (L.P.N.) programs is $3,000; the maximum award for students enrolled in a baccalaureate (B.S.N.) program is $5,000. This is a scholarship/loan program; recipients who provide at least 6 months of consecutive full-time employment as a licensed nurse in North Carolina for 1 employer qualify for service cancellation. Loans are cancelled at the rate of $417 per month for service as an R.N. or $250 per month for service as an L.P.N. Loans not repaid in service must be repaid in cash, plus 10% interest from the date of disbursement. Recipients have up to 7 years to repay loans with service or 10 years to repay in cash. **Duration:** 1 year. Students in an A.D.N. program may renew the scholarship for 1 additional year. Students in a B.S.N. program may renew the scholarship for 3 additional years. Scholarships for L.P.N. programs are nonrenewable.

Eligibility Requirements: This program is open to students at any of the 56 North Carolina Community Colleges, the 11 constituent institutions of the University of North Carolina, or the 4 private colleges and universities in North Carolina that offer nursing education instruction. Applicants must be preparing for licensure in North Carolina as a Licensed Practical Nurse (L.P.N.) or a Registered Nurse (R.N.). U.S. citizenship and North Carolina residency are required. Selection is based on academic performance, student's willingness to practice full time as an L.P.N. or R.N. in North Carolina following completion of the education program, student's willingness to comply with the rules and regulations of this program, and financial need. **Additional Information:** Information and applications are available at the financial aid office of the participating North Carolina college or university offering the level of nurse education instruction desired. This program was first funded in 1989.

2898 ■ NORTH CAROLINA STATE EDUCATION ASSISTANCE AUTHORITY

Attn: Scholarship and Grant Services
10 T.W. Alexander Drive
P.O. Box 14223
Research Triangle Park, NC 27709-4223
Tel: (919)549-8614
Free: 800-700-1775
Fax: (919)549-8481
E-mail: information@ncseaa.edu
Web Site: http://www.ncseaa.edu
To provide loans and loans-for-service to North Carolina residents who are interested in preparing for a career in health, science, or mathematics.

Title of Award: North Carolina Student Loan Program for Health, Science, and Mathematics **Area, Field, or Subject:** Allied health; Dentistry; Medicine; Nursing; Optometry; Public health; Social work **Level of Education for which Award is Granted:** Graduate, Undergraduate

Number Awarded: Varies each year; recently, a total of 497 students were receiving $3,238,569 in support through this program. **Funds Available:** Maximum loans are $3,000 per year for associate degree and certificate programs, $5,000 per year for baccalaureate degree/certificate programs, $6,500 per year for master's degree programs, or $8,500 per year for health/professional doctoral programs. The maximum amount that any student can borrow through this program is $58,000. The interest rate is 4% while the borrowers are attending school and from 10 to 15% after they leave school. Cash repayments must begin 90 days or less after completion of course work and training. Under specified conditions, certain loan recipients in qualifying disciplines may have their loans canceled through service in North Carolina. **Duration:** 1 year; renewable for 1 additional year for diploma, associate, certificate, and master's degree programs, for 2 additional years for baccalaureate degree programs, or for 3 additional years for doctoral programs.

Eligibility Requirements: North Carolina residents are eligible to apply for this program if they have been accepted as full-time students in an accredited associate, baccalaureate, master's, or doctoral program leading to a degree in 1 of the following areas: allied health (including audiology/communications assistant, cytotechnology, dental hygiene, diagnostic medical sonographer, imaging technologist, medical technology, nuclear medicine technologist, occupational therapy/assistant, physician assistant, physical therapy/assistant, radiation therapist, radiography, respiratory therapy, and speech language pathology); clinical psychology (Ph.D. level only); dentistry; dietetics and nutrition (graduate level only); mathematics education; medicine (including chiropractic medicine, emergency medicine, family medicine, geriatrics, internal medicine, obstetrics and gynecology, osteopathic medicine, pediatrics, podiatry, primary care medicine, and psychiatry); nursing (including anesthetist, family nurse practitioner, nursing administration, general nursing, and midwifery); optometry; pharmacy; public health (graduate level only); science education (including biology, chemistry, communications and technologies, computer and information sciences, engineering, and physical science); social work (graduate level only); and veterinary medicine. U.S. citizenship is required. Selection is based on academic progress, financial ability of sureties to repay all loans and accrued interest in case of applicant's default, applicant's willingness to work in underserved areas of the state or in disciplines for which there is a shortage of professionals, applicant's willingness to comply with all program regulations, and financial need. **Deadline for Receipt:** May of each year. **Additional Information:** Recipients may attend a North Carolina postsecondary institution or an eligible out-of-state institution. This program was formerly known as the North Carolina Medical Student Loan Program.

2899 ■ NORTH CAROLINA STATE EDUCATION ASSISTANCE AUTHORITY

Attn: Scholarship and Grant Services
10 T.W. Alexander Drive
P.O. Box 14103
Research Triangle Park, NC 27709-4103
Tel: (919)549-8614
Free: 800-700-1775
Fax: (919)549-8481
E-mail: information@ncseaa.edu
Web Site: http://www.ncseaa.edu
To provide scholarship/loans to students in North Carolina who wish to prepare for a career in nursing.

Title of Award: North Carolina Undergraduate Nurse Scholars Program **Area, Field, or Subject:** Nursing **Level of Education for which Award is Granted:** Undergraduate **Number Awarded:** Varies; generally, up to 450 new undergraduate degree awards are made each year. Recently, a total of 834 students were receiving $3,414,500 through this program. **Funds Available:** Annual stipends are $3,000 for candidates for an associate degree, $3,000 for candidates for a diploma in nursing, or $5,000 or $3,000 for students in a B.S.N. program. This is a scholarship/loan program; 1 year of full-time work as a nurse in North Carolina cancels 1 year of support under this program. Recipients who fail to honor the work obligation must repay the balance plus 10% interest. **Duration:** 1 year; may be renewed 1 additional year by candidates for an associate degree, registered nurses completing a B.S.N. degree, and community college transfer students and juniors in a B.S.N. program, or for 3 additional years by freshmen and nontraditional students in a B.S.N. program.

Eligibility Requirements: Applicants must be high school seniors, high school graduates, or currently-enrolled college students who are U.S. citizens, North Carolina residents, and interested in becoming a nurse. Students must plan to enter a North Carolina college, university, or hospital that prepares students for licensure as a registered nurse. Applications are encouraged from nontraditional students, including older individuals, ethnic minorities, males, and individuals with previous careers and/or degrees who are pursuing nurse education. U.S. citizenship and full-time enrollment are required. Selection is based on academic achievement, leadership potential, and the promise of service as a registered nurse in North Carolina; financial need is not considered. **Deadline for Receipt:** February of each year for B.S.N. programs; May of each year for A.D.N. and diploma students. **Additional Information:** The North Carolina General Assembly created this program in 1989; the first recipients were funded for the 1990-91 academic year.

2900 ■ NURSE EDUCATORS OF ILLINOIS

Attn: Scholarships
P.O. Box 695
Morton Grove, IL 60053
Tel: (847)983-0954
E-mail: neionline@neionline.org
Web Site: http://www.neionline.org
To provide financial assistance to undergraduate members of Nurse Educators of Illinois who are enrolled in an accredited B.S.N., A.D.N., or diploma program in nursing.

Title of Award: Nurse Educators of Illinois Undergraduate Scholarships **Area, Field, or Subject:** Nursing **Level of Education for which Award is Granted:** Undergraduate **Number Awarded:** Varies each year; recently, 2 of these scholarships were awarded. **Funds Available:** A stipend is awarded (amount not specified). **Duration:** 1 year.
Eligibility Requirements: This program is open to full- or part-time (half-time or more) students who are attending an accredited undergraduate or R.N. diploma nursing program. Applicants must be enrolled at the senior level (B.S.N.) or in their final year of an R.N. diploma or A.D.N. program at the time of the award. They must have a GPA of 3.5 or higher (official transcript is required), an above-average level of clinical achievement, leadership in an organization and/or community service, and evidence of verbal and written communication skills. Nurse Educators of Illinois membership on an individual or program level is required. **Additional Information:** Nurse Educators of Illinois was founded in 2004 as a successor to the Illinois League for Nursing.

2901 ■ NURSING FOUNDATION OF PENNSYLVANIA

Attn: Awards Committee
2578 Interstate Drive, Suite 101
Harrisburg, PA 17110
Tel: (717)657-1222; 888-707-PSNA
Fax: (717)657-3796
E-mail: panurses@panurses.org
Web Site: http://www.psna.org
To provide financial assistance to veterans, military personnel, and their dependents who are studying nursing in Pennsylvania.

Title of Award: Jack E. Barger, Sr. Memorial Nursing Scholarships **Area, Field, or Subject:** Nursing **Level of Education for which Award is Granted:** Professional, Undergraduate **Number Awarded:** 6 each year. **Funds Available:** The stipend is $1,000. **Duration:** 1 year.
Eligibility Requirements: This program is open to veterans, active-duty military personnel, and the children and spouses of veterans and active-duty military personnel. Applicants must be residents of Pennsylvania and currently enrolled in an undergraduate professional school of nursing in the state. Recipients are selected by lottery from among the qualified applicants. **Deadline for Receipt:** April of each year. **Additional Information:** This program is sponsored by the Department of Pennsylvania Veterans of Foreign Wars (VFW). Recipients must attend the VFW Convention to accept the scholarship; travel, meals, and overnight expenses are paid by the VFW.

2902 ■ NURSING FOUNDATION OF PENNSYLVANIA

Attn: Awards Committee
2578 Interstate Drive, Suite 101
Harrisburg, PA 17110
Tel: (717)657-1222; 888-707-PSNA

Fax: (717)657-3796
E-mail: panurses@panurses.org
Web Site: http://www.psna.org
To provide financial assistance to undergraduate nursing students in Pennsylvania.

Title of Award: Pauline Thompson Nursing Education Scholarship **Area, Field, or Subject:** Nursing **Level of Education for which Award is Granted:** Professional, Undergraduate **Number Awarded:** 5 each year. **Funds Available:** The stipend is $1,000. **Duration:** 1 year.
Eligibility Requirements: Applicants must be enrolled in a baccalaureate, associate degree, or R.N. to B.S.N. competition nursing program located in Pennsylvania that is accredited by the National League for Nursing. Baccalaureate students must be in their junior or senior year (application may be made at the end of the sophomore year). Associate degree students must be in their final year (application may be made at the end of the first year). Registered nurses must have been accepted into a baccalaureate program. All applicants must be Pennsylvania residents. They must be in good academic standing (GPA of 3.0 or higher) and able to show both leadership qualities and involvement in community service. Applicants must be members of the Student Nurses Association of Pennsylvania, unless there is no school chapter (applicants who are R.N.s must be members of the Pennsylvania State Nurses Association). **Deadline for Receipt:** May of each year. **Additional Information:** The recipient must attend the foundation's annual banquet to receive the scholarship. The recipient will be the guest of the foundation at the banquet and financial support for travel and overnight accommodations will be provided if necessary.

2903 ■ NURSING FOUNDATION OF RHODE ISLAND

Attn: Scholarship Committee
Corliss Landing
550 South Water Street
Providence, RI 02903
Tel: (401)421-9703
Fax: (401)421-6793
E-mail: risna@prodigy.net
Web Site: http://www.rinursingfoundation.org/StudentNurse.htm
To provide financial assistance to students currently enrolled in nursing schools in Rhode Island.

Title of Award: Nursing Foundation of Rhode Island Student Scholarships **Area, Field, or Subject:** Nursing **Level of Education for which Award is Granted:** Graduate, Undergraduate **Number Awarded:** Varies each year; recently, more than 70 of these scholarships were awarded. **Funds Available:** The stipend of the Elsie L. Drew Memorial Scholarship is $1,000. All other stipends are $500. Checks are written jointly to the recipient and the recipient's school. **Duration:** 1 year.
Eligibility Requirements: This program is open to students enrolled in a nursing program in Rhode Island who demonstrate financial need, have maintained at least a 3.0 GPA, and have demonstrated clinical proficiency, enthusiasm, and motivation in their studies. Preference is given to students who are in the latter half of their nursing program. **Deadline for Receipt:** May of each year. **Additional Information:** In addition to the Elsie L. Drew Memorial Scholarship, this program includes these other named scholarships: the Francis H. Sherman Memorial Scholarship, the Gerald and Trudy Mulvey Scholarship, and the Helen Capocci Enright Scholarship.

2904 ■ OHIO BOARD OF REGENTS

Attn: State Grants and Scholarships
57 East Main Street, Fourth Floor
P.O. Box 182452
Columbus, OH 43218-2452
Tel: (614)466-7420; 888-833-1133
Fax: (614)752-5903
E-mail: bmetheney@regents.state.oh.us
Web Site: http://www.regents.state.oh.us/sgs/nealp.htm
To provide scholarship/loans to students in Ohio who intend to study nursing.

Title of Award: Ohio Nurse Education Assistance Loan Program **Area, Field, or Subject:** Nursing **Level of Education for which Award is Granted:** Undergraduate **Number Awarded:** Varies each year; recently, 35 students received benefits through this program. **Funds Available:** Up to $3,000 per year is available. This is a scholarship/loan program; up to

100% of the loan may be forgiven at the rate of 20% per year if the recipient serves as a nurse under specified conditions for up to 5 years. If the loan is not repaid with service, it must be repaid in cash with interest at the rate of 8% per year. **Duration:** 1 year; renewable for up to 4 additional years.

Eligibility Requirements: Applicants must be Ohio residents, U.S. citizens, and enrolled at least half time in an approved nursing education program in Ohio. Applicants must demonstrate financial need and intend to engage in direct clinical practice following graduation. **Deadline for Receipt:** May of each year for fall semester; October of each year for spring semester. **Additional Information:** This program, established in 1990, is administered by the Ohio Board of Regents with assistance from the Ohio Board of Nursing.

2905 ■ ONCOLOGY NURSING SOCIETY

Attn: ONS Foundation
125 Enterprise Drive
Pittsburgh, PA 15275-1214
Tel: (412)859-6100; (866)257-4ONS
Fax: (412)859-6160
E-mail: foundation@ons.org
Web Site: http://www.ons.org/awards/foundawards/bachelors.shtml
To provide financial assistance to registered nurses who are interested in working on a bachelor's degree in oncology nursing.
Title of Award: Amgen Bachelor's Scholarships **Area, Field, or Subject:** Nursing, Oncological; Oncology **Level of Education for which Award is Granted:** Professional, Undergraduate **Number Awarded:** 2 each year. **Funds Available:** The stipend is $2,000. **Duration:** 1 year.
Eligibility Requirements: This program is open to registered nurses with a demonstrated interest in and commitment to oncology nursing. Applicants must be currently enrolled in an undergraduate degree program at an NLN- or CCNE-accredited school of nursing. They may not have previously received a bachelor's level scholarship from this sponsor. Applicants must submit an essay of 250 words or less on their role in caring for persons with cancer and a statement of their professional goals and their relationship to the advancement of oncology nursing. Financial need is not considered in the selection process. **Deadline for Receipt:** January of each year. **Additional Information:** This program, supported by Amgen, Inc., began in 2005 At the end of each year of scholarship participation, recipients must submit a summary describing their educational activities. Applications must be accompanied by a $5 fee.

2906 ■ ONCOLOGY NURSING SOCIETY

Attn: ONS Foundation
125 Enterprise Drive
Pittsburgh, PA 15275-1214
Tel: (412)859-6100; (866)257-4ONS
Fax: (412)859-6160
E-mail: foundation@ons.org
Web Site: http://www.ons.org/awards/foundawards/joshGottheil.shtml
To provide funding for further education to professional registered nurses who can demonstrate meritorious practice in bone marrow transplant (BMT) nursing.
Title of Award: Josh Gottheil Memorial Bone Marrow Transplant Career Development Awards **Area, Field, or Subject:** Nursing, Oncological; Oncology **Level of Education for which Award is Granted:** Master's, Professional, Undergraduate **Number Awarded:** 4 each year. **Funds Available:** The stipend is $2,000. Funds may be used to support a continuing education program or to supplement tuition in a bachelor's or master's program. **Duration:** 1 year.
Eligibility Requirements: This program is open to professional registered nurses who are interested in pursuing education at the bachelor's or master's degree level. Applicants must be currently employed as a registered nurse working in BMT (at least 75% of time must be devoted to patient care) or in the position of nurse manager, nurse practitioner, clinical nurse specialist, BMT coordinator, or equivalent position. They must have at least 2 years in BMT nursing practice. Candidates are evaluated on the following criteria: 1) clarity of professional goal statement; 2) demonstrated commitment to professional development in BMT nursing; 3) demonstrated commitment to continuing professional practice in BMT nursing; 4) recommendations; and 5) contributions and/or professional nursing practice. Applicants must not have previously received this career development award from the founda-

tion. **Deadline for Receipt:** November of each year. **Additional Information:** These awards were first presented in 1995.

2907 ■ ONCOLOGY NURSING SOCIETY

Attn: ONS Foundation
125 Enterprise Drive
Pittsburgh, PA 15275-1214
Tel: (412)859-6100; (866)257-4ONS
Fax: (412)859-6160
E-mail: foundation@ons.org
Web Site: http://www.ons.org/awards/foundawards/bachelors.shtml
To provide financial assistance to nurses who are interested in working on a bachelor's degree in oncology nursing.
Title of Award: Oncology Nursing Certification Corporation Bachelor's Scholarships **Area, Field, or Subject:** Nursing, Oncological; Oncology **Level of Education for which Award is Granted:** Professional, Undergraduate **Number Awarded:** Varies each year; recently, 10 of these scholarships were awarded. **Funds Available:** The stipend is $2,000. **Duration:** 1 year.
Eligibility Requirements: This program is open to registered nurses and licensed practical (vocational) nurses with a demonstrated interest in and commitment to oncology nursing. They must be currently enrolled in an undergraduate degree program at an NLN- or CCNE-accredited school of nursing. They may not have previously received a bachelor's level scholarship from this sponsor. Applicants must submit an essay of 250 words or less on their role in caring for persons with cancer and a statement of their professional goals and their relationship to the advancement of oncology nursing. Financial need is not considered in the selection process. **Deadline for Receipt:** January of each year. **Additional Information:** This program, supported by the Oncology Nursing Certification Corporation, awarded its first scholarships in 1992. At the end of each year of scholarship participation, recipients must submit a summary describing their educational activities. Applications must be accompanied by a $5 fee.

2908 ■ ONCOLOGY NURSING SOCIETY

Attn: ONS Foundation
125 Enterprise Drive
Pittsburgh, PA 15275-1214
Tel: (412)859-6100; (866)257-4ONS
Fax: (412)859-6160
E-mail: foundation@ons.org
Web Site: http://www.ons.org/awards/foundawards/bachelors.shtml
To provide financial assistance to registered nurses who are interested in working on a bachelor's degree in oncology nursing.
Title of Award: Roberta Pierce Scofield Bachelor's Scholarships **Area, Field, or Subject:** Nursing, Oncological; Oncology **Level of Education for which Award is Granted:** Professional, Undergraduate **Number Awarded:** 2 each year. **Funds Available:** The stipend is $2,000. **Duration:** 1 year.
Eligibility Requirements: This program is open to registered nurses with a demonstrated interest in and commitment to oncology nursing. Applicants must be currently enrolled in an undergraduate degree program at an NLN- or CCNE-accredited school of nursing. They may not have previously received a bachelor's level scholarship from this sponsor. Applicants must submit an essay of 250 words or less on their role in caring for persons with cancer and a statement of their professional goals and their relationship to the advancement of oncology nursing. Financial need is not considered in the selection process. **Deadline for Receipt:** January of each year. **Additional Information:** These scholarships were first awarded in 1988. At the end of each year of scholarship participation, recipients must submit a summary describing their educational activities. Applications must be accompanied by a $5 fee.

2909 ■ OREGON STUDENT ASSISTANCE COMMISSION

Attn: Grants and Scholarships Division
1500 Valley River Drive, Suite 100
Eugene, OR 97401-2146
Tel: (541)687-7395
Free: 800-452-8807
Fax: (541)687-7419
E-mail: awardinfo@mercury.osac.state.or.us
Web Site: http://www.osac.state.or.us

To provide financial assistance for college or graduate school to residents of Oregon who are interested in preparing for a public health career.
Title of Award: Lawrence R. Foster Memorial Scholarship **Area, Field, or Subject:** Medical assisting; Medical technology; Nursing; Public health **Level of Education for which Award is Granted:** Four Year College, Graduate **Number Awarded:** Varies each year; recently, 6 of these scholarships were awarded. **Funds Available:** Stipend amounts vary; recently, they were at least $4,167. **Duration:** 1 year.
Eligibility Requirements: This program is open to residents of Oregon who are attending a 4-year college or university in any state to prepare for a career in public health (not private practice). First preference is given to applicants who are either working in public health or enrolled as graduate students in that field. Second preference is given to undergraduates entering the junior or senior year of a health program, including nursing, medical technology, and physician assistant. A general preference is given to applicants from diverse cultures. Along with their application, they must submit a 1- to 2-page essay on their interest, experience, and future plans for a public health career **Deadline for Receipt:** February of each year. **Additional Information:** This program is administered by the Oregon Student Assistance Commission (OSAC) with funds provided by the Oregon Community Foundation, 1221 S.W. Yamhill, Suite 100, Portland, OR 97205, (503) 227-6846, Fax: (503) 274-7771.

2910 ■ OREGON STUDENT ASSISTANCE COMMISSION

Attn: Grants and Scholarships Division
1500 Valley River Drive, Suite 100
Eugene, OR 97401-2146
Tel: (541)687-7395
Free: 800-452-8807
Fax: (541)687-7419
E-mail: awardinfo@mercury.osac.state.or.us
Web Site: http://www.osac.state.or.us
To provide financial assistance to students in Oregon who are employed while working on an undergraduate or graduate degree in teaching or nursing.
Title of Award: Friends of Oregon Students Program **Area, Field, or Subject:** Education; Nursing **Level of Education for which Award is Granted:** Graduate, Undergraduate **Number Awarded:** Varies each year; recently, 28 of these scholarships were awarded. **Funds Available:** Stipends range from $3,000 to $5,000 per year. **Duration:** 1 year; may be renewed.
Eligibility Requirements: This program is open to students in Oregon who are working and will continue to work at least 20 hours per week while attending college or graduate school at least three-quarter time. Applicants must be interested in preparing for a career in teaching or nursing. They must be able to demonstrate a cumulative GPA of 2.5 or higher and volunteer or work experience relevant to their chosen profession. Preference is given to applicants who 1) are nontraditional students (e.g., older, returning, single parents), 2) have overcome significant personal obstacles, or 3) graduated from an alternative high school, obtained a GED, or are transferring from an Oregon community college to a 4-year college. Along with their application, they must submit essays and letters of reference on how they balance school, work, and personal life as well as their experiences in overcoming obstacles. Selection is based on work experience, community service and volunteer activities, responses to essay questions, letters of reference, and financial need; academic promise (as indicated by GPA and SAT/ACT scores) is also considered. **Deadline for Receipt:** February of each year. **Additional Information:** Funding for this program, established in 1996, is provided by the HF Fund, P.O. Box 55187, Portland, OR 97238, (503) 234-0259, E-mail: foosf@hffund.org.

2911 ■ OREGON STUDENT ASSISTANCE COMMISSION

Attn: Grants and Scholarships Division
1500 Valley River Drive, Suite 100
Eugene, OR 97401-2146
Tel: (541)687-7395
Free: 800-452-8807
Fax: (541)687-7419
E-mail: awardinfo@mercury.osac.state.or.us
Web Site: http://www.osac.state.or.us
To provide financial assistance for the study of nursing to residents of Oregon.
Title of Award: Bertha P. Singer Scholarship **Area, Field, or Subject:** Nursing **Level of Education for which Award is Granted:** Undergradu-

ate **Number Awarded:** Varies each year; recently, 23 of these scholarships were awarded. **Funds Available:** Stipend amounts vary; recently, they were at least $1,087. **Duration:** 1 year.
Eligibility Requirements: This program is open to residents of Oregon who are studying nursing at a college in the state and have a cumulative GPA of 3.0 or higher. Applicants must provide documentation of enrollment in the third year of a 4-year nursing degree program or the second year of a 2-year associate degree nursing program. **Deadline for Receipt:** February of each year.

2912 ■ PACIFICARE FOUNDATION

3100 Lake Center Drive
P.O. Box 25186
Santa Ana, CA 92799
Tel: (714)825-5233
Web Site: http://www.pacificare.com
To provide financial assistance to Latino high school seniors in designated states planning to major in a health care field in college.
Title of Award: PacifiCare Latino Health Scholars Program **Area, Field, or Subject:** Health care services; Medical technology; Medicine; Nursing; Pharmaceutical sciences; Psychology; Public health **Level of Education for which Award is Granted:** Undergraduate **Number Awarded:** Approximately 50 each year. **Funds Available:** The stipend is $2,000. **Duration:** 1 year.
Eligibility Requirements: This program is open to seniors graduating from high schools in Arizona, California, Colorado, Nevada, Oklahoma, Oregon, Texas, and Washington. Applicants must have a GPA of 3.0 or higher, be fluent in Spanish, and have been accepted as a full-time student at a university, community college, or accredited technical college. Their proposed field of study must relate to health care, including (but not limited to) nursing, medical interpretation, health claims examiner, health information technology programs, pharmacy technician, public health, psychology, or pre-medical studies. Along with their application, they must submit a 2-page essay (in both English and Spanish) on their personal and academic accomplishments, community involvement, volunteer and leadership activities, academic plans, and the reason they want a career in the health care field. **Deadline for Receipt:** June of each year. **Additional Information:** This program was established in 2003.

2913 ■ RHODE ISLAND FOUNDATION

Attn: Scholarship Coordinator
One Union Station
Providence, RI 02903
Tel: (401)274-4564
Fax: (401)331-8085
E-mail: libbym@rifoundation.org
Web Site: http://www.rifoundation.org
To provide financial assistance to students, especially residents of Rhode Island, working on a degree in nursing.
Title of Award: Albert E. and Florence W. Newton Nursing Scholarship **Area, Field, or Subject:** Nursing **Level of Education for which Award is Granted:** Professional, Undergraduate **Number Awarded:** Varies each year. Recently, 8 of these scholarships were awarded: 3 new awards and 5 renewals. **Funds Available:** A stipend is awarded (amount not specified). **Duration:** 1 year; may be renewed.
Eligibility Requirements: This program is open to 1) students enrolled in a baccalaureate nursing program; 2) second- or third-year students in a 3-year nursing program; 3) students in a 2-year associate degree nursing program; and 4) active practicing R.N.s working on a bachelor's degree in nursing. Applicants must be studying at a nursing school on a full- or part-time basis and able to demonstrate financial need. They may be enrolled at a school in any state; preference is given to residents of Rhode Island. Along with their application, they must submit an essay, up to 300 words, on their career goals, particularly as they relate to practicing in or advancing the field of nursing in Rhode Island. **Deadline for Receipt:** April of each year.

2914 ■ RHODE ISLAND FOUNDATION

Attn: Scholarship Coordinator
One Union Station
Providence, RI 02903
Tel: (401)274-4564
Fax: (401)331-8085

E-mail: libbym@rifoundation.org
Web Site: http://www.rifoundation.org
To provide financial assistance to students enrolled in nursing programs in Rhode Island.
Title of Award: Edward J. and Virginia M. Routhier Nursing Scholarship **Area, Field, or Subject:** Nursing **Level of Education for which Award is Granted:** Graduate, Professional, Undergraduate **Number Awarded:** Varies each year. Recently, 11 of these scholarships were awarded: 6 new awards and 5 renewals. **Funds Available:** A stipend is awarded (amount not specified). **Duration:** 1 year; may be renewed.
Eligibility Requirements: This program is open to students enrolled or accepted at an accredited nursing program in Rhode Island. Applicants must be 1) registered nurses (R.N.s) enrolled in a nursing baccalaureate degree program; 2) students enrolled in a baccalaureate nursing program; or 3) R.N.s working on a graduate degree (master's or Ph.D.). They must be able to demonstrate financial need and a commitment to practice in Rhode Island. Along with their application, they must submit an essay, up to 300 words, on their career goals, particularly as they relate to practicing in or advancing the field of nursing in Rhode Island. **Deadline for Receipt:** April of each year.

2915 ■ SCHOLARSHIP ADMINISTRATIVE SERVICES, INC.
Attn: AUN Program
2000 Rock Street, Suite 3
Mountain View, CA 94043
To provide financial assistance to undergraduate and graduate students working on a degree in nursing.
Title of Award: Association of United Nurses Scholarships **Area, Field, or Subject:** Nursing **Level of Education for which Award is Granted:** Graduate, Undergraduate **Number Awarded:** Up to 20 each year. **Funds Available:** The stipend is $5,000 per year. **Duration:** 1 year; may be renewed 1 additional year if the recipient maintains full-time enrollment and a GPA of 3.0 or higher.
Eligibility Requirements: This program is open to full-time students working on or planning to work on an undergraduate or graduate degree in nursing. Applicants must have a GPA of 3.0 or higher and be able to demonstrate a record of involvement in extracurricular and work activities related to nursing. Along with their application, they must submit a 1,000-word essay on their educational and career goals, why they believe nursing is essential to America, and why they have decided to prepare for a career in nursing. Financial need is not considered in the selection process. **Deadline for Receipt:** April of each year. **Additional Information:** This program is sponsored by the Association of United Nurses (AUN) and administered by Scholarship Administrative Services, Inc. AUN was established in 2005 to encourage more American students to consider a career as a nurse. Requests for applications should be accompanied by a self-addressed stamped envelope, the student's e-mail address, and the source where they found the scholarship information.

2916 ■ HAROLD B. & DOROTHY A. SNYDER SCHOLARSHIP FUND
P.O. Box 671
Moorestown, NJ 08057-0671
Tel: (856)273-9745
To provide financial assistance to undergraduate and graduate students preparing for a career in the areas of Presbyterian ministry, nursing, building construction, or engineering.
Title of Award: Harold B. & Dorothy A. Snyder Scholarships **Area, Field, or Subject:** Construction; Engineering; Nursing; Religion **Level of Education for which Award is Granted:** Master's, Undergraduate **Number Awarded:** Varies each year. **Funds Available:** The amount awarded varies, depending upon the needs of the recipient. Funds are paid directly to the recipient's institution. **Duration:** 1 year; generally renewable until completion of the recipient's degree program.
Eligibility Requirements: This program is open to U.S. citizens who are attending or planning to attend institutions of higher learning. They must be preparing for a career in the areas of Presbyterian ministry (M.Div. degree), nursing (B.S.N.), building construction, or engineering. Applicants are evaluated on the basis of achievement, need, demonstrated commitment to community service, and character. Preference is given to applicants who are full-time students and who are New Jersey residents. In some instances, preference is also given to full-time enrollees of specific institutions and to members of certain denominations and congregations or residents of certain towns. There are no other prefer-

ences as to age, sex, religion (except when applicable), race, or country of origin. Personal interviews are required. **Deadline for Receipt:** March of each year. **Additional Information:** Snyder Scholars are required, by contract, to submit periodic reports and attend meetings. The foundation will withdraw scholarship aid from any recipient who, in its opinion, has engaged in activities detrimental to the school or college being attended or to the country. In addition, the foundation will withdraw aid from any recipient (other than a divinity student) who seeks to avoid service in the U.S. armed forces as a conscientious objector.

2917 ■ STATE STUDENT ASSISTANCE COMMISSION OF INDIANA
Attn: Grant Division
150 West Market Street, Suite 500
Indianapolis, IN 46204-2811
Tel: (317)232-2350; 888-528-4719
Fax: (317)232-3260
E-mail: special@ssaci.state.in.us
Web Site: http://www.in.gov/ssaci/programs/nur.html
To provide scholarship/loans to Indiana residents who are interested in preparing for a career as a nurse.
Title of Award: Indiana Nursing Scholarship Fund Program **Area, Field, or Subject:** Nursing **Level of Education for which Award is Granted:** Undergraduate **Number Awarded:** Varies each year. **Funds Available:** The stipend is $5,000 per year. Funds may be used only for tuition and fees. Recipients agree in writing to work as a nurse in a health care setting in Indiana for at least the first 2 years after graduation. If they fail to fulfill that service obligation, they will be required to reimburse the state of Indiana. **Duration:** 1 year; may be renewed up to 3 additional years, but recipients must complete the nursing program within 6 years from the time the first scholarship is awarded.
Eligibility Requirements: Applicants must be Indiana residents, be admitted to an eligible Indiana school as a full- or part-time student to work on a certificate or bachelor's degree in nursing, be able to demonstrate financial need, be U.S. citizens or permanent resident, and have a GPA of 2.0 or higher. **Additional Information:** This program was created in 1990.

2918 ■ TEXAS HIGHER EDUCATION COORDINATING BOARD
Attn: Hinson-Hazlewood College Student Loan Program
1200 East Anderson Lane
P.O. Box 12788, Capitol Station
Austin, TX 78711-2788
Tel: (512)427-6340
Free: 800-242-3062
Fax: (512)427-6423
E-mail: loaninfo@thecb.state.tx.us
Web Site: http://www.hhloans.com
To provide educational loans to students in Texas in health-related degree programs.
Title of Award: Hinson-Hazlewood Health Education Loan Program **Area, Field, or Subject:** Dentistry; Health care services; Medicine; Medicine, Osteopathic; Nursing; Optometry; Pharmaceutical sciences; Podiatry; Public health; Veterinary science and medicine **Level of Education for which Award is Granted:** Four Year College, Graduate **Number Awarded:** Varies each year. **Funds Available:** The maximum annual loan is $12,500 for pharmacy, nursing, allied health, and public health students; or $20,000 for medicine, dentistry, optometry, osteopathy, podiatry, or veterinary medicine students. The origination fee is 3%. After a grace period of 9 months, repayment must be completed within 25 years at a minimum monthly payment of $50. The current interest rate is 5.25% which begins to accrue immediately, even while the student is in school. **Duration:** 1 year; may be renewed up to 3 additional years. The maximum total loan is $50,000 for pharmacy, nursing, allied health, and public health students or $80,000 for medicine, dentistry, optometry, osteopathy, podiatry, or veterinary medicine students.
Eligibility Requirements: This program is open to students who qualify as Texas residents and meet the academic requirements of a public or private college or university in the state. Applicants must be enrolled at least half time in a course of study leading to 1) a doctoral degree in medicine, dentistry, optometry, osteopathy, podiatry, or veterinary medicine; 2) a bachelor's or master's degree in pharmacy; 3) a graduate or equivalent degree in public health; or 4) an associate, bachelor's, or graduate degree in nursing or allied health fields. They must be able to

demonstrate financial need and enroll full time. U.S. citizenship is required. **Additional Information:** Applications must be submitted through the financial aid office at the college or university attended. This program is part of the Hinton-Hazelwood College Student Loan Program (HHCSLP).

2919 ■ TEXAS HIGHER EDUCATION COORDINATING BOARD

Attn: Grants and Special Programs
1200 East Anderson Lane
P.O. Box 12788, Capitol Station
Austin, TX 78711-2788
Tel: (512)427-6340
Free: 800-242-3062
Fax: (512)427-6127
E-mail: grantinfo@thecb.state.tx.us
Web Site: http://www.collegefortexans.com
To provide financial assistance to Texas students who are interested in preparing for a career as a professional nurse.
Title of Award: Texas Professional Nursing Scholarships **Area, Field, or Subject:** Nursing **Level of Education for which Award is Granted:** Graduate, Undergraduate **Number Awarded:** Varies each year; recently, 131 of these scholarships were awarded. **Funds Available:** The stipend depends on the need of the recipient, to a maximum of $3,000. **Duration:** 1 academic year.
Eligibility Requirements: This program is open to undergraduate or graduate students who are residents of Texas and enrolled at least half time in a program leading to licensure as a professional nurse at a college or university in the state. Applicants must be able to demonstrate financial need. **Deadline for Receipt:** Applicants should contact the financial aid director at the professional nursing school in which they plan to enroll for appropriate deadline dates. **Additional Information:** Some of these funds are targeted to students from rural communities and some to graduate students.

2920 ■ TEXAS HIGHER EDUCATION COORDINATING BOARD

Attn: Grants and Special Programs
1200 East Anderson Lane
P.O. Box 12788, Capitol Station
Austin, TX 78711-2788
Tel: (512)427-6340
Free: 800-242-3062
Fax: (512)427-6127
E-mail: grantinfo@thecb.state.tx.us
Web Site: http://www.collegefortexans.com
To provide financial assistance to Texas students who are interested in preparing for a career as a vocational nurse.
Title of Award: Texas Vocational Nursing Scholarships **Area, Field, or Subject:** Nursing **Level of Education for which Award is Granted:** Undergraduate **Number Awarded:** Varies each year; recently, 36 of these scholarships were awarded. **Funds Available:** The stipend depends on the need of the recipient, to a maximum of $1,500. **Duration:** 1 academic year.
Eligibility Requirements: This program is open to undergraduate or graduate students who are residents of Texas and enrolled at least half time in a program leading to licensure as a vocational nurse at a college or university in the state. Applicants must be able to demonstrate financial need. **Deadline for Receipt:** Applicants should contact the financial aid director at the vocational nursing school in which they plan to enroll for appropriate deadline dates. **Additional Information:** Some of these funds are targeted to students from rural communities.

2921 ■ ULMAN CANCER FUND FOR YOUNG ADULTS

Attn: Scholarship Committee
4725 Dorsey Hall Drive, Suite A
PMB 505
Ellicott City, MD 21042
Tel: (410)964-0202; 888-393-FUND
E-mail: scholarship@ulmanfund.org
Web Site: http://www.ulmanfund.org/Services/Scholarship/tabid/73/Default.aspx
To provide financial assistance to nursing students who have a parent with cancer.
Title of Award: Barbara Palo Foster Memorial Scholarship **Area, Field, or Subject:** Nursing **Level of Education for which Award is Granted:**

Undergraduate **Number Awarded:** 1 each year. **Funds Available:** The stipend is $1,000. **Duration:** 1 year.
Eligibility Requirements: This program is open to students who have or have lost a parent to cancer. Applicants must be able to demonstrate financial need. They must be between 15 and 40 years of age and enrolled in, or planning to enroll in, a postsecondary program in nursing. Along with their application, they must submit a 500-word essay on 1 of 4 assigned topics that relate to cancer. Selection is based on the quality of the essay, recommendations, their overall story of cancer survivorship, and financial need. **Deadline for Receipt:** March of each year.

2922 ■ UNITED DAUGHTERS OF THE CONFEDERACY

Attn: Education Director
328 North Boulevard
Richmond, VA 23220-4057
Tel: (804)355-1636
Fax: (804)353-1396
E-mail: hqudc@rcn.com
Web Site: http://www.hqudc.org/scholarships/scholarships.html
To provide financial assistance for nursing education to lineal descendants of Confederate veterans.
Title of Award: Phoebe Pember Memorial Scholarship **Area, Field, or Subject:** Nursing **Level of Education for which Award is Granted:** Undergraduate **Number Awarded:** 1 each year. **Funds Available:** The amount of this scholarship depends on the availability of funds. **Duration:** 1 year; may be renewed for up to 3 additional years.
Eligibility Requirements: Eligible to apply for these scholarships are lineal descendants of worthy Confederates or collateral descendants who are members of the Children of the Confederacy or the United Daughters of the Confederacy. Applicants must intend to study nursing and must submit a family financial report and certified proof of the Confederate record of 1 ancestor, with the company and regiment in which he served. They must have at least a 3.0 GPA in high school. **Deadline for Receipt:** March of each year. **Additional Information:** Information is also available from Mrs. Robert C. Kraus, Second Vice President General, 239 Deerfield Lane, Franklin, NC 28734-0112. Members of the same family may not hold scholarships simultaneously, and only 1 application per family will be accepted within any 1 year. All requests for applications must include a self-addressed stamped envelope.

2923 ■ UNITED DAUGHTERS OF THE CONFEDERACY

Attn: Education Director
328 North Boulevard
Richmond, VA 23220-4057
Tel: (804)355-1636
Fax: (804)353-1396
E-mail: hqudc@rcn.com
Web Site: http://www.hqudc.org/scholarships/scholarships.html
To provide financial assistance to mature women who are lineal descendants of Confederate veterans and plan to major in selected fields in college.
Title of Award: Walter Reed Smith Scholarship Program **Area, Field, or Subject:** Business administration; Computer and information sciences; Home Economics; Nursing; Nutrition **Level of Education for which Award is Granted:** Undergraduate **Number Awarded:** 1 each year. **Funds Available:** The amount of this scholarship depends on the availability of funds. **Duration:** 1 year; may be renewed.
Eligibility Requirements: Eligible to apply for these scholarships are women over the age of 30 who are lineal descendants of worthy Confederates or collateral descendants and members of the Children of the Confederacy or the United Daughters of the Confederacy. Applicants must intend to study business administration, computer science, home economics, nutrition, or nursing. They must submit certified proof of the Confederate record of 1 ancestor, with the company and regiment in which he served, and must have had at least a 3.0 GPA in high school. **Deadline for Receipt:** March of each year. **Additional Information:** Information is also available from Mrs. Robert C. Kraus, Second Vice President General, 239 Deerfield Lane, Franklin, NC 28734-0112. Members of the same family may not hold scholarships simultaneously,

and only 1 application per family will be accepted within any 1 year. All requests for applications must be accompanied by a self-addressed stamped envelope.

2924 ■ UNITED DAUGHTERS OF THE CONFEDERACY-VIRGINIA DIVISION

c/o Suzie Snyder, Education Committee Chair
8440 Bradshaw Road
Salem, VA 24153-2246
Tel: (540)384-6884
E-mail: Suzienotes@aol.com
Web Site: http://users.erols.com/va-udc/scholarships.html

To provide financial assistance for college to women who are Confederate descendants from Virginia and working on a degree in nursing.

Title of Award: Sally Tompkins Nursing and Applied Health Sciences Scholarship **Area, Field, or Subject:** Nursing **Level of Education for which Award is Granted:** Undergraduate **Number Awarded:** This scholarship is offered whenever a prior recipient graduates or is no longer eligible. **Funds Available:** The amount of the stipend depends on the availability of funds. Payment is made directly to the college or university the recipient attends. **Duration:** 1 year; may be renewed up to 3 additional years if the recipient maintains a GPA of 3.0 or higher.

Eligibility Requirements: This program is open to women residents of Virginia interested in working on a degree in nursing. Applicants must be 1) lineal descendants of Confederates, or 2) collateral descendants and also members of the Children of the Confederacy or the United Daughters of the Confederacy. They must submit proof of the Confederate military record of at least 1 ancestor, with the company and regiment in which he served. They must also submit a personal letter pledging to make the best possible use of the scholarship; describing their health, social, family, religious, and fraternal connections within the community; and reflecting on what a Southern heritage means to them (using the term "War Between the States" in lieu of "Civil War"). They must have a GPA of 3.0 or higher and be able to demonstrate financial need. **Deadline for Receipt:** May of the years in which a scholarship is available. **Additional Information:** Information is also available from Mrs. George W. Bryson, 10103 Rixeyville Road, Culpeper, VA 22701-4422, E-mail: brysdale@aol.com.

2925 ■ U.S. AIR FORCE

Attn: Headquarters AFROTC/RRUC
551 East Maxwell Boulevard
Maxwell AFB, AL 36112-5917
Tel: (334)953-2091; (866)423-7682
Fax: (334)953-6167
Web Site: http://www.afrotc.com/admissions/professional/nursing.php

To provide financial assistance to college students who are interested in a career as a nurse, are interested in joining Air Force ROTC, and are willing to serve as Air Force officers following completion of their bachelor's degree.

Title of Award: Air Force ROTC Nursing Scholarships **Area, Field, or Subject:** Nursing **Level of Education for which Award is Granted:** Undergraduate **Funds Available:** Awards are type 2 AFROTC scholarships that provide for payment of tuition and fees, to a maximum of $15,000 per year, plus an annual book allowance of $600. All recipients are also awarded a tax-free subsistence allowance for 10 months of each year that is $300 per month during their sophomore year, $350 during their junior year, and $400 during their senior year. **Duration:** 2 or 3 years, provided the recipient maintains a GPA of 2.5 or higher.

Eligibility Requirements: This program is open to U.S. citizens who are freshmen or sophomores in college and interested in a career as a nurse. Applicants must have a cumulative GPA of 2.5 or higher at the end of their freshman year and meet all other academic and physical requirements for participation in AFROTC. They must be interested in working on a nursing degree from an accredited program. At the time of Air Force commissioning, they may be no more than 31 years of age. They must be able to pass the Air Force Officer Qualifying Test (AFOQT) and the Air Force ROTC Physical Fitness Test. **Deadline for Receipt:** June of each year. **Additional Information:** Recipients must also complete 4 years of aerospace studies courses at 1 of the 144 colleges and universities that have an Air Force ROTC unit on campus or 1 of the approximately 900 colleges that have cross-enrollment agreements with those institutions. They must also attend a 4-week summer training camp at an Air Force

base, usually between their sophomore and junior years. Following completion of their bachelor's degree, scholarship recipients earn a commission as a second lieutenant in the Air Force and serve at least 4 years.

2926 ■ U.S. AIR FORCE

Attn: Headquarters AFROTC/RRUE
Enlisted Commissioning Section
551 East Maxwell Boulevard
Maxwell AFB, AL 36112-5917
Tel: (334)953-2091; (866)423-7682
Fax: (334)953-6167
E-mail: enlisted@afrotc.com
Web Site: http://www.afoats.af.mil/AFROTC/EnlistedComm/AECP.asp

To allow selected enlisted Air Force personnel to earn a bachelor's degree in approved majors by providing financial assistance for full-time college study.

Title of Award: Airman Education and Commissioning Program **Area, Field, or Subject:** African studies; Asian studies; Computer and information sciences; Engineering; Foreign languages; Mathematics and mathematical sciences; Meteorology; Near Eastern studies; Nursing; Physics; Russian studies **Level of Education for which Award is Granted:** Undergraduate **Number Awarded:** Approximately 60 each year. **Funds Available:** While participating in this program, cadets remain on active duty in the Air Force and receive their regular salary and benefits. They also receive payment of tuition and fees up to $15,000 per year and an annual textbook allowance of $600. **Duration:** 1 to 3 years, until completion of a bachelor's degree.

Eligibility Requirements: Eligible to participate in this program are enlisted members of the Air Force who have been accepted at a university or college (or approved crosstown institution) that is associated with AFROTC and that offers an approved major. The majors currently supported are computer science, all ABET-accredited engineering fields (not engineering technology), foreign area studies (limited to Middle East, Africa, Asia, Russia/Eurasia), foreign languages (limited to Arabic, Armenian, Azeri, Chinese, French, Georgian, Hebrew, Hindi, Indonesian, Kazakh, Pashto, Persian Farsi, Russian, Swahili, and Turkish), mathematics, meteorology, nursing, and physics. Applicants must have completed at least 1 year of time-in-service and 1 year of time-on-station. They must have scores on the Air Force Officer Qualifying Test of at least 15 on the verbal and 10 on the quantitative and be able to pass the Air Force ROTC Physical Fitness Test. Normally they should have completed at least 30 semester hours of college study with a GPA of 2.75 or higher. They must be younger than 31 years of age or otherwise able to be commissioned before they become 35 years of age. **Deadline for Receipt:** February of each year. **Additional Information:** While attending college, participants in this program attend ROTC classes at their college or university. Upon completing their degree, they are commissioned to serve in the Air Force in their area of specialization with an active-duty service commitment of at least 4 years. Further information is available from base education service officers or an Air Force ROTC unit. This program does not provide for undergraduate flying training.

2927 ■ U.S. ARMY

ROTC Cadet Command
Attn: ATCC-OP-I-S
55 Patch Road, Building 56
Fort Monroe, VA 23651-1052
Tel: (757)727-4558
Free: 800-USA-ROTC
E-mail: atccps@usaac.army.mil
Web Site: http://www.rotc.usaac.army.mil/scholarship_HPD2/index.asp

To provide financial assistance to high school seniors or graduates who are interested in enrolling in Army ROTC and major in nursing in college.

Title of Award: Partnership in Nursing Education Program **Area, Field, or Subject:** Nursing **Level of Education for which Award is Granted:** Four Year College **Number Awarded:** A limited number each year. **Funds Available:** This scholarship provides financial assistance toward college tuition and educational fees up to an annual amount of $17,000. In addition, a flat rate of $1,000 is provided for the purchase of textbooks, classroom supplies and equipment. Recipients are also awarded a stipend for up to 10 months of each year that is $250 per month during their freshman year, $300 per month during their sophomore year, $350 per month during their junior year, and $400 per month during their senior year. **Duration:** 4 years, until completion of a baccalaureate degree. A limited number of 2-year and 3-year scholarships are also available to students who are already attending an accredited B.S.N. program on a campus affiliated with ROTC.

Eligibility Requirements: Applicants for the Army Reserve Officers' Training Corps (ROTC) program must 1) be U.S. citizens; 2) be at least 17 years of age by October of the year in which they are seeking a scholarship; 3) be no more than 27 years of age when they graduate from college after 4 years; 4) score at least 920 on the SAT or 19 on the ACT; 5) have a high school GPA of 2.4 or higher; and 6) meet medical and other regulatory requirements. This program is open to ROTC scholarship applicants who wish to enroll in a nursing program at 1 of approximately 100 designated partner colleges and universities and become Army nurses after graduation. **Deadline for Receipt:** November of each year. **Additional Information:** This program was established in 1996 to ensure that ROTC cadets seeking nursing careers would be admitted to the upper-level division of a baccalaureate program. The 56 partnership nursing schools affiliated with Army ROTC have agreed to guarantee upper-level admission to students who maintain an established GPA during their first 2 years. During the summer, participants have the opportunity to participate in the Nurse Summer Training Program, a paid 3- to 4-week clinical elective at an Army hospital in the United States, Germany, or Korea. Following completion of their baccalaureate degree, participants become commissioned officers in the Army Nurse Corps. Scholarship winners must serve in the military for 8 years. That service obligation may be fulfilled 1) by serving on active duty for 4 years followed by service in the Army National Guard (ARNG), the United States Army Reserve (USAR), or the Inactive Ready Reserve (IRR) for the remainder of the 8 years; or 2) by serving 8 years in an ARNG or USAR troop program unit that includes a 3- to 6-month active-duty period for initial training.

2928 ■ U.S. ARMY RECRUITING COMMAND

Attn: RCHS-AN-AECP
1307 Third Avenue
Fort Knox, KY 40121-2726
800-223-3735
E-mail: aecp@usarec.army.mil
Web Site: http://www.usarec.army.mil/AECP

To provide financial assistance to Army enlisted personnel who are interested in earning a bachelor's degree in nursing.

Title of Award: Army Medical Department Enlisted Commissioning Program **Area, Field, or Subject:** Nursing **Level of Education for which Award is Granted:** Four Year College **Number Awarded:** Varies each year. **Funds Available:** Participants receive their regular pay and allowances plus payment of academic costs up to $3,000 per semester or $2,250 per quarter. **Duration:** Up to 24 months or completion of a bachelor's degree.

Eligibility Requirements: This program is open to active-duty enlisted soldiers, regardless of their military occupational specialty, who are able to gain acceptance as a full-time student at an accredited nursing program. Applicants must have at least 3 but no more than 10 years of active military service (a waiver to that requirement may be approved on a case-by-case basis). The college or university to which they have been admitted must be in their state (or Puerto Rico) of legal residence or current domicile and they must be able to complete a bachelor's degree at the school within 24 calendar months. **Deadline for Receipt:** July of each year. **Additional Information:** Following receipt of their degree and successful completion of the National Council for Licensure Examination-RN, participants are commissioned as second lieutenants in the Army Nurse Corps.

2929 ■ U.S. NAVY

Attn: Naval Medical Education
Code OG3
8901 Wisconsin Avenue, 16th Floor, Tower 1
Bethesda, MD 20889-5611
Tel: (301)319-4520
E-mail: mecp@nmetc.med.navy.mil
Web Site: http://nshs.med.navy.mil/mecp/mecp.htm

To provide Navy and Marine enlisted personnel with an opportunity to earn an undergraduate or master's degree in nursing while continuing to receive their regular pay and allowances.

Title of Award: Medical Enlisted Commissioning Program (MEPC) **Area, Field, or Subject:** Nursing **Level of Education for which Award is**

Granted: Master's, Undergraduate **Number Awarded:** Varies each year. **Funds Available:** Participants receive full pay and allowances for their enlisted pay grade and are eligible for advancement while in college. They are responsible for tuition, fees, books, and other expenses. If eligible, they may use the Montgomery GI Bill or the Veterans Educational Assistance Program (VEAP) educational benefits, but they may not participate in the Navy Tuition Assistance Program. **Duration:** Up to 36 months of full-time, year-round study, until completion of a B.S.N. degree or, if eligible, an M.S.N. degree.

Eligibility Requirements: This program is open to enlisted personnel who are serving on active duty in any rating of the U.S. Navy, U.S. Marine Corps, Naval Reserve (including the Training and Administration of the Reserve Program), and the Marine Corps Reserve (including the Active Reserve Program). Applicants must have completed at least 30 semester credit hours of college work (with a cumulative GPA of 2.5 or higher) so they can complete a bachelor's degree in nursing (B.S.N.) within 36 months. They must have SAT scores of at least 1000 (500 mathematics and 500 critical reading) or ACT scores of at least 42 (21 mathematics and 21 English). If they have a B.S.N. from a non-accredited institution, or can complete both a B.S.N. and M.S.N. within 36 months, they may apply for that option. At the time of commissioning, they must be younger than 35 years of age. U.S. citizenship is required. **Deadline for Receipt:** August of each year. **Additional Information:** Following graduation, participants are commissioned as ensigns in the Nurse Corps and attend Officer Indoctrination School. They incur an 8-year service obligation, of which at least 4 years must be served on active duty.

2930 ■ U.S. NAVY

Naval Education and Training Center
Attn: AEV Program Office
6490 Saufley Field Road
Pensacola, FL 32509-5204
Tel: (850)452-1001
Fax: (850)452-1357
E-mail: rick.cusimano@navy.mil
Web Site: http://www.npc.navy.mil/CareerInfo/Education

To provide financial assistance to Navy enlisted personnel who are interested in earning an undergraduate or graduate degree during off-duty hours.

Title of Award: Navy Advanced Education Voucher Program **Area, Field, or Subject:** Accounting; Business administration; Educational administration; Engineering; Engineering, Civil; Engineering, Electrical; Finance; Information science and technology; Leadership, Institutional and community; Management; Nursing; Personnel administration/human resources; Systems engineering; Technology **Level of Education for which Award is Granted:** Master's, Undergraduate **Number Awarded:** Varies each year. Recently, 30 of these positions were available: 25 for bachelor's degrees and 5 for master's degrees. **Funds Available:** This program covers 100% of graduate education costs (tuition, books, and fees), up to a maximum of $6,700 per year for a bachelor's degree or $20,000 per year for a master's degree. **Duration:** Up to 36 months from the time of enrollment for a bachelor's degree; up to 24 months from the time of enrollment for a master's degree.

Eligibility Requirements: This program is open to senior enlisted Navy personnel in ranks E-7 through E-9. Applicants should be transferring to, or currently on, shore duty with sufficient time ashore to complete a bachelor's or master's degree. Personnel at rank E-7 may have no more than 17 years time in service, E-8 no more than 20 years, or E-9 no more than 22 years. The area of study must be certified by the Naval Postgraduate School as Navy-relevant. **Deadline for Receipt:** March of each year. **Additional Information:** Recently approved majors for bachelor's degrees included accounting and finances, civil engineering, electrical engineering technology, engineering propulsion systems, human performance system integration, human resources, industrial management, information technology, leadership and management, nursing, and systems engineering and analysis. Approved fields of study for master's degrees included business administration, education and training management, emergency and disaster management, engineering and technology, homeland defense and security, human resources, information technology, leadership and management, project management, and systems engineering and analysis. Recipients of this assistance incur an obligation to remain on active duty following completion of the program for a period equal to 3 times the number of months of education completed, to a maximum obligation of 36 months.

2931 ■ U.S. NAVY

Attn: Naval Medical Education
Code OH
8901 Wisconsin Avenue
Bethesda, MD 20889-5611
Tel: (301)295-2373
Free: 800-USA-NAVY
Fax: (301)295-6014
E-mail: OH@nmetc.med.navy.mil
Web Site: http://nshs.med.navy.mil/hpsp/Pages/Programs.htm
To provide financial assistance for nursing education to students interested in serving in the Navy.

Title of Award: Navy Nurse Candidate Program **Area, Field, or Subject:** Nursing **Level of Education for which Award is Granted:** Four Year College **Number Awarded:** Varies each year. **Funds Available:** This program pays a $10,000 accession bonus upon enlistment and a stipend of $1,000 per month. Students are responsible for paying all school expenses. **Duration:** Up to 24 months.
Eligibility Requirements: This program is open to full-time students in a bachelor of science in nursing program. Prior to or during their junior year of college, applicants must enlist in the U.S. Navy Nurse Corps Reserve. Following receipt of their degree, they must be willing to serve as a nurse in the Navy.

2932 ■ U.S. NAVY

Attn: Chief of Naval Education and Training
Code N79A2
250 Dallas Street
Pensacola, FL 32508-5220
Tel: (850)452-4941
Free: 800-NAV-ROTC
Fax: (850)452-2486
E-mail: PNSC_NROTC.scholarship@navy.mil
Web Site: http://www.nrotc.navy.mil/nursingoption.cfm
To provide financial assistance to graduating high school seniors who are interested in joining Navy ROTC and majoring in nursing in college.

Title of Award: Navy Nurse Corps NROTC Scholarship Program **Area, Field, or Subject:** Nursing **Level of Education for which Award is Granted:** Undergraduate **Number Awarded:** Varies each year. **Funds Available:** This scholarship provides payment of full tuition and required educational fees, as well as $250 per semester for textbooks, supplies, and equipment. The program also provides a stipend for 10 months of the year that is $250 per month as a freshman, $300 per month as a sophomore, $350 per month as a junior, and $400 per month as a senior. **Duration:** 4 years.
Eligibility Requirements: Eligible to apply for these scholarships are graduating high school seniors who have been accepted at a college with a Navy ROTC unit on campus or a college with a cross-enrollment agreement with such a college. Applicants must be U.S. citizens between the ages of 17 and 23 who plan to study nursing in college and are willing to serve for 4 years as active-duty Navy officers in the Navy Nurse Corps following graduation from college. They must not have reached their 27th birthday by the time of college graduation and commissioning; applicants who have prior active-duty military service may be eligible for age adjustments for the amount of time equal to their prior service, up to a maximum of 36 months. They must have minimum SAT scores of 530 critical reading and 520 mathematics or minimum ACT scores of 22 in both English and mathematics. **Deadline for Receipt:** January of each year.

2933 ■ U.S. NAVY

Attn: Commander, Naval Service Training Command
250 Dallas Street, Suite A
Pensacola, FL 32508-5268
Tel: (850)452-9563
Fax: (850)452-2486
E-mail: PNSC-STA21@navy.mil
Web Site: http://www.navy.com/careers/officerplanner/enlistedtoofficer
To allow outstanding enlisted Navy personnel to complete a bachelor's degree and receive a commission in the Nurse Corps.

Title of Award: Nurse Corps Option of the Seaman to Admiral-21 Program **Area, Field, or Subject:** Nursing **Level of Education for which**

Award is Granted: Four Year College **Number Awarded:** Varies each year. **Funds Available:** Awardees continue to receive their regular Navy pay and allowances while they attend college on a full-time basis. They also receive reimbursement for tuition, fees, and books up to $10,000 per year. If base housing is available, they are eligible to live there. Participants are not eligible to receive benefits under the Navy's Tuition Assistance Program (TA), the Montgomery GI Bill (MGIB), Navy College Fund, or the Veterans Educational Assistance Program (VEAP). **Duration:** Selectees are supported for up to 36 months of full-time, year-round study or completion of a bachelor's degree, as long as they maintain a GPA of 2.5 or higher.
Eligibility Requirements: This program is open to U.S. citizens who are currently serving on active duty in the U.S. Navy or Naval Reserve, including Training and Administration of the Reserves (TAR), Selected Reserves (SELRES), and Navy Reservists on active duty except for those on active for training (ACDUTRA). Applicants must be high school graduates (or GED recipients) who are able to complete requirements for a baccalaureate degree in 36 months or less. They must be at least 18 years of age and able to complete degree requirements and be commissioned prior to age 35. Within the past 3 years, they must have taken the SAT test (and achieved scores of at least 500 on the mathematics section and 500 on the verbal or critical reading section) or the ACT test (and achieved a score of 41 or higher, including at least 21 on the mathematics portion and 20 on the English portion). **Deadline for Receipt:** July of each year. **Additional Information:** This program was established in 2001 as a replacement for the Fleet Accession to Naval Reserve Officer Training Corps (NROTC) Nurse Option. Upon acceptance into the program, selectees attend the Naval Science Institute (NSI) in Newport, Rhode Island for an 8-week program in the fundamental core concepts of being a naval officer (navigation, engineering, weapons, military history and justice, etc.). They then enter an NROTC affiliated college or university with a nursing program that confers an accredited baccalaureate degree in nursing and pursue full-time study. They become members of and drill with the NROTC unit. When they complete their bachelor's degree in nursing, they are commissioned as ensigns in the United States Naval Reserve and assigned to initial training as an officer in the Nurse Corps. After commissioning, 5 years of active service are required.

2934 ■ UNIVERSITY INTERSCHOLASTIC LEAGUE

Attn: Texas Interscholastic League Foundation
1701 Manor Road
P.O. Box 8028
Austin, TX 78713
Tel: (512)232-4938
Fax: (512)471-5908
E-mail: carolyn.scott@mail.utexas.edu
Web Site: http://www.uil.utexas.edu/tilf/scholarships.html
To provide financial assistance to students who participate in programs of the Texas Interscholastic League Foundation (TILF) and plan to study nursing.

Title of Award: Abell-Hanger Foundation Nursing Awards **Area, Field, or Subject:** Nursing **Level of Education for which Award is Granted:** Undergraduate **Number Awarded:** 1 each year. **Funds Available:** The stipend is $3,500 per year. **Duration:** 2 years.
Eligibility Requirements: This program is open to students who meet the 5 basic requirements of the TILF: 1) graduate from high school during the current year and begin college or university in Texas by the following fall; 2) enroll full time and maintain a GPA of 2.5 or higher during the first semester; 3) compete in a University Interscholastic League (UIL) academic state meet contest in accounting, calculator applications, computer applications, computer science, current issues and events, debate (cross-examination and Lincoln-Douglas), journalism (editorial writing, feature writing, headline writing, and news writing), literary criticism, mathematics, number sense, 1-act play, ready writing, science, social studies, speech (prose interpretation, poetry interpretation, informative speaking, and persuasive speaking), or spelling and vocabulary; 4) submit high school transcripts that include SAT and/or ACT scores; and 5) submit parents' latest income tax returns. Applicants for this scholarship must be planning to major in nursing. **Deadline for Receipt:** May of each year.

2935 ■ VERMONT STUDENT ASSISTANCE CORPORATION

Champlain Mill
Attn: Scholarship Programs

P.O. Box 2000
Winooski, VT 05404-2601
Tel: (802)654-3798; 888-253-4819
Fax: (802)654-3765
E-mail: info@vsac.org
Web Site: http://www.vsac.org
To provide financial assistance to high school seniors in Vermont who plan to study a field related to emergency services in college.

Title of Award: Raymond R. Mooney Scholarship **Area, Field, or Subject:** Medicine; Nursing **Level of Education for which Award is Granted:** Undergraduate **Number Awarded:** 1 each year. **Funds Available:** The stipend is $1,000. **Duration:** 1 year; may be renewed for 1 additional year.

Eligibility Requirements: This scholarship is available to high school seniors in Vermont who are enrolled or planning to enroll in an academic, vocational, or technical program in a field related to emergency services. Selection is based on financial need and required essays. **Deadline for Receipt:** April of each year. **Additional Information:** This program was established by the Vermont Police Association, which is responsible for selecting the recipients.

2936 ■ VERMONT STUDENT ASSISTANCE CORPORATION

Champlain Mill
Attn: Scholarship Programs
P.O. Box 2000
Winooski, VT 05404-2601
Tel: (802)654-3798; 888-253-4819
Fax: (802)654-3765
E-mail: info@vsac.org
Web Site: http://www.vsac.org
To provide scholarship/loans to Vermont residents who are interested in earning a nursing degree and then working within the state.

Title of Award: Vermont State Nursing Incentive Scholarship **Area, Field, or Subject:** Nursing **Level of Education for which Award is Granted:** Undergraduate **Number Awarded:** Approximately 13 each year. **Funds Available:** The maximum award is $6,000 per year. This is a scholarship/loan program. Funds are provided as an interest-free loan, but the debt is cancelled if the recipient successfully graduates from the L.P.N. or R.N. degree program and completes 1 year of employment in Vermont or within 10 miles of the Vermont border. **Duration:** 1 year.

Eligibility Requirements: This scholarship is available to high school seniors, high school graduates, and currently-enrolled college students in Vermont. Applicants must be enrolled or planning to enroll in 1) an accredited licensed practical nursing (L.P.N.) degree program; 2) the final year of an accredited associate in nursing (A.S., R.N.) degree program; or 3) the final 2 years of an accredited bachelor of science in nursing (B.S. N., R.N.) degree program. Applicants must intend to work in Vermont or within 10 miles of the Vermont border for at least 1 year following licensure as an L.P.N. or R.N. Selection is based on commitment to employment serving Vermonters, required essays, and a letter of recommendation. **Deadline for Receipt:** July of each year. **Additional Information:** This program, established in 2001, is sponsored by the Vermont Department of Health.

2937 ■ VIRGINIA DAUGHTERS OF THE AMERICAN REVOLUTION

c/o Catherine Rafferty, Scholarship Chair
10101 Sanders Court
Great Falls, VA 22066-2526
Web Site: http://www.vadar.org/vadarscholarships.htm
To provide financial assistance to high school seniors in Virginia who wish to study nursing in college.

Title of Award: Virginia Nursing Scholarships **Area, Field, or Subject:** Nursing **Level of Education for which Award is Granted:** Undergraduate **Number Awarded:** 2 each year: 1 at $1,000 and 1 at $500. **Funds Available:** Stipends are $1,000 or $500. **Duration:** 1 year.

Eligibility Requirements: This program is open to seniors graduating from high schools in Virginia who plan to attend a Virginia school of nursing. Along with their application, they must submit a 500-word letter giving their reasons for interest in preparing for a career in nursing, a transcript of grades, a letter of recommendation from a teacher or guidance counselor, and documentation of financial need. **Deadline for Receipt:** January of each year.

2938 ■ WASHINGTON HIGHER EDUCATION COORDINATING BOARD

917 Lakeridge Way
P.O. Box 43430
Olympia, WA 98504-3430
Tel: (360)753-7844
Fax: (360)753-7808
E-mail: kathy.mcvay@hecb.wa.gov
Web Site: http://www.hecb.wa.gov/financialaid/other/health.asp
To provide scholarship/loans for primary care health professional education to students who agree to work in designated areas of Washington.

Title of Award: Washington State Health Professional Scholarship Program **Area, Field, or Subject:** Dental hygiene; Dentistry; Medicine; Medicine, Osteopathic; Midwifery; Nursing; Pharmaceutical sciences **Level of Education for which Award is Granted:** Graduate, Undergraduate **Number Awarded:** Varies each year. **Funds Available:** The stipend is intended to cover eligible expenses: tuition, books, equipment, fees, and room and board. This is a scholarship/loan program. Recipients who fail to complete the course of study are required to repay the amount received, plus a penalty and interest. Scholars who fail to serve in health professional shortage areas in Washington are required to repay the scholarship, with penalty plus interest. The interest rate on the repayments is 8% for the first 4 years and 10% for the fifth year. **Duration:** Up to 5 years.

Eligibility Requirements: Applicants must be enrolled or accepted for enrollment in an accredited program leading to eligibility for licensure in Washington State in a designated health profession. They must agree to practice in Washington for 3 to 5 years following graduation, but they do not need to be Washington residents or to attend an educational institution in the state. Currently, there are no geographic restrictions for registered nurses or practical nurses. For other primary care health professionals (M.D., D.O., N.D., P.A., N.P., C.N.M., L.M.), dental care professionals (D.D.S., R.D.H.), and pharmacists, service must be in designated areas of the state. State correctional facilities, state mental health facilities, community and migrant health centers, and any other facility with more than 40% of its caseload consisting of Medicaid and sliding fee patients also qualify. **Deadline for Receipt:** April of each year.

2939 ■ WESTERN INTERSTATE COMMISSION FOR HIGHER EDUCATION

Attn: Student Exchange Programs
3035 Center Green Drive
P.O. Box 9752
Boulder, CO 80301-9752
Tel: (303)541-0210
Fax: (303)541-0291
E-mail: info-sep@wiche.edu
Web Site: http://www.wiche.edu/sep/psep
To underwrite some of the cost of out-of-state professional schooling for students in selected western states.

Title of Award: Professional Student Exchange Program **Area, Field, or Subject:** Architecture; Dentistry; Library and archival sciences; Medical assisting; Medicine; Medicine, Osteopathic; Nursing; Occupational therapy; Optometry; Pharmaceutical sciences; Physical therapy; Podiatry; Public health; Veterinary science and medicine **Level of Education for which Award is Granted:** Graduate, Undergraduate **Number Awarded:** Varies each year. **Funds Available:** The assistance consists of reduced levels of tuition, usually resident tuition in public institutions or reduced standard tuition at private schools. The home state pays a support fee to the admitting school to help cover the cost of the recipient's education. **Duration:** 1 year; may be renewed.

Eligibility Requirements: This program is open to residents of 13 western states who are interested in pursuing professional study at selected out-of-state institutions, usually because those fields of study are not available in their home states. The eligible programs, and the states whose residents are eligible, presently include: 1) architecture (master's degree), for residents of Wyoming, to study at designated institutions in Arizona, California, Colorado, Idaho, Montana, New Mexico, Oregon, Utah, or Washington); 2) dentistry, for residents of Alaska, Arizona,

Hawaii, Montana, New Mexico, North Dakota, and Wyoming, to study at designated institutions in Arizona, California, Colorado, Nevada, Oregon, or Washington; 3) library studies (master's degree), for residents of New Mexico and Wyoming, to study at designated institutions in Arizona, California, Hawaii, or Washington; 4) medicine, for residents of Montana and Wyoming, to study at designated institutions in Arizona, California, Colorado, Hawaii, Nevada, New Mexico, North Dakota, Oregon, or Utah; 5) nursing (graduate degree), for residents of Wyoming, to study at designated institutions in California, Hawaii, North Dakota, or Oregon; 6) occupational therapy (bachelors' or master's degree), for residents of Alaska, Arizona, Hawaii, Montana, and Wyoming, to study at designated institutions in Arizona, California, Idaho, New Mexico, North Dakota, Oregon, Utah, or Washington; 7) optometry, for residents of Alaska, Arizona, Colorado, Hawaii, Idaho, Montana, Nevada, New Mexico, North Dakota, Utah, Washington, and Wyoming, to study at designated institutions in California or Oregon; 8) osteopathic medicine, for residents of Arizona, Montana, New Mexico, Washington, and Wyoming, to study at designated institutions in Arizona or California; 9) pharmacy, for residents of Alaska, Hawaii, and Nevada, to study at designated institutions in Arizona, California, Colorado, Idaho, Montana, New Mexico, North Dakota, Oregon, Utah, Washington, or Wyoming; 10) physical therapy (master's or doctoral degree), for residents of Alaska, Hawaii, and Wyoming, to study at designated institutions in Arizona, California, Colorado, Idaho, Montana, New Mexico, North Dakota, Oregon, Utah, or Washington; 11) physician assistant, for residents of Alaska, Arizona, Nevada, and Wyoming, to study at designated institutions in Arizona, California, Colorado, Idaho, Oregon, Utah, or Washington; 12) podiatry, for residents of Alaska, Montana, New Mexico, Utah, and Wyoming, to study at a designated institution in California; 13) public health, for residents of Montana and New Mexico, to study at designated institutions in California, Colorado, or Washington; and 14) veterinary medicine, for residents of Arizona, Hawaii, Montana, Nevada, New Mexico, North Dakota, Utah, and Wyoming, to study at designated institutions in California, Colorado, Oregon, or Washington. The financial status of the applicants is not considered. Interested students must apply for admission and for PSEP assistance directly from the institution of their choice. They must be certified by their state of residence to become an exchange student and be seeking enrollment at the first professional degree level. **Deadline for Receipt:** In most states, the deadline for receiving completed applications for certification is in October. After obtaining certification, students must still apply to the school of their choice, which also sets its own deadline.

2940 ■ WINSTON-SALEM FOUNDATION

Attn: Director, Student Aid
860 West Fifth Street
Winston-Salem, NC 27101-2506
Tel: (336)714-3445
Fax: (336)727-0581
E-mail: info@wsfoundation.org
Web Site: http://www.wsfoundation.org/student_aid_Noncitizens.php
To provide loans for college to residents of North Carolina working on a degree in fields related to health care.
Title of Award: Oliver Joel and Ellen Pell Denny Student Loan Fund **Area, Field, or Subject:** Health care services; Nursing; Radiology; Respiratory therapy **Level of Education for which Award is Granted:** Graduate, Undergraduate **Number Awarded:** 1 or more each year, including 5 scholarships set aside for eligible noncitizens. **Funds Available:** The maximum loan is $1,200 per year. Repayment of the principal is deferred until the student borrower leaves school. There is a 60-day grace period before repayment begins. The interest rate is 7%. **Duration:** 1 year; may be renewed.
Eligibility Requirements: This program is open to North Carolina residents working on an undergraduate or graduate degree in health care fields, including (but not limited to) registered nursing, licensed practical nursing, nuclear medicine, radiography, and respiratory therapy. Applicants must have a cumulative GPA of 2.5 or higher and a family adjusted gross income of less than $80,000. Selection is based on career plans and goals, academic promise, financial need, indication of ability to repay the loan, and current income and debts. Preference is given to residents of Davidson, Davie, Forsyth, Stokes, Surry, and Yadkin coun-

ties. Some of the scholarships are set aside for eligible noncitizens. **Additional Information:** There is a $20 application fee (waived if the applicant is unable to pay).

2941 ■ WINSTON-SALEM FOUNDATION

Attn: Director, Student Aid
860 West Fifth Street
Winston-Salem, NC 27101-2506
Tel: (336)714-3445
Fax: (336)727-0581
E-mail: info@wsfoundation.org
Web Site: http://www.wsfoundation.org/student_aid_Noncitizens.php
To provide loans for college to residents of North Carolina interested in studying nursing.
Title of Award: Virginia Elizabeth and Alma Vane Taylor Student Nurse Loan Fund **Area, Field, or Subject:** Nursing **Level of Education for which Award is Granted:** Undergraduate **Number Awarded:** 1 or more each year, including 5 scholarships set aside for eligible noncitizens. **Funds Available:** The maximum loan is $1,200 per year. Repayment of the principal is deferred until the student borrower leaves school. There is a 60-day grace period before repayment begins. The interest rate is 7%. **Duration:** 1 year; may be renewed.
Eligibility Requirements: This program is open to college-bound high school seniors in North Carolina interested in working on an associate or baccalaureate degree in nursing at a school in the state. Applicants must have a high school cumulative GPA of 2.5 or higher and a family adjusted gross income less than $80,000. Selection is based on career plans and goals, academic promise, financial need, indication of ability to repay the loan, and current income and debts. Preference is given to residents of Davidson, Davie, Forsyth, Stokes, Surry, and Yadkin counties. Some of the scholarships are set aside for eligible noncitizens. **Additional Information:** There is a $20 application fee (waived if the applicant is unable to pay).

2942 ■ WISCONSIN HIGHER EDUCATIONAL AIDS BOARD

131 West Wilson Street, Room 902
P.O. Box 7885
Madison, WI 53707-7885
Tel: (608)267-2209
Fax: (608)267-2808
E-mail: cindy.lehrman@heab.state.wi.us
Web Site: http://heab.state.wi.us/programs.html
To provide scholarship/loans to nursing students in Wisconsin who are interested in working in the state following licensure.
Title of Award: Wisconsin Nursing Student Loans **Area, Field, or Subject:** Nursing **Level of Education for which Award is Granted:** Undergraduate **Number Awarded:** Varies each year. **Funds Available:** Scholarship/loans are provided up to $3,000 per year. For each of the first 2 years the student nurses and meets the eligibility criteria, 25% of the loan is forgiven. The balance remaining after forgiveness must be repaid at an interest rate up to 5%. If the student does not practice nursing and meet the eligibility criteria, the entire loan must be repaid at an interest rate up to 5%. **Duration:** 1 year; may be renewed up to 4 additional years.
Eligibility Requirements: This program is open to Wisconsin residents who are enrolled at least half time at an eligible institution in the state that prepares them to be licensed as nurses, either R.N. or L.P.N. Applicants must agree to be employed as a licensed nurse in Wisconsin following completion of their program. Financial need is considered in the selection process. **Deadline for Receipt:** Deadline dates vary by institution; check with your school's financial aid office. **Additional Information:** Eligible students should apply through their school's financial aid office.

2943 ■ WISCONSIN MEDICAL SOCIETY

Attn: Executive Director, Foundation
330 East Lakeside Street
P.O. Box 1109
Madison, WI 53701-1109
Tel: (608)442-3722; (866)442-3800
Fax: (608)442-3802
E-mail: eileenw@wismed.org
Web Site: http://www.wisconsinmedicalsociety.org
To provide financial assistance to American Indians (especially those from Wisconsin) interested in working on a degree in medicine, nursing, or allied health care.

Title of Award: Amy Louise Hunter-Wilson, M.D. Memorial Scholarship **Area, Field, or Subject:** Health care services; Medical technology; Medicine; Nursing **Level of Education for which Award is Granted:** Graduate, Undergraduate **Number Awarded:** 1 or more each year. **Funds Available:** The stipend is at least $1,000. **Duration:** 1 year.
Eligibility Requirements: This program is open to members of federally-recognized American Indian tribes who are 1) full-time students enrolled in a health career program at an accredited institution, 2) adults returning to school in an allied health field, and 3) adults working in a non-professional health-related field returning for a professional license or degree. Applicants must be working on a degree or advanced training as a doctor of medicine, nurse, or technician. Preference is given to residents of Wisconsin who are students at educational institutions in the state and applicants close to completing their degree. U.S. citizenship is required. Selection is based on financial need, academic achievement, personal qualities and strengths, and letters of recommendation. **Deadline for Receipt:** January of each year.

2944 ■ WISCONSIN MEDICAL SOCIETY

Attn: Executive Director, Foundation
330 East Lakeside Street
P.O. Box 1109
Madison, WI 53701-1109
Tel: (608)442-3722; (866)442-3800
Fax: (608)442-3802
E-mail: eileenw@wismed.org
Web Site: http://www.wisconsinmedicalsociety.org
To provide financial assistance to Wisconsin residents working on a degree in medicine, nursing, or a related field.
Title of Award: Wisconsin Medical Society General Medical Education Scholarships **Area, Field, or Subject:** Health care services; Medical assisting; Medicine; Nursing **Level of Education for which Award is Granted:** Graduate, Undergraduate **Number Awarded:** 1 or more each year. **Funds Available:** The stipend is $1,500 for medical students or $750 for registered nurses, physician assistants, and other allied health care careers. **Duration:** 1 year.
Eligibility Requirements: This program is open to Wisconsin residents who are enrolled in medical school or in a nursing, physician assistant, or other allied health career program. Preference is given to students at educational institutions in Wisconsin, those close to completing their degree, and those who show a strong interest in practicing in Wisconsin. U.S. citizenship is required. Selection is based on financial need, academic achievement, personal qualities and strengths, and letters of recommendation. **Deadline for Receipt:** March of each year.

2945 ■ WISCONSIN SPACE GRANT CONSORTIUM

c/o University of Wisconsin at Green Bay
Department of Natural and Applied Sciences
2420 Nicolet Drive
Green Bay, WI 54311-7001
Tel: (920)465-2108
Fax: (920)465-2376
E-mail: wsgc@uwgb.edu
Web Site: http://www.uwgb.edu/wsgc/students/us.asp
To provide financial assistance to undergraduate students at colleges and universities participating in the Wisconsin Space Grant Consortium (WSGC).
Title of Award: Wisconsin Space Grant Consortium Undergraduate Scholarships **Area, Field, or Subject:** Aerospace sciences; Architecture; Business administration; Engineering; Engineering, Aerospace/Aeronautical/Astronautical; Law; Medicine; Nursing; Science; Space and planetary sciences **Level of Education for which Award is Granted:** Undergraduate **Number Awarded:** Varies each year; recently, 26 of these scholarships were awarded. **Funds Available:** Stipends up to $1,500 per year are available. **Duration:** 1 academic year.
Eligibility Requirements: This program is open to undergraduate students enrolled at universities participating in the WSGC. Applicants must be U.S. citizens; be working full time on a bachelor's degree in space science, aerospace, or interdisciplinary space studies (including, but not limited to, engineering, the sciences, architecture, law, business, nursing, and medicine); and have a GPA of 3.0 or higher. The consortium especially encourages applications from underrepresented minorities, women, and students with disabilities. Selection is based on academic

performance and space-related promise. **Deadline for Receipt:** February of each year. **Additional Information:** Funding for this program is provided by the U.S. National Aeronautics and Space Administration (NASA). The schools participating in the consortium include the University of Wisconsin campuses at Fox Valley, Green Bay, La Crosse, Madison, Milwaukee, Oshkosh, Parkside, Superior, and Whitewater; Alverno College; Marquette University; College of the Menominee Nation; Carroll College; Lawrence University; Milwaukee School of Engineering; Ripon College; Medical College of Wisconsin; Western Wisconsin Technical College; and Wisconsin Lutheran College.

Nutrition

2946 ■ CALIFORNIA ADOLESCENT NUTRITION, PHYSICAL EDUCATION, AND CULINARY ARTS SCHOLARSHIPS

2140 Shattuck Avenue, Suite 610
Berkeley, CA 94704
Tel: (510)644-1533
Free: 800-200-3131
Fax: (510)644-1535
E-mail: info@canfit.org
Web Site: http://www.canfit.org/scholarships.html
To provide financial assistance to minority undergraduate and graduate students who are studying nutrition, physical education or culinary arts in California.
Title of Award: CANFit Program Scholarships **Area, Field, or Subject:** Culinary arts; Education, Physical; Nutrition; Public health; Youth **Level of Education for which Award is Granted:** Graduate, Undergraduate **Number Awarded:** 5 graduate scholarships and 10 undergraduate scholarships are available each year. **Funds Available:** Graduate stipends are $1,000 each and undergraduate stipends are $500 per year.
Eligibility Requirements: Eligible to apply are American Indians/Alaska Natives, African Americans, Asians/Pacific Islanders, and Latinos/Hispanics who are enrolled in either: 1) an approved master's or doctoral graduate program in nutrition, public health nutrition, or physical education or in a preprofessional practice program approved by the American Dietetic Association at an accredited university in California; or, 2) an approved bachelor's or professional certificate program in culinary arts, nutrition, or physical education at an accredited university or college in California. Graduate student applicants must have completed at least 12 units of graduate course work and have a cumulative GPA of 3.0 or higher; undergraduate applicants must have completed 50 semester units or the equivalent of college credits and have a cumulative GPA of 2.5 or higher. Selection is based on financial need, academic goals, and community nutrition or physical education activities. **Deadline for Receipt:** March of each year. **Additional Information:** A goal of the California Adolescent Nutrition and Fitness (CANFit) program is to improve the nutritional status and physical fitness of California's low-income multi-ethnic youth aged 10 to 14. By offering these scholarships, the program hopes to encourage more students to consider careers in adolescent nutrition and fitness.

2947 ■ INDIAN HEALTH SERVICE

Attn: Scholarship Program
801 Thompson Avenue, Suite 120
Rockville, MD 20852
Tel: (301)443-6197
Fax: (301)443-6048
E-mail: bmiller@na.ihs.gov
Web Site: http://www.ihs.gov
To provide financial assistance to Native American students who need compensatory or preprofessional education to qualify for enrollment in a health professions school.
Title of Award: Health Professions Preparatory Scholarship Program **Area, Field, or Subject:** Engineering; Health care services; Medical technology; Nursing; Nutrition; Pharmaceutical sciences; Physical therapy; Social work **Level of Education for which Award is Granted:** Undergraduate **Number Awarded:** Varies each year. **Funds Available:** Awards provide a payment directly to the school for tuition and required fees; a stipend for living expenses of approximately $1,160 per month for 10 months; a lump sum to cover the costs of books, travel, and other necessary educational expenses; and up to $400 for approved tutorial costs. **Duration:** Up to 2 years of full-time study or up to 4 years of part-time study.

Eligibility Requirements: Applicants must be American Indians or Alaska Natives; be high school graduates or the equivalent; have the capacity to complete a health professions course of study; and be enrolled or accepted for enrollment in a compensatory or preprofessional general education course or curriculum. The qualifying fields of study include premedical technology, pre-dietetics, pre-nursing, pre-pharmacy, pre-physical therapy, pre-social work, and pre-engineering. Recipients must intend to serve Indian people upon completion of professional health care education as a health care provider in the discipline for which they are enrolled at the pregraduate level. **Deadline for Receipt:** February of each year.

2948 ■ INDIAN HEALTH SERVICE

Attn: Scholarship Program
801 Thompson Avenue, Suite 120
Rockville, MD 20852
Tel: (301)443-6197
Fax: (301)443-6048
E-mail: bmiller@na.ihs.gov
Web Site: http://www.ihs.gov
To provide loans-for-service to American Indian and Alaska Native students enrolled in health professions and allied health professions programs.
Title of Award: Health Professions Scholarship Program **Area, Field, or Subject:** Counseling/Guidance; Dental hygiene; Dentistry; Health care services; Medical assisting; Medical technology; Medicine; Medicine, Osteopathic; Nursing; Nutrition; Optometry; Pharmaceutical sciences; Physical therapy; Podiatry; Psychology; Public health; Radiology; Respiratory therapy; Social work; **Level of Education for which Award is Granted:** Graduate, Undergraduate **Number Awarded:** Varies each year. **Funds Available:** Awards provide a payment directly to the school for tuition and required fees; a stipend for living expenses of approximately $1,160 per month for 12 months; a lump sum to cover the costs of books, travel, and other necessary educational expenses; and up to $400 for approved tutorial costs. Upon completion of their program of study, recipients are required to provide payback service of 1 year for each year of scholarship support at the Indian Health Service, a tribal health programs, an urban Indian health program, or in private practice in a designated health professional shortage area serving a substantial number of Indians. Recipients who fail to complete their service obligation must repay all funds received (although no interest is charged). **Duration:** 1 year; may be renewed for up to 3 additional years.
Eligibility Requirements: This program is open to American Indians and Alaska Natives who are at least high school graduates and enrolled in a full-time study program leading to a degree in a health-related professions school within the United States. Priority is given to upper-division and graduate students. Qualifying fields of study include chemical dependency counseling (bachelor's or master's degree), clinical psychology (Ph.D. only), coding specialist (certificate), counseling psychology (Ph.D. only), dental hygiene (B.S.), dentistry (D.D.S.), diagnostic radiology technology (certificate, associate, or B.S.), dietitian (B.S.), civil or environmental engineering (B.S.), environmental health (B.S.), health care administration (B.S. or M.S.), health education (B.S. or M.S.), health records (R.H.I.T. or R.H.I.A.), injury prevention specialist (certificate), medical technology (B.S.), allopathic and osteopathic medicine, nursing (A.D.N., B.S.N., or C.R.N.A), optometry, pharmacy (B.S. or Pharm.D.), physician assistant (B.S.), physical therapy (M.S. or D.P.T.), podiatry (D.P.M.), public health (M.P.H. only), public health nutrition (master's only), social work (master's only), respiratory therapy (associate), and ultrasonography. **Deadline for Receipt:** February of each year.

2949 ■ INTERNATIONAL FOODSERVICE EDITORIAL COUNCIL

P.O. Box 491
Hyde Park, NY 12538
Tel: (845)229-6973
Fax: (845)229-6993
E-mail: ifec@aol.com
Web Site: http://www.ifec-is-us.com
To provide financial assistance to undergraduate or graduate students who are interested in preparing for a career in communications in the food service industry.
Title of Award: IFEC Scholarships **Area, Field, or Subject:** Communications; Creative writing; Culinary arts; English language and literature; Food science and technology; Food service careers; Graphic art and

design; Hotel, institutional, and restaurant management; Journalism; Management; Marketing and distribution; Nutrition; Photography; Photography, Journalistic; Public relations **Level of Education for which Award is Granted:** Master's, Undergraduate **Number Awarded:** Varies each year; recently, 5 of these scholarships were awarded. **Funds Available:** The stipend is $3,000 per year. **Duration:** 1 year.
Eligibility Requirements: This program is open to currently-enrolled college students who are working on an associate, bachelor's, or master's degree. They must be enrolled full time and planning on a career in editorial, public relations, photography, food styling, or a related aspect of communications in the food service industry. The following food service majors are considered appropriate for this program: culinary arts; hospitality management; hotel, restaurant, and institutional management; dietetics; food science and technology; and nutrition. Applicable communications areas include journalism, English, mass communications, public relations, marketing, broadcast journalism, creative writing, graphic arts, and photography. Selection is based on academic record, character references, and demonstrated financial need. **Deadline for Receipt:** March of each year.

2950 ■ NATIONAL DAIRY PROMOTION AND RESEARCH BOARD

c/o Dairy Management Inc.
10255 West Higgins Road, Suite 900
Rosemont, IL 60018-5616
Tel: (847)803-2000
Fax: (847)803-2077
E-mail: marykateg@rosedmi.com
Web Site: http://www.dairycheckoff.com/DairyCheckoff/about/scholarship.htm
To provide financial assistance to undergraduate students in fields related to the dairy industry.
Title of Award: NDPRB Undergraduate Scholarship Program **Area, Field, or Subject:** Business administration; Communications; Dairy science; Economics; Education; Food science and technology; Journalism; Marketing and distribution; Nutrition; Public relations **Level of Education for which Award is Granted:** Four Year College **Number Awarded:** 20 each year: the James H. Loper Jr. Memorial Scholarship at $2,500 and 19 other scholarships at $1,500. **Funds Available:** Stipends are $2,500 or $1,500. **Duration:** 1 year; may be renewed.
Eligibility Requirements: This program is open to sophomores, juniors, and seniors enrolled in college and university programs that emphasize dairy. Eligible majors include agricultural education, business, communications and/or public relations, economics, food science, journalism, marketing, and nutrition. Fields related to production (e.g., animal science) are not eligible. Selection is based on academic performance; interest in a career in dairy; involvement in extracurricular activities, especially those relating to dairy; and evidence of leadership ability, initiative, character, and integrity. The applicant who is judged most outstanding is awarded the James H. Loper Jr. Memorial Scholarship. **Deadline for Receipt:** May of each year. **Additional Information:** Dairy Management Inc. manages this program on behalf of the National Dairy Promotion and Research Board (NDPRB).

2951 ■ NATIONAL FFA ORGANIZATION

Attn: Scholarship Office
6060 FFA Drive
P.O. Box 68960
Indianapolis, IN 46268-0960
Tel: (317)802-4321
Fax: (317)802-5321
E-mail: scholarships@ffa.org
Web Site: http://www.ffa.org
To provide financial assistance to FFA members who are interested in studying animal science, dairy science, or nutrition in college.
Title of Award: Cooperative Resources International Scholarships **Area, Field, or Subject:** Animal science and behavior; Dairy science; Nutrition **Level of Education for which Award is Granted:** Four Year College **Number Awarded:** 2 each year. **Funds Available:** The stipend is $1,000. Funds are paid directly to the recipient. **Duration:** 1 year; nonrenewable.
Eligibility Requirements: This program is open to members who are graduating high school seniors planning to enroll or students already enrolled full time in college. Applicants must be interested in working on a 4-year degree in animal science, dairy science, or nutrition. Selection is

based on academic achievement (10 points for GPA, 10 points for SAT or ACT score, 10 points for class rank), leadership in FFA activities (30 points), leadership in community activities (10 points), and participation in the Supervised Agricultural Experience (SAE) program (30 points). U.S. citizenship is required. **Deadline for Receipt:** February of each year. **Additional Information:** Funding for these scholarships is provided by Cooperative Resources International.

2952 ■ NATIONAL POULTRY AND FOOD DISTRIBUTORS ASSOCIATION

Attn: NPFDA Scholarship Foundation
958 McEver Road Extension, Unit B-8
Gainesville, GA 30504
Tel: (770)535-9901; 877-845-1545
Fax: (770)535-7385
E-mail: info@npfda.org
Web Site: http://www.npfda.org
To provide financial assistance to students enrolled in fields related to the poultry and food industries.
Title of Award: NPFDA Scholarships **Area, Field, or Subject:** Agriculture, Economic aspects; Food science and technology; Nutrition; Poultry science **Level of Education for which Award is Granted:** Four Year College **Number Awarded:** 4 each year. **Funds Available:** Stipends range from $1,500 to $2,000. **Duration:** 1 year. **Eligibility Requirements:** This program is open to full-time students entering their junior or senior year of college. Applicants must be studying poultry science, food science, agricultural economics or marketing, nutrition, or another area related to the poultry industry. Along with their application, they must submit a 1-page narrative on their goals and ambitions and their transcripts. Selection is based on academic excellence, past and current involvement in poultry and food-related activities, and professional objectives. **Deadline for Receipt:** May of each year. **Additional Information:** The National Poultry and Food Distributors Association (NPFDA) established its Scholarship Foundation in 1979. The following named scholarships are included in the program: the Albin S. Johnson Memorial Scholarship, the William Manson Family Memorial Scholarship, and the Alfred Schwartz Memorial Scholarship.

2953 ■ SIEMENS FOUNDATION

170 Wood Avenue South
Iselin, NJ 08830
877-822-5233
Fax: (732)603-5890
E-mail: foundation@sc.siemens.com
Web Site: http://www.siemens-foundation.org/scholarship
To recognize and reward outstanding high school seniors who have undertaken individual or team research projects in science, mathematics, and technology (or in combinations of those disciplines).
Title of Award: Siemens Westinghouse Competition Awards **Area, Field, or Subject:** Astronomy and astronomical sciences; Atmospheric science; Biochemistry; Biological and clinical sciences; Chemistry; Computer and information sciences; Earth sciences; Engineering, Civil; Engineering, Electrical; Engineering, Mechanical; Environmental science; Genetics; Geosciences; Materials research/science; Mathematics and mathematical sciences; Nutrition; Physics; Writing **Level of Education for which Award is Granted:** Undergraduate **Number Awarded:** In the initial round of judging, up to 300 regional semifinalists (up to 50 in each region) are selected. Of those, 60 are chosen as regional finalists (5 individuals and 5 teams in each of the 6 regions). Then 12 regional winners (1 individual and 1 team) are selected in the regional competitions, and they become the national finalists. **Funds Available:** At the regional level, finalists receive $1,000 scholarships, both as individuals and members of teams. Individual regional winners receive $3,000 scholarships. Winning regional teams receive $6,000 scholarships to be divided among the team members. Those regional winners then receive additional scholarships as national finalists. In the national competition. first-place winners receive an additional $100,000 scholarship, second place an additional $50,000 scholarship, third place an additional $40,000 scholarship, fourth place an additional $30,000 scholarship, fifth place an additional $20,000 scholarship, and sixth place an additional $10,000 scholarship. These national awards are provided both to individuals and to teams to be divided equally among team members. Scholarship money is sent directly to the recipient's college or university to cover undergraduate and/or graduate

educational expenses. Schools with regional finalists receive a $2,000 award to be used to support science, mathematics, and technology programs in their schools. **Duration:** The competition is held annually. **Eligibility Requirements:** This program is open to high school seniors who are legal or permanent U.S. residents. They must be enrolled in a high school in the United States, Puerto Rico, Guam, Virgin Islands, American Samoa, Wake and Midway Islands, or the Marianas. U.S. high school students enrolled in a Department of Defense dependents school, an accredited overseas American or international school, a foreign school as an exchange student, or a foreign school because their parent(s) live and work abroad are also eligible. Students being home-schooled qualify if they obtain the endorsement of the school district official responsible for such programs. Research projects may be submitted in mathematics and the biological and physical sciences, or involve combinations of disciplines, such as astrophysics, biochemistry, bioengineering, biology, biophysics, botany, chemistry, computer science, civil engineering, earth and atmospheric science engineering, electrical engineering, environmental sciences, fluid dynamics, genetics, geology, materials science, mathematics, mechanical engineering, nutritional science, physics, toxicology, and virology. Both individual and team projects (2 or 3 members) may be entered. All team members must meet the eligibility requirements. Team projects may include seniors, but that is not a requirement. Competition entrants must submit a detailed report on their research project, including a description of the purpose of the research, rationale for the research, pertinent scientific literature, methodology, results, discussion, and conclusion. All projects must be endorsed by a sponsoring high school (except home-schooled students, who obtain their endorsement from the district or state home-school official). Each project must have a project advisor or mentor who is a member of the instructional staff or a person approved by the endorsing high school. There are 3 judging phases to the competition. An initial review panel selects outstanding research projects from 6 different regions of the country. The students submitting these projects are identified as regional semifinalists. Out of those, the highest-rated projects from each region are selected and the students who submitted them are recognized as regional finalists. For the next phase, the regional finalists are offered all-expense paid trips to the regional competition on the campus of a regional university partner, where their projects are reviewed by a panel of judges appointed by the host institution. Regional finalists are required to prepare a poster display of their research project, make an oral presentation about the research and research findings, and respond to questions from the judges. The top-rated individual and the top-rated team project in each region are selected as regional winners to represent the region in the national competition as national finalists. At that competition, the national finalists again display their projects, make oral presentations, and respond to judges' questions. At each phase, selection is based on clarity of expression, comprehensiveness, creativity, field knowledge, future work, interpretation, literature review, presentation, scientific importance, and validity. **Deadline for Receipt:** September of each year. **Additional Information:** The program is offered by Siemens Foundation, in partnership with the College Board. Information is available from the College Board at (703) 707-8999, E-mail: spro@collegeboard.org. Students submitting the projects with the highest evaluations become part of a registry that is circulated to colleges and universities nationwide. To continue receiving scholarships, winners must attend an accredited academic institution on a full-time basis.

2954 ■ UNITED DAUGHTERS OF THE CONFEDERACY

Attn: Education Director
328 North Boulevard
Richmond, VA 23220-4057
Tel: (804)355-1636
Fax: (804)353-1396
E-mail: hqudc@rcn.com
Web Site: http://www.hqudc.org/scholarships/scholarships.html
To provide financial assistance to mature women who are lineal descendants of Confederate veterans and plan to major in selected fields in college.
Title of Award: Walter Reed Smith Scholarship Program **Area, Field, or Subject:** Business administration; Computer and information sciences; Home Economics; Nursing; Nutrition **Level of Education for which Award is Granted:** Undergraduate **Number Awarded:** 1 each year. **Funds Available:** The amount of this scholarship depends on the avail-

ability of funds. **Duration:** 1 year; may be renewed.

Eligibility Requirements: Eligible to apply for these scholarships are women over the age of 30 who are lineal descendants of worthy Confederates or collateral descendants and members of the Children of the Confederacy or the United Daughters of the Confederacy. Applicants must intend to study business administration, computer science, home economics, nutrition, or nursing. They must submit certified proof of the Confederate record of 1 ancestor, with the company and regiment in which he served, and must have had at least a 3.0 GPA in high school. **Deadline for Receipt:** March of each year. **Additional Information:** Information is also available from Mrs. Robert C. Kraus, Second Vice President General, 239 Deerfield Lane, Franklin, NC 28734-0112. Members of the same family may not hold scholarships simultaneously, and only 1 application per family will be accepted within any 1 year. All requests for applications must be accompanied by a self-addressed stamped envelope.

Optometry

2955 ■ ALASKA COMMISSION ON POSTSECONDARY EDUCATION
Attn: AlaskAdvantage Programs
3030 Vintage Boulevard
Juneau, AK 99801-7109
Tel: (907)465-6779; (866)427-5683
Fax: (907)465-5316
E-mail: customer_service@acpe.ak.us
Web Site: http://alaskaadvantage.state.ak.us/page/256
To provide educational loans to Alaska residents who attend out-of-state professional schools in specified fields through the Professional Student Exchange Program (PSEP) of the Western Interstate Commission for Higher Education (WICHE).
Title of Award: Alaska Professional Student Exchange Loan Program **Area, Field, or Subject:** Dentistry; Medical assisting; Occupational therapy; Optometry; Pharmaceutical sciences; Physical therapy; Podiatry **Level of Education for which Award is Granted:** Undergraduate **Number Awarded:** Varies each year. **Funds Available:** Loans up to the annual support fee are available, to a maximum of $17,200. No origination fee is charged. The interest rate is 6%. **Duration:** 1 year; may be renewed.
Eligibility Requirements: This program is open to residents of Alaska who are attending a professional school in another state as part of the PSEP of WICHE. The fields of study currently available are dentistry, occupational therapy, optometry, physician assistant, podiatry, pharmacy, and physical therapy. In most cases, PSEP students pay resident tuition (or reduced tuition at private institutions) and their home state pays an additional support fee to the institution. Alaska requires PSEP students to pay the tuition and support fee, and provides these loans to enable them to do so.

2956 ■ CANADIAN INSTITUTES OF HEALTH RESEARCH
Attn: Grants and Awards
160 Elgin Street, Ninth Floor
Address Locator 4809A
Ottawa, ON, Canada K1A 0W9
Tel: (613)954-1968; 888-603-4178
Fax: (613)954-1800
E-mail: info@cihr-irsc.gc.ca
Web Site: http://www.cihr-irsc.gc.ca
To provide research funding to undergraduate and graduate students interested in preparing for a career in health-related fields in Canada.
Title of Award: Health Professional Students Research Awards of the Canadian Institutes of Health Research **Area, Field, or Subject:** Dentistry; Medicine; Nursing; Optometry; Pharmaceutical sciences **Level of Education for which Award is Granted:** Graduate, Undergraduate **Number Awarded:** Varies each year. **Funds Available:** The stipend for students registered in a health professional school is $C1,417 per month. The stipend for students enrolled in a combined degree program is $C1,987 per month. **Duration:** Up to 3 months.
Eligibility Requirements: This program is open to 1) undergraduate and graduate students enrolled at Canadian schools offered programs leading to licensure in medicine, dentistry, nursing, physiotherapy, or related fields; and 2) medical students working on a combined degree (e.g., M.D./

M.Sc., M.D./Ph.D.). Applicants must have completed their first year of study and be interested in participating in a health research project. They must be citizens or permanent residents of Canada. **Deadline for Receipt:** February **Additional Information:** The Canadian Institutes of Health Research (CIHR) was formerly the Medical Research Council (MRC) of Canada. This program was formerly designated the Burroughs Wellcome Fund Student Research Awards.

2957 ■ CONNECTICUT ASSOCIATION OF OPTOMETRISTS
342 North Main Street
West Hartford, CT 06117
Tel: (860)586-7508
Fax: (860)586-7550
E-mail: info@cao.org
Web Site: http://www.cao.org
To provide financial assistance to undergraduate students from Connecticut who are enrolled in accredited colleges of optometry.
Title of Award: George Comstock Scholarship Fund **Area, Field, or Subject:** Optometry **Level of Education for which Award is Granted:** Undergraduate **Number Awarded:** 6 to 8 each year. **Funds Available:** The stipend ranges from $400 to $1,000 per year. The exact amount depends upon the recipient's scholastic performance and financial need. **Duration:** 1 year; may be renewed.
Eligibility Requirements: Applicants must be Connecticut residents enrolled in accredited colleges of optometry in the United States. Selection is based on scholarship, character, and financial need. **Deadline for Receipt:** June of each year. **Additional Information:** Information is also available from Clinton McLean, O.D., Vision Center Ltd., 880 Bridgeport Avenue, Shelton, CT 06484-4661, (203) 929-4030, Fax: (203) 929-9662, E-mail: cmclean@networksynergy.net.

2958 ■ INDIAN HEALTH SERVICE
Attn: Scholarship Program
801 Thompson Avenue, Suite 120
Rockville, MD 20852
Tel: (301)443-6197
Fax: (301)443-6048
E-mail: bmiller@na.ihs.gov
Web Site: http://www.ihs.gov
To provide loans-for-service to American Indian and Alaska Native students enrolled in health professions and allied health professions programs.
Title of Award: Health Professions Scholarship Program **Area, Field, or Subject:** Counseling/Guidance; Dental hygiene; Dentistry; Health care services; Medical assisting; Medical technology; Medicine; Medicine, Osteopathic; Nursing; Nutrition; Optometry; Pharmaceutical sciences; Physical therapy; Podiatry; Psychology; Public health; Radiology; Respiratory therapy; Social work; **Level of Education for which Award is Granted:** Graduate, Undergraduate **Number Awarded:** Varies each year. **Funds Available:** Awards provide a payment directly to the school for tuition and required fees; a stipend for living expenses of approximately $1,160 per month for 12 months; a lump sum to cover the costs of books, travel, and other necessary educational expenses; and up to $400 for approved tutorial costs. Upon completion of their program of study, recipients are required to provide payback service of 1 year for each year of scholarship support at the Indian Health Service, a tribal health programs, an urban Indian health program, or in private practice in a designated health professional shortage area serving a substantial number of Indians. Recipients who fail to complete their service obligation must repay all funds received (although no interest is charged). **Duration:** 1 year; may be renewed for up to 3 additional years.
Eligibility Requirements: This program is open to American Indians and Alaska Natives who are at least high school graduates and enrolled in a full-time study program leading to a degree in a health-related professions school within the United States. Priority is given to upper-division and graduate students. Qualifying fields of study include chemical dependency counseling (bachelor's or master's degree), clinical psychology (Ph.D. only), coding specialist (certificate), counseling psychology (Ph.D. only), dental hygiene (B.S.), dentistry (D.D.S.), diagnostic radiology technology (certificate, associate, or B.S.), dietitian (B.S.), civil or environmental engineering (B.S.), environmental health (B.S.), health care administration (B.S. or M.S.), health education (B.S. or M.S.), health records (R.H.I.T. or R.H.I.A.), injury prevention specialist (certificate), medical technology (B.

S.), allopathic and osteopathic medicine, nursing (A.D.N., B.S.N., or C.R. N.A), optometry, pharmacy (B.S. or Pharm.D.), physician assistant (B.S.), physical therapy (M.S. or D.P.T.), podiatry (D.P.M.), public health (M.P.H. only), public health nutrition (master's only), social work (master's only), respiratory therapy (associate), and ultrasonography. **Deadline for Receipt:** February of each year.

2959 ■ KOSTER INSURANCE AGENCY

Attn: Scholarship
500 Victory Road
Quincy, MA 02171
Tel: (617)770-9889
Free: 800-457-5599
Fax: (617)479-0860
E-mail: Scholarship@kosterins.com
Web Site: http://www.kosterweb.com/about/scholarship_main.php
To provide financial assistance to undergraduate students working on a degree in a health-related field.
Title of Award: Koster Insurance Health Careers Scholarship Program
Area, Field, or Subject: Biological and clinical sciences; Chemistry; Dentistry; Health care services; Nursing; Occupational therapy; Optometry; Pharmaceutical sciences; Physical therapy; Physiology; Public health; Social work **Level of Education for which Award is Granted:** Undergraduate **Number Awarded:** 5 each year. **Funds Available:** The stipend is $3,000 per year. **Duration:** 1 year; may be renewed 1 additional year.
Eligibility Requirements: This program is open to full-time undergraduates entering their second-to-last or final year of study in a health-related field, including (but not limited to) pre-medicine, nursing, public and community health, physical therapy, occupational therapy, pharmacy, biology, chemistry, physiology, social work, dentistry, and optometry. Applicants must have a GPA of 3.0 or higher and be able to demonstrate financial need. Along with their application, they must submit a 1-page essay describing their personal goals, including their reasons for preparing for a career in health care. Selection is based on motivation to pursue a career in health care, academic excellence, dedication to community service, and financial need. **Deadline for Receipt:** April of each year. **Additional Information:** This program began in 2001.

2960 ■ NORTH CAROLINA STATE EDUCATION ASSISTANCE AUTHORITY

Attn: Scholarship and Grant Services
10 T.W. Alexander Drive
P.O. Box 14223
Research Triangle Park, NC 27709-4223
Tel: (919)549-8614
Free: 800-700-1775
Fax: (919)549-8481
E-mail: information@ncseaa.edu
Web Site: http://www.ncseaa.edu
To provide loans and loans-for-service to North Carolina residents who are interested in preparing for a career in health, science, or mathematics.
Title of Award: North Carolina Student Loan Program for Health, Science, and Mathematics **Area, Field, or Subject:** Allied health; Dentistry; Medicine; Nursing; Optometry; Public health; Social work **Level of Education for which Award is Granted:** Graduate, Undergraduate **Number Awarded:** Varies each year; recently, a total of 497 students were receiving $3,238,569 in support through this program. **Funds Available:** Maximum loans are $3,000 per year for associate degree and certificate programs, $5,000 per year for baccalaureate degree/certificate programs, $6,500 per year for master's degree programs, or $8,500 per year for health/professional doctoral programs. The maximum amount that any student can borrow through this program is $58,000. The interest rate is 4% while the borrowers are attending school and from 10 to 15% after they leave school. Cash repayments must begin 90 days or less after completion of course work and training. Under specified conditions, certain loan recipients in qualifying disciplines may have their loans canceled through service in North Carolina. **Duration:** 1 year; renewable for 1 additional year for diploma, associate, certificate, and master's degree programs, for 2 additional years for baccalaureate degree programs, or for 3 additional years for doctoral programs.
Eligibility Requirements: North Carolina residents are eligible to apply for this program if they have been accepted as full-time students in an

accredited associate, baccalaureate, master's, or doctoral program leading to a degree in 1 of the following areas: allied health (including audiology/communications assistant, cytotechnology, dental hygiene, diagnostic medical sonographer, imaging technologist, medical technology, nuclear medicine technologist, occupational therapy/assistant, physician assistant, physical therapy/assistant, radiation therapist, radiography, respiratory therapy, and speech language pathology); clinical psychology (Ph.D. level only); dentistry; dietetics and nutrition (graduate level only); mathematics education; medicine (including chiropractic medicine, emergency medicine, family medicine, geriatrics, internal medicine, obstetrics and gynecology, osteopathic medicine, pediatrics, podiatry, primary care medicine, and psychiatry); nursing (including anesthetist, family nurse practitioner, nursing administration, general nursing, and midwifery); optometry; pharmacy; public health (graduate level only); science education (including biology, chemistry, communications and technologies, computer and information sciences, engineering, and physical science); social work (graduate level only); and veterinary medicine. U.S. citizenship is required. Selection is based on academic progress, financial ability of sureties to repay all loans and accrued interest in case of applicant's default, applicant's willingness to work in underserved areas of the state or in disciplines for which there is a shortage of professionals, applicant's willingness to comply with all program regulations, and financial need. **Deadline for Receipt:** May of each year. **Additional Information:** Recipients may attend a North Carolina postsecondary institution or an eligible out-of-state institution. This program was formerly known as the North Carolina Medical Student Loan Program.

2961 ■ TEXAS HIGHER EDUCATION COORDINATING BOARD

Attn: Hinson-Hazlewood College Student Loan Program
1200 East Anderson Lane
P.O. Box 12788, Capitol Station
Austin, TX 78711-2788
Tel: (512)427-6340
Free: 800-242-3062
Fax: (512)427-6423
E-mail: loaninfo@thecb.state.tx.us
Web Site: http://www.hhloans.com
To provide educational loans to students in Texas in health-related degree programs.
Title of Award: Hinson-Hazlewood Health Education Loan Program
Area, Field, or Subject: Dentistry; Health care services; Medicine; Medicine, Osteopathic; Nursing; Optometry; Pharmaceutical sciences; Podiatry; Public health; Veterinary science and medicine **Level of Education for which Award is Granted:** Four Year College, Graduate **Number Awarded:** Varies each year. **Funds Available:** The maximum annual loan is $12,500 for pharmacy, nursing, allied health, and public health students; or $20,000 for medicine, dentistry, optometry, osteopathy, podiatry, or veterinary medicine students. The origination fee is 3%. After a grace period of 9 months, repayment must be completed within 25 years at a minimum monthly payment of $50. The current interest rate is 5.25% which begins to accrue immediately, even while the student is in school. **Duration:** 1 year; may be renewed up to 3 additional years. The maximum total loan is $50,000 for pharmacy, nursing, allied health, and public health students or $80,000 for medicine, dentistry, optometry, osteopathy, podiatry, or veterinary medicine students.
Eligibility Requirements: This program is open to students who qualify as Texas residents and meet the academic requirements of a public or private college or university in the state. Applicants must be enrolled at least half time in a course of study leading to 1) a doctoral degree in medicine, dentistry, optometry, osteopathy, podiatry, or veterinary medicine; 2) a bachelor's or master's degree in pharmacy; 3) a graduate or equivalent degree in public health; or 4) an associate, bachelor's, or graduate degree in nursing or allied health fields. They must be able to demonstrate financial need and enroll full time. U.S. citizenship is required. **Additional Information:** Applications must be submitted through the financial aid office at the college or university attended. This program is part of the Hinton-Hazlewood College Student Loan Program (HHCSLP).

2962 ■ U.S. AIR FORCE

Attn: Headquarters AFROTC/RRUC
551 East Maxwell Boulevard
Maxwell AFB, AL 36112-5917

Tel: (334)953-2091; (866)423-7682

Fax: (334)953-6167

Web Site: http://www.afrotc.com/admissions/professional/biomed.php

To provide financial assistance to students who are interested in joining Air Force ROTC in college and preparing for a career as a physical therapist, optometrist, or pharmacist.

Title of Award: Air Force ROTC Biomedical Sciences Corps **Area, Field, or Subject:** Optometry; Pharmaceutical sciences; Physical therapy **Level of Education for which Award is Granted:** Undergraduate **Funds Available:** Awards are type 2 AFROTC scholarships that provide for payment of tuition and fees, to a maximum of $15,000 per year, plus an annual book allowance of $600. All recipients are also awarded a tax-free subsistence allowance for 10 months of each year that is $300 per month during their sophomore year, $350 during their junior year, and $400 during their senior year. **Duration:** 2 or 3 years, provided the recipient maintains a GPA of 2.0 or higher.

Eligibility Requirements: This program is open to U.S. citizens who are freshmen or sophomores in college and interested in a career as a physical therapist, optometrist, or pharmacist. Applicants must have a GPA of 2.0 or higher and meet all other academic and physical requirements for participation in AFROTC. At the time of their Air Force commissioning, they may be no more than 31 years of age. They must agree to serve for at least 4 years as nonline active-duty Air Force officers following graduation from college. **Deadline for Receipt:** June of each year. **Additional Information:** Recipients must also complete 4 years of aerospace studies courses at 1 of the 144 colleges and universities that have an Air Force ROTC unit on campus or 1 of the approximately 900 colleges that have cross-enrollment agreements with those institutions. They must also attend a 4-week summer training camp at an Air Force base, usually between their sophomore and junior years. Following completion of their bachelor's degree, scholarship recipients earn a commission as a second lieutenant in the Air Force and serve at least 4 years.

2963 ■ WALMAN OPTICAL COMPANY

c/o Scholarship America

Attn: Scholarship Management Services

One Scholarship Way

P.O. Box 297

St. Peter, MN 56082

Tel: (507)931-1682

Free: 800-537-4180

Fax: (507)931-9168

E-mail: smsinfo@csfa.org

Web Site: http://www.walman.com

To provide financial assistance to students enrolled at designated schools and colleges of optometry.

Title of Award: Walman Optical Company Scholarship **Area, Field, or Subject:** Optometry **Level of Education for which Award is Granted:** Four Year College, Doctorate **Number Awarded:** Varies each year. **Funds Available:** The stipend ranges from $500 to $3,000 per year, depending on the need of the recipient. **Duration:** 1 year; nonrenewable, although recipients may reapply.

Eligibility Requirements: This program is open to students currently enrolled in the second or third year of a full-time 4-year program leading to a Doctor of Optometry degree at a school selected by Walman Optical Company. Selection is based on academic record, demonstrated leadership and participation in school and community activities, honors, work experience, a statement of goals and aspirations, unusual personal or family circumstances, and an outside appraisal. **Deadline for Receipt:** April of each year. **Additional Information:** The designated schools are University of Alabama at Birmingham, School of Optometry (Birmingham, Alabama); University of California at Berkeley, School of Optometry (Berkeley, California); Southern California College of Optometry (Fullerton, California); Nova Southeastern University, Health Professions Division, College of Optometry (Ft. Lauderdale, Florida); Illinois College of Optometry (Chicago, Illinois); Indiana University, School of Optometry (Bloomington, Indiana); New England College of Optometry (Boston, Massachusetts); Michigan College of Optometry, Ferris State University (Big Rapids, Michigan); University of Missouri at St. Louis, School of Optometry (St. Louis, Missouri); State University of New York, State College of Optometry (New York, New York); Ohio State University, College of Optometry (Columbus, Ohio); Northeastern State University, College of Optometry (Tahlequah, Oklahoma); Pacific University, College of Optometry (Forest Grove, Oregon); Pennsylvania College of Optometry (Elkins Park, Pennsylvania); Inter American University of Puerto Rico, School of Optometry (San Juan, Puerto Rico); Southern College of Optometry (Memphis, Tennessee); and University of Houston, College of Optometry (Houston, Texas).

2964 ■ WESTERN INTERSTATE COMMISSION FOR HIGHER EDUCATION

Attn: Student Exchange Programs

3035 Center Green Drive

P.O. Box 9752

Boulder, CO 80301-9752

Tel: (303)541-0210

Fax: (303)541-0291

E-mail: info-sep@wiche.edu

Web Site: http://www.wiche.edu/sep/psep

To underwrite some of the cost of out-of-state professional schooling for students in selected western states.

Title of Award: Professional Student Exchange Program **Area, Field, or Subject:** Architecture; Dentistry; Library and archival sciences; Medical assisting; Medicine; Medicine, Osteopathic; Nursing; Occupational therapy; Optometry; Pharmaceutical sciences; Physical therapy; Podiatry; Public health; Veterinary science and medicine **Level of Education for which Award is Granted:** Graduate, Undergraduate **Number Awarded:** Varies each year. **Funds Available:** The assistance consists of reduced levels of tuition, usually resident tuition in public institutions or reduced standard tuition at private schools. The home state pays a support fee to the admitting school to help cover the cost of the recipient's education. **Duration:** 1 year; may be renewed.

Eligibility Requirements: This program is open to residents of 13 western states who are interested in pursuing professional study at selected out-of-state institutions, usually because those fields of study are not available in their home states. The eligible programs, and the states whose residents are eligible, presently include: 1) architecture (master's degree), for residents of Wyoming, to study at designated institutions in Arizona, California, Colorado, Idaho, Montana, New Mexico, Oregon, Utah, or Washington); 2) dentistry, for residents of Alaska, Arizona, Hawaii, Montana, New Mexico, North Dakota, and Wyoming, to study at designated institutions in Arizona, California, Colorado, Nevada, Oregon, or Washington; 3) library studies (master's degree), for residents of New Mexico and Wyoming, to study at designated institutions in Arizona, California, Hawaii, or Washington; 4) medicine, for residents of Montana and Wyoming, to study at designated institutions in Arizona, California, Colorado, Hawaii, Nevada, New Mexico, North Dakota, Oregon, or Utah; 5) nursing (graduate degree), for residents of Wyoming, to study at designated institutions in California, Hawaii, North Dakota, or Oregon; 6) occupational therapy (bachelors' or master's degree), for residents of Alaska, Arizona, Hawaii, Montana, and Wyoming, to study at designated institutions in Arizona, California, Idaho, New Mexico, North Dakota, Oregon, Utah, or Washington; 7) optometry, for residents of Alaska, Arizona, Colorado, Hawaii, Idaho, Montana, Nevada, New Mexico, North Dakota, Utah, Washington, and Wyoming, to study at designated institutions in California or Oregon; 8) osteopathic medicine, for residents of Arizona, Montana, New Mexico, Washington, and Wyoming, to study at designated institutions in Arizona or California; 9) pharmacy, for residents of Alaska, Hawaii, and Nevada, to study at designated institutions in Arizona, California, Colorado, Idaho, Montana, New Mexico, North Dakota, Oregon, Utah, Washington, or Wyoming; 10) physical therapy (master's or doctoral degree), for residents of Alaska, Hawaii, and Wyoming, to study at designated institutions in Arizona, California, Colorado, Idaho, Montana, New Mexico, North Dakota, Oregon, Utah, or Washington; 11) physician assistant, for residents of Alaska, Arizona, Nevada, and Wyoming, to study at designated institutions in Arizona, California, Colorado, Idaho, Oregon, Utah, or Washington; 12) podiatry, for residents of Alaska, Montana, New Mexico, Utah, and Wyoming, to study at a designated institution in California; 13) public health, for residents of Montana and New Mexico, to study at designated institutions in California, Colorado, or Washington; and 14) veterinary medicine, for residents of Arizona, Hawaii, Montana, Nevada, New Mexico, North Dakota, Utah, and Wyoming, to study at designated institutions in California, Colorado, Oregon, or Washington. The financial status of the applicants is not considered. Interested students must apply for admission and for PSEP assistance directly from the institution of their choice. They must be certified by their state of residence to become an exchange student and be seeking enrollment at the first professional degree level. **Deadline for Receipt:** In most states, the deadline for receiving completed applications for certification is in October. After obtaining certification, students must still apply to the school of their choice, which also sets its own deadline.

Osteopathy

2965 ■ H. FLETCHER BROWN TRUST

PNC Bank Delaware
Attn: Donald W. Davis
222 Delaware Avenue, 16th Floor
Wilmington, DE 19899
Tel: (302)429-2827
Fax: (302)429-5658
E-mail: Robbie.testa@pncadvisors.com
To provide financial assistance to residents of Delaware who are interested in studying engineering, chemistry, medicine, dentistry, or law.
Title of Award: H. Fletcher Brown Scholarship **Area, Field, or Subject:** Chemistry; Dentistry; Engineering; Law; Medicine; Medicine, Osteopathic **Level of Education for which Award is Granted:** Graduate, Professional, Undergraduate **Funds Available:** The amount of the scholarship is determined by the scholarship committee and is awarded in installments over the length of study. **Duration:** 1 year; may be renewed if the recipient maintains a GPA of 2.5 or higher and continues to be worthy of and eligible for the award.
Eligibility Requirements: This program is open to Delaware residents who were born in Delaware, are either high school seniors entering the first year of college or college seniors entering the first year of graduate school, are of good moral character, and need financial assistance from sources outside their family. Applicants must have combined mathematics and verbal SAT scores of 1000 or higher, rank in the upper 20% of their class, and come from a family whose income is less than $75,000. Their proposed fields of study must be engineering, chemistry, medicine (for an M.D. or D.O. degree only), dentistry, or law. Finalists are interviewed. **Deadline for Receipt:** March of each year.

2966 ■ INDIAN HEALTH SERVICE

Attn: Scholarship Program
801 Thompson Avenue, Suite 120
Rockville, MD 20852
Tel: (301)443-6197
Fax: (301)443-6048
E-mail: bmiller@na.ihs.gov
Web Site: http://www.ihs.gov
To provide financial support to American Indian students interested in majoring in pre-medicine or pre-dentistry in college.
Title of Award: Health Professions Pregraduate Scholarship Program **Area, Field, or Subject:** Dentistry; Medicine; Medicine, Osteopathic **Level of Education for which Award is Granted:** Undergraduate **Number Awarded:** Varies each year. **Funds Available:** Awards provide a payment directly to the school for tuition and required fees; a stipend for living expenses of approximately $1,160 per month for 10 months; a lump sum to cover the costs of books, travel, and other necessary educational expenses; and up to $400 for approved tutorial costs. **Duration:** Up to 4 years of full-time study or up to 8 years of part-time study.
Eligibility Requirements: Applicants must be American Indians or Alaska Natives; be high school graduates or the equivalent; have the capacity to complete a health professions course of study; and be enrolled or accepted for enrollment in a baccalaureate degree program to prepare for entry into a school of medicine, osteopathy, or dentistry. Priority is given to students entering their junior or senior year; support is provided to freshmen and sophomores only if remaining funds are available. Selection is based on academic performance, work experience and community background, faculty/employer recommendations, and applicant's reasons for seeking the scholarship. Recipients must intend to serve Indian people upon completion of their professional health care education. **Deadline for Receipt:** February of each year.

2967 ■ INDIAN HEALTH SERVICE

Attn: Scholarship Program
801 Thompson Avenue, Suite 120
Rockville, MD 20852

Tel: (301)443-6197
Fax: (301)443-6048
E-mail: bmiller@na.ihs.gov
Web Site: http://www.ihs.gov
To provide loans-for-service to American Indian and Alaska Native students enrolled in health professions and allied health professions programs.
Title of Award: Health Professions Scholarship Program **Area, Field, or Subject:** Counseling/Guidance; Dental hygiene; Dentistry; Health care services; Medical assisting; Medical technology; Medicine; Medicine, Osteopathic; Nursing; Nutrition; Optometry; Pharmaceutical sciences; Physical therapy; Podiatry; Psychology; Public health; Radiology; Respiratory therapy; Social work; **Level of Education for which Award is Granted:** Graduate, Undergraduate **Number Awarded:** Varies each year. **Funds Available:** Awards provide a payment directly to the school for tuition and required fees; a stipend for living expenses of approximately $1,160 per month for 12 months; a lump sum to cover the costs of books, travel, and other necessary educational expenses; and up to $400 for approved tutorial costs. Upon completion of their program of study, recipients are required to provide payback service of 1 year for each year of scholarship support at the Indian Health Service, a tribal health programs, an urban Indian health program, or in private practice in a designated health professional shortage area serving a substantial number of Indians. Recipients who fail to complete their service obligation must repay all funds received (although no interest is charged). **Duration:** 1 year; may be renewed for up to 3 additional years.
Eligibility Requirements: This program is open to American Indians and Alaska Natives who are at least high school graduates and enrolled in a full-time study program leading to a degree in a health-related professions school within the United States. Priority is given to upper-division and graduate students. Qualifying fields of study include chemical dependency counseling (bachelor's or master's degree), clinical psychology (Ph.D. only), coding specialist (certificate), counseling psychology (Ph.D. only), dental hygiene (B.S.), dentistry (D.D.S.), diagnostic radiology technology (certificate, associate, or B.S.), dietitian (B.S.), civil or environmental engineering (B.S.), environmental health (B.S.), health care administration (B.S. or M.S.), health education (B.S. or M.S.), health records (R.H.I.T. or R.H.I.A.), injury prevention specialist (certificate), medical technology (B.S.), allopathic and osteopathic medicine, nursing (A.D.N., B.S.N., or C.R.N.A), optometry, pharmacy (B.S. or Pharm.D.), physician assistant (B.S.), physical therapy (M.S. or D.P.T.), podiatry (D.P.M.), public health (M.P.H. only), public health nutrition (master's only), social work (master's only), respiratory therapy (associate), and ultrasonography. **Deadline for Receipt:** February of each year.

2968 ■ PAPA OLA LOKAHI, INC.

Attn: Native Hawaiian Health Scholarship Program
345 Queen Street, Suite 706
Honolulu, HI 96813
Tel: (808)585-8944
Fax: (808)585-8081
E-mail: nhhsp@hawaii.rr.com
Web Site: http://www.nhhsp.org
To provide scholarship/loans to Native Hawaiians for training in the health professions in exchange for service in a federally-designated health professional shortage area (HPSA) or other facility for Native Hawaiians.
Title of Award: Native Hawaiian Health Scholarship Program **Area, Field, or Subject:** Dental hygiene; Dentistry; Family/Marital therapy; Health care services; Medical assisting; Medicine; Medicine, Osteopathic; Midwifery; Nursing; Nursing, Psychiatric; Psychiatry; Psychology; Public health **Level of Education for which Award is Granted:** Graduate, Undergraduate **Number Awarded:** Varies each year, depending upon the funding available. Since the program began, 151 scholars have received support. **Funds Available:** Full coverage of tuition and fees is paid directly to the health professional school. A stipend, current set at $1,157 per month, is paid directly to the scholar. This is a scholarship/loan program. Participants are obligated to provide full-time clinical primary health care services to populations in 1) a Native Hawaiian Health Care System, or 2) an HPSA in Hawaii, medically underserved area (MUA), or another area or facility in Hawaii designated by the U.S. Department of Health and Human Services. Participants owe 1 year of service in the National Health Service Corps for each full or partial year of support received under this program. The minimum service obligation is 2 years.

Duration: 1 year; may be renewed for up to 3 additional years.
Eligibility Requirements: Applicants must be Native Hawaiians training in allopathic or osteopathic medicine, dentistry, clinical psychology, registered nursing, nurse midwifery, psychiatric nursing, public health/community nursing, social work, dental hygiene, physician assistant, public health, marriage and family therapy, or primary care nurse practitioner. They may be studying in any state. Recipients must agree to serve in a designated health-care facility in Hawaii upon completion of training. First priority is given to former scholars who have completed their previous service obligation and are seeking another year of support. Second priority is given to applicants who appear to have characteristics that increase the probability they will continue to serve underserved Native Hawaiians after the completion of their service obligations. **Deadline for Receipt:** March of each year. **Additional Information:** This program, which began in 1991, is administered by the U.S. Health Resources and Services Administration, Bureau of Health Professions, through a contract with Papa Ola Lokahi, Inc.

2969 ■ TEXAS HIGHER EDUCATION COORDINATING BOARD

Attn: Hinson-Hazlewood College Student Loan Program
1200 East Anderson Lane
P.O. Box 12788, Capitol Station
Austin, TX 78711-2788
Tel: (512)427-6340
Free: 800-242-3062
Fax: (512)427-6423
E-mail: loaninfo@thecb.state.tx.us
Web Site: http://www.hhloans.com
To provide educational loans to students in Texas in health-related degree programs.

Title of Award: Hinson-Hazlewood Health Education Loan Program **Area, Field, or Subject:** Dentistry; Health care services; Medicine; Medicine, Osteopathic; Nursing; Optometry; Pharmaceutical sciences; Podiatry; Public health; Veterinary science and medicine **Level of Education for which Award is Granted:** Four Year College, Graduate **Number Awarded:** Varies each year. **Funds Available:** The maximum annual loan is $12,500 for pharmacy, nursing, allied health, and public health students; or $20,000 for medicine, dentistry, optometry, osteopathy, podiatry, or veterinary medicine students. The origination fee is 3%. After a grace period of 9 months, repayment must be completed within 25 years at a minimum monthly payment of $50. The current interest rate is 5.25% which begins to accrue immediately, even while the student is in school. **Duration:** 1 year; may be renewed up to 3 additional years. The maximum total loan is $50,000 for pharmacy, nursing, allied health, and public health students or $80,000 for medicine, dentistry, optometry, osteopathy, podiatry, or veterinary medicine students.
Eligibility Requirements: This program is open to students who qualify as Texas residents and meet the academic requirements of a public or private college or university in the state. Applicants must be enrolled at least half time in a course of study leading to 1) a doctoral degree in medicine, dentistry, optometry, osteopathy, podiatry, or veterinary medicine; 2) a bachelor's or master's degree in pharmacy; 3) a graduate or equivalent degree in public health; or 4) an associate, bachelor's, or graduate degree in nursing or allied health fields. They must be able to demonstrate financial need and enroll full time. U.S. citizenship is required. **Additional Information:** Applications must be submitted through the financial aid office at the college or university attended. This program is part of the Hinton-Hazelwood College Student Loan Program (HHCSLP).

2970 ■ WASHINGTON HIGHER EDUCATION COORDINATING BOARD

917 Lakeridge Way
P.O. Box 43430
Olympia, WA 98504-3430
Tel: (360)753-7844
Fax: (360)753-7808
E-mail: kathy.mcvay@hecb.wa.gov
Web Site: http://www.hecb.wa.gov/financialaid/other/health.asp
To provide scholarship/loans for primary care health professional education to students who agree to work in designated areas of Washington.
Title of Award: Washington State Health Professional Scholarship Program **Area, Field, or Subject:** Dental hygiene; Dentistry; Medicine;

Medicine, Osteopathic; Midwifery; Nursing; Pharmaceutical sciences **Level of Education for which Award is Granted:** Graduate, Undergraduate **Number Awarded:** Varies each year. **Funds Available:** The stipend is intended to cover eligible expenses: tuition, books, equipment, fees, and room and board. This is a scholarship/loan program. Recipients who fail to complete the course of study are required to repay the amount received, plus a penalty and interest. Scholars who fail to serve in health professional shortage areas in Washington are required to repay the scholarship, with penalty plus interest. The interest rate on the repayments is 8% for the first 4 years and 10% for the fifth year. **Duration:** Up to 5 years.
Eligibility Requirements: Applicants must be enrolled or accepted for enrollment in an accredited program leading to eligibility for licensure in Washington State in a designated health profession. They must agree to practice in Washington for 3 to 5 years following graduation, but they do not need to be Washington residents or to attend an educational institution in the state. Currently, there are no geographic restrictions for registered nurses or practical nurses. For other primary care health professionals (M.D., D.O., N.D., P.A., N.P., C.N.M., L.M.), dental care professionals (D.D.S., R.D.H.), and pharmacists, service must be in designated areas of the state. State correctional facilities, state mental health facilities, community and migrant health centers, and any other facility with more than 40% of its caseload consisting of Medicaid and sliding fee patients also qualify. **Deadline for Receipt:** April of each year.

2971 ■ WESTERN INTERSTATE COMMISSION FOR HIGHER EDUCATION

Attn: Student Exchange Programs
3035 Center Green Drive
P.O. Box 9752
Boulder, CO 80301-9752
Tel: (303)541-0210
Fax: (303)541-0291
E-mail: info-sep@wiche.edu
Web Site: http://www.wiche.edu/sep/psep
To underwrite some of the cost of out-of-state professional schooling for students in selected western states.
Title of Award: Professional Student Exchange Program **Area, Field, or Subject:** Architecture; Dentistry; Library and archival sciences; Medical assisting; Medicine; Medicine, Osteopathic; Nursing; Occupational therapy; Optometry; Pharmaceutical sciences; Physical therapy; Podiatry; Public health; Veterinary science and medicine **Level of Education for which Award is Granted:** Graduate, Undergraduate **Number Awarded:** Varies each year. **Funds Available:** The assistance consists of reduced levels of tuition, usually resident tuition in public institutions or reduced standard tuition at private schools. The home state pays a support fee to the admitting school to help cover the cost of the recipient's education. **Duration:** 1 year; may be renewed.
Eligibility Requirements: This program is open to residents of 13 western states who are interested in pursuing professional study at selected out-of-state institutions, usually because those fields of study are not available in their home states. The eligible programs, and the states whose residents are eligible, presently include: 1) architecture (master's degree), for residents of Wyoming, to study at designated institutions in Arizona, California, Colorado, Idaho, Montana, New Mexico, Oregon, Utah, or Washington); 2) dentistry, for residents of Alaska, Arizona, Hawaii, Montana, New Mexico, North Dakota, and Wyoming, to study at designated institutions in Arizona, California, Colorado, Nevada, Oregon, or Washington; 3) library studies (master's degree), for residents of New Mexico and Wyoming, to study at designated institutions in Arizona, California, Hawaii, or Washington; 4) medicine, for residents of Montana and Wyoming, to study at designated institutions in Arizona, California, Colorado, Hawaii, Nevada, New Mexico, North Dakota, Oregon, or Utah; 5) nursing (graduate degree), for residents of Wyoming, to study at designated institutions in California, Hawaii, North Dakota, or Oregon; 6) occupational therapy (bachelors' or master's degree), for residents of Alaska, Arizona, Hawaii, Montana, and Wyoming, to study at designated institutions in Arizona, California, Idaho, New Mexico, North Dakota, Oregon, Utah, or Washington; 7) optometry, for residents of Alaska, Arizona, Colorado, Hawaii, Idaho, Montana, Nevada, New Mexico, North Dakota, Utah, Washington, and Wyoming, to study at designated institutions in California or Oregon; 8) osteopathic medicine, for residents of Arizona, Montana, New Mexico, Washington, and Wyoming, to study at

designated institutions in Arizona or California; 9) pharmacy, for residents of Alaska, Hawaii, and Nevada, to study at designated institutions in Arizona, California, Colorado, Idaho, Montana, New Mexico, North Dakota, Oregon, Utah, Washington, or Wyoming; 10) physical therapy (master's or doctoral degree), for residents of Alaska, Hawaii, and Wyoming, to study at designated institutions in Arizona, California, Colorado, Idaho, Montana, New Mexico, North Dakota, Oregon, Utah, or Washington; 11) physician assistant, for residents of Alaska, Arizona, Nevada, and Wyoming, to study at designated institutions in Arizona, California, Colorado, Idaho, Oregon, Utah, or Washington; 12) podiatry, for residents of Alaska, Montana, New Mexico, Utah, and Wyoming, to study at a designated institution in California; 13) public health, for residents of Montana and New Mexico, to study at designated institutions in California, Colorado, or Washington; and 14) veterinary medicine, for residents of Arizona, Hawaii, Montana, Nevada, New Mexico, North Dakota, Utah, and Wyoming, to study at designated institutions in California, Colorado, Oregon, or Washington. The financial status of the applicants is not considered. Interested students must apply for admission and for PSEP assistance directly from the institution of their choice. They must be certified by their state of residence to become an exchange student and be seeking enrollment at the first professional degree level. **Deadline for Receipt:** In most states, the deadline for receiving completed applications for certification is in October. After obtaining certification, students must still apply to the school of their choice, which also sets its own deadline.

Pharmacology

2972 ■ ALASKA COMMISSION ON POSTSECONDARY EDUCATION

Attn: AlaskAdvantage Programs
3030 Vintage Boulevard
Juneau, AK 99801-7109
Tel: (907)465-6779; (866)427-5683
Fax: (907)465-5316
E-mail: customer_service@acpe.ak.us
Web Site: http://alaskaadvantage.state.ak.us/page/256
To provide educational loans to Alaska residents who attend out-of-state professional schools in specified fields through the Professional Student Exchange Program (PSEP) of the Western Interstate Commission for Higher Education (WICHE).
Title of Award: Alaska Professional Student Exchange Loan Program **Area, Field, or Subject:** Dentistry; Medical assisting; Occupational therapy; Optometry; Pharmaceutical sciences; Physical therapy; Podiatry **Level of Education for which Award is Granted:** Undergraduate **Number Awarded:** Varies each year. **Funds Available:** Loans up to the annual support fee are available, to a maximum of $17,200. No origination fee is charged. The interest rate is 6%. **Duration:** 1 year; may be renewed.
Eligibility Requirements: This program is open to residents of Alaska who are attending a professional school in another state as part of the PSEP of WICHE. The fields of study currently available are dentistry, occupational therapy, optometry, physician assistant, podiatry, pharmacy, and physical therapy. In most cases, PSEP students pay resident tuition (or reduced tuition at private institutions) and their home state pays an additional support fee to the institution. Alaska requires PSEP students to pay the tuition and support fee, and provides these loans to enable them to do so.

2973 ■ ASSOCIATION FOR WOMEN IN SCIENCE-SEATTLE CHAPTER

c/o Fran Solomon, Scholarship Committee Chair
5805 16th Avenue, N.E.
Seattle, WA 98105
Tel: (206)522-6441
E-mail: fran.solomon@metrokc.gov
Web Site: http://www.scn.org/awis/undergraduate_scholarship.htm
To provide financial assistance to women undergraduates from any state majoring in science, mathematics, or engineering at colleges and universities in western Washington.
Title of Award: AWIS Seattle Scholarships **Area, Field, or Subject:** Biochemistry; Biological and clinical sciences; Chemistry; Engineering; Environmental conservation; Environmental science; Geology; Mathemat-

ics and mathematical sciences; Pharmaceutical sciences; Physics **Level of Education for which Award is Granted:** Four Year College **Number Awarded:** Varies each year; recently, 11 of these scholarships were awarded. **Funds Available:** Stipends range from $1,000 to $1,500. **Duration:** 1 year.
Eligibility Requirements: This program is open to women from any state entering their junior or senior year at a 4-year college or university in western Washington. Applicants must have a declared major in science (e.g., biological sciences, environmental science, biochemistry, chemistry, pharmacy, geology, computer science, physics), mathematics, or engineering. Along with their application, they must submit essays on the events that led to their choice of a major, their current career plans and long-term goals, and their volunteer and community activities. Financial need is considered in the selection process. At least 1 scholarship is reserved for a woman from a group that is underrepresented in science, mathematics, and engineering careers, including Native American Indians and Alaska Natives, Black/African Americans, Mexican Americans/Chicanas/Latinas, Native Pacific Islanders (Polynesians, Melanesians, and Micronesians), and women with disabilities. **Deadline for Receipt:** March of each year. **Additional Information:** This program includes the following named awards: the Virginia Badger Scholarship, the Angela Paez Memorial Scholarship, and the Fran Solomon Scholarship. Support for the program is provided by several sponsors, including the American Chemical Society, Iota Sigma Pi, Rosetta Inpharmatics, and ZymoGenetics, Inc.

2974 ■ CANADIAN INSTITUTES OF HEALTH RESEARCH

Attn: Grants and Awards
160 Elgin Street, Ninth Floor
Address Locator 4809A
Ottawa, ON, Canada K1A 0W9
Tel: (613)954-1968; 888-603-4178
Fax: (613)954-1800
E-mail: info@cihr-irsc.gc.ca
Web Site: http://www.cihr-irsc.gc.ca
To provide research funding to undergraduate and graduate students interested in preparing for a career in health-related fields in Canada.
Title of Award: Health Professional Students Research Awards of the Canadian Institutes of Health Research **Area, Field, or Subject:** Dentistry; Medicine; Nursing; Optometry; Pharmaceutical sciences **Level of Education for which Award is Granted:** Graduate, Undergraduate **Number Awarded:** Varies each year. **Funds Available:** The stipend for students registered in a health professional school is $C1,417 per month. The stipend for students enrolled in a combined degree program is $C1,987 per month. **Duration:** Up to 3 months.
Eligibility Requirements: This program is open to 1) undergraduate and graduate students enrolled at Canadian schools offered programs leading to licensure in medicine, dentistry, nursing, physiotherapy, or related fields; and 2) medical students working on a combined degree (e.g., M.D./M.Sc., M.D./Ph.D.). Applicants must have completed their first year of study and be interested in participating in a health research project. They must be citizens or permanent residents of Canada. **Deadline for Receipt:** February **Additional Information:** The Canadian Institutes of Health Research (CIHR) was formerly the Medical Research Council (MRC) of Canada. This program was formerly designated the Burroughs Wellcome Fund Student Research Awards.

2975 ■ INDIAN HEALTH SERVICE

Attn: Scholarship Program
801 Thompson Avenue, Suite 120
Rockville, MD 20852
Tel: (301)443-6197
Fax: (301)443-6048
E-mail: bmiller@na.ihs.gov
Web Site: http://www.ihs.gov
To provide financial assistance to Native American students who need compensatory or preprofessional education to qualify for enrollment in a health professions school.
Title of Award: Health Professions Preparatory Scholarship Program **Area, Field, or Subject:** Engineering; Health care services; Medical technology; Nursing; Nutrition; Pharmaceutical sciences; Physical therapy; Social work **Level of Education for which Award is Granted:** Undergraduate **Number Awarded:** Varies each year. **Funds Available:**

Awards provide a payment directly to the school for tuition and required fees; a stipend for living expenses of approximately $1,160 per month for 10 months; a lump sum to cover the costs of books, travel, and other necessary educational expenses; and up to $400 for approved tutorial costs. **Duration:** Up to 2 years of full-time study or up to 4 years of part-time study.

Eligibility Requirements: Applicants must be American Indians or Alaska Natives; be high school graduates or the equivalent; have the capacity to complete a health professions course of study; and be enrolled in or accepted for enrollment in a compensatory or preprofessional general education course or curriculum. The qualifying fields of study include premedical technology, pre-dietetics, pre-nursing, pre-pharmacy, pre-physical therapy, pre-social work, and pre-engineering. Recipients must intend to serve Indian people upon completion of professional health care education as a health care provider in the discipline for which they are enrolled at the pregraduate level. **Deadline for Receipt:** February of each year.

2976 ■ INDIAN HEALTH SERVICE

Attn: Scholarship Program
801 Thompson Avenue, Suite 120
Rockville, MD 20852
Tel: (301)443-6197
Fax: (301)443-6048
E-mail: bmiller@na.ihs.gov
Web Site: http://www.ihs.gov
To provide loans-for-service to American Indian and Alaska Native students enrolled in health professions and allied health professions programs.

Title of Award: Health Professions Scholarship Program **Area, Field, or Subject:** Counseling/Guidance; Dental hygiene; Dentistry; Health care services; Medical assisting; Medical technology; Medicine; Medicine, Osteopathic; Nursing; Nutrition; Optometry; Pharmaceutical sciences; Physical therapy; Podiatry; Psychology; Public health; Radiology; Respiratory therapy; Social work; **Level of Education for which Award is Granted:** Graduate, Undergraduate **Number Awarded:** Varies each year. **Funds Available:** Awards provide a payment directly to the school for tuition and required fees; a stipend for living expenses of approximately $1,160 per month for 12 months; a lump sum to cover the costs of books, travel, and other necessary educational expenses; and up to $400 for approved tutorial costs. Upon completion of their program of study, recipients are required to provide payback service of 1 year for each year of scholarship support at the Indian Health Service, a tribal health programs, an urban Indian health program, or in private practice in a designated health professional shortage area serving a substantial number of Indians. Recipients who fail to complete their service obligation must repay all funds received (although no interest is charged). **Duration:** 1 year; may be renewed for up to 3 additional years.

Eligibility Requirements: This program is open to American Indians and Alaska Natives who are at least high school graduates and enrolled in a full-time study program leading to a degree in a health-related professions school within the United States. Priority is given to upper-division and graduate students. Qualifying fields of study include chemical dependency counseling (bachelor's or master's degree), clinical psychology (Ph.D. only), coding specialist (certificate), counseling psychology (Ph.D. only), dental hygiene (B.S.), dentistry (D.D.S.), diagnostic radiology technology (certificate, associate, or B.S.), dietitian (B.S.), civil or environmental engineering (B.S.), environmental health (B.S.), health care administration (B.S. or M.S.), health education (B.S. or M.S.), health records (R.H.I.T. or R.H.I.A.), injury prevention specialist (certificate), medical technology (B.S.), allopathic and osteopathic medicine, nursing (A.D.N., B.S.N., or C.R.N.A), optometry, pharmacy (B.S. or Pharm.D.), physician assistant (B.S.), physical therapy (M.S. or D.P.T.), podiatry (D.P.M.), public health (M.P.H. only), public health nutrition (master's only), social work (master's only), respiratory therapy (associate), and ultrasonography. **Deadline for Receipt:** February of each year.

2977 ■ KOSTER INSURANCE AGENCY

Attn: Scholarship
500 Victory Road
Quincy, MA 02171
Tel: (617)770-9889
Free: 800-457-5599
Fax: (617)479-0860

E-mail: Scholarship@kosterins.com
Web Site: http://www.kosterweb.com/about/scholarship_main.php
To provide financial assistance to undergraduate students working on a degree in a health-related field.

Title of Award: Koster Insurance Health Careers Scholarship Program **Area, Field, or Subject:** Biological and clinical sciences; Chemistry; Dentistry; Health care services; Nursing; Occupational therapy; Optometry; Pharmaceutical sciences; Physical therapy; Physiology; Public health; Social work **Level of Education for which Award is Granted:** Undergraduate **Number Awarded:** 5 each year. **Funds Available:** The stipend is $3,000 per year. **Duration:** 1 year; may be renewed 1 additional year.

Eligibility Requirements: This program is open to full-time undergraduates entering their second-to-last or final year of study in a health-related field, including (but not limited to) pre-medicine, nursing, public and community health, physical therapy, occupational therapy, pharmacy, biology, chemistry, physiology, social work, dentistry, and optometry. Applicants must have a GPA of 3.0 or higher and be able to demonstrate financial need. Along with their application, they must submit a 1-page essay describing their personal goals, including their reasons for preparing for a career in health care. Selection is based on motivation to pursue a career in health care, academic excellence, dedication to community service, and financial need. **Deadline for Receipt:** April of each year. **Additional Information:** This program began in 2001.

2978 ■ NORTHWEST PHARMACIST COALITION

P.O. Box 22975
Seattle, WA 98122
Tel: (425)746-9618
To provide financial assistance to Washington state residents of Black ethnic origin who are interested in becoming a pharmacist.

Title of Award: Northwest Pharmacist Coalition Scholarship in Honor of Russell S. Gideon **Area, Field, or Subject:** Pharmaceutical sciences **Level of Education for which Award is Granted:** Undergraduate **Number Awarded:** 2 each year. **Funds Available:** The amount of the stipend depends on the availability of funds. **Duration:** 1 year.

Eligibility Requirements: Eligible to apply for this scholarship are high school seniors or currently-enrolled college students who are or will be enrolled in a community college or university pre-pharmacy or pharmacy program. Applicants must have discussed the pharmacy profession with at least 1 practicing pharmacist (name must be provided) and must include copies of their high school/college transcripts as part of the application process. In addition, they must submit a written essay on why they wish to be a pharmacist and why they feel they should receive this scholarship. They must be Washington residents and available for an interview with the scholarship committee in the Seattle area. **Deadline for Receipt:** April of each year.

2979 ■ PACIFICARE FOUNDATION

3100 Lake Center Drive
P.O. Box 25186
Santa Ana, CA 92799
Tel: (714)825-5233
Web Site: http://www.pacificare.com
To provide financial assistance to Latino high school seniors in designated states planning to major in a health care field in college.

Title of Award: PacifiCare Latino Health Scholars Program **Area, Field, or Subject:** Health care services; Medical technology; Medicine; Nursing; Pharmaceutical sciences; Psychology; Public health **Level of Education for which Award is Granted:** Undergraduate **Number Awarded:** Approximately 50 each year. **Funds Available:** The stipend is $2,000. **Duration:** 1 year.

Eligibility Requirements: This program is open to seniors graduating from high schools in Arizona, California, Colorado, Nevada, Oklahoma, Oregon, Texas, and Washington. Applicants must have a GPA of 3.0 or higher, be fluent in Spanish, and have been accepted as a full-time student at a university, community college, or accredited technical college. Their proposed field of study must relate to health care, including (but not limited to) nursing, medical interpretation, health claims examiner, health information technology programs, pharmacy technician, public health, psychology, or pre-medical studies. Along with their application, they must submit a 2-page essay (in both English and Spanish) on their personal and academic accomplishments, community involvement, volunteer and leadership activities, academic plans, and the reason they want a career in the health care field. **Deadline for Receipt:** June of each year. **Additional Information:** This program was established in 2003.

2980 ■ TEXAS HIGHER EDUCATION COORDINATING BOARD

Attn: Hinson-Hazlewood College Student Loan Program
1200 East Anderson Lane
P.O. Box 12788, Capitol Station
Austin, TX 78711-2788
Tel: (512)427-6340
Free: 800-242-3062
Fax: (512)427-6423
E-mail: loaninfo@thecb.state.tx.us
Web Site: http://www.hhloans.com
To provide educational loans to students in Texas in health-related degree programs.
Title of Award: Hinson-Hazlewood Health Education Loan Program **Area, Field, or Subject:** Dentistry; Health care services; Medicine; Medicine, Osteopathic; Nursing; Optometry; Pharmaceutical sciences; Podiatry; Public health; Veterinary science and medicine **Level of Education for which Award is Granted:** Four Year College, Graduate **Number Awarded:** Varies each year. **Funds Available:** The maximum annual loan is $12,500 for pharmacy, nursing, allied health, and public health students; or $20,000 for medicine, dentistry, optometry, osteopathy, podiatry, or veterinary medicine students. The origination fee is 3%. After a grace period of 9 months, repayment must be completed within 25 years at a minimum monthly payment of $50. The current interest rate is 5.25% which begins to accrue immediately, even while the student is in school. **Duration:** 1 year; may be renewed up to 3 additional years. The maximum total loan is $50,000 for pharmacy, nursing, allied health, and public health students or $80,000 for medicine, dentistry, optometry, osteopathy, podiatry, or veterinary medicine students.
Eligibility Requirements: This program is open to students who qualify as Texas residents and meet the academic requirements of a public or private college or university in the state. Applicants must be enrolled at least half time in a course of study leading to 1) a doctoral degree in medicine, dentistry, optometry, osteopathy, podiatry, or veterinary medicine; 2) a bachelor's or master's degree in pharmacy; 3) a graduate or equivalent degree in public health; or 4) an associate, bachelor's, or graduate degree in nursing or allied health fields. They must be able to demonstrate financial need and enroll full time. U.S. citizenship is required. **Additional Information:** Applications must be submitted through the financial aid office at the college or university attended. This program is part of the Hinton-Hazlewood College Student Loan Program (HHCSLP).

2981 ■ U.S. AIR FORCE

Attn: Headquarters AFROTC/RRUC
551 East Maxwell Boulevard
Maxwell AFB, AL 36112-5917
Tel: (334)953-2091; (866)423-7682
Fax: (334)953-6167
Web Site: http://www.afrotc.com/admissions/professional/biomed.php
To provide financial assistance to students who are interested in joining Air Force ROTC in college and preparing for a career as a physical therapist, optometrist, or pharmacist.
Title of Award: Air Force ROTC Biomedical Sciences Corps **Area, Field, or Subject:** Optometry; Pharmaceutical sciences; Physical therapy **Level of Education for which Award is Granted:** Undergraduate **Funds Available:** Awards are type 2 AFROTC scholarships that provide for payment of tuition and fees, to a maximum of $15,000 per year, plus an annual book allowance of $600. All recipients are also awarded a tax-free subsistence allowance for 10 months of each year that is $300 per month during their sophomore year, $350 during their junior year, and $400 during their senior year. **Duration:** 2 or 3 years, provided the recipient maintains a GPA of 2.0 or higher.
Eligibility Requirements: This program is open to U.S. citizens who are freshmen or sophomores in college and interested in a career as a physical therapist, optometrist, or pharmacist. Applicants must have a GPA of 2.0 or higher and meet all other academic and physical requirements for participation in AFROTC. At the time of their Air Force commissioning, they may be no more than 31 years of age. They must agree to serve for at least 4 years as nonline active-duty Air Force officers following gradu-

ation from college. **Deadline for Receipt:** June of each year. **Additional Information:** Recipients must also complete 4 years of aerospace studies courses at 1 of the 144 colleges and universities that have an Air Force ROTC unit on campus or 1 of the approximately 900 colleges that have cross-enrollment agreements with those institutions. They must also attend a 4-week summer training camp at an Air Force base, usually between their sophomore and junior years. Following completion of their bachelor's degree, scholarship recipients earn a commission as a second lieutenant in the Air Force and serve at least 4 years.

2982 ■ U.S. NAVY

Attn: Naval Medical Education
Code OG3
8901 Wisconsin Avenue, 16th Floor, Tower 1
Bethesda, MD 20889-5611
Tel: (301)319-4520
E-mail: mscipp@nmetc.med.navy.mil
Web Site: http://nshs.med.navy.mil/mscipp/mscipp.htm
To provide funding to Navy and Marine enlisted personnel who wish to earn an undergraduate or graduate degree in selected health care specialties while continuing to receive their regular pay and allowances.
Title of Award: Medical Service Corps Inservice Procurement Program (MSC-IPP) **Area, Field, or Subject:** Entomology; Environmental conservation; Environmental science; Health care services; Industrial hygiene; Medical assisting; Pharmaceutical sciences **Level of Education for which Award is Granted:** Four Year College, Graduate **Number Awarded:** Varies each year. Recently, 36 of these positions were available: 20 in health care administration, 10 in physician assistant, 2 in pharmacy, 2 in environmental health, 1 in industrial hygiene, and 1 in entomology. **Funds Available:** Participants receive payment of tuition, mandatory fees, a book allowance, and full pay and allowances for their enlisted pay grade. They are eligible for advancement while in college. **Duration:** 24 to 48 months of full-time, year-round study, until completion of a relevant degree.
Eligibility Requirements: This program is open to enlisted personnel who are serving on active duty in pay grades E-5 through E-9 of the U.S. Navy, U.S. Marine Corps, Naval Reserve (including the Training and Administration of the Reserve Program), and the Marine Corps Reserve (including the Active Reserve Program). Applicants must be interested in working on a degree to become commissioned in the following medical specialties: health care administration, physician assistant, pharmacy, environmental health, industrial hygiene, or entomology. If they plan to work on a graduate degree, they must have scores of at least 900 on the GRE or 470 on the GMAT; if they plan to work on a bachelor's or physician assistant degree, they must have scores of at least 1000 on the SAT (including 460 on the mathematics portion) or 42 on the ACT. They must be U.S. citizens who can be commissioned before they reach their 42nd birthday. **Deadline for Receipt:** August of each year. **Additional Information:** Following graduation, participants are commissioned in the Medical Service Corps and attend Officer Indoctrination School.

2983 ■ WASHINGTON HIGHER EDUCATION COORDINATING BOARD

917 Lakeridge Way
P.O. Box 43430
Olympia, WA 98504-3430
Tel: (360)753-7844
Fax: (360)753-7808
E-mail: kathy.mcvay@hecb.wa.gov
Web Site: http://www.hecb.wa.gov/financialaid/other/health.asp
To provide scholarship/loans for primary care health professional education to students who agree to work in designated areas of Washington.
Title of Award: Washington State Health Professional Scholarship Program **Area, Field, or Subject:** Dental hygiene; Dentistry; Medicine; Medicine, Osteopathic; Midwifery; Nursing; Pharmaceutical sciences **Level of Education for which Award is Granted:** Graduate, Undergraduate **Number Awarded:** Varies each year. **Funds Available:** The stipend is intended to cover eligible expenses: tuition, books, equipment, fees, and room and board. This is a scholarship/loan program. Recipients who fail to complete the course of study are required to repay the amount received, plus a penalty and interest. Scholars who fail to serve in health professional shortage areas in Washington are required to repay the scholarship, with penalty plus interest. The interest rate on the repay-

ments is 8% for the first 4 years and 10% for the fifth year. **Duration:** Up to 5 years.

Eligibility Requirements: Applicants must be enrolled or accepted for enrollment in an accredited program leading to eligibility for licensure in Washington State in a designated health profession. They must agree to practice in Washington for 3 to 5 years following graduation, but they do not need to be Washington residents or to attend an educational institution in the state. Currently, there are no geographic restrictions for registered nurses or practical nurses. For other primary care health professionals (M.D., D.O., N.D., P.A., N.P., C.N.M., L.M.), dental care professionals (D.D.S., R.D.H.), and pharmacists, service must be in designated areas of the state. State correctional facilities, state mental health facilities, community and migrant health centers, and any other facility with more than 40% of its caseload consisting of Medicaid and sliding fee patients also qualify. **Deadline for Receipt:** April of each year.

2984 ■ WESTERN INTERSTATE COMMISSION FOR HIGHER EDUCATION

Attn: Student Exchange Programs
3035 Center Green Drive
P.O. Box 9752
Boulder, CO 80301-9752
Tel: (303)541-0210
Fax: (303)541-0291
E-mail: info-sep@wiche.edu
Web Site: http://www.wiche.edu/sep/psep
To underwrite some of the cost of out-of-state professional schooling for students in selected western states.

Title of Award: Professional Student Exchange Program **Area, Field, or Subject:** Architecture; Dentistry; Library and archival sciences; Medical assisting; Medicine; Medicine, Osteopathic; Nursing; Occupational therapy; Optometry; Pharmaceutical sciences; Physical therapy; Podiatry; Public health; Veterinary science and medicine **Level of Education for which Award is Granted:** Graduate, Undergraduate **Number Awarded:** Varies each year. **Funds Available:** The assistance consists of reduced levels of tuition, usually resident tuition in public institutions or reduced standard tuition at private schools. The home state pays a support fee to the admitting school to help cover the cost of the recipient's education. **Duration:** 1 year; may be renewed.

Eligibility Requirements: This program is open to residents of 13 western states who are interested in pursuing professional study at selected out-of-state institutions, usually because those fields of study are not available in their home states. The eligible programs, and the states whose residents are eligible, presently include: 1) architecture (master's degree), for residents of Wyoming, to study at designated institutions in Arizona, California, Colorado, Idaho, Montana, New Mexico, Oregon, Utah, or Washington); 2) dentistry, for residents of Alaska, Arizona, Hawaii, Montana, New Mexico, North Dakota, and Wyoming, to study at designated institutions in Arizona, California, Colorado, Nevada, Oregon, or Washington; 3) library studies (master's degree), for residents of New Mexico and Wyoming, to study at designated institutions in Arizona, California, Hawaii, or Washington; 4) medicine, for residents of Montana and Wyoming, to study at designated institutions in Arizona, California, Colorado, Hawaii, Nevada, New Mexico, North Dakota, Oregon, or Utah; 5) nursing (graduate degree), for residents of Wyoming, to study at designated institutions in California, Hawaii, North Dakota, or Oregon; 6) occupational therapy (bachelors' or master's degree), for residents of Alaska, Arizona, Hawaii, Montana, and Wyoming, to study at designated institutions in Arizona, California, Idaho, New Mexico, North Dakota, Oregon, Utah, or Washington; 7) optometry, for residents of Alaska, Arizona, Colorado, Hawaii, Idaho, Montana, Nevada, New Mexico, North Dakota, Utah, Washington, and Wyoming, to study at designated institutions in California or Oregon; 8) osteopathic medicine, for residents of Arizona, Montana, New Mexico, Washington, and Wyoming, to study at designated institutions in Arizona or California; 9) pharmacy, for residents of Alaska, Hawaii, and Nevada, to study at designated institutions in Arizona, California, Colorado, Idaho, Montana, New Mexico, North Dakota, Oregon, Utah, Washington, or Wyoming; 10) physical therapy (master's or doctoral degree), for residents of Alaska, Hawaii, and Wyoming, to study at designated institutions in Arizona, California, Colorado, Idaho, Montana, New Mexico, North Dakota, Oregon, Utah, or Washington; 11) physician assistant, for residents of Alaska, Arizona, Nevada, and Wyoming, to study at designated institutions in Arizona,

California, Colorado, Idaho, Oregon, Utah, or Washington; 12) podiatry, for residents of Alaska, Montana, New Mexico, Utah, and Wyoming, to study at a designated institution in California; 13) public health, for residents of Montana and New Mexico, to study at designated institutions in California, Colorado, or Washington; and 14) veterinary medicine, for residents of Arizona, Hawaii, Montana, Nevada, New Mexico, North Dakota, Utah, and Wyoming, to study at designated institutions in California, Colorado, Oregon, or Washington. The financial status of the applicants is not considered. Interested students must apply for admission and for PSEP assistance directly from the institution of their choice. They must be certified by their state of residence to become an exchange student and be seeking enrollment at the first professional degree level. **Deadline for Receipt:** In most states, the deadline for receiving completed applications for certification is in October. After obtaining certification, students must still apply to the school of their choice, which also sets its own deadline.

Psychiatry

2985 ■ ACADEMY OF TELEVISION ARTS & SCIENCES FOUNDATION

Attn: Education Department
5220 Lankershim Boulevard
North Hollywood, CA 91601-3109
Tel: (818)754-2830
Fax: (818)761-ATAS
E-mail: collegeawards@emmys.org
Web Site: http://www.emmys.tv/foundation/index.php
To provide financial assistance to upper-division and graduate students interested in working on a project in a field related to children's media.

Title of Award: Fred Rogers Memorial Scholarship **Area, Field, or Subject:** Art, Caricatures and cartoons; Child development; Education, Early childhood; Filmmaking; Music; Psychology; Radio and television **Level of Education for which Award is Granted:** Four Year College, Graduate **Number Awarded:** 1 each year. **Funds Available:** The stipend is $10,000. **Duration:** 1 year.

Eligibility Requirements: This program is open to upper-division and graduate students interested in preparing for a career in children's media. Applicants must be able to demonstrate a commitment, either through course work or experience, to any combination of at least 2 of the following fields: early childhood education, child development, child psychology, film or television production, music, or animation. They may apply for support for any of the following areas: research on the relationship between children's media and learning or children's use of media and personal growth; development of program concepts or extended development of creative elements of an existing concept (e.g., design of puppets, scripts, storyboards, characters, music); professional internship in an organization that is relevant to the applicant's goal for use of the award. **Deadline for Receipt:** January of each year. **Additional Information:** This scholarship, first awarded in 2005, is supported by Ernst & Young.

2986 ■ AMERICAN PSYCHOLOGICAL ASSOCIATION

Attn: Education Directorate
750 First Street, N.E.
Washington, DC 20002-4242
Tel: (202)572-3013
Fax: (202)336-5962
E-mail: eleary@apa.org
Web Site: http://www.apa.org/ed/topss/apftopsscholar.html
To recognize and reward, with college scholarships, high school students who submit outstanding research papers on psychology.

Title of Award: APF/APA TOPSS Scholars Competition **Area, Field, or Subject:** Psychology; Writing **Level of Education for which Award is Granted:** Undergraduate **Number Awarded:** 3 each year. **Funds Available:** The award is $1,000. **Duration:** The competition is held annually.

Eligibility Requirements: This competition is open to high school students who have been enrolled or are currently enrolled in a psychology course. Candidates must be sponsored by a member of the American Psychological Association (APA) Teachers of Psychology in Secondary Schools (TOPSS). They must submit a paper, up to 3,000 words in length, on an assigned topic relating to psychology. Selection is based on the literature review (10 points per item) and research proposal (10 points per item). **Deadline for Receipt:** February of each year. **Additional Information:** This program is cosponsored by the American Psychological Foundation (APF).

2987 ■ CHRISTIAN LIFE RESOURCES
Attn: WELS Lutherans for Life
Scholarship Review Committee
2949 North Mayfair Road, Suite 309
Milwaukee, WI 53222-4304
Tel: (414)774-1331
Fax: (414)774-1360
Web Site: http://www.christianliferesources.com
To provide financial assistance to Lutheran high school seniors in Wisconsin who are interested in studying life-related issues in college.
Title of Award: WELS Lutherans for Life Scholarship Program **Area, Field, or Subject:** Biological and clinical sciences; Education, Special; Engineering, Biomedical; Journalism; Law; Medicine; Physical therapy; Political science; Psychology; Social work **Level of Education for which Award is Granted:** Four Year College **Number Awarded:** Varies each year; recently, 9 of these scholarships were awarded. **Funds Available:** Stipends up to $1,000 are available. **Duration:** 1 year.
Eligibility Requirements: This program is open to high school seniors who are active members of the Wisconsin Evangelical Lutheran Synod (WELS) or an affiliated church. Applicants must be planning to go to a 4-year school to prepare for a secular career in which pro-life values will be demonstrated. Acceptable fields include medicine, biotechnology/biological engineering, medical research/genetics, law/politics, journalism/media, psychology, physical therapy, social services, or special education. They must have a GPA of 3.25 or higher. Along with their application, they must submit essays on 1) the field of study they plan to enter and how it relates to pro-life issues; 2) why the scholarship should be awarded to them, including their future goals; and 3) how they have demonstrated a Christian, pro-life attitude in their life. **Deadline for Receipt:** February of each year. **Additional Information:** WELS Lutherans for Life was formerly a ministry of the Wisconsin Evangelical Lutheran Synod.

2988 ■ EPILEPSY FOUNDATION
Attn: Research Department
4351 Garden City Drive
Landover, MD 20785-7223
Tel: (301)459-3700
Free: 800-EFA-1000
Fax: (301)577-2684
E-mail: grants@efa.org
Web Site: http://www.epilepsyfoundation.org/research/grants.cfm
To provide funding to undergraduate and graduate students interested in working on a summer research training project in a field relevant to epilepsy.
Title of Award: Behavioral Sciences Student Fellowships in Epilepsy **Area, Field, or Subject:** Anthropology; Behavioral sciences; Counseling/Guidance; Economics; Epilepsy; Nursing; Political science; Psychology; Rehabilitation, Physical/Psychological; Social work; Sociology **Level of Education for which Award is Granted:** Graduate, Undergraduate **Number Awarded:** Varies each year; recently, 4 of these fellowships were awarded. **Funds Available:** The grant is $3,000. **Duration:** 3 months during the summer.
Eligibility Requirements: This program is open to undergraduate and graduate students in a behavioral science program relevant to epilepsy research or clinical care, including, but not limited to, sociology, social work, psychology, anthropology, nursing, economics, vocational rehabilitation, counseling, and political science. Applicants must be interested in working on an epilepsy research project under the supervision of a qualified mentor. Because the program is designed as a training opportunity, the quality of the training plans and environment are considered in the selection process. Other selection criteria include the quality of the proposed project, the relevance of the proposed work to epilepsy, the applicant's interest in the field of epilepsy, the applicant's qualifications, and the mentor's qualifications, including his or her commitment to the student and the project. U.S. citizenship is not required, but the project must be conducted in the United States. Applications from women, members of minority groups, and people with disabilities are especially encouraged. The program is not intended for students working on a dissertation research project. **Deadline for Receipt:** March of each year. **Additional**

Information: This program is supported by the American Epilepsy Society, Abbott Laboratories, Ortho-McNeil Pharmaceutical Corporation, and Pfizer Inc.

2989 ■ HAWAI'I COMMUNITY FOUNDATION
Attn: Scholarship Department
1164 Bishop Street, Suite 800
Honolulu, HI 96813
Tel: (808)566-5570; 888-731-3863
Fax: (808)521-6286
E-mail: scholarships@hcf-hawaii.org
Web Site: http://www.hawaiicommunityfoundation.org/scholar/scholar.php
To provide financial assistance to residents of Hawaii for undergraduate or graduate studies in fields related to achieving world cooperation and international understanding.
Title of Award: Marion Maccarrell Scott Scholarship **Area, Field, or Subject:** Anthropology; Economics; Geography; History; International affairs and relations; Law; Peace studies; Philosophy; Political science; Psychology; Sociology **Level of Education for which Award is Granted:** Graduate, Undergraduate **Number Awarded:** Varies each year; recently, 258 of these scholarships were awarded. **Funds Available:** The amounts of the awards depend on the availability of funds and the need of the recipient; recently, stipends averaged $1,749. **Duration:** 1 year.
Eligibility Requirements: This program is open to graduates of public high schools in Hawaii. They must plan to attend school as full-time students (on the undergraduate or graduate level) on the mainland, majoring in history, government, political science, anthropology, economics, geography, international relations, law, psychology, philosophy, or sociology. They must be residents of the state of Hawaii, able to demonstrate financial need, interested in attending an accredited 2- or 4-year college or university, and able to demonstrate academic achievement (GPA of 2.8 or higher). Along with their application, they must submit an essay on their commitment to world peace that includes their learning experiences (courses, clubs, community activities, or travel) related to achieving world peace and international understanding and explaining how their experiences have enhanced their ability to achieve those goals. **Deadline for Receipt:** February of each year.

2990 ■ HISPANIC SCHOLARSHIP FUND INSTITUTE
1001 Connecticut Avenue, N.W., Suite 632
Washington, DC 20036
Tel: (202)296-0009
Fax: (202)296-3633
E-mail: info@hsfi.org
Web Site: http://www.hsfi.org/scholarships/generation.asp
To provide financial assistance to Hispanic and other students majoring in designated business, engineering, social science, and science fields who are interested in employment with the U.S. Department of Energy (DOE).
Title of Award: Next Generation of Public Servants Scholarship **Area, Field, or Subject:** Accounting; Biological and clinical sciences; Business administration; Computer and information sciences; Engineering; Environmental science; Finance; Geology; Information science and technology; Management; Mathematics and mathematical sciences; Physics; Political science; Psychology; Sociology **Level of Education for which Award is Granted:** Undergraduate **Number Awarded:** Varies each year. **Funds Available:** The stipend is $3,000 per year. **Duration:** 1 year; may be renewed up to 2 additional years if the recipient maintains full-time enrollment and a GPA of 2.8 or higher.
Eligibility Requirements: This program is open to U.S. citizens enrolled full time as sophomores with a GPA of 2.8 or higher. Applicants must be interested in preparing for a career with the DOE in an energy-related field. Eligible academic majors are in the fields of business (accounting, business administration, finance, and management), engineering (biomedical, chemical, civil, computer, electrical, environmental, industrial, materials, mechanical, metallurgical, nuclear, and petroleum), social science (economics, organizational psychology, political science, and sociology), and science (biological sciences, computer science, geology, information technology, mathematics, microbiology, and physics). They must be willing to participate in co-ops with the DOE. Along with their application, they must submit a 2-page essay on why a career in public service interests them, how their academic major connects with their stated DOE career goal, why the DOE should invest in them through this program, and how they believe the DOE will benefit from this investment.

Selection is based on academic achievement, financial need, demonstrated commitment to public service, and interest in federal employment with the DOE. **Deadline for Receipt:** February of each year. **Additional Information:** This program, sponsored by DOE's Office of Economic Impact and Diversity, is administered by the Hispanic Scholarship Fund Institute as part of its effort to increase Hispanic participation in federal service.

2991 ■ INDIAN HEALTH SERVICE

Attn: Scholarship Program
801 Thompson Avenue, Suite 120
Rockville, MD 20852
Tel: (301)443-6197
Fax: (301)443-6048
E-mail: bmiller@na.ihs.gov
Web Site: http://www.ihs.gov
To provide loans-for-service to American Indian and Alaska Native students enrolled in health professions and allied health professions programs.
Title of Award: Health Professions Scholarship Program **Area, Field, or Subject:** Counseling/Guidance; Dental hygiene; Dentistry; Health care services; Medical assisting; Medical technology; Medicine; Medicine, Osteopathic; Nursing; Nutrition; Optometry; Pharmaceutical sciences; Physical therapy; Podiatry; Psychology; Public health; Radiology; Respiratory therapy; Social work; **Level of Education for which Award is Granted:** Graduate, Undergraduate **Number Awarded:** Varies each year. **Funds Available:** Awards provide a payment directly to the school for tuition and required fees; a stipend for living expenses of approximately $1,160 per month for 12 months; a lump sum to cover the costs of books, travel, and other necessary educational expenses; and up to $400 for approved tutorial costs. Upon completion of their program of study, recipients are required to provide payback service of 1 year for each year of scholarship support at the Indian Health Service, a tribal health programs, an urban Indian health program, or in private practice in a designated health professional shortage area serving a substantial number of Indians. Recipients who fail to complete their service obligation must repay all funds received (although no interest is charged). **Duration:** 1 year; may be renewed for up to 3 additional years.
Eligibility Requirements: This program is open to American Indians and Alaska Natives who are at least high school graduates and enrolled in a full-time study program leading to a degree in a health-related professions school within the United States. Priority is given to upper-division and graduate students. Qualifying fields of study include chemical dependency counseling (bachelor's or master's degree), clinical psychology (Ph.D. only), coding specialist (certificate), counseling psychology (Ph.D. only), dental hygiene (B.S.), dentistry (D.D.S.), diagnostic radiology technology (certificate, associate, or B.S.), dietitian (B.S.), civil or environmental engineering (B.S.), environmental health (B.S.), health care administration (B.S. or M.S.), health education (B.S. or M.S.), health records (R.H.I.T. or R.H.I.A.), injury prevention specialist (certificate), medical technology (B.S.), allopathic and osteopathic medicine, nursing (A.D.N., B.S.N., or C.R.N.A), optometry, pharmacy (B.S. or Pharm.D.), physician assistant (B.S.), physical therapy (M.S. or D.P.T.), podiatry (D.P.M.), public health (M.P.H. only), public health nutrition (master's only), social work (master's only), respiratory therapy (associate), and ultrasonography. **Deadline for Receipt:** February of each year.

2992 ■ PAPA OLA LOKAHI, INC.

Attn: Native Hawaiian Health Scholarship Program
345 Queen Street, Suite 706
Honolulu, HI 96813
Tel: (808)585-8944
Fax: (808)585-8081
E-mail: nhhsp@hawaii.rr.com
Web Site: http://www.nhhsp.org
To provide scholarship/loans to Native Hawaiians for training in the health professions in exchange for service in a federally-designated health professional shortage area (HPSA) or other facility for Native Hawaiians.
Title of Award: Native Hawaiian Health Scholarship Program **Area, Field, or Subject:** Dental hygiene; Dentistry; Family/Marital therapy; Health care services; Medical assisting; Medicine; Medicine, Osteopathic; Midwifery; Nursing; Nursing, Psychiatric; Psychiatry; Psychology; Public health **Level of Education for which Award is Granted:** Graduate,

Undergraduate **Number Awarded:** Varies each year, depending upon the funding available. Since the program began, 151 scholars have received support. **Funds Available:** Full coverage of tuition and fees is paid directly to the health professional school. A stipend, current set at $1,157 per month, is paid directly to the scholar. This is a scholarship/loan program. Participants are obligated to provide full-time clinical primary health care services to populations in 1) a Native Hawaiian Health Care System, or 2) an HPSA in Hawaii, medically underserved area (MUA), or another area or facility in Hawaii designated by the U.S. Department of Health and Human Services. Participants owe 1 year of service in the National Health Service Corps for each full or partial year of support received under this program. The minimum service obligation is 2 years. **Duration:** 1 year; may be renewed for up to 3 additional years.
Eligibility Requirements: Applicants must be Native Hawaiians training in allopathic or osteopathic medicine, dentistry, clinical psychology, registered nursing, nurse midwifery, psychiatric nursing, public health/community nursing, social work, dental hygiene, physician assistant, public health, marriage and family therapy, or primary care nurse practitioner. They may be studying in any state. Recipients must agree to serve in a designated health-care facility in Hawaii upon completion of training. First priority is given to former scholars who have completed their previous service obligation and are seeking another year of support. Second priority is given to applicants who appear to have characteristics that increase the probability they will continue to serve underserved Native Hawaiians after the completion of their service obligations. **Deadline for Receipt:** March of each year. **Additional Information:** This program, which began in 1991, is administered by the U.S. Health Resources and Services Administration, Bureau of Health Professions, through a contract with Papa Ola Lokahi, Inc.

2993 ■ MARYLAND HIGHER EDUCATION COMMISSION

Attn: Office of Student Financial Assistance
839 Bestgate Road, Suite 400
Annapolis, MD 21401-3013
Tel: (410)260-4594
Free: 800-974-1024
Fax: (410)974-5376
E-mail: osfamail@mhec.state.md.us
Web Site: http://www.mhec.state.md.us/financialAid/
ProgramDescriptions/prog_devdis.asp
To provide scholarship/loans to students in Maryland who are interested in working on a degree in a designated human services program.
Title of Award: Maryland Developmental Disabilities, Mental Health, Child Welfare, and Juvenile Justice Workforce Tuition Assistance Program **Area, Field, or Subject:** Counseling/Guidance; Criminal justice; Criminology; Disabilities; Education, Special; Gerontology; Law enforcement; Mental health; Nursing; Occupational therapy; Physical therapy; Psychology; Rehabilitation, Physical/Psychological; Social work **Level of Education for which Award is Granted:** Graduate, Undergraduate **Number Awarded:** Varies each year. **Funds Available:** The maximum stipend is $2,000 per year for students attending a 2-year institution or $3,000 per year for students at a 4-year institution. The total amount of all state awards may not exceed the cost of attendance as determined by the school's financial aid office or $17,800, whichever is less. Recipients must agree to work in a Maryland community-based program that is licensed by the Developmental Disabilities Administration or approved by the Mental Hygiene Administration, or in a residential program that is licensed by the Department of Human Resources or the Department of Juvenile Justice. The service obligation must begin within 6 months of graduation. The total service requirement is 2,000 hours if the award amount is $1,999 or less, 3,000 hours if the award amount is $2,000 to $3,999, or 4,000 hours if the award amount is $4,000 or more. If the service requirement is not completed, the award must be repaid with interest. **Duration:** 1 year; may be renewed if the recipient maintains satisfactory academic progress and remains enrolled in a human services degree program.
Eligibility Requirements: This program is open to high school seniors and full-time and part-time undergraduate and graduate students. Applicants and their parents must be Maryland residents attending a college or university in the state in 1 of the following human services degree programs: aging services, counseling, disability services, mental health, nursing, occupational therapy, physical therapy, psychology, rehabilitation, social work, special education, supported employment, vocational rehabilitation, or any other concentration in the healing arts or a program

providing support services to individuals with special needs including child welfare and juvenile justice. Financial need is not considered in the selection process. **Deadline for Receipt:** June of each year.

2994 ■ MISSISSIPPI OFFICE OF STUDENT FINANCIAL AID

3825 Ridgewood Road
Jackson, MS 39211-6453
Tel: (601)432-6997
Free: 800-327-2980
Fax: (601)432-6527
E-mail: sfa@ihl.state.ms.us
Web Site: http://www.ihl.state.ms.us/financialaid/hcp.html

To provide scholarship/loans to Mississippi residents who are majoring in a critical health care field in college.
Title of Award: Mississippi Health Care Professions Loan/Scholarship Program **Area, Field, or Subject:** Health care services; Occupational therapy; Physical therapy; Psychology; Speech and language pathology/audiology **Level of Education for which Award is Granted:** Four Year College, Graduate **Number Awarded:** Varies each year, depending on the availability of funds; awards are granted on a first-come, first-served basis. **Funds Available:** Under this program, $1,500 is awarded per year to undergraduate students and $3,000 per year to graduate students. This is a scholarship/loan program. Obligation can be discharged on the basis of 1 year's service in the health profession at a state-operated health institution in Mississippi for 1 year's scholarship/loan award. In the event the recipient fails to fulfill the service obligation, repayment of principal and interest is required. **Duration:** Up to 2 years for undergraduates and for graduate students in physical therapy; 1 year for graduate students in occupational therapy.
Eligibility Requirements: This program is open to Mississippi residents who are enrolled as a junior, senior, or graduate student in an approved training program in the state of Mississippi. Approved programs of study currently include speech pathology and psychology on the undergraduate level and occupational therapy and physical therapy on the graduate level. Selection is based on cumulative GPA. The highest priority is given to renewal students. **Deadline for Receipt:** March of each year. **Additional Information:** State health institutions include the following: Mississippi State Hospital, Ellisville State School, East Mississippi State Hospital, Mississippi Children's Rehabilitation Center, North Mississippi Retardation Center, Hudspeth Retardation Center, South Mississippi Retardation Center, University of Mississippi Hospital, Boswell Retardation Center, State Board of Health, Department of Mental Health, and health care facilities under the Department of Corrections.

2995 ■ OAK RIDGE INSTITUTE FOR SCIENCE AND EDUCATION

Attn: Science and Engineering Education
P.O. Box 117
Oak Ridge, TN 37831-0117
Tel: (865)576-8239
Fax: (865)241-5219
E-mail: igrid.gregory@orau.gov
Web Site: http://www.orau.gov/orise.htm

To provide financial assistance and summer research experience to undergraduate students who are working on a degree in a field of interest to the Department of Homeland Security (DHS).
Title of Award: Department of Homeland Security Undergraduate Scholarships **Area, Field, or Subject:** Agricultural sciences; Biological and clinical sciences; Communications; Computer and information sciences; Engineering; Information science and technology; Mathematics and mathematical sciences; Physical sciences; Psychology; Public administration; Religion; Social sciences; Writing **Level of Education for which Award is Granted:** Undergraduate **Number Awarded:** Approximately 50 each year. **Funds Available:** This program provides a stipend of $1,000 per month during the academic year and $5,000 for the internship plus full payment of tuition and mandatory fees. **Duration:** 2 academic years plus 10 weeks during the intervening summer.
Eligibility Requirements: This program is open to 1) full-time students who are in their second year of college attendance as of the application deadline; and 2) part-time students who have completed at least 45 but no more than 60 semester hours as of the application deadline. Applicants must be majoring in the agricultural sciences, biological and life sciences, computer and information sciences, engineering, mathematics, physical sciences, psychology, social sciences, or selected humanities (religious

studies, cultural studies, public policy, advocacy, communications, or science writing). They must have a GPA of 3.3 or higher. Along with their application, they must submit 2 statements on 1) their educational and professional goals, the kinds of research they are interested in conducting, specific questions that interest them, and how they became interested in them; and 2) how they think their interests, talents, and initiative would contribute to make the homeland safer and secure. Selection is based on those statements, academic record, references, and SAT or ACT scores, As part of their program, they must be interested in participating in summer research and development activities at a DHS-designated facility. U.S. citizenship is required. **Deadline for Receipt:** January of each year. **Additional Information:** This program, established in 2003, is funded by DHS and administered by Oak Ridge Institute for Science and Education (ORISE). Recipients must enroll full time.

2996 ■ PACIFICARE FOUNDATION

3100 Lake Center Drive
P.O. Box 25186
Santa Ana, CA 92799
Tel: (714)825-5233
Web Site: http://www.pacificare.com

To provide financial assistance to Latino high school seniors in designated states planning to major in a health care field in college.
Title of Award: PacifiCare Latino Health Scholars Program **Area, Field, or Subject:** Health care services; Medical technology; Medicine; Nursing; Pharmaceutical sciences; Psychology; Public health **Level of Education for which Award is Granted:** Undergraduate **Number Awarded:** Approximately 50 each year. **Funds Available:** The stipend is $2,000. **Duration:** 1 year.
Eligibility Requirements: This program is open to seniors graduating from high schools in Arizona, California, Colorado, Nevada, Oklahoma, Oregon, Texas, and Washington. Applicants must have a GPA of 3.0 or higher, be fluent in Spanish, and have been accepted as a full-time student at a university, community college, or accredited technical college. Their proposed field of study must relate to health care, including (but not limited to) nursing, medical interpretation, health claims examiner, health information technology programs, pharmacy technician, public health, psychology, or pre-medical studies. Along with their application, they must submit a 2-page essay (in both English and Spanish) on their personal and academic accomplishments, community involvement, volunteer and leadership activities, academic plans, and the reason they want a career in the health care field. **Deadline for Receipt:** June of each year. **Additional Information:** This program was established in 2003.

2997 ■ SUNSHINE LADY FOUNDATION, INC.

Attn: CASS Program
4900 Randall Parkway, Suite H
Wilmington, NC 28403
Tel: (910)397-7742; (866)255-7742
Fax: (910)397-0023
E-mail: mitty@sunshineladyfdn.org
Web Site: http://www.sunshineladyfdn.org/cass.html

To provide financial assistance for college or graduate study in related fields to workers at domestic violence service centers.
Title of Award: Counselor, Advocate and Support Staff Scholarship **Area, Field, or Subject:** Accounting; Business administration; Counseling/Guidance; Nonprofit sector; Psychology **Level of Education for which Award is Granted:** Graduate, Undergraduate **Number Awarded:** Varies each year. **Funds Available:** Funding, paid directly to the educational institution, is provided for tuition, fees, required books, and supplies. A maximum of 3 courses per academic term may be supported. **Duration:** 1 academic term; may be renewed if the recipient maintains a GPA of 2.5 or higher.
Eligibility Requirements: This program is open to women and men who have been employed for at least 1 year by a nonprofit domestic violence victim services provider that is willing to provide support for their study. Applicants must be interested in enrolling in a community college, 4-year degree, graduate degree, or certificate program as a full or part time student. Their program should be related to their employment, including social work, counseling, psychology, accounting, nonprofit management, or business management. Financial need is considered in the selection process. **Deadline for Receipt:** February of each year for spring quarter; April of each year for summer term; July of each year for fall quarter or

semester; November of each year for winter quarter or spring semester. **Additional Information:** This program was established in 1999.

2998 ■ U.S. MARINE CORPS

Manpower and Reserve Affairs (MMEA-85)
3280 Russell Road
Quantico, VA 22134-5103
Tel: (703)784-9264
Fax: (703)784-9843
Web Site: http://www.usmc.mil

To allow selected noncommissioned Marine Corps officers to earn a bachelor's degree in selected fields by pursuing full-time college study while continuing to receive their regular pay and allowances.

Title of Award: Marine Corps Staff Noncommissioned Officers Degree Completion Program **Area, Field, or Subject:** Accounting; Business administration; Education; Environmental conservation; Environmental science; Finance; Management; Music; Protective services; Psychology **Level of Education for which Award is Granted:** Undergraduate **Number Awarded:** Varies each year; recently, 5 Marines were selected to participate in this program. **Funds Available:** Noncommissioned officers selected to participate in this program receive their regular Marine Corps pay while attending a college or university on a full-time basis. Tuition, matriculation fees, and other expenses (such as books) must be paid by the recipient through personal funds, in-service Montgomery GI Bill benefits, student loans, or other non-Marine Corps means. **Duration:** Up to the equivalent of 2 academic years.

Eligibility Requirements: Eligible to participate in this program are regular active-duty Marines, especially in the grades of staff sergeant and gunnery sergeant. Applicants must have completed at least 2 years of postsecondary study and have been accepted by an accredited degree-granting college or university in a program offered to all matriculating students; enrollment in a multiple major program designed for adults returning to school does not qualify. The program recently was limited to the following majors: accounting, business administration with an emphasis on accounting or financial management, education, environmental safety, environmental health management, hazardous material and waste control, music, occupational safety, psychology, safety education, safety management, and waste control. **Deadline for Receipt:** April of each year. **Additional Information:** Applicants must agree to extend/reenlist for a period of 4 years beyond completion of this program.

2999 ■ WISCONSIN FOUNDATION FOR INDEPENDENT COLLEGES, INC.

Attn: College-to-Work Program
735 North Water Street, Suite 600
Milwaukee, WI 53202-4100
Tel: (414)273-5980
Fax: (414)273-5995
E-mail: wfic@wficweb.org
Web Site: http://www.wficweb.org/work.html

To provide financial assistance and work experience to students at member institutions of the Wisconsin Foundation for Independent Colleges (WFIC) who are interested in preparing for a career in a field related to Alzheimer's Disease.

Title of Award: Alzheimer's Support Center College-to-Work Program **Area, Field, or Subject:** Alzheimer's disease; Business administration; Computer and information sciences; Marketing and distribution; Psychology; Sociology **Level of Education for which Award is Granted:** Four Year College **Number Awarded:** 1 each year. **Funds Available:** The stipends are $3,500 for the scholarship and $1,500 for the internship. **Duration:** 1 year for the scholarship; 10 weeks during the summer for the internship.

Eligibility Requirements: This program is open to full-time sophomores, juniors, and seniors at WFIC member colleges and universities. Applicants should be majoring in psychology, sociology, business, marketing, or computers. They must be interested in an internship at the Alzheimer's Support Center in Janesville, Wisconsin. Along with their application, they must submit a 1-page essay that includes why they are applying for the internship, why they have selected their major and what interests them about it, why they are attending their chosen college or university, and their future career objectives. **Deadline for Receipt:** February of each year. **Additional Information:** The WFIC member schools are Alverno College, Beloit College, Cardinal Stritch University, Carroll College,

Carthage College, Concordia University of Wisconsin, Edgewood College, Lakeland College, Lawrence University, Marian College, Marquette University, Milwaukee Institute of Art & Design, Milwaukee School of Engineering, Mount Mary College, Northland College, Ripon College, St. Norbert College, Silver Lake College, Viterbo University, and Wisconsin Lutheran College. This program is sponsored by the Alzheimer's Support Center of Janesville.

Rehabilitation

3000 ■ AMERICAN COUNCIL OF THE BLIND

Attn: Coordinator, Scholarship Program
1155 15th Street, N.W., Suite 1004
Washington, DC 20005
Tel: (202)467-5081
Free: 800-424-8666
Fax: (202)467-5085
E-mail: info@acb.org
Web Site: http://www.acb.org

To provide financial assistance to undergraduate or graduate students who are blind and are interested in studying in a field of service to persons with disabilities.

Title of Award: Arnold Sadler Memorial Scholarship **Area, Field, or Subject:** Disabilities; Education, Special; Law; Rehabilitation, Physical/Psychological **Level of Education for which Award is Granted:** Graduate, Undergraduate **Number Awarded:** 1 each year. **Funds Available:** The stipend is $2,000. In addition, the winner receives a Kurzweil-1000 Reading System. **Duration:** 1 year.

Eligibility Requirements: This program is open to students in rehabilitation, education, law, or other fields of service to persons with disabilities. Applicants must be legally blind and U.S. citizens. In addition to letters of recommendation and copies of academic transcripts, applications must include an autobiographical sketch. A cumulative GPA of 3.3 or higher is generally required. Selection is based on demonstrated academic record, involvement in extracurricular and civic activities, and academic objectives. The severity of the applicant's visual impairment and his/her study methods are also taken into account. **Deadline for Receipt:** February of each year. **Additional Information:** This scholarship is funded by the Arnold Sadler Memorial Scholarship Fund. Scholarship winners are expected to be present at the council's annual conference; the council will cover all reasonable expenses connected with convention attendance.

3001 ■ AMERICAN FOUNDATION FOR THE BLIND

Attn: Scholarship Committee
11 Penn Plaza, Suite 300
New York, NY 10001
Tel: (212)502-7661
Free: 800-AFB-LINE
Fax: (212)502-7771
E-mail: afbinfo@afb.net
Web Site: http://www.afb.org/scholarships.asp

To provide financial assistance to blind undergraduate and graduate students who wish to study in the field of rehabilitation and/or education of the blind.

Title of Award: Delta Gamma Foundation Florence Margaret Harvey Memorial Scholarship **Area, Field, or Subject:** Education, Special; Rehabilitation, Physical/Psychological; Visual impairment **Level of Education for which Award is Granted:** Four Year College, Graduate **Number Awarded:** 1 each year. **Funds Available:** The stipend is $1,000. **Duration:** 1 year.

Eligibility Requirements: This program is open to legally blind juniors, seniors, or graduate students. U.S. citizenship is required. Applicants must be studying in the field of rehabilitation and/or education of visually impaired and blind persons. Along with their application, they must submit an essay that includes the field of study they are pursuing and why they have chosen it; their educational and personal goals; their work experience; any extracurricular activities with which they have been involved, including those in school, religious organizations, and the community; and how they intend to use scholarship monies that may be awarded. **Deadline for Receipt:** April of each year. **Additional Information:** This scholarship is supported by the Delta Gamma Foundation and administered by the American Foundation for the Blind.

3002 ■ AMERICAN FOUNDATION FOR THE BLIND

Attn: Scholarship Committee
11 Penn Plaza, Suite 300
New York, NY 10001
Tel: (212)502-7661
Free: 800-AFB-LINE
Fax: (212)502-7771
E-mail: afbinfo@afb.net
Web Site: http://www.afb.org/scholarships.asp
To provide financial assistance to legally blind undergraduate or graduate students studying in the field of rehabilitation and/or education of visually impaired and blind persons.

Title of Award: Rudolph Dillman Memorial Scholarship **Area, Field, or Subject:** Education, Special; Rehabilitation, Physical/Psychological; Visual impairment **Level of Education for which Award is Granted:** Graduate, Undergraduate **Number Awarded:** 4 each year: 3 without consideration of financial need and 1 to an applicant who can submit evidence of financial need. **Funds Available:** The stipend is $2,500 per year. **Duration:** 1 academic year; previous recipients may not reapply.

Eligibility Requirements: Applicants must be able to submit evidence of legal blindness, U.S. citizenship, and acceptance in an accredited undergraduate or graduate training program within the broad field of rehabilitation and/or education of blind and visually impaired persons. Along with their application, they must submit an essay that includes the field of study they are pursuing and why they have chosen it; their educational and personal goals; their work experience; any extracurricular activities with which they have been involved, including those in school, religious organizations, and the community; and how they intend to use scholarship monies that may be awarded. They may also include documentation of financial need. **Deadline for Receipt:** April of each year.

3003 ■ ASSOCIATION FOR EDUCATION AND REHABILITATION OF THE BLIND AND VISUALLY IMPAIRED OF OHIO

c/o Marjorie E. Ward
1568 Lafayette Drive
Columbus, OH 43220
E-mail: ward5@osu.edu
Web Site: http://www.aerohio.org/schgrts/schol-grant.htm
To provide financial assistance to Ohio residents who are working on an undergraduate or graduate degree in a field related to rehabilitation of the blind.

Title of Award: AERO Personnel Preparation Scholarships **Area, Field, or Subject:** Counseling/Guidance; Education, Special; Rehabilitation, Physical/Psychological; Visual impairment **Level of Education for which Award is Granted:** Four Year College, Graduate **Number Awarded:** 1 each year. **Funds Available:** The stipend is $1,000. **Duration:** 1 year; nonrenewable.

Eligibility Requirements: This program is open to undergraduate and graduate students in rehabilitation counseling, rehabilitation teaching, orientation and mobility, or education of students with visual disabilities. Applicants must be residents of Ohio, although they may be studying in any state. Undergraduates must have at least junior standing. All applicants must have a GPA of 3.0 or higher. Along with their application, they must submit 1) a short essay explaining why they have chosen their specific field as their profession and what they would like to contribute to the field; 2) a short description of volunteer or paid involvement with individuals with visual disabilities or any other disability; 3) transcripts; and 4) 3 letters of recommendation. **Deadline for Receipt:** April of each year.

3004 ■ COURAGE CENTER

Attn: EMPOWER Scholarship Program
3915 Golden Valley Road
Minneapolis, MN 55422
Tel: (763)520-0214; 888-8-INTAKE
Fax: (763)520-0392
E-mail: suep@courage.org
Web Site: http://www.courage.org
To provide financial assistance to students of color interested in preparing for a career in the medical rehabilitation field.

Title of Award: Encourage Minority Participation in Occupations with Emphasis on Rehabilitation **Area, Field, or Subject:** Rehabilitation, Physical/Psychological **Level of Education for which Award is**

Granted: Undergraduate **Number Awarded:** 2 each year. **Funds Available:** The stipend is $1,500. **Duration:** 1 year.

Eligibility Requirements: This program is open to ethnically diverse students accepted at or enrolled in an institution of higher learning. Applicants must demonstrate a career interest in the medical rehabilitation field by completing at least 200 hours of career-related volunteer service. They must have a GPA of 2.0 or higher. Selection is based on career intentions and achievements, not academic rank. **Deadline for Receipt:** April of each year. **Additional Information:** This program is also identified by its acronym as the EMPOWER Scholarship Award.

3005 ■ EPILEPSY FOUNDATION

Attn: Research Department
4351 Garden City Drive
Landover, MD 20785-7223
Tel: (301)459-3700
Free: 800-EFA-1000
Fax: (301)577-2684
E-mail: grants@efa.org
Web Site: http://www.epilepsyfoundation.org/research/grants.cfm
To provide funding to undergraduate and graduate students interested in working on a summer research training project in a field relevant to epilepsy.

Title of Award: Behavioral Sciences Student Fellowships in Epilepsy **Area, Field, or Subject:** Anthropology; Behavioral sciences; Counseling/Guidance; Economics; Epilepsy; Nursing; Political science; Psychology; Rehabilitation, Physical/Psychological; Social work; Sociology **Level of Education for which Award is Granted:** Graduate, Undergraduate **Number Awarded:** Varies each year; recently, 4 of these fellowships were awarded. **Funds Available:** The grant is $3,000. **Duration:** 3 months during the summer.

Eligibility Requirements: This program is open to undergraduate and graduate students in a behavioral science program relevant to epilepsy research or clinical care, including, but not limited to, sociology, social work, psychology, anthropology, nursing, economics, vocational rehabilitation, counseling, and political science. Applicants must be interested in working on an epilepsy research project under the supervision of a qualified mentor. Because the program is designed as a training opportunity, the quality of the training plans and environment are considered in the selection process. Other selection criteria include the quality of the proposed project, the relevance of the proposed work to epilepsy, the applicant's interest in the field of epilepsy, the applicant's qualifications, and the mentor's qualifications, including his or her commitment to the student and the project. U.S. citizenship is not required, but the project must be conducted in the United States. Applications from women, members of minority groups, and people with disabilities are especially encouraged. The program is not intended for students working on a dissertation research project. **Deadline for Receipt:** March of each year. **Additional Information:** This program is supported by the American Epilepsy Society, Abbott Laboratories, Ortho-McNeil Pharmaceutical Corporation, and Pfizer Inc.

3006 ■ MARYLAND HIGHER EDUCATION COMMISSION

Attn: Office of Student Financial Assistance
839 Bestgate Road, Suite 400
Annapolis, MD 21401-3013
Tel: (410)260-4594
Free: 800-974-1024
Fax: (410)974-5376
E-mail: osfamail@mhec.state.md.us
Web Site: http://www.mhec.state.md.us/financialAid/
ProgramDescriptions/prog_devdis.asp
To provide scholarship/loans to students in Maryland who are interested in working on a degree in a designated human services program.

Title of Award: Maryland Developmental Disabilities, Mental Health, Child Welfare, and Juvenile Justice Workforce Tuition Assistance Program **Area, Field, or Subject:** Counseling/Guidance; Criminal justice; Criminology; Disabilities; Education, Special; Gerontology; Law enforcement; Mental health; Nursing; Occupational therapy; Physical therapy; Psychology; Rehabilitation, Physical/Psychological; Social work **Level of Education for which Award is Granted:** Graduate, Undergraduate **Number Awarded:** Varies each year. **Funds Available:** The maximum stipend is $2,000 per year for students attending a 2-year institution or $3,000 per year for students at a 4-year institution. The total amount of all state awards may not exceed the cost of attendance as determined by the school's financial aid office or $17,800, whichever is less. Recipients must agree to work in a Maryland community-based program that is licensed by the Developmental Disabilities Administration or approved by the Mental Hygiene Administration, or in a residential program that is licensed by the Department of Human Resources or the Department of Juvenile Justice. The service obligation must begin within 6 months of graduation. The total service requirement is 2,000 hours if the award amount is $1,999 or less, 3,000 hours if the award amount is $2,000 to $3,999, or 4,000 hours if the award amount is $4,000 or more. If the service requirement is not completed, the award must be repaid with interest. **Duration:** 1 year; may be renewed if the recipient maintains satisfactory academic progress and remains enrolled in a human services degree program.

Eligibility Requirements: This program is open to high school seniors and full-time and part-time undergraduate and graduate students. Applicants and their parents must be Maryland residents attending a college or university in the state in 1 of the following human services degree programs: aging services, counseling, disability services, mental health, nursing, occupational therapy, physical therapy, psychology, rehabilitation, social work, special education, supported employment, vocational rehabilitation, or any other concentration in the healing arts or a program providing support services to individuals with special needs including child welfare and juvenile justice. Financial need is not considered in the selection process. **Deadline for Receipt:** June of each year.

3007 ■ NATIONAL AMBUCS, INC.

Attn: Scholarship Coordinator
P.O. Box 5127
High Point, NC 27262

Tel: (336)852-0052
Fax: (336)852-6830
E-mail: ambucs@ambucs.org
Web Site: http://www.ambucs.org
To provide financial assistance to undergraduate and graduate students who are interested in preparing for a career serving disabled citizens in various fields of clinical therapy.

Title of Award: AMBUCS Scholarships for Therapists **Area, Field, or Subject:** Occupational therapy; Physical therapy; Rehabilitation, Physical/Psychological; Speech and language pathology/audiology **Level of Education for which Award is Granted:** Four Year College, Graduate **Number Awarded:** Approximately 400 each year, with a total value of $225,000. **Funds Available:** Most of these awards range from $500 to $1,500 per year; 1 scholarship of $6,000 for 2 years is also awarded. Funds are paid directly to the recipient's school. **Duration:** 1 year.

Eligibility Requirements: This program is open to U.S. citizens who have been accepted at the upper-division or graduate level in an accredited program that qualifies the students for clinical practice in occupational therapy, physical therapy, speech language pathology, or hearing audiology. Programs for therapy assistants are not included. Applicants must submit college transcripts for the last 3 semesters, a 500-word essay on their interest in therapy as a career, and a statement of family financial circumstances. Selection is based on financial need, commitment to local community, demonstrated academic accomplishment, character for compassion and integrity, and career objectives. **Deadline for Receipt:** April of each year. **Additional Information:** This program was established in 1955; since then, the association has awarded more than $5 million for more than 9,900 scholarships.

General

3008 ■ ALABAMA SPACE GRANT CONSORTIUM

c/o University of Alabama in Huntsville
Materials Science Building, Room 205
Huntsville, AL 35899
Tel: (256)824-6800
Fax: (256)824-6061
E-mail: reasonj@uah.edu
Web Site: http://www.uah.edu/ASGC

To provide financial assistance to undergraduate students at universities participating in the Alabama Space Grant Consortium who wish to prepare for a career as a teacher of science or mathematics.
Title of Award: Teacher Education Scholarship Program of the Alabama Space Grant Consortium **Area, Field, or Subject:** Aerospace sciences; Earth sciences; Education; Environmental conservation; Environmental science; Geosciences; Mathematics and mathematical sciences; Science; Space and planetary sciences **Level of Education for which Award is Granted:** Undergraduate **Number Awarded:** Varies each year; recently, 10 of these scholarships were awarded. **Funds Available:** The stipend is $1,000 per year. **Duration:** 1 year; nonrenewable.
Eligibility Requirements: This program is open to students enrolled in or accepted for enrollment as full-time undergraduates at universities in Alabama participating in the consortium. Applicants must intend to enter the teacher certification program and teach in a pre-college setting. Priority is given to those majoring in science, mathematics, or earth/space/environmental science. Applicants should have a GPA of 3.0 or higher and must be U.S. citizens. Members of underrepresented groups in science and mathematics (minorities and women) are especially encouraged to apply. Along with their application, they must submit a 1- to 2-page statement on the reasons for their desire to enter the teaching profession, specifically the fields of science or mathematics education. **Deadline for Receipt:** February of each year. **Additional Information:** The member universities are University of Alabama in Huntsville, Alabama A&M University, University of Alabama, University of Alabama at Birmingham, University of South Alabama, Tuskegee University, and Auburn University. Funding for this program is provided by NASA.

3009 ■ ALABAMA SPACE GRANT CONSORTIUM

c/o University of Alabama in Huntsville
Materials Science Building, Room 205
Huntsville, AL 35899
Tel: (256)824-6800
Fax: (256)824-6061
E-mail: reasonj@uah.edu
Web Site: http://www.uah.edu/ASGC

To provide financial assistance to undergraduates who are studying the space sciences at universities participating in the Alabama Space Grant Consortium (ASGC).
Title of Award: Undergraduate Scholarship Program of the Alabama Space Grant Consortium **Area, Field, or Subject:** Aerospace sciences; Behavioral sciences; Biological and clinical sciences; Business administration; Communications; Computer and information sciences; Economics; Education; Engineering, Aerospace/Aeronautical/Astronautical; International affairs and relations; Law; Natural sciences; Physical sci-

ences; Public administration; Sociology; Space and planetary sciences **Level of Education for which Award is Granted:** Four Year College **Number Awarded:** Varies each year; recently, 32 of these scholarships were awarded. **Funds Available:** The stipend is $1,000 per year. **Duration:** 1 year; may be renewed 1 additional year.
Eligibility Requirements: This program is open to full-time students entering their junior or senior year at universities participating in the ASGC. Applicants must be studying in a field related to space, including the physical, natural, and biological sciences; engineering, education; economics; business; sociology; behavioral sciences; computer science; communications; law; international affairs; and public administration. They must be U.S. citizens and have a GPA of 3.0 or higher. Individuals from underrepresented groups (African Americans, Hispanic, American Indians, Pacific Islanders, Asian Americans, and women) are especially encouraged to apply. Interested students should submit a completed application with a career goal statement, personal references, a brief resume, and transcripts. Selection is based on 1) academic qualifications, 2) quality of the career goal statement, and 3) assessment of the applicant's motivation for a career in aerospace. **Deadline for Receipt:** February of each year. **Additional Information:** The member universities are University of Alabama in Huntsville, Alabama A&M University, University of Alabama, University of Alabama at Birmingham, University of South Alabama, Tuskegee University, and Auburn University. Funding for this program is provided by NASA.

3010 ■ AMERICAN ASSOCIATION OF BLACKS IN ENERGY

Attn: Scholarship Committee
927 15th Street, N.W., Suite 200
Washington, DC 20005
Tel: (202)371-9530
Fax: (202)371-9218
E-mail: aabe@aabe.org
Web Site: http://aabe.org/taxonomy_menu/24/253

To provide financial assistance to underrepresented minority high school seniors who are interested in majoring in engineering, mathematics, or physical science in college.
Title of Award: American Association of Blacks in Energy Scholarship **Area, Field, or Subject:** Engineering; Mathematics and mathematical sciences; Physical sciences **Level of Education for which Award is Granted:** Undergraduate **Number Awarded:** 6 each year (1 in each of the organization's regions); of those 6 winners, 1 is chosen to receive the Premier Award. **Funds Available:** The stipends are $1,500. The Premier Award is an additional $3,000. All funds are paid directly to the students upon proof of enrollment at an accredited college or university. **Duration:** 1 year; nonrenewable.
Eligibility Requirements: This program is open to members of minority groups underrepresented in the energy industry (African Americans, Hispanics, and Native Americans) who are graduating high school seniors. Applicants must have a "B" academic average overall and a "B" average in mathematics and science courses. They must be planning to attend an accredited college or university to major in engineering, mathematics, or the physical sciences. Along with their application, they must submit a 350-word essay covering why they should receive this scholarship, their professional career objectives, and any other pertinent information. Financial need is also considered in the selection process.

The applicant who demonstrates the most outstanding achievement and promise is presented with the Premier Award. All applications must be submitted to the local office of the sponsoring organization in the student's state. For a list of local offices, contact the scholarship committee at the national office. **Deadline for Receipt:** February of each year.

3011 ■ AMERICAN FOUNDATION FOR THE BLIND

Attn: Scholarship Committee
11 Penn Plaza, Suite 300
New York, NY 10001
Tel: (212)502-7661
Free: 800-AFB-LINE
Fax: (212)502-7771
E-mail: afbinfo@afb.net
Web Site: http://www.afb.org/scholarships.asp
To provide financial assistance to visually impaired students who wish to work on a graduate or undergraduate degree in engineering or computer, physical, or life sciences.
Title of Award: Paul and Ellen Ruckes Scholarship **Area, Field, or Subject:** Biological and clinical sciences; Computer and information sciences; Engineering; Physical sciences **Level of Education for which Award is Granted:** Graduate, Undergraduate **Number Awarded:** 1 each year. **Funds Available:** The stipend is $1,000. **Duration:** 1 year.
Eligibility Requirements: This program is open to visually impaired undergraduate or graduate students who are U.S. citizens working on a degree in engineering or the computer, physical, or life sciences. Legal blindness is not required. Along with their application, they must submit an essay that includes the field of study they are pursuing and why they have chosen it; their educational and personal goals; their work experience; any extracurricular activities with which they have been involved, including those in school, religious organizations, and the community; and how they intend to use scholarship monies that may be awarded. **Deadline for Receipt:** April of each year.

3012 ■ AMERICAN INDIAN SCIENCE AND ENGINEERING SOCIETY

Attn: Scholarship Coordinator
2305 Renard, S.E., Suite 200
P.O. Box 9828
Albuquerque, NM 87119-9828
Tel: (505)765-1052
Fax: (505)765-5608
E-mail: shirley@aises.org
Web Site: http://www.aises.org/highered/scholarships
To provide financial assistance to members of the American Indian Science and Engineering Society who are majoring in designated fields as undergraduate or graduate students.
Title of Award: A.T. Anderson Memorial Scholarship Program **Area, Field, or Subject:** Engineering; Mathematics and mathematical sciences; Medicine; Natural resources; Physical sciences; Science **Level of Education for which Award is Granted:** Graduate, Undergraduate **Number Awarded:** Varies; generally, 200 or more each year, depending upon the availability of funds from corporate and other sponsors. **Funds Available:** The annual stipend is $1,000 for undergraduates or $2,000 for graduate students. **Duration:** 1 year; nonrenewable.
Eligibility Requirements: This program is open to members of the society who can furnish proof of tribal enrollment or Certificate of Degree of Indian Blood. Applicants must be full-time students at the undergraduate or graduate school level attending an accredited 4-year college or university or a 2-year college leading to an academic degree in engineering, mathematics, medicine, natural resources, physical science, or the sciences. They must submit a 500-word essay that demonstrates their interest in and motivation to continue higher education, an understanding of the importance of college and a commitment to completion, their educational and/or career goals, and a commitment to learning and giving back to the community. Selection is based on the essay, academic achievement (GPA of 2.0 or higher), leadership potential, and commitment to helping other American Indians. Financial need is not considered. **Deadline for Receipt:** June of each year. **Additional Information:** This program was launched in 1983 in memory of A.T. Anderson, a Mohawk and a chemical engineer who worked with Albert Einstein. Anderson was 1 of the society's founders and was the society's first executive director. The program includes the following named awards: the Al Qoyawayma Award for an applicant who is majoring in science or engineering and also

has a strong interest in the arts, the Norbert S. Hill, Jr. Leadership Award, the Polingaysi Qoyawayma Award for an applicant who is working on a teaching degree in order to teach mathematics or science in a Native community or an advanced degree for personal improvement or teaching at the college level, and the Robert W. Brocksbank Scholarship.

3013 ■ AMERICAN INDIAN SCIENCE AND ENGINEERING SOCIETY

Attn: Scholarship Coordinator
2305 Renard, S.E., Suite 200
P.O. Box 9828
Albuquerque, NM 87119-9828
Tel: (505)765-1052
Fax: (505)765-5608
E-mail: shirley@aises.org
Web Site: http://www.aises.org/highered/scholarships
To provide financial assistance for college to outstanding American Indian high school seniors from designated states who are members of American Indian Science and Engineering Society (AISES).
Title of Award: Burlington Northern Santa Fe Foundation Scholarship **Area, Field, or Subject:** Business administration; Engineering; Mathematics and mathematical sciences; Medicine; Natural resources; Physical sciences; Science; Technology **Level of Education for which Award is Granted:** Four Year College **Number Awarded:** 5 new awards are made each year. **Funds Available:** The stipend is $2,500 per year. **Duration:** 4 years or until completion of a baccalaureate degree, whichever occurs first.
Eligibility Requirements: This program is open to AISES members who are high school seniors planning to attend an accredited 4-year college or university and major in business, engineering, mathematics, medicine, natural resources, physical science, science, or technology. Applicants must submit 1) proof of tribal enrollment or a Certificate of Degree of Indian Blood; 2) evidence of residence in the service area of the Burlington Northern and Santa Fe Corporation (Arizona, California, Colorado, Kansas, Minnesota, Montana, New Mexico, North Dakota, Oklahoma, Oregon, South Dakota, and Washington); 3) a statement of financial need; 4) a 500-word essay on why they chose their particular field of study, their career aspirations, an evaluation of past scholastic performance, obstacles faced as a student, and involvement in and commitment to tribal community life; and 5) high school transcripts showing a GPA of 2.0 or higher. **Deadline for Receipt:** April of each year. **Additional Information:** This program is funded by the Burlington Northern Santa Fe Foundation and administered by AISES.

3014 ■ ARIZONA STATE UNIVERSITY

Attn: Center for Meteorite Studies
P.O. Box 871404
Tempe, AZ 85287-1404
Tel: (602)965-6511
E-mail: meteorites@asu.edu
Web Site: http://meteorites.asu.edu/nininger
To recognize and reward outstanding student papers dealing with aspects of meteoritic investigation.
Title of Award: Dr. and Mrs. H.H. Nininger Meteorite Award **Area, Field, or Subject:** Physical sciences; Writing **Level of Education for which Award is Granted:** Graduate, Undergraduate **Number Awarded:** 1 each year. **Funds Available:** The prize is $2,500. **Duration:** The competition is held annually.
Eligibility Requirements: This competition is open to both undergraduate and graduate students. They are invited to submit a paper (under 10,000 words) reflecting an aspect of meteoritic investigation. Research topics may include (but are not limited to) physical and chemical properties of meteorites, origin of meteoritic material, and cratering. Observational, experimental, statistical, or theoretical investigations are allowed. Students must be the first author of the paper, but they do not have to be the sole author. Papers must have been written, submitted, or published during the first 10 and a half months of the calendar year. They must cover original research conducted by the student. **Deadline for Receipt:** November of each year. **Additional Information:** Entries not awarded the

prize may be resubmitted in the original or a revised form as long as the author is a student at an American college or university.

3015 ■ ARKANSAS DEPARTMENT OF WORKFORCE EDUCATION

Luther Hardin Building
Three Capitol Mall, Room 207
Little Rock, AR 72201-1083
Tel: (501)682-1500
Fax: (501)682-1509
Web Site: http://dwe.arkansas.gov/LoanForgiveness/atcslfp.htm

To provide forgivable loans to residents of Arkansas who are interested in pursuing technical education and working in the state.

Title of Award: Arkansas Technical Careers Student Loan Forgiveness Program **Area, Field, or Subject:** Biological and clinical sciences; Computer and information sciences; Engineering; Engineering, Biomedical; Engineering, Computer; Engineering, Electrical; Engineering, Industrial; Health care services; Physical sciences **Level of Education for which Award is Granted:** Undergraduate **Number Awarded:** Varies each year. **Funds Available:** The maximum loan is $2,500 per year. Loans are forgiven if the recipient works full time in the high demand technical field in Arkansas. Each year's loan may be forgiven with 1 year of full-time employment. Loan recipients who do not graduate from the program or work full time in the field in Arkansas must repay the loan in full. **Duration:** Up to 4 years.

Eligibility Requirements: This program is open to residents of Arkansas who are U.S. citizens or permanent residents admitted to an approved program resulting in a diploma, certificate, or degree in a high demand technical field. Applicants must indicate their intention to work in Arkansas in the field for which they receive the training. **Deadline for Receipt:** Applications must be submitted within 6 months of the completion of the program of study. **Additional Information:** The Arkansas General Assembly established this program in 1999. Recently, the designated career fields related to advanced manufacturing (including engineering and engineering technology, industrial electronics installers and repairers, machinist and machine technologies, and tool and die maker and technologist); computer and information technology (including computer engineering, computer and information sciences, electrical and electronic engineering and related technology, electromechanical instrumentation and maintenance technology, and computer installer and repairer); and biomedical and biotechnology (including biological and life sciences, physical sciences, science technologies, health professions and related sciences, bioengineering and biomedical engineering, and biomedical engineering technology and technician).

3016 ■ ASSOCIATION FOR WOMEN GEOSCIENTISTS

Attn: AWG Foundation
P.O. Box 30645
Lincoln, NE 68503-0645
E-mail: awgscholarship@yahoo.com
Web Site: http://www.awg.org/eas/ekdale.html

To provide financial assistance for a summer field camp to women majoring in geoscience at a college or university in Utah.

Title of Award: Susan Ekdale Memorial Scholarship **Area, Field, or Subject:** Earth sciences; Geosciences **Level of Education for which Award is Granted:** Undergraduate **Number Awarded:** 1 each year. **Funds Available:** The stipend is $1,000. Funds must be used to help pay field camp expenses. **Duration:** Summer months.

Eligibility Requirements: This program is open to women majoring in geoscience at a college or university in Utah who must attend a summer field camp as part of their graduation requirements. Women geoscience students from Utah attending college in other states are also eligible. Applicants must submit a 1- to 2-page essay in which they describe their personal and academic highlights, their plans for applying their geoscience education to their future work or education, their reasons for applying for the scholarship, and what they, as women, can contribute to the geosciences. Selection is based on merit and need. **Deadline for Receipt:** March of each year. **Additional Information:** This program is sponsored by the Salt Lake chapter of the Association for Women

Geoscientists. Information is also available from the Ekdale Scholarship Co-chair, Janae Wallace Boyer, P.O. Box 146100, Salt Lake City, UT 84114, (801) 537-3387.

3017 ■ FOUNDATION FOR AMATEUR RADIO, INC.

Attn: Scholarship Committee
P.O. Box 831
Riverdale, MD 20738
E-mail: aa3of@arrl.net
Web Site: http://www.amateurradio-far.org/scholarships.php

To provide funding to licensed radio amateurs who are interested in studying engineering or the physical sciences in college.

Title of Award: Chuck Reville, K3FT, Memorial Scholarship **Area, Field, or Subject:** Engineering; Physical sciences **Level of Education for which Award is Granted:** Undergraduate **Number Awarded:** 1 each year. **Funds Available:** The stipend is $1,000. **Duration:** 1 year.

Eligibility Requirements: This program is open to radio amateurs who are interested in working on a bachelor's degree in a branch of engineering or the physical sciences. There are no restrictions on license class or residence area. **Deadline for Receipt:** Requests for applications must be submitted by April of each year. **Additional Information:** Recipients must attend an accredited school (university, college, or technical institute) on a full-time basis.

3018 ■ FOUNDATION FOR AMATEUR RADIO, INC.

Attn: Scholarship Committee
P.O. Box 831
Riverdale, MD 20738
E-mail: aa3of@arrl.net
Web Site: http://www.amateurradio-far.org/scholarships.php

To provide funding to licensed radio amateurs who are interested in studying engineering or the physical sciences in college.

Title of Award: Dwight Weller, KB3LA, Memorial Scholarship **Area, Field, or Subject:** Engineering; Physical sciences **Level of Education for which Award is Granted:** Undergraduate **Number Awarded:** 1 each year. **Funds Available:** The stipend is $1,000. **Duration:** 1 year.

Eligibility Requirements: This program is open to radio amateurs who are interested in working on a bachelor's degree in a branch of engineering or the physical sciences. There are no restrictions on license class or residence area. **Deadline for Receipt:** Requests for applications must be submitted by April of each year. **Additional Information:** Recipients must attend an accredited school (university, college, or technical institute) on a full-time basis.

3019 ■ HAWAI'I COMMUNITY FOUNDATION

Attn: Scholarship Department
1164 Bishop Street, Suite 800
Honolulu, HI 96813
Tel: (808)566-5570; 888-731-3863
Fax: (808)521-6286
E-mail: scholarships@hcf-hawaii.org
Web Site: http://www.hawaiicommunityfoundation.org/scholar/scholar.php

To provide financial assistance to Hawaii residents who are interested in preparing for a career in the physical sciences.

Title of Award: William James and Dorothy Bading Lanquist Fund Scholarships **Area, Field, or Subject:** Physical sciences **Level of Education for which Award is Granted:** Graduate, Undergraduate **Number Awarded:** Varies each year; recently, 7 of these scholarships were awarded. **Funds Available:** The amounts of the awards depend on the availability of funds and the need of the recipient; recently, stipends averaged $1,000. **Duration:** 1 year.

Eligibility Requirements: This program is open to Hawaii residents who are interested in majoring in the physical sciences or related fields (but not the biological or social sciences) on the undergraduate or graduate school level. They must be able to demonstrate academic achievement (GPA of 2.7 or higher), good moral character, and financial need. In addition to filling out the standard application form, applicants must write a short statement indicating their reasons for attending college, their planned course of study, and their career goals. **Deadline for Receipt:** February of each year. **Additional Information:** Recipients may attend college in Hawaii or on the mainland. Recipients must be full-time students.

3020 ■ HISPANIC SCHOLARSHIP FUND

Attn: Selection Committee
55 Second Street, Suite 1500
San Francisco, CA 94105
Tel: (415)808-2350; 877-HSF-INFO
Fax: (415)808-2302
E-mail: highschool@hsf.net
Web Site: http://www.hsf.net/scholarship/programs/shpe.php
To provide financial assistance for college to Hispanic Americans who are interested in majoring in designated fields of science.

Title of Award: Society of Hispanic Professional Engineers Scholarship Program **Area, Field, or Subject:** Computer and information sciences; Engineering; Mathematics and mathematical sciences; Physical sciences **Level of Education for which Award is Granted:** Undergraduate **Number Awarded:** Varies each year; recently, 69 of these scholarships were awarded: 7 at $1,250, 2 at $1,307, and 60 at $2,500. **Funds Available:** Stipends range from $1,250 to $2,500 per year. **Duration:** 1 year.

Eligibility Requirements: This program is open to U.S. citizens, permanent residents, and visitors with a passport stamped I-551 who are of Hispanic heritage. Applicants may be graduating high school seniors, community college students transferring to a 4-year institution, or continuing college students as long as they have a GPA of 3.0 or higher. They must be enrolled or planning to enroll full time at an accredited college or university in the United States to major in computer science, physical science, applied science, mathematics, or engineering. Along with their application, they must submit 600-word essays on 1) how their Hispanic heritage, family upbringing, and/or role models have influenced their personal long-term goals; 2) how they contribute to their community and what they have learned from their experiences; and 3) an academic challenge they have faced and how they have overcome it. Selection is based on academic achievement, personal strengths, leadership, and financial need. **Deadline for Receipt:** June of each year. **Additional Information:** This program is jointly sponsored by the Society of Hispanic Professional Engineers (SHPE) and the Hispanic Scholarship Fund (HSF).

3021 ■ MAINE SPACE GRANT CONSORTIUM

Attn: Executive Director
87 Winthrop Street, Suite 200
Augusta, ME 04330
Tel: (207)622-4688; 877-397-7223
Fax: (207)622-4548
E-mail: shehata@msgc.org
Web Site: http://www.msgc.org/education_students.asp
To provide funding to undergraduate and graduate students at colleges and universities in Maine interested in working on projects related to space.

Title of Award: Maine Space Grant Consortium Scholarship and Fellowship Program **Area, Field, or Subject:** Aerospace sciences; Biological and clinical sciences; Computer and information sciences; Earth sciences; Engineering, Aerospace/Aeronautical/Astronautical; Geosciences; Physical sciences; Social sciences; Space and planetary sciences; Technology **Level of Education for which Award is Granted:** Graduate, Undergraduate **Number Awarded:** Varies each year. **Funds Available:** Stipends are $2,500 for undergraduates or $5,000 for graduate students. **Duration:** 1 year.

Eligibility Requirements: This program is open to U.S. citizens who are enrolled on a full-time basis in an undergraduate or graduate program at a 2- or 4-year college or university in Maine, including those not members of the Maine Space Grant Consortium. Applicants must be proposing to conduct a project on a topic of interest to the U.S. National Aeronautics and Space Administration (NASA) in biological, earth, physical, social, or space science; human exploration and development of space; or other related science, technology, computer, or engineering fields. Undergraduates must have a GPA of 3.0 or higher; graduate students must have a GPA of 3.2 or higher. Proposals may involve conducting research at their home institution, traveling to conduct research and/or to present finished project work at a NASA field center, or facilitating technology transfer from NASA to their institution and industry in Maine. Applications are especially encouraged from women, minorities, and persons with disabilities. Selection is based on the relevance of the project to NASA's mission and its

strategic enterprises, collaboration with researchers at NASA space flight centers, qualifications of the student, technical content and quality of the proposal, and recommendation from a faculty member. **Deadline for Receipt:** May or October of each year. **Additional Information:** This program is funded by NASA.

3022 ■ MAINE SPACE GRANT CONSORTIUM

Attn: Executive Director
87 Winthrop Street, Suite 200
Augusta, ME 04330
Tel: (207)622-4688; 877-397-7223
Fax: (207)622-4548
E-mail: shehata@msgc.org
Web Site: http://www.msgc.org/education_students.asp
To provide funding to undergraduate and graduate students at member institutions of the Maine Space Grant Consortium (MSGC) interested in working on projects related to space.

Title of Award: MSGC Undergraduate and Graduate Research Fellowships **Area, Field, or Subject:** Aerospace sciences; Biological and clinical sciences; Earth sciences; Engineering, Aerospace/Aeronautical/Astronautical; Geosciences; Physical sciences; Space and planetary sciences **Level of Education for which Award is Granted:** Graduate, Undergraduate **Number Awarded:** Varies each year. **Funds Available:** Stipends vary at participating institutions, ranging from $2,500 to $5,000 per year for undergraduates and from $5,000 to $15,000 per year for graduate students. **Duration:** 1 year; may be renewed.

Eligibility Requirements: This program is open to U.S. citizens who are enrolled on a full-time basis in an undergraduate or graduate program at a MSGC member institution. Applicants must be proposing to conduct a project on a topic of interest to the U.S. National Aeronautics and Space Administration (NASA) in aerospace technology, biological and physical research, space science, earth science, human exploration and development of space, and other related science or engineering fields. They may be proposing to conduct research at their home institution, spend time conducting research at a NASA flight center, facilitate the development of a liaison between researchers at their home institution and a NASA center, or facilitate technology transfer from their home institution to industry. Selection is based on the relevance of the proposed research project to NASA's mission. Applications are especially encouraged from women and minorities. **Deadline for Receipt:** Each participating institution sets its own deadline. **Additional Information:** The member institutions are the University of Maine, the University of Southern Maine, the University of New England, and Maine Maritime Academy. This program is funded by NASA.

3023 ■ MINNESOTA SPACE GRANT CONSORTIUM

c/o University of Minnesota
Department of Aerospace Engineering and Mechanics
107 Akerman Hall
110 Union Street S.E.
Minneapolis, MN 55455
Tel: (612)626-9295
Fax: (612)626-1558
E-mail: mnsgc@aem.umn.edu
Web Site: http://www.aem.umn.edu/msgc/Scholarships/sf.shtml
To provide financial assistance for space-related studies to undergraduate and graduate students in Minnesota.

Title of Award: Minnesota Space Grant Consortium Scholarships and Fellowships **Area, Field, or Subject:** Earth sciences; Engineering; Life sciences; Physical sciences; Social sciences **Level of Education for which Award is Granted:** Graduate, Undergraduate **Number Awarded:** 8 to 12 undergraduate scholarships and 2 to 3 graduate fellowships are awarded each year. **Funds Available:** This program awards approximately $125,000 in undergraduate scholarships and graduate fellowships each year. The amounts of the awards are set by each of the participating institutions, which augment funding from this program with institutional resources. **Duration:** 1 year; renewable.

Eligibility Requirements: This program is open to graduate and undergraduate full-time students at institutions that are affiliates of the Minnesota Space Grant Consortium. U.S. citizenship and a GPA of 3.2 or higher are required. Eligible fields of study include the physical sciences (astronomy, astrophysics, chemistry, computer science, mathematics, physics, planetary geoscience, and planetary science), life sciences (biology, biochemistry, botany, health science/nutrition, medicine, molecular/cellular biology, and zoology), social sciences (anthropology, architecture, art, economics, education, history, philosophy, political science/public policy, and psychology), earth sciences (atmospheric science, climatology/meteorology, environmental science, geography, geology, geophysics, and oceanography), and engineering (agricultural, aeronautical, aerospace, architectural, bioengineering, chemical, civil, computer, electrical, electronic, environmental, industrial, materials science, mechanical, mining, nuclear, petroleum, engineering science, and engineering mechanics). The Minnesota Space Grant Consortium is a component of the U.S. National Aeronautics and Space Administration (NASA) Space Grant program, which encourages participation by women, underrepresented minorities, and persons with disabilities. **Deadline for Receipt:** March of each year. **Additional Information:** This program is funded by NASA. The member institutions are: Augsburg College, Bethel College, Bemidji State University, College of St. Catherine, Carleton College, Concordia College, Fond du Lac Community College, Itasca Community College, Leech Lake Tribal College, Macalaster College, Normandale Community College, Southwest State University, University of Minnesota at Duluth, University of Minnesota at Twin Cities, and University of St. Thomas.

3024 ■ NATIONAL FFA ORGANIZATION

Attn: Scholarship Office
6060 FFA Drive
P.O. Box 68960
Indianapolis, IN 46268-0960
Tel: (317)802-4321
Fax: (317)802-5321
E-mail: scholarships@ffa.org
Web Site: http://www.ffa.org

To provide financial assistance to FFA members from designated states who are interested in studying a field related to agriculture in college.

Title of Award: Wilbur-Ellis Company Scholarships **Area, Field, or Subject:** Agribusiness; Agricultural sciences; Agriculture, Economic aspects; Animal science and behavior; Biochemistry; Business administration; Computer and information sciences; Entomology; Finance; Forestry; Genetics; Horticulture; Management; Marketing and distribution; Poultry science; Soil science **Level of Education for which Award is Granted:** Four Year College **Number Awarded:** 13 each year: 1 at $5,000, 2 at $2,000, and 10 at $1,000. **Funds Available:** Stipends are $5,000, $2,000, or $1,000 per year. Funds are paid directly to the recipient. **Duration:** 1 year; nonrenewable.

Eligibility Requirements: This program is open to members who are graduating high school seniors planning to enroll or college students currently enrolled full time. Applicants must be residents of the following states: Arizona, California, Idaho, Indiana, Michigan, Minnesota, Montana, New Mexico, North Dakota, Ohio, Oregon, South Dakota, Texas, Utah, Washington, Wisconsin, or Wyoming. They must be planning to work on a 4-year degree in agricultural production, forest management, agronomy and crop science, animal nutrition, farm and ranch management, horticulture, nursery and landscape management, plant science, poultry science, general agriculture, business management, economics, international agriculture, finance, sales and marketing, biochemistry, biotechnology, computer systems in agriculture, entomology, plant breeding and genetics, plant pathology, range science, or soil science. Their combined SAT score must be 1000 or higher and their GPA must be 3.0 or higher. Selection is based on academic achievement (10 points for GPA, 10 points for SAT or ACT score, 10 points for class rank), leadership in FFA activities (30 points), leadership in community activities (10 points), and participation in the Supervised Agricultural Experience (SAE) program (30 points). Financial need is also considered in the selection process. U.S. citizenship is required. **Deadline for Receipt:** February of each year. **Additional Information:** Funding for this scholarship is provided by the agriculture division of the Wilbur-Ellis Company.

3025 ■ OAK RIDGE INSTITUTE FOR SCIENCE AND EDUCATION

Attn: Science and Engineering Education
P.O. Box 117
Oak Ridge, TN 37831-0117
Tel: (865)576-8239
Fax: (865)241-5219
E-mail: igrid.gregory@orau.gov

Web Site: http://www.orau.gov/orise.htm

To provide financial assistance and summer research experience to undergraduate students who are working on a degree in a field of interest to the Department of Homeland Security (DHS).

Title of Award: Department of Homeland Security Undergraduate Scholarships **Area, Field, or Subject:** Agricultural sciences; Biological and clinical sciences; Communications; Computer and information sciences; Engineering; Information science and technology; Mathematics and mathematical sciences; Physical sciences; Psychology; Public administration; Religion; Social sciences; Writing **Level of Education for which Award is Granted:** Undergraduate **Number Awarded:** Approximately 50 each year. **Funds Available:** This program provides a stipend of $1,000 per month during the academic year and $5,000 for the internship plus full payment of tuition and mandatory fees. **Duration:** 2 academic years plus 10 weeks during the intervening summer.

Eligibility Requirements: This program is open to 1) full-time students who are in their second year of college attendance as of the application deadline; and 2) part-time students who have completed at least 45 but no more than 60 semester hours as of the application deadline. Applicants must be majoring in the agricultural sciences, biological and life sciences, computer and information sciences, engineering, mathematics, physical sciences, psychology, social sciences, or selected humanities (religious studies, cultural studies, public policy, advocacy, communications, or science writing). They must have a GPA of 3.3 or higher. Along with their application, they must submit 2 statements on 1) their educational and professional goals, the kinds of research they are interested in conducting, specific questions that interest them, and how they became interested in them; and 2) how they think their interests, talents, and initiative would contribute to make the homeland safer and secure. Selection is based on those statements, academic record, references, and SAT or ACT scores. As part of their program, they must be interested in participating in summer research and development activities at a DHS-designated facility. U.S. citizenship is required. **Deadline for Receipt:** January of each year. **Additional Information:** This program, established in 2003, is funded by DHS and administered by Oak Ridge Institute for Science and Education (ORISE). Recipients must enroll full time.

3026 ■ OAK RIDGE INSTITUTE FOR SCIENCE AND EDUCATION

Attn: Global Change Education Program
120 Badger Avenue, M.S. 36
P.O. Box 117
Oak Ridge, TN 37831-0117
Tel: (865)576-9655
E-mail: mary.kinney@orau.gov
Web Site: http://www.atmos.anl.gov/GCEP

To provide undergraduate students with an opportunity to conduct research during the summer on global change.

Title of Award: Global Change Summer Undergraduate Research Experience (SURE) **Area, Field, or Subject:** Atmospheric science; Earth sciences; Environmental conservation; Environmental science; Geosciences **Level of Education for which Award is Granted:** Undergraduate **Number Awarded:** 20 to 30 each year. **Funds Available:** Participants receive a weekly stipend of $475 and support for travel and housing. **Duration:** 10 to 12 weeks during the summer. Successful participants are expected to reapply for a second year of research with their mentors.

Eligibility Requirements: This program is open to undergraduates in their sophomore and junior years, although outstanding freshman and senior applicants are also considered. Applicants must be proposing to conduct research in a program area within the Department of Energy's Office of Biological and Environmental Research (DOE-BER): the atmospheric science program, the environmental meteorology program, the atmospheric radiation measurement program, the terrestrial carbon processes effort, the program for ecosystem research, and studies carried out under the direction of the National Institute for Global Environmental Change. Minority and female students are particularly encouraged to apply. U.S. citizenship is required. **Deadline for Receipt:** February of each year. **Additional Information:** This program, funded by DOE-BER, began in summer 1999. The first 2 weeks are spent in an orientation and focus session at a participating university. For the remaining 10 weeks, students conduct mentored research at 1 of the national laboratories or universities conducting BER-supported global change research.

3027 ■ OAK RIDGE INSTITUTE FOR SCIENCE AND EDUCATION
Attn: Science and Engineering Education
P.O. Box 117
Oak Ridge, TN 37831-0117
Tel: (865)241-8240
Fax: (865)241-5219
E-mail: hollingsscholarship@orau.gov
Web Site: http://www.orau.gov/orise.htm
To provide financial assistance and summer research experience to upper-division students who are working on a degree in a field of interest to the National Oceanic and Atmospheric Administration (NOAA).
Title of Award: Ernest F. Hollings Scholarship Program **Area, Field, or Subject:** Agricultural sciences; Behavioral sciences; Biological and clinical sciences; Computer and information sciences; Education; Engineering; Information science and technology; Mathematics and mathematical sciences; Physical sciences; Social sciences **Level of Education for which Award is Granted:** Four Year College **Number Awarded:** Approximately 100 each year. **Funds Available:** This program provides a stipend of $8,000 per academic year and $650 per week during the internship, a housing subsidy and limited travel reimbursement for round-trip transportation to the internship site, and travel expenses to the scholarship program conference at the completion of the internship. **Duration:** 2 academic years plus 10 weeks during the intervening summer.
Eligibility Requirements: This program is open to full-time students entering their junior year at an accredited college or university in the United States or its territories. Applicants must be majoring in a discipline related to oceanic and atmospheric science, research, technology, and education, and supportive of the purposes of NOAA's programs and mission (e.g., biological, life, and agricultural sciences; computer and information sciences; engineering; mathematics; physical sciences; social and behavioral sciences; or teacher education). They must have a GPA of 3.0 or higher. As part of their program, they must be interested in participating in summer research and development activities at NOAA headquarters (Silver Spring, Maryland) or field centers. U.S. citizenship is required. **Deadline for Receipt:** May of each year. **Additional Information:** This program, established in 2005, is funded by NOAA and administered by Oak Ridge Institute for Science and Education (ORISE).

3028 ■ PENNSYLVANIA SPACE GRANT CONSORTIUM
c/o Pennsylvania State University
2217 Earth-Engineering Sciences Building
University Park, PA 16802
Tel: (814)863-7687
Fax: (814)863-8286
E-mail: spacegrant@psu.edu
Web Site: http://www.psu.edu/spacegrant/highered/scholar.html
To provide financial assistance for space-related study to undergraduate students at universities affiliated with the Pennsylvania Space Grant Consortium.
Title of Award: Pennsylvania Space Grant Consortium Scholarships **Area, Field, or Subject:** Aerospace sciences; Biological and clinical sciences; Earth sciences; Engineering, Aerospace/Aeronautical/Astronautical; Geosciences; Physical sciences; Space and planetary sciences **Level of Education for which Award is Granted:** Undergraduate **Number Awarded:** Varies each year. **Funds Available:** The stipend is set by each participating university. At Pennsylvania State University, for instance, it is $4,000 per year. **Duration:** 1 year.
Eligibility Requirements: This program is open to full-time undergraduate students at participating universities. Applicants must be studying a field that does, or can, promote a strategic enterprise of the U.S. National Aeronautics and Space Administration (NASA): aerospace technology, earth science, human exploration and development of space, biological and physical research, or space science. U.S. citizenship is required. Students from underrepresented groups (women, minorities, rural populations, and those with disabilities) are especially encouraged to apply. **Deadline for Receipt:** Each participating university sets its own deadline. **Additional Information:** Participating institutions include California University of Pennsylvania, Carnegie Mellon University, Clarion University, Lincoln University, Pennsylvania State University, University of Pittsburgh, Susquehanna University, Lincoln University, Temple University, West

Chester University, and Pennsylvania State University at Abington. At Pennsylvania State University, the award is designated as the Sylvia Stein Memorial Space Grant Scholarship. This program is sponsored by the U.S. National Aeronautics and Space Administration (NASA).

3029 ■ ROYAL NEIGHBORS OF AMERICA
Attn: Fraternal Services
230 16th Street
Rock Island, IL 61201-8645
Tel: (309)788-4561
Free: 800-627-4762
E-mail: contact@royalneighbors.org
Web Site: http://www.royalneighbors.org/MemberBenefits/scholarships.cfm
To provide financial assistance for college to women members of the Royal Neighbors of America who plan to enter nontraditional fields.
Title of Award: Eliza D. Watt Scholarships **Area, Field, or Subject:** Computer and information sciences; Engineering; Mathematics and mathematical sciences; Physical sciences **Level of Education for which Award is Granted:** Undergraduate **Number Awarded:** 5 each year. **Funds Available:** The stipend is $2,000 per year. **Duration:** 4 years.
Eligibility Requirements: This program is open to women members of the society who are graduating high school seniors. Applicants must be planning to enter a field considered nontraditional for women, including computer science, engineering, physical sciences, teaching of nontraditional women's fields, business writing, or mathematics. **Deadline for Receipt:** December of each year. **Additional Information:** This program was established in 2004.

3030 ■ HARRY S. TRUMAN SCHOLARSHIP FOUNDATION
Attn: Executive Secretary
712 Jackson Place, N.W.
Washington, DC 20006
Tel: (202)395-4831
Fax: (202)395-6995
E-mail: office@truman.gov
Web Site: http://www.truman.gov
To provide grants-for-service for graduate school to current college juniors who are interested in preparing for a career in public service.
Title of Award: Harry S. Truman Scholarship Program **Area, Field, or Subject:** Agricultural sciences; Biological and clinical sciences; Economics; Education; Engineering; Environmental conservation; Environmental science; History; International affairs and relations; Law; Physical sciences; Political science; Public administration; Public health; Public service; Social sciences; Technology **Level of Education for which Award is Granted:** Four Year College, Graduate **Number Awarded:** 70 to 75 each year: a) 1 "state" scholarship is available to a qualified resident nominee in each of the 50 states, the District of Columbia, Puerto Rico, and the Islands (Guam, the Virgin Islands, American Samoa, and the Commonwealth of the Northern Mariana Islands); and b) up to 25 at-large scholars. **Funds Available:** The program provides up to $30,000, including up to $15,000 for the first year of graduate study and up to $15,000 for the final year of graduate study. **Duration:** Support is provided for the first and last year of graduate study.
Eligibility Requirements: Students must be nominated to be considered for this program. Nominees must be full-time students with junior standing at a 4-year institution, committed to a career in government or public service, in the upper quarter of their class, and U.S. citizens or nationals. Each participating institution may nominate up to 4 candidates (and up to 3 additional students who completed their first 2 years at a community college); community colleges and other 2-year institutions may nominate former students who are enrolled as full-time students with junior-level academic standing at accredited 4-year institutions. Selection is based on extent and quality of community service and government involvement, academic performance, leadership record, suitability of the nominee's proposed program of study for a career in public service, and writing and analytical skills. Priority is given to candidates who plan to enroll in a graduate program that specifically trains them for a career in public service, including government at any level, uniformed services, public interest organizations, nongovernmental research and/or educational organizations, public and private schools, and public service oriented nonprofit organizations. The fields of study may include agriculture, biology, engineering, environmental management, physical and social sci-

ences, and technology policy, as well as such traditional fields as economics, education, government, history, international relations, law, nonprofit management, political science, public administration, public health, and public policy. Interviews are required. **Deadline for Receipt:** February of each year. **Additional Information:** Recipients may attend graduate school in the United States or in foreign countries. Scholars are required to work in public service for 3 of the 7 years following completion of a graduate degree program funded by this program. Scholars who do not meet this service requirement, or who fail to provide timely proof to the foundation of such employment, will be required to repay funds received, along with interest.

3031 ■ VIRGINIA SPACE GRANT CONSORTIUM

Attn: Fellowship Coordinator
Old Dominion University Peninsula Center
600 Butler Farm Road
Hampton, VA 23666
Tel: (757)766-5210
Fax: (757)766-5205
E-mail: vsgc@odu.edu
Web Site: http://www.vsgc.odu.edu/Menu3_1_1.htm
To provide financial assistance for college or graduate school to students in Virginia planning a career as science, mathematics, or technology educators.
Title of Award: Virginia Space Grant Teacher Education Scholarship Program **Area, Field, or Subject:** Aerospace sciences; Earth sciences; Education; Environmental conservation; Environmental science; Geosciences; Mathematics and mathematical sciences; Science; Space and planetary sciences; Technology **Level of Education for which Award is Granted:** Four Year College, Master's **Number Awarded:** Approximately 10 each year. **Funds Available:** The maximum stipend is $1,000. **Duration:** 1 year; nonrenewable.
Eligibility Requirements: This program is open to full-time undergraduate students at the Virginia Space Grant Consortium (VSGC) colleges and universities in a track that will qualify them to teach in a pre-college setting. Priority is given to those majoring in technology education, mathematics, or science, particularly earth, space, or environmental science. Applicants may apply while seniors in high school or sophomores in a community college, with the award contingent on their enrollment at a VSGC college and entrance into a teacher certification program. They must submit a statement of academic goals and plan of study, explaining their reasons for desiring to enter the teaching profession, specifically the fields of science, mathematics, or technology education. Students currently enrolled in a VSGC college can apply when they declare their intent to enter the teacher certification program. Students enrolled in a master of education degree program leading to teacher certification in eligible fields are also eligible to apply. Applicants must be U.S. citizens with a GPA of 3.0 or higher. Since an important purpose of this program is to increase the participation of underrepresented minorities, women, and persons with disabilities in science, mathematics, and technology education, the VSGC especially encourages applications from those students. **Deadline for Receipt:** February of each year. **Additional Information:** The VSGC institutions are College of William and Mary, Hampton University, Old Dominion University, the University of Virginia, and Virginia Polytechnic Institute and State University. This program is funded by the U.S. National Aeronautics and Space Administration (NASA).

Chemistry

3032 ■ AMERICAN CHEMICAL SOCIETY

Attn: Department of Diversity Programs
1155 16th Street, N.W.
Washington, DC 20036
Tel: (202)872-6250
Free: 800-227-5558
Fax: (202)776-8003
E-mail: scholars@acs.org
Web Site: http://www.chemistry.org/scholars
To provide financial assistance to underrepresented minority students with a strong interest in chemistry and a desire to prepare for a career in a chemically-related science.
Title of Award: American Chemical Society Scholars Program **Area, Field, or Subject:** Biochemistry; Chemistry; Engineering, Chemical;

Environmental conservation; Environmental science; Materials research/science; Toxicology **Level of Education for which Award is Granted:** Undergraduate **Number Awarded:** Approximately 100 new awards are granted each year. **Funds Available:** The maximum stipend is $2,500 for the freshman year in college or $3,000 per year for sophomores, juniors, and seniors. **Duration:** 1 year; may be renewed.
Eligibility Requirements: This program is open to 1) college-bound high school seniors; 2) college freshmen, sophomores, and juniors enrolled full time at an accredited college or university; 3) community college graduates and transfer students who plan to study for a bachelor's degree; and 4) community college freshmen. Applicants must be African American, Hispanic/Latino, or American Indian. They must be majoring or planning to major in chemistry, biochemistry, chemical engineering, or other chemically-related fields, such as environmental science, materials science, or toxicology, and planning to prepare for a career in the chemical sciences or chemical technology. Students planning careers in medicine or pharmacy are not eligible. U.S. citizenship or permanent resident status is required. Selection is based on academic merit (GPA of 3.0 or higher) and financial need. **Deadline for Receipt:** February of each year. **Additional Information:** This program was established in 1994.

3033 ■ AMERICAN CHEMICAL SOCIETY

Attn: Education Division
1155 16th Street, N.W.
Washington, DC 20036
Tel: (202)872-4380
Free: 800-227-5558
E-mail: r_rasheed@acs.org
Web Site: http://www.chemistry.org/education/SEED.html
To provide financial assistance for college to high school students who participated in the American Chemical Society's Project SEED: Summer Education Experience for the Disadvantaged.
Title of Award: Project SEED Scholarships **Area, Field, or Subject:** Biochemistry; Chemistry; Engineering, Chemical; Materials research/science **Level of Education for which Award is Granted:** Undergraduate **Number Awarded:** Varies each year; recently, 29 of these scholarships were awarded. **Funds Available:** Stipends up to $5,000 per year are available. **Duration:** 1 year; nonrenewable.
Eligibility Requirements: Applicants for Project SEED must have completed the junior or senior year in high school, live within commuting distance of a sponsoring institution, have completed a course in high school chemistry, and come from an economically disadvantaged family. The standards for economic disadvantage follow federal poverty guidelines for family size, but the maximum family income is $32,000 except in cases where other factors are present that may deter a student from considering a career in science; family income may be up to $44,000 if the student is a member of an ethnic group underrepresented in the sciences (African American, Hispanic, American Indian), if the parents have not attended college, or if the family is single-parent or very large. Participants in the Project SEED program are eligible to apply for these scholarships during their senior year in high school if they plan to major in college in a chemical science or engineering field, such as chemistry, chemical engineering, biochemistry, materials science, or another closely-related field. **Deadline for Receipt:** February of each year.

3034 ■ AMERICAN COUNCIL OF THE BLIND

Attn: Coordinator, Scholarship Program
1155 15th Street, N.W., Suite 1004
Washington, DC 20005
Tel: (202)467-5081
Free: 800-424-8666
Fax: (202)467-5085
E-mail: info@acb.org
Web Site: http://www.acb.org
To provide financial assistance to blind students who are working on an undergraduate or graduate degree in science at an accredited college or university.
Title of Award: Dr. S. Bradley Burson Memorial Scholarship **Area, Field, or Subject:** Biological and clinical sciences; Chemistry; Engineering; Physics **Level of Education for which Award is Granted:** Graduate, Undergraduate **Number Awarded:** 1 each year. **Funds Available:** The stipend is $1,000. In addition, the winner receives a Kurzweil-1000 Reading System. **Duration:** 1 year.

Eligibility Requirements: This program is open to legally blind undergraduate or graduate students majoring in the "hard" sciences (i.e., biology, chemistry, physics, and engineering, but not computer science) in college. They must be U.S. citizens. In addition to letters of recommendation and copies of academic transcripts, applications must include an autobiographical sketch. A cumulative GPA of 3.3 or higher is generally required. Selection is based on demonstrated academic record, involvement in extracurricular and civic activities, and academic objectives. The severity of the applicant's visual impairment and his/her study methods are also taken into account. **Deadline for Receipt:** February of each year. **Additional Information:** Scholarship winners are expected to be present at the council's annual conference; the council will cover all reasonable expenses connected with convention attendance.

3035 ■ AMERICAN NUCLEAR SOCIETY
Attn: Scholarship Coordinator
555 North Kensington Avenue
La Grange Park, IL 60526-5592
Tel: (708)352-6611
Fax: (708)352-0499
E-mail: outreach@ans.org
Web Site: http://www.ans.org/honors/scholarships
To provide financial assistance to undergraduate and graduate students who are interested in preparing for a career in nuclear science.
Title of Award: James R. Vogt Radiochemistry Scholarship **Area, Field, or Subject:** Chemistry; Nuclear science **Level of Education for which Award is Granted:** Four Year College, Graduate **Number Awarded:** 1 each year. **Funds Available:** The stipend is $2,000 for undergraduate students or $3,000 for graduate students. **Duration:** 1 year; nonrenewable.
Eligibility Requirements: This program is open to juniors, seniors, and first-year graduate students who are enrolled in or proposing to undertake research in radio-analytical chemistry, analytical chemistry, or analytical applications of nuclear science. Applicants must be U.S. citizens or permanent residents and able to demonstrate academic achievement. **Deadline for Receipt:** January of each year.

3036 ■ AMERICAN SOCIETY FOR ENGINEERING EDUCATION
Attn: SMART Defense Scholarship Program
1818 N Street, N.W., Suite 600
Washington, DC 20036-2479
Tel: (202)331-3516
Fax: (202)265-8504
E-mail: smart@asee.org
Web Site: http://www.asee.org/resources/fellowships/smart/index.cfm
To provide scholarship/loans to upper-division and graduate students in areas of science, mathematics, and engineering that are of interest to the U.S. Department of Defense.
Title of Award: Science, Mathematics, and Research for Transformation (SMART) Defense Scholarship Program **Area, Field, or Subject:** Architecture, Naval; Behavioral sciences; Biological and clinical sciences; Chemistry; Computer and information sciences; Earth sciences; Engineering, Aerospace/Aeronautical/Astronautical; Engineering, Chemical; Engineering, Civil; Engineering, Electrical; Engineering, Materials; Engineering, Mechanical; Engineering, Ocean; Geosciences; Materials research/science; Mathematics and mathematical sciences; Oceanography; Physics **Level of Education for which Award is Granted:** Four Year College, Graduate **Number Awarded:** Varies each year; recently, 36 of these scholarships were awarded. **Funds Available:** The program provides full payment of tuition, fees, room, board, and other normal educational expenses at the recipient's institution. A book allowance of $1,000 per year is also provided. This is a scholarship/loan program; recipients must agree to serve as a civilian employee of the Department of Defense in a science and engineering position. If they fail to fulfill that service obligation, they must reimburse the federal government for all funds they received. **Duration:** Up to 24 months.
Eligibility Requirements: This program is open to upper-division and graduate students working on an undergraduate or graduate degree in any of the following fields: aeronautical and astronautical engineering; biosciences; chemical engineering; chemistry; civil engineering; cognitive, neural, and behavioral sciences; computer and computational sciences; electrical engineering; geosciences, including terrain, water, and air; materials science and engineering; mathematics; mechanical engineer-

ing; naval architecture and ocean engineering; oceanography; or physics. Applicants must be U.S. citizens who have a GPA of 3.0 or higher. Selection is based on academic records, personal statements, letters of recommendation, and GRE scores. **Deadline for Receipt:** March of each year. **Additional Information:** This program, established in 2005, is sponsored by the Army Research Laboratory, the Air Force Office of Scientific Research, the Office of Naval Research, the Air Force Research Laboratory, the Defense Advanced Research Projects Agency, the Defense Information Systems Agency, and the Defense Threat Reduction Agency.

3037 ■ APPALACHIAN COLLEGE ASSOCIATION
Attn: Director of Programs
210 Center Street
Berea, KY 40403
Tel: (859)986-4584
Fax: (859)986-9549
E-mail: kathrynb@acaweb.org
Web Site: http://www.acaweb.org
To provide financial assistance to upper-division students majoring in biology, chemistry, or mathematics at colleges and universities that are members of the Appalachian College Association (ACA) who plan to become teachers.
Title of Award: Robert Noyce Scholarships **Area, Field, or Subject:** Biological and clinical sciences; Chemistry; Education; Mathematics and mathematical sciences **Level of Education for which Award is Granted:** Four Year College **Number Awarded:** 12 each year. **Funds Available:** The stipend is $7,500 per year. Recipients must be willing to sign a promissory note with a commitment to teach in a high-need middle or high school for 2 years for every year of the scholarship. **Duration:** 1 year; may be renewed 1 additional year.
Eligibility Requirements: This program is open to full-time students entering their junior or senior year at ACA member institutions with a major in biology, chemistry, or mathematics and plans to earn a teaching license. Applicants must have a GPA of 3.0 or higher and be able to document financial need. Along with their application, they must submit a 500-word essay describing their interest in becoming a 6-12 teacher; their commitment to the Appalachian region, including the impact they hope to have as a teacher; and actual and planned progress toward becoming certified. U.S. citizenship is required. Preference is given to graduates of high schools in the Appalachian region and to applicants who express a desire to teach in a high-need middle or high school, especially schools in central Appalachia. **Deadline for Receipt:** March of each year. **Additional Information:** Funding for this program is provided by the National Science Foundation. The ACA includes member institutions in Kentucky (Alice Lloyd College, Berea College, Campbellsville University, University of the Cumberlands, Kentucky Christian University, Lindsey Wilson College, Pikeville College, and Union College), North Carolina (Brevard College, Lees-McRae College, Mars Hill College, Montreat College, and Warren Wilson College), Tennessee (Bryan College, Carson-Newman College, King College, Lee University, Lincoln Memorial University, Maryville College, Milligan College, Tennessee Wesleyan College, Tusculum College, and University of the South), Virginia (Bluefield College, Emery & Henry College, Ferrum College, and Virginia Intermont College), and West Virginia (Alderson-Broaddus College, Bethany College, Davis & Elkins College, Ohio Valley University, University of Charleston, West Virginia Wesleyan College, and Wheeling Jesuit University).

3038 ■ ARKANSAS DEPARTMENT OF HIGHER EDUCATION
Attn: Financial Aid Division
114 East Capitol Avenue
Little Rock, AR 72201-3818
Tel: (501)371-2050
Free: 800-54-STUDY
Fax: (501)371-2001
E-mail: finaid@adhe.arknet.edu
Web Site: http://www.starark.com
To provide scholarship/loans to college students in Arkansas who are interested in preparing for a teaching career in an approved subject or geographic shortage area.
Title of Award: Arkansas State Teacher Assistance Resource (STAR) Program **Area, Field, or Subject:** Biological and clinical sciences; Chemistry; Earth sciences; Education; Education, Secondary; Education,

Special; Geosciences; Linguistics; Mathematics and mathematical sciences; Physical sciences; Physics **Level of Education for which Award is Granted:** Master's, Undergraduate **Number Awarded:** Varies each year; recently, 42 of these scholarship/loans were approved. **Funds Available:** The award is $3,000 per year for students who agree to teach in either a geographic teacher shortage area or a subject teacher shortage area. For students who agree to teach in both a geographic shortage area and a subject shortage area, the award is $6,000 per year. This is a scholarship/loan program. Recipients must teach in an Arkansas geographic or subject shortage area for 1 year for each year of support they receive. If they fail to complete that teaching obligation, they must repay all funds received. **Duration:** 1 year; may be renewed for 1 additional year if the recipient is enrolled in a 4-year teacher education program or 2 additional years if enrolled in a 5-year teacher education program. Renewal requires that the recipient maintain a GPA of 2.75 or higher and complete 24 semester hours as an undergraduate or 18 semester hours as a graduate student.
Eligibility Requirements: This program is open to Arkansas residents who are full-time students enrolled 1) at a 4-year public or private college or university in the state with an approved teacher education program; 2) in an associate of arts in teaching program; or 3) in an master of arts in teaching program. Applicants must have a GPA of 2.75 or higher and be entering their sophomore, junior, or senior year (or be in a master's degree program). They must be willing to teach in a public school located in a geographic area of Arkansas designated as having a critical shortage of teachers or in a subject matter area designated as having a critical shortage of teachers. Applicants must have completed their freshman year at an accredited Arkansas public or private college or university in a major field of study leading to secondary teacher certification in 1 of the shortage areas. U.S. citizenship is required. **Deadline for Receipt:** May of each year. **Additional Information:** This program was established in 2004 as a replacement for the former Arkansas Emergency Secondary Education Loan Program. Recently, the subject areas designated as having a critical shortage of teachers were foreign language, mathematics, chemistry, physics, biology, physical science, earth science, and special education. For a list of geographic areas of Arkansas that are designated as having a critical shortage of teachers, contact the Department of Higher Education. The State Teacher Assistance Resource (STAR) program also provides that teachers who received federal student loans may have those loans repaid 1) at the rate of $3,000 per year if they teach a subject area in Arkansas that is designated as a shortage area or if they teach in a geographic area of the state with a shortage of teachers, or 2) at the rate of $6,000 per year if they teach a shortage subject area in a shortage geographic area. Students may not, however, participate in both the scholarship/loan program and the federal loan repayment program.

3039 ■ ASSOCIATION FOR IRON & STEEL TECHNOLOGY

Attn: AIST Foundation
186 Thorn Hill Road
Warrendale, PA 15086-7528
Tel: (724)776-6040
Fax: (724)776-1880
E-mail: lwharrey@aist.org
Web Site: http://www.aist.org/foundation/scholarships.htm
To provide financial assistance for college study of engineering to Canadians who are children of members of the Association for Iron & Steel Technology (AIST).
Title of Award: David H. Samson Canadian Scholarship **Area, Field, or Subject:** Chemistry; Engineering; Geology; Mathematics and mathematical sciences; Physics **Level of Education for which Award is Granted:** Undergraduate **Number Awarded:** 1 each year. **Funds Available:** The stipend is $US2,000. **Duration:** 1 year; may be renewed for up to 3 additional years.
Eligibility Requirements: This program is open to the children (natural, adopted, or ward) of Canadian citizens and landed immigrants who are members of the association. Applicants must have been accepted in an eligible full-time course of study of engineering at an accredited Canadian university. If no engineering student applies, the award may be made to an eligible student planning to major in chemistry, geology, mathematics, or physics. The scholarship may also be awarded to a student entering a community college if there is no eligible applicant entering an accredited university. The committee may also award the scholarship to a previous applicant entering the second or third year at a Canadian university or

community college if there is no eligible applicant entering the first year. Selection is based on academic achievements, extracurricular activities, and the student's written statements; financial need is not considered. **Deadline for Receipt:** June of each year. **Additional Information:** The AIST was formed in 2004 by the merger of the Iron and Steel Society (ISS) and the Association of Iron and Steel Engineers (AISE). Information is also available from Robert Kneale, AIST Northern Member Chapter, P.O. Box 1734, Cambridge, Ontario N1R 7G8, Canada.

3040 ■ ASSOCIATION FOR IRON & STEEL TECHNOLOGY-NORTHWEST CHAPTER

c/o Gerardo L. Giraldo, Secretary-Treasurer
Nucor Steel Seattle, Inc.
Washington Steel Division
2424 S.W. Andover Street
Seattle, WA 98106-1100
Tel: (206)933-2245
Fax: (206)933-2207
E-mail: gerry.giraldo@nucor-seattle.com
Web Site: http://www.aist.org/chapters/
mc_pittsburgh_scholar_guidelines.htm
To provide financial assistance to family of members of the Northwest Chapter of the Association for Iron & Steel Technology (AIST) who are interested in studying engineering in college.
Title of Award: Northwest Chapter AIST Scholarships **Area, Field, or Subject:** Business; Chemistry; Engineering; Manufacturing; Mathematics and mathematical sciences; Metallurgy; Physics **Level of Education for which Award is Granted:** Four Year College **Number Awarded:** 2 each year. **Funds Available:** The stipend is $1,000. **Duration:** 1 year.
Eligibility Requirements: This program is open to children, grandchildren, spouses, or nieces/nephews of chapter members who are high school seniors planning to attend an accredited 4-year college or university. Applicants must intend to study engineering; if there are no applicants in engineering, the award may be given to a student majoring in chemistry, mathematics, metallurgy, or physics, or to a student showing an interest in preparing for a career in the iron and steel industry. Along with their application, they must submit a 500-word essay on 1 of the following topics: 1) an accomplishment they have achieved while they have been a student, why they were successful, and how their success will influence their future plans as an engineer or an engineer in the steel industry; 2) their strengths and interests and how they will apply their skills to a career in the steel industry or as an engineer; or 3) the challenges that face the steel industry and the opportunities for graduates to improve the success of companies within the industry. Financial need is not considered in the selection process. **Deadline for Receipt:** June of each year. **Additional Information:** The AIST was formed in 2004 by the merger of the Iron and Steel Society (ISS) and the Association of Iron and Steel Engineers (AISE). The Northwest Chapter serves Alaska, Idaho, Montana, Oregon, Washington, and Wyoming.

3041 ■ ASSOCIATION FOR IRON & STEEL TECHNOLOGY-OHIO VALLEY CHAPTER

c/o Jeff McKain, Scholarship Chair
Xtek, Inc.
11451 Reading Road
Cincinnati, OH 45241
Tel: (513)733-7843; (999)332-XTEK
Fax: (513)733-7939
E-mail: jeff.mckain@xtek.com
Web Site: http://www.aist.org/chapters/ohiovalley_scholarship.htm
To provide financial assistance for college to student members and children of members of the Ohio Valley Chapter of the Association for Iron & Steel Technology (AIST).
Title of Award: Ohio Valley Chapter AIST Scholarships **Area, Field, or Subject:** Biological and clinical sciences; Chemistry; Computer and information sciences; Earth sciences; Engineering; Engineering, Electrical; Engineering, Mechanical; Environmental conservation; Environmental science; Geosciences; Information science and technology; Metallurgy; Physical sciences; Physics **Level of Education for which Award is Granted:** Undergraduate **Number Awarded:** Up to 2 each year. **Funds Available:** The stipend is $1,000 per year. **Duration:** 1 year; may be renewed up to 3 additional years provided the recipient remains enrolled full time and maintains a GPA of 3.0 or higher.

Eligibility Requirements: This program is open to high school seniors and college students who are either 1) children of Ohio Valley Chapter AIST members, or 2) student AIST members. Applicants must be accepted at, planning to attend, or currently enrolled at an accredited college or university with a major in biology, chemistry, computer programming, computer technology, electrical engineering, engineering, engineering technology, environmental engineering, environmental science, information systems technology, mechanical engineering, metallurgy, microbiology, physical science, physics, or other field approved by the scholarship committee. Along with their application, they must submit a 500-word essay on the reasons for their interests and reasons for working on a degree in their field of study, career goals and objectives, and extracurricular activities and their benefits. Selection is based on overall academic achievement (especially in mathematics and science), the essay, and extracurricular activities. **Deadline for Receipt:** February of each year. **Additional Information:** The AIST was formed in 2004 by the merger of the Iron and Steel Society (ISS) and the Association of Iron and Steel Engineers (AISE). This program was established by the former Ohio Valley District Section of AISE. The Ohio Valley Chapter covers Indiana (except for the northwestern portion), all of Kentucky, western Tennessee, and portions of southern Ohio.

3042 ■ ASSOCIATION FOR WOMEN GEOSCIENTISTS
Attn: AWG Foundation
P.O. Box 30645
Lincoln, NE 68503-0645
E-mail: awgscholarship@yahoo.com
Web Site: http://www.awg.org/eas/minority.html
To provide financial assistance to minority women who are interested in working on an undergraduate degree in the geosciences.
Title of Award: Association for Women Geoscientists Minority Scholarship **Area, Field, or Subject:** Chemistry; Earth sciences; Education; Geology; Geosciences; Hydrology; Meteorology; Oceanography **Level of Education for which Award is Granted:** Undergraduate **Number Awarded:** 1 or more each year. **Funds Available:** A total of $5,000 is available for this program each year. **Duration:** 1 year; may be renewed. **Eligibility Requirements:** This program is open to women who are African American, Hispanic, or Native American (including Eskimo, Hawaiian, Samoan, or American Indian). Applicants must be full-time students working on, or planning to work on, an undergraduate degree in the geosciences (including geology, geophysics, geochemistry, hydrology, meteorology, physical oceanography, planetary geology, or earth science education). They must submit a 500-word essay on why they have chosen to major in the geosciences and their career goals, 2 letters of recommendation, high school and/or college transcripts, and SAT or ACT scores. Financial need is not considered in the selection process. **Deadline for Receipt:** May of each year. **Additional Information:** This program, first offered in 2004, is supported by ExxonMobil Foundation.

3043 ■ ASSOCIATION FOR WOMEN IN SCIENCE-SEATTLE CHAPTER
c/o Fran Solomon, Scholarship Committee Chair
5805 16th Avenue, N.E.
Seattle, WA 98105
Tel: (206)522-6441
E-mail: fran.solomon@metrokc.gov
Web Site: http://www.scn.org/awis/undergraduate_scholarship.htm
To provide financial assistance to women undergraduates from any state majoring in science, mathematics, or engineering at colleges and universities in western Washington.
Title of Award: AWIS Seattle Scholarships **Area, Field, or Subject:** Biochemistry; Biological and clinical sciences; Chemistry; Engineering; Environmental conservation; Environmental science; Geology; Mathematics and mathematical sciences; Pharmaceutical sciences; Physics **Level of Education for which Award is Granted:** Four Year College **Number Awarded:** Varies each year; recently, 11 of these scholarships were awarded. **Funds Available:** Stipends range from $1,000 to $1,500. **Duration:** 1 year.
Eligibility Requirements: This program is open to women from any state entering their junior or senior year at a 4-year college or university in western Washington. Applicants must have a declared major in science (e.g., biological sciences, environmental science, biochemistry, chemistry, pharmacy, geology, computer science, physics), mathematics, or

engineering. Along with their application, they must submit essays on the events that led to their choice of a major, their current career plans and long-term goals, and their volunteer and community activities. Financial need is considered in the selection process. At least 1 scholarship is reserved for a woman from a group that is underrepresented in science, mathematics, and engineering careers, including Native American Indians and Alaska Natives, Black/African Americans, Mexican Americans/Chicanas/Latinas, Native Pacific Islanders (Polynesians, Melanesians, and Micronesians), and women with disabilities. **Deadline for Receipt:** March of each year. **Additional Information:** This program includes the following named awards: the Virginia Badger Scholarship, the Angela Paez Memorial Scholarship, and the Fran Solomon Scholarship. Support for the program is provided by several sponsors, including the American Chemical Society, Iota Sigma Pi, Rosetta Inpharmatics, and ZymoGenetics, Inc.

3044 ■ H. FLETCHER BROWN TRUST
PNC Bank Delaware
Attn: Donald W. Davis
222 Delaware Avenue, 16th Floor
Wilmington, DE 19899
Tel: (302)429-2827
Fax: (302)429-5658
E-mail: Robbie.testa@pncadvisors.com
To provide financial assistance to residents of Delaware who are interested in studying engineering, chemistry, medicine, dentistry, or law.
Title of Award: H. Fletcher Brown Scholarship **Area, Field, or Subject:** Chemistry; Dentistry; Engineering; Law; Medicine; Medicine, Osteopathic **Level of Education for which Award is Granted:** Graduate, Professional, Undergraduate **Funds Available:** The amount of the scholarship is determined by the scholarship committee and is awarded in installments over the length of study. **Duration:** 1 year; may be renewed if the recipient maintains a GPA of 2.5 or higher and continues to be worthy of and eligible for the award.
Eligibility Requirements: This program is open to Delaware residents who were born in Delaware, are either high school seniors entering the first year of college or college seniors entering the first year of graduate school, are of good moral character, and need financial assistance from sources outside their family. Applicants must have combined mathematics and verbal SAT scores of 1000 or higher, rank in the upper 20% of their class, and come from a family whose income is less than $75,000. Their proposed fields of study must be engineering, chemistry, medicine (for an M.D. or D.O. degree only), dentistry, or law. Finalists are interviewed. **Deadline for Receipt:** March of each year.

3045 ■ BUSINESS AND PROFESSIONAL WOMEN OF VIRGINIA
Attn: Virginia BPW Foundation
P.O. Box 4842
McLean, VA 22103-4842
Web Site: http://www.bpwva.org/Foundation.shtml
To provide financial assistance to women in Virginia who are interested in working on a bachelor's or advanced degree in science or technology.
Title of Award: Women in Science and Technology Scholarship **Area, Field, or Subject:** Actuarial science; Biological and clinical sciences; Chemistry; Computer and information sciences; Dentistry; Engineering; Engineering, Biomedical; Insurance and insurance-related fields; Mathematics and mathematical sciences; Medicine; Physics; Science; Technology **Level of Education for which Award is Granted:** Graduate, Undergraduate **Number Awarded:** At least 1 each year. **Funds Available:** Stipends range from $500 to $1,000 per year, depending on the need of the recipient; funds may be used for tuition, fees, books, transportation, living expenses, and dependent care. **Duration:** 1 year; recipients may reapply (but prior recipients are not given priority).
Eligibility Requirements: This program is open to women who are at least 18 years of age, U.S. citizens, Virginia residents, accepted at or currently studying at a Virginia college or university, and working on a bachelor's, master's, or doctoral degree in 1 of the following fields: actuarial science, biology, bioengineering, chemistry, computer science, dentistry, engineering, mathematics, medicine, physics, or a similar scientific or technical field. Applicants must have a definite plan to use their education in a scientific or technical profession. They must be able to demonstrate financial need. **Deadline for Receipt:** March of each year. **Additional Information:** Recipients must complete their studies within 2 years.

3046 ■ COMMUNITY FOUNDATION OF GREATER JACKSON
525 East Capitol Street, Suite 5B
Jackson, MS 39201
Tel: (601)974-6044
Fax: (601)974-6045
E-mail: info@cfgreaterjackson.org
Web Site: http://www.cfgreaterjackson.org
To provide financial assistance to undergraduate students in Mississippi who are preparing for a career in the field of public works.
Title of Award: APWA Scholarship Fund **Area, Field, or Subject:** Biological and clinical sciences; Chemistry; Engineering, Civil; Engineering, Electrical; Environmental science; Public administration **Level of Education for which Award is Granted:** Four Year College **Number Awarded:** 2 each year. **Funds Available:** The stipend is $1,000. **Duration:** 1 year.
Eligibility Requirements: This program is open to full-time juniors and seniors at public universities in Mississippi who are preparing to enter the field of public works. Applicants must have graduated from a high school in Mississippi. Eligible majors include civil engineering, electrical engineering, environmental engineering, public administration, biology, or chemistry. Selection is based on merit and need. **Deadline for Receipt:** April of each year. **Additional Information:** This program, established in 2000, is sponsored by the Mississippi chapter of the American Public Works Association (APWA).

3047 ■ CONGRESSIONAL BLACK CAUCUS FOUNDATION, INC.
Attn: Director, Educational Programs
1720 Massachusetts Avenue, N.W.
Washington, DC 20036
Tel: (202)263-2836
Free: 800-784-2577
Fax: (202)775-0773
E-mail: spouses@cbcfinc.org
Web Site: http://www.cbcfinc.org
To provide financial assistance to minority and other undergraduate and graduate students who reside in a Congressional district represented by an African American and are interested in preparing for a health-related career.
Title of Award: Cheerios Brand Health Initiative Scholarship **Area, Field, or Subject:** Biological and clinical sciences; Chemistry; Education, Physical; Engineering; Food service careers; Health care services; Medicine; Nursing **Level of Education for which Award is Granted:** Graduate, Undergraduate **Number Awarded:** Varies each year. **Funds Available:** A stipend is awarded (amount not specified). **Duration:** 1 year.
Eligibility Requirements: This program is open to 1) minority and other graduating high school seniors planning to attend an accredited institution of higher education and 2) currently-enrolled full-time undergraduate, graduate, and doctoral students in good academic standing with a GPA of 2.5 or higher. Applicants must reside or attend school in a Congressional district represented by a member of the Congressional Black Caucus. They must be interested in preparing for a career in a medical, food services, or other health-related field, including pre-medicine, nursing, chemistry, biology, physical education, and engineering. Along with their application, they must submit a 500-word personal statement on 1) the field of study they intend to pursue and why they have chosen that field; 2) their interests, involvement in school activities, community and public service, hobbies, special talents, sports, and other highlight areas; and 3) any other experiences, skills, or qualifications they feel should be considered. They must also be able to document financial need. **Deadline for Receipt:** April of each year. **Additional Information:** The program was established in 1998 with support from General Mills, Inc.

3048 ■ DEPARTMENT OF TRANSPORTATION
Federal Highway Administration
Attn: National Highway Institute, HNHI-20
4600 North Fairfax Drive, Suite 800
Arlington, VA 22203-1553
Tel: (703)235-0538
Fax: (703)235-0593
E-mail: transportationedu@fhwa.dot.gov
Web Site: http://www.nhi.fhwa.dot.gov/ddetfp.asp
To enable students to participate in research activities at facilities of the U.S. Department of Transportation (DOT) Federal Highway Administration in the Washington, D.C. area.

Title of Award: Eisenhower Grants for Research Fellowships **Area, Field, or Subject:** Chemistry; Economics; Engineering; Engineering, Civil; Geography; Information science and technology; Materials research/science; Operations research; Physics; Public administration; Statistics; Technology; Transportation; Urban affairs/design/planning **Level of Education for which Award is Granted:** Four Year College, Graduate **Number Awarded:** Varies each year; recently, 9 students participated in this program. **Funds Available:** Fellows receive full tuition and fees that relate to the academic credits for the approved research project and a monthly stipend of $1,450 for college seniors, $1,700 for master's students, or $2,000 for doctoral students. An allowance for travel to and from the DOT facility where the research is conducted is also provided, but selectees are responsible for their own housing accommodations. Faculty advisors are allowed 1 site review on projects over 6 months and 2 site reviews on projects over 9 months; travel and per diem are provided for those site reviews. **Duration:** Tenure is normally 3, 6, 9, or 12 months.
Eligibility Requirements: This program is open to 1) students in their junior year of a baccalaureate program who will complete their junior year before being awarded a fellowship; 2) students in their senior year of a baccalaureate program; and 3) students who have completed their baccalaureate degree and are enrolled in a program leading to a master's, Ph.D., or equivalent degree. Applicants must be U.S. citizens enrolled in an accredited U.S. institution of higher education working on a degree full time and planning to enter the transportation profession after completing their higher education. They select 1 or more projects from a current list of research projects underway at various DOT facilities; the research will be conducted with academic supervision provided by a faculty advisor from their home university (which grants academic credit for the research project) and with technical direction provided by the DOT staff. Specific requirements for the target projects vary; most require engineering backgrounds, but others involve transportation planning, information management, public administration, physics, materials science, statistical analysis, operations research, chemistry, economics, technology transfer, urban studies, geography, and urban and regional planning. The DOT encourages students at Historically Black Colleges and Universities (HBCUs) and Hispanic Serving Institutions (HSIs) to apply for these grants. Selection is based on match of the student's qualifications with the proposed research project (including the student's ability to accomplish the project in the available time), recommendation letters regarding the nominee's qualifications to conduct the research, academic records (including class standing, GPA, and transcripts), and transportation work experience (if any) including the employer's endorsement. **Deadline for Receipt:** February of each year.

3049 ■ ENVIRONMENTAL PROTECTION AGENCY
Attn: National Center for Environmental Research
Ariel Rios Building - 3500
1200 Pennsylvania Avenue, N.W.
Washington, DC 20460
Tel: (202)343-9862
E-mail: barnwell.thomas@opa.gov
Web Site: http://es.epa.gov/ncer/P3
To provide funding to teams of undergraduate and graduate students interested in conducting a research project related to environmental sustainability.
Title of Award: P3 Award Program **Area, Field, or Subject:** Agricultural sciences; Biological and clinical sciences; Chemistry; Energy-related areas; Environmental conservation; Environmental science; Information science and technology; Public health; Transportation; Water resources **Level of Education for which Award is Granted:** Graduate, Undergraduate **Number Awarded:** Varies each year. Recently, 42 Phase I grants were awarded, of which 10 were selected to receive Phase II grants. **Funds Available:** Phase I grants are $10,000. Phase II grants are $75,000. Grants cover all direct and indirect costs; cost-sharing is not required. **Duration:** 1 year for Phase I and 1 additional year for Phase II.
Eligibility Requirements: This competition is open to teams of undergraduate and graduate students at U.S. colleges and universities who are interested in conducting a research project related to the 3 components of sustainability: people, prosperity, and the planet. Projects must address the causes, effects, extent, prevention, reduction, or elimination of air, water, or solid and hazardous waste pollution. Categories include agriculture (e.g., irrigation practices, reduction or elimination of pesticides); materials and chemicals (e.g., materials

conservation, green engineering, green chemistry, biotechnology, recovery and reuse of materials); energy (e.g., reduction in air emissions, energy conservation); information technology (e.g., delivery of and access to environmental performance, technical, educational, or public health information related environmental decision making); water (e.g., quality, quantity, conservation, availability, and access); or the built environment (e.g., environmental benefits through innovative green buildings, transportation, and mobility strategies, and smart growth as it results in reduced vehicle miles traveled or reduces storm water runoff). Student teams, with a faculty advisor (who serves as the principal investigator on the grant), submit designs for Phase I of the competition. Selection of grantees is based on the extent to which the proposed project achieves the outcomes of minimizing the use and generation of hazardous substances; utilizes resources and energy effectively and efficiently; and advances the goals of economic competitiveness, human health, and environmental protection for societal benefit. Recipients of Phase I grants are then invited to apply for additional funding through a Phase I grant. **Deadline for Receipt:** February of each year. **Additional Information:** This program began in 2004. It is supported by a large number of organizations from industry, the nonprofit sector, and the federal government.

3050 ■ FOUNDATION FOR THE CAROLINAS

Attn: Senior Vice President, Scholarships
217 South Tryon Street
P.O. Box 34769
Charlotte, NC 28234-4769
Tel: (704)973-4535
Free: 800-973-7244
Fax: (704)973-4935
E-mail: jseymour@fftc.org
Web Site: http://www.fftc.org/scholarships
To provide financial assistance to college students in North and South Carolina who are preparing for a career in the plastics industry.
Title of Award: Richard Goolsby Scholarship **Area, Field, or Subject:** Business administration; Chemistry; Engineering, Chemical; Engineering, Industrial; Engineering, Mechanical; Physics **Level of Education for which Award is Granted:** Undergraduate **Number Awarded:** 1 or more each year. **Funds Available:** Stipends range up to $4,000 per year; Funds are paid directly to the recipient's school to be used for tuition, required fees, books, and supplies. **Duration:** 1 year; may be renewed. **Eligibility Requirements:** This program is open to residents of South Carolina, central North Carolina, or western North Carolina. Applicants must be entering their sophomore, junior, or senior year at a college or university in North or South Carolina and be majoring in a subject that will prepare them for a career in the plastics industry (e.g., chemistry, physics, chemical engineering, mechanical engineering, industrial engineering, business administration). They must be enrolled full time. Along with their application, they must submit a 1- to 2-page statement explaining why they are applying for the scholarship, their qualifications, and their educational and career goals in the plastics industry. Selection is based on academic performance, demonstrated interest in the plastics industry, financial need, school and community involvement, and personal achievements. **Deadline for Receipt:** February of each year.

3051 ■ HISPANIC SCHOLARSHIP FUND INSTITUTE

1001 Connecticut Avenue, N.W., Suite 632
Washington, DC 20036
Tel: (202)296-0009
Fax: (202)296-3633
E-mail: info@hsfi.org
Web Site: http://www.hsfi.org/scholarships/energy.asp
To provide financial assistance to Hispanic undergraduate students majoring in designated business, engineering, and science fields related to the U.S. Department of Energy (DOE) goals of environmental restoration and waste management.
Title of Award: Environmental Management Scholarship **Area, Field, or Subject:** Business administration; Chemistry; Computer and information sciences; Engineering, Agricultural; Engineering, Civil; Engineering, Electrical; Engineering, Industrial; Engineering, Mechanical; Engineering, Metallurgical; Engineering, Petroleum; Environmental science; Epidemiology; Geology; Hydrology; Management; Mathematics and mathematical sciences; Physics; Radiology; Toxicology **Level of Education for which**

Award is Granted: Undergraduate **Number Awarded:** Varies each year. **Funds Available:** The stipend is $3,000 per year for 4-year university students or $2,000 per year for community college students. **Duration:** 1 year.
Eligibility Requirements: This program is open to U.S. citizens and permanent residents of Hispanic background who have completed at least 12 undergraduate credits with a GPA of 3.0 or higher. Applicants must be interested in preparing for a career supportive of the DOE goals of environmental restoration and waste management. Eligible academic majors are in the fields of business (management and system analysis), engineering (agricultural, chemical, civil, electrical, environmental, industrial, mechanical, metallurgical, nuclear, and petroleum), and science (applied math/physics, chemistry, computer science, ecology, environmental, epidemiology, geology, health physics, hydrology, radiochemistry, radio-ecology, and toxicology). Along with their application, they must submit a 2-page essay on 1) how their academic major, interests, and career goals correspond to environmental restoration and waste management issues; and 2) how their Hispanic background and family upbringing have influenced their academic and personal goals. Selection is based on the essay, academic record, academic plans and career goals, financial need, commitment to DOE's goal of environmental restoration and waste management, and a letter of recommendation. **Deadline for Receipt:** March of each year. **Additional Information:** This program, which began in 1990, is sponsored by DOE's Office of Environmental Management. Recipients must enroll full time at a college or university in the United States.

3052 ■ INSTITUTE OF INTERNATIONAL EDUCATION

Attn: Lucent Global Science Scholars Program
809 United Nations Plaza
New York, NY 10017-3580
Tel: (212)984-5419
Fax: (212)984-5452
E-mail: sciencescholars@iie.org
Web Site: http://www.iie.org/programs/lucent
To provide financial assistance for college to high school students in the United States and university students in other designated countries who are interested in preparing for careers in information technology.
Title of Award: Lucent Global Science Scholars Program **Area, Field, or Subject:** Chemistry; Computer and information sciences; Engineering; Information science and technology; Mathematics and mathematical sciences; Physics **Level of Education for which Award is Granted:** Undergraduate **Number Awarded:** Varies each year. Recently, 32 students from foreign countries (5 from China, 1 from Hong Kong, and 2 from each of the other countries) and 28 from the United States received these scholarships. **Funds Available:** The stipend is $5,000 per year. **Duration:** 1 year; nonrenewable.
Eligibility Requirements: This program is open to high school seniors in the United States and first-year university students in Brazil, Canada, China, France, Germany, Hong Kong, India, Korea, Mexico, the Netherlands, Philippines, Poland, Russia, Spain, and the United Kingdom. Students from the United States must have a GPA of 3.6 or higher. Eligible majors include applied physics, chemistry, computer science, engineering, information science and technology, mathematics and applied mathematics, and physics. Selection is based on a demonstrated record of distinction in science and mathematics and a desire to prepare for a career in information technology. **Deadline for Receipt:** February of each year for students from the United States; March of each year for students from other countries. **Additional Information:** This program, established in 1999, is funded by Lucent Technologies. Students are offered internships at Lucent's research and development and manufacturing facilities in their own countries during the summer following their freshman year in the United States or the sophomore year in other countries.

3053 ■ IOTA SIGMA PI

c/o National Director for Student Awards
Vicki H. Grassian
University of Iowa
Department of Chemistry
Iowa City, IA 52242
Tel: (319)335-1392
Fax: (319)335-1270
E-mail: vicki-grassian@uiowa.edu

Web Site: http://www.iotasigmapi.info/ISPstudentawards/
ISPstudentawards.htm
To provide financial assistance to women undergraduates who have
achieved excellence in the study of chemistry or biochemistry.
Title of Award: Gladys Anderson Emerson Scholarship **Area, Field, or
Subject:** Chemistry **Level of Education for which Award is Granted:**
Four Year College **Number Awarded:** 1 each year. **Funds Available:** The
stipend is $2,000. **Duration:** 1 year.
Eligibility Requirements: The nominee must be a female chemistry or
biochemistry student who has attained at least junior standing but has at
least 1 semester of work to complete. Both the nominator and the
nominee must be members of Iota Sigma Pi, although students who are
not members but wish to apply for the scholarship may be made members
by National Council action. Selection is based on transcripts; a list of all
academic honors and professional memberships; a short essay by the
nominee describing herself, her goals in chemistry, any hobbies or talents,
and her financial need; and letters of recommendation. **Deadline for
Receipt:** February of each year. **Additional Information:** This scholarship was first awarded in 1987.

3054 ■ KOSTER INSURANCE AGENCY

Attn: Scholarship
500 Victory Road
Quincy, MA 02171
Tel: (617)770-9889
Free: 800-457-5599
Fax: (617)479-0860
E-mail: Scholarship@kosterins.com
Web Site: http://www.kosterweb.com/about/scholarship_main.php
To provide financial assistance to undergraduate students working on a
degree in a health-related field.
Title of Award: Koster Insurance Health Careers Scholarship Program
Area, Field, or Subject: Biological and clinical sciences; Chemistry;
Dentistry; Health care services; Nursing; Occupational therapy;
Optometry; Pharmaceutical sciences; Physical therapy; Physiology;
Public health; Social work **Level of Education for which Award is
Granted:** Undergraduate **Number Awarded:** 5 each year. **Funds Available:** The stipend is $3,000 per year. **Duration:** 1 year; may be renewed
1 additional year.
Eligibility Requirements: This program is open to full-time undergraduates entering their second-to-last or final year of study in a health-related
field, including (but not limited to) pre-medicine, nursing, public and community health, physical therapy, occupational therapy, pharmacy, biology,
chemistry, physiology, social work, dentistry, and optometry. Applicants
must have a GPA of 3.0 or higher and be able to demonstrate financial
need. Along with their application, they must submit a 1-page essay
describing their personal goals, including their reasons for preparing for a
career in health care. Selection is based on motivation to pursue a career
in health care, academic excellence, dedication to community service,
and financial need. **Deadline for Receipt:** April of each year. **Additional
Information:** This program began in 2001.

3055 ■ CLARE BOOTHE LUCE FUND

c/o Henry Luce Foundation, Inc.
111 West 50th Street, Suite 4601
New York, NY 10020
Tel: (212)489-7700
Fax: (212)581-9541
E-mail: jdaniels@hluce.org
Web Site: http://www.hluce.org
To provide funding to women interested in studying science or engineer-
ing at the undergraduate level at designated universities.
Title of Award: Clare Boothe Luce Scholarships in Science and
Engineering **Area, Field, or Subject:** Biological and clinical sciences;
Chemistry; Computer and information sciences; Engineering; Engineering, Aerospace/Aeronautical/Astronautical; Engineering, Civil; Engineering, Electrical; Engineering, Mechanical; Engineering, Nuclear; Mathematics and mathematical sciences; Meteorology; Physics **Level of Education
for which Award is Granted:** Undergraduate **Number Awarded:** Varies;
since the program began, more than 800 of these scholarships have been
awarded. **Funds Available:** The amount awarded is established individually by each of the participating institutions. The stipends are intended to
augment rather than replace any existing institutional support in these

fields. Each stipend is calculated to include the cost of room and board as
well as tuition and other fees or expenses. **Duration:** 2 years; in certain
special circumstances, awards for the full 4 years of undergraduate study
may be offered.
Eligibility Requirements: This program is open to female undergraduate
students (particularly juniors and seniors) majoring in biology, chemistry,
computer science, engineering (aeronautical, civil, electrical, mechanical,
nuclear, and others), mathematics, meteorology, and physics. Applicants
must be U.S. citizens attending 1 of the 12 designated colleges and
universities affiliated with this program; periodically, other institutions are
invited to participate. Premedical science majors are ineligible for this
competition. The participating institutions select the recipients without
regard to race, age, religion, ethnic background, or need. All awards are
made on the basis of merit. **Deadline for Receipt:** Varies; check with the
participating institutions for their current schedule. **Additional Information:** The participating institutions are Boston University, Colby College,
Creighton University, Fordham University, Georgetown University,
Marymount University, Mount Holyoke College, St. John's University,
Santa Clara University, Seton Hall University, Trinity College, and
University of Notre Dame.

3056 ■ MARYLAND HIGHER EDUCATION COMMISSION

Attn: Office of Student Financial Assistance
839 Bestgate Road, Suite 400
Annapolis, MD 21401-3013
Tel: (410)260-4545
Free: 800-974-1024
Fax: (410)974-5376
E-mail: osfamail@mhec.state.md.us
Web Site: http://www.mhec.state.md.us/financialAid/
ProgramDescriptions/prog_scm.asp
To provide scholarship/loans to Maryland residents who wish to prepare
for a teaching career.
Title of Award: Sharon Christa McAuliffe Memorial Teacher Education
Award **Area, Field, or Subject:** Chemistry; Classical studies; Computer
and information sciences; Earth sciences; Education; Education, English
as a second language; Education, Special; Education, Vocational-
technical; Foreign languages; Geosciences; Health care services; Hearing and deafness; Mathematics and mathematical sciences; Physical sciences; Physics; Space and planetary sciences; Visual impairment **Level
of Education for which Award is Granted:** Master's, Professional,
Undergraduate **Number Awarded:** Varies each year. **Funds Available:**
The amount of the award is based on the recipient's enrollment and housing status, to a maximum of $17,000 per year. The total amount of all
state awards may not exceed the cost of attendance as determined by the
school's financial aid office or $17,800, whichever is less. Following
graduation, recipients must teach at a Maryland public school for 1 year
for each year of financial aid received under this program. If they fail to
meet that service obligation, they must repay all funds they received with
interest. They must begin the service obligation within 12 months of
graduation. **Duration:** 1 year; may be renewed for 1 additional year if the
recipient maintains satisfactory academic progress with a cumulative GPA
of 3.0 or higher and enrollment at a 2-year or 4-year Maryland college or
university in an approved teacher education program.
Eligibility Requirements: This program is open to Maryland residents
who are college students with at least 60 semester credit hours
completed, college graduates, and teachers in a non-critical shortage
area. Applicants must have a GPA of 3.0 or higher and plan to teach in a
field identified as a critical shortage area. Selection is based on cumulative GPA, applicable work or volunteer experience, quality of academic
background in certification field, and a writing sample. **Deadline for
Receipt:** December of each year. **Additional Information:** Recently, the
eligible critical shortage areas were business education, chemistry,
computer science, earth and space science, English for speakers of other
languages, family and consumer sciences, German, health occupations,
Latin, mathematics, physical science, physics, Spanish, special education
(generic infant-grade 3, generic grades 1-8, generic grades 6-adult, hearing impaired, severely and profoundly handicapped, visually impaired),
and technology education.

3057 ■ MARYLAND SPACE GRANT CONSORTIUM

c/o Johns Hopkins University
203 Bloomberg Center for Physics and Astronomy

3400 North Charles Street
Baltimore, MD 21218-2686
Tel: (410)516-7351
Fax: (410)516-4109
E-mail: info@mdspacegrant.org
Web Site: http://www.mdspacegrant.org/scholars_about.html

To provide financial assistance to undergraduates who are interested in studying space-related fields at selected universities in Maryland that are members of the Maryland Space Grant Consortium.

Title of Award: Maryland Space Scholars Program **Area, Field, or Subject:** Aerospace sciences; Astronomy and astronomical sciences; Biological and clinical sciences; Chemistry; Computer and information sciences; Engineering; Geology; Mathematics and mathematical sciences; Physics; Space and planetary sciences **Level of Education for which Award is Granted:** Undergraduate **Number Awarded:** Varies each year; recently 16 of these scholarships were awarded (2 at Johns Hopkins University, 5 at Morgan State University, 2 at Hagerstown Community College, 2 at Towson University, and 5 at the University of Maryland at College Park). **Funds Available:** Scholars receive partial payment of tuition at the participating university they attend. **Duration:** 1 year; may be renewed if the recipient maintains a GPA of 3.0 or higher.

Eligibility Requirements: This program is open to residents of Maryland and graduates of Maryland high schools who are enrolled full time at a member institution. Applicants must be interested in preparing for a career in mathematics, science, engineering, technology, or a space-related field. They must be majoring in a relevant field, including (but not limited to) astronomy, the biological and life sciences, chemistry, computer science, engineering, geological sciences, or physics. U.S. citizenship is required. Along with their application, they must submit an essay of 200 to 500 words on how this scholarship will help them meet their educational and financial goals. This program is a component of the U.S. National Aeronautics and Space Administration (NASA) Space Grant program, which encourages participation by women, underrepresented minorities, and persons with disabilities. **Deadline for Receipt:** August of each year.

Additional Information: The participating universities are Hagerstown Community College, Johns Hopkins University, Morgan State University, Towson University, the University of Maryland at College Park, and Washington College. Funding for this program is provided by NASA.

3058 ■ MICRON TECHNOLOGY, INC.

Attn: Micron Technology Foundation
8000 South Federal Way
P.O. Box 6
Boise, ID 83707-0006
Tel: (208)368-3675
Web Site: http://www.micron.com/about/giving/foundation/scholarships.html

To provide financial assistance to high school seniors in selected states who are interested in majoring in the physical sciences.

Title of Award: Micron Science and Technology Scholars **Area, Field, or Subject:** Chemistry; Computer and information sciences; Engineering, Chemical; Engineering, Computer; Engineering, Electrical; Engineering, Mechanical; Materials research/science; Physics **Level of Education for which Award is Granted:** Undergraduate **Number Awarded:** 13 each year: 1 at $55,000 and 12 at $16,500; 2 are awarded to students from each of 5 participating states, plus 3 floating scholarships are awarded within those states. **Funds Available:** Stipends are either $55,000 or $16,500. A cash grant of $1,000 is awarded to the high school of each winner.

Eligibility Requirements: This program is open to high school seniors who reside in and attend public or private schools in Colorado, Idaho, Texas, Utah, or Virginia. Applicants must have a combined SAT score of at least 1350 or a composite ACT score of at least 30; have at least a 3.5 GPA; have demonstrated leadership in school, work, and extracurricular activities; and plan to major in engineering (electrical, computer, chemical, or mechanical), computer science, chemistry, material sciences, or physics. Selection is based on merit (in academics and leadership). **Deadline for Receipt:** January of each year. **Additional Information:** This program began in 2000. Information is also available from Scholarship

Management Services of Scholarship America, One Scholarship Way, P.O. Box 297, St. Peter, MN 56082, (507) 931-1682, (800) 537-4180, Fax: (507) 931-9168.

3059 ■ MONTANA SPACE GRANT CONSORTIUM

c/o Montana State University
416 Cobleigh Hall
P.O. Box 173835
Bozeman, MT 59717-3835
Tel: (406)994-4223
Fax: (406)994-4452
E-mail: msgc@montana.edu
Web Site: http://spacegrant.montana.edu/Text/ScholarProgram.html

To provide financial assistance to students in Montana who are interested in working on an undergraduate degree in the space sciences and/or engineering.

Title of Award: Montana Space Grant Consortium Undergraduate Scholarships **Area, Field, or Subject:** Aerospace sciences; Astronomy and astronomical sciences; Biological and clinical sciences; Chemistry; Computer and information sciences; Engineering, Aerospace/Aeronautical/Astronautical; Engineering, Chemical; Engineering, Civil; Engineering, Electrical; Engineering, Mechanical; Geology; Physics; Space and planetary sciences **Level of Education for which Award is Granted:** Undergraduate **Number Awarded:** Varies each year; recently, 23 of these scholarships were awarded. **Funds Available:** The stipend is $1,000 per year. **Duration:** 1 year; may be renewed.

Eligibility Requirements: This program is open to full-time undergraduate students at member institutions of the Montana Space Grant Consortium (MSGC) majoring in fields related to space sciences and engineering. Those fields include, but are not limited to, astronomy, biological and life sciences, chemical engineering, chemistry, civil engineering, computer sciences, electrical engineering, geological sciences, mathematics, mechanical engineering, and physics. Priority is given to students who have been involved in aerospace-related research. U.S. citizenship is required. The MSGC is a component of the U.S. National Aeronautics and Space Administration (NASA) Space Grant program, which encourages participation by women, underrepresented minorities, and persons with disabilities. **Deadline for Receipt:** March of each year. **Additional Information:** The MSGC member institutions are Blackfeet Community College, Carroll College, Chief Dull Knife College, Fort Belknap College, Fort Peck Community College, Little Big Horn College, Montana State University at Billings, Montana State University at Bozeman, Montana State University Northern, Montana Tech, Rocky Mountain College, Salish Kootenai College, Stone Child College, University of Great Falls, University of Montana, and University of Montana Western. Funding for this program is provided by NASA.

3060 ■ NATIONAL CONSORTIUM FOR GRADUATE DEGREES FOR MINORITIES IN ENGINEERING AND SCIENCE (GEM)

P.O. Box 537
Notre Dame, IN 46556
Tel: (574)631-7771
Fax: (574)287-1486
E-mail: gem.1@nd.edu
Web Site: http://www.gemfellowship.org

To provide financial assistance and summer work experience to underrepresented minority students interested in obtaining a Ph.D. degree in the life sciences, mathematics, or physical sciences.

Title of Award: GEM Ph.D. Science Fellowship Program **Area, Field, or Subject:** Biological and clinical sciences; Chemistry; Computer and information sciences; Earth sciences; Geosciences; Mathematics and mathematical sciences; Natural sciences; Physics **Level of Education for which Award is Granted:** Four Year College, Doctorate **Number Awarded:** Varies each year; recently, 40 of these fellowships were awarded. **Funds Available:** The stipend is $14,000 per year, plus tuition and fees. In addition, there is a summer internship program that provides a salary and reimbursement for travel expenses to and from the summer work site. The total value of the award is between $60,000 and $100,000, depending upon academic status at the time of application, summer employer, and graduate school attended. **Duration:** 3 to 5 years for the fellowship; 12 weeks during at least 1 summer for the internship. Fellows selected as juniors or seniors intern each summer until entrance to graduate school; fellows selected after college graduation intern at least 1 summer. ■

Eligibility Requirements: This program is open to U.S. citizens who are members of ethnic groups underrepresented in the natural sciences: Native Americans, African Americans, Latinos, Puerto Ricans, and other Hispanic Americans. Applicants must be juniors, seniors, or recent baccalaureate graduates in the life sciences, mathematics, or physical sciences (chemistry, computer science, earth sciences, and physics) with an academic record that indicates the ability to pursue doctoral studies (including a GPA of 3.0 or higher). **Deadline for Receipt:** October of each year. **Additional Information:** This program is valid only at 1 of 95 participating GEM member universities; write to GEM for a list. The fellowship award is designed to support the student in the first year of the doctoral program without working. Subsequent years are subsidized by the respective university and will usually include either a teaching or research assistantship. Recipients must participate in the GEM summer internship; failure to agree to accept the internship cancels the fellowship. Recipients must enroll in the same scientific discipline as their undergraduate major.

3061 ■ NATIONAL INVENTORS HALL OF FAME

Attn: Collegiate Inventors Competition
221 South Broadway Street
Akron, OH 44308-1595
Tel: (330)849-6887
E-mail: collegiate@invent.org
Web Site: http://www.invent.org/collegiate

To recognize and reward outstanding inventions by college or university students in the fields of science, engineering, and technology.

Title of Award: Collegiate Inventors Competition **Area, Field, or Subject:** Biological and clinical sciences; Chemistry; Computer and information sciences; Engineering; Environmental conservation; Environmental science; Inventors; Mathematics and mathematical sciences; Medicine; Physics; Science; Technology; Veterinary science and medicine **Level of Education for which Award is Granted:** Graduate, Postdoctoral, Undergraduate **Number Awarded:** 15 semifinalists are selected each year; of those, 3 individuals or teams win prizes. **Funds Available:** Finalists receive an all-expense paid trip to Washington, D.C. to participate in a final round of judging and in the awards dinner and presentation. The Grand Prize winner or team receives $25,000. Other prizes are $10,000 for an undergraduate winner or team and $15,000 for a graduate winner or team. Academic advisors of the winning entries each receive a $3,000 cash prize. Awards are unrestricted cash gifts, not scholarships or grants. **Duration:** The competition is held annually.

Eligibility Requirements: This competition is open to undergraduate and graduate students who are (or have been) enrolled full time at least part of the 12-month period prior to entry in a college or university in the United States. Entries may also be submitted by teams, up to 4 members, of whom at least 1 must meet the full-time requirement and all others must have been enrolled at least half time sometime during the preceding 24-month period. Applicants must submit a description of their invention, including a patent search and summary of current literature that describes the state of the art and identifies the originality of the invention; test data demonstrating that the idea, invention, or design is workable; the societal, economic, and environmental benefits of the invention; and supplemental material that may include photos, slides, disks, videotapes, and even samples. Entries must be original ideas and the work of a student or team and a university advisor; the invention should be reproducible and may not have been 1) made available to the public as a commercial product or process, or 2) patented or published more than 1 year prior to the date of submission for this competition. Entries are first reviewed by a committee of judges that selects the finalists. The committee is comprised of mathematicians, engineers, biologists, chemists, environmentalists, physicists, computer specialists, members of the medical and veterinary profession, and specialists in invention and development of technology. Entries are judged on the basis of originality, inventiveness, potential value to society (socially, environmentally, and economically), and range or scope of use. **Deadline for Receipt:** May of each year. **Additional Information:** This program is co-sponsored by Abbott Laboratories and

the United States Patent and Trademark Office. It was established in 1990 as the BFGoodrich Collegiate Inventors Program.

3062 ■ NATIONAL ORGANIZATION FOR THE PROFESSIONAL ADVANCEMENT OF BLACK CHEMISTS AND CHEMICAL ENGINEERS

c/o Howard University
P.O. Box 77040
Washington, DC 20013
Tel: (202)667-1699
Free: 800-776-1419
Fax: (267)200-0156
Web Site: http://www.nobcche.org

To provide financial assistance to African American undergraduates majoring in chemistry and chemical engineering.

Title of Award: NOBCChE Undergraduate Award **Area, Field, or Subject:** Chemistry; Engineering, Chemical **Level of Education for which Award is Granted:** Undergraduate **Number Awarded:** 1 each year. **Funds Available:** The stipend is $2,500. **Duration:** 1 year; nonrenewable.

Eligibility Requirements: This program is open to African American high school graduates and undergraduate students enrolled at a college or university and working on or planning to work on a bachelor's degree in chemistry or chemical engineering. Applicants must submit 3 letters of recommendation, an official transcript, and a resume. **Deadline for Receipt:** January of each year. **Additional Information:** This program is sponsored by the National Organization for the Professional Advancement of Black Chemists and Chemical Engineers (NOBCChE). Information is also available from Dr. Marlon L. Walker, Awards and Scholarships Committee Chair, National Institute of Standards and Technology, 100 Bureau Drive, Gaithersburg, MD 20899-8372, (301) 975-5593 E-mail: marlon.walker@nist.gov.

3063 ■ NATIONAL SOCIETY OF BLACK ENGINEERS

Attn: Programs Department
1454 Duke Street
Alexandria, VA 22314
Tel: (703)549-2207
Fax: (703)683-5312
E-mail: scholarships@nsbe.org
Web Site: http://www.nsbe.org/programs/schol_jnj.php

To provide financial assistance to members of the National Society of Black Engineers (NSBE) who are majoring in designated engineering fields.

Title of Award: Johnson & Johnson NSBE Corporate Scholarship Program **Area, Field, or Subject:** Biological and clinical sciences; Chemistry; Computer and information sciences; Engineering; Engineering, Biomedical; Engineering, Chemical; Engineering, Computer; Engineering, Electrical; Engineering, Industrial; Engineering, Materials; Engineering, Mechanical; Logistics **Level of Education for which Award is Granted:** Four Year College **Number Awarded:** 13 each year: 1 national award and 12 regional awards (2 in each NSBE region). **Funds Available:** The national stipend is $2,000; the regional stipends are $1,500. **Duration:** 1 year.

Eligibility Requirements: This program is open to members of the society who are entering their junior or senior year in college and majoring in biology, chemistry, computer science, operations/logistics, or the following fields of engineering: biomedical, chemical, computer, electrical, industrial, material, or mechanical. Applicants must have a GPA of 3.2 or higher and a demonstrated interest in employment with Johnson & Johnson. Along with their application, they must submit a resume and official transcript. **Deadline for Receipt:** January of each year.

3064 ■ NEBRASKA ACADEMY OF SCIENCES

c/o University of Nebraska
302 Morrill Hall
14th and U Streets
P.O. Box 880339
Lincoln, NE 68588-0339
Tel: (402)472-2644
E-mail: nebacad@unl.edu
Web Site: http://www.neacadsci.org/Info/coll_scholarship.htm

To provide financial assistance to upper-division students majoring in science at colleges and universities in Nebraska.

Title of Award: C. Bertrand and Marian Othmer Scultz Collegiate Scholarship **Area, Field, or Subject:** Biological and clinical sciences;

Chemistry; Geology; Physics **Level of Education for which Award is Granted:** Four Year College **Number Awarded:** 1 each year. **Funds Available:** The stipend is $3,000 per year. **Duration:** 1 year; may be renewed 1 additional year.

Eligibility Requirements: This program is open to student entering their junior or senior year at 4-year colleges and universities in Nebraska. Applicants must have a declared major in a natural science discipline (chemistry, physics, biology, or geology). They must be preparing for a career in a science-related industry, science teaching, or scientific research. A member of the Nebraska Academy of Sciences must provide a letter of nomination. **Deadline for Receipt:** January of each year. **Additional Information:** This scholarship was first awarded in 2006.

3065 ■ NEW HAMPSHIRE POSTSECONDARY EDUCATION COMMISSION

3 Barrell Court, Suite 300
Concord, NH 03301-8543
Tel: (603)271-2555
Fax: (603)271-2696
E-mail: pedes@pec.state.nh.us
Web Site: http://www.state.nh.us/postsecondary/finwork.html
To provide scholarship/loans to New Hampshire residents who are interested in attending college to prepare for careers in designated professions.

Title of Award: New Hampshire Workforce Incentive Program Forgivable Loans **Area, Field, or Subject:** Chemistry; Education; Education, Special; Linguistics; Mathematics and mathematical sciences; Nursing; Physical sciences; Physics; Science **Level of Education for which Award is Granted:** Graduate, Undergraduate **Number Awarded:** Varies each year. **Funds Available:** The stipend is $500 per semester ($1,000 per year). This is a scholarship/loan program; recipients must agree to pursue, within New Hampshire, the professional career for which they receive training. Recipients of loans for 1 year have their notes cancelled upon completion of 1 year of full-time service; repayment by service must be completed within 3 years from the date of licensure, certification, or completion of the program. Recipients of loans for more than 1 year have their notes cancelled upon completion of 2 years of full-time service; repayment by service must be completed within 5 years from the date of licensure, certification, or completion of the program. If the note is not cancelled because of service, the recipient must repay the loan within 2 years. **Duration:** 1 year; may be renewed.

Eligibility Requirements: This program is open to residents of New Hampshire who wish to prepare for careers in fields designated by the commission as shortage areas. Currently, the career shortage areas are chemistry, general science, mathematics, physical sciences, physics, special education, world languages, and nursing (L.P.N. through graduate). Applicants must be enrolled as a junior, senior, or graduate student at a college in New Hampshire and must be able to demonstrate financial need. **Deadline for Receipt:** May of each year for fall semester; December of each year for spring semester. **Additional Information:** The time for repayment of the loan, either in cash or through professional service, is extended while the recipient is 1) engaged in a course of study, at least on a half-time basis, at an institution of higher education; 2) serving on active duty as a member of the armed forces of the United States, or as a member of VISTA, the Peace Corps, or AmeriCorps, for a period up to 3 years; 3) temporarily totally disabled for a period up to 3 years; or 4) unable to secure employment because of the need to care for a disabled spouse, child, or parent for a period up to 12 months. The repayment obligation is cancelled if the recipient is unable to work because of a permanent total disability, receives relief under federal bankruptcy laws, or dies. This program went into effect in 1999.

3066 ■ NEW JERSEY UTILITIES ASSOCIATION

50 West State Street, Suite 1117
Trenton, NJ 08608
Tel: (609)392-1000
Fax: (609)396-4231
Web Site: http://www.njua.org
To provide financial assistance to minority, female, and disabled high school seniors in New Jersey interested in majoring in selected subjects in college.

Title of Award: New Jersey Utilities Association Scholarships **Area, Field, or Subject:** Accounting; Biological and clinical sciences; Business

administration; Chemistry; Engineering; Environmental conservation; Environmental science **Level of Education for which Award is Granted:** Undergraduate **Number Awarded:** 2 each year. **Funds Available:** The stipend is $1,500 per year. **Duration:** 4 years.

Eligibility Requirements: Eligible to apply for this scholarship are women, minorities (Black, Hispanic, American Indian/Alaska Native, or Asian American/Pacific Islander), and persons with disabilities who are high school seniors in New Jersey. They must be able to demonstrate financial need, be planning to enroll on a full-time basis at an institute of higher education, and be planning to work on a bachelor's degree in engineering, environmental science, chemistry, biology, business administration, or accounting. Children of employees of any New Jersey Utilities Association-member company are ineligible. Selection is based on overall academic excellence and demonstrated financial need. **Deadline for Receipt:** March of each year.

3067 ■ OAK RIDGE INSTITUTE FOR SCIENCE AND EDUCATION

Attn: Science and Engineering Education
P.O. Box 117
Oak Ridge, TN 37831-0117
Tel: (865)576-9279
Fax: (865)241-5220
E-mail: coxre@orau.gov
Web Site: http://www.orau.gov/orise.htm
To provide financial assistance and research experience to undergraduate students at minority serving institutions who are majoring in scientific fields of interest to the National Oceanic and Atmospheric Administration (NOAA).

Title of Award: National Oceanic and Atmospheric Administration Educational Partnership Program with Minority Serving Institutions Undergraduate Scholarships **Area, Field, or Subject:** Atmospheric science; Biological and clinical sciences; Cartography/Surveying; Chemistry; Computer and information sciences; Engineering; Environmental conservation; Environmental science; Geography; Mathematics and mathematical sciences; Meteorology; Photogrammetry; Physical sciences; Physics **Level of Education for which Award is Granted:** Four Year College **Number Awarded:** 10 each year. **Funds Available:** This program provides payment of tuition and fees (to a maximum of $4,000 per year) and a stipend during the internship of $650 per week. **Duration:** 1 academic year and 2 summers.

Eligibility Requirements: This program is open to juniors and seniors at minority serving institutions, including Hispanic Serving Institutions (HSIs), Historically Black Colleges and Universities (HBCUs), and Tribal Colleges and Universities (TCUs). Applicants must be majoring in atmospheric science, biology, cartography, chemistry, computer science, engineering, environmental science, geodesy, geography, marine science, mathematics, meteorology, photogrammetry, physical science, physics, or remote sensing. They must also be interested in participating in a research internship at a NOAA site. U.S. citizenship is required. **Deadline for Receipt:** January of each year. **Additional Information:** This program is funded by NOAA through an interagency agreement with the U.S. Department of Energy and administered by Oak Ridge Institute for Science and Education (ORISE).

3068 ■ OHIO SPACE GRANT CONSORTIUM

c/o Ohio Aerospace Institute
22800 Cedar Point Road
Cleveland, OH 44142
Tel: (440)962-3032
Free: 800-828-OSGC
Fax: (440)962-3057
E-mail: osgc@oai.org
Web Site: http://www.osgc.org/Scholarship.html
To provide financial assistance to students in their junior year at selected universities in Ohio who wish to working on a bachelor's degree in an aerospace-related field.

Title of Award: Ohio Space Grant Consortium Junior Scholarships **Area, Field, or Subject:** Astronomy and astronomical sciences; Biological and clinical sciences; Chemistry; Computer and information sciences; Engineering, Aerospace/Aeronautical/Astronautical; Engineering, Chemical; Engineering, Civil; Engineering, Computer; Engineering, Electrical; Engineering, Industrial; Engineering, Materials; Engineering, Mechanical; Engineering, Petroleum; Geography; Geology; Materials research/

science; Mathematics and mathematical sciences; Physics; Space and planetary sciences **Level of Education for which Award is Granted:** Four Year College **Number Awarded:** Varies each year; recently, 20 of these scholarships were awarded. **Funds Available:** The stipend is $2,000. **Duration:** 1 year; recipients may apply for a senior scholarship if they maintain satisfactory academic performance and good progress on their research project.

Eligibility Requirements: These scholarships are available to U.S. citizens who expect to complete within 2 years the requirements for a bachelor of science degree in an aerospace-related discipline (aeronautical engineering, aerospace engineering, astronomy, biology, chemical engineering, chemistry, civil engineering, computer engineering and science, control engineering, electrical engineering, engineering mechanics, geography, geology, industrial engineering, manufacturing engineering, materials science and engineering, mathematics, mechanical engineering, petroleum engineering, physics, and systems engineering). Applicants must be attending a member university of the Ohio Space Grant Consortium (OSGC) or another participating university. They must propose and initiate a research project on campus under the guidance of a faculty member. Along with their application, they must submit a 1-page personal objective statement that discusses their career goals and anticipated benefits to be derived from this program. Women, underrepresented minorities, and persons with disabilities are particularly encouraged to apply. **Deadline for Receipt:** February of each year. **Additional Information:** These scholarships are funded through the National Space Grant College and Fellowship Program administered by the National Aeronautics and Space Administration (NASA), with matching funds provided by the member universities, the Ohio Aerospace Institute, and private industry. The OSGC member universities include the University of Akron, Case Western Reserve University, Central State University, University of Cincinnati, Cleveland State University, University of Dayton, Ohio State University, Ohio University, University of Toledo, Wilberforce University, and Wright State University. Other participating universities are Cedarville University, Marietta College (petroleum engineering), Miami University (manufacturing engineering), Ohio Northern University (mechanical engineering), and Youngstown State University (mechanical and industrial engineering). Recipients are required to attend the annual spring research symposium sponsored by the OSGC and present a poster on their research project.

3069 ■ OREGON UNIVERSITY SYSTEM

Attn: Chancellor's Office, Industry Affairs Division
Capital Center, Suite 1065
18640 N.W. Walker Road
Beaverton, OR 97006-8966
Tel: (503)725-2918
Fax: (503)775-2921
E-mail: aeaschol@ous.edu
Web Site: http://www.ous.edu/ecs/scholarships.html
To provide financial assistance to Oregon high school seniors interested in studying designated computer and engineering fields at selected public universities in the state.
Title of Award: AeA Technology Scholarship Program **Area, Field, or Subject:** Biochemistry; Chemistry; Computer and information sciences; Engineering; Engineering, Chemical; Engineering, Computer; Engineering, Electrical; Engineering, Industrial; Engineering, Mechanical; Mathematics and mathematical sciences; Physics **Level of Education for which Award is Granted:** Undergraduate **Number Awarded:** Varies each year; recently, this program awarded 25 new scholarships. **Funds Available:** The stipend is $2,500 per year. **Duration:** 1 year; may be renewed up to 3 additional years if the recipient maintains a GPA of 3.0 or higher.
Eligibility Requirements: This program is open to seniors graduating from high schools in Oregon who plan to attend Eastern Oregon University, Oregon Institute of Technology, Oregon State University, Portland State University, Southern Oregon University, Western Oregon University, or the University of Oregon. Applicants must be planning to major in biochemistry, chemical engineering, chemistry, computer engineering, computer science, electrical engineering, electronic engineering, engineering technology, industrial engineering, mathematics, mechanical engineering, or physics (not all majors are available at each institution). Women and ethnic minorities underrepresented in the technology industry (Black Americans, Hispanic Americans, and Native

Americans) are strongly encouraged to apply. Selection is based on academic performance; college entrance examination scores; mathematics, science, and technology course work; achievements; leadership; civic participation; interests; employment; insight into and commitment to a career in technology; and communication skill. **Deadline for Receipt:** March of each year. **Additional Information:** This program was established in 1999 by Intel, which offered it to the Oregon Council of the AeA (formerly American Electronics Association) in the following year. Currently, Intel and other Oregon AeA member companies (such as Xerox and Hewlett Packard) provide ongoing support.

3070 ■ PLASTICS INSTITUTE OF AMERICA

c/o University of Massachusetts at Lowell
Attn: Plastics Pioneers Association
333 Aiken Street
Lowell, MA 01854
Tel: (978)934-3130
Fax: (978)458-4141
E-mail: info@plasticsinstitute.org
Web Site: http://www.plasticsinstitute.org/scholarships.php
To provide financial assistance to college students taking courses related to plastics technology.
Title of Award: Plastics Pioneers Association Scholarships **Area, Field, or Subject:** Chemistry; Engineering, Materials; Technology **Level of Education for which Award is Granted:** Undergraduate **Number Awarded:** Varies each year; recently, 15 of these scholarships were awarded. **Funds Available:** The stipend is $1,500 per year. **Duration:** 1 year; may be renewed for 1 additional year.
Eligibility Requirements: This program is open to students enrolled in a 2-year, 4-year, or certificate program. Applicants must be studying plastics/polymer science, engineering, technology, and management. They must be U.S. citizens and interested in preparing for a career in the plastics industry. Selection is based on academic record, extracurricular activities, recommendations, and an essay on their interest in a career in plastics. **Deadline for Receipt:** March of each year. **Additional Information:** This program is funded by the Education Fund of the Plastics Pioneers Association and administered by the Plastics Institute of America.

3071 ■ SEALASKA CORPORATION

Attn: Sealaska Heritage Institute
One Sealaska Plaza, Suite 301
Juneau, AK 99801-1249
Tel: (907)586-9166; 888-311-4992
Fax: (907)586-9293
E-mail: scholarship@sealaska.com
Web Site: http://www.sealaskaheritage.org/programs/university_scholarships.htm
To provide financial assistance for undergraduate or graduate study to Native Alaskans who have a connection to Sealaska Corporation and are majoring in designated fields.
Title of Award: Sealaska Heritage Institute 7(i) Scholarships **Area, Field, or Subject:** Business administration; Chemistry; Engineering, Chemical; Health care services; Mathematics and mathematical sciences; Natural resources; Physics **Level of Education for which Award is Granted:** Graduate, Undergraduate **Number Awarded:** Varies each year. **Funds Available:** The amount of the award depends on the availability of funds, the number of qualified applicants, class standing, and cumulative GPA. **Duration:** 1 year; may be renewed up to 5 years for a bachelor's degree, up to 3 years for a master's degree, up to 2 years for a doctorate, or up to 3 years for vocational study. The maximum total support is limited to 9 years. Renewal depends on recipients' maintaining full-time enrollment and a GPA of 2.5 or higher.
Eligibility Requirements: This program is open to 1) Alaska Natives who are enrolled to Sealaska Corporation, and 2) Native lineal descendants of Alaska Natives enrolled to Sealaska Corporation, whether or not the applicant owns Sealaska Corporation stock. Applicants must be enrolled or accepted for enrollment as full-time undergraduate or graduate students. Along with their application, they must submit 2 essays: 1) their personal history and educational goals, and 2) their expected contributions to the Alaska Native or Native American community. Financial need is also considered in the selection process. The following areas of study qualify for these awards: natural resources (environmental sciences, engineer-

ing, conservation biology, environmental law, fisheries, geology, marine science/biology, forestry, wildlife management, and mining technology); business administration (accounting, finance, marketing, international business, international commerce and trade, management of information systems, human resources management, economics, computer information systems, and industrial management); and other special fields (cadastral surveys, chemistry, equipment/machinery operators, industrial safety specialists, health specialists, plastics engineers, trade specialists, physics, mathematics, and marine trades and occupations). **Deadline for Receipt:** February of each year. **Additional Information:** Funding for this program is provided from Alaska Native Claims Settlement Act (ANSCA) Section 7(i) revenue sharing provisions. Sealaska sponsors a number of other scholarships, including the Cape Fox Scholarships and the Sealaska Heritage Institute Scholarships.

3072 ■ SIEMENS FOUNDATION

170 Wood Avenue South
Iselin, NJ 08830
877-822-5233
Fax: (732)603-5890
E-mail: foundation@sc.siemens.com
Web Site: http://www.siemens-foundation.org/awards
To recognize and reward high school students with exceptional scores on the Advanced Placement (AP) examinations in mathematics and the sciences.

Title of Award: Siemens Awards for Advanced Placement **Area, Field, or Subject:** Biological and clinical sciences; Chemistry; Computer and information sciences; Environmental conservation; Environmental science; Mathematics and mathematical sciences; Physics; Statistics **Level of Education for which Award is Granted:** Professional, Undergraduate **Number Awarded:** 24 regional scholarships (2 females and 2 males in each of the 6 regions), 2 national scholarships (1 female and 1 male), 12 high school awards (in each region, 1 to a school for improvement in the number and percentage of students taking AP examinations, 1 to an urban school for providing access to AP mathematics and science to minorities), and 18 teacher awards (in each region, 2 for commitment to students and the AP program, 1 for teaching minorities) are awarded each year. **Funds Available:** Regional scholarships are $3,000; national winners receive additional $5,000 scholarships. Awards to teachers and to schools are $1,000. **Duration:** The awards are presented annually.

Eligibility Requirements: All students in U.S. high schools are eligible to be considered for these awards (including home-schooled students and those in U.S. territories). Each fall, the College Board identifies the male and female seniors in each of its regions who have earned the highest number of scores on 7 AP exams: biology, calculus BC, chemistry, computer science AB, environmental science, physics C (physics C: mechanics and physics C: electricity each count as half), and statistics. Males and females are considered separately. Regional winners receive all-expense paid trips to Washington, D.C., where national winners are announced. The program also recognizes and rewards monetarily 1) schools that have shown the greatest improvement in the number and percentage of students taking AP examinations in biology, calculus, chemistry, computer science, environmental science, physics, and statistics in the past year; and 2) non-magnet urban schools that provide access to AP mathematics and science to a significant number of underrepresented minority students. In addition, teachers are rewarded for their commitment to students and the AP program. Additional teachers are recognized because they have successfully taught AP mathematics and/or science to underrepresented minority students in non-magnet urban schools. **Deadline for Receipt:** There is no application or nomination process for these awards. The College Board identifies the students, teachers, and high schools for the Siemens Foundation. **Additional Information:** Information from the College Board is available at (703) 707-8999.

3073 ■ SIEMENS FOUNDATION

170 Wood Avenue South
Iselin, NJ 08830
877-822-5233
Fax: (732)603-5890
E-mail: foundation@sc.siemens.com
Web Site: http://www.siemens-foundation.org/scholarship

To recognize and reward outstanding high school seniors who have undertaken individual or team research projects in science, mathematics, and technology (or in combinations of those disciplines).

Title of Award: Siemens Westinghouse Competition Awards **Area, Field, or Subject:** Astronomy and astronomical sciences; Atmospheric science; Biochemistry; Biological and clinical sciences; Chemistry; Computer and information sciences; Earth sciences; Engineering, Civil; Engineering, Electrical; Engineering, Mechanical; Environmental science; Genetics; Geosciences; Materials research/science; Mathematics and mathematical sciences; Nutrition; Physics; Writing **Level of Education for which Award is Granted:** Undergraduate **Number Awarded:** In the initial round of judging, up to 300 regional semifinalists (up to 50 in each region) are selected. Of those, 60 are chosen as regional finalists (5 individuals and 5 teams in each of the 6 regions). Then 12 regional winners (1 individual and 1 team) are selected in the regional competitions, and they become the national finalists. **Funds Available:** At the regional level, finalists receive $1,000 scholarships, both as individuals and members of teams. Individual regional winners receive $3,000 scholarships. Winning regional teams receive $6,000 scholarships to be divided among the team members. Those regional winners then receive additional scholarships as national finalists. In the national competition. first-place winners receive an additional $100,000 scholarship, second place an additional $50,000 scholarship, third place an additional $40,000 scholarship, fourth place an additional $30,000 scholarship, fifth place an additional $20,000 scholarship, and sixth place an additional $10,000 scholarship. Those national awards are provided both to individuals and to teams to be divided equally among team members. Scholarship money is sent directly to the recipient's college or university to cover undergraduate and/or graduate educational expenses. Schools with regional finalists receive a $2,000 award to be used to support science, mathematics, and technology programs in their schools. **Duration:** The competition is held annually.

Eligibility Requirements: This program is open to high school seniors who are legal or permanent U.S. residents. They must be enrolled in a high school in the United States, Puerto Rico, Guam, Virgin Islands, American Samoa, Wake and Midway Islands, or the Marianas. U.S. high school students enrolled in a Department of Defense dependents school, an accredited overseas American or international school, a foreign school as an exchange student, or a foreign school because their parent(s) live and work abroad are also eligible. Students being home-schooled qualify if they obtain the endorsement of the school district official responsible for such programs. Research projects may be submitted in mathematics and the biological and physical sciences, or involve combinations of disciplines, such as astrophysics, biochemistry, bioengineering, biology, biophysics, botany, chemistry, computer science, civil engineering, earth and atmospheric science engineering, electrical engineering, environmental sciences, fluid dynamics, genetics, geology, materials science, mathematics, mechanical engineering, nutritional science, physics, toxicology, and virology. Both individual and team projects (2 or 3 members) may be entered. All team members must meet the eligibility requirements. Team projects may include seniors, but that is not a requirement. Competition entrants must submit a detailed report on their research project, including a description of the purpose of the research, rationale for the research, pertinent scientific literature, methodology, results, discussion, and conclusion. All projects must be endorsed by a sponsoring high school (except home-schooled students, who obtain their endorsement from the district or state home-school official). Each project must have a project advisor or mentor who is a member of the instructional staff or a person approved by the endorsing high school. There are 3 judging phases to the competition. An initial review panel selects outstanding research projects from 6 different regions of the country. The students submitting these projects are identified as regional semifinalists. Out of those, the highest-rated projects from each region are selected and the students who submitted them are recognized as regional finalists. For the next phase, the regional finalists are offered all-expense paid trips to the regional competition on the campus of a regional university partner, where their projects are reviewed by a panel of judges appointed by the host institution. Regional finalists are required to prepare a poster display of their research project, make an oral presentation about the research and research findings, and respond to questions from the judges. The top-rated individual and the top-rated team project in each region are selected as regional winners to represent the region in the national competition as national finalists. At that competition, the national finalists again display their projects, make oral presentations, and respond to judges' questions. At each phase, selection is based on clarity of expression, comprehensiveness, creativity, field knowledge, future work, interpretation, literature review, presentation, scientific importance, and validity. **Deadline for Receipt:** September of each year. **Additional Information:** The program is offered by Siemens Foundation, in partnership with the College Board. Information is available from the College Board at (703) 707-8999, E-mail: spro@collegeboard.org. Students submitting the projects with the highest evaluations become part of a registry that is circulated to colleges and universities nationwide. To continue receiving scholarships, winners must attend an accredited academic institution on a full-time basis.

3074 ■ SOCIETY OF PLASTICS ENGINEERS
Attn: SPE Foundation
14 Fairfield Drive
Brookfield, CT 06804-0403
Tel: (203)740-5447
Fax: (203)775-1157
E-mail: foundation@4spe.org
Web Site: http://www.4spe.org/foundation/scholarships.php
To provide financial assistance to undergraduate students who have a career interest in the plastics industry.
Title of Award: American Plastics Council (APC)/SPE Plastics Environmental Division Scholarship **Area, Field, or Subject:** Chemistry; Engineering, Chemical; Engineering, Industrial; Engineering, Materials; Engineering, Mechanical; Physics **Level of Education for which Award is Granted:** Undergraduate **Number Awarded:** 1 each year. **Funds Available:** The stipend is $2,500 per year. Funds are paid directly to the recipient's school. **Duration:** 1 year.
Eligibility Requirements: This program is open to full-time undergraduate students at 4-year colleges or in 2-year technical programs. Applicants must 1) have a demonstrated or expressed interest in the plastics industry; 2) be majoring in or taking courses that would be beneficial to a career in the plastics or polymer industry (e.g., plastics engineering, polymer sciences, chemistry, physics, chemical engineering, mechanical engineering, or industrial engineering); 3) be in good academic standing at their school; and 4) be able to document financial need. Along with their application, they must submit 3 letters of recommendation; a high school and/or college transcript; and a 1- to 2-page statement telling why they are interested in the scholarship, their qualifications, and their educational and career goals in the plastics industry. **Deadline for Receipt:** January of each year. **Additional Information:** This scholarship is awarded annually in the names of corporations cited as the *Excellence in Plastics Impact on the Environment* by the Plastics Environmental Division of the Society of Plastics Engineers (SPE).

3075 ■ SOCIETY OF PLASTICS ENGINEERS
Attn: SPE Foundation
14 Fairfield Drive
Brookfield, CT 06804-0403
Tel: (203)740-5447
Fax: (203)775-1157
E-mail: foundation@4spe.org
Web Site: http://www.4spe.org/foundation/scholarships.php
To provide financial assistance to undergraduate and graduate students who have a career interest in the plastics industry.
Title of Award: Composites Division/Harold Giles Scholarship **Area, Field, or Subject:** Chemistry; Engineering, Chemical; Engineering, Industrial; Engineering, Materials; Engineering, Mechanical; Physics **Level of Education for which Award is Granted:** Graduate, Undergraduate **Number Awarded:** 1 each year. **Funds Available:** The stipend is $1,000 per year. Funds are paid directly to the recipient's school. **Duration:** 1 year.
Eligibility Requirements: This program is open to full-time undergraduate and graduate students at 4-year colleges or in 2-year technical programs. Applicants must 1) have a demonstrated or expressed interest in the plastics industry; 2) be majoring in or taking courses that would be beneficial to a career in the plastics or polymer industry (e.g., plastics engineering, polymer sciences, chemistry, physics, chemical engineering, mechanical engineering, or industrial engineering); 3) be in good academic standing at their school; and 4) be able to document financial need. Along with their application, they must submit 3 letters of recom-

mendation; a high school and/or college transcript; and a 1- to 2-page statement telling why they are interested in the scholarship, their qualifications, and their educational and career goals in the plastics industry. **Deadline for Receipt:** January of each year.

3076 ■ SOCIETY OF PLASTICS ENGINEERS
Attn: SPE Foundation
14 Fairfield Drive
Brookfield, CT 06804-0403
Tel: (203)740-5447
Fax: (203)775-1157
E-mail: foundation@4spe.org
Web Site: http://www.4spe.org/foundation/scholarships.php
To provide financial assistance to undergraduate students who have a career interest in the plastics industry.
Title of Award: Robert E. Cramer/Product Design and Development Division/Mid-Michigan Section Scholarship **Area, Field, or Subject:** Chemistry; Engineering, Chemical; Engineering, Industrial; Engineering, Materials; Engineering, Mechanical; Physics **Level of Education for which Award is Granted:** Undergraduate **Number Awarded:** 1 each year. **Funds Available:** The stipend is $1,000 per year. Funds are paid directly to the recipient's school. **Duration:** 1 year.
Eligibility Requirements: This program is open to full-time undergraduate students at 4-year colleges or in 2-year technical programs. Applicants must 1) have a demonstrated or expressed interest in the plastics industry; 2) be majoring in or taking courses that would be beneficial to a career in the plastics or polymer industry (e.g., plastics engineering, polymer sciences, chemistry, physics, chemical engineering, mechanical engineering, or industrial engineering); 3) be in good academic standing at their school; and 4) be able to document financial need. Along with their application, they must submit 3 letters of recommendation; a high school and/or college transcript; and a 1- to 2-page statement telling why they are interested in the scholarship, their qualifications, and their educational and career goals in the plastics industry. **Deadline for Receipt:** January of each year.

3077 ■ SOCIETY OF PLASTICS ENGINEERS
Attn: SPE Foundation
14 Fairfield Drive
Brookfield, CT 06804-0403
Tel: (203)740-5447
Fax: (203)775-1157
E-mail: foundation@4spe.org
Web Site: http://www.4spe.org/foundation/scholarships.php
To provide financial assistance to undergraduate students who have a career interest in the plastics industry.
Title of Award: Robert G. Dailey/Detroit Section Scholarship **Area, Field, or Subject:** Chemistry; Engineering, Chemical; Engineering, Industrial; Engineering, Materials; Engineering, Mechanical; Physics **Level of Education for which Award is Granted:** Undergraduate **Number Awarded:** 1 each year. **Funds Available:** The stipend is $4,000 per year. Funds are paid directly to the recipient's school. **Duration:** 1 year.
Eligibility Requirements: This program is open to full-time undergraduate students at 4-year colleges or in 2-year technical programs. Applicants must 1) have a demonstrated or expressed interest in the plastics industry; 2) be majoring in or taking courses that would be beneficial to a career in the plastics or polymer industry (e.g., plastics engineering, polymer sciences, chemistry, physics, chemical engineering, mechanical engineering, or industrial engineering); 3) be in good academic standing at their school; and 4) be able to document financial need. Along with their application, they must submit 3 letters of recommendation; a high school and/or college transcript; and a 1- to 2-page statement telling why they are interested in the scholarship, their qualifications, and their educational and career goals in the plastics industry. **Deadline for Receipt:** January of each year.

3078 ■ SOCIETY OF PLASTICS ENGINEERS
Attn: SPE Foundation
14 Fairfield Drive
Brookfield, CT 06804-0403
Tel: (203)740-5447
Fax: (203)775-1157
E-mail: foundation@4spe.org

Web Site: http://www.4spe.org/foundation/scholarships.php
To provide financial assistance to Mexican American undergraduate and graduate students who have a career interest in the plastics industry.
Title of Award: Fleming/Blaszcak Scholarship **Area, Field, or Subject:** Chemistry; Engineering, Chemical; Engineering, Industrial; Engineering, Materials; Engineering, Mechanical; Physics **Level of Education for which Award is Granted:** Four Year College, Graduate **Number Awarded:** 1 each year. **Funds Available:** The stipend is $2,000 per year. Funds are paid directly to the recipient's school. **Duration:** 1 year.
Eligibility Requirements: This program is open to full-time undergraduate and graduate students of Mexican descent who are enrolled in a 4-year college or university. Applicants must be U.S. citizens or legal residents. They must 1) have a demonstrated or expressed interest in the plastics industry; 2) be majoring in or taking courses that would be beneficial to a career in the plastics or polymer industry (e.g., plastics engineering, polymer sciences, chemistry, physics, chemical engineering, mechanical engineering, or industrial engineering); 3) be in good academic standing at their school; and 4) be able to document financial need. Along with their application, they must submit 3 letters of recommendation; a high school and/or college transcript; a 1- to 2-page statement telling why they are interested in the scholarship, their qualifications, and their educational and career goals in the plastics industry; and documentation of their Mexican heritage. **Deadline for Receipt:** January of each year. **Additional Information:** This program is sponsored by Cal Mold Inc. and Formula Plastics.

3079 ■ SOCIETY OF PLASTICS ENGINEERS

Attn: SPE Foundation
14 Fairfield Drive
Brookfield, CT 06804-0403
Tel: (203)740-5447
Fax: (203)775-1157
E-mail: foundation@4spe.org
Web Site: http://www.4spe.org/foundation/scholarships.php
To provide financial assistance to undergraduate and graduate students who have a career interest in the plastics industry and experience in the thermoset industry.
Title of Award: Thermoset Division/James I. MacKenzie Scholarship **Area, Field, or Subject:** Chemistry; Engineering, Chemical; Engineering, Industrial; Engineering, Materials; Engineering, Mechanical; Physics **Level of Education for which Award is Granted:** Graduate, Undergraduate **Number Awarded:** 2 each year: 1 to an undergraduate and 1 to a graduate student. **Funds Available:** The stipend is $1,000 per year. Funds are paid directly to the recipient's school. **Duration:** 1 year.
Eligibility Requirements: This program is open to full-time undergraduate and graduate students at either a 4-year college or in a 2-year technical program. Applicants must have experience in the thermoset industry, such as courses taken, research conducted, or jobs held. They must 1) have a demonstrated or expressed interest in the plastics industry; 2) be majoring in or taking courses that would be beneficial to a career in the plastics or polymer industry (e.g., plastics engineering, polymer sciences, chemistry, physics, chemical engineering, mechanical engineering, or industrial engineering); 3) be in good academic standing at their school; and 4) be able to document financial need. Along with their application, they must submit 3 letters of recommendation; a high school and/or college transcript; a 1- to 2-page statement telling why they are interested in the scholarship, their qualifications, and their educational and career goals in the plastics industry; and a statement detailing their exposure to the thermoset industry. **Deadline for Receipt:** January of each year.

3080 ■ SOCIETY OF PLASTICS ENGINEERS

Attn: SPE Foundation
14 Fairfield Drive
Brookfield, CT 06804-0403
Tel: (203)740-5447
Fax: (203)775-1157
E-mail: foundation@4spe.org
Web Site: http://www.4spe.org/foundation/scholarships.php
To provide financial assistance to undergraduate and graduate students who have a career interest in the plastics industry.
Title of Award: Ted Neward Scholarships **Area, Field, or Subject:** Chemistry; Engineering, Chemical; Engineering, Industrial; Engineering, Materials; Engineering, Mechanical; Physics **Level of Education for**

which Award is Granted: Graduate, Undergraduate **Number Awarded:** 3 each year. **Funds Available:** The stipend is $3,000 per year. Funds are paid directly to the recipient's school. **Duration:** 1 year.
Eligibility Requirements: This program is open to full-time undergraduate and graduate students at 4-year colleges or in 2-year technical programs. Applicants must 1) have a demonstrated or expressed interest in the plastics industry; 2) be majoring in or taking courses that would be beneficial to a career in the plastics or polymer industry (e.g., plastics engineering, polymer sciences, chemistry, physics, chemical engineering, mechanical engineering, or industrial engineering); 3) be in good academic standing at their school; and 4) be able to document financial need. U.S. citizenship is required. Along with their application, they must submit 3 letters of recommendation; a high school and/or college transcript; and a 1- to 2-page statement telling why they are interested in the scholarship, their qualifications, and their educational and career goals in the plastics industry. **Deadline for Receipt:** January of each year.

3081 ■ SOCIETY OF PLASTICS ENGINEERS

Attn: SPE Foundation
14 Fairfield Drive
Brookfield, CT 06804-0403
Tel: (203)740-5447
Fax: (203)775-1157
E-mail: foundation@4spe.org
Web Site: http://www.4spe.org/foundation/scholarships.php
To provide financial assistance to undergraduate students who have a career interest in the plastics industry.
Title of Award: Polymer Modifiers and Additives Division Scholarships **Area, Field, or Subject:** Chemistry; Engineering, Chemical; Engineering, Industrial; Engineering, Materials; Engineering, Mechanical; Physics **Level of Education for which Award is Granted:** Undergraduate **Number Awarded:** 4 each year. **Funds Available:** The stipend is $4,000 per year. Funds are paid directly to the recipient's school. **Duration:** 1 year.
Eligibility Requirements: This program is open to full-time undergraduate students at 4-year colleges or in 2-year technical programs. Applicants must 1) have a demonstrated or expressed interest in the plastics industry; 2) be majoring in or taking courses that would be beneficial to a career in the plastics or polymer industry (e.g., plastics engineering, polymer sciences, chemistry, physics, chemical engineering, mechanical engineering, or industrial engineering); 3) be in good academic standing at their school; and 4) be able to document financial need. Along with their application, they must submit 3 letters of recommendation; a high school and/or college transcript; and a 1- to 2-page statement telling why they are interested in the scholarship, their qualifications, and their educational and career goals in the plastics industry. **Deadline for Receipt:** January of each year.

3082 ■ SOCIETY OF PLASTICS ENGINEERS

Attn: SPE Foundation
14 Fairfield Drive
Brookfield, CT 06804-0403
Tel: (203)740-5447
Fax: (203)775-1157
E-mail: foundation@4spe.org
Web Site: http://www.4spe.org/foundation/scholarships.php
To provide financial assistance to undergraduate and graduate students who have a career interest in the plastics industry.
Title of Award: Society of Plastics Engineers Foundation Scholarships **Area, Field, or Subject:** Chemistry; Engineering, Chemical; Engineering, Industrial; Engineering, Materials; Engineering, Mechanical; Physics **Level of Education for which Award is Granted:** Graduate, Undergraduate **Number Awarded:** 10 to 12 each year. **Funds Available:** Stipends range up to $4,000 per year. Funds are paid directly to the recipient's school. **Duration:** 1 year; may be renewed for up to 3 additional years.
Eligibility Requirements: This program is open to full-time undergraduate and graduate students at 4-year colleges or in 2-year technical programs. Applicants must 1) have a demonstrated or expressed interest in the plastics industry; 2) be majoring in or taking courses that would be beneficial to a career in the plastics or polymer industry (e.g., plastics engineering, polymer sciences, chemistry, physics, chemical engineering, mechanical engineering, or industrial engineering); 3) be in good

academic standing at their school; and 4) be able to document financial need. Along with their application, they must submit 3 letters of recommendation; a high school or college transcript; and a 1- to 2-page statement telling why they are interested in the scholarship, their qualifications, and their educational and career goals in the plastics industry. **Deadline for Receipt:** January of each year.

3083 ■ SOCIETY OF PLASTICS ENGINEERS

Attn: SPE Foundation
14 Fairfield Drive
Brookfield, CT 06804-0403
Tel: (203)740-5447
Fax: (203)775-1157
E-mail: foundation@4spe.org
Web Site: http://www.4spe.org/foundation/scholarships.php
To provide college scholarships to students who have a career interest in the plastics industry and experience in the thermoforming industry.
Title of Award: Thermoforming Division Memorial Scholarships **Area, Field, or Subject:** Chemistry; Engineering, Chemical; Engineering, Industrial; Engineering, Materials; Engineering, Mechanical; Physics **Level of Education for which Award is Granted:** Graduate, Undergraduate **Number Awarded:** 2 each year. **Funds Available:** The stipend is $5,000 per year. Funds are paid directly to the recipient's school. **Duration:** 1 year.
Eligibility Requirements: This program is open to full-time undergraduate and graduate students at either a 4-year college or in a 2-year technical program. Applicants must have experience in the thermoforming industry, such as courses taken, research conducted, or jobs held. They must 1) have a demonstrated or expressed interest in the plastics industry; 2) be majoring in or taking courses that would be beneficial to a career in the plastics or polymer industry (e.g., plastics engineering, polymer sciences, chemistry, physics, chemical engineering, mechanical engineering, or industrial engineering); 3) be in good academic standing at their school; and 4) be able to document financial need. Along with their application, they must submit 3 letters of recommendation; a high school and/or college transcript; a 1to 2-page statement telling why they are interested in the scholarship, their qualifications, and their educational and career goals in the plastics industry; and a statement detailing their exposure to the thermoforming industry. **Deadline for Receipt:** January of each year.

3084 ■ SOCIETY OF PLASTICS ENGINEERS

Attn: SPE Foundation
14 Fairfield Drive
Brookfield, CT 06804-0403
Tel: (203)740-5447
Fax: (203)775-1157
E-mail: foundation@4spe.org
Web Site: http://www.4spe.org/foundation/scholarships.php
To provide financial assistance to undergraduate students who have a career interest in the plastics industry.
Title of Award: Vinyl Plastics Division Scholarship **Area, Field, or Subject:** Chemistry; Engineering, Chemical; Engineering, Industrial; Engineering, Materials; Engineering, Mechanical; Physics **Level of Education for which Award is Granted:** Undergraduate **Number Awarded:** 1 each year. **Funds Available:** The stipend is $1,000 per year. Funds are paid directly to the recipient's school. **Duration:** 1 year.
Eligibility Requirements: This program is open to full-time undergraduate students at 4-year colleges or in 2-year technical programs. Applicants must 1) have a demonstrated or expressed interest in the plastics industry; 2) be majoring in or taking courses that would be beneficial to a career in the plastics or polymer industry (e.g., plastics engineering, polymer sciences, chemistry, physics, chemical engineering, mechanical engineering, or industrial engineering); 3) be in good academic standing at their school; and 4) be able to document financial need. Along with their application, they must submit 3 letters of recommendation; a high school and/or college transcript; and a 1- to 2-page statement telling why they are interested in the scholarship, their qualifications, and their educational and career goals in the plastics industry. Preference is given to applicants

with experience in the vinyl industry, such as courses taken, research conducted, or jobs held. **Deadline for Receipt:** January of each year.

3085 ■ TEXAS SPACE GRANT CONSORTIUM

Attn: Administrative Assistant
3925 West Braker Lane, Suite 200
Austin, TX 78759
Tel: (512)471-3583
Free: 800-248-8742
Fax: (512)471-3585
E-mail: scholarships@tsgc.utexas.edu
Web Site: http://www.tsgc.utexas.edu/grants
To provide financial assistance to upper-division and medical students at Texas universities working on degrees in the fields of space science and engineering.
Title of Award: Columbia Crew Memorial Undergraduate Scholarships **Area, Field, or Subject:** Aerospace sciences; Biological and clinical sciences; Chemistry; Engineering, Aerospace/Aeronautical/Astronautical; Engineering, Chemical; Engineering, Electrical; Engineering, Industrial; Engineering, Mechanical; Geology; Mathematics and mathematical sciences; Physics; Space and planetary sciences **Level of Education for which Award is Granted:** Doctorate, Undergraduate **Number Awarded:** Varies each year; recently, 29 of these scholarships were awarded. **Funds Available:** The stipend is $1,000. **Duration:** 1 year; nonrenewable.
Eligibility Requirements: Applicants must be U.S. citizens, eligible for financial assistance, and registered for full-time study at a participating college or university. Applicants must be a sophomore at a 2-year institution, a junior or senior at a 4-year institution, or a first- or second-year student at a medical school. Supported fields of study have included aerospace engineering, biology, chemical engineering, chemistry, electrical engineering, geology, industrial engineering, mathematics, mechanical engineering, and physics. The program encourages participation by members of groups underrepresented in science and engineering (persons with disabilities, women, African Americans, Hispanic Americans, Native Americans, and Pacific Islanders). Selection is based on excellence in academics, participation in space education projects, participation in research projects, and exhibited leadership qualities. **Deadline for Receipt:** March of each year. **Additional Information:** In 2003, the Texas Space Grant Consortium renamed its undergraduate scholarship program in honor of the 7 Space Shuttle Columbia astronauts. The participating universities are Baylor University, Lamar University, Prairie View A&M University, Rice University, San Jacinto College, Southern Methodist University, Sul Ross State University, Texas A&M University (including Kingsville and Corpus Christi campuses), Texas Christian University, Texas Southern University, Texas Tech University, Trinity University, University of Houston (including Clear Lake and Downtown campuses), University of Texas at Arlington, University of Texas at Austin, University of Texas at Dallas, University of Texas at El Paso, University of Texas at San Antonio, and University of Texas/Pan American. This program is funded by the National Aeronautics and Space Administration (NASA).

3086 ■ U.S. AIR FORCE

Attn: Headquarters AFROTC/RRUC
551 East Maxwell Boulevard
Maxwell AFB, AL 36112-5917
Tel: (334)953-2091; (866)423-7682
Fax: (334)953-6167
Web Site: http://www.afrotc.com/scholarships/hsschol/types.php
To provide financial assistance to high school seniors or graduates who are interested in joining Air Force ROTC in college and are willing to serve as Air Force officers following completion of their bachelor's degree.
Title of Award: Air Force ROTC High School Scholarships **Area, Field, or Subject:** Architecture; Chemistry; Computer and information sciences; Engineering, Aerospace/Aeronautical/Astronautical; Engineering, Architectural; Engineering, Civil; Engineering, Computer; Engineering, Electrical; Engineering, Mechanical; Environmental science; General studies/Field of study not specified; Mathematics and mathematical sciences; Meteorology; Operations research; Physics **Level of Education for which Award is Granted:** Four Year College **Number Awarded:** Approximately 2,000 each year. **Funds Available:** Type 1 scholarships provide payment of full tuition and most laboratory fees, as well as $600 for books. Type 2 scholarships pay the same benefits except tuition is

capped at $15,000 per year; students who attend an institution where tuition exceeds $15,000 must pay the difference. Type 7 scholarships pay full tuition and most laboratory fees, but students must attend a college or university where the tuition is less than $9,000 per year or a public college or university where they qualify for the in-state tuition rate; they may not attend an institution with higher tuition and pay the difference. Approximately 5% of scholarship offers are for Type 1, approximately 20% are for Type 2, and approximately 75% are for type 7. All recipients are also awarded a tax-free subsistence allowance for 10 months of each year that is $250 per month as a freshman, $300 per month as a sophomore, $350 per month as a junior, and $400 per month as a senior. **Duration:** 4 years.

Eligibility Requirements: This program is open to high school seniors who are U.S. citizens at least 17 of age and have been accepted at a college or university with an Air Force ROTC unit on campus or a college with a cross-enrollment agreement with such a college. Applicants must have a cumulative GPA of 3.0 or higher and an ACT composite score of 24 or higher or an SAT score of 1100 (mathematics and verbal portion only) or higher. At the time of their commissioning in the Air Force, they must be no more than 31 years of age. They must agree to serve for at least 4 years as active-duty Air Force officers following graduation from college. **Deadline for Receipt:** November of each year. **Additional Information:** Recently, approximately 70% of these scholarships were offered to students planning to major in the science and technical fields of architecture, chemistry, computer science, engineering (aeronautical, aerospace, astronautical, architectural, civil, computer, electrical, environmental, or mechanical), mathematics, meteorology and atmospheric sciences, operations research, or physics. Approximately 30% were offered to students in all other fields. While scholarship recipients can major in any subject, they must enroll in 4 years of aerospace studies courses at 1 of the 144 colleges and universities that have an Air Force ROTC unit on campus; students may also attend nearly 900 other colleges that have cross-enrollment agreements with the institutions that have an Air Force ROTC unit on campus. Recipients must attend a 4-week summer training camp at an Air Force base, usually between their sophomore and junior years. Most cadets incur a 4-year active-duty commitment. Pilots incur a 10-year active-duty service commitment after successfully completing Specialized Undergraduate Pilot Training and navigators incur a 6-year commitment after successfully completing Specialized Undergraduate Navigator Training. The minimum service obligation for intelligence and Air Battle Management career fields is 5 years.

3087 ■ U.S. AIR FORCE

Attn: Headquarters AFROTC/RRUC
551 East Maxwell Boulevard
Maxwell AFB, AL 36112-5917
Tel: (334)953-2091; (866)423-7682
Fax: (334)953-6167
Web Site: http://www.afrotc.com/scholarships/incolschol/incolProgram.php

To provide financial assistance to undergraduate students who are willing to join Air Force ROTC in college and serve as Air Force officers following completion of their bachelor's degree.

Title of Award: Air Force ROTC In-College Scholarship Program **Area, Field, or Subject:** Architecture; Chemistry; Computer and information sciences; Engineering; Engineering, Aerospace/Aeronautical/Astronautical; Engineering, Architectural; Engineering, Civil; Engineering, Computer; Engineering, Electrical; Engineering, Mechanical; Environmental science; General studies/Field of study not specified; Mathematics and mathematical sciences; Meteorology; Operations research; Physics **Level of Education for which Award is Granted:** Undergraduate **Number Awarded:** Varies each year. **Funds Available:** Cadets selected in Phase 1 are awarded type 2 AFROTC scholarships that provide for payment of tuition and fees, to a maximum of $15,000 per year. A limited number of cadets selected in Phase 2 are also awarded type 2 AFROTC scholarships, but most are awarded type 3 AFROTC scholarships with tuition capped at $9,000 per year. Cadets selected in Phase 3 are awarded type 6 AFROTC scholarships with tuition capped at $3,000 per year. All recipients are also awarded a book allowance of $600 and a tax-free subsistence allowance for 10 months of each year that is $300 per month during the sophomore

year, $350 during the junior year, and $400 during the senior year. **Duration:** 3 years for students selected as freshmen or 2 years for students selected as sophomores.

Eligibility Requirements: This program is open to U.S. citizens enrolled as freshmen or sophomores at 1 of the 144 colleges and universities that have an Air Force ROTC unit on campus. Applicants must have a cumulative GPA of 2.5 or higher and be able to pass the Air Force Officer Qualifying Test and the Air Force ROTC Physical Fitness Test. At the time of commissioning, they may be no more than 31 years of age. They must agree to serve for at least 4 years as active-duty Air Force officers following graduation from college. Phase 1 is open to students enrolled in the Air Force ROTC program who do not currently have a scholarship but now wish to apply. Phase 2 is open to Phase 1 nonselects and students not enrolled in Air Force ROTC. Phase 3 is open only to Phase 2 nonselects. Recently, the program gave preference to students majoring in the science and technical fields of architecture, chemistry, computer science, engineering (aeronautical, aerospace, astronautical, architectural, civil, computer, electrical, environmental, or mechanical), mathematics, meteorology and atmospheric sciences, operations research, or physics. **Deadline for Receipt:** January of each year. **Additional Information:** While scholarship recipients can major in any subject, they must complete 4 years of aerospace studies courses at 1 of the 144 colleges or universities that have an Air Force ROTC unit on campus. Recipients must also attend a 4-week summer training camp at an Air Force base, usually between their sophomore and junior years; 2-year scholarship awardees attend in the summer after their junior year. Current military personnel are eligible for early release from active duty in order to enter the Air Force ROTC program. Following completion of their bachelor's degree, scholarship recipients earn a commission as a second lieutenant in the Air Force and serve at least 4 years.

3088 ■ U.S. AIR FORCE

Attn: Headquarters AFROTC/RRUE
Enlisted Commissioning Section
551 East Maxwell Boulevard
Maxwell AFB, AL 36112-5917
Tel: (334)953-2091; (866)423-7682
Fax: (334)953-6167
E-mail: enlisted@afrotc.com
Web Site: http://www.afoats.af.mil/AFROTC/EnlistedComm/ASCP.asp

To allow selected enlisted Air Force personnel to earn a bachelor's degree in approved majors by providing financial assistance for full-time college study.

Title of Award: Airman Scholarship and Commissioning Program **Area, Field, or Subject:** Architecture; Atmospheric science; Chemistry; Computer and information sciences; Engineering; Engineering, Aerospace/Aeronautical/Astronautical; Engineering, Architectural; Engineering, Civil; Engineering, Computer; Engineering, Electrical; Engineering, Mechanical; Environmental science; General studies/Field of study not specified; Mathematics and mathematical sciences; Meteorology; Operations research; Physics **Level of Education for which Award is Granted:** Undergraduate **Number Awarded:** Varies each year. **Funds Available:** Awards are type 2 AFROTC scholarships that provide for payment of tuition and fees, to a maximum of $15,000 per year, plus an annual book allowance of $600. All recipients are also awarded a tax-free subsistence allowance for 10 months of each year that is $300 per month during their sophomore year, $350 during their junior year, and $400 during their senior year. **Duration:** 2 to 4 years, until completion of a bachelor's degree.

Eligibility Requirements: This program is open to active-duty enlisted members of the Air Force who have completed at least 1 year of continuous active duty and at least 1 year on station. Applicants normally must have completed at least 24 semester hours of graded college credit with a cumulative college GPA of 2.5 or higher. If they have not completed 24 hours of graded college credit, they must have an ACT score of 24 or higher or an SAT combined verbal and mathematics score of 1100 or higher. They must also have scores on the Air Force Officer Qualifying Test (AFOQT) of 15 or more on the verbal scale and 10 or more on the quantitative scale and be able to pass the Air Force ROTC Physical Fitness Test. Applicants must have been accepted at a college or university (including crosstown schools) offering the AFROTC 4-year program. When they complete the program and receive their commission, they may not be 31 years of age or older. U.S. citizenship is required. Recently, awards were presented according to the following priorities: 1) computer, electrical, and environmental engineering; 2) aeronautical, aerospace, architectural, astronautical, civil, and mechanical engineering and meteorology and atmospheric sciences; 3) all other ABET-accredited engineering majors, architecture, chemistry, computer science, mathematics, operations research, and physics; 4) all other majors. **Deadline for Receipt:** October of each year. **Additional Information:** Selectees separate from the active-duty Air Force, join an AFROTC detachment, and become full-time students. Upon completing their degree, they are commissioned as officers and returned to active duty in the Air Force with a 4-year service obligation. Further information is available from base education service officers or an Air Force ROTC unit.

3089 ■ U.S. AIR FORCE

Attn: Headquarters AFROTC/RRUE
Enlisted Commissioning Section
551 East Maxwell Boulevard
Maxwell AFB, AL 36112-5917
Tel: (334)953-2091; (866)423-7682
Fax: (334)953-6167
E-mail: enlisted@afrotc.com
Web Site: http://www.afoats.af.mil/AFROTC/EnlistedComm/POC-ERP.asp

To allow selected enlisted Air Force personnel to earn a baccalaureate degree by providing financial assistance for full-time college study.

Title of Award: Professional Officer Course Early Release Program **Area, Field, or Subject:** Architecture; Atmospheric science; Chemistry; Computer and information sciences; Engineering; Engineering, Aerospace/Aeronautical/Astronautical; Engineering, Architectural; Engineering, Civil; Engineering, Computer; Engineering, Electrical; Engineering, Mechanical; Environmental science; General studies/Field of study not specified; Mathematics and mathematical sciences; Meteorology; Operations research; Physics **Level of Education for which Award is Granted:** Undergraduate **Number Awarded:** Varies each year. **Funds Available:** Participants receive a stipend for 10 months of the year that is $350 per month during the first year and $400 per month during the second year. Scholarship recipients earn the Professional Officer Course Incentive of $3,000 per year for tuition and $600 per year for books. **Duration:** 2 years (no more and no less).
Eligibility Requirements: Eligible to participate in this program are enlisted members of the Air Force under the age of 30 (or otherwise able to be commissioned before becoming 35 years of age) who have completed at least 1 year on continuous active duty, have served on station for at least 1 year, and have no more than 2 years remaining to complete their initial baccalaureate degree. Scholarship applicants must be younger than 31 years of age when they graduate and earn their commission. All applicants must have been accepted at a college or university offering the AFROTC 4-year program and must have a cumulative college GPA of 2.5 or higher. Their Air Force Officer Qualifying Test (AFOQT) scores must be at least 15 on the verbal and 10 on the quantitative. Applicants who have not completed 24 units of college work must have an ACT composite score of 24 or higher or an SAT combined verbal and mathematics score of 1100 or higher. U.S. citizenship is required. Recently, awards were presented according to the following priorities: 1) computer, electrical, and environmental engineering; 2) aeronautical, aerospace, architectural, astronautical, civil, and mechanical engineering and meteorology and atmospheric sciences; 3) all other ABET-accredited engineering majors, architecture, chemistry, computer science, mathematics, operations research, and physics; 4) all other majors. **Deadline for Receipt:** October of each year. **Additional Information:** Upon completing their degree, selectees are commissioned as officers in the Air Force with a 4-year service obligation. Further information is available from base education service officers or an Air Force ROTC unit.

3090 ■ U.S. NAVY

Attn: Navy Personnel Command
5722 Integrity Drive
Millington, TN 38054-5057
Tel: (901)874-3070; 888-633-9674
Fax: (901)874-2651

E-mail: nukeprograms@cnrc.navy.mil
Web Site: http://www.cnrc.navy.mil/nucfield/college/officer_options.htm
To provide financial assistance to college juniors and seniors who wish to serve in the Navy's nuclear propulsion training program following graduation.

Title of Award: Nuclear Propulsion Officer Candidate (NUPOC) Program **Area, Field, or Subject:** Chemistry; Engineering; General studies/Field of study not specified; Mathematics and mathematical sciences; Physics **Level of Education for which Award is Granted:** Four Year College **Number Awarded:** Varies each year. **Funds Available:** Participants become Active Reserve enlisted Navy personnel and receive a salary of up to $2,500 per month; the exact amount depends on the local cost of living and other factors. A bonus of $10,000 is also paid at the time of enlistment and another $2,000 upon completion of nuclear power training. **Duration:** Up to 30 months, until completion of a bachelor's degree.
Eligibility Requirements: This program is open to U.S. citizens who are entering their junior or senior year of college as a full-time student. Strong technical majors (mathematics, physics, chemistry, or an engineering field) are encouraged but not required. Applicants must have completed at least 1 year of calculus and 1 year of physics and must have earned a grade of "C" or better in all mathematics, science, and technical courses. Normally, they must be 26 years of age or younger at the expected date of commissioning, although applicants for the design and research specialty may be 29 years old. **Additional Information:** Following graduation, participants attend Officer Candidate School in Pensacola, Florida for 4 months and receive their commissions. They have a service obligation of 8 years (of which at least 5 years must be on active duty), beginning with 6 months at the Navy Nuclear Power Training Command in Charleston, South Carolina and 6 more months of hands-on training at a nuclear reactor facility. Further information on this program is available from a local Navy recruiter or the Navy Recruiting Command, 801 North Randolph Street, Arlington, VA 22203-1991.

3091 ■ UNIVERSITY INTERSCHOLASTIC LEAGUE

Attn: Texas Interscholastic League Foundation
1701 Manor Road
P.O. Box 8028
Austin, TX 78713
Tel: (512)232-4938
Fax: (512)471-5908
E-mail: carolyn.scott@mail.utexas.edu
Web Site: http://www.uil.utexas.edu/tilf/scholarships.html
To provide financial assistance to students who participate in programs of the Texas Interscholastic League Foundation (TILF) and plan to major in chemistry, biochemistry, or chemical engineering.

Title of Award: Welch Foundation Scholarships **Area, Field, or Subject:** Biochemistry; Chemistry; Engineering, Chemical **Level of Education for which Award is Granted:** Undergraduate **Number Awarded:** 20 each year. **Funds Available:** The stipend is $3,500 per year. **Duration:** 4 years.
Eligibility Requirements: This program is open to students who meet the 5 basic requirements of the TILF: 1) graduate from high school during the current year and begin college or university in Texas by the following fall; 2) enroll full time at an approved institution and maintain a GPA of 2.5 or higher during the first semester; 3) compete in a University Interscholastic League (UIL) academic state meet contest in accounting, calculator applications, computer applications, computer science, current issues and events, debate (cross-examination and Lincoln-Douglas), journalism (editorial writing, feature writing, headline writing, and news writing), literary criticism, mathematics, number sense, 1-act play, ready writing, science, social studies, speech (prose interpretation, poetry interpretation, informative speaking, and persuasive speaking), or spelling and vocabulary; 4) submit high school transcripts that include SAT and/or ACT scores; and 5) submit parents' latest income tax returns. Applicants for this scholarship must major in chemistry, biochemistry, or chemical engineering and be interested in engaging in chemical research at the graduate level. Along with their application, they must submit a 50-word essay on why they desire to major in chemistry, biochemistry, or chemical engineering. **Deadline for Receipt:** May of each year. **Additional**

Information: This scholarships may be used at 56 approved colleges and universities in Texas. For a list, contact UIL.

3092 ■ WASHINGTON HIGHER EDUCATION COORDINATING BOARD

917 Lakeridge Way
P.O. Box 43430
Olympia, WA 98504-3430
Tel: (360)753-7851; 888-535-0747
Fax: (360)753-7808
E-mail: futureteachers@hecb.wa.gov
Web Site: http://www.hecb.wa.gov/financialaid/other/alternative.asp
To provide forgivable loans to K-12 classified employees in Washington who are interested in attending a college or university in order to become a teacher.

Title of Award: Washington Conditional Scholarships for Alternative Teaching Certification **Area, Field, or Subject:** Chemistry; Education; Education, Bilingual and cross-cultural; Education, Elementary; Education, English as a second language; Education, Secondary; Education, Special; Foreign languages; Mathematics and mathematical sciences; Physics; Technology **Level of Education for which Award is Granted:** Professional, Undergraduate **Number Awarded:** Approximately 25 each year. **Funds Available:** The maximum award is $4,000 per academic year. These awards are in the form of loans that can be forgiven in exchange for teaching service. Each 2 years of eligible teaching service results in the forgiveness of 1 year of loan. **Duration:** 1 year; may be renewed up to 4 additional years.
Eligibility Requirements: This program is open to Washington residents who are currently employed as a classified instructional employee in a K-12 public school. Applicants must 1) have a transferable associate degree and be seeking residency teacher certification with endorsements in special education or English as a second language; or 2) have a bachelor's degree and subject matter expertise in a shortage area and be seeking residency teacher certification in a subject matter shortage area (currently defined as special education, English as a second language, chemistry, physics, Japanese, mathematics, and technology education). to enroll in an accredited Washington college or university and work as a teacher in a K-12 public school in the state after completing initial teacher certification. Selection is based on academic ability, a statement demonstrating commitment to the teaching profession, the applicant's ability to serve as a positive role model as a K-12 public school teacher, length and quality of contributions to the Washington K-12 public school, and recommendations from a current teacher or school official describing the applicant's potential as a future teacher. The priority in making awards is: 1) eligible renewal applicants who are within 2 years of completing their initial teacher certification requirements; 2) all other eligible renewable applicants; 3) eligible new applicants who are within 2 years of completing their initial teacher certification requirements; and 4) all other new eligible applicants. **Deadline for Receipt:** October of each year. **Additional Information:** This program was established by the Washington legislature in 2001. It is administered by the Washington Higher Education Coordinator Board, but the Washington State Professional Educator Standards Board selects the recipients.

Geology

3093 ■ AMERICAN GEOLOGICAL INSTITUTE

Attn: Minority Participation Program
4220 King Street
Alexandria, VA 22302-1502
Tel: (703)379-2480
Fax: (703)379-7563
E-mail: cmm@agiweb.org
Web Site: http://www.agiweb.org/mpp/index.html
To provide financial assistance to underrepresented minority undergraduate and graduate students interested in working on a degree in the geosciences.

Title of Award: Minority Geoscience Student Scholarships **Area, Field, or Subject:** Education; Geology; Hydrology; Meteorology; Oceanography **Level of Education for which Award is Granted:** Graduate, Undergraduate **Number Awarded:** Varies each year; recently, 19 of these scholarships were awarded. **Funds Available:** Stipends range from $500 to $3,000 per year. **Duration:** 1 academic year; renewable if the recipient maintains satisfactory performance.

Eligibility Requirements: This program is open to members of ethnic minority groups underrepresented in the geosciences (Blacks, Hispanics, American Indians, Eskimos, Hawaiians, and Samoans). U.S. citizenship or permanent resident status is required. Applicants must be full-time students enrolled in an accredited institution working on an undergraduate or graduate degree in the geosciences, including geology, geophysics, hydrology, meteorology, physical oceanography, planetary geology, and earth science education; students in other natural sciences, mathematics, or engineering are not eligible. Selection is based on a 250-word essay on career goals and why the applicant has chosen a geoscience as a major, work experience, recommendations, honors and awards, extracurricular activities, and financial need. **Deadline for Receipt:** March of each year.
Additional Information: Funding for this program is provided by ExxonMobil Corporation, ConocoPhillips, ChevronTexaco Corporation, Marathon Corporation, and the Seismological Society of America.

3094 ■ ASSOCIATION OF ENVIRONMENTAL AND ENGINEERING GEOLOGISTS

Attn: AEG Foundation
300 South Jackson Street, Suite 100
P.O. Box 460518
Denver, CO 80246
Tel: (303)757-2926
Fax: (303)757-2969
E-mail: aeg@aegweb.org
Web Site: http://www.aegfoundation.org/index2.php
To provide financial assistance for college or graduate school to student members of the Association of Environmental and Engineering Geologists.

Title of Award: Marliave Scholar Award **Area, Field, or Subject:** Engineering, Geological; Geology **Level of Education for which Award is Granted:** Four Year College, Graduate **Number Awarded:** 1 each year. **Funds Available:** The stipend is $1,000. **Duration:** 1 year.
Eligibility Requirements: Applicants must be college seniors or graduate students in engineering geology or geological engineering, must be enrolled full time in a college or university offering a degree program directly applicable to engineering geology or geological engineering, and must be a student member of the association. Along with their application, they must submit official transcripts covering all undergraduate and graduate work, 3 letters of reference, copies of pertinent publications and abstracts, and a 2-page statement of career goals. Selection is based on demonstrated ability, academic record, potential for contributions to the profession, character, and activities in student/professional societies. Financial need is not considered. **Deadline for Receipt:** April of each year. **Additional Information:** This program was established in 1968. Information is also available from Paul M. Santi, Colorado School of Mines, Department of Geology and Geological Engineering, Berthoud Hall, Golden, CO 80401, (303) 273-3108, E-mail: psanti@mines.edu.

3095 ■ ASSOCIATION OF ENVIRONMENTAL AND ENGINEERING GEOLOGISTS

Attn: AEG Foundation
300 South Jackson Street, Suite 100
P.O. Box 460518
Denver, CO 80246
Tel: (303)757-2926
Fax: (303)757-2969
E-mail: aeg@aegweb.org
Web Site: http://www.aegfoundation.org/index2.php
To provide financial assistance to members of the Association of Environmental and Engineering Geologists (AEG) who are working on an undergraduate degree in geology or a graduate degree with an environmental or engineering geology emphasis.

Title of Award: Martin L. Stout Scholarship **Area, Field, or Subject:** Engineering, Geological; Geology **Level of Education for which Award is Granted:** Four Year College, Graduate **Number Awarded:** 1 each year. **Funds Available:** The stipend is $1,000. **Duration:** 1 year.
Eligibility Requirements: This program is open to student members of the association who are undergraduate geology majors in their sophomore through senior year or graduate students with an environmental or engineering geology emphasis. Applicants must submit a 500-word essay on either of the following questions: 1) how they intend to become a competent professional environmental and/or engineering geologist, or 2)

why they need to become a competent field geologist. Selection is based on the essay and letters of recommendation. **Deadline for Receipt:** January of each year. **Additional Information:** This program was established in 1994 by the Southern California section of the Association of Engineering Geologists and transferred to the AEG Foundation in 2004. Information is also available from Robert A. Larson, 13376 Azores Avenue, Sylmar, CA 91342, (818) 362-0363, E-mail: ralarson@rampageusa.com.

3096 ■ ASSOCIATION FOR IRON & STEEL TECHNOLOGY

Attn: AIST Foundation
186 Thorn Hill Road
Warrendale, PA 15086-7528
Tel: (724)776-6040
Fax: (724)776-1880
E-mail: lwharrey@aist.org
Web Site: http://www.aist.org/foundation/scholarships.htm
To provide financial assistance for college study of engineering to Canadians who are children of members of the Association for Iron & Steel Technology (AIST).
Title of Award: David H. Samson Canadian Scholarship **Area, Field, or Subject:** Chemistry; Engineering; Geology; Mathematics and mathematical sciences; Physics **Level of Education for which Award is Granted:** Undergraduate **Number Awarded:** 1 each year. **Funds Available:** The stipend is $US2,000. **Duration:** 1 year; may be renewed for up to 3 additional years.
Eligibility Requirements: This program is open to the children (natural, adopted, or ward) of Canadian citizens and landed immigrants who are members of the association. Applicants must have been accepted in an eligible full-time course of study of engineering at an accredited Canadian university. If no engineering student applies, the award may be made to an eligible student planning to major in chemistry, geology, mathematics, or physics. The scholarship may also be awarded to a student entering a community college if there is no eligible applicant entering an accredited university. The committee may also award the scholarship to a previous applicant entering the second or third year at a Canadian university or community college if there is no eligible applicant entering the first year. Selection is based on academic achievements, extracurricular activities, and the student's written statements; financial need is not considered. **Deadline for Receipt:** June of each year. **Additional Information:** The AIST was formed in 2004 by the merger of the Iron and Steel Society (ISS) and the Association of Iron and Steel Engineers (AISE). Information is also available from Robert Kneale, AIST Northern Member Chapter, P.O. Box 1734, Cambridge, Ontario N1R 7G8, Canada.

3097 ■ ASSOCIATION OF STATE DAM SAFETY OFFICIALS

Attn: Scholarship Coordinator
450 Old Vine Street, Second Floor
Lexington, KY 40507
Tel: (859)257-5140
Fax: (859)323-1958
E-mail: info@damsafety.org
Web Site: http://www.damsafety.org
To provide financial assistance for undergraduate education to students interested in fields related to dam safety.
Title of Award: Association of State Dam Safety Officials Scholarships **Area, Field, or Subject:** Engineering, Civil; Engineering, Hydraulic; Geology; Hydrology **Level of Education for which Award is Granted:** Four Year College **Number Awarded:** 2 or 3 each year. **Funds Available:** The stipend is $5,000 per year. **Duration:** 1 year; junior recipients may reapply for their senior year.
Eligibility Requirements: Applicants must be college seniors with a GPA of 2.5 or higher studying civil engineering or a related field. They must have a demonstrated interest in preparing for a career in hydraulics, hydrology, or geotechnical disciplines related to the design, construction, and operation of dams. U.S. citizenship is required. Selection is based on academic achievement, financial need, work experience and activities, and a 2-page essay on their proposed course of study and why dam safety is important. **Deadline for Receipt:** March of each year. **Additional Information:** This program was established in 1992.

3098 ■ ASSOCIATION FOR WOMEN GEOSCIENTISTS

Attn: AWG Foundation
P.O. Box 30645
Lincoln, NE 68503-0645

E-mail: awgscholarship@yahoo.com
Web Site: http://www.awg.org/eas/minority.html
To provide financial assistance to minority women who are interested in working on an undergraduate degree in the geosciences.
Title of Award: Association for Women Geoscientists Minority Scholarship **Area, Field, or Subject:** Chemistry; Earth sciences; Education; Geology; Geosciences; Hydrology; Meteorology; Oceanography **Level of Education for which Award is Granted:** Undergraduate **Number Awarded:** 1 or more each year. **Funds Available:** A total of $5,000 is available for this program each year. **Duration:** 1 year; may be renewed.
Eligibility Requirements: This program is open to women who are African American, Hispanic, or Native American (including Eskimo, Hawaiian, Samoan, or American Indian). Applicants must be full-time students working on, or planning to work on, an undergraduate degree in the geosciences (including geology, geophysics, geochemistry, hydrology, meteorology, physical oceanography, planetary geology, or earth science education). They must submit a 500-word essay on why they have chosen to major in the geosciences and their career goals, 2 letters of recommendation, high school and/or college transcripts, and SAT or ACT scores. Financial need is not considered in the selection process. **Deadline for Receipt:** May of each year. **Additional Information:** This program, first offered in 2004, is supported by ExxonMobil Foundation.

3099 ■ ASSOCIATION FOR WOMEN GEOSCIENTISTS

Attn: AWG Foundation
P.O. Box 30645
Lincoln, NE 68503-0645
E-mail: awgscholarship@yahoo.com
Web Site: http://www.awg.org/members/po_scholarships.html
To provide financial assistance to minority women working on an undergraduate or graduate degree in the geosciences in the Potomac Bay region.
Title of Award: William Rucker Greenwood Scholarship **Area, Field, or Subject:** Earth sciences; Geology; Geosciences **Level of Education for which Award is Granted:** Graduate, Undergraduate **Number Awarded:** 1 each year. **Funds Available:** The stipend is $1,000. The recipient also is granted a 1-year membership in the Association for Women Geoscientists (AWG). **Duration:** 1 year.
Eligibility Requirements: This program is open to minority women who are currently enrolled as full-time undergraduate or graduate geoscience majors in an accredited, degree-granting college or university in Delaware, the District of Columbia, Maryland, Virginia, or West Virginia. Selection is based on the applicant's 1) participation in geoscience or earth science educational activities, and 2) potential for leadership as a future geoscience professional. **Deadline for Receipt:** April of each year. **Additional Information:** This program is sponsored by the AWG Potomac Area Chapter. Information is also available from Laurel M. Bybell, U.S. Geological Survey, 926 National Center, Reston, VA 20192.

3100 ■ ASSOCIATION FOR WOMEN IN SCIENCE-SEATTLE CHAPTER

c/o Fran Solomon, Scholarship Committee Chair
5805 16th Avenue, N.E.
Seattle, WA 98105
Tel: (206)522-6441
E-mail: fran.solomon@metrokc.gov
Web Site: http://www.scn.org/awis/undergraduate_scholarship.htm
To provide financial assistance to women undergraduates from any state majoring in science, mathematics, or engineering at colleges and universities in western Washington.
Title of Award: AWIS Seattle Scholarships **Area, Field, or Subject:** Biochemistry; Biological and clinical sciences; Chemistry; Engineering; Environmental conservation; Environmental science; Geology; Mathematics and mathematical sciences; Pharmaceutical sciences; Physics **Level of Education for which Award is Granted:** Four Year College **Number Awarded:** Varies each year; recently, 11 of these scholarships were awarded. **Funds Available:** Stipends range from $1,000 to $1,500. **Duration:** 1 year.
Eligibility Requirements: This program is open to women from any state entering their junior or senior year at a 4-year college or university in western Washington. Applicants must have a declared major in science (e.g., biological sciences, environmental science, biochemistry, chemistry, pharmacy, geology, computer science, physics), mathematics, or

engineering. Along with their application, they must submit essays on the events that led to their choice of a major, their current career plans and long-term goals, and their volunteer and community activities. Financial need is considered in the selection process. At least 1 scholarship is reserved for a woman from a group that is underrepresented in science, mathematics, and engineering careers, including Native American Indians and Alaska Natives, Black/African Americans, Mexican Americans/Chicanas/Latinas, Native Pacific Islanders (Polynesians, Melanesians, and Micronesians), and women with disabilities. **Deadline for Receipt:** March of each year. **Additional Information:** This program includes the following named awards: the Virginia Badger Scholarship, the Angela Paez Memorial Scholarship, and the Fran Solomon Scholarship. Support for the program is provided by several sponsors, including the American Chemical Society, Iota Sigma Pi, Rosetta Inpharmatics, and ZymoGenetics, Inc.

3101 ■ BROWN AND CALDWELL

Attn: Scholarship Program
201 North Civic Drive, Suite 115
P.O. Box 8045
Walnut Creek, CA 94596
Tel: (925)937-9010
Fax: (925)937-9026
E-mail: scholarships@brwncald.com
Web Site: http://www.brownandcaldwell.com
To provide financial assistance to minority students working on an undergraduate degree in an environmental or engineering field.
Title of Award: Brown and Caldwell Minority Scholarship **Area, Field, or Subject:** Biological and clinical sciences; Engineering, Chemical; Engineering, Civil; Environmental conservation; Environmental science; Geology; Hydrology; Industrial hygiene; Toxicology **Level of Education for which Award is Granted:** Four Year College **Number Awarded:** 1 each year. **Funds Available:** The stipend is $3,000. **Duration:** 1 year.
Eligibility Requirements: This program is open to members of minority groups (African Americans, Hispanics, Asians, Pacific Islanders, Native Americans, and Alaska Natives) who are full-time students in their junior year at an accredited 4-year college or university. Applicants must have a GPA of 3.0 or higher with a declared major in civil, chemical, or environmental engineering or an environmental science (e.g., biology, ecology, geology, hydrogeology, industrial hygiene, toxicology). Along with their application, they must submit an essay (up to 250 words) on why they chose to major in an environmental discipline. They must be U.S. citizens or permanent resident and available to participate in a summer internship at a Brown and Caldwell office. Financial need is not considered in the selection process. **Deadline for Receipt:** February of each year. **Additional Information:** As part of the paid summer internship at a Brown and Caldwell office in 1 of more than 40 cities in the country, the program provides a mentor to guide the intern through the company's information and communications resources.

3102 ■ BROWN AND CALDWELL

Attn: Scholarship Program
201 North Civic Drive, Suite 115
P.O. Box 8045
Walnut Creek, CA 94596
Tel: (925)937-9010
Fax: (925)937-9026
E-mail: scholarships@brwncald.com
Web Site: http://www.brownandcaldwell.com
To provide financial assistance to undergraduate students working on an degree in an environmental or engineering field.
Title of Award: Dr. W. Wesley Eckenfelder Scholarship **Area, Field, or Subject:** Biological and clinical sciences; Engineering, Chemical; Engineering, Civil; Environmental conservation; Environmental science; Geology; Hydrology; Industrial hygiene; Toxicology **Level of Education for which Award is Granted:** Four Year College **Number Awarded:** 1 each year. **Funds Available:** The stipend is $3,000. **Duration:** 1 year.
Eligibility Requirements: This program is open to U.S. citizens and permanent residents enrolled as full-time students in their junior year at an accredited 4-year college or university. Applicants must have a GPA of 3.0 or higher with a declared major in civil, chemical, or environmental engineering or an environmental science (e.g., biology, ecology, geology, hydrogeology, industrial hygiene, toxicology). Along with their application,

they must submit an essay (up to 250 words) on why they chose to major in an environmental discipline. Financial need is not considered in the selection process. **Deadline for Receipt:** February of each year. **Additional Information:** This scholarship was first awarded in 1999.

3103 ■ GEOLOGICAL SOCIETY OF AMERICA

Attn: Program Officer-Grants, Awards and Recognition
3300 Penrose Place
P.O. Box 9140
Boulder, CO 80301-9140
Tel: (303)357-1028
Free: 800-472-1988
Fax: (303)357-1070
E-mail: awards@geosociety.org
Web Site: http://www.geosociety.org
To provide support to undergraduate student members of the Geological Society of America (GSA) interested in conducting research at universities in designated sections of the United States.
Title of Award: Geological Society of America Undergraduate Student Research Grants **Area, Field, or Subject:** Geology **Level of Education for which Award is Granted:** Undergraduate **Number Awarded:** 1 or more each year in each of the 4 sections. **Funds Available:** Grant amounts vary. **Duration:** 1 year.
Eligibility Requirements: This program is open to undergraduate students who are interested in conducting research and are majoring in geology at universities in 4 GSA sections: north-central, northeastern, south-central, and southeastern. Applicants must be student associates of the GSA. Applications from women, minorities, and persons with disabilities are strongly encouraged. **Deadline for Receipt:** January of each year. **Additional Information:** Within the 4 participating sections, information is available from the secretary. For the name and address of the 4 section secretaries, contact the sponsor.

3104 ■ GEOLOGICAL SOCIETY OF AMERICA-NORTHEASTERN SECTION

Attn: Stephen G. Pollock, Secretary
University of Southern Maine
Department of Geosciences
37 College Avenue
Gorham, ME 04038-1091
Tel: (207)780-5353
Fax: (207)228-8361
E-mail: pollock@usm.maine.edu.
Web Site: http://www.geosociety.org/grants/negrant.htm
To provide support to undergraduate student members of the Geological Society of America (GSA) interested in conducting research at universities in the northeastern part of the United States.
Title of Award: Northeastern Section Undergraduate Student Research Grants **Area, Field, or Subject:** Geology **Level of Education for which Award is Granted:** Undergraduate **Number Awarded:** 1 or more each year. **Funds Available:** Grant amounts vary. **Duration:** 1 year.
Eligibility Requirements: This program is open to undergraduate students who are majoring in geology at universities located within the geographic area of the Northeastern Section. Applicants must be a student associate or member of the GSA. Women, minorities, and persons with disabilities are strongly encouraged to apply. **Deadline for Receipt:** February of each year. **Additional Information:** This program is sponsored by the Geological Society of America's Northeastern Section, which covers Connecticut, Delaware, the District of Columbia, Maine, Maryland, Massachusetts, New Hampshire, New Jersey, New York, Pennsylvania, Rhode Island, Vermont, New Brunswick, Newfoundland, Nova Scotia, Prince Edward Island, Quebec, and eastern Ontario.

3105 ■ GEOLOGICAL SOCIETY OF AMERICA-SOUTHEASTERN SECTION

Attn: Donald W. Neal, Secretary
East Carolina University
Department of Geology
Greenville, NC 27858-4353
Tel: (252)328-4392
Fax: (252)328-4391
E-mail: neald@mail.ecu.edu.
Web Site: http://core.ecu.edu/geology/neal/segsa/research.html

To provide support to undergraduate student members of the Geological Society of America (GSA) interested in conducting research at universities in the southeastern part of the United States.

Title of Award: Southeastern Section Undergraduate Student Research Grants **Area, Field, or Subject:** Geology **Level of Education for which Award is Granted:** Undergraduate **Number Awarded:** 1 or more each year. **Funds Available:** Grant amounts vary. **Duration:** 1 year.

Eligibility Requirements: This program is open to undergraduate students who are majoring in geology at universities located within the geographic area of the southeastern section. Applicants must be student associate members of the GSA. Applications from women, minorities, and persons with disabilities are strongly encouraged. **Deadline for Receipt:** January of each year. **Additional Information:** This program is sponsored by the Geological Society of America's Southeastern Section, which covers Alabama, Florida, Georgia, Kentucky, Mississippi, North Carolina, South Carolina, Tennessee, Virginia, and West Virginia.

3106 ■ HISPANIC SCHOLARSHIP FUND INSTITUTE

1001 Connecticut Avenue, N.W., Suite 632
Washington, DC 20036
Tel: (202)296-0009
Fax: (202)296-3633
E-mail: info@hsfi.org
Web Site: http://www.hsfi.org/scholarships/energy.asp

To provide financial assistance to Hispanic undergraduate students majoring in designated business, engineering, and science fields related to the U.S. Department of Energy (DOE) goals of environmental restoration and waste management.

Title of Award: Environmental Management Scholarship **Area, Field, or Subject:** Business administration; Chemistry; Computer and information sciences; Engineering, Agricultural; Engineering, Civil; Engineering, Electrical; Engineering, Industrial; Engineering, Mechanical; Engineering, Metallurgical; Engineering, Petroleum; Environmental science; Epidemiology; Geology; Hydrology; Management; Mathematics and mathematical sciences; Physics; Radiology; Toxicology **Level of Education for which Award is Granted:** Undergraduate **Number Awarded:** Varies each year. **Funds Available:** The stipend is $3,000 per year for 4-year university students or $2,000 per year for community college students. **Duration:** 1 year.

Eligibility Requirements: This program is open to U.S. citizens and permanent residents of Hispanic background who have completed at least 12 undergraduate credits with a GPA of 3.0 or higher. Applicants must be interested in preparing for a career supportive of the DOE goals of environmental restoration and waste management. Eligible academic majors are in the fields of business (management and system analysis), engineering (agricultural, chemical, civil, electrical, environmental, industrial, mechanical, metallurgical, nuclear, and petroleum), and science (applied math/physics, chemistry, computer science, ecology, environmental, epidemiology, geology, health physics, hydrology, radiochemistry, radio-ecology, and toxicology). Along with their application, they must submit a 2-page essay on 1) how their academic major, interests, and career goals correspond to environmental restoration and waste management issues; and 2) how their Hispanic background and family upbringing have influenced their academic and personal goals. Selection is based on the essay, academic record, academic plans and career goals, financial need, commitment to DOE's goal of environmental restoration and waste management, and a letter of recommendation. **Deadline for Receipt:** March of each year. **Additional Information:** This program, which began in 1990, is sponsored by DOE's Office of Environmental Management. Recipients must enroll full time at a college or university in the United States.

3107 ■ HISPANIC SCHOLARSHIP FUND INSTITUTE

1001 Connecticut Avenue, N.W., Suite 632
Washington, DC 20036
Tel: (202)296-0009
Fax: (202)296-3633
E-mail: info@hsfi.org
Web Site: http://www.hsfi.org/scholarships/generation.asp

To provide financial assistance to Hispanic and other students majoring in designated business, engineering, social science, and science fields who are interested in employment with the U.S. Department of Energy (DOE).

Title of Award: Next Generation of Public Servants Scholarship **Area, Field, or Subject:** Accounting; Biological and clinical sciences; Business administration; Computer and information sciences; Engineering; Environmental science; Finance; Geology; Information science and technology; Management; Mathematics and mathematical sciences; Physics; Political science; Psychology; Sociology **Level of Education for which Award is Granted:** Undergraduate **Number Awarded:** Varies each year. **Funds Available:** The stipend is $3,000 per year. **Duration:** 1 year; may be renewed up to 2 additional years if the recipient maintains full-time enrollment and a GPA of 2.8 or higher.

Eligibility Requirements: This program is open to U.S. citizens enrolled full time as sophomores with a GPA of 2.8 or higher. Applicants must be interested in preparing for a career with the DOE in an energy-related field. Eligible academic majors are in the fields of business (accounting, business administration, finance, and management), engineering (biomedical, chemical, civil, computer, electrical, environmental, industrial, materials, mechanical, metallurgical, nuclear, and petroleum), social science (economics, organizational psychology, political science, and sociology), and science (biological sciences, computer science, geology, information technology, mathematics, microbiology, and physics). They must be willing to participate in co-ops with the DOE. Along with their application, they must submit a 2-page essay on why a career in public service interests them, how their academic major connects with their stated DOE career goal, why the DOE should invest in them through this program, and how they believe the DOE will benefit from this investment. Selection is based on academic achievement, financial need, demonstrated commitment to public service, and interest in federal employment with the DOE. **Deadline for Receipt:** February of each year. **Additional Information:** This program, sponsored by DOE's Office of Economic Impact and Diversity, is administered by the Hispanic Scholarship Fund Institute as part of its effort to increase Hispanic participation in federal service.

3108 ■ MARYLAND SPACE GRANT CONSORTIUM

c/o Johns Hopkins University
203 Bloomberg Center for Physics and Astronomy
3400 North Charles Street
Baltimore, MD 21218-2686
Tel: (410)516-7351
Fax: (410)516-4109
E-mail: info@mdspacegrant.org
Web Site: http://www.mdspacegrant.org/scholars_about.html

To provide financial assistance to undergraduates who are interested in studying space-related fields at selected universities in Maryland that are members of the Maryland Space Grant Consortium.

Title of Award: Maryland Space Scholars Program **Area, Field, or Subject:** Aerospace sciences; Astronomy and astronomical sciences; Biological and clinical sciences; Chemistry; Computer and information sciences; Engineering; Geology; Mathematics and mathematical sciences; Physics; Space and planetary sciences **Level of Education for which Award is Granted:** Undergraduate **Number Awarded:** Varies each year; recently 16 of these scholarships were awarded (2 at Johns Hopkins University, 5 at Morgan State University, 2 at Hagerstown Community College, 2 at Towson University, and 5 at the University of Maryland at College Park). **Funds Available:** Scholars receive partial payment of tuition at the participating university they attend. **Duration:** 1 year; may be renewed if the recipient maintains a GPA of 3.0 or higher.

Eligibility Requirements: This program is open to residents of Maryland and graduates of Maryland high schools who are enrolled full time at a member institution. Applicants must be interested in preparing for a career in mathematics, science, engineering, technology, or a space-related field. They must be majoring in a relevant field, including (but not limited to) astronomy, the biological and life sciences, chemistry, computer science, engineering, geological sciences, or physics. U.S. citizenship is required. Along with their application, they must submit an essay of 200 to 500 words on how this scholarship will help them meet their educational and financial goals. This program is a component of the U.S. National Aeronautics and Space Administration (NASA) Space Grant program, which encourages participation by women, underrepresented minorities, and persons with disabilities. **Deadline for Receipt:** August of each year. **Additional Information:** The participating universities are Hagerstown Community College, Johns Hopkins University, Morgan State University,

Towson University, the University of Maryland at College Park, and Washington College. Funding for this program is provided by NASA.

3109 ■ MONTANA SPACE GRANT CONSORTIUM
c/o Montana State University
416 Cobleigh Hall
P.O. Box 173835
Bozeman, MT 59717-3835
Tel: (406)994-4223
Fax: (406)994-4452
E-mail: msgc@montana.edu
Web Site: http://spacegrant.montana.edu/Text/ScholarProgram.html
To provide financial assistance to students in Montana who are interested in working on an undergraduate degree in the space sciences and/or engineering.
Title of Award: Montana Space Grant Consortium Undergraduate Scholarships **Area, Field, or Subject:** Aerospace sciences; Astronomy and astronomical sciences; Biological and clinical sciences; Chemistry; Computer and information sciences; Engineering, Aerospace/Aeronautical/Astronautical; Engineering, Chemical; Engineering, Civil; Engineering, Electrical; Engineering, Mechanical; Geology; Physics; Space and planetary sciences **Level of Education for which Award is Granted:** Undergraduate **Number Awarded:** Varies each year; recently, 23 of these scholarships were awarded. **Funds Available:** The stipend is $1,000 per year. **Duration:** 1 year; may be renewed.
Eligibility Requirements: This program is open to full-time undergraduate students at member institutions of the Montana Space Grant Consortium (MSGC) majoring in fields related to space sciences and engineering. Those fields include, but are not limited to, astronomy, biological and life sciences, chemical engineering, chemistry, civil engineering, computer sciences, electrical engineering, geological sciences, mathematics, mechanical engineering, and physics. Priority is given to students who have been involved in aerospace-related research. U.S. citizenship is required. The MSGC is a component of the U.S. National Aeronautics and Space Administration (NASA) Space Grant program, which encourages participation by women, underrepresented minorities, and persons with disabilities. **Deadline for Receipt:** March of each year. **Additional Information:** The MSGC member institutions are Blackfeet Community College, Carroll College, Chief Dull Knife College, Fort Belknap College, Fort Peck Community College, Little Big Horn College, Montana State University at Billings, Montana State University at Bozeman, Montana State University Northern, Montana Tech, Rocky Mountain College, Salish Kootenai College, Stone Child College, University of Great Falls, University of Montana, and University of Montana Western. Funding for this program is provided by NASA.

3110 ■ NATIONAL SPELEOLOGICAL SOCIETY
2813 Cave Avenue
Huntsville, AL 35810-4413
Tel: (256)852-1300
Fax: (256)851-9241
E-mail: nss@caves.org
Web Site: http://www.caves.org
To recognize and reward young members of the National Speleological Society (NSS) who present outstanding papers at the annual convention.
Title of Award: James G. Mitchell Award **Area, Field, or Subject:** Cave studies **Level of Education for which Award is Granted:** Graduate, Undergraduate **Number Awarded:** 1 each year. **Funds Available:** A cash award is provided. **Duration:** The award is presented annually.
Eligibility Requirements: This program is open to members of the society under 25 years of age who present outstanding scientific papers at a session of the annual convention. Selection is based on how well the papers exemplify sound methods of scientific research and presentation and, secondarily, on their contribution of knowledge. **Additional Information:** This award was first presented in 1970.

3111 ■ NEBRASKA ACADEMY OF SCIENCES
c/o University of Nebraska
302 Morrill Hall
14th and U Streets
P.O. Box 880339
Lincoln, NE 68588-0339
Tel: (402)472-2644

E-mail: nebacad@unl.edu
Web Site: http://www.neacadsci.org/Info/coll_scholarship.htm
To provide financial assistance to upper-division students majoring in science at colleges and universities in Nebraska.
Title of Award: C. Bertrand and Marian Othmer Scultz Collegiate Scholarship **Area, Field, or Subject:** Biological and clinical sciences; Chemistry; Geology; Physics **Level of Education for which Award is Granted:** Four Year College **Number Awarded:** 1 each year. **Funds Available:** The stipend is $3,000 per year. **Duration:** 1 year; may be renewed 1 additional year.
Eligibility Requirements: This program is open to student entering their junior or senior year at 4-year colleges and universities in Nebraska. Applicants must have a declared major in a natural science discipline (chemistry, physics, biology, or geology). They must be preparing for a career in a science-related industry, science teaching, or scientific research. A member of the Nebraska Academy of Sciences must provide a letter of nomination. **Deadline for Receipt:** January of each year. **Additional Information:** This scholarship was first awarded in 2006.

3112 ■ OHIO SPACE GRANT CONSORTIUM
c/o Ohio Aerospace Institute
22800 Cedar Point Road
Cleveland, OH 44142
Tel: (440)962-3032
Free: 800-828-OSGC
Fax: (440)962-3057
E-mail: osgc@oai.org
Web Site: http://www.osgc.org/Scholarship.html
To provide financial assistance to students in their junior year at selected universities in Ohio who wish to working on a bachelor's degree in an aerospace-related field.
Title of Award: Ohio Space Grant Consortium Junior Scholarships **Area, Field, or Subject:** Astronomy and astronomical sciences; Biological and clinical sciences; Chemistry; Computer and information sciences; Engineering, Aerospace/Aeronautical/Astronautical; Engineering, Chemical; Engineering, Civil; Engineering, Computer; Engineering, Electrical; Engineering, Industrial; Engineering, Materials; Engineering, Mechanical; Engineering, Petroleum; Geography; Geology; Materials research/science; Mathematics and mathematical sciences; Physics; Space and planetary sciences **Level of Education for which Award is Granted:** Four Year College **Number Awarded:** Varies each year; recently, 20 of these scholarships were awarded. **Funds Available:** The stipend is $2,000. **Duration:** 1 year; recipients may apply for a senior scholarship if they maintain satisfactory academic performance and good progress on their research project.
Eligibility Requirements: These scholarships are available to U.S. citizens who expect to complete within 2 years the requirements for a bachelor of science degree in an aerospace-related discipline (aeronautical engineering, aerospace engineering, astronomy, biology, chemical engineering, chemistry, civil engineering, computer engineering and science, control engineering, electrical engineering, engineering mechanics, geography, geology, industrial engineering, manufacturing engineering, materials science and engineering, mathematics, mechanical engineering, petroleum engineering, physics, and systems engineering). Applicants must be attending a member university of the Ohio Space Grant Consortium (OSGC) or another participating university. They must propose and initiate a research project on campus under the guidance of a faculty member. Along with their application, they must submit a 1-page personal objective statement that discusses their career goals and anticipated benefits to be derived from this program. Women, underrepresented minorities, and persons with disabilities are particularly encouraged to apply. **Deadline for Receipt:** February of each year. **Additional Information:** These scholarships are funded through the National Space Grant College and Fellowship Program administered by the National Aeronautics and Space Administration (NASA), with matching funds provided by the member universities, the Ohio Aerospace Institute, and private industry. The OSGC member universities include the University of Akron, Case Western Reserve University, Central State University, University of Cincinnati, Cleveland State University, University of Dayton, Ohio State University, Ohio University, University of Toledo, Wilberforce University, and Wright State University. Other participating universities are Cedarville University, Marietta College (petroleum engineering), Miami

University (manufacturing engineering), Ohio Northern University (mechanical engineering), and Youngstown State University (mechanical and industrial engineering). Recipients are required to attend the annual spring research symposium sponsored by the OSGC and present a poster on their research project.

3113 ■ ROCKY MOUNTAIN COAL MINING INSTITUTE

Attn: Executive Director
8057 South Yukon Way
Littleton, CO 80128-5510
Tel: (303)948-3300
Fax: (303)948-1132
E-mail: mail@rmcmi.org
Web Site: http://www.rmcmi.org
To provide financial assistance to college students from Rocky Mountain states who are preparing for a career in the mining industry.
Title of Award: Rocky Mountain Coal Mining Institute Scholarships **Area, Field, or Subject:** Business; Engineering, Electrical; Engineering, Geological; Engineering, Mechanical; Engineering, Metallurgical; Engineering, Mining and Mineral; Environmental science; Geology; Metallurgy; Mining **Level of Education for which Award is Granted:** Four Year College **Number Awarded:** 8 each year (1 from each of the participating states). **Funds Available:** The stipend is $2,000 per year. Funds are disbursed to the recipient's institution to be used as a tuition credit. during the junior, senior, and/or fifth year of undergraduate study. **Duration:** 2 years; renewable, if the recipient continues in school as a full-time student in good academic standing.
Eligibility Requirements: This program is open to full-time sophomores or juniors in college who are U.S. citizens and residents of Arizona, Colorado, Montana, New Mexico, North Dakota, Texas, Utah, or Wyoming. Applicants must be working on a degree in engineering (e.g., electrical, environmental, geological, mechanical, metallurgical, mining) or in a mining-related field (e.g., geology, mineral processing, metallurgy). They may be attending school in 1 of those states or another school approved by the sponsor (e.g., University of Missouri at Rolla, South Dakota School of Mines). Preference is given to students who are particularly interested in western coal as a career. Interviews are required. **Deadline for Receipt:** January of each year.

3114 ■ SOCIETY FOR MINING, METALLURGY, AND EXPLORATION, INC.

Attn: Student Center
8307 Shaffer Parkway
Littleton, CO 80127-4102
Tel: (303)973-9550
Free: 800-763-3132
Fax: (303)973-3845
E-mail: sme@smenet.org
Web Site: http://www.smenet.org/education/students/sme_scholarships.cfm
To provide financial assistance to upper-division student members of the Society for Mining, Metallurgy, and Exploration (SME) who are majoring in fields that will develop their skills related to mining and the environment.
Title of Award: Environmental Division Scholarship **Area, Field, or Subject:** Economics; Engineering, Mining and Mineral; Environmental conservation; Environmental science; Geology; Metallurgy **Level of Education for which Award is Granted:** Four Year College **Number Awarded:** 1 or more each year. **Funds Available:** A total of $2,000 is awarded each year. **Duration:** 1 year.
Eligibility Requirements: Applicants must 1) be majoring in a field related to the minerals industry (e.g., geology, minerals engineering, mining engineering, or mineral economics) at a 4-year college or university, 2) have completed at least their sophomore year in college, 3) be a U.S. citizen, and 4) be a student member of the society. They must be of good character, be of sound health, have demonstrated scholastic aptitude (GPA of 3.0 or higher), and be able to demonstrate financial need. Candidates for these scholarships must be working on an undergraduate

degree related to mining and the environment with a faculty advisor who has special interests in an environmentally-oriented program. **Deadline for Receipt:** October of each year.

3115 ■ SOCIETY FOR MINING, METALLURGY, AND EXPLORATION, INC.

Attn: Student Center
8307 Shaffer Parkway
Littleton, CO 80127-4102
Tel: (303)973-9550
Free: 800-763-3132
Fax: (303)973-3845
E-mail: sme@smenet.org
Web Site: http://www.smenet.org/education/students/sme_scholarships.cfm
To provide financial assistance to upper-division and graduate student members of the Society for Mining, Metallurgy, and Exploration (SME) who are majoring in fields that will prepare them for a career in industrial minerals.
Title of Award: Gerald V. Henderson Industrial Minerals Memorial Scholarship **Area, Field, or Subject:** Economics; Engineering, Mining and Mineral; Geology; Metallurgy **Level of Education for which Award is Granted:** Four Year College, Graduate **Number Awarded:** 1 or more each year. **Funds Available:** A total of $2,000 is awarded each year. **Duration:** 1 year.
Eligibility Requirements: Applicants must 1) be majoring in a field related to the minerals industry (e.g., geology, minerals engineering, mining engineering, or mineral economics) at a 4-year college or university, 2) have completed at least their sophomore year in college, 3) be a U.S. citizen, and 4) be a student member of the society. They must be of good character, be of sound health, have demonstrated scholastic aptitude (GPA of 3.0 or higher), and be able to demonstrate financial need. Candidates for these scholarships may be proposed by any of the following: mining and minerals companies; local sections of the society; state mining institutes; high school principals; industrial minerals associations; manufacturers of mining and processing equipment; minerals research organizations; or geology and mining engineering departments at colleges or universities. An interview may be required. **Deadline for Receipt:** October of each year.

3116 ■ SOCIETY FOR MINING, METALLURGY, AND EXPLORATION, INC.

Attn: Student Center
8307 Shaffer Parkway
Littleton, CO 80127-4102
Tel: (303)973-9550
Free: 800-763-3132
Fax: (303)973-3845
E-mail: sme@smenet.org
Web Site: http://www.smenet.org/education/students/sme_scholarships.cfm
To provide financial assistance to student members of the Society for Mining, Metallurgy, and Exploration (SME) who are preparing for a career in the minerals industry.
Title of Award: Mining and Exploration Division Scholarships **Area, Field, or Subject:** Engineering, Mining and Mineral; Geology; Metallurgy **Level of Education for which Award is Granted:** Four Year College **Number Awarded:** Up to 4 each year. **Funds Available:** The stipend is $1,500. **Duration:** 1 year.
Eligibility Requirements: Applicants must have completed their sophomore year in college and be majoring in mining, geology, or a related field of specialization at an ABET-accredited college or university. They must be U.S. citizens or permanent residents, be able to demonstrate financial need, have a strong academic record, and be a student member of the society. Only 1 candidate from each eligible department may be nominated each academic year. **Deadline for Receipt:** November of each year.

3117 ■ SOUTH DAKOTA SPACE GRANT CONSORTIUM

Attn: Deputy Director and Outreach Coordinator
South Dakota School of Mines and Technology
Mineral Industries Building, Room 228
501 East St. Joseph Street
Rapid City, SD 57701-3995

Tel: (605)394-1975
Fax: (605)394-5360
E-mail: Thomas.Durkin@sdsmt.edu
Web Site: http://www.sdsmt.edu/space
To provide funding to undergraduate and graduate students for space-related activities in South Dakota.
Title of Award: South Dakota Space Grant Consortium Graduate Fellowships and Undergraduate Scholarships **Area, Field, or Subject:** Aerospace sciences; Earth sciences; Engineering, Aerospace/Aeronautical/Astronautical; Environmental conservation; Environmental science; Geology; Geosciences; Mathematics and mathematical sciences; Space and planetary sciences; Technology **Level of Education for which Award is Granted:** Graduate, Undergraduate **Number Awarded:** Varies each year. Approximately $70,000 is available for this program annually. **Funds Available:** Stipends range from $1,000 to $7,500. **Duration:** 1 academic year, semester, or summer.
Eligibility Requirements: This program is open to undergraduate and graduate students at member and affiliated institutions of the South Dakota Space Grant Consortium. Applicants must be interested in 1) earth- and space-science related educational and research projects in fields relevant to the goals of the U.S. National Aeronautics and Space Administration (NASA); or 2) eventual employment with NASA or in a NASA-related career field in science, technology, engineering, and mathematics (STEM) education. Activities may include student research and educational efforts in remote sensing, GIS, global and regional geoscience, environmental science, and K-12 educational outreach; exposure to NASA-relevant projects; and internship experiences at various NASA centers and the Earth Resources Observation and Science (EROS) Center in Sioux Falls. U.S. citizenship is required. Women, members of underrepresented groups (African Americans, Hispanics, Pacific Islanders, Asian Americans, Native Americans, and persons with disabilities), and Tribal College students are specifically encouraged to apply. Selection is based on academic qualifications of the application (preference is given to students with a GPA of 3.0 or higher), quality of the application and its career goal statement, and assessment of the applicant's motivation toward an earth science, aerospace, or engineering career or research. **Deadline for Receipt:** January of each year. **Additional Information:** Member institutions include South Dakota School of Mines and Technology, South Dakota State University, and Augustana College. Educational affiliates include Black Hills State University, the University of South Dakota, Dakota State University, Lower Brule Community College, Oglala Lakota College, Sinte Gleska University, and Lake Area Technical Institute.

3118 ■ TEXAS SPACE GRANT CONSORTIUM

Attn: Administrative Assistant
3925 West Braker Lane, Suite 200
Austin, TX 78759
Tel: (512)471-3583
Free: 800-248-8742
Fax: (512)471-3585
E-mail: scholarships@tsgc.utexas.edu
Web Site: http://www.tsgc.utexas.edu/grants
To provide financial assistance to upper-division and medical students at Texas universities working on degrees in the fields of space science and engineering.
Title of Award: Columbia Crew Memorial Undergraduate Scholarships **Area, Field, or Subject:** Aerospace sciences; Biological and clinical sciences; Chemistry; Engineering, Aerospace/Aeronautical/Astronautical; Engineering, Chemical; Engineering, Electrical; Engineering, Industrial; Engineering, Mechanical; Geology; Mathematics and mathematical sciences; Physics; Space and planetary sciences **Level of Education for which Award is Granted:** Doctorate, Undergraduate **Number Awarded:** Varies each year; recently, 29 of these scholarships were awarded. **Funds Available:** The stipend is $1,000. **Duration:** 1 year; nonrenewable.
Eligibility Requirements: Applicants must be U.S. citizens, eligible for financial assistance, and registered for full-time study at a participating college or university. Applicants must be a sophomore at a 2-year institution, a junior or senior at a 4-year institution, or a first- or second-year student at a medical school. Supported fields of study have included aerospace engineering, biology, chemical engineering, chemistry, electrical engineering, geology, industrial engineering, mathematics, mechanical

engineering, and physics. The program encourages participation by members of groups underrepresented in science and engineering (persons with disabilities, women, African Americans, Hispanic Americans, Native Americans, and Pacific Islanders). Selection is based on excellence in academics, participation in space education projects, participation in research projects, and exhibited leadership qualities. **Deadline for Receipt:** March of each year. **Additional Information:** In 2003, the Texas Space Grant Consortium renamed its undergraduate scholarship program in honor of the 7 Space Shuttle Columbia astronauts. The participating universities are Baylor University, Lamar University, Prairie View A&M University, Rice University, San Jacinto College, Southern Methodist University, Sul Ross State University, Texas A&M University (including Kingsville and Corpus Christi campuses), Texas Christian University, Texas Southern University, Texas Tech University, Trinity University, University of Houston (including Clear Lake and Downtown campuses), University of Texas at Arlington, University of Texas at Austin, University of Texas at Dallas, University of Texas at El Paso, University of Texas at San Antonio, and University of Texas/Pan American. This program is funded by the National Aeronautics and Space Administration (NASA).

Geophysics

3119 ■ SOCIETY OF EXPLORATION GEOPHYSICISTS

Attn: SEG Foundation
8801 South Yale, Suite 500
P.O. Box 702740
Tulsa, OK 74170-2740
Tel: (918)497-5513
Fax: (918)497-5557
E-mail: scholarships@seg.org
Web Site: http://seg.org/business/foundation/scholarships/index.shtml
To provide financial assistance to upper-division students working on a degree in geophysical engineering.
Title of Award: Ralph W. Baird Scholarship **Area, Field, or Subject:** Engineering; Geophysics **Level of Education for which Award is Granted:** Undergraduate **Number Awarded:** 1 each year. **Funds Available:** Stipends range from $1,000 to $3,000 per year. **Duration:** 1 academic year.
Eligibility Requirements: This program is open to juniors and seniors working on a degree in geophysical engineering. Along with their application, they must submit a 150-word essay on how they plan to use geophysics in their future. Financial need is not considered in the selection process. **Deadline for Receipt:** January of each year.

3120 ■ SOCIETY OF EXPLORATION GEOPHYSICISTS

Attn: SEG Foundation
8801 South Yale, Suite 500
P.O. Box 702740
Tulsa, OK 74170-2740
Tel: (918)497-5513
Fax: (918)497-5557
E-mail: scholarships@seg.org
Web Site: http://seg.org/business/foundation/scholarships/index.shtml
To provide financial assistance to undergraduate and graduate students who are interested in studying applied geophysics in Colorado.
Title of Award: Denver Geophysical Society Scholarships **Area, Field, or Subject:** Geophysics **Level of Education for which Award is Granted:** Graduate, Undergraduate **Number Awarded:** 1 or more each year. **Funds Available:** The stipend ranges from $1,000 to $3,000 per year. **Duration:** 1 academic year; may be renewable, based on scholastic standing, availability of funds, and continuance of a course of study leading to a career in applied geophysics.
Eligibility Requirements: This program is open to 1) high school students planning to enter college in the fall, and 2) undergraduate or graduate students whose grades are above average. Preference is given to students at Colorado School of Mines; if no qualified students from that school apply, students at other colleges and universities in Colorado are considered. Applicants must intend to work on a degree directed toward a career in applied geophysics or a closely-related field. Along with their application, they must submit a 150-word essay on how they plan to use geophysics in their future. Financial need is not considered in the selection process. **Deadline for Receipt:** January of each year. **Additional**

Information: This program is sponsored by the Denver Geophysical Society.

3121 ■ SOCIETY OF EXPLORATION GEOPHYSICISTS

Attn: SEG Foundation
8801 South Yale, Suite 500
P.O. Box 702740
Tulsa, OK 74170-2740
Tel: (918)497-5513
Fax: (918)497-5557
E-mail: scholarships@seg.org
Web Site: http://seg.org/business/foundation/scholarships/index.shtml
To provide financial assistance to undergraduate and graduate students at universities in the United States and Canada who are interested in studying applied geophysics.
Title of Award: Excel Geophysics Scholarship **Area, Field, or Subject:** Geophysics **Level of Education for which Award is Granted:** Graduate, Undergraduate **Number Awarded:** 1 each year. **Funds Available:** Stipends range from $1,000 to $3,000 per year. **Duration:** 1 academic year; may be renewable, based on scholastic standing, availability of funds, and continuance of a course of study leading to a career in applied geophysics.
Eligibility Requirements: This program is open to 1) high school students planning to enter college in the fall, and 2) undergraduate or graduate students whose grades are above average. Applicants must intend to work on a degree directed toward a career in applied geophysics or a closely-related field at a university in the United States or Canada. Along with their application, they must submit a 150-word essay on how they plan to use geophysics in their future. Financial need is not considered in the selection process. **Deadline for Receipt:** January of each year. **Additional Information:** This program is sponsored by Excel Geophysics.

3122 ■ SOCIETY OF EXPLORATION GEOPHYSICISTS

Attn: SEG Foundation
8801 South Yale, Suite 500
P.O. Box 702740
Tulsa, OK 74170-2740
Tel: (918)497-5513
Fax: (918)497-5557
E-mail: scholarships@seg.org
Web Site: http://seg.org/business/foundation/scholarships/index.shtml
To provide financial assistance to undergraduate and graduate students from Alaska who are interested in studying applied geophysics.
Title of Award: Geophysical Society of Alaska Scholarship **Area, Field, or Subject:** Geophysics **Level of Education for which Award is Granted:** Graduate, Undergraduate **Number Awarded:** 1 each year. **Funds Available:** The stipend ranges from $1,000 to $3,000 per year. **Duration:** 1 academic year; may be renewable, based on scholastic standing, availability of funds, and continuance of a course of study leading to a career in applied geophysics.
Eligibility Requirements: This program is open to 1) high school students planning to enter college in the fall, and 2) undergraduate or graduate students whose grades are above average. Applicants must intend to work on a degree directed toward a career in applied geophysics or a closely-related field. They must be residents of Alaska or a student at a college or university in the state. Along with their application, they must submit a 150-word essay on how they plan to use geophysics in their future. Financial need is not considered in the selection process. **Deadline for Receipt:** January of each year. **Additional Information:** This program is sponsored by the Geophysical Society of Alaska.

3123 ■ SOCIETY OF EXPLORATION GEOPHYSICISTS

Attn: SEG Foundation
8801 South Yale, Suite 500
P.O. Box 702740
Tulsa, OK 74170-2740
Tel: (918)497-5513
Fax: (918)497-5557
E-mail: scholarships@seg.org
Web Site: http://seg.org/business/foundation/scholarships/index.shtml
To provide financial assistance to undergraduate and graduate students who are interested in studying applied geophysics in Texas.

Title of Award: Geophysical Society of Houston Scholarships **Area, Field, or Subject:** Geophysics **Level of Education for which Award is Granted:** Graduate, Undergraduate **Number Awarded:** 1 or more each year. **Funds Available:** The stipend ranges from $1,000 to $3,000 per year. **Duration:** 1 academic year; may be renewable, based on scholastic standing, availability of funds, and continuance of a course of study leading to a career in applied geophysics.
Eligibility Requirements: This program is open to 1) high school students planning to enter college in the fall, and 2) undergraduate or graduate students whose grades are above average. Preference is given to students at schools in Houston, Texas; if no qualified students from that area apply, students at other colleges and universities in Texas are considered. Applicants must intend to work on a degree directed toward a career in applied geophysics or a closely-related field. Along with their application, they must submit a 150-word essay on how they plan to use geophysics in their future. Financial need is not considered in the selection process. **Deadline for Receipt:** January of each year. **Additional Information:** This program is sponsored by the Geophysical Society of Houston.

3124 ■ SOCIETY OF EXPLORATION GEOPHYSICISTS

Attn: SEG Foundation
8801 South Yale, Suite 500
P.O. Box 702740
Tulsa, OK 74170-2740
Tel: (918)497-5513
Fax: (918)497-5557
E-mail: scholarships@seg.org
Web Site: http://seg.org/business/foundation/scholarships/index.shtml
To provide financial assistance to undergraduate and graduate students who are interested in studying applied geophysics in Oklahoma.
Title of Award: Geophysical Society of Oklahoma City Scholarship **Area, Field, or Subject:** Geophysics **Level of Education for which Award is Granted:** Graduate, Undergraduate **Number Awarded:** 1 each year. **Funds Available:** Stipends range from $1,000 to $3,000 per year. **Duration:** 1 academic year; may be renewable, based on scholastic standing, availability of funds, and continuance of a course of study leading to a career in applied geophysics.
Eligibility Requirements: This program is open to 1) high school students planning to enter college in the fall, and 2) undergraduate or graduate students whose grades are above average. Applicants must intend to attend a college or university in Oklahoma to work on a degree directed toward a career in applied geophysics or a closely-related field. Along with their application, they must submit a 150-word essay on how they plan to use geophysics in their future. Financial need is not considered in the selection process. **Deadline for Receipt:** January of each year. **Additional Information:** This program is sponsored by the Geophysical Society of Oklahoma City.

3125 ■ SOCIETY OF EXPLORATION GEOPHYSICISTS

Attn: SEG Foundation
8801 South Yale, Suite 500
P.O. Box 702740
Tulsa, OK 74170-2740
Tel: (918)497-5513
Fax: (918)497-5557
E-mail: scholarships@seg.org
Web Site: http://seg.org/business/foundation/scholarships/index.shtml
To provide financial assistance to undergraduate and graduate students from Oklahoma who are interested in studying applied geophysics.
Title of Award: Geophysical Society of Tulsa Scholarships **Area, Field, or Subject:** Geophysics **Level of Education for which Award is Granted:** Graduate, Undergraduate **Number Awarded:** 1 or more each year. **Funds Available:** Stipends range from $1,000 to $3,000 per year. **Duration:** 1 academic year; may be renewable, based on scholastic standing, availability of funds, and continuance of a course of study leading to a career in applied geophysics.
Eligibility Requirements: This program is open to 1) high school students planning to enter college in the fall, and 2) undergraduate or graduate students whose grades are above average. Applicants must intend to work on a degree directed toward a career in applied geophysics or a closely-related field. They must be residents of Oklahoma or students at a college or university in the state. Along with their application, they

must submit a 150-word essay on how they plan to use geophysics in their future. Financial need is not considered in the selection process. **Deadline for Receipt:** January of each year. **Additional Information:** This program is sponsored by the Geophysical Society of Tulsa.

3126 ■ SOCIETY OF EXPLORATION GEOPHYSICISTS

Attn: SEG Foundation
8801 South Yale, Suite 500
P.O. Box 702740
Tulsa, OK 74170-2740
Tel: (918)497-5513
Fax: (918)497-5557
E-mail: scholarships@seg.org
Web Site: http://seg.org/business/foundation/scholarships/index.shtml
To provide financial assistance to undergraduate and graduate students who are interested in studying applied geophysics in Texas.
Title of Award: GSH/Carlton-Farren Scholarship **Area, Field, or Subject:** Geophysics **Level of Education for which Award is Granted:** Graduate, Undergraduate **Number Awarded:** 1 each year. **Funds Available:** The stipend ranges from $5,000 to $6,000 per year. **Duration:** 1 academic year; may be renewable, based on scholastic standing, availability of funds, and continuance of a course of study leading to a career in applied geophysics.
Eligibility Requirements: This program is open to 1) high school students planning to enter college in the fall, and 2) undergraduate or graduate students whose grades are above average. Preference is given to students at schools in Houston, Texas; if no qualified students from that area apply, students at other colleges and universities in Texas are considered. Applicants must intend to work on a degree directed toward a career in applied geophysics or a closely-related field. Along with their application, they must submit a 150-word essay on how they plan to use geophysics in their future. Financial need is not considered in the selection process. **Deadline for Receipt:** January of each year. **Additional Information:** This program is sponsored by the Geophysical Society of Houston (GSH).

3127 ■ SOCIETY OF EXPLORATION GEOPHYSICISTS

Attn: SEG Foundation
8801 South Yale, Suite 500
P.O. Box 702740
Tulsa, OK 74170-2740
Tel: (918)497-5513
Fax: (918)497-5557
E-mail: scholarships@seg.org
Web Site: http://seg.org/business/foundation/scholarships/index.shtml
To provide financial assistance to undergraduate and graduate students who are interested in the field of applied geophysics related to mining or electrical methods.
Title of Award: G.W. Hohmann Scholarships **Area, Field, or Subject:** Business; Geophysics; Mining **Level of Education for which Award is Granted:** Graduate, Undergraduate **Number Awarded:** 2 each year: 1 for an undergraduate and 1 for a graduate student. **Funds Available:** The stipend is $3,000 per year for graduate students or $1,000 per year for undergraduates. **Duration:** 1 academic year; may be renewable, based on scholastic standing, availability of funds, and continuance of a course of study leading to a career in applied geophysics.
Eligibility Requirements: This program is open to 1) high school students planning to enter college in the fall, and 2) undergraduate or graduate students whose grades are above average. Applicants must intend to work on a degree directed toward a career in applied geophysics with an emphasis on mining or electrical methods. Along with their application, they must submit a 150-word essay on how they plan to use geophysics in their future. Financial need is not considered in the selection process. **Deadline for Receipt:** January of each year.

3128 ■ SOCIETY OF EXPLORATION GEOPHYSICISTS

Attn: SEG Foundation
8801 South Yale, Suite 500
P.O. Box 702740
Tulsa, OK 74170-2740
Tel: (918)497-5513
Fax: (918)497-5557
E-mail: scholarships@seg.org

Web Site: http://seg.org/business/foundation/scholarships/index.shtml
To provide financial assistance to women undergraduate and graduate students who are interested in the field of applied geophysics.
Title of Award: Barbara McBride Scholarship **Area, Field, or Subject:** Geophysics **Level of Education for which Award is Granted:** Graduate, Undergraduate **Number Awarded:** 1 each year. **Funds Available:** The stipend ranges from $1,000 to $3,000 per year. **Duration:** 1 academic year; may be renewable, based on scholastic standing, availability of funds, and continuance of a course of study leading to a career in applied geophysics.
Eligibility Requirements: This program is open to women who are 1) high school students planning to enter college in the fall, or 2) undergraduate or graduate students whose grades are above average. Applicants must intend to work on a degree directed toward a career in applied geophysics or a closely-related field. Along with their application, they must submit a 150-word essay on how they plan to use geophysics in their future. Financial need is not considered in the selection process. **Deadline for Receipt:** January of each year.

3129 ■ SOCIETY OF EXPLORATION GEOPHYSICISTS

Attn: SEG Foundation
8801 South Yale, Suite 500
P.O. Box 702740
Tulsa, OK 74170-2740
Tel: (918)497-5513
Fax: (918)497-5557
E-mail: scholarships@seg.org
Web Site: http://seg.org/business/foundation/scholarships/index.shtml
To provide financial assistance to undergraduate and graduate students who are interested in the field of applied geophysics.
Title of Award: SEG Scholarship Program **Area, Field, or Subject:** Geophysics **Level of Education for which Award is Granted:** Graduate, Undergraduate **Number Awarded:** Varies each year; recently, 70 renewals and 66 new scholarships were awarded. The total value of the scholarships was $268,100. **Funds Available:** The stipends generally range from $500 to $14,000 per year and average $1,500 per year. **Duration:** 1 academic year; may be renewable, based on scholastic standing, availability of funds, and continuance of a course of study leading to a career in applied geophysics.
Eligibility Requirements: This program is open to 1) high school students planning to enter college in the fall, and 2) undergraduate or graduate students whose grades are above average. Applicants must intend to work on a degree directed toward a career in applied geophysics or a closely-related field. Along with their application, they must submit a 150-word essay on how they plan to use geophysics in their future. Financial need is not considered in the selection process. Some of the scholarships are set aside for students at recognized colleges or universities in countries outside of the United States. **Deadline for Receipt:** January of each year. **Additional Information:** This program includes a number of named scholarships; among them are the Donald R. Allen Memorial Scholarship, the Ted Born Memorial Scholarship, the Michael Forrest Scholarship, the Jim and Ruth Harrison Scholarship, the Jene and Marvin Hewitt Scholarship, the Fred Hilterman Scholarship, the Landmark Graphics Scholarship, the Permian Basic Geophysical Society Scholarship, the Schlumberger Scholarship, the WesternGeco Scholarship, the WesternGeco/Henry Salvatori Scholarship, and the David Worthington Scholarship.

3130 ■ SOCIETY OF EXPLORATION GEOPHYSICISTS

Attn: SEG Foundation
8801 South Yale, Suite 500
P.O. Box 702740
Tulsa, OK 74170-2740
Tel: (918)497-5513
Fax: (918)497-5557
E-mail: scholarships@seg.org
Web Site: http://seg.org/business/foundation/scholarships/index.shtml
To provide financial assistance to undergraduate and graduate students who are interested in studying applied geophysics.
Title of Award: Shell Oil International Scholarships **Area, Field, or Subject:** Geophysics **Level of Education for which Award is Granted:** Graduate, Undergraduate **Number Awarded:** 1 or more each year. **Funds Available:** Stipends range from $1,000 to $3,000 per year. **Dura-**

tion: 1 academic year; may be renewable, based on scholastic standing, availability of funds, and continuance of a course of study leading to a career in applied geophysics.

Eligibility Requirements: This program is open to 1) high school students planning to enter college in the fall, and 2) undergraduate or graduate students whose grades are above average. Applicants must intend to work on a degree directed toward a career in applied geophysics or a closely-related field; preference is given to undergraduates. Along with their application, they must submit a 150-word essay on how they plan to use geophysics in their future. Financial need is not considered in the selection process. **Deadline for Receipt:** January of each year. **Additional Information:** This program is sponsored by Shell Oil International.

3131 ■ SOCIETY OF EXPLORATION GEOPHYSICISTS

Attn: SEG Foundation
8801 South Yale, Suite 500
P.O. Box 702740
Tulsa, OK 74170-2740
Tel: (918)497-5513
Fax: (918)497-5557
E-mail: scholarships@seg.org
Web Site: http://seg.org/business/foundation/scholarships/index.shtml
To provide financial assistance to undergraduate and graduate students who are interested in the field of applied geophysics.

Title of Award: Veritas DGC Scholarship **Area, Field, or Subject:** Geophysics **Level of Education for which Award is Granted:** Graduate, Undergraduate **Number Awarded:** 1 each year. **Funds Available:** The stipend ranges from $1,000 to $3,000 per year. **Duration:** 1 academic year; may be renewable, based on scholastic standing, availability of funds, and continuance of a course of study leading to a career in applied geophysics.

Eligibility Requirements: This program is open to 1) high school students planning to enter college in the fall, and 2) undergraduate or graduate students whose grades are above average. Applicants must intend to work on a degree directed toward a career in applied geophysics. Along with their application, they must submit a 150-word essay on how they plan to use geophysics in their future. Financial need is not considered in the selection process. **Deadline for Receipt:** January of each year.

Meteorology

3132 ■ AMERICAN GEOLOGICAL INSTITUTE

Attn: Minority Participation Program
4220 King Street
Alexandria, VA 22302-1502
Tel: (703)379-2480
Fax: (703)379-7563
E-mail: cmm@agiweb.org
Web Site: http://www.agiweb.org/mpp/index.html
To provide financial assistance to underrepresented minority undergraduate and graduate students interested in working on a degree in the geosciences.

Title of Award: Minority Geoscience Student Scholarships **Area, Field, or Subject:** Education; Geology; Hydrology; Meteorology; Oceanography **Level of Education for which Award is Granted:** Graduate, Undergraduate **Number Awarded:** Varies each year; recently, 19 of these scholarships were awarded. **Funds Available:** Stipends range from $500 to $3,000 per year. **Duration:** 1 academic year; renewable if the recipient maintains satisfactory performance.

Eligibility Requirements: This program is open to members of ethnic minority groups underrepresented in the geosciences (Blacks, Hispanics, American Indians, Eskimos, Hawaiians, and Samoans). U.S. citizenship or permanent resident status is required. Applicants must be full-time students enrolled in an accredited institution working on an undergraduate or graduate degree in the geosciences, including geology, geophysics, hydrology, meteorology, physical oceanography, planetary geology, and earth science education; students in other natural sciences, mathematics, or engineering are not eligible. Selection is based on a 250-word essay on career goals and why the applicant has chosen a geoscience as a major, work experience, recommendations, honors and awards, extracurricular

activities, and financial need. **Deadline for Receipt:** March of each year. **Additional Information:** Funding for this program is provided by ExxonMobil Corporation, ConocoPhillips, ChevronTexaco Corporation, Marathon Corporation, and the Seismological Society of America.

3133 ■ AMERICAN METEOROLOGICAL SOCIETY

Attn: Fellowship/Scholarship Program
45 Beacon Street
Boston, MA 02108-3693
Tel: (617)227-2426
Fax: (617)742-8718
E-mail: scholar@ametsoc.org
Web Site: http://www.ametsoc.org/amsstudentinfo/scholfeldocs/index.html
To provide financial assistance to undergraduates majoring in meteorology or an aspect of atmospheric sciences.

Title of Award: AMS Undergraduate Scholarships **Area, Field, or Subject:** Atmospheric science; Hydrology; Meteorology; Oceanography **Level of Education for which Award is Granted:** Four Year College **Number Awarded:** 11 each year. **Funds Available:** Stipends range from $700 to $5,000 per year. **Duration:** 1 year.

Eligibility Requirements: This program is open to full-time students entering their final year of undergraduate study and majoring in meteorology or an aspect of the atmospheric or related oceanic and hydrologic sciences. Applicants must intend to make atmospheric or related sciences their career. They must be U.S. citizens or permanent residents enrolled at a U.S. institution and have a cumulative GPA of 3.25 or higher. Along with their application, they must submit 200-word essays on 1) their most important achievements that qualify them for this scholarship, and 2) their career goals in the atmospheric or related oceanic or hydrologic fields. Selection is based on academic excellence and achievement; financial need is not considered. The sponsor specifically encourages applications from women, minorities, and students with disabilities who are traditionally underrepresented in the atmospheric and related oceanic sciences. **Deadline for Receipt:** February of each year. **Additional Information:** This program includes the following named scholarships: the Howard H. Hanks, Jr. Scholarship in Meteorology ($700), the AMS 75th Anniversary Endowed Scholarship ($2,000), the Om and Saraswati (Sara) Bahethi Scholarship ($2,000), the Howard T. Orville Endowed Scholarship in Meteorology ($5,000), the George S. Benton Scholarship ($3,500), the Carl W. Kreitzberg Endowed Scholarship ($2,000), the Dr. Pedro Grau Undergraduate Scholarship ($2,500), the Guillermo Salazar Rodriguez Scholarship ($2,500), the John R. Hope Endowed Scholarship in Atmospheric Science ($2,500), the Richard and Helen Hagemeyer Scholarship ($3,000), and the Werner A. Baum Endowed Scholarship ($5,000). Requests for an application must be accompanied by a self-addressed stamped envelope.

3134 ■ AMERICAN METEOROLOGICAL SOCIETY

Attn: Fellowship/Scholarship Program
45 Beacon Street
Boston, MA 02108-3693
Tel: (617)227-2426
Fax: (617)742-8718
E-mail: scholar@ametsoc.org
Web Site: http://www.ametsoc.org/amsstudentinfo/scholfeldocs/index.html
To provide financial assistance to undergraduates majoring in meteorology or an aspect of atmospheric sciences with an interest in applied meteorology.

Title of Award: Loren W. Crow Memorial Scholarship **Area, Field, or Subject:** Atmospheric science; Hydrology; Meteorology; Oceanography **Level of Education for which Award is Granted:** Four Year College **Number Awarded:** 1 each year. **Funds Available:** The stipend is $2,000 per year. **Duration:** 1 year.

Eligibility Requirements: This program is open to full-time students entering their final year of undergraduate study and majoring in meteorology or an aspect of the atmospheric or related oceanic and hydrologic sciences. Applicants must intend to make atmospheric or related sciences their career, with preference for students who have demonstrated a strong interest in applied meteorology. They must be U.S. citizens or permanent residents enrolled at a U.S. institution and have a cumulative GPA of 3.25 or higher. Along with their application, they must submit 200-word essays on 1) their most important achievements that qualify them for this scholarship, and 2) their career goals in the atmospheric or related oceanic or hydrologic fields. Selection is based on academic excellence and achievement; financial need is not considered. The sponsor specifically encourages applications from women, minorities, and students with disabilities who are traditionally underrepresented in the atmospheric and related oceanic sciences. **Deadline for Receipt:** February of each year. **Additional Information:** Requests for an application must be accompanied by a self-addressed stamped envelope.

3135 ■ AMERICAN METEOROLOGICAL SOCIETY

Attn: Fellowship/Scholarship Program
45 Beacon Street
Boston, MA 02108-3693
Tel: (617)227-2426
Fax: (617)742-8718
E-mail: scholar@ametsoc.org
Web Site: http://www.ametsoc.org/amsstudentinfo/scholfeldocs/index.html
To provide financial assistance to undergraduates majoring in meteorology or an aspect of atmospheric sciences with an interest in statistical meteorology.
Title of Award: Bob Glahn Scholarship in Statistical Meteorology **Area, Field, or Subject:** Atmospheric science; Hydrology; Meteorology; Oceanography; Statistics **Level of Education for which Award is Granted:** Four Year College **Number Awarded:** 1 each year. **Funds Available:** The stipend is $2,500 per year. **Duration:** 1 year.
Eligibility Requirements: This program is open to full-time students entering their final year of undergraduate study and majoring in meteorology or an aspect of the atmospheric or related oceanic and hydrologic sciences. Applicants must intend to make atmospheric or related sciences their career, with preference for students who have demonstrated a strong interest in statistical meteorology. They must be U.S. citizens or permanent residents enrolled at a U.S. institution and have a cumulative GPA of 3.25 or higher. Along with their application, they must submit 200-word essays on 1) their most important achievements that qualify them for this scholarship, and 2) their career goals in the atmospheric or related oceanic or hydrologic fields. Selection is based on academic excellence and achievement; financial need is not considered. The sponsor specifically encourages applications from women, minorities, and students with disabilities who are traditionally underrepresented in the atmospheric and related oceanic sciences. **Deadline for Receipt:** February of each year. **Additional Information:** Requests for an application must be accompanied by a self-addressed stamped envelope.

3136 ■ AMERICAN METEOROLOGICAL SOCIETY

Attn: Fellowship/Scholarship Program
45 Beacon Street
Boston, MA 02108-3693
Tel: (617)227-2426
Fax: (617)742-8718
E-mail: scholar@ametsoc.org
Web Site: http://www.ametsoc.org/amsstudentinfo/scholfeldocs/index.html
To provide financial assistance to underrepresented minority students entering college and planning to major in meteorology or an aspect of atmospheric sciences.
Title of Award: Industry Minority Scholarships **Area, Field, or Subject:** Atmospheric science; Hydrology; Meteorology; Oceanography **Level of Education for which Award is Granted:** Four Year College **Number Awarded:** Varies each year; recently, 10 of these scholarships were awarded. **Funds Available:** The stipend is $3,000 per year. **Duration:** 1 year; may be renewed for the second year of college study.
Eligibility Requirements: This program is open to members of minority groups traditionally underrepresented in the sciences (Hispanics, Native Americans, and Black/African Americans) who are entering their freshman year at a college or university and planning to work on a degree in the atmospheric or related oceanic and hydrologic sciences. Applicants must submit an official high school transcript showing grades from the past 3 years, a letter of recommendation from a high school teacher or guidance counselor, a copy of scores from an SAT or similar national entrance exam, and a 500-word essay on how they would use their college education in atmospheric sciences (or a closely-related field) to make their com-

munity a better place in which to live. Selection is based on the essay and academic performance in high school. **Deadline for Receipt:** February of each year. **Additional Information:** This program is funded by grants from industry and by donations to the American Meteorological Society (AMS) 21st Century Campaign. Requests for an application must be accompanied by a self-addressed stamped envelope.

3137 ■ AMERICAN METEOROLOGICAL SOCIETY

Attn: Fellowship/Scholarship Program
45 Beacon Street
Boston, MA 02108-3693
Tel: (617)227-2426
Fax: (617)742-8718
E-mail: scholar@ametsoc.org
Web Site: http://www.ametsoc.org/amsstudentinfo/scholfeldocs/index.html
To provide financial assistance to undergraduates majoring in meteorology or an aspect of atmospheric sciences with an interest in weather forecasting.
Title of Award: Ethan and Allan Murphy Endowed Memorial Scholarship **Area, Field, or Subject:** Atmospheric science; Hydrology; Meteorology; Oceanography **Level of Education for which Award is Granted:** Four Year College **Number Awarded:** 1 each year. **Funds Available:** The stipend is $2,000 per year. **Duration:** 1 year.
Eligibility Requirements: This program is open to full-time students entering their final year of undergraduate study and majoring in meteorology or an aspect of the atmospheric or related oceanic and hydrologic sciences. Applicants must intend to make atmospheric or related sciences their career and be able to demonstrate, through curricular or extracurricular activities, an interest in weather forecasting or in the value and utilization of forecasts. They must be U.S. citizens or permanent residents enrolled at a U.S. institution and have a cumulative GPA of 3.25 or higher. Along with their application, they must submit 200-word essays on 1) their most important achievements that qualify them for this scholarship, and 2) their career goals in the atmospheric or related oceanic or hydrologic fields. Selection is based on academic excellence and achievement; financial need is not considered. The sponsor specifically encourages applications from women, minorities, and students with disabilities who are traditionally underrepresented in the atmospheric and related oceanic sciences. **Deadline for Receipt:** February of each year. **Additional Information:** Requests for an application must be accompanied by a self-addressed stamped envelope.

3138 ■ AMERICAN METEOROLOGICAL SOCIETY

Attn: Fellowship/Scholarship Program
45 Beacon Street
Boston, MA 02108-3693
Tel: (617)227-2426
Fax: (617)742-8718
E-mail: scholar@ametsoc.org
Web Site: http://www.ametsoc.org/amsstudentinfo/scholfeldocs/index.html
To provide financial assistance to students majoring in meteorology or some aspect of atmospheric sciences who demonstrate financial need.
Title of Award: Mark J. Schroeder Endowed Scholarship in Meteorology **Area, Field, or Subject:** Atmospheric science; Hydrology; Meteorology; Oceanography **Level of Education for which Award is Granted:** Four Year College **Number Awarded:** 1 each year. **Funds Available:** The stipend is $5,000. **Duration:** 1 year.
Eligibility Requirements: This program is open to full-time students entering their final year of undergraduate study and majoring in meteorology or an aspect of the atmospheric or related oceanic and hydrologic sciences. Applicants must intend to make atmospheric or related sciences their career. They must be U.S. citizens or permanent residents enrolled at a U.S. institution and have a cumulative GPA of 3.25 or higher. Along with their application, they must submit 200-word essays on 1) their most important achievements that qualify them for this scholarship, and 2) their career goals in the atmospheric or related oceanic or hydrologic fields. Selection is based on academic excellence and achievement and financial need. The sponsor specifically encourages applications from women, minorities, and students with disabilities who are traditionally underrepresented in the atmospheric and related oceanic sciences. **Deadline for Receipt:** February of each year. **Additional Information:**

This scholarship was established in 1995. Requests for an application must be accompanied by a self-addressed stamped envelope.

3139 ■ ASSOCIATION FOR WOMEN GEOSCIENTISTS

Attn: AWG Foundation
P.O. Box 30645
Lincoln, NE 68503-0645
E-mail: awgscholarship@yahoo.com
Web Site: http://www.awg.org/eas/minority.html

To provide financial assistance to minority women who are interested in working on an undergraduate degree in the geosciences.

Title of Award: Association for Women Geoscientists Minority Scholarship **Area, Field, or Subject:** Chemistry; Earth sciences; Education; Geology; Geosciences; Hydrology; Meteorology; Oceanography **Level of Education for which Award is Granted:** Undergraduate **Number Awarded:** 1 or more each year. **Funds Available:** A total of $5,000 is available for this program each year. **Duration:** 1 year; may be renewed. **Eligibility Requirements:** This program is open to women who are African American, Hispanic, or Native American (including Eskimo, Hawaiian, Samoan, or American Indian). Applicants must be full-time students working on, or planning to work on, an undergraduate degree in the geosciences (including geology, geophysics, geochemistry, hydrology, meteorology, physical oceanography, planetary geology, or earth science education). They must submit a 500-word essay on why they have chosen to major in the geosciences and their career goals, 2 letters of recommendation, high school and/or college transcripts, and SAT or ACT scores. Financial need is not considered in the selection process. **Deadline for Receipt:** May of each year. **Additional Information:** This program, first offered in 2004, is supported by ExxonMobil Foundation.

3140 ■ HANSCOM OFFICERS' WIVES' CLUB

Attn: Scholarship Chair
P.O. Box 557
Bedford, MA 01730
Tel: (781)275-1251
E-mail: scholarship@hanscomowd.org
Web Site: http://www.hanscomowc.org

To provide financial assistance to children of military personnel and veterans in New England who are interested in studying aeronautics and space in college.

Title of Award: COL Chuck Jones Memorial Award **Area, Field, or Subject:** Aeronautics; Aerospace sciences; Communications; Engineering; Meteorology; Space and planetary sciences **Level of Education for which Award is Granted:** Undergraduate **Number Awarded:** 1 each year. **Funds Available:** The stipend is $2,000. **Duration:** 1 year; nonrenewable. **Eligibility Requirements:** This program is open to college-bound high school seniors living in New England who are dependents of active-duty, retired, or deceased military members of any branch of service. Also eligible are dependents of military recruiters working in the New York area and students living elsewhere but whose military sponsor is stationed at Hanscom Air Force Base. Applicants must demonstrate qualities of responsibility, leadership, scholastics, citizenship, and diversity of interest. They must have a valid military identification card and be planning to work on a college degree in a field related to aeronautics and space (including communications, meteorology, air/space maintenance, manufacturing processing, engineering, and the astronaut program). Along with their application, they must submit a 2-page essay on their educational goals, how their educational experience will help prepare them to pursue future goals, and how they intend to apply their education to better their community. **Deadline for Receipt:** March of each year. **Additional Information:** This program was established to honor a victim of an airplane crash on September 11, 2001. It is sponsored by the Paul Revere Chapter of the Air Force Association.

3141 ■ HANSCOM OFFICERS' WIVES' CLUB

Attn: Scholarship Chair
P.O. Box 557
Bedford, MA 01730
Tel: (781)275-1251
E-mail: scholarship@hanscomowd.org
Web Site: http://www.hanscomowc.org

To provide financial assistance to children of military personnel and veterans in New England who are interested in studying aviation in college.

Title of Award: Brian Sweeney Memorial Award **Area, Field, or Subject:** Aviation; Engineering, Aerospace/Aeronautical/Astronautical; Engineering, Civil; Environmental science; Meteorology; Protective services **Level of Education for which Award is Granted:** Undergraduate **Number Awarded:** 1 each year. **Funds Available:** The stipend is $2,000. **Duration:** 1 year; nonrenewable. **Eligibility Requirements:** This program is open to college-bound high school seniors living in New England who are dependents of active-duty, retired, or deceased military members of any branch of service. Also eligible are dependents of military recruiters working in the New York area and students living elsewhere but whose military sponsor is stationed at Hanscom Air Force Base. Applicants must demonstrate qualities of responsibility, leadership, scholastics, citizenship, and diversity of interest. They must have a valid military identification card and be planning to work on a college degree in a field related to aviation (including civil, aeronautical, and environmental engineering; maintenance; management; aviation safety and security; and meteorology). Along with their application, they must submit a 2-page essay on their educational goals, how their educational experience will help prepare them to pursue future goals, and how they intend to apply their education to better their community. **Deadline for Receipt:** March of each year. **Additional Information:** This program was established to honor a victim of an airplane crash on September 11, 2001. It is sponsored by the Paul Revere Chapter of the Air Force Association.

3142 ■ CLARE BOOTHE LUCE FUND

c/o Henry Luce Foundation, Inc.
111 West 50th Street, Suite 4601
New York, NY 10020
Tel: (212)489-7700
Fax: (212)581-9541
E-mail: jdaniels@hluce.org
Web Site: http://www.hluce.org

To provide funding to women interested in studying science or engineering at the undergraduate level at designated universities.

Title of Award: Clare Boothe Luce Scholarships in Science and Engineering **Area, Field, or Subject:** Biological and clinical sciences; Chemistry; Computer and information sciences; Engineering; Engineering, Aerospace/Aeronautical/Astronautical; Engineering, Civil; Engineering, Electrical; Engineering, Mechanical; Engineering, Nuclear; Mathematics and mathematical sciences; Meteorology; Physics **Level of Education for which Award is Granted:** Undergraduate **Number Awarded:** Varies; since the program began, more than 800 of these scholarships have been awarded. **Funds Available:** The amount awarded is established individually by each of the participating institutions. The stipends are intended to augment rather than replace any existing institutional support in these fields. Each stipend is calculated to include the cost of room and board as well as tuition and other fees or expenses. **Duration:** 2 years; in certain special circumstances, awards for the full 4 years of undergraduate study may be offered. **Eligibility Requirements:** This program is open to female undergraduate students (particularly juniors and seniors) majoring in biology, chemistry, computer science, engineering (aeronautical, civil, electrical, mechanical, nuclear, and others), mathematics, meteorology, and physics. Applicants must be U.S. citizens attending 1 of the 12 designated colleges and universities affiliated with this program; periodically, other institutions are invited to participate. Premedical science majors are ineligible for this competition. The participating institutions select the recipients without regard to race, age, religion, ethnic background, or need. All awards are made on the basis of merit. **Deadline for Receipt:** Varies; check with the participating institutions for their current schedule. **Additional Information:** The participating institutions are Boston University, Colby College, Creighton University, Fordham University, Georgetown University, Marymount University, Mount Holyoke College, St. John's University, Santa Clara University, Seton Hall University, Trinity College, and University of Notre Dame.

3143 ■ NAVAL WEATHER SERVICE ASSOCIATION

c/o Jim Stone, Secretary-Treasurer
600 East Fifth Street, Apartment 179
Waverly, OH 45690-1500

E-mail: jstone@navalweather.org

Web Site: http://www.navalweather.org/NWSA_Scholarships.htm

To provide financial assistance to high school seniors and currently-enrolled undergraduates who plan to work on a college degree in selected science or engineering fields.

Title of Award: Naval Weather Service Association Scholarship **Area, Field, or Subject:** Engineering, Aerospace/Aeronautical/Astronautical; Meteorology; Oceanography **Level of Education for which Award is Granted:** Undergraduate **Number Awarded:** 1 or more each year. **Funds Available:** Stipends range from $500 to $2,000. Funds may be used to pay for tuition, fees, books, supplies, equipment, or any other educational expenses. **Duration:** 1 year; recipients may reapply.

Eligibility Requirements: This program is open to students who are enrolled or planning to enroll in an undergraduate program in meteorology, oceanography, or aerospace engineering. Applicants must be U.S. citizens and sponsored by a member of the association. Priority is given to graduating high school seniors, but current undergraduates are also eligible. Students planning to attend junior or community colleges may apply when they intend to transfer to a 4-year college or university. Selection is based on academic record, leadership skills, character, all-around ability, and financial need. **Deadline for Receipt:** April of each year. **Additional Information:** The Naval Weather Service Association is a nonprofit organization open to retired and active-duty meteorological and oceanographic personnel of the Navy and Marine Corps.

3144 ■ OAK RIDGE INSTITUTE FOR SCIENCE AND EDUCATION

Attn: Science and Engineering Education

P.O. Box 117

Oak Ridge, TN 37831-0117

Tel: (865)576-9279

Fax: (865)241-5220

E-mail: coxre@orau.gov

Web Site: http://www.orau.gov/orise.htm

To provide financial assistance and research experience to undergraduate students at minority serving institutions who are majoring in scientific fields of interest to the National Oceanic and Atmospheric Administration (NOAA).

Title of Award: National Oceanic and Atmospheric Administration Educational Partnership Program with Minority Serving Institutions Undergraduate Scholarships **Area, Field, or Subject:** Atmospheric science; Biological and clinical sciences; Cartography/Surveying; Chemistry; Computer and information sciences; Engineering; Environmental conservation; Environmental science; Geography; Mathematics and mathematical sciences; Meteorology; Photogrammetry; Physical sciences; Physics **Level of Education for which Award is Granted:** Four Year College **Number Awarded:** 10 each year. **Funds Available:** This program provides payment of tuition and fees (to a maximum of $4,000 per year) and a stipend during the internship of $650 per week. **Duration:** 1 academic year and 2 summers.

Eligibility Requirements: This program is open to juniors and seniors at minority serving institutions, including Hispanic Serving Institutions (HSIs), Historically Black Colleges and Universities (HBCUs), and Tribal Colleges and Universities (TCUs). Applicants must be majoring in atmospheric science, biology, cartography, chemistry, computer science, engineering, environmental science, geodesy, geography, marine science, mathematics, meteorology, photogrammetry, physical science, physics, or remote sensing. They must also be interested in participating in a research internship at a NOAA site. U.S. citizenship is required. **Deadline for Receipt:** January of each year. **Additional Information:** This program is funded by NOAA through an interagency agreement with the U.S. Department of Energy and administered by Oak Ridge Institute for Science and Education (ORISE).

3145 ■ U.S. AIR FORCE

Attn: Headquarters AFROTC/RRUC

551 East Maxwell Boulevard

Maxwell AFB, AL 36112-5917

Tel: (334)953-2091; (866)423-7682

Fax: (334)953-6167

Web Site: http://www.afrotc.com/scholarships/incolschol/expressSchol.php

To provide financial assistance to students who are interested in joining Air Force ROTC and majoring in critical Air Force officer fields in college.

Title of Award: Air Force ROTC Express Scholarships **Area, Field, or Subject:** Atmospheric science; Engineering, Aerospace/Aeronautical/Astronautical; Engineering, Civil; Engineering, Computer; Engineering, Electrical; Engineering, Mechanical; Environmental science; Meteorology **Level of Education for which Award is Granted:** Undergraduate **Funds Available:** Awards are type 2 AFROTC scholarships that provide for payment of tuition and fees, to a maximum of $15,000 per year, plus an annual book allowance of $600. All recipients are also awarded a tax-free monthly subsistence allowance that is $250 for freshmen, $300 for sophomores, $350 for juniors, and $400 for seniors. **Duration:** 3 and a half years, until completion of a bachelor's degree.

Eligibility Requirements: This program is open to U.S. citizens who are completing at least their first year of college and are working on a degree in fields that may change annually but are of critical interest to the Air Force. Applicants must have a GPA of 2.5 or higher and meet all other academic and physical requirements for participation in AFROTC. At the time of their Air Force commissioning, they may be no more than 31 years of age. They must be able to pass the Air Force Officer Qualifying Test (AFOQT) and the Air Force ROTC Physical Fitness Test. years as active-duty Air Force officers following graduation from college. **Additional Information:** Recently, freshmen were eligible if they were majoring in computer, electrical, or environmental engineering. Sophomores and juniors were eligible if they were majoring in those fields, meteorology and atmospheric sciences, or in the following engineering disciplines: aeronautical, aerospace, astronautical, civil, or mechanical. Recipients must also complete 4 years of aerospace studies courses at 1 of the 144 colleges and universities that have an Air Force ROTC unit on campus or 1 of the approximately 900 colleges that have cross-enrollment agreements with those institutions. They must also attend a 4-week summer training camp at an Air Force base, usually between their sophomore and junior years. Following completion of their bachelor's degree, scholarship recipients earn a commission as a second lieutenant in the Air Force and serve at least 4 years.

3146 ■ U.S. AIR FORCE

Attn: Headquarters AFROTC/RRUC

551 East Maxwell Boulevard

Maxwell AFB, AL 36112-5917

Tel: (334)953-2091; (866)423-7682

Fax: (334)953-6167

Web Site: http://www.afrotc.com/scholarships/hsschol/types.php

To provide financial assistance to high school seniors or graduates who are interested in joining Air Force ROTC in college and are willing to serve as Air Force officers following completion of their bachelor's degree.

Title of Award: Air Force ROTC High School Scholarships **Area, Field, or Subject:** Architecture; Chemistry; Computer and information sciences; Engineering, Aerospace/Aeronautical/Astronautical; Engineering, Architectural; Engineering, Civil; Engineering, Computer; Engineering, Electrical; Engineering, Mechanical; Environmental science; General studies/Field of study not specified; Mathematics and mathematical sciences; Meteorology; Operations research; Physics **Level of Education for which Award is Granted:** Four Year College **Number Awarded:** Approximately 2,000 each year. **Funds Available:** Type 1 scholarships provide payment of full tuition and most laboratory fees, as well as $600 for books. Type 2 scholarships pay the same benefits except tuition is capped at $15,000 per year; students who attend an institution where tuition exceeds $15,000 must pay the difference. Type 7 scholarships pay full tuition and most laboratory fees, but students must attend a college or university where the tuition is less than $9,000 per year or a public college or university where they qualify for the in-state tuition rate; they may not attend an institution with higher tuition and pay the difference. Approximately 5% of scholarship offers are for Type 1, approximately 20% are for Type 2, and approximately 75% are for type 7. All recipients are also awarded a tax-free subsistence allowance for 10 months of each year that is $250 per month as a freshman, $300 per month as a sophomore, $350 per month as a junior, and $400 per month as a senior. **Duration:** 4 years.

Eligibility Requirements: This program is open to high school seniors who are U.S. citizens at least 17 of age and have been accepted at a college or university with an Air Force ROTC unit on campus or a college with a cross-enrollment agreement with such a college. Applicants must have a cumulative GPA of 3.0 or higher and an ACT composite score of 24 or higher or an SAT score of 1100 (mathematics and verbal portion only) or higher. At the time of their commissioning in the Air Force, they must be no more than 31 years of age. They must agree to serve for at least 4 years as active-duty Air Force officers following graduation from college. **Deadline for Receipt:** November of each year. **Additional Information:** Recently, approximately 70% of these scholarships were offered to students planning to major in the science and technical fields of architecture, chemistry, computer science, engineering (aeronautical, aerospace, astronautical, architectural, civil, computer, electrical, environmental, or mechanical), mathematics, meteorology and atmospheric sciences, operations research, or physics. Approximately 30% were offered to students in all other fields. While scholarship recipients can major in any subject, they must enroll in 4 years of aerospace studies courses at 1 of the 144 colleges and universities that have an Air Force ROTC unit on campus; students may also attend nearly 900 other colleges that have cross-enrollment agreements with the institutions that have an Air Force ROTC unit on campus. Recipients must attend a 4-week summer training camp at an Air Force base, usually between their sophomore and junior years. Most cadets incur a 4-year active-duty commitment. Pilots incur a 10-year active-duty service commitment after successfully completing Specialized Undergraduate Pilot Training and navigators incur a 6-year commitment after successfully completing Specialized Undergraduate Navigator Training. The minimum service obligation for intelligence and Air Battle Management career fields is 5 years.

3147 ■ U.S. AIR FORCE
Attn: Headquarters AFROTC/RRUC
551 East Maxwell Boulevard
Maxwell AFB, AL 36112-5917
Tel: (334)953-2091; (866)423-7682
Fax: (334)953-6167
Web Site: http://www.afrotc.com/scholarships/incolschol/incolProgram.php
To provide financial assistance to undergraduate students who are willing to join Air Force ROTC in college and serve as Air Force officers following completion of their bachelor's degree.
Title of Award: Air Force ROTC In-College Scholarship Program **Area, Field, or Subject:** Architecture; Chemistry; Computer and information sciences; Engineering, Aerospace/Aeronautical/Astronautical; Engineering, Architectural; Engineering, Civil; Engineering, Computer; Engineering, Electrical; Engineering, Mechanical; Environmental science; General studies/Field of study not specified; Mathematics and mathematical sciences; Meteorology; Operations research; Physics **Level of Education for which Award is Granted:** Undergraduate **Number Awarded:** Varies each year. **Funds Available:** Cadets selected in Phase 1 are awarded type 2 AFROTC scholarships that provide for payment of tuition and fees, to a maximum of $15,000 per year. A limited number of cadets selected in Phase 2 are also awarded type 2 AFROTC scholarships, but most are awarded type 3 AFROTC scholarships with tuition capped at $9,000 per year. Cadets selected in Phase 3 are awarded type 6 AFROTC scholarships with tuition capped at $3,000 per year. All recipients are also awarded a book allowance of $600 and a tax-free subsistence allowance for 10 months of each year that is $300 per month during the sophomore year, $350 during the junior year, and $400 during the senior year. **Duration:** 3 years for students selected as freshmen or 2 years for students selected as sophomores.
Eligibility Requirements: This program is open to U.S. citizens enrolled as freshmen or sophomores at 1 of the 144 colleges and universities that have an Air Force ROTC unit on campus. Applicants must have a cumulative GPA of 2.5 or higher and be able to pass the Air Force Officer Qualifying Test and the Air Force ROTC Physical Fitness Test. At the time of commissioning, they may be no more than 31 years of age. They must agree to serve for at least 4 years as active-duty Air Force officers following graduation from college. Phase 1 is open to students enrolled in the Air Force ROTC program who do not currently have a scholarship but now wish to apply. Phase 2 is open to Phase 1 nonselects and students not enrolled in Air Force ROTC. Phase 3 is open only to Phase 2 nonselects. Recently, the program gave preference to students majoring in the science and technical fields of architecture, chemistry, computer science, engineering (aeronautical, aerospace, astronautical, architectural, civil, computer, electrical, environmental, or mechanical), mathematics, meteorology and atmospheric sciences, operations research, or physics. **Deadline for Receipt:** January of each year. **Additional Information:**

While scholarship recipients can major in any subject, they must complete 4 years of aerospace studies courses at 1 of the 144 colleges or universities that have an Air Force ROTC unit on campus. Recipients must also attend a 4-week summer training camp at an Air Force base, usually between their sophomore and junior years; 2-year scholarship awardees attend in the summer after their junior year. Current military personnel are eligible for early release from active duty in order to enter the Air Force ROTC program. Following completion of their bachelor's degree, scholarship recipients earn a commission as a second lieutenant in the Air Force and serve at least 4 years.

3148 ■ U.S. AIR FORCE
Attn: Headquarters AFROTC/RRUE
Enlisted Commissioning Section
551 East Maxwell Boulevard
Maxwell AFB, AL 36112-5917
Tel: (334)953-2091; (866)423-7682
Fax: (334)953-6167
E-mail: enlisted@afrotc.com
Web Site: http://www.afoats.af.mil/AFROTC/EnlistedComm/AECP.asp
To allow selected enlisted Air Force personnel to earn a bachelor's degree in approved majors by providing financial assistance for full-time college study.
Title of Award: Airman Education and Commissioning Program **Area, Field, or Subject:** African studies; Asian studies; Computer and information sciences; Engineering; Foreign languages; Mathematics and mathematical sciences; Meteorology; Near Eastern studies; Nursing; Physics; Russian studies **Level of Education for which Award is Granted:** Undergraduate **Number Awarded:** Approximately 60 each year. **Funds Available:** While participating in this program, cadets remain on active duty in the Air Force and receive their regular salary and benefits. They also receive payment of tuition and fees up to $15,000 per year and an annual textbook allowance of $600. **Duration:** 1 to 3 years, until completion of a bachelor's degree.
Eligibility Requirements: Eligible to participate in this program are enlisted members of the Air Force who have been accepted at a university or college (or approved crosstown institution) that is associated with AFROTC and that offers an approved major. The majors currently supported are computer science, all ABET-accredited engineering fields (not engineering technology), foreign area studies (limited to Middle East, Africa, Asia, Russia/Eurasia), foreign languages (limited to Arabic, Armenian, Azeri, Chinese, French, Georgian, Hebrew, Hindi, Indonesian, Kazakh, Pashto, Persian Farsi, Russian, Swahili, and Turkish), mathematics, meteorology, nursing, and physics. Applicants must have completed at least 1 year of time-in-service and 1 year of time-on-station. They must have scores on the Air Force Officer Qualifying Test of at least 15 on the verbal and 10 on the quantitative and be able to pass the Air Force ROTC Physical Fitness Test. Normally they should have completed at least 30 semester hours of college study with a GPA of 2.75 or higher. They must be younger than 31 years of age or otherwise able to be commissioned before they become 35 years of age. **Deadline for Receipt:** February of each year. **Additional Information:** While attending college, participants in this program attend ROTC classes at their college or university. Upon completing their degree, they are commissioned to serve in the Air Force in their area of specialization with an active-duty service commitment of at least 4 years. Further information is available from base education service officers or an Air Force ROTC unit. This program does not provide for undergraduate flying training.

3149 ■ U.S. AIR FORCE
Attn: Headquarters AFROTC/RRUE
Enlisted Commissioning Section
551 East Maxwell Boulevard
Maxwell AFB, AL 36112-5917
Tel: (334)953-2091; (866)423-7682
Fax: (334)953-6167
E-mail: enlisted@afrotc.com
Web Site: http://www.afoats.af.mil/AFROTC/EnlistedComm/ASCP.asp
To allow selected enlisted Air Force personnel to earn a bachelor's degree in approved majors by providing financial assistance for full-time college study.
Title of Award: Airman Scholarship and Commissioning Program **Area, Field, or Subject:** Architecture; Atmospheric science; Chemistry;

Computer and information sciences; Engineering; Engineering, Aerospace/Aeronautical/Astronautical; Engineering, Architectural; Engineering, Civil; Engineering, Computer; Engineering, Electrical; Engineering, Mechanical; Environmental science; General studies/Field of study not specified; Mathematics and mathematical sciences; Meteorology; Operations research; Physics **Level of Education for which Award is Granted:** Undergraduate **Number Awarded:** Varies each year. **Funds Available:** Awards are type 2 AFROTC scholarships that provide for payment of tuition and fees, to a maximum of $15,000 per year, plus an annual book allowance of $600. All recipients are also awarded a tax-free subsistence allowance for 10 months of each year that is $300 per month during their sophomore year, $350 during their junior year, and $400 during their senior year. **Duration:** 2 to 4 years, until completion of a bachelor's degree.

Eligibility Requirements: This program is open to active-duty enlisted members of the Air Force who have completed at least 1 year of continuous active duty and at least 1 year on station. Applicants normally must have completed at least 24 semester hours of graded college credit with a cumulative college GPA of 2.5 or higher. If they have not completed 24 hours of graded college credit, they must have an ACT score of 24 or higher or an SAT combined verbal and mathematics score of 1100 or higher. They must also have scores on the Air Force Officer Qualifying Test (AFOQT) of 15 or more on the verbal scale and 10 or more on the quantitative scale and be able to pass the Air Force ROTC Physical Fitness Test. Applicants must have been accepted at a college or university (including crosstown schools) offering the AFROTC 4-year program. When they complete the program and receive their commission, they may not be 31 years of age or older. U.S. citizenship is required. Recently, awards were presented according to the following priorities: 1) computer, electrical, and environmental engineering; 2) aeronautical, aerospace, architectural, astronautical, civil, and mechanical engineering and meteorology and atmospheric sciences; 3) all other ABET-accredited engineering majors, architecture, chemistry, computer science, mathematics, operations research, and physics; 4) all other majors. **Deadline for Receipt:** October of each year. **Additional Information:** Selectees separate from the active-duty Air Force, join an AFROTC detachment, and become full-time students. Upon completing their degree, they are commissioned as officers and returned to active duty in the Air Force with a 4-year service obligation. Further information is available from base education service officers or an Air Force ROTC unit.

3150 ■ U.S. AIR FORCE

Attn: Headquarters AFROTC/RRUE
Enlisted Commissioning Section
551 East Maxwell Boulevard
Maxwell AFB, AL 36112-5917
Tel: (334)953-2091; (866)423-7682
Fax: (334)953-6167
E-mail: enlisted@afrotc.com
Web Site: http://www.afoats.af.mil/AFROTC/EnlistedComm/POC-ERP.asp

To allow selected enlisted Air Force personnel to earn a baccalaureate degree by providing financial assistance for full-time college study.

Title of Award: Professional Officer Course Early Release Program **Area, Field, or Subject:** Architecture; Atmospheric science; Chemistry; Computer and information sciences; Engineering; Engineering, Aerospace/Aeronautical/Astronautical; Engineering, Architectural; Engineering, Civil; Engineering, Computer; Engineering, Electrical; Engineering, Mechanical; Environmental science; General studies/Field of study not specified; Mathematics and mathematical sciences; Meteorology; Operations research; Physics **Level of Education for which Award is Granted:** Undergraduate **Number Awarded:** Varies each year. **Funds Available:** Participants receive a stipend for 10 months of the year that is $350 per month during the first year and $400 per month during the second year. Scholarship recipients earn the Professional Officer Course Incentive of $3,000 per year for tuition and $600 per year for books. **Duration:** 2 years (no more and no less).

Eligibility Requirements: Eligible to participate in this program are enlisted members of the Air Force under the age of 30 (or otherwise able to be commissioned before becoming 35 years of age) who have completed at least 1 year on continuous active duty, have served on station for at least 1 year, and have no more than 2 years remaining to complete their initial baccalaureate degree. Scholarship applicants must

be younger than 31 years of age when they graduate and earn their commission. All applicants must have been accepted at a college or university offering the AFROTC 4-year program and must have a cumulative college GPA of 2.5 or higher. Their Air Force Officer Qualifying Test (AFOQT) scores must be at least 15 on the verbal and 10 on the quantitative. Applicants who have not completed 24 units of college work must have an ACT composite score of 24 or higher or an SAT combined verbal and mathematics score of 1100 or higher. U.S. citizenship is required. Recently, awards were presented according to the following priorities: 1) computer, electrical, and environmental engineering; 2) aeronautical, aerospace, architectural, astronautical, civil, and mechanical engineering and meteorology and atmospheric sciences; 3) all other ABET-accredited engineering majors, architecture, chemistry, computer science, mathematics, operations research, and physics; 4) all other majors. **Deadline for Receipt:** October of each year. **Additional Information:** Upon completing their degree, selectees are commissioned as officers in the Air Force with a 4-year service obligation. Further information is available from base education service officers or an Air Force ROTC unit.

Physics

3151 ■ AMERICAN ASSOCIATION OF PHYSICS TEACHERS

Attn: Scholarship Committee
One Physics Ellipse
College Park, MD 20740
Tel: (301)209-3344
Fax: (301)209-0845
E-mail: aapt-prog@aapt.org
Web Site: http://www.aapt.org/Grants/lotze.cfm

To provide financial assistance to high school seniors or currently-enrolled college students interested in preparing for a career as a high school physics teacher.

Title of Award: Barbara Lotze Scholarship for Future Teachers **Area, Field, or Subject:** Education; Education, Secondary; Physics **Level of Education for which Award is Granted:** Undergraduate **Number Awarded:** Generally, 1 each year. **Funds Available:** The stipend is $2,000 per year. **Duration:** 1 year; may be renewed for up to 3 additional years.

Eligibility Requirements: Eligible to apply are high school seniors, high school graduates, and currently-enrolled undergraduate students in or planning to enter a physics teacher preparation program. All applicants must be U.S. citizens. All other considerations being equal, applicants from Allegheny College are given preference. **Deadline for Receipt:** Applications may be submitted at any time.

3152 ■ AMERICAN COUNCIL OF THE BLIND

Attn: Coordinator, Scholarship Program
1155 15th Street, N.W., Suite 1004
Washington, DC 20005
Tel: (202)467-5081
Free: 800-424-8666
Fax: (202)467-5085
E-mail: info@acb.org
Web Site: http://www.acb.org

To provide financial assistance to blind students who are working on an undergraduate or graduate degree in science at an accredited college or university.

Title of Award: Dr. S. Bradley Burson Memorial Scholarship **Area, Field, or Subject:** Biological and clinical sciences; Chemistry; Engineering; Physics **Level of Education for which Award is Granted:** Graduate, Undergraduate **Number Awarded:** 1 each year. **Funds Available:** The stipend is $1,000. In addition, the winner receives a Kurzweil-1000 Reading System. **Duration:** 1 year.

Eligibility Requirements: This program is open to legally blind undergraduate or graduate students majoring in the "hard" sciences (i.e., biology, chemistry, physics, and engineering, but not computer science) in college. They must be U.S. citizens. In addition to letters of recommendation and copies of academic transcripts, applications must include an autobiographical sketch. A cumulative GPA of 3.3 or higher is generally required. Selection is based on demonstrated academic record, involvement in extracurricular and civic activities, and academic objectives. The severity of the applicant's visual impairment and his/her study methods are also taken into account. **Deadline for Receipt:** February of each year. **Additional Information:** Scholarship winners are expected to be present at the council's annual conference; the council will cover all reasonable expenses connected with convention attendance.

3153 ■ AMERICAN PHYSICAL SOCIETY

Attn: Apker Award Committee
One Physics Ellipse
College Park, MD 20740-3844
Tel: (301)209-3233
Fax: (301)209-0865
E-mail: chodos@aps.org
Web Site: http://www.aps.org/praw/apker/index.cfm
To recognize and reward undergraduate students for outstanding work in physics.

Title of Award: Leroy Apker Award **Area, Field, or Subject:** Physics **Level of Education for which Award is Granted:** Four Year College **Number Awarded:** 2 recipients each year: 1 to a student at a Ph.D. granting institution and 1 at a non-Ph.D. granting institution. **Funds Available:** The award consists of a $5,000 honorarium for the student, a certificate citing the work and school of the recipient, and an allowance for travel expenses to the meeting of the American Physical Society (APS) at which the prize is presented. Each of the finalists receives an honorarium of $2,000 and a certificate. Each of the physics departments whose nominees are selected as recipients and finalists receives a certificate and an award; the departmental award is $5,000 for recipients and $1,000 for finalists. **Duration:** The award is presented annually.

Eligibility Requirements: This program is open to undergraduate students at colleges and universities in the United States. Nominees should have completed or be completing the requirements for an undergraduate degree with an excellent academic record and should have demonstrated exceptional potential for scientific research by making an original contribution to physics. Each department of physics in the United States may nominate only 1 student. Each nomination packet should include the student's academic transcript, a description of the original contribution written by the student (such as a manuscript or reprint of a research publication or senior thesis), a 1,000-word summary, and 2 letters of recommendation. **Deadline for Receipt:** June of each year. **Additional Information:** This award was established in 1978.

3154 ■ AMERICAN PHYSICAL SOCIETY

Attn: Committee on Minorities
One Physics Ellipse
College Park, MD 20740-3844
Tel: (301)209-3232
Fax: (301)209-0865
Web Site: http://www.aps.org/educ/com/scholars/index.cfm
To provide financial assistance to underrepresented minority students interested in studying physics on the undergraduate level.

Title of Award: APS Scholarships for Minority Undergraduate Students Who Major in Physics **Area, Field, or Subject:** Physics **Level of Education for which Award is Granted:** Undergraduate **Number Awarded:** Usually, 20 to 25 of these scholarships are awarded each year. **Funds Available:** Stipends are $2,000 per year in the first year or $3,000 in the second year; funds must be used for tuition, room, and board. In addition, $500 is awarded to the host department. **Duration:** 1 year; renewable for 1 additional year with the approval of the APS selection committee.

Eligibility Requirements: Any African American, Hispanic American, or Native American who plans to major in physics and who is a high school senior or college freshman or sophomore may apply. U.S. citizenship or permanent resident status is required. The selection committee especially encourages applications from students who are attending or planning to attend institutions with historically or predominantly Black, Hispanic, or Native American enrollment. Selection is based on commitment to the study of physics and plans to work on a physics baccalaureate degree. **Deadline for Receipt:** January of each year. **Additional Information:** APS conducts this program, which began in 1980 as the Corporate-Sponsored Scholarships for Minority Undergraduate Students Who Major in Physics, in conjunction with the Corporate Associates of the American Institute of Physics. Each scholarship is sponsored by a corporation, which is normally designated as the sponsor. A corporation generally sponsors from 1 to 10 scholarships, depending upon its size and utilization of physics in the business.

3155 ■ AMERICAN SOCIETY FOR ENGINEERING EDUCATION

Attn: SMART Defense Scholarship Program
1818 N Street, N.W., Suite 600
Washington, DC 20036-2479
Tel: (202)331-3516
Fax: (202)265-8504
E-mail: smart@asee.org
Web Site: http://www.asee.org/resources/fellowships/smart/index.cfm
To provide scholarship/loans to upper-division and graduate students in areas of science, mathematics, and engineering that are of interest to the U.S. Department of Defense.

Title of Award: Science, Mathematics, and Research for Transformation (SMART) Defense Scholarship Program **Area, Field, or Subject:** Architecture, Naval; Behavioral sciences; Biological and clinical sciences; Chemistry; Computer and information sciences; Earth sciences; Engineering, Aerospace/Aeronautical/Astronautical; Engineering, Chemical; Engineering, Civil; Engineering, Electrical; Engineering, Materials; Engineering, Mechanical; Engineering, Ocean; Geosciences; Materials research/science; Mathematics and mathematical sciences; Oceanography; Physics **Level of Education for which Award is Granted:** Four Year College, Graduate **Number Awarded:** Varies each year; recently, 36 of these scholarships were awarded. **Funds Available:** The program provides full payment of tuition, fees, room, board, and other normal educational expenses at the recipient's institution. A book allowance of $1,000 per year is also provided. This is a scholarship/loan program; recipients must agree to serve as a civilian employee of the Department of Defense in a science and engineering position. If they fail to fulfill that service obligation, they must reimburse the federal government for all funds they received. **Duration:** Up to 24 months.

Eligibility Requirements: This program is open to upper-division and graduate students working on an undergraduate or graduate degree in any of the following fields: aeronautical and astronautical engineering; biosciences; chemical engineering; chemistry; civil engineering; cognitive, neural, and behavioral sciences; computer and computational sciences; electrical engineering; geosciences, including terrain, water, and air; materials science and engineering; mathematics; mechanical engineering; naval architecture and ocean engineering; oceanography; or physics. Applicants must be U.S. citizens who have a GPA of 3.0 or higher. Selection is based on academic records, personal statements, letters of recommendation, and GRE scores. **Deadline for Receipt:** March of each year. **Additional Information:** This program, established in 2005, is sponsored by the Army Research Laboratory, the Air Force Office of Scientific Research, the Office of Naval Research, the Air Force Research Laboratory, the Defense Advanced Research Projects Agency, the Defense Information Systems Agency, and the Defense Threat Reduction Agency.

3156 ■ ARKANSAS DEPARTMENT OF HIGHER EDUCATION

Attn: Financial Aid Division
114 East Capitol Avenue
Little Rock, AR 72201-3818
Tel: (501)371-2050
Free: 800-54-STUDY
Fax: (501)371-2001
E-mail: finaid@adhe.arknet.edu
Web Site: http://www.starark.com
To provide scholarship/loans to college students in Arkansas who are interested in preparing for a teaching career in an approved subject or geographic shortage area.

Title of Award: Arkansas State Teacher Assistance Resource (STAR) Program **Area, Field, or Subject:** Biological and clinical sciences; Chemistry; Earth sciences; Education; Education, Secondary; Education, Special; Geosciences; Linguistics; Mathematics and mathematical sciences; Physical sciences; Physics **Level of Education for which Award is Granted:** Master's, Undergraduate **Number Awarded:** Varies each year; recently, 42 of these scholarship/loans were approved. **Funds Available:** The award is $3,000 per year for students who agree to teach in either a geographic teacher shortage area or a subject teacher shortage area. For students who agree to teach in both a geographic shortage area and a subject shortage area, the award is $6,000 per year. This is a scholarship/loan program. Recipients must teach in an Arkansas geographic or subject shortage area for 1 year for each year of support they receive. If they fail to complete that teaching obligation, they must repay all funds received. **Duration:** 1 year; may be renewed for 1 additional year if the recipient is enrolled in a 4-year teacher education program or 2 additional years if enrolled in a 5-year teacher education program. Renewal requires that the recipient maintain a GPA of 2.75 or higher and complete 24 semester hours as an undergraduate or 18 semester hours as a graduate student.

Eligibility Requirements: This program is open to Arkansas residents who are full-time students enrolled 1) at a 4-year public or private college or university in the state with an approved teacher education program; 2) in an associate of arts in teaching program; or 3) in an master of arts in teaching program. Applicants must have a GPA of 2.75 or higher and be entering their sophomore, junior, or senior year (or be in a master's degree program). They must be willing to teach in a public school located in a geographic area of Arkansas designated as having a critical shortage of teachers or in a subject matter area designated as having a critical shortage of teachers. Applicants must have completed their freshman year at an accredited Arkansas public or private college or university in a major field of study leading to secondary teacher certification in 1 of the shortage areas. U.S. citizenship is required. **Deadline for Receipt:** May of each year. **Additional Information:** This program was established in 2004 as a replacement for the former Arkansas Emergency Secondary Education Loan Program. Recently, the subject areas designated as having a critical shortage of teachers were foreign language, mathematics, chemistry, physics, biology, physical science, earth science, and special education. For a list of geographic areas of Arkansas that are designated as having a critical shortage of teachers, contact the Department of Higher Education. The State Teacher Assistance Resource (STAR) program also provides that teachers who received federal student loans may have those loans repaid 1) at the rate of $3,000 per year if they teach a subject area in Arkansas that is designated as a shortage area or if they teach in a geographic area of the state with a shortage of teachers, or 2) at the rate of $6,000 per year if they teach a shortage subject area in a shortage geographic area. Students may not, however, participate in both the scholarship/loan program and the federal loan repayment program.

3157 ■ ARMED FORCES COMMUNICATIONS AND ELECTRONICS ASSOCIATION

Attn: AFCEA Educational Foundation
4400 Fair Lakes Court
Fairfax, VA 22033-3899
Tel: (703)631-6149
Free: 800-336-4583
Fax: (703)631-4693
E-mail: scholarship@afcea.org
Web Site: http://www.afcea.org/education/scholarships/undergraduate/pub1.asp
To provide financial assistance to undergraduate students who are working full time on a degree by means of a distance-learning or on-line program.

Title of Award: AFCEA Distance-Learning/On-Line Scholarships **Area, Field, or Subject:** Computer and information sciences; Engineering, Chemical; Engineering, Computer; Engineering, Electrical; Mathematics and mathematical sciences; Physics; Systems engineering **Level of Education for which Award is Granted:** Four Year College **Number Awarded:** 1 each year. **Funds Available:** The stipend is $1,000. **Duration:** 1 year.

Eligibility Requirements: This program is open to U.S. citizens working full time on a bachelor's degree by means of a distance-learning or on-line program affiliated with a major, accredited 4-year college or university in the United States. Applicants must have completed at least 1 year of course work based on a 30-semester hour equivalent; classes in progress at the time of application cannot be used towards the 1-year minimum completion requirement. Completed courses must include at least 2 semesters of calculus (not pre-calculus). Majors are limited to the fields of engineering (chemical, computer, electrical, or systems), mathematics, physics, or computer science. Selection is based primarily on academic excellence. **Deadline for Receipt:** July of each year.

3158 ■ ARMED FORCES COMMUNICATIONS AND ELECTRONICS ASSOCIATION

Attn: AFCEA Educational Foundation
4400 Fair Lakes Court
Fairfax, VA 22033-3899
Tel: (703)631-6149

Free: 800-336-4583
Fax: (703)631-4693
E-mail: scholarship@afcea.org
Web Site: http://www.afcea.org/education/scholarships/rotc/rotc1.asp
To provide financial assistance to ROTC cadets who are majoring in fields related to communications and electronics.

Title of Award: AFCEA ROTC Scholarships **Area, Field, or Subject:** Computer and information sciences; Electronics; Engineering, Aerospace/Aeronautical/Astronautical; Engineering, Chemical; Engineering, Computer; Engineering, Electrical; Mathematics and mathematical sciences; Physics; Systems engineering **Level of Education for which Award is Granted:** Four Year College **Number Awarded:** 36 each year, divided equally among Army, Navy/Marine Corps, and Air Force ROTC programs; for each service, 6 are awarded to rising juniors, 6 to rising seniors. **Funds Available:** The stipend is $2,000. **Duration:** 1 year; may be renewed.

Eligibility Requirements: This program is open to ROTC cadets majoring in electronics, engineering (aerospace, chemical, computer, electrical, or systems), mathematics, physics, or computer science. Applicants must be nominated by their ROTC professor, be entering their junior or senior year, be U.S. citizens, be of good moral character, have demonstrated academic excellence, be motivated to complete a college education and serve as officers in the U.S. armed forces, and be able to demonstrate financial need. **Deadline for Receipt:** March of each year.

3159 ■ ARMED FORCES COMMUNICATIONS AND ELECTRONICS ASSOCIATION

Attn: AFCEA Educational Foundation
4400 Fair Lakes Court
Fairfax, VA 22033-3899
Tel: (703)631-6149
Free: 800-336-4583
Fax: (703)631-4693
E-mail: scholarship@afcea.org
Web Site: http://www.afcea.org/education/scholarships/workingstudents/ws1.asp
To provide financial assistance to undergraduate students who are working part time on a degree in engineering or the sciences while already employed.

Title of Award: AFCEA Scholarship for Working Professionals **Area, Field, or Subject:** Computer and information sciences; Engineering, Aerospace/Aeronautical/Astronautical; Engineering, Chemical; Engineering, Electrical; Mathematics and mathematical sciences; Physics; Systems engineering **Level of Education for which Award is Granted:** Undergraduate **Number Awarded:** 1 each year. **Funds Available:** The stipend is $1,500. **Duration:** 1 year; may be renewed.

Eligibility Requirements: This program is open to part-time students entering their sophomore, junior, or senior year at an accredited 2-year or 4-year college or university in the United States while already employed in a science or technology field. Applicants must be U.S. citizens working toward a degree in engineering (aerospace, chemical, electrical, or systems), mathematics, physics, or computer science with a GPA of 3.4 or higher. They must be able to demonstrate academic achievement, patriotism, and potential to contribute to the American work force. **Deadline for Receipt:** September of each year. **Additional Information:** This program was established in 2002.

3160 ■ ARMED FORCES COMMUNICATIONS AND ELECTRONICS ASSOCIATION

Attn: AFCEA Educational Foundation
4400 Fair Lakes Court
Fairfax, VA 22033-3899
Tel: (703)631-6149
Free: 800-336-4583
Fax: (703)631-4693
E-mail: scholarship@afcea.org
Web Site: http://www.afcea.org/education/scholarships/undergraduate/genemm.asp
To provide funding to veterans, military personnel, and their family members who are majoring in specified scientific fields in college.

Title of Award: General Emmett Paige Scholarships **Area, Field, or Subject:** Computer and information sciences; Engineering, Aerospace/Aeronautical/Astronautical; Engineering, Chemical; Engineering,

Computer; Engineering, Electrical; Mathematics and mathematical sciences; Physics **Level of Education for which Award is Granted:** Four Year College **Number Awarded:** Varies each year; recently, 11 of these scholarships were awarded. **Funds Available:** The stipend is $2,000. **Duration:** 1 year; may be renewed.

Eligibility Requirements: This program is open to veterans, persons on active duty in the uniformed military services, and their spouses or dependents who are currently enrolled full time in an accredited 4-year college or university in the United States. Graduating high school seniors are not eligible, but veterans entering college as freshmen may apply. Spouses or dependents must be sophomores or juniors. Applicants must be U.S. citizens, be of good moral character, have demonstrated academic excellence, be motivated to complete a college education, and be working toward a degree in engineering (aerospace, chemical, computer, or electrical), mathematics, physics, or computer science with a GPA of 3.4 or higher. They must provide a copy of Discharge Form DD214, Certificate of Service, or facsimile of their current Department of Defense or Coast Guard Identification Card. **Deadline for Receipt:** February of each year.

3161 ■ ARMED FORCES COMMUNICATIONS AND ELECTRONICS ASSOCIATION

Attn: AFCEA Educational Foundation
4400 Fair Lakes Court
Fairfax, VA 22033-3899
Tel: (703)631-6149
Free: 800-336-4583
Fax: (703)631-4693
E-mail: scholarship@afcea.org
Web Site: http://www.afcea.org/education/scholarships/undergraduate/veteran.asp

To provide financial assistance to veterans and military personnel who served in Afghanistan or Iraq and are working on an undergraduate degree in fields related to the support of U.S. intelligence enterprises.

Title of Award: Veterans of Enduring Freedom-Afghanistan and Iraqi Freedom Combat Operations Scholarship **Area, Field, or Subject:** Computer and information sciences; Engineering; Engineering, Aerospace/Aeronautical/Astronautical; Engineering, Computer; Engineering, Electrical; Mathematics and mathematical sciences; Physics; Systems engineering **Level of Education for which Award is Granted:** Undergraduate **Number Awarded:** 1 or more each year. **Funds Available:** The stipend is $2,000. **Duration:** 1 year.

Eligibility Requirements: This program is open to active-duty and honorably discharged U.S. military veterans, Reservists, and National Guard personnel who served in combat operations of Enduring Freedom-Afghanistan or Iraqi Freedom. Applicants must be enrolled at a 2- or 4-year institution in the United States and working on an undergraduate degree in computer engineering technology, computer information systems, electronics engineering technology, engineering (aerospace, computer, electrical, or systems), mathematics, physics, or computer science. Along with their application, they must submit an essay that includes a brief synopsis of relevant work experience (including military assignments), a brief statement of career goals after graduation, and a explanation of how their academic and career goals will contribute to the areas related to communications, intelligence and/or information systems, and the mission of the Armed Forces Communications and Electronics Association (AFCEA). Financial need is also considered in the selection process. **Deadline for Receipt:** October of each year. **Additional Information:** This scholarship was first offered in 2005.

3162 ■ ARMED FORCES COMMUNICATIONS AND ELECTRONICS ASSOCIATION

Attn: AFCEA Educational Foundation
4400 Fair Lakes Court
Fairfax, VA 22033-3899
Tel: (703)631-6149
Free: 800-336-4583
Fax: (703)631-4693
E-mail: scholarship@afcea.org
Web Site: http://www.afcea.org/education/scholarships/undergraduate/pub2.asp

To provide financial assistance to undergraduate students who are working full time on a degree in engineering or the sciences.

Title of Award: General John A. Wickham Scholarships **Area, Field, or Subject:** Computer and information sciences; Engineering, Aerospace/Aeronautical/Astronautical; Engineering, Chemical; Engineering, Computer; Engineering, Electrical; Mathematics and mathematical sciences; Physics; Systems engineering **Level of Education for which Award is Granted:** Four Year College **Number Awarded:** Varies each year; recently, 11 of these scholarships were awarded. **Funds Available:** The stipend is $2,000. **Duration:** 1 year; may be renewed.

Eligibility Requirements: This program is open to full-time students entering their junior or senior year at an accredited degree-granting 4-year college or university in the United States. Applicants must be U.S. citizens working toward a degree in engineering (aerospace, chemical, computer, electrical, or systems), mathematics, physics, or computer science with a GPA of 3.5 or higher. They must be able to demonstrate academic achievement, patriotism, and potential to contribute to the American work force. **Deadline for Receipt:** April of each year.

3163 ■ ARMED FORCES COMMUNICATIONS AND ELECTRONICS ASSOCIATION

Attn: AFCEA Educational Foundation
4400 Fair Lakes Court
Fairfax, VA 22033-3899
Tel: (703)631-6149
Free: 800-336-4583
Fax: (703)631-4693
E-mail: scholarship@afcea.org
Web Site: http://www.afcea.org/education/scholarships/undergraduate/sgtjean.asp

To provide funding to members and veterans of the U.S. Marine Corps (USMC) who are majoring in specified fields in college.

Title of Award: Marine Sgt. Jeannette L. Winters Memorial Scholarship **Area, Field, or Subject:** Computer and information sciences; Engineering, Aerospace/Aeronautical/Astronautical; Engineering, Computer; Engineering, Electrical; Mathematics and mathematical sciences; Physics; Systems engineering **Level of Education for which Award is Granted:** Undergraduate **Number Awarded:** 1 each year. **Funds Available:** The stipend is $2,000. **Duration:** 1 year.

Eligibility Requirements: This program is open to USMC personnel currently on active duty, in the Reserves, or honorably-discharged veterans who are enrolled full or part time in an accredited college or university in the United States. Applicants must be U.S. citizens, be of good moral character, have demonstrated academic excellence, be motivated to complete a college education, and be working on a degree in engineering (aerospace, computer, electrical, or systems), mathematics, physics, or computer science with a GPA of 3.0 or higher. They must provide a copy of Discharge Form DD214, Certificate of Service, or facsimile of their current Department of Defense Identification Card. **Deadline for Receipt:** September of each year. **Additional Information:** This program was established in 2002 to honor a Marine who died when her KC-130 aircraft crashed in Pakistan.

3164 ■ ASSOCIATION FOR IRON & STEEL TECHNOLOGY

Attn: AIST Foundation
186 Thorn Hill Road
Warrendale, PA 15086-7528
Tel: (724)776-6040
Fax: (724)776-1880
E-mail: lwharrey@aist.org
Web Site: http://www.aist.org/foundation/scholarships.htm

To provide financial assistance for college study of engineering to Canadians who are children of members of the Association for Iron & Steel Technology (AIST).

Title of Award: David H. Samson Canadian Scholarship **Area, Field, or Subject:** Chemistry; Engineering; Geology; Mathematics and mathematical sciences; Physics **Level of Education for which Award is Granted:** Undergraduate **Number Awarded:** 1 each year. **Funds Available:** The stipend is $US2,000. **Duration:** 1 year; may be renewed for up to 3 additional years.

Eligibility Requirements: This program is open to the children (natural, adopted, or ward) of Canadian citizens and landed immigrants who are members of the association. Applicants must have been accepted in an eligible full-time course of study of engineering at an accredited Canadian university. If no engineering student applies, the award may be made to an eligible student planning to major in chemistry, geology, mathematics, or physics. The scholarship may also be awarded to a student entering a community college if there is no eligible applicant entering an accredited university. The committee may also award the scholarship to a previous applicant entering the second or third year at a Canadian university or community college if there is no eligible applicant entering the first year. Selection is based on academic achievements, extracurricular activities, and the student's written statements; financial need is not considered. **Deadline for Receipt:** June of each year. **Additional Information:** The AIST was formed in 2004 by the merger of the Iron and Steel Society (ISS) and the Association of Iron and Steel Engineers (AISE). Information is also available from Robert Kneale, AIST Northern Member Chapter, P.O. Box 1734, Cambridge, Ontario N1R 7G8, Canada.

3165 ■ ASSOCIATION FOR IRON & STEEL TECHNOLOGY-NORTHWEST CHAPTER

c/o Gerardo L. Giraldo, Secretary-Treasurer
Nucor Steel Seattle, Inc.
Washington Steel Division
2424 S.W. Andover Street
Seattle, WA 98106-1100
Tel: (206)933-2245
Fax: (206)933-2207
E-mail: gerry.giraldo@nucor-seattle.com
Web Site: http://www.aist.org/chapters/
mc_pittsburgh_scholar_guidelines.htm
To provide financial assistance to family of members of the Northwest Chapter of the Association for Iron & Steel Technology (AIST) who are interested in studying engineering in college.
Title of Award: Northwest Chapter AIST Scholarships **Area, Field, or Subject:** Business; Chemistry; Engineering; Manufacturing; Mathematics and mathematical sciences; Metallurgy; Physics **Level of Education for which Award is Granted:** Four Year College **Number Awarded:** 2 each year. **Funds Available:** The stipend is $1,000. **Duration:** 1 year.
Eligibility Requirements: This program is open to children, grandchildren, spouses, or nieces/nephews of chapter members who are high school seniors planning to attend an accredited 4-year college or university. Applicants must intend to study engineering; if there are no applicants in engineering, the award may be given to a student majoring in chemistry, mathematics, metallurgy, or physics, or to a student showing an interest in preparing for a career in the iron and steel industry. Along with their application, they must submit a 500-word essay on 1 of the following topics: 1) an accomplishment they have achieved while they have been a student, why they were successful, and how their success will influence their future plans as an engineer or an engineer in the steel industry; 2) their strengths and interests and how they will apply their skills to a career in the steel industry or as an engineer; or 3) the challenges that face the steel industry and the opportunities for graduates to improve the success of companies within the industry. Financial need is not considered in the selection process. **Deadline for Receipt:** June of each year. **Additional Information:** The AIST was formed in 2004 by the merger of the Iron and Steel Society (ISS) and the Association of Iron and Steel Engineers (AISE). The Northwest Chapter serves Alaska, Idaho, Montana, Oregon, Washington, and Wyoming.

3166 ■ ASSOCIATION FOR IRON & STEEL TECHNOLOGY-OHIO VALLEY CHAPTER

c/o Jeff McKain, Scholarship Chair
Xtek, Inc.
11451 Reading Road
Cincinnati, OH 45241
Tel: (513)733-7843; (999)332-XTEK
Fax: (513)733-7939
E-mail: jeff.mckain@xtek.com
Web Site: http://www.aist.org/chapters/ohiovalley_scholarship.htm
To provide financial assistance for college to student members and children of members of the Ohio Valley Chapter of the Association for Iron & Steel Technology (AIST).
Title of Award: Ohio Valley Chapter AIST Scholarships **Area, Field, or Subject:** Biological and clinical sciences; Chemistry; Computer and information sciences; Earth sciences; Engineering; Engineering, Electrical; Engineering, Mechanical; Environmental conservation; Environmental science; Geosciences; Information science and technology; Metallurgy;

Physical sciences; Physics **Level of Education for which Award is Granted:** Undergraduate **Number Awarded:** Up to 2 each year. **Funds Available:** The stipend is $1,000 per year. **Duration:** 1 year; may be renewed up to 3 additional years provided the recipient remains enrolled full time and maintains a GPA of 3.0 or higher.
Eligibility Requirements: This program is open to high school seniors and college students who are either 1) children of Ohio Valley Chapter AIST members, or 2) student AIST members. Applicants must be accepted at, planning to attend, or currently enrolled at an accredited college or university with a major in biology, chemistry, computer programming, computer technology, electrical engineering, engineering, engineering technology, environmental engineering, environmental science, information systems technology, mechanical engineering, metallurgy, microbiology, physical science, physics, or other field approved by the scholarship committee. Along with their application, they must submit a 500-word essay on the reasons for their interests and reasons for working on a degree in their field of study, career goals and objectives, and extracurricular activities and their benefits. Selection is based on overall academic achievement (especially in mathematics and science), the essay, and extracurricular activities. **Deadline for Receipt:** February of each year. **Additional Information:** The AIST was formed in 2004 by the merger of the Iron and Steel Society (ISS) and the Association of Iron and Steel Engineers (AISE). This program was established by the former Ohio Valley District Section of AISE. The Ohio Valley Chapter covers Indiana (except for the northwestern portion), all of Kentucky, western Tennessee, and portions of southern Ohio.

3167 ■ ASSOCIATION OF OLD CROWS

Attn: AOC Educational Foundation
1000 North Payne Street
Alexandria, VA 22314-1652
Tel: (703)549-1600
Fax: (703)549-2589
Web Site: http://www.crows.org
To provide financial assistance to military enlisted personnel who are pursuing off-duty college-level education programs in fields related to electronics.
Title of Award: Association of Old Crows Enlisted Tuition Grants **Area, Field, or Subject:** Electronics; Engineering, Electrical; Mathematics and mathematical sciences; Physics **Level of Education for which Award is Granted:** Undergraduate **Number Awarded:** Varies each year; recently, a total of $160,000 per year was available for this program. **Funds Available:** Support is provided to supplement the funding available through the tuition assistance programs. **Duration:** 1 semester; may be renewed.
Eligibility Requirements: This program is open to military enlisted personnel (rank of E-4 and above) who are utilizing the tuition assistance programs of the services to study electrical engineering, physics, mathematics, and related areas during their off-duty hours. Selection is based on academic excellence and financial need. **Additional Information:** Funding is provided by local chapters of this organization, which was founded by World War II veterans who had engaged in electronic warfare to disrupt enemy communications and radars. The program was code-named "Raven" and its operators became known as Old Crows. For information on a chapter in your area, contact the AOC Educational Foundation.

3168 ■ ASSOCIATION FOR WOMEN IN SCIENCE-SEATTLE CHAPTER

c/o Fran Solomon, Scholarship Committee Chair
5805 16th Avenue, N.E.
Seattle, WA 98105
Tel: (206)522-6441
E-mail: fran.solomon@metrokc.gov
Web Site: http://www.scn.org/awis/undergraduate_scholarship.htm
To provide financial assistance to women undergraduates from any state majoring in science, mathematics, or engineering at colleges and universities in western Washington.
Title of Award: AWIS Seattle Scholarships **Area, Field, or Subject:** Biochemistry; Biological and clinical sciences; Chemistry; Engineering; Environmental conservation; Environmental science; Geology; Mathematics and mathematical sciences; Pharmaceutical sciences; Physics **Level of Education for which Award is Granted:** Four Year College **Number Awarded:** Varies each year; recently, 11 of these scholarships were

awarded. **Funds Available:** Stipends range from $1,000 to $1,500. **Duration:** 1 year.

Eligibility Requirements: This program is open to women from any state entering their junior or senior year at a 4-year college or university in western Washington. Applicants must have a declared major in science (e.g., biological sciences, environmental science, biochemistry, chemistry, pharmacy, geology, computer science, physics), mathematics, or engineering. Along with their application, they must submit essays on the events that led to their choice of a major, their current career plans and long-term goals, and their volunteer and community activities. Financial need is considered in the selection process. At least 1 scholarship is reserved for a woman from a group that is underrepresented in science, mathematics, and engineering careers, including Native American Indians and Alaska Natives, Black/African Americans, Mexican Americans/ Chicanas/Latinas, Native Pacific Islanders (Polynesians, Melanesians, and Micronesians), and women with disabilities. **Deadline for Receipt:** March of each year. **Additional Information:** This program includes the following named awards: the Virginia Badger Scholarship, the Angela Paez Memorial Scholarship, and the Fran Solomon Scholarship. Support for the program is provided by several sponsors, including the American Chemical Society, Iota Sigma Pi, Rosetta Inpharmatics, and ZymoGenetics, Inc.

3169 ■ BUSINESS AND PROFESSIONAL WOMEN OF VIRGINIA

Attn: Virginia BPW Foundation
P.O. Box 4842
McLean, VA 22103-4842
Web Site: http://www.bpwva.org/Foundation.shtml
To provide financial assistance to women in Virginia who are interested in working on a bachelor's or advanced degree in science or technology.
Title of Award: Women in Science and Technology Scholarship **Area, Field, or Subject:** Actuarial science; Biological and clinical sciences; Chemistry; Computer and information sciences; Dentistry; Engineering; Engineering, Biomedical; Insurance and insurance-related fields; Mathematics and mathematical sciences; Medicine; Physics; Science; Technology **Level of Education for which Award is Granted:** Graduate, Undergraduate **Number Awarded:** At least 1 each year. **Funds Available:** Stipends range from $500 to $1,000 per year, depending on the need of the recipient; funds may be used for tuition, fees, books, transportation, living expenses, and dependent care. **Duration:** 1 year; recipients may reapply (but prior recipients are not given priority).
Eligibility Requirements: This program is open to women who are at least 18 years of age, U.S. citizens, Virginia residents, accepted at or currently studying at a Virginia college or university, and working on a bachelor's, master's, or doctoral degree in 1 of the following fields: actuarial science, biology, bioengineering, chemistry, computer science, dentistry, engineering, mathematics, medicine, physics, or a similar scientific or technical field. Applicants must have a definite plan to use their education in a scientific or technical profession. They must be able to demonstrate financial need. **Deadline for Receipt:** March of each year. **Additional Information:** Recipients must complete their studies within 2 years.

3170 ■ DEPARTMENT OF TRANSPORTATION

Federal Highway Administration
Attn: National Highway Institute, HNHI-20
4600 North Fairfax Drive, Suite 800
Arlington, VA 22203-1553
Tel: (703)235-0538
Fax: (703)235-0593
E-mail: transportationedu@fhwa.dot.gov
Web Site: http://www.nhi.fhwa.dot.gov/ddetfp.asp
To enable students to participate in research activities at facilities of the U.S. Department of Transportation (DOT) Federal Highway Administration in the Washington, D.C. area.
Title of Award: Eisenhower Grants for Research Fellowships **Area, Field, or Subject:** Chemistry; Economics; Engineering; Engineering, Civil; Geography; Information science and technology; Materials research/ science; Operations research; Physics; Public administration; Statistics; Technology; Transportation; Urban affairs/design/planning **Level of Education for which Award is Granted:** Four Year College, Graduate **Number Awarded:** Varies each year; recently, 9 students participated in this program. **Funds Available:** Fellows receive full tuition and fees that

relate to the academic credits for the approved research project and a monthly stipend of $1,450 for college seniors, $1,700 for master's students, or $2,000 for doctoral students. An allowance for travel to and from the DOT facility where the research is conducted is also provided, but selectees are responsible for their own housing accommodations. Faculty advisors are allowed 1 site review on projects over 6 months and 2 site reviews on projects over 9 months; travel and per diem are provided for those site reviews. **Duration:** Tenure is normally 3, 6, 9, or 12 months.
Eligibility Requirements: This program is open to 1) students in their junior year of a baccalaureate program who will complete their junior year before being awarded a fellowship; 2) students in their senior year of a baccalaureate program; and 3) students who have completed their baccalaureate degree and are enrolled in a program leading to a master's, Ph.D., or equivalent degree. Applicants must be U.S. citizens enrolled in an accredited U.S. institution of higher education working on a degree full time and planning to enter the transportation profession after completing their higher education. They select 1 or more projects from a current list of research projects underway at various DOT facilities; the research will be conducted with academic supervision provided by a faculty advisor from their home university (which grants academic credit for the research project) and with technical direction provided by the DOT staff. Specific requirements for the target projects vary; most require engineering backgrounds, but others involve transportation planning, information management, public administration, physics, materials science, statistical analysis, operations research, chemistry, economics, technology transfer, urban studies, geography, and urban and regional planning. The DOT encourages students at Historically Black Colleges and Universities (HBCUs) and Hispanic Serving Institutions (HSIs) to apply for these grants. Selection is based on match of the student's qualifications with the proposed research project (including the student's ability to accomplish the project in the available time), recommendation letters regarding the nominee's qualifications to conduct the research, academic records (including class standing, GPA, and transcripts), and transportation work experience (if any) including the employer's endorsement. **Deadline for Receipt:** February of each year.

3171 ■ FOUNDATION FOR THE CAROLINAS

Attn: Senior Vice President, Scholarships
217 South Tryon Street
P.O. Box 34769
Charlotte, NC 28234-4769
Tel: (704)973-4535
Free: 800-973-7244
Fax: (704)973-4935
E-mail: jseymour@fftc.org
Web Site: http://www.fftc.org/scholarships
To provide financial assistance to college students in North and South Carolina who are preparing for a career in the plastics industry.
Title of Award: Richard Goolsby Scholarship **Area, Field, or Subject:** Business administration; Chemistry; Engineering, Chemical; Engineering, Industrial; Engineering, Mechanical; Physics **Level of Education for which Award is Granted:** Undergraduate **Number Awarded:** 1 or more each year. **Funds Available:** Stipends range up to $4,000 per year; Funds are paid directly to the recipient's school to be used for tuition, required fees, books, and supplies. **Duration:** 1 year; may be renewed.
Eligibility Requirements: This program is open to residents of South Carolina, central North Carolina, or western North Carolina. Applicants must be entering their sophomore, junior, or senior year at a college or university in North or South Carolina and be majoring in a subject that will prepare them for a career in the plastics industry (e.g., chemistry, physics, chemical engineering, mechanical engineering, industrial engineering, business administration). They must be enrolled full time. Along with their application, they must submit a 1- to 2-page statement explaining why they are applying for the scholarship, their qualifications, and their educational and career goals in the plastics industry. Selection is based on academic performance, demonstrated interest in the plastics industry, financial need, school and community involvement, and personal achievements. **Deadline for Receipt:** February of each year.

3172 ■ HAWAI'I COMMUNITY FOUNDATION

Attn: Scholarship Department
1164 Bishop Street, Suite 800
Honolulu, HI 96813

Tel: (808)566-5570; 888-731-3863
Fax: (808)521-6286
E-mail: scholarships@hcf-hawaii.org
Web Site: http://www.hawaiicommunityfoundation.org/scholar/scholar.php
To provide financial assistance for college to Hawaii residents who are interested in majoring in a scientific field.
Title of Award: Shuichi, Katsu and Itsuyo Suga Scholarship **Area, Field, or Subject:** Mathematics and mathematical sciences; Physics; Science; Technology **Level of Education for which Award is Granted:** Graduate, Undergraduate **Number Awarded:** Varies each year; recently, 9 of these scholarships were awarded. **Funds Available:** The amounts of the awards depend on the availability of funds and the need of the recipient; recently, stipends averaged $1,000. **Duration:** 1 year.
Eligibility Requirements: This program is open to Hawaii residents who plan to attend an accredited 2- or 4-year college or university as a full-time undergraduate or graduate student. Applicants must be planning to study mathematics, physics, science, or technology. They must be able to demonstrate academic achievement (GPA of 3.0 or higher), good moral character, and financial need. Along with their application, they must submit a short statement indicating their reasons for attending college, planned course of study, and career goals. **Deadline for Receipt:** February of each year. **Additional Information:** Recipients may attend college in Hawaii or on the mainland.

3173 ■ HISPANIC ENGINEER NATIONAL ACHIEVEMENT AWARDS CONFERENCE
3900 Whiteside Street
Los Angeles, CA 90063
Tel: (323)262-0997
Fax: (323)262-0946
E-mail: info@henaac.org
Web Site: http://www.henaac.org/scholarships
To provide financial assistance to Hispanic undergraduate students majoring in engineering and related fields.
Title of Award: Northrop Grumman/HENAAC Scholars Program **Area, Field, or Subject:** Architecture, Naval; Computer and information sciences; Engineering, Aerospace/Aeronautical/Astronautical; Engineering, Chemical; Engineering, Civil; Engineering, Computer; Engineering, Electrical; Engineering, Industrial; Engineering, Mechanical; Engineering, Ocean; Information science and technology; Mathematics and mathematical sciences; Physics **Level of Education for which Award is Granted:** Undergraduate **Number Awarded:** 5 each year. **Funds Available:** The stipend is $5,000. **Duration:** 1 year; recipients may reapply.
Eligibility Requirements: This program is open to Hispanic undergraduate students who are enrolled full time in the following engineering fields: aerospace, chemical, civil, computer, electrical, industrial, manufacturing, marine, mechanical, ocean, or structural. Students majoring in computer science, information science, mathematics, naval architecture, and physics are also eligible. Applicants must be U.S. citizens and have a GPA of 3.0 or higher. Academic achievement and campus community activities are considered in the selection process. **Deadline for Receipt:** April of each year. **Additional Information:** This program is sponsored by Northrop Grumman as part of its effort to support the mission of the Hispanic Engineer National Achievement Awards Conference (HENAAC) to promote technical excellence and leadership in the Hispanic community.

3174 ■ HISPANIC SCHOLARSHIP FUND INSTITUTE
1001 Connecticut Avenue, N.W., Suite 632
Washington, DC 20036
Tel: (202)296-0009
Fax: (202)296-3633
E-mail: info@hsfi.org
Web Site: http://www.hsfi.org/scholarships/energy.asp
To provide financial assistance to Hispanic undergraduate students majoring in designated business, engineering, and science fields related to the U.S. Department of Energy (DOE) goals of environmental restoration and waste management.
Title of Award: Environmental Management Scholarship **Area, Field, or Subject:** Business administration; Chemistry; Computer and information sciences; Engineering, Agricultural; Engineering, Civil; Engineering, Electrical; Engineering, Industrial; Engineering, Mechanical; Engineering,

Metallurgical; Engineering, Petroleum; Environmental science; Epidemiology; Geology; Hydrology; Management; Mathematics and mathematical sciences; Physics; Radiology; Toxicology **Level of Education for which Award is Granted:** Undergraduate **Number Awarded:** Varies each year. **Funds Available:** The stipend is $3,000 per year for 4-year university students or $2,000 per year for community college students. **Duration:** 1 year.
Eligibility Requirements: This program is open to U.S. citizens and permanent residents of Hispanic background who have completed at least 12 undergraduate credits with a GPA of 3.0 or higher. Applicants must be interested in preparing for a career supportive of the DOE goals of environmental restoration and waste management. Eligible academic majors are in the fields of business (management and system analysis), engineering (agricultural, chemical, civil, electrical, environmental, industrial, mechanical, metallurgical, nuclear, and petroleum), and science (applied math/physics, chemistry, computer science, ecology, environmental, epidemiology, geology, health physics, hydrology, radiochemistry, radio-ecology, and toxicology). Along with their application, they must submit a 2-page essay on 1) how their academic major, interests, and career goals correspond to environmental restoration and waste management issues; and 2) how their Hispanic background and family upbringing have influenced their academic and personal goals. Selection is based on the essay, academic record, academic plans and career goals, financial need, commitment to DOE's goal of environmental restoration and waste management, and a letter of recommendation. **Deadline for Receipt:** March of each year. **Additional Information:** This program, which began in 1990, is sponsored by DOE's Office of Environmental Management. Recipients must enroll full time at a college or university in the United States.

3175 ■ HISPANIC SCHOLARSHIP FUND INSTITUTE
1001 Connecticut Avenue, N.W., Suite 632
Washington, DC 20036
Tel: (202)296-0009
Fax: (202)296-3633
E-mail: info@hsfi.org
Web Site: http://www.hsfi.org/scholarships/generation.asp
To provide financial assistance to Hispanic and other students majoring in designated business, engineering, social science, and science fields who are interested in employment with the U.S. Department of Energy (DOE).
Title of Award: Next Generation of Public Servants Scholarship **Area, Field, or Subject:** Accounting; Biological and clinical sciences; Business administration; Computer and information sciences; Engineering; Environmental science; Finance; Geology; Information science and technology; Management; Mathematics and mathematical sciences; Physics; Political science; Psychology; Sociology **Level of Education for which Award is Granted:** Undergraduate **Number Awarded:** Varies each year. **Funds Available:** The stipend is $3,000 per year. **Duration:** 1 year; may be renewed up to 2 additional years if the recipient maintains full-time enrollment and a GPA of 2.8 or higher.
Eligibility Requirements: This program is open to U.S. citizens enrolled full time as sophomores with a GPA of 2.8 or higher. Applicants must be interested in preparing for a career with the DOE in an energy-related field. Eligible academic majors are in the fields of business (accounting, business administration, finance, and management), engineering (biomedical, chemical, civil, computer, electrical, environmental, industrial, materials, mechanical, metallurgical, nuclear, and petroleum), social science (economics, organizational psychology, political science, and sociology), and science (biological sciences, computer science, geology, information technology, mathematics, microbiology, and physics). They must be willing to participate in co-ops with the DOE. Along with their application, they must submit a 2-page essay on why a career in public service interests them, how their academic major connects with their stated DOE career goal, why the DOE should invest in them through this program, and how they believe the DOE will benefit from this investment. Selection is based on academic achievement, financial need, demonstrated commitment to public service, and interest in federal employment with the DOE. **Deadline for Receipt:** February of each year. **Additional Information:** This program, sponsored by DOE's Office of Economic

Impact and Diversity, is administered by the Hispanic Scholarship Fund Institute as part of its effort to increase Hispanic participation in federal service.

3176 ■ INSTITUTE OF INTERNATIONAL EDUCATION
Attn: Lucent Global Science Scholars Program
809 United Nations Plaza
New York, NY 10017-3580
Tel: (212)984-5419
Fax: (212)984-5452
E-mail: sciencescholars@iie.org
Web Site: http://www.iie.org/programs/lucent
To provide financial assistance for college to high school students in the United States and university students in other designated countries who are interested in preparing for careers in information technology.
Title of Award: Lucent Global Science Scholars Program **Area, Field, or Subject:** Chemistry; Computer and information sciences; Engineering; Information science and technology; Mathematics and mathematical sciences; Physics **Level of Education for which Award is Granted:** Undergraduate **Number Awarded:** Varies each year. Recently, 32 students from foreign countries (5 from China, 1 from Hong Kong, and 2 from each of the other countries) and 28 from the United States received these scholarships. **Funds Available:** The stipend is $5,000 per year. **Duration:** 1 year; nonrenewable.
Eligibility Requirements: This program is open to high school seniors in the United States and first-year university students in Brazil, Canada, China, France, Germany, Hong Kong, India, Korea, Mexico, the Netherlands, Philippines, Poland, Russia, Spain, and the United Kingdom. Students from the United States must have a GPA of 3.6 or higher. Eligible majors include applied physics, chemistry, computer science, engineering, information science and technology, mathematics and applied mathematics, and physics. Selection is based on a demonstrated record of distinction in science and mathematics and a desire to prepare for a career in information technology. **Deadline for Receipt:** February of each year for students from the United States; March of each year for students from other countries. **Additional Information:** This program, established in 1999, is funded by Lucent Technologies. Students are offered internships at Lucent's research and development and manufacturing facilities in their own countries during the summer following their freshman year in the United States or the sophomore year in other countries.

3177 ■ CLARE BOOTHE LUCE FUND
c/o Henry Luce Foundation, Inc.
111 West 50th Street, Suite 4601
New York, NY 10020
Tel: (212)489-7700
Fax: (212)581-9541
E-mail: jdaniels@hluce.org
Web Site: http://www.hluce.org
To provide funding to women interested in studying science or engineering at the undergraduate level at designated universities.
Title of Award: Clare Boothe Luce Scholarships in Science and Engineering **Area, Field, or Subject:** Biological and clinical sciences; Chemistry; Computer and information sciences; Engineering; Engineering, Aerospace/Aeronautical/Astronautical; Engineering, Civil; Engineering, Electrical; Engineering, Mechanical; Engineering, Nuclear; Mathematics and mathematical sciences; Meteorology; Physics **Level of Education for which Award is Granted:** Undergraduate **Number Awarded:** Varies; since the program began, more than 800 of these scholarships have been awarded. **Funds Available:** The amount awarded is established individually by each of the participating institutions. The stipends are intended to augment rather than replace any existing institutional support in these fields. Each stipend is calculated to include the cost of room and board as well as tuition and other fees or expenses. **Duration:** 2 years; in certain special circumstances, awards for the full 4 years of undergraduate study may be offered.
Eligibility Requirements: This program is open to female undergraduate students (particularly juniors and seniors) majoring in biology, chemistry, computer science, engineering (aeronautical, civil, electrical, mechanical, nuclear, and others), mathematics, meteorology, and physics. Applicants must be U.S. citizens attending 1 of the 12 designated colleges and universities affiliated with this program; periodically, other institutions are invited to participate. Premedical science majors are ineligible for this

competition. The participating institutions select the recipients without regard to race, age, religion, ethnic background, or need. All awards are made on the basis of merit. **Deadline for Receipt:** Varies; check with the participating institutions for their current schedule. **Additional Information:** The participating institutions are Boston University, Colby College, Creighton University, Fordham University, Georgetown University, Marymount University, Mount Holyoke College, St. John's University, Santa Clara University, Seton Hall University, Trinity College, and University of Notre Dame.

3178 ■ MARYLAND HIGHER EDUCATION COMMISSION
Attn: Office of Student Financial Assistance
839 Bestgate Road, Suite 400
Annapolis, MD 21401-3013
Tel: (410)260-4545
Free: 800-974-1024
Fax: (410)974-5376
E-mail: osfamail@mhec.state.md.us
Web Site: http://www.mhec.state.md.us/financialAid/ProgramDescriptions/prog_scm.asp
To provide scholarship/loans to Maryland residents who wish to prepare for a teaching career.
Title of Award: Sharon Christa McAuliffe Memorial Teacher Education Award **Area, Field, or Subject:** Chemistry; Classical studies; Computer and information sciences; Earth sciences; Education; Education, English as a second language; Education, Special; Education, Vocational-technical; Foreign languages; Geosciences; Health care services; Hearing and deafness; Mathematics and mathematical sciences; Physical sciences; Physics; Space and planetary sciences; Visual impairment **Level of Education for which Award is Granted:** Master's, Professional, Undergraduate **Number Awarded:** Varies each year. **Funds Available:** The amount of the award is based on the recipient's enrollment and housing status, to a maximum of $17,000 per year. The total amount of all state awards may not exceed the cost of attendance as determined by the school's financial aid office or $17,800, whichever is less. Following graduation, recipients must teach at a Maryland public school for 1 year for each year of financial aid received under this program. If they fail to meet that service obligation, they must repay all funds they received with interest. They must begin the service obligation within 12 months of graduation. **Duration:** 1 year; may be renewed for 1 additional year if the recipient maintains satisfactory academic progress with a cumulative GPA of 3.0 or higher and enrollment at a 2-year or 4-year Maryland college or university in an approved teacher education program.
Eligibility Requirements: This program is open to Maryland residents who are college students with at least 60 semester credit hours completed, college graduates, and teachers in a non-critical shortage area. Applicants must have a GPA of 3.0 or higher and plan to teach in a field identified as a critical shortage area. Selection is based on cumulative GPA, applicable work or volunteer experience, quality of academic background in certification field, and a writing sample. **Deadline for Receipt:** December of each year. **Additional Information:** Recently, the eligible critical shortage areas were business education, chemistry, computer science, earth and space science, English for speakers of other languages, family and consumer sciences, German, health occupations, Latin, mathematics, physical science, physics, Spanish, special education (generic infant-grade 3, generic grades 1-8, generic grades 6-adult, hearing impaired, severely and profoundly handicapped, visually impaired), and technology education.

3179 ■ MARYLAND SPACE GRANT CONSORTIUM
c/o Johns Hopkins University
203 Bloomberg Center for Physics and Astronomy
3400 North Charles Street
Baltimore, MD 21218-2686
Tel: (410)516-7351
Fax: (410)516-4109
E-mail: info@mdspacegrant.org
Web Site: http://www.mdspacegrant.org/scholars_about.html
To provide financial assistance to undergraduates who are interested in studying space-related fields at selected universities in Maryland that are members of the Maryland Space Grant Consortium.
Title of Award: Maryland Space Scholars Program **Area, Field, or Subject:** Aerospace sciences; Astronomy and astronomical sciences;

Biological and clinical sciences; Chemistry; Computer and information sciences; Engineering; Geology; Mathematics and mathematical sciences; Physics; Space and planetary sciences **Level of Education for which Award is Granted:** Undergraduate **Number Awarded:** Varies each year; recently 16 of these scholarships were awarded (2 at Johns Hopkins University, 5 at Morgan State University, 2 at Hagerstown Community College, 2 at Towson University, and 5 at the University of Maryland at College Park). **Funds Available:** Scholars receive partial payment of tuition at the participating university they attend. **Duration:** 1 year; may be renewed if the recipient maintains a GPA of 3.0 or higher.

Eligibility Requirements: This program is open to residents of Maryland and graduates of Maryland high schools who are enrolled full time at a member institution. Applicants must be interested in preparing for a career in mathematics, science, engineering, technology, or a space-related field. They must be majoring in a relevant field, including (but not limited to) astronomy, the biological and life sciences, chemistry, computer science, engineering, geological sciences, or physics. U.S. citizenship is required. Along with their application, they must submit an essay of 200 to 500 words on how this scholarship will help them meet their educational and financial goals. This program is a component of the U.S. National Aeronautics and Space Administration (NASA) Space Grant program, which encourages participation by women, underrepresented minorities, and persons with disabilities. **Deadline for Receipt:** August of each year. **Additional Information:** The participating universities are Hagerstown Community College, Johns Hopkins University, Morgan State University, Towson University, the University of Maryland at College Park, and Washington College. Funding for this program is provided by NASA.

3180 ■ MICRON TECHNOLOGY, INC.
Attn: Micron Technology Foundation
8000 South Federal Way
P.O. Box 6
Boise, ID 83707-0006
Tel: (208)368-3675
Web Site: http://www.micron.com/about/giving/foundation/scholarships.html
To provide financial assistance to high school seniors in selected states who are interested in majoring in the physical sciences.

Title of Award: Micron Science and Technology Scholars **Area, Field, or Subject:** Chemistry; Computer and information sciences; Engineering, Chemical; Engineering, Computer; Engineering, Electrical; Engineering, Mechanical; Materials research/science; Physics **Level of Education for which Award is Granted:** Undergraduate **Number Awarded:** 13 each year: 1 at $55,000 and 12 at $16,500; 2 are awarded to students from each of 5 participating states, plus 3 floating scholarships are awarded within those states. **Funds Available:** Stipends are either $55,000 or $16,500. A cash grant of $1,000 is awarded to the high school of each winner.

Eligibility Requirements: This program is open to high school seniors who reside in and attend public or private schools in Colorado, Idaho, Texas, Utah, or Virginia. Applicants must have a combined SAT score of at least 1350 or a composite ACT score of at least 30; have at least a 3.5 GPA; have demonstrated leadership in school, work, and extracurricular activities; and plan to major in engineering (electrical, computer, chemical, or mechanical), computer science, chemistry, material sciences, or physics. Selection is based on merit (in academics and leadership). **Deadline for Receipt:** January of each year. **Additional Information:** This program began in 2000. Information is also available from Scholarship Management Services of Scholarship America, One Scholarship Way, P.O. Box 297, St. Peter, MN 56082, (507) 931-1682, (800) 537-4180, Fax: (507) 931-9168.

3181 ■ MICROSOFT CORPORATION
Attn: National Minority Technical Scholarship
One Microsoft Way
Redmond, WA 98052-8303
Tel: (425)882-8080
E-mail: scholars@microsoft.com
Web Site: http://www.microsoft.com/college/ss_overview.mspx
To provide financial assistance and summer work experience to undergraduate students, especially members of underrepresented groups, interested in preparing for a career in computer science or other related technical fields.

Title of Award: Microsoft National Scholarships **Area, Field, or Subject:** Computer and information sciences; Engineering, Computer; Engineering, Electrical; Mathematics and mathematical sciences; Physics; Technology **Level of Education for which Award is Granted:** Undergraduate **Number Awarded:** Varies. A total of $540,000 is available for this program each year. **Funds Available:** Scholarships cover 100% of the tuition as posted by the financial aid office of the university or college the recipient designates. Scholarships are made through that school and are not transferable to other academic institutions. Funds may be used for tuition only and may not be used for other costs on the recipient's bursar bill, such as room and board. **Duration:** 1 year.

Eligibility Requirements: This program is open to students who are enrolled full time and making satisfactory progress toward an undergraduate degree in computer science, computer engineering, or a related technical discipline (such as electrical engineering, mathematics, or physics) with a demonstrated interest in computer science. Applicants must be enrolled at a 4-year college or university in the United States, Canada, or Mexico. They must have a GPA of 3.0 or higher. Although all students who meet the eligibility criteria may apply, a large majority of scholarships are awarded to women, underrepresented minorities (African Americans, Hispanics, and Native Americans), and students with disabilities. Along with their application, students must submit an essay that describes the following 4 items: 1) how they demonstrate their passion for technology outside the classroom; 2) the toughest technical problem they have worked on, how they addressed the problem, their role in reaching the outcome if it was team-based, and the final outcome; 3) a situation that demonstrates initiative and their willingness to go above and beyond; and 4) how they are currently funding their college education. **Deadline for Receipt:** January of each year. **Additional Information:** Selected recipients are offered a paid summer internship where they will have a chance to develop Microsoft products.

3182 ■ MONTANA SPACE GRANT CONSORTIUM
c/o Montana State University
416 Cobleigh Hall
P.O. Box 173835
Bozeman, MT 59717-3835
Tel: (406)994-4223
Fax: (406)994-4452
E-mail: msgc@montana.edu
Web Site: http://spacegrant.montana.edu/Text/ScholarProgram.html
To provide financial assistance to students in Montana who are interested in working on an undergraduate degree in the space sciences and/or engineering.

Title of Award: Montana Space Grant Consortium Undergraduate Scholarships **Area, Field, or Subject:** Aerospace sciences; Astronomy and astronomical sciences; Biological and clinical sciences; Chemistry; Computer and information sciences; Engineering, Aerospace/Aeronautical/Astronautical; Engineering, Chemical; Engineering, Civil; Engineering, Electrical; Engineering, Mechanical; Geology; Physics; Space and planetary sciences **Level of Education for which Award is Granted:** Undergraduate **Number Awarded:** Varies each year; recently, 23 of these scholarships were awarded. **Funds Available:** The stipend is $1,000 per year. **Duration:** 1 year; may be renewed.

Eligibility Requirements: This program is open to full-time undergraduate students at member institutions of the Montana Space Grant Consortium (MSGC) majoring in fields related to space sciences and engineering. Those fields include, but are not limited to, astronomy, biological and life sciences, chemical engineering, chemistry, civil engineering, computer sciences, electrical engineering, geological sciences, mathematics, mechanical engineering, and physics. Priority is given to students who have been involved in aerospace-related research. U.S. citizenship is required. The MSGC is a component of the U.S. National Aeronautics and Space Administration (NASA) Space Grant program, which encourages participation by women, underrepresented minorities, and persons with disabilities. **Deadline for Receipt:** March of each year. **Additional Information:** The MSGC member institutions are Blackfeet Community College, Carroll College, Chief Dull Knife College, Fort Belknap College, Fort Peck Community College, Little Big Horn College, Montana State University at Billings, Montana State University at Bozeman, Montana State University Northern, Montana Tech, Rocky Mountain College, Salish Kootenai College, Stone Child College, University of Great Falls, University of Montana, and University of

Montana Western. Funding for this program is provided by NASA.

3183 ■ NATIONAL CONSORTIUM FOR GRADUATE DEGREES FOR MINORITIES IN ENGINEERING AND SCIENCE (GEM)

P.O. Box 537
Notre Dame, IN 46556
Tel: (574)631-7771
Fax: (574)287-1486
E-mail: gem.1@nd.edu
Web Site: http://www.gemfellowship.org

To provide financial assistance and summer work experience to underrepresented minority students interested in obtaining a Ph.D. degree in the life sciences, mathematics, or physical sciences.

Title of Award: GEM Ph.D. Science Fellowship Program **Area, Field, or Subject:** Biological and clinical sciences; Chemistry; Computer and information sciences; Earth sciences; Geosciences; Mathematics and mathematical sciences; Natural sciences; Physics **Level of Education for which Award is Granted:** Four Year College, Doctorate **Number Awarded:** Varies each year; recently, 40 of these fellowships were awarded. **Funds Available:** The stipend is $14,000 per year, plus tuition and fees. In addition, there is a summer internship program that provides a salary and reimbursement for travel expenses to and from the summer work site. The total value of the award is between $60,000 and $100,000, depending upon academic status at the time of application, summer employer, and graduate school attended. **Duration:** 3 to 5 years for the fellowship; 12 weeks during at least 1 summer for the internship. Fellows selected as juniors or seniors intern each summer until entrance to graduate school; fellows selected after college graduation intern at least 1 summer.

Eligibility Requirements: This program is open to U.S. citizens who are members of ethnic groups underrepresented in the natural sciences: Native Americans, African Americans, Latinos, Puerto Ricans, and other Hispanic Americans. Applicants must be juniors, seniors, or recent baccalaureate graduates in the life sciences, mathematics, or physical sciences (chemistry, computer science, earth sciences, and physics) with an academic record that indicates the ability to pursue doctoral studies (including a GPA of 3.0 or higher). **Deadline for Receipt:** October of each year. **Additional Information:** This program is valid only at 1 of 95 participating GEM member universities; write to GEM for a list. The fellowship award is designed to support the student in the first year of the doctoral program without working. Subsequent years are subsidized by the respective university and will usually include either a teaching or research assistantship. Recipients must participate in the GEM summer internship; failure to agree to accept the internship cancels the fellowship. Recipients must enroll in the same scientific discipline as their undergraduate major.

3184 ■ NATIONAL INVENTORS HALL OF FAME

Attn: Collegiate Inventors Competition
221 South Broadway Street
Akron, OH 44308-1595
Tel: (330)849-6887
E-mail: collegiate@invent.org
Web Site: http://www.invent.org/collegiate

To recognize and reward outstanding inventions by college or university students in the fields of science, engineering, and technology.

Title of Award: Collegiate Inventors Competition **Area, Field, or Subject:** Biological and clinical sciences; Chemistry; Computer and information sciences; Engineering; Environmental conservation; Environmental science; Inventors; Mathematics and mathematical sciences; Medicine; Physics; Science; Technology; Veterinary science and medicine **Level of Education for which Award is Granted:** Graduate, Postdoctoral, Undergraduate **Number Awarded:** 15 semifinalists are selected each year; of those, 3 individuals or teams win prizes. **Funds Available:** Finalists receive an all-expense paid trip to Washington, D.C. to participate in a final round of judging and in the awards dinner and presentation. The Grand Prize winner or team receives $25,000. Other prizes are $10,000 for an undergraduate winner or team and $15,000 for a graduate winner or team. Academic advisors of the winning entries each receive a $3,000 cash prize. Awards are unrestricted cash gifts, not scholarships or grants. **Duration:** The competition is held annually.

Eligibility Requirements: This competition is open to undergraduate and graduate students who are (or have been) enrolled full time at least part of the 12-month period prior to entry in a college or university in the United States. Entries may also be submitted by teams, up to 4 members, of whom at least 1 must meet the full-time requirement and all others must have been enrolled at least half time sometime during the preceding 24-month period. Applicants must submit a description of their invention, including a patent search and summary of current literature that describes the state of the art and identifies the originality of the invention; test data demonstrating that the idea, invention, or design is workable; the societal, economic, and environmental benefits of the invention; and supplemental material that may include photos, slides, disks, videotapes, and even samples. Entries must be original ideas and the work of a student or team and a university advisor; the invention should be reproducible and may not have been 1) made available to the public as a commercial product or process, or 2) patented or published more than 1 year prior to the date of submission for this competition. Entries are first reviewed by a committee of judges that selects the finalists. The committee is comprised of mathematicians, engineers, biologists, chemists, environmentalists, physicists, computer specialists, members of the medical and veterinary profession, and specialists in invention and development of technology. Entries are judged on the basis of originality, inventiveness, potential value to society (socially, environmentally, and economically), and range or scope of use. **Deadline for Receipt:** May of each year. **Additional Information:** This program is co-sponsored by Abbott Laboratories and the United States Patent and Trademark Office. It was established in 1990 as the BFGoodrich Collegiate Inventors Program.

3185 ■ NATIONAL SOCIETY OF BLACK ENGINEERS

Attn: Programs Department
1454 Duke Street
Alexandria, VA 22314
Tel: (703)549-2207
Fax: (703)683-5312
E-mail: scholarships@nsbe.org
Web Site: http://www.nsbe.org/programs/schol_micro.php

To provide financial assistance to members of the National Society of Black Engineers (NSBE) who are majoring in computer science or engineering.

Title of Award: Microsoft Corporation NSBE Scholarships **Area, Field, or Subject:** Computer and information sciences; Engineering, Computer; Mathematics and mathematical sciences; Physics **Level of Education for which Award is Granted:** Undergraduate **Number Awarded:** 3 each year. **Funds Available:** The stipend is $5,000. **Duration:** 1 year.

Eligibility Requirements: This program is open to members of the society who are undergraduate students majoring in computer engineering, computer science, or mathematics/physics with a demonstrated interest in computer science. Applicants must have a GPA of 3.0 or higher. They must submit a 300-word essay on their "passion for technology" outside of the classroom. **Deadline for Receipt:** January of each year. **Additional Information:** This program is supported by Microsoft Corporation.

3186 ■ NATIONAL SOCIETY OF BLACK ENGINEERS

Attn: Programs Department
1454 Duke Street
Alexandria, VA 22314
Tel: (703)549-2207
Fax: (703)683-5312
E-mail: scholarships@nsbe.org
Web Site: http://www.nsbe.org/programs/schol_ng.php

To provide financial assistance to members of the National Society of Black Engineers (NSBE) who are working on an undergraduate degree in designated science and engineering fields.

Title of Award: Northrop Grumman NSBE Scholarships **Area, Field, or Subject:** Architecture, Naval; Computer and information sciences; Engineering, Aerospace/Aeronautical/Astronautical; Engineering, Chemical; Engineering, Civil; Engineering, Computer; Engineering, Electrical; Engineering, Industrial; Engineering, Mechanical; Engineering, Ocean; Mathematics and mathematical sciences; Physics **Level of Education for which Award is Granted:** Undergraduate **Number Awarded:** 5 each year. **Funds Available:** The stipend is $5,000. **Duration:** 1 year.

Eligibility Requirements: This program is open to members of the society who are U.S. citizens currently enrolled in college. Applicants must be majoring in computer science, information science, mathematics, naval architecture, physics, or the following engineering fields: aerospace, chemical, civil (structural), computer, electrical, industrial, manufacturing, marine, mechanical, or ocean. They must have a GPA of 3.0 or higher and demonstrate an interest in employment with Northrop Grumman Corporation. **Deadline for Receipt:** January of each year.

3187 ■ NEBRASKA ACADEMY OF SCIENCES

c/o University of Nebraska
302 Morrill Hall
14th and U Streets
P.O. Box 880339
Lincoln, NE 68588-0339
Tel: (402)472-2644
E-mail: nebacad@unl.edu
Web Site: http://www.neacadsci.org/Info/coll_scholarship.htm
To provide financial assistance to upper-division students majoring in science at colleges and universities in Nebraska.
Title of Award: C. Bertrand and Marian Othmer Scultz Collegiate Scholarship **Area, Field, or Subject:** Biological and clinical sciences; Chemistry; Geology; Physics **Level of Education for which Award is Granted:** Four Year College **Number Awarded:** 1 each year. **Funds Available:** The stipend is $3,000 per year. **Duration:** 1 year; may be renewed 1 additional year.
Eligibility Requirements: This program is open to student entering their junior or senior year at 4-year colleges and universities in Nebraska. Applicants must have a declared major in a natural science discipline (chemistry, physics, biology, or geology). They must be preparing for a career in a science-related industry, science teaching, or scientific research. A member of the Nebraska Academy of Sciences must provide a letter of nomination. **Deadline for Receipt:** January of each year. **Additional Information:** This scholarship was first awarded in 2006.

3188 ■ NEW HAMPSHIRE POSTSECONDARY EDUCATION COMMISSION

3 Barrell Court, Suite 300
Concord, NH 03301-8543
Tel: (603)271-2555
Fax: (603)271-2696
E-mail: pedes@pec.state.nh.us
Web Site: http://www.state.nh.us/postsecondary/finwork.html
To provide scholarship/loans to New Hampshire residents who are interested in attending college to prepare for careers in designated professions.
Title of Award: New Hampshire Workforce Incentive Program Forgivable Loans **Area, Field, or Subject:** Chemistry; Education; Education, Special; Linguistics; Mathematics and mathematical sciences; Nursing; Physical sciences; Physics **Level of Education for which Award is Granted:** Graduate, Undergraduate **Number Awarded:** Varies each year. **Funds Available:** The stipend is $500 per semester ($1,000 per year). This is a scholarship/loan program; recipients must agree to pursue, within New Hampshire, the professional career for which they receive training. Recipients of loans for 1 year have their notes cancelled upon completion of 1 year of full-time service; repayment by service must be completed within 3 years from the date of licensure, certification, or completion of the program. Recipients of loans for more than 1 year have their notes cancelled upon completion of 2 years of full-time service; repayment by service must be completed within 5 years from the date of licensure, certification, or completion of the program. If the note is not cancelled because of service, the recipient must repay the loan within 2 years. **Duration:** 1 year; may be renewed.
Eligibility Requirements: This program is open to residents of New Hampshire who wish to prepare for careers in fields designated by the commission as shortage areas. Currently, the career shortage areas are chemistry, general science, mathematics, physical sciences, physics, special education, world languages, and nursing (L.P.N. through graduate). Applicants must be enrolled as a junior, senior, or graduate student at a college in New Hampshire and must be able to demonstrate financial need. **Deadline for Receipt:** May of each year for fall semester; December of each year for spring semester. **Additional Information:** The time for repayment of the loan, either in cash or through professional service, is extended while the recipient is 1) engaged in a course of study, at least on a half-time basis, at an institution of higher education; 2) serving on active duty as a member of the armed forces of the United States,

or as a member of VISTA, the Peace Corps, or AmeriCorps, for a period up to 3 years; 3) temporarily totally disabled for a period up to 3 years; or 4) unable to secure employment because of the need to care for a disabled spouse, child, or parent for a period up to 12 months. The repayment obligation is cancelled if the recipient is unable to work because of a permanent total disability, receives relief under federal bankruptcy laws, or dies. This program went into effect in 1999.

3189 ■ NEW HAMPSHIRE SPACE GRANT CONSORTIUM

c/o University of New Hampshire
Institute for the Study of Earth, Oceans, and Space
Morse Hall
39 College Road
Durham, NH 03824-3525
Tel: (603)862-0094
Fax: (603)862-1915
E-mail: nhspacegrant@unh.edu
Web Site: http://www.nhsgc.sr.unh.edu
To provide financial assistance to students at member institutions of the New Hampshire Space Grant Consortium (NHSGC) who are interested in participating in space-related activities.
Title of Award: New Hampshire Space Grant Consortium Project Support **Area, Field, or Subject:** Aerospace sciences; Astronomy and astronomical sciences; Atmospheric science; Biological and clinical sciences; Computer and information sciences; Earth sciences; Engineering, Aerospace/Aeronautical/Astronautical; Geosciences; Oceanography; Physics; Space and planetary sciences **Level of Education for which Award is Granted:** Graduate, Undergraduate **Number Awarded:** Varies each year. **Funds Available:** The amount of the award depends on the nature of the project. **Duration:** From 1 quarter to 1 year.
Eligibility Requirements: This program is open to students at member institutions of the NHSGC. Applicants must be studying space physics, astrophysics, astronomy, or aspects of computer science, engineering, earth sciences, ocean sciences, atmospheric sciences, or life sciences that utilize space technology and/or adopt a planetary view of the global environment. U.S. citizenship is required. The New Hampshire Space Grant Consortium is a component of the U.S. National Aeronautics and Space Administration (NASA) Space Grant program, which encourages participation by women, underrepresented minorities, and persons with disabilities. **Deadline for Receipt:** Each participating college or university sets its own deadline. **Additional Information:** This program is funded by NASA. Currently, projects operating through this program include space grant fellowships at the University of New Hampshire, Agnes M. Lindsay Trust/NASA Challenge Scholars Initiative at the New Hampshire Community Technical College System, Presidential Scholars Research Assistantships at Dartmouth College, and Women in Science Internships at Dartmouth.

3190 ■ OAK RIDGE INSTITUTE FOR SCIENCE AND EDUCATION

Attn: Science and Engineering Education
P.O. Box 117
Oak Ridge, TN 37831-0117
Tel: (865)576-9279
Fax: (865)241-5220
E-mail: coxre@orau.gov
Web Site: http://www.orau.gov/orise.htm
To provide financial assistance and research experience to undergraduate students at minority serving institutions who are majoring in scientific fields of interest to the National Oceanic and Atmospheric Administration (NOAA).
Title of Award: National Oceanic and Atmospheric Administration Educational Partnership Program with Minority Serving Institutions Undergraduate Scholarships **Area, Field, or Subject:** Atmospheric science; Biological and clinical sciences; Cartography/Surveying; Chemistry; Computer and information sciences; Engineering; Environmental conservation; Environmental science; Geography; Mathematics and mathematical sciences; Meteorology; Photogrammetry; Physical sciences; Physics **Level of Education for which Award is Granted:** Four Year College **Number Awarded:** 10 each year. **Funds Available:** This program provides payment of tuition and fees (to a maximum of $4,000 per year) and a stipend during the internship of $650 per week. **Duration:** 1 academic year and 2 summers.
Eligibility Requirements: This program is open to juniors and seniors at minority serving institutions, including Hispanic Serving Institutions (HSIs),

Historically Black Colleges and Universities (HBCUs), and Tribal Colleges and Universities (TCUs). Applicants must be majoring in atmospheric science, biology, cartography, chemistry, computer science, engineering, environmental science, geodesy, geography, marine science, mathematics, meteorology, photogrammetry, physical science, physics, or remote sensing. They must also be interested in participating in a research internship at a NOAA site. U.S. citizenship is required. **Deadline for Receipt:** January of each year. **Additional Information:** This program is funded by NOAA through an interagency agreement with the U.S. Department of Energy and administered by Oak Ridge Institute for Science and Education (ORISE).

3191 ■ OHIO SPACE GRANT CONSORTIUM

c/o Ohio Aerospace Institute
22800 Cedar Point Road
Cleveland, OH 44142
Tel: (440)962-3032
Free: 800-828-OSGC
Fax: (440)962-3057
E-mail: osgc@oai.org
Web Site: http://www.osgc.org/Scholarship.html

To provide financial assistance to students in their junior year at selected universities in Ohio who wish to working on a bachelor's degree in an aerospace-related field.

Title of Award: Ohio Space Grant Consortium Junior Scholarships **Area, Field, or Subject:** Astronomy and astronomical sciences; Biological and clinical sciences; Chemistry; Computer and information sciences; Engineering, Aerospace/Aeronautical/Astronautical; Engineering, Chemical; Engineering, Civil; Engineering, Computer; Engineering, Electrical; Engineering, Industrial; Engineering, Materials; Engineering, Mechanical; Engineering, Petroleum; Geography; Geology; Materials research/science; Mathematics and mathematical sciences; Physics; Space and planetary sciences **Level of Education for which Award is Granted:** Four Year College **Number Awarded:** Varies each year; recently, 20 of these scholarships were awarded. **Funds Available:** The stipend is $2,000. **Duration:** 1 year; recipients may apply for a senior scholarship if they maintain satisfactory academic performance and good progress on their research project.

Eligibility Requirements: These scholarships are available to U.S. citizens who expect to complete within 2 years the requirements for a bachelor of science degree in an aerospace-related discipline (aeronautical engineering, aerospace engineering, astronomy, biology, chemical engineering, chemistry, civil engineering, computer engineering and science, control engineering, electrical engineering, engineering mechanics, geography, geology, industrial engineering, manufacturing engineering, materials science and engineering, mathematics, mechanical engineering, petroleum engineering, physics, and systems engineering). Applicants must be attending a member university of the Ohio Space Grant Consortium (OSGC) or another participating university. They must propose and initiate a research project on campus under the guidance of a faculty member. Along with their application, they must submit a 1-page personal objective statement that discusses their career goals and anticipated benefits to be derived from this program. Women, underrepresented minorities, and persons with disabilities are particularly encouraged to apply. **Deadline for Receipt:** February of each year. **Additional Information:** These scholarships are funded through the National Space Grant College and Fellowship Program administered by the National Aeronautics and Space Administration (NASA), with matching funds provided by the member universities, the Ohio Aerospace Institute, and private industry. The OSGC member universities include the University of Akron, Case Western Reserve University, Central State University, University of Cincinnati, Cleveland State University, University of Dayton, Ohio State University, Ohio University, University of Toledo, Wilberforce University, and Wright State University. Other participating universities are Cedarville University, Marietta College (petroleum engineering), Miami University (manufacturing engineering), Ohio Northern University (mechanical engineering), and Youngstown State University (mechanical and industrial engineering). Recipients are required to attend the annual spring research symposium sponsored by the OSGC and present a poster on their research project.

3192 ■ OREGON UNIVERSITY SYSTEM

Attn: Chancellor's Office, Industry Affairs Division
Capital Center, Suite 1065
18640 N.W. Walker Road
Beaverton, OR 97006-8966
Tel: (503)725-2918
Fax: (503)775-2921
E-mail: aeaschol@ous.edu
Web Site: http://www.ous.edu/ecs/scholarships.html

To provide financial assistance to Oregon high school seniors interested in studying designated computer and engineering fields at selected public universities in the state.

Title of Award: AeA Technology Scholarship Program **Area, Field, or Subject:** Biochemistry; Chemistry; Computer and information sciences; Engineering; Engineering, Chemical; Engineering, Computer; Engineering, Electrical; Engineering, Industrial; Engineering, Mechanical; Mathematics and mathematical sciences; Physics **Level of Education for which Award is Granted:** Undergraduate **Number Awarded:** Varies each year; recently, this program awarded 25 new scholarships. **Funds Available:** The stipend is $2,500 per year. **Duration:** 1 year; may be renewed up to 3 additional years if the recipient maintains a GPA of 3.0 or higher.

Eligibility Requirements: This program is open to seniors graduating from high schools in Oregon who plan to attend Eastern Oregon University, Oregon Institute of Technology, Oregon State University, Portland State University, Southern Oregon University, Western Oregon University, or the University of Oregon. Applicants must be planning to major in biochemistry, chemical engineering, chemistry, computer engineering, computer science, electrical engineering, electronic engineering, engineering technology, industrial engineering, mathematics, mechanical engineering, or physics (not all majors are available at each institution). Women and ethnic minorities underrepresented in the technology industry (Black Americans, Hispanic Americans, and Native Americans) are strongly encouraged to apply. Selection is based on academic performance; college entrance examination scores; mathematics, science, and technology course work; achievements; leadership; civic participation; interests; employment; insight into and commitment to a career in technology; and communication skill. **Deadline for Receipt:** March of each year. **Additional Information:** This program was established in 1999 by Intel, which offered it to the Oregon Council of the AeA (formerly American Electronics Association) in the following year. Currently, Intel and other Oregon AeA member companies (such as Xerox and Hewlett Packard) provide ongoing support.

3193 ■ SEALASKA CORPORATION

Attn: Sealaska Heritage Institute
One Sealaska Plaza, Suite 301
Juneau, AK 99801-1249
Tel: (907)586-9166; 888-311-4992
Fax: (907)586-9293
E-mail: scholarship@sealaska.com
Web Site: http://www.sealaskaheritage.org/programs/university_scholarships.htm

To provide financial assistance for undergraduate or graduate study to Native Alaskans who have a connection to Sealaska Corporation and are majoring in designated fields.

Title of Award: Sealaska Heritage Institute 7(i) Scholarships **Area, Field, or Subject:** Business administration; Chemistry; Engineering, Chemical; Health care services; Mathematics and mathematical sciences; Natural resources; Physics **Level of Education for which Award is Granted:** Graduate, Undergraduate **Number Awarded:** Varies each year. **Funds Available:** The amount of the award depends on the availability of funds, the number of qualified applicants, class standing, and cumulative GPA. **Duration:** 1 year; may be renewed up to 5 years for a bachelor's degree, up to 3 years for a master's degree, up to 2 years for a doctorate, or up to 3 years for vocational study. The maximum total support is limited to 9 years. Renewal depends on recipients' maintaining full-time enrollment and a GPA of 2.5 or higher.

Eligibility Requirements: This program is open to 1) Alaska Natives who are enrolled to Sealaska Corporation, and 2) Native lineal descendants of Alaska Natives enrolled to Sealaska Corporation, whether or not the applicant owns Sealaska Corporation stock. Applicants must be enrolled or accepted for enrollment as full-time undergraduate or graduate students. Along with their application, they must submit 2 essays: 1) their personal history and educational goals, and 2) their expected contributions to the Alaska Native or Native American community. Financial need is also considered in the selection process. The following areas of study qualify for these awards: natural resources (environmental sciences, engineering, conservation biology, environmental law, fisheries, geology, marine science/biology, forestry, wildlife management, and mining technology); business administration (accounting, finance, marketing, international business, international commerce and trade, management of information systems, human resources management, economics, computer information systems, and industrial management); and other special fields (cadastral surveys, chemistry, equipment/machinery operators, industrial safety specialists, health specialists, plastics engineers, trade specialists, physics, mathematics, and marine trades and occupations). **Deadline for Receipt:** February of each year. **Additional Information:** Funding for this program is provided from Alaska Native Claims Settlement Act (ANSCA) Section 7(i) revenue sharing provisions. Sealaska sponsors a number of other scholarships, including the Cape Fox Scholarships and the Sealaska Heritage Institute Scholarships.

3194 ■ SIEMENS FOUNDATION

170 Wood Avenue South
Iselin, NJ 08830
877-822-5233
Fax: (732)603-5890
E-mail: foundation@sc.siemens.com
Web Site: http://www.siemens-foundation.org/awards
To recognize and reward high school students with exceptional scores on the Advanced Placement (AP) examinations in mathematics and the sciences.

Title of Award: Siemens Awards for Advanced Placement **Area, Field, or Subject:** Biological and clinical sciences; Chemistry; Computer and information sciences; Environmental conservation; Environmental science; Mathematics and mathematical sciences; Physics; Statistics **Level of Education for which Award is Granted:** Professional, Undergraduate **Number Awarded:** 24 regional scholarships (2 females and 2 males in each of the 6 regions), 2 national scholarships (1 female and 1 male), 12 high school awards (in each region, 1 to a school for improvement in the number and percentage of students taking AP examinations, 1 to an urban school for providing access to AP mathematics and science to minorities), and 18 teacher awards (in each region, 2 for commitment to students and the AP program, 1 for teaching minorities) are awarded each year. **Funds Available:** Regional scholarships are $3,000; national winners receive additional $5,000 scholarships. Awards to teachers and to schools are $1,000. **Duration:** The awards are presented annually.

Eligibility Requirements: All students in U.S. high schools are eligible to be considered for these awards (including home-schooled students and those in U.S. territories). Each fall, the College Board identifies the male and female seniors in each of its regions who have earned the highest number of scores on 7 AP exams: biology, calculus BC, chemistry, computer science AB, environmental science, physics C (physics C: mechanics and physics C: electricity each count as half), and statistics. Males and females are considered separately. Regional winners receive all-expense paid trips to Washington, D.C., where national winners are announced. The program also recognizes and rewards monetarily 1) schools that have shown the greatest improvement in the number and percentage of students taking AP examinations in biology, calculus, chemistry, computer science, environmental science, physics, and statistics in the past year; and 2) non-magnet urban schools that provide access to AP mathematics and science to a significant number of underrepresented minority students. In addition, teachers are rewarded for their commitment to students and the AP program. Additional teachers are recognized because they have successfully taught AP mathematics and/or science to underrepresented minority students in non-magnet urban schools. **Deadline for Receipt:** There is no application or nomination process for these awards. The College Board identifies the students, teachers, and high schools for the Siemens Foundation. **Additional Information:** Information from the College Board is available at (703) 707-8999.

3195 ■ SIEMENS FOUNDATION

170 Wood Avenue South
Iselin, NJ 08830
877-822-5233
Fax: (732)603-5890
E-mail: foundation@sc.siemens.com

Web Site: http://www.siemens-foundation.org/scholarship
To recognize and reward outstanding high school seniors who have undertaken individual or team research projects in science, mathematics, and technology (or in combinations of those disciplines).

Title of Award: Siemens Westinghouse Competition Awards **Area, Field, or Subject:** Astronomy and astronomical sciences; Atmospheric science; Biochemistry; Biological and clinical sciences; Chemistry; Computer and information sciences; Earth sciences; Engineering, Civil; Engineering, Electrical; Engineering, Mechanical; Environmental science; Genetics; Geosciences; Materials research/science; Mathematics and mathematical sciences; Nutrition; Physics; Writing **Level of Education for which Award is Granted:** Undergraduate **Number Awarded:** In the initial round of judging, up to 300 regional semifinalists (up to 50 in each region) are selected. Of those, 60 are chosen as regional finalists (5 individuals and 5 teams in each of the 6 regions). Then 12 regional winners (1 individual and 1 team) are selected in the regional competitions, and they become the national finalists. **Funds Available:** At the regional level, finalists receive $1,000 scholarships, both as individuals and members of teams. Individual regional winners receive $3,000 scholarships. Winning regional teams receive $6,000 scholarships to be divided among the team members. Those regional winners then receive additional scholarships as national finalists. In the national competition, first-place winners receive an additional $100,000 scholarship, second place an additional $50,000 scholarship, third place an additional $40,000 scholarship, fourth place an additional $30,000 scholarship, fifth place an additional $20,000 scholarship, and sixth place an additional $10,000 scholarship. Those national awards are provided both to individuals and to teams to be divided equally among team members. Scholarship money is sent directly to the recipient's college or university to cover undergraduate and/or graduate educational expenses. Schools with regional finalists receive a $2,000 award to be used to support science, mathematics, and technology programs in their schools. **Duration:** The competition is held annually.

Eligibility Requirements: This program is open to high school seniors who are legal or permanent U.S. residents. They must be enrolled in a high school in the United States, Puerto Rico, Guam, Virgin Islands, American Samoa, Wake and Midway Islands, or the Marianas. U.S. high school students enrolled in a Department of Defense dependents school, an accredited overseas American or international school, a foreign school as an exchange student, or a foreign school because their parent(s) live and work abroad are also eligible. Students being home-schooled qualify if they obtain the endorsement of the school district official responsible for such programs. Research projects may be submitted in mathematics and the biological and physical sciences, or involve combinations of disciplines, such as astrophysics, biochemistry, bioengineering, biology, biophysics, botany, chemistry, computer science, civil engineering, earth and atmospheric science engineering, electrical engineering, environmental sciences, fluid dynamics, genetics, geology, materials science, mathematics, mechanical engineering, nutritional science, physics, toxicology, and virology. Both individual and team projects (2 or 3 members) may be entered. All team members must meet the eligibility requirements. Team projects may include seniors, but that is not a requirement. Competition entrants must submit a detailed report on their research project, including a description of the purpose of the research, rationale for the research, pertinent scientific literature, methodology, results, discussion, and conclusion. All projects must be endorsed by a sponsoring high school (except home-schooled students, who obtain their endorsement from the district or state home-school official). Each project must have a project advisor or mentor who is a member of the instructional staff or a person approved by the endorsing high school. There are 3 judging phases to the competition. An initial review panel selects outstanding research projects from 6 different regions of the country. The students submitting these projects are identified as regional semifinalists. Out of those, the highest-rated projects from each region are selected and the students who submitted them are recognized as regional finalists. For the next phase, the regional finalists are offered all-expense paid trips to the regional competition on the campus of a regional university partner, where their projects are reviewed by a panel of judges appointed by the host institution. Regional finalists are required to prepare a poster display of their research project, make an oral presentation about the research and research findings, and respond to questions from the judges. The top-rated individual and the top-rated team project in each region are selected as regional winners to represent the region in the national competition as national finalists. At that competition, the national finalists again display their projects, make oral presentations, and respond to judges' questions. At each phase, selection is based on clarity of expression, comprehensiveness, creativity, field knowledge, future work, interpretation, literature review, presentation, scientific importance, and validity. **Deadline for Receipt:** September of each year. **Additional Information:** The program is offered by Siemens Foundation, in partnership with the College Board. Information is available from the College Board at (703) 707-8999, E-mail: spro@collegeboard.org. Students submitting the projects with the highest evaluations become part of a registry that is circulated to colleges and universities nationwide. To continue receiving scholarships, winners must attend an accredited academic institution on a full-time basis.

3196 ■ SOCIETY OF AUTOMOTIVE ENGINEERS

Attn: Scholarship Administrator
400 Commonwealth Drive
Warrendale, PA 15096-0001
Tel: (724)772-4047
Fax: (724)776-3049
E-mail: scholarships@sae.org
Web Site: http://students.sae.org/awdscholar/scholarships/hillquist
To provide financial assistance to college juniors who are majoring in mechanical or automotive engineering.
Title of Award: Ralph K. Hillquist Honorary SAE Scholarship **Area, Field, or Subject:** Engineering, Automotive; Engineering, Mechanical; Physics **Level of Education for which Award is Granted:** Four Year College **Number Awarded:** 1 each odd-numbered year. **Funds Available:** The stipend is $1,000. **Duration:** 1 year; nonrenewable.
Eligibility Requirements: This program is open to juniors enrolled full time at U.S. universities. Applicants must have a declared major in mechanical engineering or an automotive-related engineering discipline, with preference given to those who have completed studies or courses in the areas of expertise related to noise and vibration (e.g., statics, dynamics, physics, vibration). They must be U.S. citizens with a GPA of 3.0 or higher and significant academic and leadership achievements. along with their application, they must submit a 300-word essay on the single experience that most strongly convinced them or confirmed their decision to prepare for a career in engineering. Financial need is not considered in the selection process. **Deadline for Receipt:** January of each odd-numbered year. **Additional Information:** This scholarship, first awarded in 2005, is funded by the Noise & Vibration Conference of the Society of Automotive Engineers (SAE).

3197 ■ SOCIETY OF FLIGHT TEST ENGINEERS

44814 North Elm Avenue
P.O. Box 4037
Lancaster, CA 93539-4037
Tel: (661)949-2095
Fax: (661)949-2096
E-mail: sfte@sfte.org
Web Site: http://www.sfte.org
To provide financial assistance for college to student members and children of members of the Society of Flight Test Engineers (SFTE).
Title of Award: Society of Flight Test Engineers Scholarships **Area, Field, or Subject:** Computer and information sciences; Engineering; Mathematics and mathematical sciences; Physics **Level of Education for which Award is Granted:** Undergraduate **Number Awarded:** 1 or more each year. **Funds Available:** Stipends range from $200 to $2,000. **Duration:** 1 year; recipients may reapply.
Eligibility Requirements: This program is open to college students who have completed at least their freshman year. Applicants must be a student member of SFTE or the child of a member. They must be working on an undergraduate degree in engineering, computer sciences, mathematics, physics, or another technical discipline. Selection is based primarily on academic achievement; financial need is not considered. **Deadline for Receipt:** June of each year.

3198 ■ SOCIETY OF PHYSICS STUDENTS

c/o American Institute of Physics
One Physics Ellipse
College Park, MD 20740-3843
Tel: (301)209-3007

Fax: (301)209-0839
E-mail: sps@aip.org
Web Site: http://www.spsnational.org/programs/two_year.htm
To provide financial assistance to members of the Society of Physics Students (SPS) who are transitioning from a 2-year college into a physics bachelor's degree program.
Title of Award: Peggy Dixon Two-Year College Scholarship **Area, Field, or Subject:** Physics **Level of Education for which Award is Granted:** Four Year College **Number Awarded:** 1 each year. **Funds Available:** The stipend is $2,000. **Duration:** 1 year.
Eligibility Requirements: This program is open to students at 2-year colleges who are entering a bachelor's degree program in physics. Applicants must have completed at least 1 semester or quarter of the introductory physics sequence and be currently enrolled in the appropriate subsequent physics courses. They must be members of the society. Selection is based on 1) high scholarship performance both in physics and overall studies, 2) potential for continued scholastic development in physics, and 3) active participation in society programs; those 3 criteria are given equal weight. **Deadline for Receipt:** February of each year. **Additional Information:** This program is sponsored by the Sigma Pi Sigma Trust Fund and the American Institute of Physics.

3199 ■ SOCIETY OF PHYSICS STUDENTS

c/o American Institute of Physics
One Physics Ellipse
College Park, MD 20740-3843
Tel: (301)209-3007
Fax: (301)209-0839
E-mail: sps@aip.org
Web Site: http://www.spsnational.org/programs/hlevy.htm
To provide financial assistance to members of the Society of Physics Students (SPS) in their final year of undergraduate study.
Title of Award: Herbert Levy Memorial Scholarship **Area, Field, or Subject:** Physics **Level of Education for which Award is Granted:** Four Year College **Number Awarded:** 1 each year. **Funds Available:** The stipend is $2,000. **Duration:** 1 year.
Eligibility Requirements: This program is open to undergraduate students in any year of college who are active members of the society. Selection is based on 1) high scholarship performance both in physics and overall studies, 2) potential and intention for continued scholastic development in physics, 3) active participation in society programs, and 4) financial need. **Deadline for Receipt:** February of each year.

3200 ■ SOCIETY OF PHYSICS STUDENTS

c/o American Institute of Physics
One Physics Ellipse
College Park, MD 20740-3843
Tel: (301)209-3007
Fax: (301)209-0839
E-mail: sps@aip.org
Web Site: http://www.spsnational.org/programs/icpstravel.htm
To provide funding to members of the Society of Physics Students (SPS) who wish to attend the annual conference of the International Association of Physics Students (IAPS).
Title of Award: Outstanding Student Award for Undergraduate Research **Area, Field, or Subject:** Physics **Level of Education for which Award is Granted:** Four Year College, Graduate **Number Awarded:** Varies each year; recently, 3 of these awards were granted. **Funds Available:** Winners receive a $500 honorarium and a $500 award for their SPS chapter. **Duration:** These awards are presented annually.
Eligibility Requirements: This program is open to members of the society who wish to present a paper at the International Conference of Physics Students (ICPS), conducted by the IAPS. Normally, applicants are upper-division undergraduates or first- or second-year graduate students. Selection is based on the quality of an abstract, letters of recommendation, and demonstration of active participation in the society. **Deadline for Receipt:** April of each year. **Additional Information:** The ICPS is usually held in Europe; in previous years it has been in Turkey, Portugal, Austria, Russia, Denmark, Hungary, Finland, Croatia, and

Ireland. This program was formerly known as the International Conference of Physics Students Travel Award.

3201 ■ SOCIETY OF PHYSICS STUDENTS
c/o American Institute of Physics
One Physics Ellipse
College Park, MD 20740-3843
Tel: (301)209-3007
Fax: (301)209-0839
E-mail: sps@aip.org
Web Site: http://www.spsnational.org/programs/future_teacher.htm
To provide financial assistance to members of the Society of Physics Students (SPS) interested in preparing for a career as a physics teacher. **Title of Award:** SPS Future Teacher Scholarship **Area, Field, or Subject:** Education; Physics **Level of Education for which Award is Granted:** Four Year College **Number Awarded:** 1 each year. **Funds Available:** The stipend is $2,000. **Duration:** 1 year.
Eligibility Requirements: This program is open to full-time college juniors who are active members of the society. Applicants must be enrolled in a teacher education program with plans to prepare for a career in physics education. Selection is based on 1) high scholarship performance both in physics and overall studies, 2) potential for continued scholastic development in physics, 3) active participation in society programs, and 4) a statement of experiences and ambitions with regard to teaching physics. **Deadline for Receipt:** February of each year. **Additional Information:** This program is sponsored by the Sigma Pi Sigma Trust Fund and the American Institute of Physics.

3202 ■ SOCIETY OF PHYSICS STUDENTS
c/o American Institute of Physics
One Physics Ellipse
College Park, MD 20740-3843
Tel: (301)209-3007
Fax: (301)209-0839
E-mail: sps@aip.org
Web Site: http://www.spsnational.org/programs/scholarships.htm
To provide financial assistance to members of the Society of Physics Students (SPS) in their final year of undergraduate study.
Title of Award: SPS Leadership Scholarships **Area, Field, or Subject:** Physics **Level of Education for which Award is Granted:** Four Year College **Number Awarded:** Varies each year; recently, 26 of these scholarships were awarded. **Funds Available:** Stipends are $5,000 or $2,000. **Duration:** 1 year.
Eligibility Requirements: Eligible are full-time college juniors majoring in physics who are active members of the society. Selection is based on 1) high scholarship performance both in physics and overall studies, 2) potential for continued scholastic development in physics, and 3) active participation in society programs; those 3 criteria are given equal weight. **Deadline for Receipt:** February of each year. **Additional Information:** This program is sponsored by the Sigma Pi Sigma Trust Fund and the American Institute of Physics.

3203 ■ SOCIETY OF PLASTICS ENGINEERS
Attn: SPE Foundation
14 Fairfield Drive
Brookfield, CT 06804-0403
Tel: (203)740-5447
Fax: (203)775-1157
E-mail: foundation@4spe.org
Web Site: http://www.4spe.org/foundation/scholarships.php
To provide financial assistance to undergraduate students who have a career interest in the plastics industry.
Title of Award: American Plastics Council (APC)/SPE Plastics Environmental Division Scholarship **Area, Field, or Subject:** Chemistry; Engineering, Chemical; Engineering, Industrial; Engineering, Materials; Engineering, Mechanical; Physics **Level of Education for which Award is Granted:** Undergraduate **Number Awarded:** 1 each year. **Funds Available:** The stipend is $2,500 per year. Funds are paid directly to the recipient's school. **Duration:** 1 year.
Eligibility Requirements: This program is open to full-time undergraduate students at 4-year colleges or in 2-year technical programs. Applicants must 1) have a demonstrated or expressed interest in the plastics industry; 2) be majoring in or taking courses that would be beneficial to a

career in the plastics or polymer industry (e.g., plastics engineering, polymer sciences, chemistry, physics, chemical engineering, mechanical engineering, or industrial engineering); 3) be in good academic standing at their school; and 4) be able to document financial need. Along with their application, they must submit 3 letters of recommendation; a high school and/or college transcript; and a 1- to 2-page statement telling why they are interested in the scholarship, their qualifications, and their educational and career goals in the plastics industry. **Deadline for Receipt:** January of each year. **Additional Information:** This scholarship is awarded annually in the names of corporations cited as the *Excellence in Plastics Impact on the Environment* by the Plastics Environmental Division of the Society of Plastics Engineers (SPE).

3204 ■ SOCIETY OF PLASTICS ENGINEERS
Attn: SPE Foundation
14 Fairfield Drive
Brookfield, CT 06804-0403
Tel: (203)740-5447
Fax: (203)775-1157
E-mail: foundation@4spe.org
Web Site: http://www.4spe.org/foundation/scholarships.php
To provide financial assistance to undergraduate and graduate students who have a career interest in the plastics industry.
Title of Award: Composites Division/Harold Giles Scholarship **Area, Field, or Subject:** Chemistry; Engineering, Chemical; Engineering, Industrial; Engineering, Materials; Engineering, Mechanical; Physics **Level of Education for which Award is Granted:** Graduate, Undergraduate **Number Awarded:** 1 each year. **Funds Available:** The stipend is $1,000 per year. Funds are paid directly to the recipient's school. **Duration:** 1 year.
Eligibility Requirements: This program is open to full-time undergraduate and graduate students at 4-year colleges or in 2-year technical programs. Applicants must 1) have a demonstrated or expressed interest in the plastics industry; 2) be majoring in or taking courses that would be beneficial to a career in the plastics or polymer industry (e.g., plastics engineering, polymer sciences, chemistry, physics, chemical engineering, mechanical engineering, or industrial engineering); 3) be in good academic standing at their school; and 4) be able to document financial need. Along with their application, they must submit 3 letters of recommendation; a high school and/or college transcript; and a 1- to 2-page statement telling why they are interested in the scholarship, their qualifications, and their educational and career goals in the plastics industry. **Deadline for Receipt:** January of each year.

3205 ■ SOCIETY OF PLASTICS ENGINEERS
Attn: SPE Foundation
14 Fairfield Drive
Brookfield, CT 06804-0403
Tel: (203)740-5447
Fax: (203)775-1157
E-mail: foundation@4spe.org
Web Site: http://www.4spe.org/foundation/scholarships.php
To provide financial assistance to undergraduate students who have a career interest in the plastics industry.
Title of Award: Robert E. Cramer/Product Design and Development Division/Mid-Michigan Section Scholarship **Area, Field, or Subject:** Chemistry; Engineering, Chemical; Engineering, Industrial; Engineering, Materials; Engineering, Mechanical; Physics **Level of Education for which Award is Granted:** Undergraduate **Number Awarded:** 1 each year. **Funds Available:** The stipend is $1,000 per year. Funds are paid directly to the recipient's school. **Duration:** 1 year.
Eligibility Requirements: This program is open to full-time undergraduate students at 4-year colleges or in 2-year technical programs. Applicants must 1) have a demonstrated or expressed interest in the plastics industry; 2) be majoring in or taking courses that would be beneficial to a career in the plastics or polymer industry (e.g., plastics engineering, polymer sciences, chemistry, physics, chemical engineering, mechanical engineering, or industrial engineering); 3) be in good academic standing at their school; and 4) be able to document financial need. Along with their application, they must submit 3 letters of recommendation; a high school and/or college transcript; and a 1- to 2-page statement telling why they are interested in the scholarship, their qualifications, and their educational and career goals in the plastics industry. **Deadline for Receipt:** January of each year.

3206 ■ SOCIETY OF PLASTICS ENGINEERS

Attn: SPE Foundation
14 Fairfield Drive
Brookfield, CT 06804-0403
Tel: (203)740-5447
Fax: (203)775-1157
E-mail: foundation@4spe.org
Web Site: http://www.4spe.org/foundation/scholarships.php
To provide financial assistance to undergraduate students who have a career interest in the plastics industry.
Title of Award: Robert G. Dailey/Detroit Section Scholarship **Area, Field, or Subject:** Chemistry; Engineering, Chemical; Engineering, Industrial; Engineering, Materials; Engineering, Mechanical; Physics **Level of Education for which Award is Granted:** Undergraduate **Number Awarded:** 1 each year. **Funds Available:** The stipend is $4,000 per year. Funds are paid directly to the recipient's school. **Duration:** 1 year.
Eligibility Requirements: This program is open to full-time undergraduate students at 4-year colleges or in 2-year technical programs. Applicants must 1) have a demonstrated or expressed interest in the plastics industry; 2) be majoring in or taking courses that would be beneficial to a career in the plastics or polymer industry (e.g., plastics engineering, polymer sciences, chemistry, physics, chemical engineering, mechanical engineering, or industrial engineering); 3) be in good academic standing at their school; and 4) be able to document financial need. Along with their application, they must submit 3 letters of recommendation; a high school and/or college transcript; and a 1- to 2-page statement telling why they are interested in the scholarship, their qualifications, and their educational and career goals in the plastics industry. **Deadline for Receipt:** January of each year.

3207 ■ SOCIETY OF PLASTICS ENGINEERS

Attn: SPE Foundation
14 Fairfield Drive
Brookfield, CT 06804-0403
Tel: (203)740-5447
Fax: (203)775-1157
E-mail: foundation@4spe.org
Web Site: http://www.4spe.org/foundation/scholarships.php
To provide financial assistance to Mexican American undergraduate and graduate students who have a career interest in the plastics industry.
Title of Award: Fleming/Blaszcak Scholarship **Area, Field, or Subject:** Chemistry; Engineering, Chemical; Engineering, Industrial; Engineering, Materials; Engineering, Mechanical; Physics **Level of Education for which Award is Granted:** Four Year College, Graduate **Number Awarded:** 1 each year. **Funds Available:** The stipend is $2,000 per year. Funds are paid directly to the recipient's school. **Duration:** 1 year.
Eligibility Requirements: This program is open to full-time undergraduate and graduate students of Mexican descent who are enrolled in a 4-year college or university. Applicants must be U.S. citizens or legal residents. They must 1) have a demonstrated or expressed interest in the plastics industry; 2) be majoring in or taking courses that would be beneficial to a career in the plastics or polymer industry (e.g., plastics engineering, polymer sciences, chemistry, physics, chemical engineering, mechanical engineering, or industrial engineering); 3) be in good academic standing at their school; and 4) be able to document financial need. Along with their application, they must submit 3 letters of recommendation; a high school and/or college transcript; a 1- to 2-page statement telling why they are interested in the scholarship, their qualifications, and their educational and career goals in the plastics industry; and documentation of their Mexican heritage. **Deadline for Receipt:** January of each year. **Additional Information:** This program is sponsored by Cal Mold Inc. and Formula Plastics.

3208 ■ SOCIETY OF PLASTICS ENGINEERS

Attn: SPE Foundation
14 Fairfield Drive
Brookfield, CT 06804-0403
Tel: (203)740-5447
Fax: (203)775-1157
E-mail: foundation@4spe.org
Web Site: http://www.4spe.org/foundation/scholarships.php
To provide financial assistance to undergraduate and graduate students who have a career interest in the plastics industry and experience in the thermoset industry.

Title of Award: Thermoset Division/James I. MacKenzie Scholarship **Area, Field, or Subject:** Chemistry; Engineering, Chemical; Engineering, Industrial; Engineering, Materials; Engineering, Mechanical; Physics **Level of Education for which Award is Granted:** Graduate, Undergraduate **Number Awarded:** 2 each year: 1 to an undergraduate and 1 to a graduate student. **Funds Available:** The stipend is $1,000 per year. Funds are paid directly to the recipient's school. **Duration:** 1 year.
Eligibility Requirements: This program is open to full-time undergraduate and graduate students at either a 4-year college or in a 2-year technical program. Applicants must have experience in the thermoset industry, such as courses taken, research conducted, or jobs held. They must 1) have a demonstrated or expressed interest in the plastics industry; 2) be majoring in or taking courses that would be beneficial to a career in the plastics or polymer industry (e.g., plastics engineering, polymer sciences, chemistry, physics, chemical engineering, mechanical engineering, or industrial engineering); 3) be in good academic standing at their school; and 4) be able to document financial need. Along with their application, they must submit 3 letters of recommendation; a high school and/or college transcript; a 1- to 2-page statement telling why they are interested in the scholarship, their qualifications, and their educational and career goals in the plastics industry; and a statement detailing their exposure to the thermoset industry. **Deadline for Receipt:** January of each year.

3209 ■ SOCIETY OF PLASTICS ENGINEERS

Attn: SPE Foundation
14 Fairfield Drive
Brookfield, CT 06804-0403
Tel: (203)740-5447
Fax: (203)775-1157
E-mail: foundation@4spe.org
Web Site: http://www.4spe.org/foundation/scholarships.php
To provide financial assistance to undergraduate and graduate students who have a career interest in the plastics industry.
Title of Award: Ted Neward Scholarships **Area, Field, or Subject:** Chemistry; Engineering, Chemical; Engineering, Industrial; Engineering, Materials; Engineering, Mechanical; Physics **Level of Education for which Award is Granted:** Graduate, Undergraduate **Number Awarded:** 3 each year. **Funds Available:** The stipend is $3,000 per year. Funds are paid directly to the recipient's school. **Duration:** 1 year.
Eligibility Requirements: This program is open to full-time undergraduate and graduate students at 4-year colleges or in 2-year technical programs. Applicants must 1) have a demonstrated or expressed interest in the plastics industry; 2) be majoring in or taking courses that would be beneficial to a career in the plastics or polymer industry (e.g., plastics engineering, polymer sciences, chemistry, physics, chemical engineering, mechanical engineering, or industrial engineering); 3) be in good academic standing at their school; and 4) be able to document financial need. U.S. citizenship is required. Along with their application, they must submit 3 letters of recommendation; a high school and/or college transcript; and a 1- to 2-page statement telling why they are interested in the scholarship, their qualifications, and their educational and career goals in the plastics industry. **Deadline for Receipt:** January of each year.

3210 ■ SOCIETY OF PLASTICS ENGINEERS

Attn: SPE Foundation
14 Fairfield Drive
Brookfield, CT 06804-0403
Tel: (203)740-5447
Fax: (203)775-1157
E-mail: foundation@4spe.org
Web Site: http://www.4spe.org/foundation/scholarships.php
To provide financial assistance to undergraduate students who have a career interest in the plastics industry.
Title of Award: Polymer Modifiers and Additives Division Scholarships **Area, Field, or Subject:** Chemistry; Engineering, Chemical; Engineering, Industrial; Engineering, Materials; Engineering, Mechanical; Physics **Level of Education for which Award is Granted:** Undergraduate **Number Awarded:** 4 each year. **Funds Available:** The stipend is $4,000 per year. Funds are paid directly to the recipient's school. **Duration:** 1 year.
Eligibility Requirements: This program is open to full-time undergraduate students at 4-year colleges or in 2-year technical programs. Applicants must 1) have a demonstrated or expressed interest in the plastics

industry; 2) be majoring in or taking courses that would be beneficial to a career in the plastics or polymer industry (e.g., plastics engineering, polymer sciences, chemistry, physics, chemical engineering, mechanical engineering, or industrial engineering); 3) be in good academic standing at their school; and 4) be able to document financial need. Along with their application, they must submit 3 letters of recommendation; a high school and/or college transcript; and a 1- to 2-page statement telling why they are interested in the scholarship, their qualifications, and their educational and career goals in the plastics industry. **Deadline for Receipt:** January of each year.

3211 ■ SOCIETY OF PLASTICS ENGINEERS
Attn: SPE Foundation
14 Fairfield Drive
Brookfield, CT 06804-0403
Tel: (203)740-5447
Fax: (203)775-1157
E-mail: foundation@4spe.org
Web Site: http://www.4spe.org/foundation/scholarships.php
To provide financial assistance to undergraduate and graduate students who have a career interest in the plastics industry.
Title of Award: Society of Plastics Engineers Foundation Scholarships **Area, Field, or Subject:** Chemistry; Engineering, Chemical; Engineering, Industrial; Engineering, Materials; Engineering, Mechanical; Physics **Level of Education for which Award is Granted:** Graduate, Undergraduate **Number Awarded:** 10 to 12 each year. **Funds Available:** Stipends range up to $4,000 per year. Funds are paid directly to the recipient's school. **Duration:** 1 year; may be renewed for up to 3 additional years.
Eligibility Requirements: This program is open to full-time undergraduate and graduate students at 4-year colleges or in 2-year technical programs. Applicants must 1) have a demonstrated or expressed interest in the plastics industry; 2) be majoring in or taking courses that would be beneficial to a career in the plastics or polymer industry (e.g., plastics engineering, polymer sciences, chemistry, physics, chemical engineering, mechanical engineering, or industrial engineering); 3) be in good academic standing at their school; and 4) be able to document financial need. Along with their application, they must submit 3 letters of recommendation; a high school and/or college transcript; and a 1- to 2-page statement telling why they are interested in the scholarship, their qualifications, and their educational and career goals in the plastics industry.
Deadline for Receipt: January of each year.

3212 ■ SOCIETY OF PLASTICS ENGINEERS
Attn: SPE Foundation
14 Fairfield Drive
Brookfield, CT 06804-0403
Tel: (203)740-5447
Fax: (203)775-1157
E-mail: foundation@4spe.org
Web Site: http://www.4spe.org/foundation/scholarships.php
To provide college scholarships to students who have a career interest in the plastics industry and experience in the thermoforming industry.
Title of Award: Thermoforming Division Memorial Scholarships **Area, Field, or Subject:** Chemistry; Engineering, Chemical; Engineering, Industrial; Engineering, Materials; Engineering, Mechanical; Physics **Level of Education for which Award is Granted:** Graduate, Undergraduate **Number Awarded:** 2 each year. **Funds Available:** The stipend is $5,000 per year. Funds are paid directly to the recipient's school. **Duration:** 1 year.
Eligibility Requirements: This program is open to full-time undergraduate and graduate students at either a 4-year college or in a 2-year technical program. Applicants must have experience in the thermoforming industry, such as courses taken, research conducted, or jobs held. They must 1) have a demonstrated or expressed interest in the plastics industry; 2) be majoring in or taking courses that would be beneficial to a career in the plastics or polymer industry (e.g., plastics engineering, polymer sciences, chemistry, physics, chemical engineering, mechanical engineering, or industrial engineering); 3) be in good academic standing at their school; and 4) be able to document financial need. Along with their application, they must submit 3 letters of recommendation; a high school and/or college transcript; a 1to 2-page statement telling why they are interested in the scholarship, their qualifications, and their educational and

career goals in the plastics industry; and a statement detailing their exposure to the thermoforming industry. **Deadline for Receipt:** January of each year.

3213 ■ SOCIETY OF PLASTICS ENGINEERS
Attn: SPE Foundation
14 Fairfield Drive
Brookfield, CT 06804-0403
Tel: (203)740-5447
Fax: (203)775-1157
E-mail: foundation@4spe.org
Web Site: http://www.4spe.org/foundation/scholarships.php
To provide financial assistance to undergraduate students who have a career interest in the plastics industry.
Title of Award: Vinyl Plastics Division Scholarship **Area, Field, or Subject:** Chemistry; Engineering, Chemical; Engineering, Industrial; Engineering, Materials; Engineering, Mechanical; Physics **Level of Education for which Award is Granted:** Undergraduate **Number Awarded:** 1 each year. **Funds Available:** The stipend is $1,000 per year. Funds are paid directly to the recipient's school. **Duration:** 1 year.
Eligibility Requirements: This program is open to full-time undergraduate students at 4-year colleges or in 2-year technical programs. Applicants must 1) have a demonstrated or expressed interest in the plastics industry; 2) be majoring in or taking courses that would be beneficial to a career in the plastics or polymer industry (e.g., plastics engineering, polymer sciences, chemistry, physics, chemical engineering, mechanical engineering, or industrial engineering); 3) be in good academic standing at their school; and 4) be able to document financial need. Along with their application, they must submit 3 letters of recommendation; a high school and/or college transcript; and a 1- to 2-page statement telling why they are interested in the scholarship, their qualifications, and their educational and career goals in the plastics industry. Preference is given to applicants with experience in the vinyl industry, such as courses taken, research conducted, or jobs held. **Deadline for Receipt:** January of each year.

3214 ■ TEXAS SPACE GRANT CONSORTIUM
Attn: Administrative Assistant
3925 West Braker Lane, Suite 200
Austin, TX 78759
Tel: (512)471-3583
Free: 800-248-8742
Fax: (512)471-3585
E-mail: scholarships@tsgc.utexas.edu
Web Site: http://www.tsgc.utexas.edu/grants
To provide financial assistance to upper-division and medical students at Texas universities working on degrees in the fields of space science and engineering.
Title of Award: Columbia Crew Memorial Undergraduate Scholarships **Area, Field, or Subject:** Aerospace sciences; Biological and clinical sciences; Chemistry; Engineering, Aerospace/Aeronautical/Astronautical; Engineering, Chemical; Engineering, Electrical; Engineering, Industrial; Engineering, Mechanical; Geology; Mathematics and mathematical sciences; Physics; Space and planetary sciences **Level of Education for which Award is Granted:** Doctorate, Undergraduate **Number Awarded:** Varies each year; recently, 29 of these scholarships were awarded. **Funds Available:** The stipend is $1,000. **Duration:** 1 year; nonrenewable.
Eligibility Requirements: Applicants must be U.S. citizens, eligible for financial assistance, and registered for full-time study at a participating college or university. Applicants must be a sophomore at a 2-year institution, a junior or senior at a 4-year institution, or a first- or second-year student at a medical school. Supported fields of study have included aerospace engineering, biology, chemical engineering, chemistry, electrical engineering, geology, industrial engineering, mathematics, mechanical engineering, and physics. The program encourages participation by members of groups underrepresented in science and engineering (persons with disabilities, women, African Americans, Hispanic Americans, Native Americans, and Pacific Islanders). Selection is based on excellence in academics, participation in space education projects, participation in research projects, and exhibited leadership qualities. **Deadline for Receipt:** March of each year. **Additional Information:** In 2003, the Texas Space Grant Consortium renamed its undergraduate scholarship program in honor of the 7 Space Shuttle Columbia astronauts. The participating

universities are Baylor University, Lamar University, Prairie View A&M University, Rice University, San Jacinto College, Southern Methodist University, Sul Ross State University, Texas A&M University (including Kingsville and Corpus Christi campuses), Texas Christian University, Texas Southern University, Texas Tech University, Trinity University, University of Houston (including Clear Lake and Downtown campuses), University of Texas at Arlington, University of Texas at Austin, University of Texas at Dallas, University of Texas at El Paso, University of Texas at San Antonio, and University of Texas/Pan American. This program is funded by the National Aeronautics and Space Administration (NASA).

3215 ■ U.S. AIR FORCE

Attn: Headquarters AFROTC/RRUC
551 East Maxwell Boulevard
Maxwell AFB, AL 36112-5917
Tel: (334)953-2091; (866)423-7682
Fax: (334)953-6167
Web Site: http://www.afrotc.com/scholarships/hsschol/types.php
To provide financial assistance to high school seniors or graduates who are interested in joining Air Force ROTC in college and are willing to serve as Air Force officers following completion of their bachelor's degree.
Title of Award: Air Force ROTC High School Scholarships **Area, Field, or Subject:** Architecture; Chemistry; Computer and information sciences; Engineering, Aerospace/Aeronautical/Astronautical; Engineering, Architectural; Engineering, Civil; Engineering, Computer; Engineering, Electrical; Engineering, Mechanical; Environmental science; General studies/Field of study not specified; Mathematics and mathematical sciences; Meteorology; Operations research; Physics **Level of Education for which Award is Granted:** Four Year College **Number Awarded:** Approximately 2,000 each year. **Funds Available:** Type 1 scholarships provide payment of full tuition and most laboratory fees, as well as $600 for books. Type 2 scholarships pay the same benefits except tuition is capped at $15,000 per year; students who attend an institution where tuition exceeds $15,000 must pay the difference. Type 7 scholarships pay full tuition and most laboratory fees, but students must attend a college or university where the tuition is less than $9,000 per year or a public college or university where they qualify for the in-state tuition rate; they may not attend an institution with higher tuition and pay the difference. Approximately 5% of scholarship offers are for Type 1, approximately 20% are for Type 2, and approximately 75% are for type 7. All recipients are also awarded a tax-free subsistence allowance for 10 months of each year that is $250 per month as a freshman, $300 per month as a sophomore, $350 per month as a junior, and $400 per month as a senior. **Duration:** 4 years.
Eligibility Requirements: This program is open to high school seniors who are U.S. citizens at least 17 of age and have been accepted at a college or university with an Air Force ROTC unit on campus or a college with a cross-enrollment agreement with such a college. Applicants must have a cumulative GPA of 3.0 or higher and an ACT composite score of 24 or higher or an SAT score of 1100 (mathematics and verbal portion only) or higher. At the time of their commissioning in the Air Force, they must be no more than 31 years of age. They must agree to serve for at least 4 years as active-duty Air Force officers following graduation from college. **Deadline for Receipt:** November of each year. **Additional Information:** Recently, approximately 70% of these scholarships were offered to students planning to major in the science and technical fields of architecture, chemistry, computer science, engineering (aeronautical, aerospace, astronautical, architectural, civil, computer, electrical, environmental, or mechanical), mathematics, meteorology and atmospheric sciences, operations research, or physics. Approximately 30% were offered to students in all other fields. While scholarship recipients can major in any subject, they must enroll in 4 years of aerospace studies courses at 1 of the 144 colleges and universities that have an Air Force ROTC unit on campus; students may also attend nearly 900 other colleges that have cross-enrollment agreements with the institutions that have an Air Force ROTC unit on campus. Recipients must attend a 4-week summer training camp at an Air Force base, usually between their sophomore and junior years. Most cadets incur a 4-year active-duty commitment. Pilots incur a 10-year active-duty service commitment after successfully completing Specialized Undergraduate Pilot Training and navigators incur a 6-year commitment after successfully completing

Specialized Undergraduate Navigator Training. The minimum service obligation for intelligence and Air Battle Management career fields is 5 years.

3216 ■ U.S. AIR FORCE

Attn: Headquarters AFROTC/RRUC
551 East Maxwell Boulevard
Maxwell AFB, AL 36112-5917
Tel: (334)953-2091; (866)423-7682
Fax: (334)953-6167
Web Site: http://www.afrotc.com/scholarships/incolschol/
incolProgram.php
To provide financial assistance to undergraduate students who are willing to join Air Force ROTC in college and serve as Air Force officers following completion of their bachelor's degree.
Title of Award: Air Force ROTC In-College Scholarship Program **Area, Field, or Subject:** Architecture; Chemistry; Computer and information sciences; Engineering, Aerospace/Aeronautical/Astronautical; Engineering, Architectural; Engineering, Civil; Engineering, Computer; Engineering, Electrical; Engineering, Mechanical; Environmental science; General studies/Field of study not specified; Mathematics and mathematical sciences; Meteorology; Operations research; Physics **Level of Education for which Award is Granted:** Undergraduate **Number Awarded:** Varies each year. **Funds Available:** Cadets selected in Phase 1 are awarded type 2 AFROTC scholarships that provide for payment of tuition and fees, to a maximum of $15,000 per year. A limited number of cadets selected in Phase 2 are also awarded type 2 AFROTC scholarships, but most are awarded type 3 AFROTC scholarships with tuition capped at $9,000 per year. Cadets selected in Phase 3 are awarded type 6 AFROTC scholarships with tuition capped at $3,000 per year. All recipients are also awarded a book allowance of $600 and a tax-free subsistence allowance for 10 months of each year that is $300 per month during the sophomore year, $350 during the junior year, and $400 during the senior year. **Duration:** 3 years for students selected as freshmen or 2 years for students selected as sophomores.
Eligibility Requirements: This program is open to U.S. citizens enrolled as freshmen or sophomores at 1 of the 144 colleges and universities that have an Air Force ROTC unit on campus. Applicants must have a cumulative GPA of 2.5 or higher and be able to pass the Air Force Officer Qualifying Test and the Air Force ROTC Physical Fitness Test. At the time of commissioning, they may be no more than 31 years of age. They must agree to serve for at least 4 years as active-duty Air Force officers following graduation from college. Phase 1 is open to students enrolled in the Air Force ROTC program who do not currently have a scholarship but now wish to apply. Phase 2 is open to Phase 1 nonselects and students not enrolled in Air Force ROTC. Phase 3 is open only to Phase 2 nonselects. Recently, the program gave preference to students majoring in the science and technical fields of architecture, chemistry, computer science, engineering (aeronautical, aerospace, astronautical, architectural, civil, computer, electrical, environmental, or mechanical), mathematics, meteorology and atmospheric sciences, operations research, or physics. **Deadline for Receipt:** January of each year. **Additional Information:** While scholarship recipients can major in any subject, they must complete 4 years of aerospace studies courses at 1 of the 144 colleges or universities that have an Air Force ROTC unit on campus. Recipients must also attend a 4-week summer training camp at an Air Force base, usually between their sophomore and junior years; 2-year scholarship awardees attend in the summer after their junior year. Current military personnel are eligible for early release from active duty in order to enter the Air Force ROTC program. Following completion of their bachelor's degree, scholarship recipients earn a commission as a second lieutenant in the Air Force and serve at least 4 years.

3217 ■ U.S. AIR FORCE

Attn: Headquarters AFROTC/RRUE
Enlisted Commissioning Section
551 East Maxwell Boulevard
Maxwell AFB, AL 36112-5917
Tel: (334)953-2091; (866)423-7682
Fax: (334)953-6167
E-mail: enlisted@afrotc.com
Web Site: http://www.afoats.af.mil/AFROTC/EnlistedComm/AECP.asp

To allow selected enlisted Air Force personnel to earn a bachelor's degree in approved majors by providing financial assistance for full-time college study.

Title of Award: Airman Education and Commissioning Program **Area, Field, or Subject:** African studies; Asian studies; Computer and information sciences; Engineering; Foreign languages; Mathematics and mathematical sciences; Meteorology; Near Eastern studies; Nursing; Physics; Russian studies **Level of Education for which Award is Granted:** Undergraduate **Number Awarded:** Approximately 60 each year. **Funds Available:** While participating in this program, cadets remain on active duty in the Air Force and receive their regular salary and benefits. They also receive payment of tuition and fees up to $15,000 per year and an annual textbook allowance of $600. **Duration:** 1 to 3 years, until completion of a bachelor's degree.

Eligibility Requirements: Eligible to participate in this program are enlisted members of the Air Force who have been accepted at a university or college (or approved crosstown institution) that is associated with AFROTC and that offers an approved major. The majors currently supported are computer science, all ABET-accredited engineering fields (not engineering technology), foreign area studies (limited to Middle East, Africa, Asia, Russia/Eurasia), foreign languages (limited to Arabic, Armenian, Azeri, Chinese, French, Georgian, Hebrew, Hindi, Indonesian, Kazakh, Pashto, Persian Farsi, Russian, Swahili, and Turkish), mathematics, meteorology, nursing, and physics. Applicants must have completed at least 1 year of time-in-service and 1 year of time-on-station. They must have scores on the Air Force Officer Qualifying Test of at least 15 on the verbal and 10 on the quantitative and be able to pass the Air Force ROTC Physical Fitness Test. Normally they should have completed at least 30 semester hours of college study with a GPA of 2.75 or higher. They must be younger than 31 years of age or otherwise able to be commissioned before they become 35 years of age. **Deadline for Receipt:** February of each year. **Additional Information:** While attending college, participants in this program attend ROTC classes at their college or university. Upon completing their degree, they are commissioned to serve in the Air Force in their area of specialization with an active-duty service commitment of at least 4 years. Further information is available from base education service officers or an Air Force ROTC unit. This program does not provide for undergraduate flying training.

3218 ■ U.S. AIR FORCE
Attn: Headquarters AFROTC/RRUE
Enlisted Commissioning Section
551 East Maxwell Boulevard
Maxwell AFB, AL 36112-5917
Tel: (334)953-2091; (866)423-7682
Fax: (334)953-6167
E-mail: enlisted@afrotc.com
Web Site: http://www.afoats.af.mil/AFROTC/EnlistedComm/ASCP.asp
To allow selected enlisted Air Force personnel to earn a bachelor's degree in approved majors by providing financial assistance for full-time college study.

Title of Award: Airman Scholarship and Commissioning Program **Area, Field, or Subject:** Architecture; Atmospheric science; Chemistry; Computer and information sciences; Engineering; Engineering, Aerospace/Aeronautical/Astronautical; Engineering, Architectural; Engineering, Civil; Engineering, Computer; Engineering, Electrical; Engineering, Mechanical; Environmental science; General studies/Field of study not specified; Mathematics and mathematical sciences; Meteorology; Operations research; Physics **Level of Education for which Award is Granted:** Undergraduate **Number Awarded:** Varies each year. **Funds Available:** Awards are type 2 AFROTC scholarships that provide for payment of tuition and fees, to a maximum of $15,000 per year, plus an annual book allowance of $600. All recipients are also awarded a tax-free subsistence allowance for 10 months of each year that is $300 per month during their sophomore year, $350 during their junior year, and $400 during their senior year. **Duration:** 2 to 4 years, until completion of a bachelor's degree.

Eligibility Requirements: This program is open to active-duty enlisted members of the Air Force who have completed at least 1 year of continuous active duty and at least 1 year on station. Applicants normally must have completed at least 24 semester hours of graded college credit with a cumulative college GPA of 2.5 or higher. If they have not completed 24 hours of graded college credit, they must have an ACT score of 24 or

higher or an SAT combined verbal and mathematics score of 1100 or higher. They must also have scores on the Air Force Officer Qualifying Test (AFOQT) of 15 or more on the verbal scale and 10 or more on the quantitative scale and be able to pass the Air Force ROTC Physical Fitness Test. Applicants must have been accepted at a college or university (including crosstown schools) offering the AFROTC 4-year program. When they complete the program and receive their commission, they may not be 31 years of age or older. U.S. citizenship is required. Recently, awards were presented according to the following priorities: 1) computer, electrical, and environmental engineering; 2) aeronautical, aerospace, architectural, astronautical, civil, and mechanical engineering and meteorology and atmospheric sciences; 3) all other ABET-accredited engineering majors, architecture, chemistry, computer science, mathematics, operations research, and physics; 4) all other majors. **Deadline for Receipt:** October of each year. **Additional Information:** Selectees separate from the active-duty Air Force, join an AFROTC detachment, and become full-time students. Upon completing their degree, they are commissioned as officers and returned to active duty in the Air Force with a 4-year service obligation. Further information is available from base education service officers or an Air Force ROTC unit.

3219 ■ U.S. AIR FORCE
Attn: Headquarters AFROTC/RRUE
Enlisted Commissioning Section
551 East Maxwell Boulevard
Maxwell AFB, AL 36112-5917
Tel: (334)953-2091; (866)423-7682
Fax: (334)953-6167
E-mail: enlisted@afrotc.com
Web Site: http://www.afoats.af.mil/AFROTC/EnlistedComm/POC-ERP.asp
To allow selected enlisted Air Force personnel to earn a baccalaureate degree by providing financial assistance for full-time college study.

Title of Award: Professional Officer Course Early Release Program **Area, Field, or Subject:** Architecture; Atmospheric science; Chemistry; Computer and information sciences; Engineering; Engineering, Aerospace/Aeronautical/Astronautical; Engineering, Architectural; Engineering, Civil; Engineering, Computer; Engineering, Electrical; Engineering, Mechanical; Environmental science; General studies/Field of study not specified; Mathematics and mathematical sciences; Meteorology; Operations research; Physics **Level of Education for which Award is Granted:** Undergraduate **Number Awarded:** Varies each year. **Funds Available:** Participants receive a stipend for 10 months of the year that is $350 per month during the first year and $400 per month during the second year. Scholarship recipients earn the Professional Officer Course Incentive of $3,000 per year for tuition and $600 per year for books. **Duration:** 2 years (no more and no less).

Eligibility Requirements: Eligible to participate in this program are enlisted members of the Air Force under the age of 30 (or otherwise able to be commissioned before becoming 35 years of age) who have completed at least 1 year on continuous active duty, have served on station for at least 1 year, and have no more than 2 years remaining to complete their initial baccalaureate degree. Scholarship applicants must be younger than 31 years of age when they graduate and earn their commission. All applicants must have been accepted at a college or university offering the AFROTC 4-year program and must have a cumulative college GPA of 2.5 or higher. Their Air Force Officer Qualifying Test (AFOQT) scores must be at least 15 on the verbal and 10 on the quantitative. Applicants who have not completed 24 units of college work must have an ACT composite score of 24 or higher or an SAT combined verbal and mathematics score of 1100 or higher. U.S. citizenship is required. Recently, awards were presented according to the following priorities: 1) computer, electrical, and environmental engineering; 2) aeronautical, aerospace, architectural, astronautical, civil, and mechanical engineering and meteorology and atmospheric sciences; 3) all other ABET-accredited engineering majors, architecture, chemistry, computer science, mathematics, operations research, and physics; 4) all other majors. **Deadline for Receipt:** October of each year. **Additional Information:** Upon completing their degree, selectees are commissioned as officers in the Air Force with a 4-year service obligation. Further information is available from base education service officers or an Air Force ROTC unit.

3220 ■ U.S. NAVY

Attn: Navy Personnel Command
5722 Integrity Drive
Millington, TN 38054-5057
Tel: (901)874-3070; 888-633-9674
Fax: (901)874-2651
E-mail: nukeprograms@cnrc.navy.mil
Web Site: http://www.cnrc.navy.mil/nucfield/college/officer_options.htm
To provide financial assistance to college juniors and seniors who wish to serve in the Navy's nuclear propulsion training program following graduation.

Title of Award: Nuclear Propulsion Officer Candidate (NUPOC) Program **Area, Field, or Subject:** Chemistry; Engineering; General studies/Field of study not specified; Mathematics and mathematical sciences; Physics **Level of Education for which Award is Granted:** Four Year College **Number Awarded:** Varies each year. **Funds Available:** Participants become Active Reserve enlisted Navy personnel and receive a salary of up to $2,500 per month; the exact amount depends on the local cost of living and other factors. A bonus of $10,000 is also paid at the time of enlistment and another $2,000 upon completion of nuclear power training. **Duration:** Up to 30 months, until completion of a bachelor's degree.

Eligibility Requirements: This program is open to U.S. citizens who are entering their junior or senior year of college as a full-time student. Strong technical majors (mathematics, physics, chemistry, or an engineering field) are encouraged but not required. Applicants must have completed at least 1 year of calculus and 1 year of physics and must have earned a grade of "C" or better in all mathematics, science, and technical courses. Normally, they must be 26 years of age or younger at the expected date of commissioning, although applicants for the design and research specialty may be 29 years old. **Additional Information:** Following graduation, participants attend Officer Candidate School in Pensacola, Florida for 4 months and receive their commissions. They have a service obligation of 8 years (of which at least 5 years must be on active duty), beginning with 6 months at the Navy Nuclear Power Training Command in Charleston, South Carolina and 6 more months of hands-on training at a nuclear reactor facility. Further information on this program is available from a local Navy recruiter or the Navy Recruiting Command, 801 North Randolph Street, Arlington, VA 22203-1991.

3221 ■ WASHINGTON HIGHER EDUCATION COORDINATING BOARD

917 Lakeridge Way
P.O. Box 43430
Olympia, WA 98504-3430

Tel: (360)753-7851; 888-535-0747
Fax: (360)753-7808
E-mail: futureteachers@hecb.wa.gov
Web Site: http://www.hecb.wa.gov/financialaid/other/alternative.asp
To provide forgivable loans to K-12 classified employees in Washington who are interested in attending a college or university in order to become a teacher.

Title of Award: Washington Conditional Scholarships for Alternative Teaching Certification **Area, Field, or Subject:** Chemistry; Education; Education, Bilingual and cross-cultural; Education, Elementary; Education, English as a second language; Education, Secondary; Education, Special; Foreign languages; Mathematics and mathematical sciences; Physics; Technology **Level of Education for which Award is Granted:** Professional, Undergraduate **Number Awarded:** Approximately 25 each year. **Funds Available:** The maximum award is $4,000 per academic year. These awards are in the form of loans that can be forgiven in exchange for teaching service. Each 2 years of eligible teaching service results in the forgiveness of 1 year of loan. **Duration:** 1 year; may be renewed up to 4 additional years.

Eligibility Requirements: This program is open to Washington residents who are currently employed as a classified instructional employee in a K-12 public school. Applicants must 1) have a transferable associate degree and be seeking residency teacher certification with endorsements in special education or English as a second language; or 2) have a bachelor's degree and subject matter expertise in a shortage area and be seeking residency teacher certification in a subject matter shortage area (currently defined as special education, English as a second language, chemistry, physics, Japanese, mathematics, and technology education). to enroll in an accredited Washington college or university and work as a teacher in a K-12 public school in the state after completing initial teacher certification. Selection is based on academic ability, a statement demonstrating commitment to the teaching profession, the applicant's ability to serve as a positive role model as a K-12 public school teacher, length and quality of contributions to the Washington K-12 public school, and recommendations from a current teacher or school official describing the applicant's potential as a future teacher. The priority in making awards is: 1) eligible renewal applicants who are within 2 years of completing their initial teacher certification requirements; 2) all other eligible renewable applicants; 3) eligible new applicants who are within 2 years of completing their initial teacher certification requirements; and 4) all other new eligible applicants. **Deadline for Receipt:** October of each year. **Additional Information:** This program was established by the Washington legislature in 2001. It is administered by the Washington Higher Education Coordinator Board, but the Washington State Professional Educator Standards Board selects the recipients.

General

3222 ■ AIR & WASTE MANAGEMENT ASSOCIATION-CONNECTICUT CHAPTER
Attn: Ray Yarmac, Secretary
Sci-Tech, Inc.
185 Silas Deane Highway
Wethersfield, CT 06109
Tel: (860)257-0767
E-mail: ryarmac@sce-techinc.com
Web Site: http://www.awma-nes.org/connecticut_chapter.htm
To provide financial assistance to residents of Connecticut who are interested in studying fields related to air and waste management in college.
Title of Award: Connecticut Chapter Scholarship **Area, Field, or Subject:** Air pollution; Engineering; Environmental conservation; Environmental science; Science **Level of Education for which Award is Granted:** Undergraduate **Number Awarded:** 1 each year. **Funds Available:** The stipend is $1,000. **Duration:** 1 year; recipients may reapply.
Eligibility Requirements: This program is open to 1) seniors graduating from high schools in Connecticut who plan to enroll full time in college, and 2) Connecticut residents already enrolled full time in college. Applicants must be interested in working on a degree in science or engineering leading to careers in the environmental field, especially air pollution control or waste management. Selection is based on their proposed plan of study, transcripts, work experience, and volunteer and extracurricular activities; financial need is not considered. **Deadline for Receipt:** April of each year.

3223 ■ CHINESE HISTORICAL SOCIETY OF SOUTHERN CALIFORNIA
Attn: Scholarship Chair
415 Bernard Street
P.O. Box 862647
Los Angeles, CA 90086-2647
Tel: (323)222-0856
E-mail: chssc@chssc.org
Web Site: http://www.chssc.org
To provide financial assistance to students from any state who who attending college in southern California and interested in majoring in Chinese American studies.
Title of Award: CHSSC Scholarship **Area, Field, or Subject:** Asian studies; Humanities; Social sciences **Level of Education for which Award is Granted:** Graduate, Undergraduate **Number Awarded:** 1 each year. **Funds Available:** The stipend is $1,000. **Duration:** 1 year.
Eligibility Requirements: This program is open to undergraduate and graduate students from any state who are attending an accredited college or university in southern California on a full-time basis, have earned at least a 3.0 GPA, and are have an academic interest related to Chinese American studies in the humanities or social sciences. Applicants must submit a 300- to 500-word essay in English on the importance to them of Chinese American studies; a statement of additional factors, such as financial need, family circumstances, employment history, and campus and community activities that may advance their application; transcripts;

and an optional letter of recommendation. Finalists are interviewed. **Deadline for Receipt:** March of each year. **Additional Information:** This program began in 1992. Information is also available from Susie Ling, E-mail: shling@pasadena.edu.

3224 ■ FOUNDATION FOR AMATEUR RADIO, INC.
Attn: Scholarship Committee
P.O. Box 831
Riverdale, MD 20738
E-mail: aa3of@arrl.net
Web Site: http://www.amateurradio-far.org/scholarships.php
To provide funding to licensed radio amateurs who are interested in studying humanities or the social sciences in college.
Title of Award: Kevin Barry Perdue Memorial Scholarship **Area, Field, or Subject:** Humanities; Social sciences **Level of Education for which Award is Granted:** Undergraduate **Number Awarded:** 1 each year. **Funds Available:** The stipend is $2,000. **Duration:** 1 year.
Eligibility Requirements: Applicants must have at least a technician class license and intend to pursue a course of study in the liberal arts, humanities, or social sciences. They must intend to earn a bachelor's degree from a U.S. college or university. **Deadline for Receipt:** Requests for applications must be submitted by April of each year. **Additional Information:** Recipients must attend an accredited school (university, college, or technical institute) on a full-time basis.

3225 ■ FRAMELINE
Attn: Film and Video Completion Fund
145 Ninth Street, Suite 300
San Francisco, CA 94103
Tel: (415)703-8650
Fax: (415)861-1404
E-mail: info@frameline.org
Web Site: http://www.frameline.org/fund
To provide funding to lesbian and gay film/video artists.
Title of Award: Horizons/Frameline Film and Video Completion Fund **Area, Field, or Subject:** Filmmaking; Homosexuality **Level of Education for which Award is Granted:** Graduate, Professional, Undergraduate **Number Awarded:** Varies each year; recently, 4 of these grants were awarded. **Funds Available:** Grants range from $3,000 to $5,000.
Eligibility Requirements: This program is open to lesbian and gay artists who are in the last stages of the production of documentary, educational, animated, or experimental projects about or of interest to lesbians, gay men, bisexuals, and transgender people and their communities. Applicants may be independent artists, students, producers, or nonprofit corporations. They must be interested in completion or post-production work, including subtitling or conversion from video to film (or vice versa). In particular, women and people of color are encouraged to apply. Selection is based on financial need, the contribution the grant will make to completing the project, assurances that the project will be completed, and the statement the project makes about lesbian, gay, bisexual, and transgender people and/or issues of concern to them and their communi-

ties. Grants are not awarded for script development, research, pre-production, or production work. **Deadline for Receipt:** October of each year.

3226 ■ MAINE SPACE GRANT CONSORTIUM

Attn: Executive Director
87 Winthrop Street, Suite 200
Augusta, ME 04330
Tel: (207)622-4688; 877-397-7223
Fax: (207)622-4548
E-mail: shehata@msgc.org
Web Site: http://www.msgc.org/education_students.asp
To provide funding to undergraduate and graduate students at colleges and universities in Maine interested in working on projects related to space.
Title of Award: Maine Space Grant Consortium Scholarship and Fellowship Program **Area, Field, or Subject:** Aerospace sciences; Biological and clinical sciences; Computer and information sciences; Earth sciences; Engineering, Aerospace/Aeronautical/Astronautical; Geosciences; Physical sciences; Social sciences; Space and planetary sciences; Technology **Level of Education for which Award is Granted:** Graduate, Undergraduate **Number Awarded:** Varies each year. **Funds Available:** Stipends are $2,500 for undergraduates or $5,000 for graduate students. **Duration:** 1 year.
Eligibility Requirements: This program is open to U.S. citizens who are enrolled on a full-time basis in an undergraduate or graduate program at a 2- or 4-year college or university in Maine, including those not members of the Maine Space Grant Consortium. Applicants must be proposing to conduct a project on a topic of interest to the U.S. National Aeronautics and Space Administration (NASA) in biological, earth, physical, social, or space science; human exploration and development of space; or other related science, technology, computer, or engineering fields. Undergraduates must have a GPA of 3.0 or higher; graduate students must have a GPA of 3.2 or higher. Proposals may involve conducting research at their home institution, traveling to conduct research and/or to present finished project work at a NASA field center, or facilitating technology transfer from NASA to their institution and industry in Maine. Applications are especially encouraged from women, minorities, and persons with disabilities. Selection is based on the relevance of the project to NASA's mission and its strategic enterprises, collaboration with researchers at NASA space flight centers, qualifications of the student, technical content and quality of the proposal, and recommendation from a faculty member. **Deadline for Receipt:** May or October of each year. **Additional Information:** This program is funded by NASA.

3227 ■ MINNESOTA SPACE GRANT CONSORTIUM

c/o University of Minnesota
Department of Aerospace Engineering and Mechanics
107 Akerman Hall
110 Union Street S.E.
Minneapolis, MN 55455
Tel: (612)626-9295
Fax: (612)626-1558
E-mail: mnsgc@aem.umn.edu
Web Site: http://www.aem.umn.edu/msgc/Scholarships/sf.shtml
To provide financial assistance for space-related studies to undergraduate and graduate students in Minnesota.
Title of Award: Minnesota Space Grant Consortium Scholarships and Fellowships **Area, Field, or Subject:** Earth sciences; Engineering; Life sciences; Physical sciences; Social sciences **Level of Education for which Award is Granted:** Graduate, Undergraduate **Number Awarded:** 8 to 12 undergraduate scholarships and 2 to 3 graduate fellowships are awarded each year. **Funds Available:** This program awards approximately $125,000 in undergraduate scholarships and graduate fellowships each year. The amounts of the awards are set by each of the participating institutions, which augment funding from this program with institutional resources. **Duration:** 1 year; renewable.
Eligibility Requirements: This program is open to graduate and undergraduate full-time students at institutions that are affiliates of the Minnesota Space Grant Consortium. U.S. citizenship and a GPA of 3.2 or higher are required. Eligible fields of study include the physical sciences (astronomy, astrophysics, chemistry, computer science, mathematics, physics, planetary geoscience, and planetary science), life sciences (biol-

ogy, biochemistry, botany, health science/nutrition, medicine, molecular/cellular biology, and zoology), social sciences (anthropology, architecture, art, economics, education, history, philosophy, political science/public policy, and psychology), earth sciences (atmospheric science, climatology/meteorology, environmental science, geography, geology, geophysics, and oceanography), and engineering (agricultural, aeronautical, aerospace, architectural, bioengineering, chemical, civil, computer, electrical, electronic, environmental, industrial, materials science, mechanical, mining, nuclear, petroleum, engineering science, and engineering mechanics). The Minnesota Space Grant Consortium is a component of the U.S. National Aeronautics and Space Administration (NASA) Space Grant program, which encourages participation by women, underrepresented minorities, and persons with disabilities. **Deadline for Receipt:** March of each year. **Additional Information:** This program is funded by NASA. The member institutions are: Augsburg College, Bethel College, Bemidji State University, College of St. Catherine, Carleton College, Concordia College, Fond du Lac Community College, Itasca Community College, Leech Lake Tribal College, Macalaster College, Normandale Community College, Southwest State University, University of Minnesota at Duluth, University of Minnesota at Twin Cities, and University of St. Thomas.

3228 ■ OAK RIDGE INSTITUTE FOR SCIENCE AND EDUCATION

Attn: Science and Engineering Education
P.O. Box 117
Oak Ridge, TN 37831-0117
Tel: (865)576-9279
Fax: (865)241-5219
E-mail: coxre@orau.gov
Web Site: http://www.orau.gov/orise.htm
To provide scholarships and internship experience to students at Historically Black Colleges and Universities (HBCUs) working on undergraduate degrees in areas related to the Office of Civilian Radioactive Waste Management (OCRWM).
Title of Award: Office of Civilian Radioactive Waste Management Historically Black Colleges and Universities Undergraduate Scholarship Program **Area, Field, or Subject:** Energy-related areas; Engineering; Mathematics and mathematical sciences; Nuclear science; Science; Social sciences **Level of Education for which Award is Granted:** Four Year College **Number Awarded:** 10 each year. **Funds Available:** The program provides for payment of tuition and fees (to a maximum of $8,000) plus a monthly stipend of $600. **Duration:** 2 years.
Eligibility Requirements: This program is open to juniors and seniors at HBCUs who are working on a degree in science, mathematics, engineering, engineering technology, or social sciences. As part of their program, they must be willing to participate in an internship at a U.S. Department of Energy (DOE) site conducting activities for the OCRWM. **Deadline for Receipt:** January of each year. **Additional Information:** This program is funded by DOE/OCRWM and administered by Oak Ridge Institute for Science and Education (ORISE).

3229 ■ PENNSYLVANIA ASSOCIATION OF FAMILY AND CONSUMER SCIENCES

c/o Diane Brown, Scholarship Chair
146 North Cacoosing Drive
Sinking Spring, PA 19608
E-mail: dvb146ncd@comcast.net
Web Site: http://www.pafcs.org/pafcsawards.htm
To provide financial assistance to graduate student members of the Pennsylvania Association of Family and Consumer Sciences (PAFCS).
Title of Award: PAFCS Graduate Scholarship **Area, Field, or Subject:** Consumer affairs **Level of Education for which Award is Granted:** Four Year College, Graduate **Number Awarded:** 1 each year. **Funds Available:** The stipend is $1,500. **Duration:** 1 year.
Eligibility Requirements: This program is open to student members of the association enrolled in a graduate program in family and consumer sciences. Along with their application, they must submit a statement of 200 to 300 words on their professional goals, a 200- to 300-word descrip-

tion of their research topic and its focus, transcripts, a current vita, and a 1-page biographical sketch. **Deadline for Receipt:** January of each year.

3230 ■ PENNSYLVANIA ASSOCIATION OF FAMILY AND CONSUMER SCIENCES

c/o Diane Brown, Scholarship Chair
146 North Cacoosing Drive
Sinking Spring, PA 19608
E-mail: dvb146ncd@comcast.net
Web Site: http://www.pafcs.org/pafcsawards.htm
To provide financial assistance to undergraduate student members of the Pennsylvania Association of Family and Consumer Sciences (PAFCS).
Title of Award: PAFCS Undergraduate Scholarship **Area, Field, or Subject:** Consumer affairs **Level of Education for which Award is Granted:** Four Year College **Number Awarded:** 2 each year. **Funds Available:** The stipend is $1,000. **Duration:** 1 year.
Eligibility Requirements: This program is open to student members of the association entering their junior or senior year of college. Applicants must be enrolled full time in an aspect of family and consumer sciences education. Along with their application, they must submit a 200-word essay on their professional goals and how they think they can contribute to the family and consumer sciences profession. Financial need is also considered in the selection process. **Deadline for Receipt:** January of each year.

3231 ■ TEXAS 4-H YOUTH DEVELOPMENT FOUNDATION

Attn: Executive Director
Texas A&M University
7606 Eastmark Drive, Suite 101
College Station, TX 77843-2473
Tel: (979)845-1213
Fax: (979)845-6495
E-mail: texas4-hscholarships@tamu.edu
Web Site: http://texas4-h.tamu.edu/scholarships
To provide financial assistance to 4-H members in Texas who plan to work on a technical certificate in selected science or social science fields at an institution in the state.
Title of Award: Texas 4-H Technical Certification Scholarship Program **Area, Field, or Subject:** Science; Social sciences **Level of Education for which Award is Granted:** Two Year College, Vocational/Occupational **Number Awarded:** The foundation awards approximately 170 scholarships, worth more than $1.2 million, for all of its programs each year. **Funds Available:** Scholarships range from $1,500 to $15,000, depending on the contributions from various donors. **Duration:** 1 year.
Eligibility Requirements: This program is open to graduating seniors at high schools in Texas who have been actively participating in 4-H and plan to attend an institution in the state to work on a technical certificate in an approved major. Applicants must have passed all sections of the TAAS, THEA, and/or TAKS test. Some scholarships require applicants to demonstrate financial need; selection for those awards is based on GPA (10%), 4-H experience (60%), financial need (20%), and a personal interview (10%). For other scholarships, selection is based on GPA (10%), 4-H experience (80%), and a personal interview (10%). **Deadline for Receipt:** Students submit their applications to their county extension office, which must forward them to the district extension office by February of each year. **Additional Information:** The approved majors and courses of study include accounting associate, aircraft pilot training technology, applied graphic design technology, aquaculture technology, auctioneering services, automotive body/collision technology, automotive technology, aviation maintenance technology, aviation technology, biomedical equipment technology, biotechnology, business/office administration, caption reporting proficiency, carpentry, chemical laboratory technology, child development, commercial art and advertising, computer aided design and drafting, computer information systems, computer maintenance technology, computer network administration/technology, computer science technology, construction management and technology, court/realtime reporting, criminal justice, dental assistant, dental hygiene, diagnostic medical sonography, diesel and heavy equipment technology, dietary management, digital imaging technology, digital media design, drafting and design technology, echocardiology technology, e-commerce technology, educational assistant, electrical technology, electronics engineering technology, emergency medical services, environmental health and safety technology, farrier technology, fire science, food service/culinary arts, GIS/

GPS technology, golf course and landscape management, HVAC technology, histology technology, horticulture technology, hotel and restaurant management, industrial maintenance and engineering technology, information management/technology, instrument and control technology, interpretation preparation program/deaf, invasive cardiovascular technology, logistics technology, machining technology, marketing, meat technology, mechanical engineering technology, media communications and information technology, medical assistant, medical data specialist, medical laboratory technology, mental health associate, mortuary science, music, nuclear medicine, nursing (associate degree and vocational), occupational therapy assistant, paralegal/legal assistant, pharmacy technology, phlebotomy, physical therapist assistant, plastics technology, process technology, radiation therapy, radiography, radio-television, ranch and feedlot operations, real estate, respiratory care, semiconductor manufacturing, surgical technology, telecommunications technology, travel/ exposition/meeting management, veterinary technology, video technology, and welding technology. Students who apply to the Texas FFA Association or the Texas chapter of Family, Career and Community Leaders of America (FCCLA) for a scholarship will have their 4-H application voided.

3232 ■ TEXAS EXTENSION ASSOCIATION OF FAMILY AND CONSUMER SCIENCE

c/o Marsha Blair, CEA-FCS
1212 Houston Street, Suite 2
Levelland, TX 79336-3515
Tel: (806)894-3159
Fax: (806)897-3104
E-mail: ml-blair@tamu.edu
Web Site: http://teafcs.tamu.edu/awards.html
To provide financial assistance to members of 4-H who are enrolled in a field related to family and consumer sciences at a Texas college or university.
Title of Award: Ann Sonner Scholarship **Area, Field, or Subject:** Consumer affairs **Level of Education for which Award is Granted:** Four Year College **Number Awarded:** 1 each year. **Funds Available:** The stipend is $1,000. **Duration:** 1 year.
Eligibility Requirements: This program is open to students entering their junior or senior year at a college or university in Texas with a major in a field related to family and consumer sciences. Applicants must have actively participated in 4-H for 3 years and have a GPA of 2.5 or higher. Selection is based on academic ability (25%), leadership and character (25%), participation in 4-H (25%), and financial need (25%). **Deadline for Receipt:** February of each year.

Anthropology

3233 ■ EPILEPSY FOUNDATION

Attn: Research Department
4351 Garden City Drive
Landover, MD 20785-7223
Tel: (301)459-3700
Free: 800-EFA-1000
Fax: (301)577-2684
E-mail: grants@efa.org
Web Site: http://www.epilepsyfoundation.org/research/grants.cfm
To provide funding to undergraduate and graduate students interested in working on a summer research training project in a field relevant to epilepsy.
Title of Award: Behavioral Sciences Student Fellowships in Epilepsy **Area, Field, or Subject:** Anthropology; Behavioral sciences; Counseling/ Guidance; Economics; Epilepsy; Nursing; Political science; Psychology; Rehabilitation, Physical/Psychological; Social work; Sociology **Level of Education for which Award is Granted:** Graduate, Undergraduate **Number Awarded:** Varies each year; recently, 4 of these fellowships were awarded. **Funds Available:** The grant is $3,000. **Duration:** 3 months during the summer.
Eligibility Requirements: This program is open to undergraduate and graduate students in a behavioral science program relevant to epilepsy research or clinical care, including, but not limited to, sociology, social work, psychology, anthropology, nursing, economics, vocational rehabilitation, counseling, and political science. Applicants must be interested in working on an epilepsy research project under the supervision of a quali-

fied mentor. Because the program is designed as a training opportunity, the quality of the training plans and environment are considered in the selection process. Other selection criteria include the quality of the proposed project, the relevance of the proposed work to epilepsy, the applicant's interest in the field of epilepsy, the applicant's qualifications, and the mentor's qualifications, including his or her commitment to the student and the project. U.S. citizenship is not required, but the project must be conducted in the United States. Applications from women, members of minority groups, and people with disabilities are especially encouraged. The program is not intended for students working on a dissertation research project. **Deadline for Receipt:** March of each year. **Additional Information:** This program is supported by the American Epilepsy Society, Abbott Laboratories, Ortho-McNeil Pharmaceutical Corporation, and Pfizer Inc.

3234 ■ HAWAI'I COMMUNITY FOUNDATION

Attn: Scholarship Department
1164 Bishop Street, Suite 800
Honolulu, HI 96813
Tel: (808)566-5570; 888-731-3863
Fax: (808)521-6286
E-mail: scholarships@hcf-hawaii.org
Web Site: http://www.hawaiicommunityfoundation.org/scholar/scholar.php
To provide financial assistance to Hawaii residents who are interested in preparing for a career in early childhood education.
Title of Award: Henry and Dorothy Castle Memorial Fund Scholarship **Area, Field, or Subject:** Child care; Education, Early childhood; Education, Elementary **Level of Education for which Award is Granted:** Graduate, Undergraduate **Number Awarded:** Varies each year; recently, 10 of these scholarships were awarded. **Funds Available:** The amounts of the awards depend on the availability of funds and the need of the recipient; recently, stipends averaged $2,000. **Duration:** 1 year.
Eligibility Requirements: This program is open to Hawaii residents who are interested in pursuing full-time undergraduate or graduate studies in the field of early childhood education (birth through third grade), including child care and preschool. They must be able to demonstrate academic achievement (GPA of 2.7 or higher), good moral character, and financial need. In addition to filling out the standard application form, applicants must 1) write a short statement indicating their reasons for attending college, their planned course of study, and their career goals, and 2) write an essay that states their interests and goals in studying early childhood education and how they plan to contribute to the field. **Deadline for Receipt:** February of each year. **Additional Information:** Recipients may attend college in Hawaii or on the mainland. This scholarship is funded by the Samuel N. and Mary Castle Foundation.

3235 ■ HAWAI'I COMMUNITY FOUNDATION

Attn: Scholarship Department
1164 Bishop Street, Suite 800
Honolulu, HI 96813
Tel: (808)566-5570; 888-731-3863
Fax: (808)521-6286
E-mail: scholarships@hcf-hawaii.org
Web Site: http://www.hawaiicommunityfoundation.org/scholar/scholar.php
To provide financial assistance to residents of Hawaii for undergraduate or graduate studies in fields related to achieving world cooperation and international understanding.
Title of Award: Marion Maccarrell Scott Scholarship **Area, Field, or Subject:** Anthropology; Economics; Geography; History; International affairs and relations; Law; Peace studies; Philosophy; Political science; Psychology; Sociology **Level of Education for which Award is Granted:** Graduate, Undergraduate **Number Awarded:** Varies each year; recently, 258 of these scholarships were awarded. **Funds Available:** The amounts of the awards depend on the availability of funds and the need of the recipient; recently, stipends averaged $1,749. **Duration:** 1 year.
Eligibility Requirements: This program is open to graduates of public high schools in Hawaii. They must plan to attend school as full-time students (on the undergraduate or graduate level) on the mainland, majoring in history, government, political science, anthropology, economics, geography, international relations, law, psychology, philosophy, or sociology. They must be residents of the state of Hawaii, able to demonstrate financial need, interested in attending an accredited 2- or 4-year college or university, and able to demonstrate academic achievement (GPA of 2.8

or higher). Along with their application, they must submit an essay on their commitment to world peace that includes their learning experiences (courses, clubs, community activities, or travel) related to achieving world peace and international understanding and explaining how their experiences have enhanced their ability to achieve those goals. **Deadline for Receipt:** February of each year.

3236 ■ KONIAG INCORPORATED

Attn: Koniag Education Foundation
6927 Old Seward Highway, Suite 103
Anchorage, AK 99518-2283
Tel: (907)562-9093; 888-562-9093
Fax: (907)562-9023
E-mail: kcf@alaska.net
Web Site: http://www.koniageducation.org
To provide financial assistance to Alaska Natives of the Koniag region who are enrolled in undergraduate or graduate study in a field related to Alutiiq culture.
Title of Award: Larry Matfay Cultural Heritage Scholarship **Area, Field, or Subject:** Anthropology; History; Native American studies **Level of Education for which Award is Granted:** Four Year College, Graduate **Number Awarded:** 1 each year. **Funds Available:** The stipend is $1,000. Funds are sent directly to the recipient's school and may be used for tuition, books, supplies, room, board, and transportation. **Duration:** 1 year; may be renewed.
Eligibility Requirements: This program is open to college juniors, seniors, and graduate students who are 1) Alaska Natives enrolled under Section 5 of the Alaska Native Claims Settlement Act to the Koniag region, or 2) direct or legally adopted descendants of those original enrollees. Applicants must supply proof of eligibility and documentation of financial need. They must have a GPA of 2.5 or higher cumulatively (3.0 or higher within their major) and be majoring in anthropology, history, Alaska Native or American Indian studies, or another discipline that involves research and learning about Alutiiq culture. Along with their application, they must submit 1) a 300- to 600-word letter that includes their personal and family history, their schooling or work history, and their educational and life goals; and 2) a 200- to 400-word essay on how their education may benefit the Alutiiq people. **Deadline for Receipt:** March of each year. **Additional Information:** Recipients are also eligible to apply for a Koniag Education Foundation Academic Achievement/Graduate Scholarship. The Koniag Education Foundation was established in 1993 by the directors of Koniag, Inc. The Koniag region covers Kodiak Island, many smaller islands, and a portion of the Alaska Peninsula.

3237 ■ MARYLAND HIGHER EDUCATION COMMISSION

Attn: Office of Student Financial Assistance
839 Bestgate Road, Suite 400
Annapolis, MD 21401-3013
Tel: (410)260-4563
Free: 800-974-1024
Fax: (410)974-5376
E-mail: osfamail@mhec.state.md.us
Web Site: http://www.mhec.state.md.us/financialAid/
ProgramDescriptions/prog_child.asp
To provide scholarship/loans to students in Maryland who wish to prepare for a career as a child care provider.
Title of Award: Maryland Child Care Provider Scholarship Program **Area, Field, or Subject:** Child care; Child development; Education, Early childhood **Level of Education for which Award is Granted:** Professional, Undergraduate **Number Awarded:** Varies each year. **Funds Available:** Stipends at 4-year institutions are $2,000 per year for full-time study, $1,000 for part-time; at community colleges, annual stipends are $1,000 for full-time study, $500 for part-time. The total amount of all state awards may not exceed the cost of attendance as determined by the school's financial aid office or $17,800, whichever is less. Within 12 months of graduation, recipients must provide 1 year of child care service in Maryland for each year of financial aid received under this program; failure to comply with that service obligation will require the recipient to repay the scholarship money with interest. Teaching in a public school in Maryland does not fulfill the service requirement. **Duration:** 1 year; may be renewed for up to 3 additional years of full-time study provided the recipient maintains a GPA of 2.0 or higher.
Eligibility Requirements: Eligible are residents of Maryland who are enrolled or plan to enroll in a program leading to an associate or

bachelor's degree in a Maryland institution of higher education that offers an undergraduate program in early childhood education or child development. Full-time enrollment is required, although part-time study is allowed if the applicant is employed for a minimum of 15 hours per week at a child care or family day care center. Financial need is not considered in the selection process. **Deadline for Receipt:** June of each year.

Behavioral Sciences

3238 ■ ACADEMY OF TELEVISION ARTS & SCIENCES FOUNDATION

Attn: Education Department
5220 Lankershim Boulevard
North Hollywood, CA 91601-3109
Tel: (818)754-2830
Fax: (818)761-ATAS
E-mail: collegeawards@emmys.org
Web Site: http://www.emmys.tv/foundation/index.php

To provide financial assistance to upper-division and graduate students interested in working on a project in a field related to children's media. **Title of Award:** Fred Rogers Memorial Scholarship **Area, Field, or Subject:** Art, Caricatures and cartoons; Child development; Education, Early childhood; Filmmaking; Music; Psychology; Radio and television **Level of Education for which Award is Granted:** Four Year College, Graduate **Number Awarded:** 1 each year. **Funds Available:** The stipend is $10,000. **Duration:** 1 year.

Eligibility Requirements: This program is open to upper-division and graduate students interested in preparing for a career in children's media. Applicants must be able to demonstrate a commitment, either through course work or experience, to any combination of at least 2 of the following fields: early childhood education, child development, child psychology, film or television production, music, or animation. They may apply for support for any of the following areas: research on the relationship between children's media and learning or children's use of media and personal growth; development of program concepts or extended development of creative elements of an existing concept (e.g., design of puppets, scripts, storyboards, characters, music); professional internship in an organization that is relevant to the applicant's goal for use of the award. **Deadline for Receipt:** January of each year. **Additional Information:** This scholarship, first awarded in 2005, is supported by Ernst & Young.

3239 ■ ALABAMA SPACE GRANT CONSORTIUM

c/o University of Alabama in Huntsville
Materials Science Building, Room 205
Huntsville, AL 35899
Tel: (256)824-6800
Fax: (256)824-6061
E-mail: reasonj@uah.edu
Web Site: http://www.uah.edu/ASGC

To provide financial assistance to undergraduates who are studying the space sciences at universities participating in the Alabama Space Grant Consortium (ASGC). **Title of Award:** Undergraduate Scholarship Program of the Alabama Space Grant Consortium **Area, Field, or Subject:** Aerospace sciences; Behavioral sciences; Biological and clinical sciences; Business administration; Communications; Computer and information sciences; Economics; Education; Engineering, Aerospace/Aeronautical/Astronautical; International affairs and relations; Law; Natural sciences; Physical sciences; Public administration; Sociology; Space and planetary sciences **Level of Education for which Award is Granted:** Four Year College **Number Awarded:** Varies each year; recently, 32 of these scholarships were awarded. **Funds Available:** The stipend is $1,000 per year. **Duration:** 1 year; may be renewed 1 additional year.

Eligibility Requirements: This program is open to full-time students entering their junior or senior year at universities participating in the ASGC. Applicants must be studying in a field related to space, including the physical, natural, and biological sciences; engineering; education; economics; business; sociology; behavioral sciences; computer science; communications; law; international affairs; and public administration. They must be U.S. citizens and have a GPA of 3.0 or higher. Individuals from underrepresented groups (African Americans, Hispanic, American Indians, Pacific Islanders, Asian Americans, and women) are especially

encouraged to apply. Interested students should submit a completed application with a career goal statement, personal references, a brief resume, and transcripts. Selection is based on 1) academic qualifications, 2) quality of the career goal statement, and 3) assessment of the applicant's motivation for a career in aerospace. **Deadline for Receipt:** February of each year. **Additional Information:** The member universities are University of Alabama in Huntsville, Alabama A&M University, University of Alabama, University of Alabama at Birmingham, University of South Alabama, Tuskegee University, and Auburn University. Funding for this program is provided by NASA.

3240 ■ AMERICAN LEGION

Attn: Americanism and Children & Youth Division
P.O. Box 1055
Indianapolis, IN 46206-1055
Tel: (317)630-1249
Fax: (317)630-1223
E-mail: acy@legion.org
Web Site: http://www.legion.org

To recognize and reward high school students who participate in an oratorical contest on a theme related to the U.S. constitution. **Title of Award:** American Legion National High School Oratorical Contest **Area, Field, or Subject:** General studies/Field of study not specified; Patriotism; Speech, Debate, and Forensics **Level of Education for which Award is Granted:** Undergraduate **Number Awarded:** 3 national winners; hundreds of sectional, regional, and departmental winners. **Funds Available:** Scholarship awards are presented to the 3 finalists in the national contest: $18,000 to the first-place winner; $16,000 to the second-place winner; and $14,000 to the third-place winner. Each Department (state) winner who participates in the first round of the national contest receives a $1,500 scholarship; each first-round winner who advances to and participates in the second round, but does not advance to the final round, receives an additional $1,500 scholarship. **Duration:** The competition is held annually.

Eligibility Requirements: This program is open to U.S. citizens under the age of 20 who are currently enrolled in junior high or high school (grades 9-12). Students enter the contest through their Department (state) American Legion (many of these departments offer scholarships to participants in their state, in addition to the scholarships offered through the national program; check with your state department for further information). Each department then chooses 1 contestant to enter the regional contest. Regional winners compete in sectional contests; sectional winners compete on the national level. In all competitions, participants are evaluated on both the content and presentation of their prepared and extemporaneous speeches, which must deal with some aspect of the American Constitution or principles of government under the Constitution. **Deadline for Receipt:** The dates of departmental competitions vary; check with your local American Legion post. The national competition is generally held in April. **Additional Information:** The National Organization of the American Legion pays the travel costs of Department winners and their chaperones as they progress in national competition. Scholarships may be used to attend any accredited college or university in the United States. All contestants must be accompanied by a chaperone.

3241 ■ AMERICAN LEGION

Attn: Department of Pennsylvania
Attn: Scholarship Secretary
P.O. Box 2324
Harrisburg, PA 17105-2324
Tel: (717)730-9100
Fax: (717)975-2836
E-mail: hq@pa-legion.com
Web Site: http://www.pa-legion.com/essay.shtml

To recognize and reward high school students in Pennsylvania who submit outstanding essays on a patriotic topic. **Title of Award:** Pennsylvania Legion State High School Essay Contest **Area, Field, or Subject:** General studies/Field of study not specified; Patriotism; Writing **Level of Education for which Award is Granted:** Undergraduate **Number Awarded:** 3 state winners are selected each year. **Funds Available:** At the state level, the first-place winner receives a $3,500 scholarship, second a $3,000 scholarship, and third a $2,500 scholarship. If winners choose not to attend college, prizes are $300 for first place, $200 for second, and $200 for third. Local posts, counties, districts, and sections also offer awards. **Duration:** The competition is held annually.

Eligibility Requirements: This program is open to students who are currently enrolled in grades 9-12 in a Pennsylvania public, parochial, private, or home school. Applicants must submit an essay, from 600 to 1,000 words, on a topic that changes annually but relates to a patriotic theme; a recent topic was "America-Sweet Land of Liberty." Competitions are held at the level of local American Legion post, county, district, inter-district, sectional, and then state. Selection is based on proper English structure, accuracy, extent of information, and originality. **Deadline for Receipt:** Applications must be submitted to the local American Legion post by February of each year.

3242 ■ AMERICAN SOCIETY FOR ENGINEERING EDUCATION

Attn: SMART Defense Scholarship Program
1818 N Street, N.W., Suite 600
Washington, DC 20036-2479
Tel: (202)331-3516
Fax: (202)265-8504
E-mail: smart@asee.org
Web Site: http://www.asee.org/resources/fellowships/smart/index.cfm
To provide scholarship/loans to upper-division and graduate students in areas of science, mathematics, and engineering that are of interest to the U.S. Department of Defense.

Title of Award: Science, Mathematics, and Research for Transformation (SMART) Defense Scholarship Program **Area, Field, or Subject:** Architecture, Naval; Behavioral sciences; Biological and clinical sciences; Chemistry; Computer and information sciences; Earth sciences; Engineering, Aerospace/Aeronautical/Astronautical; Engineering, Chemical; Engineering, Civil; Engineering, Electrical; Engineering, Materials; Engineering, Mechanical; Engineering, Ocean; Geosciences; Materials research/science; Mathematics and mathematical sciences; Oceanography; Physics **Level of Education for which Award is Granted:** Four Year College, Graduate **Number Awarded:** Varies each year; recently, 36 of these scholarships were awarded. **Funds Available:** The program provides full payment of tuition, fees, room, board, and other normal educational expenses at the recipient's institution. A book allowance of $1,000 per year is also provided. This is a scholarship/loan program; recipients must agree to serve as a civilian employee of the Department of Defense in a science and engineering position. If they fail to fulfill that service obligation, they must reimburse the federal government for all funds they received. **Duration:** Up to 24 months.

Eligibility Requirements: This program is open to upper-division and graduate students working on an undergraduate or graduate degree in any of the following fields: aeronautical and astronautical engineering; biosciences; chemical engineering; chemistry; civil engineering; cognitive, neural, and behavioral sciences; computer and computational sciences; electrical engineering; geosciences, including terrain, water, and air; materials science and engineering; mathematics; mechanical engineering; naval architecture and ocean engineering; oceanography; or physics. Applicants must be U.S. citizens who have a GPA of 3.0 or higher. Selection is based on academic records, personal statements, letters of recommendation, and GRE scores. **Deadline for Receipt:** March of each year.

Additional Information: This program, established in 2005, is sponsored by the Army Research Laboratory, the Air Force Office of Scientific Research, the Office of Naval Research, the Air Force Research Laboratory, the Defense Advanced Research Projects Agency, the Defense Information Systems Agency, and the Defense Threat Reduction Agency.

3243 ■ ARKANSAS DEPARTMENT OF HIGHER EDUCATION

Attn: Financial Aid Division
114 East Capitol Avenue
Little Rock, AR 72201-3818
Tel: (501)371-2050
Free: 800-54-STUDY
Fax: (501)371-2001
E-mail: finaid@adhe.arknet.edu
Web Site: http://www.arkansashighered.com/mteachers.html
To provide scholarship/loans to minority undergraduates in Arkansas who want to become teachers.

Title of Award: Arkansas Minority Teacher Scholars Program **Area, Field, or Subject:** Counseling/Guidance; Education; Education,

Elementary; Linguistics; Mathematics and mathematical sciences; Science **Level of Education for which Award is Granted:** Four Year College **Number Awarded:** Varies each year; recently, 97 of these scholarship/loans were approved. **Funds Available:** Awards up to $5,000 per year are available. This is a scholarship/loan program. The loan will be forgiven at the rate of 20% for each year the recipient teaches full time in an Arkansas public school (or 33% per year if the obligation is fulfilled in 3 years as described above). If the loan is not forgiven by service, it must be repaid with interest at a rate up to 5% points above the Federal Reserve discount rate. **Duration:** 1 year; may be renewed for 1 additional year if the recipient remains a full-time student with a GPA of 2.5 or higher.

Eligibility Requirements: Applicants must be minority (African American, Native American, Hispanic, or Asian American) residents of Arkansas who are U.S. citizens and enrolled as full-time juniors or seniors in an approved teacher certification program at an Arkansas public or independent 4-year institution. They must have a cumulative GPA of 2.5 or higher and be willing to teach in an Arkansas public school for at least 5 years after completion of their teaching certificate (3 years if the teaching is in 1 of the 42 counties of Arkansas designated as the Delta Region; or if the teaching is in mathematics, science, or foreign language; or if the recipient is an African American male and teaches at the elementary level; or if the service is as a guidance counselor). **Deadline for Receipt:** May of each year.

3244 ■ ASSOCIATION FOR EDUCATION AND REHABILITATION OF THE BLIND AND VISUALLY IMPAIRED OF OHIO

c/o Marjorie E. Ward
1568 Lafayette Drive
Columbus, OH 43220
E-mail: ward5@osu.edu
Web Site: http://www.aerohio.org/schgrts/schol-grant.htm
To provide financial assistance to Ohio residents who are working on an undergraduate or graduate degree in a field related to rehabilitation of the blind.

Title of Award: AERO Personnel Preparation Scholarships **Area, Field, or Subject:** Counseling/Guidance; Education, Special; Rehabilitation, Physical/Psychological; Visual impairment **Level of Education for which Award is Granted:** Four Year College, Graduate **Number Awarded:** 1 each year. **Funds Available:** The stipend is $1,000. **Duration:** 1 year; nonrenewable.

Eligibility Requirements: This program is open to undergraduate and graduate students in rehabilitation counseling, rehabilitation teaching, orientation and mobility, or education of students with visual disabilities. Applicants must be residents of Ohio, although they may be studying in any state. Undergraduates must have at least junior standing. All applicants must have a GPA of 3.0 or higher. Along with their application, they must submit 1) a short essay explaining why they have chosen their specific field as their profession and what they would like to contribute to the field; 2) a short description of volunteer or paid involvement with individuals with visual disabilities or any other disability; 3) transcripts; and 4) 3 letters of recommendation. **Deadline for Receipt:** April of each year.

3245 ■ CATCHING THE DREAM

8200 Mountain Road, N.E., Suite 203
Albuquerque, NM 87110-7835
Tel: (505)262-2351
Fax: (505)262-0534
E-mail: NScholarsh@aol.com
Web Site: http://www.catchingthedream.org
To provide financial assistance to American Indian paraprofessionals in the education field who wish to return to college or graduate school.

Title of Award: Native American Leadership in Education (NALE) Program **Area, Field, or Subject:** Counseling/Guidance; Education; Educational administration **Level of Education for which Award is Granted:** Graduate, Professional, Undergraduate **Number Awarded:** Varies; generally, 15 or more each year. **Funds Available:** Stipends range from $500 to $5,000. **Duration:** 1 year; may be renewed.

Eligibility Requirements: This program is open to paraprofessionals who are working in Indian schools and who plan to return to school to complete their degree in education, counseling, or school administration. Applicants must be able to provide proof that they are at least one-quarter Indian blood and a member of a U.S. tribe that is federally-recognized, state-recognized, or terminated. Along with their application, they must submit documentation of financial need, 3 letters of recommendation, copies of applications and responses for at least 15 other sources of funding, official transcripts, standardized test scores (ACT, SAT, GRE, MCAT, LSAT, etc.), and an essay explaining their goals in life, college plans, and career plans (especially how those plans include working with and benefiting Indians). Selection is based on merit and potential for improving the lives of Indian people. **Deadline for Receipt:** April of each year for fall term; September of each year for spring and winter terms; March of each year for summer school. **Additional Information:** The sponsor was formerly known as the Native American Scholarship Fund.

3246 ■ COMMUNITY FOUNDATION OF GREATER JACKSON

525 East Capitol Street, Suite 5B
Jackson, MS 39201
Tel: (601)974-6044
Fax: (601)974-6045
E-mail: info@cfgreaterjackson.org
Web Site: http://www.cfgreaterjackson.org
To provide financial assistance to upper-division students in Mississippi and Louisiana who are preparing for a career in the field of juvenile justice.
Title of Award: Anthony "Tony" Gobar Juvenile Justice Scholarship Fund **Area, Field, or Subject:** Counseling/Guidance; Criminal justice; Criminology; Law enforcement; Political science **Level of Education for which Award is Granted:** Four Year College **Number Awarded:** 1 each year. **Funds Available:** A stipend is awarded (amount not specified). **Duration:** 1 year.
Eligibility Requirements: This program is open to full-time juniors and seniors at public universities in Mississippi and at Southern University in Louisiana who are preparing to enter the field of juvenile justice. Applicants must have demonstrated a strong commitment to community and public service. They must be U.S. citizens with a GPA of 2.5 or higher. Eligible majors include criminal justice, counseling, and political science. Selection is based on merit and need. **Deadline for Receipt:** April of each year. **Additional Information:** This program was established in 2005.

3247 ■ DELAWARE HIGHER EDUCATION COMMISSION

Carvel State Office Building
820 North French Street
Wilmington, DE 19801
Tel: (302)577-3240
Free: 800-292-7935
Fax: (302)577-6765
E-mail: dhec@doe.k12.de.us
Web Site: http://www.doe.state.de.us/high-ed/christa.htm
To provide scholarship/loans for teacher training to Delaware residents with outstanding academic records.
Title of Award: Christa McAuliffe Teacher Scholarship/Loan **Area, Field, or Subject:** Counseling/Guidance; Education; Education, Bilingual and cross-cultural; Education, English as a second language; Education, Special; English language and literature; Library and archival sciences; Linguistics; Mathematics and mathematical sciences; Reading; Technology **Level of Education for which Award is Granted:** Undergraduate **Number Awarded:** Up to 50 each year. **Funds Available:** Funds up to the cost of tuition, fees, and other direct educational expenses are provided. This is a scholarship/loan program; if the recipient performs required service at a school in Delaware, the loan is forgiven at the rate of 1 year of assistance for each year of service. **Duration:** 1 year; may be renewed for up to 3 additional years.
Eligibility Requirements: This program is open to Delaware residents who are enrolled or accepted for enrollment at a Delaware college or university in a program leading to teacher qualification. Preference is given to applicants planning to teach in an area of critical need. High school seniors must rank in the top half of their class and have a combined score of at least 1570 on the SAT; applicants who are already enrolled in college must have a cumulative GPA of 2.75 or higher. Selection is based on academic achievement. U.S. citizenship or permanent resident status is required. **Deadline for Receipt:** March of each year. **Additional Information:** The areas of critical need recently included bilingual education, business education, English, foreign languages,

English to speakers of other languages, mathematics, reading, science, school librarianship, special education, and technology education.

3248 ■ EPILEPSY FOUNDATION

Attn: Research Department
4351 Garden City Drive
Landover, MD 20785-7223
Tel: (301)459-3700
Free: 800-EFA-1000
Fax: (301)577-2684
E-mail: grants@efa.org
Web Site: http://www.epilepsyfoundation.org/research/grants.cfm
To provide funding to undergraduate and graduate students interested in working on a summer research training project in a field relevant to epilepsy.
Title of Award: Behavioral Sciences Student Fellowships in Epilepsy **Area, Field, or Subject:** Anthropology; Behavioral sciences; Counseling/Guidance; Economics; Epilepsy; Nursing; Political science; Psychology; Rehabilitation, Physical/Psychological; Social work; Sociology **Level of Education for which Award is Granted:** Graduate, Undergraduate **Number Awarded:** Varies each year; recently, 4 of these fellowships were awarded. **Funds Available:** The grant is $3,000. **Duration:** 3 months during the summer.
Eligibility Requirements: This program is open to undergraduate and graduate students in a behavioral science program relevant to epilepsy research or clinical care, including, but not limited to, sociology, social work, psychology, anthropology, nursing, economics, vocational rehabilitation, counseling, and political science. Applicants must be interested in working on an epilepsy research project under the supervision of a qualified mentor. Because the program is designed as a training opportunity, the quality of the training plans and environment are considered in the selection process. Other selection criteria include the quality of the proposed project, the relevance of the proposed work to epilepsy, the applicant's interest in the field of epilepsy, the applicant's qualifications, and the mentor's qualifications, including his or her commitment to the student and the project. U.S. citizenship is not required, but the project must be conducted in the United States. Applications from women, members of minority groups, and people with disabilities are especially encouraged. The program is not intended for students working on a dissertation research project. **Deadline for Receipt:** March of each year. **Additional Information:** This program is supported by the American Epilepsy Society, Abbott Laboratories, Ortho-McNeil Pharmaceutical Corporation, and Pfizer Inc.

3249 ■ FINANCE AUTHORITY OF MAINE

Attn: Education Finance Programs
5 Community Drive
P.O. Box 949
Augusta, ME 04332-0949
Tel: (207)623-3263
Free: 800-228-3734
Fax: (207)623-0095
E-mail: info@famemaine.com
Web Site: http://www.famemaine.com/html/education/fameprogs.html
To provide scholarship/loans to high school seniors, college students, and graduate students in Maine who are interested in preparing for a career as a teacher.
Title of Award: Educators for Maine Program **Area, Field, or Subject:** Child development; Education; Speech and language pathology/audiology **Level of Education for which Award is Granted:** Graduate, Undergraduate **Funds Available:** Full-time undergraduate students receive $3,000 per academic year; postbaccalaureate students receive $2,000 per academic year. This is a scholarship/loan program. Recipients may receive 1 year of loan forgiveness by completing 1 year of full-time teaching in a Maine public or private elementary or secondary school. The repayment option can be accelerated to 2 years of loan forgiveness for each year of teaching if the service is conducted in an educator shortage area or underserved subject area. If the loan recipient does not meet the service obligation, the total amount borrowed must be repaid at 9% interest; undergraduate borrowers must complete repayment within 10 years of graduation or withdrawal from school; postbaccalaureate students must complete repayment within 5 years of graduation or withdrawal from school. **Duration:** 1 year; may be renewed up to 3 additional years if the

recipient remains a Maine resident and maintains a cumulative GPA of 2.5 or higher.

Eligibility Requirements: This program is open to 1) high school seniors planning to attend college to prepare for a career in education; 2) currently-enrolled college students; and 3) postbaccalaureate students who are enrolled or planning to enroll in a program leading to certification as a teacher, speech pathologist, or child care provider. Applicants must be residents of Maine with a GPA of 3.0 or higher. Selection is based on academic achievement, activities, community service, and an essay; financial need is not considered. Preference is given to applicants planning to teach a shortage subject. **Deadline for Receipt:** March of each year. **Additional Information:** These scholarship/loans may be used at any accredited postsecondary institution offering certificate, 2-year, 4-year, or graduate programs that lead to an associate, baccalaureate, master's, or doctoral degree. This program was formerly known as Teachers for Maine. Undergraduate recipients must attend school on a full-time basis, but postbaccalaureate students and teachers are not required to enroll as full-time students.

3250 ■ FINANCE AUTHORITY OF MAINE

Attn: Education Finance Programs
5 Community Drive
P.O. Box 949
Augusta, ME 04332-0949
Tel: (207)623-3263
Free: 800-228-3734
Fax: (207)623-0095
E-mail: info@famemaine.com
Web Site: http://www.famemaine.com/html/education/fameprogs.html
To provide financial assistance to Maine residents interested in improving their skills in the child development field.

Title of Award: Maine Quality Child Care Education Scholarship Program **Area, Field, or Subject:** Child development **Level of Education for which Award is Granted:** Graduate, Professional, Undergraduate **Number Awarded:** Varies each year; scholarships are awarded on a first-come, first-served basis. **Funds Available:** The stipend is $500 per course or $2,000 per year. **Duration:** 1 semester or 1 year.

Eligibility Requirements: This program is open to residents of Maine who either currently work as a child care provider or express an interest in becoming a child care provider. Applicants must be enrolled or planning to enroll in an accredited college or university in Maine, another state, or a foreign country. They must be able to demonstrate financial need (total household adjusted gross income cannot exceed 300% of the federal poverty guidelines). **Deadline for Receipt:** Applications may be submitted at any time.

3251 ■ FLEET RESERVE ASSOCIATION

Attn: Americanism Essay Contest
125 North West Street
Alexandria, VA 22314-2754
Tel: (703)683-1400
Free: 800-372-1924
Fax: (703)549-6610
E-mail: fra@fra.org
Web Site: http://www.fra.org/Content/fra/AboutFRA/EssayContest/default.htm
To recognize and reward outstanding high school student essays on Americanism.

Title of Award: Fleet Reserve Association Americanism Essay Contest **Area, Field, or Subject:** Patriotism; Writing **Level of Education for which Award is Granted:** Undergraduate **Number Awarded:** 1 Grand Prize and 18 grade-level prizes (3 for each grade from 7 through 12) are offered on the national level. Many smaller prizes are awarded on the local and regional levels. **Funds Available:** The Grand National Prize is a $15,000 U.S. savings bond. For each grade level, first place is a $5,000 U.S. savings bond, second place is a $3,000 U.S. savings bond, and third place is a $2,000 U.S. savings bond. Additional prizes are awarded to students winning at local branch and regional levels of competition. **Duration:** The competition is held annually.

Eligibility Requirements: Any student, grade 7-12, may enter this contest. The contest is not restricted to children of the Fleet Reserve Association (FRA) or its Ladies Auxiliary. However, each entrant must be sponsored by an FRA member, branch, or Ladies Auxiliary unit. Essays must be on the annual theme (recently: "What My Vote Will Mean to Me") and cannot exceed 350 words. Students may submit only 1 entry per year. Essays are first graded on the FRA branch level and the top essays from each branch are forwarded to the regional level. From there, the top essays in each region are sent to the national level to be graded. **Deadline for Receipt:** November of each year.

3252 ■ HAWAI'I COMMUNITY FOUNDATION

Attn: Scholarship Department
1164 Bishop Street, Suite 800
Honolulu, HI 96813
Tel: (808)566-5570; 888-731-3863
Fax: (808)521-6286
E-mail: scholarships@hcf-hawaii.org
Web Site: http://www.hawaiicommunityfoundation.org/scholar/scholar.php
To provide financial assistance to residents of Hawaii for undergraduate or graduate studies in fields related to achieving world cooperation and international understanding.

Title of Award: Marion Maccarrell Scott Scholarship **Area, Field, or Subject:** Anthropology; Economics; Geography; History; International affairs and relations; Law; Peace studies; Philosophy; Political science; Psychology; Sociology **Level of Education for which Award is Granted:** Graduate, Undergraduate **Number Awarded:** Varies each year; recently, 258 of these scholarships were awarded. **Funds Available:** The amounts of the awards depend on the availability of funds and the need of the recipient; recently, stipends averaged $1,749. **Duration:** 1 year.

Eligibility Requirements: This program is open to graduates of public high schools in Hawaii. They must plan to attend school as full-time students (on the undergraduate or graduate level) on the mainland, majoring in history, government, political science, anthropology, economics, geography, international relations, law, psychology, philosophy, or sociology. They must be residents of the state of Hawaii, able to demonstrate financial need, interested in attending an accredited 2- or 4-year college or university, and able to demonstrate academic achievement (GPA of 2.8 or higher). Along with their application, they must submit an essay on their commitment to world peace that includes their learning experiences (courses, clubs, community activities, or travel) related to achieving world peace and international understanding and explaining how their experiences have enhanced their ability to achieve those goals. **Deadline for Receipt:** February of each year.

3253 ■ INDIAN HEALTH SERVICE

Attn: Scholarship Program
801 Thompson Avenue, Suite 120
Rockville, MD 20852
Tel: (301)443-6197
Fax: (301)443-6048
E-mail: bmiller@na.ihs.gov
Web Site: http://www.ihs.gov
To provide loans-for-service to American Indian and Alaska Native students enrolled in health professions and allied health professions programs.

Title of Award: Health Professions Scholarship Program **Area, Field, or Subject:** Counseling/Guidance; Dental hygiene; Dentistry; Health care services; Medical assisting; Medical technology; Medicine; Medicine, Osteopathic; Nursing; Nutrition; Optometry; Pharmaceutical sciences; Physical therapy; Podiatry; Psychology; Public health; Radiology; Respiratory therapy; Social work; **Level of Education for which Award is Granted:** Graduate, Undergraduate **Number Awarded:** Varies each year. **Funds Available:** Awards provide a payment directly to the school for tuition and required fees; a stipend for living expenses of approximately $1,160 per month for 12 months; a lump sum to cover the costs of books, travel, and other necessary educational expenses; and up to $400 for approved tutorial costs. Upon completion of their program of study, recipients are required to provide payback service of 1 year for each year of scholarship support at the Indian Health Service, a tribal health programs, an urban Indian health program, or in private practice in a designated health professional shortage area serving a substantial number of Indians. Recipients who fail to complete their service obligation must repay all funds received (although no interest is charged). **Duration:** 1 year; may be renewed for up to 3 additional years.

Eligibility Requirements: This program is open to American Indians and Alaska Natives who are at least high school graduates and enrolled in a full-time study program leading to a degree in a health-related professions school within the United States. Priority is given to upper-division and graduate students. Qualifying fields of study include chemical dependency counseling (bachelor's or master's degree), clinical psychology (Ph.D. only), coding specialist (certificate), counseling psychology (Ph.D. only), dental hygiene (B.S.), dentistry (D.D.S.), diagnostic radiology technology (certificate, associate, or B.S.), dietitian (B.S.), civil or environmental engineering (B.S.), environmental health (B.S.), health care administration (B.S. or M.S.), health education (B.S. or M.S.), health records (R.H.I.T. or R.H.I.A.), injury prevention specialist (certificate), medical technology (B.S.), allopathic and osteopathic medicine, nursing (A.D.N., B.S.N., or C.R.N.A), optometry, pharmacy (B.S. or Pharm.D.), physician assistant (B.S.), physical therapy (M.S. or D.P.T.), podiatry (D.P.M.), public health (M.P.H. only), public health nutrition (master's only), social work (master's only), respiratory therapy (associate), and ultrasonography. **Deadline for Receipt:** February of each year.

3254 ■ LADIES AUXILIARY TO THE VETERANS OF FOREIGN WARS

c/o National Headquarters
406 West 34th Street
Kansas City, MO 64111
Tel: (816)561-8655
Fax: (816)931-4753
E-mail: info@ladiesauxvfg.com
Web Site: http://www.ladiesauxvfw.com
To recognize and reward high school students who submit outstanding works of art on patriotic themes.
Title of Award: Young American Creative Patriotic Art Scholarships **Area, Field, or Subject:** Art; Patriotism **Level of Education for which Award is Granted:** Undergraduate **Number Awarded:** 3 national winners are selected each year. **Funds Available:** National awards are $10,000 for first prize, $5,000 for second prize, and $2,500 for third prize. Funds must be used for continued art education or for art supplies.
Eligibility Requirements: Any student who is a U.S. citizen in grades 9-12 may enter. Home-schooled students are eligible; foreign exchange students are not. Entrants may submit art on paper or canvas using water color, pencil, pastel, charcoal, tempera, crayon, acrylic, pen-and-ink, or oil. Digital art may be submitted, but it must be on paper or canvas. Competitions are held in individual Veterans of Foreign Wars (VFW) Auxiliaries, then at department, and finally national levels. Students must be sponsored by an Auxiliary; they must attend school in the same state as the sponsoring Auxiliary. Entries are judged on the originality of concept, presentation, and patriotism expressed; content, how it relates to patriotism, and clarity of ideas; design technique; total impact of work; and uniqueness. **Deadline for Receipt:** March of each year. **Additional Information:** First prize also includes an all-expense paid trip to the annual VFW Auxiliary National Community Service Conference and display of the art on the cover of the National *Ladies Auxiliary VFW Magazine* and on the Auxiliary web site. Second- and third-place winners are featured in the magazine and on the web site. National winners may not compete again.

3255 ■ PAPA OLA LOKAHI, INC.

Attn: Native Hawaiian Health Scholarship Program
345 Queen Street, Suite 706
Honolulu, HI 96813
Tel: (808)585-8944
Fax: (808)585-8081
E-mail: nhhsp@hawaii.rr.com
Web Site: http://www.nhhsp.org
To provide scholarship/loans to Native Hawaiians for training in the health professions in exchange for service in a federally-designated health professional shortage area (HPSA) or other facility for Native Hawaiians.
Title of Award: Native Hawaiian Health Scholarship Program **Area, Field, or Subject:** Dental hygiene; Dentistry; Family/Marital therapy; Health care services; Medical assisting; Medicine; Medicine, Osteopathic; Midwifery; Nursing; Nursing, Psychiatric; Psychiatry; Psychology; Public health **Level of Education for which Award is Granted:** Graduate, Undergraduate **Number Awarded:** Varies each year, depending upon the funding available. Since the program began, 151 scholars have received support. **Funds Available:** Full coverage of tuition and fees is paid directly to the health professional school. A stipend, current set at $1,157 per month, is paid directly to the scholar. This is a scholarship/loan

program. Participants are obligated to provide full-time clinical primary health care services to populations in 1) a Native Hawaiian Health Care System, or 2) an HPSA in Hawaii, medically underserved area (MUA), or another area or facility in Hawaii designated by the U.S. Department of Health and Human Services. Participants owe 1 year of service in the National Health Service Corps for each full or partial year of support received under this program. The minimum service obligation is 2 years. **Duration:** 1 year; may be renewed for up to 3 additional years.
Eligibility Requirements: Applicants must be Native Hawaiians training in allopathic or osteopathic medicine, dentistry, clinical psychology, registered nursing, nurse midwifery, psychiatric nursing, public health/community nursing, social work, dental hygiene, physician assistant, public health, marriage and family therapy, or primary care nurse practitioner. They may be studying in any state. Recipients must agree to serve in a designated health-care facility in Hawaii upon completion of training. First priority is given to former scholars who have completed their previous service obligation and are seeking another year of support. Second priority is given to applicants who appear to have characteristics that increase the probability they will continue to serve underserved Native Hawaiians after the completion of their service obligations. **Deadline for Receipt:** March of each year. **Additional Information:** This program, which began in 1991, is administered by the U.S. Health Resources and Services Administration, Bureau of Health Professions, through a contract with Papa Ola Lokahi, Inc.

3256 ■ MAINE ROADS SCHOLARSHIP FUND

c/o University of Southern Maine, Muskie School
400 Congress Street
P.O. Box 15010
Portland, ME 04112
888-900-0055
Fax: (207)780-5817
E-mail: sturner@usm.maine.edu
Web Site: http://muskie.usm.maine.edu/maineroads/scholarship.html
To provide financial assistance to child care providers in Maine who are working on an undergraduate or graduate degree at an institution in the state.
Title of Award: Maine Roads Degree Scholarship **Area, Field, or Subject:** Child development; Education, Early childhood; Parks and recreation; Social work **Level of Education for which Award is Granted:** Graduate, Professional, Undergraduate **Number Awarded:** Varies each year. **Funds Available:** Stipends range up to $1,800 for undergraduate students or up to $2,400 for graduate students. **Duration:** 1 year.
Eligibility Requirements: This program is open to child care providers who are residents of Maine working on a bachelor's, master's, or doctoral degree at an institution of higher education in the state. Applicants must have a family income that does not exceed 300% of the federal poverty level (currently, that means an income of $26,940 for a family of 1, rising to $92,880 for a family of 8). They must have experience within the past 2 years working in the child care and early education field in licensed or certified child care facilities or resource development centers. Courses of study may include early childhood education, child development, recreation and leisure services with a special needs focus, social work with an emphasis on early childhood, or child care administration. Along with their application, they must submit brief statements on their plans to work directly with children after completing their degree and how earning their degree will impact their work in child care. **Deadline for Receipt:** June or October of each year.

3257 ■ MARYLAND HIGHER EDUCATION COMMISSION

Attn: Office of Student Financial Assistance
839 Bestgate Road, Suite 400
Annapolis, MD 21401-3013
Tel: (410)260-4563
Free: 800-974-1024
Fax: (410)974-5376
E-mail: osfamail@mhec.state.md.us
Web Site: http://www.mhec.state.md.us/financialAid/ProgramDescriptions/prog_child.asp
To provide scholarship/loans to students in Maryland who wish to prepare for a career as a child care provider.
Title of Award: Maryland Child Care Provider Scholarship Program **Area, Field, or Subject:** Child care; Child development; Education, Early child-

hood **Level of Education for which Award is Granted:** Professional, Undergraduate **Number Awarded:** Varies each year. **Funds Available:** Stipends at 4-year institutions are $2,000 per year for full-time study, $1,000 for part-time; at community colleges, annual stipends are $1,000 for full-time study, $500 for part-time. The total amount of all state awards may not exceed the cost of attendance as determined by the school's financial aid office or $17,800, whichever is less. Within 12 months of graduation, recipients must provide 1 year of child care service in Maryland for each year of financial aid received under this program; failure to comply with that service obligation will require the recipient to repay the scholarship money with interest. Teaching in a public school in Maryland does not fulfill the service requirement. **Duration:** 1 year; may be renewed for up to 3 additional years of full-time study provided the recipient maintains a GPA of 2.0 or higher.

Eligibility Requirements: Eligible are residents of Maryland who are enrolled or plan to enroll in a program leading to an associate or bachelor's degree in a Maryland institution of higher education that offers an undergraduate program in early childhood education or child development. Full-time enrollment is required, although part-time study is allowed if the applicant is employed for a minimum of 15 hours per week at a child care or family day care center. Financial need is not considered in the selection process. **Deadline for Receipt:** June of each year.

3258 ■ MARYLAND HIGHER EDUCATION COMMISSION
Attn: Office of Student Financial Assistance
839 Bestgate Road, Suite 400
Annapolis, MD 21401-3013
Tel: (410)260-4594
Free: 800-974-1024
Fax: (410)974-5376
E-mail: osfamail@mhec.state.md.us
Web Site: http://www.mhec.state.md.us/financialAid/
ProgramDescriptions/prog_devdis.asp
To provide scholarship/loans to students in Maryland who are interested in working on a degree in a designated human services program.
Title of Award: Maryland Developmental Disabilities, Mental Health, Child Welfare, and Juvenile Justice Workforce Tuition Assistance Program **Area, Field, or Subject:** Counseling/Guidance; Criminal justice; Criminology; Disabilities; Education, Special; Gerontology; Law enforcement; Mental health; Nursing; Occupational therapy; Physical therapy; Psychology; Rehabilitation, Physical/Psychological; Social work **Level of Education for which Award is Granted:** Graduate, Undergraduate **Number Awarded:** Varies each year. **Funds Available:** The maximum stipend is $2,000 per year for students attending a 2-year institution or $3,000 per year for students at a 4-year institution. The total amount of all state awards may not exceed the cost of attendance as determined by the school's financial aid office or $17,800, whichever is less. Recipients must agree to work in a Maryland community-based program that is licensed by the Developmental Disabilities Administration or approved by the Mental Hygiene Administration, or in a residential program that is licensed by the Department of Human Resources or the Department of Juvenile Justice. The service obligation must begin within 6 months of graduation. The total service requirement is 2,000 hours if the award amount is $1,999 or less, 3,000 hours if the award amount is $2,000 to $3,999, or 4,000 hours if the award amount is $4,000 or more. If the service requirement is not completed, the award must be repaid with interest. **Duration:** 1 year; may be renewed if the recipient maintains satisfactory academic progress and remains enrolled in a human services degree program.

Eligibility Requirements: This program is open to high school seniors and full-time and part-time undergraduate and graduate students. Applicants and their parents must be Maryland residents attending a college or university in the state in 1 of the following human services degree programs: aging services, counseling, disability services, mental health, nursing, occupational therapy, physical therapy, psychology, rehabilitation, social work, special education, supported employment, vocational rehabilitation, or any other concentration in the healing arts or a program providing support services to individuals with special needs including child welfare and juvenile justice. Financial need is not considered in the selection process. **Deadline for Receipt:** June of each year.

3259 ■ NATIONAL INSTITUTE OF GENERAL MEDICAL SCIENCES
Attn: Division of Minority Opportunities in Research
45 Center Drive, Suite 2AS37
Bethesda, MD 20892-6200

Tel: (301)594-3900
Fax: (301)480-2753
E-mail: at21z@nih.gov
Web Site: http://www.nih.gov/nigms
To enable faculty at minority and minority-serving institutions to complete a Ph.D. degree in the biomedical sciences.
Title of Award: Minority Access to Research Careers (MARC) Faculty Predoctoral Fellowships **Area, Field, or Subject:** Behavioral sciences; Biomedical sciences; Mathematics and mathematical sciences **Level of Education for which Award is Granted:** Four Year College, Professional, Doctorate **Funds Available:** The fellowships provide a stipend of $32,820 per year and a supplement that offsets the cost of tuition, fees, and health insurance at a rate of 100% up to $3,000 and 60% of costs above $3,000. An institutional allowance of $2,750 per year is also provided. **Duration:** Up to 5 years.

Eligibility Requirements: This program is open to full-time faculty in a biomedical or behavioral science department (including mathematics) at minority and minority-serving institutions who lack a Ph.D. degree. The institution must be a college or university where the candidate has been employed for at least 3 years and that has substantial enrollments of students in biomedical and related sciences from minority groups underrepresented in those sciences. The candidate must have been accepted into the doctoral program at a research university, institution, or center with active biomedical and behavioral science research faculties. They must be sponsored by their home institution, which must have granted them a study leave and where they are expected to return after completing their doctoral degree. Only U.S. citizens, nationals, and permanent residents are eligible. **Deadline for Receipt:** April or December of each year.

3260 ■ NATIONAL INSTITUTES OF HEALTH
Attn: Office of Loan Repayment and Scholarship
2 Center Drive, Room 2E24
Bethesda, MD 20892-0230
800-528-7689
Fax: (301)480-5481
E-mail: ugsp@nih.gov
Web Site: http://ugsp.info.nih.gov
To provide loans-for-service for undergraduate education in the life sciences to students from disadvantaged backgrounds.
Title of Award: National Institutes of Health Undergraduate Scholarship Program **Area, Field, or Subject:** Behavioral sciences; Biomedical sciences; Social sciences **Level of Education for which Award is Granted:** Undergraduate **Number Awarded:** 15 each year. **Funds Available:** Stipends are available up to $20,000 per year, to be used for tuition, educational expenses (such as books and lab fees), and qualified living expenses while attending a college or university. Recipients incur a service obligation to work as an employee of the NIH in Bethesda, Maryland for 10 consecutive weeks (during the summer) during the sponsored year and, upon graduation, for 52 weeks for each academic year of scholarship support. The NIH 52-week employment obligation may be deferred if the recipient goes to graduate or medical school. **Duration:** 1 year; may be renewed for up to 3 additional years.

Eligibility Requirements: This program is open to U.S. citizens, nationals, and permanent residents who are enrolled or accepted for enrollment as full-time students at accredited institutions of higher education and committed to careers in biomedical, behavioral, and social science health-related research. Applicants must come from a family that meets federal standards of low income, currently defined as a family with an annual income below $18,620 for a 1-person family, ranging to below $63,140 for families of 8 or more. They must have a GPA of 3.5 or higher or be in the top 5% of their class. Selection is based on commitment to a career in biomedical, behavioral, or social science health-related research as an employee of the National Institutes of Health (NIH); academic achievements; recommendations and evaluations of skills, abilities, and goals; and relevant extracurricular activities. Applicants are ranked according to the following priorities: first, juniors and seniors who have completed 2 years of undergraduate course work including 4 core science courses in biology, chemistry, physics, and calculus; second, other undergraduates who have completed those 4 core science courses; third, freshmen and sophomores at accredited undergraduate institutions; and fourth, high school seniors who have been accepted for enrollment as full-time students at accredited undergraduate institutions. The sponsor especially encourages applications from underrepresented minorities, women, and individuals with disabilities. **Deadline for Receipt:** February of each year.

3261 ■ OAK RIDGE INSTITUTE FOR SCIENCE AND EDUCATION

Attn: Science and Engineering Education
P.O. Box 117
Oak Ridge, TN 37831-0117
Tel: (865)241-8240
Fax: (865)241-5219
E-mail: hollingsscholarship@orau.gov
Web Site: http://www.orau.gov/orise.htm

To provide financial assistance and summer research experience to upper-division students who are working on a degree in a field of interest to the National Oceanic and Atmospheric Administration (NOAA).

Title of Award: Ernest F. Hollings Scholarship Program **Area, Field, or Subject:** Agricultural sciences; Behavioral sciences; Biological and clinical sciences; Computer and information sciences; Education; Engineering; Information science and technology; Mathematics and mathematical sciences; Physical sciences; Social sciences **Level of Education for which Award is Granted:** Four Year College **Number Awarded:** Approximately 100 each year. **Funds Available:** This program provides a stipend of $8,000 per academic year and $650 per week during the internship, a housing subsidy and limited travel reimbursement for round-trip transportation to the internship site, and travel expenses to the scholarship program conference at the completion of the internship. **Duration:** 2 academic years plus 10 weeks during the intervening summer.

Eligibility Requirements: This program is open to full-time students entering their junior year at an accredited college or university in the United States or its territories. Applicants must be majoring in a discipline related to oceanic and atmospheric science, research, technology, and education, and supportive of the purposes of NOAA's programs and mission (e.g., biological, life, and agricultural sciences; computer and information sciences; engineering; mathematics; physical sciences; social and behavioral sciences; or teacher education). They must have a GPA of 3.0 or higher. As part of their program, they must be interested in participating in summer research and development activities at NOAA headquarters (Silver Spring, Maryland) or field centers. U.S. citizenship is required. **Deadline for Receipt:** May of each year. **Additional Information:** This program, established in 2005, is funded by NOAA and administered by Oak Ridge Institute for Science and Education (ORISE).

3262 ■ ORDER SONS OF ITALY IN AMERICA

Attn: Sons of Italy Foundation
219 E Street, N.E.
Washington, DC 20002
Tel: (202)547-5106
Fax: (202)546-8168
E-mail: scholarships@osia.org
Web Site: http://www.osia.org/public/scholarships/grants.asp

To provide financial assistance for college to high school seniors of Italian descent who write about the principles of liberty, freedom, and equality in the United States.

Title of Award: Henry Salvatori Scholarship **Area, Field, or Subject:** General studies/Field of study not specified; Patriotism; Writing **Level of Education for which Award is Granted:** Four Year College **Number Awarded:** 1 each year. **Funds Available:** The stipend is $25,000. **Duration:** 1 year; nonrenewable.

Eligibility Requirements: Eligible are U.S. citizens of Italian descent who are high school seniors planning to enroll as full-time students in an undergraduate program at an accredited 4-year college or university. Applications must be accompanied by essays, from 750 to 1,000 words, on the relevance to the United States today of the Declaration of Independence, the Constitution, or the Bill of Rights and the meaning of those documents to the principles of liberty, freedom, and equality in the 21st century. The scholarship is presented to a student who has demonstrated exceptional leadership, distinguished scholarship, and an understanding of the principles for which the country was founded. **Deadline for Receipt:** February of each year. **Additional Information:** Applications must be accompanied by a $25 processing fee.

3263 ■ SUNSHINE LADY FOUNDATION, INC.

Attn: CASS Program
4900 Randall Parkway, Suite H
Wilmington, NC 28403

Tel: (910)397-7742; (866)255-7742
Fax: (910)397-0023
E-mail: mitty@sunshineladyfdn.org
Web Site: http://www.sunshineladyfdn.org/cass.html

To provide financial assistance for college or graduate study in related fields to workers at domestic violence service centers.

Title of Award: Counselor, Advocate and Support Staff Scholarship **Area, Field, or Subject:** Accounting; Business administration; Counseling/Guidance; Nonprofit sector; Psychology **Level of Education for which Award is Granted:** Graduate, Undergraduate **Number Awarded:** Varies each year. **Funds Available:** Funding, paid directly to the educational institution, is provided for tuition, fees, required books, and supplies. A maximum of 3 courses per academic term may be supported. **Duration:** 1 academic term; may be renewed if the recipient maintains a GPA of 2.5 or higher.

Eligibility Requirements: This program is open to women and men who have been employed for at least 1 year by a nonprofit domestic violence victim services provider that is willing to provide support for their study. Applicants must be interested in enrolling in a community college, 4-year degree, graduate degree, or certificate program as a full or part time student. Their program should be related to their employment, including social work, counseling, psychology, accounting, nonprofit management, or business management. Financial need is considered in the selection process. **Deadline for Receipt:** February of each year for spring quarter; April of each year for summer term; July of each year for fall quarter or semester; November of each year for winter quarter or spring semester. **Additional Information:** This program was established in 1999.

3264 ■ VETERANS OF FOREIGN WARS OF THE UNITED STATES

VFW Building
406 West 34th Street
Kansas City, MO 64111
Tel: (816)968-1117
Fax: (816)968-1149
E-mail: KHarmer@vfw.org
Web Site: http://www.vfw.org

To recognize and reward, with college scholarships, outstanding high school students in a national broadcast scriptwriting competition dealing with freedom and democracy.

Title of Award: Voice of Democracy Scholarship Program **Area, Field, or Subject:** General studies/Field of study not specified; Patriotism; Writing **Level of Education for which Award is Granted:** Undergraduate **Number Awarded:** Recently, a total of 54 of these scholarships were awarded. In addition to the 5 top winners, other scholarships included 2 at $5,000, 1 at $4,000, 1 at $3,500, 2 at $3,000, 2 at $2,500, 9 at $2,000, 7 at $1,500, and 25 at $1,000. **Funds Available:** A total of $145,000 in national scholarships is awarded each year; first place is $25,000, second $16,000, third $10,000, fourth $7,000, and fifth $5,000. Other state winners receive scholarships that may vary each year but range from $1,000 to $5,000. Winners in each state also receive an all-expense paid trip to Washington, D.C. for the national competition. **Duration:** The competition is held annually.

Eligibility Requirements: This competition is open to students in grades 9-12 at high schools and home schools in the United States, its territories and possessions, and U.S. military and civilian dependent overseas schools. Contestants prepare a script, from 3 to 5 minutes in length, on a topic chosen annually but related to freedom and democracy; a recent theme was "How I Demonstrate My Freedom." Students record the script themselves on audiocassette and submit it for sponsorship by a local post or auxiliary of the Veterans of Foreign Wars (VFW). Scripts must reflect the entrant's own original thinking. Selection is based on delivery (35 points), content (35 points), and originality (30 points). **Deadline for Receipt:** October of each year. **Additional Information:** The first-place award is designated the T.C. Selman Memorial Scholarship Award. The second-place award is designated the Charles Kuralt Memorial Scholarship Award.

3265 ■ WATTS CHARITY ASSOCIATION, INC.

6245 Bristol Parkway, Suite 224
Culver City, CA 90230
Tel: (323)671-0394
Fax: (323)778-2613
E-mail: wattscharity@yahoo.com

Web Site: http://4watts.tripod.com/id5.html

To provide financial assistance to upper-division college students majoring in child development, teaching, or social services.

Title of Award: Joyce Washington Scholarship **Area, Field, or Subject:** Child development; Education; Social work **Level of Education for which Award is Granted:** Four Year College **Number Awarded:** 1 each year. **Funds Available:** A stipend is awarded (amount not specified). **Duration:** 1 year.

Eligibility Requirements: This program is open to U.S. citizens of African American descent who are enrolled full time as a college or university junior. Applicants must be majoring in child development, teaching, or the study of social services. They must have a GPA of 3.0 or higher, be between 17 and 24 years of age, and be able to demonstrate that they intend to continue their education for at least 2 years. Along with their application, they must submit 1) a 1-paragraph statement on why they should be awarded a Watts Foundation scholarship, and 2) a 1- to 2-page essay on a specific type of cancer, based either on how it has impacted their life or on researched information. **Deadline for Receipt:** May of each year. **Additional Information:** Royce R. Watts, Sr. established the Watts Charity Association after he learned he had cancer in 2001.

Business and Economics

3266 ■ ALABAMA BANKERS ASSOCIATION

Attn: Scholarship Applications
534 Adams Avenue
Montgomery, AL 36104
Tel: (334)834-1890
Free: 800-239-5521
Fax: (334)834-4443
E-mail: info@alabamabankers.org
Web Site: http://www.alabamabankers.org

To provide financial assistance to seniors at colleges and universities in Alabama who are interested in a career in banking.

Title of Award: Kenneth R. McCartha Scholarship **Area, Field, or Subject:** Banking; Business administration; Finance **Level of Education for which Award is Granted:** Four Year College **Number Awarded:** 1 or more each year. **Funds Available:** The stipend is $1,500. **Duration:** 1 year.

Eligibility Requirements: This program is open to residents of Alabama entering their senior year at 4-year colleges and universities in the state. Applicants must be majoring in banking, finance, or business and have plans to enter the banking profession. They must be enrolled full time and have a GPA of 2.0 or higher. Selection is based on academic record, probability of entering banking or a bank-related field of employment after graduation, character, leadership, potential for development, and financial need. **Deadline for Receipt:** February of each year.

3267 ■ ALABAMA SPACE GRANT CONSORTIUM

c/o University of Alabama in Huntsville
Materials Science Building, Room 205
Huntsville, AL 35899
Tel: (256)824-6800
Fax: (256)824-6061
E-mail: reasonj@uah.edu
Web Site: http://www.uah.edu/ASGC

To provide financial assistance to undergraduates who are studying the space sciences at universities participating in the Alabama Space Grant Consortium (ASGC).

Title of Award: Undergraduate Scholarship Program of the Alabama Space Grant Consortium **Area, Field, or Subject:** Aerospace sciences; Behavioral sciences; Biological and clinical sciences; Business administration; Communications; Computer and information sciences; Economics; Education; Engineering, Aerospace/Aeronautical/Astronautical; International affairs and relations; Law; Natural sciences; Physical sciences; Public administration; Sociology; Space and planetary sciences **Level of Education for which Award is Granted:** Four Year College **Number Awarded:** Varies each year; recently, 32 of these scholarships were awarded. **Funds Available:** The stipend is $1,000 per year. **Duration:** 1 year; may be renewed 1 additional year.

Eligibility Requirements: This program is open to full-time students entering their junior or senior year at universities participating in the

ASGC. Applicants must be studying in a field related to space, including the physical, natural, and biological sciences; engineering, education; economics; business; sociology; behavioral sciences; computer science; communications; law; international affairs; and public administration. They must be U.S. citizens and have a GPA of 3.0 or higher. Individuals from underrepresented groups (African Americans, Hispanic, American Indians, Pacific Islanders, Asian Americans, and women) are especially encouraged to apply. Interested students should submit a completed application with a career goal statement, personal references, a brief resume, and transcripts. Selection is based on 1) academic qualifications, 2) quality of the career goal statement, and 3) assessment of the applicant's motivation for a career in aerospace. **Deadline for Receipt:** February of each year. **Additional Information:** The member universities are University of Alabama in Huntsville, Alabama A&M University, University of Alabama, University of Alabama at Birmingham, University of South Alabama, Tuskegee University, and Auburn University. Funding for this program is provided by NASA.

3268 ■ ALASKA COMMISSION ON POSTSECONDARY EDUCATION

Attn: AlaskAdvantage Programs
3030 Vintage Boulevard
Juneau, AK 99801-7109
Tel: (907)465-2962
Free: 800-441-2962
Fax: (907)465-5316
E-mail: customer_service@acpe.ak.us
Web Site: http://alaskaadvantage.state.ak.us/page/257

To provide financial assistance to Alaska residents who are interested in working on an undergraduate or graduate degree in fisheries or related fields.

Title of Award: A.W. "Winn" Brindle Memorial Education Loan Program **Area, Field, or Subject:** Business; Fisheries sciences/management; Food science and technology **Level of Education for which Award is Granted:** Graduate, Undergraduate **Number Awarded:** Varies each year, depending upon the amount of contributions made to the fund by private donors and fisheries businesses. **Funds Available:** Loans are awarded to cover the cost of tuition, fees, books, supplies, room, board, and transportation costs. An origination fee of 3% is deducted from the eligible loan amount. The interest rate charged is 5%. This is a partial scholarship/loan program; recipients are eligible for up to 50% forgiveness upon graduation if they return to Alaska to secure employment in a fisheries-related field. **Duration:** Up to 5 years of undergraduate study and up to 5 years of graduate study, or a combined maximum of 8 years of study. Recipients have up to 15 years to repay the loans.

Eligibility Requirements: This program is open to full-time undergraduate and graduate students in Alaska who are interested in working on a degree at an accredited college or university that will lead to a career in fisheries, fishery science, fishery management, seafood processing, food technology, or other fishery-related fields. Applicants who have been nominated by program donors are given preference for receipt of funds. **Additional Information:** This program is funded by private donations and contributions from fisheries businesses in exchange for tax credits. A fisheries business is entitled to a tax credit of up to 5% of its business tax liability for contributions made during the tax year to this scholarship/loan fund. Businesses and other donors are encouraged to nominate individuals for receipt of these funds.

3269 ■ AMERICAN CONCRETE INSTITUTE

Attn: Concrete Research and Education Foundation
38800 Country Club Drive
P.O. Box 9094
Farmington Hills, MI 48333-9094
Tel: (248)848-3700
Fax: (248)848-3701
E-mail: scholarships@concrete.org
Web Site: http://www.concrete.org/STUDENTS/STU_SCHOLAR.HTM

To provide funding to undergraduate and graduate students preparing for a career in the field of concrete.

Title of Award: ACI Student Fellowship Program **Area, Field, or Subject:** Business; Construction; Engineering **Level of Education for which Award is Granted:** Graduate, Undergraduate **Number Awarded:** Varies each year; recently, 3 of these fellowships were awarded. **Funds Available:** The stipend is $10,000 per year; funds may be used for tuition, residence, books, and materials. Other financial benefits include reimbursement of expenses associated with attending the ACI convention and reimbursement of expenses associated with an internship. **Duration:** 2 years; may be renewed, including through graduate school for students who first receive an award as an undergraduate.

Eligibility Requirements: This program is open to full-time undergraduate and graduate students in engineering, construction management, and other appropriate fields. Applicants must first be nominated by a faculty member of the American Concrete Institute (ACI). They may be residing anywhere in the world, but graduate study must take place in the United States or Canada. **Deadline for Receipt:** November of each year.

3270 ■ AMERICAN CONCRETE INSTITUTE

Attn: Concrete Research and Education Foundation
38800 Country Club Drive
P.O. Box 9094
Farmington Hills, MI 48333-9094
Tel: (248)848-3700
Fax: (248)848-3701
E-mail: scholarships@concrete.org
Web Site: http://www.concrete.org/STUDENTS/STU_SCHOLAR.HTM
To provide funding to undergraduate students preparing for a career in the field of concrete construction.

Title of Award: Peter D. Courtois Concrete Construction Scholarships **Area, Field, or Subject:** Business; Construction; Engineering; Technology **Level of Education for which Award is Granted:** Four Year College **Number Awarded:** 1 each year. **Funds Available:** The stipend is $1,000. **Duration:** 1 year.

Eligibility Requirements: This program is open to undergraduate students in the United States or Canada who have achieved senior status in a 4-year or longer program in engineering, construction, or technology. Selection is based on demonstrated interest and ability to work in the field of concrete construction. **Deadline for Receipt:** November of each year.

3271 ■ AMERICAN CONCRETE INSTITUTE-GREATER MICHIGAN CHAPTER

c/o Ruben Ramos, President
Testing Engineers and Consultants
1343 Rochester Road
P.O. Box 249
Troy, MI 48099-0249
Tel: (248)588-6514
Fax: (248)588-6232
E-mail: rramos@tectest.com
Web Site: http://www.acigmc.org/Scholarship.html
To provide financial assistance to upper-division students from Michigan and Ontario who are working on a degree related to concrete.

Title of Award: Greater Michigan Chapter ACI Concrete Scholarship **Area, Field, or Subject:** Business; Construction; Engineering, Materials; Materials research/science **Level of Education for which Award is Granted:** Four Year College **Number Awarded:** 1 each year. **Funds Available:** The stipend is $2,000. **Duration:** 1 year.

Eligibility Requirements: This program is open to residents of Michigan and Ontario. Applicants must be enrolled full time at a designated university in the area and studying an engineering or technical field emphasizing concrete or masonry design, construction, or materials. **Deadline for Receipt:** March of each year. **Additional Information:** The participating universities are the University of Michigan, Wayne State University, Michigan State University, Michigan Technological University, Lawrence Technological University, University of Detroit-Mercy, and University of Windsor.

3272 ■ AMERICAN CONCRETE INSTITUTE-ILLINOIS CHAPTER

c/o Mike Morrison, Scholarship Committee
Construction Technology Laboratories
5400 Old Orchard Road
Skokie, IL 60077
Tel: (847)972-3314
Fax: (847)965-6541
E-mail: mmorrison@ctlgroup.com
Web Site: http://www.concrete.org/CHAPTERS/
Chapter_Scholarships.asp?cid=C034

To provide financial assistance to upper-division students from Illinois working on a degree related to the concrete industry.

Title of Award: Illinois ACI Chapter Scholarship Award **Area, Field, or Subject:** Business; Construction **Level of Education for which Award is Granted:** Four Year College **Number Awarded:** 1 each year. **Funds Available:** The stipend is $2,500. **Duration:** 1 year.

Eligibility Requirements: This program is open to students who are residents of Illinois or enrolled at a university in the states. Applicants must have completed at least 2 years of undergraduate study in a field related to concrete design, materials, construction, or any combination of those. They must submit a statement on why they should receive the scholarship (financial need is not an important consideration); a statement on their interest in concrete; undergraduate records of academic performance; and their plan for continuing education. **Deadline for Receipt:** April of each year.

3273 ■ AMERICAN CONCRETE INSTITUTE-INDIANA CHAPTER

c/o Brian Stater
Bowen Engineering Corporation, Inc.
10315 Allisonville Road
Fishers, IN 46038
Tel: (317)842-2616
Fax: (317)841-4257
E-mail: brian@bowenengineering.com
Web Site: http://www.concrete.org/CHAPTERS/
Chapter_Scholarships.asp?cid=C048
To provide financial assistance to students in Indiana working on a degree in a field related to the concrete industry.

Title of Award: Indiana Chapter ACI Scholarships **Area, Field, or Subject:** Business; Construction **Level of Education for which Award is Granted:** Undergraduate **Number Awarded:** 3 each year: 1 each at $3,000, $2,000, and $1,000. **Funds Available:** Stipends are $3,000, $2,000, or $1,000. **Duration:** 1 year

Eligibility Requirements: This program is open to sophomores and juniors at colleges and universities in Indiana who are preparing for a career in concrete design or construction. Applicants must submit information on their work experience, career objectives, reasons for seeking this scholarship, and financial need. **Deadline for Receipt:** March of each year.

3274 ■ AMERICAN CONCRETE INSTITUTE-NEBRASKA CHAPTER

Attn: Scholarships
6901 Vine Street
Lincoln, NE 68505
Tel: (402)466-4233
E-mail: rdelorm@msn.com
Web Site: http://www.acinebraska.org/students/StudentsUGScholar2.html
To provide financial assistance to students entering their senior year at a college or university in Nebraska and majoring in a field related to the concrete industry.

Title of Award: Nebraska Chapter ACI Undergraduate Student Award **Area, Field, or Subject:** Business; Construction; Engineering; Technology **Level of Education for which Award is Granted:** Four Year College **Number Awarded:** 1 each year. **Funds Available:** The stipend is $1,000. **Duration:** 1 year.

Eligibility Requirements: This program is open to students entering their senior year at a 4-year college or university in Nebraska. Applicants must be majoring in a field of engineering, construction, or technology to prepare for a career in concrete construction. Along with their application, they must submit a 500-word essay explaining their interest, experience, ability, and career objectives as they relate to concrete construction. **Deadline for Receipt:** December of each year.

3275 ■ AMERICAN INDIAN COLLEGE FUND

Attn: Scholarship Department
8333 Greenwood Boulevard
Denver, CO 80221
Tel: (303)426-8900
Free: 800-776-FUND
Fax: (303)426-1200
E-mail: info@collegefund.org
Web Site: http://www.collegefund.org/scholarships/main.html

To provide financial assistance to Native American college students who are majoring in designated fields at specified colleges and universities. **Title of Award:** Ford Motor Company/American Indian College Fund Corporate Scholars Program **Area, Field, or Subject:** Accounting; Engineering, Computer; Engineering, Electrical; Engineering, Mechanical; Finance; Information science and technology; Marketing and distribution; Operations research **Level of Education for which Award is Granted:** Undergraduate **Number Awarded:** Varies each year. **Funds Available:** The stipend is $8,000 per year. **Duration:** 1 year; may be renewed. **Eligibility Requirements:** This program is open to American Indians, Alaska Natives, and Hawaii Natives who have proof of enrollment or descendancy and have achieved at least sophomore status at 1 of 102 designated college and universities. Applicants must have a GPA of 3.0 or higher and be able to demonstrate financial need. They must have declared a major in accounting, computer engineering, electrical engineering, finance, information systems, marketing, mechanical engineering, or operations management. Along with their application, they must submit a 1-page personal essay on how they can become a role model and make a difference in their chosen field. Leadership and commitment to the American Indian community are also considered in the selection process. **Deadline for Receipt:** November of each year. **Additional Information:** This program is funded by the Ford Motor Company.

3276 ■ AMERICAN INDIAN COLLEGE FUND

Attn: Scholarship Department
8333 Greenwood Boulevard
Denver, CO 80221
Tel: (303)426-8900
Free: 800-776-FUND
Fax: (303)426-1200
E-mail: info@collegefund.org
Web Site: http://www.collegefund.org/scholarships/main.html
To provide financial assistance to American Indian students currently enrolled full time at a tribal college or university to prepare for a career in business and the financial services industry.
Title of Award: Morgan Stanley Tribal College Scholars Program **Area, Field, or Subject:** Accounting; Banking; Business administration; Finance; Information science and technology; Marketing and distribution **Level of Education for which Award is Granted:** Undergraduate **Number Awarded:** 10 each year. **Funds Available:** The stipend is $2,500. **Duration:** 1 year.
Eligibility Requirements: Eligible to apply are American Indians or Alaska Natives who are enrolled full time in either an associate's or bachelor's degree program at an accredited tribal college or university. Applicants must be able to demonstrate exceptional academic achievement (GPA of 3.0 or higher), as well as leadership, service, and commitment to the American Indian community. They must be interested in a career in business and the financial services industry (e.g., information technology, investment banking, marketing, financial accounting). Along with their application, they must submit official college transcripts; personal essays (500 words or less) on their personal and academic background, a role model who has motivated them, and an experience or risk they have taken and its impact on them; 2 letters of recommendation; tribal enrollment information; a statement regarding any financial hardship they have; and a color photograph. **Deadline for Receipt:** April of each year. **Additional Information:** This scholarship is sponsored by Morgan Stanley, in partnership with the American Indian College Fund.

3277 ■ AMERICAN SOCIETY OF MILITARY COMPTROLLERS

Attn: National Awards Committee
415 North Alfred Street
Alexandria, VA 22314
Tel: (703)549-0360
Free: 800-462-5637
E-mail: asmchq@aol.com
Web Site: http://www.asmconline.org/national/nationalawards.shtml
To provide financial assistance for continuing education to members of the American Society of Military Comptrollers (ASMC).
Title of Award: ASMC Members' Continuing Education Program Award **Area, Field, or Subject:** Accounting; Business administration; Computer and information sciences; Economics; Finance; Operations research; Public administration **Level of Education for which Award is Granted:**

Graduate, Professional, Undergraduate **Number Awarded:** 15 each year: 1 at $5,000 (the Dick Vincent Scholarship), 4 at $2,500, and 10 at $1,000. **Funds Available:** Stipends are $5,000, $2,500, or $1,000 per year. **Duration:** 1 year.
Eligibility Requirements: Applicants for this assistance must have been members of the society for at least 2 full years and must have been active in the local chapter at some level (board member, committee chair or member, volunteer for chapter events, etc.). They must be enrolled in or planning to enroll in an academic institution in a field of study directly related to financial resource management, including business administration, economics, public administration, computer science, or operations research related to financial management, accounting, and finance. As part of the selection process, they must submit an essay of up to 500 words on their academic and career goals and financial need. **Deadline for Receipt:** March of each year. **Additional Information:** The ASMC is open to all financial management professionals employed by the U.S. Department of Defense and Coast Guard, both civilian and military. The applicant whose service to the society is judged the most exceptional is designated the Dick Vincent Scholarship Winner.

3278 ■ AMERICAN SOCIETY OF MILITARY COMPTROLLERS

Attn: National Awards Committee
415 North Alfred Street
Alexandria, VA 22314
Tel: (703)549-0360
Free: 800-462-5637
E-mail: asmchq@aol.com
Web Site: http://www.asmconline.org/national/nationalawards.shtml
To provide financial assistance to high school seniors and recent graduates interested in preparing for a career in financial management.
Title of Award: ASMC National Scholarship Program **Area, Field, or Subject:** Accounting; Business administration; Computer and information sciences; Economics; Finance; Operations research; Public administration **Level of Education for which Award is Granted:** Undergraduate **Number Awarded:** 10 each year: 5 at $2,000 and 5 at $1,000. **Funds Available:** Stipends are $2,000 or $1,000 per year. **Duration:** 1 year.
Eligibility Requirements: This program is open to high school seniors and to people who graduated from high school during the preceding 6 months. Applicants must be planning to enter college in a field of study directly related to financial resource management, including business administration, economics, public administration, computer science, or operations research related to financial management, accounting, and finance. They must be endorsed by a chapter of the American Society of Military Comptrollers (ASMC). Selection is based on scholastic achievement, leadership ability, extracurricular activities, career and academic goals, and financial need. **Deadline for Receipt:** March of each year. **Additional Information:** The ASMC is open to all financial management professionals employed by the U.S. Department of Defense and Coast Guard, both civilian and military.

3279 ■ AMERICAN SOCIETY OF MILITARY COMPTROLLERS-MOUNT VERNON CHAPTER

Attn: Awards and Scholarships Director
P.O. Box 99
Fort Belvoir, VA 22060-0099
To provide financial assistance to high school seniors in the Washington, D.C. area who plan to work on an undergraduate degree related to financial management.
Title of Award: Mount Vernon Chapter Scholarships **Area, Field, or Subject:** Accounting; Business administration; Computer and information sciences; Economics; Finance; Operations research; Public administration **Level of Education for which Award is Granted:** Undergraduate **Number Awarded:** Several each year. **Funds Available:** The stipend is $1,000. **Duration:** 1 year.
Eligibility Requirements: This program is open to seniors graduating from high schools in Maryland, Virginia, and Washington, D.C. and to recent (within the past 6 months) graduates of those high schools. Applicants must be entering a field of study directly related to financial management (business administration, economics, public administration, computer science, operations research related to financial management, accounting, and finance). Along with their application, they must submit a 250-word essay on their career and academic goals and their financial need. Selection is based on academic achievement, leadership ability,

extracurricular activities, career and academic goals, and financial need. **Deadline for Receipt:** March of each year.

3280 ■ AMERICAN SOCIETY OF MILITARY COMPTROLLERS-WASHINGTON CHAPTER

Attn: Shirley Simpkins
P.O. Box 16237
Arlington, VA 22215-1237
Tel: (202)781-2785
E-mail: Scholarships@Washington-ASMC.org
Web Site: http://www.washington-asmc.org/stuaward.htm
To provide financial assistance to high school seniors in the Washington, D.C. area who plan to work on an undergraduate degree related to financial operations.
Title of Award: Washington Chapter Scholarships **Area, Field, or Subject:** Accounting; Business administration; Economics; Finance; Operations research; Public administration **Level of Education for which Award is Granted:** Undergraduate **Number Awarded:** 10 each year. **Funds Available:** The stipend is $1,500. **Duration:** 1 year.
Eligibility Requirements: This program is open to seniors graduating from high schools in Maryland, Virginia, and Washington, D.C. Applicants must be entering a field of study directly related to financial operations (business administration, economics, public administration, operations research related to financial management, accounting, and finance. finance). Along with their application, they must submit 3 letters of recommendation, an official transcript, and SAT scores. Selection is based on academic achievement, leadership ability, extracurricular activities, career goals, and financial need. **Deadline for Receipt:** January of each year.

3281 ■ ASSOCIATION FOR IRON & STEEL TECHNOLOGY

Attn: AIST Foundation
186 Thorn Hill Road
Warrendale, PA 15086-7528
Tel: (724)776-6040
Fax: (724)776-1880
E-mail: lwharrey@aist.org
Web Site: http://www.aist.org/foundation/scholarships.htm
To provide financial assistance for college to students interested in preparing for a career in the iron and steel or steel-related industries.
Title of Award: Association for Iron & Steel Technology Scholarships **Area, Field, or Subject:** Business; Engineering; Manufacturing; Materials research/science; Metallurgy **Level of Education for which Award is Granted:** Undergraduate **Number Awarded:** 7 each year, including 3 Willy Korf Memorial Fund Scholarships, 2 Ronald E. Lincoln Memorial Scholarship, and 2 Benjamin F. Fairless Scholarships. **Funds Available:** The stipend is $2,000. **Duration:** 1 year; recipients may reapply.
Eligibility Requirements: This program is open to full-time students majoring in metallurgy, materials science, or engineering at accredited universities in North America. Applicants must have a GPA of 3.0 or higher and a demonstrated interest in the iron and steel industry. Along with their application, they must submit 3 letters of recommendation; a resume with work experience and extracurricular activities, noting any leadership positions; a current academic transcript; and a 2-page essay on their professional goals, explaining why they are interested in a career in the steel industry and how their skills could be applied to enhance the industry. Financial need is not considered in the selection process. **Deadline for Receipt:** April of each year. **Additional Information:** The AIST was formed in 2004 by the merger of the Iron and Steel Society (ISS) and the Association of Iron and Steel Engineers (AISE).

3282 ■ ASSOCIATION FOR IRON & STEEL TECHNOLOGY

Attn: AIST Foundation
186 Thorn Hill Road
Warrendale, PA 15086-7528
Tel: (724)776-6040
Fax: (724)776-1880
E-mail: lwharrey@aist.org
Web Site: http://www.aist.org/femet/femet_scholarship.htm
To provide financial assistance and work experience to college juniors working on a degree in metallurgy or materials sciences.
Title of Award: Ferrous Metallurgy Education Today (FeMET) Scholarships **Area, Field, or Subject:** Business; Manufacturing; Materials research/science; Metallurgy **Level of Education for which Award is**

Granted: Four Year College **Number Awarded:** 10 each year. **Funds Available:** The program provides a stipend of $5,000 for the junior year, a paid internship during the following summer, and a stipend of $5,000 for the senior year. **Duration:** 2 years.
Eligibility Requirements: This program is open to full-time students entering their junior year in a metallurgy or materials science program at a college or university in North America (Canada, Mexico, and the United States). Applicants must have a GPA of 3.0 or higher and a demonstrated interest in the iron and steel industry. They must be available for employment at a steel company during the summer after their junior year; students unable to accept an internship will not be considered. Along with their application, they must submit a 2-page essay on their professional goals, why they are interested in a career in the steel industry, and how their skills could be applied to enhance the industry. Selection is based on the essay; a resume with work experience and extracurricular activities, noting any leadership positions; letters of recommendation; a current academic transcript; and a list of the source and amount of other grants and scholarships. **Deadline for Receipt:** April of each year. **Additional Information:** The AIST was formed in 2004 by the merger of the Iron and Steel Society (ISS) and the Association of Iron and Steel Engineers (AISE). This program was established in 2005 by the AIST Foundation and the American Iron and Steel Institute, (202) 452-7143, E-mail: blakshmi@steel.org.

3283 ■ ASSOCIATION FOR IRON & STEEL TECHNOLOGY

Attn: AIST Foundation
186 Thorn Hill Road
Warrendale, PA 15086-7528
Tel: (724)776-6040
Fax: (724)776-1880
E-mail: lwharrey@aist.org
Web Site: http://www.aist.org/foundation/scholarships.htm
To provide financial assistance for college to students interested in preparing for a career in the iron and steel or steel-related industries.
Title of Award: William E. Schwabe Memorial Scholarship **Area, Field, or Subject:** Business; Engineering; Manufacturing; Materials research/science; Metallurgy **Level of Education for which Award is Granted:** Undergraduate **Number Awarded:** 1 each year. **Funds Available:** The stipend is $1,500. **Duration:** 1 year; recipients may reapply.
Eligibility Requirements: This program is open to full-time students majoring in metallurgy, materials science, or engineering at accredited universities in North America. Applicants must have a GPA of 3.0 or higher and a demonstrated interest in the iron and steel industry. Along with their application, they must submit 3 letters of recommendation; a resume with work experience and extracurricular activities, noting any leadership positions; a current academic transcript; and a 2-page essay on their professional goals, explaining why they are interested in a career in the steel industry and how their skills could be applied to enhance the industry. Financial need is not considered in the selection process. **Deadline for Receipt:** April of each year. **Additional Information:** The AIST was formed in 2004 by the merger of the Iron and Steel Society (ISS) and the Association of Iron and Steel Engineers (AISE). This scholarship was established in 2005 by the Steel Manufacturers Association.

3284 ■ ASSOCIATION FOR IRON & STEEL TECHNOLOGY-BALTIMORE CHAPTER

c/o Thomas J. Russo
Mittal Steel USA
5111 North Point Boulevard
Sparrows Point, MD 21219-1014
Tel: (410)388-6370
Fax: (410)388-3772
E-mail: tom.russo@mittalsteel.com
Web Site: http://www.aist.org/chapters/mc_baltimore_scholar.htm
To provide financial assistance to family of members of the Baltimore Chapter of the Association for Iron & Steel Technology (AIST) who are interested in studying engineering or metallurgy in college.
Title of Award: Baltimore Chapter AIST Scholarship **Area, Field, or Subject:** Business; Engineering; Manufacturing; Metallurgy **Level of Education for which Award is Granted:** Undergraduate **Number Awarded:** 1 each year. **Funds Available:** The stipend is $1,500. **Duration:** 1 year.
Eligibility Requirements: This program is open to children, grandchildren, and spouses of chapter members who are high school seniors or

full-time undergraduates at an accredited college or university. Applicants must be studying or planning to study engineering or metallurgy with a demonstrated interest in a career in the iron and steel industry. Along with their application, they must submit 1) a 500-word essay on an accomplishment that they have achieved while they have been a student; 2) a 500-word essay on their interest and/or involvement in the iron and steel industry; 3) SAT/ACT scores; and 4) high school and/or college transcripts. Selection is based on academic achievement, extracurricular activities, and the essays; financial need is not considered. **Deadline for Receipt:** April of each year. **Additional Information:** The AIST was formed in 2004 by the merger of the Iron and Steel Society (ISS) and the Association of Iron and Steel Engineers (AISE). The Baltimore Chapter covers the District of Columbia, Maryland, and northern Virginia.

3285 ■ ASSOCIATION FOR IRON & STEEL TECHNOLOGY-DETROIT CHAPTER

c/o Judith A. Quinn, Secretary
14201 Robbe Road
Belleville, MI 48111
Tel: (313)319-2815
E-mail: judieqn@aol.com
Web Site: http://www.aist.org/chapters/detroit_scholarship.htm
To provide financial assistance to family of members of the Detroit Chapter of the Association for Iron & Steel Technology (AIST) who are interested in studying engineering, materials science, or metallurgy in college.
Title of Award: Detroit Chapter AIST Scholarship **Area, Field, or Subject:** Business; Engineering; Manufacturing; Materials research/science; Metallurgy **Level of Education for which Award is Granted:** Undergraduate **Number Awarded:** 1 each year. **Funds Available:** The stipend is $3,500. **Duration:** 1 year.
Eligibility Requirements: This program is open to children and grandchildren of chapter members who are high school seniors or full-time undergraduates at an accredited college or university. They must be studying or planning to study engineering, materials science, or metallurgy; if there are no applicants in those fields, the award may be given to a student majoring in another field relating to iron and steel production. Applicants must have a GPA of 3.0 or higher and a demonstrated interest in a career in the iron and steel industry. Along with their application, they must submit a 2-page essay on their professional goals, why they are interested in a career in the steel industry, and how their skills could be applied to enhance the industry. Financial need is not considered in the selection process. **Deadline for Receipt:** April of each year. **Additional Information:** The AIST was formed in 2004 by the merger of the Iron and Steel Society (ISS) and the Association of Iron and Steel Engineers (AISE). The Detroit Chapter serves Michigan and northwestern Ohio.

3286 ■ ASSOCIATION FOR IRON & STEEL TECHNOLOGY-NORTHWEST CHAPTER

c/o Gerardo L. Giraldo, Secretary-Treasurer
Nucor Steel Seattle, Inc.
Washington Steel Division
2424 S.W. Andover Street
Seattle, WA 98106-1100
Tel: (206)933-2245
Fax: (206)933-2207
E-mail: gerry.giraldo@nucor-seattle.com
Web Site: http://www.aist.org/chapters/
mc_pittsburgh_scholar_guidelines.htm
To provide financial assistance to family of members of the Northwest Chapter of the Association for Iron & Steel Technology (AIST) who are interested in studying engineering in college.
Title of Award: Northwest Chapter AIST Scholarships **Area, Field, or Subject:** Business; Chemistry; Engineering; Manufacturing; Mathematics and mathematical sciences; Metallurgy; Physics **Level of Education for which Award is Granted:** Four Year College **Number Awarded:** 2 each year. **Funds Available:** The stipend is $1,000. **Duration:** 1 year.
Eligibility Requirements: This program is open to children, grandchildren, spouses, or nieces/nephews of chapter members who are high school seniors planning to attend an accredited 4-year college or university. Applicants must intend to study engineering; if there are no applicants in engineering, the award may be given to a student majoring in chemistry, mathematics, metallurgy, or physics, or to a student showing

an interest in preparing for a career in the iron and steel industry. Along with their application, they must submit a 500-word essay on 1 of the following topics: 1) an accomplishment they have achieved while they have been a student, why they were successful, and how their success will influence their future plans as an engineer or an engineer in the steel industry; 2) their strengths and interests and how they will apply their skills to a career in the steel industry or as an engineer; or 3) the challenges that face the steel industry and the opportunities for graduates to improve the success of companies within the industry. Financial need is not considered in the selection process. **Deadline for Receipt:** June of each year. **Additional Information:** The AIST was formed in 2004 by the merger of the Iron and Steel Society (ISS) and the Association of Iron and Steel Engineers (AISE). The Northwest Chapter serves Alaska, Idaho, Montana, Oregon, Washington, and Wyoming.

3287 ■ ASSOCIATION FOR IRON & STEEL TECHNOLOGY-PITTSBURGH CHAPTER

c/o Paul D. Conley
Allegheny Ludlum
100 River Road
Brackenridge, PA 15014-1597
Tel: (724)226-5000
Web Site: http://www.aist.org/chapters/
mc_pittsburgh_scholar_guidelines.htm
To provide financial assistance to family of members of the Pittsburgh Chapter of the Association for Iron & Steel Technology (AIST) who are interested in studying engineering or metallurgy in college.
Title of Award: Pittsburgh Chapter AIST Scholarships **Area, Field, or Subject:** Business; Engineering; Manufacturing; Metallurgy **Level of Education for which Award is Granted:** Undergraduate **Number Awarded:** Up to 2 each year. **Funds Available:** The stipend is $2,500. **Duration:** 1 year.
Eligibility Requirements: This program is open to children, grandchildren, or spouses of chapter members who are high school seniors or full-time undergraduates at an accredited college or university. Applicants must be studying or planning to study engineering or metallurgy; if there are no applicants in those fields, the award may be given to a student majoring in another field relating to iron and steel production. Along with their application, they must submit a 500-word essay on 1 of the following topics: 1) an accomplishment they have achieved while they have been a student, why they were successful, and how their success will influence their future plans as an engineer or an engineer in the steel industry; 2) their strengths and interests and how they will apply their skills to a career in the steel industry or as an engineer; or 3) they challenges that face the steel industry and the opportunities for graduates to improve the success of companies within the industry. Financial need is not considered in the selection process. **Deadline for Receipt:** June of each year. **Additional Information:** The AIST was formed in 2004 by the merger of the Iron and Steel Society (ISS) and the Association of Iron and Steel Engineers (AISE). The Pittsburgh Chapter serves western Pennsylvania, West Virginia, and southeastern Ohio. This program includes the Lawrence G. Maloney Scholarship.

3288 ■ ASSOCIATION FOR IRON & STEEL TECHNOLOGY-SOUTHEAST CHAPTER

c/o Mike Hutson, Secretary
803 Floyd Street
Kings Mountain, NC 28086-3130
Tel: (704)730-8320
Fax: (704)730-8321
E-mail: Mike@johnhutsoncompany.com
Web Site: http://www.aist.org/chapters/
mc_southeast_scholar_guidelines.htm
To provide financial assistance to the families of members of the Southeast Chapter of the Association for Iron & Steel Technology (AIST) who are interested in studying engineering or science in college.
Title of Award: Gene Suave Scholarship **Area, Field, or Subject:** Business; Engineering; Manufacturing; Science **Level of Education for which Award is Granted:** Undergraduate **Number Awarded:** 1 each year. **Funds Available:** The stipend is $1,000. **Duration:** 1 year.
Eligibility Requirements: This program is open to high school seniors and undergraduate students who are the children, stepchildren, grandchildren, or spouses of active Southeast Chapter members for 2

consecutive years. Applicants must plan to work full or part time on a degree in engineering or the sciences. If no engineering or science student applies, the award may be presented to an applicant studying another major related to iron and steel production. Applicants must submit a 250-word essay on their extracurricular involvement in high school and why they should be the recipient of the scholarship. Financial need is not considered. **Deadline for Receipt:** June of each year. **Additional Information:** The AIST was formed in 2004 by the merger of the Iron and Steel Society (ISS) and the Association of Iron and Steel Engineers (AISE). The Southeast Chapter covers the states of North Carolina, South Carolina, Georgia, and Florida as well as portions of southern Virginia and eastern Tennessee.

3289 ■ BRISTOL BAY NATIVE CORPORATION

Attn: BBNC Education Foundation
800 Cordova Street, Suite 200
Anchorage, AK 99501-6299
Tel: (907)278-3602
Free: 800-426-3602
Fax: (907)276-3925
E-mail: pelagiol@bbnc.net
Web Site: http://www.bbnc.net
To provide financial assistance to shareholders of Bristol Bay Native Corporation (BBNC) who are interested in majoring in banking in college. **Title of Award:** Wells Fargo-BBNC Scholarship Fund **Area, Field, or Subject:** Banking **Level of Education for which Award is Granted:** Undergraduate **Funds Available:** The stipend is $5,000 per year. **Duration:** 1 year.

Eligibility Requirements: This program is open to BBNC shareholders who are enrolled full time as a college junior or senior to prepare for a career in banking. Applicants must have a GPA of 2.0 or higher and be able to demonstrate financial need. Along with their application, they must submit an essay on their career goals and desire to succeed in their chosen field of study. Selection is based on the essay (35%), cumulative GPA (40%), financial need (20%), and letters of recommendation (5%). based on academic standing, financial need, and a written essay. **Deadline for Receipt:** April of each year. **Additional Information:** The funding for this program is provided equally by Wells Fargo Bank and the Bristol Bay Native Corporation Education Foundation.

3290 ■ CALIFORNIA STATE UNIVERSITY

Office of the Chancellor
Attn: Lori Redfearn, Vice President
401 Golden Shore, Sixth Floor
Long Beach, CA 90802-4210
Tel: (562)951-4815
E-mail: lredfearn@calstate.edu
Web Site: http://www.calstate.edu/foundation/scholarship.shtml
To provide financial assistance to graduate students majoring in designated fields at campuses of the California State University (CSU) system.
Title of Award: Glenn and Dorothy Dumke Fellowship **Area, Field, or Subject:** Economics; History, American; Library and archival sciences; Political science; Public administration **Level of Education for which Award is Granted:** Four Year College, Master's **Number Awarded:** 1 each year. **Funds Available:** The stipend is $1,000 per year. **Duration:** 1 year.

Eligibility Requirements: This program is open to students working on a graduate degree at CSU campuses in public policy, American history, economics, archival management, or government.

3291 ■ JORGE MAS CANOSA FREEDOM FOUNDATION

c/o Cuban American National Foundation
1312 S.W. 27th Avenue
P.O. Box 440069
Miami, FL 33144-9926
Tel: (305)592-7768
Fax: (305)592-7889
Web Site: http://www.canf.org
To provide financial assistance to students of Cuban descent who are working on an undergraduate or graduate degree in selected subject areas.
Title of Award: Mas Family Scholarship Program **Area, Field, or Subject:** Business administration; Communications; Economics;

Engineering; International affairs and relations; Journalism **Level of Education for which Award is Granted:** Graduate, Undergraduate **Funds Available:** The amount of the award depends on the cost of tuition at the recipient's selected institution, on the family's situation, and on the amount of funds received from other sources. The amount of the yearly award cannot exceed $10,000. Full scholarships are not awarded to students who will be receiving full tuition scholarships and/or stipendiary support from other sources. **Duration:** 1 year; recipients may reapply and are given preference over other candidates.

Eligibility Requirements: This program is open to students who are direct descendants of those who left Cuba or were born in Cuba themselves. Applicants must be or have been in the top 10% of their high school graduating class and have be able to meet federal standards of financial need. At least 1 parent or 2 grandparents must have been born in Cuba. Both undergraduate and graduate students may apply, provided they are majoring in 1 of the following subjects: engineering, business, international relations, economics, communications, or journalism. Selection is based on academic performance, leadership qualities, financial need, potential to contribute to the advancement of a free society, and likelihood of succeeding in their chosen field. Finalists may be interviewed. **Deadline for Receipt:** March of each year. **Additional Information:** This program was previously offered by the Cuban American National Foundation.

3292 ■ CATCHING THE DREAM

8200 Mountain Road, N.E., Suite 203
Albuquerque, NM 87110-7835
Tel: (505)262-2351
Fax: (505)262-0534
E-mail: NScholarsh@aol.com
Web Site: http://www.catchingthedream.org
To provide financial assistance for college to American Indian students interested in studying a field related to economic development for tribes. **Title of Award:** Tribal Business Management (TBM) Program **Area, Field, or Subject:** Banking; Business administration; Economics; Finance; Hotel, institutional, and restaurant management; Management **Level of Education for which Award is Granted:** Undergraduate **Number Awarded:** Varies; generally, 30 to 35 each year. **Funds Available:** Stipends range from $500 to $5,000. **Duration:** 1 year.

Eligibility Requirements: This program is open to American Indians who can provide proof that they are at least one-quarter Indian blood and a member of a U.S. tribe that is federally-recognized, state-recognized, or terminated. Applicants must be enrolled or planning to enroll full time and major in the 1 of the following fields: business administration, finance, management, economics, banking, hotel management, or other fields related to economic development for tribes. They may be entering freshmen, undergraduate students, graduate students, or Ph.D. candidates. Along with their application, they must submit documentation of financial need, 3 letters of recommendation, copies of applications and responses for at least 15 other sources of funding, official transcripts, standardized test scores (ACT, SAT, GRE, MCAT, LSAT, etc.), and an essay explaining their goals in life, college plans, and career plans (especially how those plans include working with and benefiting Indians). Selection is based on merit and potential for improving the lives of Indian people. **Deadline for Receipt:** April of each year for fall term; September of each year for spring and winter terms; March of each year for summer school. **Additional Information:** The sponsor was formerly known as the Native American Scholarship Fund. This program was established in 2003.

3293 ■ CFA INSTITUTE

Attn: 11 September Memorial Scholarship Fund
560 Ray C. Hunt Drive
P.O. Box 3668
Charlottesville, VA 22903-0668
Tel: (434)951-5499
Free: 800-237-8132
Fax: (434)951-5262
E-mail: 11septemberfund@cfainstitute.org
Web Site: http://www.cfainstitute.org/research/products/
About_September_Scholarship.html
To provide financial assistance to people and their families who were disabled or killed in the September 11 terrorist attacks and who wish to major in designated fields in college.

Title of Award: CFA Institute 11 September Memorial Scholarship **Area, Field, or Subject:** Accounting; Business administration; Economics; Finance **Level of Education for which Award is Granted:** Undergraduate **Number Awarded:** Varies each year; recently, 12 of these scholarships were awarded. **Funds Available:** Stipends range from $2,000 to $13,000 per year, depending on the need of the recipient. **Duration:** 1 year; renewable up to 4 additional years.

Eligibility Requirements: College scholarships are offered to those who meet the following 2 criteria: 1) they were permanently disabled in the attacks, or were the spouses, domestic partners, or children of anyone killed or permanently disabled in the attacks, and 2) they will be working on a college-level education in finance, economics, accounting, or business ethics. Applicants may be residents of any state or country. Selection is based on demonstrated commitment to high levels of professional ethics, academic record, and financial need. **Deadline for Receipt:** May of each year. **Additional Information:** The CFA (Chartered Financial Analyst) Institute was formerly the Association for Investment Management and Research (AIMR). It lost at least 60 of its members and CFA candidates in the terrorist attacks of 11 September. This program is managed by Scholarship America, One Scholarship Way, P.O. Box 297, St. Peter, MN 56082, (507) 931-1682, (800) 537-4180, Fax: (507) 931-9168, E-mail: smsinfo@csfa.org.

3294 ■ CHICAGO URBAN LEAGUE

Attn: Education Department
4510 South Michigan Avenue
Chicago, IL 60653-3898
Tel: (773)451-3565
Fax: (773)285-7772
E-mail: info@cul-chicago.org
Web Site: http://www.cul-chicago.org
To provide financial assistance to Illinois residents of color interested in studying a field related to automotive technology in college.

Title of Award: Mercedes-Benz Scholarships **Area, Field, or Subject:** Accounting; Automotive technology; Business; Business administration; Computer and information sciences; Engineering, Automotive; Transportation **Level of Education for which Award is Granted:** Undergraduate **Number Awarded:** 4 each year. **Funds Available:** The stipend is $1,000 per year. **Duration:** 4 years.

Eligibility Requirements: This program is open to Illinois residents of color who are graduating high school seniors with a GPA of 2.5 or higher and planning to enroll as full-time undergraduate students at a 4-year college or university, Triton College, or 1 of the City Colleges of Chicago. Applicants must be planning to major in automotive technology or a field related to the automotive industry (e.g., engineering, computer science, business, or accounting). They must be able to demonstrate financial need. **Deadline for Receipt:** May of each year. **Additional Information:** This program is offered as part of the Chicago Urban League's Whitney M. Young, Jr. Memorial Scholarship Fund, established in 1970.

3295 ■ CHICKASAW FOUNDATION

P.O. Box 1726
Ada, OK 74821-1726
Tel: (580)421-9030
Fax: (580)421-9031
Web Site: http://www.cflink.org
To provide financial assistance to members of the Chickasaw Nation who are preparing for a career in banking.

Title of Award: Bank2 Banking Scholarship **Area, Field, or Subject:** Accounting; Banking; Business administration; Finance **Level of Education for which Award is Granted:** Four Year College **Number Awarded:** 1 each year. **Funds Available:** The stipend is $3,000 per year. **Duration:** 1 year.

Eligibility Requirements: This program is open to Chickasaw students who are currently enrolled at a 4-year college or university as a full-time undergraduate student. Applicants must be majoring in finance, business, or accounting and preparing for a career in banking. Along with their application, they must submit high school or college transcripts, 2 letters of recommendation, a copy of their Certificate of Degree of Indian Blood, a copy of their Chickasaw Nation citizenship card, and a 1-page essay on their long-term goals and plans for achieving them. Financial need is not considered in the selection process. **Deadline for Receipt:** May of each year. **Additional Information:** This program is supported by Bank2,

headquartered in Oklahoma City and owned by the Chickasaw Nation.

3296 ■ CHICKASAW FOUNDATION

P.O. Box 1726
Ada, OK 74821-1726
Tel: (580)421-9030
Fax: (580)421-9031
Web Site: http://www.cflink.org
To provide financial assistance to members of the Chickasaw Nation who are preparing for a career in banking.

Title of Award: Bank2 Ta-ossaa-asha' Scholarships **Area, Field, or Subject:** Accounting; Banking; Business administration; Finance **Level of Education for which Award is Granted:** Undergraduate **Number Awarded:** 3 each year. **Funds Available:** The stipend is $1,000 per year. **Duration:** 1 year.

Eligibility Requirements: This program is open to Chickasaw students who are currently enrolled at an accredited institution of higher education as a full-time undergraduate student. Applicants must be majoring in finance, business, or accounting and preparing for a career in banking. Along with their application, they must submit high school or college transcripts, 2 letters of recommendation, a copy of their Certificate of Degree of Indian Blood, a copy of their Chickasaw Nation citizenship card, and a 1-page essay on their long-term goals and plans for achieving them. Financial need is not considered in the selection process. **Deadline for Receipt:** May of each year. **Additional Information:** This program is supported by Bank2, headquartered in Oklahoma City and owned by the Chickasaw Nation.

3297 ■ COLORADO MOTOR CARRIERS ASSOCIATION

Attn: Scholarship Committee
4060 Elati Street
Denver, CO 80216
Tel: (303)433-3375
Fax: (303)477-6977
E-mail: meredith@cmca.com
Web Site: http://www.cmca.com/scholarship.htm
To provide financial assistance to Colorado residents preparing for a career in the trucking industry as diesel mechanics.

Title of Award: Colorado Motor Carriers Association Diesel Scholarship **Area, Field, or Subject:** Business; Mechanics and repairs; Transportation **Level of Education for which Award is Granted:** Undergraduate **Number Awarded:** Varies each year. **Funds Available:** A stipend is awarded (amount not specified). **Duration:** 1 year.

Eligibility Requirements: This program is open to Colorado residents currently enrolled in a diesel mechanic school with good standing in both GPA and attendance. Applicants must be preparing for a career in the trucking industry but need assistance to do so. Preference is given to students currently employed in the industry. Along with their application, they must submit a 300-word essay on themselves, their goals, what they imagine as their future, and why they chose this industry. **Deadline for Receipt:** March of each year.

3298 ■ COLORADO MOTOR CARRIERS ASSOCIATION

Attn: Scholarship Committee
4060 Elati Street
Denver, CO 80216
Tel: (303)433-3375
Fax: (303)477-6977
E-mail: meredith@cmca.com
Web Site: http://www.cmca.com/scholarship.htm
To provide financial assistance for college to employees and family members of member company employees of the Colorado Motor Carriers Association (CMCA).

Title of Award: Ray Smith Scholarship **Area, Field, or Subject:** Business; General studies/Field of study not specified; Transportation **Level of Education for which Award is Granted:** Undergraduate **Number Awarded:** Varies each year; recently, 16 of these scholarships were awarded. **Funds Available:** A stipend is awarded (amount not specified). Funds may be used for tuition, books, supplies, and laboratory and/or other fees. **Duration:** 1 year; may be renewed.

Eligibility Requirements: This program is open to high school seniors and older college bound students. Applicants must be an employee of a CMCA member company or an immediate family member of an employee.

Along with their application, they must submit a 300-word essay on themselves and their goals. Selection is based on the essay, GPA, academic honors or awards received, involvement in leadership or extracurricular school activities, involvement in community or other organizations, and 3 letters of recommendation. Financial need is not considered. Preference is given to applicants preparing for a career in transportation or another field demonstrating a positive benefit for the trucking industry. **Deadline for Receipt:** March of each year.

3299 ■ COLORADO READY MIXED CONCRETE ASSOCIATION/ COLORADO ROCK PRODUCTS ASSOCIATION

Attn: Scholarship Fund
6855 South Havana Street, Suite 540
Centennial, CO 80112
Tel: (303)290-0303
Fax: (303)290-8008
E-mail: pschauer@crmca.org
Web Site: http://www.crmca.org/scholarships/default.php
To provide financial assistance to upper-division students from Colorado who are preparing for a career in areas of interest to the Colorado Ready Mixed Concrete Association (CRMCA) and the Colorado Rock Products Association (CRPA).
Title of Award: CRMCA/CRPA Scholarships **Area, Field, or Subject:** Architecture; Business; Construction; Engineering; Engineering, Materials; Materials research/science **Level of Education for which Award is Granted:** Four Year College **Number Awarded:** 4 each year. **Funds Available:** The stipend is $1,000. Funds are paid directly to the student's institution. **Duration:** 1 year.
Eligibility Requirements: This program is open to full-time juniors and seniors at colleges and universities in Colorado who have a GPA of 3.0 or higher. Applicants must be preparing for a career in such fields as aggregate extraction, building construction, road building, municipal utility construction, building design, heavy equipment design, materials research or application, or other fields associated with the use of aggregates or concrete. Preference is given to students whose home residence is Colorado, have graduated from a high school in Colorado, and have a parent employed in concrete or aggregate production industries or associated or auxiliary industries. Along with their application, they must submit a brief resume of their current activities and work experience, 3 letters of character reference, and a 1-page statement on their plans for the future and career. Financial need is not considered in the selection process. **Deadline for Receipt:** July of each year.

3300 ■ COMMUNITY FOUNDATION FOR GREATER ATLANTA, INC.

50 Hurt Plaza, Suite 449
Atlanta, GA 30303
Tel: (404)688-5525
Fax: (404)688-3060
E-mail: vweekes@atlcf.org
Web Site: http://www.atlcf.org/GrantsScholarships/Scholarships/ RonAutry.aspx
To provide financial assistance to Georgia residents who are majoring in journalism at a 4-year college or university.
Title of Award: Ron Autry Scholarship **Area, Field, or Subject:** Advertising; Journalism; Personnel administration/human resources **Level of Education for which Award is Granted:** Four Year College **Number Awarded:** 1 each year. **Funds Available:** The maximum stipend is $2,000 per year. **Duration:** 1 year.
Eligibility Requirements: This program is open to legal residents of Georgia who are enrolled as a junior or senior at a college or university and preparing for a career in journalism or the newspaper industry (news, advertising, circulation, or human resources). Applicants must be enrolled full time, have a GPA of 2.0 or higher and be able to demonstrate financial need. Along with their application, they must submit a 500-word essay on a topic that changes annually; recently, applicants were invited to write on the topic: "What has been the impact of the Jayson Blair scandal on Black journalists and what should be done to avoid plagiarism?" **Deadline for Receipt:** March of each year. **Additional Information:** This program is sponsored by the Atlanta Association of Black Journalists (AABJ), P.O. Box 54128, Atlanta, GA 30308, (404) 508-4612. Applications may be submitted to the Community Foundation for Greater Atlanta or directly to the AABJ. The recipient is selected by the AABJ.

3301 ■ CONGRESSIONAL BLACK CAUCUS FOUNDATION, INC.

Attn: Director, Educational Programs
1720 Massachusetts Avenue, N.W.
Washington, DC 20036
Tel: (202)263-2836
Free: 800-784-2577
Fax: (202)775-0773
E-mail: spouses@cbcfinc.org
Web Site: http://www.cbcfinc.org
To provide financial assistance to minority and other undergraduate and graduate students who reside in a Congressional district represented by an African American and are interested in studying the performing arts in college.
Title of Award: CBC Spouses Performing Arts Scholarship **Area, Field, or Subject:** Business; Music; Performing arts **Level of Education for which Award is Granted:** Graduate, Undergraduate **Number Awarded:** 10 each year. **Funds Available:** The stipend is $3,000. **Duration:** 1 year.
Eligibility Requirements: This program is open to 1) minority and other graduating high school seniors planning to attend an accredited institution of higher education and 2) currently-enrolled full-time undergraduate, graduate, and doctoral students in good academic standing with a GPA of 2.5 or higher. Applicants must reside or attend school in a Congressional district represented by a member of the Congressional Black Caucus (CBC). They must be interested in preparing for a career in the performing arts, music, or a related field in the entertainment industry. Along with their application, they must submit a videotape of their performance and a 500-word personal statement on 1) the field of study they intend to pursue and why they have chosen that field; 2) their interests, involvement in school activities, community and public service, hobbies, special talents, sports, and other highlight areas; and 3) any other experiences, skills, or qualifications they feel should be considered. They must also be able to document financial need. **Deadline for Receipt:** April of each year. **Additional Information:** This program, established in 2000, is sponsored by Heineken USA.

3302 ■ COOK INLET REGION, INC.

Attn: CIRI Foundation
2600 Cordova Street, Suite 206
Anchorage, AK 99503
Tel: (907)263-5582
Free: 800-764-3382
Fax: (907)263-5588
E-mail: tcf@ciri.com
Web Site: http://www.thecirifoundation.org/scholarship.html
To provide financial assistance for undergraduate or graduate studies in business-related fields to Alaska Natives who are original enrollees to Cook Inlet Region, Inc. (CIRI) and their lineal descendants.
Title of Award: Carl H. Marrs Scholarship Fund **Area, Field, or Subject:** Accounting; Business administration; Economics; Finance; Management **Level of Education for which Award is Granted:** Four Year College, Graduate **Number Awarded:** Varies each year; recently, 2 of these scholarships were awarded. **Funds Available:** The stipend is $18,000 per year. **Duration:** 1 year; may be renewed.
Eligibility Requirements: This program is open to Alaska Native enrollees to CIRI under the Alaska Native Claims Settlement Act (ANCSA) of 1971 and their lineal descendants. There are no Alaska residency requirements or age limitations. Applicants must be accepted or enrolled full time in a 4-year undergraduate or a graduate degree program in business administration, economics, finance, organizational management, accounting, or a similar field. They must have a GPA of 3.7 or higher. Selection is based on academic achievement, rigor of course work or degree program, quality of a statement of purpose, student financial contribution, financial need, grade level, previous work performance, education and community activities, letters of recommendation, seriousness of purpose, and practicality of educational and professional goals. **Deadline for Receipt:** May of each year. **Additional Information:** This program was established in 2001. Recipients must enroll in school on a full-time basis.

3303 ■ EDWARD DAVIS EDUCATION FOUNDATION

585 East Larned Street, Suite 100
Detroit, MI 48226

Tel: (313)963-2209; 877-847-9060

Web Site: http://www.automag.com/EDEFoundation/default.asp

To provide financial assistance to minority students interested in preparing for a career in an automotive-related profession.

Title of Award: Edward Davis Scholarship Fund **Area, Field, or Subject:** Business; Transportation **Level of Education for which Award is Granted:** Undergraduate **Funds Available:** Stipends range from $1,000 to $2,500. **Duration:** 1 year.

Eligibility Requirements: This program is open to minority high school seniors or currently-enrolled college students who are interested in preparing for a career in the automotive industry. Applicants must have a GPA of 2.7 or higher. Along with their application, they must submit a 250-word essay on what diversity in the automotive industry means to them. They should be able to demonstrate leadership qualities as defined by a record of involvement and participation in extracurricular and community activities. U.S. citizenship is required. **Deadline for Receipt:** November of each year. **Additional Information:** This scholarship, established in 1998, honors the first African American to own a new car dealership.

3304 ■ DECA

1908 Association Drive

Reston, VA 20191-1594

Tel: (703)860-5000

Fax: (703)860-4013

E-mail: decainc@aol.com

Web Site: http://www.deca.org/student.html

To recognize and reward (with college scholarships) DECA members who develop outstanding advertising campaigns for display on the Internet.

Title of Award: 7 Up Challenge **Area, Field, or Subject:** Advertising; Internet design and development; Marketing and distribution **Level of Education for which Award is Granted:** Undergraduate **Number Awarded:** 4 finalists are selected in each category in each round (for a total of 16 finalists); from among those, 2 grand-prize winners (1 in each category) are selected. **Funds Available:** Each finalist receives a $500 award. The grand-prize winners receive $2,500 college scholarships. **Duration:** The competition is held annually.

Eligibility Requirements: This competition is open to high school DECA members who submit entries in either of 2 categories: 1) a web campaign of at least 400 x 400 pixels with up to 4 links and up to 500K in size; or 2) a banner ad of approximately 450 x 60 pixels, 72 dpi, and up to 20K. In either category, the campaign must promote brand awareness of lemon-lime and/or cherry-flavored soft drinks, involve the consumer, and utilize the themes of college basketball and/or music. Entries are received in 2 rounds, with finalists selected in each category in each round. Grand-prize winners are selected from among the finalists on the basis of how well and creatively the campaign or banner ad promotes the soft drinks, overall appearance, content of copy, ease of use, identification, layout, and impact. **Deadline for Receipt:** November of each year for the first round; February of each year for the second round. **Additional Information:** This program is sponsored by the Seven Up Division of Dr Pepper/Seven Up, Inc.

3305 ■ DECA

1908 Association Drive

Reston, VA 20191-1594

Tel: (703)860-5000

Fax: (703)860-4013

E-mail: decainc@aol.com

Web Site: http://www.deca.org/student.html

To provide financial assistance for college to DECA members who are also members of an academy of hospitality and tourism affiliated with the National Academy Foundation.

Title of Award: American Express Foundation of Hospitality and Tourism Academy Scholarships **Area, Field, or Subject:** Food service careers; Hotel, institutional, and restaurant management; Management; Marketing and distribution; Travel and tourism **Level of Education for which Award is Granted:** Undergraduate **Number Awarded:** 2 each year. **Funds Available:** The stipend is $1,000. **Duration:** 1 year.

Eligibility Requirements: This program is open to DECA members who are high school seniors and also members of an academy of hospitality and tourism affiliated with the National Academy Foundation. Applicants must be interested in enrolling in a 2-year or 4-year course of study in marketing, merchandising, or management at an accredited institution or

university. Selection based on DECA involvement, leadership, and grades. Applicants may also include a statement in support of financial need and it will be reviewed. **Deadline for Receipt:** February of each year. **Additional Information:** This program is sponsored by American Express.

3306 ■ DECA

1908 Association Drive

Reston, VA 20191-1594

Tel: (703)860-5000

Fax: (703)860-4013

E-mail: decainc@aol.com

Web Site: http://www.deca.org/student.html

To provide financial assistance to DECA members interested in working on a college degree in marketing, entrepreneurship, or management.

Title of Award: Harry A. Applegate Scholarship Award **Area, Field, or Subject:** Business administration; Management; Marketing and distribution **Level of Education for which Award is Granted:** Undergraduate **Number Awarded:** Varies each year; recently, 20 of these scholarships were awarded. **Funds Available:** The stipend is $1,000. Funds are paid directly to the recipient's college or university. **Duration:** 1 year.

Eligibility Requirements: This program is open to DECA members in either the high school or Delta Epsilon Chi (collegiate) division. Applicants must intend to work full time on a 2- or 4-year degree in marketing, entrepreneurship, or management. Complete applications are to be submitted to the state advisor. Each state is told the number of applications it may forward to the national organization. Selection is based on DECA involvement, leadership ability, community service, and grades. The program is merit based, but applicants may include a statement in support of financial need and it will be reviewed. **Deadline for Receipt:** Each state sets its own deadline, usually in January.

3307 ■ DECA

1908 Association Drive

Reston, VA 20191-1594

Tel: (703)860-5000

Fax: (703)860-4013

E-mail: decainc@aol.com

Web Site: http://www.deca.org/student.html

To provide financial assistance to DECA members interested in studying business or marketing education in college.

Title of Award: Coca-Cola DECA Scholarships **Area, Field, or Subject:** Business administration; Education; Marketing and distribution **Level of Education for which Award is Granted:** Undergraduate **Number Awarded:** Up to 5 each year. **Funds Available:** The stipend is $1,000. **Duration:** 1 year.

Eligibility Requirements: This program is open to DECA members who are interested in working full time on a 2-year or 4-year degree in marketing, business, or marketing education. Applicants must be able to demonstrate evidence of DECA activities, academic achievement, leadership ability, and community service involvement. Selection is based on merit, not financial need. **Deadline for Receipt:** February of each year. **Additional Information:** This program, established in 2002, is sponsored by the Coca-Cola Company.

3308 ■ DECA

1908 Association Drive

Reston, VA 20191-1594

Tel: (703)860-5000

Fax: (703)860-4013

E-mail: decainc@aol.com

Web Site: http://www.deca.org/student.html

To provide financial assistance for college to DECA members interested in the hospitality industry.

Title of Award: Marriott International Scholarships **Area, Field, or Subject:** Business administration; Food service careers; Hotel, institutional, and restaurant management; Marketing and distribution **Level of Education for which Award is Granted:** Undergraduate **Number Awarded:** Up to 6 each year. **Funds Available:** The stipend is $1,000. **Duration:** 1 year.

Eligibility Requirements: This program is open to DECA members who are interested in working full time on a 2-year or 4-year degree in business or marketing to prepare for a career in the hospitality industry. Applicants must be able to demonstrate evidence of DECA activities, academic achievement, leadership ability, and interest or experience in the hospitality industry. Selection is based on merit, not financial need. **Deadline for Receipt:** February of each year. **Additional Information:** This program is sponsored by Marriott International, Inc.

3309 ■ DECA
1908 Association Drive
Reston, VA 20191-1594
Tel: (703)860-5000
Fax: (703)860-4013
E-mail: decainc@aol.com
Web Site: http://www.deca.org/student.html
To provide financial assistance to DECA members interested in studying management or marketing education in college.
Title of Award: Otis Spunkmeyer Student Scholarships **Area, Field, or Subject:** Education; Management; Marketing and distribution **Level of Education for which Award is Granted:** Undergraduate **Number Awarded:** 15 each year. **Funds Available:** The stipend is $1,000. **Duration:** 1 year.
Eligibility Requirements: This program is open to DECA members who are interested in working full time on a 2-year or 4-year degree in marketing, management, or marketing education. Applicants must be able to demonstrate evidence of DECA activities, academic achievement, leadership ability, and community service involvement. Selection is based on merit, not financial need. **Deadline for Receipt:** February of each year. **Additional Information:** This program is sponsored by Otis Spunkmeyer, Inc.

3310 ■ DECA
1908 Association Drive
Reston, VA 20191-1594
Tel: (703)860-5000
Fax: (703)860-4013
E-mail: decainc@aol.com
Web Site: http://www.deca.org/student.html
To provide financial assistance to DECA members interested in studying business or marketing education in college.
Title of Award: Walgreens DECA Scholarships **Area, Field, or Subject:** Business administration; Education; Marketing and distribution **Level of Education for which Award is Granted:** Undergraduate **Number Awarded:** Up to 5 each year. **Funds Available:** The stipend is $1,000. **Duration:** 1 year.
Eligibility Requirements: This program is open to DECA members who are interested in working full time on a 2-year or 4-year degree in marketing, business, or marketing education. Applicants must be able to demonstrate evidence of DECA activities, academic achievement, leadership ability, and community service involvement. Selection is based on merit, not financial need. **Deadline for Receipt:** February of each year. **Additional Information:** This program, established in 2004, is sponsored by Walgreens.

3311 ■ DEPARTMENT OF TRANSPORTATION
Federal Highway Administration
Attn: National Highway Institute, HNHI-20
4600 North Fairfax Drive, Suite 800
Arlington, VA 22203-1553
Tel: (703)235-0538
Fax: (703)235-0593
E-mail: transportationedu@fhwa.dot.gov
Web Site: http://www.nhi.fhwa.dot.gov/ddetfp.asp
To enable students to participate in research activities at facilities of the U.S. Department of Transportation (DOT) Federal Highway Administration in the Washington, D.C. area.
Title of Award: Eisenhower Grants for Research Fellowships **Area, Field, or Subject:** Chemistry; Economics; Engineering; Engineering, Civil; Geography; Information science and technology; Materials research/science; Operations research; Physics; Public administration; Statistics; Technology; Transportation; Urban affairs/design/planning **Level of Education for which Award is Granted:** Four Year College, Graduate **Number Awarded:** Varies each year; recently, 9 students participated in this program. **Funds Available:** Fellows receive full tuition and fees that relate to the academic credits for the approved research project and a

monthly stipend of $1,450 for college seniors, $1,700 for master's students, or $2,000 for doctoral students. An allowance for travel to and from the DOT facility where the research is conducted is also provided, but selectees are responsible for their own housing accommodations. Faculty advisors are allowed 1 site review on projects over 6 months and 2 site reviews on projects over 9 months; travel and per diem are provided for those site reviews. **Duration:** Tenure is normally 3, 6, 9, or 12 months.
Eligibility Requirements: This program is open to 1) students in their junior year of a baccalaureate program who will complete their junior year before being awarded a fellowship; 2) students in their senior year of a baccalaureate program; and 3) students who have completed their baccalaureate degree and are enrolled in a program leading to a master's, Ph.D., or equivalent degree. Applicants must be U.S. citizens enrolled in an accredited U.S. institution of higher education working on a degree full time and planning to enter the transportation profession after completing their higher education. They select 1 or more projects from a current list of research projects underway at various DOT facilities; the research will be conducted with academic supervision provided by a faculty advisor from their home university (which grants academic credit for the research project) and with technical direction provided by the DOT staff. Specific requirements for the target projects vary; most require engineering backgrounds, but others involve transportation planning, information management, public administration, physics, materials science, statistical analysis, operations research, chemistry, economics, technology transfer, urban studies, geography, and urban and regional planning. The DOT encourages students at Historically Black Colleges and Universities (HBCUs) and Hispanic Serving Institutions (HSIs) to apply for these grants. Selection is based on match of the student's qualifications with the proposed research project (including the student's ability to accomplish the project in the available time), recommendation letters regarding the nominee's qualifications to conduct the research, academic records (including class standing, GPA, and transcripts), and transportation work experience (if any) including the employer's endorsement. **Deadline for Receipt:** February of each year.

3312 ■ ELECTRONIC DOCUMENT SYSTEMS FOUNDATION
Attn: EDSF Scholarship Awards
24238 Hawthorne Boulevard
Torrance, CA 90505-6505
Tel: (310)541-1481
Fax: (310)541-4803
Web Site: http://www.edsf.org/scholarships.cfm
To provide financial assistance to college juniors, seniors, and graduate students interested in working with electronic documents as a career.
Title of Award: Wayne Alexander Memorial Scholarship **Area, Field, or Subject:** Computer and information sciences; Graphic art and design; Internet design and development; Marketing and distribution; Printing trades and industries; Telecommunications systems **Level of Education for which Award is Granted:** Four Year College, Graduate **Number Awarded:** 1 each year. **Funds Available:** The stipend is $2,000. **Duration:** 1 year.
Eligibility Requirements: This program is open to juniors, seniors, and graduate students who are working full time on a degree in the field of document communication, including marketing, graphic communication and arts, e-commerce, imaging science, printing, web authoring, electronic publishing, computer science, or telecommunications. Priority consideration is given to students at the University of Central Florida. Applicants must submit a statement of their career goals in the field of document communications, an essay on a topic related to their view of the future of the document management and production industry, a list of current professional and college extracurricular activities and achievements, college transcripts (GPA of 3.0 or higher), samples of their creative work, and 2 letters of recommendation. Financial need is not considered. **Deadline for Receipt:** May of each year. **Additional Information:** This program is sponsored by AXIS Inc.

3313 ■ ELECTRONIC DOCUMENT SYSTEMS FOUNDATION
Attn: EDSF Scholarship Awards
24238 Hawthorne Boulevard
Torrance, CA 90505-6505
Tel: (310)541-1481
Fax: (310)541-4803
Web Site: http://www.edsf.org/scholarships.cfm

To provide financial assistance to college juniors, seniors, and graduate students interested in working with electronic documents as a career.

Title of Award: EDSF Board of Directors Scholarships **Area, Field, or Subject:** Computer and information sciences; Graphic art and design; Internet design and development; Marketing and distribution; Printing trades and industries; Telecommunications systems **Level of Education for which Award is Granted:** Four Year College, Graduate **Number Awarded:** 20 each year. **Funds Available:** The stipend is $2,000. **Duration:** 1 year.

Eligibility Requirements: This program is open to juniors, seniors, and graduate students who are working full time on a degree in the field of document communication, including marketing, graphic communication and arts, e-commerce, imaging science, printing, web authoring, electronic publishing, computer science, or telecommunications. Applicants must submit a statement of their career goals in the field of document communications, an essay on a topic related to their view of the future of the document management and production industry, a list of current professional and college extracurricular activities and achievements, college transcripts (GPA of 3.0 or higher), samples of their creative work, and 2 letters of recommendation. Financial need is not considered. **Deadline for Receipt:** May of each year.

3314 ■ ELECTRONIC DOCUMENT SYSTEMS FOUNDATION

Attn: EDSF Scholarship Awards
24238 Hawthorne Boulevard
Torrance, CA 90505-6505
Tel: (310)541-1481
Fax: (310)541-4803
Web Site: http://www.edsf.org/scholarships.cfm
To provide financial assistance to students in technical schools and community colleges who are interested in working with electronic documents as a career.

Title of Award: EDSF Board of Directors Technical and Community College Scholarship **Area, Field, or Subject:** Computer and information sciences; Graphic art and design; Internet design and development; Marketing and distribution; Printing trades and industries; Telecommunications systems **Level of Education for which Award is Granted:** Two Year College, Vocational/Occupational **Number Awarded:** 5 each year. **Funds Available:** The stipend is $1,000. **Duration:** 1 year.

Eligibility Requirements: This program is open to first- and second-year students at technical and trade schools and community colleges. Applicants must be working on a degree in the field of electronic document communication, including marketing, graphic communication and arts, e-commerce, imaging science, printing, web authoring, electronic publishing, computer science, or telecommunications. They must submit a 1-page essay on 1 of the following topics: 1) a definition of their career goals in the field of document management and communications; 2) a recent technological change and how it has or will affect the document communication industry; or 3) a definition of the document communication industry. Selection is based on the essay, extracurricular activities and achievements, high school transcripts (GPA of 3.0 or higher), samples of creative work, and 2 letters of recommendation. Financial need is not considered. **Deadline for Receipt:** May of each year.

3315 ■ ELECTRONIC DOCUMENT SYSTEMS FOUNDATION

Attn: EDSF Scholarship Awards
24238 Hawthorne Boulevard
Torrance, CA 90505-6505
Tel: (310)541-1481
Fax: (310)541-4803
Web Site: http://www.edsf.org/scholarships.cfm
To provide financial assistance to upper-division and graduate students interested in working with electronic documents as a career.

Title of Award: David Hoods Memorial Scholarship **Area, Field, or Subject:** Computer and information sciences; Graphic art and design; Internet design and development; Marketing and distribution; Printing trades and industries; Public relations; Telecommunications systems **Level of Education for which Award is Granted:** Four Year College, Graduate **Number Awarded:** 1 each year. **Funds Available:** The stipend is $2,000. **Duration:** 1 year.

Eligibility Requirements: This program is open to full-time juniors, seniors, and graduate students who demonstrate a strong interest in working with electronic documents as a career (including graphic com-

munications, document management, document content, and/or document distribution). Special consideration is given to students interested in marketing and public relations. Applicants must submit a statement of their career goals in the field of document communications, an essay on a topic related to their view of the future of the document management and production industry, a list of current professional and college extracurricular activities and achievements, college transcripts (GPA of 3.0 or higher), samples of their creative work, and 2 letters of recommendation. Financial need is not considered. **Deadline for Receipt:** May of each year.

3316 ■ ELECTRONIC DOCUMENT SYSTEMS FOUNDATION

Attn: EDSF Scholarship Awards
24238 Hawthorne Boulevard
Torrance, CA 90505-6505
Tel: (310)541-1481
Fax: (310)541-4803
Web Site: http://www.edsf.org/scholarships.cfm
To provide financial assistance to college juniors, seniors, and graduate students interested in working with electronic documents as a career.

Title of Award: John A. Lopiano Scholarship **Area, Field, or Subject:** Computer and information sciences; Graphic art and design; Internet design and development; Marketing and distribution; Printing trades and industries; Telecommunications systems **Level of Education for which Award is Granted:** Four Year College, Graduate **Number Awarded:** 1 each year. **Funds Available:** The stipend is $2,000. **Duration:** 1 year.

Eligibility Requirements: This program is open to juniors, seniors, and graduate students who are working full time on a degree in the field of document communication, including marketing, graphic communication and arts, e-commerce, imaging science, printing, web authoring, electronic publishing, computer science, or telecommunications. Priority consideration is given to students who work in or whose family member has worked or currently works in a segment of the high volume transaction output (HVTO) industry. Applicants must submit a statement of their career goals in the field of document communications, an essay on a topic related to their view of the future of the document management and production industry, a list of current professional and college extracurricular activities and achievements, college transcripts (GPA of 3.0 or higher), samples of their creative work, and 2 letters of recommendation. Financial need is not considered. **Deadline for Receipt:** May of each year. **Additional Information:** This program is sponsored by COPI/OutputLinks.

3317 ■ EPILEPSY FOUNDATION

Attn: Research Department
4351 Garden City Drive
Landover, MD 20785-7223
Tel: (301)459-3700
Free: 800-EFA-1000
Fax: (301)577-2684
E-mail: grants@efa.org
Web Site: http://www.epilepsyfoundation.org/research/grants.cfm
To provide funding to undergraduate and graduate students interested in working on a summer research training project in a field relevant to epilepsy.

Title of Award: Behavioral Sciences Student Fellowships in Epilepsy **Area, Field, or Subject:** Anthropology; Behavioral sciences; Counseling/Guidance; Economics; Epilepsy; Nursing; Political science; Psychology; Rehabilitation, Physical/Psychological; Social work; Sociology **Level of Education for which Award is Granted:** Graduate, Undergraduate **Number Awarded:** Varies each year; recently, 4 of these fellowships were awarded. **Funds Available:** The grant is $3,000. **Duration:** 3 months during the summer.

Eligibility Requirements: This program is open to undergraduate and graduate students in a behavioral science program relevant to epilepsy research or clinical care, including, but not limited to, sociology, social work, psychology, anthropology, nursing, economics, vocational rehabilitation, counseling, and political science. Applicants must be interested in working on an epilepsy research project under the supervision of a qualified mentor. Because the program is designed as a training opportunity, the quality of the training plans and environment are considered in the selection process. Other selection criteria include the quality of the proposed project, the relevance of the proposed work to epilepsy, the applicant's interest in the field of epilepsy, the applicant's qualifications, and the mentor's qualifications, including his or her commitment to the student and the project. U.S. citizenship is not required, but the project must be conducted in the United States. Applications from women, members of minority groups, and people with disabilities are especially encouraged. The program is not intended for students working on a dissertation research project. **Deadline for Receipt:** March of each year. **Additional Information:** This program is supported by the American Epilepsy Society, Abbott Laboratories, Ortho-McNeil Pharmaceutical Corporation, and Pfizer Inc.

3318 ■ FASHION GROUP INTERNATIONAL OF WASHINGTON

Attn: Julie Caine Brooks, Scholarship Chair
P.O. Box 1288
Great Falls, VA 22066
To provide financial assistance for college or graduate school to residents of Maryland, Virginia, and Washington, D. C. interested in preparing for a career in fashion or a fashion-related field.
Title of Award: Washington Fashion Group International Scholarship **Area, Field, or Subject:** Fashion design; Interior design; Journalism; Marketing and distribution; Photography; Textile science **Level of Education for which Award is Granted:** Graduate, Undergraduate **Number Awarded:** 1 each year. **Funds Available:** The maximum stipend is $5,000. **Duration:** 1 year; nonrenewable
Eligibility Requirements: This program is open to residents of Washington, D.C. and all cities and counties in Maryland and Virginia. Applicants must be graduating high school seniors or current undergraduate or graduate students enrolled in a fashion or fashion-related degree program (commercial arts, textiles and clothing design, interior design, journalism, merchandising, or photography). They must submit a 200-word personal statement on their career goals and motivation for entering a fashion-related career. Selection is based on that statement, academic achievement, creative ability, related work activity (paid or unpaid), extracurricular activities and awards, and 3 letters of reference. Finalists are interviewed and asked to submit portfolio material of their work. **Deadline for Receipt:** April of each year.

3319 ■ FISHER COMMUNICATIONS

Attn: Minority Scholarship
100 Fourth Avenue North, Suite 510
Seattle, WA 98109
Tel: (206)404-7000
Fax: (206)404-6037
E-mail: Info@fsci.com
Web Site: http://www.fsci.com/x100.xml
To provide financial assistance to minority college students in selected states who are interested in preparing for a career in broadcasting, marketing, or journalism.
Title of Award: Fisher Broadcasting Scholarships for Minorities **Area, Field, or Subject:** Broadcasting; Journalism; Marketing and distribution **Level of Education for which Award is Granted:** Undergraduate **Number Awarded:** Varies; a total of $10,000 is available for this program each year. **Funds Available:** A stipend is awarded (amount not specified). **Duration:** 1 year; recipients may reapply.
Eligibility Requirements: This program is open to students of non-white origin who are U.S. citizens, have a GPA of 2.5 or higher, and are at least sophomores enrolled in 1) a broadcasting, marketing, or journalism curriculum leading to a bachelor's degree at an accredited 4-year college or university; 2) a broadcast curriculum at an accredited community college, transferable to a 4-year baccalaureate degree program; or 3) a broadcast curriculum at an accredited vocational/technical school. Applicants must be either 1) residents of Washington, Oregon, Idaho, or Montana; or 2) attending a school in those states. They must submit an essay that explains their financial need, education and career goals, and school activities; a copy of their college transcript; and 2 letters of recommendation. Selection is based on need, academic achievement, and personal qualities. **Deadline for Receipt:** April of each year. **Additional Information:** This program began in 1987.

3320 ■ FLORIDA SEA GRANT COLLEGE PROGRAM

Attn: Director
University of Florida
Building 803 McCarty Drive

P.O. Box 110400
Gainesville, FL 32611-0400
Tel: (352)392-5870
Fax: (352)392-5113
Web Site: http://www.flseagrant.org/students/scholarships/index.htm
To provide financial assistance to undergraduate or graduate students working on a degree in a marine science-related field at any Florida university that participates in the Florida Sea Grant College Program.
Title of Award: Aylesworth Foundation for the Advancement of Marine Science Scholarships **Area, Field, or Subject:** Biological and clinical sciences; Economics; Engineering; Food science and technology; Marine biology **Level of Education for which Award is Granted:** Graduate, Undergraduate **Number Awarded:** Generally, 4 or more each year. **Funds Available:** The maximum stipend awarded is 65% of the annual official university or college cost of attendance or $4,000, whichever is less. **Duration:** 1 year; renewable until the recipient completes the degree.
Eligibility Requirements: Eligible to be nominated by their department chair are undergraduate or graduate students who are working on a degree in an academic discipline that has direct application in marine science (ranging from biology and engineering to economics and food science) at a university or college in Florida that participates in the Florida Sea Grant College Program. Financial need is the principal factor used in the selection process, although academic record, leadership, and personal character are also considered. Florida residents are given preference. **Deadline for Receipt:** November of each year. **Additional Information:** The Florida Sea Grant College Program, established in 1986, operates as a partnership between the Florida Board of Education and the U.S. National Oceanic and Atmospheric Administration. The participating institutions are Florida A&M University, Florida Gulf Coast University, Florida Atlantic University, Florida Institute of Technology, Florida International University, Florida State University, Harbor Branch Oceanographic Institution, Mote Marine Laboratory, New College of Florida, Nova Southeastern University, University of Central Florida, University of Florida, University of Miami, University of North Florida, University of South Florida, and University of West Florida. These scholarships are sponsored by the Aylesworth Foundation for the Advancement of Marine Science, the Southeastern Fisheries Association, and the Florida Sea Grant College Program.

3321 ■ FOUNDRY EDUCATIONAL FOUNDATION

1695 North Penny Lane
Schaumburg, IL 60173
Tel: (847)490-9200
Fax: (847)890-6270
E-mail: info@fefoffice.org
Web Site: http://www.fefinc.org
To provide financial assistance to undergraduate students, especially those in Wisconsin, who are interested in preparing for a career in the die casting industry.
Title of Award: AFS Wisconsin Past President Fund **Area, Field, or Subject:** Business; Manufacturing **Level of Education for which Award is Granted:** Undergraduate **Number Awarded:** 1 each year. **Funds Available:** The stipends range from $500 to $2,000 per year. **Duration:** 1 year.
Eligibility Requirements: This program is open to full-time undergraduate and graduate students who are U.S. citizens, have taken or plan to take courses in the die-casting process, and can demonstrate their intention to prepare for a career in the die-casting industry. Preference is given first to residents of Wisconsin within the area of the American Foundrymen's Society (AFS) chapter, then to residents of Wisconsin outside the AFS area, then to residents of states adjacent to Wisconsin, then to residents of other states. Preference is also given to students attending a college or university with an agreement with the Foundry Educational Foundation (FEF), then to students attending school in Wisconsin, then to students attending school in an adjacent state. In addition, preference is given to applicants who are currently participating in a co-op program involving the cast metal industry, who have work experience in the cast metal industry, who have any manufacturing work experience, and who have any work experience. **Deadline for Receipt:** January of each year.

Additional Information: This scholarship is provided by the Wisconsin Chapter of the American Foundrymen's Society (AFS).

3322 ■ FOUNDRY EDUCATIONAL FOUNDATION

1695 North Penny Lane
Schaumburg, IL 60173
Tel: (847)490-9200
Fax: (847)890-6270
E-mail: info@fefoffice.org
Web Site: http://www.fefinc.org
To provide financial assistance to undergraduate students who are interested in preparing for a career in the die casting industry.
Title of Award: David Laine Memorial Scholarship **Area, Field, or Subject:** Business; Manufacturing **Level of Education for which Award is Granted:** Undergraduate **Number Awarded:** 4 each year. **Funds Available:** The stipends range from $500 to $2,000 per year. **Duration:** 1 year.
Eligibility Requirements: This program is open to full-time undergraduate students who are h citizens of the United States, Canada, or Mexico, Applicants must have worked in the die casting industry for at least 3 months within the past year. Along with their application, they must submit a paper on their activities and results from their work in the die casing industry. **Deadline for Receipt:** September of each year. **Additional Information:** This scholarship, established in 1975, is jointly sponsored by the North American Die Casting Association and the Foundry Educational Foundation.

3323 ■ FOUNDRY EDUCATIONAL FOUNDATION

1695 North Penny Lane
Schaumburg, IL 60173
Tel: (847)490-9200
Fax: (847)890-6270
E-mail: info@fefoffice.org
Web Site: http://www.fefinc.org
To provide financial assistance to undergraduate and graduate students who are interested in preparing for a career in the ductile iron industry.
Title of Award: Keith Dwight Millis Scholarship **Area, Field, or Subject:** Business; Manufacturing **Level of Education for which Award is Granted:** Graduate, Undergraduate **Number Awarded:** 1 each year. **Funds Available:** The stipend is $2,000 per year. **Duration:** 1 year.
Eligibility Requirements: This program is open to full-time undergraduate and graduate students who are citizens of any country, are enrolled in a college or university in the United States, and have a demonstrated interest in ductile iron. Applicants must be registered with the Foundry Educational Foundation (FEF), but they are not required to attend FEF schools. As part of their application, they must explain their interest in ductile iron. **Deadline for Receipt:** October of each year. **Additional Information:** This scholarship is jointly sponsored by the Ductile Iron Society and the Foundry Educational Foundation.

3324 ■ FOUNDRY EDUCATIONAL FOUNDATION

1695 North Penny Lane
Schaumburg, IL 60173
Tel: (847)490-9200
Fax: (847)890-6270
E-mail: info@fefoffice.org
Web Site: http://www.fefinc.org
To provide financial assistance to college students in Indiana and adjoining states who are interested in preparing for a career in the die casting industry.
Title of Award: NADCA Indiana Chapter 25 Scholarship Fund **Area, Field, or Subject:** Business; Manufacturing **Level of Education for which Award is Granted:** Undergraduate **Number Awarded:** 1 each year. **Funds Available:** The stipends range from $500 to $2,000 per year. **Duration:** 1 year.
Eligibility Requirements: This program is open to full-time students who are U.S. citizens, have taken or plan to take courses in the die-casting process, and can demonstrate their intention to prepare for a career in the die-casting industry. Preference is given first to residents of central Indiana, then to residents of Indiana outside the central area, then to residents of states adjacent to Indiana. Preference is also given to students attending an Indiana college or university with an agreement with the Foundry Educational Foundation (FEF), then to students attending

school in Indiana, then to students attending an FEF school in an adjacent state. Preference is also given to applicants pursuing programs deemed most useful to the die casting industry, then to candidates with the best scholastic record. In addition, preference is given (in order) to applicants who are currently participating in a co-op program involving the die casting industry, who have work experience in the die casting industry, who have work experience in the cast metal industry, and who have any manufacturing work experience. Finally, preference is given to applicants who know or have worked for or with a member of Indiana Chapter 25 of the North American Die Casting Association. **Deadline for Receipt:** May of each year.

3325 ■ FOUNDRY EDUCATIONAL FOUNDATION

1695 North Penny Lane
Schaumburg, IL 60173
Tel: (847)490-9200
Fax: (847)890-6270
E-mail: info@fefoffice.org
Web Site: http://www.fefinc.org
To provide financial assistance to college students in Illinois and adjacent states who are interested in preparing for a career in the metal-casting industry.
Title of Award: Roy W. Schroeder Scholarship **Area, Field, or Subject:** Business; Manufacturing **Level of Education for which Award is Granted:** Undergraduate **Number Awarded:** 1 each year. **Funds Available:** The stipends range from $500 to $2,000 per year. **Duration:** 1 year.
Eligibility Requirements: This program is open to full-time students who are U.S. citizens, have taken or plan to take courses in metal casting, and can demonstrate their intention to prepare for a career in the metal-casting industry. Preference is given first to residents within the area of the American Foundrymen's Society (AFS) Chicago chapter, then to residents of Illinois, then to residents of states adjacent to Illinois. Preference is also given to students attending a college or university with an agreement with the Foundry Educational Foundation (FEF), then to students attending school in Illinois, then to students attending a school that meets FEF guidelines. In addition, preference is given first to applicants who have expressed interest in metal casting through job experience, then to candidates with the best scholastic record. **Deadline for Receipt:** October of each year.

3326 ■ FOUNDRY EDUCATIONAL FOUNDATION

1695 North Penny Lane
Schaumburg, IL 60173
Tel: (847)490-9200
Fax: (847)890-6270
E-mail: info@fefoffice.org
Web Site: http://www.fefinc.org
To provide financial assistance to undergraduate students from Minnesota, Wisconsin, and Iowa who are interested in preparing for a career in the die casting industry.
Title of Award: Twin City Chapter AFS Memorial Scholarship Fund **Area, Field, or Subject:** Business; Engineering, Metallurgical; Manufacturing **Level of Education for which Award is Granted:** Undergraduate **Number Awarded:** 1 each year. **Funds Available:** The stipends range from $500 to $2,000 per year. **Duration:** 1 year.
Eligibility Requirements: This program is open to full-time undergraduate students who are U.S. citizens, have taken or plan to take courses in the die-casting process, and can demonstrate their intention to prepare for a career in the die-casting industry. Preference is given first to residents of Minnesota, then to residents of western Wisconsin, then to residents of northern Iowa. Preference is also given to students attending a college or university with an agreement with the Foundry Educational Foundation (FEF) and to students enrolled in foundry-related courses. **Deadline for Receipt:** October of each year. **Additional Information:** This scholarship is provided by the Twin City Chapter of the American Foundrymen's Society (AFS).

3327 ■ GEORGIA CONCRETE & PRODUCTS ASSOCIATION

Attn: Scholarship Committee
100 Crescent Centre Parkway, Suite 110
Tucker, GA 30084
Tel: (770)621-9324
Fax: (770)621-9380

Web Site: http://www.gcpa.org/scholarships.htm
To provide financial assistance for college to high school seniors in Georgia or contiguous states, especially those interested in studying concrete industry management at Middle Tennessee State University (MTSU).

Title of Award: Georgia Concrete & Products Association Scholarships **Area, Field, or Subject:** Business; Business administration; Construction; Science **Level of Education for which Award is Granted:** Undergraduate **Number Awarded:** The scholarship is awarded to 1 student at MTSU or 2 other students each year. **Funds Available:** If the scholarship is awarded to a student at MTSU, the stipend is $2,000 per year. For other scholarship winners, the stipend is $1,000. **Duration:** For students at MTSU, support is provided for 4 years, as long as the recipient maintains full-time enrollment and a GPA of 2.5 or higher. For other students, the scholarship is for 1 year and nonrenewable.

Eligibility Requirements: This program is open to seniors graduating from high schools in Georgia or its contiguous states (Alabama, Florida, North Carolina, South Carolina, and Tennessee) who are recommended by an employee of a member company of the Georgia Concrete & Products Association. First priority is given to applicants planning to major in concrete industry management at MTSU. They must have an ACT score of at least 20 and a GPA of 2.8 or higher. Along with their application, they must submit an essay of 250 to 300 words on themselves, their goals, their aspirations, their desire for this scholarship, and why they are interested in a career in concrete industry management. If no MTSU student applies or qualifies, scholarships are awarded to the most outstanding applicants planning to major in business or the sciences at the college or university of their choice. **Deadline for Receipt:** March of each year.

3328 ■ H.H. HARRIS FOUNDATION

Attn: Trustee
30 South Wacker Drive, Suite 2300
Chicago, IL 60606
Tel: (312)346-7900
Fax: (312)346-0904
E-mail: JohnHH@aol.com
Web Site: http://www.afsinc.org/Harris.htm
To provide financial assistance to students and professionals in the metallurgical and casting of metals field.

Title of Award: H.H. Harris Foundation Scholarships **Area, Field, or Subject:** Business; Manufacturing; Metallurgy **Level of Education for which Award is Granted:** Graduate, Professional, Undergraduate **Number Awarded:** Varies each year. **Funds Available:** Stipends are at least $1,000. **Duration:** 1 year.

Eligibility Requirements: This program is open to U.S. citizens who are enrolled in an undergraduate or graduate program in the metallurgical and casting of metals field. Preference is given to undergraduates. Along with their application, they must submit documentation of financial need and a statement of purpose that summarizes their career plans and goals with regard to the cast metal and/or metallurgical fields. **Deadline for Receipt:** June of each year.

3329 ■ HARVEST EDUCATION FOUNDATION

P.O. Box 100
Romeo, MI 48065-0100
Tel: (586)752-6066
Web Site: http://www.marvac.org/harvestapp.html
To provide financial assistance for college to Michigan residents interested in preparing for a career in the manufactured homes, recreational vehicles, or campground industries.

Title of Award: HARVEST Scholarships **Area, Field, or Subject:** Design; Engineering; Management; Marketing and distribution; Personnel administration/human resources **Level of Education for which Award is Granted:** Undergraduate **Number Awarded:** 1 or more each year. **Funds Available:** A stipend is awarded (amount not specified). **Duration:** 1 year; may be renewed.

Eligibility Requirements: This program is open to Michigan students enrolled or planning to enroll at an accredited college or university to prepare for a career in the manufactured homes, recreational vehicles, or campground industries. Fields of study may include engineering, marketing, management, service, design, human resources, or any other discipline that will serve the needs of the industries. Applicants must

submit an essay of 200 to 300 words on their career goals and why they feel they deserve this scholarship. Selection is based on merit and/or financial need. **Deadline for Receipt:** March of each year. **Additional Information:** The HARVEST Education Foundation is a joint venture of the Michigan Manufactured Housing Association and the Michigan Association of Recreation Vehicles and Campgrounds, both at 2222 Association Drive, Okemos, MI 48864-5978, (517) 349-3300, E-mail: michhome@michhome.org and marvac@marvac.org.

3330 ■ HAWAI'I COMMUNITY FOUNDATION

Attn: Scholarship Department
1164 Bishop Street, Suite 800
Honolulu, HI 96813
Tel: (808)566-5570; 888-731-3863
Fax: (808)521-6286
E-mail: scholarships@hcf-hawaii.org
Web Site: http://www.hawaiicommunityfoundation.org/scholar/scholar.php
To provide financial assistance to Hawaii residents who are interested in studying marketing, law, or travel industry management in college or graduate school.

Title of Award: Bick Bickson Scholarship Fund **Area, Field, or Subject:** Law; Marketing and distribution; Travel and tourism **Level of Education for which Award is Granted:** Graduate, Undergraduate **Number Awarded:** Varies each year; recently, 2 of these scholarships were awarded. **Funds Available:** The amounts of the awards depend on the availability of funds and the need of the recipient; recently, stipends averaged $1,250. **Duration:** 1 year.

Eligibility Requirements: This program is open to Hawaii residents who are interested in majoring in marketing, law, or travel industry management on the undergraduate or graduate school level. They must be able to demonstrate academic achievement (GPA of 2.7 or higher), good moral character, and financial need. In addition to filling out the standard application form, applicants must write a short statement indicating their reasons for attending college, their planned course of study, and their career goals. **Deadline for Receipt:** February of each year. **Additional Information:** Recipients may attend college in Hawaii or on the mainland. Recipients must be full-time students.

3331 ■ HAWAI'I COMMUNITY FOUNDATION

Attn: Scholarship Department
1164 Bishop Street, Suite 800
Honolulu, HI 96813
Tel: (808)566-5570; 888-731-3863
Fax: (808)521-6286
E-mail: scholarships@hcf-hawaii.org
Web Site: http://www.hawaiicommunityfoundation.org/scholar/scholar.php
To provide financial assistance to Hawaii residents who are interested in preparing for a career in the arts.

Title of Award: PHG Foundation Scholarship **Area, Field, or Subject:** Art; Art industries and trade; Crafts **Level of Education for which Award is Granted:** Graduate, Undergraduate **Number Awarded:** Varies each year; recently, 5 of these scholarships were awarded. **Funds Available:** The amounts of the awards depend on the availability of funds and the need of the recipient; recently, stipends averaged $1,000. **Duration:** 1 year.

Eligibility Requirements: This program is open to Hawaii residents who are interested in majoring in art or arts and crafts (not video, film, culinary arts, or the performing arts). They may be studying full or part time, on the undergraduate or graduate school level. They must be able to demonstrate academic achievement (GPA of 2.7 or higher), good moral character, and financial need. In addition to filling out the standard application form, applicants must write a short statement indicating their reasons for attending college, their planned course of study, and their career goals. **Deadline for Receipt:** February of each year. **Additional Information:** Recipients may attend college in Hawaii or on the mainland. This scholarship was established by a foundation created by the Pacific Handcrafters Guild (PHG), P.O. Box 602, Waimanalo, HI 98795, (808) 948-3890.

3332 ■ HAWAI'I COMMUNITY FOUNDATION

Attn: Scholarship Department
1164 Bishop Street, Suite 800
Honolulu, HI 96813

Tel: (808)566-5570; 888-731-3863

Fax: (808)521-6286

E-mail: scholarships@hcf-hawaii.org

Web Site: http://www.hawaiicommunityfoundation.org/scholar/scholar.php

To provide financial assistance to residents of Hawaii for undergraduate or graduate studies in fields related to achieving world cooperation and international understanding.

Title of Award: Marion Maccarrell Scott Scholarship **Area, Field, or Subject:** Anthropology; Economics; Geography; History; International affairs and relations; Law; Peace studies; Philosophy; Political science; Psychology; Sociology **Level of Education for which Award is Granted:** Graduate, Undergraduate **Number Awarded:** Varies each year; recently, 258 of these scholarships were awarded. **Funds Available:** The amounts of the awards depend on the availability of funds and the need of the recipient; recently, stipends averaged $1,749. **Duration:** 1 year.

Eligibility Requirements: This program is open to graduates of public high schools in Hawaii. They must plan to attend school as full-time students (on the undergraduate or graduate level) on the mainland, majoring in history, government, political science, anthropology, economics, geography, international relations, law, psychology, philosophy, or sociology. They must be residents of the state of Hawaii, able to demonstrate financial need, interested in attending an accredited 2- or 4-year college or university, and able to demonstrate academic achievement (GPA of 2.8 or higher). Along with their application, they must submit an essay on their commitment to world peace that includes their learning experiences (courses, clubs, community activities, or travel) related to achieving world peace and international understanding and explaining how their experiences have enhanced their ability to achieve those goals. **Deadline for Receipt:** February of each year.

3333 ■ HISPANIC SCHOLARSHIP FUND

Attn: Selection Committee

55 Second Street, Suite 1500

San Francisco, CA 94105

Tel: (415)808-2350; 877-HSF-INFO

Fax: (415)808-2302

E-mail: college1@hsf.net

Web Site: http://www.hsf.net/scholarship/programs/citigroup.php

To provide financial assistance to Hispanic upper-division students working on a degree related to business at designated universities.

Title of Award: HSF/Citigroup Fellows Program **Area, Field, or Subject:** Business administration; Economics; Finance **Level of Education for which Award is Granted:** Four Year College **Number Awarded:** 1 or more each year. **Funds Available:** The stipend is $5,000 per year. **Duration:** 2 years (the junior and senior years of college).

Eligibility Requirements: This program is open to U.S. citizens, permanent residents, and visitors with a passport stamped I-551 who are of Hispanic heritage. Applicants must be 1) residents of or enrolled full time at a 4-year college or university in the New York City metropolitan area, the Miami/Fort Lauderdale area, Tampa, Dallas, Los Angeles, or the San Francisco Bay area; or 2) enrolled full time at Columbia University, Cornell University, Dartmouth University, Duke University, Georgetown University, Harvard University, New York University, Northwestern University, Princeton University, Rutgers University, Stanford University, University of California at Los Angeles, University of Chicago, University of Pennsylvania, University of Virginia, University of Texas at Austin, or Yale University. They must be entering their junior year with a GPA of 3.2 or higher and a major in business, economics, finance, or business administration. Along with their application, they must submit 600-word essays on 1) how their Hispanic heritage, family upbringing, and/or role models have influenced their personal long-term goals; 2) how they contribute to their community and what they have learned from their experiences; and 3) an academic challenge they have faced and how they have overcome it. Selection is based on academic achievement, personal strengths, leadership, and financial need. **Deadline for Receipt:** April of each year. **Additional Information:** This program is funded by the Citigroup Foundation, which also arranges for a Citigroup employee to be paired with each student recipient as a mentor. Students are also invited

to a professional development conference in the fall of their junior and senior years, with all expenses paid by the foundation.

3334 ■ HISPANIC SCHOLARSHIP FUND

Attn: Selection Committee

55 Second Street, Suite 1500

San Francisco, CA 94105

Tel: (415)808-2350; 877-HSF-INFO

Fax: (415)808-2302

E-mail: college1@hsf.net

Web Site: http://www.hsf.net/scholarship/programs/jpmorgan.php

To provide financial assistance to Hispanic upper-division students working on a degree in a field related to business.

Title of Award: JPMorganChase Scholarship Program of the Hispanic Scholarship Fund **Area, Field, or Subject:** Business administration; Economics; Finance **Level of Education for which Award is Granted:** Undergraduate **Number Awarded:** 1 or more each year. **Funds Available:** The stipend is $2,500. **Duration:** 1 year.

Eligibility Requirements: This program is open to U.S. citizens, permanent residents, and visitors with a passport stamped I-551 who are of Hispanic heritage. Applicants must be currently enrolled full time as a sophomore or junior at an accredited 4-year college or university in the United States, Puerto Rico, or the U.S. Virgin Islands. They must be majoring in business administration, finance, or economics with a GPA of 3.0 or higher. Along with their application, they must submit 600-word essays on 1) how their Hispanic heritage, family upbringing, and/or role models have influenced their personal long-term goals; 2) how they contribute to their community and what they have learned from their experiences; and 3) an academic challenge they have faced and how they have overcome it. Selection is based on academic achievement, personal strengths, leadership, and financial need. **Deadline for Receipt:** November of each year. **Additional Information:** This program is jointly sponsored by JPMorganChase and the Hispanic Scholarship Fund (HSF).

3335 ■ IMPERIAL POLK ADVERTISING FEDERATION

Attn: Scholarship Program

P.O. Box 24201

Lakeland, FL 33802-4201

Tel: (863)858-3736

Fax: (863)858-3736

Web Site: http://www.polkadfed.com

To provide financial assistance to undergraduate students majoring in fields related to advertising at Florida colleges.

Title of Award: William E. Gregory Scholarship **Area, Field, or Subject:** Advertising; Communications; Graphic art and design; Marketing and distribution **Level of Education for which Award is Granted:** Undergraduate **Number Awarded:** 1 or more each year. **Funds Available:** A total of $2,000 is available for this program each year. **Duration:** 1 year; nonrenewable.

Eligibility Requirements: This program is open to full-time undergraduate students at universities, colleges, and technical schools in Florida. Applicants must be working on a degree in advertising, communications, graphic design, or marketing. They must have a GPA of 3.0 or higher. Along with their application, they must submit 1) a 500-word essay describing their future professional and educational goals; and 2) a project they have recently completed for a class or internship. Financial need is not considered in the selection process. **Deadline for Receipt:** November of each year. **Additional Information:** Information is also available from Samantha Hocker, Scholarship Chair, (863) 701-7789, E-mail: shocker@keisercollege.edu.

3336 ■ INTERNATIONAL FOODSERVICE EDITORIAL COUNCIL

P.O. Box 491

Hyde Park, NY 12538

Tel: (845)229-6973

Fax: (845)229-6993

E-mail: ifec@aol.com

Web Site: http://www.ifec-is-us.com

To provide financial assistance to undergraduate or graduate students who are interested in preparing for a career in communications in the food service industry.

Title of Award: IFEC Scholarships **Area, Field, or Subject:** Communications; Creative writing; Culinary arts; English language and literature;

Food science and technology; Food service careers; Graphic art and design; Hotel, institutional, and restaurant management; Journalism; Management; Marketing and distribution; Nutrition; Photography; Photography, Journalistic; Public relations **Level of Education for which Award is Granted:** Master's, Undergraduate **Number Awarded:** Varies each year; recently, 5 of these scholarships were awarded. **Funds Available:** The stipend is $3,000 per year. **Duration:** 1 year.

Eligibility Requirements: This program is open to currently-enrolled college students who are working on an associate, bachelor's, or master's degree. They must be enrolled full time and planning on a career in editorial, public relations, photography, food styling, or a related aspect of communications in the food service industry. The following food service majors are considered appropriate for this program: culinary arts; hospitality management; hotel, restaurant, and institutional management; dietetics; food science and technology; and nutrition. Applicable communications areas include journalism, English, mass communications, public relations, marketing, broadcast journalism, creative writing, graphic arts, and photography. Selection is based on academic record, character references, and demonstrated financial need. **Deadline for Receipt:** March of each year.

3337 ■ IOWA READY MIXED CONCRETE ASSOCIATION

Attn: Scholarship Committee
380 S.E. Delaware Avenue
Ankeny, IA 50021
Tel: (515)965-4575
Fax: (515)963-4010
Web Site: http://www.iowareadymix.org
To provide financial assistance to undergraduates at colleges and universities in Iowa who are preparing for a career in the concrete, construction, or engineering industries.

Title of Award: Iowa Ready Mixed Concrete Association Scholarship Program **Area, Field, or Subject:** Business; Construction; Engineering **Level of Education for which Award is Granted:** Four Year College **Number Awarded:** At least 3 scholarships at $1,000 and 4 at $500 are awarded each year. **Funds Available:** Stipends are $1,000 or $500. **Duration:** 1 year.

Eligibility Requirements: This program is open to students who have achieved at least sophomore status at a 4-year college or university in Iowa. Applicants must be working on a degree in an area that will prepare them for a career in the ready mixed concrete or construction and engineering industries. Preference is given to applicants who are residents of Iowa, related to an employee of a member company of the Iowa Ready Mixed Concrete Association, and experienced in the ready mixed concrete industry. Along with their application, they must submit a 1-page essay explaining their career goals, why they are applying for a scholarship, and why they might consider employment in the ready mixed concrete, construction, or engineering fields. **Deadline for Receipt:** December of each year.

3338 ■ KNIGHT RIDDER, INC.

Attn: Office of Diversity
50 West San Fernando Street, Suite 1200
San Jose, CA 95113
Tel: (408)938-7734
Fax: (408)938-7755
Web Site: http://www.kri.com/career/internships.html
To provide financial assistance and work experience to students at selected Historically Black Colleges and Universities (HBCUs) who are studying advertising, business, or journalism.

Title of Award: Knight Ridder HBCU Scholarships **Area, Field, or Subject:** Advertising; Business administration; Journalism **Level of Education for which Award is Granted:** Four Year College **Number Awarded:** Varies each year. **Funds Available:** The stipend is $2,500 per year. Recipients also work as an intern at a Knight Ridder newspaper during the summer after their junior year and receive a salary according to the newspaper's normal scale. **Duration:** 1 year; may be renewed for 1 additional year, if the recipient maintains a GPA of 3.0 or higher.

Eligibility Requirements: This program is open to students at selected HBCUs who are entering their junior year. Applicants must be majoring in advertising, business, or journalism. **Additional Information:** The participating HBCUs are Howard University, Florida A&M University, Morehouse College, and Spelman College. Further information is avail-

able from the placement office at those institutions.

3339 ■ KNIGHT RIDDER, INC.

Attn: Office of Diversity
50 West San Fernando Street, Suite 1200
San Jose, CA 95113
Tel: (408)938-7734
Fax: (408)938-7755
Web Site: http://www.knightridder.com/career/internships.html
To provide financial assistance and work experience to minority high school seniors who are interested in going to college to prepare for a career in journalism.

Title of Award: Knight Ridder Minority Scholars Program **Area, Field, or Subject:** Advertising; Graphic art and design; Information science and technology; Journalism; Marketing and distribution; Photography, Journalistic **Level of Education for which Award is Granted:** Undergraduate **Number Awarded:** Up to 5 each year: 2 for news, 2 for business, and 1 for either. **Funds Available:** The stipend is $5,000 per year for the freshman and sophomore year and $15,000 per year for the junior and senior year. **Duration:** 1 year; may be renewed for up to 3 additional years, if the recipient maintains a GPA of 3.0 or higher and satisfactory performance on internships.

Eligibility Requirements: This program is open to minority seniors graduating from high schools in areas served by Knight Ridder. Applicants must be interested in attending college to prepare for a career in the newspaper industry. They first apply to their local Knight Ridder newspaper and compete for local scholarships; selected winners are then nominated for this award. Both "news" and "business" students are eligible. **Additional Information:** Recipients are offered an internship opportunity at a Knight Ridder newspaper during the summer. News scholars work in the newsroom, writing and editing stories, taking photographs, crafting illustrations, and designing news pages. Business scholars complete internships in advertising, marketing, information technology, circulation, and other areas essential to the industry. At the end of the sophomore year, recipients must agree to work at a Knight Ridder newspaper for 1 year after graduation.

3340 ■ KNIGHT RIDDER NEWSPAPERS-WASHINGTON BUREAU

Attn: Anthony Pugh
700 12th Street, N.W., Suite 1000
Washington, DC 20005-3994
Tel: (202)383-6013
Fax: (202)383-3738
E-mail: tpugh@krwashington.com
Web Site: http://www.krwashington.com
To provide financial assistance to minority high school seniors from the Washington, D.C. area who are interested in attending college to prepare for a career in the newspaper industry.

Title of Award: Washington Bureau Minority Scholarships **Area, Field, or Subject:** Advertising; Business administration; Computer and information sciences; Graphic art and design; Journalism; Photography, Journalistic **Level of Education for which Award is Granted:** Undergraduate **Number Awarded:** 2 each year. **Funds Available:** The stipend is $1,000. **Duration:** 1 year.

Eligibility Requirements: This program is open to minority seniors graduating from high schools in the metropolitan area of Washington, D.C. Applicants must be able to demonstrate an interest in journalism, but they are not required to have been school newspaper reporters or editors. They may be photographers, graphic artists, computer experts, delivery workers with an interest in circulation, or business and advertising staff members. Along with their application, they must submit a transcript of grades (with a GPA of 3.0 or higher), SAT/ACT scores, 2 letters of recommendation, a list of journalism or business experience, information on extracurricular activities, up to 5 samples of work with bylines (for journalism applicants), and a 500-word essay on why they want to prepare for a career in journalism or communication business. **Deadline for Receipt:** January of each year. **Additional Information:** The recipients of these scholarships are entered into competition for the Knight Ridder Minority Scholarship Program of $40,000 over 4 years.

3341 ■ KNOWLEDGE MATTERS, INC.

85 Woodland Drive
Florence, MA 01062

Tel: (413)587-9940; 877-965-3276
Fax: (413)584-8485
E-mail: info@KnowledgeMatters.com
Web Site: http://www.KnowledgeMatters.com/scholarships
To provide financial assistance for college to high school students enrolled in business or marketing courses.
Title of Award: Virtual Business Scholarship **Area, Field, or Subject:** Business administration; Marketing and distribution **Level of Education for which Award is Granted:** Undergraduate **Number Awarded:** 3 each year. **Funds Available:** The highest-ranked applicant receives a $1,000 scholarship, second a $500 scholarship, and third a $250 scholarship. **Duration:** 1 year.
Eligibility Requirements: This program is open to high school juniors and seniors enrolled in business or marketing courses. Applicants must be able to demonstrate excellence in business or marketing classes and interest and accomplishment in the use of technologies in those subjects. They must be nominated by their teacher, who works in coordination with the adviser for their state organization of Business Professionals of America (BPA), Future Business Leaders of America (FBLA), or DECA. Along with their application, they must submit an essay on what they have gained from their technology experiences within the business and marketing subject areas. **Deadline for Receipt:** March of each year.

3342 ■ LOWE'S COMPANIES, INC.
Attn: Scholarship Program
P.O. Box 1111
North Wilkesboro, NC 28656
Tel: (336)658-4104
Free: 800-44-LOWES
Web Site: http://www.lowes.com/scholarships
To provide financial assistance to students at selected community and technical colleges who are preparing for a career in a business or technical field related to Lowe's stores.
Title of Award: Lowe's Educational Scholarship Program **Area, Field, or Subject:** Business; Construction; Drafting; Electronics; Heating, air conditioning, and refrigeration; Horticulture **Level of Education for which Award is Granted:** Two Year College, Vocational/Occupational **Number Awarded:** Varies each year; since the program was established, more than 150 of these scholarships have been awarded. **Funds Available:** Stipends are $2,000 for full-time students, $1,000 for three-quarter time students, or $800 for half-time students. **Duration:** 1 year; may be renewed if the recipient qualifies for employment at Lowe's.
Eligibility Requirements: This program is open to students who are at least 18 years of age and currently enrolled in a community or technical college that is cooperating with Lowe's stores. Applicants must intend to prepare for a career in an approved discipline within the business division (business management, business administration) or vocational/technical division (air conditioning, heating and refrigeration, construction, electrical or electronics, industrial maintenance, machining, mechanical drafting and design, plumbing, carpentry, or horticulture) of Lowe's. They must have completed at least 1 semester with a GPA of 2.0 or higher. Applications are accepted from current Lowe's employees, but students working for another major retailer are not eligible. **Additional Information:** This program was established in 1999. Currently, 32 community and technical colleges are participating in the program. For a list, contact Lowe's.

3343 ■ MARINE TRADES ASSOCIATION OF NEW JERSEY
Attn: Executive Director
2516 Highway 35, Second Floor
Manasquan, NJ 08736
Tel: (732)292-1051
Fax: (732)292-1041
E-mail: info@mtanj.org
Web Site: http://www.mtanj.org
To provide financial assistance to residents of New Jersey interested in attending a vocational/technical school to prepare for a career in the marine trades.
Title of Award: Marine Trades Association of New Jersey Scholarships **Area, Field, or Subject:** Business; Transportation **Level of Education for which Award is Granted:** Vocational/Occupational **Number Awarded:** 1 each year. **Funds Available:** The stipend is $1,500. **Duration:** 1 year.
Eligibility Requirements: This program is open to New Jersey residents who are recent high school graduates. Applicants must desire to succeed

in a marine industry vocational/technical program and to prepare for a career in the recreational marine industry in New Jersey. Selection is based on personal character and ability. **Deadline for Receipt:** April of each year.

3344 ■ MICHIGAN AGGREGATES ASSOCIATION
3474 Alaiedon Parkway, Suite 700
Okemos, MI 48864
Tel: (517)381-1732
Fax: (517)381-1796
E-mail: contactmaa@miagg.org
Web Site: http://www.miagg.org
To provide financial assistance to undergraduate and graduate students affiliated with the Michigan Aggregates Association (MAA).
Title of Award: Michigan Aggregates Association Scholarships **Area, Field, or Subject:** Business; Engineering, Mining and Mineral; Mining **Level of Education for which Award is Granted:** Graduate, Undergraduate **Number Awarded:** 1 or more each year. **Funds Available:** The stipend is $1,000. **Duration:** 1 year; nonrenewable.
Eligibility Requirements: This program is open to students entering or attending an accredited institution of higher education who are immediate relatives of an MAA member or an MAA member employee or relative. Applicants must be working on an undergraduate or graduate degree in a field related to the extraction of mineral resources. Along with their application, they must submit an essay (up to 250 words) on their interest in the aggregate/mineral extraction industry. Financial need is not considered in the selection process. **Deadline for Receipt:** April of each year.

3345 ■ NATIONAL ASSOCIATION OF NEGRO BUSINESS AND PROFESSIONAL WOMEN'S CLUBS
Attn: Scholarship Committee
1806 New Hampshire Avenue, N.W.
Washington, DC 20009-3208
Tel: (202)483-4206
Fax: (202)462-7253
E-mail: nanbpwc@aol.com
Web Site: http://www.nanbpwc.org/ScholarshipApplications.asp
To provide financial assistance to African American women studying journalism, economics, or a related field in college.
Title of Award: Dr. Julianne Malveaux Scholarship **Area, Field, or Subject:** Economics; Journalism **Level of Education for which Award is Granted:** Undergraduate **Number Awarded:** 1 or more each year. **Funds Available:** The stipend is $1,000. **Duration:** 1 year.
Eligibility Requirements: This program is open to African American women enrolled in an accredited college or university as a sophomore or junior. Applicants must have a GPA of 3.0 or higher and be majoring in journalism, economics, or a related field. **Deadline for Receipt:** February of each year.

3346 ■ NATIONAL ASSOCIATION OF WOMEN IN CONSTRUCTION-GRANITE STATE CHAPTER 218
c/o Bayview Construction Corporation
170 West Road, Suite 10
Portsmouth, NH 03801
Web Site: http://www.geocities.com/nawicnh/scholarship.htm
To provide financial assistance to New Hampshire residents who are majoring in a construction-related field.
Title of Award: Granite State Chapter NAWIC Scholarships **Area, Field, or Subject:** Business; Construction; Engineering; Engineering, Electrical **Level of Education for which Award is Granted:** Undergraduate **Number Awarded:** 1 each year. **Funds Available:** The stipend is $1,000. **Duration:** 1 year.
Eligibility Requirements: This program is open to New Hampshire residents (male or female) who are entering 1) the final year of a 2-year school or 2) the junior or senior year of a 4-year school. Applicants must be majoring in a construction-related field (e.g., engineering, electrical, plumbing, carpentry, or general construction) and have a GPA of 2.0 or higher. Along with their application, they must submit a 150-word essay on why they have chosen the construction industry for their career. **Deadline for Receipt:** March of each year. **Additional Information:** The recipient's education institution may not utilize this scholarship as a reduction from previously granted financial aid of any form.

3347 ■ NATIONAL ASSOCIATION OF WOMEN IN CONSTRUCTION-MAINE CHAPTER 276

P.O. Box 366
Hallowell, ME 04347
Tel: (207)623-4683
E-mail: nawicmaine@aol.com
Web Site: http://www.nawicmaine.org
To provide financial assistance to Maine residents who are working on a college degree in a field related to construction.

Title of Award: Maine Chapter 276 Scholarships **Area, Field, or Subject:** Architecture; Business; Construction; Engineering, Civil; Welding **Level of Education for which Award is Granted:** Undergraduate **Number Awarded:** Varies each year; recently, 7 of these scholarships were awarded. **Funds Available:** Stipends range from $500 to $1,000. **Duration:** 1 year.

Eligibility Requirements: This program is open to residents of Maine who are enrolled in a postsecondary educational program. Applicants must be preparing for a career in construction, including carpentry, civil engineering, architecture, welding, electrical, plumbing, or construction management. Along with their application, they must submit a 50-word statement on why they have chosen a career in construction. Selection is based on academic achievement and financial need. **Deadline for Receipt:** April of each year. **Additional Information:** Information is also available from Joyce Newman, 3 Hillcrest Street, Hallowell, ME 04347.

3348 ■ NATIONAL DAIRY PROMOTION AND RESEARCH BOARD

c/o Dairy Management Inc.
10255 West Higgins Road, Suite 900
Rosemont, IL 60018-5616
Tel: (847)803-2000
Fax: (847)803-2077
E-mail: marykateg@rosedmi.com
Web Site: http://www.dairycheckoff.com/DairyCheckoff/about/scholarship.htm
To provide financial assistance to undergraduate students in fields related to the dairy industry.

Title of Award: NDPRB Undergraduate Scholarship Program **Area, Field, or Subject:** Business administration; Communications; Dairy science; Economics; Education; Food science and technology; Journalism; Marketing and distribution; Nutrition; Public relations **Level of Education for which Award is Granted:** Four Year College **Number Awarded:** 20 each year: the James H. Loper Jr. Memorial Scholarship at $2,500 and 19 other scholarships at $1,500. **Funds Available:** Stipends are $2,500 or $1,500. **Duration:** 1 year; may be renewed.

Eligibility Requirements: This program is open to sophomores, juniors, and seniors enrolled in college and university programs that emphasize dairy. Eligible majors include agricultural education, business, communications and/or public relations, economics, food science, journalism, marketing, and nutrition. Fields related to production (e.g., animal science) are not eligible. Selection is based on academic performance; interest in a career in dairy; involvement in extracurricular activities, especially those relating to dairy; and evidence of leadership ability, initiative, character, and integrity. The applicant who is judged most outstanding is awarded the James H. Loper Jr. Memorial Scholarship. **Deadline for Receipt:** May of each year. **Additional Information:** Dairy Management Inc. manages this program on behalf of the National Dairy Promotion and Research Board (NDPRB).

3349 ■ NATIONAL FFA ORGANIZATION

Attn: Scholarship Office
6060 FFA Drive
P.O. Box 68960
Indianapolis, IN 46268-0960
Tel: (317)802-4321
Fax: (317)802-5321
E-mail: scholarships@ffa.org
Web Site: http://www.ffa.org
To provide financial assistance to women and minority FFA members who are interested in studying specified agribusiness fields in college.

Title of Award: BASF Agricultural Products Scholarships **Area, Field, or Subject:** Agribusiness; Marketing and distribution **Level of Education for which Award is Granted:** Four Year College **Number Awarded:** 7 each year. **Funds Available:** The stipend is $1,000. Funds are paid directly to the recipient. **Duration:** 1 year; nonrenewable.

Eligibility Requirements: This program is open to members who are either graduating high school seniors planning to enroll in college or students already enrolled in college. Applicants must 1) be interested in working full time on a 4-year degree in agricultural marketing, merchandising, or sales; 2) be women or members of a minority group; 3) have a GPA of 3.0 or higher; 4) have participated in community service; and 5) be able to demonstrate strong leadership skills and financial need. Selection is based on academic achievement (10 points for GPA, 10 points for SAT or ACT score, 10 points for class rank), leadership in FFA activities (30 points), leadership in community activities (10 points), and participation in the Supervised Agricultural Experience (SAE) program (30 points). U.S. citizenship is required. **Deadline for Receipt:** February of each year. **Additional Information:** Funding for these scholarships is provided by BASF Agricultural Products.

3350 ■ NATIONAL FFA ORGANIZATION

Attn: Scholarship Office
6060 FFA Drive
P.O. Box 68960
Indianapolis, IN 46268-0960
Tel: (317)802-4321
Fax: (317)802-5321
E-mail: scholarships@ffa.org
Web Site: http://www.ffa.org
To provide financial assistance to FFA members from selected states interested in studying field related to agribusiness in college.

Title of Award: Burlington Northern Santa Fe Corporation Scholarships **Area, Field, or Subject:** Agribusiness; Agriculture, Economic aspects; Finance; Marketing and distribution **Level of Education for which Award is Granted:** Four Year College **Number Awarded:** 10 each year: 1 from each of the eligible states. **Funds Available:** The stipend is $1,250 per year. Funds are paid directly to the recipient. **Duration:** 1 year; may be renewed up to 3 additional years provided the recipient maintains a GPA of 3.0 or higher.

Eligibility Requirements: This program is open to members who are graduating high school seniors planning to enroll full time in college. Applicants must be residents of California, Illinois, Iowa, Kansas, Minnesota, Montana, Nebraska, North Dakota, South Dakota, or Texas planning to work on a 4-year degree in the following areas of agriculture: business management, finance, economics, sales, and marketing. They must have a GPA of 3.0 or higher. Selection is based on academic achievement (10 points for GPA, 10 points for SAT or ACT score, 10 points for class rank), leadership in FFA activities (30 points), leadership in community activities (10 points), and participation in the Supervised Agricultural Experience (SAE) program (30 points). U.S. citizenship is required. **Deadline for Receipt:** February of each year. **Additional Information:** Funding for these scholarships is provided by the Burlington Northern Santa Fe Foundation.

3351 ■ NATIONAL FFA ORGANIZATION

Attn: Scholarship Office
6060 FFA Drive
P.O. Box 68960
Indianapolis, IN 46268-0960
Tel: (317)802-4321
Fax: (317)802-5321
E-mail: scholarships@ffa.org
Web Site: http://www.ffa.org
To provide financial assistance for college to FFA members who are interested in majoring in selected fields of agribusiness.

Title of Award: CNH Capital Scholarships **Area, Field, or Subject:** Agribusiness; Finance; Management; Marketing and distribution **Level of Education for which Award is Granted:** Four Year College **Number Awarded:** 26 each year. **Funds Available:** The stipend is $1,250 per year. Funds are paid directly to the recipient. **Duration:** 1 year; nonrenewable.

Eligibility Requirements: This program is open to members who are graduating high school seniors planning to enroll full time in college or undergraduates already enrolled. Applicants must be working on or planning to work on a 4-year degree in the following areas of agriculture: management, finance, marketing, or sales. They must have a GPA of 3.5 or higher. Selection is based on academic achievement (10 points for GPA, 10 points for SAT or ACT score, 10 points for class rank), leadership in FFA activities (30 points), leadership in community activities (10 points), and participation in the Supervised Agricultural Experience (SAE) program (30 points). U.S. citizenship is required. **Deadline for Receipt:** February of each year. **Additional Information:** Funding for these scholarships is provided by CNH Capital.

3352 ■ NATIONAL FFA ORGANIZATION

Attn: Scholarship Office
6060 FFA Drive
P.O. Box 68960
Indianapolis, IN 46268-0960
Tel: (317)802-4321
Fax: (317)802-5321
E-mail: scholarships@ffa.org
Web Site: http://www.ffa.org
To provide financial assistance to FFA members who are interested in studying agriculture in college.

Title of Award: Garst Seed Company Scholarship **Area, Field, or Subject:** Agribusiness; Agricultural sciences; Communications; Education; Marketing and distribution **Level of Education for which Award is Granted:** Four Year College **Number Awarded:** 25 each year: 10 to students with any agricultural major, 5 to students majoring in agricultural communications or education, and 10 to students in agricultural marketing, merchandising, or sales. **Funds Available:** The stipend is $1,000. Funds are paid directly to the recipient. **Duration:** 1 year; nonrenewable.
Eligibility Requirements: This program is open to members who are graduating high school seniors planning to enroll or students currently enrolled full time in college. Applicants must be interested in working on a 4-year college degree in agriculture; in agricultural communications or education; or in agricultural marketing, merchandising, or sales. Selection is based on academic achievement (10 points for GPA, 10 points for SAT or ACT score, 10 points for class rank), leadership in FFA activities (30 points), leadership in community activities (10 points), and participation in the Supervised Agricultural Experience (SAE) program (30 points). U.S. citizenship is required. **Deadline for Receipt:** February of each year. **Additional Information:** Funding for this scholarship is provided by Garst Seed Company.

3353 ■ NATIONAL FFA ORGANIZATION

Attn: Scholarship Office
6060 FFA Drive
P.O. Box 68960
Indianapolis, IN 46268-0960
Tel: (317)802-4321
Fax: (317)802-5321
E-mail: scholarships@ffa.org
Web Site: http://www.ffa.org
To provide financial assistance to FFA members from selected states who are interested in studying agriculture or agribusiness in college.

Title of Award: Mid-States Wool Growers Cooperative Association Scholarship **Area, Field, or Subject:** Agribusiness; Agricultural sciences; Business **Level of Education for which Award is Granted:** Four Year College **Number Awarded:** 1 each year. **Funds Available:** The stipend is $1,000. Funds are paid directly to the recipient. **Duration:** 1 year; nonrenewable.
Eligibility Requirements: This program is open to members who are graduating high school seniors planning to enroll full time in college. Applicants must be residents of Illinois, Indiana, Iowa, Kansas, Kentucky, Michigan, Minnesota, Missouri, Nebraska, North Carolina, North Dakota, Ohio, Oklahoma, Pennsylvania, South Dakota, Virginia, or Wisconsin interested in working on a 4-year degree in agriculture or agribusiness. They must be sheep producers or from a family of sheep producers with an operation of 20 or more ewes; advisors must confirm this sheep involvement. Selection is based on academic achievement (10 points for GPA, 10 points for SAT or ACT score, 10 points for class rank), leadership in FFA activities (30 points), leadership in community activities (10 points), and participation in the Supervised Agricultural Experience (SAE) program (30 points). U.S. citizenship is required. **Deadline for Receipt:** February of each year. **Additional Information:** Funding for this scholarship is provided by the Mid-States Wool Growers Cooperative Association.

3354 ■ NATIONAL FFA ORGANIZATION

Attn: Scholarship Office
6060 FFA Drive

P.O. Box 68960
Indianapolis, IN 46268-0960
Tel: (317)802-4321
Fax: (317)802-5321
E-mail: scholarships@ffa.org
Web Site: http://www.ffa.org
To provide financial assistance to FFA members who wish to study agribusiness and related fields in college.

Title of Award: National FFA Scholarships for Undergraduates in the Social Sciences **Area, Field, or Subject:** Agribusiness; Agriculture, Economic aspects; Education; Finance; Marketing and distribution **Level of Education for which Award is Granted:** Undergraduate **Number Awarded:** Varies; generally, a total of approximately 1,000 scholarships are awarded annually by the association. **Funds Available:** Stipends vary, but most are at least $1,000. **Duration:** 1 year or more.
Eligibility Requirements: This program is open to current and former members of the organization who are working or planning to work full time on a degree in fields related to business and the social sciences; this includes: agribusiness, agricultural economics, agricultural education, agricultural finance, and agricultural marketing. For most of the scholarships, applicants must be high school seniors; others are open to students currently enrolled in college. The program includes a large number of designated scholarships that specify the locations where the members must live, the schools they must attend, the fields of study they must pursue, or other requirements. Some consider family income in the selection process, but most do not. Selection is based on academic achievement (10 points for GPA, 10 points for SAT or ACT score, 10 points for class rank), leadership in FFA activities (30 points), leadership in community activities (10 points), and participation in the Supervised Agricultural Experience (SAE) program (30 points). U.S. citizenship is required. **Deadline for Receipt:** February of each year. **Additional Information:** Funding for these scholarships is provided by many different corporate sponsors.

3355 ■ NATIONAL FFA ORGANIZATION

Attn: Scholarship Office
6060 FFA Drive
P.O. Box 68960
Indianapolis, IN 46268-0960
Tel: (317)802-4321
Fax: (317)802-5321
E-mail: scholarships@ffa.org
Web Site: http://www.ffa.org
To provide financial assistance to current or former FFA members who are interested in studying a field related to agriculture at a college or university in designated states.

Title of Award: Norfolk Southern Foundation Scholarships **Area, Field, or Subject:** Agribusiness; Agricultural sciences; Communications; Education; Engineering, Agricultural; Finance; Forestry; Management; Marketing and distribution **Level of Education for which Award is Granted:** Four Year College **Number Awarded:** 3 each year. **Funds Available:** The stipend is $1,000. Funds are paid directly to the recipient. **Duration:** 1 year; nonrenewable.
Eligibility Requirements: This program is open to members who are either graduating high school seniors planning to enroll in college or students already enrolled in college. Applicants must be interested in working full time on a 4-year degree in agricultural and forestry production, communication, education, engineering, finance, management, marketing, merchandising, sales, or agricultural science. They must be planning to attend a college or university in Alabama, Delaware, Georgia, Illinois, Indiana, Louisiana, Maryland, Michigan, Missouri, New York, North Carolina, Ohio, Pennsylvania, South Carolina, Tennessee, or Virginia. Selection is based on academic achievement (10 points for GPA, 10 points for SAT or ACT score, 10 points for class rank), leadership in FFA activities (30 points), leadership in community activities (10 points), and participation in the Supervised Agricultural Experience (SAE) program (30 points). U.S. citizenship is required. **Deadline for Receipt:** February of each year. **Additional Information:** Funding for these scholarships is provided by the Norfolk Southern Foundation.

3356 ■ NATIONAL FFA ORGANIZATION

Attn: Scholarship Office
6060 FFA Drive

P.O. Box 68960
Indianapolis, IN 46268-0960
Tel: (317)802-4321
Fax: (317)802-5321
E-mail: scholarships@ffa.org
Web Site: http://www.ffa.org
To provide financial assistance to FFA members interested in studying fields related to communications in college.
Title of Award: Progressive Farmer Magazine Scholarships **Area, Field, or Subject:** Advertising; Agricultural sciences; Communications; Journalism **Level of Education for which Award is Granted:** Four Year College **Number Awarded:** 1 each year. **Funds Available:** The stipend is $1,000 per year. Funds are paid directly to the recipient. **Duration:** 1 year; nonrenewable.
Eligibility Requirements: This program is open to members who are graduating high school seniors planning to enroll full time in college. Applicants must be interested in working on a 4-year degree in communications, journalism, or advertising. Selection is based on academic achievement (10 points for GPA, 10 points for SAT or ACT score, 10 points for class rank), leadership in FFA activities (30 points), leadership in community activities (10 points), and participation in the Supervised Agricultural Experience (SAE) program (30 points). U.S. citizenship is required. **Deadline for Receipt:** February of each year. **Additional Information:** Funding for these scholarships is provided by *Progressive Farmer Magazine.*

3357 ■ NATIONAL FFA ORGANIZATION

Attn: Scholarship Office
6060 FFA Drive
P.O. Box 68960
Indianapolis, IN 46268-0960
Tel: (317)802-4321
Fax: (317)802-5321
E-mail: scholarships@ffa.org
Web Site: http://www.ffa.org
To provide financial assistance to FFA members who are studying a field related to communications, business, or education in college.
Title of Award: Solutions Inc. Results Through Creative Marketing Scholarships **Area, Field, or Subject:** Agribusiness; Agricultural sciences; Communications; Education; Marketing and distribution **Level of Education for which Award is Granted:** Four Year College **Number Awarded:** 3 each year. **Funds Available:** The stipend is $1,000 per year. Funds are paid directly to the recipient. **Duration:** 1 year; nonrenewable.
Eligibility Requirements: This program is open to members currently enrolled full time in college and working on a 4-year degree in agricultural communications, marketing, merchandising, sales, or as an education specialist. Applicants must have a GPA of 3.0 or higher. Selection is based on academic achievement (10 points for GPA, 10 points for SAT or ACT score, 10 points for class rank), leadership in FFA activities (30 points), leadership in community activities (10 points), and participation in the Supervised Agricultural Experience (SAE) program (30 points). U.S. citizenship is required. **Deadline for Receipt:** February of each year. **Additional Information:** This program is sponsored by the creative marketing firm Solutions Inc. Results Through Creative Marketing.

3358 ■ NATIONAL FFA ORGANIZATION

Attn: Scholarship Office
6060 FFA Drive
P.O. Box 68960
Indianapolis, IN 46268-0960
Tel: (317)802-4321
Fax: (317)802-5321
E-mail: scholarships@ffa.org
Web Site: http://www.ffa.org
To provide financial assistance to FFA members who are interested in studying fields related to agriculture, business, engineering, or nursing in college.
Title of Award: Tyson Foods Scholarships **Area, Field, or Subject:** Agribusiness; Agricultural sciences; Business; Business administration; Engineering; Food science and technology; Management; Nursing; Packaging **Level of Education for which Award is Granted:** Undergraduate **Number Awarded:** 10 each year. **Funds Available:** The stipend is $1,000. Funds are paid directly to the recipient. **Duration:** 1 year; nonrenewable.

Eligibility Requirements: This program is open to members who are either high school seniors or already enrolled full time in college. Applicants must be working on or planning to work on a 2-year or 4-year degree in agriculture, food science, food technology, supply chain management, product development, product development, product packaging, nursing, engineering, or business. They must reside in a community in which a Tyson Foods processing facility is located. Selection is based on academic achievement (10 points for GPA, 10 points for SAT or ACT score, 10 points for class rank), leadership in FFA activities (30 points), leadership in community activities (10 points), and participation in the Supervised Agricultural Experience (SAE) program (30 points). U.S. citizenship is required. **Deadline for Receipt:** February of each year. **Additional Information:** Funding for these scholarships is provided by Tyson Foods, Inc.

3359 ■ NATIONAL FFA ORGANIZATION

Attn: Scholarship Office
6060 FFA Drive
P.O. Box 68960
Indianapolis, IN 46268-0960
Tel: (317)802-4321
Fax: (317)802-5321
E-mail: scholarships@ffa.org
Web Site: http://www.ffa.org
To provide financial assistance to FFA members from California interested in studying agribusiness in college.
Title of Award: Valent USA Corporation Scholarships **Area, Field, or Subject:** Agribusiness; Marketing and distribution **Level of Education for which Award is Granted:** Four Year College **Number Awarded:** 2 each year. **Funds Available:** The stipend is $1,000 per year. Funds are paid directly to the recipient. **Duration:** 1 year; nonrenewable.
Eligibility Requirements: This program is open to members who are residents of California current enrolled full time in a 2- or 4-year degree program in agricultural marketing, merchandising, or sales. Preference is given to students who are focusing on California specialty agriculture. Applicants must come from a family that earns 50% or more of its income from production agriculture in the area of grapes, fruit, tree fruit, or vegetables. Selection is based on academic achievement (10 points for GPA, 10 points for SAT or ACT score, 10 points for class rank), leadership in FFA activities (30 points), leadership in community activities (10 points), and participation in the Supervised Agricultural Experience (SAE) program (30 points). U.S. citizenship is required. **Deadline for Receipt:** February of each year. **Additional Information:** Funding for these scholarships is provided by Valent USA Corporation.

3360 ■ NATIONAL FFA ORGANIZATION

Attn: Scholarship Office
6060 FFA Drive
P.O. Box 68960
Indianapolis, IN 46268-0960
Tel: (317)802-4321
Fax: (317)802-5321
E-mail: scholarships@ffa.org
Web Site: http://www.ffa.org
To provide financial assistance and work experience to FFA members from dairy-producing states interested in studying agribusiness in college.
Title of Award: WestfaliaSurge Scholarships **Area, Field, or Subject:** Agribusiness; Dairy science; Marketing and distribution **Level of Education for which Award is Granted:** Four Year College **Number Awarded:** 12 each year: 2 corporate scholarships at $2,000 each and 10 dealer scholarships at $1,000 each. **Funds Available:** Stipends are $2,000 or $1,000 per year. Funds are paid directly to the recipient. **Duration:** 1 year; nonrenewable.
Eligibility Requirements: This program is open to members who are graduating high school seniors planning to enroll or college students currently enrolled full time. Applicants must be residents of 1 of the top 20 dairy states: Arizona, California, Florida, Idaho, Illinois, Indiana, Iowa, Kentucky, Michigan, Minnesota, Missouri, New Mexico, New York, Ohio, Pennsylvania, Texas, Vermont, Virginia, Washington, or Wisconsin. They must be interested in working on a 4-year degree in agribusiness with an emphasis on dairy science or dairy production, agricultural marketing, and/or sales. Selection is based on academic achievement (10 points for GPA, 10 points for SAT or ACT score, 10 points for class rank), leadership

in FFA activities (30 points), leadership in community activities (10 points), and participation in the Supervised Agricultural Experience (SAE) program (30 points). Financial need is also considered. U.S. citizenship is required. **Deadline for Receipt:** February of each year. **Additional Information:** Funding for these scholarships is provided by WestfaliaSurge, Inc. of Naperville, Illinois and participating dealers. The firm also offers recipients internship opportunities each summer of their college career if they meet certain requirements.

3361 ■ NATIONAL FFA ORGANIZATION

Attn: Scholarship Office
6060 FFA Drive
P.O. Box 68960
Indianapolls, IN 46268-0960
Tel: (317)802-4321
Fax: (317)802-5321
E-mail: scholarships@ffa.org
Web Site: http://www.ffa.org
To provide financial assistance to FFA members from designated states who are interested in studying a field related to agriculture in college.
Title of Award: Wilbur-Ellis Company Scholarships **Area, Field, or Subject:** Agribusiness; Agricultural sciences; Agriculture, Economic aspects; Animal science and behavior; Biochemistry; Business administration; Computer and information sciences; Entomology; Finance; Forestry; Genetics; Horticulture; Management; Marketing and distribution; Poultry science; Soil science **Level of Education for which Award is Granted:** Four Year College **Number Awarded:** 13 each year: 1 at $5,000, 2 at $2,000, and 10 at $1,000. **Funds Available:** Stipends are $5,000, $2,000, or $1,000 per year. Funds are paid directly to the recipient. **Duration:** 1 year; nonrenewable.
Eligibility Requirements: This program is open to members who are graduating high school seniors planning to enroll or college students currently enrolled full time. Applicants must be residents of the following states: Arizona, California, Idaho, Indiana, Michigan, Minnesota, Montana, New Mexico, North Dakota, Ohio, Oregon, South Dakota, Texas, Utah, Washington, Wisconsin, or Wyoming. They must be planning to work on a 4-year degree in agricultural production, forest management, agronomy and crop science, animal nutrition, farm and ranch management, horticulture, nursery and landscape management, plant science, poultry science, general agriculture, business management, economics, international agriculture, finance, sales and marketing, biochemistry, biotechnology, computer systems in agriculture, entomology, plant breeding and genetics, plant pathology, range science, or soil science. Their combined SAT score must be 1000 or higher and their GPA must be 3.0 or higher. Selection is based on academic achievement (10 points for GPA, 10 points for SAT or ACT score, 10 points for class rank), leadership in FFA activities (30 points), leadership in community activities (10 points), and participation in the Supervised Agricultural Experience (SAE) program (30 points). Financial need is also considered in the selection process. U.S. citizenship is required. **Deadline for Receipt:** February of each year. **Additional Information:** Funding for this scholarship is provided by the agriculture division of the Wilbur-Ellis Company.

3362 ■ NATIONAL INDIAN GAMING ASSOCIATION

Attn: Spirit of Sovereignty Foundation
224 Second Street, S.E.
Washington, DC 20003
Tel: (480)820-2464
E-mail: info@spiritfund.com
Web Site: http://www.spiritfund.com/student.htm
To provide financial assistance to Native American upper-division and graduate students who are working on a degree in a business-related field.
Title of Award: Spirit of Sovereignty Scholarships **Area, Field, or Subject:** Business administration; Computer and information sciences; Economics; Hotel, institutional, and restaurant management; Information science and technology **Level of Education for which Award is Granted:** Four Year College, Graduate **Number Awarded:** 1 or more each year. **Funds Available:** A stipend is awarded (amount not specified). **Duration:** 1 year.
Eligibility Requirements: This program is open to college juniors, seniors, and graduate students who are working on a degree in business or a related field (e.g., hotel management, information systems, computer

science, economics, human resources). Applicants must submit a copy of their Certificate of Degree of Indian Blood (CDIB), current transcript, 2 letters of recommendation, and a 250-word essay that describes their extracurricular activities related to involvement of American Indian programs at their institution, volunteer and community work related to American Indian communities, potential for future interaction and support to Indian communities, tribal and community involvement, and potential to give strong representation to the American Indian community to non-Native constituents. **Deadline for Receipt:** February of each year.

3363 ■ NATIONAL SECURITY AGENCY

Attn: Office of Recruitment and Staffing (Roberts)
9800 Savage Road, Suite 6779
P.O. Box 1661, Suite 6779
Fort Meade, MD 20755-6779
Tel: (410)854-4725; (866)672-4473
Web Site: http://www.nsa.gov/careers/students_4.cfm
To provide financial assistance and work experience to college sophomores and juniors interested in preparing for a career with the National Security Agency (NSA) as a global network analyst.
Title of Award: Pat Roberts Intelligence Scholars Program for Global Network Analysts **Area, Field, or Subject:** Banking; Computer and information sciences; Finance; Information science and technology; International affairs and relations; Political science; Telecommunications systems **Level of Education for which Award is Granted:** Undergraduate **Number Awarded:** Varies each year. **Funds Available:** The stipend is $25,000 per year. During the summer after application, students participate in a Global Network Analysis internship. After graduation, they have an employment obligation to NSA equal to 1.5 times the length of educational support provided. **Duration:** 1 year; may be renewed 1 additional year. The summer internship program is for 12 weeks.
Eligibility Requirements: This program is open to college sophomore and juniors whose academic program includes 1 of the following areas of emphasis: 1) technical studies (computer science major with a minor in political science or international relations); 2) topical studies (terrorism, proliferation or related sciences, international banking and finance, or telecommunications and information systems networks); or 3) disciplines (technical intelligence analysis, information assurance, networks, and telecommunications). Applicants must be enrolled full time with a GPA of 3.0 or higher. Along with their application, they must submit a 1-page essay describing how the proposed program of study will improve their ability to analyze information and to think and write critically. U.S. citizenship and eligibility to obtain a high-level security clearance are required **Deadline for Receipt:** October of each year. **Additional Information:** After graduation, participants enter NSA's Global Network Analysis Internship Program as a full-time employee.

3364 ■ NATIONAL SECURITY AGENCY

Attn: Office of Recruitment and Staffing (Roberts)
9800 Savage Road, Suite 6779
P.O. Box 1661, Suite 6779
Fort Meade, MD 20755-6779
Tel: (410)854-4725; (866)672-4473
Web Site: http://www.nsa.gov/careers/students_4.cfm
To provide financial assistance to college juniors interested in preparing for a career with the National Security Agency (NSA) as an intelligence analyst.
Title of Award: Pat Roberts Intelligence Scholars Program for Intelligence Analysts **Area, Field, or Subject:** Asian studies; Banking; Finance; Foreign languages; Geography; Information science and technology; International affairs and relations; Library and archival sciences; Near Eastern studies; South Asian studies; Telecommunications systems **Level of Education for which Award is Granted:** Four Year College **Number Awarded:** Varies each year. **Funds Available:** The stipend is $25,000 per year. After graduation, recipients have an employment obligation to NSA equal to 1.5 times the length of educational support provided. **Duration:** 1 year (the senior year of college).
Eligibility Requirements: This program is open to college juniors whose academic program includes 1 of the following areas of emphasis: 1) regional studies (Middle East or south, east, or central Asia); 2) topical studies (terrorism, proliferation or related sciences, international banking and finance, or telecommunications and information systems networks); or 3) disciplines (intelligence analysis, philosophy, or international rela-

tions; familiarity with foreign languages, particularly Arabic, Chinese, Dari, Farsi, Hindi, Korean, Pashto, Urdu, or a central Asian language is desirable; highly qualified applicants studying social network analysis, library science, or geographic information systems may also be considered). Applicants must be enrolled full time with a GPA of 3.0 or higher. Along with their application, they must submit a 1-page essay describing how the proposed program of study will improve their ability to analyze information and to think and write critically. U.S. citizenship and eligibility to obtain a high-level security clearance are required **Deadline for Receipt:** October of each year. **Additional Information:** After graduation, participants enter NSA's Intelligence Analysis Development Program as a full-time employee.

3365 ■ NEBRASKA ACTUARIES CLUB

c/o Bob Jurgensmeier
Lincoln Beneficial Life
2940 South 84th Street, Suite 1A3
Lincoln, NE 68506
Fax: (402)328-6116
E-mail: bjurg@allstate.com
Web Site: http://www.n-a-c.org/Scholarships/Scholarships.PHP
To provide financial assistance to students in Nebraska who are preparing for an actuarial career.
Title of Award: Nebraska Actuaries Club Scholarships **Area, Field, or Subject:** Actuarial science; Economics; Insurance and insurance-related fields; Mathematics and mathematical sciences; Statistics **Level of Education for which Award is Granted:** Undergraduate **Number Awarded:** 3 each year: 2 to Nebraska high school graduates attending the University of Nebraska system (designated Madden Scholarships and supported by the Nebraska Insurance Federation) and 1 to graduates from other states attending a college or university in Nebraska (supported by the Nebraska Actuaries Club). **Funds Available:** The stipend is $1,000. **Duration:** 1 year.
Eligibility Requirements: This program is open to 1) seniors graduating from high schools in Nebraska and planning to attend a campus of the University of Nebraska; and 2) seniors graduating from high schools anywhere in the United States and planning to attend a college or university in Nebraska. Applicants must intend to major in actuarial science, mathematics, statistics, or economics and prepare for a career as an actuary. They must be able to demonstrate mathematical ability. Along with their application, they must submit an essay on their interest in actuarial science and why they would like to be an actuary. Financial need is not considered in the selection process. **Deadline for Receipt:** March of each year. **Additional Information:** This program is jointly sponsored by the Nebraska Actuaries Club and the Nebraska Insurance Federation.

3366 ■ NEBRASKA BANKERS ASSOCIATION

Attn: Educational Foundation
233 South 13th Street, Suite 700
P.O. Box 80008
Lincoln, NE 68501-0008
Tel: (402)474-1555
Fax: (402)474-2148
E-mail: karen.miller@nebankers.org
Web Site: http://www.nebankers.org/public/consumer.html
To provide financial assistance to Nebraska residents working on a degree in business at a college or university in the state.
Title of Award: Nebraska Bankers Educational Foundation Scholarships **Area, Field, or Subject:** Accounting; Business administration; Economics; Finance **Level of Education for which Award is Granted:** Undergraduate **Number Awarded:** 8 each year (including 4 designated as William B. Brandt Memorial Scholarships). **Funds Available:** The stipend is $1,000. **Duration:** 1 year.
Eligibility Requirements: This program is open to residents of Nebraska who are enrolled as juniors or seniors at a college or university in the state (except for the University of Nebraska). Applicants must be working on a bachelor of science in business administration with an emphasis on finance, accounting, or economics and have a GPA of 3.0 or higher. Along with their application, they must submit an essay of 100 to 200 words on how the banking industry has impacted their community or the role they expect the banking industry to play in their future. Financial need is not considered in the selection process. **Deadline for Receipt:** January of each year.

3367 ■ NEBRASKA EDUCATIONAL OFFICE PROFESSIONALS AS-SOCIATION

P.O. Box 83872
Lincoln, NE 68501-3872
Web Site: http://neopa.unl.edu/awards.html
To provide financial assistance to residents of Nebraska who are interested in preparing for an office-related career.
Title of Award: Nebraska Educational Office Professionals Association Student Scholarship **Area, Field, or Subject:** Accounting; Computer and information sciences; Law; Marketing and distribution; Publishing; Secretarial sciences **Level of Education for which Award is Granted:** Undergraduate **Number Awarded:** 1 each year. **Funds Available:** The stipend is $1,000. **Duration:** 1 year.
Eligibility Requirements: This program is open to residents of Nebraska who are graduating high school seniors or students currently enrolled in a postsecondary educational institution. Applicants must have completed 2 or more business education courses (in high school, college, or a combination) from among the following: computer classes, keyboarding/ typing, marketing, accounting, office practices and procedures, bookkeeping, business communication, desktop publishing, and/or business law. They must submit a 1-page essay on why they are choosing an office-related career or vocation, 3 letters of recommendation, and high school or college transcripts. Selection is based on academic achievement, initiative of the student, and financial need. **Deadline for Receipt:** December of each year. **Additional Information:** Information is also available from Edie Schleiger, Scholarship Director, University of Nebraska at Lincoln, Office of Admissions, 1410 Q Street, Lincoln, NE 68588-0417.

3368 ■ NEBRASKA PRESS ASSOCIATION FOUNDATION

845 S Street
Lincoln, NE 68508
Tel: (402)476-2851
Free: 800-369-2850
Fax: (402)476-2942
E-mail: nebpress@nebpress.com
Web Site: http://www.nebpress.com
To provide financial assistance to high school seniors in Nebraska who are interested in preparing for a career in print journalism.
Title of Award: Nebraska Press Association Foundation Scholarships **Area, Field, or Subject:** Advertising; Journalism; Photography, Journalistic **Level of Education for which Award is Granted:** Undergraduate **Funds Available:** The stipend is $1,250. **Duration:** 1 year.
Eligibility Requirements: This program is open to high school seniors in Nebraska who are interested in attending a college or university in the state and majoring in print journalism. Preference is given to students with specific interests in news, editorial, photography, circulation, production, or advertising. Applicants must submit information on their academic accomplishments, reasons for applying for this scholarship (including their career plans), and family financial situation. **Deadline for Receipt:** February of each year.

3369 ■ NEWSPAPER ASSOCIATION OF AMERICA

Attn: ATHENA Awards
1921 Gallows Road, Suite 600
Vienna, VA 22182-3900
Tel: (703)902-1656
Fax: (703)902-1935
E-mail: pagap@naa.org
Web Site: http://www.athenaawards.com
To recognize and reward outstanding creative advertisements in the newspaper industry.
Title of Award: Award To Honor Excellence in Newspaper Advertising (ATHENA) **Area, Field, or Subject:** Advertising **Level of Education for which Award is Granted:** Graduate, Professional, Undergraduate **Number Awarded:** Varies each year; recently, 50 prizes were awarded, including 1 grand prize, 1 student prize, 9 gold awards, 13 silver awards, and 26 bronze awards (of which 7 were in the student division). **Funds Available:** The grand prize is $100,000; the student ad prize is $5,000. Gold, silver, and bronze medals are also awarded. **Duration:** The competition is held annually.
Eligibility Requirements: Entries must be published in a newspaper for the first time during the preceding calendar year. They may be submitted by agencies, clients, printing companies, and/or newspapers. Nomina-

tions may be made in any of 10 categories: automotive, beverage, business products and services, entertainment, financial, health care products and services, leisure and travel, media, public service, and student ads. **Deadline for Receipt:** April of each year. **Additional Information:** This program was revived in 1997 after a prolonged hiatus.

3370 ■ RHODE ISLAND FOUNDATION

Attn: Scholarship Coordinator
One Union Station
Providence, RI 02903
Tel: (401)274-4564
Fax: (401)331-8085
E-mail: libbym@rifoundation.org
Web Site: http://www.rifoundation.org
To provide financial assistance to residents of Rhode Island who are enrolled in college to prepare for a career in advertising.
Title of Award: J.D. Edsal Advertising Scholarship **Area, Field, or Subject:** Advertising; Broadcasting; Filmmaking; Graphic art and design; Marketing and distribution; Public relations; Radio and television **Level of Education for which Award is Granted:** Undergraduate **Number Awarded:** 2 each year. **Funds Available:** The stipend is $1,500. **Duration:** 1 year.
Eligibility Requirements: This program is open to residents of Rhode Island who are enrolled full time as undergraduates at the sophomore level or above. Applicants must be preparing for a career in advertising and majoring in a related field (e.g., broadcast production, graphic design, interactive film, marketing, public relations, television, or video). Along with their application, they must submit an essay (up to 300 words) on the impact they would like to have on the advertising industry. Financial need is also considered in the selection process. **Deadline for Receipt:** April of each year.

3371 ■ RHODE ISLAND FOUNDATION

Attn: Scholarship Coordinator
One Union Station
Providence, RI 02903
Tel: (401)274-4564
Fax: (401)331-8085
E-mail: libbym@rifoundation.org
Web Site: http://www.rifoundation.org
To provide financial assistance to Rhode Island students of color interested in preparing for a career in communications.
Title of Award: RDW Group, Inc. Minority Scholarship for Communications **Area, Field, or Subject:** Advertising; Art; Communications; Filmmaking; Graphic art and design **Level of Education for which Award is Granted:** Graduate, Undergraduate **Number Awarded:** 1 each year. **Funds Available:** The stipend is $2,000. **Duration:** 1 year; nonrenewable.
Eligibility Requirements: This program is open to minority undergraduate and graduate students who are Rhode Island residents. Applicants must intend to major in communications (including computer graphics, art, cinematography, or other fields that would prepare them for a career in advertising). They must be able to demonstrate financial need and a commitment to a career in communications. Along with their application, they must submit an essay (up to 300 words) on the impact they would like to have on the communications field. **Deadline for Receipt:** April of each year. **Additional Information:** This program is sponsored by the RDW Group, Inc.

3372 ■ RHODE ISLAND FOUNDATION

Attn: Scholarship Coordinator
One Union Station
Providence, RI 02903
Tel: (401)274-4564
Fax: (401)331-8085
E-mail: libbym@rifoundation.org
Web Site: http://www.rifoundation.org
To provide financial assistance to Rhode Island undergraduates of color interested in preparing for a career in banking.
Title of Award: Raymond H. Trott Scholarship for Banking **Area, Field, or Subject:** Banking **Level of Education for which Award is Granted:** Four Year College **Number Awarded:** 1 each year. **Funds Available:** The stipend is $1,000. **Duration:** 1 year; nonrenewable.

Eligibility Requirements: This program is open to minority residents of Rhode Island who are entering their senior year in college. Applicants must plan to prepare for a career in banking and be able to demonstrate financial need. Along with their application, they must submit an essay (up to 300 words) on the impact they would like to have on the banking industry. **Deadline for Receipt:** June of each year. **Additional Information:** This program was established in 1980.

3373 ■ ROCKY MOUNTAIN COAL MINING INSTITUTE

Attn: Executive Director
8057 South Yukon Way
Littleton, CO 80128-5510
Tel: (303)948-3300
Fax: (303)948-1132
E-mail: mail@rmcmi.org
Web Site: http://www.rmcmi.org
To provide financial assistance to college students from Rocky Mountain states who are preparing for a career in the mining industry.
Title of Award: Rocky Mountain Coal Mining Institute Scholarships **Area, Field, or Subject:** Business; Engineering, Electrical; Engineering, Geological; Engineering, Mechanical; Engineering, Metallurgical; Engineering, Mining and Mineral; Environmental science; Geology; Metallurgy; Mining **Level of Education for which Award is Granted:** Four Year College **Number Awarded:** 8 each year (1 from each of the participating states). **Funds Available:** The stipend is $2,000 per year. Funds are disbursed to the recipient's institution to be used as a tuition credit. during the junior, senior, and/or fifth year of undergraduate study. **Duration:** 2 years; renewable, if the recipient continues in school as a full-time student in good academic standing.
Eligibility Requirements: This program is open to full-time sophomores or juniors in college who are U.S. citizens and residents of Arizona, Colorado, Montana, New Mexico, North Dakota, Texas, Utah, or Wyoming. Applicants must be working on a degree in engineering (e.g., electrical, environmental, geological, mechanical, metallurgical, mining) or in a mining-related field (e.g., geology, mineral processing, metallurgy). They may be attending school in 1 of those states or another school approved by the sponsor (e.g., University of Missouri at Rolla, South Dakota School of Mines). Preference is given to students who are particularly interested in western coal as a career. Interviews are required. **Deadline for Receipt:** January of each year.

3374 ■ SIGMA ALPHA IOTA PHILANTHROPIES, INC.

One Tunnel Road
Asheville, NC 28805
Tel: (828)251-0606
Fax: (828)251-0644
E-mail: philonline@sai-national.org
Web Site: http://www.sai-national.org/phil/philmustech.html
To provide financial assistance for college to members of Sigma Alpha Iota (an organization of women musicians).
Title of Award: Dorothy Cooke Whinery Music Business/Technology Scholarship **Area, Field, or Subject:** Business; Business administration; Management; Marketing and distribution; Music; Performing arts; Technology **Level of Education for which Award is Granted:** Four Year College **Number Awarded:** 1 each year. **Funds Available:** The stipend is $2,000. **Duration:** 1 year.
Eligibility Requirements: This program is open to members of the organization entering their junior or senior year of college. Applicants must be working on a degree in the field of music business or music technology, including music marketing, music business administration, entertainment industry, commercial music, recording and production, music management, or other related fields. They must have a GPA of 3.0 or higher. Along with their application, they must submit a statement of purpose that includes their career goals. **Deadline for Receipt:** March of each year. **Additional Information:** This program was established in 2003. There is a $25 nonrefundable application fee.

3375 ■ SOCIETY OF EXPLORATION GEOPHYSICISTS

Attn: SEG Foundation
8801 South Yale, Suite 500
P.O. Box 702740
Tulsa, OK 74170-2740
Tel: (918)497-5513

Fax: (918)497-5557
E-mail: scholarships@seg.org
Web Site: http://seg.org/business/foundation/scholarships/index.shtml
To provide financial assistance to undergraduate and graduate students who are interested in the field of applied geophysics related to mining or electrical methods.
Title of Award: G.W. Hohmann Scholarships **Area, Field, or Subject:** Business; Geophysics; Mining **Level of Education for which Award is Granted:** Graduate, Undergraduate **Number Awarded:** 2 each year: 1 for an undergraduate and 1 for a graduate student. **Funds Available:** The stipend is $3,000 per year for graduate students or $1,000 per year for undergraduates. **Duration:** 1 academic year; may be renewable, based on scholastic standing, availability of funds, and continuance of a course of study leading to a career in applied geophysics.
Eligibility Requirements: This program is open to 1) high school students planning to enter college in the fall, and 2) undergraduate or graduate students whose grades are above average. Applicants must intend to work on a degree directed toward a career in applied geophysics with an emphasis on mining or electrical methods. Along with their application, they must submit a 150-word essay on how they plan to use geophysics in their future. Financial need is not considered in the selection process. **Deadline for Receipt:** January of each year.

3376 ■ SOCIETY FOR MINING, METALLURGY, AND EXPLORATION, INC.

Attn: Student Center
8307 Shaffer Parkway
Littleton, CO 80127-4102
Tel: (303)973-9550
Free: 800-763-3132
Fax: (303)973-3845
E-mail: sme@smenet.org
Web Site: http://www.smenet.org/education/students/sme_scholarships.cfm
To provide financial assistance to upper-division student members of the Society for Mining, Metallurgy, and Exploration (SME) who are majoring in fields that will develop their skills related to mining and the environment.
Title of Award: Environmental Division Scholarship **Area, Field, or Subject:** Economics; Engineering, Mining and Mineral; Environmental conservation; Environmental science; Geology; Metallurgy **Level of Education for which Award is Granted:** Four Year College **Number Awarded:** 1 or more each year. **Funds Available:** A total of $2,000 is awarded each year. **Duration:** 1 year.
Eligibility Requirements: Applicants must 1) be majoring in a field related to the minerals industry (e.g., geology, minerals engineering, mining engineering, or mineral economics) at a 4-year college or university, 2) have completed at least their sophomore year in college, 3) be a U.S. citizen, and 4) be a student member of the society. They must be of good character, be of sound health, have demonstrated scholastic aptitude (GPA of 3.0 or higher), and be able to demonstrate financial need. Candidates for these scholarships must be working on an undergraduate degree related to mining and the environment with a faculty advisor who has special interests in an environmentally-oriented program. **Deadline for Receipt:** October of each year.

3377 ■ SOCIETY FOR MINING, METALLURGY, AND EXPLORATION, INC.

Attn: Student Center
8307 Shaffer Parkway
Littleton, CO 80127-4102
Tel: (303)973-9550
Free: 800-763-3132
Fax: (303)973-3845
E-mail: sme@smenet.org
Web Site: http://www.smenet.org/education/students/sme_scholarships.cfm
To provide financial assistance to upper-division and graduate student members of the Society for Mining, Metallurgy, and Exploration (SME) who are majoring in fields that will prepare them for a career in industrial minerals.
Title of Award: Gerald V. Henderson Industrial Minerals Memorial Scholarship **Area, Field, or Subject:** Economics; Engineering, Mining and Mineral; Geology; Metallurgy **Level of Education for which Award**

is Granted: Four Year College, Graduate **Number Awarded:** 1 or more each year. **Funds Available:** A total of $2,000 is awarded each year. **Duration:** 1 year.
Eligibility Requirements: Applicants must 1) be majoring in a field related to the minerals industry (e.g., geology, minerals engineering, mining engineering, or mineral economics) at a 4-year college or university, 2) have completed at least their sophomore year in college, 3) be a U.S. citizen, and 4) be a student member of the society. They must be of good character, be of sound health, have demonstrated scholastic aptitude (GPA of 3.0 or higher), and be able to demonstrate financial need. Candidates for these scholarships may be proposed by any of the following: mining and minerals companies; local sections of the society; state mining institutes; high school principals; industrial minerals associations; manufacturers of mining and processing equipment; minerals research organizations; or geology and mining engineering departments at colleges or universities. An interview may be required. **Deadline for Receipt:** October of each year.

3378 ■ SOCIETY OF PETROLEUM ENGINEERS-ALASKA SECTION

c/o Lara D. Bennett
ConocoPhillips Alaska, Inc.
P.O. Box 100360
Anchorage, AK 99510-0360
Tel: (907)265-6427
E-mail: Lara.D.Bennett@conocophilips.com
Web Site: http://alaska.spe.org/section.cfm?id=17
To provide financial assistance to college students from Alaska who are majoring in engineering in college.
Title of Award: Alaska Section SPE Scholarships **Area, Field, or Subject:** Business; Energy-related areas; Engineering, Petroleum **Level of Education for which Award is Granted:** Undergraduate **Number Awarded:** 8 each year. **Funds Available:** Stipends range from $1,500 to $2,500. **Duration:** 1 year.
Eligibility Requirements: This program is open to students entering or attending an accredited university to work on an undergraduate degree in petroleum engineering, a related discipline, or a career in the petroleum exploration and production industry. Applicants must meet 1 of the following requirements: 1) graduating or graduated from a high school in Alaska; 2) currently enrolled in a college in Alaska; or 3) a dependent of a member of the Society of Petroleum Engineers (SPE) Alaska Section. Along with their application, they must submit essay on their continuing goals in college, eventual career plans, and what role they think the petroleum industry will play in their personal life and the future of Alaska. Financial need is not considered in the selection process. **Deadline for Receipt:** January of each year.

3379 ■ SOCIETY OF PETROLEUM ENGINEERS-POWDER RIVER BASIN SECTION

P.O. Box 3977
Gillette, WY 82717-3977
To provide financial assistance to Wyoming students interested in preparing for a career in the oil and gas industry.
Title of Award: Powder River Basin Section Annual Scholarship Awards **Area, Field, or Subject:** Business; Energy-related areas; Engineering, Petroleum **Level of Education for which Award is Granted:** Undergraduate **Number Awarded:** 5 to 15 each year. **Funds Available:** Stipends range from $250 to $1,000. **Duration:** 1 year.
Eligibility Requirements: This program is open to Wyoming students preparing for a career in the oil and gas industry. Applicants should be majoring in engineering (especially petroleum engineering and petroleum technology), although some of the scholarships may go to non-engineering students. They must be enrolled full time as entering freshmen, sophomores, juniors, or seniors in a 4-year program or freshmen or sophomores in a 2-year program and have a GPA of 2.75 or higher. Along with their application, they must submit a letter that covers their academic qualifications, primary career interests, extracurricular activities, and names of 2 references. Financial need is not considered in the selection process. **Deadline for Receipt:** March of each year. **Additional Information:** Information is also available from Bob Christofferson, Citation Oil

and Gas Corporation, 1016 East Lincoln, Gillette, WY 82716, (307) 682-4853, E-mail: bchristofferson@cogc.com.

3380 ■ SOCIETY OF PETROLEUM ENGINEERS-SALT LAKE PETROLEUM SECTION

c/o Roberto Suarez-Rivera
TerraTek
1935 South Fremont Drive
Salt Lake City, UT 84104
Tel: (801)584-2432
Free: 800-372-2522
Fax: (801)584-2406
E-mail: rsuarez@terratek.com
Web Site: http://saltlake.spe.org
To provide financial assistance to engineering students in Utah who are preparing for a career in the petroleum industry.
Title of Award: Richard E. Wyman Scholarship Awards **Area, Field, or Subject:** Business; Energy-related areas; Engineering **Level of Education for which Award is Granted:** Undergraduate **Number Awarded:** 2 each year. **Funds Available:** The stipend is $1,000. **Duration:** 1 year.
Eligibility Requirements: This program is open to students enrolled or planning to enroll at an accredited college or university in Utah in a program leading to a degree in engineering. Applicants must be interested in preparing for a career in the petroleum industry. College students must be recommended by a member of the faculty at their school. High school seniors must be recommended by a member of the Society of Petroleum Engineers (SPE). **Deadline for Receipt:** February of each year.

3381 ■ SOUTH CAROLINA COMMISSION ON HIGHER EDUCATION

Attn: Director of Student Services
1333 Main Street, Suite 200
Columbia, SC 29201
Tel: (803)737-2260; 877-349-7183
Fax: (803)737-2297
E-mail: dbrown@che.sc.gov
Web Site: http://www.che.sc.gov
To provide scholarship/loans to teachers in South Carolina who wish to improve their content knowledge and degree programs.
Title of Award: South Carolina Teaching Scholarship Grants Program **Area, Field, or Subject:** Art; Dance; Economics; Education; Education, Early childhood; Education, Elementary; Education, Music; Education, Secondary; Education, Special; Geography; History; Linguistics; Mathematics and mathematical sciences; Music; Political science; Science **Level of Education for which Award is Granted:** Graduate, Professional, Undergraduate **Number Awarded:** Varies each year. **Funds Available:** The stipend is $1,000 per fiscal year. This is a scholarship/loan program. Recipients must sign a commitment to teach in South Carolina public schools for at least 1 year following completion of the scholarship grant year and agree to refund the scholarship amount if the 1-year teaching commitment is not honored. **Duration:** 1 year; may be renewed if recipients maintain a GPA of 3.0 or higher. They may receive up to 3 grants in a 5 year period.
Eligibility Requirements: This program is open to residents of South Carolina who have a professional teaching certificate and are under contract as a teacher in a public school in the state. Applicants must be 1) accepted as a degree-seeking graduate student in the teaching field at the master's level and enrolled at an eligible institution in the state; or 2) enrolled for graduate or undergraduate courses in their current teaching field or in a teaching field in which they wish to add on certification. Proposed fields of study must relate to core content areas of English, reading or language arts, mathematics, science, foreign languages, civics and government, economics, arts (advanced fine arts, art, dance, drama, music, and speech), history, or geography; early childhood, elementary education, middle level education, secondary education, and special education also qualify. Priority is given to classroom teachers (not administrators, counselors, media specialists, or other support personnel) whose teaching specialties are critical need subject areas. Continuing graduate students must have a GPA of 3.0 or higher. U.S. citizenship or permanent resident status is required. **Deadline for Receipt:** December of each year for second summer session and fall semester; June of each

year for spring semester and first summer session. **Additional Information:** This program was established in 2001.

3382 ■ SOUTH DAKOTA ASSOCIATION OF PLUMBING, HEATING, & COOLING CONTRACTORS

Attn: Educational Foundation
P.O. Box 336
Pierre, SD 57501
Tel: (605)224-2528
Free: 800-640-PHCC
Fax: (605)224-1543
E-mail: PHCC@midco.net
Web Site: http://sdaphcc.tripod.com
To provide financial assistance for college to high school seniors and college freshmen in South Dakota who are preparing for a career in plumbing, heating and cooling, construction, or business management.
Title of Award: SDAPHCC Educational Foundation Scholarships **Area, Field, or Subject:** Business; Business administration; Construction; Heating, air conditioning, and refrigeration **Level of Education for which Award is Granted:** Undergraduate **Number Awarded:** 2 each year: 1 at $1,000 and 1 at $500. **Funds Available:** Stipends are $1,000 or $500. **Duration:** 1 year.
Eligibility Requirements: This program is open to high school seniors and college freshmen in South Dakota who are preparing for a career in plumbing, heating and cooling, construction, or business management. Applicants must be sponsored by a member of the South Dakota Association of Plumbing, Heating & Cooling Contractors (SDAPHCC). **Deadline for Receipt:** December of each year.

3383 ■ SOUTH DAKOTA BANKERS ASSOCIATION

Attn: Foundation
109 West Missouri Avenue
P.O. Box 1081
Pierre, SD 57501-1081
Tel: (605)224-1653
Fax: (605)224-7835
Web Site: http://www.sdba.com/SDBA/Foundation/scholarships.htm
To provide financial assistance to students at South Dakota colleges or universities who are preparing for a career in banking or finance.
Title of Award: Herman Lerdal Scholarship **Area, Field, or Subject:** Banking; Business administration; Finance **Level of Education for which Award is Granted:** Four Year College **Number Awarded:** 1 each year. **Funds Available:** The stipend is $1,000. **Duration:** 1 year.
Eligibility Requirements: This program is open to juniors at colleges or universities in South Dakota who are working on a business-related degree in preparation for a career in banking or finance. Applicants must have at least a 3.0 GPA. Along with their application, they must submit a statement on their career interests, a description of their special talents and leadership abilities, a statement on obstacles they have overcome, and 3 letters of recommendation. Financial need is not considered in the selection process. **Deadline for Receipt:** March of each year.

3384 ■ SWEDISH WOMEN'S EDUCATION ASSOCIATION INTERNATIONAL-SOUTH FLORIDA CHAPTER

c/o Yorti Nelson, Scholarship Committee
3759 Mykonos Court
Boca Raton, FL 33486
Tel: (561)997-2050
Fax: (561)997-8010
E-mail: florida@swea.org
Web Site: http://www.chapters-swea.org/florida
To provide financial assistance to Florida residents interested in studying in Sweden or an area related to Swedish studies.
Title of Award: South Florida SWEA Scholarship **Area, Field, or Subject:** Art; Art industries and trade; Crafts; Design; Environmental conservation; Environmental science; Foreign languages; General studies/Field of study not specified; Literature; Music; Swedish studies **Level of Education for which Award is Granted:** Graduate, Professional, Undergraduate **Number Awarded:** 1 each year. **Funds Available:** The stipend is $3,000.
Eligibility Requirements: This program is open to all residents of Florida interested in participating in an exchange program in Sweden. Applicants may also propose to study in the United States, if the studies specifically

emphasize Sweden and Swedish aspects, including 1) Swedish language; 2) Swedish culture or traditions; 3) environmental science; 4) a health care program promoting better health for women and children; or 5) handicraft, art, glass art, music, literature, or design. Study proposals must be well-defined in time and content. Along with their application, they must submit a transcript from college, university, or vocational school; curriculum vitae; project proposal, describing the planned studies, length of studies, and goals; financial statement; and letter of recommendation from an instructor. **Deadline for Receipt:** January of each year. **Additional Information:** Within 3 months after the end of studies or the project, the recipient must report to the scholarship committee or, if possible, accept an invitation to an organization meeting to share the experience.

3385 ■ TEXAS DECA

Attn: State Advisor
P.O. Box 13062
Austin, TX 78711-3062
Tel: (979)481-3370
Fax: (409)741-2248
E-mail: lhamff@texasdeca.org
Web Site: http://www.texasdeca.org/scholarships.htm
To provide financial assistance for college to members of DECA whose teachers are members of Marketing Educators of Texas (MET).
Title of Award: Marketing Educators of Texas Scholarships **Area, Field, or Subject:** Marketing and distribution **Level of Education for which Award is Granted:** Undergraduate **Number Awarded:** 2 each year. **Funds Available:** The stipend is $1,000. **Duration:** 1 year.
Eligibility Requirements: This program is open to seniors graduating from high schools in Texas who are members of DECA. Applicants must be participants in a marketing education program whose teacher or coordinator is a current MET member. They must be planning to attend a technical school, community college, or university in Texas to prepare for a career in marketing or a related field. Along with their application, they must submit a 200-word essay on the topic, "What Marketing Means to Me." Selection is based on the essay, DECA activities, community service, work and/or school activities and accomplishments, scholarship, neatness of their application form, and 2 letters of reference. **Deadline for Receipt:** December of each year. **Additional Information:** This program consists of the following named scholarships: the Ann Reed Memorial Scholarship and the Tom Ponder Memorial Scholarship. Information on this program is also available from Mary Ann Canell, 219 Blount Street, Nacogdoches, TX 75965.

3386 ■ HARRY S. TRUMAN SCHOLARSHIP FOUNDATION

Attn: Executive Secretary
712 Jackson Place, N.W.
Washington, DC 20006
Tel: (202)395-4831
Fax: (202)395-6995
E-mail: office@truman.gov
Web Site: http://www.truman.gov
To provide grants-for-service for graduate school to current college juniors who are interested in preparing for a career in public service.
Title of Award: Harry S. Truman Scholarship Program **Area, Field, or Subject:** Agricultural sciences; Biological and clinical sciences; Economics; Education; Engineering; Environmental conservation; Environmental science; History; International affairs and relations; Law; Physical sciences; Political science; Public administration; Public health; Public service; Social sciences; Technology **Level of Education for which Award is Granted:** Four Year College, Graduate **Number Awarded:** 70 to 75 each year: a) 1 "state" scholarship is available to a qualified resident nominee in each of the 50 states, the District of Columbia, Puerto Rico, and the Islands (Guam, the Virgin Islands, American Samoa, and the Commonwealth of the Northern Mariana Islands); and b) up to 25 at-large scholars. **Funds Available:** The program provides up to $30,000, including up to $15,000 for the first year of graduate study and up to $15,000 for the final year of graduate study. **Duration:** Support is provided for the first and last year of graduate study.
Eligibility Requirements: Students must be nominated to be considered for this program. Nominees must be full-time students with junior standing at a 4-year institution, committed to a career in government or public service, in the upper quarter of their class, and U.S. citizens or nationals. Each participating institution may nominate up to 4 candidates (and up to

3 additional students who completed their first 2 years at a community college); community colleges and other 2-year institutions may nominate former students who are enrolled as full-time students with junior-level academic standing at accredited 4-year institutions. Selection is based on extent and quality of community service and government involvement, academic performance, leadership record, suitability of the nominee's proposed program of study for a career in public service, and writing and analytical skills. Priority is given to candidates who plan to enroll in a graduate program that specifically trains them for a career in public service, including government at any level, uniformed services, public interest organizations, nongovernmental research and/or educational organizations, public and private schools, and public service oriented nonprofit organizations. The fields of study may include agriculture, biology, engineering, environmental management, physical and social sciences, and technology policy, as well as such traditional fields as economics, education, government, history, international relations, law, nonprofit management, political science, public administration, public health, and public policy. Interviews are required. **Deadline for Receipt:** February of each year. **Additional Information:** Recipients may attend graduate school in the United States or in foreign countries. Scholars are required to work in public service for 3 of the 7 years following completion of a graduate degree program funded by this program. Scholars who do not meet this service requirement, or who fail to provide timely proof to the foundation of such employment, will be required to repay funds received, along with interest.

3387 ■ MORRIS K. UDALL FOUNDATION

130 South Scott Avenue
Tucson, AZ 85701-1922
Tel: (520)670-5529
Fax: (520)670-5530
Web Site: http://www.udall.gov/scholarship
To provide financial assistance to 1) college sophomores and juniors who intend to prepare for a career in environmental public policy and 2) Native American and Alaska Native students who intend to prepare for a career in health care or tribal public policy.
Title of Award: Morris K. Udall Scholarships **Area, Field, or Subject:** Business administration; Economics; Education; Environmental conservation; Environmental science; Health care services; Native American studies; Natural resources; Political science; Public administration; Public health; Urban affairs/design/planning **Level of Education for which Award is Granted:** Undergraduate **Number Awarded:** Approximately 80 scholarships and 50 honorable mentions are awarded each year. **Funds Available:** The maximum stipend for scholarship winners is $5,000 per year. Funds are to be used for tuition, fees, books, and room and board. Honorable mention stipends are $350. **Duration:** 1 year; recipients nominated as sophomores may be renominated in their junior year.
Eligibility Requirements: Each 2-year and 4-year college and university in the United States and its possessions may nominate up to 6 sophomores or juniors from either or both categories of this program: 1) students who intend to prepare for a career in environmental public policy, and 2) Native American and Alaska Native students who intend to prepare for a career in health care or tribal public policy. For the first category, the program seeks future leaders across a wide spectrum of environmental fields, such as policy, engineering, science, education, urban planning and renewal, business, health, justice, and economics. For the second category, the program seeks future Native American and Alaska Native leaders in public and community health care, tribal government, and public policy affecting Native American communities, including land and resource management, economic development, and education. Nominees must be U.S. citizens, nationals, or permanent residents with a GPA of 3.0 or higher. Along with their application, they must submit an 800-word essay discussing a significant public speech, legislative act, or public policy statement by former Congressman Morris K. Udall and its impact on their field of study, interests, and career goals. Selection is based on demonstrated commitment to 1) environmental issues through substantial commitment to and participation in 1 or more of the following: campus activities, research, community service, or public service; or 2) tribal public policy or Native American health through substantial contributions to and participation in 1 or more of the following: campus activities, tribal involvement, community or public service, or research; a course of study and proposed career likely to lead to position where nominee can make significant contributions to the shaping of environmental, tribal public

policy, or Native American health care issues, whether through scientific advances, public or political service, or community action; and leadership, character, desire to make a difference, and general well-roundedness. **Deadline for Receipt:** Faculty representatives must submit their nominations by early March of each year.

3388 ■ VERMONT STUDENT ASSISTANCE CORPORATION

Champlain Mill
Attn: Scholarship Programs
P.O. Box 2000
Winooski, VT 05404-2601
Tel: (802)654-3798; 888-253-4819
Fax: (802)654-3765
E-mail: info@vsac.org
Web Site: http://www.vsac.org
To provide financial assistance to residents of Vermont who are interested in majoring in arts or crafts in college.
Title of Award: Vermont Hand Crafters Artisanship Scholarships **Area, Field, or Subject:** Art industries and trade; Crafts; Visual arts **Level of Education for which Award is Granted:** Undergraduate **Number Awarded:** Varies each year; recently, 5 of these scholarships were awarded. **Funds Available:** Stipends range from $500 to $1,000. **Duration:** 1 year.
Eligibility Requirements: This scholarship is available to high school seniors, high school graduates, and currently-enrolled college students in Vermont who are enrolled or planning to enroll at least half time in a postsecondary degree program in the visual arts (particularly arts and crafts). Applicants must have been residents of Vermont for at least 2 years. Selection is based on financial need, academic achievement, a portfolio, a letter of recommendation, required essays, and a personal interview (if necessary). **Deadline for Receipt:** June of each year.

3389 ■ VERMONT STUDENT ASSISTANCE CORPORATION

Champlain Mill
Attn: Scholarship Programs
P.O. Box 2000
Winooski, VT 05404-2601
Tel: (802)654-3798; 888-253-4819
Fax: (802)654-3765
E-mail: info@vsac.org
Web Site: http://www.vsac.org
To provide financial assistance to residents of Vermont and New Hampshire who are interested in working on a degree in direct marketing.
Title of Award: Vermont/New Hampshire Direct Marketing Group Scholarship **Area, Field, or Subject:** Marketing and distribution **Level of Education for which Award is Granted:** Undergraduate **Number Awarded:** 1 or more each year. **Funds Available:** The maximum stipend is $1,000. **Duration:** 1 year; recipients may reapply.
Eligibility Requirements: This scholarship is available to high school seniors, high school graduates, and currently-enrolled college students in New Hampshire and Vermont. Applicants must be enrolled or planning to enroll in an education or training program in a field related to direct marketing. Selection is based on academic achievement, financial need, a letter of recommendation, and required essays. **Deadline for Receipt:** June of each year.

3390 ■ WISCONSIN FOUNDATION FOR INDEPENDENT COLLEGES, INC.

Attn: College-to-Work Program
735 North Water Street, Suite 600
Milwaukee, WI 53202-4100
Tel: (414)273-5980
Fax: (414)273-5995
E-mail: wfic@wficweb.org
Web Site: http://www.wficweb.org/work.html
To provide financial assistance and work experience to students at member institutions of the Wisconsin Foundation for Independent Colleges (WFIC) who are interested in preparing for a career in a field related to Alzheimer's Disease.
Title of Award: Alzheimer's Support Center College-to-Work Program **Area, Field, or Subject:** Alzheimer's disease; Business administration; Computer and information sciences; Marketing and distribution; Psychology; Sociology **Level of Education for which Award is Granted:** Four

Year College **Number Awarded:** 1 each year. **Funds Available:** The stipends are $3,500 for the scholarship and $1,500 for the internship. **Duration:** 1 year for the scholarship; 10 weeks during the summer for the internship.
Eligibility Requirements: This program is open to full-time sophomores, juniors, and seniors at WFIC member colleges and universities. Applicants should be majoring in psychology, sociology, business, marketing, or computers. They must be interested in an internship at the Alzheimer's Support Center in Janesville, Wisconsin. Along with their application, they must submit a 1-page essay that includes why they are applying for the internship, why they have selected their major and what interests them about it, why they are attending their chosen college or university, and their future career objectives. **Deadline for Receipt:** February of each year. **Additional Information:** The WFIC member schools are Alverno College, Beloit College, Cardinal Stritch University, Carroll College, Carthage College, Concordia University of Wisconsin, Edgewood College, Lakeland College, Lawrence University, Marian College, Marquette University, Milwaukee Institute of Art & Design, Milwaukee School of Engineering, Mount Mary College, Northland College, Ripon College, St. Norbert College, Silver Lake College, Viterbo University, and Wisconsin Lutheran College. This program is sponsored by the Alzheimer's Support Center of Janesville.

3391 ■ WISCONSIN FOUNDATION FOR INDEPENDENT COLLEGES, INC.

Attn: College-to-Work Program
735 North Water Street, Suite 600
Milwaukee, WI 53202-4100
Tel: (414)273-5980
Fax: (414)273-5995
E-mail: wfic@wficweb.org
Web Site: http://www.wficweb.org/work.html
To provide financial assistance and work experience to students majoring in fields related to business at member institutions of the Wisconsin Foundation for Independent Colleges (WFIC).
Title of Award: Appleton College-to-Work Program **Area, Field, or Subject:** Accounting; Business administration; Communications; Finance; Marketing and distribution; Personnel administration/human resources **Level of Education for which Award is Granted:** Four Year College **Number Awarded:** 2 each year. **Funds Available:** The stipends are $3,500 for the scholarship and $1,500 for the internship. **Duration:** 1 year for the scholarship; 10 weeks for the internship.
Eligibility Requirements: This program is open to full-time juniors and seniors at WFIC member colleges or universities. Minority students are encouraged to apply. Applicants must be preparing for a career in accounting, business, communications, finance, human resources, or marketing. They must be interested in a summer internship at Appleton (formerly Appleton Papers). Along with their application, they must submit a 1-page essay that includes why they are applying for the internship, why they have selected their major and what interests them about it, why they are attending their chosen college or university, and their future career objectives. **Deadline for Receipt:** February of each year. **Additional Information:** The WFIC member schools are Alverno College, Beloit College, Cardinal Stritch University, Carroll College, Carthage College, Concordia University of Wisconsin, Edgewood College, Lakeland College, Lawrence University, Marian College, Marquette University, Milwaukee Institute of Art & Design, Milwaukee School of Engineering, Mount Mary College, Northland College, Ripon College, St. Norbert College, Silver Lake College, Viterbo University, and Wisconsin Lutheran College. This program is sponsored by Appleton. The WFIC's College to Work Program includes a number of other financial assistance and work experience programs for eligible students majoring in fields related to business, including the Banta College-to-Work Program (also for engineering students), Blue Cross Blue Shield of Wisconsin College-to-Work Program, Johnson Financial Group College-to-Work Program, JohnsonDiversey College-to-Work Program, Johnsonville Sausage College-to-Work Program, M3 College-to-Work Program, Marsh College-to-Work Program, Modine Manufacturing College-to-Work Program, Opportunities, Inc. College-to-Work Program, Rock County Habitat for Humanity College-to-

Work Program, Wausau Benefits College-to-Work Scholarship, and West Bend Mutual College-to-Work Scholarship.

3392 ■ WISCONSIN FOUNDATION FOR INDEPENDENT COLLEGES, INC.

Attn: College-to-Work Program
735 North Water Street, Suite 600
Milwaukee, WI 53202-4100
Tel: (414)273-5980
Fax: (414)273-5995
E-mail: wfic@wficweb.org
Web Site: http://www.wficweb.org/work.html
To provide financial assistance and work experience to students majoring in fields related to technology at member institutions of the Wisconsin Foundation for Independent Colleges (WFIC).
Title of Award: Jefferson County Literacy Council College-to-Work Program **Area, Field, or Subject:** Computer and information sciences; Education; General studies/Field of study not specified; Internet design and development; Marketing and distribution **Level of Education for which Award is Granted:** Four Year College **Number Awarded:** 1 each year. **Funds Available:** The stipends are $3,500 for the scholarship and $1,500 for the internship. **Duration:** 1 year for the scholarship; 10 weeks during the summer for the internship.
Eligibility Requirements: This program is open to full-time sophomores, juniors, and seniors at WFIC member colleges and universities. Applicants may be studying any field, but preference is given to majors in computer technology, education, marketing, sales, or website design. They must be interested in an internship at the Jefferson County Literacy Council in Fort Atkinson, Wisconsin. Along with their application, they must submit a 1-page essay that includes why they are applying for the internship, why they have selected their major and what interests them about it, why they are attending their chosen college or university, and their future career objectives. **Deadline for Receipt:** February of each year. **Additional Information:** The WFIC member schools are Alverno College, Beloit College, Cardinal Stritch University, Carroll College, Carthage College, Concordia University of Wisconsin, Edgewood College, Lakeland College, Lawrence University, Marian College, Marquette University, Milwaukee Institute of Art & Design, Milwaukee School of Engineering, Mount Mary College, Northland College, Ripon College, St. Norbert College, Silver Lake College, Viterbo University, and Wisconsin Lutheran College. This program is sponsored by the Jefferson County Literacy Council.

3393 ■ WISCONSIN FOUNDATION FOR INDEPENDENT COLLEGES, INC.

Attn: College-to-Work Program
735 North Water Street, Suite 600
Milwaukee, WI 53202-4100
Tel: (414)273-5980
Fax: (414)273-5995
E-mail: wfic@wficweb.org
Web Site: http://www.wficweb.org/work.html
To provide financial assistance and work experience to minority students majoring in fields related to the fashion industry at member institutions of the Wisconsin Foundation for Independent Colleges (WFIC).
Title of Award: Jockey International College-to-Work Program **Area, Field, or Subject:** Art; Computer and information sciences; Fashion design; Finance; Graphic art and design; Marketing and distribution **Level of Education for which Award is Granted:** Four Year College **Number Awarded:** 1 each year. **Funds Available:** The stipend is $1,500 for the scholarship; the internship is paid hourly. **Duration:** 1 year for the scholarship; 10 weeks for the internship.
Eligibility Requirements: This program is open to minority students who are full-time juniors and seniors at WFIC member colleges or universities. Applicants may be majoring in any liberal arts field, but they must be preparing for or considering a career in art, computer science/MIS, fashion design, fashion merchandising, finance, graphic design, human resources, international business, or marketing. They must be interested in an internship at Jockey International in Kenosha, Wisconsin. Along with their application, they must submit a 1-page essay that includes why they are applying for the internship, why they have selected their major and what interests them about it, why they are attending their chosen college or university, and their future career objectives. **Deadline for Receipt:**

February of each year. **Additional Information:** The WFIC member schools are Alverno College, Beloit College, Cardinal Stritch University, Carroll College, Carthage College, Concordia University of Wisconsin, Edgewood College, Lakeland College, Lawrence University, Marian College, Marquette University, Milwaukee Institute of Art & Design, Milwaukee School of Engineering, Mount Mary College, Northland College, Ripon College, St. Norbert College, Silver Lake College, Viterbo University, and Wisconsin Lutheran College. This program is sponsored by Jockey International, Inc.

3394 ■ WISCONSIN FOUNDATION FOR INDEPENDENT COLLEGES, INC.

Attn: Program Manager
735 North Water Street, Suite 600
Milwaukee, WI 53202-4100
Tel: (414)273-5980
Fax: (414)273-5995
E-mail: wfic@wficweb.org
Web Site: http://www.wficweb.org/scholar.html
To provide financial assistance to students majoring in selected fields at member institutions of the Wisconsin Foundation for Independent Colleges (WFIC).
Title of Award: Sentry Insurance Foundation Scholarships **Area, Field, or Subject:** Architecture; Business administration; Design; Economics; Information science and technology; Interior design; Mathematics and mathematical sciences **Level of Education for which Award is Granted:** Four Year College **Number Awarded:** 20 each year: 1 at each of the participating schools. **Funds Available:** The stipend is $1,000. **Duration:** 1 year.
Eligibility Requirements: This program is open to student enrolled or planning to enroll at WFIC member colleges and universities. Applicants must have a declared major in 1 of the following fields: business, economics, mathematics, management information systems, industrial design, communication design, or interior architecture and design. They must have a GPA of 3.3 or higher; entering freshmen must rank in the top 25% of their high school class. Financial need is considered in the selection process. **Deadline for Receipt:** Each participating college sets its own deadline. **Additional Information:** The WFIC member schools are Alverno College, Beloit College, Cardinal Stritch University, Carroll College, Carthage College, Concordia University of Wisconsin, Edgewood College, Lakeland College, Lawrence University, Marian College, Marquette University, Milwaukee Institute of Art & Design, Milwaukee School of Engineering, Mount Mary College, Northland College, Ripon College, St. Norbert College, Silver Lake College, Viterbo University, and Wisconsin Lutheran College. This program is supported by the Sentry Insurance Foundation.

3395 ■ WOMEN'S JEWELRY ASSOCIATION

Attn: Scholarship Committee
373 B Route 46 West, Building E, Suite 215
Fairfield, NJ 07004
Tel: (973)575-7190
Fax: (973)575-1445
E-mail: info@womensjewelry.org
Web Site: http://www.womensjewelry.org/scholarships.html
To provide financial assistance for college to women who are interested in careers in jewelry.
Title of Award: Women's Jewelry Association Scholarship **Area, Field, or Subject:** Business administration; Crafts; Finance; Marketing and distribution; Metallurgy **Level of Education for which Award is Granted:** Undergraduate **Number Awarded:** Varies each year. Recently, 12 of these scholarships were awarded: 1 at $5,000, 2 at $3,000, 1 at $2,500, 1 at $1,500 and 7 at $1,000. **Funds Available:** Stipends range from $500 to $5,000 per year. **Duration:** 1 year.
Eligibility Requirements: Women who are enrolled in a jewelry-related curriculum at an institution of higher learning located anywhere in the United States are eligible to apply. Eligible fields of study range from design to gemological analysis and include metalsmithing, finance, business, and marketing. Applicants must submit 2 letters of recommendation, a short essay explaining why they wish to prepare for a career in jewelry/toolmaking and their aspirations for the future, 3 slides showing examples of their work, and a list of 3 courses related to jewelry that have been most important to them. Financial need is considered in the selection

process. **Deadline for Receipt:** April of each year. **Additional Information:** This program includes the June Herman Scholarship of $5,000, awarded for the first time in 2001.

3396 ■ WORLDSTUDIO FOUNDATION
200 Varick Street, Suite 507
New York, NY 10014
Tel: (212)366-1317
Fax: (212)807-0024
E-mail: scholarshipcoordinator@worldstudio.org
Web Site: http://www.worldstudio.org/schol/index.html
To provide financial support for college or graduate school to art students of Native American heritage.
Title of Award: Worldstudio Foundation Indigenous Peoples Award **Area, Field, or Subject:** Art; Art industries and trade; Crafts; Native American studies **Level of Education for which Award is Granted:** Graduate, Undergraduate **Number Awarded:** 1 or more each year. **Funds Available:** The stipend ranges from $1,000 to $2,000. **Duration:** 1 academic year. Recipients may reapply.
Eligibility Requirements: This program is open to art students affiliated with Native American, Alaska Native/Inuit, or other indigenous tribes of the Americas. Applicants must be interested in maintaining traditional art, designs, or crafts. They must be undergraduate or graduate students at an accredited college or university in the United States with a GPA of 2.0 or higher. Selection is based on the quality of submitted work, a written statement of purpose, financial need, and academic record. **Deadline for Receipt:** March of each year.

3397 ■ WORLDSTUDIO FOUNDATION
200 Varick Street, Suite 507
New York, NY 10014
Tel: (212)366-1317
Fax: (212)807-0024
E-mail: scholarshipcoordinator@worldstudio.org
Web Site: http://www.worldstudio.org/schol/index.html
To provide financial assistance to undergraduate and graduate students, especially minorities, who wish to study fine or commercial arts, design, or architecture.
Title of Award: Worldstudio Foundation Scholarships **Area, Field, or Subject:** Advertising; Architecture; Art; Art industries and trade; Crafts; Design; Fashion design; Filmmaking; Graphic art and design; Interior design; Landscape architecture and design; Photography; Urban affairs/design/planning **Level of Education for which Award is Granted:** Graduate, Undergraduate **Number Awarded:** Varies each year; recently, 24 scholarships and 7 honorable mentions were awarded. **Funds Available:** Basic scholarships range from $1,000 to $2,000, but awards between $3,000 and $5,000 are also presented at the discretion of the jury. Honorable mentions are $100. Funds are paid directly to the recipient's school. **Duration:** 1 academic year. Recipients may reapply.
Eligibility Requirements: This program is open to undergraduate and graduate students who are currently enrolled or planning to enroll at an accredited college or university and major in 1 of the following areas: advertising (art direction only), architecture, crafts, environmental graphics, fashion design, film/video (direction or cinematography only), film/theater design (including set, lighting, and costume design), fine arts, furniture design, graphic design, industrial/product design, interior design, landscape architecture, new media, photography, surface/textile design, or urban planning. Although not required, minority status is a significant factor in the selection process. International students may apply if they are enrolled at a U.S. college or university. Applicants must have a GPA of 2.0 or higher. Along with their application, they must submit a 600-word statement of purpose that includes a brief autobiography, an explanation of how their experiences have influenced their creative work and/or their career plans, and how they see themselves contributing to the community at large in the future. Selection is based on that statement, the quality of submitted work, financial need, minority status, and academic record. **Deadline for Receipt:** March of each year. **Additional Information:** The foundation encourages the scholarship recipients to focus on ways that their work can address issues of social and environmental responsibility. This program includes the following named awards: the Sherry and Gary Baker Award, the Bobolink Foundation Award, the Bombay Sapphire Awards, the Richard and Jean Coyne Family Foundation Awards, the David A. Dechman Foundation Awards, the Philip and Edina Jennison

Award, the Kraus Family Foundation Awards, the Dena McKelvey Award. the New York Design Center Award, the Rudin Foundation Awards, the Starr Foundation Awards, and the John F. Wright III Award.

Communications

3398 ■ ACADEMY OF TELEVISION ARTS & SCIENCES FOUNDATION
Attn: Education Department
5220 Lankershim Boulevard
North Hollywood, CA 91601-3109
Tel: (818)754-2830
Fax: (818)761-ATAS
E-mail: collegeawards@emmys.org
Web Site: http://www.emmys.tv/foundation/index.php
To provide financial assistance to upper-division and graduate students interested in working on a project in a field related to children's media.
Title of Award: Fred Rogers Memorial Scholarship **Area, Field, or Subject:** Art, Caricatures and cartoons; Child development; Education, Early childhood; Filmmaking; Music; Psychology; Radio and television **Level of Education for which Award is Granted:** Four Year College, Graduate **Number Awarded:** 1 each year. **Funds Available:** The stipend is $10,000. **Duration:** 1 year.
Eligibility Requirements: This program is open to upper-division and graduate students interested in preparing for a career in children's media. Applicants must be able to demonstrate a commitment, either through course work or experience, to any combination of at least 2 of the following fields: early childhood education, child development, child psychology, film or television production, music, or animation. They may apply for support for any of the following areas: research on the relationship between children's media and learning or children's use of media and personal growth; development of program concepts or extended development of creative elements of an existing concept (e.g., design of puppets, scripts, storyboards, characters, music); professional internship in an organization that is relevant to the applicant's goal for use of the award. **Deadline for Receipt:** January of each year. **Additional Information:** This scholarship, first awarded in 2005, is supported by Ernst & Young.

3399 ■ ALABAMA SPACE GRANT CONSORTIUM
c/o University of Alabama in Huntsville
Materials Science Building, Room 205
Huntsville, AL 35899
Tel: (256)824-6800
Fax: (256)824-6061
E-mail: reasonj@uah.edu
Web Site: http://www.uah.edu/ASGC
To provide financial assistance to undergraduates who are studying the space sciences at universities participating in the Alabama Space Grant Consortium (ASGC).
Title of Award: Undergraduate Scholarship Program of the Alabama Space Grant Consortium **Area, Field, or Subject:** Aerospace sciences; Behavioral sciences; Biological and clinical sciences; Business administration; Communications; Computer and information sciences; Economics; Education; Engineering, Aerospace/Aeronautical/Astronautical; International affairs and relations; Law; Natural sciences; Physical sciences; Public administration; Sociology; Space and planetary sciences **Level of Education for which Award is Granted:** Four Year College **Number Awarded:** Varies each year; recently, 32 of these scholarships were awarded. **Funds Available:** The stipend is $1,000 per year. **Duration:** 1 year; may be renewed 1 additional year.
Eligibility Requirements: This program is open to full-time students entering their junior or senior year at universities participating in the ASGC. Applicants must be studying in a field related to space, including the physical, natural, and biological sciences; engineering, education; economics; business; sociology; behavioral sciences; computer science; communications; law; international affairs; and public administration. They must be U.S. citizens and have a GPA of 3.0 or higher. Individuals from underrepresented groups (African Americans, Hispanic, American Indians, Pacific Islanders, Asian Americans, and women) are especially encouraged to apply. Interested students should submit a completed application with a career goal statement, personal references, a brief resume, and transcripts. Selection is based on 1) academic qualifications,

2) quality of the career goal statement, and 3) assessment of the applicant's motivation for a career in aerospace. **Deadline for Receipt:** February of each year. **Additional Information:** The member universities are University of Alabama in Huntsville, Alabama A&M University, University of Alabama, University of Alabama at Birmingham, University of South Alabama, Tuskegee University, and Auburn University. Funding for this program is provided by NASA.

3400 ■ AMERICAN FEDERATION OF TELEVISION AND RADIO ARTISTS

Attn: AFTRA/Heller Memorial Foundation, Inc.
260 Madison Avenue, Seventh Floor
New York, NY 10016
Tel: (212)532-0800
Fax: (212)532-2242
E-mail: info@aftra.com
Web Site: http://www.aftra.org/benefits/scholarship.htm
To provide financial assistance to undergraduate and graduate students who are members or the dependent children of members of the American Federation of Television and Radio Artists (AFTRA).
Title of Award: AFTRA/Heller Memorial Foundation Scholarships **Area, Field, or Subject:** Communications; General studies/Field of study not specified; Industrial and labor relations; Journalism; Performing arts **Level of Education for which Award is Granted:** Graduate, Undergraduate **Number Awarded:** 12 to 15 each year. **Funds Available:** Stipends up to $2,500 per year are available. **Duration:** 1 year; nonrenewable.
Eligibility Requirements: This program is open to AFTRA members and the dependent children of AFTRA members (or deceased members) in good standing for at least 5 years. Applicants may be interested in working on a bachelor's or advanced degree in any field, including broadcast journalism and labor relations, or professional training in the performing arts. Selection is based on academic achievement and financial need. **Deadline for Receipt:** April of each year.

3401 ■ AMERICAN FOUNDATION FOR TRANSLATION AND INTERPRETATION

Columbia Plaza, Suite 101
350 East Michigan Avenue
Kalamazoo, MI 49007
Tel: (269)383-6893
E-mail: aftiorg@aol.com
Web Site: http://www.afti.org
To provide financial assistance to undergraduate and graduate students in translator or interpreter education programs.
Title of Award: JTG Scholarship in Scientific and Technical Translation or Interpretation **Area, Field, or Subject:** Translating **Level of Education for which Award is Granted:** Graduate, Undergraduate **Number Awarded:** 1 each year. **Funds Available:** The stipend is $2,500. **Duration:** 1 year; nonrenewable.
Eligibility Requirements: This program is open to students enrolled or planning to enroll in graduate or undergraduate programs in scientific and technical translation on in interpretation at accredited U.S. colleges and universities. Applicants must be full-time students who have completed at least 1 year of postsecondary education and have at least 1 year of academic work remaining to complete their program of study. They must have a GPA of 3.0 or higher overall and 3.5 or higher in translation and interpretation related courses. U.S. citizenship is required. Along with their application, they must submit an essay of 300 to 500 words on their interests and goals as they relate to the field of translation or interpretation. Selection is based on the essay, demonstrated achievement in translation and interpretation, academic record, and 3 letters of recommendation. **Deadline for Receipt:** May of each year. **Additional Information:** This program, established in 2001, is supported by the American Translators Association (ATA) and JTG, Inc. of Alexandria, Virginia. Information is also available from the ATA, 225 Reinekers Lane, Suite 590, Alexandria, VA 22314, (703) 683-6100, Fax: (703) 683-6122, E-mail: ata@atanet.org.

3402 ■ AMERICAN RADIO RELAY LEAGUE

Attn: ARRL Foundation
225 Main Street
Newington, CT 06111
Tel: (860)594-0397

Fax: (860)594-0259
E-mail: foundation@arrl.org
Web Site: http://www.arrl.org/arrlf/scholgen.html
To provide financial assistance to licensed radio amateurs who are interested in working on an undergraduate or graduate degree, especially in electronics or communications.
Title of Award: Irving W. Cook, WA0CGS, Scholarship **Area, Field, or Subject:** Communications; Electronics; General studies/Field of study not specified **Level of Education for which Award is Granted:** Graduate, Undergraduate **Number Awarded:** 1 each year. **Funds Available:** The stipend is $1,000. **Duration:** 1 year.
Eligibility Requirements: This program is open to undergraduate or graduate students at accredited institutions who are licensed radio amateurs (any class). Applicants must submit an essay on the role amateur radio has played in their lives and provide documentation of financial need. Preference is given to applicants from Kansas who are majoring in electronics, communications, or related fields. **Deadline for Receipt:** January of each year. **Additional Information:** Recipients may attend school in any state.

3403 ■ AMERICAN RADIO RELAY LEAGUE

Attn: ARRL Foundation
225 Main Street
Newington, CT 06111
Tel: (860)594-0397
Fax: (860)594-0259
E-mail: foundation@arrl.org
Web Site: http://www.arrl.org/arrlf/scholgen.html
To provide financial assistance to licensed radio amateurs, particularly from Arizona and selected counties in California, who are interested in working on an undergraduate or graduate degree, particularly in electronics, communications, or related fields.
Title of Award: Charles N. Fisher Memorial Scholarship **Area, Field, or Subject:** Communications; Electronics; General studies/Field of study not specified **Level of Education for which Award is Granted:** Graduate, Undergraduate **Number Awarded:** 1 each year. **Funds Available:** The stipend is $1,000. **Duration:** 1 year.
Eligibility Requirements: This program is open to undergraduate or graduate students at accredited institutions who are licensed radio amateurs (any class). Applicants must submit an essay on the role amateur radio has played in their lives and provide documentation of financial need. Preference is given to students who are 1) residents of Arizona or selected counties in California (Los Angeles, Orange, San Diego, Santa Barbara), and 2) majoring in electronics, communications, or related fields. **Deadline for Receipt:** January of each year.

3404 ■ AMERICAN RADIO RELAY LEAGUE

Attn: ARRL Foundation
225 Main Street
Newington, CT 06111
Tel: (860)594-0397
Fax: (860)594-0259
E-mail: foundation@arrl.org
Web Site: http://www.arrl.org/arrlf/scholgen.html
To provide financial assistance to licensed radio amateurs who are interested in working on an undergraduate or graduate degree, particularly in electronics or communications.
Title of Award: Paul and Helen L. Grauer Scholarship **Area, Field, or Subject:** Communications; Electronics; General studies/Field of study not specified **Level of Education for which Award is Granted:** Graduate, Undergraduate **Number Awarded:** 1 each year. **Funds Available:** The stipend is $1,000. **Duration:** 1 year.
Eligibility Requirements: This program is open to undergraduate or graduate students at accredited institutions who are licensed radio amateurs of the novice class or higher. Preference is given to students who are 1) residents of Iowa, Kansas, Missouri, or Nebraska and attending schools in those states, and 2) majoring in electronics, communications, or related fields. Applicants must submit an essay on the role

amateur radio has played in their lives and provide documentation of financial need. **Deadline for Receipt:** January of each year.

3405 ■ AMERICAN RADIO RELAY LEAGUE

Attn: ARRL Foundation
225 Main Street
Newington, CT 06111
Tel: (860)594-0397
Fax: (860)594-0259
E-mail: foundation@arrl.org
Web Site: http://www.arrl.org/arrlf/scholgen.html
To provide financial assistance to licensed radio amateurs from designated states who are interested in working on an undergraduate or graduate degree, particularly in electronics or communications.
Title of Award: L. Phil Wicker Scholarship **Area, Field, or Subject:** Communications; Electronics; General studies/Field of study not specified **Level of Education for which Award is Granted:** Graduate, Undergraduate **Number Awarded:** 1 each year. **Funds Available:** The stipend is $1,000. **Duration:** 1 year.
Eligibility Requirements: This program is open to undergraduate or graduate students at accredited institutions who are licensed radio amateurs of general class. Preference is given to students who are 1) residents of North Carolina, South Carolina, Virginia, or West Virginia and attending school in those states, and 2) majoring in electronics, communications, or related fields. Applicants must submit an essay on the role amateur radio has played in their lives and provide documentation of financial need. **Deadline for Receipt:** January of each year.

3406 ■ ARAB AMERICAN INSTITUTE FOUNDATION

Attn: Scholarship Administrator
1600 K Street, N.W., Suite 601
Washington, DC 20006
Tel: (202)429-9210
Fax: (202)429-9214
E-mail: aaif@aaiusa.org
Web Site: http://www.aaiusa.org/foundation/154/student-resource-center
To provide financial assistance to Arab American students interested in working on an undergraduate or graduate degree in journalism.
Title of Award: Al Muammar Scholarships for Journalism **Area, Field, or Subject:** Communications; Journalism **Level of Education for which Award is Granted:** Graduate, Undergraduate **Number Awarded:** Up to 4 each year. **Funds Available:** The stipend is $5,000. **Duration:** 1 year.
Eligibility Requirements: This program is open to U.S. citizens and permanent residents of Arab descent who are enrolled full time at an accredited college or university in the United States. Applicants must be undergraduates or college seniors admitted to a graduate program. They must have a GPA of 3.3 or higher and a demonstrated commitment to the field of print or broadcast journalism. Selection is based on sensitivity to Arab American issues, demonstrated community involvement, initiative in social advocacy and civic empowerment, journalistic ability, academic ability, commitment to the field of journalism, and financial need. **Deadline for Receipt:** February of each year. **Additional Information:** These scholarships were first awarded in 2006.

3407 ■ ARKANSAS DEPARTMENT OF HIGHER EDUCATION

Attn: Financial Aid Division
114 East Capitol Avenue
Little Rock, AR 72201-3818
Tel: (501)371-2050
Free: 800-54-STUDY
Fax: (501)371-2001
E-mail: finaid@adhe.arknet.edu
Web Site: http://www.arkansashighered.com/mteachers.html
To provide scholarship/loans to minority undergraduates in Arkansas who want to become teachers.
Title of Award: Arkansas Minority Teacher Scholars Program **Area, Field, or Subject:** Counseling/Guidance; Education; Education, Elementary; Linguistics; Mathematics and mathematical sciences; Science **Level of Education for which Award is Granted:** Four Year College **Number Awarded:** Varies each year; recently, 97 of these scholarship/loans were approved. **Funds Available:** Awards up to $5,000 per year are available. This is a scholarship/loan program. The loan will be forgiven at the rate of 20% for each year the recipient teaches full time

in an Arkansas public school (or 33% per year if the obligation is fulfilled in 3 years as described above). If the loan is not forgiven by service, it must be repaid with interest at a rate up to 5% points above the Federal Reserve discount rate. **Duration:** 1 year; may be renewed for 1 additional year if the recipient remains a full-time student with a GPA of 2.5 or higher.
Eligibility Requirements: Applicants must be minority (African American, Native American, Hispanic, or Asian American) residents of Arkansas who are U.S. citizens and enrolled as full-time juniors or seniors in an approved teacher certification program at an Arkansas public or independent 4-year institution. They must have a cumulative GPA of 2.5 or higher and be willing to teach in an Arkansas public school for at least 5 years after completion of their teaching certificate (3 years if the teaching is in 1 of the 42 counties of Arkansas designated as the Delta Region; or if the teaching is in mathematics, science, or foreign language; or if the recipient is an African American male and teaches at the elementary level; or if the service is as a guidance counselor). **Deadline for Receipt:** May of each year.

3408 ■ ARKANSAS DEPARTMENT OF HIGHER EDUCATION

Attn: Financial Aid Division
114 East Capitol Avenue
Little Rock, AR 72201-3818
Tel: (501)371-2050
Free: 800-54-STUDY
Fax: (501)371-2001
E-mail: finaid@adhe.arknet.edu
Web Site: http://www.starark.com
To provide scholarship/loans to college students in Arkansas who are interested in preparing for a teaching career in an approved subject or geographic shortage area.
Title of Award: Arkansas State Teacher Assistance Resource (STAR) Program **Area, Field, or Subject:** Biological and clinical sciences; Chemistry; Earth sciences; Education; Education, Secondary; Education, Special; Geosciences; Linguistics; Mathematics and mathematical sciences; Physical sciences; Physics **Level of Education for which Award is Granted:** Master's, Undergraduate **Number Awarded:** Varies each year; recently, 42 of these scholarship/loans were approved. **Funds Available:** The award is $3,000 per year for students who agree to teach in either a geographic teacher shortage area or a subject teacher shortage area. For students who agree to teach in both a geographic shortage area and a subject shortage area, the award is $6,000 per year. This is a scholarship/loan program. Recipients must teach in an Arkansas geographic or subject shortage area for 1 year for each year of support they receive. If they fail to complete that teaching obligation, they must repay all funds received. **Duration:** 1 year; may be renewed for 1 additional year if the recipient is enrolled in a 4-year teacher education program or 2 additional years if enrolled in a 5-year teacher education program. Renewal requires that the recipient maintain a GPA of 2.75 or higher and complete 24 semester hours as an undergraduate or 18 semester hours as a graduate student.
Eligibility Requirements: This program is open to Arkansas residents who are full-time students enrolled 1) at a 4-year public or private college or university in the state with an approved teacher education program; 2) in an associate of arts in teaching program; or 3) in an master of arts in teaching program. Applicants must have a GPA of 2.75 or higher and be entering their sophomore, junior, or senior year (or be in a master's degree program). They must be willing to teach in a public school located in a geographic area of Arkansas designated as having a critical shortage of teachers or in a subject matter area designated as having a critical shortage of teachers. Applicants must have completed their freshman year at an accredited Arkansas public or private college or university in a major field of study leading to secondary teacher certification in 1 of the shortage areas. U.S. citizenship is required. **Deadline for Receipt:** May of each year. **Additional Information:** This program was established in 2004 as a replacement for the former Arkansas Emergency Secondary Education Loan Program. Recently, the subject areas designated as having a critical shortage of teachers were foreign language, mathematics, chemistry, physics, biology, physical science, earth science, and special education. For a list of geographic areas of Arkansas that are designated as having a critical shortage of teachers, contact the Department of Higher Education. The State Teacher Assistance Resource (STAR) program also provides that teachers who received federal student loans may have those loans repaid 1) at the rate of $3,000 per year if they teach

a subject area in Arkansas that is designated as a shortage area or if they teach in a geographic area of the state with a shortage of teachers, or 2) at the rate of $6,000 per year if they teach a shortage subject area in a shortage geographic area. Students may not, however, participate in both the scholarship/loan program and the federal loan repayment program.

3409 ■ ASIAN AMERICAN JOURNALISTS ASSOCIATION

Attn: Student Programs Coordinator
1182 Market Street, Suite 320
San Francisco, CA 94102
Tel: (415)346-2051
Fax: (415)346-6343
E-mail: brandons@aaja.org
Web Site: http://www.aaja.org/programs/for_students/scholarships
To provide financial assistance to student members of the Asian American Journalists Association (AAJA) interested in careers in broadcast, photo, or print journalism.
Title of Award: Cox Foundation Scholarships **Area, Field, or Subject:** Communications; Graphic art and design; Journalism; Photography, Journalistic **Level of Education for which Award is Granted:** Graduate, Undergraduate **Number Awarded:** Varies each year. **Funds Available:** The stipend is $2,500. **Duration:** 1 year; may be renewed.
Eligibility Requirements: This program is open to AAJA members who are high school seniors or college students (graduate or undergraduate) enrolled full time in accredited institutions. Applicants must submit a 500-word essay on their involvement or interest in the Asian American community and how, if they are awarded this scholarship, they would contribute to the field of journalism and/or media issues involving the Asian American and Pacific Islander community. Selection is based on scholastic ability, commitment to journalism, sensitivity to Asian American and Pacific Islander issues as demonstrated by community involvement, journalistic ability, and financial need. **Deadline for Receipt:** April of each year. **Additional Information:** This program is supported by the Cox Foundation.

3410 ■ ASIAN AMERICAN JOURNALISTS ASSOCIATION

Attn: Student Programs Coordinator
1182 Market Street, Suite 320
San Francisco, CA 94102
Tel: (415)346-2051
Fax: (415)346-6343
E-mail: brandons@aaja.org
Web Site: http://www.aaja.org/programs/for_students/scholarships
To provide financial assistance to male Asian American students who are members of the Asian American Journalists Association (AAJA) and interested in a career in broadcast journalism.
Title of Award: Minoru Yasui Memorial Scholarship Award **Area, Field, or Subject:** Communications; Journalism **Level of Education for which Award is Granted:** Graduate, Undergraduate **Number Awarded:** 1 each year. **Funds Available:** The stipend is $2,000. **Duration:** 1 year.
Eligibility Requirements: This program is open to Asian American male high school seniors, undergraduates, or graduate students enrolled full time at an accredited college or university in a broadcast journalism program. Applicants must be AAJA members. Along with their application, they must submit a 500-word essay on their involvement or interest in the Asian American community and how, if they are awarded this scholarship, they would contribute to the field of journalism and/or media issues involving the Asian American and Pacific Islander community. Selection is based on scholastic ability, commitment to journalism, sensitivity to Asian American and Pacific Islander issues as demonstrated by community involvement, journalistic ability, and financial need. **Deadline for Receipt:** April of each year. **Additional Information:** This scholarship honors Minoru Yasui, a civil rights advocate and attorney who was 1 of 3 Nisei to challenge the internment of Japanese Americans during World War II.

3411 ■ ASIAN AMERICAN JOURNALISTS ASSOCIATION-PORTLAND CHAPTER

c/o Tracy Jan
The Oregonian
Metro East News Bureau
295 N.E. Second Street
Gresham, OR 97030
Tel: (503)294-5970

E-mail: tracyjan@news.oregonian.com
Web Site: http://chapters.aaja.org/Portland/scholar.html
To provide financial assistance to undergraduate and graduate journalism students in Oregon and southwestern Washington area who have been involved in the Asian American community.
Title of Award: Portland Chapter AAJA Scholarships **Area, Field, or Subject:** Communications; Journalism; Photography, Journalistic **Level of Education for which Award is Granted:** Graduate, Undergraduate **Number Awarded:** 1 each year. **Funds Available:** Stipends up to $2,000 are available. **Duration:** 1 year.
Eligibility Requirements: This program is open to high school seniors, undergraduates, and graduate students who live or attend school in Oregon or the Vancouver, Washington area. Applicants must be enrolled or planning to enroll full time in a journalism program and be able to demonstrate involvement in the Asian American community. Along with their application, they must submit an essay (up to 750 words) on how they became interested in journalism or how they see themselves contributing to the Asian American community. They must also submit work samples (print: up to 3 articles; radio: up to 3 different stories on standard audio tapes; television: up to 3 different stories on a VHS tape; photojournalism: a portfolio of up to 15 entries). Selection is based on scholastic ability, commitment to journalism, sensitivity to Asian American issues as demonstrated by community involvement, journalistic ability, and financial need. **Deadline for Receipt:** March of each year.

3412 ■ ASIAN AMERICAN JOURNALISTS ASSOCIATION-TEXAS CHAPTER

c/o Julie Tam, Scholarship Chair
KLTV-TV ABC 7
105 West Ferguson
P.O. Box 957
Tyler, TX 75710
Tel: (903)597-5588
Fax: (903)510-7847
E-mail: julie@julietam.com
Web Site: http://chapters.aaja.org/Texas/schol.html
To provide financial assistance to members of the Asian American Journalists Association (AAJA) in Texas who are working on an undergraduate or graduate degree in journalism.
Title of Award: Texas Chapter Scholarships **Area, Field, or Subject:** Communications; Journalism; Photography, Journalistic **Level of Education for which Award is Granted:** Graduate, Undergraduate **Number Awarded:** 2 each year. **Funds Available:** The stipend is $1,000 per year. **Duration:** 1 year.
Eligibility Requirements: This program is open to graduating high school seniors, undergraduates, and graduate students who are either Texas residents or planning to attend an accredited college or university in Texas. Applicants must be AAJA members. Along with their application, they must submit a 250-word autobiography that explains why they are interested in a career in journalism, a 500-word essay on the role of ethnic diversity in news coverage (both for the subjects of the news events and also the journalists involved), their most recent official transcript, a statement of financial need, 2 letters of recommendation, and a resume. Work samples to be submitted are 2 legible clips from print journalism students; 3 to 5 prints or slides with captions or descriptions from print photojournalism students; 2 VHS taped excerpts with corresponding scripts from television broadcast students; 2 edited VHS excepts from television photojournalism students; 3 taped cassette excerpts with corresponding scripts from radio broadcast students; or 3 legible online articles from web journalism students. Selection is based on commitment to the field of journalism, awareness of Asian American issues, journalistic ability, scholastic ability, and financial need. **Deadline for Receipt:** April of each year.

3413 ■ ASSOCIATED PRESS TELEVISION/RADIO ASSOCIATION OF CALIFORNIA AND NEVADA

c/o Roberta Gonzales
CBS 5 TV
855 Battery Street
San Francisco, CA 94111
Tel: (415)362-5550
E-mail: gonzales@kpix.cbs.com
Web Site: http://www.aptra.org

To provide financial assistance to students at colleges and universities in California and Nevada who are interested in broadcast journalism careers.

Title of Award: Kathryn Dettman Memorial Journalism Scholarship Award **Area, Field, or Subject:** Communications; Journalism **Level of Education for which Award is Granted:** Undergraduate **Number Awarded:** 1 each year. **Funds Available:** The stipend is $1,500 per year. **Duration:** 1 year.

Eligibility Requirements: This program is open to students at colleges and universities in California and Nevada. Applicants must have a broadcast journalism career objective. Selection is based on a 500-word essay on why the students wish to pursue broadcast journalism; another 500-word essay on their honors, awards, and broadcast experience; 3 letters of recommendation; and a statement of how they are financing their education. **Deadline for Receipt:** December of each year.

3414 ■ ASSOCIATED PRESS TELEVISION/RADIO ASSOCIATION OF CALIFORNIA AND NEVADA

c/o Roberta Gonzales
CBS 5 TV
855 Battery Street
San Francisco, CA 94111
Tel: (415)362-5550
E-mail: gonzales@kpix.cbs.com
Web Site: http://www.aptra.org

To provide financial assistance to students at colleges and universities in California and Nevada who are interested in broadcast journalism careers.

Title of Award: Clete Roberts Memorial Journalism Scholarship Award **Area, Field, or Subject:** Communications; Journalism **Level of Education for which Award is Granted:** Undergraduate **Number Awarded:** 2 each year. **Funds Available:** The stipend is $1,500 per year. **Duration:** 1 year.

Eligibility Requirements: This program is open to students at colleges and universities in California and Nevada. Applicants must have a broadcast journalism career objective. Selection is based on a 500-word essay on why the students wish to pursue broadcast journalism; another 500-word essay on their honors, awards, and broadcast experience; 3 letters of recommendation; and a statement of how they are financing their education. **Deadline for Receipt:** December of each year.

3415 ■ JORGE MAS CANOSA FREEDOM FOUNDATION

c/o Cuban American National Foundation
1312 S.W. 27th Avenue
P.O. Box 440069
Miami, FL 33144-9926
Tel: (305)592-7768
Fax: (305)592-7889
Web Site: http://www.canf.org

To provide financial assistance to students of Cuban descent who are working on an undergraduate or graduate degree in selected subject areas.

Title of Award: Mas Family Scholarship Program **Area, Field, or Subject:** Business administration; Communications; Economics; Engineering; International affairs and relations; Journalism **Level of Education for which Award is Granted:** Graduate, Undergraduate **Funds Available:** The amount of the award depends on the cost of tuition at the recipient's selected institution, on the family's situation, and on the amount of funds received from other sources. The amount of the yearly award cannot exceed $10,000. Full scholarships are not awarded to students who will be receiving full tuition scholarships and/or stipendiary support from other sources. **Duration:** 1 year; recipients may reapply and are given preference over other candidates.

Eligibility Requirements: This program is open to students who are direct descendants of those who left Cuba or were born in Cuba themselves. Applicants must be or have been in the top 10% of their high school graduating class and have be able to meet federal standards of financial need. At least 1 parent or 2 grandparents must have been born in Cuba. Both undergraduate and graduate students may apply, provided they are majoring in 1 of the following subjects: engineering, business, international relations, economics, communications, or journalism. Selection is based on academic performance, leadership qualities, financial need, potential to contribute to the advancement of a free society, and

likelihood of succeeding in their chosen field. Finalists may be interviewed. **Deadline for Receipt:** March of each year. **Additional Information:** This program was previously offered by the Cuban American National Foundation.

3416 ■ CLASSICAL ASSOCIATION OF THE MIDDLE WEST AND SOUTH

c/o Eleanor Winsor Leach
Indiana University
Department of Classical Studies
547 Ballantine Hall
Bloomington, IN 47405
Tel: (812)855-4129
E-mail: leach@indiana.edu
Web Site: http://www.camws.org/awards/MAScollege.html

To provide financial assistance to undergraduate students majoring in classics at a college or university in the area of the Classical Association of the Middle West and South (CAMWS).

Title of Award: Manson A. Stewart Scholarships **Area, Field, or Subject:** Classical studies; Foreign languages **Level of Education for which Award is Granted:** Undergraduate **Number Awarded:** Varies each year; recently, 6 of these scholarships were awarded. **Funds Available:** The award is $1,000. **Duration:** 1 year.

Eligibility Requirements: This program is open to undergraduate students who are majoring in classics at the sophomore or junior level at a college or university in the geographic area served by the association. Candidates must be nominated by the chair of their department or program; students then fill out an application and send it along with transcripts and letters of recommendation from 2 members of the association. Nominees are expected to take at least 2 courses in Latin or Greek during the junior or senior year in which the scholarship is held. **Deadline for Receipt:** February of each year.

3417 ■ CLASSICAL ASSOCIATION OF NEW ENGLAND

c/o Allen M. Ware
University of Connecticut
Department of History
Box U-103
Storrs, CT 06269-2103
Tel: (860)486-3722
Fax: (860)486-0641
E-mail: ward@uconnvm.uconn.edu
Web Site: http://www.caneweb.org

To provide financial assistance to upper-division and graduate students in New England who are working on certification as a teacher of Latin or Greek.

Title of Award: CANE Certification Scholarship **Area, Field, or Subject:** Classical studies; Education, Secondary; Foreign languages **Level of Education for which Award is Granted:** Four Year College, Master's **Number Awarded:** 1 each year. **Funds Available:** The stipend is $1,500. Funds are intended to cover tuition and fees. **Duration:** 1 year or summer session.

Eligibility Requirements: This program is open to junior and senior undergraduates at colleges and universities in New England and to holders of a master's degree. Applicants must be preparing for secondary school certification as a teacher of Latin or Greek or both in a New England state. Full-time, part-time, and summer programs qualify. Along with their application, they must submit 2 letters of recommendation from college classicists, a letter attesting to their ability to communicate and work with young people and inspire them to high levels of achievement, a 1,000-word personal statement explaining why they are preparing for a career as a secondary school classicist, high school and college transcripts, and a description of their program and the expenses involved. **Deadline for Receipt:** February of each year.

3418 ■ COMMUNITIES FOUNDATION OF TEXAS

Attn: Scholarship Department
5500 Caruth Haven Lane
Dallas, TX 75225-8146
Tel: (214)750-4222
Fax: (214)750-4210
E-mail: grants@cftexas.org
Web Site: http://www.cftexas.org

To provide financial assistance to upper-division and graduate students who are working on a degree in journalism and have an interest in aviation.

Title of Award: George E. Haddaway Scholarship **Area, Field, or Subject:** Aviation; Communications; Journalism **Level of Education for which Award is Granted:** Four Year College, Graduate **Number Awarded:** 1 each year. **Funds Available:** The stipend is $2,500 per year. **Duration:** 1 year; nonrenewable.

Eligibility Requirements: This program is open to college juniors, seniors, and graduate students who can demonstrate interest in aviation by such activities as 1) current or former membership in the aviation program of a college or university, the Boy or Girl Scouts of America, the Civil Air Patrol, or a similar organization; or 2) pursuit or completion of the requirements for an aircraft license. Applicants must be working on a baccalaureate or advanced degree in print or electronic journalism and have completed at least 52 hours of college course work with a GPA of 2.75 or higher. They must be able to demonstrate financial need. Along with their application, they must submit an essay (200 to 500 words) describing their interest in aviation and how they might combine that interest with a career in journalism. U.S. citizenship is required. **Deadline for Receipt:** March of each year.

3419 ■ COOK INLET REGION, INC.
Attn: CIRI Foundation
2600 Cordova Street, Suite 206
Anchorage, AK 99503
Tel: (907)263-5582
Free: 800-764-3382
Fax: (907)263-5588
E-mail: tcf@ciri.com
Web Site: http://www.thecirifoundation.org/scholarship.html
To provide financial assistance for undergraduate or graduate studies in telecommunications or broadcast to Alaska Natives and their lineal descendants.

Title of Award: Cap Lathrop Endowment Scholarship Fund **Area, Field, or Subject:** Communications; Radio and television; Telecommunications systems **Level of Education for which Award is Granted:** Graduate, Undergraduate **Number Awarded:** 1 each year. **Funds Available:** The stipend is $3,500 per year. Funds must be used for tuition, university fees, books, required class supplies, and campus housing and meal plans for students who must live away from their permanent home to attend college. Checks are sent directly to the recipient's school. **Duration:** 1 year (2 semesters).

Eligibility Requirements: This program is open to Alaska Native enrollees under the Alaska Native Claims Settlement Act (ANCSA) of 1971 and their lineal descendants. Proof of eligibility must be submitted. Applicants may be enrollees of any of the 13 ANCSA regional corporations, but preference is given to original enrollees/descendants of Cook Inlet Region, Inc. (CIRI) who have a GPA of 3.0 or higher. There are no Alaska residency requirements or age limitations. Applicants must be accepted or enrolled full time in a 2-year undergraduate, 4-year undergraduate, or graduate degree program. They must be majoring in telecommunications or broadcast and planning to work in the telecommunications or broadcast industry in Alaska after graduation. Selection is based on academic achievement, rigor of course work or degree program, quality of a statement of purpose, student financial contribution, financial need, grade level, previous work performance, education and community activities, letters of recommendation, seriousness of purpose, and practicality of educational and professional goals. **Deadline for Receipt:** May of each year. **Additional Information:** This program was established in 1997. Recipients must attend school on a full-time basis and must plan to work in the broadcast or telecommunications industry in Alaska upon completion of their academic degree.

3420 ■ COOK INLET REGION, INC.
Attn: CIRI Foundation
2600 Cordova Street, Suite 206
Anchorage, AK 99503
Tel: (907)263-5582
Free: 800-764-3382
Fax: (907)263-5588
E-mail: tcf@ciri.com
Web Site: http://www.thecirifoundation.org/scholarship.html

To provide financial assistance for undergraduate or graduate studies in selected liberal arts to Alaska Natives who are original enrollees to Cook Inlet Region, Inc. (CIRI) and their lineal descendants.

Title of Award: Lawrence Matson Memorial Endowment Fund Scholarships **Area, Field, or Subject:** Art; Communications; Education; Law; Linguistics; Social sciences **Level of Education for which Award is Granted:** Four Year College, Graduate **Number Awarded:** Varies each year; recently, 1 of these scholarships (at $7,000 per year) was awarded. **Funds Available:** The stipend is $9,000 per year, $7,000 per year, or $2,000 per semester, depending on GPA. **Duration:** 1 year (2 semesters).

Eligibility Requirements: This program is open to Alaska Native enrollees to CIRI under the Alaska Native Claims Settlement Act (ANCSA) of 1971 and their lineal descendants. There are no Alaska residency requirements or age limitations. Applicants must be accepted or enrolled full time in a 4-year undergraduate or a graduate degree program in the following liberal arts fields: language, education, social sciences, arts, communications, or law. They must have a GPA of 2.5 or higher. Selection is based on academic achievement, rigor of course work or degree program, quality of a statement of purpose, student financial contribution, financial need, grade level, previous work performance, education and community activities, letters of recommendation, seriousness of purpose, and practicality of educational and professional goals. **Deadline for Receipt:** May of each year. **Additional Information:** This fund was established in 1989. Recipients must attend school on a full-time basis.

3421 ■ DELAWARE HIGHER EDUCATION COMMISSION
Carvel State Office Building
820 North French Street
Wilmington, DE 19801
Tel: (302)577-3240
Free: 800-292-7935
Fax: (302)577-6765
E-mail: dhec@doe.k12.de.us
Web Site: http://www.doe.state.de.us/high-ed/christa.htm
To provide scholarship/loans for teacher training to Delaware residents with outstanding academic records.

Title of Award: Christa McAuliffe Teacher Scholarship/Loan **Area, Field, or Subject:** Counseling/Guidance; Education; Education, Bilingual and cross-cultural; Education, English as a second language; Education, Special; English language and literature; Library and archival sciences; Linguistics; Mathematics and mathematical sciences; Reading; Technology **Level of Education for which Award is Granted:** Undergraduate **Number Awarded:** Up to 50 each year. **Funds Available:** Funds up to the cost of tuition, fees, and other direct educational expenses are provided. This is a scholarship/loan program; if the recipient performs required service at a school in Delaware, the loan is forgiven at the rate of 1 year of assistance for each year of service. **Duration:** 1 year; may be renewed for up to 3 additional years.

Eligibility Requirements: This program is open to Delaware residents who are enrolled or accepted for enrollment at a Delaware college or university in a program leading to teacher qualification. Preference is given to applicants planning to teach in an area of critical need. High school seniors must rank in the top half of their class and have a combined score of at least 1570 on the SAT; applicants who are already enrolled in college must have a cumulative GPA of 2.75 or higher. Selection is based on academic achievement. U.S. citizenship or permanent resident status is required. **Deadline for Receipt:** March of each year. **Additional Information:** The areas of critical need recently included bilingual education, business education, English, foreign languages, English to speakers of other languages, mathematics, reading, science, school librarianship, special education, and technology education.

3422 ■ DELTA SIGMA THETA SORORITY, INC.
1707 New Hampshire Avenue, N.W.
Washington, DC 20009
Tel: (202)986-2400
Fax: (202)986-2513
E-mail: dstemail@deltasigmatheta.org
Web Site: http://www.deltasigmatheta.org
To provide financial assistance to members of Delta Sigma Theta who are interested in preparing for a career in journalism or another area of communications.

Title of Award: Julia Bumry Jones Scholarship Program **Area, Field, or Subject:** Communications; Journalism **Level of Education for which**

Award is Granted: Four Year College, Graduate **Funds Available:** The stipends range from $1,000 to $2,000. The funds may be used to cover tuition, fees, and living expenses. **Duration:** 1 year; may be renewed up to 2 additional years.
Eligibility Requirements: Applicants must be college seniors or graduate students who are interested in preparing for a career in journalism or another area of communications and who are active, dues-paying members of Delta Sigma Theta. **Deadline for Receipt:** March of each year. **Additional Information:** Winners may also receive financial assistance from other sources. Confirmation of registration must be received before stipends are paid.

3423 ■ DETROIT FREE PRESS
Attn: High School Journalism Directors
600 West Fort Street
Detroit, MI 48226
Tel: (313)222-6428
Free: 800-678-6400
Fax: (313)222-8874
E-mail: highschools@freepress.com
Web Site: http://www.freep.com
To provide financial assistance for college to minority high school seniors the circulation area of the *Detroit Free Press* who are interested in a career in journalism or newspaper business operations.
Title of Award: Detroit Free Press Minority Scholarships **Area, Field, or Subject:** Business administration; Communications; Journalism **Level of Education for which Award is Granted:** Four Year College **Number Awarded:** 3 each year, of whom at least 2 are nominated for the national scholarships. **Funds Available:** The stipend is $1,000. **Duration:** 1 year.
Eligibility Requirements: This program is open to minority high school seniors in Michigan, the greater Toledo metropolitan area, and the greater Windsor metropolitan area. Applicants must be planning to attend a 4-year college or university to major in journalism, communications, or a related field. They must be interested in preparing for a career in journalism or newspaper business operations. Along with their application, they must submit 2 letters of recommendation, a transcript of grades, SAT/ACT scores, up to 5 samples of work with bylines (for journalism applicants), and an essay on "Why Journalism or the Newspaper Business is the Life for Me." **Deadline for Receipt:** January of each year. **Additional Information:** The recipients of these scholarships may be entered into competition for the Knight Ridder Minority Scholarship Program of $40,000 over 4 years.

3424 ■ ELECTRONIC DOCUMENT SYSTEMS FOUNDATION
Attn: EDSF Scholarship Awards
24238 Hawthorne Boulevard
Torrance, CA 90505-6505
Tel: (310)541-1481
Fax: (310)541-4803
Web Site: http://www.edsf.org/scholarships.cfm
To provide financial assistance to college juniors, seniors, and graduate students interested in working with electronic documents as a career.
Title of Award: Wayne Alexander Memorial Scholarship **Area, Field, or Subject:** Computer and information sciences; Graphic art and design; Internet design and development; Marketing and distribution; Printing trades and industries; Telecommunications systems **Level of Education for which Award is Granted:** Four Year College, Graduate **Number Awarded:** 1 each year. **Funds Available:** The stipend is $2,000. **Duration:** 1 year.
Eligibility Requirements: This program is open to juniors, seniors, and graduate students who are working full time on a degree in the field of document communication, including marketing, graphic communication and arts, e-commerce, imaging science, printing, web authoring, electronic publishing, computer science, or telecommunications. Priority consideration is given to students at the University of Central Florida. Applicants must submit a statement of their career goals in the field of document communications, an essay on a topic related to their view of the future of the document management and production industry, a list of current professional and college extracurricular activities and achievements, college transcripts (GPA of 3.0 or higher), samples of their creative work, and 2 letters of recommendation. Financial need is not considered. **Deadline for Receipt:** May of each year. **Additional Information:** This program is sponsored by AXIS Inc.

3425 ■ ELECTRONIC DOCUMENT SYSTEMS FOUNDATION
Attn: EDSF Scholarship Awards
24238 Hawthorne Boulevard
Torrance, CA 90505-6505
Tel: (310)541-1481
Fax: (310)541-4803
Web Site: http://www.edsf.org/scholarships.cfm
To provide financial assistance to college juniors, seniors, and graduate students interested in working with electronic documents as a career.
Title of Award: EDSF Board of Directors Scholarships **Area, Field, or Subject:** Computer and information sciences; Graphic art and design; Internet design and development; Marketing and distribution; Printing trades and industries; Telecommunications systems **Level of Education for which Award is Granted:** Four Year College, Graduate **Number Awarded:** 20 each year. **Funds Available:** The stipend is $2,000. **Duration:** 1 year.
Eligibility Requirements: This program is open to juniors, seniors, and graduate students who are working full time on a degree in the field of document communication, including marketing, graphic communication and arts, e-commerce, imaging science, printing, web authoring, electronic publishing, computer science, or telecommunications. Applicants must submit a statement of their career goals in the field of document communications, an essay on a topic related to their view of the future of the document management and production industry, a list of current professional and college extracurricular activities and achievements, college transcripts (GPA of 3.0 or higher), samples of their creative work, and 2 letters of recommendation. Financial need is not considered. **Deadline for Receipt:** May of each year.

3426 ■ ELECTRONIC DOCUMENT SYSTEMS FOUNDATION
Attn: EDSF Scholarship Awards
24238 Hawthorne Boulevard
Torrance, CA 90505-6505
Tel: (310)541-1481
Fax: (310)541-4803
Web Site: http://www.edsf.org/scholarships.cfm
To provide financial assistance to students in technical schools and community colleges who are interested in working with electronic documents as a career.
Title of Award: EDSF Board of Directors Technical and Community College Scholarship **Area, Field, or Subject:** Computer and information sciences; Graphic art and design; Internet design and development; Marketing and distribution; Printing trades and industries; Telecommunications systems **Level of Education for which Award is Granted:** Two Year College, Vocational/Occupational **Number Awarded:** 5 each year. **Funds Available:** The stipend is $1,000. **Duration:** 1 year.
Eligibility Requirements: This program is open to first- and second-year students at technical and trade schools and community colleges. Applicants must be working on a degree in the field of electronic document communication, including marketing, graphic communication and arts, e-commerce, imaging science, printing, web authoring, electronic publishing, computer science, or telecommunications. They must submit a 1-page essay on 1 of the following topics: 1) a definition of their career goals in the field of document management and communications; 2) a recent technological change and how it has or will affect the document communication industry; or 3) a definition of the document communication industry. Selection is based on the essay, extracurricular activities and achievements, high school transcripts (GPA of 3.0 or higher), samples of creative work, and 2 letters of recommendation. Financial need is not considered. **Deadline for Receipt:** May of each year.

3427 ■ ELECTRONIC DOCUMENT SYSTEMS FOUNDATION
Attn: EDSF Scholarship Awards
24238 Hawthorne Boulevard
Torrance, CA 90505-6505
Tel: (310)541-1481
Fax: (310)541-4803
Web Site: http://www.edsf.org/scholarships.cfm
To provide financial assistance to upper-division and graduate students interested in working with electronic documents as a career.
Title of Award: David Hoods Memorial Scholarship **Area, Field, or Subject:** Computer and information sciences; Graphic art and design; Internet design and development; Marketing and distribution; Printing

trades and industries; Public relations; Telecommunications systems **Level of Education for which Award is Granted:** Four Year College, Graduate **Number Awarded:** 1 each year. **Funds Available:** The stipend is $2,000. **Duration:** 1 year.

Eligibility Requirements: This program is open to full-time juniors, seniors, and graduate students who demonstrate a strong interest in working with electronic documents as a career (including graphic communications, document management, document content, and/or document distribution). Special consideration is given to students interested in marketing and public relations. Applicants must submit a statement of their career goals in the field of document communications, an essay on a topic related to their view of the future of the document management and production industry, a list of current professional and college extracurricular activities and achievements, college transcripts (GPA of 3.0 or higher), samples of their creative work, and 2 letters of recommendation. Financial need is not considered. **Deadline for Receipt:** May of each year.

3428 ■ ELECTRONIC DOCUMENT SYSTEMS FOUNDATION
Attn: EDSF Scholarship Awards
24238 Hawthorne Boulevard
Torrance, CA 90505-6505
Tel: (310)541-1481
Fax: (310)541-4803
Web Site: http://www.edsf.org/scholarships.cfm
To provide financial assistance to college juniors, seniors, and graduate students interested in working with electronic documents as a career.
Title of Award: John A. Lopiano Scholarship **Area, Field, or Subject:** Computer and information sciences; Graphic art and design; Internet design and development; Marketing and distribution; Printing trades and industries; Telecommunications systems **Level of Education for which Award is Granted:** Four Year College, Graduate **Number Awarded:** 1 each year. **Funds Available:** The stipend is $2,000. **Duration:** 1 year.
Eligibility Requirements: This program is open to juniors, seniors, and graduate students who are working full time on a degree in the field of document communication, including marketing, graphic communication and arts, e-commerce, imaging science, printing, web authoring, electronic publishing, computer science, or telecommunications. Priority consideration is given to students who work in or whose family member has worked or currently works in a segment of the high volume transaction output (HVTO) industry. Applicants must submit a statement of their career goals in the field of document communications, an essay on a topic related to their view of the future of the document management and production industry, a list of current professional and college extracurricular activities and achievements, college transcripts (GPA of 3.0 or higher), samples of their creative work, and 2 letters of recommendation. Financial need is not considered. **Deadline for Receipt:** May of each year. **Additional Information:** This program is sponsored by COPI/OutputLinks.

3429 ■ EVANGELICAL PRESS ASSOCIATION
Attn: Scholarships
P.O. Box 28129
Crystal, MN 55428
Tel: (763)535-4793
Fax: (763)535-4794
E-mail: director@epassoc.org
Web Site: http://www.epassoc.org/scholarships.html
To provide financial assistance to upper-division and graduate students interested in preparing for a career in Christian journalism.
Title of Award: Evangelical Press Association Scholarships **Area, Field, or Subject:** Communications; Journalism; Religion **Level of Education for which Award is Granted:** Four Year College, Graduate **Number Awarded:** Several each year. **Funds Available:** Stipends range from $500 to $2,000. **Duration:** 1 year.
Eligibility Requirements: This program is open to entering juniors, seniors, and graduate students who have at least 1 years of full-time study remaining. Applicants must be majoring or minoring in journalism or communications, preferably with an interest in the field of Christian journalism. They must be enrolled at an accredited Christian or secular college or university in the United States or Canada with a GPA of 3.0 or higher. Along with their application, they must submit a biographical sketch that includes their birth date, hometown, family, and something

about the factors that shaped their interest in Christian journalism; a copy of their academic record; references from their pastor and from an instructor; samples of published writing from church or school publications; and an original essay (from 500 to 700 words) on the state of journalism today. **Deadline for Receipt:** March of each year. **Additional Information:** This program includes the Mel Larson Memorial Scholarship.

3430 ■ FISHER COMMUNICATIONS
Attn: Minority Scholarship
100 Fourth Avenue North, Suite 510
Seattle, WA 98109
Tel: (206)404-7000
Fax: (206)404-6037
E-mail: Info@fsci.com
Web Site: http://www.fsci.com/x100.xml
To provide financial assistance to minority college students in selected states who are interested in preparing for a career in broadcasting, marketing, or journalism.
Title of Award: Fisher Broadcasting Scholarships for Minorities **Area, Field, or Subject:** Broadcasting; Journalism; Marketing and distribution **Level of Education for which Award is Granted:** Undergraduate **Number Awarded:** Varies; a total of $10,000 is available for this program each year. **Funds Available:** A stipend is awarded (amount not specified). **Duration:** 1 year; recipients may reapply.
Eligibility Requirements: This program is open to students of non-white origin who are U.S. citizens, have a GPA of 2.5 or higher, and are at least sophomores enrolled in 1) a broadcasting, marketing, or journalism curriculum leading to a bachelor's degree at an accredited 4-year college or university; 2) a broadcast curriculum at an accredited community college, transferable to a 4-year baccalaureate degree program; or 3) a broadcast curriculum at an accredited vocational/technical school. Applicants must be either 1) residents of Washington, Oregon, Idaho, or Montana; or 2) attending a school in those states. They must submit an essay that explains their financial need, education and career goals, and school activities; a copy of their college transcript; and 2 letters of recommendation. Selection is based on need, academic achievement, and personal qualities. **Deadline for Receipt:** April of each year. **Additional Information:** This program began in 1987.

3431 ■ FLORIDA STATE ASSOCIATION OF SUPERVISORS OF ELECTIONS
c/o David H. Stafford
Escambia County Supervisor of Elections
213 Palafox Place, Suite 4
P.O. Box 12601
Pensacola, FL 32591-2601
Tel: (850)595-3900
Fax: (850)595-3914
E-mail: soe@escambiavotes.com
Web Site: http://www.gotvflorida.com/scholarship.htm
To provide financial assistance to Florida residents who are interested in majoring in business, political science, or communications in college.
Title of Award: Florida State Association of Supervisors of Elections Scholarship **Area, Field, or Subject:** Business administration; Communications; Journalism; Political science; Public administration **Level of Education for which Award is Granted:** Four Year College **Number Awarded:** 3 each year. **Funds Available:** The stipend is $1,200 per year. **Duration:** 1 year; recipients may reapply.
Eligibility Requirements: This program is open to residents of Florida who have completed 2 years of undergraduate study and are enrolled or planning to enroll full time at a 4-year college or university in the state. Applicants must be majoring in business administration, political science/public administration, or journalism/mass communications and have a GPA of 2.0 or higher. They must be U.S. citizens registered to vote in Florida. Along with their application, they must submit 2 letters of recommendation, a resume of high school and/or college activities, and documentation of financial need. Applications should be submitted to the student's county Supervisor of Elections. Each county's supervisor will review the applications received and select 1 finalist to be sent to the association for consideration. **Deadline for Receipt:** March of each year. **Additional Information:** This program includes the following named scholarships: the Joe Oldmixon Scholarship, the Jimmy Whitehouse Scholarship, and the Dorothy Walker Ruggles Scholarship.

3432 ■ HANSCOM OFFICERS' WIVES' CLUB

Attn: Scholarship Chair
P.O. Box 557
Bedford, MA 01730
Tel: (781)275-1251
E-mail: scholarship@hanscomowd.org
Web Site: http://www.hanscomowc.org
To provide financial assistance to children of military personnel and veterans in New England who are interested in studying aeronautics and space in college.
Title of Award: COL Chuck Jones Memorial Award **Area, Field, or Subject:** Aeronautics; Aerospace sciences; Communications; Engineering; Meteorology; Space and planetary sciences **Level of Education for which Award is Granted:** Undergraduate **Number Awarded:** 1 each year. **Funds Available:** The stipend is $2,000. **Duration:** 1 year; nonrenewable.
Eligibility Requirements: This program is open to college-bound high school seniors living in New England who are dependents of active-duty, retired, or deceased military members of any branch of service. Also eligible are dependents of military recruiters working in the New York area and students living elsewhere but whose military sponsor is stationed at Hanscom Air Force Base. Applicants must demonstrate qualities of responsibility, leadership, scholastics, citizenship, and diversity of interest. They must have a valid military identification card and be planning to work on a college degree in a field related to aeronautics and space (including communications, meteorology, air/space maintenance, manufacturing processing, engineering, and the astronaut program). Along with their application, they must submit a 2-page essay on their educational goals, how their educational experience will help prepare them to pursue future goals, and how they intend to apply their education to better their community. **Deadline for Receipt:** March of each year. **Additional Information:** This program was established to honor a victim of an airplane crash on September 11, 2001. It is sponsored by the Paul Revere Chapter of the Air Force Association.

3433 ■ HAWAI'I COMMUNITY FOUNDATION

Attn: Scholarship Department
1164 Bishop Street, Suite 800
Honolulu, HI 96813
Tel: (808)566-5570; 888-731-3863
Fax: (808)521-6286
E-mail: scholarships@hcf-hawaii.org
Web Site: http://www.hawaiicommunityfoundation.org/scholar/scholar.php
To provide financial assistance to Hawaii residents who are interested in preparing for a career in journalism.
Title of Award: Edward Payson and Bernice Pi'ilani Irwin Scholarship **Area, Field, or Subject:** Communications; Journalism **Level of Education for which Award is Granted:** Four Year College, Graduate **Number Awarded:** Varies each year; recently, 24 of these scholarships were awarded. **Funds Available:** The amounts of the awards depend on the availability of funds and the need of the recipient; recently, stipends averaged $1,840. **Duration:** 1 year.
Eligibility Requirements: This program is open to Hawaii residents who are studying journalism or communications as college juniors, seniors, or graduate students. They must be able to demonstrate academic achievement (GPA of 2.7 or higher), good moral character, and financial need. In addition to filling out the standard application form, applicants must write a short statement indicating their reasons for attending college, their planned course of study, their career goals, and why they have chosen to major in journalism. **Deadline for Receipt:** February of each year. **Additional Information:** Recipients may attend college in Hawaii or on the mainland.

3434 ■ HISPANIC SCHOLARSHIP FUND

Attn: Selection Committee
55 Second Street, Suite 1500
San Francisco, CA 94105
Tel: (415)808-2350; 877-HSF-INFO
Fax: (415)808-2302
E-mail: college1@hsf.net
Web Site: http://www.hsf.net/scholarship/programs/mcnamara.php
To provide funding to Hispanic undergraduate and graduate students interested in beginning and completing an art project.

Title of Award: McNamara Family Creative Arts Project Grants **Area, Field, or Subject:** Communications; Creative writing; Filmmaking; Performing arts **Level of Education for which Award is Granted:** Graduate, Undergraduate **Number Awarded:** 1 or more each year. **Funds Available:** Grants range from $5,000 to $20,000. **Duration:** These are 1-time grants.
Eligibility Requirements: This program is open to U.S. citizens, permanent residents, and visitors with a passport stamped I-551. Applicants must be of Hispanic heritage and working full time on an undergraduate or graduate degree at an accredited college or university in the United States, Puerto Rico, or the U.S. Virgin Islands. They must have completed at least 12 undergraduate units with a GPA of 3.0 or higher and be majoring in the arts, including (but not limited to) media, film, performing arts, communications, and writing. Along with their application, they must submit a 3-page concept paper describing the art project for which they are seeking funding, a portfolio of their work, and 600-word essays on 1) how their Hispanic heritage, family upbringing, and/or role models have influenced their personal long-term goals; 2) how they contribute to their community and what they have learned from their experiences; and 3) an academic challenge they have faced and how they have overcome it. Selection is based on those submissions, academic record, plans and career goals, community service, and financial need. **Deadline for Receipt:** May of each year. **Additional Information:** This program is offered by the Hispanic Scholarship Fund (HSF) in partnership with the McNamara Family Foundation.

3435 ■ ILLUMINATING ENGINEERING SOCIETY OF NORTH AMERICA-GOLDEN GATE SECTION

c/o Phil Hall
1514 Gibbons Drive
Alameda, CA 94501
Tel: (510)208-5005
Fax: (510)864-8511
E-mail: mrcatisbac@aol.com
Web Site: http://www.iesgg.org
To provide financial assistance to undergraduate or graduate students interested in studying or conducting research in lighting.
Title of Award: Robert W. Thunen Memorial Scholarships **Area, Field, or Subject:** Architecture; Engineering, Electrical; Filmmaking; Interior design; Lighting science; Radio and television **Level of Education for which Award is Granted:** Four Year College, Graduate **Number Awarded:** At least 2 each year. **Funds Available:** The stipend is $2,500. **Duration:** 1 year.
Eligibility Requirements: Applicants must be enrolled full time as an upper-division or graduate student at an accredited 4-year educational institution in northern California, northern Nevada, Oregon, or Washington and be studying architecture, electrical engineering, film/TV, lighting design, theater, or vision with an emphasis on lighting. Undergraduate students must be proposing course work related to potential employment in the lighting field. Graduate students must be proposing to conduct a research project that will further the lighting field or industry. Financial need is not considered in the selection process. **Deadline for Receipt:** March of each year. **Additional Information:** This program was established in 1986.

3436 ■ IMPERIAL POLK ADVERTISING FEDERATION

Attn: Scholarship Program
P.O. Box 24201
Lakeland, FL 33802-4201
Tel: (863)858-3736
Fax: (863)858-3736
Web Site: http://www.polkadfed.com
To provide financial assistance to undergraduate students majoring in fields related to advertising at Florida colleges.
Title of Award: William E. Gregory Scholarship **Area, Field, or Subject:** Advertising; Communications; Graphic art and design; Marketing and distribution **Level of Education for which Award is Granted:** Undergraduate **Number Awarded:** 1 or more each year. **Funds Available:** A total of $2,000 is available for this program each year. **Duration:** 1 year; nonrenewable.
Eligibility Requirements: This program is open to full-time undergraduate students at universities, colleges, and technical schools in Florida. Applicants must be working on a degree in advertising, communications,

graphic design, or marketing. They must have a GPA of 3.0 or higher. Along with their application, they must submit 1) a 500-word essay describing their future professional and educational goals; and 2) a project they have recently completed for a class or internship. Financial need is not considered in the selection process. **Deadline for Receipt:** November of each year. **Additional Information:** Information is also available from Samantha Hocker, Scholarship Chair, (863) 701-7789, E-mail: shocker@keisercollege.edu.

3437 ■ INTERNATIONAL COMMUNICATIONS INDUSTRIES ASSOCIATION, INC.
Attn: Director of Strategic Initiatives
11242 Waples Mill Road, Suite 200
Fairfax, VA 22030
Tel: (703)273-7200
Free: 800-659-7469
Fax: (703)278-8082
E-mail: dwilbert@infocomm.org
Web Site: http://www.infocomm.org/Foundation/Scholarships/College.cfm
To provide financial assistance to college students in their final year of study who are interested in preparing for a career in the audiovisual industry.
Title of Award: International Communications Industries Association College Scholarships **Area, Field, or Subject:** Electronics; Information science and technology; Journalism; Telecommunications systems **Level of Education for which Award is Granted:** Graduate, Undergraduate **Number Awarded:** Varies each year; recently, 7 of these scholarships were awarded. **Funds Available:** The stipend is $2,500. **Duration:** 1 year.
Eligibility Requirements: This program is open to 1) college juniors completing their bachelor's degree in the following year; 2) college seniors who plan to enter graduate school; and 3) students in their final year of study for an associate degree. Applicants must have a GPA of 2.75 or higher in a program of audio, visual, audiovisual, electronics, telecommunications, technical theater, data networking, software development, or information technology. Students in other programs, such as journalism, may be eligible if they can demonstrate a relationship to career goals in the audiovisual industry. Along with their application, they must submit essays on why they are applying for this scholarship, why they are interested in the audiovisual industry, and their professional plans following graduation. Minority and women candidates are especially encouraged to apply. Selection is based on the essays, presentation of the application, GPA, work experience, and letters of recommendation. **Deadline for Receipt:** April of each year. **Additional Information:** Recipients are required to work during the summer as paid interns with a manufacturer, dealer, designer, or other firm that is a member of the International Communications Industries Association.

3438 ■ INTERNATIONAL COMMUNICATIONS INDUSTRIES ASSOCIATION, INC.
Attn: Director of Strategic Initiatives
11242 Waples Mill Road, Suite 200
Fairfax, VA 22030
Tel: (703)273-7200
Free: 800-659-7469
Fax: (703)278-8082
E-mail: dwilbert@infocomm.org
Web Site: http://www.infocomm.org/Foundation/Scholarships
To provide financial assistance for college to dependents of members of the International Communications Industries Association (ICIA) interested in preparing for a career in the audiovisual industry.
Title of Award: Scholarships for Dependents of ICIA Members **Area, Field, or Subject:** Electronics; Information science and technology; Journalism; Telecommunications systems **Level of Education for which Award is Granted:** Undergraduate **Number Awarded:** Varies each year; recently, 3 of these scholarships were awarded. **Funds Available:** The stipend is $1,500. **Duration:** 1 year.
Eligibility Requirements: This program is open to graduating high school seniors and current college students who are the children, stepchildren, and spouses of employees at ICIA member companies. Applicants must have a GPA of 2.75 or higher and be majoring or planning to major in audio, visual, audiovisual, electronics, telecommunications, technical theater, data networking, software development, or information

technology. Students in other programs, such as journalism, may be eligible if they can demonstrate a relationship to career goals in the audiovisual industry. Along with their application, they must submit 1) an essay of 150 to 200 words on the career path they see themselves pursuing in the next 5 years and why, and 2) an essay of 250 to 300 words on the experience or person that most influenced them in selecting the audiovisual industry as their career of choice. Minority and women candidates are especially encouraged to apply. Selection is based on the essays, presentation of the application, GPA, work experience, and letters of recommendation. **Deadline for Receipt:** April of each year.

3439 ■ INTERNATIONAL FOODSERVICE EDITORIAL COUNCIL
P.O. Box 491
Hyde Park, NY 12538
Tel: (845)229-6973
Fax: (845)229-6993
E-mail: ifec@aol.com
Web Site: http://www.ifec-is-us.com
To provide financial assistance to undergraduate or graduate students who are interested in preparing for a career in communications in the food service industry.
Title of Award: IFEC Scholarships **Area, Field, or Subject:** Communications; Creative writing; Culinary arts; English language and literature; Food science and technology; Food service careers; Graphic art and design; Hotel, institutional, and restaurant management; Journalism; Management; Marketing and distribution; Nutrition; Photography; Photography, Journalistic; Public relations **Level of Education for which Award is Granted:** Master's, Undergraduate **Number Awarded:** Varies each year; recently, 5 of these scholarships were awarded. **Funds Available:** The stipend is $3,000 per year. **Duration:** 1 year.
Eligibility Requirements: This program is open to currently-enrolled college students who are working on an associate, bachelor's, or master's degree. They must be enrolled full time and planning on a career in editorial, public relations, photography, food styling, or a related aspect of communications in the food service industry. The following food service majors are considered appropriate for this program: culinary arts; hospitality management; hotel, restaurant, and institutional management; dietetics; food science and technology; and nutrition. Applicable communications areas include journalism, English, mass communications, public relations, marketing, broadcast journalism, creative writing, graphic arts, and photography. Selection is based on academic record, character references, and demonstrated financial need. **Deadline for Receipt:** March of each year.

3440 ■ KANSAS AFRICAN AMERICAN LEGISLATIVE CAUCUS
c/o Dale M. Dennis
State Department of Education
120 East Tenth Street
Topeka, KS 66612
To provide financial assistance African American college students in Kansas who are interested in a career in politics.
Title of Award: Kansas African American Legislative Caucus Scholarships **Area, Field, or Subject:** Communications; General studies/Field of study not specified; Political science **Level of Education for which Award is Granted:** Undergraduate **Number Awarded:** 2 each year: 1 female and 1 male. **Funds Available:** The stipend is $1,000. **Duration:** 1 year.
Eligibility Requirements: This program is open to residents of Kansas of African American ethnic background who are attending a college or university in the state. Applicants must have a GPA of 2.6 or higher. Selection is based on academic achievement, leadership ability, and community involvement. Preference is given to students majoring in communications or political science. Males and females are judged separately. **Deadline for Receipt:** March of each year. **Additional Information:** This program is funded by past and present African American members of the Kansas Legislature.

3441 ■ LEBANESE AMERICAN HERITAGE CLUB
Attn: Arab American Scholarship Foundation
4337 Maple Road
Dearborn, MI 48126
Tel: (313)846-8480
Fax: (313)846-2710

E-mail: lahc@lahc.org

Web Site: http://www.lahc.org/scholarship.htm

To provide financial assistance for college or graduate school to Americans of Arab descent who reside in Michigan.

Title of Award: Lebanese American Heritage Club Scholarships **Area, Field, or Subject:** Communications; General studies/Field of study not specified **Level of Education for which Award is Granted:** Graduate, Undergraduate **Number Awarded:** 1 or more each year. **Funds Available:** The stipend is $1,000. Funds are paid directly to the recipient's institution. **Duration:** 1 year; recipients may reapply.

Eligibility Requirements: This program is open to students who are already in college or graduate school. Only full-time students may apply. Applicants must be of Arab descent, be U.S. citizens or permanent residents, reside in the state of Michigan, and be able to demonstrate financial need. Undergraduate students must have at least a 3.0 GPA; graduate students must have at least a 3.5. Applicants must submit a completed application form, official copies of academic transcripts, 2 letters of recommendation, financial aid transcripts, copies of their current Student Aid Report, and a 500-word essay on their educational background, field of study, future goals, and contributions to their community. Preference is given to students who are working on a degree in mass communications. **Deadline for Receipt:** April of each year. **Additional Information:** This program was established in 1989. Since then, more than half a million dollars has been awarded.

3442 ■ LUSO-AMERICAN EDUCATION FOUNDATION

Attn: Administrative Director

7080 Donlon Way, Suite 202

P.O. Box 2967

Dublin, CA 94568

Tel: (925)828-3883

Fax: (925)828-3883

Web Site: http://www.luso-american.org/laef

To provide financial assistance for undergraduate study in Portuguese language to students in California.

Title of Award: Herbert Fernandes Scholarship **Area, Field, or Subject:** Foreign languages; Portuguese studies **Level of Education for which Award is Granted:** Four Year College **Number Awarded:** 1 each year. **Funds Available:** The stipend is $1,000. **Duration:** 1 year; renewable.

Eligibility Requirements: This program is open to students of Portuguese descent who are sophomores, juniors, or seniors at 4-year colleges or universities with a GPA of 3.5 or higher. Applicants must be California residents who are interested or involved in the Luso-American community and have taken or will enroll in Portuguese language classes. Selection is based on promise of success in college, financial need, qualities of leadership, vocational promise, and sincerity of purpose. **Deadline for Receipt:** February of each year.

3443 ■ LUSO-AMERICAN EDUCATION FOUNDATION

Attn: Administrative Director

7080 Donlon Way, Suite 202

P.O. Box 2967

Dublin, CA 94568

Tel: (925)828-3883

Fax: (925)828-3883

Web Site: http://www.luso-american.org/laef

To provide financial assistance to undergraduate students with a Portuguese connection in California.

Title of Award: Luso-American Education Foundation General Fund Scholarship **Area, Field, or Subject:** Foreign languages; General studies/Field of study not specified **Level of Education for which Award is Granted:** Four Year College **Number Awarded:** 1 or more each year. **Funds Available:** The stipend is $1,000. **Duration:** 1 year; may be renewed.

Eligibility Requirements: Applicants must meet at least 1 of the following requirements: 1) be of Portuguese descent; 2) be planning to enroll in Portuguese classes in a 4-year college or university; or 3) be a member of an organization whose scholarships are administered by the Luso-American Education Foundation. All applicants must be California residents younger than 21 years of age, have graduated from an accredited high school by the summer of the year of the award, and have a GPA of 3.0 or higher. Selection is based on promise of success in college, financial need, qualities of leadership, vocational promise, and sincerity of

purpose. **Deadline for Receipt:** February of each year. **Additional Information:** Funds may be utilized only at 4-year colleges and universities; but recipients who wish to attend a community college may request that funds be held in reserve for 2 years until they are ready to transfer to a 4-year institution.

3444 ■ MAINE COMMUNITY FOUNDATION

Attn: Program Director

245 Main Street

Ellsworth, ME 04605

Tel: (207)667-9735; 877-700-6800

Fax: (207)667-0447

E-mail: info@mainecf.org

Web Site: http://www.mainecf.org/html/scholarships/index.html

To provide financial assistance to Maine residents who are interested in studying journalism in college.

Title of Award: Guy P. Gannett Scholarship Fund **Area, Field, or Subject:** Communications; Journalism **Level of Education for which Award is Granted:** Graduate, Undergraduate **Number Awarded:** 1 or more each year. **Funds Available:** A stipend is paid (amount not specified). **Duration:** 1 year; may be renewed.

Eligibility Requirements: This program is open to graduates of Maine high schools (public and private) and to Maine residents who were schooled at home during their last year of secondary education. Applicants must be attending either an undergraduate (including a trade school or a technical institute program) or a graduate program at an accredited postsecondary institution in the United States. They must be majoring in journalism or a related field, including all forms of print, broadcast, or electronic media. Selection is based on academic achievement, financial need, and a demonstrated interest in a career in a form of journalism. Preference is given to renewal applicants. **Deadline for Receipt:** April of each year. **Additional Information:** This program was established in 2000.

3445 ■ MARYLAND ASSOCIATION OF PRIVATE COLLEGES AND CAREER SCHOOLS

Attn: Scholarship Committee

3100 Dunglow Road

Baltimore, MD 21222

Tel: (410)282-4012

Fax: (410)282-4133

E-mail: mdapcs@yahoo.com

Web Site: http://www.mapccs.org/scholarships.html

To provide financial assistance to students interested in attending selected private career schools in Maryland.

Title of Award: Maryland Association of Private Colleges and Career Schools Scholarships **Area, Field, or Subject:** Broadcasting; Cosmetology; Drafting; Health care services; Mechanics and repairs; Medicine; Holistic/alternative; Secretarial sciences **Level of Education for which Award is Granted:** Vocational/Occupational **Number Awarded:** Varies each year; since the program was established in 1983, more than $3 million in scholarships have been awarded. **Funds Available:** Individual awards range from $500 to more than $5,000. The H.R. Leslie Scholarship is $1,000. Funds must be applied for full or partial payment of tuition. Recently, a total of $164,000 was awarded. **Duration:** 1 year.

Eligibility Requirements: This program is open to high school seniors and graduates who are interested in attending a participating private career school in Maryland. Applicants should be interested in working on a degree in such business or technical areas as cosmetology, barbering, diesel mechanics, automotive technology, massage therapy, allied health, secretarial sciences, or drafting. The H.R. Leslie Scholarship is open to any student who applies to a member school. Selection is based on GPA, involvement in school and community activities, recommendations from school officials, desire, and potential to succeed in their career field. Financial need is not considered in the selection process. **Deadline for Receipt:** March of each year. **Additional Information:** The participating schools are All State Career School (Baltimore) American Beauty Academy (Wheaton), Americare School of Allied Health (Silver Spring), Avara's Academy of Hair Design (Baltimore), Baltimore School of Massage, Baltimore Studio of Hair Design, Bladensburg Barber School (Bladensburg), Broadcasting Institute of Maryland (Baltimore), Diesel Institute of America (Grantsville), Frederick School of Cosmetology (Frederick), Hair Academy (New Carrollton), Holistic Massage Training

Institute (Baltimore), International Beauty School (Bel Air), Lincoln Technical Institute (Columbia), Medix School (Towson), Savage Neon (Baltimore), and Von Lee School of Aesthetics (Pikesville). Scholarships can be used only to attend the schools listed above.

3446 ■ MARYLAND HIGHER EDUCATION COMMISSION

Attn: Office of Student Financial Assistance
839 Bestgate Road, Suite 400
Annapolis, MD 21401-3013
Tel: (410)260-4545
Free: 800-974-1024
Fax: (410)974-5376
E-mail: osfamail@mhec.state.md.us
Web Site: http://www.mhec.state.md.us/financialAid/
ProgramDescriptions/prog_scm.asp
To provide scholarship/loans to Maryland residents who wish to prepare for a teaching career.

Title of Award: Sharon Christa McAuliffe Memorial Teacher Education Award **Area, Field, or Subject:** Chemistry; Classical studies; Computer and information sciences; Earth sciences; Education; Education, English as a second language; Education, Special; Education, Vocational-technical; Foreign languages; Geosciences; Health care services; Hearing and deafness; Mathematics and mathematical sciences; Physical sciences; Physics; Space and planetary sciences; Visual impairment **Level of Education for which Award is Granted:** Master's, Professional, Undergraduate **Number Awarded:** Varies each year. **Funds Available:** The amount of the award is based on the recipient's enrollment and housing status, to a maximum of $17,000 per year. The total amount of all state awards may not exceed the cost of attendance as determined by the school's financial aid office or $17,800, whichever is less. Following graduation, recipients must teach at a Maryland public school for 1 year for each year of financial aid received under this program. If they fail to meet that service obligation, they must repay all funds they received with interest. They must begin the service obligation within 12 months of graduation. **Duration:** 1 year; may be renewed for 1 additional year if the recipient maintains satisfactory academic progress with a cumulative GPA of 3.0 or higher and enrollment at a 2-year or 4-year Maryland college or university in an approved teacher education program.

Eligibility Requirements: This program is open to Maryland residents who are college students with at least 60 semester credit hours completed, college graduates, and teachers in a non-critical shortage area. Applicants must have a GPA of 3.0 or higher and plan to teach in a field identified as a critical shortage area. Selection is based on cumulative GPA, applicable work or volunteer experience, quality of academic background in certification field, and a writing sample. **Deadline for Receipt:** December of each year. **Additional Information:** Recently, the eligible critical shortage areas were business education, chemistry, computer science, earth and space science, English for speakers of other languages, family and consumer sciences, German, health occupations, Latin, mathematics, physical science, physics, Spanish, special education (generic Infant-grade 3, generic grades 1-8, generic grades 6-adult, hearing impaired, severely and profoundly handicapped, visually impaired), and technology education.

3447 ■ MASSACHUSETTS OFFICE OF STUDENT FINANCIAL ASSISTANCE

454 Broadway, Suite 200
Revere, MA 02151
Tel: (617)727-9420
Fax: (617)727-0667
E-mail: osfa@osfa.mass.edu
Web Site: http://www.osfa.mass.edu
To provide scholarship/loans to educational paraprofessionals in Massachusetts who are interested in completing a college degree and becoming certified as teachers.

Title of Award: Massachusetts Paraprofessional Teacher Preparation Grant Program **Area, Field, or Subject:** Education; Education, Bilingual and cross-cultural; Education, Special; Linguistics; Mathematics and mathematical sciences; Science **Level of Education for which Award is Granted:** Undergraduate **Number Awarded:** Varies each year. **Funds Available:** Grants depend on the type of institution attended. At public universities, the maximum award is $625 per credit, to a total of $7,500 per academic year. At state colleges, the maximum award is $450 per

credit, to a total of $6,000 per academic year. At community colleges, the maximum award is $250 per credit, to a total of $4,000 per academic year. This is a scholarship/loan program. Recipients must agree to teach in a Massachusetts public school 1 year for each year of full or partial grant received. If they fail to complete that teaching obligation, they must repay the amount of the grant received. **Duration:** Until completion of an undergraduate degree, provided the recipient maintains satisfactory academic progress.

Eligibility Requirements: This program is open to Massachusetts residents who 1) have been employed as paraprofessionals in public schools in the state for at least 2 years, or 2) are working on a degree in an area of high need (recently defined as bilingual education, foreign languages, mathematics, science, and special education). Applicants must be enrolled full time in an undergraduate degree program leading to teacher certification at a Massachusetts public institution. U.S. citizenship or permanent resident status is required. Applicants must submit a Free Application for Federal Student Aid (FAFSA), but financial need is not required.

3448 ■ MINNESOTA HIGHER EDUCATION SERVICES OFFICE

1450 Energy Park Drive, Suite 350
St. Paul, MN 55108-5227
Tel: (651)642-0567
Free: 800-657-3866
Fax: (651)642-0675
E-mail: info@heso.state.mn.us
Web Site: http://www.mheso.state.mn.us
To provide financial assistance for college to outstanding high school seniors or graduates in Minnesota.

Title of Award: Minnesota Academic Excellence Scholarship **Area, Field, or Subject:** Art; Creative writing; English language and literature; Linguistics; Mathematics and mathematical sciences; Science; Social sciences **Level of Education for which Award is Granted:** Undergraduate **Number Awarded:** Varies each year. **Funds Available:** Scholarships at public institutions cover the cost of full-time attendance; scholarships at private institutions cover an amount equal to the lesser of the actual tuition and fees charged by the institution or the tuition and fees in comparable public institutions. **Duration:** 1 year; may be renewed up to 3 additional years.

Eligibility Requirements: This program is open to Minnesota residents who have demonstrated outstanding ability, achievement, and potential in English, creative writing, fine arts, foreign language, mathematics, science, or social science. Applicants must have been admitted as full-time students at a branch of the University of Minnesota, a Minnesota state university, or a private, baccalaureate degree-granting college or university in Minnesota. **Additional Information:** This program was established by the Minnesota Legislature in 1991. Funds for this program come from the sale of special collegiate license plates.

3449 ■ NATIONAL ASSOCIATION OF BLACK TELECOMMUNICATIONS PROFESSIONALS, INC.

c/o Cynthia L. Newman
2020 Pennsylvania Avenue, N.W.
Box 735
Washington, DC 20006
800-946-6228
E-mail: office@nabtp.org
Web Site: http://www.nabtp.org/about/scholarships.shtml
To provide financial assistance to students who are working on a degree in telecommunications or a related field and are interested in participating in the activities of the National Association of Black Telecommunications Professionals (NABTP).

Title of Award: NABTP Collegian Scholarship **Area, Field, or Subject:** Business administration; Communications; Computer and information sciences; Engineering; Telecommunications systems **Level of Education for which Award is Granted:** Undergraduate **Number Awarded:** 1 each year. **Funds Available:** The stipend is $2,000 per year. **Duration:** 1 year; may be renewed for 2 or 3 additional years if the recipient maintains a GPA of 3.0 or higher and active involvement in NABTP.

Eligibility Requirements: This program is open to students majoring in telecommunications or a related field (e.g., computer science, business, engineering, mass communications) at an accredited college or university. Applicants must submit an essay on their educational and career goals, the skill sets and values they are able to bring to NABTP as a possible intern, and how they see active involvement in NABTP supportive to their career path and educational goals. As an option, they may also submit an essay in which they provide a profile of a majority owned African American telecommunications company, including CEO name, number of employees, percentage of minority ownership, annual revenue, address, phone number, web site address, company product and/or services, and company successes. Selection is based on the essays, GPA, notable achievements, and financial need. **Deadline for Receipt:** July of each year.

3450 ■ NATIONAL DAIRY PROMOTION AND RESEARCH BOARD
c/o Dairy Management Inc.
10255 West Higgins Road, Suite 900
Rosemont, IL 60018-5616
Tel: (847)803-2000
Fax: (847)803-2077
E-mail: marykateg@rosedmi.com
Web Site: http://www.dairycheckoff.com/DairyCheckoff/about/scholarship.htm
To provide financial assistance to undergraduate students in fields related to the dairy industry.
Title of Award: NDPRB Undergraduate Scholarship Program **Area, Field, or Subject:** Business administration; Communications; Dairy science; Economics; Education; Food science and technology; Journalism; Marketing and distribution; Nutrition; Public relations **Level of Education for which Award is Granted:** Four Year College **Number Awarded:** 20 each year: the James H. Loper Jr. Memorial Scholarship at $2,500 and 19 other scholarships at $1,500. **Funds Available:** Stipends are $2,500 or $1,500. **Duration:** 1 year; may be renewed.
Eligibility Requirements: This program is open to sophomores, juniors, and seniors enrolled in college and university programs that emphasize dairy. Eligible majors include agricultural education, business, communications and/or public relations, economics, food science, journalism, marketing, and nutrition. Fields related to production (e.g., animal science) are not eligible. Selection is based on academic performance; interest in a career in dairy; involvement in extracurricular activities, especially those relating to dairy; and evidence of leadership ability, initiative, character, and integrity. The applicant who is judged most outstanding is awarded the James H. Loper Jr. Memorial Scholarship. **Deadline for Receipt:** May of each year. **Additional Information:** Dairy Management Inc. manages this program on behalf of the National Dairy Promotion and Research Board (NDPRB).

3451 ■ NATIONAL FFA ORGANIZATION
Attn: Scholarship Office
6060 FFA Drive
P.O. Box 68960
Indianapolis, IN 46268-0960
Tel: (317)802-4321
Fax: (317)802-5321
E-mail: scholarships@ffa.org
Web Site: http://www.ffa.org
To provide financial assistance to FFA members from Florida and Georgia who are interested in studying fields related to agriculture in college.
Title of Award: Chevron Corporation Scholarships **Area, Field, or Subject:** Agricultural sciences; Communications; Education; Environmental conservation; Environmental science; Natural resources; Wildlife conservation, management, and science **Level of Education for which Award is Granted:** Undergraduate **Number Awarded:** 2 each year.
Funds Available: The stipend is $1,000. Funds are paid directly to the recipient. **Duration:** 1 year; nonrenewable.
Eligibility Requirements: This program is open to members who are graduating high school seniors planning to enroll full time in college. Applicants must be residents of Florida or Georgia planning to work on a 2-year or 4-year degree in agricultural communications and education, environmental engineering, environmental science, natural resource management, wildlife management, or public service and administration in agriculture. Preference is given to those who have shown outstanding leadership. Selection is based on academic achievement (10 points for GPA, 10 points for SAT or ACT score, 10 points for class rank), leadership in FFA activities (30 points), leadership in community activities (10 points), and participation in the Supervised Agricultural Experience (SAE) program

(30 points). U.S. citizenship is required. **Deadline for Receipt:** February of each year. **Additional Information:** Funding for these scholarships is provided by ChevronTexaco Corporation.

3452 ■ NATIONAL FFA ORGANIZATION
Attn: Scholarship Office
6060 FFA Drive
P.O. Box 68960
Indianapolis, IN 46268-0960
Tel: (317)802-4321
Fax: (317)802-5321
E-mail: scholarships@ffa.org
Web Site: http://www.ffa.org
To provide financial assistance to FFA members interested in studying dairy science in college.
Title of Award: Hoard's Dairyman Scholarship **Area, Field, or Subject:** Agricultural sciences; Communications; Dairy science **Level of Education for which Award is Granted:** Four Year College **Number Awarded:** 1 each year. **Funds Available:** The stipend is $1,000 per year. Funds are paid directly to the recipient. **Duration:** 1 year; nonrenewable.
Eligibility Requirements: This program is open to members who are graduating high school seniors planning to enroll full time in college. Applicants must be interested in working on a 4-year degree in dairy science. Preference is given to applicants with agricultural journalism experience. Selection is based on academic achievement (10 points for GPA, 10 points for SAT or ACT score, 10 points for class rank), leadership in FFA activities (30 points), leadership in community activities (10 points), and participation in the Supervised Agricultural Experience (SAE) program (30 points). U.S. citizenship is required. **Deadline for Receipt:** February of each year. **Additional Information:** Funding for this scholarship is provided by W.D. Hoard & Sons Company, publisher of *Hoard's Dairyman*.

3453 ■ NATIONAL FFA ORGANIZATION
Attn: Scholarship Office
6060 FFA Drive
P.O. Box 68960
Indianapolis, IN 46268-0960
Tel: (317)802-4321
Fax: (317)802-5321
E-mail: scholarships@ffa.org
Web Site: http://www.ffa.org
To provide financial assistance to FFA members who are interested in studying agriculture in college.
Title of Award: Garst Seed Company Scholarship **Area, Field, or Subject:** Agribusiness; Agricultural sciences; Communications; Education; Marketing and distribution **Level of Education for which Award is Granted:** Four Year College **Number Awarded:** 25 each year: 10 to students with any agricultural major, 5 to students majoring in agricultural communications or education, and 10 to students in agricultural marketing, merchandising, or sales. **Funds Available:** The stipend is $1,000. Funds are paid directly to the recipient. **Duration:** 1 year; nonrenewable.
Eligibility Requirements: This program is open to members who are graduating high school seniors planning to enroll or students currently enrolled full time in college. Applicants must be interested in working on a 4-year college degree in agriculture; in agricultural communications or education; or in agricultural marketing, merchandising, or sales. Selection is based on academic achievement (10 points for GPA, 10 points for SAT or ACT score, 10 points for class rank), leadership in FFA activities (30 points), leadership in community activities (10 points), and participation in the Supervised Agricultural Experience (SAE) program (30 points). U.S. citizenship is required. **Deadline for Receipt:** February of each year. **Additional Information:** Funding for this scholarship is provided by Garst Seed Company.

3454 ■ NATIONAL FFA ORGANIZATION
Attn: Scholarship Office
6060 FFA Drive
P.O. Box 68960
Indianapolis, IN 46268-0960
Tel: (317)802-4321
Fax: (317)802-5321
E-mail: scholarships@ffa.org

Web Site: http://www.ffa.org
To provide financial assistance to FFA members who wish to study agricultural journalism and related fields in college.

Title of Award: National FFA Scholarships for Undergraduates in the Humanities **Area, Field, or Subject:** Agricultural sciences; Communications; Horticulture; Landscape architecture and design **Level of Education for which Award is Granted:** Undergraduate **Number Awarded:** Varies; generally, a total of approximately 1,000 scholarships are awarded annually by the association. **Funds Available:** Stipends vary, but most are at least $1,000. **Duration:** 1 year or more.

Eligibility Requirements: This program is open to current and former members of the organization who are working or planning to work full time on a degree in fields related to agricultural journalism and communications, floriculture, and landscape design. For most of the scholarships, applicants must be high school seniors; others are open to students currently enrolled in college. The program includes a large number of designated scholarships that specify the locations where the members must live, the schools they must attend, the fields of study they must pursue, or other requirements. Some consider family income in the selection process, but most do not. Selection is based on academic achievement (10 points for GPA, 10 points for SAT or ACT score, 10 points for class rank), leadership in FFA activities (30 points), leadership in community activities (10 points), and participation in the Supervised Agricultural Experience (SAE) program (30 points). U.S. citizenship is required. **Deadline for Receipt:** February of each year. **Additional Information:** Funding for these scholarships is provided by many different corporate sponsors.

3455 ■ NATIONAL FFA ORGANIZATION
Attn: Scholarship Office
6060 FFA Drive
P.O. Box 68960
Indianapolis, IN 46268-0960
Tel: (317)802-4321
Fax: (317)802-5321
E-mail: scholarships@ffa.org
Web Site: http://www.ffa.org
To provide financial assistance to current or former FFA members who are interested in studying a field related to agriculture at a college or university in designated states.

Title of Award: Norfolk Southern Foundation Scholarships **Area, Field, or Subject:** Agribusiness; Agricultural sciences; Communications; Education; Engineering, Agricultural; Finance; Forestry; Management; Marketing and distribution **Level of Education for which Award is Granted:** Four Year College **Number Awarded:** 3 each year. **Funds Available:** The stipend is $1,000. Funds are paid directly to the recipient. **Duration:** 1 year; nonrenewable.

Eligibility Requirements: This program is open to members who are either graduating high school seniors planning to enroll in college or students already enrolled in college. Applicants must be interested in working full time on a 4-year degree in agricultural and forestry production, communication, education, engineering, finance, management, marketing, merchandising, sales, or agricultural science. They must be planning to attend a college or university in Alabama, Delaware, Georgia, Illinois, Indiana, Louisiana, Maryland, Michigan, Missouri, New York, North Carolina, Ohio, Pennsylvania, South Carolina, Tennessee, or Virginia. Selection is based on academic achievement (10 points for GPA, 10 points for SAT or ACT score, 10 points for class rank), leadership in FFA activities (30 points), leadership in community activities (10 points), and participation in the Supervised Agricultural Experience (SAE) program (30 points). U.S. citizenship is required. **Deadline for Receipt:** February of each year. **Additional Information:** Funding for these scholarships is provided by the Norfolk Southern Foundation.

3456 ■ NATIONAL FFA ORGANIZATION
Attn: Scholarship Office
6060 FFA Drive
P.O. Box 68960
Indianapolis, IN 46268-0960
Tel: (317)802-4321
Fax: (317)802-5321
E-mail: scholarships@ffa.org
Web Site: http://www.ffa.org

To provide financial assistance to FFA members who are interested in studying agriculture, especially agricultural communications, at a 4-year institution.

Title of Award: Primedia Business Magazines & Media Scholarship **Area, Field, or Subject:** Agricultural sciences; Communications **Level of Education for which Award is Granted:** Four Year College **Number Awarded:** 1 each year. **Funds Available:** The stipend is $1,000. Funds are paid directly to the recipient. **Duration:** 1 year; nonrenewable.

Eligibility Requirements: This program is open to members who are graduating high school seniors planning to enroll full time in college. Applicants must be interested in working on a 4-year degree in an agricultural-related major, preferably agricultural journalism or agricultural communications. They must live on a family-owned farm and at least 50% of their family income must come from production agriculture. Selection is based on academic achievement (10 points for GPA, 10 points for SAT or ACT score, 10 points for class rank), leadership in FFA activities (30 points), leadership in community activities (10 points), and participation in the Supervised Agricultural Experience (SAE) program (30 points). Financial need is also considered. U.S. citizenship is required. **Deadline for Receipt:** February of each year. **Additional Information:** Funding for this scholarship is provided by Primedia Business Magazines & Media.

3457 ■ NATIONAL FFA ORGANIZATION
Attn: Scholarship Office
6060 FFA Drive
P.O. Box 68960
Indianapolis, IN 46268-0960
Tel: (317)802-4321
Fax: (317)802-5321
E-mail: scholarships@ffa.org
Web Site: http://www.ffa.org
To provide financial assistance to FFA members interested in studying fields related to communications in college.

Title of Award: Progressive Farmer Magazine Scholarships **Area, Field, or Subject:** Advertising; Agricultural sciences; Communications; Journalism **Level of Education for which Award is Granted:** Four Year College **Number Awarded:** 1 each year. **Funds Available:** The stipend is $1,000 per year. Funds are paid directly to the recipient. **Duration:** 1 year; nonrenewable.

Eligibility Requirements: This program is open to members who are graduating high school seniors planning to enroll full time in college. Applicants must be interested in working on a 4-year degree in communications, journalism, or advertising. Selection is based on academic achievement (10 points for GPA, 10 points for SAT or ACT score, 10 points for class rank), leadership in FFA activities (30 points), leadership in community activities (10 points), and participation in the Supervised Agricultural Experience (SAE) program (30 points). U.S. citizenship is required. **Deadline for Receipt:** February of each year. **Additional Information:** Funding for these scholarships is provided by *Progressive Farmer Magazine.*

3458 ■ NATIONAL FFA ORGANIZATION
Attn: Scholarship Office
6060 FFA Drive
P.O. Box 68960
Indianapolis, IN 46268-0960
Tel: (317)802-4321
Fax: (317)802-5321
E-mail: scholarships@ffa.org
Web Site: http://www.ffa.org
To provide financial assistance to FFA members who are studying a field related to communications, business, or education in college.

Title of Award: Solutions Inc. Results Through Creative Marketing Scholarships **Area, Field, or Subject:** Agribusiness; Agricultural sciences; Communications; Education; Marketing and distribution **Level of Education for which Award is Granted:** Four Year College **Number Awarded:** 3 each year. **Funds Available:** The stipend is $1,000 per year. Funds are paid directly to the recipient. **Duration:** 1 year; nonrenewable.

Eligibility Requirements: This program is open to members currently enrolled full time in college and working on a 4-year degree in agricultural communications, marketing, merchandising, sales, or as an education specialist. Applicants must have a GPA of 3.0 or higher. Selection is based on academic achievement (10 points for GPA, 10 points for SAT or ACT score, 10 points for class rank), leadership in FFA activities (30 points), leadership in community activities (10 points), and participation in the Supervised Agricultural Experience (SAE) program (30 points). U.S. citizenship is required. **Deadline for Receipt:** February of each year. **Additional Information:** This program is sponsored by the creative marketing firm Solutions Inc. Results Through Creative Marketing.

3459 ■ NATIONAL FFA ORGANIZATION

Attn: Scholarship Office
6060 FFA Drive
P.O. Box 68960
Indianapolis, IN 46268-0960
Tel: (317)802-4321
Fax: (317)802-5321
E-mail: scholarships@ffa.org
Web Site: http://www.ffa.org
To provide financial assistance to FFA members who are interested in studying journalism in college.
Title of Award: Vance Publishing Corporation Scholarship **Area, Field, or Subject:** Agricultural sciences; Communications; Journalism **Level of Education for which Award is Granted:** Four Year College **Number Awarded:** 1 each year. **Funds Available:** The stipend is $1,000. Funds are paid directly to the recipient. **Duration:** 1 year; nonrenewable.
Eligibility Requirements: This program is open to members who are graduating high school seniors planning to enroll full time in college. Applicants must be interested in working on a 4-year degree with a preference for agricultural journalism. Selection is based on academic achievement (10 points for GPA, 10 points for SAT or ACT score, 10 points for class rank), leadership in FFA activities (30 points), leadership in community activities (10 points), and participation in the Supervised Agricultural Experience (SAE) program (30 points). U.S. citizenship is required. **Deadline for Receipt:** February of each year. **Additional Information:** Funding for this scholarship is provided by Vance Publishing Corporation.

3460 ■ NATIONAL MILITARY INTELLIGENCE ASSOCIATION

Attn: Scholarship Fund
P.O. Box 489
Hamilton, VA 20159
Tel: (540)338-1143
Fax: (703)738-7487
E-mail: NMIA@adelphia.net
Web Site: http://www.nmia.org/Scholarship.html
To provide financial assistance for college to the children of members of the National Military Intelligence Association (NMIA).
Title of Award: NMIA Merit Scholarship Program **Area, Field, or Subject:** General studies/Field of study not specified; Linguistics **Level of Education for which Award is Granted:** Undergraduate **Number Awarded:** 1 or more each year. **Funds Available:** The stipend is $1,000. **Duration:** 1 year; nonrenewable.
Eligibility Requirements: This program is open to children of NMIA members who are attending, or planning to attend, an accredited college or university to work on a bachelor's degree. **Additional Information:** Membership in the NMIA is open to military and civil service personnel; Reserve, National Guard, retired, and former service personnel; and U.O. civilians in the industrial sector supporting the U.S. intelligence system. This program includes the Vernon Walters Scholarship for a student working on a degree in a foreign language, offered in cooperation with the Intelligence Scholarship Foundation.

3461 ■ NATIONAL SECURITY AGENCY

Attn: Office of Recruitment and Staffing (Roberts)
9800 Savage Road, Suite 6779
P.O. Box 1661, Suite 6779
Fort Meade, MD 20755-6779
Tel: (410)854-4725; (866)672-4473
Web Site: http://www.nsa.gov/careers/students_4.cfm
To provide financial assistance and work experience to college sophomores and juniors interested in preparing for a career with the National Security Agency (NSA) as a global network analyst.
Title of Award: Pat Roberts Intelligence Scholars Program for Global Network Analysts **Area, Field, or Subject:** Banking; Computer and information sciences; Finance; Information science and technology;

International affairs and relations; Political science; Telecommunications systems **Level of Education for which Award is Granted:** Undergraduate **Number Awarded:** Varies each year. **Funds Available:** The stipend is $25,000 per year. During the summer after application, students participate in a Global Network Analysis internship. After graduation, they have an employment obligation to NSA equal to 1.5 times the length of educational support provided. **Duration:** 1 year; may be renewed 1 additional year. The summer internship program is for 12 weeks.
Eligibility Requirements: This program is open to college sophomore and juniors whose academic program includes 1 of the following areas of emphasis: 1) technical studies (computer science major with a minor in political science or international relations); 2) topical studies (terrorism, proliferation or related sciences, international banking and finance, or telecommunications and information systems networks); or 3) disciplines (technical intelligence analysis, information assurance, networks, and telecommunications). Applicants must be enrolled full time with a GPA of 3.0 or higher. Along with their application, they must submit a 1-page essay describing how the proposed program of study will improve their ability to analyze information and to think and write critically. U.S. citizenship and eligibility to obtain a high-level security clearance are required **Deadline for Receipt:** October of each year. **Additional Information:** After graduation, participants enter NSA's Global Network Analysis Internship Program as a full-time employee.

3462 ■ NATIONAL SECURITY AGENCY

Attn: Office of Recruitment and Staffing (Roberts)
9800 Savage Road, Suite 6779
P.O. Box 1661, Suite 6779
Fort Meade, MD 20755-6779
Tel: (410)854-4725; (866)672-4473
Web Site: http://www.nsa.gov/careers/students_4.cfm
To provide financial assistance to college juniors interested in preparing for a career with the National Security Agency (NSA) as an intelligence analyst.
Title of Award: Pat Roberts Intelligence Scholars Program for Intelligence Analysts **Area, Field, or Subject:** Asian studies; Banking; Finance; Foreign languages; Geography; Information science and technology; International affairs and relations; Library and archival sciences; Near Eastern studies; South Asian studies; Telecommunications systems **Level of Education for which Award is Granted:** Four Year College **Number Awarded:** Varies each year. **Funds Available:** The stipend is $25,000 per year. After graduation, recipients have an employment obligation to NSA equal to 1.5 times the length of educational support provided. **Duration:** 1 year (the senior year of college).
Eligibility Requirements: This program is open to college juniors whose academic program includes 1 of the following areas of emphasis: 1) regional studies (Middle East or south, east, or central Asia); 2) topical studies (terrorism, proliferation or related sciences, international banking and finance, or telecommunications and information systems networks); or 3) disciplines (intelligence analysis, philosophy, or international relations; familiarity with foreign languages, particularly Arabic, Chinese, Dari, Farsi, Hindi, Korean, Pashto, Urdu, or a central Asian language is desirable; highly qualified applicants studying social network analysis, library science, or geographic information systems may also be considered). Applicants must be enrolled full time with a GPA of 3.0 or higher. Along with their application, they must submit a 1-page essay describing how the proposed program of study will improve their ability to analyze information and to think and write critically. U.S. citizenship and eligibility to obtain a high-level security clearance are required **Deadline for Receipt:** October of each year. **Additional Information:** After graduation, participants enter NSA's Intelligence Analysis Development Program as a full-time employee.

3463 ■ NATIONAL SECURITY AGENCY

Attn: Office of Recruitment and Staffing (Roberts)
9800 Savage Road, Suite 6779
P.O. Box 1661, Suite 6779
Fort Meade, MD 20755-6779
Tel: (410)854-4725; (866)672-4473
Web Site: http://www.nsa.gov/careers/students_4.cfm
To provide financial assistance to graduate students interested in preparing for a career with the National Security Agency (NSA) as a language analyst.

Title of Award: Pat Roberts Intelligence Scholars Program for Language Analysts **Area, Field, or Subject:** Foreign languages **Level of Education for which Award is Granted:** Four Year College, Graduate **Number Awarded:** Varies each year. **Funds Available:** The stipend is $25,000 per year. After graduation, recipients have an employment obligation to NSA equal to 1.5 times the length of educational support provided. **Duration:** 1 year; may be renewed 1 additional year.
Eligibility Requirements: This program is open to graduate students working on a master's or doctoral degree in foreign languages, especially Arabic Chinese, Dari, Farsi, Hindi, Korean, Philippine languages, Russian, and Urdu. Applicants must be enrolled full time with a GPA of 3.0 or higher. Along with their application, they must submit a 1-page essay on why they are interested in utilizing their language skills at NSA. U.S. citizenship and eligibility to obtain a high-level security clearance are required **Deadline for Receipt:** October of each year. **Additional Information:** After graduation, participants enter NSA's Language Analysis New Hire Program.

3464 ■ NATIONAL SECURITY AGENCY

Attn: Office of Recruitment and Staffing (Stokes)
9800 Savage Road, Suite 6779
P.O. Box 1661, Suite 6779
Fort Meade, MD 20755-6779
Tel: (410)854-4725; (866)672-4473
Web Site: http://www.nsa.gov/careers/students_4.cfm
To provide minority and other high school seniors and college sophomores with scholarship/loans and work experience at the National Security Agency (NSA).
Title of Award: Stokes Educational Scholarship Program **Area, Field, or Subject:** Asian studies; Computer and information sciences; Engineering, Computer; Engineering, Electrical; Finance; Foreign languages; International affairs and relations; Mathematics and mathematical sciences; Near Eastern studies; South Asian studies **Level of Education for which Award is Granted:** Undergraduate **Number Awarded:** Varies each year. **Funds Available:** Participants receive college tuition for up to 4 years, reimbursement for books and certain fees, a year-round salary, and a housing allowance and travel reimbursement during summer employment if the distance between the agency and school exceeds 75 miles. Following graduation, participants must work for the agency for 1 and a half times their length of study, usually 5 years. Students who leave agency employment earlier must repay the tuition cost. **Duration:** Up to 4 years, followed by employment at the agency for 5 years.
Eligibility Requirements: This program is open to graduating high school seniors, particularly minorities, who 1) are planning a college major in electrical or computer engineering, computer science, international affairs, international finance, mathematics, area studies (Middle East or south, east, or central Asia), foreign languages (recent language interests included Arabic, Chinese, Farsi, and Korean); 2) have minimum scores of 1600 on the SAT (1100 on critical reading and mathematics, 500 in writing) or 25 on the ACT; 3) have a GPA of 3.0 or higher; 4) are U.S. citizens; and 5) demonstrate leadership abilities. Also eligible are college sophomores who are U.S. citizens, have a GPA of 3.0 or higher, and are majoring in the eligible fields. Applicants must include a 1-page essay on why they want to have a career with the NSA. **Deadline for Receipt:** November of each year. **Additional Information:** Participants must attend classes full time and work at the agency during the summer in jobs tailored to their course of study. They must maintain at least a 3.0 GPA. This program, established in 1986, was formerly known as the National Security Agency Undergraduate Training Program.

3465 ■ NEW HAMPSHIRE POSTSECONDARY EDUCATION COMMISSION

3 Barrell Court, Suite 300
Concord, NH 03301-8543
Tel: (603)271-2555
Fax: (603)271-2696
E-mail: pedes@pec.state.nh.us
Web Site: http://www.state.nh.us/postsecondary/finwork.html
To provide scholarship/loans to New Hampshire residents who are interested in attending college to prepare for careers in designated professions.
Title of Award: New Hampshire Workforce Incentive Program Forgivable Loans **Area, Field, or Subject:** Chemistry; Education; Education, Special;

Linguistics; Mathematics and mathematical sciences; Nursing; Physical sciences; Physics; Science **Level of Education for which Award is Granted:** Graduate, Undergraduate **Number Awarded:** Varies each year. **Funds Available:** The stipend is $500 per semester ($1,000 per year). This is a scholarship/loan program; recipients must agree to pursue, within New Hampshire, the professional career for which they receive training. Recipients of loans for 1 year have their notes cancelled upon completion of 1 year of full-time service; repayment by service must be completed within 3 years from the date of licensure, certification, or completion of the program. Recipients of loans for more than 1 year have their notes cancelled upon completion of 2 years of full-time service; repayment by service must be completed within 5 years from the date of licensure, certification, or completion of the program. If the note is not cancelled because of service, the recipient must repay the loan within 2 years. **Duration:** 1 year; may be renewed.
Eligibility Requirements: This program is open to residents of New Hampshire who wish to prepare for careers in fields designated by the commission as shortage areas. Currently, the career shortage areas are chemistry, general science, mathematics, physical sciences, physics, special education, world languages, and nursing (L.P.N. through graduate). Applicants must be enrolled as a junior, senior, or graduate student at a college in New Hampshire and must be able to demonstrate financial need. **Deadline for Receipt:** May of each year for fall semester; December of each year for spring semester. **Additional Information:** The time for repayment of the loan, either in cash or through professional service, is extended while the recipient is 1) engaged in a course of study, at least on a half-time basis, at an institution of higher education; 2) serving on active duty as a member of the armed forces of the United States, or as a member of VISTA, the Peace Corps, or AmeriCorps, for a period up to 3 years; 3) temporarily totally disabled for a period up to 3 years; or 4) unable to secure employment because of the need to care for a disabled spouse, child, or parent for a period up to 12 months. The repayment obligation is cancelled if the recipient is unable to work because of a permanent total disability, receives relief under federal bankruptcy laws, or dies. This program went into effect in 1999.

3466 ■ NEW YORK STATE LEGION PRESS ASSOCIATION

c/o Scholarship Chairman
American Legion (NYSLPA)
P.O. Box 650
East Aurora, NY 14052
To provide financial assistance to the children of members of the American Legion or American Legion Auxiliary in New York who are interested in careers in communications.
Title of Award: New York State Legion Press Association Scholarship **Area, Field, or Subject:** Communications; Graphic art and design; Journalism; Public relations **Level of Education for which Award is Granted:** Four Year College **Number Awarded:** 1 each year. **Funds Available:** The stipend is $1,000. **Duration:** 1 year.
Eligibility Requirements: This program is open to New York residents who are the children of members of the American Legion or American Legion Auxiliary, or members of the Sons of the American Legion, or junior members of the American Legion Auxiliary, or graduates of the New York Boys State or Girls State. Applicants must be entering or attending an accredited 4-year college or university, working on a degree in communications (including public relations, journalism, reprographics, newspaper design or management, or other related fields acceptable to the scholarship committee). Along with their application, they must submit a 500-word essay on why they chose the field of communications as a future vocation. Financial need and class standing are not considered. **Deadline for Receipt:** May of each year.

3467 ■ NORTH CAROLINA 4-H DEVELOPMENT FUND

c/o North Carolina State University
Department of 4-H Youth Development
202 Ricks Hall
P.O. Box 7606
Raleigh, NC 27695-7606
Tel: (919)515-8486
Fax: (919)515-7812
Web Site: http://www.nc4h.org
To provide financial assistance to students in North Carolina who are members of 4-H and interested in majoring in communications in college.

Title of Award: Ray Wilkinson Communications Scholarship **Area, Field, or Subject:** Communications **Level of Education for which Award is Granted:** Undergraduate **Number Awarded:** 1 each year. **Funds Available:** The stipend is $1,000 per year. **Duration:** 1 year.
Eligibility Requirements: This program is open to 4-H members who are graduating from high schools in North Carolina. Applicants must be planning to major in communications at a college or university in the state. If no entering freshman is eligible, the award may be given to a continuing upperclassman. Selection is based on accomplishments in 4-H (50%), academic achievement as indicated by GPA and class rank (25%), and aptitude for college as indicated by grades and SAT or ACT scores (25%). **Deadline for Receipt:** January of each year.

3468 ■ OAK RIDGE INSTITUTE FOR SCIENCE AND EDUCATION

Attn: Science and Engineering Education
P.O. Box 117
Oak Ridge, TN 37831-0117
Tel: (865)576-8239
Fax: (865)241-5219
E-mail: igrid.gregory@orau.gov
Web Site: http://www.orau.gov/orise.htm
To provide financial assistance and summer research experience to undergraduate students who are working on a degree in a field of interest to the Department of Homeland Security (DHS).
Title of Award: Department of Homeland Security Undergraduate Scholarships **Area, Field, or Subject:** Agricultural sciences; Biological and clinical sciences; Communications; Computer and information sciences; Engineering; Information science and technology; Mathematics and mathematical sciences; Physical sciences; Psychology; Public administration; Religion; Social sciences; Writing **Level of Education for which Award is Granted:** Undergraduate **Number Awarded:** Approximately 50 each year. **Funds Available:** This program provides a stipend of $1,000 per month during the academic year and $5,000 for the internship plus full payment of tuition and mandatory fees. **Duration:** 2 academic years plus 10 weeks during the intervening summer.
Eligibility Requirements: This program is open to 1) full-time students who are in their second year of college attendance as of the application deadline; and 2) part-time students who have completed at least 45 but no more than 60 semester hours as of the application deadline. Applicants must be majoring in the agricultural sciences, biological and life sciences, computer and information sciences, engineering, mathematics, physical sciences, psychology, social sciences, or selected humanities (religious studies, cultural studies, public policy, advocacy, communications, or science writing). They must have a GPA of 3.3 or higher. Along with their application, they must submit 2 statements on 1) their educational and professional goals, the kinds of research they are interested in conducting, specific questions that interest them, and how they became interested in them; and 2) how they think their interests, talents, and initiative would contribute to make the homeland safer and secure. Selection is based on those statements, academic record, references, and SAT or ACT scores. As part of their program, they must be interested in participating in summer research and development activities at a DHS-designated facility. U.S. citizenship is required. **Deadline for Receipt:** January of each year.
Additional Information: This program, established in 2003, is funded by DHS and administered by Oak Ridge Institute for Science and Education (ORISE). Recipients must enroll full time.

3469 ■ OHIO CLASSICAL CONFERENCE

c/o Amy J. Sawan, Scholarship Committee
Medina Senior High School
777 East Union Street
Medina, OH 44256
Tel: (330)636-3200
E-mail: LIAMOT@aol.com
Web Site: http://dept.kent.edu/mcls/classics/occ
To provide financial assistance to Ohio residents preparing for a career as a Latin teacher.
Title of Award: Ohio Classical Conference Scholarship for Prospective Latin Teachers **Area, Field, or Subject:** Classical studies; Education, Elementary; Education, Secondary; Foreign languages **Level of Education for which Award is Granted:** Undergraduate **Number Awarded:** 1 each year. **Funds Available:** The stipend is $1,500. **Duration:** 1 year; nonrenewable.

Eligibility Requirements: This program is open to residents of Ohio enrolled at least at the sophomore level at a college or university in the United States. Applicants must be taking courses leading to a career in the teaching of Latin at the K-12 level in a public, private, or parochial school. They must submit college transcripts, 2 letters of recommendation (including 1 from a member of their classics department), a prospectus of courses completed and to be taken as part of the program, and a 1-page statement of their academic goals and reasons for applying for the scholarship. **Deadline for Receipt:** March of each year.

3470 ■ OHIO CLASSICAL CONFERENCE

c/o Amy J. Sawan, Scholarship Committee
Medina Senior High School
777 East Union Street
Medina, OH 44256
Tel: (330)636-3200
E-mail: LIAMOT@aol.com
Web Site: http://dept.kent.edu/mcls/classics/occ
To provide financial assistance to Ohio high school seniors planning to study Latin in college.
Title of Award: Ohio Classical Conference Scholarship for the Study of Latin **Area, Field, or Subject:** Classical studies; Foreign languages **Level of Education for which Award is Granted:** Undergraduate **Number Awarded:** 1 each year. **Funds Available:** The stipend is $1,500. **Duration:** 1 year; nonrenewable.
Eligibility Requirements: This program is open to seniors graduating from high schools in Ohio and entering a college or university in the United States. Applicants must be planning to study Latin, although they do not need to major in Latin or classics. They must submit an official high school transcript, 2 letters of recommendation (including 1 from their high school Latin teacher), and a 1-page statement on their reasons for studying Latin or the classics. **Deadline for Receipt:** March of each year.

3471 ■ OKLAHOMA STATE REGENTS FOR HIGHER EDUCATION

Attn: Director of Scholarship and Grant Programs
655 Research Parkway, Suite 200
P.O. Box 108850
Oklahoma City, OK 73101-8850
Tel: (405)225-9239
Free: 800-858-1840
Fax: (405)225-9230
E-mail: studentinfo@osrhe.edu
Web Site: http://www.okhighered.org/student-center/financial-aid/future-teach.shtml
To provide forgivable loans to Oklahoma residents who are interested in teaching (particularly in teacher shortage fields) in Oklahoma.
Title of Award: Oklahoma Future Teachers Scholarship Program **Area, Field, or Subject:** Education; Education, Special; English language and literature; Linguistics; Mathematics and mathematical sciences; Science **Level of Education for which Award is Granted:** Graduate, Undergraduate **Number Awarded:** Varies each year; recently, 136 students received support through this program. **Funds Available:** Full-time students receive up to $1,500 per year if they have completed 60 hours or more or up to $1,000 if they have completed fewer than 60 hours; part-time students receive up to $750 per year if they have completed 60 hours or more or up to $500 per year if they have completed fewer than 60 hours. Funds are paid directly to the institution on the student's behalf. This is a forgivable loan program; recipients must agree to teach in Oklahoma public schools for 3 years following graduation and licensure. **Duration:** 1 year; may be renewable for up to 3 additional years as long as the recipient maintains a GPA of 2.5 or higher.
Eligibility Requirements: Candidates for this program must be nominated by institutions of higher education in Oklahoma. Nominees may be high school seniors, high school graduates, or currently-enrolled undergraduate or graduate students. They must 1) rank in the top 15% of their high school graduating class; 2) have an ACT or SAT score ranking in the top 15% for high school graduates of the same year; 3) have been admitted into a professional education program at an accredited Oklahoma institution of higher education; or 4) have achieved an undergraduate record of outstanding success as defined by the institution. Both part-time and full-time students are eligible, but preference is given to full-time students. Applicants must be interested in teaching in critical shortage areas in the state upon graduation. These areas change periodi-

cally but recently have included special education, mathematics, science, English, and foreign languages. **Deadline for Receipt:** September of each year.

3472 ■ ORDER SONS OF ITALY IN AMERICA

Attn: Sons of Italy Foundation
219 E Street, N.E.
Washington, DC 20002
Tel: (202)547-5106
Fax: (202)546-8168
E-mail: scholarships@osia.org
Web Site: http://www.osia.org/public/scholarships/grants.asp
To provide financial assistance to upper-division students majoring in Italian.

Title of Award: Sons of Italy Italian Language Scholarship **Area, Field, or Subject:** Foreign languages **Level of Education for which Award is Granted:** Four Year College **Number Awarded:** 1 or more each year. **Funds Available:** Stipends range from $4,000 to $25,000. **Duration:** 1 year; nonrenewable.

Eligibility Requirements: This program is open to U.S. citizens of Italian descent who are enrolled as full-time undergraduate juniors or seniors at an accredited 4-year college or university. Applicants must be majoring in the Italian language. They must submit an essay of 750 to 1,000 words in Italian on how they plan to use their degree in Italian language in their career. Financial need is not considered in the selection process. **Deadline for Receipt:** February of each year. **Additional Information:** Applications must be accompanied by a $25 processing fee.

3473 ■ OREGON ASSOCIATION OF BROADCASTERS

Attn: Scholarship Committee
7150 S.W. Hampton Street, Suite 214
Portland, OR 97223-8366
Tel: (503)443-2299
Fax: (503)443-2488
E-mail: theoab@theoab.org
Web Site: http://www.theoab.org/eduopps_foundation.htm
To provide financial assistance to students in Oregon who are interested in majoring in broadcast-related fields in college.

Title of Award: Oregon Association of Broadcasters Scholarships **Area, Field, or Subject:** Broadcasting; Communications; Journalism **Level of Education for which Award is Granted:** Undergraduate **Number Awarded:** 6 each year: 2 to graduating high school seniors and 4 to students currently enrolled in 2- or 4-year college broadcast programs. **Funds Available:** The stipend is $1,000. **Duration:** 1 year.

Eligibility Requirements: This program is open to Oregon residents who are either enrolled or accepted for enrollment at a 2- or 4-year public or private college or university in the state. Applicants must be planning to enroll or be currently enrolled in a full-time undergraduate course of study, majoring in broadcast journalism, production, management, or another broadcast-related field. They must be graduating high school seniors, first- or second-year students in a 2-year program, or sophomores, juniors, or seniors in a 4-year program. Preference is given to applicants with at least a 3.0 cumulative GPA and demonstrated academic and/or professional experience in broadcasting or other electronic-media fields. Along with their application, students must submit an essay that explains their reasons for choosing a broadcast major and includes any broadcast activities in which they have participated, their first job preference after college, their 10-year goals, any other scholarships they have received, and any academic honors they have received. Financial need is not considered in the selection process. **Deadline for Receipt:** February of each year.

3474 ■ PHILADELPHIA NEWSPAPERS, INC.

Attn: Ivan Sample
400 North Broad Street
P.O. Box 8263
Philadelphia, PA 19101
Tel: (215)854-2429
Fax: (215)854-2578
E-mail: isample@phillynews.com
Web Site: http://www.philly.com/mld/philly/living/education
To provide financial assistance to minority high school seniors from the circulation area of Philadelphia Newspapers Inc. (PNI) who are interested in a career in journalism or communications.

Title of Award: PNI Knight Ridder Minority Scholars Program **Area, Field, or Subject:** Communications; Journalism **Level of Education for which Award is Granted:** Undergraduate **Number Awarded:** 3 each year. **Funds Available:** The stipend is $1,000. **Duration:** 1 year; nonrenewable.

Eligibility Requirements: This program is open to minority seniors graduating from high schools in the service area of the PNI newspapers (the *Philadelphia Inquirer* and the *Philadelphia Daily News*) in Delaware, New Jersey, and Pennsylvania. Applicants must be interested in majoring in journalism in college. Along with their application, they must submit 2 letters of recommendation, transcripts of grades, SAT or ACT scores, up to 5 samples of work with bylines, and an essay on why they want to prepare for a career in the journalism or communication business. **Deadline for Receipt:** January of each year. **Additional Information:** The recipients of these scholarships are automatically entered into competition for the Knight Ridder Minority Scholarship Program of $40,000 over 4 years.

3475 ■ PRESS CLUB OF NEW ORLEANS

Attn: Scholarship Committee
203 Carondelet Street, Suite 415
New Orleans, LA 70130
Tel: (504)523-1010
E-mail: pressclubneworleans@cox.net
Web Site: http://www.pressclubneworleans.org
To provide financial assistance to students in Louisiana who will be majoring in journalism.

Title of Award: Press Club of New Orleans Journalism Scholarship Program **Area, Field, or Subject:** Communications; Journalism **Level of Education for which Award is Granted:** Undergraduate **Number Awarded:** 1 or more each year. **Funds Available:** A total of $5,000 is awarded each year. **Duration:** 1 year.

Eligibility Requirements: This program is open to Louisiana residents who will be enrolled in university-level print or broadcast journalism programs during the upcoming academic year. Applicants must submit 1) a brief (1 to 3 pages) written statement outlining their course of study, career goals, and financial need, and 2) examples of their published work, including newspaper stories, tapes, columns, and/or editorials. **Deadline for Receipt:** April of each year. **Additional Information:** Recipients may attend school in any state.

3476 ■ RHODE ISLAND FOUNDATION

Attn: Scholarship Coordinator
One Union Station
Providence, RI 02903
Tel: (401)274-4564
Fax: (401)331-8085
E-mail: libbym@rifoundation.org
Web Site: http://www.rifoundation.org
To provide financial assistance to residents of Rhode Island who are enrolled in college to prepare for a career in advertising.

Title of Award: J.D. Edsal Advertising Scholarship **Area, Field, or Subject:** Advertising; Broadcasting; Filmmaking; Graphic art and design; Marketing and distribution; Public relations; Radio and television **Level of Education for which Award is Granted:** Undergraduate **Number Awarded:** 2 each year. **Funds Available:** The stipend is $1,500. **Duration:** 1 year.

Eligibility Requirements: This program is open to residents of Rhode Island who are enrolled full time as undergraduates at the sophomore level or above. Applicants must be preparing for a career in advertising and majoring in a related field (e.g., broadcast production, graphic design, interactive film, marketing, public relations, television, or video). Along with their application, they must submit an essay (up to 300 words) on the impact they would like to have on the advertising industry. Financial need is also considered in the selection process. **Deadline for Receipt:** April of each year.

3477 ■ RHODE ISLAND FOUNDATION

Attn: Scholarship Coordinator
One Union Station
Providence, RI 02903
Tel: (401)274-4564
Fax: (401)331-8085

E-mail: libbym@rifoundation.org

Web Site: http://www.rifoundation.org

To provide financial assistance to Rhode Island students of color interested in preparing for a career in communications.

Title of Award: RDW Group, Inc. Minority Scholarship for Communications **Area, Field, or Subject:** Advertising; Art; Communications; Filmmaking; Graphic art and design **Level of Education for which Award is Granted:** Graduate, Undergraduate **Number Awarded:** 1 each year. **Funds Available:** The stipend is $2,000. **Duration:** 1 year; nonrenewable.

Eligibility Requirements: This program is open to minority undergraduate and graduate students who are Rhode Island residents. Applicants must intend to major in communications (including computer graphics, art, cinematography, or other fields that would prepare them for a career in advertising). They must be able to demonstrate financial need and a commitment to a career in communications. Along with their application, they must submit an essay (up to 300 words) on the impact they would like to have on the communications field. **Deadline for Receipt:** April of each year. **Additional Information:** This program is sponsored by the RDW Group, Inc.

3478 ■ SOUTH CAROLINA COMMISSION ON HIGHER EDUCATION

Attn: Director of Student Services

1333 Main Street, Suite 200

Columbia, SC 29201

Tel: (803)737-2260; 877-349-7183

Fax: (803)737-2297

E-mail: dbrown@che.sc.gov

Web Site: http://www.che.sc.gov

To provide scholarship/loans to teachers in South Carolina who wish to improve their content knowledge and degree programs.

Title of Award: South Carolina Teaching Scholarship Grants Program **Area, Field, or Subject:** Art; Dance; Economics; Education; Education, Early childhood; Education, Elementary; Education, Music; Education, Secondary; Education, Special; Geography; History; Linguistics; Mathematics and mathematical sciences; Music; Political science; Science **Level of Education for which Award is Granted:** Graduate, Professional, Undergraduate **Number Awarded:** Varies each year. **Funds Available:** The stipend is $1,000 per fiscal year. This is a scholarship/loan program. Recipients must sign a commitment to teach in South Carolina public schools for at least 1 year following completion of the scholarship grant year and agree to refund the scholarship amount if the 1-year teaching commitment is not honored. **Duration:** 1 year; may be renewed if recipients maintain a GPA of 3.0 or higher. They may receive up to 3 grants in a 5-year period.

Eligibility Requirements: This program is open to residents of South Carolina who have a professional teaching certificate and are under contract as a teacher in a public school in the state. Applicants must be 1) accepted as a degree-seeking graduate student in the teaching field at the master's level and enrolled at an eligible institution in the state; or 2) enrolled for graduate or undergraduate courses in their current teaching field or in a teaching field in which they wish to add on certification. Proposed fields of study must relate to core content areas of English, reading or language arts, mathematics, science, foreign languages, civics and government, economics, arts (advanced fine arts, art, dance, drama, music, and speech), history, or geography; early childhood, elementary education, middle level education, secondary education, and special education also qualify. Priority is given to classroom teachers (not administrators, counselors, media specialists, or other support personnel) whose teaching specialties are critical need subject areas. Continuing graduate students must have a GPA of 3.0 or higher. U.S. citizenship or permanent resident status is required. **Deadline for Receipt:** December of each year for second summer session and fall semester; June of each year for spring semester and first summer session. **Additional Information:** This program was established in 2001.

3479 ■ SOUTH CAROLINA STUDENT LOAN CORPORATION

Interstate Center

16 Berryhill Road, Suite 210

P.O. Box 21487

Columbia, SC 29221-1487

Tel: (803)798-0916

Free: 800-347-2752

Fax: (803)772-9410

Web Site: http://www.slc.sc.edu

To provide scholarship/loans to students in South Carolina who wish to teach certain subjects or in certain geographic areas.

Title of Award: South Carolina Teacher Loan Program **Area, Field, or Subject:** Agricultural sciences; Classical studies; Consumer affairs; Dance; Education, Elementary; Education, Music; Education, Special; English language and literature; Foreign languages; Library and archival sciences; Mathematics and mathematical sciences; Science; Speech and language pathology/audiology; Technology **Level of Education for which Award is Granted:** Graduate, Undergraduate **Number Awarded:** Varies each year. **Funds Available:** Freshmen and sophomores may borrow up to $2,500 per academic year; juniors, seniors, and graduate students may borrow up to $5,000 per academic year. This is a scholarship/loan program; loans are forgivable at the rate of 20% or $3,000, whichever is greater, for each full year of teaching in an area (either geographic or subject) of critical need; for students who teach in both critical subject and geographic areas, the rate of cancellation is 33% or $5,000, whichever is greater, per year. Borrowers who fail to teach in either a critical subject or geographic area must repay the loan at an annual interest rate that varies (currently, 5.37%) but is capped at 10.25%. **Duration:** 1 year; may be renewed for a total of 5 years of undergraduate and 5 years of graduate study.

Eligibility Requirements: Eligible to apply are residents of South Carolina who are planning to teach in certain critical geographic areas of the state, or to teach in critical subject areas. Entering freshmen must have ranked in the top 40% of their high school class and have an ACT or SAT score greater than the South Carolina average (recently 986 on the SAT or 19.3 on the ACT); enrolled undergraduates or entering graduate students must have at least a 2.75 cumulative GPA; graduate students who have completed at least 1 term must have a GPA of 3.5 or better. Undergraduate students at South Carolina colleges must have taken and passed the Education Entrance Exam; students at institutions outside South Carolina must have completed the necessary prerequisites required at that institution. Only U.S. citizens may apply. **Deadline for Receipt:** May of each year. **Additional Information:** Recently, the critical subject areas include mathematics, science (biology, chemistry, physics, and general science), media specialist, special education, industrial technology, foreign languages (Spanish, French, Latin, and German), family and consumer science, art, music, business education, English and language arts, dance, speech and drama/theater, and agriculture. For a list of critical geographic area, contact the sponsor.

3480 ■ SWEDISH WOMEN'S EDUCATION ASSOCIATION INTERNATIONAL-SOUTH FLORIDA CHAPTER

c/o Yerti Nelson, Scholarship Committee

3759 Mykonos Court

Boca Raton, FL 33486

Tel: (561)997-2050

Fax: (561)997-8010

E-mail: florida@swea.org

Web Site: http://www.chapters-swea.org/florida

To provide financial assistance to Florida residents interested in studying in Sweden or an area related to Swedish studies.

Title of Award: South Florida SWEA Scholarship **Area, Field, or Subject:** Art; Art industries and trade; Crafts; Design; Environmental conservation; Environmental science; Foreign languages; General studies/Field of study not specified; Literature; Music; Swedish studies **Level of Education for which Award is Granted:** Graduate, Professional, Undergraduate **Number Awarded:** 1 each year. **Funds Available:** The stipend is $3,000.

Eligibility Requirements: This program is open to all residents of Florida interested in participating in an exchange program in Sweden. Applicants may also propose to study in the United States, if the studies specifically emphasize Sweden and Swedish aspects, including 1) Swedish language; 2) Swedish culture or traditions; 3) environmental science; 4) a health care program promoting better health for women and children; or 5) handicraft, art, glass art, music, literature, or design. Study proposals must be well-defined in time and content. Along with their application, they must submit a transcript from college, university, or vocational school; curriculum vitae; project proposal, describing the planned studies, length of studies, and goals; financial statement; and letter of recommendation from an instructor. **Deadline for Receipt:** January of each year. **Additional**

Information: Within 3 months after the end of studies or the project, the recipient must report to the scholarship committee or, if possible, accept an invitation to an organization meeting to share the experience.

3481 ■ TEXAS CLASSICAL ASSOCIATION

c/o Andrew Riggsby, Scholarship Committee Chair
University of Texas at Austin
Waggener 123
Austin, TX 78712-1181
Tel: (512)471-5742
E-mail: ariggsby@utxvms.cc.utexas.edu
Web Site: http://www.txclassics.org/schol.htm
To provide financial assistance to high school seniors in Texas who plan to study Latin or Greek in college.
Title of Award: TSJCL Lourania Miller Scholarship **Area, Field, or Subject:** Classical studies; Foreign languages **Level of Education for which Award is Granted:** Undergraduate **Number Awarded:** 1 each year. **Funds Available:** The stipend is $1,000. **Duration:** 1 year.
Eligibility Requirements: This program is open to residents of Texas who have been active members of the Texas Classical Association (TCA) for at least 2 years. Applicants must be graduating from high school and planning to continue their study of Latin and Greek during their freshman year in college. Enrollment in Latin cannot be at a beginning level. Courses in classical civilization are not accepted. **Deadline for Receipt:** June of each year. **Additional Information:** This program is offered jointly by the Texas State Junior Classical League (TSJCL) and TCA.

3482 ■ TEXAS CLASSICAL ASSOCIATION

c/o Andrew Riggsby, Scholarship Committee Chair
University of Texas at Austin
Waggener 123
Austin, TX 78712-1181
Tel: (512)471-5742
E-mail: ariggsby@utxvms.cc.utexas.edu
Web Site: http://www.txclassics.org/schol.htm
To provide financial assistance to high school seniors in Texas who plan to study Latin or Greek in college.
Title of Award: TSJCL Gareth Morgan Scholarship **Area, Field, or Subject:** Classical studies; Foreign languages **Level of Education for which Award is Granted:** Undergraduate **Number Awarded:** 1 each year. **Funds Available:** The stipend is $1,000. **Duration:** 1 year.
Eligibility Requirements: This program is open to residents of Texas who have been active members of the Texas Classical Association (TCA) for at least 2 years. Applicants must be graduating from high school and planning to continue their study of Latin and Greek during their freshman year in college. Enrollment in Latin cannot be at a beginning level. Courses in classical civilization are not accepted. **Deadline for Receipt:** June of each year. **Additional Information:** This program is offered jointly by the Texas State Junior Classical League (TSJCL) and TCA.

3483 ■ U.S. AIR FORCE

Attn: Headquarters AFROTC/RRUE
Enlisted Commissioning Section
551 East Maxwell Boulevard
Maxwell AFB, AL 36112-5917
Tel: (334)953-2091; (866)423-7682
Fax: (334)953-6167
E-mail: enlisted@afrotc.com
Web Site: http://www.afoats.af.mil/AFROTC/EnlistedComm/AECP.asp
To allow selected enlisted Air Force personnel to earn a bachelor's degree in approved majors by providing financial assistance for full-time college study.
Title of Award: Airman Education and Commissioning Program **Area, Field, or Subject:** African studies; Asian studies; Computer and information sciences; Engineering; Foreign languages; Mathematics and mathematical sciences; Meteorology; Near Eastern studies; Nursing; Physics; Russian studies **Level of Education for which Award is Granted:** Undergraduate **Number Awarded:** Approximately 60 each year. **Funds Available:** While participating in this program, cadets remain on active duty in the Air Force and receive their regular salary and benefits. They also receive payment of tuition and fees up to $15,000 per year and an annual textbook allowance of $600. **Duration:** 1 to 3 years, until completion of a bachelor's degree.

Eligibility Requirements: Eligible to participate in this program are enlisted members of the Air Force who have been accepted at a university or college (or approved crosstown institution) that is associated with AFROTC and that offers an approved major. The majors currently supported are computer science, all ABET-accredited engineering fields (not engineering technology), foreign area studies (limited to Middle East, Africa, Asia, Russia/Eurasia), foreign languages (limited to Arabic, Armenian, Azeri, Chinese, French, Georgian, Hebrew, Hindi, Indonesian, Kazakh, Pashto, Persian Farsi, Russian, Swahili, and Turkish), mathematics, meteorology, nursing, and physics. Applicants must have completed at least 1 year of time-in-service and 1 year of time-on-station. They must have scores on the Air Force Officer Qualifying Test of at least 15 on the verbal and 10 on the quantitative and be able to pass the Air Force ROTC Physical Fitness Test. Normally they should have completed at least 30 semester hours of college study with a GPA of 2.75 or higher. They must be younger than 31 years of age or otherwise able to be commissioned before they become 35 years of age. **Deadline for Receipt:** February of each year. **Additional Information:** While attending college, participants in this program attend ROTC classes at their college or university. Upon completing their degree, they are commissioned to serve in the Air Force in their area of specialization with an active-duty service commitment of at least 4 years. Further information is available from base education service officers or an Air Force ROTC unit. This program does not provide for undergraduate flying training.

3484 ■ US PAN ASIAN AMERICAN CHAMBER OF COMMERCE

Attn: Scholarship Coordinator
1329 18th Street, N.W.
Washington, DC 20036
Tel: (202)296-5221
Fax: (202)296-5225
E-mail: administrator@uspaacc.com
Web Site: http://www.uspaacc.com/web/programs/
bernadette_Wong_yu.htm
To provide financial assistance to high school seniors who are interested in studying Chinese language or Chinese studies at a college or university in the United States or China.
Title of Award: Bernadette Wong Yu Scholarship **Area, Field, or Subject:** Chinese studies; Foreign languages **Level of Education for which Award is Granted:** Undergraduate **Number Awarded:** 1 each year. **Funds Available:** The maximum stipend is $3,000. Funds are paid directly to the recipient's college or university. **Duration:** 1 year.
Eligibility Requirements: This program is open to high school seniors who are U.S. citizens or permanent residents. Applicants must be planning to begin full-time study of Chinese language or Chinese studies at an accredited postsecondary educational institution in the United States or China. Along with their application, they must submit a 500-word essay on "Why I am interested in the Chinese culture." Selection is based on academic excellence (GPA of 3.3 or higher), community service involvement, and financial need. **Deadline for Receipt:** February of each year. **Additional Information:** Funding is not provided for correspondence courses, Internet courses, or study in a country other than the United States or China.

3485 ■ VESALIUS TRUST FOR VISUAL COMMUNICATIONS IN THE HEALTH SCIENCES

Attn: Wendy Hiller Gee, Student Grants and Scholarships
Krames-West Coast
1100 Grundy Lane
San Bruno, CA 94066
Tel: (650)244-4320
E-mail: wendy.hillergee@krames.com
Web Site: http://www.vesaliustrust.org/scholarships.html
To provide funding to students working on a research project in biocommunications.
Title of Award: Vesalius Trust Student Research Grants **Area, Field, or Subject:** Communications; Illustrators and illustrations; Medicine **Level of Education for which Award is Granted:** Graduate, Undergraduate **Number Awarded:** Varies each year. Recently, 19 of these grants were awarded, including 1 designated as the Alan Cole Scholarship and 5 designated as the Vesalian Scholarships. **Funds Available:** Grant amounts vary each year. **Duration:** 1 year.
Eligibility Requirements: This program is open to undergraduate and graduate students who have completed at least 1 year of a biocommuni-

cations program in medical illustrating. Applicants must be interested in conducting a research project under the guidance of a faculty preceptor. Selection is based on the background and education of the applicant (20%); an evaluation by the preceptor of the student's ability to complete the project and its potential contributions (10%); the project concept and subject matter (30%); project design (20%); and production plan (20%). **Deadline for Receipt:** November of each year. **Additional Information:** The top-ranked applicant receives the Alan Cole Scholarship. Other recipients whose projects show evidence of significant merit are designated Vesalian Scholarships.

3486 ■ WASHINGTON HIGHER EDUCATION COORDINATING BOARD

917 Lakeridge Way
P.O. Box 43430
Olympia, WA 98504-3430
Tel: (360)753-7851; 888-535-0747
Fax: (360)753-7808
E-mail: futureteachers@hecb.wa.gov
Web Site: http://www.hecb.wa.gov/financialaid/other/alternative.asp
To provide forgivable loans to K-12 classified employees in Washington who are interested in attending a college or university in order to become a teacher.
Title of Award: Washington Conditional Scholarships for Alternative Teaching Certification **Area, Field, or Subject:** Chemistry; Education; Education, Bilingual and cross-cultural; Education, Elementary; Education, English as a second language; Education, Secondary; Education, Special; Foreign languages; Mathematics and mathematical sciences; Physics; Technology **Level of Education for which Award is Granted:** Professional, Undergraduate **Number Awarded:** Approximately 25 each year. **Funds Available:** The maximum award is $4,000 per academic year. These awards are in the form of loans that can be forgiven in exchange for teaching service. Each 2 years of eligible teaching service results in the forgiveness of 1 year of loan. **Duration:** 1 year; may be renewed up to 4 additional years.
Eligibility Requirements: This program is open to Washington residents who are currently employed as a classified instructional employee in a K-12 public school. Applicants must 1) have a transferable associate degree and be seeking residency teacher certification with endorsements in special education or English as a second language; or 2) have a bachelor's degree and subject matter expertise in a shortage area and be seeking residency teacher certification in a subject matter shortage area (currently defined as special education, English as a second language, chemistry, physics, Japanese, mathematics, and technology education). to enroll in an accredited Washington college or university and work as a teacher in a K-12 public school in the state after completing initial teacher certification. Selection is based on academic ability, a statement demonstrating commitment to the teaching profession, the applicant's ability to serve as a positive role model as a K-12 public school teacher, length and quality of contributions to the Washington K-12 public school, and recommendations from a current teacher or school official describing the applicant's potential as a future teacher. The priority in making awards is: 1) eligible renewal applicants who are within 2 years of completing their initial teacher certification requirements; 2) all other eligible renewable applicants; 3) eligible new applicants who are within 2 years of completing their initial teacher certification requirements; and 4) all other new eligible applicants. **Deadline for Receipt:** October of each year. **Additional Information:** This program was established by the Washington legislature in 2001. It is administered by the Washington Higher Education Coordinator Board, but the Washington State Professional Educator Standards Board selects the recipients.

3487 ■ WISCONSIN FOUNDATION FOR INDEPENDENT COLLEGES, INC.

Attn: College-to-Work Program
735 North Water Street, Suite 600
Milwaukee, WI 53202-4100
Tel: (414)273-5980
Fax: (414)273-5995
E-mail: wfic@wficweb.org
Web Site: http://www.wficweb.org/work.html
To provide financial assistance and work experience to students majoring in fields related to business at member institutions of the Wisconsin Foundation for Independent Colleges (WFIC).

Title of Award: Appleton College-to-Work Program **Area, Field, or Subject:** Accounting; Business administration; Communications; Finance; Marketing and distribution; Personnel administration/human resources **Level of Education for which Award is Granted:** Four Year College **Number Awarded:** 2 each year. **Funds Available:** The stipends are $3,500 for the scholarship and $1,500 for the internship. **Duration:** 1 year for the scholarship; 10 weeks for the internship.
Eligibility Requirements: This program is open to full-time juniors and seniors at WFIC member colleges or universities. Minority students are encouraged to apply. Applicants must be preparing for a career in accounting, business, communications, finance, human resources, or marketing. They must be interested in a summer internship at Appleton (formerly Appleton Papers). Along with their application, they must submit a 1-page essay that includes why they are applying for the internship, why they have selected their major and what interests them about it, why they are attending their chosen college or university, and their future career objectives. **Deadline for Receipt:** February of each year. **Additional Information:** The WFIC member schools are Alverno College, Beloit College, Cardinal Stritch University, Carroll College, Carthage College, Concordia University of Wisconsin, Edgewood College, Lakeland College, Lawrence University, Marian College, Marquette University, Milwaukee Institute of Art & Design, Milwaukee School of Engineering, Mount Mary College, Northland College, Ripon College, St. Norbert College, Silver Lake College, Viterbo University, and Wisconsin Lutheran College. This program is sponsored by Appleton. The WFIC's College to Work Program includes a number of other financial assistance and work experience programs for eligible students majoring in fields related to business, including the Banta College-to-Work Program (also for engineering students), Blue Cross Blue Shield of Wisconsin College-to-Work Program, Johnson Financial Group College-to-Work Program, JohnsonDiversey College-to-Work Program, Johnsonville Sausage College-to-Work Program, M3 College-to-Work Program, Marsh College-to-Work Program, Modine Manufacturing College-to-Work Program, Opportunities, Inc. College-to-Work Program, Rock County Habitat for Humanity College-to-Work Program, Wausau Benefits College-to-Work Scholarship, and West Bend Mutual College-to-Work Scholarship.

3488 ■ WISCONSIN FOUNDATION FOR INDEPENDENT COLLEGES, INC.

Attn: College-to-Work Program
735 North Water Street, Suite 600
Milwaukee, WI 53202-4100
Tel: (414)273-5980
Fax: (414)273-5995
E-mail: wfic@wficweb.org
Web Site: http://www.wficweb.org/work.html
To provide financial assistance and work experience to students majoring in fields related to communications at member institutions of the Wisconsin Foundation for Independent Colleges (WFIC).
Title of Award: Manitowoc American Red Cross College-to-Work Program **Area, Field, or Subject:** Communications; English language and literature; General studies/Field of study not specified; Graphic art and design; Public relations **Level of Education for which Award is Granted:** Four Year College **Number Awarded:** 1 each year. **Funds Available:** The stipends are $3,500 for the scholarship and $1,500 for the internship. **Duration:** 1 year for the scholarship; 10 weeks for the internship.
Eligibility Requirements: This program is open to full-time sophomores, juniors, and seniors at private colleges and universities in Wisconsin. Applicants must be interested in an internship at the Manitowoc/Calumet County Chapter of the American Red Cross in Manitowoc. Preference is given to 1) students attending Lakeland College or Silver Lake College; 2) residents of Manitowoc County attending another WFIC member institution; and 3) students majoring in communications, English, graphic design, or public relations. Along with their application, they must submit a 1-page essay that includes why they are applying for the internship, why they have selected their major and what interests them about it, why they are attending their chosen college or university, and their future career objectives. **Deadline for Receipt:** February of each year. **Additional Information:** The other WFIC schools are Alverno College, Beloit College, Cardinal Stritch University, Carroll College, Carthage College, Concordia University of Wisconsin, Edgewood College, Lawrence University, Marian College, Marquette University, Milwaukee Institute of

Art & Design, Milwaukee School of Engineering, Mount Mary College, Northland College, Ripon College, St. Norbert College, Viterbo University, and Wisconsin Lutheran College. This program is sponsored by the Manitowoc/Calumet County Chapter of the American Red Cross. The WFIC's College-to-Work Program includes a number of other financial assistance and work experience programs aimed at eligible students interested in majoring in fields related to communications, journalism, media, and related fields, including the Post-Crescent College-to-Work Program and Reporter College-to-Work Program.

Education

3489 ■ 100TH INFANTRY BATTALION VETERANS CLUB

Attn: Scholarship Committee
520 Kamoku Street
Honolulu, HI 96826
Tel: (808)732-5216
E-mail: daisyy@hgea.net
Web Site: http://emedia.leeward.hawaii.edu/mnakano
To provide financial assistance to high school seniors and college students who plan to major or are majoring in education and exemplify the sponsor's motto of "Continuing Service."
Title of Award: Major James W. Lovell Scholarships **Area, Field, or Subject:** Education **Level of Education for which Award is Granted:** Undergraduate **Number Awarded:** 2 each year. **Funds Available:** The stipend is $1,000. **Duration:** 1 year; nonrenewable.
Eligibility Requirements: This program is open to high school seniors planning to attend an institution of higher learning and full-time undergraduate students at community colleges, vocational/trade schools, 4-year colleges, and universities. Applicants must have a GPA of 2.5 or higher and be able to demonstrate civic responsibility and community service. They must be majoring or planning to major in education. Along with their application, they must submit a 4-page essay that explains how lifelong learning (including academic success, experiential learning, intellectual growth, social and economic growth, leadership skills, and civic responsibility) is important for citizens and their state and country. Selection is based on that essay and the applicant's demonstration that he or she can effectively promote the legacy of the 100th Infantry Battalion and its motto of "Continuing Service." Financial need is not considered. **Deadline for Receipt:** April of each year.

3490 ■ ACADEMY OF TELEVISION ARTS & SCIENCES FOUNDATION

Attn: Education Department
5220 Lankershim Boulevard
North Hollywood, CA 91601-3109
Tel: (818)754-2830
Fax: (818)761-ATAS
E-mail: collegeawards@emmys.org
Web Site: http://www.emmys.tv/foundation/index.php
To provide financial assistance to upper-division and graduate students interested in working on a project in a field related to children's media.
Title of Award: Fred Rogers Memorial Scholarship **Area, Field, or Subject:** Art, Caricatures and cartoons; Child development; Education, Early childhood; Filmmaking; Music; Psychology; Radio and television **Level of Education for which Award is Granted:** Four Year College, Graduate **Number Awarded:** 1 each year. **Funds Available:** The stipend is $10,000. **Duration:** 1 year.
Eligibility Requirements: This program is open to upper-division and graduate students interested in preparing for a career in children's media. Applicants must be able to demonstrate a commitment, either through course work or experience, to any combination of at least 2 of the following fields: early childhood education, child development, child psychology, film or television production, music, or animation. They may apply for support for any of the following areas: research on the relationship between children's media and learning or children's use of media and personal growth; development of program concepts or extended development of creative elements of an existing concept (e.g., design of puppets, scripts, storyboards, characters, music); professional internship in an organization that is relevant to the applicant's goal for use of the award. **Deadline for Receipt:** January of each year. **Additional Information:** This scholarship, first awarded in 2005, is supported by Ernst & Young.

3491 ■ ALABAMA ALLIANCE FOR SCIENCE, ENGINEERING, MATHEMATICS, AND SCIENCE EDUCATION

Attn: Project Director
University of Alabama at Birmingham
Campbell Hall, Room 401
1300 University Boulevard
Birmingham, AL 35294-1170
Tel: (205)934-8762
Fax: (205)934-1650
E-mail: LDale@uab.edu
Web Site: http://www.uab.edu/istp/alabama.html
To provide financial assistance to underrepresented minority students at designated institutions in Alabama who are interested in preparing for a career as a science teacher.
Title of Award: Science Teacher Preparation Program **Area, Field, or Subject:** Education; Education, Elementary; Education, Secondary **Level of Education for which Award is Granted:** Master's, Undergraduate **Number Awarded:** Varies each year. **Funds Available:** The stipend is $1,000 per year. **Duration:** 1 year; may be renewed.
Eligibility Requirements: This program is open to members of underrepresented minority groups who have been unconditionally admitted to a participating Alabama college or university. Applicants may 1) be entering freshmen or junior college transfer students who intend to major in science education and become certified to teach in elementary, middle, or high school; 2) have earned a degree in mathematics, science, or education and are seeking to become certified to teach; or 3) have earned a degree in mathematics, science, or education and are enrolled in a fifth-year education program leading to a master's degree and certification. **Additional Information:** Support for this program is provided by the National Science Foundation. The participating institutions are Alabama A&M University, Alabama State University, Auburn University, Miles College, Stillman College, Talladega College, Tuskegee University, University of Alabama at Birmingham, and University of Alabama in Huntsville.

3492 ■ ALABAMA SPACE GRANT CONSORTIUM

c/o University of Alabama in Huntsville
Materials Science Building, Room 205
Huntsville, AL 35899
Tel: (256)824-6800
Fax: (256)824-6061
E-mail: reasonj@uah.edu
Web Site: http://www.uah.edu/ASGC
To provide financial assistance to undergraduate students at universities participating in the Alabama Space Grant Consortium who wish to prepare for a career as a teacher of science or mathematics.
Title of Award: Teacher Education Scholarship Program of the Alabama Space Grant Consortium **Area, Field, or Subject:** Aerospace sciences; Earth sciences; Education; Environmental conservation; Environmental science; Geosciences; Mathematics and mathematical sciences; Science; Space and planetary sciences **Level of Education for which Award is Granted:** Undergraduate **Number Awarded:** Varies each year; recently, 10 of these scholarships were awarded. **Funds Available:** The stipend is $1,000 per year. **Duration:** 1 year; nonrenewable.
Eligibility Requirements: This program is open to students enrolled in or accepted for enrollment as full-time undergraduates at universities in Alabama participating in the consortium. Applicants must intend to enter the teacher certification program and teach in a pre-college setting. Priority is given to those majoring in science, mathematics, or earth/space/environmental science. Applicants should have a GPA of 3.0 or higher and must be U.S. citizens. Members of underrepresented groups in science and mathematics (minorities and women) are especially encouraged to apply. Along with their application, they must submit a 1- to 2-page statement on the reasons for their desire to enter the teaching profession, specifically the fields of science or mathematics education. **Deadline for Receipt:** February of each year. **Additional Information:** The member universities are University of Alabama in Huntsville, Alabama A&M University, University of Alabama, University of Alabama at Birmingham, University of South Alabama, Tuskegee University, and Auburn University. Funding for this program is provided by NASA.

3493 ■ ALABAMA SPACE GRANT CONSORTIUM

c/o University of Alabama in Huntsville
Materials Science Building, Room 205
Huntsville, AL 35899

Tel: (256)824-6800
Fax: (256)824-6061
E-mail: reasonj@uah.edu
Web Site: http://www.uah.edu/ASGC
To provide financial assistance to undergraduates who are studying the space sciences at universities participating in the Alabama Space Grant Consortium (ASGC).

Title of Award: Undergraduate Scholarship Program of the Alabama Space Grant Consortium **Area, Field, or Subject:** Aerospace sciences; Behavioral sciences; Biological and clinical sciences; Business administration; Communications; Computer and information sciences; Economics; Education; Engineering, Aerospace/Aeronautical/Astronautical; International affairs and relations; Law; Natural sciences; Physical sciences; Public administration; Sociology; Space and planetary sciences **Level of Education for which Award is Granted:** Four Year College **Number Awarded:** Varies each year; recently, 32 of these scholarships were awarded. **Funds Available:** The stipend is $1,000 per year. **Duration:** 1 year; may be renewed 1 additional year.

Eligibility Requirements: This program is open to full-time students entering their junior or senior year at universities participating in the ASGC. Applicants must be studying in a field related to space, including the physical, natural, and biological sciences; engineering, education; economics; business; sociology; behavioral sciences; computer science; communications; law; international affairs; and public administration. They must be U.S. citizens and have a GPA of 3.0 or higher. Individuals from underrepresented groups (African Americans, Hispanic, American Indians, Pacific Islanders, Asian Americans, and women) are especially encouraged to apply. Interested students should submit a completed application with a career goal statement, personal references, a brief resume, and transcripts. Selection is based on 1) academic qualifications, 2) quality of the career goal statement, and 3) assessment of the applicant's motivation for a career in aerospace. **Deadline for Receipt:** February of each year. **Additional Information:** The member universities are University of Alabama in Huntsville, Alabama A&M University, University of Alabama, University of Alabama at Birmingham, University of South Alabama, Tuskegee University, and Auburn University. Funding for this program is provided by NASA.

3494 ■ ALASKA COMMISSION ON POSTSECONDARY EDUCATION
Attn: AlaskAdvantage Programs
3030 Vintage Boulevard
Juneau, AK 99801-7109
Tel: (907)465-2962
Free: 800-441-2962
Fax: (907)465-5316
E-mail: customer_service@acpe.ak.us
Web Site: http://alaskaadvantage.state.ak.us/page/254
To provide forgivable loans to Alaska high school graduates who wish to prepare for a teaching career in a rural elementary or secondary school in the state.

Title of Award: Alaska Teacher Education Loan Program **Area, Field, or Subject:** Education, Elementary; Education, Secondary **Level of Education for which Award is Granted:** Four Year College **Number Awarded:** Varies each year; recently, 187 of these scholarship/loans were issued. **Funds Available:** This is a scholarship/loan program. Students may borrow up to $7,500 per year for in-state or out-of-state study. Loans may be used for tuition, room and board, books and supplies, and transportation costs (up to 2 round trips between the student's home community and the school of attendance). An origination fee of 3% of the amount loaned is added to the principal balance to be repaid. The interest rate charged is 6%. If the borrower is employed after graduation as a teacher in a rural elementary or secondary school in Alaska, he or she may be eligible for up to 100% forgiveness of the total loan. **Duration:** Loans may be awarded for up to a maximum of 5 years of undergraduate study. Repayment must begin no later than 12 months from the time the borrower terminates full-time student status. The loan must be repaid within 15 years.

Eligibility Requirements: Alaska high school graduates who are enrolled or who intend to enroll in a 4-year bachelor's degree program in elementary or secondary teacher education or a fifth-year teacher certification program may be nominated by a rural school district for receipt of this loan. Nominees must meet all the eligibility criteria of the AlaskAdvantage Education Loan Programs. Currently, only rural school

districts may nominate loan recipients. Rural is defined as communities with a population of 5,500 or less that are not on road or rail to Anchorage or Fairbanks or with a population of 1,500 or less that are on road or rail to Anchorage or Fairbanks. **Deadline for Receipt:** June of each year. **Additional Information:** Students cannot receive an Alaska Teachers Education Loan and an Alaska Supplemental Education Loan simultaneously, although their family members may borrow an Alaska Family Education Loan on their behalf.

3495 ■ ALASKA COMMISSION ON POSTSECONDARY EDUCATION
Attn: AlaskAdvantage Programs
3030 Vintage Boulevard
Juneau, AK 99801-7109
Tel: (907)465-6779; (866)427-5683
Fax: (907)465-5316
E-mail: customer_service@acpe.ak.us
Web Site: http://alaskaadvantage.state.ak.us/page/276
To provide financial assistance to Alaska residents who attend college in the state to prepare for a career in designated fields with a workforce shortage.

Title of Award: AlaskAdvantage Educational Grants **Area, Field, or Subject:** Education; Health care services; Social work **Level of Education for which Award is Granted:** Undergraduate **Number Awarded:** Varies each year; students with the greatest financial need are awarded support until funds are exhausted. **Funds Available:** Grants range from $500 to $2,000 per year, depending on the need of the recipient. **Duration:** 1 year; may be renewed as long as the recipient remains enrolled at least half time, makes satisfactory academic progress, and continues to meet residency and financial need requirements.

Eligibility Requirements: This program is open to residents of Alaska who have been admitted to an undergraduate degree or vocational certificate program at a qualifying institution in the state. Applicants must be planning to work on a degree or certificate in a field that the state has designated as a workforce shortage area; currently, those are allied health sciences, community or social service, and teaching. They must be able to demonstrate financial need and SAT or ACT scores in the top quartile. U.S. citizenship or permanent resident status is required. **Deadline for Receipt:** April of each year.

3496 ■ ALEXANDER CHRISTIAN FOUNDATION OF INDIANA
312 East Main Street, Suite B
P.O. Box 246
Greenfield, IN 46140-0246
Tel: (317)467-1223
Web Site: http://www.acfindiana.org
To provide financial assistance to members of the Christian Church or Church of Christ (Independent) in Indiana who are preparing for a church-related vocation.

Title of Award: Alexander Christian Foundation of Indiana Scholarships **Area, Field, or Subject:** Education, Religious; Music; Religion **Level of Education for which Award is Granted:** Graduate, Undergraduate **Number Awarded:** Varies each year. **Funds Available:** Stipends range from $1,200 to $2,000 per year. **Duration:** 1 year; may be renewed.

Eligibility Requirements: This program is open to members of the Christian Church or Church of Christ (Independent) in Indiana who are candidates for a church-related vocation or currently working full time on an appropriate undergraduate or graduate degree. Applicants must be attending or planning to attend a college or seminary affiliated with the Christian Churches/Churches of Christ. Students at Christian colleges must have a GPA of 3.0 or higher. Along with their application, they must submit an essay of 500 to 1,000 words on "Why I Desire to Serve Christ in a Church-Related Vocation." Selection is based on that essay, evaluations of the applicant's character and motivation by their home church minister and an elder of their church, and transcripts. **Deadline for Receipt:** February of each year. **Additional Information:** This program was established in 1964. Church-related vocations include preaching ministry, youth ministry, missions ministry, music ministry, counseling ministry, and education ministry.

3497 ■ ALPHA DELTA KAPPA
1615 West 92nd Street
Kansas City, MO 64114-3296
Tel: (816)363-5525

Free: 800-247-2311
Fax: (816)363-4010
E-mail: dfrost@www.alphadeltakappa.org
Web Site: http://www.alphadeltakappa.org/public/ite_information.htm
To offer scholarships to foreign women who are interested in learning American educational techniques.
Title of Award: International Teacher Education Scholarship **Area, Field, or Subject:** Education **Level of Education for which Award is Granted:** Master's, Undergraduate **Number Awarded:** Varies each year; recently, 5 of these scholarships were awarded. **Funds Available:** The stipend is $10,000. **Duration:** 1 year.
Eligibility Requirements: This program is open to single women between 20 and 35 years of age from countries other than the United States who are interested in full-time teacher training in the United States. Applicants must have completed at least 1 year of college and rank in the top 25% of their class. Students who have received an undergraduate degree are also eligible, but doctoral study is beyond the scope of this program. Applicants must have well-rounded personalities and should display qualities of leadership. Awards are not granted to members of Alpha Delta Kappa. **Deadline for Receipt:** December of each year. **Additional Information:** The scholarships, first awarded in 1963, are tenable in the United States at any accredited institution of higher learning. The recipient is expected to live in an American college or university dormitory. Should there be no available dormitory space, she is to live in university or college approved housing. After the scholarship year, the recipient is to return to her home country to work for at least 1 year in her major field of study or related field of education. Should further qualification for employment in her field be necessary in the student's homeland, she will be allowed an additional amount of time, not to exceed 3 years, before beginning her year of work.

3498 ■ AMERICAN ASSOCIATION OF PHYSICS TEACHERS

Attn: Scholarship Committee
One Physics Ellipse
College Park, MD 20740
Tel: (301)209-3344
Fax: (301)209-0845
E-mail: aapt-prog@aapt.org
Web Site: http://www.aapt.org/Grants/lotze.cfm
To provide financial assistance to high school seniors or currently-enrolled college students interested in preparing for a career as a high school physics teacher.
Title of Award: Barbara Lotze Scholarship for Future Teachers **Area, Field, or Subject:** Education; Education, Secondary; Physics **Level of Education for which Award is Granted:** Undergraduate **Number Awarded:** Generally, 1 each year. **Funds Available:** The stipend is $2,000 per year. **Duration:** 1 year; may be renewed for up to 3 additional years.
Eligibility Requirements: Eligible to apply are high school seniors, high school graduates, and currently-enrolled undergraduate students in or planning to enter a physics teacher preparation program. All applicants must be U.S. citizens. All other considerations being equal, applicants from Allegheny College are given preference. **Deadline for Receipt:** Applications may be submitted at any time.

3499 ■ AMERICAN COUNCIL OF THE BLIND

Attn: Coordinator, Scholarship Program
1155 15th Street, N.W., Suite 1004
Washington, DC 20005
Tel: (202)467-5081
Free: 800-424-8666
Fax: (202)467-5085
E-mail: info@acb.org
Web Site: http://www.acb.org
To provide financial assistance to undergraduate or graduate students who are blind and are interested in studying in a field of service to persons with disabilities.
Title of Award: Arnold Sadler Memorial Scholarship **Area, Field, or Subject:** Disabilities; Education, Special; Law; Rehabilitation, Physical/Psychological **Level of Education for which Award is Granted:** Graduate, Undergraduate **Number Awarded:** 1 each year. **Funds Available:** The stipend is $2,000. In addition, the winner receives a Kurzweil-1000 Reading System. **Duration:** 1 year.

Eligibility Requirements: This program is open to students in rehabilitation, education, law, or other fields of service to persons with disabilities. Applicants must be legally blind and U.S. citizens. In addition to letters of recommendation and copies of academic transcripts, applications must include an autobiographical sketch. A cumulative GPA of 3.3 or higher is generally required. Selection is based on demonstrated academic record, involvement in extracurricular and civic activities, and academic objectives. The severity of the applicant's visual impairment and his/her study methods are also taken into account. **Deadline for Receipt:** February of each year. **Additional Information:** This scholarship is funded by the Arnold Sadler Memorial Scholarship Fund. Scholarship winners are expected to be present at the council's annual conference; the council will cover all reasonable expenses connected with convention attendance.

3500 ■ AMERICAN FOUNDATION FOR THE BLIND

Attn: Scholarship Committee
11 Penn Plaza, Suite 300
New York, NY 10001
Tel: (212)502-7661
Free: 800-AFB-LINE
Fax: (212)502-7771
E-mail: afbinfo@afb.net
Web Site: http://www.afb.org/scholarships.asp
To provide financial assistance to blind undergraduate and graduate students who wish to study in the field of rehabilitation and/or education of the blind.
Title of Award: Delta Gamma Foundation Florence Margaret Harvey Memorial Scholarship **Area, Field, or Subject:** Education, Special; Rehabilitation, Physical/Psychological; Visual impairment **Level of Education for which Award is Granted:** Four Year College, Graduate **Number Awarded:** 1 each year. **Funds Available:** The stipend is $1,000. **Duration:** 1 year.
Eligibility Requirements: This program is open to legally blind juniors, seniors, or graduate students. U.S. citizenship is required. Applicants must be studying in the field of rehabilitation and/or education of visually impaired and blind persons. Along with their application, they must submit an essay that includes the field of study they are pursuing and why they have chosen it; their educational and personal goals; their work experience; any extracurricular activities with which they have been involved, including those in school, religious organizations, and the community; and how they intend to use scholarship monies that may be awarded. **Deadline for Receipt:** April of each year. **Additional Information:** This scholarship is supported by the Delta Gamma Foundation and administered by the American Foundation for the Blind.

3501 ■ AMERICAN FOUNDATION FOR THE BLIND

Attn: Scholarship Committee
11 Penn Plaza, Suite 300
New York, NY 10001
Tel: (212)502-7661
Free: 800-AFB-LINE
Fax: (212)502-7771
E-mail: afbinfo@afb.net
Web Site: http://www.afb.org/scholarships.asp
To provide financial assistance to legally blind undergraduate or graduate students studying in the field of rehabilitation and/or education of visually impaired and blind persons.
Title of Award: Rudolph Dillman Memorial Scholarship **Area, Field, or Subject:** Education, Special; Rehabilitation, Physical/Psychological; Visual impairment **Level of Education for which Award is Granted:** Graduate, Undergraduate **Number Awarded:** 4 each year: 3 without consideration of financial need and 1 to an applicant who can submit evidence of financial need. **Funds Available:** The stipend is $2,500 per year. **Duration:** 1 academic year; previous recipients may not reapply.
Eligibility Requirements: Applicants must be able to submit evidence of legal blindness, U.S. citizenship, and acceptance in an accredited undergraduate or graduate training program within the broad field of rehabilitation and/or education of blind and visually impaired persons. Along with their application, they must submit an essay that includes the field of study they are pursuing and why they have chosen it; their educational and personal goals; their work experience; any extracurricular activities with which they have been involved, including those in school, religious organizations, and the community; and how they intend to use

scholarship monies that may be awarded. They may also include documentation of financial need. **Deadline for Receipt:** April of each year.

3502 ■ AMERICAN GEOLOGICAL INSTITUTE

Attn: Minority Participation Program
4220 King Street
Alexandria, VA 22302-1502
Tel: (703)379-2480
Fax: (703)379-7563
E-mail: cmm@agiweb.org
Web Site: http://www.agiweb.org/mpp/index.html
To provide financial assistance to underrepresented minority undergraduate and graduate students interested in working on a degree in the geosciences.
Title of Award: Minority Geoscience Student Scholarships **Area, Field, or Subject:** Education; Geology; Hydrology; Meteorology; Oceanography **Level of Education for which Award is Granted:** Graduate, Undergraduate **Number Awarded:** Varies each year; recently, 19 of these scholarships were awarded. **Funds Available:** Stipends range from $500 to $3,000 per year. **Duration:** 1 academic year; renewable if the recipient maintains satisfactory performance.
Eligibility Requirements: This program is open to members of ethnic minority groups underrepresented in the geosciences (Blacks, Hispanics, American Indians, Eskimos, Hawaiians, and Samoans). U.S. citizenship or permanent resident status is required. Applicants must be full-time students enrolled in an accredited institution working on an undergraduate or graduate degree in the geosciences, including geology, geophysics, hydrology, meteorology, physical oceanography, planetary geology, and earth science education; students in other natural sciences, mathematics, or engineering are not eligible. Selection is based on a 250-word essay on career goals and why the applicant has chosen a geoscience as a major, work experience, recommendations, honors and awards, extracurricular activities, and financial need. **Deadline for Receipt:** March of each year.
Additional Information: Funding for this program is provided by ExxonMobil Corporation, ConocoPhillips, ChevronTexaco Corporation, Marathon Corporation, and the Seismological Society of America.

3503 ■ AMERICAN LEGION

Attn: Department of New Hampshire
State House Annex
25 Capitol Street, Room 431
Concord, NH 03301-6312
Tel: (603)271-2211
Fax: (603)271-5352
To provide financial assistance to students in New Hampshire who are interested in becoming a teacher.
Title of Award: Christa McAuliffe Memorial Scholarship **Area, Field, or Subject:** Education **Level of Education for which Award Is Granted:** Undergraduate **Number Awarded:** 1 each year. **Funds Available:** The stipend is $1,000. **Duration:** 1 year.
Eligibility Requirements: Students who are or will be graduates of a New Hampshire high school and have been New Hampshire residents for at least 3 years may apply for this scholarship if they are entering their first year of college to study education. **Deadline for Receipt:** April of each year.

3504 ■ AMERICAN LEGION AUXILIARY

Attn: Department of Maryland
1589 Sulphur Spring Road, Suite 105
Baltimore, MD 21227
Tel: (410)242-9519
Fax: (410)242-9553
E-mail: anna@alamd.org
To provide financial assistance for college to the daughters of veterans who are Maryland residents and wish to study arts, sciences, business, public administration, education, or a medical field.
Title of Award: Maryland Legion Auxiliary Children and Youth Fund Scholarship **Area, Field, or Subject:** Art; Business administration; Education; Medicine; Public administration; Science **Level of Education for which Award is Granted:** Undergraduate **Number Awarded:** 1 each year. **Funds Available:** The stipend is $2,000. **Duration:** 1 year; may be renewed up to 3 additional years.

Eligibility Requirements: Eligible for this scholarship are Maryland senior high girls with veteran parents who wish to study arts, sciences, business, public administration, education, or a medical field other than nursing at a college or university in the state. Preference is given to children of members of the American Legion or American Legion Auxiliary. Selection is based on character (30%), Americanism (20%), leadership (10%), scholarship (20%), and financial need (20%). **Deadline for Receipt:** April of each year.

3505 ■ APPALACHIAN COLLEGE ASSOCIATION

Attn: Director of Programs
210 Center Street
Berea, KY 40403
Tel: (859)986-4584
Fax: (859)986-9549
E-mail: kathrynb@acaweb.org
Web Site: http://www.acaweb.org
To provide financial assistance to upper-division students majoring in biology, chemistry, or mathematics at colleges and universities that are members of the Appalachian College Association (ACA) who plan to become teachers.
Title of Award: Robert Noyce Scholarships **Area, Field, or Subject:** Biological and clinical sciences; Chemistry; Education; Mathematics and mathematical sciences **Level of Education for which Award is Granted:** Four Year College **Number Awarded:** 12 each year. **Funds Available:** The stipend is $7,500 per year. Recipients must be willing to sign a promissory note with a commitment to teach in a high-need middle or high school for 2 years for every year of the scholarship. **Duration:** 1 year; may be renewed 1 additional year.
Eligibility Requirements: This program is open to full-time students entering their junior or senior year at ACA member institutions with a major in biology, chemistry, or mathematics and plans to earn a teaching license. Applicants must have a GPA of 3.0 or higher and be able to document financial need. Along with their application, they must submit a 500-word essay describing their interest in becoming a 6-12 teacher; their commitment to the Appalachian region, including the impact they hope to have as a teacher; and actual and planned progress toward becoming certified. U.S. citizenship is required. Preference is given to graduates of high schools in the Appalachian region and to applicants who express a desire to teach in a high-need middle or high school, especially schools in central Appalachia. **Deadline for Receipt:** March of each year. **Additional Information:** Funding for this program is provided by the National Science Foundation. The ACA includes member institutions in Kentucky (Alice Lloyd College, Berea College, Campbellsville University, University of the Cumberlands, Kentucky Christian University, Lindsey Wilson College, Pikeville College, and Union College), North Carolina (Brevard College, Lees-McRae College, Mars Hill College, Montreat College, and Warren Wilson College), Tennessee (Bryan College, Carson-Newman College, King College, Lee University, Lincoln Memorial University, Maryville College, Milligan College, Tennessee Wesleyan College, Tusculum College, and University of the South), Virginia (Bluefield College, Emery & Henry College, Ferrum College, and Virginia Intermont College), and West Virginia (Alderson-Broaddus College, Bethany College, Davis & Elkins College, Ohio Valley University, University of Charleston, West Virginia Wesleyan College, and Wheeling Jesuit University).

3506 ■ ARKANSAS DEPARTMENT OF HIGHER EDUCATION

Attn: Financial Aid Division
114 East Capitol Avenue
Little Rock, AR 72201-3818
Tel: (501)371-2050
Free: 800-54-STUDY
Fax: (501)371-2001
E-mail: finaid@adhe.arknet.edu
Web Site: http://www.arkansashighered.com/mmasters.html
To provide fellowship/loans to minority graduate students in Arkansas who want to become teachers in selected subject areas.
Title of Award: Arkansas Minority Masters Fellows Program **Area, Field, or Subject:** Education **Level of Education for which Award is Granted:** Four Year College, Master's **Number Awarded:** Varies each year; recently, 25 of these fellowship/loans were approved. **Funds Available:** The stipend is up to $7,500 per year for full-time students (or up to $2,500

per summer for part-time summer students). This is a fellowship/loan program. The loan will be forgiven at the rate of 50% for each year the recipient teaches full time in an Arkansas public school or public institution of higher education. If the recipient does not attend college on a full-time basis, withdraws from an approved teacher education program, or does not fulfill the required teaching obligation, the loan must be repaid in full with interest at a rate up to 5 percentage points above the Federal Reserve discount rate. **Duration:** 1 year; may be renewed if the recipient remains a full-time student with a GPA of 3.0 or higher.

Eligibility Requirements: Applicants must be minority (African American, Hispanic, Native American, or Asian American) residents of Arkansas who are U.S. citizens and enrolled as full-time master's degree students at an Arkansas public or independent institution with a cumulative GPA of 2.75 or higher. Also eligible are minority students in the fifth year of a 5-year teacher certification program. Recipients must be willing to teach in an Arkansas public school or public institution of higher education for at least 2 years after completion of their education. Preference is given to applicants who completed their baccalaureate degrees within the previous 2 years. **Deadline for Receipt:** May of each year.

3507 ■ ARKANSAS DEPARTMENT OF HIGHER EDUCATION
Attn: Financial Aid Division
114 East Capitol Avenue
Little Rock, AR 72201-3818
Tel: (501)371-2050
Free: 800-54-STUDY
Fax: (501)371-2001
E-mail: finaid@adhe.arknet.edu
Web Site: http://www.arkansashighered.com/mteachers.html
To provide scholarship/loans to minority undergraduates in Arkansas who want to become teachers.

Title of Award: Arkansas Minority Teacher Scholars Program **Area, Field, or Subject:** Counseling/Guidance; Education; Education, Elementary; Linguistics; Mathematics and mathematical sciences; Science **Level of Education for which Award is Granted:** Four Year College **Number Awarded:** Varies each year; recently, 97 of these scholarship/loans were approved. **Funds Available:** Awards up to $5,000 per year are available. This is a scholarship/loan program. The loan will be forgiven at the rate of 20% for each year the recipient teaches full time in an Arkansas public school (or 33% per year if the obligation is fulfilled in 3 years as described above). If the loan is not forgiven by service, it must be repaid with interest at a rate up to 5% points above the Federal Reserve discount rate. **Duration:** 1 year; may be renewed for 1 additional year if the recipient remains a full-time student with a GPA of 2.5 or higher.

Eligibility Requirements: Applicants must be minority (African American, Native American, Hispanic, or Asian American) residents of Arkansas who are U.S. citizens and enrolled as full-time juniors or seniors in an approved teacher certification program at an Arkansas public or independent 4-year institution. They must have a cumulative GPA of 2.5 or higher and be willing to teach in an Arkansas public school for at least 5 years after completion of their teaching certificate (3 years if the teaching is in 1 of the 42 counties of Arkansas designated as the Delta Region; or if the teaching is in mathematics, science, or foreign language; or if the recipient is an African American male and teaches at the elementary level; or if the service is as a guidance counselor). **Deadline for Receipt:** May of each year.

3508 ■ ARKANSAS DEPARTMENT OF HIGHER EDUCATION
Attn: Financial Aid Division
114 East Capitol Avenue
Little Rock, AR 72201-3818
Tel: (501)371-2050
Free: 800-54-STUDY
Fax: (501)371-2001
E-mail: finaid@adhe.arknet.edu
Web Site: http://www.starark.com
To provide scholarship/loans to college students in Arkansas who are interested in preparing for a teaching career in an approved subject or geographic shortage area.

Title of Award: Arkansas State Teacher Assistance Resource (STAR) Program **Area, Field, or Subject:** Biological and clinical sciences; Chemistry; Earth sciences; Education; Education, Secondary; Education, Special; Geosciences; Linguistics; Mathematics and mathematical sci-

ences; Physical sciences; Physics **Level of Education for which Award is Granted:** Master's, Undergraduate **Number Awarded:** Varies each year; recently, 42 of these scholarship/loans were approved. **Funds Available:** The award is $3,000 per year for students who agree to teach in either a geographic teacher shortage area or a subject teacher shortage area. For students who agree to teach in both a geographic shortage area and a subject shortage area, the award is $6,000 per year. This is a scholarship/loan program. Recipients must teach in an Arkansas geographic or subject shortage area for 1 year for each year of support they receive. If they fail to complete that teaching obligation, they must repay all funds received. **Duration:** 1 year; may be renewed for 1 additional year if the recipient is enrolled in a 4-year teacher education program or 2 additional years if enrolled in a 5-year teacher education program. Renewal requires that the recipient maintain a GPA of 2.75 or higher and complete 24 semester hours as an undergraduate or 18 semester hours as a graduate student.

Eligibility Requirements: This program is open to Arkansas residents who are full-time students enrolled 1) at a 4-year public or private college or university in the state with an approved teacher education program; 2) in an associate of arts in teaching program; or 3) in an master of arts in teaching program. Applicants must have a GPA of 2.75 or higher and be entering their sophomore, junior, or senior year (or be in a master's degree program). They must be willing to teach in a public school located in a geographic area of Arkansas designated as having a critical shortage of teachers or in a subject matter area designated as having a critical shortage of teachers. Applicants must have completed their freshman year at an accredited Arkansas public or private college or university in a major field of study leading to secondary teacher certification in 1 of the shortage areas. U.S. citizenship is required. **Deadline for Receipt:** May of each year. **Additional Information:** This program was established in 2004 as a replacement for the former Arkansas Emergency Secondary Education Loan Program. Recently, the subject areas designated as having a critical shortage of teachers were foreign language, mathematics, chemistry, physics, biology, physical science, earth science, and special education. For a list of geographic areas of Arkansas that are designated as having a critical shortage of teachers, contact the Department of Higher Education. The State Teacher Assistance Resource (STAR) program also provides that teachers who received federal student loans may have those loans repaid 1) at the rate of $3,000 per year if they teach a subject area in Arkansas that is designated as a shortage area or if they teach in a geographic area of the state with a shortage of teachers, or 2) at the rate of $6,000 per year if they teach a shortage subject area in a shortage geographic area. Students may not, however, participate in both the scholarship/loan program and the federal loan repayment program.

3509 ■ ASSOCIATION FOR EDUCATION AND REHABILITATION OF THE BLIND AND VISUALLY IMPAIRED OF OHIO
c/o Marjorie E. Ward
1568 Lafayette Drive
Columbus, OH 43220
E-mail: ward5@osu.edu
Web Site: http://www.aerohio.org/schgrts/schol-grant.htm
To provide financial assistance to Ohio residents who are working on an undergraduate or graduate degree in a field related to rehabilitation of the blind.

Title of Award: AERO Personnel Preparation Scholarships **Area, Field, or Subject:** Counseling/Guidance; Education, Special; Rehabilitation, Physical/Psychological; Visual impairment **Level of Education for which Award is Granted:** Four Year College, Graduate **Number Awarded:** 1 each year. **Funds Available:** The stipend is $1,000. **Duration:** 1 year; nonrenewable.

Eligibility Requirements: This program is open to undergraduate and graduate students in rehabilitation counseling, rehabilitation teaching, orientation and mobility, or education of students with visual disabilities. Applicants must be residents of Ohio, although they may be studying in any state. Undergraduates must have at least junior standing. All applicants must have a GPA of 3.0 or higher. Along with their application, they must submit 1) a short essay explaining why they have chosen their specific field as their profession and what they would like to contribute to the field; 2) a short description of volunteer or paid involvement with individuals with visual disabilities or any other disability; 3) transcripts; and 4) 3 letters of recommendation. **Deadline for Receipt:** April of each year.

3510 ■ ASSOCIATION OF RETIRED TEACHERS OF CONNECTICUT
240 Pomeroy Avenue, Suite 201
Meriden, CT 06450-7170
Tel: (203)639-9628; (866)343-ARTC
E-mail: artc@artcinc.org
Web Site: http://www.artcinc.org/Appl.htm
To provide financial assistance to high school seniors in Connecticut who are interested in majoring in education in college.
Title of Award: Glenn Moon Scholarships **Area, Field, or Subject:** Education **Level of Education for which Award is Granted:** Undergraduate **Number Awarded:** 4 each year: 1 at $1,500 and 3 at $1,000. **Funds Available:** Stipends are $1,500 or $1,000. **Duration:** 1 year; the $1,500 award may be renewed up to 3 additional years; the $1,000 awards are nonrenewable.
Eligibility Requirements: Connecticut high school seniors who intend to become teachers are eligible to apply. Applicants must submit an autobiographical essay that includes their reasons for wishing to teach, history of teaching and/or tutoring experience, desired teaching level and/or subject area, and experiences that influenced their selection of teaching as a career. Selection is based on the essay, academic record, financial need, character and personality, interests, and educational activities. **Deadline for Receipt:** March of each year. **Additional Information:** This program was established in 1979. Information is also available from T.M. Barton, 361 Woodland Street, Bristol, CT 06010.

3511 ■ ASSOCIATION OF TEXAS PROFESSIONAL EDUCATORS
Attn: Scholarships
305 East Huntland Drive, Suite 300
Austin, TX 78752-3792
Tel: (512)467-0071
Free: 800-777-ATPE
Fax: (512)467-2203
E-mail: atpe@atpe.org
Web Site: http://www.atpe.org/Awards/bjordaninfo.htm
To provide financial assistance to undergraduate and graduate students enrolled in educator preparation programs at predominantly ethnic minority institutions in Texas.
Title of Award: Barbara Jordan Memorial Scholarship **Area, Field, or Subject:** Education **Level of Education for which Award is Granted:** Four Year College, Graduate **Number Awarded:** Up to 6 each year. **Funds Available:** The stipend is $1,500 per year. **Duration:** 1 year.
Eligibility Requirements: This program is open to juniors, seniors, and graduate students enrolled in educator preparation programs at predominantly ethnic minority institutions in Texas. Applicants must submit a 2-page essay on their personal philosophy toward education, why they want to become an educator, who influenced them the most in making their career decision, and why they are applying for the scholarship. Financial need is not considered in the selection process. **Deadline for Receipt:** May of each year. **Additional Information:** The qualifying institutions are Huston-Tillotson College, Jarvis Christian College, Our Lady of the Lake University, Paul Quinn College, Prairie View A&M University, St. Mary's University of San Antonio, Our Ross State University, Sul Ross State University Rio Grande College, Texas A&M International University, Texas A&M University at Kingsville, Texas Southern University, University of Houston, University of Houston-Downtown, University of Texas at Brownsville and Texas Southmost College, University of Texas at El Paso, University of Texas at San Antonio, University of Texas-Pan American, University of the Incarnate Word, and Wiley College.

3512 ■ ASSOCIATION OF TEXAS PROFESSIONAL EDUCATORS
Attn: Scholarships
305 East Huntland Drive, Suite 300
Austin, TX 78752-3792
Tel: (512)467-0071
Free: 800-777-ATPE
Fax: (512)467-2203
E-mail: atpe@atpe.org
Web Site: http://www.atpe.org/Awards/fwiesnerinfo.htm
To provide financial assistance to undergraduate and graduate students enrolled in educator preparation programs at institutions in Texas.

Title of Award: Fred Wiesner Educational Excellence Scholarship **Area, Field, or Subject:** Education **Level of Education for which Award is Granted:** Four Year College, Graduate **Number Awarded:** 4 each year: 3 to undergraduates and 1 to a graduate student. **Funds Available:** The stipend is $1,500 per year. **Duration:** 1 year.
Eligibility Requirements: This program is open to juniors, seniors, and graduate students enrolled in educator preparation programs at colleges and universities in Texas. Applicants must submit a 2-page essay on their personal philosophy toward education, why they want to become an educator, who influenced them the most in making their career decision, and why they are applying for the scholarship. Financial need is not considered in the selection process. **Deadline for Receipt:** May of each year.

3513 ■ ASSOCIATION FOR WOMEN GEOSCIENTISTS
Attn: AWG Foundation
P.O. Box 30645
Lincoln, NE 68503-0645
E-mail: awgscholarship@yahoo.com
Web Site: http://www.awg.org/eas/minority.html
To provide financial assistance to minority women who are interested in working on an undergraduate degree in the geosciences.
Title of Award: Association for Women Geoscientists Minority Scholarship **Area, Field, or Subject:** Chemistry; Earth sciences; Education; Geology; Geosciences; Hydrology; Meteorology; Oceanography **Level of Education for which Award is Granted:** Undergraduate **Number Awarded:** 1 or more each year. **Funds Available:** A total of $5,000 is available for this program each year. **Duration:** 1 year; may be renewed.
Eligibility Requirements: This program is open to women who are African American, Hispanic, or Native American (including Eskimo, Hawaiian, Samoan, or American Indian). Applicants must be full-time students working on, or planning to work on, an undergraduate degree in the geosciences (including geology, geophysics, geochemistry, hydrology, meteorology, physical oceanography, planetary geology, or earth science education). They must submit a 500-word essay on why they have chosen to major in the geosciences and their career goals, 2 letters of recommendation, high school and/or college transcripts, and SAT or ACT scores. Financial need is not considered in the selection process. **Deadline for Receipt:** May of each year. **Additional Information:** This program, first offered in 2004, is supported by ExxonMobil Foundation.

3514 ■ CALIFORNIA ADOLESCENT NUTRITION, PHYSICAL EDUCATION, AND CULINARY ARTS SCHOLARSHIPS
2140 Shattuck Avenue, Suite 610
Berkeley, CA 94704
Tel: (510)644-1533
Free: 800-200-3131
Fax: (510)644-1535
E-mail: info@canfit.org
Web Site: http://www.canfit.org/scholarships.html
To provide financial assistance to minority undergraduate and graduate students who are studying nutrition, physical education or culinary arts in California.
Title of Award: CANFit Program Scholarships **Area, Field, or Subject:** Culinary arts; Education; Physical; Nutrition; Public health; Youth **Level of Education for which Award is Granted:** Graduate, Undergraduate **Number Awarded:** 5 graduate scholarships and 10 undergraduate scholarships are available each year. **Funds Available:** Graduate stipends are $1,000 each and undergraduate stipends are $500 per year.
Eligibility Requirements: Eligible to apply are American Indians/Alaska Natives, African Americans, Asians/Pacific Islanders, and Latinos/Hispanics who are enrolled in either: 1) an approved master's or doctoral graduate program in nutrition, public health nutrition, or physical education or in a preprofessional practice program approved by the American Dietetic Association at an accredited university in California; or, 2) an approved bachelor's or professional certificate program in culinary arts, nutrition, or physical education at an accredited university or college in California. Graduate student applicants must have completed at least 12 units of graduate course work and have a cumulative GPA of 3.0 or higher; undergraduate applicants must have completed 50 semester units or the equivalent of college credits and have a cumulative GPA of 2.5 or higher. Selection is based on financial need, academic goals, and community nutrition or physical education activities. **Deadline for Receipt:**

March of each year. **Additional Information:** A goal of the California Adolescent Nutrition and Fitness (CANFit) program is to improve the nutritional status and physical fitness of California's low-income multi-ethnic youth aged 10 to 14. By offering these scholarships, the program hopes to encourage more students to consider careers in adolescent nutrition and fitness.

3515 ■ CALIFORNIA STATE FAIR

Attn: Friends of the Fair Scholarship Program
1600 Exposition Boulevard
P.O. Box 15649
Sacramento, CA 95852
Tel: (916)274-5969
E-mail: wross@calexpo.com
Web Site: http://www.bigfun.org
To provide financial assistance to residents of California who are working on a teacher credential.
Title of Award: California State Fair Teacher Credential Scholarships **Area, Field, or Subject:** Education **Level of Education for which Award is Granted:** Professional, Undergraduate **Number Awarded:** 2 each year: 1 at $1,500 and 1 at $500. **Funds Available:** Stipends are $1,500 or $500. **Duration:** 1 year.
Eligibility Requirements: This program is open to residents of California currently working on a teacher credential at a college or university in the state. Reentry professionals are also eligible. Applicants must have a GPA of 3.0 or higher. Along with their application, they must submit a 2-page essay on why they are pursuing their desired career and life goals. Selection is based on personal commitment, goals established for their chosen field, leadership potential, and civic accomplishments. **Deadline for Receipt:** March of each year. **Additional Information:** The Friends of the Fair Scholarship Program was established in 1993.

3516 ■ CALIFORNIA STATE FAIR

Attn: Friends of the Fair Scholarship Program
1600 Exposition Boulevard
P.O. Box 15649
Sacramento, CA 95852
Tel: (916)274-5969
E-mail: wross@calexpo.com
Web Site: http://www.bigfun.org
To provide financial assistance for college to residents of California who are interested in majoring in designated fields or preparing for a career in the Fair industry.
Title of Award: Eddie G. Cole Memorial Scholarships **Area, Field, or Subject:** Agricultural sciences; Education, Physical; Equine studies **Level of Education for which Award is Granted:** Undergraduate **Number Awarded:** 2 each year: 1 at $1,000 and 1 at $500. **Funds Available:** Stipends are $1,000 or $500. **Duration:** 1 year.
Eligibility Requirements: This program is open to residents of California currently working on an undergraduate degree at a college or university in the state. Applicants be 1) majoring in physical education, agriculture, or equine studies; or 2) preparing for a career in the Fair industry. They must have a GPA of 3.0 or higher. Along with their application, they must submit a 2-page essay on why they are pursuing their desired career and life goals. Selection is based on personal commitment, goals established for their chosen field, leadership potential, and civic accomplishments. **Deadline for Receipt:** March of each year. **Additional Information:** The Friends of the Fair Scholarship Program was established in 1993.

3517 ■ CANADIAN INSTITUTE OF UKRAINIAN STUDIES

c/o University of Alberta
450 Athabasca Hall
Edmonton, AB, Canada T6G 2E8
E-mail: cius@ualberta.ca
Web Site: http://www.ualberta.ca/CIUS/cius-grants.htm
To provide financial assistance to Canadian undergraduate students majoring in a field related to Ukrainian or Ukrainian Canadian studies.
Title of Award: Leo J. Krysa Family Undergraduate Scholarship **Area, Field, or Subject:** Canadian studies; Education; European studies; Humanities; Social sciences; Ukrainian studies **Level of Education for which Award is Granted:** Four Year College **Number Awarded:** 1 each year. **Funds Available:** The maximum stipend is $C3,500. **Duration:** 8 months; nonrenewable.

Eligibility Requirements: This program is open to Canadian citizens and permanent residents who are entering the final year of study for an undergraduate degree at a college or university in Canada. Applicants' programs must emphasize Ukrainian and/or Ukrainian Canadian studies, through a combination of Ukrainian and east European or Canadian courses in education, history, humanities, or the social sciences. Selection is based on overall academic record, performance in Ukrainian-content courses, a working sample, and community involvement. **Deadline for Receipt:** February of each year. **Additional Information:** Recipients may attend any Canadian university.

3518 ■ CATCHING THE DREAM

8200 Mountain Road, N.E., Suite 203
Albuquerque, NM 87110-7835
Tel: (505)262-2351
Fax: (505)262-0534
E-mail: NScholarsh@aol.com
Web Site: http://www.catchingthedream.org
To provide financial assistance to American Indian students who are interested in working on an undergraduate or graduate degree in selected fields.
Title of Award: MESBEC Program **Area, Field, or Subject:** Business administration; Computer and information sciences; Education; Engineering; Mathematics and mathematical sciences; Science **Level of Education for which Award is Granted:** Four Year College, Graduate **Number Awarded:** Varies; generally, 30 to 35 each year. **Funds Available:** Stipends range from $500 to $5,000. **Duration:** 1 year; may be renewed.
Eligibility Requirements: This program is open to American Indians who can provide proof that they are at least one-quarter Indian blood and a member of a U.S. tribe that is federally-recognized, state-recognized, or terminated. Applicants must be enrolled or planning to enroll full time and major in the 1 of the following fields: mathematics, engineering, science, business administration, education, or computer science. They may be entering freshmen, undergraduate students, graduate students, or Ph.D. candidates. Along with their application, they must submit documentation of financial need, 3 letters of recommendation, copies of applications and responses for at least 15 other sources of funding, official transcripts, standardized test scores (ACT, SAT, GRE, MCAT, LSAT, etc.), and an essay explaining their goals in life, college plans, and career plans (especially how those plans include working with and benefiting Indians). Selection is based on merit and potential for improving the lives of Indian people. **Deadline for Receipt:** April of each year for fall term; September of each year for spring and winter terms; March of each year for summer school. **Additional Information:** MESBEC is an acronym that stands for the priority areas of this program: mathematics, engineering, science, business, education, and computers. The sponsor was formerly known as the Native American Scholarship Fund.

3519 ■ CATCHING THE DREAM

8200 Mountain Road, N.E., Suite 203
Albuquerque, NM 87110-7835
Tel: (505)262-2351
Fax: (505)262-0534
E-mail: NScholarsh@aol.com
Web Site: http://www.catchingthedream.org
To provide financial assistance to American Indian paraprofessionals in the education field who wish to return to college or graduate school.
Title of Award: Native American Leadership in Education (NALE) Program **Area, Field, or Subject:** Counseling/Guidance; Education; Educational administration **Level of Education for which Award is Granted:** Graduate, Professional, Undergraduate **Number Awarded:** Varies; generally, 15 or more each year. **Funds Available:** Stipends range from $500 to $5,000. **Duration:** 1 year; may be renewed.
Eligibility Requirements: This program is open to paraprofessionals who are working in Indian schools and who plan to return to school to complete their degree in education, counseling, or school administration. Applicants must be able to provide proof that they are at least one-quarter Indian blood and a member of a U.S. tribe that is federally-recognized, state-recognized, or terminated. Along with their application, they must submit documentation of financial need, 3 letters of recommendation, copies of applications and responses for at least 15 other sources of funding, official transcripts, standardized test scores (ACT, SAT, GRE, MCAT, LSAT, etc.), and an essay explaining their goals in life, college plans, and career plans

(especially how those plans include working with and benefiting Indians). Selection is based on merit and potential for improving the lives of Indian people. **Deadline for Receipt:** April of each year for fall term; September of each year for spring and winter terms; March of each year for summer school. **Additional Information:** The sponsor was formerly known as the Native American Scholarship Fund.

3520 ■ CHICKASAW FOUNDATION

P.O. Box 1726
Ada, OK 74821-1726
Tel: (580)421-9030
Fax: (580)421-9031
Web Site: http://www.cflink.org
To provide financial assistance to members of the Chickasaw Nation who are majoring or minoring in American history.
Title of Award: Colbert "Bud" Baker Scholarship **Area, Field, or Subject:** Education; History, American; Law; Native American studies **Level of Education for which Award is Granted:** Four Year College **Number Awarded:** 1 each year. **Funds Available:** The stipend is $1,000 per year. **Duration:** 1 year.
Eligibility Requirements: This program is open to Chickasaw students who are currently enrolled full time at an accredited institution of higher education. Applicants must be classified as juniors or seniors at a 4-year college. They must be majoring in history or majoring in education or pre-law with a minor in history. The history emphasis must be on Chickasaw tribal history or Native American studies. Along with their application, they must submit high school or college transcripts, 2 letters of recommendation, a copy of their Certificate of Degree of Indian Blood, a copy of their Chickasaw Nation citizenship card, and a 1-page essay on their long-term goals and plans for achieving them. Financial need is not considered in the selection process. **Deadline for Receipt:** May of each year.

3521 ■ CHICKASAW FOUNDATION

P.O. Box 1726
Ada, OK 74821-1726
Tel: (580)421-9030
Fax: (580)421-9031
Web Site: http://www.cflink.org
To provide financial assistance to members of the Chickasaw Nation interested in studying education in college.
Title of Award: Mary K. Moreland and Daniel T. Jenks Scholarship **Area, Field, or Subject:** Education **Level of Education for which Award is Granted:** Undergraduate **Number Awarded:** 1 each year. **Funds Available:** The stipend is $1,500. **Duration:** 1 year.
Eligibility Requirements: This program is open to Chickasaw students who are currently enrolled full time as an undergraduate at an accredited 4-year college. Applicants must be majoring in education and have a GPA of 3.0 or higher. Along with their application, they must submit high school or college transcripts, 2 letters of recommendation, a copy of their Certificate of Degree of Indian Blood, a copy of their Chickasaw Nation citizenship card, and a 1-page essay on their long-term goals and plans for achieving them. Financial need is not considered in the selection process. **Deadline for Receipt:** May of each year.

3522 ■ CHRISTIAN LIFE RESOURCES

Attn: WELS Lutherans for Life
Scholarship Review Committee
2949 North Mayfair Road, Suite 309
Milwaukee, WI 53222-4304
Tel: (414)774-1331
Fax: (414)774-1360
Web Site: http://www.christianliferesources.com
To provide financial assistance to Lutheran high school seniors in Wisconsin who are interested in studying life-related issues in college.
Title of Award: WELS Lutherans for Life Scholarship Program **Area, Field, or Subject:** Biological and clinical sciences; Education, Special; Engineering, Biomedical; Journalism; Law; Medicine; Physical therapy; Political science; Psychology; Social work **Level of Education for which Award is Granted:** Four Year College **Number Awarded:** Varies each year; recently, 9 of these scholarships were awarded. **Funds Available:** Stipends up to $1,000 are available. **Duration:** 1 year.

Eligibility Requirements: This program is open to high school seniors who are active members of the Wisconsin Evangelical Lutheran Synod (WELS) or an affiliated church. Applicants must be planning to go to a 4-year school to prepare for a secular career in which pro-life values will be demonstrated. Acceptable fields include medicine, biotechnology/biological engineering, medical research/genetics, law/politics, journalism/media, psychology, physical therapy, social services, or special education. They must have a GPA of 3.25 or higher. Along with their application, they must submit essays on 1) the field of study they plan to enter and how it relates to pro-life issues; 2) why the scholarship should be awarded to them, including their future goals; and 3) how they have demonstrated a Christian, pro-life attitude in their life. **Deadline for Receipt:** February of each year. **Additional Information:** WELS Lutherans for Life was formerly a ministry of the Wisconsin Evangelical Lutheran Synod.

3523 ■ CLASSICAL ASSOCIATION OF NEW ENGLAND

c/o Allen M. Ware
University of Connecticut
Department of History
Box U-103
Storrs, CT 06269-2103
Tel: (860)486-3722
Fax: (860)486-0641
E-mail: ward@uconnvm.uconn.edu
Web Site: http://www.caneweb.org
To provide financial assistance to upper-division and graduate students in New England who are working on certification as a teacher of Latin or Greek.
Title of Award: CANE Certification Scholarship **Area, Field, or Subject:** Classical studies; Education, Secondary; Foreign languages **Level of Education for which Award is Granted:** Four Year College, Master's **Number Awarded:** 1 each year. **Funds Available:** The stipend is $1,500. Funds are intended to cover tuition and fees. **Duration:** 1 year or summer session.
Eligibility Requirements: This program is open to junior and senior undergraduates at colleges and universities in New England and to holders of a master's degree. Applicants must be preparing for secondary school certification as a teacher of Latin or Greek or both in a New England state. Full-time, part-time, and summer programs qualify. Along with their application, they must submit 2 letters of recommendation from college classicists, a letter attesting to their ability to communicate and work with young people and inspire them to high levels of achievement, a 1,000-word personal statement explaining why they are preparing for a career as a secondary school classicist, high school and college transcripts, and a description of their program and the expenses involved. **Deadline for Receipt:** February of each year.

3524 ■ COLORADO COMMISSION ON HIGHER EDUCATION

1380 Lawrence Street, Suite 1200
Denver, CO 80204
Tel: (303)866-2723
Fax: (303)866-4266
E-mail: cche@state.co.us
Web Site: http://www.state.co.us/cche/finaid/students/stateaid/types.html
To provide funding to Colorado undergraduate education students who need assistance in paying for their education while they are working as student teachers.
Title of Award: Colorado Supplemental Leveraging Educational Assistance Partnership (SLEAP) **Area, Field, or Subject:** Education **Level of Education for which Award is Granted:** Undergraduate **Number Awarded:** Varies each year. **Funds Available:** The amount of assistance varies, to a maximum of $5,000 per year. **Duration:** 1 year.
Eligibility Requirements: This program is open to residents of Colorado who are enrolled in an undergraduate or postbaccalaureate teacher education program in the states. Applicants must be engaged full time in a student teaching assignment as preparation for teacher education licensure. They must be able to demonstrate financial need. U.S. citizenship or permanent resident status is required. **Deadline for Receipt:** Each participating institution sets its own deadlines. **Additional Informa-**

tion: Applications are available either from the Colorado Commission on Higher Education or from the financial aid office of eligible Colorado institutions.

3525 ■ COMMUNITY FOUNDATION OF GREATER NEW BRITAIN

Attn: Scholarship Manager
74A Vine Street
New Britain, CT 06052-1431
Tel: (860)229-6018
Fax: (860)225-2666
E-mail: cfarmer@cfgnb.org
Web Site: http://www.cfgnb.org
To provide financial assistance to minority college students in Connecticut who are interested in preparing for a teaching career.
Title of Award: Alma Exley Scholarship **Area, Field, or Subject:** Education **Level of Education for which Award is Granted:** Four Year College **Number Awarded:** 2 each year: 1 to a 4-year student and 1 to an ARC student. **Funds Available:** The stipend is $1,500 per year for students at a 4-year college or university or $500 for a student in the ARC program. **Duration:** 2 years for students at 4-year colleges or universities; 1 year for students in the ARC program.
Eligibility Requirements: This program is open to students of color (African Americans, Asian Americans, Hispanic Americans, and Native Americans) enrolled in a teacher preparation program in Connecticut. Applicant must 1) have been admitted to a traditional teacher preparation program at an accredited 4-year college or university in the state, or 2) be participating in the Alternate Route to Certification (ARC) program sponsored by the Connecticut Department of Higher Education. **Deadline for Receipt:** October of each year.

3526 ■ CONGRESSIONAL BLACK CAUCUS FOUNDATION, INC.

Attn: Director, Educational Programs
1720 Massachusetts Avenue, N.W.
Washington, DC 20036
Tel: (202)263-2836
Free: 800-784-2577
Fax: (202)775-0773
E-mail: spouses@cbcfinc.org
Web Site: http://www.cbcfinc.org
To provide financial assistance to minority and other undergraduate and graduate students who reside in a Congressional district represented by an African American and are interested in preparing for a health-related career.
Title of Award: Cheerios Brand Health Initiative Scholarship **Area, Field, or Subject:** Biological and clinical sciences; Chemistry; Education, Physical; Engineering; Food service careers; Health care services; Medicine; Nursing **Level of Education for which Award is Granted:** Graduate, Undergraduate **Number Awarded:** Varies each year. **Funds Available:** A stipend is awarded (amount not specified). **Duration:** 1 year.
Eligibility Requirements: This program is open to 1) minority and other graduating high school seniors planning to attend an accredited institution of higher education and 2) currently-enrolled full-time undergraduate, graduate, and doctoral students in good academic standing with a GPA of 2.5 or higher. Applicants must reside or attend school in a Congressional district represented by a member of the Congressional Black Caucus. They must be interested in preparing for a career in a medical, food services, or other health-related field, including pre-medicine, nursing, chemistry, biology, physical education, and engineering. Along with their application, they must submit a 500-word personal statement on 1) the field of study they intend to pursue and why they have chosen that field; 2) their interests, involvement in school activities, community and public service, hobbies, special talents, sports, and other highlight areas; and 3) any other experiences, skills, or qualifications they feel should be considered. They must also be able to document financial need. **Deadline for Receipt:** April of each year. **Additional Information:** The program was established in 1998 with support from General Mills, Inc.

3527 ■ CONNECTICUT DEPARTMENT OF HIGHER EDUCATION

Attn: Office of Student Financial Aid
61 Woodland Street
Hartford, CT 06105-2326
Tel: (860)947-1855
Fax: (860)947-1838

E-mail: mtip@ctdhe.org
Web Site: http://www.ctdhe.org/SFA/sfa.htm
To provide financial assistance and loan repayment to minority upper-division college students in Connecticut who are interested in teaching at public schools in the state.
Title of Award: Connecticut Minority Teacher Incentive Program **Area, Field, or Subject:** Education **Level of Education for which Award is Granted:** Four Year College **Number Awarded:** Varies each year. **Funds Available:** The maximum stipend is $5,000 per year. In addition, if recipients complete a credential and teach at a public school in Connecticut, they may receive up to $2,500 per year, for up to 4 years, to help pay off college loans. **Duration:** Up to 2 years.
Eligibility Requirements: This program is open to minority juniors and seniors enrolled full time in Connecticut college and university teacher preparation programs. Students must be nominated by the education dean at their institution. **Deadline for Receipt:** September of each year.

3528 ■ CONNECTICUT DEPARTMENT OF HIGHER EDUCATION

Attn: Education and Employment Information Center
61 Woodland Street
Hartford, CT 06105-2326
Tel: (860)947-1846
Free: 800-842-0229
Fax: (860)947-1311
E-mail: setig@ctdhe.org
Web Site: http://www.ctdhe.org/SFA/sfa.htm
To provide financial assistance to undergraduate and graduate students in Connecticut who are preparing for a career as a special education teacher.
Title of Award: Connecticut Special Education Teacher Incentive Grant **Area, Field, or Subject:** Education, Special; Hearing and deafness; Visual impairment **Level of Education for which Award is Granted:** Four Year College, Graduate **Number Awarded:** Varies each year. **Funds Available:** The stipend is $5,000 per year for full-time study or $2,000 per year for part-time graduate study. **Duration:** 1 year.
Eligibility Requirements: This program is open to full-time juniors and seniors and full- or part-time graduate students who are residents of Connecticut. Applicants must be enrolled in 1) special education teacher preparation programs at selected universities in Connecticut; or 2) out-of-state teacher preparation programs seeking cross-endorsement for teaching "low-incidence student" areas. They must be nominated by the dean of education at their school and have a stated intent to teach in a Connecticut public school, an approved private special education facility, or a Regional Educational Service Center. Priority is given to minority (African American, Hispanic/Latino, Asian American, and Native American) and bilingual students and to Connecticut residents enrolled in an approved out-of-state program. **Deadline for Receipt:** August of each year. **Additional Information:** The approved in-state programs are at Central Connecticut State University, Fairfield University, Saint Joseph College, Southern Connecticut State University, University of Connecticut, and University of Hartford. The programs for students seeking cross-endorsement certification for teaching students who are blind and partially-sighted or visually impaired are at Hunter College of CUNY (New York, New York), Dominican College (Orangeburg, New York), Teachers College of Columbia University (New York, New York), and University of Northern Colorado (Greeley, Colorado). The programs for students seeking cross-endorsement certification for teaching students who are deaf or hearing-impaired are at Hunter College, Teachers College, Clarke School for the Deaf at Smith College (Northampton, Massachusetts), and Boston University (Boston, Massachusetts).

3529 ■ CONTINENTAL SOCIETY, DAUGHTERS OF INDIAN WARS

c/o Mrs. Donald C. Trolinger, Scholarship Chair
61300 East 110 Road
Miami, OK 74354-4726
E-mail: ottawahillpt@neok.com
To provide financial assistance to Native American college students who are interested in preparing for a career in education.
Title of Award: Continental Society, Daughters of Indian Wars Scholarship **Area, Field, or Subject:** Education; Social work **Level of Education for which Award is Granted:** Four Year College **Number Awarded:** 1 each year. **Funds Available:** The stipend is $1,000. **Duration:** 1 year; may be renewed.

Eligibility Requirements: Applicants must be certified tribal members of a federally-recognized tribe, plan to prepare for a career in education or social service, plan to work on a reservation, be a junior at an accredited college, have earned at least a 3.0 GPA, and carry at least 10 quarter hours or 8 semester hours. Selection is based primarily on academic achievement and commitment to the field of study; financial need is not necessary but is considered. **Deadline for Receipt:** June of each year.

3530 ■ COOK INLET REGION, INC.
Attn: CIRI Foundation
2600 Cordova Street, Suite 206
Anchorage, AK 99503
Tel: (907)263-5582
Free: 800-764-3382
Fax: (907)263-5588
E-mail: tcf@ciri.com
Web Site: http://www.thecirifoundation.org/scholarship.html
To provide financial assistance for undergraduate or graduate studies in selected fields to Alaska Natives who are original enrollees to Cook Inlet Region, Inc. (CIRI) and their lineal descendants.
Title of Award: CIRI Foundation Special Excellence Scholarships **Area, Field, or Subject:** Business administration; Education; Engineering; General studies/Field of study not specified; Health care services; Mathematics and mathematical sciences; Science **Level of Education for which Award is Granted:** Four Year College, Graduate **Number Awarded:** 1 or more each year. **Funds Available:** The stipend is $18,000 per year. **Duration:** 1 year; may be renewed.
Eligibility Requirements: This program is open to Alaska Native enrollees to CIRI under the Alaska Native Claims Settlement Act (ANCSA) of 1971 and their lineal descendants. There are no Alaska residency requirements or age limitations. Applicants must be accepted or enrolled full time in a 4-year undergraduate or a graduate degree program. They must have a GPA of 3.7 or higher. Preference is given to students working on a degree in business, education, mathematics, sciences, health services, or engineering. Selection is based on academic achievement, rigor of course work or degree program, quality of a statement of purpose, student financial contribution, financial need, grade level, previous work performance, education and community activities, letters of recommendation, seriousness of purpose, and practicality of educational and professional goals. **Deadline for Receipt:** May of each year. **Additional Information:** This program was established in 1997. Recipients must enroll in school on a full-time basis.

3531 ■ COOK INLET REGION, INC.
Attn: CIRI Foundation
2600 Cordova Street, Suite 206
Anchorage, AK 99503
Tel: (907)263-5582
Free: 800-764-3382
Fax: (907)263-5588
E-mail: tcf@ciri.com
Web Site: http://www.thecirifoundation.org/scholarship.html
To provide financial assistance for undergraduate or graduate studies in selected liberal arts to Alaska Natives who are original enrollees to Cook Inlet Region, Inc. (CIRI) and their lineal descendants.
Title of Award: Lawrence Matson Memorial Endowment Fund Scholarships **Area, Field, or Subject:** Art; Communications; Education; Law; Linguistics; Social sciences **Level of Education for which Award is Granted:** Four Year College, Graduate **Number Awarded:** Varies each year; recently, 1 of these scholarships (at $7,000 per year) was awarded. **Funds Available:** The stipend is $9,000 per year, $7,000 per year, or $2,000 per semester, depending on GPA. **Duration:** 1 year (2 semesters).
Eligibility Requirements: This program is open to Alaska Native enrollees to CIRI under the Alaska Native Claims Settlement Act (ANCSA) of 1971 and their lineal descendants. There are no Alaska residency requirements or age limitations. Applicants must be accepted or enrolled full time in a 4-year undergraduate or a graduate degree program in the following liberal arts fields: language, education, social sciences, arts, communications, or law. They must have a GPA of 2.5 or higher. Selection is based on academic achievement, rigor of course work or degree program, quality of a statement of purpose, student financial contribution, financial need, grade level, previous work performance, education and community activities, letters of recommendation, seriousness of purpose,

and practicality of educational and professional goals. **Deadline for Receipt:** May of each year. **Additional Information:** This fund was established in 1989. Recipients must attend school on a full-time basis.

3532 ■ DECA
1908 Association Drive
Reston, VA 20191-1594
Tel: (703)860-5000
Fax: (703)860-4013
E-mail: decainc@aol.com
Web Site: http://www.deca.org/student.html
To provide financial assistance to DECA members interested in studying business or marketing education in college.
Title of Award: Coca-Cola DECA Scholarships **Area, Field, or Subject:** Business administration; Education; Marketing and distribution **Level of Education for which Award is Granted:** Undergraduate **Number Awarded:** Up to 5 each year. **Funds Available:** The stipend is $1,000. **Duration:** 1 year.
Eligibility Requirements: This program is open to DECA members who are interested in working full time on a 2-year or 4-year degree in marketing, business, or marketing education. Applicants must be able to demonstrate evidence of DECA activities, academic achievement, leadership ability, and community service involvement. Selection is based on merit, not financial need. **Deadline for Receipt:** February of each year. **Additional Information:** This program, established in 2002, is sponsored by the Coca-Cola Company.

3533 ■ DECA
1908 Association Drive
Reston, VA 20191-1594
Tel: (703)860-5000
Fax: (703)860-4013
E-mail: decainc@aol.com
Web Site: http://www.deca.org/student.html
To provide financial assistance to DECA members interested in studying management or marketing education in college.
Title of Award: Otis Spunkmeyer Student Scholarships **Area, Field, or Subject:** Education; Management; Marketing and distribution **Level of Education for which Award is Granted:** Undergraduate **Number Awarded:** 15 each year. **Funds Available:** The stipend is $1,000. **Duration:** 1 year.
Eligibility Requirements: This program is open to DECA members who are interested in working full time on a 2-year or 4-year degree in marketing, management, or marketing education. Applicants must be able to demonstrate evidence of DECA activities, academic achievement, leadership ability, and community service involvement. Selection is based on merit, not financial need. **Deadline for Receipt:** February of each year. **Additional Information:** This program is sponsored by Otis Spunkmeyer, Inc.

3534 ■ DECA
1908 Association Drive
Reston, VA 20191-1594
Tel: (703)860-5000
Fax: (703)860-4013
E-mail: decainc@aol.com
Web Site: http://www.deca.org/student.html
To provide financial assistance to DECA members interested in studying business or marketing education in college.
Title of Award: Walgreens DECA Scholarships **Area, Field, or Subject:** Business administration; Education; Marketing and distribution **Level of Education for which Award is Granted:** Undergraduate **Number Awarded:** Up to 5 each year. **Funds Available:** The stipend is $1,000. **Duration:** 1 year.
Eligibility Requirements: This program is open to DECA members who are interested in working full time on a 2-year or 4-year degree in marketing, business, or marketing education. Applicants must be able to demonstrate evidence of DECA activities, academic achievement, leadership ability, and community service involvement. Selection is based on

merit, not financial need. **Deadline for Receipt:** February of each year. **Additional Information:** This program, established in 2004, is sponsored by Walgreens.

3535 ■ DELAWARE HIGHER EDUCATION COMMISSION
Carvel State Office Building
820 North French Street
Wilmington, DE 19801
Tel: (302)577-3240
Free: 800-292-7935
Fax: (302)577-6765
E-mail: dhec@doe.k12.de.us
Web Site: http://www.doe.state.de.us/high-ed/christa.htm
To provide scholarship/loans for teacher training to Delaware residents with outstanding academic records.
Title of Award: Christa McAuliffe Teacher Scholarship/Loan **Area, Field, or Subject:** Counseling/Guidance; Education; Education, Bilingual and cross-cultural; Education, English as a second language; Education, Special; English language and literature; Library and archival sciences; Linguistics; Mathematics and mathematical sciences; Reading; Technology **Level of Education for which Award is Granted:** Undergraduate **Number Awarded:** Up to 50 each year. **Funds Available:** Funds up to the cost of tuition, fees, and other direct educational expenses are provided. This is a scholarship/loan program; if the recipient performs required service at a school in Delaware, the loan is forgiven at the rate of 1 year of assistance for each year of service. **Duration:** 1 year; may be renewed for up to 3 additional years.
Eligibility Requirements: This program is open to Delaware residents who are enrolled or accepted for enrollment at a Delaware college or university in a program leading to teacher qualification. Preference is given to applicants planning to teach in an area of critical need. High school seniors must rank in the top half of their class and have a combined score of at least 1570 on the SAT; applicants who are already enrolled in college must have a cumulative GPA of 2.75 or higher. Selection is based on academic achievement. U.S. citizenship or permanent resident status is required. **Deadline for Receipt:** March of each year. **Additional Information:** The areas of critical need recently included bilingual education, business education, English, foreign languages, English to speakers of other languages, mathematics, reading, science, school librarianship, special education, and technology education.

3536 ■ DELAWARE STATE EDUCATION ASSOCIATION
Attn: Scholarship Committee
136 East Water Street
Dover, DE 19901
Tel: (302)734-5834; (866)734-5834
Fax: (302)674-8499
E-mail: info@dsea.org
Web Site: http://www.dsea.org/aboutdsea/dsea/scholarship.htm
To provide scholarship/loans to high school seniors in Delaware who are interested in preparing for a teaching career.
Title of Award: Christopher K. Smith Memorial Scholarship **Area, Field, or Subject:** Education **Level of Education for which Award is Granted:** Four Year College **Number Awarded:** 1 each year. **Funds Available:** The stipend is $1,000. Funds are paid directly to the recipient. This is a scholarship/loan program. Recipients are expected to be employed for 1 year as a teacher in a public school district within 1 year of graduation. If this does not happen, the scholarship is viewed as a loan and must be repaid with interest. **Duration:** 1 year.
Eligibility Requirements: This program is open to seniors graduating from public high schools in Delaware who are interested in preparing for a career in teaching. Selection is based on class rank, GPA, standardized test scores, school activities, awards and honors, career plans, and letters of reference. **Deadline for Receipt:** March of each year. **Additional Information:** Recipients are expected to work on a 4-year college degree leading to a Delaware teacher certificate and to teach in a public school (preferably in Delaware) for at least 1 year.

3537 ■ FBLA/PBL FOUNDATION
Attn: Scholarships
P.O. Box 3021010
Montgomery, AL 36130-2101
Tel: (334)242-9109

To provide financial assistance for college to members of Future Business Leaders of America (FBLA) and Phi Beta Lambda (PBL).
Title of Award: FBLA/PBL Foundation Scholarships **Area, Field, or Subject:** Business administration; Education **Level of Education for which Award is Granted:** Undergraduate **Number Awarded:** 1 in each FBLA/PBL district. **Funds Available:** The stipend is $1,000. **Duration:** 1 year.
Eligibility Requirements: This program is open to high school seniors who are members of FBLA and college students who are members of PBL. Applicants must be enrolled or planning to enroll in a business education program at a college or university. Along with their application, they must submit an essay on a topic administered to them by their adviser at their home site. Selection is based on that essay (20%), FBLA/PBL involvement and leadership (25%), community involvement (20%), honors and awards other than FBLA/PBL (15%), GPA (10%), and financial need (10%). **Deadline for Receipt:** September of each year.

3538 ■ FINANCE AUTHORITY OF MAINE
Attn: Education Finance Programs
5 Community Drive
P.O. Box 949
Augusta, ME 04332-0949
Tel: (207)623-3263
Free: 800-228-3734
Fax: (207)623-0095
E-mail: info@famemaine.com
Web Site: http://www.famemaine.com/html/education/fameprogs.html
To provide scholarship/loans to high school seniors, college students, and graduate students in Maine who are interested in preparing for a career as a teacher.
Title of Award: Educators for Maine Program **Area, Field, or Subject:** Child development; Education; Speech and language pathology/audiology **Level of Education for which Award is Granted:** Graduate, Undergraduate **Funds Available:** Full-time undergraduate students receive $3,000 per academic year; postbaccalaureate students receive $2,000 per academic year. This is a scholarship/loan program. Recipients may receive 1 year of loan forgiveness by completing 1 year of full-time teaching in a Maine public or private elementary or secondary school. The repayment option can be accelerated to 2 years of loan forgiveness for each year of teaching if the service is conducted in an educator shortage area or underserved subject area. If the loan recipient does not meet the service obligation, the total amount borrowed must be repaid at 9% interest; undergraduate borrowers must complete repayment within 10 years of graduation or withdrawal from school; postbaccalaureate students must complete repayment within 5 years of graduation or withdrawal from school. **Duration:** 1 year; may be renewed up to 3 additional years if the recipient remains a Maine resident and maintains a cumulative GPA of 2.5 or higher.
Eligibility Requirements: This program is open to 1) high school seniors planning to attend college to prepare for a career in education; 2) currently-enrolled college students; and 3) postbaccalaureate students who are enrolled or planning to enroll in a program leading to certification as a teacher, speech pathologist, or child care provider. Applicants must be residents of Maine with a GPA of 3.0 or higher. Selection is based on academic achievement, activities, community service, and an essay; financial need is not considered. Preference is given to applicants planning to teach a shortage subject. **Deadline for Receipt:** March of each year. **Additional Information:** These scholarship/loans may be used at any accredited postsecondary institution offering certificate, 2-year, 4-year, or graduate programs that lead to an associate, baccalaureate, master's, or doctoral degree. This program was formerly known as Teachers for Maine. Undergraduate recipients must attend school on a full-time basis, but postbaccalaureate students and teachers are not required to enroll as full-time students.

3539 ■ BILL AND MELINDA GATES FOUNDATION
P.O. Box 10500
Fairfax, VA 22031-8044
877-690-GMSP
Web Site: http://www.gmsp.org
To provide financial assistance to outstanding low-income minority students, particularly those interested in majoring in specific fields in college.

Title of Award: Gates Millennium Undergraduate Scholars Program **Area, Field, or Subject:** Education; Engineering; General studies/Field of study not specified; Mathematics and mathematical sciences; Science **Level of Education for which Award is Granted:** Undergraduate **Number Awarded:** Under the Gates Millennium Scholars Program, a total of 4,000 students receive support each year. **Funds Available:** The program covers the cost of tuition, fees, books, and living expenses not paid for by grants and scholarships already committed as part of the recipient's financial aid package. **Duration:** 4 years or the completion of the undergraduate degree, if the recipient maintains at least a 3.0 GPA.

Eligibility Requirements: This program is open to African Americans, Alaska Natives, American Indians, Hispanic Americans, and Asian Pacific Islander Americans who are graduating high school seniors with a GPA of 3.3 or higher. Principals, teachers, guidance counselors, tribal higher education representatives, and other professional educators are invited to nominate students with outstanding academic qualifications, especially those likely to succeed in the fields of mathematics, science, engineering, education, or library science. Nominees should have significant financial need and demonstrated leadership abilities through participation in community service, extracurricular, or other activities. U.S. citizenship or permanent resident status is required. Nominees must be planning to enter an accredited college or university as a full-time, degree-seeking freshman in the following fall. **Deadline for Receipt:** January of each year. **Additional Information:** This program, established in 1999, is funded by the Bill and Melinda Gates Foundation and administered by the United Negro College Fund with support from the American Indian Graduate Center, the Hispanic Scholarship Fund, and the Organization of Chinese Americans.

3540 ■ GENERAL FEDERATION OF WOMEN'S CLUBS OF CONNECTICUT

c/o Hamden Women's Club
Antoinette Antonucci, Co-President
26 Country Way
Wallingford, CT 06492
Tel: (203)265-9407
E-mail: gfwcct@yahoo.com
Web Site: http://www.gfwcct.org
To provide financial assistance to women in Connecticut who are working on an undergraduate or graduate degree in education.

Title of Award: Phipps Memorial Scholarship **Area, Field, or Subject:** Education **Level of Education for which Award is Granted:** Four Year College, Master's **Number Awarded:** 1 each year. **Funds Available:** The stipend is $1,000. **Duration:** 1 year.

Eligibility Requirements: This program is open to female residents of Connecticut who have completed at least 2 years of college. Applicants must have a GPA of 3.0 or higher and be working on a bachelor's or master's degree in education. **Deadline for Receipt:** February of each year.

3541 ■ GENERAL FEDERATION OF WOMEN'S CLUBS OF CONNECTICUT

c/o Hamden Women's Club
Antoinette Antonucci, Co-President
26 Country Way
Wallingford, CT 06492
Tel: (203)265-9407
E-mail: gfwcct@yahoo.com
Web Site: http://www.gfwcct.org
To provide financial assistance to women in Connecticut who are working on an undergraduate or graduate degree in education.

Title of Award: Dorothy E. Schoelzel Memorial Scholarship **Area, Field, or Subject:** Education **Level of Education for which Award is Granted:** Four Year College, Master's **Number Awarded:** 1 each year. **Funds Available:** The stipend is $1,000. **Duration:** 1 year.

Eligibility Requirements: This program is open to female residents of Connecticut who have completed at least 3 years of college. Applicants must have a GPA of 3.0 or higher and be working on a bachelor's or master's degree in education. **Deadline for Receipt:** February of each year.

3542 ■ GEORGIA BUSINESS EDUCATION ASSOCIATION

c/o Ruth Lee, Awards Chair
Mitchell Baker High School
1000 Newton Road
Camilla, GA 31730
Tel: (229)336-2173
E-mail: ruth_lee@mitchell.k12.ga.us
Web Site: http://www.georgiagbea.org
To provide financial assistance to student members of the Georgia Business Education Association (GBEA) who are enrolled in an undergraduate program of student.

Title of Award: Georgia Business Education Association College Student Scholarship **Area, Field, or Subject:** Education **Level of Education for which Award is Granted:** Undergraduate **Number Awarded:** 1 or more each year **Funds Available:** A stipend is awarded (amount not specified). **Duration:** 1 year.

Eligibility Requirements: This program is open to GBEA student members enrolled full time in an approved business education program of study. Applicants must have a GPA of 3.0 or higher. Along with their application, they must submit a statement of commitment, 3 letters of recommendation, and a transcript. **Deadline for Receipt:** January of each year.

3543 ■ GEORGIA STUDENT FINANCE COMMISSION

Attn: Scholarships and Grants Division
2082 East Exchange Place, Suite 200
Tucker, GA 30084-5305
Tel: (770)724-9000
Free: 800-505-GSFC
Fax: (770)724-9089
E-mail: info@mail.gsfc.state.ga.us
Web Site: http://www.gsfc.org
To provide forgivable loans to residents of Georgia who are preparing for a second career as a teacher.

Title of Award: Georgia Destination Teacher Program **Area, Field, or Subject:** Education, Elementary; Education, Secondary **Level of Education for which Award is Granted:** Undergraduate **Number Awarded:** Varies each year. **Funds Available:** The maximum total loan is $5,000. Within 6 months of completion of the program, recipients must become a teacher and repay the loan by working in a high-need school in a high-need district in Georgia. **Duration:** 1 year; may be renewed.

Eligibility Requirements: This program is open to second career candidates (including paraprofessionals) preparing to become teachers at high-need schools in Georgia. Applicants must be interested in attending designated institutions of the University System of Georgia. **Additional Information:** Interested students should contact a program liaison at a college or university for their region of the state: Region 1 (Albany State College); Region 2 (Armstrong Atlantic State University); Region 3 (Georgia State University); Region 4 (Georgia Southwestern State University); Region 5 (Georgia Southern University or East Georgia College); Region 6 (Valdosta State University, Waycross College, South Georgia College, or Abraham Baldwin Agricultural College).

3544 ■ GEORGIA STUDENT FINANCE COMMISSION

Attn: Scholarships and Grants Division
2082 East Exchange Place, Suite 200
Tucker, GA 30084-5305
Tel: (770)724-9000
Free: 800-505-GSFC
Fax: (770)724-9089
E-mail: info@mail.gsfc.state.ga.us
Web Site: http://www.gsfc.org/gsfc/grants/dsp_gcmts.cfm
To provide financial assistance to Georgia residents who wish to prepare for a career as a teacher.

Title of Award: Charles McDaniel Teacher Scholarships **Area, Field, or Subject:** Education, Elementary; Education, Secondary **Level of Education for which Award is Granted:** Four Year College **Number Awarded:** Varies each year; recently, 4 of these scholarships were awarded. **Funds Available:** The stipend is $1,000 per year. **Duration:** 1 year.

Eligibility Requirements: This program is open to residents of Georgia who graduated from a public high school in the state and are currently enrolled as full-time juniors or seniors in a college or department of education within an approved Georgia public institution. Each of the public colleges in Georgia that offers a teaching degree may nominate 1 student for these scholarships. Nominees must be working toward an initial baccalaureate degree, have a GPA of 3.25 or higher, and indicate a strong desire to prepare for a career as an elementary or secondary school teacher. They must submit an essay discussing their professional goals, reasons for pursuing a teaching career at the elementary or secondary level, and accomplishments, experiences, and honors that relate to teaching.

3545 ■ GEORGIA STUDENT FINANCE COMMISSION

Attn: Scholarships and Grants Division
2082 East Exchange Place, Suite 200
Tucker, GA 30084-5305
Tel: (770)724-9000
Free: 800-505-GSFC
Fax: (770)724-9089
E-mail: hope@mail.gsfc.state.ga.us
Web Site: http://www.gsfc.org/GSFA/SCL/
dsp_teacher_prom_scholarship.cfm
To provide forgivable loans to students in Georgia who are preparing for a career as a teacher.
Title of Award: PROMISE Teacher Scholarship Program **Area, Field, or Subject:** Education, Early childhood; Education, Elementary; Education, Secondary **Level of Education for which Award is Granted:** Four Year College **Number Awarded:** 600 each year. **Funds Available:** Full-time students may borrow up to a maximum of $3,000 per year and part-time students up to $1,500; loan funds may be used for tuition and fees, room and board, and any other part of the student's cost of attendance budget. Loans are forgiven at the rate of $1,500 for each year that the recipient teaches in a Georgia public school system at the preschool, elementary, middle, or secondary level. Otherwise, all money received must be repaid with interest at a rate up to 10%. **Duration:** 1 year; may be renewed 1 additional year if the recipient maintains satisfactory academic progress (a continuing 3.0 GPA is not required).
Eligibility Requirements: This program is open to students entering their junior year in a teacher education program at an approved college or university in Georgia. Applicants must have a cumulative GPA of 3.0 or higher and be certified by the college of education teacher certification official at their institution. They do not need to be residents of Georgia but must be U.S. citizens or permanent residents. **Additional Information:** This program is administered by the Georgia Student Finance Authority as a component of its Helping Outstanding Pupils Educationally (HOPE) program.

3546 ■ GOLDEN APPLE FOUNDATION

Attn: Director of Scholars, Recruitment and Placement
8 South Michigan Avenue, Suite 700
Chicago, IL 60603-3463
Tel: (312)407-0433
Fax: (312)407-0344
E-mail: kilduff@goldenapple.org
Web Site: http://www.goldenapple.org/scholars.htm
To provide scholarship/loans to high school seniors in Illinois who wish to study education at an Illinois college and teach in the state.
Title of Award: Golden Apple Scholars of Illinois **Area, Field, or Subject:** Education **Level of Education for which Award is Granted:** Undergraduate **Number Awarded:** Up to 100 each year. **Funds Available:** Scholars receive a scholarship/loan of $2,500 per year to apply toward their educational expenses and a stipend of $2,000 per year for participating in a summer teaching internship. If they complete a bachelor's degree and teach for 5 years in an Illinois school of need, the loan is forgiven. Schools of need are defined as those either having Chapter I status by the U.S. Department of Education or having mediocre to poor PSAE or ISAT scores. **Duration:** 4 years, provided the recipient maintains a GPA of 2.0 or higher during the freshman year and 2.5 or higher in subsequent years. Students who enter the program as sophomores receive 2 years of support.
Eligibility Requirements: This program is open to high school seniors at schools in Illinois. Students must be nominated by a teacher, principal, guidance counselor, or other non-family adult; self-nominations are also accepted. Nominees must be committed to teaching as a profession and must be interested in attending 1 of 53 designated colleges and universities in Illinois. A limited number of openings are also available to sophomores at those designated Illinois institutions. The program strongly encourages nomination of prospective teachers for which there is currently a shortage, especially minority and bilingual teachers. **Deadline for Receipt:** Nominations must be submitted by November of each year. **Ad-**

ditional Information: During the annual summer institutes, scholars participate in teaching internships and seminars on the art and craft of teaching. This program was established in 1988.

3547 ■ HAWAI'I COMMUNITY FOUNDATION

Attn: Scholarship Department
1164 Bishop Street, Suite 800
Honolulu, HI 96813
Tel: (808)566-5570; 888-731-3863
Fax: (808)521-6286
E-mail: scholarships@hcf-hawaii.org
Web Site: http://www.hawaiicommunityfoundation.org/scholar/scholar.php
To provide financial assistance to Hawaii residents who are working on an undergraduate or graduate degree in education.
Title of Award: Alma White-Delta Kappa Gamma Scholarship **Area, Field, or Subject:** Education **Level of Education for which Award is Granted:** Four Year College, Graduate **Number Awarded:** Varies each year; recently, 4 of these scholarships were awarded. **Funds Available:** The amounts of the awards depend on the availability of funds and the need of the recipient; recently, stipends averaged $1,000. **Duration:** 1 year.
Eligibility Requirements: This program is open to Hawaii residents who are enrolled in an education program (as a junior, senior, or graduate student). They must be able to demonstrate academic achievement (GPA of 2.7 or higher), good moral character, and financial need. Applications must be accompanied by a short statement indicating reasons for attending college, planned course of study, and career goals. Recipients must attend college on a full-time basis. **Deadline for Receipt:** February of each year. **Additional Information:** This program was established in 1998.

3548 ■ HAWAI'I COMMUNITY FOUNDATION

Attn: Scholarship Department
1164 Bishop Street, Suite 800
Honolulu, HI 96813
Tel: (808)566-5570; 888-731-3863
Fax: (808)521-6286
E-mail: scholarships@hcf-hawaii.org
Web Site: http://www.hawaiicommunityfoundation.org/scholar/scholar.php
To provide financial assistance to seniors at designated high schools in Hawaii who are interested in studying education in college.
Title of Award: Ron Bright Scholarship **Area, Field, or Subject:** Education **Level of Education for which Award is Granted:** Undergraduate **Number Awarded:** Varies each year; recently, 3 of these scholarships were awarded. **Funds Available:** The amounts of the awards depend on the availability of funds and the need of the recipient; recently, stipends averaged $1,000. **Duration:** 1 year.
Eligibility Requirements: This program is open to seniors at Castle, Kahuku, Kailua, Kalaheo, and Olomana high schools who plan to major in education in college. Preference is given to students with extracurricular activities in the performing arts. Applicants must be able to demonstrate academic achievement (GPA of 2.7 or higher), good moral character, and financial need. **Deadline for Receipt:** February of each year. **Additional Information:** Recipients may attend college in Hawaii or on the mainland.

3549 ■ HAWAI'I COMMUNITY FOUNDATION

Attn: Scholarship Department
1164 Bishop Street, Suite 800
Honolulu, HI 96813
Tel: (808)566-5570; 888-731-3863
Fax: (808)521-6286
E-mail: scholarships@hcf-hawaii.org
Web Site: http://www.hawaiicommunityfoundation.org/scholar/scholar.php
To provide financial assistance to Hawaii residents who are interested in preparing for a career in early childhood education.
Title of Award: Henry and Dorothy Castle Memorial Fund Scholarship **Area, Field, or Subject:** Child care; Education, Early childhood; Education, Elementary **Level of Education for which Award is Granted:** Graduate, Undergraduate **Number Awarded:** Varies each year; recently, 10 of these scholarships were awarded. **Funds Available:** The amounts of the awards depend on the availability of funds and the need of the recipient; recently, stipends averaged $2,000. **Duration:** 1 year.
Eligibility Requirements: This program is open to Hawaii residents who are interested in pursuing full-time undergraduate or graduate studies in

the field of early childhood education (birth through third grade), including child care and preschool. They must be able to demonstrate academic achievement (GPA of 2.7 or higher), good moral character, and financial need. In addition to filling out the standard application form, applicants must 1) write a short statement indicating their reasons for attending college, their planned course of study, and their career goals, and 2) write an essay that states their interests and goals in studying early childhood education and how they plan to contribute to the field. **Deadline for Receipt:** February of each year. **Additional Information:** Recipients may attend college in Hawaii or on the mainland. This scholarship is funded by the Samuel N. and Mary Castle Foundation.

3550 ■ HAWAI'I COMMUNITY FOUNDATION

Attn: Scholarship Department
1164 Bishop Street, Suite 800
Honolulu, HI 96813
Tel: (808)566-5570; 888-731-3863
Fax: (808)521-6286
E-mail: scholarships@hcf-hawaii.org
Web Site: http://www.hawaiicommunityfoundation.org/scholar/scholar.php
To provide financial assistance to Hawaii residents who are interested in preparing for a career that will fill gaps in the local job market.
Title of Award: Hawai'i Community Foundation Community Scholarship Fund **Area, Field, or Subject:** Architecture; Art; Education; Humanities; Social sciences **Level of Education for which Award is Granted:** Graduate, Undergraduate **Number Awarded:** Varies each year; recently, 97 of these scholarships were awarded. **Funds Available:** The amount awarded varies; recently, stipends averaged $1,000. **Duration:** 1 year.
Eligibility Requirements: This program is open to students in Hawaii who show potential for filling a community need; demonstrate accomplishment, motivation, initiative, and vision; are residents of the state of Hawaii; intend to return to, or stay in, Hawaii to work; are able to demonstrate financial need; are interested in attending an accredited 2- or 4-year college or university as a full-time student at either the undergraduate or graduate level; plan to major in the arts, architecture, education, humanities, or social science; and are able to demonstrate academic achievement (GPA of 3.0 or higher). **Deadline for Receipt:** February of each year. **Additional Information:** Recipients may attend school in Hawaii or on the mainland. This fund was established in 1947.

3551 ■ HAWAI'I COMMUNITY FOUNDATION

Attn: Scholarship Department
1164 Bishop Street, Suite 800
Honolulu, HI 96813
Tel: (808)566-5570; 888-731-3863
Fax: (808)521-6286
E-mail: scholarships@hcf-hawaii.org
Web Site: http://www.hawaiicommunityfoundation.org/scholar/scholar.php
To provide financial assistance to Hawaii residents who are interested in preparing for a career in designated health fields.
Title of Award: Dr. Alvin and Monica Saake Foundation Scholarships **Area, Field, or Subject:** Athletics; Education, Physical; Medicine, Sports; Occupational therapy; Parks and recreation; Physical therapy **Level of Education for which Award is Granted:** Four Year College, Graduate **Number Awarded:** Varies each year; recently, 19 of these scholarships were awarded. **Funds Available:** The amounts of the awards depend on the availability of funds and the need of the recipient; recently, stipends averaged $2,895. **Duration:** 1 year.
Eligibility Requirements: This program is open to Hawaii residents who are enrolled as full-time juniors, seniors, or graduate students. Applicants must be majoring in kinesiology, leisure science, physical education, athletic training, exercise science, sports medicine, physical therapy, or occupational therapy. They must be able to demonstrate academic achievement (GPA of 2.7 or higher), good moral character, and financial need. In addition to filling out the standard application form, applicants must write a short statement indicating their reasons for attending college, their planned course of study, and their career goals. **Deadline for Receipt:** February of each year. **Additional Information:** Recipients may attend college in Hawaii or on the mainland.

3552 ■ HAWAI'I COMMUNITY FOUNDATION

Attn: Scholarship Department
1164 Bishop Street, Suite 800
Honolulu, HI 96813

Tel: (808)566-5570; 888-731-3863
Fax: (808)521-6286
E-mail: scholarships@hcf-hawaii.org
Web Site: http://www.hawaiicommunityfoundation.org/scholar/scholar.php
To provide financial assistance to Hawaii residents who are nontraditional students planning to major in education.
Title of Award: Dr. Hans and Clara Zimmerman Foundation Education Scholarships **Area, Field, or Subject:** Education **Level of Education for which Award is Granted:** Undergraduate **Number Awarded:** Varies each year; recently, 61 of these scholarships were awarded. **Funds Available:** The amount of the award depends on the availability of funds and the need of the recipient; recently, stipends averaged $1,620. **Duration:** 1 year.
Eligibility Requirements: This program is open to Hawaii residents who have worked for at least 2 years and are returning to school as full-time students majoring in education. Applicants must be able to demonstrate academic achievement (GPA of 2.8 or higher), good moral character, and financial need. In addition to filling out the standard application form, they must write a short statement describing their community service and how their college education will help them achieve their career goals. Preference is given to students of Hawaiian ancestry, students from the neighboring islands who plan to teach in Hawaii, and students with some teaching experience. **Deadline for Receipt:** February of each year. **Additional Information:** This scholarship was established in 1997.

3553 ■ HOPI TRIBE

Attn: Office of Education
P.O. Box 123
Kykotsmovi, AZ 86039
Tel: (928)734-3533
Free: 800-762-9630
Fax: (928)734-9575
E-mail: IPolingyumptewa@hopi.nsn.us
Web Site: http://www.hopi.nsn.us/education_htgsp.asp
To encourage Hopi students to get an undergraduate or graduate degree in an area of interest to the Hopi Tribe.
Title of Award: Hopi Tribal Priority Scholarship **Area, Field, or Subject:** Business administration; Education; Engineering; Environmental conservation; Environmental science; Health care services; Law; Medicine **Level of Education for which Award is Granted:** Four Year College, Graduate **Number Awarded:** Varies each year. **Funds Available:** The stipend covers all educational expenses. **Duration:** 1 year; may be renewed.
Eligibility Requirements: This program is open to enrolled members of the Hopi Tribe. They must be college juniors, seniors, or graduate students whose degree is in a subject area that is of priority interest to the Hopi Tribe. Those areas are law, natural resources, education, medicine, health, engineering, or business. This is a highly competitive scholarship. Selection is based on academic merit and the likelihood that the applicants will use their training and expertise for tribal goals and objectives. **Deadline for Receipt:** July of each year. **Additional Information:** Recipients must attend school on a full-time basis.

3554 ■ IDAHO SPACE GRANT CONSORTIUM

c/o University of Idaho
College of Engineering
P.O. Box 441011
Moscow, ID 83844-1011
Tel: (208)885-6438
Fax: (208)885-1399
E-mail: isgc@uidaho.edu
Web Site: http://isgc.uidaho.edu
To provide financial assistance for study in space-related fields to undergraduate students at institutions belonging to the Idaho Space Grant Consortium (ISGC).
Title of Award: Idaho Space Grant Consortium Scholarship Program **Area, Field, or Subject:** Aerospace sciences; Education; Engineering, Aerospace/Aeronautical/Astronautical; Mathematics and mathematical sciences; Science; Space and planetary sciences **Level of Education for which Award is Granted:** Undergraduate **Number Awarded:** Varies each year; recently, 24 of these scholarships were awarded. **Funds Available:** The stipend is up to $1,000 per year. Funds are to be used to pay for registration at colleges in the consortium. **Duration:** 1 year; may be renewed.

Eligibility Requirements: This program is open to full-time undergraduate students at ISGC member institutions. Applicants must be majoring in engineering, mathematics, science, or science/math education and have a cumulative GPA of 3.0 or higher. They should be planning to work on a 4-year degree in a space-related field. Along with their application, they must submit a 500-word essay on their future career and educational goals and why they believe the U.S. National Aeronautics and Space Administration (NASA) should support their education. U.S. citizenship is required. As a component of the NASA Space Grant program, the ISGC encourages participation by women, underrepresented minorities, and persons with disabilities. **Deadline for Receipt:** February of each year. **Additional Information:** Members of the consortium include Albertson College of Idaho, Boise State University, College of Southern Idaho, Idaho State University, Lewis Clark State College, North Idaho College, Northwest Nazarene College, Brigham Young University of Idaho, and the University of Idaho. This program is funded by NASA.

3555 ■ IDAHO STATE BOARD OF EDUCATION

Len B. Jordan Office Building
650 West State Street, Room 307
P.O. Box 83720
Boise, ID 83720-0037
Tel: (208)332-1574
Fax: (208)334-2632
E-mail: board@osbe.state.id.us
Web Site: http://www.idahoboardofed.org/scholarships/loan.asp
To provide scholarship/loans to Idaho students who wish to prepare for a teaching or nursing career in Idaho.
Title of Award: Idaho Education Incentive Loan Forgiveness **Area, Field, or Subject:** Education; Nursing **Level of Education for which Award is Granted:** Undergraduate **Number Awarded:** Approximately 45 each year. **Funds Available:** This is a scholarship/loan program. Loans are forgiven if the recipient pursues a teaching or nursing career within Idaho for at least 2 years. **Duration:** 1 year; renewable.
Eligibility Requirements: Applicants must have graduated from a secondary school in Idaho within the previous 2 years and rank within the upper 15% of their graduating high school class or have earned a cumulative GPA in college of 3.0 or higher. They must enroll as a full-time student at an Idaho public college or university, working on a degree that will qualify them to receive an Idaho teaching certificate or write the licensure examination approved by the Board of Nursing for a registered nurse.

3556 ■ IDAHO STATE BOARD OF EDUCATION

Len B. Jordan Office Building
650 West State Street, Room 307
P.O. Box 83720
Boise, ID 83720-0037
Tel: (208)332-1574
Fax: (208)334-2632
E-mail: board@osbe.state.id.us
Web Site: http://www.idahoboardofed.org/scholarships/gyo.asp
To provide financial assistance to students at selected Idaho colleges and universities who are interested in becoming teachers of bilingual education or English as a Second Language (ESL) or to Native American education students.
Title of Award: Idaho Grow Your Own Teacher Scholarship Program **Area, Field, or Subject:** Education; Education, Bilingual and cross-cultural; Education, English as a second language **Level of Education for which Award is Granted:** Professional, Undergraduate **Number Awarded:** Varies each year. **Funds Available:** The stipend is $3,000 per year for full-time students; the stipend for part-time students depends on the number of credit hours and the fee charged to part-time students at the participating college or university. **Duration:** 1 year.
Eligibility Requirements: This program is open to Idaho school district employees and volunteers who are 1) interested in completing an associate and/or baccalaureate degree in education with a bilingual or ESL endorsement, or 2) Native Americans preparing to teach in Idaho school districts with a significant Native American student population. Applicants

must be attending Boise State University, the College of Southern Idaho, Lewis-Clark State College, or Idaho State University.

3557 ■ ILLINOIS STUDENT ASSISTANCE COMMISSION

Attn: Scholarship and Grant Services
1755 Lake Cook Road
Deerfield, IL 60015-5209
Tel: (847)948-8550
Free: 800-899-ISAC
Fax: (847)831-8549
E-mail: collegezone@isac.org
Web Site: http://www.collegezone.com
To provide scholarship/loans to college students in Illinois who are interested in training or retraining for a teaching career in academic shortage areas.
Title of Award: Illinois Future Teacher Corps Program **Area, Field, or Subject:** Education; Education, Bilingual and cross-cultural; Education, Early childhood; Education, Elementary; Education, Music; Education, Physical; Education, Secondary; Education, Special; Hearing and deafness; Visual impairment **Level of Education for which Award is Granted:** Four Year College **Number Awarded:** Varies each year, depending on the availability of funds. **Funds Available:** This program pays tuition and fees, room and board, or a commuter allowance at academic institutions in Illinois. The maximum award is $5,000 or $10,000 (and may even be increased by an additional $5,000), depending on the teaching commitment the recipient makes. Funds are paid directly to the school. This is a scholarship/loan program. Recipients must agree to teach in an Illinois public, private, or parochial preschool, elementary school, or secondary school for 1 year for each full year of assistance received. The teaching obligation must be completed within 5 years of completion of the degree or certificate program for which the scholarship was awarded. That time period may be extended if the recipient serves in the U.S. armed forces, enrolls full time in a graduate program related to teaching, becomes temporarily disabled, is unable to find employment as a teacher, or takes additional courses on at least a half-time basis to teach in a specialized teacher shortage discipline. Recipients who fail to honor this work obligation must repay the award with interest. **Duration:** 1 year; may be renewed.
Eligibility Requirements: This program is open to Illinois residents who are enrolled at the junior level or higher at an institution of higher education in the state. Applicants must be planning to prepare for a career as a preschool, elementary, or secondary school teacher. Preference is given to students working on a degree in designated teacher shortage disciplines, making a commitment to teach at a hard-to-staff school, and/or planning to teach minority students. Recently, the teacher shortage disciplines included behavior disordered, bilingual teacher (K-12), cross categorical (seeking certification in 2 or more areas of special education), general special education (including blind and deaf specialties and early childhood special education), learning disabled, mathematics (K-12), music (K-12), physical education (K-12), reading and English language arts (K-12), and speech and language impaired. Preference is given to renewal applicants. Selection is based on cumulative GPA, expected family contribution, and minority student status. **Deadline for Receipt:** Priority consideration is given to applications submitted by February of each year. **Additional Information:** This program was formerly known as the David A. DeBolt Teacher Shortage Scholarship Program.

3558 ■ ILLINOIS STUDENT ASSISTANCE COMMISSION

Attn: Scholarship and Grant Services
1755 Lake Cook Road
Deerfield, IL 60015-5209
Tel: (847)948-8550
Free: 800-899-ISAC
Fax: (847)831-8549
E-mail: collegezone@isac.org
Web Site: http://www.collegezone.com
To provide scholarship/loans to students in Illinois who are interested in training or retraining for a career in special education.
Title of Award: Illinois Special Education Teacher Tuition Waiver Program **Area, Field, or Subject:** Disabilities; Education, Special **Level of Education for which Award is Granted:** Four Year College, Graduate, Professional **Number Awarded:** 250 each year. **Funds Available:** This program waives tuition and fees at 12 participating Illinois public 4-year universi-

ties. Recipients must agree to teach full time in a special education discipline at an Illinois public, private, or parochial school for 2 of the 5 years immediately following graduation or termination of enrollment. That teaching requirement may be postponed if the recipient serves in the U.S. armed forces, enrolls full time in a graduate or postgraduate program, becomes temporarily disabled, is unable to find employment as a teacher, or withdraws from a course of study leading to a teacher certification in special education but remains enrolled full time in another academic discipline. Participants who fail to fulfill that teaching requirement must repay the entire amount of the tuition waiver prorated to the fraction of the teaching requirement not completed, plus interest at a rate of 5% per year. **Duration:** Up to 4 continuous calendar years.
Eligibility Requirements: Eligible for support under this program are Illinois residents who are enrolled or planning to enroll in an Illinois public institution of higher education to prepare for a career as a public, private, or parochial elementary or secondary school teacher in the state. Applicants must be undergraduate or graduate students seeking certification in an area of special education. They must rank in the upper half of their Illinois high school graduating class. Current teachers who have a valid teaching certificate that is not in the discipline of special education are also eligible. **Deadline for Receipt:** February of each year. **Additional Information:** The participating universities are Chicago State University, Eastern Illinois University, Governors State University, Illinois State University, Northeastern Illinois University, Northern Illinois University, Southern Illinois University at Carbondale, Southern Illinois University at Edwardsville, University of Illinois at Chicago, University of Illinois at Springfield, University of Illinois at Urbana, and Western Illinois University.

3559 ■ ILLINOIS STUDENT ASSISTANCE COMMISSION
Attn: Scholarship and Grant Services
1755 Lake Cook Road
Deerfield, IL 60015-5209
Tel: (847)948-8550
Free: 800-899-ISAC
Fax: (847)831-8549
E-mail: collegezone@isac.org
Web Site: http://www.collegezone.com
To provide scholarship/loans to minority students in Illinois who plan to become teachers at the preschool, elementary, or secondary level.
Title of Award: Minority Teachers of Illinois Scholarship Program **Area, Field, or Subject:** Education, Early childhood; Education, Elementary; Education, Secondary **Level of Education for which Award is Granted:** Undergraduate **Number Awarded:** Varies each year. **Funds Available:** Grants up to $5,000 per year are awarded. This is a scholarship/loan program. Recipients must agree to teach full time 1 year for each year of support received. The teaching agreement may be fulfilled at a public, private, or parochial preschool, elementary school, or secondary school in Illinois; at least 30% of the student body at those schools must be minority. It must be fulfilled within the 5-year period following the completion of the undergraduate program for which the scholarship was awarded. The time period may be extended if the recipient serves in the U.S. armed forces, enrolls full time in a graduate program related to teaching, becomes temporarily disabled, is unable to find employment as a teacher at a qualifying school, or takes additional courses on at least a half-time basis to obtain certification as a teacher in Illinois. Recipients who fail to honor this work obligation must repay the award with 5% interest. **Duration:** 1 year.
Eligibility Requirements: Applicants must be Illinois residents, U.S. citizens or eligible noncitizens, members of a minority group (African American/Black, Hispanic American, Asian American, or Native American), and high school graduates or holders of a General Educational Development (GED) certificate. They must be enrolled in college full time at the sophomore level or above, have a GPA of 2.5 or higher, not be in default on any student loan, and be enrolled or accepted for enrollment in a teacher education program. **Deadline for Receipt:** Priority consideration is given to applications received by February of each year.

3560 ■ INTERNATIONAL FOUNDATION FOR GENDER EDUCATION
Attn: Transgender Scholarship and Education Legacy Fund
P.O. Box 540229
Waltham, MA 02454-0229
Tel: (781)899-2212
Fax: (781)899-5703

E-mail: carrie@tself.org
Web Site: http://www.tself.org
To provide financial assistance to transgender students who are working on an undergraduate or graduate degree in the caring professions.
Title of Award: Transgender Scholarship and Education Legacy Fund Awards **Area, Field, or Subject:** Education; Health care services; Law; Religion; Social work **Level of Education for which Award is Granted:** Graduate, Undergraduate **Number Awarded:** Varies each year; recently, 4 of these scholarships were awarded. **Funds Available:** Stipends average $2,000. Funds are paid directly to the student. **Duration:** 1 year; nonrenewable.
Eligibility Requirements: This program is open to undergraduate and graduate students who are living full time in a gender or sex role that differs from that assigned to them at birth and who are "out and proud" about their transgender identity. Applicants must be working on a degree in the helping and caring professions, including, but not limited to, social services, health care, religious instruction, education, and the law. They may be of any age or nationality, but they must be attending or planning to attend a college, university, trade school, or technical college in the United States or Canada. Selection is based on affirmation of transgender identity; demonstration of integrity and honesty; participation and leadership in community activities; service as role model, mentor, colleague, or advisor for the transgender communities; and service as transgender role model, mentor, colleague, or advisor to non-transpeople in the helping and caring professions. **Deadline for Receipt:** January of each year. **Additional Information:** This program includes the TSELF Youth Award (for applicants under 22 years of age entering their first or second year of postsecondary education); the TSELF Schools Education Award (for applicants working on a degree in education and teaching); the Lee Frances Heller Memorial Award (for Christian students or applicants who are or will be attending a college, university, or other institution for religious studies); the HIV/AIDS Prevention and Treatment Award (for applicants who have been involved in HIV/AIDS prevention, care, and treatment activities); and the Chicago Gender Society Leadership Award (for applicants who have been involved in community building activities).

3561 ■ JEWISH FEDERATION OF GREATER HARTFORD, INC.
Attn: Endowment Foundation
333 Bloomfield Avenue
West Hartford, CT 06117
Tel: (860)523-7460
Fax: (860)231-0576
E-mail: grants@jcfhartford.org
Web Site: http://www.jcfhartford.org
To provide financial assistance for college to students in Connecticut interested in Jewish education.
Title of Award: Hebrew Ladies Sheltering Home Scholarships **Area, Field, or Subject:** Education, Religious; Jewish studies; Religion **Level of Education for which Award is Granted:** Undergraduate **Number Awarded:** 2 to 3 each year. **Funds Available:** The stipend is $1,000. **Duration:** 1 year.
Eligibility Requirements: This program is open to Jewish residents of Connecticut who are graduating high school seniors. Applicants must be interested in working on a degree in Jewish education. U.S. citizenship is required. Selection is based on academic record and financial need. **Deadline for Receipt:** April of each year.

3562 ■ KANSAS BOARD OF REGENTS
Attn: Student Financial Aid
1000 S.W. Jackson Street, Suite 520
Topeka, KS 66612-1368
Tel: (785)296-3518
Fax: (785)296-0983
E-mail: dlindeman@ksbor.org
Web Site: http://www.kansasregents.com/financial_aid/teacher.html
To provide scholarship/loans to high school seniors, high school graduates, and selected undergraduates who are interested in preparing for a career as a teacher in Kansas.
Title of Award: Kansas Teacher Service Scholarships **Area, Field, or Subject:** Education; Education, Special; Science **Level of Education for which Award is Granted:** Undergraduate **Number Awarded:** Approximately 100 each year. **Funds Available:** Participants receive $5,000 per year. This is a scholarship/loan program. Recipients must teach in

Kansas 1 year for every year of funding received, or they must repay the amount received with interest at 5% over the federal PLUS rate. The teaching must be in the specific curriculum area or in an underserved geographic area (recently including Wichita, Leavenworth, Garden City, and Kansas City). **Duration:** 1 year; may be renewed for up to 3 additional years or up to 4 additional years for designated 5-year courses of study requiring graduate work.

Eligibility Requirements: This program is open to Kansas residents who plan to enter the teaching profession in specific curriculum areas; recently, those included special education, mathematics, and science. Applicants must submit evidence of completion of the Kansas Scholars Curriculum (4 years of English, 4 years of mathematics, 3 years of science, 3 years of social studies, 2 years of foreign language, and 1 year of computer technology), ACT or SAT scores, high school GPA, high school class rank, and (if relevant) college transcripts and letters of recommendation from a college or university official. First priority goes to applicants who are in the final 2 years of study in teacher education and have submitted a college transcript and 1 letter of recommendation from a college official. Special consideration is given to minority applicants (academic performance being similar), because minorities continue to be underrepresented in the teaching profession in Kansas schools. Second priority goes to students who have completed the Kansas Scholars Curriculum and have competitive GPAs, ACT scores, and class rank. **Deadline for Receipt:** March of each year. **Additional Information:** There is a $10 application fee.

3563 ■ KANSAS FEDERATION OF BUSINESS & PROFESSIONAL WOMEN'S CLUBS, INC.

Attn: Kansas BPW Educational Foundation
c/o Diane Smith, Executive Secretary
10418 Haskins
Lenexa, KS 66215-2162
E-mail: desmith@fcbankonline.com
Web Site: http://www.bpwkansas.org/bpw_foundation.htm
To provide financial assistance to residents of Kansas who are preparing for a career in special education in the state.
Title of Award: Dena Nigus Memorial Scholarship **Area, Field, or Subject:** Education, Special **Level of Education for which Award is Granted:** Four Year College, Graduate **Number Awarded:** 1 or more each year. **Funds Available:** A stipend is awarded (amount not specified). **Duration:** 1 year; may be renewed for a total of 4 semesters or 2 summers if the recipient maintains a GPA of 3.0 or higher.

Eligibility Requirements: This program is open to Kansas residents (men and women) who are college juniors, seniors, or graduate students and preparing to teach special education in the state. Applicants must submit a 3-page personal biography in which they express their career goals, the direction they want to take in the future, their proposed field of study, their reason for selecting that field, the institutions they plan to attend and why, their circumstances for reentering school (if a factor), and what makes them uniquely qualified for this scholarship. They must also be able to document financial need. Applications must be submitted through a local organization of the sponsor. **Deadline for Receipt:** December of each year.

3564 ■ MAINE COMMUNITY FOUNDATION

Attn: Program Director
245 Main Street
Ellsworth, ME 04605
Tel: (207)667-9735; 877-700-6800
Fax: (207)667-0447
E-mail: info@mainecf.org
Web Site: http://www.mainecf.org/html/scholarships/index.html
To provide financial assistance to seniors at designated high schools in Maine who are interested in attending college to prepare for a career coaching or teaching sports at the secondary school level.
Title of Award: Billy Brown Scholarship **Area, Field, or Subject:** Athletics; Education, Physical **Level of Education for which Award is Granted:** Four Year College **Number Awarded:** 1 or more each year. **Funds Available:** A stipend is awarded (amount not specified). Funds must be used for tuition, room, board, books, laboratory fees, and equipment. **Duration:** 1 year.

Eligibility Requirements: Applicants must have attended Portland, Deering, Catherine McAuley, Chevrus, Waynflete, South Portland, Cape Elizabeth, Scarborough, or Yarmouth high schools in Maine. They are not required to be graduating seniors, but they must be entering the first year of postsecondary education at a 4-year institution. They must be planning to coach or teach sports in secondary education, including baseball, soccer, and softball. Selection is based on financial need, scholastic talent, and demonstrated dedication to coaching or teaching those sports. **Deadline for Receipt:** April of each year. **Additional Information:** This program began in 1999.

3565 ■ MAINE ROADS SCHOLARSHIP FUND

c/o University of Southern Maine, Muskie School
400 Congress Street
P.O. Box 15010
Portland, ME 04112
888-900-0055
Fax: (207)780-5817
E-mail: sturner@usm.maine.edu
Web Site: http://muskie.usm.maine.edu/maineroads/scholarship.html
To provide financial assistance to child care providers in Maine who are working on an undergraduate or graduate degree at an institution in the state.
Title of Award: Maine Roads Degree Scholarship **Area, Field, or Subject:** Child development; Education, Early childhood; Parks and recreation; Social work **Level of Education for which Award is Granted:** Graduate, Professional, Undergraduate **Number Awarded:** Varies each year. **Funds Available:** Stipends range up to $1,800 for undergraduate students or up to $2,400 for graduate students. **Duration:** 1 year.

Eligibility Requirements: This program is open to child care providers who are residents of Maine working on a bachelor's, master's, or doctoral degree at an institution of higher education in the state. Applicants must have a family income that does not exceed 300% of the federal poverty level (currently, that means an income of $26,940 for a family of 1, rising to $92,880 for a family of 8). They must have experience within the past 2 years working in the child care and early education field in licensed or certified child care facilities or resource development centers. Courses of study may include early childhood education, child development, recreation and leisure services with a special needs focus, social work with an emphasis on early childhood, or child care administration. Along with their application, they must submit brief statements on their plans to work directly with children after completing their degree and how earning their degree will impact their work in child care. **Deadline for Receipt:** June or October of each year.

3566 ■ MARYLAND HIGHER EDUCATION COMMISSION

Attn: Office of Student Financial Assistance
839 Bestgate Road, Suite 400
Annapolis, MD 21401-3013
Tel: (410)260-4563
Free: 800-974-1024
Fax: (410)974-5376
E-mail: osfamail@mhec.state.md.us
Web Site: http://www.mhec.state.md.us/financialAid/
ProgramDescriptions/prog_child.asp
To provide scholarship/loans to students in Maryland who wish to prepare for a career as a child care provider.
Title of Award: Maryland Child Care Provider Scholarship Program **Area, Field, or Subject:** Child care; Child development; Education, Early childhood **Level of Education for which Award is Granted:** Professional, Undergraduate **Number Awarded:** Varies each year. **Funds Available:** Stipends at 4-year institutions are $2,000 per year for full-time study, $1,000 for part-time; at community colleges, annual stipends are $1,000 for full-time study, $500 for part-time. The total amount of all state awards may not exceed the cost of attendance as determined by the school's financial aid office or $17,800, whichever is less. Within 12 months of graduation, recipients must provide 1 year of child care service in Maryland for each year of financial aid received under this program; failure to comply with that service obligation will require the recipient to repay the scholarship money with interest. Teaching in a public school in Maryland does not fulfill the service requirement. **Duration:** 1 year; may be renewed for up to 3 additional years of full-time study provided the recipient maintains a GPA of 2.0 or higher.

Eligibility Requirements: Eligible are residents of Maryland who are enrolled or plan to enroll in a program leading to an associate or bachelor's degree in a Maryland institution of higher education that offers an undergraduate program in early childhood education or child development. Full-time enrollment is required, although part-time study is allowed if the applicant is employed for a minimum of 15 hours per week at a child care or family day care center. Financial need is not considered in the selection process. **Deadline for Receipt:** June of each year.

3567 ■ MARYLAND HIGHER EDUCATION COMMISSION

Attn: Office of Student Financial Assistance
839 Bestgate Road, Suite 400
Annapolis, MD 21401-3013
Tel: (410)260-4594
Free: 800-974-1024
Fax: (410)974-5376
E-mail: osfamail@mhec.state.md.us
Web Site: http://www.mhec.state.md.us/financialAid/ProgramDescriptions/prog_devdis.asp
To provide scholarship/loans to students in Maryland who are interested in working on a degree in a designated human services program.
Title of Award: Maryland Developmental Disabilities, Mental Health, Child Welfare, and Juvenile Justice Workforce Tuition Assistance Program **Area, Field, or Subject:** Counseling/Guidance; Criminal justice; Criminology; Disabilities; Education, Special; Gerontology; Law enforcement; Mental health; Nursing; Occupational therapy; Physical therapy; Psychology; Rehabilitation, Physical/Psychological; Social work **Level of Education for which Award is Granted:** Graduate, Undergraduate **Number Awarded:** Varies each year. **Funds Available:** The maximum stipend is $2,000 per year for students attending a 2-year institution or $3,000 per year for students at a 4-year institution. The total amount of all state awards may not exceed the cost of attendance as determined by the school's financial aid office or $17,800, whichever is less. Recipients must agree to work in a Maryland community-based program that is licensed by the Developmental Disabilities Administration or approved by the Mental Hygiene Administration, or in a residential program that is licensed by the Department of Human Resources or the Department of Juvenile Justice. The service obligation must begin within 6 months of graduation. The total service requirement is 2,000 hours if the award amount is $1,999 or less, 3,000 hours if the award amount is $2,000 to $3,999, or 4,000 hours if the award amount is $4,000 or more. If the service requirement is not completed, the award must be repaid with interest. **Duration:** 1 year; may be renewed if the recipient maintains satisfactory academic progress and remains enrolled in a human services degree program.
Eligibility Requirements: This program is open to high school seniors and full-time and part-time undergraduate and graduate students. Applicants and their parents must be Maryland residents attending a college or university in the state in 1 of the following human services degree programs: aging services, counseling, disability services, mental health, nursing, occupational therapy, physical therapy, psychology, rehabilitation, social work, special education, supported employment, vocational rehabilitation, or any other concentration in the healing arts or a program providing support services to individuals with special needs including child welfare and juvenile justice. Financial need is not considered in the selection process. **Deadline for Receipt:** June of each year.

3568 ■ MARYLAND HIGHER EDUCATION COMMISSION

Attn: Office of Student Financial Assistance
839 Bestgate Road, Suite 400
Annapolis, MD 21401-3013
Tel: (410)260-4569
Free: 800-974-1024
Fax: (410)974-5376
E-mail: osfamail@mhec.state.md.us
Web Site: http://www.mhec.state.md.us/financialAid/ProgramDescriptions/prog_dste.asp
To provide scholarship/loans to students in Maryland interested in preparing for a career as a teacher.
Title of Award: Maryland Distinguished Scholar Teacher Education Awards **Area, Field, or Subject:** Education **Level of Education for which Award is Granted:** Undergraduate **Number Awarded:** Varies each year. **Funds Available:** The award is $3,000 per year. The total amount of all state awards may not exceed the cost of attendance as determined by the school's financial aid office or $17,800, whichever is less. This is a scholarship/loan program. Recipients must teach in a

Maryland public school 1 year for each year the award was received or the award must be repaid with interest. They must begin the service obligation within 9 months of graduation. **Duration:** 1 year; may be renewed for up to 3 additional years, if the recipient maintains a 3.0 GPA and full-time enrollment.
Eligibility Requirements: This program is open to Maryland residents who have been awarded a Maryland Distinguished Scholar award. Applicants must be enrolled full time in an approved teacher education program at an approved Maryland institution. Financial need is not required. **Deadline for Receipt:** June of each year.

3569 ■ MARYLAND HIGHER EDUCATION COMMISSION

Attn: Office of Student Financial Assistance
839 Bestgate Road, Suite 400
Annapolis, MD 21401-3013
Tel: (410)260-4545
Free: 800-974-1024
Fax: (410)974-5376
E-mail: osfamail@mhec.state.md.us
Web Site: http://www.mhec.state.md.us/financialAid/ProgramDescriptions/prog_scm.asp
To provide scholarship/loans to Maryland residents who wish to prepare for a teaching career.
Title of Award: Sharon Christa McAuliffe Memorial Teacher Education Award **Area, Field, or Subject:** Chemistry; Classical studies; Computer and information sciences; Earth sciences; Education; Education, English as a second language; Education, Special; Education, Vocational-technical; Foreign languages; Geosciences; Health care services; Hearing and deafness; Mathematics and mathematical sciences; Physical sciences; Physics; Space and planetary sciences; Visual impairment **Level of Education for which Award is Granted:** Master's, Professional, Undergraduate **Number Awarded:** Varies each year. **Funds Available:** The amount of the award is based on the recipient's enrollment and housing status, to a maximum of $17,000 per year. The total amount of all state awards may not exceed the cost of attendance as determined by the school's financial aid office or $17,800, whichever is less. Following graduation, recipients must teach at a Maryland public school for 1 year for each year of financial aid received under this program. If they fail to meet that service obligation, they must repay all funds they received with interest. They must begin the service obligation within 12 months of graduation. **Duration:** 1 year; may be renewed for 1 additional year if the recipient maintains satisfactory academic progress with a cumulative GPA of 3.0 or higher and enrollment at a 2-year or 4-year Maryland college or university in an approved teacher education program.
Eligibility Requirements: This program is open to Maryland residents who are college students with at least 60 semester credit hours completed, college graduates, and teachers in a non-critical shortage area. Applicants must have a GPA of 3.0 or higher and plan to teach in a field identified as a critical shortage area. Selection is based on cumulative GPA, applicable work or volunteer experience, quality of academic background in certification field, and a writing sample. **Deadline for Receipt:** December of each year. **Additional Information:** Recently, the eligible critical shortage areas were business education, chemistry, computer science, earth and space science, English for speakers of other languages, family and consumer sciences, German, health occupations, Latin, mathematics, physical science, physics, Spanish, special education (generic infant-grade 3, generic grades 1-8, generic grades 6-adult, hearing impaired, severely and profoundly handicapped, visually impaired), and technology education.

3570 ■ MARYLAND STATE GRANGE

Attn: Master
8743 Old Kiln Road
Thurmont, MD 21788-1219
Tel: (301)447-2075
Fax: (301)447-2019
E-mail: rlt-rox@juno.com
To provide financial assistance for college or graduate school to Maryland residents who are either deaf or preparing to work with hearing-impaired people.
Title of Award: Maryland State Grange Deaf Scholarship **Area, Field, or Subject:** Education, Special; General studies/Field of study not specified; Hearing and deafness **Level of Education for which Award is Granted:**

Graduate, Undergraduate **Number Awarded:** 1 or more each year. **Funds Available:** A stipend is awarded (amount not specified). **Duration:** 1 year; may be renewed if the recipient maintains a GPA of 3.0 or higher. **Eligibility Requirements:** This program is open to residents of Maryland who graduated from a high school in the state and are attending college or graduate school in the state. Applicants must be 1) deaf or hearing impaired, or 2) preparing for a career working with deaf or hearing-impaired people. **Deadline for Receipt:** May of each year. **Additional Information:** Information is also available from Donna D. Wiles, Deaf Activities Director, 5543 Buffalo Road, Mount Airy, MD 21771, (301) 829-0545.

3571 ■ MASSACHUSETTS OFFICE OF STUDENT FINANCIAL ASSISTANCE
454 Broadway, Suite 200
Revere, MA 02151
Tel: (617)727-9420
Fax: (617)727-0667
E-mail: osfa@osfa.mass.edu
Web Site: http://www.osfa.mass.edu
To provide scholarship/loans to students at colleges and universities in Massachusetts who are interested in becoming teachers in the state following graduation.
Title of Award: Massachusetts Incentive Program for Aspiring Teachers **Area, Field, or Subject:** Education, Elementary; Education, Secondary **Level of Education for which Award is Granted:** Undergraduate **Number Awarded:** Varies each year. **Funds Available:** Eligible students are entitled to a tuition waiver equal to the resident tuition rate at the state college or university campus where they are enrolled. If they do not complete their college education within 4 years of entering the program, or if they fail to complete their 2-year teaching commitment within 4 years following graduation from college, they must pay the state the full amount of the tuition waivers granted, with interest. **Duration:** 2 years, provided the recipient maintains a GPA of 3.0 or higher.
Eligibility Requirements: This program is open to students enrolled in their third or fourth year of a Massachusetts state-approved teacher certification program field with teacher shortages. Applicants must 1) have been residents of Massachusetts for at least 1 year and 2) be U.S. citizens or permanent residents. They must be attending 1 of the 9 Massachusetts state colleges or the 4 campuses of the University of Massachusetts and have a cumulative GPA of 3.0 or higher. A condition of the program is that they must commit to teaching for 2 years in a public school in Massachusetts upon successful completion of a bachelor's degree.

3572 ■ MASSACHUSETTS OFFICE OF STUDENT FINANCIAL ASSISTANCE
454 Broadway, Suite 200
Revere, MA 02151
Tel: (617)727-9420
Fax: (617)727-0667
E-mail: osfa@osfa.mass.edu
Web Site: http://www.osfa.mass.edu
To provide scholarship/loans to educational paraprofessionals in Massachusetts who are interested in completing a college degree and becoming certified as teachers.
Title of Award: Massachusetts Paraprofessional Teacher Preparation Grant Program **Area, Field, or Subject:** Education; Education, Bilingual and cross-cultural; Education, Special; Linguistics; Mathematics and mathematical sciences; Science **Level of Education for which Award is Granted:** Undergraduate **Number Awarded:** Varies each year. **Funds Available:** Grants depend on the type of institution attended. At public universities, the maximum award is $625 per credit, to a total of $7,500 per academic year. At state colleges, the maximum award is $450 per credit, to a total of $6,000 per academic year. At community colleges, the maximum award is $250 per credit, to a total of $4,000 per academic year. This is a scholarship/loan program. Recipients must agree to teach in a Massachusetts public school 1 year for each year of full or partial grant received. If they fail to complete that teaching obligation, they must repay the amount of the grant received. **Duration:** Until completion of an undergraduate degree, provided the recipient maintains satisfactory academic progress.
Eligibility Requirements: This program is open to Massachusetts residents who 1) have been employed as paraprofessionals in public

schools in the state for at least 2 years, or 2) are working on a degree in an area of high need (recently defined as bilingual education, foreign languages, mathematics, science, and special education). Applicants must be enrolled full time in an undergraduate degree program leading to teacher certification at a Massachusetts public institution. U.S. citizenship or permanent resident status is required Applicants must submit a Free Application for Federal Student Aid (FAFSA), but financial need is not required.

3573 ■ MAUI COMMUNITY COLLEGE
Attn: Liko A'e Native Hawaiian Scholarship Program
310 West Ka'ahumanu Avenue
Kahului, HI 96732-1617
Tel: (808)984-3553
E-mail: lhokoana@hawaii.edu
Web Site: http://www.likoae.org/scholarship_info.asp
To provide financial assistance for college or graduate school to Native Hawaiian students.
Title of Award: Liko A'e Scholarships **Area, Field, or Subject:** Education; General studies/Field of study not specified **Level of Education for which Award is Granted:** Graduate, Undergraduate **Number Awarded:** Varies each year. **Funds Available:** A stipend is awarded (amount not specified). Child care assistance is also provided. **Duration:** 1 year.
Eligibility Requirements: This program is open to U.S. citizens who are descendants of the aboriginal inhabitants of the Hawaiian Islands prior to 1778. Applicants must be enrolled or accepted as full- or part-time students in an accredited 2- or 4-year degree-granting institution of higher education. Undergraduates must have a GPA of 2.0 or higher and graduate students must have a GPA of 3.0 or higher. Selection is based on merit (as judged by GPA and responses to essay questions) and financial need. Preference is given to students working on degrees in professions in which Native Hawaiians are underrepresented. Some of the scholarships are designated for students from smaller rural communities who are working on a degree in education. **Deadline for Receipt:** Deadlines are in May, August, November, and February. **Additional Information:** This program was established in 2003 by a grant from the U.S. Department of Education and is administered by Maui Community College.

3574 ■ MEMORIAL FOUNDATION FOR JEWISH CULTURE
50 Broadway, 34th Floor
New York, NY 10004
Tel: (212)425-6606
Fax: (212)425-6602
E-mail: office@mfjc.org
Web Site: http://www.mfjc.org
To assist well-qualified individuals to train for careers in a field related to Jewish community service.
Title of Award: International Scholarship Program for Community Service **Area, Field, or Subject:** Education; Jewish studies; Religion; Social work **Level of Education for which Award is Granted:** Graduate, Undergraduate **Funds Available:** The amount of the grant varies, depending on the country in which the student will be trained and other considerations. **Duration:** 1 year; may be renewed.
Eligibility Requirements: The scholarship is open to any individual, regardless of country of origin, who is presently receiving or plans to undertake training in his/her chosen field at a recognized yeshiva, teacher training seminary, school of social work, university, or other educational institution. Applicants must be interested in pursuing professional training for careers in Jewish education, Jewish social service, the rabbinate, or as religious functionaries (e.g., shohatim, mohalim) in Diaspora Jewish communities in need of such personnel. Students planning to serve in the United States, Canada, or Israel are not eligible. **Deadline for Receipt:** November of each year. **Additional Information:** Recipients must agree to serve for at least 2 to 3 years in a Jewish-deprived Diaspora community where their skills are needed after completing their training.

3575 ■ MINNESOTA BUSINESS EDUCATORS, INC.
c/o Kathryn Larson, MBEI Awards Chair
Owatonna High School
333 East School Street
Owatonna, MN 55060
Tel: (507)444-8800
E-mail: klarson1@owatonna.k12.mn.us

Web Site: http://www.mbei-online.org

To provide financial assistance for college to members of Minnesota Business Educators, Inc. (MBEI) who are enrolled in a business teaching licensure program at a Minnesota college or university.

Title of Award: Minnesota Business Educators Award for Business Education Teaching Majors **Area, Field, or Subject:** Education **Level of Education for which Award is Granted:** Undergraduate **Number Awarded:** 1 each year. **Funds Available:** A stipend is awarded (amount not specified). **Duration:** 1 year.

Eligibility Requirements: This program is open to student members of MBEI enrolled as a major in a business teacher licensure program at a Minnesota college or university. Applicants must submit a letter indicating why they merit this award, a 2-page resume, 2 letters of recommendation, and a transcript. **Deadline for Receipt:** February of each year. **Additional Information:** This award was first presented in 1989.

3576 ■ MISSISSIPPI OFFICE OF STUDENT FINANCIAL AID

3825 Ridgewood Road
Jackson, MS 39211-6453
Tel: (601)432-6997
Free: 800-327-2980
Fax: (601)432-6527
E-mail: sfa@ihl.state.ms.us
Web Site: http://www.ihl.state.ms.us/financialaid/cnar.html

To provide scholarship/loans to students in Mississippi interested in preparing for a career as a teacher and willing to work in selected areas of the state or teach in specified subject areas.

Title of Award: Mississippi Critical Needs Alternate Route Teacher Loan/Scholarship Program **Area, Field, or Subject:** Education; Education, Special **Level of Education for which Award is Granted:** Four Year College **Number Awarded:** Varies each year, depending on the availability of funds; awards are granted on a first-come, first-served basis. **Funds Available:** The program provides payment of tuition and required fees (at the in-state rate only), an allowance for room and board equal to the state average for a Mississippi resident, and an allowance for books. This is a scholarship/loan program; recipients must sign a contract agreeing to teach 1 year for each year the award is received in an accredited public school or public school district in a critical teacher geographic shortage area of Mississippi as defined at the time of graduation. If the recipient fails to remain enrolled in a teacher education program or fails to fulfill the service obligation, repayment of principal and interest is required. **Duration:** 1 year; may be renewed 1 additional year if the recipient maintains a GPA of 2.5 or higher, meets the satisfactory academic progress standards of their institution, and remains enrolled in a program of study leading to an Alternate Route teacher license.

Eligibility Requirements: This program is normally open to juniors and seniors at Mississippi 4-year colleges and universities. Mississippi residency is not required. Applicants must be enrolled in a program of study leading to an Alternate Route teacher license and be working on their first bachelor's degree. They must have passed Praxis I; agree to employment immediately after completing their degree as a full-time classroom teacher in a Mississippi public school located in a critical teacher shortage area of the state or in a subject shortage area; participate in entrance counseling; and have a cumulative GPA of 2.5 or higher. **Deadline for Receipt:** March of each year. **Additional Information:** A list of the current critical teacher shortage areas is available from the Mississippi Department of Education. Current subject shortage areas are mathematics, science (chemistry, physics, and biology only), foreign language (French, German, and Spanish only), and special education. Recipients are not eligible for funds from other state aid programs.

3577 ■ MISSISSIPPI OFFICE OF STUDENT FINANCIAL AID

3825 Ridgewood Road
Jackson, MS 39211-6453
Tel: (601)432-6997
Free: 800-327-2980
Fax: (601)432-6527
E-mail: sfa@ihl.state.ms.us
Web Site: http://www.ihl.state.ms.us/financialaid/cntp.html

To provide scholarship/loans to students in Mississippi interested in preparing for a career as a teacher and willing to work in selected areas of the state or teach in specified subject areas.

Title of Award: Mississippi Critical Needs Teacher Loan/Scholarship Program **Area, Field, or Subject:** Education; Education, Special **Level of Education for which Award is Granted:** Four Year College **Number Awarded:** Varies each year, depending on the availability of funds; awards are granted on a first-come, first-served basis. **Funds Available:** The program provides payment of tuition and required fees (at the in-state rate only), an allowance for room and board equal to the state average for a Mississippi resident, and an allowance for books. This is a scholarship/loan program; recipients must sign a contract agreeing to teach 1 year for each year the award is received in an accredited public school or public school district in a critical teacher geographic shortage area of Mississippi as defined at the time of graduation. If the recipient fails to remain enrolled in a teacher education program or fails to fulfill the service obligation, repayment of principal and interest is required. **Duration:** 1 year; may be renewed 1 additional year if the recipient maintains a GPA of 2.5 or higher, meets the satisfactory academic progress standards of their institution, and remains enrolled in a program of study leading to a Class "A" teacher educator license.

Eligibility Requirements: This program is normally open to juniors and seniors at Mississippi 4-year colleges and universities. Mississippi residency is not required. While in high school applicants must have passed Praxis I, had an ACT score of 21 or higher, or had an SAT score of 860 or higher. While in college, they must enroll in a program of study leading to a Class "A" teacher educator license; agree to employment immediately after completing their degree as a full-time classroom teacher in a Mississippi public school located in a critical teacher shortage area of the state or in a subject shortage area; participate in entrance counseling; and have a cumulative GPA of 2.5 or higher. **Deadline for Receipt:** March of each year. **Additional Information:** This program was established in 1998. A list of the current critical teacher shortage areas is available from the Mississippi Department of Education. Current subject shortage areas are mathematics, science (chemistry, physics, and biology only), foreign language (French, German, and Spanish only), and special education. Recipients are not eligible for funds from other state aid programs.

3578 ■ MISSISSIPPI OFFICE OF STUDENT FINANCIAL AID

3825 Ridgewood Road
Jackson, MS 39211-6453
Tel: (601)432-6997
Free: 800-327-2980
Fax: (601)432-6527
E-mail: sfa@ihl.state.ms.us
Web Site: http://www.ihl.state.ms.us/financialaid/wwar.html

To provide scholarship/loans to Mississippi residents working on an Alternative Route teacher educator license.

Title of Award: William Winter Alternative Route Teacher Scholar Loan Program **Area, Field, or Subject:** Education **Level of Education for which Award is Granted:** Four Year College **Number Awarded:** Varies each year, depending on the availability of funds; awards are granted on a first-come, first-served basis. **Funds Available:** Loans are provided up to $4,000 per academic year. For each year of service as a full-time classroom teacher in an accredited public school or public school district in Mississippi, 1 year's loan will be forgiven. **Duration:** 1 year; may be renewed 1 additional year if the recipient maintains a GPA of 2.5 or higher, remains enrolled full time in a program of study leading to an Alternative Route teacher educator license, exhibits satisfactory academic progress, and documents that Praxis II has been passed after no more than 3 semesters of participation in this program.

Eligibility Requirements: This program is open to Mississippi residents who are enrolled full time as juniors or seniors at an accredited Mississippi 4-year public or private college or university. Applicants must be enrolled in a program of study leading to an Alternative Route teacher educator license with a cumulative GPA of 2.5 or higher. They must have passed Praxis I and agree to employment immediately upon degree completion as a full-time classroom teacher in a Mississippi public school. **Deadline for Receipt:** March of each year. **Additional Information:** Recipients may not defer the service obligation to work on an advanced degree.

3579 ■ MISSISSIPPI OFFICE OF STUDENT FINANCIAL AID

3825 Ridgewood Road
Jackson, MS 39211-6453
Tel: (601)432-6997
Free: 800-327-2980
Fax: (601)432-6527
E-mail: sfa@ihl.state.ms.us

Web Site: http://www.ihl.state.ms.us/financialaid/wwts.html
To provide scholarship/loans to Mississippi residents working on a Class "A" teacher educator license.

Title of Award: William Winter Teacher Scholar Loan Program **Area, Field, or Subject:** Education **Level of Education for which Award is Granted:** Four Year College **Number Awarded:** Varies each year, depending on the availability of funds; awards are granted on a first-come, first-served basis. **Funds Available:** Loans are provided up to $4,000 per academic year. For each year of service as a full-time classroom teacher in an accredited public school or public school district in Mississippi, 1 year's loan will be forgiven. **Duration:** 1 year; may be renewed 1 additional year if the recipient maintains a GPA of 2.5 or higher, remains enrolled full time in a program of study leading to a Class "A" teacher educator license, exhibits satisfactory academic progress, and documents that Praxis II has been passed after no more than 3 semesters of participation in this program.
Eligibility Requirements: This program is open to Mississippi residents who are enrolled full time as juniors or seniors at an accredited Mississippi 4-year public or private college or university. Applicants must be enrolled in a program of study leading to a Class "A" teacher educator license with a cumulative GPA of 2.5 or higher. They must be able to document that they have passed Praxis I or have an ACT score of 21 or higher with a minimum of 18 on all sub-scores. Programs of study that do not qualify include, but are not limited to, speech and language pathology, psychological and counseling services, and recreational therapy. **Deadline for Receipt:** March of each year. **Additional Information:** The Mississippi legislature established this program in 1987. Recipients may not defer the service obligation to work on an advanced degree.

3580 ■ MORRIS SCHOLARSHIP FUND

Attn: Scholarship Selection Committee
525 S.W. Fifth Street, Suite A
Des Moines, IA 50309-4501
Tel: (515)282-8192
Fax: (515)282-9117
E-mail: morris@assoc-mgmt.com
Web Site: http://www.morrisscholarship.org
To provide financial assistance to African Americans in Iowa interested in preparing to work with "at risk" students.

Title of Award: Nelson Urban Scholarship Fund **Area, Field, or Subject:** Education, Elementary; Education, Secondary **Level of Education for which Award is Granted:** Graduate, Undergraduate **Number Awarded:** At least 2 each year. **Funds Available:** The awards generally range from $2,500 to $5,000. **Duration:** 1 year.
Eligibility Requirements: This program is open to African Americans who are Iowa residents, enrolled full or part time at the undergraduate or graduate school level, and interested in working with "at risk" minority students in the elementary or secondary schools. **Deadline for Receipt:** January of each year.

3581 ■ P. BUCKLEY MOSS SOCIETY

20 Stoneridge Drive, Suite 102
Waynesboro, VA 22980
Tel: (540)943-5678
Fax: (540)949-8408
E-mail: society@mosssociety.org
Web Site: http://www.mosssociety.org
To provide financial assistance to students working on a bachelor's or master's degree in special education.

Title of Award: Judith Cary Memorial Scholarship **Area, Field, or Subject:** Education, Special **Level of Education for which Award is Granted:** Four Year College, Master's **Number Awarded:** 2 each year. **Funds Available:** The stipend is $1,000. Funds are paid to the recipient's college or university. **Duration:** 1 year.
Eligibility Requirements: Eligible to be nominated for this scholarship are students who have completed at least 2 years of undergraduate study and are working on a bachelor's or master's degree in special education. Nominations may be submitted by society members only. The nomination packet must include proof of acceptance into a specific program to teach special needs students, 2 letters of recommendation, a short essay on school and community work activities and achievements, and an essay of 250 to 500 words on their career goals, teaching philosophies, reasons for choosing this career, and ways in which they plan to make a difference in

the lives of special needs students. Financial need is not considered in the selection process. **Deadline for Receipt:** March of each year. **Additional Information:** This program was established in 1999.

3582 ■ NATIONAL ASSOCIATION OF EDUCATIONAL OFFICE PROFESSIONALS

Attn: NAEOP Foundation
P.O. Box 12619
Wichita, KS 67277-2619
Tel: (316)942-4822
Fax: (316)942-7100
E-mail: naeop@naeop.org
Web Site: http://www.naeop.org/foundation.htm
To provide financial assistance to students interested in preparing for an office-related career.

Title of Award: Marion T. Wood National Scholarships **Area, Field, or Subject:** Education; Secretarial sciences **Level of Education for which Award is Granted:** Undergraduate **Number Awarded:** Varies each year. **Funds Available:** The stipend is $1,000. **Duration:** 1 year.
Eligibility Requirements: This program is open to business education students preparing for an office-related career, preferably in the field of education. **Deadline for Receipt:** February of each year.

3583 ■ NATIONAL DAIRY PROMOTION AND RESEARCH BOARD

c/o Dairy Management Inc.
10255 West Higgins Road, Suite 900
Rosemont, IL 60018-5616
Tel: (847)803-2000
Fax: (847)803-2077
E-mail: marykateg@rosedmi.com
Web Site: http://www.dairycheckoff.com/DairyCheckoff/about/scholarship.htm
To provide financial assistance to undergraduate students in fields related to the dairy industry.

Title of Award: NDPRB Undergraduate Scholarship Program **Area, Field, or Subject:** Business administration; Communications; Dairy science; Economics; Education; Food science and technology; Journalism; Marketing and distribution; Nutrition; Public relations **Level of Education for which Award is Granted:** Four Year College **Number Awarded:** 20 each year: the James H. Loper Jr. Memorial Scholarship at $2,500 and 19 other scholarships at $1,500. **Funds Available:** Stipends are $2,500 or $1,500. **Duration:** 1 year; may be renewed.
Eligibility Requirements: This program is open to sophomores, juniors, and seniors enrolled in college and university programs that emphasize dairy. Eligible majors include agricultural education, business, communications and/or public relations, economics, food science, journalism, marketing, and nutrition. Fields related to production (e.g., animal science) are not eligible. Selection is based on academic performance; interest in a career in dairy; involvement in extracurricular activities, especially those relating to dairy; and evidence of leadership ability, initiative, character, and integrity. The applicant who is judged most outstanding is awarded the James H. Loper Jr. Memorial Scholarship. **Deadline for Receipt:** May of each year. **Additional Information:** Dairy Management Inc. manages this program on behalf of the National Dairy Promotion and Research Board (NDPRB).

3584 ■ NATIONAL FEDERATION OF THE BLIND

c/o Peggy Elliott, Scholarship Committee Chair
805 Fifth Avenue
Grinnell, IA 50112
Tel: (641)236-3366
Web Site: http://www.nfb.org/sch_intro.htm
To provide financial assistance to blind undergraduate or graduate students who wish to prepare for a career as a teacher.

Title of Award: Educator of Tomorrow Award **Area, Field, or Subject:** Education; Education, Elementary; Education, Secondary **Level of Education for which Award is Granted:** Graduate, Undergraduate **Number Awarded:** 1 each year. **Funds Available:** The stipend is $3,000. **Duration:** 1 year; recipients may resubmit applications up to 2 additional years.
Eligibility Requirements: This program is open to legally blind students who are working on or planning to work full time on an undergraduate or graduate degree. Applicants must be preparing for a career in elementary,

secondary, or postsecondary teaching. Selection is based on academic excellence, service to the community, and financial need. **Deadline for Receipt:** March of each year. **Additional Information:** Scholarships are awarded at the federation convention in July. Recipients attend the convention at federation expense; that funding is in addition to the scholarship grant.

3585 ■ NATIONAL FEDERATION OF THE BLIND
c/o Peggy Elliott, Scholarship Committee Chair
805 Fifth Avenue
Grinnell, IA 50112
Tel: (641)236-3366
Web Site: http://www.nfb.org/sch_intro.htm
To provide financial assistance to blind undergraduate and graduate students working on a degree in the field of education, especially those planning to major in education of disabled youth.
Title of Award: Sally S. Jacobsen Scholarship **Area, Field, or Subject:** Education; Education, Special **Level of Education for which Award is Granted:** Graduate, Undergraduate **Number Awarded:** 1 each year. **Funds Available:** The stipend is $5,000. **Duration:** 1 year; recipients may resubmit applications up to 2 additional years.
Eligibility Requirements: This program is open to legally blind students who are working on or planning to work full time on an undergraduate or graduate degree in education. Preference is given to applicants planning to specialize in education of disabled youth. Selection is based on academic excellence, service to the community, and financial need. **Deadline for Receipt:** March of each year. **Additional Information:** Scholarships are awarded at the federation convention in July. Recipients attend the convention at federation expense; that funding is in addition to the scholarship grant.

3586 ■ NATIONAL FEDERATION OF THE BLIND OF CONNECTICUT
580 Burnside Avenue, Suite 1
East Hartford, CT 06108
Tel: (860)289-1971
E-mail: info@nfbct.org
Web Site: http://www.nfbct.org/html/bcmsch.htm
To provide financial assistance for college or graduate school to students in Connecticut who plan to become a teacher of the blind and visually impaired.
Title of Award: Brian Cummins Memorial Scholarship **Area, Field, or Subject:** Education, Special; Visual impairment **Level of Education for which Award is Granted:** Graduate, Undergraduate **Number Awarded:** 1 each year. **Funds Available:** The stipend is $5,000. **Duration:** 1 year.
Eligibility Requirements: This program is open to graduate and undergraduate students enrolled full time at colleges and universities in Connecticut who are preparing for a career as a certified teacher of the blind and visually impaired. Applicants must be planning to reside in Connecticut and work as a teacher of the blind and visually impaired. Along with their application, they must submit a letter on their career goals and how the scholarship might help them achieve those. Applicants do not need to be blind or members of the National Federation of the Blind of Connecticut. Selection is based on academic quality, service to the community, and financial need. **Deadline for Receipt:** September of each year. **Additional Information:** This program was established to honor Brian Cummins, who lost his life in the World Trade Center on September 11, 2001.

3587 ■ NATIONAL FFA ORGANIZATION
Attn: Scholarship Office
6060 FFA Drive
P.O. Box 68960
Indianapolis, IN 46268-0960
Tel: (317)802-4321
Fax: (317)802-5321
E-mail: scholarships@ffa.org
Web Site: http://www.ffa.org
To provide financial assistance to FFA members from Florida and Georgia who are interested in studying fields related to agriculture in college.
Title of Award: Chevron Corporation Scholarships **Area, Field, or Subject:** Agricultural sciences; Communications; Education; Environmental conservation; Environmental science; Natural resources; Wildlife conservation, management, and science **Level of Education for which**

Award is Granted: Undergraduate **Number Awarded:** 2 each year. **Funds Available:** The stipend is $1,000. Funds are paid directly to the recipient. **Duration:** 1 year; nonrenewable.
Eligibility Requirements: This program is open to members who are graduating high school seniors planning to enroll full time in college. Applicants must be residents of Florida or Georgia planning to work on a 2-year or 4-year degree in agricultural communications and education, environmental engineering, environmental science, natural resource management, wildlife management, or public service and administration in agriculture. Preference is given to those who have shown outstanding leadership. Selection is based on academic achievement (10 points for GPA, 10 points for SAT or ACT score, 10 points for class rank), leadership in FFA activities (30 points), leadership in community activities (10 points), and participation in the Supervised Agricultural Experience (SAE) program (30 points). U.S. citizenship is required. **Deadline for Receipt:** February of each year. **Additional Information:** Funding for these scholarships is provided by ChevronTexaco Corporation.

3588 ■ NATIONAL FFA ORGANIZATION
Attn: Scholarship Office
6060 FFA Drive
P.O. Box 68960
Indianapolis, IN 46268-0960
Tel: (317)802-4321
Fax: (317)802-5321
E-mail: scholarships@ffa.org
Web Site: http://www.ffa.org
To provide financial assistance to FFA members who are interested in studying agriculture in college.
Title of Award: Garst Seed Company Scholarship **Area, Field, or Subject:** Agribusiness; Agricultural sciences; Communications; Education; Marketing and distribution **Level of Education for which Award is Granted:** Four Year College **Number Awarded:** 25 each year: 10 to students with any agricultural major, 5 to students majoring in agricultural communications or education, and 10 to students in agricultural marketing, merchandising, or sales. **Funds Available:** The stipend is $1,000. Funds are paid directly to the recipient. **Duration:** 1 year; nonrenewable.
Eligibility Requirements: This program is open to members who are graduating high school seniors planning to enroll or students currently enrolled full time in college. Applicants must be interested in working on a 4-year college degree in agriculture; in agricultural communications or education; or in agricultural marketing, merchandising, or sales. Selection is based on academic achievement (10 points for GPA, 10 points for SAT or ACT score, 10 points for class rank), leadership in FFA activities (30 points), leadership in community activities (10 points), and participation in the Supervised Agricultural Experience (SAE) program (30 points). U.S. citizenship is required. **Deadline for Receipt:** February of each year. **Additional Information:** Funding for this scholarship is provided by Garst Seed Company.

3589 ■ NATIONAL FFA ORGANIZATION
Attn: Scholarship Office
6060 FFA Drive
P.O. Box 68960
Indianapolis, IN 46268-0960
Tel: (317)802-4321
Fax: (317)802-5321
E-mail: scholarships@ffa.org
Web Site: http://www.ffa.org
To provide financial assistance to FFA members interested in studying agricultural education in college.
Title of Award: Elmer J. and Hester Jane Johnson Honorary Scholarship **Area, Field, or Subject:** Education **Level of Education for which Award is Granted:** Four Year College **Number Awarded:** 1 each year. **Funds Available:** The stipend is $1,000. Funds are paid directly to the recipient. **Duration:** 1 year; nonrenewable.
Eligibility Requirements: This program is open to members who are graduating high school seniors planning to enroll full time in college. Applicants must be planning to work on a 4-year college degree in

agricultural education. Selection is based on financial need, leadership ability, and academic standing. **Deadline for Receipt:** February of each year.

3590 ■ NATIONAL FFA ORGANIZATION
Attn: Scholarship Office
6060 FFA Drive
P.O. Box 68960
Indianapolis, IN 46268-0960
Tel: (317)802-4321
Fax: (317)802-5321
E-mail: scholarships@ffa.org
Web Site: http://www.ffa.org
To provide financial assistance to FFA members interested in working on a degree in agricultural education in college.
Title of Award: Monsanto Roadrunners Scholarships **Area, Field, or Subject:** Education **Level of Education for which Award is Granted:** Four Year College **Number Awarded:** At least 2 each year. **Funds Available:** The stipend is $1,500. **Duration:** 1 year; nonrenewable.
Eligibility Requirements: This program is open to FFA members who are high school seniors and whose families are actively engaged in production agriculture. Applicants must be planning to work full time on a 4-year degree in agricultural education. They must have an ACT composite score of 18 or higher or an SAT combined verbal and math score of 850 or higher. Selection is based on academic achievement (10 points for GPA, 10 points for SAT or ACT score, 10 points for class rank), leadership in FFA activities (30 points), leadership in community activities (10 points), and participation in the Supervised Agricultural Experience (SAE) program (30 points). U.S. citizenship is required. **Deadline for Receipt:** February of each year. **Additional Information:** This program is funded by employees of Monsanto Company who combine their passion for running and commitment to agricultural education by running in marathons to raise funds for scholarships.

3591 ■ NATIONAL FFA ORGANIZATION
Attn: Scholarship Office
6060 FFA Drive
P.O. Box 68960
Indianapolis, IN 46268-0960
Tel: (317)802-4321
Fax: (317)802-5321
E-mail: scholarships@ffa.org
Web Site: http://www.ffa.org
To provide financial assistance to FFA members interested in studying agricultural education in college.
Title of Award: National FFA Alumni Association Scholarships **Area, Field, or Subject:** Education **Level of Education for which Award is Granted:** Four Year College **Number Awarded:** 5 each year. **Funds Available:** The stipend is $1,000. Funds are paid directly to the recipient. **Duration:** 1 year; nonrenewable.
Eligibility Requirements: This program is open to members who are either graduating high school seniors planning to enroll full time in college or students already enrolled in college on a full-time basis. Applicants must be working on or planning to work on a 4-year degree in agricultural education to prepare for a career as an agriculture teacher. They must be an alumni member or from an FFA chapter with an active alumni affiliate. Selection is based on academic achievement (10 points for GPA, 10 points for SAT or ACT score, 10 points for class rank), leadership in FFA activities (30 points), leadership in community activities (10 points), and participation in the Supervised Agricultural Experience (SAE) program (30 points). U.S. citizenship is required. **Deadline for Receipt:** February of each year. **Additional Information:** Funding for these scholarships is provided by the National FFA Alumni Association.

3592 ■ NATIONAL FFA ORGANIZATION
Attn: Scholarship Office
6060 FFA Drive
P.O. Box 68960
Indianapolis, IN 46268-0960
Tel: (317)802-4321
Fax: (317)802-5321
E-mail: scholarships@ffa.org
Web Site: http://www.ffa.org

To provide financial assistance to FFA members interested in studying agricultural education in college.
Title of Award: National FFA Foundation/AERO Staff Scholarship **Area, Field, or Subject:** Education **Level of Education for which Award is Granted:** Four Year College **Number Awarded:** 1 each year. **Funds Available:** The stipend is $1,000. Funds are paid directly to the recipient. **Duration:** 1 year; nonrenewable.
Eligibility Requirements: This program is open to members who are graduating high school seniors planning to enroll full time in college. Applicants must be interested in working on a 4-year degree in agricultural education. Selection is based on academic achievement (10 points for GPA, 10 points for SAT or ACT score, 10 points for class rank), leadership in FFA activities (30 points), leadership in community activities (10 points), and participation in the Supervised Agricultural Experience (SAE) program (30 points). U.S. citizenship is required. **Deadline for Receipt:** February of each year. **Additional Information:** Funding for this scholarship is provided by staff and board members of the National FFA Organization, National FFA Foundation, and the Agricultural Education Related Organizations (AERO).

3593 ■ NATIONAL FFA ORGANIZATION
Attn: Scholarship Office
6060 FFA Drive
P.O. Box 68960
Indianapolis, IN 46268-0960
Tel: (317)802-4321
Fax: (317)802-5321
E-mail: scholarships@ffa.org
Web Site: http://www.ffa.org
To provide financial assistance to FFA members who wish to study agribusiness and related fields in college.
Title of Award: National FFA Scholarships for Undergraduates in the Social Sciences **Area, Field, or Subject:** Agribusiness; Agriculture, Economic aspects; Education; Finance; Marketing and distribution **Level of Education for which Award is Granted:** Undergraduate **Number Awarded:** Varies; generally, a total of approximately 1,000 scholarships are awarded annually by the association. **Funds Available:** Stipends vary, but most are at least $1,000. **Duration:** 1 year or more.
Eligibility Requirements: This program is open to current and former members of the organization who are working or planning to work full time on a degree in fields related to business and the social sciences; this includes: agribusiness, agricultural economics, agricultural education, agricultural finance, and agricultural marketing. For most of the scholarships, applicants must be high school seniors; others are open to students currently enrolled in college. The program includes a large number of designated scholarships that specify the locations where the members must live, the schools they must attend, the fields of study they must pursue, or other requirements. Some consider family income in the selection process, but most do not. Selection is based on academic achievement (10 points for GPA, 10 points for SAT or ACT score, 10 points for class rank), leadership in FFA activities (30 points), leadership in community activities (10 points), and participation in the Supervised Agricultural Experience (SAE) program (30 points). U.S. citizenship is required. **Deadline for Receipt:** February of each year. **Additional Information:** Funding for these scholarships is provided by many different corporate sponsors.

3594 ■ NATIONAL FFA ORGANIZATION
Attn: Scholarship Office
6060 FFA Drive
P.O. Box 68960
Indianapolis, IN 46268-0960
Tel: (317)802-4321
Fax: (317)802-5321
E-mail: scholarships@ffa.org
Web Site: http://www.ffa.org
To provide financial assistance to current or former FFA members who are interested in studying a field related to agriculture at a college or university in designated states.
Title of Award: Norfolk Southern Foundation Scholarships **Area, Field, or Subject:** Agribusiness; Agricultural sciences; Communications; Education; Engineering, Agricultural; Finance; Forestry; Management; Marketing and distribution **Level of Education for which Award is Granted:** Four

Year College **Number Awarded:** 3 each year. **Funds Available:** The stipend is $1,000. Funds are paid directly to the recipient. **Duration:** 1 year; nonrenewable.

Eligibility Requirements: This program is open to members who are either graduating high school seniors planning to enroll in college or students already enrolled in college. Applicants must be interested in working full time on a 4-year degree in agricultural and forestry production, communication, education, engineering, finance, management, marketing, merchandising, sales, or agricultural science. They must be planning to attend a college or university in Alabama, Delaware, Georgia, Illinois, Indiana, Louisiana, Maryland, Michigan, Missouri, New York, North Carolina, Ohio, Pennsylvania, South Carolina, Tennessee, or Virginia. Selection is based on academic achievement (10 points for GPA, 10 points for SAT or ACT score, 10 points for class rank), leadership in FFA activities (30 points), leadership in community activities (10 points), and participation in the Supervised Agricultural Experience (SAE) program (30 points). U.S. citizenship is required. **Deadline for Receipt:** February of each year. **Additional Information:** Funding for these scholarships is provided by the Norfolk Southern Foundation.

3595 ■ NATIONAL FFA ORGANIZATION
Attn: Scholarship Office
6060 FFA Drive
P.O. Box 68960
Indianapolis, IN 46268-0960
Tel: (317)802-4321
Fax: (317)802-5321
E-mail: scholarships@ffa.org
Web Site: http://www.ffa.org
To provide financial assistance to FFA members from designated states who are interested in studying agricultural education in college.
Title of Award: Pioneer Hi-Bred International Scholarships **Area, Field, or Subject:** Education **Level of Education for which Award is Granted:** Four Year College **Number Awarded:** 12 each year. **Funds Available:** The stipend is $1,000. Funds are paid directly to the recipient. **Duration:** 1 year; nonrenewable.

Eligibility Requirements: This program is open to members who are graduating high school seniors planning to enroll full time in college. Applicants must be residents of Colorado, Illinois, Indiana, Iowa, Kansas, Minnesota, Missouri, or Nebraska and interested in working on a 4-year degree in agricultural education. Selection is based on academic achievement (10 points for GPA, 10 points for SAT or ACT score, 10 points for class rank), leadership in FFA activities (30 points), leadership in community activities (10 points), and participation in the Supervised Agricultural Experience (SAE) program (30 points). U.S. citizenship is required. **Deadline for Receipt:** February of each year. **Additional Information:** Funding for these scholarships is provided by Pioneer Hi-Bred International, Inc. of Des Moines, Iowa.

3596 ■ NATIONAL FFA ORGANIZATION
Attn: Scholarship Office
6060 FFA Drive
P.O. Box 68960
Indianapolis, IN 46268-0960
Tel: (317)802-4321
Fax: (317)802-5321
E-mail: scholarships@ffa.org
Web Site: http://www.ffa.org
To provide financial assistance to FFA members who are studying a field related to communications, business, or education in college.
Title of Award: Solutions Inc. Results Through Creative Marketing Scholarships **Area, Field, or Subject:** Agribusiness; Agricultural sciences; Communications; Education; Marketing and distribution **Level of Education for which Award is Granted:** Four Year College **Number Awarded:** 3 each year. **Funds Available:** The stipend is $1,000 per year. Funds are paid directly to the recipient. **Duration:** 1 year; nonrenewable.

Eligibility Requirements: This program is open to members currently enrolled full time in college and working on a 4-year degree in agricultural communications, marketing, merchandising, sales, or as an education specialist. Applicants must have a GPA of 3.0 or higher. Selection is based on academic achievement (10 points for GPA, 10 points for SAT or ACT score, 10 points for class rank), leadership in FFA activities (30 points), leadership in community activities (10 points), and participation in the

Supervised Agricultural Experience (SAE) program (30 points). U.S. citizenship is required. **Deadline for Receipt:** February of each year. **Additional Information:** This program is sponsored by the creative marketing firm Solutions Inc. Results Through Creative Marketing.

3597 ■ NATIONAL FFA ORGANIZATION
Attn: Scholarship Office
6060 FFA Drive
P.O. Box 68960
Indianapolis, IN 46268-0960
Tel: (317)802-4321
Fax: (317)802-5321
E-mail: scholarships@ffa.org
Web Site: http://www.ffa.org
To provide financial assistance to FFA members interested in working on a degree in agricultural education in college.
Title of Award: Bernie Staller Endowment Fund Scholarship **Area, Field, or Subject:** Education **Level of Education for which Award is Granted:** Four Year College **Number Awarded:** 1 or more each year. **Funds Available:** The stipend is $2,500. **Duration:** 1 year; nonrenewable.

Eligibility Requirements: This program is open to FFA members who are high school seniors planning to enroll full time in college. Applicants must be planning to work on a 4-year degree in agricultural education and have career plans to teach at the secondary level. Selection is based on academic achievement (10 points for GPA, 10 points for SAT or ACT score, 10 points for class rank), leadership in FFA activities (30 points), leadership in community activities (10 points), and participation in the Supervised Agricultural Experience (SAE) program (30 points). U.S. citizenship is required. **Deadline for Receipt:** February of each year.

3598 ■ NATIONAL SORORITY OF PHI DELTA KAPPA, INC.-DELTA BETA CHAPTER
c/o Nancy Thompson, Chapter Scholarship Chair
4703 Broadhill Drive
Austin, TX 78723
Tel: (512)926-6309
To provide financial assistance to African American high school seniors who plan to study education in college.
Title of Award: Carmer Mercer Scholarship **Area, Field, or Subject:** Education **Level of Education for which Award is Granted:** Undergraduate **Number Awarded:** 1 each year. **Funds Available:** The stipend is $1,000. **Duration:** 1 year.

Eligibility Requirements: This program is open to African American graduating high school seniors who are planning a 4-year college and major in the field of education. Along with their application, they must submit documentation of financial need, high school transcripts, 2 letters of recommendation, SAT and/or ACT scores, a list of honors and awards received in high school, and a list of extracurricular, community, and volunteer activities. **Deadline for Receipt:** January of each year.

3599 ■ NATIONAL URBAN LEAGUE
Attn: Scholarship Coordinator
120 Wall Street
New York, NY 10005
Tel: (212)558-5300; 888-839-0467
Fax: (212)344-5332
E-mail: info@nul.org
Web Site: http://www.nul.org/jerrybartowscholarship.html
To provide financial assistance to undergraduate students at Historically Black Colleges and Universities (HBCUs) that are participating in the Black Executive Exchange Program (BEEP).
Title of Award: Jerry Bartow Scholarship Fund **Area, Field, or Subject:** Business administration; Education; Management; Technology **Level of Education for which Award is Granted:** Undergraduate **Number Awarded:** 2 each year. **Funds Available:** The stipend is $1,500 per year. **Duration:** 1 year.

Eligibility Requirements: This program is open to African American sophomores, juniors, and seniors at HBCUs that are participating in the BEEP. Applicants must be majoring in business, management, technology, and/or education. **Deadline for Receipt:** January of each year. **Additional Information:** This program was established in 1997 by ITT Hartford Insurance Company. Recipients are required to attend the annual BEEP conference to accept the award. Travel and hotel arrangements are provided by BEEP.

3600 ■ NAVY WIVES CLUB OF AMERICA

P.O. Box 54022
Millington, TN 38053-6022
(866)511-NWCA
E-mail: nwca@navywivesclubsofamerica.org
Web Site: http://www.navywivesclubsofamerica.org/nwc/scholarships.htm
To provide financial assistance for college or medical school to the children of naval personnel.

Title of Award: Navy Wives Club of America National Scholarships **Area, Field, or Subject:** Education, Special; General studies/Field of study not specified; Medicine **Level of Education for which Award is Granted:** Doctorate, Undergraduate **Number Awarded:** 41 each year: 6 to freshmen, 18 for renewals, 4 to current undergraduates applying for the first time, 2 to medical students, 2 to students majoring in special education, and 9 to children of NWCA members. **Funds Available:** The stipend is $1,500. **Duration:** 1 year; may be renewed up to 3 additional years.

Eligibility Requirements: Applicants for these scholarships must be the children (natural born, legally adopted, or stepchildren) of enlisted members of the Navy, Marine Corps, or Coast Guard on active duty, retired with pay, or deceased. Applicants must be attending or planning to attend an accredited college or university. Along with their application, they must submit an essay on their career objectives and the reasons they chose those objectives. Selection is based on academic standing, moral character, and financial need. Some scholarships are reserved for students majoring in special education, medical students, and children of members of Navy Wives Club of American (NWCA). **Deadline for Receipt:** May of each year. **Additional Information:** Information is also available from the NWCA Scholarship Foundation Director, Susan Quinn, 1644A Jana Court, Norfolk, VA 23503. Membership in the NWCA is open to spouses of enlisted personnel serving in the Navy, Marine Corps, Coast Guard, and the active Reserve units of those services; spouses of enlisted personnel who have been honorable discharged, retired, or transferred to the Fleet Reserve on completion of duty; and widows of enlisted personnel in those services.

3601 ■ NEW HAMPSHIRE POSTSECONDARY EDUCATION COMMISSION

3 Barrell Court, Suite 300
Concord, NH 03301-8543
Tel: (603)271-2555
Fax: (603)271-2696
E-mail: pedes@pec.state.nh.us
Web Site: http://www.state.nh.us/postsecondary/finwork.html
To provide scholarship/loans to New Hampshire residents who are interested in attending college to prepare for careers in designated professions.

Title of Award: New Hampshire Workforce Incentive Program Forgivable Loans **Area, Field, or Subject:** Chemistry; Education; Education, Special; Linguistics; Mathematics and mathematical sciences; Nursing; Physical sciences; Physics; Science **Level of Education for which Award is Granted:** Graduate, Undergraduate **Number Awarded:** Varies each year. **Funds Available:** The stipend is $500 per semester ($1,000 per year). This is a scholarship/loan program; recipients must agree to pursue, within New Hampshire, the professional career for which they receive training. Recipients of loans for 1 year have their notes cancelled upon completion of 1 year of full-time service; repayment by service must be completed within 3 years from the date of licensure, certification, or completion of the program. Recipients of loans for more than 1 year have their notes cancelled upon completion of 2 years of full-time service; repayment by service must be completed within 5 years from the date of licensure, certification, or completion of the program. If the note is not cancelled because of service, the recipient must repay the loan within 2 years. **Duration:** 1 year; may be renewed.

Eligibility Requirements: This program is open to residents of New Hampshire who wish to prepare for careers in fields designated by the commission as shortage areas. Currently, the career shortage areas are chemistry, general science, mathematics, physical sciences, physics, special education, world languages, and nursing (L.P.N. through graduate). Applicants must be enrolled as a junior, senior, or graduate student at a college in New Hampshire and must be able to demonstrate financial need. **Deadline for Receipt:** May of each year for fall semester; December of each year for spring semester. **Additional Information:** The time for repayment of the loan, either in cash or through professional

service, is extended while the recipient is 1) engaged in a course of study, at least on a half-time basis, at an institution of higher education; 2) serving on active duty as a member of the armed forces of the United States, or as a member of VISTA, the Peace Corps, or AmeriCorps, for a period up to 3 years; 3) temporarily totally disabled for a period up to 3 years; or 4) unable to secure employment because of the need to care for a disabled spouse, child, or parent for a period up to 12 months. The repayment obligation is cancelled if the recipient is unable to work because of a permanent total disability, receives relief under federal bankruptcy laws, or dies. This program went into effect in 1999.

3602 ■ NEW JERSEY SCHOOLWOMEN'S CLUB

c/o Judy Jordan
67 Spray Way
Lavallette, NJ 08735
To provide financial assistance for college to female high school seniors in New Jersey who intend to prepare for a career in education.

Title of Award: New Jersey Schoolwomen's Club Scholarships **Area, Field, or Subject:** Education **Level of Education for which Award is Granted:** Undergraduate **Number Awarded:** 2 each year. **Funds Available:** The stipend is $1,000. **Duration:** 1 year.

Eligibility Requirements: This program is open to women graduating from high schools in New Jersey. Applicants must be planning to attend a 4-year college or university to prepare for a career in the field of education. They must have an academic average of "C+" or higher and a combined SAT mathematics and critical reading score of at least 950. Selection is based on academic achievement, community involvement, and extracurricular activities. **Deadline for Receipt:** February of each year. **Additional Information:** This program includes the Patricia Barber Scholarship and the Jeanette Hodge Scholarship.

3603 ■ NEW MEXICO ASSOCIATION OF SCHOOL BUSINESS OFFICIALS

Attn: Executive Director
P.O. Box 7535
Albuquerque, NM 87194-7535
Tel: (505)821-1887
E-mail: jmontano110@comcast.net
Web Site: http://www.nmasbo.org
To provide financial assistance to high school seniors in New Mexico who plan to study education in college.

Title of Award: NMASBO Scholarships **Area, Field, or Subject:** Education **Level of Education for which Award is Granted:** Undergraduate **Number Awarded:** 6 each year. **Funds Available:** The stipend is $1,000. **Duration:** 1 year.

Eligibility Requirements: This program is open to seniors graduating from high schools in New Mexico with a GPA of 3.0 or higher. Applicants must be planning to attend a college or university in the state to work full time on a degree related to education. **Deadline for Receipt:** April of each year.

3604 ■ NORTH CAROLINA BUSINESS EDUCATION ASSOCIATION

c/o Betsy Tobin, Past President
700 East Stonewall Street, Suite 400
Charlotte, NC 28202
Tel: (980)343-2384
E-mail: betsy.tobin@cms.k12.nc.us
Web Site: http://www.ncbea.org/bunch.htm
To provide financial assistance to high school seniors in North Carolina who plan to study business or business education in college.

Title of Award: John M. Bunch Student Scholarship **Area, Field, or Subject:** Business administration; Education **Level of Education for which Award is Granted:** Undergraduate **Number Awarded:** 1 or more each year. **Funds Available:** Stipends are $1,000 or $500. Funds are disbursed through the financial aid office at the recipient's college. **Duration:** 1 year.

Eligibility Requirements: This program is open to seniors graduating from high schools in North Carolina who have taken 1 or more business education subjects. Applicants must be planning to attend a technical school, community college, college, or university in North Carolina to prepare for a career in business and/or business education. Along with their application, they must submit a 500-word essay on their future goals or aspirations and how college can help them achieve those goals.

Financial need is not considered in the selection process. **Deadline for Receipt:** August of each year. **Additional Information:** This program was established in 1993.

3605 ■ NORTH CAROLINA STATE EDUCATION ASSISTANCE AUTHORITY

Attn: Teacher Assistant Scholarship Fund
P.O. Box 13663
Research Triangle Park, NC 27709-3663
Tel: (919)248-8614
Free: 800-700-1775
Fax: (919)248-6632
E-mail: eew@ncseaa.edu
Web Site: http://www.ncseaa.edu/TAS.htm

To provide financial assistance to public school teacher assistants in North Carolina who are interested in working on a college degree to become a teacher.

Title of Award: North Carolina Teacher Assistant Scholarship Fund **Area, Field, or Subject:** Education **Level of Education for which Award is Granted:** Four Year College, Professional **Number Awarded:** Varies each year. Recently, a total of 239 students were receiving $957,100 in support through this program. **Funds Available:** The stipend is $1,600 per semester (including summer sessions). A student can receive up to $4,800 per year or $28,000 per lifetime. **Duration:** 1 year; may be renewed if the recipient completes at least 12 semester hours with a GPA of 2.8 or higher.
Eligibility Requirements: This program is open to teacher assistants employed full time in North Carolina public schools. Applicants must be enrolled in at least 6 semester hours pursuing teacher licensure at an accredited 4-year college in North Carolina with a teacher education program. They must have a GPA of 2.8 or higher and remain employed as a teacher assistant while attending college part time. **Deadline for Receipt:** February of each year.

3606 ■ NORTH CAROLINA TEACHING FELLOWS COMMISSION

Koger Center, Cumberland Building
3739 National Drive, Suite 210
Raleigh, NC 27612
Tel: (919)781-6833
Fax: (919)781-6527
E-mail: tfellows@ncforum.org
Web Site: http://www.teachingfellows.org

To provide scholarship/loans to high school seniors in North Carolina who wish to prepare for a career in teaching.

Title of Award: North Carolina Teaching Fellows Scholarship Program **Area, Field, or Subject:** Education **Level of Education for which Award is Granted:** Undergraduate **Number Awarded:** Up to 400 each year. Approximately 20% of the program's recipients are minority and 30% are male. **Funds Available:** The maximum stipend is $6,500 per year. This is a scholarship/loan program; recipients must teach in a North Carolina public school 1 year for each year of support received. If they cannot fulfill the service requirement, they must repay the loan with 10% interest. **Duration:** 1 year; renewable for up to 3 additional years if the recipient maintains full-time enrollment and a GPA of 2.25 or higher for the freshman year and 2.50 or higher in the sophomore year.
Eligibility Requirements: This program is open to seniors at high schools in North Carolina who are interested in preparing for a career as a teacher and have been accepted for enrollment at a participating school in the state. Applicants must demonstrate superior achievement on the basis of high school grades, class standing, SAT scores, a writing sample, community service, extracurricular activities, and references from teachers and members of the community. U.S. citizenship is required. A particular goal of the program is to recruit and retain greater numbers of male and minority teacher education candidates in North Carolina. **Deadline for Receipt:** October of each year. **Additional Information:** The participating schools are Appalachian State University, East Carolina University, Elon College, Meredith College, North Carolina A&T State University, University of North Carolina at Asheville, North Carolina Central University, North Carolina State University, University of North Carolina at Pembroke, University of North Carolina at Chapel Hill, University of North Carolina at Charlotte, University of North Carolina at Greensboro, University of North Carolina at Wilmington, and Western Carolina University. This program was established in 1986 and the first fellows were named in 1987.

3607 ■ OAK RIDGE INSTITUTE FOR SCIENCE AND EDUCATION

Attn: Science and Engineering Education
P.O. Box 117
Oak Ridge, TN 37831-0117
Tel: (865)241-8240
Fax: (865)241-5219
E-mail: hollingsscholarship@orau.gov
Web Site: http://www.orau.gov/orise.htm

To provide financial assistance and summer research experience to upper-division students who are working on a degree in a field of interest to the National Oceanic and Atmospheric Administration (NOAA).

Title of Award: Ernest F. Hollings Scholarship Program **Area, Field, or Subject:** Agricultural sciences; Behavioral sciences; Biological and clinical sciences; Computer and information sciences; Education; Engineering; Information science and technology; Mathematics and mathematical sciences; Physical sciences; Social sciences **Level of Education for which Award is Granted:** Four Year College **Number Awarded:** Approximately 100 each year. **Funds Available:** This program provides a stipend of $8,000 per academic year and $650 per week during the internship, a housing subsidy and limited travel reimbursement for round-trip transportation to the internship site, and travel expenses to the scholarship program conference at the completion of the internship. **Duration:** 2 academic years plus 10 weeks during the intervening summer.
Eligibility Requirements: This program is open to full-time students entering their junior year at an accredited college or university in the United States or its territories. Applicants must be majoring in a discipline related to oceanic and atmospheric science, research, technology, and education, and supportive of the purposes of NOAA's programs and mission (e.g., biological, life, and agricultural sciences; computer and information sciences; engineering; mathematics; physical sciences; social and behavioral sciences; or teacher education). They must have a GPA of 3.0 or higher. As part of their program, they must be interested in participating in summer research and development activities at NOAA headquarters (Silver Spring, Maryland) or field centers. U.S. citizenship is required. **Deadline for Receipt:** May of each year. **Additional Information:** This program, established in 2005, is funded by NOAA and administered by Oak Ridge Institute for Science and Education (ORISE).

3608 ■ OHIO BUSINESS TEACHERS ASSOCIATION

c/o Victoria Hammer, President
University of Cincinnati
Raymond Walters College
9555 Plainfield Road
Cincinnati, OH 45236
Tel: (513)745-5791
Fax: (513)745-5771
E-mail: victoria.hammer@uc.edu
Web Site: http://www.rwc.uc.edu/obta

To provide financial assistance to undergraduate and graduate students and professionals in Ohio who are interested in business education.

Title of Award: Ohio Business Teachers Association Scholarships **Area, Field, or Subject:** Business administration; Education **Level of Education for which Award is Granted:** Graduate, Professional, Undergraduate **Number Awarded:** 1 each year. **Funds Available:** The stipend is $1,000. **Duration:** 1 year.
Eligibility Requirements: This program is open to 1) undergraduate students enrolled full time in a 4-year bachelor's degree program in the field of business education at an accredited Ohio institution; 2) graduate students at Ohio institutions who are members of the Ohio Business Teachers Association (OBTA) and/or the business education division of the Ohio Vocational Association (OVA) and are enrolled in course work for regular academic credit in business, business education, or a directly-related field; and 3) professional educators who are currently employed as a teacher and/or administrator in business education in Ohio, are current members of OBTA and/or the business education division of OVA, and have the equivalent of 3 academic years of teaching in business education. Applicants must have a GPA of 3.0 or higher. **Deadline for Receipt:** August of each year.

3609 ■ OHIO CLASSICAL CONFERENCE

c/o Amy J. Sawan, Scholarship Committee
Medina Senior High School
777 East Union Street
Medina, OH 44256

Tel: (330)636-3200
E-mail: LIAMOT@aol.com
Web Site: http://dept.kent.edu/mcls/classics/occ
To provide financial assistance to Ohio residents preparing for a career as a Latin teacher.
Title of Award: Ohio Classical Conference Scholarship for Prospective Latin Teachers **Area, Field, or Subject:** Classical studies; Education, Elementary; Education, Secondary; Foreign languages **Level of Education for which Award is Granted:** Undergraduate **Number Awarded:** 1 each year. **Funds Available:** The stipend is $1,500. **Duration:** 1 year; nonrenewable.
Eligibility Requirements: This program is open to residents of Ohio enrolled at least at the sophomore level at a college or university in the United States. Applicants must be taking courses leading to a career in the teaching of Latin at the K-12 level in a public, private, or parochial school. They must submit college transcripts, 2 letters of recommendation (including 1 from a member of their classics department), a prospectus of courses completed and to be taken as part of the program, and a 1-page statement of their academic goals and reasons for applying for the scholarship. **Deadline for Receipt:** March of each year.

3610 ■ OKLAHOMA STATE REGENTS FOR HIGHER EDUCATION

Attn: Director of Scholarship and Grant Programs
655 Research Parkway, Suite 200
P.O. Box 108850
Oklahoma City, OK 73101-8850
Tel: (405)225-9239
Free: 800-858-1840
Fax: (405)225-9230
E-mail: studentinfo@osrhe.edu
Web Site: http://www.okhighered.org/student-center/financial-aid/future-teach.shtml
To provide forgivable loans to Oklahoma residents who are interested in teaching (particularly in teacher shortage fields) in Oklahoma.
Title of Award: Oklahoma Future Teachers Scholarship Program **Area, Field, or Subject:** Education; Education, Special; English language and literature; Linguistics; Mathematics and mathematical sciences; Science **Level of Education for which Award is Granted:** Graduate, Undergraduate **Number Awarded:** Varies each year; recently, 136 students received support through this program. **Funds Available:** Full-time students receive up to $1,500 per year if they have completed 60 hours or more or up to $1,000 if they have completed fewer than 60 hours; part-time students receive up to $750 per year if they have completed 60 hours or more or up to $500 per year if they have completed fewer than 60 hours. Funds are paid directly to the institution on the student's behalf. This is a forgivable loan program; recipients must agree to teach in Oklahoma public schools for 3 years following graduation and licensure. **Duration:** 1 year; may be renewable for up to 3 additional years as long as the recipient maintains a GPA of 2.5 or higher.
Eligibility Requirements: Candidates for this program must be nominated by institutions of higher education in Oklahoma. Nominees may be high school seniors, high school graduates, or currently-enrolled undergraduate or graduate students. They must 1) rank in the top 15% of their high school graduating class; 2) have an ACT or SAT score ranking in the top 15% for high school graduates of the same year; 3) have been admitted into a professional education program at an accredited Oklahoma institution of higher education; or 4) have achieved an undergraduate record of outstanding success as defined by the institution. Both part-time and full-time students are eligible, but preference is given to full-time students. Applicants must be interested in teaching in critical shortage areas in the state upon graduation. These areas change periodically but recently have included special education, mathematics, science, English, and foreign languages. **Deadline for Receipt:** September of each year.

3611 ■ OMAHA VOLUNTEERS FOR HANDICAPPED CHILDREN

c/o Lois Carlson
2010 Country Club Avenue
Omaha, NE 68104
Tel: (402)553-0378
To provide financial assistance for college to Nebraska residents who have a physical disability or are preparing for a career related to people with orthopedic impairments or physical disabilities.

Title of Award: Omaha Volunteers for Handicapped Children Scholarships **Area, Field, or Subject:** Disabilities; Education, Special; General studies/Field of study not specified **Level of Education for which Award is Granted:** Undergraduate **Number Awarded:** 5 to 10 each year. **Funds Available:** The stipend is $1,000 per year. **Duration:** 1 year; may be renewed.
Eligibility Requirements: This program is open to residents of Nebraska who are U.S. citizens. First priority applicants must have an orthopedic impairment or physical disability and be 1) high school seniors with a GPA of 2.25 or higher and accepted into the school of their choice or 2) college students making satisfactory progress toward graduation. Second priority applicants must be enrolled in the college of their choice and preparing for a teaching or health-related career of service to people with orthopedic impairments or physical disabilities. All applicants must submit a 250-word essay on their future goals and need for the scholarship. **Deadline for Receipt:** July of each year.

3612 ■ OREGON NASA SPACE GRANT CONSORTIUM

c/o Oregon State University
92 Kerr Administration Building
Corvallis, OR 97331-2103
Tel: (541)737-2414
Fax: (541)737-9946
E-mail: spacegrant@oregonstate.edu
Web Site: http://www.oregonspacegrant.orst.edu/programs/education/undergraduate.html
To provide financial assistance for study in space-related fields to undergraduate students at colleges and universities that are members of the Oregon Space Grant Consortium (OSGC).
Title of Award: Oregon Space Grant Undergraduate Scholarship Program **Area, Field, or Subject:** Aerospace sciences; Education; Engineering, Aerospace/Aeronautical/Astronautical; Mathematics and mathematical sciences; Space and planetary sciences; Technology **Level of Education for which Award is Granted:** Undergraduate **Number Awarded:** Varies each year. **Funds Available:** The stipend is $2,000. **Duration:** 1 year.
Eligibility Requirements: This program is open to U.S. citizens enrolled full time at OSGC member institutions. Applicants must be working on 1) a baccalaureate degree in a science, technology, engineering, or mathematics (STEM) field (including mathematics or science education) related to the mission of the U.S. National Aeronautics and Space Administration (NASA); or 2) an associate degree in applied science and planning to transfer to a 4-year institution to complete a baccalaureate in the same fields. Along with their application, they must submit a letter of intent of 250 to 300 words on their career goals as they relate to NASA and how this scholarship will contribute to those goals. Selection is based on scholastic achievement, aerospace-related career goals, and 2 letters of recommendation. Applications are especially encouraged from members of underrepresented groups (women, minorities, and people with disabilities). **Deadline for Receipt:** January of each year. **Additional Information:** Institutions that are members of OSG include Oregon State University, Portland State University, the University of Oregon, Southern Oregon University, Eastern Oregon University, Western Oregon University, George Fox University, Lane Community College, Linfield College, Portland Community College, and Oregon Institute of Technology. This program is funded by NASA.

3613 ■ OREGON STUDENT ASSISTANCE COMMISSION

Attn: Grants and Scholarships Division
1500 Valley River Drive, Suite 100
Eugene, OR 97401-2146
Tel: (541)687-7395
Free: 800-452-8807
Fax: (541)687-7419
E-mail: awardinfo@mercury.osac.state.or.us
Web Site: http://www.osac.state.or.us
To provide financial assistance to Oregon residents majoring in education on the undergraduate or graduate school level.
Title of Award: James Carlson Memorial Scholarship **Area, Field, or Subject:** Education, Elementary; Education, Secondary **Level of Education for which Award is Granted:** Four Year College, Graduate **Number Awarded:** Varies each year; recently, 3 of these scholarships were awarded. **Funds Available:** Stipend amounts vary; recently, they were at least $1,300. **Duration:** 1 year.

Eligibility Requirements: This program is open to residents of Oregon who are U.S. citizens or permanent residents. Applicants must be either 1) college seniors or fifth-year students majoring in elementary or secondary education or 2) graduate students working on an elementary or secondary certificate. Full-time enrollment and financial need are required. Priority is given to 1) members of African American, Asian American, Hispanic, or Native American ethnic groups; 2) dependents of members of the Oregon Education Association; and 3) applicants committed to teaching autistic children. **Deadline for Receipt:** February of each year. **Additional Information:** This program is administered by the Oregon Student Assistance Commission (OSAC) with funds provided by the Oregon Community Foundation, 1221 S.W. Yamhill, Suite 100, Portland, OR 97205, (503) 227-6846, Fax: (503) 274-7771.

3614 ■ OREGON STUDENT ASSISTANCE COMMISSION

Attn: Grants and Scholarships Division
1500 Valley River Drive, Suite 100
Eugene, OR 97401-2146
Tel: (541)687-7395
Free: 800-452-8807
Fax: (541)687-7419
E-mail: awardinfo@mercury.osac.state.or.us
Web Site: http://www.osac.state.or.us

To provide financial assistance to students in Oregon who are employed while working on an undergraduate or graduate degree in teaching or nursing.

Title of Award: Friends of Oregon Students Program **Area, Field, or Subject:** Education; Nursing **Level of Education for which Award is Granted:** Graduate, Undergraduate **Number Awarded:** Varies each year; recently, 28 of these scholarships were awarded. **Funds Available:** Stipends range from $3,000 to $5,000 per year. **Duration:** 1 year; may be renewed.

Eligibility Requirements: This program is open to students in Oregon who are working and will continue to work at least 20 hours per week while attending college or graduate school at least three-quarter time. Applicants must be interested in preparing for a career in teaching or nursing. They must be able to demonstrate a cumulative GPA of 2.5 or higher and volunteer or work experience relevant to their chosen profession. Preference is given to applicants who 1) are nontraditional students (e.g., older, returning, single parents), 2) have overcome significant personal obstacles, or 3) graduated from an alternative high school, obtained a GED, or are transferring from an Oregon community college to a 4-year college. Along with their application, they must submit essays and letters of reference on how they balance school, work, and personal life as well as their experiences in overcoming obstacles. Selection is based on work experience, community service and volunteer activities, responses to essay questions, letters of reference, and financial need; academic promise (as indicated by GPA and SAT/ACT scores) is also considered. **Deadline for Receipt:** February of each year. **Additional Information:** Funding for this program, established in 1996, is provided by the HF Fund, P.O. Box 55187, Portland, OR 97238, (503) 234-0259, E-mail: foosf@hffund.org.

3615 ■ POLISH ROMAN CATHOLIC UNION OF AMERICA

Attn: Education Fund Scholarship Program
984 North Milwaukee Avenue
Chicago, IL 60622-4101
Tel: (773)782-2600
Free: 800-772-8632
Fax: (773)278-4595
E-mail: info@prcua.org
Web Site: http://www.prcua.org/benefits/educationfundscholarship.htm

To provide financial assistance to undergraduate and graduate education students of Polish heritage.

Title of Award: Jean C. Osajda Fund **Area, Field, or Subject:** Education **Level of Education for which Award is Granted:** Graduate, Undergraduate **Number Awarded:** 1 or more each year. **Funds Available:** A stipend is awarded (amount not specified). Funds are paid directly to the institution. **Duration:** 1 year.

Eligibility Requirements: This program is open to students enrolled full time as sophomores, juniors, and seniors in an undergraduate program or full or part time as a graduate or professional school student. Applicants must be majoring in education. Selection is based on academic achievement, Polonia involvement, and community service. **Deadline for Receipt:** May of each year.

3616 ■ SCHOLARSHIP ADMINISTRATIVE SERVICES, INC.

Attn: ABE Program
2000 Rock Street, Suite 3
Mountain View, CA 94043

To provide financial assistance to students working on a bachelor's or master's degree in business education.

Title of Award: American Business Educators Scholarships **Area, Field, or Subject:** Education; Education, Secondary **Level of Education for which Award is Granted:** Master's, Undergraduate **Number Awarded:** Up to 20 each year. **Funds Available:** The stipend is $5,000 per year. **Duration:** 1 year; may be renewed 1 additional year if the recipient maintains full-time enrollment and a GPA of 3.0 or higher.

Eligibility Requirements: This program is open to full-time students working on or planning to work on a bachelor's or master's degree in business education. Applicants must have a GPA of 3.0 or higher and be able to demonstrate a record of involvement in extracurricular and work activities related to business. Along with their application, they must submit a 1,000-word essay on their educational and career goals, why they believe business is essential to America, and how they plan to make an impact as a business teacher at the secondary level. Financial need is not considered in the selection process. **Deadline for Receipt:** April of each year. **Additional Information:** This program is sponsored by American Business Educators (ABE) and administered by Scholarship Administrative Services, Inc. ABE was established in 2004 to encourage more American students to consider a career as a business teacher at the secondary level. Requests for applications should be accompanied by a self-addressed stamped envelope, the student's e-mail address, and the source where they found the scholarship information.

3617 ■ SEATTLE MARINERS WOMEN'S CLUB

P.O. Box 4100
Seattle, WA 98104
Tel: (206)628-3555

To provide financial assistance to high school athletes in Washington state who are interested in preparing for an athletic-related career.

Title of Award: Bev and Wes Stock Scholarship **Area, Field, or Subject:** Athletics; Education, Physical **Level of Education for which Award is Granted:** Undergraduate **Number Awarded:** 1 each year. **Funds Available:** The stipend is $1,000. **Duration:** 1 year; nonrenewable.

Eligibility Requirements: This program is open to athletes who display good character both on and off the playing field. They must be graduating high school seniors in Washington state who are planning to prepare for an athletic-related career and will be attending a college or university in the coming academic year. There is no application form. Applicants must submit a typewritten essay outlining why they are applying for the scholarship, their extracurricular activities, their goals, and how receiving the scholarship will be an advantage to them. Also required are a transcript and 3 letters of recommendation. Selection is based on merit. **Deadline for Receipt:** May of each year. **Additional Information:** No telephone inquiries are permitted.

3618 ■ SOCIETY OF PHYSICS STUDENTS

c/o American Institute of Physics
One Physics Ellipse
College Park, MD 20740-3843
Tel: (301)209-3007
Fax: (301)209-0839
E-mail: sps@aip.org
Web Site: http://www.spsnational.org/programs/future_teacher.htm

To provide financial assistance to members of the Society of Physics Students (SPS) interested in preparing for a career as a physics teacher.

Title of Award: SPS Future Teacher Scholarship **Area, Field, or Subject:** Education; Physics **Level of Education for which Award is Granted:** Four Year College **Number Awarded:** 1 each year. **Funds Available:** The stipend is $2,000. **Duration:** 1 year.

Eligibility Requirements: This program is open to full-time college juniors who are active members of the society. Applicants must be enrolled in a teacher education program with plans to prepare for a career in physics education. Selection is based on 1) high scholarship performance both in physics and overall studies, 2) potential for continued scholastic development in physics, 3) active participation in society programs, and 4) a statement of experiences and ambitions with regard to teaching physics. **Deadline for Receipt:** February of each year. **Ad-**

ditional Information: This program is sponsored by the Sigma Pi Sigma Trust Fund and the American Institute of Physics.

3619 ■ SOUTH CAROLINA ALLIANCE OF BLACK SCHOOL EDUCATORS

Attn: Executive Director
P.O. Box 11737
Columbia, SC 29211
Tel: (803)786-6478
Fax: (803)735-1159
E-mail: jrobin2000@msn.com
Web Site: http://www.scabse.com
To provide financial assistance to residents of South Carolina, especially minorities, interested in preparing for a career as a classroom teacher.
Title of Award: South Carolina Alliance of Black School Educators Scholarships **Area, Field, or Subject:** Education **Level of Education for which Award is Granted:** Undergraduate **Number Awarded:** 4 each year. **Funds Available:** The stipend is $1,000. **Duration:** 1 year.
Eligibility Requirements: This program is open to residents of South Carolina who are high school seniors or college undergraduates planning to attend or attending a college or university in the state. Applicants must be majoring, or planning to major, in education and become a classroom teacher in the state. They should be able to help meet a goal of the program to increase the number of ethnic minorities in South Carolina classrooms. Along with their application, they must submit 1-page essays on 1) what they hope their colleagues and former students will say about them at the close of their career, and 2) the approaches they will take to honor the diversity of the students in their classes. Selection is based on scholarship (20%); school, community, and employment activities (20%); written expression and commitment (40%); and recommendations (20%). **Deadline for Receipt:** March of each year. **Additional Information:** This program parallels the goals of the South Carolina Center for Educator Recruitment, Retention, and Advancement (CERRA), which administers this program. Information is also available from CERRA, Stewart House at Winthop University, Rock Hill, SC 29733, (803) 323-4032, Fax: (803) 323-4044.

3620 ■ SOUTH CAROLINA BUSINESS EDUCATION ASSOCIATION

c/o Anne M. London, Scholarship Committee Chair
837 Stiles Drive
Charleston, SC 29412
E-mail: anne_london@charleston.k12.sc.us
Web Site: http://www.scbea.org/scholarship.htm
To provide financial assistance to students seeking certification in a business and marketing education program at a college or university in South Carolina.
Title of Award: South Carolina Business Education Association Scholarships **Area, Field, or Subject:** Education **Level of Education for which Award is Granted:** Four Year College **Number Awarded:** 1 or more each year. **Funds Available:** A stipend is awarded (amount not specified). **Duration:** I year.
Eligibility Requirements: This program is open to students seeking initial certification in the upper division of a state-approved business and marketing education program at South Carolina colleges and universities. Applicants must submit a 300-word essay on why they would like to receive this scholarship. Selection is based on that essay, academic record, honors received, extracurricular activities, work experience, and financial need. **Deadline for Receipt:** January of each year.

3621 ■ SOUTH CAROLINA CENTER FOR EDUCATOR RECRUITMENT, RETENTION, AND ADVANCEMENT

Attn: South Carolina Teaching Fellows Program
Ward House at Winthrop University
Rock Hill, SC 29733
Tel: (803)323-4032
Free: 800-476-2387
Fax: (803)323-4044
Web Site: http://www.cerra.org/fellows.asp
To provide loans-for-service to high school seniors in South Carolina interested in preparing for a career as a teacher in the state.
Title of Award: South Carolina Teaching Fellows Program **Area, Field, or Subject:** Education **Level of Education for which Award is Granted:** Undergraduate **Number Awarded:** 200 each year. **Funds Available:** The

stipend is $6,000 per year, including $5,700 for tuition and board and $300 for summer enrichment programs administered by the sponsor. Fellows must agree to teach in South Carolina 1 year for each year they receive the fellowship. **Duration:** 4 years.
Eligibility Requirements: This program is open to high school seniors who are legal residents of South Carolina and enrolled in a public, private, or home school. The initial application requires documentation of academic achievement and school activities, a separate indicator for Teacher Cadet and ProTeam participation, 3 references, and a short narrative on why the applicant wants to become a teacher. Based on those applications, semifinalists are invited to regional interviews, where they first write a 30-minute response to an education-related question and then appear before an interview committee. Final selection is based on communication, problem solving ability, knowledge of world and educational issues, originality, and commitment to teaching as demonstrated in those responses and interviews. **Deadline for Receipt:** October of each year. **Additional Information:** The South Carolina General Assembly established this program in 1999. The participating institutions are Anderson College, Charleston Southern University, College of Charleston, Columbia College, Furman University, Lander University, Newberry College, South Carolina State University, University of South Carolina at Columbia, University of South Carolina Upstate, and Winthrop University.

3622 ■ SOUTH CAROLINA COMMISSION ON HIGHER EDUCATION

Attn: Director of Student Services
1333 Main Street, Suite 200
Columbia, SC 29201
Tel: (803)737-2260; 877-349-7183
Fax: (803)737-2297
E-mail: dbrown@che.sc.gov
Web Site: http://www.che.sc.gov
To provide scholarship/loans to teachers in South Carolina who wish to improve their content knowledge and degree programs.
Title of Award: South Carolina Teaching Scholarship Grants Program **Area, Field, or Subject:** Art; Dance; Economics; Education; Education, Early childhood; Education, Elementary; Education, Music; Education, Secondary; Education, Special; Geography; History; Linguistics; Mathematics and mathematical sciences; Music; Political science; Science **Level of Education for which Award is Granted:** Graduate, Professional, Undergraduate **Number Awarded:** Varies each year. **Funds Available:** The stipend is $1,000 per fiscal year. This is a scholarship/loan program. Recipients must sign a commitment to teach in South Carolina public schools for at least 1 year following completion of the scholarship grant year and agree to refund the scholarship amount if the 1-year teaching commitment is not honored. **Duration:** 1 year; may be renewed if recipients maintain a GPA of 3.0 or higher. They may receive up to 3 grants in a 5-year period.
Eligibility Requirements: This program is open to residents of South Carolina who have a professional teaching certificate and are under contract as a teacher in a public school in the state. Applicants must be 1) accepted as a degree-seeking graduate student in the teaching field at the master's level and enrolled at an eligible institution in the state; or 2) enrolled for graduate or undergraduate courses in their current teaching field or in a teaching field in which they wish to add on certification. Proposed fields of study must relate to core content areas of English, reading or language arts, mathematics, science, foreign languages, civics and government, economics, arts (advanced fine arts, art, dance, drama, music, and speech), history, or geography; early childhood, elementary education, middle level education, secondary education, and special education also qualify. Priority is given to classroom teachers (not administrators, counselors, media specialists, or other support personnel) whose teaching specialties are critical need subject areas. Continuing graduate students must have a GPA of 3.0 or higher. U.S. citizenship or permanent resident status is required. **Deadline for Receipt:** December of each year for second summer session and fall semester; June of each year for spring semester and first summer session. **Additional Information:** This program was established in 2001.

3623 ■ SOUTH CAROLINA SPACE GRANT CONSORTIUM

c/o College of Charleston
Department of Geology and Environmental Sciences
66 George Street
Charleston, SC 29424

Tel: (843)953-5463
Fax: (843)953-5446
E-mail: scozzarot@cofc.edu
Web Site: http://www.cofc.edu/~scsgrant/scholar/overview.html
To provide financial assistance to upper-division and graduate students in South Carolina who are preparing for a career as a science and mathematics teacher.

Title of Award: South Carolina Space Grant Consortium Pre-Service Teacher Scholarships **Area, Field, or Subject:** Aerospace sciences; Astronomy and astronomical sciences; Education; Engineering; Engineering, Aerospace/Aeronautical/Astronautical; Environmental conservation; Environmental science; Science; Space and planetary sciences **Level of Education for which Award is Granted:** Four Year College, Graduate **Number Awarded:** Varies each year. **Funds Available:** The stipend is $2,000. Funds may be used for such expenses as 1) partial payment of tuition; 2) travel and registration for attending science and mathematics education workshops or conferences for the purpose of professional development; 3) purchase of supplies for student teaching activities; or 4) other supportive activities that lead to successful professional development and graduation as an educator in South Carolina. **Duration:** 1 year. **Eligibility Requirements:** This program is open to juniors, seniors, and graduate students at member institutions of the South Carolina Space Grant Consortium. Applicants must be working on a teaching certificate in science, mathematics, or engineering. Their areas of interest may include, but are not limited to, the basic sciences, astronomy, science education, planetary science, environmental studies, or engineering. U.S. citizenship is required. Selection is based on academic qualifications of the applicant; 2 letters of recommendation; a description of past activities, current interests, and future plans concerning a space science or aerospace-related field; a sample lesson plan using curriculum materials available from the U.S. National Aeronautics and Space Administration (NASA); and faculty sponsorship. Women, minorities, and persons with disabilities are encouraged to apply. **Deadline for Receipt:** January of each year. **Additional Information:** Members of the consortium are Benedict College, The Citadel, College of Charleston, Clemson University, Coastal Carolina University, Furman University, University of South Carolina, Wofford College, South Carolina State University, The Medical University of South Carolina, and University of the Virgin Islands. This program is funded by NASA.

3624 ■ SOUTH CAROLINA STUDENT LOAN CORPORATION

Interstate Center
16 Berryhill Road, Suite 210
P.O. Box 21487
Columbia, SC 29221-1487
Tel: (803)798-0916
Free: 800-347-2752
Fax: (803)772-9410
Web Site: http://www.slc.sc.edu
To provide scholarship/loans to students in South Carolina who wish to teach certain subjects or in certain geographic areas.

Title of Award: South Carolina Teacher Loan Program **Area, Field, or Subject:** Agricultural sciences; Classical studies; Consumer affairs; Dance; Education, Elementary; Education, Music; Education, Special; English language and literature; Foreign languages; Library and archival sciences; Mathematics and mathematical sciences; Science; Speech and language pathology/audiology; Technology **Level of Education for which Award is Granted:** Graduate, Undergraduate **Number Awarded:** Varies each year. **Funds Available:** Freshmen and sophomores may borrow up to $2,500 per academic year; juniors, seniors, and graduate students may borrow up to $5,000 per academic year. This is a scholarship/loan program; loans are forgivable at the rate of 20% or $3,000, whichever is greater, for each full year of teaching in an area (either geographic or subject) of critical need; for students who teach in both critical subject and geographic areas, the rate of cancellation is 33% or $5,000, whichever is greater, per year. Borrowers who fail to teach in either a critical subject or geographic area must repay the loan at an annual interest rate that varies (currently, 5.37%) but is capped at 10.25%. **Duration:** 1 year; may be renewed for a total of 5 years of undergraduate and 5 years of graduate study.

Eligibility Requirements: Eligible to apply are residents of South Carolina who are planning to teach in certain critical geographic areas of the state, or to teach in critical subject areas. Entering freshmen must have ranked in the top 40% of their high school class and have an ACT or SAT score greater than the South Carolina average (recently 986 on the SAT or 19.3 on the ACT); enrolled undergraduates or entering graduate students must have at least a 2.75 cumulative GPA; graduate students who have completed at least 1 term must have a GPA of 3.5 or better. Undergraduate students at South Carolina colleges must have taken and passed the Education Entrance Exam; students at institutions outside South Carolina must have completed the necessary prerequisites required at that institution. Only U.S. citizens may apply. **Deadline for Receipt:** May of each year. **Additional Information:** Recently, the critical subject areas include mathematics, science (biology, chemistry, physics, and general science), media specialist, special education, industrial technology, foreign languages (Spanish, French, Latin, and German), family and consumer science, art, music, business education, English and language arts, dance, speech and drama/theater, and agriculture. For a list of critical geographic area, contact the sponsor.

3625 ■ SOUTH DAKOTA BOARD OF REGENTS

Attn: Scholarship Committee
306 East Capitol Avenue, Suite 200
Pierre, SD 57501-2545
Tel: (605)773-3455
Fax: (605)773-2422
E-mail: info@ris.sdbor.edu
Web Site: http://www.sdbor.edu/administration/academics/Scholarships.htm
To provide financial assistance to high school seniors planning to attend a public university in South Dakota and major in elementary education.

Title of Award: Annis Irene Fowler/Kaden Scholarship **Area, Field, or Subject:** Education, Elementary **Level of Education for which Award is Granted:** Undergraduate **Number Awarded:** 1 each year. **Funds Available:** The stipend is $1,000; funds are allocated to the institution for distribution to the student. **Duration:** 1 year; nonrenewable.

Eligibility Requirements: This program is open to first-time entering freshmen at public universities in South Dakota. Applicants must have a GPA of 3.0 or higher and an intent to major in elementary education. They must submit an essay (from 1,000 to 1,500 words) on a topic that changes annually; recently, the topic related to advantages and disadvantages of No Child Left Behind laws. Special consideration is given to students who demonstrate motivational ability, who have a disability, or who are self-supporting. **Deadline for Receipt:** February of each year.

3626 ■ SOUTH DAKOTA BOARD OF REGENTS

Attn: Scholarship Committee
306 East Capitol Avenue, Suite 200
Pierre, SD 57501-2545
Tel: (605)773-3455
Fax: (605)773-2422
E-mail: info@ris.sdbor.edu
Web Site: http://www.sdbor.edu/administration/academics/Scholarships.htm
To provide financial assistance to students at public universities in South Dakota who are enrolled in a teacher education program.

Title of Award: Haines Memorial Scholarship **Area, Field, or Subject:** Education **Level of Education for which Award is Granted:** Undergraduate **Number Awarded:** 1 each year. **Funds Available:** The stipend is $2,150; funds are allocated to the institution for distribution to the student. **Duration:** 1 year; nonrenewable.

Eligibility Requirements: This program is open to sophomores, juniors, and seniors at public universities in South Dakota. Applicants must have a GPA of 2.5 or higher and a declared major in a teacher education program. They must submit a statement that describes their personal philosophy and their philosophy of education. **Deadline for Receipt:** February of each year.

3627 ■ SOUTH DAKOTA BOARD OF REGENTS

Attn: Scholarship Committee
306 East Capitol Avenue, Suite 200
Pierre, SD 57501-2545
Tel: (605)773-3455
Fax: (605)773-2422
E-mail: info@ris.sdbor.edu
Web Site: http://www.sdbor.edu

To provide assistance for additional training to certain elementary and secondary school teachers and vocational instructors in South Dakota.
Title of Award: South Dakota Tuition Reduction for Certain Teachers **Area, Field, or Subject:** Education, Elementary; Education, Secondary; Education, Vocational-technical **Level of Education for which Award is Granted:** Graduate, Professional, Undergraduate **Number Awarded:** Varies each year. **Funds Available:** Qualified teachers and instructors are entitled to pay only 50% of tuition (but 100% of required fees) at a South Dakota state-supported institution of higher education. **Duration:** Recipients are entitled to the tuition reduction as long as they meet the eligibility requirements and maintain a GPA of 3.0 or higher.
Eligibility Requirements: This program is open to teachers and vocational instructors who are residents of South Dakota and employed by an accredited elementary or secondary school as a teacher or vocational instructor. Applicants must be required by state law, administrative rules, or an employment contract to pursue additional undergraduate or graduate education as a condition of employment or to maintain a certificate to teach. **Additional Information:** The tuition reduction can by used for a maximum of 6 credit hours per academic year.

3628 ■ STATE STUDENT ASSISTANCE COMMISSION OF INDIANA
Attn: Grant Division
150 West Market Street, Suite 500
Indianapolis, IN 46204-2811
Tel: (317)232-2350; 888-528-4719
Fax: (317)232-3260
E-mail: special@ssaci.state.in.us
Web Site: http://www.in.gov/ssaci/programs/m-teach.html
To provide scholarship/loans to Black and Hispanic undergraduate students in Indiana interested in preparing for a teaching career and to other residents of the state preparing for a career in special education, occupational therapy, or physical therapy.
Title of Award: Indiana Minority Teacher/Special Education Services Scholarship **Area, Field, or Subject:** Education, Elementary; Education, Secondary; Education, Special; Occupational therapy; Physical therapy **Level of Education for which Award is Granted:** Undergraduate **Number Awarded:** Varies each year. **Funds Available:** Up to $1,000 annually; if students demonstrate financial need, they may receive up to $4,000 annually. For 3 out of the 5 years following graduation, recipients must teach full time in an elementary or secondary school in Indiana or practice as an occupational or physical therapist at a school or rehabilitation facility in the state. If they fail to meet that service requirement, they are required to reimburse the state of Indiana for all funds received. **Duration:** 1 year; may be renewed up to 3 additional years if recipients maintain a 2.0 GPA. They may, however, take up to 6 years to complete the program from the start of receiving the first scholarship.
Eligibility Requirements: This program is open to 1) Black and Hispanic students seeking teacher certification; 2) students seeking special education teaching certification; or 3) students seeking occupational or physical therapy certification. Applicants must be Indiana residents and U.S. citizens who are enrolled or accepted for enrollment as full-time students at an academic institution in Indiana. Students who are already enrolled in college must have a GPA of 2.0 or higher. Applicants must be preparing to teach in an accredited elementary or secondary school in Indiana or to work as an occupational or physical therapist at a school or rehabilitation facility. Financial need may be considered, but it is not a requirement. Preference is given to minorities and to students enrolling in college for the first time. **Deadline for Receipt:** Each participating college or university establishes its filing deadline for this program. **Additional Information:** This program was established in 1988 to address the critical shortage of Black and Hispanic teachers in Indiana. An amendment in 1990 added the field of special education, and in 1991 the fields of occupational and physical therapy were added. Participating colleges in Indiana select the recipients. Students must submit their application to the financial aid office of the college they plan to attend (not to the State Student Assistance Commission of Indiana).

3629 ■ TENNESSEE STUDENT ASSISTANCE CORPORATION
Parkway Towers
404 James Robertson Parkway, Suite 1950
Nashville, TN 37243-0820
Tel: (615)741-1346
Free: 800-342-1663

Fax: (615)741-6101
E-mail: tsac@mail.state.tn.us
Web Site: http://www.tnscholardollars.com/mon_college/minority_teach.htm
To provide scholarship/loans to minority Tennesseans who wish to enter the teaching field.
Title of Award: Tennessee Minority Teaching Fellows Program **Area, Field, or Subject:** Education **Level of Education for which Award is Granted:** Undergraduate **Number Awarded:** 20 new awards are granted each year. **Funds Available:** The scholarship/loan is $5,000 per year. Recipients incur an obligation to teach at the K-12 level in a Tennessee public school 1 year for each year the award is received. **Duration:** 1 year; may be renewed for up to 3 additional years.
Eligibility Requirements: This program is open to minority residents of Tennessee who are either high school seniors planning to attend a college or university in the state or continuing college students at a Tennessee college or university. High school seniors must have a GPA of 2.75 or higher and either have an ACT score of at least 18 (or its SAT equivalent) or rank in the top 25% of their high school class. Continuing college students must have a college GPA of 2.5 or higher. All applicants must agree to teach at the K-12 level in a Tennessee public school following graduation from college. **Deadline for Receipt:** April of each year. **Additional Information:** This program was established in 1989.

3630 ■ TENNESSEE STUDENT ASSISTANCE CORPORATION
Parkway Towers
404 James Robertson Parkway, Suite 1950
Nashville, TN 37243-0820
Tel: (615)741-1346
Free: 800-342-1663
Fax: (615)741-6101
E-mail: tsac@mail.state.tn.us
Web Site: http://www.tnscholardollars.com/mon_college/tn_teach_sch.htm
To provide scholarship/loans to students in Tennessee who are interested in preparing for a teaching career.
Title of Award: Tennessee Teaching Scholars Program **Area, Field, or Subject:** Education, Early childhood; Education, Elementary; Education, Secondary **Level of Education for which Award is Granted:** Four Year College, Master's **Number Awarded:** 185 each year. **Funds Available:** Loans up to $4,500 per year are available. For each year of teaching in Tennessee, 1 year of the loan is forgiven. **Duration:** 1 year; may be renewed for up to 3 additional years, provided the recipient maintains a 2.75 GPA.
Eligibility Requirements: This program is open to college juniors, seniors, and postbaccalaureate students in approved teacher education programs in Tennessee. They must be U.S. citizens, be Tennessee residents, have earned a GPA of 2.75 or higher, and agree to teach at the public preschool, elementary, or secondary level in Tennessee. **Deadline for Receipt:** April of each year.

3631 ■ TEXAS BUSINESS AND TECHNOLOGY EDUCATORS ASSOCIATION
c/o Mona Fannon, Scholarship Committee Chair
Route 2 Box 8-14
Fritch, TX 79036
Tel: (806)857-9320
E-mail: mona.fannon@borgerisd.net
Web Site: http://www.tbtea.org
To provide financial assistance for college to members of Business Professionals of America (BPA) or Future Business Leaders of America (FBLA) in Texas.
Title of Award: Texas Business and Technology Educators Association Scholarships **Area, Field, or Subject:** Business administration; Computer and information sciences; Education; Information science and technology **Level of Education for which Award is Granted:** Undergraduate **Number Awarded:** 4 each year. **Funds Available:** The stipend is $1,000. **Duration:** 1 year.
Eligibility Requirements: This program is open to seniors graduating from high schools in Texas who are members of BPA or FBLA (or were members during their junior year). Applicants must have a GPA of 2.75 or higher and be nominated by a teacher who is a member of the Texas Business and Technology Educators Association. They must be planning

to attend college to prepare for a career in business, business education, computer science, computer information systems, or a related field. Along with their application, they must submit a 1-page letter describing why they deserve this scholarship, defining their career goals, and including any information regarding financial need. **Deadline for Receipt:** February of each year.

3632 ■ HARRY S. TRUMAN SCHOLARSHIP FOUNDATION

Attn: Executive Secretary
712 Jackson Place, N.W.
Washington, DC 20006
Tel: (202)395-4831
Fax: (202)395-6995
E-mail: office@truman.gov
Web Site: http://www.truman.gov

To provide grants-for-service for graduate school to current college juniors who are interested in preparing for a career in public service.

Title of Award: Harry S. Truman Scholarship Program **Area, Field, or Subject:** Agricultural sciences; Biological and clinical sciences; Economics; Education; Engineering; Environmental conservation; Environmental science; History; International affairs and relations; Law; Physical sciences; Political science; Public administration; Public health; Public service; Social sciences; Technology **Level of Education for which Award is Granted:** Four Year College, Graduate **Number Awarded:** 70 to 75 each year: a) 1 "state" scholarship is available to a qualified resident nominee in each of the 50 states, the District of Columbia, Puerto Rico, and the Islands (Guam, the Virgin Islands, American Samoa, and the Commonwealth of the Northern Mariana Islands); and b) up to 25 at-large scholars. **Funds Available:** The program provides up to $30,000, including up to $15,000 for the first year of graduate study and up to $15,000 for the final year of graduate study. **Duration:** Support is provided for the first and last year of graduate study.

Eligibility Requirements: Students must be nominated to be considered for this program. Nominees must be full-time students with junior standing at a 4-year institution, committed to a career in government or public service, in the upper quarter of their class, and U.S. citizens or nationals. Each participating institution may nominate up to 4 candidates (and up to 3 additional students who completed their first 2 years at a community college); community colleges and other 2-year institutions may nominate former students who are enrolled as full-time students with junior-level academic standing at accredited 4-year institutions. Selection is based on extent and quality of community service and government involvement, academic performance, leadership record, suitability of the nominee's proposed program of study for a career in public service, and writing and analytical skills. Priority is given to candidates who plan to enroll in a graduate program that specifically trains them for a career in public service, including government at any level, uniformed services, public interest organizations, nongovernmental research and/or educational organizations, public and private schools, and public service oriented nonprofit organizations. The fields of study may include agriculture, biology, engineering, environmental management, physical and social sciences, and technology policy, as well as such traditional fields as economics, education, government, history, international relations, law, nonprofit management, political science, public administration, public health, and public policy. Interviews are required. **Deadline for Receipt:** February of each year. **Additional Information:** Recipients may attend graduate school in the United States or in foreign countries. Scholars are required to work in public service for 3 of the 7 years following completion of a graduate degree program funded by this program. Scholars who do not meet this service requirement, or who fail to provide timely proof to the foundation of such employment, will be required to repay funds received, along with interest.

3633 ■ MORRIS K. UDALL FOUNDATION

130 South Scott Avenue
Tucson, AZ 85701-1922
Tel: (520)670-5529
Fax: (520)670-5530
Web Site: http://www.udall.gov/scholarship

To provide financial assistance to 1) college sophomores and juniors who intend to prepare for a career in environmental public policy and 2) Native American and Alaska Native students who intend to prepare for a career in health care or tribal public policy.

Title of Award: Morris K. Udall Scholarships **Area, Field, or Subject:** Business administration; Economics; Education; Environmental conservation; Environmental science; Health care services; Native American studies; Natural resources; Political science; Public administration; Public health; Urban affairs/design/planning **Level of Education for which Award is Granted:** Undergraduate **Number Awarded:** Approximately 80 scholarships and 50 honorable mentions are awarded each year. **Funds Available:** The maximum stipend for scholarship winners is $5,000 per year. Funds are to be used for tuition, fees, books, and room and board. Honorable mention stipends are $350. **Duration:** 1 year; recipients nominated as sophomores may be renominated in their junior year.

Eligibility Requirements: Each 2-year and 4-year college and university in the United States and its possessions may nominate up to 6 sophomores or juniors from either or both categories of this program: 1) students who intend to prepare for a career in environmental public policy, and 2) Native American and Alaska Native students who intend to prepare for a career in health care or tribal public policy. For the first category, the program seeks future leaders across a wide spectrum of environmental fields, such as policy, engineering, science, education, urban planning and renewal, business, health, justice, and economics. For the second category, the program seeks future Native American and Alaska Native leaders in public and community health care, tribal government, and public policy affecting Native American communities, including land and resource management, economic development, and education. Nominees must be U.S. citizens, nationals, or permanent residents with a GPA of 3.0 or higher. Along with their application, they must submit an 800-word essay discussing a significant public speech, legislative act, or public policy statement by former Congressman Morris K. Udall and its impact on their field of study, interests, and career goals. Selection is based on demonstrated commitment to 1) environmental issues through substantial commitment to and participation in 1 or more of the following: campus activities, research, community service, or public service; or 2) tribal public policy or Native American health through substantial contributions to and participation in 1 or more of the following: campus activities, tribal involvement, community or public service, or research; a course of study and proposed career likely to lead to position where nominee can make significant contributions to the shaping of environmental, tribal public policy, or Native American health care issues, whether through scientific advances, public or political service, or community action; and leadership, character, desire to make a difference, and general well-roundedness. **Deadline for Receipt:** Faculty representatives must submit their nominations by early March of each year.

3634 ■ U.S. MARINE CORPS

Manpower and Reserve Affairs (MMEA-85)
3280 Russell Road
Quantico, VA 22134-5103
Tel: (703)784-9264
Fax: (703)784-9843
Web Site: http://www.usmc.mil

To allow selected noncommissioned Marine Corps officers to earn a bachelor's degree in selected fields by pursuing full-time college study while continuing to receive their regular pay and allowances.

Title of Award: Marine Corps Staff Noncommissioned Officers Degree Completion Program **Area, Field, or Subject:** Accounting; Business administration; Education; Environmental conservation; Environmental science; Finance; Management; Music; Protective services; Psychology **Level of Education for which Award is Granted:** Undergraduate **Number Awarded:** Varies each year; recently, 5 Marines were selected to participate in this program. **Funds Available:** Noncommissioned officers selected to participate in this program receive their regular Marine Corps pay while attending a college or university on a full-time basis. Tuition, matriculation fees, and other expenses (such as books) must be paid by the recipient through personal funds, in-service Montgomery GI Bill benefits, student loans, or other non-Marine Corps means. **Duration:** Up to the equivalent of 2 academic years.

Eligibility Requirements: Eligible to participate in this program are regular active-duty Marines, especially in the grades of staff sergeant and gunnery sergeant. Applicants must have completed at least 2 years of postsecondary study and have been accepted by an accredited degree-granting college or university in a program offered to all matriculating students; enrollment in a multiple major program designed for adults returning to school does not qualify. The program recently was limited to the following majors: accounting, business administration with an emphasis on accounting or financial management, education, environmental safety, environmental health management, hazardous material and waste control, music, occupational safety, psychology, safety education, safety management, and waste control. **Deadline for Receipt:** April of each year. **Additional Information:** Applicants must agree to extend/reenlist for a period of 4 years beyond completion of this program.

3635 ■ UNIVERSITY INTERSCHOLASTIC LEAGUE

Attn: Texas Interscholastic League Foundation
1701 Manor Road
P.O. Box 8028
Austin, TX 78713
Tel: (512)232-4938
Fax: (512)471-5908
E-mail: carolyn.scott@mail.utexas.edu
Web Site: http://www.uil.utexas.edu/tilf/scholarships.html
To provide financial assistance to students who participate in programs of the Texas Interscholastic League Foundation (TILF) and plan to teach in the public school system after graduating from college.

Title of Award: Red Oak Foundation Scholarships **Area, Field, or Subject:** Education, Elementary; Education, Secondary **Level of Education for which Award is Granted:** Four Year College **Number Awarded:** 3 each year. **Funds Available:** The stipend is $1,200 per year. **Duration:** 4 years.

Eligibility Requirements: This program is open to students who meet the 5 basic requirements of the TILF: 1) graduate from high school during the current year and enroll at a 4-year public college or university in Texas (or Baylor University or Texas Wesleyan University) by the following fall; 2) enroll full time and maintain a GPA of 2.75 or higher during the first semester; 3) compete in a University Interscholastic League (UIL) academic state meet contest in accounting, calculator applications, computer applications, computer science, current issues and events, debate (cross-examination and Lincoln-Douglas), journalism (editorial writing, feature writing, headline writing, and news writing), literary criticism, mathematics, number sense, 1-act play, ready writing, science, social studies, speech (prose interpretation, poetry interpretation, informative speaking, and persuasive speaking), or spelling and vocabulary; 4) submit high school transcripts that include SAT and/or ACT scores; and 5) submit parents' latest income tax returns. Applicants for this scholarship must have declared their intention to teach grades K-12 in the public school system. **Deadline for Receipt:** May of each year.

3636 ■ UNIVERSITY INTERSCHOLASTIC LEAGUE

Attn: Texas Interscholastic League Foundation
1701 Manor Road
P.O. Box 8028
Austin, TX 78713
Tel: (512)232-4938
Fax: (512)471-5908
E-mail: carolyn.scott@mail.utexas.edu
Web Site: http://www.uil.utexas.edu/tilf/scholarships.html
To provide financial assistance to students who participate in programs of the Texas Interscholastic League Foundation (TILF) and plan to enter the teaching profession.

Title of Award: Dr. B.J. Stamps Memorial Endowment Scholarship **Area, Field, or Subject:** Education **Level of Education for which Award is Granted:** Undergraduate **Number Awarded:** 2 each year (1 at $1,000 and 1 at $500). **Funds Available:** Stipends are $1,000 or $500 per year. **Duration:** 1 year; nonrenewable.

Eligibility Requirements: This program is open to students who meet the 5 basic requirements of the TILF: 1) graduate from high school during the current year and begin college or university in Texas by the following fall; 2) enroll full time and maintain a GPA of 2.5 or higher during the first semester; 3) compete in a University Interscholastic League (UIL) academic state meet contest in accounting, calculator applications, computer applications, computer science, current issues and events, debate (cross-examination and Lincoln-Douglas), journalism (editorial writing, feature writing, headline writing, and news writing), literary criticism, mathematics, number sense, 1-act play, ready writing, science, social studies, speech (prose interpretation, poetry interpretation, informative speaking, and persuasive speaking), or spelling and vocabulary; 4) submit high school transcripts that include SAT and/or ACT scores; and 5)

submit parents' latest income tax returns. Applicants for this scholarship must have declared their intention to enter the teaching profession. **Deadline for Receipt:** May of each year.

3637 ■ UNIVERSITY INTERSCHOLASTIC LEAGUE

Attn: Texas Interscholastic League Foundation
1701 Manor Road
P.O. Box 8028
Austin, TX 78713
Tel: (512)232-4938
Fax: (512)471-5908
E-mail: carolyn.scott@mail.utexas.edu
Web Site: http://www.uil.utexas.edu/tilf/scholarships.html
To provide financial assistance to students who participate in programs of the Texas Interscholastic League Foundation (TILF) and plan to enter the teaching profession after graduating from college.

Title of Award: J.O. Webb Memorial Scholarship **Area, Field, or Subject:** Education **Level of Education for which Award is Granted:** Four Year College **Number Awarded:** 1 each year. **Funds Available:** The stipend is $1,000. **Duration:** 1 year; nonrenewable.

Eligibility Requirements: This program is open to students who meet the 5 basic requirements of the TILF: 1) graduate from high school during the current year and enroll at a designated university in Texas by the following fall; 2) enroll full time and maintain a GPA of 2.5 or higher during the first semester; 3) compete in a University Interscholastic League (UIL) academic state meet contest in accounting, calculator applications, computer applications, computer science, current issues and events, debate (cross-examination and Lincoln-Douglas), journalism (editorial writing, feature writing, headline writing, and news writing), literary criticism, mathematics, number sense, 1-act play, ready writing, science, social studies, speech (prose interpretation, poetry interpretation, informative speaking, and persuasive speaking), or spelling and vocabulary; 4) submit high school transcripts that include SAT and/or ACT scores; and 5) submit parents' latest income tax returns. Preference for this scholarship is given to students planning to enter the teaching profession. **Deadline for Receipt:** May of each year. **Additional Information:** The designated universities are University of North Texas, Sam Houston State University, West Texas A&M University, Texas Women's University, and Southwest Texas State University.

3638 ■ UTAH HIGHER EDUCATION ASSISTANCE AUTHORITY

Board of Regents Building, The Gateway
60 South 400 West
Salt Lake City, UT 84101-1284
Tel: (801)321-7294; 877-336-7378
Fax: (801)321-7299
E-mail: uheaa@utahsbr.edu
Web Site: http://www.uheaa.org/scholarships.htm
To provide scholarship/loans to undergraduate students in Utah interested in becoming elementary or secondary school teachers.

Title of Award: Terrel H. Bell Teaching Incentive Loan Program **Area, Field, or Subject:** Education, Elementary; Education, Secondary **Level of Education for which Award is Granted:** Undergraduate **Number Awarded:** Varies each year. **Funds Available:** Students at public institutions in Utah receive a waiver of tuition and fees; students at participating private institutions in the state receive a stipend of $995 per semester. Recipients must teach in Utah public schools for a period equal to the time they received assistance. If they fail to complete the degree or perform the required teaching service, they must repay all funds received with 9% interest. **Duration:** Up to 4 years.

Eligibility Requirements: Applicants must be either 1) seniors at high schools in Utah or 2) teacher education students currently enrolled in a college or university in Utah who have completed 24 semester units or more. They must plan to teach in Utah public schools following graduation from college. Selection is based on high school GPA, ACT or SAT scores, ethnicity, and intended teaching field. **Deadline for Receipt:** March of each year. **Additional Information:** This program was formerly known as the Utah Career Teaching Scholarship Program.

3639 ■ VERMONT ASSOCIATION OF EDUCATIONAL OFFICE PROFESSIONALS

Attn: Scholarships
c/o Linda Hendrickson

495 Old Route 100
Moretown, VT 05660
Tel: (802)828-0449
Web Site: http://www.vaeop.org/scholarship.htm
To provide financial assistance for college to high school seniors in Vermont who plan to enter an office-related profession.
Title of Award: Marion T. Wood Vermont Scholarship **Area, Field, or Subject:** Education; General studies/Field of study not specified **Level of Education for which Award is Granted:** Undergraduate **Number Awarded:** 1 each year. **Funds Available:** The stipend is $1,000. **Duration:** 1 year.
Eligibility Requirements: This program is open to graduating high school seniors in Vermont who plan to attend a postsecondary school and enter an office-related profession (preferable in the field of education). Selection is based on academic record, an essay on career plans, 3 letters of recommendation, and financial need. **Deadline for Receipt:** February of each year. **Additional Information:** The recipient is also entered in the competition for the $1,000 National Association of Education Office Professionals Award.

3640 ■ VERMONT STUDENT ASSISTANCE CORPORATION
Champlain Mill
Attn: Scholarship Programs
P.O. Box 2000
Winooski, VT 05404-2601
Tel: (802)654-3798; 888-253-4819
Fax: (802)654-3765
E-mail: info@vsac.org
Web Site: http://www.vsac.org
To provide financial assistance to Vermont residents who are studying business or education at a college in the state.
Title of Award: Jedidiah Zabrosky Scholarship **Area, Field, or Subject:** Business administration; Education **Level of Education for which Award is Granted:** Undergraduate **Number Awarded:** 1 each year. **Funds Available:** The stipend is $2,000. **Duration:** 1 year.
Eligibility Requirements: This scholarship is available to residents of Vermont who currently attend a public college in the state. Applicants must be working on a 2-year or 4-year degree in business or education and be employed at least 10 hours per week. Selection is based on academic achievement (GPA of 2.5 or higher), school and community involvement, letters of recommendation, required essays, and financial need. **Deadline for Receipt:** April of each year. **Additional Information:** This program was established in 2002.

3641 ■ VIRGINIA CONGRESS OF PARENTS AND TEACHERS
1027 Wilmer Avenue
Richmond, VA 23227-2419
Tel: (804)264-1234; (866)4VA-KIDS
Fax: (804)264-4014
E-mail: info@vapta.org
Web Site: http://www.vapta.org/Programs/student_programs.htm
To provide financial assistance to high school seniors in Virginia who are interested in preparing for a teaching or related career.
Title of Award: Virginia PTA Scholarships **Area, Field, or Subject:** Education **Level of Education for which Award is Granted:** Undergraduate **Number Awarded:** Varies each year. Recently, 24 of these scholarships were awarded: the 2 named scholarships at $1,200 and 22 scholarships at $1,000. **Funds Available:** The stipend is either $1,000 or $1,200 (for the 2 named scholarships) per year. **Duration:** 1 year.
Eligibility Requirements: This program is open to seniors graduating from high schools in Virginia that are PTA or PTSA members. Applicants must be planning to attend a college or university in Virginia to prepare for a career in teaching or another youth-serving profession. They must have a GPA of 2.5 or higher. Selection is based on academic achievement and financial need. **Deadline for Receipt:** February of each year. **Additional Information:** This program includes 2 named scholarships: M. Frieda Koontz Scholarship ($1,200) and S. John Davis Scholarship ($1,200).

3642 ■ VIRGINIA SPACE GRANT CONSORTIUM
Attn: Fellowship Coordinator
Old Dominion University Peninsula Center
600 Butler Farm Road
Hampton, VA 23666

Tel: (757)766-5210
Fax: (757)766-5205
E-mail: vsgc@odu.edu
Web Site: http://www.vsgc.odu.edu/Menu3_1_1.htm
To provide financial assistance for college or graduate school to students in Virginia planning a career as science, mathematics, or technology educators.
Title of Award: Virginia Space Grant Teacher Education Scholarship Program **Area, Field, or Subject:** Aerospace sciences; Earth sciences; Education; Environmental conservation; Environmental science; Geosciences; Mathematics and mathematical sciences; Science; Space and planetary sciences; Technology **Level of Education for which Award is Granted:** Four Year College, Master's **Number Awarded:** Approximately 10 each year. **Funds Available:** The maximum stipend is $1,000. **Duration:** 1 year; nonrenewable.
Eligibility Requirements: This program is open to full-time undergraduate students at the Virginia Space Grant Consortium (VSGC) colleges and universities in a track that will qualify them to teach in a pre-college setting. Priority is given to those majoring in technology education, mathematics, or science, particularly earth, space, or environmental science. Applicants may apply while seniors in high school or sophomores in a community college, with the award contingent on their enrollment at a VSGC college and entrance into a teacher certification program. They must submit a statement of academic goals and plan of study, explaining their reasons for desiring to enter the teaching profession, specifically the fields of science, mathematics, or technology education. Students currently enrolled in a VSGC college can apply when they declare their intent to enter the teacher certification program. Students enrolled in a master of education degree program leading to teacher certification in eligible fields are also eligible to apply. Applicants must be U.S. citizens with a GPA of 3.0 or higher. Since an important purpose of this program is to increase the participation of underrepresented minorities, women, and persons with disabilities in science, mathematics, and technology education, the VSGC especially encourages applications from those students. **Deadline for Receipt:** February of each year. **Additional Information:** The VSGC institutions are College of William and Mary, Hampton University, Old Dominion University, the University of Virginia, and Virginia Polytechnic Institute and State University. This program is funded by the U.S. National Aeronautics and Space Administration (NASA).

3643 ■ IZAAK WALTON LEAGUE OF AMERICA-MINNESOTA DIVISION
Attn: Scholarship Committee
555 Park Street, Suite 140
St. Paul, MN 55103-2110
Tel: (651)221-0215
E-mail: ikes@minnesotaikes.org
Web Site: http://www.minnesotaikes.org
To provide financial assistance to Minnesota residents who are studying an environmental field in college.
Title of Award: Minnesota Division Scholarship **Area, Field, or Subject:** Education; Environmental conservation; Environmental law; Environmental science; Wildlife conservation, management, and science **Level of Education for which Award is Granted:** Undergraduate **Number Awarded:** 1 or more each year. **Funds Available:** The stipend is $1,000 per year. **Duration:** 1 year; may be renewed.
Eligibility Requirements: This program is open to residents of Minnesota who are in at least their second year of college. Applicants must be majoring in environmental education, environmental law, wildlife management, or some other conservation-oriented program. They must be U.S. citizens and able to demonstrate financial need. Along with their application, they must submit a 1-page essay on their belief in conservation and what the future holds for them (including their educational plans and career goals), a transcript, a description of their program of study, and 2 letters of recommendation. An interview may be requested. **Deadline for Receipt:** May of each year.

3644 ■ WASHINGTON HIGHER EDUCATION COORDINATING BOARD
917 Lakeridge Way
P.O. Box 43430
Olympia, WA 98504-3430
Tel: (360)753-7851; 888-535-0747
Fax: (360)753-7808

E-mail: futureteachers@hecb.wa.gov
Web Site: http://www.hecb.wa.gov/financialaid/other/alternative.asp
To provide forgivable loans to K-12 classified employees in Washington who are interested in attending a college or university in order to become a teacher.
Title of Award: Washington Conditional Scholarships for Alternative Teaching Certification **Area, Field, or Subject:** Chemistry; Education; Education, Bilingual and cross-cultural; Education, Elementary; Education, English as a second language; Education, Secondary; Education, Special; Foreign languages; Mathematics and mathematical sciences; Physics; Technology **Level of Education for which Award is Granted:** Professional, Undergraduate **Number Awarded:** Approximately 25 each year. **Funds Available:** The maximum award is $4,000 per academic year. These awards are in the form of loans that can be forgiven in exchange for teaching service. Each 2 years of eligible teaching service results in the forgiveness of 1 year of loan. **Duration:** 1 year; may be renewed up to 4 additional years.
Eligibility Requirements: This program is open to Washington residents who are currently employed as a classified instructional employee in a K-12 public school. Applicants must 1) have a transferable associate degree and be seeking residency teacher certification with endorsements in special education or English as a second language; or 2) have a bachelor's degree and subject matter expertise in a shortage area and be seeking residency teacher certification in a subject matter shortage area (currently defined as special education, English as a second language, chemistry, physics, Japanese, mathematics, and technology education). to enroll in an accredited Washington college or university and work as a teacher in a K-12 public school in the state after completing initial teacher certification. Selection is based on academic ability, a statement demonstrating commitment to the teaching profession, the applicant's ability to serve as a positive role model as a K-12 public school teacher, length and quality of contributions to the Washington K-12 public school, and recommendations from a current teacher or school official describing the applicant's potential as a future teacher. The priority in making awards is: 1) eligible renewal applicants who are within 2 years of completing their initial teacher certification requirements; 2) all other eligible renewable applicants; 3) eligible new applicants who are within 2 years of completing their initial teacher certification requirements; and 4) all other new eligible applicants. **Deadline for Receipt:** October of each year. **Additional Information:** This program was established by the Washington legislature in 2001. It is administered by the Washington Higher Education Coordinator Board, but the Washington State Professional Educator Standards Board selects the recipients.

3645 ■ WASHINGTON STATE BUSINESS EDUCATION ASSOCIATION

c/o Jackie Floetke, Awards & Scholarship Chair
P.O. Box 138
Wilson Creek, WA 98860
Tel: (509)345-2541
E-mail: jfloetke@wilsoncreek.org
Web Site: http://www.wsbea.org/scholarships.htm
To provide financial assistance for graduate school to members of the Washington State Business Education Association (WSBEA).
Title of Award: Dr. F. Ross Byrd Scholarship **Area, Field, or Subject:** Education; Educational administration **Level of Education for which Award is Granted:** Four Year College, Graduate **Number Awarded:** 1 or more each year. **Funds Available:** The stipend is $1,000. **Duration:** 1 year.
Eligibility Requirements: This program is open to members of WSBEA who are enrolled in graduate school with at least 1 semester or quarter remaining before graduation. Applicants must be working on an advanced degree in business education or a related field (e.g., vocational administration, business and marketing, curriculum). Along with their application, they must submit a statement of their need for this scholarship, a description of their leadership activities, information on their work experience, and a 300-word essay on why they want an advanced degree in business education. **Deadline for Receipt:** April of each year.

3646 ■ WASHINGTON STATE BUSINESS EDUCATION ASSOCIATION

c/o Jackie Floetke, Awards & Scholarship Chair
P.O. Box 138
Wilson Creek, WA 98860

Tel: (509)345-2541
E-mail: jfloetke@wilsoncreek.org
Web Site: http://www.wsbea.org/scholarships.htm
To provide financial assistance for college to members of Phi Beta Lambda (PBL) in Washington.
Title of Award: Doris Y. and John L. Gerber Scholarship **Area, Field, or Subject:** Education **Level of Education for which Award is Granted:** Four Year College **Number Awarded:** 1 or more each year. **Funds Available:** The stipend is $1,000. **Duration:** 1 year.
Eligibility Requirements: This program is open to members of PBL who are juniors or seniors majoring in business education at a college or university in Washington. Applicants must be nominated by their advisor, who must be a current member of the Washington State Business Education Association (WSBEA). Along with their application, they must submit a statement of their need for this scholarship, a description of their leadership activities, a description of their community service activities, information on their work experience, and a 300-word essay on why becoming a business educator is important to them. **Deadline for Receipt:** November of each year.

3647 ■ WATTS CHARITY ASSOCIATION, INC.

6245 Bristol Parkway, Suite 224
Culver City, CA 90230
Tel: (323)671-0394
Fax: (323)778-2613
E-mail: wattscharity@yahoo.com
Web Site: http://4watts.tripod.com/id5.html
To provide financial assistance to upper-division college students majoring in child development, teaching, or social services.
Title of Award: Joyce Washington Scholarship **Area, Field, or Subject:** Child development; Education; Social work **Level of Education for which Award is Granted:** Four Year College **Number Awarded:** 1 each year. **Funds Available:** A stipend is awarded (amount not specified). **Duration:** 1 year.
Eligibility Requirements: This program is open to U.S. citizens of African American descent who are enrolled full time as a college or university junior. Applicants must be majoring in child development, teaching, or the study of social services. They must have a GPA of 3.0 or higher, be between 17 and 24 years of age, and be able to demonstrate that they intend to continue their education for at least 2 years. Along with their application, they must submit 1) a 1-paragraph statement on why they should be awarded a Watts Foundation scholarship, and 2) a 1- to 2-page essay on a specific type of cancer, based either on how it has impacted their life or on researched information. **Deadline for Receipt:** May of each year. **Additional Information:** Royce R. Watts, Sr. established the Watts Charity Association after he learned he had cancer in 2001.

3648 ■ WISCONSIN FOUNDATION FOR INDEPENDENT COLLEGES, INC.

Attn: College-to-Work Program
735 North Water Street, Suite 600
Milwaukee, WI 53202-4100
Tel: (414)273-5980
Fax: (414)273-5995
E-mail: wfic@wficweb.org
Web Site: http://www.wficweb.org/work.html
To provide financial assistance and work experience to students majoring in education at member institutions of the Wisconsin Foundation for Independent Colleges (WFIC).
Title of Award: Hedberg Public Library College-to-Work Program **Area, Field, or Subject:** Education **Level of Education for which Award is Granted:** Four Year College **Number Awarded:** 1 each year. **Funds Available:** The stipends are $3,500 for the scholarship and $1,500 for the internship. **Duration:** 1 year for the scholarship; 10 weeks during the summer for the internship.
Eligibility Requirements: This program is open to full-time sophomores, juniors, and seniors at WFIC member colleges and universities. Applicants must be majoring in education and be able to demonstrate an interest in working with children of all ages. They must be interested in an internship at the Hedberg Public Library in Janesville, Wisconsin. Along with their application, they must submit a 1-page essay that includes why they are applying for the internship, why they have selected their major and what interests them about it, why they are attending their chosen col-

lege or university, and their future career objectives. **Deadline for Receipt:** February of each year. **Additional Information:** The WFIC member schools are Alverno College, Beloit College, Cardinal Stritch University, Carroll College, Carthage College, Concordia University of Wisconsin, Edgewood College, Lakeland College, Lawrence University, Marian College, Marquette University, Milwaukee Institute of Art & Design, Milwaukee School of Engineering, Mount Mary College, Northland College, Ripon College, St. Norbert College, Silver Lake College, Viterbo University, and Wisconsin Lutheran College. This program is sponsored by the Hedberg Public Library.

3649 ■ WISCONSIN FOUNDATION FOR INDEPENDENT COLLEGES, INC.

Attn: College-to-Work Program
735 North Water Street, Suite 600
Milwaukee, WI 53202-4100
Tel: (414)273-5980
Fax: (414)273-5995
E-mail: wfic@wficweb.org
Web Site: http://www.wficweb.org/work.html
To provide financial assistance and work experience to students majoring in fields related to social work at member institutions of the Wisconsin Foundation for Independent Colleges (WFIC).
Title of Award: Holiday House of Manitowoc County College-to-Work Program **Area, Field, or Subject:** Education; General studies/Field of study not specified; Occupational therapy; Social work **Level of Education for which Award is Granted:** Four Year College **Number Awarded:** 1 each year. **Funds Available:** The stipends are $3,500 for the scholarship and $1,500 for the internship. **Duration:** 1 year for the scholarship; 10 weeks for the internship.
Eligibility Requirements: This program is open to full-time sophomores, juniors, and seniors at private colleges and universities in Wisconsin. Applicants must be interested in an internship at Holiday House of Manitowoc County. Preference is given to 1) students attending Lakeland College or Silver Lake College; 2) residents of Manitowoc County attending another WFIC member institution; and 3) students majoring in education, occupational therapy, or social work. Along with their application, they must submit a 1-page essay that includes why they are applying for the internship, why they have selected their major and what interests them about it, why they are attending their chosen college or university, and their future career objectives. **Deadline for Receipt:** February of each year. **Additional Information:** The other WFIC schools are Alverno College, Beloit College, Cardinal Stritch University, Carroll College, Carthage College, Concordia University of Wisconsin, Edgewood College, Lawrence University, Marian College, Marquette University, Milwaukee Institute of Art & Design, Milwaukee School of Engineering, Mount Mary College, Northland College, Ripon College, St. Norbert College, Viterbo University, and Wisconsin Lutheran College. This program is sponsored by Holiday House of Manitowoc County, Inc. The WFIC's College-to-Work Program includes a number of other financial assistance and work experience programs aimed at eligible students interested in majoring in fields related to social work, including the Lutheran Social Services College-to-Work Program, Manitowoc County Domestic Violence Center College-to-Work Program, and YWCA of Rock County College-to-Work Program.

3650 ■ WISCONSIN FOUNDATION FOR INDEPENDENT COLLEGES, INC.

Attn: College-to-Work Program
735 North Water Street, Suite 600
Milwaukee, WI 53202-4100
Tel: (414)273-5980
Fax: (414)273-5995
E-mail: wfic@wficweb.org
Web Site: http://www.wficweb.org/work.html
To provide financial assistance and work experience to students majoring in fields related to technology at member institutions of the Wisconsin Foundation for Independent Colleges (WFIC).
Title of Award: Jefferson County Literacy Council College-to-Work Program **Area, Field, or Subject:** Computer and information sciences; Education; General studies/Field of study not specified; Internet design and development; Marketing and distribution **Level of Education for which Award is Granted:** Four Year College **Number Awarded:** 1 each year. **Funds Available:** The stipends are $3,500 for the scholarship and

$1,500 for the internship. **Duration:** 1 year for the scholarship; 10 weeks during the summer for the internship.
Eligibility Requirements: This program is open to full-time sophomores, juniors, and seniors at WFIC member colleges and universities. Applicants may be studying any field, but preference is given to majors in computer technology, education, marketing, sales, or website design. They must be interested in an internship at the Jefferson County Literacy Council in Fort Atkinson, Wisconsin. Along with their application, they must submit a 1-page essay that includes why they are applying for the internship, why they have selected their major and what interests them about it, why they are attending their chosen college or university, and their future career objectives. **Deadline for Receipt:** February of each year. **Additional Information:** The WFIC member schools are Alverno College, Beloit College, Cardinal Stritch University, Carroll College, Carthage College, Concordia University of Wisconsin, Edgewood College, Lakeland College, Lawrence University, Marian College, Marquette University, Milwaukee Institute of Art & Design, Milwaukee School of Engineering, Mount Mary College, Northland College, Ripon College, St. Norbert College, Silver Lake College, Viterbo University, and Wisconsin Lutheran College. This program is sponsored by the Jefferson County Literacy Council.

3651 ■ WISCONSIN FOUNDATION FOR INDEPENDENT COLLEGES, INC.

Attn: College-to-Work Program
735 North Water Street, Suite 600
Milwaukee, WI 53202-4100
Tel: (414)273-5980
Fax: (414)273-5995
E-mail: wfic@wficweb.org
Web Site: http://www.wficweb.org/work.html
To provide financial assistance and work experience to students majoring in fields related to history at member institutions of the Wisconsin Foundation for Independent Colleges (WFIC).
Title of Award: Milton Historical Society College-to-Work Program **Area, Field, or Subject:** African-American studies; Education; History, American; Museum science **Level of Education for which Award is Granted:** Four Year College **Number Awarded:** 1 each year. **Funds Available:** The stipends are $3,500 for the scholarship and $1,500 for the internship. **Duration:** 1 year for the scholarship; 10 weeks during the summer for the internship.
Eligibility Requirements: This program is open to full-time sophomores, juniors, and seniors at WFIC member colleges and universities. Preference is given to students majoring in African American studies, American history, museum science, or history education. Applicants must be interested in an internship at the Milton Historical Society in Milton, Wisconsin. Along with their application, they must submit a 1-page essay that includes why they are applying for the internship, why they have selected their major and what interests them about it, why they are attending their chosen college or university, and their future career objectives. **Deadline for Receipt:** February of each year. **Additional Information:** The WFIC member schools are Alverno College, Beloit College, Cardinal Stritch University, Carroll College, Carthage College, Concordia University of Wisconsin, Edgewood College, Lakeland College, Lawrence University, Marian College, Marquette University, Milwaukee Institute of Art & Design, Milwaukee School of Engineering, Mount Mary College, Northland College, Ripon College, St. Norbert College, Silver Lake College, Viterbo University, and Wisconsin Lutheran College. This program is sponsored by the Milton Historical Society.

3652 ■ WISCONSIN HIGHER EDUCATIONAL AIDS BOARD

131 West Wilson Street, Room 902
P.O. Box 7885
Madison, WI 53707-7885
Tel: (608)267-2212
Fax: (608)267-2808
E-mail: mary.kuzdas@heab.state.wi.us
Web Site: http://heab.state.wi.us/programs.html
To provide scholarship/loans to minorities in Wisconsin who are interested in teaching in Wisconsin school districts with large minority enrollments.
Title of Award: Wisconsin Minority Teacher Loans **Area, Field, or Subject:** Education **Level of Education for which Award is Granted:** Four Year College **Number Awarded:** Varies each year. **Funds Available:** Scholarship/loans are provided up to $2,500 per year. For each year

the student teaches in an eligible school district, 25% of the loan is forgiven; if the student does not teach in an eligible district, the loan must be repaid at an interest rate of 5%. **Duration:** 1 year; may be renewed 1 additional year.

Eligibility Requirements: African Americans, Hispanic Americans, and American Indians in Wisconsin are eligible to apply if they are enrolled full time as juniors or seniors in an independent or public institution in the state. The program also includes students who were admitted to the United States after December 31, 1975 and who are a former citizen of Laos, Vietnam, or Cambodia or whose ancestor was a citizen of 1 of those countries. Applicants must be enrolled in a program leading to teaching licensure and must agree to teach in a Wisconsin school district in which minority students constitute at least 29% of total enrollment or in a school district participating in the inter-district pupil transfer program. **Deadline for Receipt:** Deadline dates vary by institution; check with your school's financial aid office. **Additional Information:** Eligible students should apply through their school's financial aid office.

3653 ■ WISCONSIN HIGHER EDUCATIONAL AIDS BOARD
131 West Wilson Street, Room 902
P.O. Box 7885
Madison, WI 53707-7885
Tel: (608)266-1665
Fax: (608)267-2808
E-mail: john.whitt@heab.state.wi.us
Web Site: http://heab.state.wi.us/programs.html
To provide scholarship/loans to residents of Wisconsin who are interested in teaching the visually impaired at a school in the state.
Title of Award: Wisconsin Teacher of the Visually Impaired Loans **Area, Field, or Subject:** Education, Special **Level of Education for which Award is Granted:** Four Year College **Number Awarded:** Varies each year. **Funds Available:** Scholarship/loans are provided up to $10,000 per year, or a lifetime maximum of $40,000. For each of the first 2 years the student teaches and meets the eligibility criteria, 25% of the loan is forgiven; for the third year, 50% of the loan is forgiven. If the student does not teach and meet the eligibility criteria, the loan must be repaid at an interest rate of 5%. **Duration:** 1 year; may be renewed up to 3 additional years.
Eligibility Requirements: This program is open to residents of Wisconsin who are enrolled at least half time at an in-state or eligible out-of-state institution in a program that prepares them to be licensed as teachers of the visually impaired or as orientation and mobility instructors. Applicants must agree to be a licensed teacher or an orientation and mobility instructor in a Wisconsin school district, the Wisconsin Center for the Blind and Visually Impaired, or a cooperative educational service agency. Financial need is considered in the selection process. **Deadline for Receipt:** Deadline dates vary by institution; check with your school's financial aid office. **Additional Information:** Eligible students should apply through their school's financial aid office.

3654 ■ WORLD WIDE BARACA PHILATHEA UNION
610 South Harlem Avenue
Freeport, IL 61032-4833
To provide financial assistance to students preparing for Christian ministry, Christian missionary work, or Christian education.
Title of Award: World Wide Baraca Philathea Union Scholarship **Area, Field, or Subject:** Education, Religious; Religion **Level of Education for which Award is Granted:** Master's, Undergraduate **Funds Available:** Stipends are paid directly to the recipient's school upon receipt of the first semester transcript and a letter confirming attendance. **Duration:** 1 year; may be renewed.
Eligibility Requirements: Eligible to apply for this support are students enrolled in an accredited college or seminary who are majoring in Christian ministry, Christian missionary work, or Christian education (e.g., church youth pastor, writer of Sunday school curriculum). **Deadline for Receipt:** March of each year.

History

3655 ■ AMERICAN HELLENIC EDUCATIONAL PROGRESSIVE AS-SOCIATION
Attn: AHEPA Educational Foundation
1909 Q Street, N.W., Suite 500
Washington, DC 20009

Tel: (202)232-6300
Fax: (202)232-2140
Web Site: http://www.ahepa.org/ahepa
To provide financial assistance for college to students with a connection to the American Hellenic Educational Progressive Association (AHEPA), particularly those interested in majoring in political science or history.
Title of Award: George Leber Scholarship **Area, Field, or Subject:** General studies/Field of study not specified; History; International affairs and relations; Political science **Level of Education for which Award is Granted:** Undergraduate **Number Awarded:** Varies each year; recently, 2 of these scholarships were awarded. **Funds Available:** The annual stipend ranges from $500 to $2,000. **Duration:** 1 year.
Eligibility Requirements: This program is open to 1) members in good standing of the Order of Ahepa, Daughters of Penelope, Sons of Pericles, or Maids of Athena, and 2) the children of Order of Ahepa or Daughters of Penelope members in good standing. Applicants must be currently enrolled or planning to enroll in a college or university in the following fall. They may major in any area, but preference is given to upper-division students majoring in political science, history, or international relations. Selection is based on academic achievement, extracurricular activities, athletic achievements, work experience, and community service. Financial need is not considered. **Deadline for Receipt:** March of each year. **Additional Information:** A processing fee of $20 must accompany each application.

3656 ■ ENGLISH-SPEAKING UNION OF THE UNITED STATES-WASHINGTON DC AREA BRANCH
1604 New Hampshire Avenue, N.W.
Washington, DC 20009
Tel: (202)234-4602
Fax: (202)234-4639
E-mail: esuwdc@msn.com
Web Site: http://www.esuwdc.org/fellowships.html
To provide funding to residents of the metropolitan Washington area who are interested in conducting research or other projects anywhere in the world on a topic that relates to the English-speaking tradition.
Title of Award: Helen Gladstone Williams Scholarships **Area, Field, or Subject:** Art; General studies/Field of study not specified; History; Philosophy **Level of Education for which Award is Granted:** Graduate, Professional, Postdoctoral, Undergraduate **Number Awarded:** 1 or more each year. **Funds Available:** The grant ranges up to $5,000.
Eligibility Requirements: This program is open to permanent residents of the Washington, D.C. metropolitan area who have at least a bachelor's degree. Applicants must be interested in conducting a project, either independently or in conjunction with an accredited institution, on a subject that relates to English-speaking traditions in locales other than, or in addition to, the United States. They must submit a 2-page summary that describes the course of study to be undertaken and discusses how it would advance the objectives of the sponsoring organization, a brief resume of academic and employment experience, and 3 letters of support. Applicants who do not have a diploma at the bachelor's level or above must also submit a transcript from an accredited institution of higher learning that indicates progress toward a degree to be bestowed in the near future. Projects should focus primarily on endeavors that shed light on history, philosophy, the arts, or other aspects of culture. Selection is based on the significance of the project in relation to the field(s) it seeks to address, the project's relevance to the aims and values of the sponsoring organization, the credentials of the applicant, and the likelihood that the project will be completed successfully and on schedule. **Deadline for Receipt:** March of each year.

3657 ■ HANDWEAVERS GUILD OF AMERICA, INC.
Attn: Scholarship Chair
1255 Buford Highway, Suite 211
Suwanee, GA 30024
Tel: (678)730-0010
Fax: (678)730-0836
E-mail: hga@weavespindye.org
Web Site: http://www.weavespindye.org
To provide financial assistance to undergraduate and graduate students working on a degree in the field of fiber arts.
Title of Award: Dendel Scholarships **Area, Field, or Subject:** Art conservation; History; Textile science **Level of Education for which**

Award is Granted: Graduate, Undergraduate **Number Awarded:** Varies; more than $4,000 is available for this program each year. **Funds Available:** The amount of the award depends on the availability of funds. Recipients may use the funds for tuition, materials (e.g., film for photographs), or travel. **Duration:** 1 year.

Eligibility Requirements: This program is open to undergraduate and graduate students enrolled in accredited colleges and universities in the United States, its possessions, and Canada. Applicants must be working on a degree in the field of fiber arts, including training for research, textile history, and conservation. Along with their application, they must submit 1) an essay on their study goals and how those fit into their future plans, and 2) 5 to 16 slides of their work. Selection is based on artistic and technical merit; financial need is not considered. **Deadline for Receipt:** March of each year.

3658 ■ HANDWEAVERS GUILD OF AMERICA, INC.

Attn: Scholarship Chair
1255 Buford Highway, Suite 211
Suwanee, GA 30024
Tel: (678)730-0010
Fax: (678)730-0836
E-mail: hga@weavespindye.org
Web Site: http://www.weavespindye.org
To provide financial assistance to undergraduate and graduate students working on a degree in the field of fiber arts.

Title of Award: HGA Scholarships **Area, Field, or Subject:** Art conservation; History; Textile science **Level of Education for which Award is Granted:** Graduate, Undergraduate **Number Awarded:** Varies; more than $4,000 is available for this program each year. **Funds Available:** The amount of the award depends on the availability of funds. Use of funds is restricted to tuition. **Duration:** 1 year.

Eligibility Requirements: This program is open to undergraduate and graduate students enrolled in accredited colleges and universities in the United States, its possessions, and Canada. Applicants must be working on a degree in the field of fiber arts, including training for research, textile history, and conservation. Along with their application, they must submit 1) an essay on their study goals and how they fit into their future plans, and 2) 5 to 16 slides of their work. Selection is based on artistic and technical merit; financial need is not considered. **Deadline for Receipt:** March of each year.

3659 ■ HAWAI'I COMMUNITY FOUNDATION

Attn: Scholarship Department
1164 Bishop Street, Suite 800
Honolulu, HI 96813
Tel: (808)566-5570; 888-731-3863
Fax: (808)521-6286
E-mail: scholarships@hcf-hawaii.org
Web Site: http://www.hawaiicommunityfoundation.org/scholar/scholar.php
To provide financial assistance to residents of Hawaii for undergraduate or graduate studies in fields related to achieving world cooperation and international understanding.

Title of Award: Marion Maccarrell Scott Scholarship **Area, Field, or Subject:** Anthropology; Economics; Geography; History; International affairs and relations; Law; Peace studies; Philosophy; Political science; Psychology; Sociology **Level of Education for which Award is Granted:** Graduate, Undergraduate **Number Awarded:** Varies each year; recently, 258 of these scholarships were awarded. **Funds Available:** The amounts of the awards depend on the availability of funds and the need of the recipient; recently, stipends averaged $1,749. **Duration:** 1 year.

Eligibility Requirements: This program is open to graduates of public high schools in Hawaii. They must plan to attend school as full-time students (on the undergraduate or graduate level) on the mainland, majoring in history, government, political science, anthropology, economics, geography, international relations, law, psychology, philosophy, or sociology. They must be residents of the state of Hawaii, able to demonstrate financial need, interested in attending an accredited 2- or 4-year college or university, and able to demonstrate academic achievement (GPA of 2.8 or higher). Along with their application, they must submit an essay on their commitment to world peace that includes their learning experiences (courses, clubs, community activities, or travel) related to achieving world peace and international understanding and explaining how their experiences have enhanced their ability to achieve those goals. **Deadline for Receipt:** February of each year.

3660 ■ KONIAG INCORPORATED

Attn: Koniag Education Foundation
6927 Old Seward Highway, Suite 103
Anchorage, AK 99518-2283
Tel: (907)562-9093; 888-562-9093
Fax: (907)562-9023
E-mail: kef@alaska.net
Web Site: http://www.koniageducation.org
To provide financial assistance to Alaska Natives of the Koniag region who are enrolled in undergraduate or graduate study in a field related to Alutiiq culture.

Title of Award: Larry Matfay Cultural Heritage Scholarship **Area, Field, or Subject:** Anthropology; History; Native American studies **Level of Education for which Award is Granted:** Four Year College, Graduate **Number Awarded:** 1 each year. **Funds Available:** The stipend is $1,000. Funds are sent directly to the recipient's school and may be used for tuition, books, supplies, room, board, and transportation. **Duration:** 1 year; may be renewed.

Eligibility Requirements: This program is open to college juniors, seniors, and graduate students who are 1) Alaska Natives enrolled under Section 5 of the Alaska Native Claims Settlement Act to the Koniag region, or 2) direct or legally adopted descendants of those original enrollees. Applicants must supply proof of eligibility and documentation of financial need. They must have a GPA of 2.5 or higher cumulatively (3.0 or higher within their major) and be majoring in anthropology, history, Alaska Native or American Indian studies, or another discipline that involves research and learning about Alutiiq culture. Along with their application, they must submit 1) a 300- to 600-word letter that includes their personal and family history, their schooling or work history, and their educational and life goals; and 2) a 200- to 400-word essay on how their education may benefit the Alutiiq people. **Deadline for Receipt:** March of each year. **Additional Information:** Recipients are also eligible to apply for a Koniag Education Foundation Academic Achievement/Graduate Scholarship. The Koniag Education Foundation was established in 1993 by the directors of Koniag, Inc. The Koniag region covers Kodiak Island, many smaller islands, and a portion of the Alaska Peninsula.

3661 ■ MASSACHUSETTS DEMOCRATIC PARTY

Attn: Executive Director
56 Roland Street, North Lobby, Suite 203
Boston, MA 02129
Tel: (617)776-2676
Fax: (617)776-2579
E-mail: Susan.Thompson@massdems.org
Web Site: http://www.massdems.org/involved/internship.htm
To provide financial assistance for college to Massachusetts residents, with preference given to registered Democrats.

Title of Award: John F. Kennedy Scholarship **Area, Field, or Subject:** History; Political science **Level of Education for which Award is Granted:** Four Year College **Number Awarded:** 2 each year: 1 is set aside specifically for a female and 1 for a male. **Funds Available:** The stipend is $1,500. **Duration:** 1 year.

Eligibility Requirements: This program is open to Massachusetts residents who are entering their third or fourth year of study at a college or university anywhere in the United States. Applicants must be majoring in political science, government, or history. They must be able to demonstrate a serious commitment to the study of American politics and be qualified to receive financial aid (as certified by their financial aid officer). Males and females compete separately. Preference is given to registered Democrats who have a GPA of 3.0 or higher. Finalists may be interviewed in Boston. **Deadline for Receipt:** April of each year.

3662 ■ SOUTH CAROLINA COMMISSION ON HIGHER EDUCATION

Attn: Director of Student Services
1333 Main Street, Suite 200
Columbia, SC 29201
Tel: (803)737-2260; 877-349-7183
Fax: (803)737-2297
E-mail: dbrown@che.sc.gov
Web Site: http://www.che.sc.gov
To provide scholarship/loans to teachers in South Carolina who wish to improve their content knowledge and degree programs.

Title of Award: South Carolina Teaching Scholarship Grants Program **Area, Field, or Subject:** Art; Dance; Economics; Education; Education,

Early childhood; Education, Elementary; Education, Music; Education, Secondary; Education, Special; Geography; History; Linguistics; Mathematics and mathematical sciences; Music; Political science; Science **Level of Education for which Award is Granted:** Graduate, Professional, Undergraduate **Number Awarded:** Varies each year. **Funds Available:** The stipend is $1,000 per fiscal year. This is a scholarship/loan program. Recipients must sign a commitment to teach in South Carolina public schools for at least 1 year following completion of the scholarship grant year and agree to refund the scholarship amount if the 1-year teaching commitment is not honored. **Duration:** 1 year; may be renewed if recipients maintain a GPA of 3.0 or higher. They may receive up to 3 grants in a 5-year period.

Eligibility Requirements: This program is open to residents of South Carolina who have a professional teaching certificate and are under contract as a teacher in a public school in the state. Applicants must be 1) accepted as a degree-seeking graduate student in the teaching field at the master's level and enrolled at an eligible institution in the state; or 2) enrolled for graduate or undergraduate courses in their current teaching field or in a teaching field in which they wish to add on certification. Proposed fields of study must relate to core content areas of English, reading or language arts, mathematics, science, foreign languages, civics and government, economics, arts (advanced fine arts, art, dance, drama, music, and speech), history, or geography; early childhood, elementary education, middle level education, secondary education, and special education also qualify. Priority is given to classroom teachers (not administrators, counselors, media specialists, or other support personnel) whose teaching specialties are critical need subject areas. Continuing graduate students must have a GPA of 3.0 or higher. U.S. citizenship or permanent resident status is required. **Deadline for Receipt:** December of each year for second summer session and fall semester; June of each year for spring semester and first summer session. **Additional Information:** This program was established in 2001.

3663 ■ TEXAS FEDERATION OF BUSINESS AND PROFESSIONAL WOMEN'S FOUNDATION, INC.

Attn: TFBPW Foundation
803 Forest Ridge Drive, Suite 207
Bedford, TX 76022
Tel: (817)283-0862
Fax: (817)283-0872
E-mail: bpwtx@swbell.net
Web Site: http://www.bpwtx.org/foundation.asp
To provide financial assistance to women in Texas who are preparing to enter selected professions.
Title of Award: Hermine Dalkowitz Tobolowsky Scholarship **Area, Field, or Subject:** History; Law; Political science; Public administration; Women's studies **Level of Education for which Award is Granted:** Graduate, Undergraduate **Number Awarded:** 1 or more each year. **Funds Available:** A stipend is awarded (amount not specified). **Duration:** 1 year.
Eligibility Requirements: This program is open to women in Texas who are interested in attending school to prepare for a career in law, public service, government, political science, or women's history. Applicants must have completed at least 2 semesters of study at an accredited college or university in Texas, have a GPA of 3.0 or higher, and be U.S. citizens. Selection is based on academic achievement and financial need. **Deadline for Receipt:** April of each year. **Additional Information:** This program was established in 1995.

3664 ■ HARRY S. TRUMAN SCHOLARSHIP FOUNDATION

Attn: Executive Secretary
712 Jackson Place, N.W.
Washington, DC 20006
Tel: (202)395-4831
Fax: (202)395-6995
E-mail: office@truman.gov
Web Site: http://www.truman.gov
To provide grants-for-service for graduate school to current college juniors who are interested in preparing for a career in public service.
Title of Award: Harry S. Truman Scholarship Program **Area, Field, or Subject:** Agricultural sciences; Biological and clinical sciences; Economics; Education; Engineering; Environmental conservation; Environmental science; History; International affairs and relations; Law; Physical sci-

ences; Political science; Public administration; Public health; Public service; Social sciences; Technology **Level of Education for which Award is Granted:** Four Year College, Graduate **Number Awarded:** 70 to 75 each year: a) 1 "state" scholarship is available to a qualified resident nominee in each of the 50 states, the District of Columbia, Puerto Rico, and the Islands (Guam, the Virgin Islands, American Samoa, and the Commonwealth of the Northern Mariana Islands); and b) up to 25 at-large scholars. **Funds Available:** The program provides up to $30,000, including up to $15,000 for the first year of graduate study and up to $15,000 for the final year of graduate study. **Duration:** Support is provided for the first and last year of graduate study.
Eligibility Requirements: Students must be nominated to be considered for this program. Nominees must be full-time students with junior standing at a 4-year institution, committed to a career in government or public service, in the upper quarter of their class, and U.S. citizens or nationals. Each participating institution may nominate up to 4 candidates (and up to 3 additional students who completed their first 2 years at a community college); community colleges and other 2-year institutions may nominate former students who are enrolled as full-time students with junior-level academic standing at accredited 4-year institutions. Selection is based on extent and quality of community service and government involvement, academic performance, leadership record, suitability of the nominee's proposed program of study for a career in public service, and writing and analytical skills. Priority is given to candidates who plan to enroll in a graduate program that specifically trains them for a career in public service, including government at any level, uniformed services, public interest organizations, nongovernmental research and/or educational organizations, public and private schools, and public service oriented nonprofit organizations. The fields of study may include agriculture, biology, engineering, environmental management, physical and social sciences, and technology policy, as well as such traditional fields as economics, education, government, history, international relations, law, nonprofit management, political science, public administration, public health, and public policy. Interviews are required. **Deadline for Receipt:** February of each year. **Additional Information:** Recipients may attend graduate school in the United States or in foreign countries. Scholars are required to work in public service for 3 of the 7 years following completion of a graduate degree program funded by this program. Scholars who do not meet this service requirement, or who fail to provide timely proof to the foundation of such employment, will be required to repay funds received, along with interest.

3665 ■ VERMONT STUDENT ASSISTANCE CORPORATION

Champlain Mill
Attn: Scholarship Programs
P.O. Box 2000
Winooski, VT 05404-2601
Tel: (802)654-3798; 888-253-4819
Fax: (802)654-3765
E-mail: info@vsac.org
Web Site: http://www.vsac.org
To provide financial assistance to upper-division students at colleges and universities in Vermont who are majoring in history.
Title of Award: Town of Williston Historical Society Scholarship **Area, Field, or Subject:** History **Level of Education for which Award is Granted:** Four Year College **Number Awarded:** 1 each year. **Funds Available:** The stipend is $1,000. **Duration:** 1 year; nonrenewable.
Eligibility Requirements: This program is open to juniors and seniors at colleges and universities in Vermont working on a 4-year degree in history. Applicants must be residents of Vermont. Selection is based on required essays. **Deadline for Receipt:** May of each year. **Additional Information:** The Town of Williston Historical Society established this scholarship in 2002.

3666 ■ VIRGINIA DAUGHTERS OF THE AMERICAN REVOLUTION

c/o Catherine Rafferty, Scholarship Chair
10101 Sanders Court
Great Falls, VA 22066-2526
Web Site: http://www.vadar.org/vadarscholarships.htm
To provide financial assistance to high school seniors in Virginia who wish to study designated fields in college.
Title of Award: Virginia DAR Scholarships **Area, Field, or Subject:** Environmental conservation; Environmental science; Forestry; Geneal-

ogy; History, American; Home Economics; Medicine; Science **Level of Education for which Award is Granted:** Undergraduate **Number Awarded:** 2 each year: 1 at $1,000 and 1 at $500. **Funds Available:** Stipends are $1,000 or $500. **Duration:** 1 year.

Eligibility Requirements: This program is open to seniors graduating from high schools in Virginia who plan to attend a Virginia college or university. Applicants must be planning to work on a degree in the field of science, medicine, conservation, ecology, forestry, home arts, genealogical research, or American history. Along with their application, they must submit a 1,000-word letter giving their reasons for interest in the scholarship, a transcript of grades, a letter of recommendation from a teacher in their chosen field, and documentation of financial need. **Deadline for Receipt:** January of each year.

3667 ■ WISCONSIN FOUNDATION FOR INDEPENDENT COLLEGES, INC.

Attn: College-to-Work Program
735 North Water Street, Suite 600
Milwaukee, WI 53202-4100
Tel: (414)273-5980
Fax: (414)273-5995
E-mail: wfic@wficweb.org
Web Site: http://www.wficweb.org/work.html

To provide financial assistance and work experience to students majoring in fields related to history at member institutions of the Wisconsin Foundation for Independent Colleges (WFIC).

Title of Award: Milton Historical Society College-to-Work Program **Area, Field, or Subject:** African-American studies; Education; History, American; Museum science **Level of Education for which Award is Granted:** Four Year College **Number Awarded:** 1 each year. **Funds Available:** The stipends are $3,500 for the scholarship and $1,500 for the internship. **Duration:** 1 year for the scholarship; 10 weeks during the summer for the internship.

Eligibility Requirements: This program is open to full-time sophomores, juniors, and seniors at WFIC member colleges and universities. Preference is given to students majoring in African American studies, American history, museum science, or history education. Applicants must be interested in an internship at the Milton Historical Society in Milton, Wisconsin. Along with their application, they must submit a 1-page essay that includes why they are applying for the internship, why they have selected their major and what interests them about it, why they are attending their chosen college or university, and their future career objectives. **Deadline for Receipt:** February of each year. **Additional Information:** The WFIC member schools are Alverno College, Beloit College, Cardinal Stritch University, Carroll College, Carthage College, Concordia University of Wisconsin, Edgewood College, Lakeland College, Lawrence University, Marian College, Marquette University, Milwaukee Institute of Art & Design, Milwaukee School of Engineering, Mount Mary College, Northland College, Ripon College, St. Norbert College, Silver Lake College, Viterbo University, and Wisconsin Lutheran College. This program is sponsored by the Milton Historical Society.

International Affairs

3668 ■ ALABAMA COMMISSION ON HIGHER EDUCATION

Attn: Grants and Scholarships Department
100 North Union Street
P.O. Box 302000
Montgomery, AL 36130-2000
Tel: (334)242-2274
E-mail: wwall@ache.state.al.us
Web Site: http://www.ache.state.al.us/StudentAsst/Programs.htm

To provide financial assistance to performing artists interested in attending a junior or community college in Alabama.

Title of Award: Alabama Junior and Community College Performing Arts Scholarships **Area, Field, or Subject:** Performing arts **Level of Education for which Award is Granted:** Two Year College **Number Awarded:** Varies each year. **Funds Available:** Awards cover up to the cost of in-state tuition.

Eligibility Requirements: Eligible are full-time students enrolled in public junior and community colleges in Alabama. Selection is based on artistic talent as determined through competitive auditions. **Additional Informa-**

tion: Further information is available from financial aid officers at the appropriate Alabama junior or community college.

3669 ■ ALABAMA SPACE GRANT CONSORTIUM

c/o University of Alabama in Huntsville
Materials Science Building, Room 205
Huntsville, AL 35899
Tel: (256)824-6800
Fax: (256)824-6061
E-mail: reasonj@uah.edu
Web Site: http://www.uah.edu/ASGC

To provide financial assistance to undergraduates who are studying the space sciences at universities participating in the Alabama Space Grant Consortium (ASGC).

Title of Award: Undergraduate Scholarship Program of the Alabama Space Grant Consortium **Area, Field, or Subject:** Aerospace sciences; Behavioral sciences; Biological and clinical sciences; Business administration; Communications; Computer and information sciences; Economics; Education; Engineering, Aerospace/Aeronautical/Astronautical; International affairs and relations; Law; Natural sciences; Physical sciences; Public administration; Sociology; Space and planetary sciences **Level of Education for which Award is Granted:** Four Year College **Number Awarded:** Varies each year; recently, 32 of these scholarships were awarded. **Funds Available:** The stipend is $1,000 per year. **Duration:** 1 year; may be renewed 1 additional year.

Eligibility Requirements: This program is open to full-time students entering their junior or senior year at universities participating in the ASGC. Applicants must be studying in a field related to space, including the physical, natural, and biological sciences; engineering, education; economics; business; sociology; behavioral sciences; computer science; communications; law; international affairs; and public administration. They must be U.S. citizens and have a GPA of 3.0 or higher. Individuals from underrepresented groups (African Americans, Hispanic, American Indians, Pacific Islanders, Asian Americans, and women) are especially encouraged to apply. Interested students should submit a completed application with a career goal statement, personal references, a brief resume, and transcripts. Selection is based on 1) academic qualifications, 2) quality of the career goal statement, and 3) assessment of the applicant's motivation for a career in aerospace. **Deadline for Receipt:** February of each year. **Additional Information:** The member universities are University of Alabama in Huntsville, Alabama A&M University, University of Alabama, University of Alabama at Birmingham, University of South Alabama, Tuskegee University, and Auburn University. Funding for this program is provided by NASA.

3670 ■ AMERICAN FEDERATION OF TELEVISION AND RADIO ARTISTS

Attn: AFTRA/Heller Memorial Foundation, Inc.
260 Madison Avenue, Seventh Floor
New York, NY 10016
Tel: (212)532-0800
Fax: (212)532-2242
E-mail: info@aftra.com
Web Site: http://www.aftra.org/benefits/scholarship.htm

To provide financial assistance to undergraduate and graduate students who are members or the dependent children of members of the American Federation of Television and Radio Artists (AFTRA).

Title of Award: AFTRA/Heller Memorial Foundation Scholarships **Area, Field, or Subject:** Communications; General studies/Field of study not specified; Industrial and labor relations; Journalism; Performing arts **Level of Education for which Award is Granted:** Graduate, Undergraduate **Number Awarded:** 12 to 15 each year. **Funds Available:** Stipends up to $2,500 per year are available. **Duration:** 1 year; nonrenewable.

Eligibility Requirements: This program is open to AFTRA members and the dependent children of AFTRA members (or deceased members) in good standing for at least 5 years. Applicants may be interested in working on a bachelor's or advanced degree in any field, including broadcast journalism and labor relations, or professional training in the performing arts. Selection is based on academic achievement and financial need. **Deadline for Receipt:** April of each year.

3671 ■ AMERICAN HELLENIC EDUCATIONAL PROGRESSIVE ASSOCIATION

Attn: AHEPA Educational Foundation
1909 Q Street, N.W., Suite 500
Washington, DC 20009
Tel: (202)232-6300
Fax: (202)232-2140
Web Site: http://www.ahepa.org/ahepa

To provide financial assistance for college to students with a connection to the American Hellenic Educational Progressive Association (AHEPA), particularly those interested in majoring in political science or history. **Title of Award:** George Leber Scholarship **Area, Field, or Subject:** General studies/Field of study not specified; History; International affairs and relations; Political science **Level of Education for which Award is Granted:** Undergraduate **Number Awarded:** Varies each year; recently, 2 of these scholarships were awarded. **Funds Available:** The annual stipend ranges from $500 to $2,000. **Duration:** 1 year.

Eligibility Requirements: This program is open to 1) members in good standing of the Order of Ahepa, Daughters of Penelope, Sons of Pericles, or Maids of Athena, and 2) the children of Order of Ahepa or Daughters of Penelope members in good standing. Applicants must be currently enrolled or planning to enroll in a college or university in the following fall. They may major in any area, but preference is given to upper-division students majoring in political science, history, or international relations. Selection is based on academic achievement, extracurricular activities, athletic achievements, work experience, and community service. Financial need is not considered. **Deadline for Receipt:** March of each year. **Additional Information:** A processing fee of $20 must accompany each application.

3672 ■ AMERICAN INDIAN ARTS COUNCIL, INC.

Attn: Scholarship Committee
725 Preston Forest Shopping Center, Suite B
Dallas, TX 75230
Tel: (214)891-9640
Fax: (214)891-0221
E-mail: aiac@flash.net

To provide financial assistance to American Indian undergraduates or graduate students planning a career in the arts or arts administration. **Title of Award:** American Indian Arts Council Scholarship Program **Area, Field, or Subject:** Art; Creative writing; Management; Performing arts; Visual arts **Level of Education for which Award is Granted:** Graduate, Undergraduate **Number Awarded:** Varies each year. **Funds Available:** Stipends range from $250 to $1,000 per semester. **Duration:** 1 semester; may be renewed if the recipient maintains a GPA of 2.5 or higher.

Eligibility Requirements: This program is open to American Indian undergraduate and graduate students who are preparing for a career in fine arts, visual and performing arts, communication arts, creative writing, or arts administration or management. Applicants must be currently enrolled in and attending a fully-accredited college or university. They must provide official tribal documentation verifying American Indian heritage and have a GPA of 2.5 or higher. Applicants majoring in the visual or performing arts (including writing) must submit slides, photographs, videotapes, audio tapes, or other examples of their work. Letters of recommendation are required. Awards are based on either merit or merit and financial need. If the applicants wish to be considered for a need-based award, a letter from their financial aid office is required to verify financial need. **Deadline for Receipt:** September of each year for the fall semester; March of each year for the spring semester. **Additional Information:** This program was established in 1993.

3673 ■ AMERICAN RADIO RELAY LEAGUE

Attn: ARRL Foundation
225 Main Street
Newington, CT 06111
Tel: (860)594-0397
Fax: (860)594-0259
E-mail: foundation@arrl.org
Web Site: http://www.arrl.org/arrlf/scholgen.html

To provide financial assistance to licensed radio amateurs who are members of the American Radio Relay League (ARRL) and interested in working on an undergraduate or graduate degree in international studies. **Title of Award:** Donald Riebhoff Memorial Scholarship **Area, Field, or Subject:** International affairs and relations **Level of Education for which Award is Granted:** Graduate, Undergraduate **Number Awarded:** 1 each year. **Funds Available:** The stipend is $1,000. **Duration:** 1 year.

Eligibility Requirements: This program is open to undergraduate or graduate students who are licensed radio amateurs of technician class. Applicants must be ARRL members majoring in international studies at an accredited postsecondary institution. They must submit an essay on the role amateur radio has played in their lives and provide documentation of financial need. **Deadline for Receipt:** January of each year.

3674 ■ ALEXANDER GRAHAM BELL ASSOCIATION FOR THE DEAF

Attn: Financial Aid Coordinator
3417 Volta Place, N.W.
Washington, DC 20007-2778
Tel: (202)337-5220
Fax: (202)337-8314
E-mail: financialaid@agbell.org
Web Site: http://www.agbell.org/
DesktopDefault.aspx?p=College_Scholarship_Awards

To provide financial aid to hearing impaired students who are participating in extracurricular activities in arts and sciences. **Title of Award:** Arts and Sciences Awards **Area, Field, or Subject:** Art; Performing arts; Science **Level of Education for which Award is Granted:** Undergraduate **Number Awarded:** Varies each year. **Funds Available:** The amount of the award varies, depending upon the cost of the program in which the recipient is enrolled. **Duration:** 1 year; may be renewed upon reapplication.

Eligibility Requirements: Applicants must be diagnosed as having a moderate to profound hearing loss (55 dB or greater loss in the better ear in the speech frequencies of 500, 1000, and 2000 Hz) and must use speech, residual hearing, and/or speechreading as their primary form of communication. They must be between 6 and 19 years of age and enrolled in an art or science program as an extracurricular activity during after-school time, summer, or weekends. Recreational summer camps, sports camps or sports, and travel and study abroad programs that do not have an explicit arts or science focus are not eligible. **Deadline for Receipt:** Applications must be requested between December and February of each year and submitted by May of each year.

3675 ■ BULLETIN OF THE ATOMIC SCIENTISTS

Attn: Rieser Fellowship
6042 South Kimbark Avenue
Chicago, IL 60637-2806
Tel: (773)702-2555
Fax: (773)702-0725
Web Site: http://www.thebulletin.org/about_us/rieser_fellowships.htm

To provide funding to undergraduate students interested in developing a project, at home or abroad, that will enable them to investigate the role of scientists in formulating public policy and in addressing global security policy challenges. **Title of Award:** Leonard M. Rieser Fellowship in Science, Technology, and Global Security **Area, Field, or Subject:** International affairs and relations; Public administration; Science; Technology **Level of Education for which Award is Granted:** Undergraduate **Number Awarded:** 3 to 5 each year. **Funds Available:** Stipends range from $2,500 to $5,000. **Duration:** 1 year; nonrenewable.

Eligibility Requirements: This program is open to students at U.S. colleges and universities who are interested in exploring the connections between science, technology, global security, and public policy. Applicants must be seeking funding to 1) provide a stipend for an otherwise unpaid full-time internship; 2) underwrite the cost of travel or transportation to support academic research; 3) participate in or travel to professional conferences where they present academic research; or 4) underwrite the production costs of a special project, ranging from laboratory work to the making of a documentary film. The proposed activity may take place in the United States or abroad. Along with their application, they must submit a narrative (from 800 to 1,000 words) describing the intended use of the fellowship; a 1-page personal essay explaining how they would benefit from the fellowship and the experience being proposed; a detail project budget; and 2 letters of recommendation. Selection is based on demonstrated interest in the fields of science, technology, and public policy, international affairs, or global security policy. Science students are especially encouraged to apply. **Deadline for Receipt:** March of each year. **Additional Information:** This program was established in 1999.

3676 ■ CALIFORNIA ALLIANCE FOR ARTS EDUCATION

495 East Colorado Boulevard
Pasadena, CA 91101
Tel: (626)578-9315
Fax: (626)578-9894
E-mail: eyaa@artsed411.org
Web Site: http://www.artsed411.org/projects/eya.stm

To provide financial assistance to outstanding high school seniors in California who are interested in training to become professional performing artists.

Title of Award: Emerging Young Artist Awards **Area, Field, or Subject:** Art; Dance; Illustrators and illustrations; Music; Painting; Performing arts; Playwriting; Sculpture; Visual arts **Level of Education for which Award is Granted:** Four Year College **Number Awarded:** 12 each year: 4 winners (1 in each category) and 8 runners-up (2 in each category). **Funds Available:** The stipend is $5,000 per year for the winners (for a total of $20,000) and 1-time awards of $1,000 for the runners-up. **Duration:** The winners receive a 4-year scholarship.

Eligibility Requirements: High school seniors in California are eligible to apply in 1 or more of the following categories: dance, music, theater, or visual arts (including painting, drawing, illustration, and sculpture). Applicants must be planning to enter a 4-year institution or accredited professional training program in 1 of those areas. They must be able to demonstrate financial need. Students who apply in the areas of dance, music, and theater must submit a performance work sample. If they advance to the semifinals and finals, they are requested to demonstrate ability with a live performance. **Deadline for Receipt:** January of each year. **Additional Information:** There is a $10 application fee. Awards are not given in non-performance areas (e.g., music composition, technical theater, or choreography).

3677 ■ CALIFORNIA STATE FAIR

Attn: Friends of the Fair Scholarship Program
1600 Exposition Boulevard
P.O. Box 15649
Sacramento, CA 95852
Tel: (916)274-5969
E-mail: wross@calexpo.com
Web Site: http://www.bigfun.org

To provide financial assistance to residents of California who are studying the arts in college.

Title of Award: California State Fair Arts Scholarships **Area, Field, or Subject:** Cinema; Dance; Filmmaking; Music; Performing arts; Visual arts **Level of Education for which Award is Granted:** Undergraduate **Number Awarded:** 2 each year: 1 at $1,500 and 1 at $500. **Funds Available:** Stipends are $1,500 or $500. **Duration:** 1 year.

Eligibility Requirements: This program is open to residents of California currently working on an undergraduate degree at a college or university in the state. Applicants must be studying the arts, including visual arts, dance, music, film, etc. They must have a GPA of 3.0 or higher. Along with their application, they must submit a 2-page essay on why they are pursuing their desired career and life goals. Selection is based on personal commitment, goals established for their chosen field, leadership potential, and civic accomplishments. **Deadline for Receipt:** March of each year. **Additional Information:** The Friends of the Fair Scholarship Program was established in 1993.

3678 ■ CALIFORNIA STATE FAIR

Attn: Friends of the Fair Scholarship Program
1600 Exposition Boulevard
P.O. Box 15649
Sacramento, CA 95852
Tel: (916)274-5969
E-mail: wross@calexpo.com
Web Site: http://www.bigfun.org

To provide financial assistance to residents of California working on an undergraduate or graduate degree in international studies at a college or university in the state.

Title of Award: California State Fair International Studies Scholarships **Area, Field, or Subject:** International affairs and relations **Level of Education for which Award is Granted:** Graduate, Undergraduate **Number Awarded:** 2 each year: 1 at $2,500 and 1 at $1,000. **Funds Available:** Stipends are $2,500 or $1,000. **Duration:** 1 year.

Eligibility Requirements: This program is open to residents of California who are enrolled as undergraduate or graduate students at a college or university in the state. Applicants must be studying or majoring in international studies. They must have a GPA of 3.0 or higher. Along with their application, they must submit a 500-word essay on global trade and economic development as it relates to California. Selection is based on personal commitment, goals established for their chosen field, leadership potential, and civic accomplishments. **Deadline for Receipt:** March of each year. **Additional Information:** The Friends of the Fair Scholarship Program was established in 1993.

3679 ■ JORGE MAS CANOSA FREEDOM FOUNDATION

c/o Cuban American National Foundation
1312 S.W. 27th Avenue
P.O. Box 440069
Miami, FL 33144-9926
Tel: (305)592-7768
Fax: (305)592-7889
Web Site: http://www.canf.org

To provide financial assistance to students of Cuban descent who are working on an undergraduate or graduate degree in selected subject areas.

Title of Award: Mas Family Scholarship Program **Area, Field, or Subject:** Business administration; Communications; Economics; Engineering; International affairs and relations; Journalism **Level of Education for which Award is Granted:** Graduate, Undergraduate **Funds Available:** The amount of the award depends on the cost of tuition at the recipient's selected institution, on the family's situation, and on the amount of funds received from other sources. The amount of the yearly award cannot exceed $10,000. Full scholarships are not awarded to students who will be receiving full tuition scholarships and/or stipendiary support from other sources. **Duration:** 1 year; recipients may reapply and are given preference over other candidates.

Eligibility Requirements: This program is open to students who are direct descendants of those who left Cuba or were born in Cuba themselves. Applicants must be or have been in the top 10% of their high school graduating class and have be able to meet federal standards of financial need. At least 1 parent or 2 grandparents must have been born in Cuba. Both undergraduate and graduate students may apply, provided they are majoring in 1 of the following subjects: engineering, business, international relations, economics, communications, or journalism. Selection is based on academic performance, leadership qualities, financial need, potential to contribute to the advancement of a free society, and likelihood of succeeding in their chosen field. Finalists may be interviewed. **Deadline for Receipt:** March of each year. **Additional Information:** This program was previously offered by the Cuban American National Foundation.

3680 ■ CHICKASAW FOUNDATION

P.O. Box 1726
Ada, OK 74821-1726
Tel: (580)421-9030
Fax: (580)421-9031
Web Site: http://www.cflink.org

To provide financial assistance to members of the Chickasaw Nation who are majoring in fields of interest to ComputerCraft Corporation.

Title of Award: ComputerCraft Corporation Scholarship **Area, Field, or Subject:** Biological and clinical sciences; Engineering, Computer; General studies/Field of study not specified; Graphic art and design; International affairs and relations **Level of Education for which Award is Granted:** Undergraduate **Number Awarded:** 1 each year. **Funds Available:** The stipend is $1,500 per year. **Duration:** 1 year.

Eligibility Requirements: This program is open to Chickasaw students who are currently enrolled full time as an undergraduate student. The sponsor recruits computer engineers, graphic designers, biologists, conference managers, and international trade specialists. Preference may be given to those majors, but all fields of study are eligible. Applicants must have a GPA of 2.5 or higher. Along with their application, they must submit high school or college transcripts, 2 letters of recommendation, a copy of their Certificate of Degree of Indian Blood, a copy of their Chickasaw Nation citizenship card, and a 1-page essay on their long-term goals and plans for achieving them. Financial need is not considered in the selection process. **Deadline for Receipt:** May of each year.

3681 ■ CONGRESSIONAL BLACK CAUCUS FOUNDATION, INC.

Attn: Director, Educational Programs
1720 Massachusetts Avenue, N.W.
Washington, DC 20036
Tel: (202)263-2836
Free: 800-784-2577
Fax: (202)775-0773
E-mail: spouses@cbcfinc.org
Web Site: http://www.cbcfinc.org

To provide financial assistance to minority and other undergraduate and graduate students who reside in a Congressional district represented by an African American and are interested in studying the performing arts in college.

Title of Award: CBC Spouses Performing Arts Scholarship **Area, Field, or Subject:** Business; Music; Performing arts **Level of Education for which Award is Granted:** Graduate, Undergraduate **Number Awarded:** 10 each year. **Funds Available:** The stipend is $3,000. **Duration:** 1 year. **Eligibility Requirements:** This program is open to 1) minority and other graduating high school seniors planning to attend an accredited institution of higher education and 2) currently-enrolled full-time undergraduate, graduate, and doctoral students in good academic standing with a GPA of 2.5 or higher. Applicants must reside or attend school in a Congressional district represented by a member of the Congressional Black Caucus (CBC). They must be interested in preparing for a career in the performing arts, music, or a related field in the entertainment industry. Along with their application, they must submit a videotape of their performance and a 500-word personal statement on 1) the field of study they intend to pursue and why they have chosen that field; 2) their interests, involvement in school activities, community and public service, hobbies, special talents, sports, and other highlight areas; and 3) any other experiences, skills, or qualifications they feel should be considered. They must also be able to document financial need. **Deadline for Receipt:** April of each year. **Additional Information:** This program, established in 2000, is sponsored by

Heineken USA.

3682 ■ CONNECTICUT ASSOCIATION OF SCHOOLS

Attn: Executive Director
30 Realty Drive
Cheshire, CT 06410
Tel: (203)250-1111
Fax: (203)250-1345
E-mail: msavage@casciac.org
Web Site: http://www.casciac.org

To provide financial assistance to high school seniors in Connecticut who plan to study the arts in college.

Title of Award: Bruce Eagleson Memorial Scholarship Awards **Area, Field, or Subject:** Architecture; Dance; Design; Music; Performing arts; Visual arts **Level of Education for which Award is Granted:** Undergraduate **Number Awarded:** 3 each year: 1 at $10,000 and 2 at $5,000. **Funds Available:** Stipends are $10,000 or $5,000. **Duration:** 1 year. **Eligibility Requirements:** This program is open to seniors graduating from high schools in Connecticut who plan to enroll in college to study the arts, including (but not limited to) visual arts, music, theater, dance, design, and architecture. Applicants must be able to demonstrate 1) considerable experience in the arts as evidenced by involvement in shows, exhibits, performances, video productions, or similar activities; 2) involvement in service to peers and/or community through artistic or other activities; and 3) financial need. Along with their application, they must submit a 250-word statement on what led them to their decision to prepare for a career in the arts. **Deadline for Receipt:** March of each year. **Additional Information:** This program is sponsored by Westfield

Corporation in honor of its former East Coast Vice-President of Management who was killed while working for the company at the World Trade Center on September 11, 2001.

3683 ■ COOK INLET REGION, INC.

Attn: CIRI Foundation
2600 Cordova Street, Suite 206
Anchorage, AK 99503
Tel: (907)263-5582
Free: 800-764-3382
Fax: (907)263-5588
E-mail: tcf@ciri.com
Web Site: http://www.thecirifoundation.org/scholarship.html

To provide financial assistance for undergraduate or graduate studies in the literary, performing, and visual arts to Alaska Natives who are original enrollees to Cook Inlet Region, Inc. (CIRI) and their lineal descendants.

Title of Award: Susie Qimmiqsak Bevins Endowment Scholarship Fund **Area, Field, or Subject:** Literature; Performing arts; Visual arts; Writing **Level of Education for which Award is Granted:** Graduate, Undergraduate **Number Awarded:** Varies each year; recently, 1 of these scholarships (at $2,000 per semester) was awarded. **Funds Available:** The stipend is $2,000 per semester. **Duration:** 1 semester; recipients may reapply. **Eligibility Requirements:** This program is open to Alaska Native enrollees to CIRI under the Alaska Native Claims Settlement Act (ANCSA) of 1971 and their lineal descendants. There are no Alaska residency requirements or age limitations. Applicants must be accepted or enrolled full time in a 2-year, 4-year, or graduate degree program in the literary, visual, or performing arts. Selection is based on academic achievement, rigor of course work or degree program, quality of a statement of purpose, student financial contribution, financial need, grade level, previous work performance, education and community activities, letters of recommendation, seriousness of purpose, and practicality of educational and professional goals. **Deadline for Receipt:** May of each year. **Additional Information:** This program was established in 1990. Recipients must attend school on a full-time basis.

3684 ■ DEFENSE INTELLIGENCE AGENCY

Attn: DAH-2
Bolling Air Force Base
Building 6000
Washington, DC 20340-5100
Tel: (202)231-4713
Fax: (202)231-4889
Web Site: http://www.dia.mil

To provide loans-for-service and work experience to women, minority, and disabled high school seniors interested in majoring in specified fields and working for the U.S. Defense Intelligence Agency (DIA).

Title of Award: Defense Intelligence Agency Undergraduate Training Assistance Program **Area, Field, or Subject:** Computer and information sciences; Geography; International affairs and relations; Political science **Level of Education for which Award is Granted:** Undergraduate **Number Awarded:** Only a few are awarded each year. **Funds Available:** Students accepted into this program receive tuition (up to $18,000 per year) at an accredited college or university selected by the student and endorsed by the sponsor; reimbursement for books and needed supplies; an annual salary to cover college room and board expenses and for summer employment; and a position at the sponsoring agency after graduation. Recipients must work for DIA after college graduation for at least 1 and a half times the length of study. For participants who leave DIA earlier than scheduled, the agency arranges for payments to reimburse DIA for the total cost of education (including the employee's pay and allowances). **Duration:** 4 years. **Eligibility Requirements:** This program is open to women, minorities, and individuals with disabilities who are graduating high school seniors and interested in majoring in 1 of the following fields in college: geography, foreign area studies, international relations, or political science. Applicants must have a high school GPA of 3.0 or higher, have an SAT score of 1000 or higher or an ACT score of 21 or higher, be able to demonstrate financial need (household income ceiling of $65,000 for a family of 4 or $80,000 for a family of 5 or more), be U.S. citizens and from a family of U.S. citizens, and demonstrate leadership abilities through extracurricular activities, civic involvement, volunteer work, or part-time employment. **Deadline for Receipt:** November of each year. **Additional Information:** Recipients are provided a challenging summer internship and guaranteed a job at the agency in their field of study upon graduation. Recipients must attend school on a full-time basis.

3685 ■ DELTA SIGMA THETA SORORITY, INC.

1707 New Hampshire Avenue, N.W.
Washington, DC 20009
Tel: (202)986-2400
Fax: (202)986-2513
E-mail: dstemail@deltasigmatheta.org
Web Site: http://www.deltasigmatheta.org
To provide financial assistance to members of Delta Sigma Theta who are interested in careers in the performing or creative arts.
Title of Award: Myra Davis Hemmings Scholarship **Area, Field, or Subject:** Art; Performing arts **Level of Education for which Award is Granted:** Undergraduate **Number Awarded:** 1 each year. **Funds Available:** The amount awarded varies, depending upon the recipient's financial need. Funds must be used for tuition or school expenses only. **Duration:** 1 year; may be renewed.
Eligibility Requirements: Applicants must be active, dues-paying members of Delta Sigma Theta and majoring in the performing or the creative arts. They must submit transcripts of all college records. Selection is based on meritorious achievement. **Deadline for Receipt:** March of each year.

3686 ■ DREW UNIVERSITY

Attn: Office of International and Off-Campus Programs
Brothers College Room 115
36 Madison Avenue
Madison, NJ 07940-4036
Tel: (973)408-3438
Fax: (973)408-3768
E-mail: intlprog@drew.edu
Web Site: http://depts.drew.edu/offcamp/non-DrewScholarships.htm
To provide financial assistance to students from any college who wish to participate in the off-campus programs in the United States or abroad sponsored by Drew University.
Title of Award: Drew University Off Campus Programs Scholarships **Area, Field, or Subject:** Art; British studies; English language and literature; European studies; General studies/Field of study not specified; Performing arts; Political science **Level of Education for which Award is Granted:** Undergraduate **Number Awarded:** Varies each year. **Funds Available:** Grants up to $3,000 per semester are available to be applied to the cost of the programs. **Duration:** 1 semester.
Eligibility Requirements: Students from any American college or university who have been accepted to participate in 1 of the off-campus programs sponsored by Drew University may apply for financial aid if the university's financial aid office determines that they meet the standards of financial need. Applicants for semester programs must be entering their junior or senior year and have a GPA of 2.7 or higher. **Deadline for Receipt:** April of each year for the fall semester; November of each year for the spring semester. **Additional Information:** The programs available recently included a Washington semester on American politics, a semester on the United Nations in New York, a New York semester on contemporary art and culture, a semester on the new Europe, a program in Eritrea on developing countries, and a London semester on British politics, history, drama, or literature.

3687 ■ FOUNDATION FOR THE CAROLINAS

Attn: Senior Vice President, Scholarships
217 South Tryon Street
P.O. Box 34769
Charlotte, NC 28234-4769
Tel: (704)973-4535
Free: 800-973-7244
Fax: (704)973-4935
E-mail: jseymour@fftc.org
Web Site: http://www.fftc.org/scholarships
To provide financial assistance to college students from North Carolina who are interested in the arts.
Title of Award: Spirit Square Center for Arts and Education Scholarship **Area, Field, or Subject:** Art; Performing arts **Level of Education for**

which **Award is Granted:** Undergraduate **Number Awarded:** 1 or more each year. **Funds Available:** Stipends range up to $4,000 per year; Funds are paid directly to the recipient's school to be used for tuition, required fees, books, and supplies. **Duration:** 1 year; may be renewed.
Eligibility Requirements: This program is open to college juniors and seniors who can demonstrate an interest and career potential in the arts. Along with their application, they must submit a 1- to 2-page statement expressing their reasons for applying for the scholarship, their interest in the arts, and their educational and career goals in the arts. Selection is based on academic achievement (preferably a GPA of 3.0 or higher) school and community involvement, personal achievements, and commitment to and demonstrated potential for a career in the arts. Preference is given to residents of Mecklenburg and surrounding counties in North Carolina attending colleges and universities in that state. **Deadline for Receipt:** February of each year.

3688 ■ HAWAI'I COMMUNITY FOUNDATION

Attn: Scholarship Department
1164 Bishop Street, Suite 800
Honolulu, HI 96813
Tel: (808)566-5570; 888-731-3863
Fax: (808)521-6286
E-mail: scholarships@hcf-hawaii.org
Web Site: http://www.hawaiicommunityfoundation.org/scholar/scholar.php
To provide financial assistance to residents of Hawaii for undergraduate or graduate studies in fields related to achieving world cooperation and international understanding.
Title of Award: Marion Maccarrell Scott Scholarship **Area, Field, or Subject:** Anthropology; Economics; Geography; History; International affairs and relations; Law; Peace studies; Philosophy; Political science; Psychology; Sociology **Level of Education for which Award is Granted:** Graduate, Undergraduate **Number Awarded:** Varies each year; recently, 258 of these scholarships were awarded. **Funds Available:** The amounts of the awards depend on the availability of funds and the need of the recipient; recently, stipends averaged $1,749. **Duration:** 1 year.
Eligibility Requirements: This program is open to graduates of public high schools in Hawaii. They must plan to attend school as full-time students (on the undergraduate or graduate level) on the mainland, majoring in history, government, political science, anthropology, economics, geography, international relations, law, psychology, philosophy, or sociology. They must be residents of the state of Hawaii, able to demonstrate financial need, interested in attending an accredited 2- or 4-year college or university, and able to demonstrate academic achievement (GPA of 2.8 or higher). Along with their application, they must submit an essay on their commitment to world peace that includes their learning experiences (courses, clubs, community activities, or travel) related to achieving world peace and international understanding and explaining how their experiences have enhanced their ability to achieve those goals. **Deadline for Receipt:** February of each year.

3689 ■ HISPANIC SCHOLARSHIP FUND

Attn: Selection Committee
55 Second Street, Suite 1500
San Francisco, CA 94105
Tel: (415)808-2350; 877-HSF-INFO
Fax: (415)808-2302
E-mail: college1@hsf.net
Web Site: http://www.hsf.net/scholarship/programs/mcnamara.php
To provide funding to Hispanic undergraduate and graduate students interested in beginning and completing an art project.
Title of Award: McNamara Family Creative Arts Project Grants **Area, Field, or Subject:** Communications; Creative writing; Filmmaking; Performing arts **Level of Education for which Award is Granted:** Graduate, Undergraduate **Number Awarded:** 1 or more each year. **Funds Available:** Grants range from $5,000 to $20,000. **Duration:** These are 1-time grants.
Eligibility Requirements: This program is open to U.S. citizens, permanent residents, and visitors with a passport stamped I-551. Applicants must be of Hispanic heritage and working full time on an undergraduate or graduate degree at an accredited college or university in the United States, Puerto Rico, or the U.S. Virgin Islands. They must have completed at least 12 undergraduate units with a GPA of 3.0 or higher and be majoring in the arts, including (but not limited to) media,

film, performing arts, communications, and writing. Along with their application, they must submit a 3-page concept paper describing the art project for which they are seeking funding, a portfolio of their work, and 600-word essays on 1) how their Hispanic heritage, family upbringing, and/or role models have influenced their personal long-term goals; 2) how they contribute to their community and what they have learned from their experiences; and 3) an academic challenge they have faced and how they have overcome it. Selection is based on those submissions, academic record, plans and career goals, community service, and financial need. **Deadline for Receipt:** May of each year. **Additional Information:** This program is offered by the Hispanic Scholarship Fund (HSF) in partnership with the McNamara Family Foundation.

3690 ■ NATIONAL ASSOCIATION FOR THE ADVANCEMENT OF COLORED PEOPLE

Attn: ACT-SO Director
4805 Mt. Hope Drive
Baltimore, MD 21215
Tel: (410)580-5650
E-mail: ACTSO@naacpnet.org
Web Site: http://www.naacp.org/programs/actso/actso_index.html

To recognize and reward outstanding African American high school students who distinguish themselves in the Afro-Academic, Cultural, Technological and Scientific Olympics (ACT-SO) program.

Title of Award: Afro-Academic, Cultural, Technological and Scientific Olympics (ACT-SO) **Area, Field, or Subject:** Art; Business administration; Humanities; Performing arts; Science; Visual arts **Level of Education for which Award is Granted:** Undergraduate **Number Awarded:** 75 each year: 3 in each of 25 categories. **Funds Available:** In each category, the first-prize winner receives a gold medal and a $2,000 scholarship, the second-prize winner receives a silver medal and a $1,500 scholarship, and the third-prize winner receives a bronze medal and a $1,000 scholarship. **Duration:** The competition has been held annually since 1977.

Eligibility Requirements: This competition is open to high school students (grades 9-12) of African descent who are U.S. citizens and amateurs in the category in which they wish to participate. Competitions are held in 25 categories in 5 general areas: humanities (music composition, original essay, playwriting, and poetry), sciences (architecture, biology, chemistry, computer science, mathematics, physics/electronics, physics/energy, and physics/general), performing arts (dance, dramatics, music instrumental/classical, music instrumental/contemporary, music vocal/classical, music vocal/contemporary, and oratory), visual arts (drawing, painting, photography, sculpture, and filmmaking/video), and business (entrepreneurship). Competition is first conducted by local chapters of the NAACP; winners in each event at the local level then compete at the national level. **Deadline for Receipt:** Local competitions usually take place between March and May. The national finals are held each year in July.

3691 ■ NATIONAL SECURITY AGENCY

Attn: Office of Recruitment and Staffing (Roberts)
9800 Savage Road, Suite 6779
P.O. Box 1661, Suite 6779
Fort Meade, MD 20755-6779
Tel: (410)854-4725; (866)672-4473
Web Site: http://www.nsa.gov/careers/students_4.cfm

To provide financial assistance and work experience to college sophomores and juniors interested in preparing for a career with the National Security Agency (NSA) as a global network analyst.

Title of Award: Pat Roberts Intelligence Scholars Program for Global Network Analysts **Area, Field, or Subject:** Banking; Computer and information sciences; Finance; Information science and technology; International affairs and relations; Political science; Telecommunications systems **Level of Education for which Award is Granted:** Undergraduate **Number Awarded:** Varies each year. **Funds Available:** The stipend is $25,000 per year. During the summer after application, students participate in a Global Network Analysis internship. After graduation, they have an employment obligation to NSA equal to 1.5 times the length of educational support provided. **Duration:** 1 year; may be renewed 1 additional year. The summer internship program is for 12 weeks.

Eligibility Requirements: This program is open to college sophomore and juniors whose academic program includes 1 of the following areas of emphasis: 1) technical studies (computer science major with a minor in

political science or international relations); 2) topical studies (terrorism, proliferation or related sciences, international banking and finance, or telecommunications and information systems networks); or 3) disciplines (technical intelligence analysis, information assurance, networks, and telecommunications). Applicants must be enrolled full time with a GPA of 3.0 or higher. Along with their application, they must submit a 1-page essay describing how the proposed program of study will improve their ability to analyze information and to think and write critically. U.S. citizenship and eligibility to obtain a high-level security clearance are required **Deadline for Receipt:** October of each year. **Additional Information:** After graduation, participants enter NSA's Global Network Analysis Internship Program as a full-time employee.

3692 ■ NATIONAL SECURITY AGENCY

Attn: Office of Recruitment and Staffing (Roberts)
9800 Savage Road, Suite 6779
P.O. Box 1661, Suite 6779
Fort Meade, MD 20755-6779
Tel: (410)854-4725; (866)672-4473
Web Site: http://www.nsa.gov/careers/students_4.cfm

To provide financial assistance to college juniors interested in preparing for a career with the National Security Agency (NSA) as an intelligence analyst.

Title of Award: Pat Roberts Intelligence Scholars Program for Intelligence Analysts **Area, Field, or Subject:** Asian studies; Banking; Finance; Foreign languages; Geography; Information science and technology; International affairs and relations; Library and archival sciences; Near Eastern studies; South Asian studies; Telecommunications systems **Level of Education for which Award is Granted:** Four Year College **Number Awarded:** Varies each year. **Funds Available:** The stipend is $25,000 per year. After graduation, recipients have an employment obligation to NSA equal to 1.5 times the length of educational support provided. **Duration:** 1 year (the senior year of college).

Eligibility Requirements: This program is open to college juniors whose academic program includes 1 of the following areas of emphasis: 1) regional studies (Middle East or south, east, or central Asia); 2) topical studies (terrorism, proliferation or related sciences, international banking and finance, or telecommunications and information systems networks); or 3) disciplines (intelligence analysis, philosophy, or international relations; familiarity with foreign languages, particularly Arabic, Chinese, Dari, Farsi, Hindi, Korean, Pashto, Urdu, or a central Asian language is desirable; highly qualified applicants studying social network analysis, library science, or geographic information systems may also be considered). Applicants must be enrolled full time with a GPA of 3.0 or higher. Along with their application, they must submit a 1-page essay describing how the proposed program of study will improve their ability to analyze information and to think and write critically. U.S. citizenship and eligibility to obtain a high-level security clearance are required **Deadline for Receipt:** October of each year. **Additional Information:** After graduation, participants enter NSA's Intelligence Analysis Development Program as a full-time employee.

3693 ■ NATIONAL SECURITY AGENCY

Attn: Office of Recruitment and Staffing (Stokes)
9800 Savage Road, Suite 6779
P.O. Box 1661, Suite 6779
Fort Meade, MD 20755-6779
Tel: (410)854-4725; (866)672-4473
Web Site: http://www.nsa.gov/careers/students_4.cfm

To provide minority and other high school seniors and college sophomores with scholarship/loans and work experience at the National Security Agency (NSA).

Title of Award: Stokes Educational Scholarship Program **Area, Field, or Subject:** Asian studies; Computer and information sciences; Engineering, Computer; Engineering, Electrical; Finance; Foreign languages; International affairs and relations; Mathematics and mathematical sciences; Near Eastern studies; South Asian studies **Level of Education for which Award is Granted:** Undergraduate **Number Awarded:** Varies each year. **Funds Available:** Participants receive college tuition for up to 4 years, reimbursement for books and certain fees, a year-round salary, and a housing allowance and travel reimbursement during summer employment if the distance between the agency and school exceeds 75 miles. Following graduation, participants must work for the agency for 1

and a half times their length of study, usually 5 years. Students who leave agency employment earlier must repay the tuition cost. **Duration:** Up to 4 years, followed by employment at the agency for 5 years.
Eligibility Requirements: This program is open to graduating high school seniors, particularly minorities, who 1) are planning a college major in electrical or computer engineering, computer science, international affairs, international finance, mathematics, area studies (Middle East or south, east, or central Asia), foreign languages (recent language interests included Arabic, Chinese, Farsi, and Korean); 2) have minimum scores of 1600 on the SAT (1100 on critical reading and mathematics, 500 in writing) or 25 on the ACT; 3) have a GPA of 3.0 or higher; 4) are U.S. citizens; and 5) demonstrate leadership abilities. Also eligible are college sophomores who are U.S. citizens, have a GPA of 3.0 or higher, and are majoring in the eligible fields. Applicants must include a 1-page essay on why they want to have a career with the NSA. **Deadline for Receipt:** November of each year. **Additional Information:** Participants must attend classes full time and work at the agency during the summer in jobs tailored to their course of study. They must maintain at least a 3.0 GPA. This program, established in 1986, was formerly known as the National Security Agency Undergraduate Training Program.

3694 ■ PRINCESS GRACE AWARDS

Attn: Executive Director
150 East 58th Street, 25th Floor
New York, NY 10155
Tel: (212)317-1470
Fax: (212)317-1473
E-mail: pgfusa@pgfusa.com
Web Site: http://www.pgfusa.com/awards/theater/index.html
To provide financial support to students and professionals interested in acting, directing, and scenic, lighting, sound, and costume design.
Title of Award: Theater Awards **Area, Field, or Subject:** Fashion design; Lighting science; Performing arts **Level of Education for which Award is Granted:** Four Year College, Master's, Professional **Number Awarded:** Varies each year. Recently, 6 of these grants were awarded: 2 as scholarships, 2 as apprenticeships, and 2 as fellowships. **Funds Available:** Grants range from $5,000 to $25,000. Companies receiving apprenticeships and fellowships are entitled to additional support equal to 15-20% of the award to be used for general operating expenses. **Duration:** Up to 1 year.
Eligibility Requirements: Nominations for these grants are invited from the artistic directors of theater companies and the deans and department chairs of professional schools of theater. Nominees may be actors, directors, or designers (costume, scenic, sound, and lighting). Grants are available as 1) scholarships for tuition for the last year of professional training at a nonprofit school in the United States; 2) apprenticeships for salary assistance for individual artists who are "learning the trade" under the supervision of a skilled staff person or mentor; and 3) fellowships for salary assistance for individual artists who are "advanced" members of a company and are ready to assume significant production responsibilities on 1 or more mainstage production(s). Professional companies must employ professional artistic and management staff, have been in continuous operation as a professional company for at least 3 years, provide a total of 20 weeks of research and performance for the current and previous 3 years, and have demonstrated the ability to raise public and other private funds. Artists must have been with the company for less than 5 years. All nominees must be U.S. citizens or permanent residents. Individuals may not submit an application independently. **Deadline for Receipt:** March of each year. **Additional Information:** This program includes the following named awards: the Robert and Gloria Hausman Theater Award, the Faberge Theater Award, the Gant Gaither Theater Award, the George C. Wolfe Theater Award, the Pierre Cardin Theater Award, and the Grace Le Vine Theater Award.

3695 ■ DONNA REED FOUNDATION FOR THE PERFORMING ARTS

1305 Broadway
Denison, IA 51442
Tel: (712)263-3334
Free: 800-336-4692
Fax: (712)263-8026
E-mail: info@donnareed.org
Web Site: http://www.donnareed.org

To provide financial assistance to high school seniors interested in studying the performing arts in college.
Title of Award: Donna Reed Performing Arts Scholarships **Area, Field, or Subject:** Music; Music, Vocal; Performing arts **Level of Education for which Award is Granted:** Undergraduate **Number Awarded:** 9 each year: in each of the 3 divisions, 1 national winner and 2 other finalists receive awards. In addition, each of the 9 national finalists receive free tuition and all expenses to participate in the Donna Reed Festival and Workshops for the Performing Arts. Another 3 scholarships (1 in each division) are awarded to Iowa residents, and another 3 scholarships (1 in each division) are awarded to residents of Crawford County, Iowa. **Funds Available:** National winners receive $1,000 per year and finalists receive $500. Funds may be used for an accredited postsecondary or approved program of study of the recipient's choice. Iowa winners receive $1,000 scholarships and Crawford County winners receive $500 scholarships. **Duration:** Scholarships for national winners are for 4 years. Scholarships for other winners are for 1 year.
Eligibility Requirements: This program is open to high school seniors who wish to pursue an education or a career in 1 of the following 3 performing arts: acting, vocal (classical, jazz, popular), or musical theater. Applicants must graduate or have graduated from high school during the period between September prior to applying and August after applying. They must submit audio or videotapes; based on those tapes, finalists are invited to a live competition in June at the Donna Reed Festival and Workshops for the Performing Arts in Denison, Iowa. Selection is based on talent. Grades and financial need are not considered. U.S. citizenship or permanent resident status is required. Separate award are presented to residents of Iowa and to residents of Crawford County, Iowa. **Deadline for Receipt:** February of each year. **Additional Information:** The widower and friends of the actress Donna Reed established this foundation in 1987, the year after her death. It is based in, and the workshops are held in, Denison, Iowa, Donna Reed's birthplace. A $40 application fee is required for the first discipline category the applicant enters; additional entries require an additional $30 fee. Fees may be waived in cases of financial need.

3696 ■ SCREEN ACTORS GUILD FOUNDATION

Attn: Administrative Director
5757 Wilshire Boulevard
Los Angeles, CA 90036-3600
Tel: (323)549-6649
Fax: (323)549-6710
E-mail: dlloyd@sag.org
Web Site: http://www.sagfoundation.org/scholarship/transitional.shtml
To provide financial assistance to members of the Screen Actors Guild (SAG) who wish to return to school to obtain additional training to broaden or change their careers.
Title of Award: John L. Dales Transitional Scholarships **Area, Field, or Subject:** Performing arts **Level of Education for which Award is Granted:** Professional, Undergraduate **Number Awarded:** Varies each year, depending on the availability of funds. **Funds Available:** The amount of the awards depends on the availability of funds.
Eligibility Requirements: Applicants must have been members of SAG for at least 10 years and have earned an aggregate of at least $60,000 from work under SAG jurisdiction. Applicants must submit information on their academic background and financial need, an essay of 250 to 500 words on a topic of their choice, and 2 letters of recommendation. The proposed study may be undertaken at an accredited college, university, specialty/adult school, or trade/vocational school. **Deadline for Receipt:** March of each year.

3697 ■ SERVICE EMPLOYEES INTERNATIONAL UNION

Attn: Education Department
1313 L Street, N.W.
Washington, DC 20005
Tel: (202)898-3326
Free: 800-448-SEIU
Fax: (202)898-3348
Web Site: http://www.seiu.org/mbe/scholarships/moefoner.cfm
To provide financial assistance to members and children of members of the Service Employees International Union (SEIU) who are interested in studying the visual or performing arts in college.
Title of Award: Moe Foner Scholarship Program for Visual and Performing Arts **Area, Field, or Subject:** Art; Performing arts **Level of Education

for which Award is Granted: Undergraduate **Number Awarded:** 1 each year. **Funds Available:** The stipend is $5,000. **Duration:** 1 year; nonrenewable.

Eligibility Requirements: This program is open to members of an SEIU local or affiliated union and their children. Applicants must be working on or planning to work on a degree or training program in the visual or performing arts at a 2-year or 4-year college or university, community college, technical or trade school, or an alternate course of study or training in an arts-related field. Along with their application, they must submit a 200-word essay describing what the labor movement has meant to them and their family; a 200-word essay describing their educational and career goals in the visual or performing arts (including how they plan to use this education to improve the lives of working families and work for economic and social justice); a high school transcript; and either 1) an essay of 500 words or less identifying a workplace issue and how they would use visual and performing arts to reflect the stories and struggles of working people, or 2) 6 copies of their creative work, showing how they would interpret the theme of working people and their struggles through the visual or performing arts. Selection is based on originality, clarity, and commitment to social and economic justice in the workplace. **Deadline for Receipt:** February of each year. **Additional Information:** This program is administered by Scholarship Program Administrators, Inc., 1201 Eighth Avenue South, P.O. Box 23737, Nashville, TN 27202-3737, (615) 320-3149, Fax: (615) 320-3151, E-mail: info@spaprog.com.

3698 ■ SIGMA ALPHA IOTA PHILANTHROPIES, INC.

One Tunnel Road
Asheville, NC 28805
Tel: (828)251-0606
Fax: (828)251-0644
E-mail: philonline@sai-national.org
Web Site: http://www.sai-national.org/phil/philmustech.html
To provide financial assistance for college to members of Sigma Alpha Iota (an organization of women musicians).

Title of Award: Dorothy Cooke Whinery Music Business/Technology Scholarship **Area, Field, or Subject:** Business; Business administration; Management; Marketing and distribution; Music; Performing arts; Technology **Level of Education for which Award is Granted:** Four Year College **Number Awarded:** 1 each year. **Funds Available:** The stipend is $2,000. **Duration:** 1 year.

Eligibility Requirements: This program is open to members of the organization entering their junior or senior year of college. Applicants must be working on a degree in the field of music business or music technology, including music marketing, music business administration, entertainment industry, commercial music, recording and production, music management, or other related fields. They must have a GPA of 3.0 or higher. Along with their application, they must submit a statement of purpose that includes their career goals. **Deadline for Receipt:** March of each year. **Additional Information:** This program was established in 2003. There is a $25 nonrefundable application fee.

3699 ■ HARRY S. TRUMAN SCHOLARSHIP FOUNDATION

Attn: Executive Secretary
712 Jackson Place, N.W.
Washington, DC 20006
Tel: (202)395-4831
Fax: (202)395-6995
E-mail: office@truman.gov
Web Site: http://www.truman.gov
To provide grants-for-service for graduate school to current college juniors who are interested in preparing for a career in public service.

Title of Award: Harry S. Truman Scholarship Program **Area, Field, or Subject:** Agricultural sciences; Biological and clinical sciences; Economics; Education; Engineering; Environmental conservation; Environmental science; History; International affairs and relations; Law; Physical sciences; Political science; Public administration; Public health; Public service; Social sciences; Technology **Level of Education for which Award is Granted:** Four Year College, Graduate **Number Awarded:** 70 to 75 each year: a) 1 "state" scholarship is available to a qualified resident nominee in each of the 50 states, the District of Columbia, Puerto Rico, and the Islands (Guam, the Virgin Islands, American Samoa, and the Commonwealth of the Northern Mariana Islands); and b) up to 25 at-large scholars. **Funds Available:** The program provides up to $30,000, includ-

ing up to $15,000 for the first year of graduate study and up to $15,000 for the final year of graduate study. **Duration:** Support is provided for the first and last year of graduate study.

Eligibility Requirements: Students must be nominated to be considered for this program. Nominees must be full-time students with junior standing at a 4-year institution, committed to a career in government or public service, in the upper quarter of their class, and U.S. citizens or nationals. Each participating institution may nominate up to 4 candidates (and up to 3 additional students who completed their first 2 years at a community college); community colleges and other 2-year institutions may nominate former students who are enrolled as full-time students with junior-level academic standing at accredited 4-year institutions. Selection is based on extent and quality of community service and government involvement, academic performance, leadership record, suitability of the nominee's proposed program of study for a career in public service, and writing and analytical skills. Priority is given to candidates who plan to enroll in a graduate program that specifically trains them for a career in public service, including government at any level, uniformed services, public interest organizations, nongovernmental research and/or educational organizations, public and private schools, and public service oriented nonprofit organizations. The fields of study may include agriculture, biology, engineering, environmental management, physical and social sciences, and technology policy, as well as such traditional fields as economics, education, government, history, international relations, law, nonprofit management, political science, public administration, public health, and public policy. Interviews are required. **Deadline for Receipt:** February of each year. **Additional Information:** Recipients may attend graduate school in the United States or in foreign countries. Scholars are required to work in public service for 3 of the 7 years following completion of a graduate degree program funded by this program. Scholars who do not meet this service requirement, or who fail to provide timely proof to the foundation of such employment, will be required to repay funds received, along with interest.

Law

3700 ■ 100TH INFANTRY BATTALION VETERANS CLUB

Attn: Scholarship Committee
520 Kamoku Street
Honolulu, HI 96826
Tel: (808)732-5216
E-mail: daisyy@hgea.net
Web Site: http://emedia.leeward.hawaii.edu/mnakano
To provide financial assistance to high school seniors and college students who major in business, political science, or law and exemplify the sponsor's motto of "Continuing Service."

Title of Award: Sakae Takahashi Scholarship **Area, Field, or Subject:** Business administration; Law; Political science **Level of Education for which Award is Granted:** Undergraduate **Number Awarded:** 1 each year. **Funds Available:** The stipend is $1,000. **Duration:** 1 year; nonrenewable.

Eligibility Requirements: This program is open to high school seniors planning to attend an institution of higher learning and full-time undergraduate students at community colleges, vocational/trade schools, 4-year colleges, and universities. Applicants must have a GPA of 2.5 or higher and be able to demonstrate civic responsibility and community service. They must be majoring or planning to major in business, political science, or law. Along with their application, they must submit a 4-page on the characteristics of positive leaders and the ways in which they are an extraordinary leader. Selection is based on that essay and the applicant's demonstration that he or she can effectively promote the legacy of the 100th Infantry Battalion and its motto of "Continuing Service." Financial need is not considered. **Deadline for Receipt:** April of each year.

3701 ■ ALABAMA SPACE GRANT CONSORTIUM

c/o University of Alabama in Huntsville
Materials Science Building, Room 205
Huntsville, AL 35899
Tel: (256)824-6800
Fax: (256)824-6061
E-mail: reasonj@uah.edu

Web Site: http://www.uah.edu/ASGC

To provide financial assistance to undergraduates who are studying the space sciences at universities participating in the Alabama Space Grant Consortium (ASGC).

Title of Award: Undergraduate Scholarship Program of the Alabama Space Grant Consortium **Area, Field, or Subject:** Aerospace sciences; Behavioral sciences; Biological and clinical sciences; Business administration; Communications; Computer and information sciences; Economics; Education; Engineering, Aerospace/Aeronautical/Astronautical; International affairs and relations; Law; Natural sciences; Physical sciences; Public administration; Sociology; Space and planetary sciences **Level of Education for which Award is Granted:** Four Year College **Number Awarded:** Varies each year; recently, 32 of these scholarships were awarded. **Funds Available:** The stipend is $1,000 per year. **Duration:** 1 year; may be renewed 1 additional year.

Eligibility Requirements: This program is open to full-time students entering their junior or senior year at universities participating in the ASGC. Applicants must be studying in a field related to space, including the physical, natural, and biological sciences; engineering, education; economics; business; sociology; behavioral sciences; computer science; communications; law; international affairs; and public administration. They must be U.S. citizens and have a GPA of 3.0 or higher. Individuals from underrepresented groups (African Americans, Hispanic, American Indians, Pacific Islanders, Asian Americans, and women) are especially encouraged to apply. Interested students should submit a completed application with a career goal statement, personal references, a brief resume, and transcripts. Selection is based on 1) academic qualifications, 2) quality of the career goal statement, and 3) assessment of the applicant's motivation for a career in aerospace. **Deadline for Receipt:** February of each year. **Additional Information:** The member universities are University of Alabama in Huntsville, Alabama A&M University, University of Alabama, University of Alabama at Birmingham, University of South Alabama, Tuskegee University, and Auburn University. Funding for this program is provided by NASA.

3702 ■ ALASKA COMMISSION ON POSTSECONDARY EDUCATION

Attn: AlaskAdvantage Programs
3030 Vintage Boulevard
Juneau, AK 99801-7109
Tel: (907)465-2962
Free: 800-441-2962
Fax: (907)465-5316
E-mail: customer_service@acpe.ak.us
Web Site: http://alaskaadvantage.state.ak.us/page/255

To provide scholarship/loans to Alaska residents who are interested in working on an undergraduate degree in law enforcement.

Title of Award: Michael Murphy Education Loan **Area, Field, or Subject:** Criminal justice; Criminology; Law enforcement **Level of Education for which Award is Granted:** Undergraduate **Number Awarded:** Varies each year. **Funds Available:** Loans up to $1,000 per year are available. No interest is charged. An origination fee of 3% of the amount disbursed is added to the principal balance to be repaid. This is a scholarship/loan program. Recipients are forgiven 20% of the total loan for each 1-year period they are employed full time in Alaska law enforcement or related fields, up to 5 years. **Duration:** 1 year; may be renewed.

Eligibility Requirements: This program is open to full-time undergraduates working on a degree in law enforcement, probation and parole, penology, or other closely-related field anywhere in the United States. Applicants must have been residents of Alaska for at least 2 years, be high school graduates or equivalent, and demonstrate financial need. **Deadline for Receipt:** March of each year. **Additional Information:** This program is funded by private donations and by voluntary contributions from state employees who may contribute 1 or more days of annual leave to the fund. Information is also available from Alaska State Troopers, Attn: Recruitment Supervisor, 5700 East Tudor Road, Anchorage, AK 99507, (907) 269-5759, Fax: (907) 269-5751.

3703 ■ AMERICAN COUNCIL OF THE BLIND

Attn: Coordinator, Scholarship Program
1155 15th Street, N.W., Suite 1004
Washington, DC 20005
Tel: (202)467-5081
Free: 800-424-8666

Fax: (202)467-5085
E-mail: info@acb.org
Web Site: http://www.acb.org

To provide financial assistance to undergraduate or graduate students who are blind and are interested in studying in a field of service to persons with disabilities.

Title of Award: Arnold Sadler Memorial Scholarship **Area, Field, or Subject:** Disabilities; Education, Special; Law; Rehabilitation, Physical/Psychological **Level of Education for which Award is Granted:** Graduate, Undergraduate **Number Awarded:** 1 each year. **Funds Available:** The stipend is $2,000. In addition, the winner receives a Kurzweil-1000 Reading System. **Duration:** 1 year.

Eligibility Requirements: This program is open to students in rehabilitation, education, law, or other fields of service to persons with disabilities. Applicants must be legally blind and U.S. citizens. In addition to letters of recommendation and copies of academic transcripts, applications must include an autobiographical sketch. A cumulative GPA of 3.3 or higher is generally required. Selection is based on demonstrated academic record, involvement in extracurricular and civic activities, and academic objectives. The severity of the applicant's visual impairment and his/her study methods are also taken into account. **Deadline for Receipt:** February of each year. **Additional Information:** This scholarship is funded by the Arnold Sadler Memorial Scholarship Fund. Scholarship winners are expected to be present at the council's annual conference; the council will cover all reasonable expenses connected with convention attendance.

3704 ■ AMERICAN SOCIETY OF CRIMINOLOGY

Attn: Awards Committee
1314 Kinnear Road, Suite 212
Columbus, OH 43212-1156
Tel: (614)292-9207
Fax: (614)292-6767
E-mail: asc41@infinet.com
Web Site: http://www.asc41.com/uminorfel.htm

To provide financial assistance to ethnic minority undergraduate students interested in conducting a research project in criminology and criminal justice.

Title of Award: American Society of Criminology Undergraduate Student Minority Scholar/Mentor Research Grants **Area, Field, or Subject:** Criminal justice; Criminology; Law enforcement **Level of Education for which Award is Granted:** Four Year College **Number Awarded:** Varies each year; recently, 4 of these grants were awarded. **Funds Available:** The grant provides $5,000 per year for research support and a $1,500 travel grant to attend the ASC annual meetings. **Duration:** 2 years (the junior and senior year of college).

Eligibility Requirements: This program is open to undergraduate students who are members of historically disadvantaged and underrepresented ethnic and racial groups. Applicants must be entering their junior year in a program in criminology and criminal justice. They must be interested in conducting a research project under the mentorship of a faculty member, who must act as a co-applicant for the funding. Along with the application, students must provide a personal statement on their career goals in criminology and another statement on how the grant would enable them to focus more time on their academic work and better achieve their career goals. Faculty members must provide 1) a written recommendation for why the student has the academic potential and career aspirations to complete graduate student in criminology successfully and prepare for an academic career; 2) student transcripts and other supporting materials; 3) a description of the proposed collaborative research project that will result in a presentation at the annual meeting of the American Society of Criminology (ASC) in the student's senior years; and 4) a description of other mentoring activities and proposed contact with the student during the junior and senior years. Selection is based on the student's potential for completing doctoral work in criminology and the quality of the proposed mentoring relationship. **Deadline for Receipt:** April of each year. **Additional Information:** This program began in 2004. Information is also available from Todd R. Clear, Minority Scholar/Mentor Committee Chair, John Jay College of Criminal Justice, 899 Tenth Avenue, New York, NY 10019, (212) 237-8470.

3705 ■ APPALACHIAN COLLEGE ASSOCIATION

Attn: Director of Programs
210 Center Street
Berea, KY 40403

Tel: (859)986-4584
Fax: (859)986-9549
E-mail: kathrynb@acaweb.org
Web Site: http://www.acaweb.org
To provide financial assistance to upper-division students at colleges and universities that are members of the Appalachian College Association (ACA) who plan to become lawyers.
Title of Award: Barbara Paul Robinson Scholarship **Area, Field, or Subject:** Law **Level of Education for which Award is Granted:** Four Year College **Number Awarded:** 1 each year. **Funds Available:** The stipend is $2,500 per year. **Duration:** 1 year; may be renewed 1 additional year.
Eligibility Requirements: This program is open to full-time students entering their junior or senior year at ACA member institutions with an interest in law. Applicants must have a GPA of 3.0 or higher and be able to document financial need. They must intend to become an attorney and serve the Appalachian people. Along with their application, they must submit a 500-word essay describing their personal and academic background and professional goals as a conscientious attorney, including any steps toward applying for law school or legal internships. **Deadline for Receipt:** January of each year. **Additional Information:** The ACA includes member institutions in Kentucky (Alice Lloyd College, Berea College, Campbellsville University, University of the Cumberlands, Kentucky Christian University, Lindsey Wilson College, Pikeville College, and Union College), North Carolina (Brevard College, Lees-McRae College, Mars Hill College, Montreat College, and Warren Wilson College), Tennessee (Bryan College, Carson-Newman College, King College, Lee University, Lincoln Memorial University, Maryville College, Milligan College, Tennessee Wesleyan College, Tusculum College, and University of the South), Virginia (Bluefield College, Emery & Henry College, Ferrum College, and Virginia Intermont College), and West Virginia (Alderson-Broaddus College, Bethany College, Davis & Elkins College, Ohio Valley University, University of Charleston, West Virginia Wesleyan College, and Wheeling Jesuit University).

3706 ■ BOYS & GIRLS CLUBS OF GREATER SAN DIEGO
Attn: Scholarships
4635 Clairemont Mesa Boulevard
San Diego, CA 92117
Tel: (619)298-3520; (866)SD-YOUTH
Fax: (619)298-3615
Web Site: http://www.sdyouth.org/scholarships.htm
To provide financial assistance to graduating male high school seniors who plan to study designated fields in college.
Title of Award: Spence Reese Scholarships **Area, Field, or Subject:** Engineering; Law; Medicine; Political science **Level of Education for which Award is Granted:** Undergraduate **Number Awarded:** 4 each year: 1 in each of the designated fields. **Funds Available:** The stipend is $2,000 per year. **Duration:** 4 years.
Eligibility Requirements: Applicants must be graduating male high school seniors planning to study law, medicine, engineering, or political science in college. They may live anywhere in the United States, but must attend an interview in San Diego, California. Selection is based on academic standing, potential for good citizenship, academic ability, and financial need. **Deadline for Receipt:** April of each year. **Additional Information:** Travel expenses for the interview are reimbursed by the sponsor. A $10 processing fee must accompany all applications.

3707 ■ H. FLETCHER BROWN TRUST
PNC Bank Delaware
Attn: Donald W. Davis
222 Delaware Avenue, 16th Floor
Wilmington, DE 19899
Tel: (302)429-2827
Fax: (302)429-5658
E-mail: Robbie.testa@pncadvisors.com
To provide financial assistance to residents of Delaware who are interested in studying engineering, chemistry, medicine, dentistry, or law.
Title of Award: H. Fletcher Brown Scholarship **Area, Field, or Subject:** Chemistry; Dentistry; Engineering; Law; Medicine; Medicine, Osteopathic **Level of Education for which Award is Granted:** Graduate, Professional, Undergraduate **Funds Available:** The amount of the scholarship is determined by the scholarship committee and is awarded in installments

over the length of study. **Duration:** 1 year; may be renewed if the recipient maintains a GPA of 2.5 or higher and continues to be worthy of and eligible for the award.
Eligibility Requirements: This program is open to Delaware residents who were born in Delaware, are either high school seniors entering the first year of college or college seniors entering the first year of graduate school, are of good moral character, and need financial assistance from sources outside their family. Applicants must have combined mathematics and verbal SAT scores of 1000 or higher, rank in the upper 20% of their class, and come from a family whose income is less than $75,000. Their proposed fields of study must be engineering, chemistry, medicine (for an M.D. or D.O. degree only), dentistry, or law. Finalists are interviewed. **Deadline for Receipt:** March of each year.

3708 ■ BUSINESS AND PROFESSIONAL WOMEN OF VIRGINIA
Attn: Virginia BPW Foundation
P.O. Box 4842
McLean, VA 22103-4842
Web Site: http://www.bpwva.org/Foundation.shtml
To provide financial assistance to mature women in Virginia who are interested in upgrading their skills or education at a college, law school, or medical school in the state.
Title of Award: Buena M. Chesshir Memorial Women's Educational Scholarship **Area, Field, or Subject:** General studies/Field of study not specified; Law; Medicine **Level of Education for which Award is Granted:** Graduate, Professional, Undergraduate **Number Awarded:** 1 or more each year. **Funds Available:** Stipends range from $100 to $1,000 per year; funds may be used for tuition, fees, books, transportation, living expenses, and dependent care. **Duration:** Recipients must complete their course of study within 2 years.
Eligibility Requirements: This program is open to women who are residents of Virginia, U.S. citizens, and at least 25 years of age. Applicants must have been accepted into an accredited program or course of study at a Virginia institution, have a definite plan to use their training to improve their chances for upward mobility in the work force, and be graduating within 2 years. Undergraduate applicants may by majoring in any field, but graduate student applicants must be working on a degree in law or medicine. Selection is based on demonstrated financial need and defined career goals. **Deadline for Receipt:** March of each year.

3709 ■ CHICKASAW FOUNDATION
P.O. Box 1726
Ada, OK 74821-1726
Tel: (580)421-9030
Fax: (580)421-9031
Web Site: http://www.cflink.org
To provide financial assistance to members of the Chickasaw Nation who are majoring or minoring in American history.
Title of Award: Colbert "Bud" Baker Scholarship **Area, Field, or Subject:** Education; History, American; Law; Native American studies **Level of Education for which Award is Granted:** Four Year College **Number Awarded:** 1 each year. **Funds Available:** The stipend is $1,000 per year. **Duration:** 1 year.
Eligibility Requirements: This program is open to Chickasaw students who are currently enrolled full time at an accredited institution of higher education. Applicants must be classified as juniors or seniors at a 4-year college. They must be majoring in history or majoring in education or pre-law with a minor in history. The history emphasis must be on Chickasaw tribal history or Native American studies. Along with their application, they must submit high school or college transcripts, 2 letters of recommendation, a copy of their Certificate of Degree of Indian Blood, a copy of their Chickasaw Nation citizenship card, and a 1-page essay on their long-term goals and plans for achieving them. Financial need is not considered in the selection process. **Deadline for Receipt:** May of each year.

3710 ■ CHRISTIAN LIFE RESOURCES
Attn: WELS Lutherans for Life
Scholarship Review Committee
2949 North Mayfair Road, Suite 309
Milwaukee, WI 53222-4304
Tel: (414)774-1331
Fax: (414)774-1360
Web Site: http://www.christianliferesources.com

To provide financial assistance to Lutheran high school seniors in Wisconsin who are interested in studying life-related issues in college. **Title of Award:** WELS Lutherans for Life Scholarship Program **Area, Field, or Subject:** Biological and clinical sciences; Education, Special; Engineering, Biomedical; Journalism; Law; Medicine; Physical therapy; Political science; Psychology; Social work **Level of Education for which Award is Granted:** Four Year College **Number Awarded:** Varies each year; recently, 9 of these scholarships were awarded. **Funds Available:** Stipends up to $1,000 are available. **Duration:** 1 year.

Eligibility Requirements: This program is open to high school seniors who are active members of the Wisconsin Evangelical Lutheran Synod (WELS) or an affiliated church. Applicants must be planning to go to a 4-year school to prepare for a secular career in which pro-life values will be demonstrated. Acceptable fields include medicine, biotechnology/biological engineering, medical research/genetics, law/politics, journalism/media, psychology, physical therapy, social services, or special education. They must have a GPA of 3.25 or higher. Along with their application, they must submit essays on 1) the field of study they plan to enter and how it relates to pro-life issues; 2) why the scholarship should be awarded to them, including their future goals; and 3) how they have demonstrated a Christian, pro-life attitude in their life. **Deadline for Receipt:** February of each year. **Additional Information:** WELS Lutherans for Life was formerly a ministry of the Wisconsin Evangelical Lutheran Synod.

3711 ■ COMMUNITY FOUNDATION OF GREATER JACKSON
525 East Capitol Street, Suite 5B
Jackson, MS 39201
Tel: (601)974-6044
Fax: (601)974-6045
E-mail: info@cfgreaterjackson.org
Web Site: http://www.cfgreaterjackson.org
To provide financial assistance to upper-division students in Mississippi and Louisiana who are preparing for a career in the field of juvenile justice.
Title of Award: Anthony "Tony" Gobar Juvenile Justice Scholarship Fund **Area, Field, or Subject:** Counseling/Guidance; Criminal justice; Criminology; Law enforcement; Political science **Level of Education for which Award is Granted:** Four Year College **Number Awarded:** 1 each year. **Funds Available:** A stipend is awarded (amount not specified). **Duration:** 1 year.

Eligibility Requirements: This program is open to full-time juniors and seniors at public universities in Mississippi and at Southern University in Louisiana who are preparing to enter the field of juvenile justice. Applicants must have demonstrated a strong commitment to community and public service. They must be U.S. citizens with a GPA of 2.5 or higher. Eligible majors include criminal justice, counseling, and political science. Selection is based on merit and need. **Deadline for Receipt:** April of each year. **Additional Information:** This program was established in 2005.

3712 ■ CONNECTICUT ASSOCIATION OF WOMEN POLICE
P.O. Box 1653
Hartford, CT 06144-1653
E-mail: admin@cawp.net
Web Site: http://www.cawp.net
To provide financial assistance to high school seniors in Connecticut who are interested in studying criminal justice in college.
Title of Award: Connecticut Association of Women Police Scholarships **Area, Field, or Subject:** Criminal justice; Criminology; Law enforcement **Level of Education for which Award is Granted:** Four Year College **Number Awarded:** Varies each year; recently, 5 of these scholarships were awarded. **Funds Available:** A stipend is awarded (amount not specified). **Duration:** 1 year.

Eligibility Requirements: This program is open to seniors graduating from high schools in Connecticut who are interested in attending a 4-year college or university to prepare for a career in criminal justice. Applicants must submit a personal essay of 200 to 250 words on their personal goals and why they should be selected for this scholarship. Selection is based on the essay and financial need. **Deadline for Receipt:** April of each year.

3713 ■ COOK INLET REGION, INC.
Attn: CIRI Foundation
2600 Cordova Street, Suite 206
Anchorage, AK 99503

Tel: (907)263-5582
Free: 800-764-3382
Fax: (907)263-5588
E-mail: tcf@ciri.com
Web Site: http://www.thecirifoundation.org/scholarship.html
To provide financial assistance for undergraduate or graduate studies leading to a career in the law to Alaska Natives who are original enrollees to Cook Inlet Region, Inc. (CIRI) and their lineal descendants.
Title of Award: John N. Colberg Endowment Scholarship Fund **Area, Field, or Subject:** Law **Level of Education for which Award is Granted:** Four Year College, Graduate **Number Awarded:** Varies each year; recently, 1 of these scholarships (at $7,000 per year) was awarded. **Funds Available:** The stipend is $9,000 per year, $7,000 per year, or $2,000 per semester, depending on GPA. **Duration:** 1 year (2 semesters).

Eligibility Requirements: This program is open to Alaska Native enrollees to CIRI under the Alaska Native Claims Settlement Act (ANCSA) of 1971 and their lineal descendants. There are no Alaska residency requirements or age limitations. Applicants must be accepted or enrolled full time in a 4-year undergraduate or a graduate degree program. They must be working on a degree leading to the study of law and have a GPA of 2.5 or higher. Selection is based on academic achievement, rigor of course work or degree program, quality of a statement of purpose, student financial contribution, financial need, grade level, previous work performance, education and community activities, letters of recommendation, seriousness of purpose, and practicality of educational and professional goals. **Deadline for Receipt:** May of each year. **Additional Information:** Recipients must attend school on a full-time basis.

3714 ■ COOK INLET REGION, INC.
Attn: CIRI Foundation
2600 Cordova Street, Suite 206
Anchorage, AK 99503
Tel: (907)263-5582
Free: 800-764-3382
Fax: (907)263-5588
E-mail: tcf@ciri.com
Web Site: http://www.thecirifoundation.org/scholarship.html
To provide financial assistance for undergraduate or graduate studies in selected liberal arts to Alaska Natives who are original enrollees to Cook Inlet Region, Inc. (CIRI) and their lineal descendants.
Title of Award: Lawrence Matson Memorial Endowment Fund Scholarships **Area, Field, or Subject:** Art; Communications; Education; Law; Linguistics; Social sciences **Level of Education for which Award is Granted:** Four Year College, Graduate **Number Awarded:** Varies each year; recently, 1 of these scholarships (at $7,000 per year) was awarded. **Funds Available:** The stipend is $9,000 per year, $7,000 per year, or $2,000 per semester, depending on GPA. **Duration:** 1 year (2 semesters).

Eligibility Requirements: This program is open to Alaska Native enrollees to CIRI under the Alaska Native Claims Settlement Act (ANCSA) of 1971 and their lineal descendants. There are no Alaska residency requirements or age limitations. Applicants must be accepted or enrolled full time in a 4-year undergraduate or a graduate degree program in the following liberal arts fields: language, education, social sciences, arts, communications, or law. They must have a GPA of 2.5 or higher. Selection is based on academic achievement, rigor of course work or degree program, quality of a statement of purpose, student financial contribution, financial need, grade level, previous work performance, education and community activities, letters of recommendation, seriousness of purpose, and practicality of educational and professional goals. **Deadline for Receipt:** May of each year. **Additional Information:** This fund was established in 1989. Recipients must attend school on a full-time basis.

3715 ■ HAWAI'I COMMUNITY FOUNDATION
Attn: Scholarship Department
1164 Bishop Street, Suite 800
Honolulu, HI 96813
Tel: (808)566-5570; 888-731-3863
Fax: (808)521-6286
E-mail: scholarships@hcf-hawaii.org
Web Site: http://www.hawaiicommunityfoundation.org/scholar/scholar.php
To provide financial assistance to Hawaii residents who are interested in studying marketing, law, or travel industry management in college or graduate school.

Title of Award: Bick Bickson Scholarship Fund **Area, Field, or Subject:** Law; Marketing and distribution; Travel and tourism **Level of Education for which Award is Granted:** Graduate, Undergraduate **Number Awarded:** Varies each year; recently, 2 of these scholarships were awarded. **Funds Available:** The amounts of the awards depend on the availability of funds and the need of the recipient; recently, stipends averaged $1,250. **Duration:** 1 year.
Eligibility Requirements: This program is open to Hawaii residents who are interested in majoring in marketing, law, or travel industry management on the undergraduate or graduate school level. They must be able to demonstrate academic achievement (GPA of 2.7 or higher), good moral character, and financial need. In addition to filling out the standard application form, applicants must write a short statement indicating their reasons for attending college, their planned course of study, and their career goals. **Deadline for Receipt:** February of each year. **Additional Information:** Recipients may attend college in Hawaii or on the mainland. Recipients must be full-time students.

3716 ■ HAWAI'I COMMUNITY FOUNDATION

Attn: Scholarship Department
1164 Bishop Street, Suite 800
Honolulu, HI 96813
Tel: (808)566-5570; 888-731-3863
Fax: (808)521-6286
E-mail: scholarships@hcf-hawaii.org
Web Site: http://www.hawaiicommunityfoundation.org/scholar/scholar.php
To provide financial assistance to residents of Hawaii for undergraduate or graduate studies in fields related to achieving world cooperation and international understanding.
Title of Award: Marion Maccarrell Scott Scholarship **Area, Field, or Subject:** Anthropology; Economics; Geography; History; International affairs and relations; Law; Peace studies; Philosophy; Political science; Psychology; Sociology **Level of Education for which Award is Granted:** Graduate, Undergraduate **Number Awarded:** Varies each year; recently, 258 of these scholarships were awarded. **Funds Available:** The amounts of the awards depend on the availability of funds and the need of the recipient; recently, stipends averaged $1,749. **Duration:** 1 year.
Eligibility Requirements: This program is open to graduates of public high schools in Hawaii. They must plan to attend school as full-time students (on the undergraduate or graduate level) on the mainland, majoring in history, government, political science, anthropology, economics, geography, international relations, law, psychology, philosophy, or sociology. They must be residents of the state of Hawaii, able to demonstrate financial need, interested in attending an accredited 2- or 4-year college or university, and able to demonstrate academic achievement (GPA of 2.8 or higher). Along with their application, they must submit an essay on their commitment to world peace that includes their learning experiences (courses, clubs, community activities, or travel) related to achieving world peace and international understanding and explaining how their experiences have enhanced their ability to achieve those goals. **Deadline for Receipt:** February of each year.

3717 ■ HOPI TRIBE

Attn: Office of Education
P.O. Box 123
Kykotsmovi, AZ 86039
Tel: (928)734-3533
Free: 800-762-9630
Fax: (928)734-9575
E-mail: IPolingyumptewa@hopi.nsn.us
Web Site: http://www.hopi.nsn.us/education_htgsp.asp
To encourage Hopi students to get an undergraduate or graduate degree in an area of interest to the Hopi Tribe.
Title of Award: Hopi Tribal Priority Scholarship **Area, Field, or Subject:** Business administration; Education; Engineering; Environmental conservation; Environmental science; Health care services; Law; Medicine **Level of Education for which Award is Granted:** Four Year College, Graduate **Number Awarded:** Varies each year. **Funds Available:** The stipend covers all educational expenses. **Duration:** 1 year; may be renewed.
Eligibility Requirements: This program is open to enrolled members of the Hopi Tribe. They must be college juniors, seniors, or graduate students whose degree is in a subject area that is of priority interest to the

Hopi Tribe. Those areas are law, natural resources, education, medicine, health, engineering, or business. This is a highly competitive scholarship. Selection is based on academic merit and the likelihood that the applicants will use their training and expertise for tribal goals and objectives. **Deadline for Receipt:** July of each year. **Additional Information:** Recipients must attend school on a full-time basis.

3718 ■ INTERNATIONAL FOUNDATION FOR GENDER EDUCATION

Attn: Transgender Scholarship and Education Legacy Fund
P.O. Box 540229
Waltham, MA 02454-0229
Tel: (781)899-2212
Fax: (781)899-5703
E-mail: carrie@tself.org
Web Site: http://www.tself.org
To provide financial assistance to transgender students who are working on an undergraduate or graduate degree in the caring professions.
Title of Award: Transgender Scholarship and Education Legacy Fund Awards **Area, Field, or Subject:** Education; Health care services; Law; Religion; Social work **Level of Education for which Award is Granted:** Graduate, Undergraduate **Number Awarded:** Varies each year; recently, 4 of these scholarships were awarded. **Funds Available:** Stipends average $2,000. Funds are paid directly to the student. **Duration:** 1 year; nonrenewable.
Eligibility Requirements: This program is open to undergraduate and graduate students who are living full time in a gender or sex role that differs from that assigned to them at birth and who are "out and proud" about their transgender identity. Applicants must be working on a degree in the helping and caring professions, including, but not limited to, social services, health care, religious instruction, education, and the law. They may be of any age or nationality, but they must be attending or planning to attend a college, university, trade school, or technical college in the United States or Canada. Selection is based on affirmation of transgender identity; demonstration of integrity and honesty; participation and leadership in community activities; service as role model, mentor, colleague, or advisor for the transgender communities; and service as transgender role model, mentor, colleague, or advisor to non-transpeople in the helping and caring professions. **Deadline for Receipt:** January of each year. **Additional Information:** This program includes the TSELF Youth Award (for applicants under 22 years of age entering their first or second year of postsecondary education); the TSELF Schools Education Award (for applicants working on a degree in education and teaching); the Lee Frances Heller Memorial Award (for Christian students or applicants who are or will be attending a college, university, or other institution for religious studies); the HIV/AIDS Prevention and Treatment Award (for applicants who have been involved in HIV/AIDS prevention, care, and treatment activities); and the Chicago Gender Society Leadership Award (for applicants who have been involved in community building activities).

3719 ■ MARYLAND HIGHER EDUCATION COMMISSION

Attn: Office of Student Financial Assistance
839 Bestgate Road, Suite 400
Annapolis, MD 21401-3013
Tel: (410)260-4594
Free: 800-974-1024
Fax: (410)974-5376
E-mail: osfamail@mhec.state.md.us
Web Site: http://www.mhec.state.md.us/financialAid/
ProgramDescriptions/prog_devdis.asp
To provide scholarship/loans to students in Maryland who are interested in working on a degree in a designated human services program.
Title of Award: Maryland Developmental Disabilities, Mental Health, Child Welfare, and Juvenile Justice Workforce Tuition Assistance Program **Area, Field, or Subject:** Counseling/Guidance; Criminal justice; Criminology; Disabilities; Education, Special; Gerontology; Law enforcement; Mental health; Nursing; Occupational therapy; Physical therapy; Psychology; Rehabilitation, Physical/Psychological; Social work **Level of Education for which Award is Granted:** Graduate, Undergraduate **Number Awarded:** Varies each year. **Funds Available:** The maximum stipend is $2,000 per year for students attending a 2-year institution or $3,000 per year for students at a 4-year institution. The total amount of all state awards may not exceed the cost of attendance as determined by the school's financial aid office or $17,800, whichever is less. Recipients must

agree to work in a Maryland community-based program that is licensed by the Developmental Disabilities Administration or approved by the Mental Hygiene Administration, or in a residential program that is licensed by the Department of Human Resources or the Department of Juvenile Justice. The service obligation must begin within 6 months of graduation. The total service requirement is 2,000 hours if the award amount is $1,999 or less, 3,000 hours if the award amount is $2,000 to $3,999, or 4,000 hours if the award amount is $4,000 or more. If the service requirement is not completed, the award must be repaid with interest. **Duration:** 1 year; may be renewed if the recipient maintains satisfactory academic progress and remains enrolled in a human services degree program.

Eligibility Requirements: This program is open to high school seniors and full-time and part-time undergraduate and graduate students. Applicants and their parents must be Maryland residents attending a college or university in the state in 1 of the following human services degree programs: aging services, counseling, disability services, mental health, nursing, occupational therapy, physical therapy, psychology, rehabilitation, social work, special education, supported employment, vocational rehabilitation, or any other concentration in the healing arts or a program providing support services to individuals with special needs including child welfare and juvenile justice. Financial need is not considered in the selection process. **Deadline for Receipt:** June of each year.

3720 ■ MICHIGAN LAW ENFORCEMENT EDUCATION PROGRAM

c/o Scholarship Committee
667 East Big Beaver Road, Suite 205
Troy, MI 48083
800-451-1220
To provide financial assistance for college to high school students in Michigan who are interested in preparing for a career in a field related to public safety.

Title of Award: LEEP Dream Scholarship **Area, Field, or Subject:** Criminal justice; Criminology; Emergency and disaster services; Fires and fire prevention; Law enforcement **Level of Education for which Award is Granted:** Undergraduate **Number Awarded:** Several each year. **Funds Available:** The stipend is $1,000. **Duration:** 1 year.

Eligibility Requirements: This program is open to seniors graduating from high schools in Michigan who are interested in preparing for a career as a law enforcement officer, police-fire dispatcher, corrections officer, fire fighter, or emergency medical technician. Applicants must be planning to attend a Michigan 4-year university, community college, or vocational training institution that grants a degree, certificate, or license in public safety or related field. **Deadline for Receipt:** May of each year.

3721 ■ MICHIGAN SHERIFFS' ASSOCIATION

Attn: Educational Services
515 North Capitol Avenue
Lansing, MI 48933
Tel: (517)485-3135
Fax: (517)485-1013
Web Site: http://www.michigansheriff.com
To provide financial assistance to high school seniors in Michigan who are interested in attending college to prepare for a career in criminal justice.

Title of Award: Bernard Grysen Memorial Criminal Justice Scholarships **Area, Field, or Subject:** Criminal justice; Criminology; Law enforcement **Level of Education for which Award is Granted:** Undergraduate **Number Awarded:** 10 each year: 2 in each of the association's districts. **Funds Available:** The stipend is $1,000. **Duration:** 1 year.

Eligibility Requirements: This program is open to seniors graduating from high schools in Michigan who are planning to attend a college or university in the state to prepare for a career in criminal justice. Applicants must be able to demonstrate high academic standing, high moral character, and a high degree of activity in civic and governmental affairs relating to law enforcement. They must be nominated by a member of the Michigan Sheriffs' Association. Along with their application, they must submit a 300-word essay on why they are preparing for a career in criminal justice. Financial need is not considered in the selection process. **Deadline for Receipt:** April of each year. **Additional Information:** This program was established in 1995.

3722 ■ MORRIS SCHOLARSHIP FUND

Attn: Scholarship Selection Committee
525 S.W. Fifth Street, Suite A
Des Moines, IA 50309-4501

Tel: (515)282-8192
Fax: (515)282-9117
E-mail: morris@assoc-mgmt.com
Web Site: http://www.morrisscholarship.org
To provide financial assistance to minority undergraduate, graduate, and law students in Iowa.

Title of Award: Morris Scholarship **Area, Field, or Subject:** General studies/Field of study not specified; Law **Level of Education for which Award is Granted:** Graduate, Undergraduate **Number Awarded:** Varies each year; recently, 11 of these scholarships were awarded. **Funds Available:** The stipend is $1,500 per year. **Duration:** 1 year; may be renewed.

Eligibility Requirements: This program is open to minority students (African Americans, Asian/Pacific Islanders, Hispanics, or Native Americans) who are interested in studying at a college, graduate school, or law school. Applicants must be either Iowa residents and high school graduates who are attending a college or university anywhere in the United States or non-Iowa residents who are attending a college or university in Iowa; preference is given to native Iowans who are attending an Iowa college or university. Along with their application, they must submit an essay of 250 to 500 words on why they are applying for this scholarship, activities or organizations in which they are involved, and their future plans. Selection is based on the essay, academic achievement (GPA of 2.5 or higher), community service, and financial need. **Deadline for Receipt:** January of each year. **Additional Information:** This fund was established in 1978 in honor of the J.B. Morris family, who founded the Iowa branch of the National Association for the Advancement of Colored People and published the *Iowa Bystander* newspaper.

3723 ■ NALS OF MICHIGAN

c/o Angela Head, Scholarship Chair
155 North 22nd Street
Battle Creek, MI 49015-1762
Tel: (269)964-9951
E-mail: angeenmad@yahoo.com
Web Site: http://www.nalsofmichigan.org/Scholarship.htm
To provide financial assistance to residents of Michigan interested in a career in the legal field.

Title of Award: NALS of Michigan Scholarships **Area, Field, or Subject:** Paralegal studies; Secretarial sciences **Level of Education for which Award is Granted:** Undergraduate **Number Awarded:** 2 each year. **Funds Available:** The stipend is $1,000. Funds are to be used for tuition or books. **Duration:** 1 year; nonrenewable.

Eligibility Requirements: This program is open to high school seniors, students currently enrolled in a school of higher education, and members of NALS of Michigan. Applicants must be interested in a career in the legal field (e.g., legal secretary) and have at least a "B" average or (if a percentile system is used) 90% or higher. Along with their application, they must submit an official transcript, 2 letters of recommendation, and a 1-page autobiographical statement that includes a description of their goals and desires. Selection is based on scholastic or legal career achievements, future career goals, leadership ability, and financial need. **Deadline for Receipt:** January of each year. **Additional Information:** NALS formerly stood for National Association of Legal Secretaries.

3724 ■ NATIONAL FEDERATION OF THE BLIND

c/o Peggy Elliott, Scholarship Committee Chair
805 Fifth Avenue
Grinnell, IA 50112
Tel: (641)236-3366
Web Site: http://www.nfb.org/sch_intro.htm
To provide financial assistance for college or graduate school to blind students studying or planning to study law, medicine, engineering, architecture, or the natural sciences.

Title of Award: Howard Brown Rickard Scholarships **Area, Field, or Subject:** Architecture; Engineering; Law; Medicine; Natural sciences **Level of Education for which Award is Granted:** Graduate, Undergraduate **Number Awarded:** 1 each year. **Funds Available:** The stipend is $3,000. **Duration:** 1 year; recipients may resubmit applications up to 2 additional years.

Eligibility Requirements: This program is open to legally blind students who are enrolled in or planning to enroll in a full-time undergraduate or graduate course of study. Applicants must be studying or planning to study law, medicine, engineering, architecture, or the natural sciences.

Selection is based on academic excellence, service to the community, and financial need. **Deadline for Receipt:** March of each year. **Additional Information:** Scholarships are awarded at the federation convention in July. Recipients attend the convention at federation expense; that funding is in addition to the scholarship grant.

3725 ■ NEBRASKA EDUCATIONAL OFFICE PROFESSIONALS ASSOCIATION
P.O. Box 83872
Lincoln, NE 68501-3872
Web Site: http://neopa.unl.edu/awards.html
To provide financial assistance to residents of Nebraska who are interested in preparing for an office-related career.
Title of Award: Nebraska Educational Office Professionals Association Student Scholarship **Area, Field, or Subject:** Accounting; Computer and information sciences; Law; Marketing and distribution; Publishing; Secretarial sciences **Level of Education for which Award is Granted:** Undergraduate **Number Awarded:** 1 each year. **Funds Available:** The stipend is $1,000. **Duration:** 1 year.
Eligibility Requirements: This program is open to residents of Nebraska who are graduating high school seniors or students currently enrolled in a postsecondary educational institution. Applicants must have completed 2 or more business education courses (in high school, college, or a combination) from among the following: computer classes, keyboarding/typing, marketing, accounting, office practices and procedures, bookkeeping, business communication, desktop publishing, and/or business law. They must submit a 1-page essay on why they are choosing an office-related career or vocation, 3 letters of recommendation, and high school or college transcripts. Selection is based on academic achievement, initiative of the student, and financial need. **Deadline for Receipt:** December of each year. **Additional Information:** Information is also available from Edie Schleiger, Scholarship Director, University of Nebraska at Lincoln, Office of Admissions, 1410 Q Street, Lincoln, NE 68588-0417.

3726 ■ NEBRASKA LEGAL PROFESSIONALS ASSOCIATION
c/o Diane Horak, Scholarship Chair
7111 Cedar Creek Circle
Lincoln, NE 68516-3056
Tel: (402)423-5077
Fax: (402)466-2288
To provide financial assistance to residents of Nebraska enrolled in a law-related program.
Title of Award: Nebraska Legal Professionals Scholarship **Area, Field, or Subject:** Law; Paralegal studies; Secretarial sciences **Level of Education for which Award is Granted:** Undergraduate **Number Awarded:** 2 each year. **Funds Available:** The stipend is $1,000 for first place and $500 for second. **Duration:** 1 year.
Eligibility Requirements: This program is open to residents of Nebraska enrolled full time in a pre-law, paralegal, legal secretary, or other law-related program. Applicants must submit a certified copy of their latest transcript; a resume covering their educational history, school and community activities, and work history for the last 5 years; a 1-page personal statement on why they wish to become a legal secretary/paralegal or why they wish to continue their formal legal secretarial/paralegal education; and a copy of their acceptance to the school of their choice. **Deadline for Receipt:** March of each year. **Additional Information:** This scholarship was first awarded in 2000.

3727 ■ NORTH CAROLINA STATE EDUCATION ASSISTANCE AUTHORITY
Attn: Scholarship and Grant Services
10 T.W. Alexander Drive
P.O. Box 14103
Research Triangle Park, NC 27709-4103
Tel: (919)549-8614
Free: 800-700-1775
Fax: (919)549-8481
E-mail: information@ncseaa.edu
Web Site: http://www.ncseaa.edu
To provide financial assistance to children of deceased or disabled North Carolina law enforcement officers who are majoring in criminal justice in college.
Title of Award: North Carolina Sheriffs' Association Undergraduate Criminal Justice Scholarships **Area, Field, or Subject:** Criminal justice;

Criminology; Law enforcement **Level of Education for which Award is Granted:** Undergraduate **Number Awarded:** Up to 10 each year: 1 at each of the participating universities. **Funds Available:** The stipend is $2,000 per year. **Duration:** 1 year; nonrenewable.
Eligibility Requirements: Eligible for this program are North Carolina residents studying criminal justice at any of the 10 state institutions offering that major: Appalachian State University, East Carolina University, Elizabeth City State University, Fayetteville State University, North Carolina Central University, North Carolina State University, the University of North Carolina at Pembroke, the University of North Carolina at Charlotte, the University of North Carolina at Wilmington, and Western Carolina University. First priority in selection is given to children of law enforcement officers killed in the line of duty; second priority is given to children of sheriffs or deputy sheriffs who are deceased, retired (regular or disability), or currently active in law enforcement in North Carolina; third priority is given to other resident criminal justice students meeting their institution's academic and financial need criteria. **Additional Information:** Funding for this program is provided by the North Carolina Sheriffs' Association. Recipients are selected by the financial aid office at the university they plan to attend or are currently attending; after selection, students obtain a letter of endorsement from the sheriff of the county in North Carolina where they reside.

3728 ■ NORTH CENTRAL TEXAS COUNCIL OF GOVERNMENTS
Attn: Transportation Department
616 Six Flags Drive, Centerpoint Two
P.O. Box 5888
Arlington, TX 76005-5888
Tel: (817)695-9242
Fax: (817)640-7806
Web Site: http://www.nctcog.org/trans/admin/fellowship
To provide financial assistance to ethnic minorities, women, and economically disadvantaged persons who are interested in obtaining an undergraduate or graduate degree and work experience in a transportation-related field in Texas.
Title of Award: Transportation Fellowship Program **Area, Field, or Subject:** Engineering, Civil; Environmental conservation; Environmental science; Geography; Law; Management; Transportation; Urban affairs/design/planning **Level of Education for which Award is Granted:** Graduate, Undergraduate **Funds Available:** The stipend is $2,000. **Duration:** 1 year; may be renewed if the recipient maintains a GPA of 3.0 or higher.
Eligibility Requirements: This program is open to ethnic minorities (African Americans, Hispanics, American Indians, Alaskan Natives, Asians, and Pacific Islanders), women, and those who are economically disadvantaged. Only U.S. citizens or permanent residents may apply. They must attend or be willing to attend a college or university within the 16-county North Central Texas region as an undergraduate or graduate student. Applicants must have a GPA of 2.5 or higher. They may be enrolled full or part time, but they must be majoring in a designated transportation-related field: transportation planning, transportation or civil engineering, urban and regional planning, transportation/environmental sciences, transportation law, urban or spatial geography, logistics, geographic information systems, or transportation management. Selection is based on financial need, interest in a professional career in transportation, and the ability to complete the program. **Deadline for Receipt:** March of each year. **Additional Information:** These fellowships are financed by the Federal Highway Administration, Federal Transit Administration, and the Texas Department of Transportation, in conjunction with local governments in north central Texas. An important part of the fellowship is an internship with a local agency (city or county), school, or transportation agency.

3729 ■ NORTHEASTERN ASSOCIATION OF FORENSIC SCIENTISTS
c/o Peter Diaczuk, Executive Secretary
John Jay College of Criminal Justice
445 West 59th Street
New York, NY 10019
Tel: (212)237-8896
E-mail: pdiaczuk@jjay.cuny.edu
Web Site: http://www.neafs.org/scholarship.htm
To provide financial assistance to upper-division and graduate students working on a degree in forensic science at colleges and universities in designated northeastern states.

Title of Award: George W. Neighbor, Jr. Memorial Scholarship **Area, Field, or Subject:** Criminal justice **Level of Education for which Award is Granted:** Four Year College, Graduate **Number Awarded:** 1 or more each year. **Funds Available:** A stipend is awarded (amount not specified). **Duration:** 1 year.
Eligibility Requirements: This program is open to full-time college juniors and seniors and full- or part-time graduate students enrolled in a forensic science or related science program. Applicants must be attending a college or university in Connecticut, Maine, Massachusetts, New Hampshire, New Jersey, New York, Pennsylvania, Rhode Island, or Vermont. Along with their application, they must submit a letter describing their personal goals, achievements, and reasons why they should be considered for this award. **Deadline for Receipt:** April of each year. **Additional Information:** Information is also available from Margaret Lafond, NYSP FIC, State Campus Building 30, 1220 Washington Avenue, Albany, NY 12226-3000, E-mail: mlafond@troopers.state.ny.us.

3730 ■ PEACE OFFICERS RESEARCH ASSOCIATION OF CALIFORNIA
Attn: Peace Officers Research and Education Foundation
4010 Truxel Road
Sacramento, CA 95834-3725
Tel: (916)928-3777
Free: 800-937-6722
Fax: (916)928-3760
E-mail: membership@porac.org
Web Site: http://www.porac.org/scholarship.html
To provide financial assistance for college to relatives of members of the Peace Officers Research Association of California (PORAC) and to members who are medically retired.
Title of Award: PORAC Scholarships **Area, Field, or Subject:** Criminal justice; Criminology; General studies/Field of study not specified; Law enforcement **Level of Education for which Award is Granted:** Undergraduate **Number Awarded:** Varies each year; recently, 16 of these scholarships were awarded. **Funds Available:** The stipend is $1,000. **Duration:** 1 year.
Eligibility Requirements: This program is open to California residents who are 1) family members of law enforcement officers who have died in the line of duty; 2) dependents whose parent or legal guardian is an active PORAC member; 3) spouses and dependents of deceased PORAC members; and 4) PORAC members who have medically retired. Applicants must submit a composition, up to 750 words, on "My goals, present and future: why I am applying for this scholarship and its importance to me." They may be interested in scholastic or vocational study, but they are encouraged to consider law enforcement as a career. Selection is based on the essay, academic achievement (GPA of 2.0 or higher for dependents), school activities, community service, and financial need. **Deadline for Receipt:** March of each year. **Additional Information:** Recipients must enroll full time.

3731 ■ STUDENT PRESS LAW CENTER
Attn: Executive Director
1101 Wilson Boulevard, Suite 1100
Arlington, VA 22209-2211
Tel: (703)807-1904
E-mail: splc@splc.org
Web Site: http://www.splc.org/legalfellow.asp
To provide financial assistance and work experience to undergraduate and graduate students interested in news writing and media law.
Title of Award: Scripps Howard Foundation Journalism Internships **Area, Field, or Subject:** Journalism; Law **Level of Education for which Award is Granted:** Graduate, Undergraduate **Number Awarded:** The number of internships varies each year; up to 2 scholarships are awarded to undergraduate summer interns. **Funds Available:** Full-time interns during the fall and spring receive a stipend of $3,000. Full-time interns during the summer receive a stipend of $2,300. The scholarship stipend is $600. **Duration:** 1 semester or summer for the internships; 1 year for the scholarship.
Eligibility Requirements: This program is open to undergraduate and graduate students who have experience in news writing and an interest in media law. Applicants must be interested in working at the Student Press Law Center during the summer, fall, or spring. Summer interns who are undergraduates on the staff of a student publication that is a member of

the Associated Collegiate Press are also eligible to apply for a scholarship for the academic year following their internship. Selection of scholarship recipients is based on journalism experience, writing ability, and commitment to freedom of the press. **Deadline for Receipt:** Students are encouraged to submit applications for summer internships by January of each year, for fall internships by May of each year, and for spring internships by October of each year. **Additional Information:** This program, which began in 2002, is sponsored by the Scripps Howard Foundation. Interns research, write, and help edit the *Report,* the publication of the Student Press Law Center that chronicles student press cases and controversies from around the country. They also participate in issue-oriented seminars organized by the Center and the Reporters Committee for Freedom of the Press. Further information on the scholarships is available from the Associated Collegiate Press, 2221 University Avenue, S.E., Minneapolis, MN 55414, (612) 625-8335.

3732 ■ TEXAS FEDERATION OF BUSINESS AND PROFESSIONAL WOMEN'S FOUNDATION, INC.
Attn: TFBPW Foundation
803 Forest Ridge Drive, Suite 207
Bedford, TX 76022
Tel: (817)283-0862
Fax: (817)283-0872
E-mail: bpwtx@swbell.net
Web Site: http://www.bpwtx.org/foundation.asp
To provide financial assistance to women in Texas who are preparing to enter selected professions.
Title of Award: Hermine Dalkowitz Tobolowsky Scholarship **Area, Field, or Subject:** History; Law; Political science; Public administration; Women's studies **Level of Education for which Award is Granted:** Graduate, Undergraduate **Number Awarded:** 1 or more each year. **Funds Available:** A stipend is awarded (amount not specified). **Duration:** 1 year.
Eligibility Requirements: This program is open to women in Texas who are interested in attending school to prepare for a career in law, public service, government, political science, or women's history. Applicants must have completed at least 2 semesters of study at an accredited college or university in Texas, have a GPA of 3.0 or higher, and be U.S. citizens. Selection is based on academic achievement and financial need. **Deadline for Receipt:** April of each year. **Additional Information:** This program was established in 1995.

3733 ■ TEXAS WOMEN IN LAW ENFORCEMENT
Attn: Scholarship Awards Chair
P.O. Box 925185
Houston, TX 77292-5185
E-mail: mem4204@aol.com
Web Site: http://www.acob.com/twle/scholar_award.html
To provide financial assistance for college to members of the Texas Women in Law Enforcement (TWLE) and their relatives.
Title of Award: Vanessa Rudloff Scholarship Program **Area, Field, or Subject:** Criminal justice; Criminology; General studies/Field of study not specified; Law enforcement **Level of Education for which Award is Granted:** Professional, Undergraduate **Number Awarded:** At least 4 each year. **Funds Available:** The stipend is $1,000. **Duration:** 1 year.
Eligibility Requirements: Members of TWLE must have been active for the past 2 years, must be currently in good standing with their department, must submit a 1-page essay stating why they deserve the scholarship, and must be majoring in criminal justice or a related field. Relatives of TWLE members must be the spouse, child, brother, sister, niece, nephew, or grandchild of the member; must be in the top 25% of their graduating class; must have a GPA of 3.0 or higher; must score at least 950 on the SAT or 21 on the ACT; must submit 2 letters of recommendation; and must submit a 1-page essay stating why they deserve the scholarship. For these relatives, the sponsor must have been an active member of TWLE for the past 2 years. **Deadline for Receipt:** March of each year.

3734 ■ HARRY S. TRUMAN SCHOLARSHIP FOUNDATION
Attn: Executive Secretary
712 Jackson Place, N.W.
Washington, DC 20006
Tel: (202)395-4831
Fax: (202)395-6995

E-mail: office@truman.gov

Web Site: http://www.truman.gov

To provide grants-for-service for graduate school to current college juniors who are interested in preparing for a career in public service.

Title of Award: Harry S. Truman Scholarship Program **Area, Field, or Subject:** Agricultural sciences; Biological and clinical sciences; Economics; Education; Engineering; Environmental conservation; Environmental science; History; International affairs and relations; Law; Physical sciences; Political science; Public administration; Public health; Public service; Social sciences; Technology **Level of Education for which Award is Granted:** Four Year College, Graduate **Number Awarded:** 70 to 75 each year: a) 1 "state" scholarship is available to a qualified resident nominee in each of the 50 states, the District of Columbia, Puerto Rico, and the Islands (Guam, the Virgin Islands, American Samoa, and the Commonwealth of the Northern Mariana Islands); and b) up to 25 at-large scholars. **Funds Available:** The program provides up to $30,000, including up to $15,000 for the first year of graduate study and up to $15,000 for the final year of graduate study. **Duration:** Support is provided for the first and last year of graduate study.

Eligibility Requirements: Students must be nominated to be considered for this program. Nominees must be full-time students with junior standing at a 4-year institution, committed to a career in government or public service, in the upper quarter of their class, and U.S. citizens or nationals. Each participating institution may nominate up to 4 candidates (and up to 3 additional students who completed their first 2 years at a community college); community colleges and other 2-year institutions may nominate former students who are enrolled as full-time students with junior-level academic standing at accredited 4-year institutions. Selection is based on extent and quality of community service and government involvement, academic performance, leadership record, suitability of the nominee's proposed program of study for a career in public service, and writing and analytical skills. Priority is given to candidates who plan to enroll in a graduate program that specifically trains them for a career in public service, including government at any level, uniformed services, public interest organizations, nongovernmental research and/or educational organizations, public and private schools, and public service oriented nonprofit organizations. The fields of study may include agriculture, biology, engineering, environmental management, physical and social sciences, and technology policy, as well as such traditional fields as economics, education, government, history, international relations, law, nonprofit management, political science, public administration, public health, and public policy. Interviews are required. **Deadline for Receipt:** February of each year. **Additional Information:** Recipients may attend graduate school in the United States or in foreign countries. Scholars are required to work in public service for 3 of the 7 years following completion of a graduate degree program funded by this program. Scholars who do not meet this service requirement, or who fail to provide timely proof to the foundation of such employment, will be required to repay funds received, along with interest.

3735 ■ U.S. MARINE CORPS

Attn: Marine Corps Recruiting Command

3280 Russell Road

Quantico, VA 22134-5103

Tel: (703)784-9449

Fax: (703)784-9859

E-mail: wendelrf@mcrc.usmc.mil

Web Site: http://www.usmc.mil

To provide financial assistance to students interested in serving in the Marines following completion of a bachelor's or law degree.

Title of Award: Platoon Leaders Class Marine Corps Tuition Assistance Program **Area, Field, or Subject:** General studies/Field of study not specified; Law **Level of Education for which Award is Granted:** Doctorate, Undergraduate **Number Awarded:** Up to 1,200 each year. **Funds Available:** This program provides reimbursement of tuition, books, and required fees, up to a maximum of $5,200 per academic year. If participants are also members of the Marine Corps Reserves, they may also use any Montgomery GI Bill benefits to which they are entitled. **Duration:** Up to 3 consecutive years, or completion of a bachelor's or law degree.

Eligibility Requirements: This program is open to full-time students enrolled in a bachelor's or law (J.D. or equivalent) degree program. When they complete their degree, undergraduates must be under 27 years of age (or up to 30 if they have prior military service) and law students must be younger than 31 (or 35 if they have prior military service). All applicants must have a GPA of 2.0 or higher and may not be on academic, disciplinary, social, or moral probation. They must be able to meet all medical and other requirements for entry into the Marine Corps Platoon Leader Class (PLC) Program. Applications may be submitted after they have completed the first summer of officer candidate training (usually after 1 year of college or law school). **Deadline for Receipt:** December of each year. **Additional Information:** Participants who successfully obtain a bachelor's or law degree and complete officer candidate training are commissioned second lieutenants in the Regular Marine Corps. This program was established in 1999. Participants incur a 60-month active-duty service obligation.

3736 ■ VERMONT STUDENT ASSISTANCE CORPORATION

Champlain Mill

Attn: Scholarship Programs

P.O. Box 2000

Winooski, VT 05404-2601

Tel: (802)654-3798; 888-253-4819

Fax: (802)654-3765

E-mail: info@vsac.org

Web Site: http://www.vsac.org

To provide financial assistance to high school seniors in Vermont who are interested in majoring in law enforcement in college.

Title of Award: Erwin Bugbee Memorial Scholarship **Area, Field, or Subject:** Criminal justice; Criminology; Law enforcement **Level of Education for which Award is Granted:** Undergraduate **Number Awarded:** 1 each year. **Funds Available:** The stipend is $1,000. **Duration:** 1 year.

Eligibility Requirements: This scholarship is available to high school seniors in Vermont who are interested in working on a degree in law enforcement in college. Selection is based on required essays and financial need. **Deadline for Receipt:** April of each year. **Additional Information:** This program was established by the Vermont Police Association, which is responsible for selecting the recipients.

3737 ■ VERMONT STUDENT ASSISTANCE CORPORATION

Champlain Mill

Attn: Scholarship Programs

P.O. Box 2000

Winooski, VT 05404-2601

Tel: (802)654-3798; 888-253-4819

Fax: (802)654-3765

E-mail: info@vsac.org

Web Site: http://www.vsac.org

To provide financial assistance to residents of Vermont who are interested in majoring in law enforcement in college.

Title of Award: Vermont Sheriffs' Association Scholarship **Area, Field, or Subject:** Criminal justice; Criminology; Law enforcement **Level of Education for which Award is Granted:** Undergraduate **Number Awarded:** 2 each year. **Funds Available:** The stipend is $1,000. **Duration:** 1 year.

Eligibility Requirements: This program is open to residents of Vermont who are graduating high school seniors, high school graduates, or current college students. Applicants must be interested in working on a college degree in law enforcement. Selection is based on academic achievement, required essays, and financial need. **Deadline for Receipt:** June of each year.

3738 ■ VIRGINIA SHERIFFS' INSTITUTE

701 East Franklin Street, Suite 706

Richmond, VA 23219

Tel: (804)225-7152

Fax: (804)225-7162

E-mail: vsavsi@virginiasheriffs.orb

Web Site: http://www.virginiasheriffs.org/vsi/scholarship/index.htm

To provide financial assistance to Virginia residents who are majoring or planning to major in law enforcement or criminal justice in college.

Title of Award: VSI Scholarship Program **Area, Field, or Subject:** Criminal justice; Criminology; Law enforcement **Level of Education for which Award is Granted:** Undergraduate **Number Awarded:** Varies each year. **Funds Available:** A stipend is awarded (amount not specified). Checks are made payable directly to the recipient's educational institution. **Duration:** 1 year; may be renewed.

Eligibility Requirements: This program is open to Virginia residents who live in areas where the sheriffs are members of the Virginia Sheriff's Institute and authorized the Institute to conduct a direct mail special appeal to raise funds for the scholarship program. Applicants must be attending or planning to attend a college or university in Virginia and major in law enforcement or criminal justice. Along with their application, they must submit a short essay on their proposed course of college study, how they reached that decision, what they expect to gain from college, and their personal goals and ambitions. Financial need is not considered in the selection process. **Deadline for Receipt:** April of each year.

3739 ■ JAMES D. VOELKER FOUNDATION
P.O. Box 15222
Lansing, MI 48901-5222
Web Site: http://www.voelkerfdn.org/Scholarships.asp
To provide financial assistance to students enrolled in Wisconsin or Michigan tribes who are interested in pursuing a legal education.
Title of Award: James D. Voelker Foundation Native American Scholarship **Area, Field, or Subject:** Law **Level of Education for which Award is Granted:** Graduate, Undergraduate **Number Awarded:** 1 or more each year. **Funds Available:** The amount awarded varies annually; recently, the scholarships were at least $4,000 each. **Duration:** 1 year.
Eligibility Requirements: This program is open to students who are enrolled members of a federally-recognized Michigan or Wisconsin tribe (applicants may live in any state) and are interested in studying law and working toward a career that will benefit Native American people. Applicants do not need to be currently enrolled in law school, but if they apply as undergraduates they must ultimately intend to attend law school. Selection is based on academic achievements and financial need (preference is given to applicants with the greatest need). **Additional Information:** Recipients must provide an annual report on their progress.

3740 ■ WISCONSIN SPACE GRANT CONSORTIUM
c/o University of Wisconsin at Green Bay
Department of Natural and Applied Sciences
2420 Nicolet Drive
Green Bay, WI 54311-7001
Tel: (920)465-2108
Fax: (920)465-2376
E-mail: wsgc@uwgb.edu
Web Site: http://www.uwgb.edu/wsgc/students/us.asp
To provide financial assistance to undergraduate students at colleges and universities participating in the Wisconsin Space Grant Consortium (WSGC).
Title of Award: Wisconsin Space Grant Consortium Undergraduate Scholarships **Area, Field, or Subject:** Aerospace sciences; Architecture; Business administration; Engineering; Engineering, Aerospace/Aeronautical/Astronautical; Law; Medicine; Nursing; Science; Space and planetary sciences **Level of Education for which Award is Granted:** Undergraduate **Number Awarded:** Varies each year; recently, 26 of these scholarships were awarded. **Funds Available:** Stipends up to $1,500 per year are available. **Duration:** 1 academic year.
Eligibility Requirements: This program is open to undergraduate students enrolled at universities participating in the WSGC. Applicants must be U.S. citizens; be working full time on a bachelor's degree in space science, aerospace, or interdisciplinary space studies (including, but not limited to, engineering, the sciences, architecture, law, business, nursing, and medicine); and have a GPA of 3.0 or higher. The consortium especially encourages applications from underrepresented minorities, women, and students with disabilities. Selection is based on academic performance and space-related promise. **Deadline for Receipt:** February of each year. **Additional Information:** Funding for this program is provided by the U.S. National Aeronautics and Space Administration (NASA). The schools participating in the consortium include the University of Wisconsin campuses at Fox Valley, Green Bay, La Crosse, Madison, Milwaukee, Oshkosh, Parkside, Superior, and Whitewater; Alverno College; Marquette University; College of the Menominee Nation; Carroll College; Lawrence University; Milwaukee School of Engineering; Ripon College; Medical College of Wisconsin; Western Wisconsin Technical College; and Wisconsin Lutheran College.

3741 ■ WOMEN IN FEDERAL LAW ENFORCEMENT
Attn: Scholarship Coordinator
2200 Wilson Boulevard, Suite 102

PMB 204
Arlington, VA 22201-3324
Tel: (703)548-9211; (866)399-4353
Fax: (410)451-7373
E-mail: WIFLE@comcast.net
Web Site: http://www.wifle.com/scholarshipfund/wiflescholarship.htm
To provide financial assistance for college or graduate school to women interested in preparing for a career in law enforcement.
Title of Award: Women in Federal Law Enforcement Scholarship **Area, Field, or Subject:** Computer and information sciences; Criminal justice; Criminology; Law enforcement **Level of Education for which Award is Granted:** Four Year College, Graduate **Number Awarded:** Several each year. **Funds Available:** Stipends range from $500 to $2,000. **Duration:** 1 year; may be renewed.
Eligibility Requirements: This program is open to women who are enrolled full time at an accredited 4-year college or university (or at a community college in the process of transferring to a 4-year school). Applicants must be preparing for a career in law enforcement (including special agents, forensic scientists, intelligence analysts, fingerprint and firearms examiners, bomb technicians, public information specialists, computer specialists, attorneys, and other related fields). They must have completed at least 1 year of college and have a GPA of 3.0 or higher. Students in graduate and postgraduate programs are also eligible, but those working on an associate degree are not. Along with their application, they must submit a 500-word essay describing a community project in which they have been involved and the results or impact to the community. Selection is based on academic potential, achievement, and commitment to serving communities in the field of law enforcement. **Deadline for Receipt:** April of each year. **Additional Information:** Information is also available from the WIFLE Scholarship Fund, P.O. Box 1480, Edgewater, MD 21037-7480.

3742 ■ WYOMING PEACE OFFICERS ASSOCIATION
c/o Valerie Sullivan, Chair, Scholarship Committee
1556 Riverbend Drive
Douglas, WY 82633-2056
Tel: (307)358-3617
To provide financial assistance for college to members of the Wyoming Peace Officers Association, to their dependents, or to nonmembers in Wyoming who are preparing for a career in law enforcement.
Title of Award: Wyoming Peace Officers Association Scholarship **Area, Field, or Subject:** Criminal justice; Criminology; General studies/Field of study not specified; Law enforcement **Level of Education for which Award is Granted:** Undergraduate **Funds Available:** Recipients are awarded up to $500 per semester or up to $1,000 per year. Funds are paid after a semester is successfully completed. **Duration:** 1 semester; may be renewed for a total of 4 semesters or 2 years.
Eligibility Requirements: There are 4 categories of applicants: 1) dependents of active, lifetime, or deceased members of the Wyoming Peace Officers Association who will be studying (in any subject) on a full-time basis during the scholarship year; 2) Wyoming residents majoring in law enforcement on a full-time basis at a Wyoming community college or the University of Wyoming; 3) active or retired Wyoming law enforcement officers who are members of the Wyoming Peace Officers Association and enrolled full or part time in a law enforcement major at a Wyoming community college or the University of Wyoming; and 4) pre-service students who have completed or will complete a peace officer basic course or detention officer basic course offered by the Wyoming Law Enforcement Academy and are, if currently employed by a law enforcement agency, a member of the Wyoming Peace Officers Association. **Deadline for Receipt:** July of each year.

Law Enforcement

3743 ■ ALASKA COMMISSION ON POSTSECONDARY EDUCATION
Attn: AlaskAdvantage Programs
3030 Vintage Boulevard
Juneau, AK 99801-7109
Tel: (907)465-2962
Free: 800-441-2962
Fax: (907)465-5316
E-mail: customer_service@acpe.ak.us

Web Site: http://alaskaadvantage.state.ak.us/page/255

To provide scholarship/loans to Alaska residents who are interested in working on an undergraduate degree in law enforcement.

Title of Award: Michael Murphy Education Loan **Area, Field, or Subject:** Criminal justice; Criminology; Law enforcement **Level of Education for which Award is Granted:** Undergraduate **Number Awarded:** Varies each year. **Funds Available:** Loans up to $1,000 per year are available. No interest is charged. An origination fee of 3% of the amount disbursed is added to the principal balance to be repaid. This is a scholarship/loan program. Recipients are forgiven 20% of the total loan for each 1-year period they are employed full time in Alaska law enforcement or related fields, up to 5 years. **Duration:** 1 year; may be renewed.

Eligibility Requirements: This program is open to full-time undergraduates working on a degree in law enforcement, probation and parole, penology, or other closely-related field anywhere in the United States. Applicants must have been residents of Alaska for at least 2 years, be high school graduates or equivalent, and demonstrate financial need. **Deadline for Receipt:** March of each year. **Additional Information:** This program is funded by private donations and by voluntary contributions from state employees who may contribute 1 or more days of annual leave to the fund. Information is also available from Alaska State Troopers, Attn: Recruitment Supervisor, 5700 East Tudor Road, Anchorage, AK 99507, (907) 269-5759, Fax: (907) 269-5751.

3744 ■ AMERICAN SOCIETY OF CRIMINOLOGY

Attn: Awards Committee
1314 Kinnear Road, Suite 212
Columbus, OH 43212-1156
Tel: (614)292-9207
Fax: (614)292-6767
E-mail: asc41@infinet.com
Web Site: http://www.asc41.com/uminorfel.htm

To provide financial assistance to ethnic minority undergraduate students interested in conducting a research project in criminology and criminal justice.

Title of Award: American Society of Criminology Undergraduate Student Minority Scholar/Mentor Research Grants **Area, Field, or Subject:** Criminal justice; Criminology; Law enforcement **Level of Education for which Award is Granted:** Four Year College **Number Awarded:** Varies each year; recently, 4 of these grants were awarded. **Funds Available:** The grant provides $5,000 per year for research support and a $1,500 travel grant to attend the ASC annual meetings. **Duration:** 2 years (the junior and senior year of college).

Eligibility Requirements: This program is open to undergraduate students who are members of historically disadvantaged and underrepresented ethnic and racial groups. Applicants must be entering their junior year in a program in criminology and criminal justice. They must be interested in conducting a research project under the mentorship of a faculty member, who must act as a co-applicant for the funding. Along with the application, students must provide a personal statement on their career goals in criminology and another statement on how the grant would enable them to focus more time on their academic work and better achieve their career goals. Faculty members must provide 1) a written recommendation for why the student has the academic potential and career aspirations to complete graduate student in criminology successfully and prepare for an academic career; 2) student transcripts and other supporting materials; 3) a description of the proposed collaborative research project that will result in a presentation at the annual meeting of the American Society of Criminology (ASC) in the student's senior years; and 4) a description of other mentoring activities and proposed contact with the student during the junior and senior years. Selection is based on the student's potential for completing doctoral work in criminology and the quality of the proposed mentoring relationship. **Deadline for Receipt:** April of each year. **Additional Information:** This program began in 2004. Information is also available from Todd R. Clear, Minority Scholar/Mentor Committee Chair, John Jay College of Criminal Justice, 899 Tenth Avenue, New York, NY 10019, (212) 237-8470.

3745 ■ COMMUNITY FOUNDATION OF GREATER JACKSON

525 East Capitol Street, Suite 5B
Jackson, MS 39201
Tel: (601)974-6044
Fax: (601)974-6045

E-mail: info@cfgreaterjackson.org
Web Site: http://www.cfgreaterjackson.org

To provide financial assistance to upper-division students in Mississippi and Louisiana who are preparing for a career in the field of juvenile justice.

Title of Award: Anthony "Tony" Gobar Juvenile Justice Scholarship Fund **Area, Field, or Subject:** Counseling/Guidance; Criminal justice; Criminology; Law enforcement; Political science **Level of Education for which Award is Granted:** Four Year College **Number Awarded:** 1 each year. **Funds Available:** A stipend is awarded (amount not specified). **Duration:** 1 year.

Eligibility Requirements: This program is open to full-time juniors and seniors at public universities in Mississippi and at Southern University in Louisiana who are preparing to enter the field of juvenile justice. Applicants must have demonstrated a strong commitment to community and public service. They must be U.S. citizens with a GPA of 2.5 or higher. Eligible majors include criminal justice, counseling, and political science. Selection is based on merit and need. **Deadline for Receipt:** April of each year. **Additional Information:** This program was established in 2005.

3746 ■ CONNECTICUT ASSOCIATION OF WOMEN POLICE

P.O. Box 1653
Hartford, CT 06144-1653
E-mail: admin@cawp.net
Web Site: http://www.cawp.net

To provide financial assistance to high school seniors in Connecticut who are interested in studying criminal justice in college.

Title of Award: Connecticut Association of Women Police Scholarships **Area, Field, or Subject:** Criminal justice; Criminology; Law enforcement **Level of Education for which Award is Granted:** Four Year College **Number Awarded:** Varies each year; recently, 5 of these scholarships were awarded. **Funds Available:** A stipend is awarded (amount not specified). **Duration:** 1 year.

Eligibility Requirements: This program is open to seniors graduating from high schools in Connecticut who are interested in attending a 4-year college or university to prepare for a career in criminal justice. Applicants must submit a personal essay of 200 to 250 words on their personal goals and why they should be selected for this scholarship. Selection is based on the essay and financial need. **Deadline for Receipt:** April of each year.

3747 ■ MARYLAND HIGHER EDUCATION COMMISSION

Attn: Office of Student Financial Assistance
839 Bestgate Road, Suite 400
Annapolis, MD 21401-3013
Tel: (410)260-4594
Free: 800-974-1024
Fax: (410)974-5376
E-mail: osfamail@mhec.state.md.us
Web Site: http://www.mhec.state.md.us/financialAid/
ProgramDescriptions/prog_devdis.asp

To provide scholarship/loans to students in Maryland who are interested in working on a degree in a designated human services program.

Title of Award: Maryland Developmental Disabilities, Mental Health, Child Welfare, and Juvenile Justice Workforce Tuition Assistance Program **Area, Field, or Subject:** Counseling/Guidance; Criminal justice; Criminology; Disabilities; Education, Special; Gerontology; Law enforcement; Mental health; Nursing; Occupational therapy; Physical therapy; Psychology; Rehabilitation, Physical/Psychological; Social work **Level of Education for which Award is Granted:** Graduate, Undergraduate **Number Awarded:** Varies each year. **Funds Available:** The maximum stipend is $2,000 per year for students attending a 2-year institution or $3,000 per year for students at a 4-year institution. The total amount of all state awards may not exceed the cost of attendance as determined by the school's financial aid office or $17,800, whichever is less. Recipients must agree to work in a Maryland community-based program that is licensed by the Developmental Disabilities Administration or approved by the Mental Hygiene Administration, or in a residential program that is licensed by the Department of Human Resources or the Department of Juvenile Justice. The service obligation must begin within 6 months of graduation. The total service requirement is 2,000 hours if the award amount is $1,999 or less, 3,000 hours if the award amount is $2,000 to $3,999, or 4,000 hours if the award amount is $4,000 or more. If the service requirement is not

completed, the award must be repaid with interest. **Duration:** 1 year; may be renewed if the recipient maintains satisfactory academic progress and remains enrolled in a human services degree program.
Eligibility Requirements: This program is open to high school seniors and full-time and part-time undergraduate and graduate students. Applicants and their parents must be Maryland residents attending a college or university in the state in 1 of the following human services degree programs: aging services, counseling, disability services, mental health, nursing, occupational therapy, physical therapy, psychology, rehabilitation, social work, special education, supported employment, vocational rehabilitation, or any other concentration in the healing arts or a program providing support services to individuals with special needs including child welfare and juvenile justice. Financial need is not considered in the selection process. **Deadline for Receipt:** June of each year.

3748 ■ MICHIGAN LAW ENFORCEMENT EDUCATION PROGRAM

c/o Scholarship Committee
667 East Big Beaver Road, Suite 205
Troy, MI 48083
800-451-1220
To provide financial assistance for college to high school students in Michigan who are interested in preparing for a career in a field related to public safety.
Title of Award: LEEP Dream Scholarship **Area, Field, or Subject:** Criminal justice; Criminology; Emergency and disaster services; Fires and fire prevention; Law enforcement **Level of Education for which Award is Granted:** Undergraduate **Number Awarded:** Several each year. **Funds Available:** The stipend is $1,000. **Duration:** 1 year.
Eligibility Requirements: This program is open to seniors graduating from high schools in Michigan who are interested in preparing for a career as a law enforcement officer, police-fire dispatcher, corrections officer, fire fighter, or emergency medical technician. Applicants must be planning to attend a Michigan 4-year university, community college, or vocational training institution that grants a degree, certificate, or license in public safety or related field. **Deadline for Receipt:** May of each year.

3749 ■ MICHIGAN SHERIFFS' ASSOCIATION

Attn: Educational Services
515 North Capitol Avenue
Lansing, MI 48933
Tel: (517)485-3135
Fax: (517)485-1013
Web Site: http://www.michigansheriff.com
To provide financial assistance to high school seniors in Michigan who are interested in attending college to prepare for a career in criminal justice.
Title of Award: Bernard Grysen Memorial Criminal Justice Scholarships **Area, Field, or Subject:** Criminal justice; Criminology; Law enforcement **Level of Education for which Award is Granted:** Undergraduate **Number Awarded:** 10 each year: 2 in each of the association's districts. **Funds Available:** The stipend is $1,000. **Duration:** 1 year.
Eligibility Requirements: This program is open to seniors graduating from high schools in Michigan who are planning to attend a college or university in the state to prepare for a career in criminal justice. Applicants must be able to demonstrate high academic standing, high moral character, and a high degree of activity in civic and governmental affairs relating to law enforcement. They must be nominated by a member of the Michigan Sheriffs' Association. Along with their application, they must submit a 300-word essay on why they are preparing for a career in criminal justice. Financial need is not considered in the selection process. **Deadline for Receipt:** April of each year. **Additional Information:** This program was established in 1995.

3750 ■ NORTH CAROLINA STATE EDUCATION ASSISTANCE AUTHORITY

Attn: Scholarship and Grant Services
10 T.W. Alexander Drive
P.O. Box 14103
Research Triangle Park, NC 27709-4103
Tel: (919)549-8614
Free: 800-700-1775
Fax: (919)549-8481
E-mail: information@ncseaa.edu
Web Site: http://www.ncseaa.edu

To provide financial assistance to children of deceased or disabled North Carolina law enforcement officers who are majoring in criminal justice in college.
Title of Award: North Carolina Sheriffs' Association Undergraduate Criminal Justice Scholarships **Area, Field, or Subject:** Criminal justice; Criminology; Law enforcement **Level of Education for which Award is Granted:** Undergraduate **Number Awarded:** Up to 10 each year: 1 at each of the participating universities. **Funds Available:** The stipend is $2,000 per year. **Duration:** 1 year; nonrenewable.
Eligibility Requirements: Eligible for this program are North Carolina residents studying criminal justice at any of the 10 state institutions offering that major: Appalachian State University, East Carolina University, Elizabeth City State University, Fayetteville State University, North Carolina Central University, North Carolina State University, the University of North Carolina at Pembroke, the University of North Carolina at Charlotte, the University of North Carolina at Wilmington, and Western Carolina University. First priority in selection is given to children of law enforcement officers killed in the line of duty; second priority is given to children of sheriffs or deputy sheriffs who are deceased, retired (regular or disability), or currently active in law enforcement in North Carolina; third priority is given to other resident criminal justice students meeting their institution's academic and financial need criteria. **Additional Information:** Funding for this program is provided by the North Carolina Sheriffs' Association. Recipients are selected by the financial aid office at the university they plan to attend or are currently attending; after selection, students obtain a letter of endorsement from the sheriff of the county in North Carolina where they reside.

3751 ■ PEACE OFFICERS RESEARCH ASSOCIATION OF CALIFORNIA

Attn: Peace Officers Research and Education Foundation
4010 Truxel Road
Sacramento, CA 95834-3725
Tel: (916)928-3777
Free: 800-937-6722
Fax: (916)928-3760
E-mail: membership@porac.org
Web Site: http://www.porac.org/scholarship.html
To provide financial assistance for college to relatives of members of the Peace Officers Research Association of California (PORAC) and to members who are medically retired.
Title of Award: PORAC Scholarships **Area, Field, or Subject:** Criminal justice; Criminology; General studies/Field of study not specified; Law enforcement **Level of Education for which Award is Granted:** Undergraduate **Number Awarded:** Varies each year; recently, 16 of these scholarships were awarded. **Funds Available:** The stipend is $1,000. **Duration:** 1 year.
Eligibility Requirements: This program is open to California residents who are 1) family members of law enforcement officers who have died in the line of duty; 2) dependents whose parent or legal guardian is an active PORAC member; 3) spouses and dependents of deceased PORAC members; and 4) PORAC members who have medically retired. Applicants must submit a composition, up to 750 words, on "My goals, present and future: why I am applying for this scholarship and its importance to me." They may be interested in scholastic or vocational study, but they are encouraged to consider law enforcement as a career. Selection is based on the essay, academic achievement (GPA of 2.0 or higher for dependents), school activities, community service, and financial need. **Deadline for Receipt:** March of each year. **Additional Information:** Recipients must enroll full time.

3752 ■ TEXAS WOMEN IN LAW ENFORCEMENT

Attn: Scholarship Awards Chair
P.O. Box 925185
Houston, TX 77292-5185
E-mail: mem4204@aol.com
Web Site: http://www.acob.com/twle/scholar_award.html
To provide financial assistance for college to members of the Texas Women in Law Enforcement (TWLE) and their relatives.
Title of Award: Vanessa Rudloff Scholarship Program **Area, Field, or Subject:** Criminal justice; Criminology; General studies/Field of study not specified; Law enforcement **Level of Education for which Award is Granted:** Professional, Undergraduate **Number Awarded:** At least 4 each year. **Funds Available:** The stipend is $1,000. **Duration:** 1 year.

Eligibility Requirements: Members of TWLE must have been active for the past 2 years, must be currently in good standing with their department, must submit a 1-page essay stating why they deserve the scholarship, and must be majoring in criminal justice or a related field. Relatives of TWLE members must be the spouse, child, brother, sister, niece, nephew, or grandchild of the member; must be in the top 25% of their graduating class; must have a GPA of 3.0 or higher; must score at least 950 on the SAT or 21 on the ACT; must submit 2 letters of recommendation; and must submit a 1-page essay stating why they deserve the scholarship. For these relatives, the sponsor must have been an active member of TWLE for the past 2 years. **Deadline for Receipt:** March of each year.

3753 ■ VERMONT STUDENT ASSISTANCE CORPORATION

Champlain Mill
Attn: Scholarship Programs
P.O. Box 2000
Winooski, VT 05404-2601
Tel: (802)654-3798; 888-253-4819
Fax: (802)654-3765
E-mail: info@vsac.org
Web Site: http://www.vsac.org
To provide financial assistance to high school seniors in Vermont who are interested in majoring in law enforcement in college.
Title of Award: Erwin Bugbee Memorial Scholarship **Area, Field, or Subject:** Criminal justice; Criminology; Law enforcement **Level of Education for which Award is Granted:** Undergraduate **Number Awarded:** 1 each year. **Funds Available:** The stipend is $1,000. **Duration:** 1 year.
Eligibility Requirements: This scholarship is available to high school seniors in Vermont who are interested in working on a degree in law enforcement in college. Selection is based on required essays and financial need. **Deadline for Receipt:** April of each year. **Additional Information:** This program was established by the Vermont Police Association, which is responsible for selecting the recipients.

3754 ■ VERMONT STUDENT ASSISTANCE CORPORATION

Champlain Mill
Attn: Scholarship Programs
P.O. Box 2000
Winooski, VT 05404-2601
Tel: (802)654-3798; 888-253-4819
Fax: (802)654-3765
E-mail: info@vsac.org
Web Site: http://www.vsac.org
To provide financial assistance to residents of Vermont who are interested in majoring in law enforcement in college.
Title of Award: Vermont Sheriffs' Association Scholarship **Area, Field, or Subject:** Criminal justice; Criminology; Law enforcement **Level of Education for which Award is Granted:** Undergraduate **Number Awarded:** 2 each year. **Funds Available:** The stipend is $1,000. **Duration:** 1 year.
Eligibility Requirements: This program is open to residents of Vermont who are graduating high school seniors, high school graduates, or current college students. Applicants must be interested in working on a college degree in law enforcement. Selection is based on academic achievement, required essays, and financial need. **Deadline for Receipt:** June of each year.

3755 ■ VIRGINIA SHERIFFS' INSTITUTE

701 East Franklin Street, Suite 706
Richmond, VA 23219
Tel: (804)225-7152
Fax: (804)225-7162
E-mail: vsavsi@virginiasheriffs.orb
Web Site: http://www.virginiasheriffs.org/vsi/scholarship/index.htm
To provide financial assistance to Virginia residents who are majoring or planning to major in law enforcement or criminal justice in college.
Title of Award: VSI Scholarship Program **Area, Field, or Subject:** Criminal justice; Criminology; Law enforcement **Level of Education for which Award is Granted:** Undergraduate **Number Awarded:** Varies each year. **Funds Available:** A stipend is awarded (amount not specified). Checks are made payable directly to the recipient's educational institution. **Duration:** 1 year; may be renewed.
Eligibility Requirements: This program is open to Virginia residents who live in areas where the sheriffs are members of the Virginia Sheriff's

Institute and authorized the Institute to conduct a direct mail special appeal to raise funds for the scholarship program. Applicants must be attending or planning to attend a college or university in Virginia and major in law enforcement or criminal justice. Along with their application, they must submit a short essay on their proposed course of college study, how they reached that decision, what they expect to gain from college, and their personal goals and ambitions. Financial need is not considered in the selection process. **Deadline for Receipt:** April of each year.

3756 ■ WOMEN IN FEDERAL LAW ENFORCEMENT

Attn: Scholarship Coordinator
2200 Wilson Boulevard, Suite 102
PMB 204
Arlington, VA 22201-3324
Tel: (703)548-9211; (866)399-4353
Fax: (410)451-7373
E-mail: WIFLE@comcast.net
Web Site: http://www.wifle.com/scholarshipfund/wiflescholarship.htm
To provide financial assistance for college or graduate school to women interested in preparing for a career in law enforcement.
Title of Award: Women in Federal Law Enforcement Scholarship **Area, Field, or Subject:** Computer and information sciences; Criminal justice; Criminology; Law enforcement **Level of Education for which Award is Granted:** Four Year College, Graduate **Number Awarded:** Several each year. **Funds Available:** Stipends range from $500 to $2,000. **Duration:** 1 year; may be renewed.
Eligibility Requirements: This program is open to women who are enrolled full time at an accredited 4-year college or university (or at a community college in the process of transferring to a 4-year school). Applicants must be preparing for a career in law enforcement (including special agents, forensic scientists, intelligence analysts, fingerprint and firearms examiners, bomb technicians, public information specialists, computer specialists, attorneys, and other related fields). They must have completed at least 1 year of college and have a GPA of 3.0 or higher. Students in graduate and postgraduate programs are also eligible, but those working on an associate degree are not. Along with their application, they must submit a 500-word essay describing a community project in which they have been involved and the results or impact to the community. Selection is based on academic potential, achievement, and commitment to serving communities in the field of law enforcement. **Deadline for Receipt:** April of each year. **Additional Information:** Information is also available from the WIFLE Scholarship Fund, P.O. Box 1480, Edgewater, MD 21037-7480.

3757 ■ WYOMING PEACE OFFICERS ASSOCIATION

c/o Valerie Sullivan, Chair, Scholarship Committee
1556 Riverbend Drive
Douglas, WY 82633-2056
Tel: (307)358-3617
To provide financial assistance for college to members of the Wyoming Peace Officers Association, to their dependents, or to nonmembers in Wyoming who are preparing for a career in law enforcement.
Title of Award: Wyoming Peace Officers Association Scholarship **Area, Field, or Subject:** Criminal justice; Criminology; General studies/Field of study not specified; Law enforcement **Level of Education for which Award is Granted:** Undergraduate **Funds Available:** Recipients are awarded up to $500 per semester or up to $1,000 per year. Funds are paid after a semester is successfully completed. **Duration:** 1 semester; may be renewed for a total of 4 semesters or 2 years.
Eligibility Requirements: There are 4 categories of applicants: 1) dependents of active, lifetime, or deceased members of the Wyoming Peace Officers Association who will be studying (in any subject) on a full-time basis during the scholarship year; 2) Wyoming residents majoring in law enforcement on a full-time basis at a Wyoming community college or the University of Wyoming; 3) active or retired Wyoming law enforcement officers who are members of the Wyoming Peace Officers Association and enrolled full or part time in a law enforcement major at a Wyoming community college or the University of Wyoming; and 4) pre-service students who have completed or will complete a peace officer basic course or detention officer basic course offered by the Wyoming Law Enforcement

Academy and are, if currently employed by a law enforcement agency, a member of the Wyoming Peace Officers Association. **Deadline for Receipt:** July of each year.

Political Science

3758 ■ 100TH INFANTRY BATTALION VETERANS CLUB

Attn: Scholarship Committee
520 Kamoku Street
Honolulu, HI 96826
Tel: (808)732-5216
E-mail: daisyy@hgea.net
Web Site: http://emedia.leeward.hawaii.edu/mnakano
To provide financial assistance to high school seniors and college students who major in business, political science, or law and exemplify the sponsor's motto of "Continuing Service."
Title of Award: Sakae Takahashi Scholarship **Area, Field, or Subject:** Business administration; Law; Political science **Level of Education for which Award is Granted:** Undergraduate **Number Awarded:** 1 each year. **Funds Available:** The stipend is $1,000. **Duration:** 1 year; nonrenewable.
Eligibility Requirements: This program is open to high school seniors planning to attend an institution of higher learning and full-time undergraduate students at community colleges, vocational/trade schools, 4-year colleges, and universities. Applicants must have a GPA of 2.5 or higher and be able to demonstrate civic responsibility and community service. They must be majoring or planning to major in business, political science, or law. Along with their application, they must submit a 4-page on the characteristics of positive leaders and the ways in which they are an extraordinary leader. Selection is based on that essay and the applicant's demonstration that he or she can effectively promote the legacy of the 100th Infantry Battalion and its motto of "Continuing Service." Financial need is not considered. **Deadline for Receipt:** April of each year.

3759 ■ AMERICAN HELLENIC EDUCATIONAL PROGRESSIVE ASSOCIATION

Attn: AHEPA Educational Foundation
1909 Q Street, N.W., Suite 500
Washington, DC 20009
Tel: (202)232-6300
Fax: (202)232-2140
Web Site: http://www.ahepa.org/ahepa
To provide financial assistance for college to students with a connection to the American Hellenic Educational Progressive Association (AHEPA), particularly those interested in majoring in political science or history.
Title of Award: George Leber Scholarship **Area, Field, or Subject:** General studies/Field of study not specified; History; International affairs and relations; Political science **Level of Education for which Award is Granted:** Undergraduate **Number Awarded:** Varies each year; recently, 2 of these scholarships were awarded. **Funds Available:** The annual stipend ranges from $500 to $2,000. **Duration:** 1 year.
Eligibility Requirements: This program is open to 1) members in good standing of the Order of Ahepa, Daughters of Penelope, Sons of Pericles, or Maids of Athena, and 2) the children of Order of Ahepa or Daughters of Penelope members in good standing. Applicants must be currently enrolled or planning to enroll in a college or university in the following fall. They may major in any area, but preference is given to upper-division students majoring in political science, history, or international relations. Selection is based on academic achievement, extracurricular activities, athletic achievements, work experience, and community service. Financial need is not considered. **Deadline for Receipt:** March of each year. **Additional Information:** A processing fee of $20 must accompany each application.

3760 ■ BOYS & GIRLS CLUBS OF GREATER SAN DIEGO

Attn: Scholarships
4635 Clairemont Mesa Boulevard
San Diego, CA 92117
Tel: (619)298-3520; (866)SD-YOUTH
Fax: (619)298-3615
Web Site: http://www.sdyouth.org/scholarships.htm

To provide financial assistance to graduating male high school seniors who plan to study designated fields in college.
Title of Award: Spence Reese Scholarships **Area, Field, or Subject:** Engineering; Law; Medicine; Political science **Level of Education for which Award is Granted:** Undergraduate **Number Awarded:** 4 each year: 1 in each of the designated fields. **Funds Available:** The stipend is $2,000 per year. **Duration:** 4 years.
Eligibility Requirements: Applicants must be graduating male high school seniors planning to study law, medicine, engineering, or political science in college. They may live anywhere in the United States, but must attend an interview in San Diego, California. Selection is based on academic standing, potential for good citizenship, academic ability, and financial need. **Deadline for Receipt:** April of each year. **Additional Information:** Travel expenses for the interview are reimbursed by the sponsor. A $10 processing fee must accompany all applications.

3761 ■ CALIFORNIA STATE UNIVERSITY

Office of the Chancellor
Attn: Lori Redfearn, Vice President
401 Golden Shore, Sixth Floor
Long Beach, CA 90802-4210
Tel: (562)951-4815
E-mail: lredfearn@calstate.edu
Web Site: http://www.calstate.edu/foundation/scholarship.shtml
To provide financial assistance to graduate students majoring in designated fields at campuses of the California State University (CSU) system.
Title of Award: Glenn and Dorothy Dumke Fellowship **Area, Field, or Subject:** Economics; History, American; Library and archival sciences; Political science; Public administration **Level of Education for which Award is Granted:** Four Year College, Master's **Number Awarded:** 1 each year. **Funds Available:** The stipend is $1,000 per year. **Duration:** 1 year.
Eligibility Requirements: This program is open to students working on a graduate degree at CSU campuses in public policy, American history, economics, archival management, or government.

3762 ■ CHRISTIAN LIFE RESOURCES

Attn: WELS Lutherans for Life
Scholarship Review Committee
2949 North Mayfair Road, Suite 309
Milwaukee, WI 53222-4304
Tel: (414)774-1331
Fax: (414)774-1360
Web Site: http://www.christianliferesources.com
To provide financial assistance to Lutheran high school seniors in Wisconsin who are interested in studying life-related issues in college.
Title of Award: WELS Lutherans for Life Scholarship Program **Area, Field, or Subject:** Biological and clinical sciences; Education, Special; Engineering, Biomedical; Journalism; Law; Medicine; Physical therapy; Political science; Psychology; Social work **Level of Education for which Award is Granted:** Four Year College **Number Awarded:** Varies each year; recently, 9 of these scholarships were awarded. **Funds Available:** Stipends up to $1,000 are available. **Duration:** 1 year.
Eligibility Requirements: This program is open to high school seniors who are active members of the Wisconsin Evangelical Lutheran Synod (WELS) or an affiliated church. Applicants must be planning to go to a 4-year school to prepare for a secular career in which pro-life values will be demonstrated. Acceptable fields include medicine, biotechnology/biological engineering, medical research/genetics, law/politics, journalism/media, psychology, physical therapy, social services, or special education. They must have a GPA of 3.25 or higher. Along with their application, they must submit essays on 1) the field of study they plan to enter and how it relates to pro-life issues; 2) why the scholarship should be awarded to them, including their future goals; and 3) how they have demonstrated a Christian, pro-life attitude in their life. **Deadline for Receipt:** February of each year. **Additional Information:** WELS Lutherans for Life was formerly a ministry of the Wisconsin Evangelical Lutheran Synod.

3763 ■ COMMUNITY FOUNDATION OF GREATER JACKSON

525 East Capitol Street, Suite 5B
Jackson, MS 39201
Tel: (601)974-6044

Fax: (601)974-6045
E-mail: info@cfgreaterjackson.org
Web Site: http://www.cfgreaterjackson.org
To provide financial assistance to upper-division students in Mississippi and Louisiana who are preparing for a career in the field of juvenile justice.

Title of Award: Anthony "Tony" Gobar Juvenile Justice Scholarship Fund **Area, Field, or Subject:** Counseling/Guidance; Criminal justice; Criminology; Law enforcement; Political science **Level of Education for which Award is Granted:** Four Year College **Number Awarded:** 1 each year. **Funds Available:** A stipend is awarded (amount not specified). **Duration:** 1 year.

Eligibility Requirements: This program is open to full-time juniors and seniors at public universities in Mississippi and at Southern University in Louisiana who are preparing to enter the field of juvenile justice. Applicants must have demonstrated a strong commitment to community and public service. They must be U.S. citizens with a GPA of 2.5 or higher. Eligible majors include criminal justice, counseling, and political science. Selection is based on merit and need. **Deadline for Receipt:** April of each year. **Additional Information:** This program was established in 2005.

3764 ■ COMMUNITY FOUNDATION OF MIDDLE TENNESSEE

Attn: Scholarship Committee
3833 Cleghorn Avenue, Suite 400
Nashville, TN 37215-2519
Tel: (615)321-4939; 888-540-5200
Fax: (615)327-2746
E-mail: mail@cfmt.org
Web Site: http://www.cfmt.org/scholarship_info.htm
To provide financial assistance for college to residents of Tennessee preparing for a career in government or politics.

Title of Award: George Oliver Benton Memorial Scholarship **Area, Field, or Subject:** Political science **Level of Education for which Award is Granted:** Four Year College **Number Awarded:** 1 or more each year. **Funds Available:** Stipends range from $500 to $2,500 per year. Funds are paid to the recipient's school and must be used for tuition, fees, books, supplies, room, board, or miscellaneous expenses. **Duration:** 1 year; recipients may reapply.

Eligibility Requirements: This program is open to residents of Tennessee who have served or are serving as legislative interns. Applicants must be enrolled or planning to enroll in a 4-year college or university. Special consideration is given to students whose extracurricular activities indicate in interest in government. Interested students must submit a completed application, their high school and/or college transcript, and 2 letters of recommendation. Selection is based on academic record, standardized test scores, extracurricular activities, work experience, community involvement, recommendations, and financial need. **Deadline for Receipt:** March of each year. **Additional Information:** Recipients may attend college anywhere in the United States. They must attend school on a full-time basis. This program was established in 2001.

3765 ■ DEFENSE INTELLIGENCE AGENCY

Attn: DAH-2
Bolling Air Force Base
Building 6000
Washington, DC 20340-5100
Tel: (202)231-4713
Fax: (202)231-4889
Web Site: http://www.dia.mil
To provide loans-for-service and work experience to women, minority, and disabled high school seniors interested in majoring in specified fields and working for the U.S. Defense Intelligence Agency (DIA).

Title of Award: Defense Intelligence Agency Undergraduate Training Assistance Program **Area, Field, or Subject:** Computer and information sciences; Geography; International affairs and relations; Political science **Level of Education for which Award is Granted:** Undergraduate **Number Awarded:** Only a few are awarded each year. **Funds Available:** Students accepted into this program receive tuition (up to $18,000 per year) at an accredited college or university selected by the student and endorsed by the sponsor; reimbursement for books and needed supplies; an annual salary to cover college room and board expenses and for summer employment; and a position at the sponsoring agency after graduation. Recipients must work for DIA after college graduation for at least 1

and a half times the length of study. For participants who leave DIA earlier than scheduled, the agency arranges for payments to reimburse DIA for the total cost of education (including the employee's pay and allowances). **Duration:** 4 years.

Eligibility Requirements: This program is open to women, minorities, and individuals with disabilities who are graduating high school seniors and interested in majoring in 1 of the following fields in college: geography, foreign area studies, international relations, or political science. Applicants must have a high school GPA of 3.0 or higher, have an SAT score of 1000 or higher or an ACT score of 21 or higher, be able to demonstrate financial need (household income ceiling of $65,000 for a family of 4 or $80,000 for a family of 5 or more), be U.S. citizens and from a family of U.S. citizens, and demonstrate leadership abilities through extracurricular activities, civic involvement, volunteer work, or part-time employment. **Deadline for Receipt:** November of each year. **Additional Information:** Recipients are provided a challenging summer internship and guaranteed a job at the agency in their field of study upon graduation. Recipients must attend school on a full-time basis.

3766 ■ DREW UNIVERSITY

Attn: Office of International and Off-Campus Programs
Brothers College Room 115
36 Madison Avenue
Madison, NJ 07940-4036
Tel: (973)408-3438
Fax: (973)408-3768
E-mail: intlprog@drew.edu
Web Site: http://depts.drew.edu/offcamp/non-DrewScholarships.htm
To provide financial assistance to students from any college who wish to participate in the off-campus programs in the United States or abroad sponsored by Drew University.

Title of Award: Drew University Off Campus Programs Scholarships **Area, Field, or Subject:** Art; British studies; English language and literature; European studies; General studies/Field of study not specified; Performing arts; Political science **Level of Education for which Award is Granted:** Undergraduate **Number Awarded:** Varies each year. **Funds Available:** Grants up to $3,000 per semester are available to be applied to the cost of the programs. **Duration:** 1 semester.

Eligibility Requirements: Students from any American college or university who have been accepted to participate in 1 of the off-campus programs sponsored by Drew University may apply for financial aid if the university's financial aid office determines that they meet the standards of financial need. Applicants for semester programs must be entering their junior or senior year and have a GPA of 2.7 or higher. **Deadline for Receipt:** April of each year for the fall semester; November of each year for the spring semester. **Additional Information:** The programs available recently included a Washington semester on American politics, a semester on the United Nations in New York, a New York semester on contemporary art and culture, a semester on the new Europe, a program in Eritrea on developing countries, and a London semester on British politics, history, drama, or literature.

3767 ■ EPILEPSY FOUNDATION

Attn: Research Department
4351 Garden City Drive
Landover, MD 20785-7223
Tel: (301)459-3700
Free: 800-EFA-1000
Fax: (301)577-2684
E-mail: grants@efa.org
Web Site: http://www.epilepsyfoundation.org/research/grants.cfm
To provide funding to undergraduate and graduate students interested in working on a summer research training project in a field relevant to epilepsy.

Title of Award: Behavioral Sciences Student Fellowships in Epilepsy **Area, Field, or Subject:** Anthropology; Behavioral sciences; Counseling/Guidance; Economics; Epilepsy; Nursing; Political science; Psychology; Rehabilitation, Physical/Psychological; Social work; Sociology **Level of Education for which Award is Granted:** Graduate, Undergraduate **Number Awarded:** Varies each year; recently, 4 of these fellowships were awarded. **Funds Available:** The grant is $3,000. **Duration:** 3 months during the summer.

Eligibility Requirements: This program is open to undergraduate and graduate students in a behavioral science program relevant to epilepsy research or clinical care, including, but not limited to, sociology, social work, psychology, anthropology, nursing, economics, vocational rehabilitation, counseling, and political science. Applicants must be interested in working on an epilepsy research project under the supervision of a qualified mentor. Because the program is designed as a training opportunity, the quality of the training plans and environment are considered in the selection process. Other selection criteria include the quality of the proposed project, the relevance of the proposed work to epilepsy, the applicant's interest in the field of epilepsy, the applicant's qualifications, and the mentor's qualifications, including his or her commitment to the student and the project. U.S. citizenship is not required, but the project must be conducted in the United States. Applications from women, members of minority groups, and people with disabilities are especially encouraged. The program is not intended for students working on a dissertation research project. **Deadline for Receipt:** March of each year. **Additional Information:** This program is supported by the American Epilepsy Society, Abbott Laboratories, Ortho-McNeil Pharmaceutical Corporation, and Pfizer Inc.

3768 ■ FLORIDA STATE ASSOCIATION OF SUPERVISORS OF ELECTIONS

c/o David H. Stafford
Escambia County Supervisor of Elections
213 Palafox Place, Suite 4
P.O. Box 12601
Pensacola, FL 32591-2601
Tel: (850)595-3900
Fax: (850)595-3914
E-mail: soe@escambiavotes.com
Web Site: http://www.gotvflorida.com/scholarship.htm
To provide financial assistance to Florida residents who are interested in majoring in business, political science, or communications in college.
Title of Award: Florida State Association of Supervisors of Elections Scholarship **Area, Field, or Subject:** Business administration; Communications; Journalism; Political science; Public administration **Level of Education for which Award is Granted:** Four Year College **Number Awarded:** 3 each year. **Funds Available:** The stipend is $1,200 per year. **Duration:** 1 year; recipients may reapply.
Eligibility Requirements: This program is open to residents of Florida who have completed 2 years of undergraduate study and are enrolled or planning to enroll full time at a 4-year college or university in the state. Applicants must be majoring in business administration, political science/public administration, or journalism/mass communications and have a GPA of 2.0 or higher. They must be U.S. citizens registered to vote in Florida. Along with their application, they must submit 2 letters of recommendation, a resume of high school and/or college activities, and documentation of financial need. Applications should be submitted to the student's county Supervisor of Elections. Each county's supervisor will review the applications received and select 1 finalist to be sent to the association for consideration. **Deadline for Receipt:** March of each year. **Additional Information:** This program includes the following named scholarships: the Joe Oldmixon Scholarship, the Jimmy Whitehouse Scholarship, and the Dorothy Walker Ruggles Scholarship.

3769 ■ HAWAI'I COMMUNITY FOUNDATION

Attn: Scholarship Department
1164 Bishop Street, Suite 800
Honolulu, HI 96813
Tel: (808)566-5570; 888-731-3863
Fax: (808)521-6286
E-mail: scholarships@hcf-hawaii.org
Web Site: http://www.hawaiicommunityfoundation.org/scholar/scholar.php
To provide financial assistance to residents of Hawaii for undergraduate or graduate studies in fields related to achieving world cooperation and international understanding.
Title of Award: Marion Maccarrell Scott Scholarship **Area, Field, or Subject:** Anthropology; Economics; Geography; History; International affairs and relations; Law; Peace studies; Philosophy; Political science; Psychology; Sociology **Level of Education for which Award is Granted:** Graduate, Undergraduate **Number Awarded:** Varies each year; recently, 258 of these scholarships were awarded. **Funds Available:** The amounts of the awards depend on the availability of funds and the need of the recipient; recently, stipends averaged $1,749. **Duration:** 1 year.

Eligibility Requirements: This program is open to graduates of public high schools in Hawaii. They must plan to attend school as full-time students (on the undergraduate or graduate level) on the mainland, majoring in history, government, political science, anthropology, economics, geography, international relations, law, psychology, philosophy, or sociology. They must be residents of the state of Hawaii, able to demonstrate financial need, interested in attending an accredited 2- or 4-year college or university, and able to demonstrate academic achievement (GPA of 2.8 or higher). Along with their application, they must submit an essay on their commitment to world peace that includes their learning experiences (courses, clubs, community activities, or travel) related to achieving world peace and international understanding and explaining how their experiences have enhanced their ability to achieve those goals. **Deadline for Receipt:** February of each year.

3770 ■ HISPANIC SCHOLARSHIP FUND INSTITUTE

1001 Connecticut Avenue, N.W., Suite 632
Washington, DC 20036
Tel: (202)296-0009
Fax: (202)296-3633
E-mail: info@hsfi.org
Web Site: http://www.hsfi.org/scholarships/generation.asp
To provide financial assistance to Hispanic and other students majoring in designated business, engineering, social science, and science fields who are interested in employment with the U.S. Department of Energy (DOE).
Title of Award: Next Generation of Public Servants Scholarship **Area, Field, or Subject:** Accounting; Biological and clinical sciences; Business administration; Computer and information sciences; Engineering; Environmental science; Finance; Geology; Information science and technology; Management; Mathematics and mathematical sciences; Physics; Political science; Psychology; Sociology **Level of Education for which Award is Granted:** Undergraduate **Number Awarded:** Varies each year. **Funds Available:** The stipend is $3,000 per year. **Duration:** 1 year; may be renewed up to 2 additional years if the recipient maintains full-time enrollment and a GPA of 2.8 or higher.
Eligibility Requirements: This program is open to U.S. citizens enrolled full time as sophomores with a GPA of 2.8 or higher. Applicants must be interested in preparing for a career with the DOE in an energy-related field. Eligible academic majors are in the fields of business (accounting, business administration, finance, and management), engineering (biomedical, chemical, civil, computer, electrical, environmental, industrial, materials, mechanical, metallurgical, nuclear, and petroleum), social science (economics, organizational psychology, political science, and sociology), and science (biological sciences, computer science, geology, information technology, mathematics, microbiology, and physics). They must be willing to participate in co-ops with the DOE. Along with their application, they must submit a 2-page essay on why a career in public service interests them, how their academic major connects with their stated DOE career goal, why the DOE should invest in them through this program, and how they believe the DOE will benefit from this investment. Selection is based on academic achievement, financial need, demonstrated commitment to public service, and interest in federal employment with the DOE. **Deadline for Receipt:** February of each year. **Additional Information:** This program, sponsored by DOE's Office of Economic Impact and Diversity, is administered by the Hispanic Scholarship Fund Institute as part of its effort to increase Hispanic participation in federal service.

3771 ■ KANSAS AFRICAN AMERICAN LEGISLATIVE CAUCUS

c/o Dale M. Dennis
State Department of Education
120 East Tenth Street
Topeka, KS 66612
To provide financial assistance African American college students in Kansas who are interested in a career in politics.
Title of Award: Kansas African American Legislative Caucus Scholarships **Area, Field, or Subject:** Communications; General studies/Field of study not specified; Political science **Level of Education for which Award is Granted:** Undergraduate **Number Awarded:** 2 each year: 1 female and 1 male. **Funds Available:** The stipend is $1,000. **Duration:** 1 year.
Eligibility Requirements: This program is open to residents of Kansas of African American ethnic background who are attending a college or

university in the state. Applicants must have a GPA of 2.6 or higher. Selection is based on academic achievement, leadership ability, and community involvement. Preference is given to students majoring in communications or political science. Males and females are judged separately. **Deadline for Receipt:** March of each year. **Additional Information:** This program is funded by past and present African American members of the Kansas Legislature.

3772 ■ MASSACHUSETTS DEMOCRATIC PARTY

Attn: Executive Director
56 Roland Street, North Lobby, Suite 203
Boston, MA 02129
Tel: (617)776-2676
Fax: (617)776-2579
E-mail: Susan.Thompson@massdems.org
Web Site: http://www.massdems.org/involved/internship.htm
To provide financial assistance for college to Massachusetts residents, with preference given to registered Democrats.
Title of Award: John F. Kennedy Scholarship **Area, Field, or Subject:** History; Political science **Level of Education for which Award is Granted:** Four Year College **Number Awarded:** 2 each year: 1 is set aside specifically for a female and 1 for a male. **Funds Available:** The stipend is $1,500. **Duration:** 1 year.
Eligibility Requirements: This program is open to Massachusetts residents who are entering their third or fourth year of study at a college or university anywhere in the United States. Applicants must be majoring in political science, government, or history. They must be able to demonstrate a serious commitment to the study of American politics and be qualified to receive financial aid (as certified by their financial aid officer). Males and females compete separately. Preference is given to registered Democrats who have a GPA of 3.0 or higher. Finalists may be interviewed in Boston. **Deadline for Receipt:** April of each year.

3773 ■ NATIONAL NAVAL OFFICERS ASSOCIATION-WASHINGTON, D.C. CHAPTER

Attn: Scholarship Program
2701 Park Center Drive, B704
Alexandria, VA 22302
E-mail: williams.stephen@hq.navy.mil
Web Site: http://www.dcnnoa.org
To provide financial assistance to African American high school seniors from the Washington, D.C. area who are interested in majoring in designated fields in college.
Title of Award: DCNNOA/Advanced Concepts and Technologies Scholarship **Area, Field, or Subject:** Computer and information sciences; Political science; Public administration **Level of Education for which Award is Granted:** Undergraduate **Number Awarded:** 1 each year. **Funds Available:** The stipend is $1,000 per year. **Duration:** 1 year; nonrenewable.
Eligibility Requirements: This program is open to African American seniors at high schools in the Washington, D.C. metropolitan area who plan to enroll full time at an accredited 2-year or 4-year college or university. Applicants must be planning to major in governmental affairs, political science, or computer science. They must have a GPA of 2.5 or higher and be U.S. citizens or permanent residents. Selection is based on academic achievement, community involvement, interpersonal and leadership skills, creativity, drive, and maturity. **Deadline for Receipt:** April of each year. **Additional Information:** Recipients are not required to join or affiliate with the military in any way. This program is sponsored by Advanced Concepts and Technologies, Inc.

3774 ■ NATIONAL SECURITY AGENCY

Attn: Office of Recruitment and Staffing (Roberts)
9800 Savage Road, Suite 6779
P.O. Box 1661, Suite 6779
Fort Meade, MD 20755-6779
Tel: (410)854-4725; (866)672-4473
Web Site: http://www.nsa.gov/careers/students_4.cfm
To provide financial assistance and work experience to college sophomores and juniors interested in preparing for a career with the National Security Agency (NSA) as a global network analyst.
Title of Award: Pat Roberts Intelligence Scholars Program for Global Network Analysts **Area, Field, or Subject:** Banking; Computer and information sciences; Finance; Information science and technology;

International affairs and relations; Political science; Telecommunications systems **Level of Education for which Award is Granted:** Undergraduate **Number Awarded:** Varies each year. **Funds Available:** The stipend is $25,000 per year. During the summer after application, students participate in a Global Network Analysis internship. After graduation, they have an employment obligation to NSA equal to 1.5 times the length of educational support provided. **Duration:** 1 year; may be renewed 1 additional year. The summer internship program is for 12 weeks.
Eligibility Requirements: This program is open to college sophomore and juniors whose academic program includes 1 of the following areas of emphasis: 1) technical studies (computer science major with a minor in political science or international relations); 2) topical studies (terrorism, proliferation or related sciences, international banking and finance, or telecommunications and information systems networks); or 3) disciplines (technical intelligence analysis, information assurance, networks, and telecommunications). Applicants must be enrolled full time with a GPA of 3.0 or higher. Along with their application, they must submit a 1-page essay describing how the proposed program of study will improve their ability to analyze information and to think and write critically. U.S. citizenship and eligibility to obtain a high-level security clearance are required **Deadline for Receipt:** October of each year. **Additional Information:** After graduation, participants enter NSA's Global Network Analysis Internship Program as a full-time employee.

3775 ■ SOUTH CAROLINA COMMISSION ON HIGHER EDUCATION

Attn: Director of Student Services
1333 Main Street, Suite 200
Columbia, SC 29201
Tel: (803)737-2260; 877-349-7183
Fax: (803)737-2297
E-mail: dbrown@che.sc.gov
Web Site: http://www.che.sc.gov
To provide scholarship/loans to teachers in South Carolina who wish to improve their content knowledge and degree programs.
Title of Award: South Carolina Teaching Scholarship Grants Program **Area, Field, or Subject:** Art; Dance; Economics; Education; Education, Early childhood; Education, Elementary; Education, Music; Education, Secondary; Education, Special; Geography; History; Linguistics; Mathematics and mathematical sciences; Music; Political science; Science **Level of Education for which Award is Granted:** Graduate, Professional, Undergraduate **Number Awarded:** Varies each year. **Funds Available:** The stipend is $1,000 per fiscal year. This is a scholarship/loan program. Recipients must sign a commitment to teach in South Carolina public schools for at least 1 year following completion of the scholarship grant year and agree to refund the scholarship amount if the 1-year teaching commitment is not honored. **Duration:** 1 year; may be renewed if recipients maintain a GPA of 3.0 or higher. They may receive up to 3 grants in a 5-year period.
Eligibility Requirements: This program is open to residents of South Carolina who have a professional teaching certificate and are under contract as a teacher in a public school in the state. Applicants must be 1) accepted as a degree-seeking graduate student in the teaching field at the master's level and enrolled at an eligible institution in the state; or 2) enrolled for graduate or undergraduate courses in their current teaching field or in a teaching field in which they wish to add on certification. Proposed fields of study must relate to core content areas of English, reading or language arts, mathematics, science, foreign languages, civics and government, economics, arts (advanced fine arts, art, dance, drama, music, and speech), history, or geography; early childhood, elementary education, middle level education, secondary education, and special education also qualify. Priority is given to classroom teachers (not administrators, counselors, media specialists, or other support personnel) whose teaching specialties are critical need subject areas. Continuing graduate students must have a GPA of 3.0 or higher. U.S. citizenship or permanent resident status is required. **Deadline for Receipt:** December of each year for second summer session and fall semester; June of each year for spring semester and first summer session. **Additional Information:** This program was established in 2001.

3776 ■ TEXAS FEDERATION OF BUSINESS AND PROFESSIONAL WOMEN'S FOUNDATION, INC.

Attn: TFBPW Foundation
803 Forest Ridge Drive, Suite 207
Bedford, TX 76022

Tel: (817)283-0862
Fax: (817)283-0872
E-mail: bpwtx@swbell.net
Web Site: http://www.bpwtx.org/foundation.asp
To provide financial assistance to women in Texas who are preparing to enter selected professions.
Title of Award: Hermine Dalkowitz Tobolowsky Scholarship **Area, Field, or Subject:** History; Law; Political science; Public administration; Women's studies **Level of Education for which Award is Granted:** Graduate, Undergraduate **Number Awarded:** 1 or more each year. **Funds Available:** A stipend is awarded (amount not specified). **Duration:** 1 year.
Eligibility Requirements: This program is open to women in Texas who are interested in attending school to prepare for a career in law, public service, government, political science, or women's history. Applicants must have completed at least 2 semesters of study at an accredited college or university in Texas, have a GPA of 3.0 or higher, and be U.S. citizens. Selection is based on academic achievement and financial need. **Deadline for Receipt:** April of each year. **Additional Information:** This program was established in 1995.

3777 ■ HARRY S. TRUMAN SCHOLARSHIP FOUNDATION

Attn: Executive Secretary
712 Jackson Place, N.W.
Washington, DC 20006
Tel: (202)395-4831
Fax: (202)395-6995
E-mail: office@truman.gov
Web Site: http://www.truman.gov
To provide grants-for-service for graduate school to current college juniors who are interested in preparing for a career in public service.
Title of Award: Harry S. Truman Scholarship Program **Area, Field, or Subject:** Agricultural sciences; Biological and clinical sciences; Economics; Education; Engineering; Environmental conservation; Environmental science; History; International affairs and relations; Law; Physical sciences; Political science; Public administration; Public health; Public service; Social sciences; Technology **Level of Education for which Award is Granted:** Four Year College, Graduate **Number Awarded:** 70 to 75 each year: a) 1 "state" scholarship is available to a qualified resident nominee in each of the 50 states, the District of Columbia, Puerto Rico, and the Islands (Guam, the Virgin Islands, American Samoa, and the Commonwealth of the Northern Mariana Islands); and b) up to 25 at-large scholars. **Funds Available:** The program provides up to $30,000, including up to $15,000 for the first year of graduate study and up to $15,000 for the final year of graduate study. **Duration:** Support is provided for the first and last year of graduate study.
Eligibility Requirements: Students must be nominated to be considered for this program. Nominees must be full-time students with junior standing at a 4-year institution, committed to a career in government or public service, in the upper quarter of their class, and U.S. citizens or nationals. Each participating institution may nominate up to 4 candidates (and up to 3 additional students who completed their first 2 years at a community college); community colleges and other 2-year institutions may nominate former students who are enrolled as full-time students with junior-level academic standing at accredited 4-year institutions. Selection is based on extent and quality of community service and government involvement, academic performance, leadership record, suitability of the nominee's proposed program of study for a career in public service, and writing and analytical skills. Priority is given to candidates who plan to enroll in a graduate program that specifically trains them for a career in public service, including government at any level, uniformed services, public interest organizations, nongovernmental research and/or educational organizations, public and private schools, and public service oriented nonprofit organizations. The fields of study may include agriculture, biology, engineering, environmental management, physical and social sciences, and technology policy, as well as such traditional fields as economics, education, government, history, international relations, law, nonprofit management, political science, public administration, public health, and public policy. Interviews are required. **Deadline for Receipt:** February of each year. **Additional Information:** Recipients may attend graduate school in the United States or in foreign countries. Scholars are required to work in public service for 3 of the 7 years following completion of a graduate degree program funded by this program. Scholars who do not

meet this service requirement, or who fail to provide timely proof to the foundation of such employment, will be required to repay funds received, along with interest.

3778 ■ MORRIS K. UDALL FOUNDATION

130 South Scott Avenue
Tucson, AZ 85701-1922
Tel: (520)670-5529
Fax: (520)670-5530
Web Site: http://www.udall.gov/scholarship
To provide financial assistance to 1) college sophomores and juniors who intend to prepare for a career in environmental public policy and 2) Native American and Alaska Native students who intend to prepare for a career in health care or tribal public policy.
Title of Award: Morris K. Udall Scholarships **Area, Field, or Subject:** Business administration; Economics; Education; Environmental conservation; Environmental science; Health care services; Native American studies; Natural resources; Political science; Public administration; Public health; Urban affairs/design/planning **Level of Education for which Award is Granted:** Undergraduate **Number Awarded:** Approximately 80 scholarships and 50 honorable mentions are awarded each year. **Funds Available:** The maximum stipend for scholarship winners is $5,000 per year. Funds are to be used for tuition, fees, books, and room and board. Honorable mention stipends are $350. **Duration:** 1 year; recipients nominated as sophomores may be renominated in their junior year.
Eligibility Requirements: Each 2-year and 4-year college and university in the United States and its possessions may nominate up to 6 sophomores or juniors from either or both categories of this program: 1) students who intend to prepare for a career in environmental public policy, and 2) Native American and Alaska Native students who intend to prepare for a career in health care or tribal public policy. For the first category, the program seeks future leaders across a wide spectrum of environmental fields, such as policy, engineering, science, education, urban planning and renewal, business, health, justice, and economics. For the second category, the program seeks future Native American and Alaska Native leaders in public and community health care, tribal government, and public policy affecting Native American communities, including land and resource management, economic development, and education. Nominees must be U.S. citizens, nationals, or permanent residents with a GPA of 3.0 or higher. Along with their application, they must submit an 800-word essay discussing a significant public speech, legislative act, or public policy statement by former Congressman Morris K. Udall and its impact on their field of study, interests, and career goals. Selection is based on demonstrated commitment to 1) environmental issues through substantial commitment to and participation in 1 or more of the following: campus activities, research, community service, or public service; or 2) tribal public policy or Native American health through substantial contributions to and participation in 1 or more of the following: campus activities, tribal involvement, community or public service, or research; a course of study and proposed career likely to lead to position where nominee can make significant contributions to the shaping of environmental, tribal public policy, or Native American health care issues, whether through scientific advances, public or political service, or community action; and leadership, character, desire to make a difference, and general well-roundedness. **Deadline for Receipt:** Faculty representatives must submit their nominations by early March of each year.

3779 ■ WATTS CHARITY ASSOCIATION, INC.

6245 Bristol Parkway, Suite 224
Culver City, CA 90230
Tel: (323)671-0394
Fax: (323)778-2613
E-mail: wattscharity@yahoo.com
Web Site: http://4watts.tripod.com/id5.html
To provide financial assistance to upper-division college students interested in health, civil rights, or administration.
Title of Award: Royce R. Watts Sr. Scholarship **Area, Field, or Subject:** Business administration; Civil rights; Health care services; Human rights; Medicine; Public administration **Level of Education for which Award is Granted:** Four Year College **Number Awarded:** 1 each year. **Funds Available:** A stipend is awarded (amount not specified). **Duration:** 1 year.
Eligibility Requirements: This program is open to U.S. citizens of African American descent who are enrolled full time as a college or university

junior. Applicants must have an interest in health and pre-medicine, community activities and civil rights, or administration. They must have a GPA of 3.0 or higher, be between 17 and 24 years of age, and be able to demonstrate that they intend to continue their education for at least 2 years. Along with their application, they must submit 1) a 1-paragraph statement on why they should be awarded a Watts Foundation scholarship, and 2) a 1- to 2-page essay on a specific type of cancer, based either on how it has impacted their life or on researched information. **Deadline for Receipt:** May of each year. **Additional Information:** Royce R. Watts, Sr. established the Watts Charity Association after he learned he had cancer in 2001.

Psychology

3780 ■ PARAPSYCHOLOGY FOUNDATION, INC.
Attn: Executive Director
P.O. Box 1562
New York, NY 10021-0043
Tel: (212)628-1550
Fax: (212)628-1559
E-mail: info@parapsychology.org
Web Site: http://www.parapsychology.org
To provide financial assistance to undergraduate or graduate students interested in studying or conducting research in parapsychology.
Title of Award: Eileen J. Garrett Scholarship for Parapsychological Research **Area, Field, or Subject:** Parapsychology **Level of Education for which Award is Granted:** Graduate, Undergraduate **Number Awarded:** 1 each year. **Funds Available:** The stipend is $3,000. **Duration:** 1 year.
Eligibility Requirements: This program is open to undergraduate and graduate students attending accredited colleges and universities who plan to pursue parapsychological studies or research. Funding is restricted to study, research, and experimentation in the field of parapsychology; it is not for general study, nor is it for those with merely a general interest in the subject matter. Applicants must demonstrate a previous academic interest in parapsychology by including, with the application form, a sample of writings on the subject. Letters of reference are also required from 3 individuals who are familiar with the applicant's work and/or studies in parapsychology. **Deadline for Receipt:** July of each year. **Additional Information:** This scholarship was first awarded in 1984.

Public Administration

3781 ■ ALABAMA SPACE GRANT CONSORTIUM
c/o University of Alabama in Huntsville
Materials Science Building, Room 205
Huntsville, AL 35899
Tel: (256)824-6800
Fax: (256)824-6061
E-mail: reasonj@uah.edu
Web Site: http://www.uah.edu/ASGC
To provide financial assistance to undergraduates who are studying the space sciences at universities participating in the Alabama Space Grant Consortium (ASGC).
Title of Award: Undergraduate Scholarship Program of the Alabama Space Grant Consortium **Area, Field, or Subject:** Aerospace sciences; Behavioral sciences; Biological and clinical sciences; Business administration; Communications; Computer and information sciences; Economics; Education; Engineering, Aerospace/Aeronautical/Astronautical; International affairs and relations; Law; Natural sciences; Physical sciences; Public administration; Sociology; Space and planetary sciences **Level of Education for which Award is Granted:** Four Year College **Number Awarded:** Varies each year; recently, 32 of these scholarships were awarded. **Funds Available:** The stipend is $1,000 per year. **Duration:** 1 year; may be renewed 1 additional year.
Eligibility Requirements: This program is open to full-time students entering their junior or senior year at universities participating in the ASGC. Applicants must be studying in a field related to space, including the physical, natural, and biological sciences; engineering, education; economics; business; sociology; behavioral sciences; computer science; communications; law; international affairs; and public administration. They

must be U.S. citizens and have a GPA of 3.0 or higher. Individuals from underrepresented groups (African Americans, Hispanic, American Indians, Pacific Islanders, Asian Americans, and women) are especially encouraged to apply. Interested students should submit a completed application with a career goal statement, personal references, a brief resume, and transcripts. Selection is based on 1) academic qualifications, 2) quality of the career goal statement, and 3) assessment of the applicant's motivation for a career in aerospace. **Deadline for Receipt:** February of each year. **Additional Information:** The member universities are University of Alabama in Huntsville, Alabama A&M University, University of Alabama, University of Alabama at Birmingham, University of South Alabama, Tuskegee University, and Auburn University. Funding for this program is provided by NASA.

3782 ■ AMERICAN COLLEGE OF MEDICAL PRACTICE EXECUTIVES
Attn: ACMPE Scholarship Fund Inc.
104 Inverness Terrace East
Englewood, CO 80112-5306
Tel: (303)799-1111; 877-ASK-MGMA
Fax: (303)643-4439
E-mail: acmpe@mgma.com
Web Site: http://www.mgma.com/academics/scholar.cfm
To provide financial assistance to practitioners in medical practice management interested in pursuing professional development through undergraduate or graduate education.
Title of Award: ACMPE Leaders Scholarships **Area, Field, or Subject:** Business administration; Health care services; Management; Public health **Level of Education for which Award is Granted:** Graduate, Professional, Undergraduate **Number Awarded:** 4 each year. **Funds Available:** The stipend is $3,000. Funds are paid directly to the recipient's college or university. **Duration:** 1 year.
Eligibility Requirements: This program is open to professionals working on an undergraduate or graduate degree in a program relevant to medical practice management, including public health, business administration, health care administration, or other related areas. Students working on a degree in medicine, physical therapy, nursing, or other clinically-related professions are not eligible. Applicants must submit a letter describing their career goals and objectives relevant to medical practice management; a resume; 2 reference letters commenting on their performance, character, potential to succeed, and need for scholarship support; and either documentation indicating acceptance into an undergraduate or graduate program or academic transcripts indicating undergraduate or graduate work completed to date. **Deadline for Receipt:** April of each year. **Additional Information:** This program is managed by Scholarship Program Administrators, Inc. 1201 Eighth Avenue South, P.O. Box 23737, Nashville, TN 27202-3737, (615) 320-3149, (800) 310-4053, Fax: (615) 320-3151, E-mail: info@spaprog.com. It was established to honor past presidents of the American College of Medical Practice Executives (ACMPE), Ernest S. Moscatello, Edgar J. Saux, Charles Wallace, Robert W. "Win" Baker, the Medical Group Management Association (MGMA) Academic Practice Assembly (APA), the MGMA Anesthesia Administration Assembly (AAA), and the MGMA Integrated Health Care Organizations Society (IHOS).

3783 ■ AMERICAN COLLEGE OF MEDICAL PRACTICE EXECUTIVES
Attn: ACMPE Scholarship Fund Inc.
104 Inverness Terrace East
Englewood, CO 80112-5306
Tel: (303)799-1111; 877-ASK-MGMA
Fax: (303)643-4439
E-mail: acmpe@mgma.com
Web Site: http://www.mgma.com/academics/scholar.cfm
To provide financial assistance to undergraduate and graduate students who are interested in preparing for a career in medical group management.
Title of Award: Richard L. Davis/Barbara B. Watson National Scholarship **Area, Field, or Subject:** Business administration; Health care services; Management; Public health **Level of Education for which Award is Granted:** Graduate, Undergraduate **Number Awarded:** 1 each year. **Funds Available:** The stipend is $1,500. Funds are paid directly to the recipient's college or university. **Duration:** 1 year.
Eligibility Requirements: This program is open to full-time students working on an undergraduate or graduate degree in a program relevant to

medical practice management, including public health, business administration, health care administration, or other related areas. Students working on a degree in medicine, physical therapy, nursing, or other clinically-related professions are not eligible. Applicants must submit a letter describing their career goals and objectives relevant to medical practice management; a resume; 3 reference letters commenting on their performance, character, potential to succeed, and need for scholarship support; and either documentation indicating acceptance into an undergraduate or graduate college or university or academic transcripts indicating undergraduate or graduate work completed to date. **Deadline for Receipt:** April of each year. **Additional Information:** This program is managed by Scholarship Program Administrators, Inc. 1201 Eighth Avenue South, P.O. Box 23737, Nashville, TN 27202-3737, (615) 320-3149, (800) 310-4053, Fax: (615) 320-3151, E-mail: info@spaprog.com.

3784 ■ AMERICAN COLLEGE OF MEDICAL PRACTICE EXECUTIVES
Attn: ACMPE Scholarship Fund Inc.
104 Inverness Terrace East
Englewood, CO 80112-5306
Tel: (303)799-1111; 877-ASK-MGMA
Fax: (303)643-4439
E-mail: acmpe@mgma.com
Web Site: http://www.mgma.com/academics/scholar.cfm
To provide financial assistance to individuals currently employed in medical group management who wish to pursue professional development on the undergraduate or graduate level.
Title of Award: Richard L. Davis Managers Scholarship **Area, Field, or Subject:** Business administration; Health care services; Management; Public health **Level of Education for which Award is Granted:** Graduate, Professional, Undergraduate **Number Awarded:** 1 each year. **Funds Available:** The stipend is $1,500. Funds are paid directly to the recipient's college or university. **Duration:** 1 year.
Eligibility Requirements: This program is open to medical group management professionals who want to pursue professional development through undergraduate or graduate education in a program relevant to medical practice management, including public health, business administration, health care administration, or other related areas. Professionals interested in studying medicine, physical therapy, nursing, or other clinically-related professions are not eligible. Applicants must submit a letter describing their career goals and objectives relevant to medical practice management; a resume; 3 reference letters commenting on their performance, character, potential to succeed, and need for scholarship support; and either documentation indicating acceptance into an undergraduate or graduate college or university or academic transcripts indicating undergraduate or graduate work completed to date. **Deadline for Receipt:** April of each year. **Additional Information:** This program is managed by Scholarship Program Administrators, Inc. 1201 Eighth Avenue South, P.O. Box 23737, Nashville, TN 27202-3737, (615) 320-3149, (800) 310-4053, Fax: (615) 320-3151, E-mail: info@spaprog.com.

3785 ■ AMERICAN COLLEGE OF MEDICAL PRACTICE EXECUTIVES
Attn: ACMPE Scholarship Fund Inc.
104 Inverness Terrace East
Englewood, CO 80112-5306
Tel: (303)799-1111; 877-ASK-MGMA
Fax: (303)643-4439
E-mail: acmpe@mgma.com
Web Site: http://www.mgma.com/academics/scholar.cfm
To provide financial assistance to undergraduate or graduate students who are interested in preparing for a career in medical group management.
Title of Award: Harry J. Harwick Scholarships **Area, Field, or Subject:** Business administration; Health care services; Management; Public health **Level of Education for which Award is Granted:** Graduate, Undergraduate **Number Awarded:** 2 each year. **Funds Available:** The stipend is $5,000. Funds are paid directly to the recipient's college or university. **Duration:** 1 year.
Eligibility Requirements: Eligible are 1) graduate students enrolled in a program accredited by the Accrediting Commission on Education for Health Services Administration and 2) undergraduate students enrolled in a program that is a member of the Association of University Programs in Health Administration. Applicants must be working on a degree in a program relevant to medical practice management, including public

health, business administration, health care administration, or other related areas. Students working on a degree in medicine, physical therapy, nursing, or other clinically-related professions are not eligible. Along with their application, they must submit a letter describing their career goals and objectives relevant to medical practice management; a resume; 3 reference letters commenting on their performance, character, potential to succeed, and need for scholarship support; and either documentation indicating acceptance into an undergraduate or graduate college or university or academic transcripts indicating undergraduate or graduate work completed to date. **Deadline for Receipt:** April of each year. **Additional Information:** This program is managed by Scholarship Program Administrators, Inc. 1201 Eighth Avenue South, P.O. Box 23737, Nashville, TN 27202-3737, (615) 320-3149, (800) 310-4053, Fax: (615) 320-3151, E-mail: info@spaprog.com.

3786 ■ AMERICAN COLLEGE OF MEDICAL PRACTICE EXECUTIVES
Attn: ACMPE Scholarship Fund Inc.
104 Inverness Terrace East
Englewood, CO 80112-5306
Tel: (303)799-1111; 877-ASK-MGMA
Fax: (303)643-4439
E-mail: acmpe@mgma.com
Web Site: http://www.mgma.com/academics/scholar.cfm
To provide financial assistance to undergraduate or graduate women in Georgia who are working on a degree in health care or health care administration.
Title of Award: Constance L. Lloyd Scholarship **Area, Field, or Subject:** Business administration; Health care services; Management; Public health **Level of Education for which Award is Granted:** Graduate, Undergraduate **Number Awarded:** 1 each year. **Funds Available:** The stipend is $2,500. Funds are paid directly to the recipient's college or university. **Duration:** 1 year.
Eligibility Requirements: This program is open to women enrolled at the undergraduate or graduate level at an accredited college or university in Georgia who are working on either an administrative or clinically-related degree in the health care field. Students working on a degree in medicine, physical therapy, nursing, or other clinically-related professions are not eligible. Applicants must submit a letter describing their career goals and objectives relevant to medical practice management; a resume; 3 reference letters commenting on their performance, character, potential to succeed, and need for scholarship support; and either documentation indicating acceptance into an undergraduate or graduate program or academic transcripts indicating undergraduate or graduate work completed to date. **Deadline for Receipt:** April of each year. **Additional Information:** This program, established in 1993, is managed by Scholarship Program Administrators, Inc. 1201 Eighth Avenue South, P.O. Box 23737, Nashville, TN 27202-3737, (615) 320-3149, (800) 310-4053, Fax: (615) 320-3151, E-mail: info@spaprog.com.

3787 ■ AMERICAN COLLEGE OF MEDICAL PRACTICE EXECUTIVES
Attn: ACMPE Scholarship Fund Inc.
104 Inverness Terrace East
Englewood, CO 80112-5306
Tel: (303)799-1111; 877-ASK-MGMA
Fax: (303)643-4439
E-mail: acmpe@mgma.com
Web Site: http://www.mgma.com/academics/scholar.cfm
To provide financial assistance to members of the Medical Group Management Association (MGMA) Midwest Section who are interested in undergraduate or graduate education.
Title of Award: MGMA Midwest Section Scholarships **Area, Field, or Subject:** Business administration; Health care services; Management; Public health **Level of Education for which Award is Granted:** Graduate, Professional, Undergraduate **Number Awarded:** 1 each year. **Funds Available:** The stipend is $2,000. Funds are paid directly to the recipient's college or university. **Duration:** 1 year.
Eligibility Requirements: Eligible to apply are individuals resident in the MGMA Midwest Section (Illinois, Indiana, Iowa, Michigan, Minnesota, Nebraska, North Dakota, Ohio, South Dakota, and Wisconsin) who wish to work on an undergraduate or graduate degree in medical practice management, including public health, business administration, health care administration, or other related areas. Students working on a degree in medicine, physical therapy, nursing, or other clinically-related professions

are not eligible. Applicants must submit a letter describing their career goals and objectives relevant to medical practice management; a resume; 3 reference letters commenting on their performance, character, potential to succeed, and need for scholarship support; and either documentation indicating acceptance into an undergraduate or graduate college or university or academic transcripts indicating undergraduate or graduate work completed to date. **Deadline for Receipt:** April of each year. **Additional Information:** This program is managed by Scholarship Program Administrators, Inc. 1201 Eighth Avenue South, P.O. Box 23737, Nashville, TN 27202-3737, (615) 320-3149, (800) 310-4053, Fax: (615) 320-3151, E-mail: info@spaprog.com.

3788 ■ AMERICAN COLLEGE OF MEDICAL PRACTICE EXECUTIVES
Attn: ACMPE Scholarship Fund Inc.
104 Inverness Terrace East
Englewood, CO 80112-5306
Tel: (303)799-1111; 877-ASK-MGMA
Fax: (303)643-4439
E-mail: acmpe@mgma.com
Web Site: http://www.mgma.com/academics/scholar.cfm
To provide financial assistance to members of the Medical Group Management Association (MGMA) Western Section who are interested in undergraduate or graduate education.
Title of Award: MGMA Western Section Scholarships **Area, Field, or Subject:** Business administration; Health care services; Management; Public health **Level of Education for which Award is Granted:** Graduate, Professional, Undergraduate **Number Awarded:** 1 each year. **Funds Available:** The stipend is $2,000. Funds are paid directly to the recipient's college or university. **Duration:** 1 year.
Eligibility Requirements: Eligible to apply are individuals who reside in and have been members of the MGMA Western Section (Alaska, Arizona, California, Colorado, Hawaii, Idaho, Montana, Nevada, New Mexico, Oregon, Utah, Washington, and Wyoming) for at least 2 years. Applicants must wish to work on an undergraduate or graduate degree in medical practice management, including public health, business administration, health care administration, or other related areas. Students working on a degree in medicine, physical therapy, nursing, or other clinically-related professions are not eligible. Applicants must submit a letter describing their career goals and objectives relevant to medical practice management; a resume; 3 reference letters commenting on their performance, character, potential to succeed, and need for scholarship support; and either documentation indicating acceptance into an undergraduate or graduate college or university or academic transcripts indicating undergraduate or graduate work completed to date. **Deadline for Receipt:** April of each year. **Additional Information:** This program is managed by Scholarship Program Administrators, Inc. 1201 Eighth Avenue South, P.O. Box 23737, Nashville, TN 27202-3737, (615) 320-3149, (800) 310-4053, Fax: (615) 320-3151, E-mail: info@spaprog.com.

3789 ■ AMERICAN COLLEGE OF MEDICAL PRACTICE EXECUTIVES
Attn: ACMPE Scholarship Fund Inc.
104 Inverness Terrace East
Englewood, CO 80112-5306
Tel: (303)799-1111; 877-ASK-MGMA
Fax: (303)643-4439
E-mail: acmpe@mgma.com
Web Site: http://www.mgma.com/academics/scholar.cfm
To provide financial assistance to residents of Ohio and West Virginia who are working on an undergraduate or graduate degree in health care management related to hematology or oncology.
Title of Award: Oncology Practice Alliance Scholarship **Area, Field, or Subject:** Business administration; Health care services; Management; Oncology; Public health **Level of Education for which Award is Granted:** Graduate, Undergraduate **Number Awarded:** 1 each year. **Funds Available:** The stipend is at least $1,000. Funds are paid directly to the recipient's college or university. **Duration:** 1 year.
Eligibility Requirements: This program is open to full-time students working on an undergraduate or graduate degree in a program relevant to medical practice management (e.g., public health, business administration, health care administration) with a specialty in oncology or hematology. Students working on a degree in medicine, physical therapy, nursing, or other clinically-related professions are not eligible. Applicants must have been residents of Ohio or West Virginia for at least 12 months prior to applying. They must submit a letter describing their career goals and

objectives relevant to medical practice management; a resume; 3 reference letters commenting on their performance, character, potential to succeed, and need for scholarship support; and either documentation indicating acceptance into an undergraduate or graduate program or academic transcripts indicating undergraduate or graduate work completed to date. **Deadline for Receipt:** April of each year. **Additional Information:** This program is managed by Scholarship Program Administrators, Inc. 1201 Eighth Avenue South, P.O. Box 23737, Nashville, TN 27202-3737, (615) 320-3149, (800) 310-4053, Fax: (615) 320-3151, E-mail: info@spaprog. com.

3790 ■ AMERICAN DENTAL HYGIENISTS' ASSOCIATION
Attn: Institute for Oral Health
444 North Michigan Avenue, Suite 3400
Chicago, IL 60611
Tel: (312)440-8918
Free: 800-735-4916
Fax: (312)440-8929
E-mail: institute@adha.net
Web Site: http://www.adha.org/institute/Scholarship/index.htm
To provide financial assistance to students in a baccalaureate or graduate degree program in dental hygiene who demonstrate strong potential in public health or community dental health.
Title of Award: Irene E. Newman Scholarship **Area, Field, or Subject:** Dental hygiene; Public health **Level of Education for which Award is Granted:** Graduate, Four Year College **Number Awarded:** 1 each year. **Funds Available:** Stipends range from $1,000 to $2,000. **Duration:** 1 year.
Eligibility Requirements: This program is open to students who have completed at least 1 year in a dental hygiene program at the baccalaureate, master's, or doctoral level with a GPA of at least 3.0. Applicants must demonstrate strong potential in public health or community dental health. They must be active members of the Student American Dental Hygienists' Association (SADHA) or the American Dental Hygienists' Association (ADHA) and be able to document financial need of at least $1,500. Along with their application, they must submit a statement that covers their long-term career goals, their intended contribution to the dental hygiene profession, their professional interests, and the manner in which their degree will enhance their professional capacity. Graduate applicants must also include a description of the research in which they are involved or would like to become involved and a list of past and/or present involvement in professional and/or community activities. and full-time enrollment. Selection is based on their potential in public health or community dental health. **Deadline for Receipt:** April of each year.

3791 ■ AMERICAN LEGION AUXILIARY
Attn: Department of Maryland
1589 Sulphur Spring Road, Suite 105
Baltimore, MD 21227
Tel: (410)242-9519
Fax: (410)242-9553
E-mail: anna@alamd.org
To provide financial assistance for college to the daughters of veterans who are Maryland residents and wish to study arts, sciences, business, public administration, education, or a medical field.
Title of Award: Maryland Legion Auxiliary Children and Youth Fund Scholarship **Area, Field, or Subject:** Art; Business administration; Education; Medicine; Public administration; Science **Level of Education for which Award is Granted:** Undergraduate **Number Awarded:** 1 each year. **Funds Available:** The stipend is $2,000. **Duration:** 1 year; may be renewed up to 3 additional years.
Eligibility Requirements: Eligible for this scholarship are Maryland senior high girls with veteran parents who wish to study arts, sciences, business, public administration, education, or a medical field other than nursing at a college or university in the state. Preference is given to children of members of the American Legion or American Legion Auxiliary. Selection is based on character (30%), Americanism (20%), leadership (10%), scholarship (20%), and financial need (20%). **Deadline for Receipt:** April of each year.

3792 ■ AMERICAN PLANNING ASSOCIATION
Attn: Federal Planning Division
122 South Michigan Avenue, Suite 1600
Chicago, IL 60603-6107

Tel: (312)431-9100
Fax: (312)431-9985
E-mail: fpd-info@list.planning.org
Web Site: http://www.FedPlan.org
To provide financial assistance to undergraduate and graduate students preparing for a career in planning, especially as it relates to activities of the federal government.
Title of Award: Federal Planning Division Annual Student Scholarship **Area, Field, or Subject:** Public administration; Urban affairs/design/planning **Level of Education for which Award is Granted:** Four Year College, Graduate **Number Awarded:** 1 or more each year. **Funds Available:** Stipends range from $500 to $2,500. **Duration:** 1 year.
Eligibility Requirements: This program is open to juniors, seniors, and graduate students at U.S. and Canadian accredited colleges and universities. Applicants must be preparing for a career in public service, especially at the federal level, as a planner. They must have a GPA of 3.0 or higher. Along with their application, they must submit an essay that addresses the federal government's role in managing its lands and resources in the best interests of the United States. Selection is based primarily on the essay, which is judged on clarity of message, freshness of idea, and potential for implementation. **Deadline for Receipt:** November of each year. **Additional Information:** This program began in 2004. Information is also available from Justin Hollander, U.S. General Services Administration, 26 Federal Plaza, Room 1609, New York, NY 10278, (212) 264-1622, E-mail: Justin.Hollander@gsa.gov.

3793 ■ AMERICAN PLANNING ASSOCIATION

Attn: Planning and the Black Community Division
122 South Michigan Avenue, Suite 1600
Chicago, IL 60603-6107
Tel: (312)431-9100
Fax: (312)431-9985
E-mail: info_pbcd@planning.org
Web Site: http://www.planning.org/blackcommunity/scholarship.htm
To provide financial assistance to African American undergraduate students interested in majoring in planning or a related field.
Title of Award: Planning and the Black Community Division Scholarship **Area, Field, or Subject:** Environmental conservation; Environmental science; Geography; Public administration; Transportation; Urban affairs/design/planning **Level of Education for which Award is Granted:** Four Year College **Number Awarded:** 1 each year. **Funds Available:** The stipend is $2,500. **Duration:** 1 year.
Eligibility Requirements: This program is open to full-time African American undergraduate students entering their junior or senior year. Applicants must be majoring in planning or a related field (e.g., geography, environmental sciences, public administration, transportation, or urban studies) with a GPA of 3.0 or higher. They must submit a 2-page personal statement on the importance of urban planning to the African American community and how they see themselves making a contribution to the urban planning profession. U.S. citizenship is required. **Deadline for Receipt:** October of each year. **Additional Information:** Information is also available from Sigmund Shipp, Hunter College, Department of Urban Affairs and Planning, 695 Park Avenue, New York, NY 10021.

3794 ■ AMERICAN SOCIETY OF MILITARY COMPTROLLERS

Attn: National Awards Committee
415 North Alfred Street
Alexandria, VA 22314
Tel: (703)549-0360
Free: 800-462-5637
E-mail: asmchq@aol.com
Web Site: http://www.asmconline.org/national/nationalawards.shtml
To provide financial assistance for continuing education to members of the American Society of Military Comptrollers (ASMC).
Title of Award: ASMC Members' Continuing Education Program Award **Area, Field, or Subject:** Accounting; Business administration; Computer and information sciences; Economics; Finance; Operations research; Public administration **Level of Education for which Award is Granted:** Graduate, Professional, Undergraduate **Number Awarded:** 15 each year: 1 at $5,000 (the Dick Vincent Scholarship), 4 at $2,500, and 10 at $1,000. **Funds Available:** Stipends are $5,000, $2,500, or $1,000 per year. **Duration:** 1 year.

Eligibility Requirements: Applicants for this assistance must have been members of the society for at least 2 full years and must have been active in the local chapter at some level (board member, committee chair or member, volunteer for chapter events, etc.). They must be enrolled in or planning to enroll in an academic institution in a field of study directly related to financial resource management, including business administration, economics, public administration, computer science, or operations research related to financial management, accounting, and finance. As part of the selection process, they must submit an essay of up to 500 words on their academic and career goals and financial need. **Deadline for Receipt:** March of each year. **Additional Information:** The ASMC is open to all financial management professionals employed by the U.S. Department of Defense and Coast Guard, both civilian and military. The applicant whose service to the society is judged the most exceptional is designated the Dick Vincent Scholarship Winner.

3795 ■ AMERICAN SOCIETY OF MILITARY COMPTROLLERS

Attn: National Awards Committee
415 North Alfred Street
Alexandria, VA 22314
Tel: (703)549-0360
Free: 800-462-5637
E-mail: asmchq@aol.com
Web Site: http://www.asmconline.org/national/nationalawards.shtml
To provide financial assistance to high school seniors and recent graduates interested in preparing for a career in financial management.
Title of Award: ASMC National Scholarship Program **Area, Field, or Subject:** Accounting; Business administration; Computer and information sciences; Economics; Finance; Operations research; Public administration **Level of Education for which Award is Granted:** Undergraduate **Number Awarded:** 10 each year: 5 at $2,000 and 5 at $1,000. **Funds Available:** Stipends are $2,000 or $1,000 per year. **Duration:** 1 year.
Eligibility Requirements: This program is open to high school seniors and to people who graduated from high school during the preceding 6 months. Applicants must be planning to enter college in a field of study directly related to financial resource management, including business administration, economics, public administration, computer science, or operations research related to financial management, accounting, and finance. They must be endorsed by a chapter of the American Society of Military Comptrollers (ASMC). Selection is based on scholastic achievement, leadership ability, extracurricular activities, career and academic goals, and financial need. **Deadline for Receipt:** March of each year. **Additional Information:** The ASMC is open to all financial management professionals employed by the U.S. Department of Defense and Coast Guard, both civilian and military.

3796 ■ AMERICAN SOCIETY OF MILITARY COMPTROLLERS- MOUNT VERNON CHAPTER

Attn: Awards and Scholarships Director
P.O. Box 99
Fort Belvoir, VA 22060-0099
To provide financial assistance to high school seniors in the Washington, D.C. area who plan to work on an undergraduate degree related to financial management.
Title of Award: Mount Vernon Chapter Scholarships **Area, Field, or Subject:** Accounting; Business administration; Computer and information sciences; Economics; Finance; Operations research; Public administration **Level of Education for which Award is Granted:** Undergraduate **Number Awarded:** Several each year. **Funds Available:** The stipend is $1,000. **Duration:** 1 year.
Eligibility Requirements: This program is open to seniors graduating from high schools in Maryland, Virginia, and Washington, D.C. and to recent (within the past 6 months) graduates of those high schools. Applicants must be entering a field of study directly related to financial management (business administration, economics, public administration, computer science, operations research related to financial management, accounting, and finance). Along with their application, they must submit a 250-word essay on their career and academic goals and their financial need. Selection is based on academic achievement, leadership ability,

extracurricular activities, career and academic goals, and financial need. **Deadline for Receipt:** March of each year.

3797 ■ AMERICAN SOCIETY OF MILITARY COMPTROLLERS-WASHINGTON CHAPTER

Attn: Shirley Simpkins
P.O. Box 16237
Arlington, VA 22215-1237
Tel: (202)781-2785
E-mail: Scholarships@Washington-ASMC.org
Web Site: http://www.washington-asmc.org/stuaward.htm
To provide financial assistance to high school seniors in the Washington, D.C. area who plan to work on an undergraduate degree related to financial operations.
Title of Award: Washington Chapter Scholarships **Area, Field, or Subject:** Accounting; Business administration; Economics; Finance; Operations research; Public administration **Level of Education for which Award is Granted:** Undergraduate **Number Awarded:** 10 each year. **Funds Available:** The stipend is $1,500. **Duration:** 1 year.
Eligibility Requirements: This program is open to seniors graduating from high schools in Maryland, Virginia, and Washington, D.C. Applicants must be entering a field of study directly related to financial operations (business administration, economics, public administration, operations research related to financial management, accounting, and finance). Along with their application, they must submit 3 letters of recommendation, an official transcript, and SAT scores. Selection is based on academic achievement, leadership ability, extracurricular activities, career goals, and financial need. **Deadline for Receipt:** January of each year.

3798 ■ ASSOCIATION OF CALIFORNIA WATER AGENCIES

Attn: Scholarship Program
910 K Street, Suite 100
Sacramento, CA 95814-3514
Tel: (916)441-4545
Fax: (916)325-4849
E-mail: lavonnew@acwa.com
Web Site: http://www.acwa.com/news_info/scholarships
To provide financial assistance to upper-division students in California who are majoring in water resources-related fields of study.
Title of Award: Association of California Water Agencies Scholarships **Area, Field, or Subject:** Agricultural sciences; Engineering; Environmental conservation; Environmental science; Public administration; Water resources **Level of Education for which Award is Granted:** Four Year College **Number Awarded:** At least 6 each year. **Funds Available:** The stipend is $1,500. Funds are paid directly to the recipient's school. **Duration:** 1 year.
Eligibility Requirements: This program is open to California residents attending selected colleges and universities in the state. Applicants must be full-time students in their junior or senior year at the time of the award and majoring in a field related to or identified with water resources, including engineering, agricultural and/or urban water supply, environmental sciences, or public administration. Along with their application, they must submit 2-page essay on key water-related issues they would address if given the opportunity, why they have chosen a career in the water resources field, and how their educational and career goals relate to a future in California water resources. Selection is based on scholastic achievement, commitment to a career in the field of water resources, and financial need. **Deadline for Receipt:** March of each year. **Additional Information:** Recipients must attend a college or university in California approved by the sponsor.

3799 ■ ASSOCIATION OF CALIFORNIA WATER AGENCIES

Attn: Scholarship Program
910 K Street, Suite 100
Sacramento, CA 95814-3514
Tel: (916)441-4545
Fax: (916)325-4849
E-mail: lavonnew@acwa.com
Web Site: http://www.acwa.com/news_info/scholarships
To provide financial assistance to upper-division students in California who are majoring in water resources-related fields of study.
Title of Award: Clair A. Hill Scholarship **Area, Field, or Subject:** Agricultural sciences; Engineering; Environmental conservation;

Environmental science; Public administration; Water resources **Level of Education for which Award is Granted:** Undergraduate **Number Awarded:** 1 each year. **Funds Available:** The stipend is $3,000. Funds are paid directly to the recipient's school. **Duration:** 1 year.
Eligibility Requirements: Applicants must be California residents attending public colleges or universities in the state. They should 1) have completed their sophomore work, 2) be full-time students in their junior or senior year at the time of the award, and 3) be majoring in a field related to or identified with water resources, including engineering, agricultural sciences, urban water supply, environmental sciences, and public administration. Selection is based on scholastic achievement, career plans, and financial need. **Deadline for Receipt:** March of each year. **Additional Information:** This program is administered each year by the current recipient of the Association of California Water Agencies Clair A. Hill Agency Award for Excellence, which is presented annually to a public water agency in recognition of outstanding and innovative water management programs. The winning agency generally selects a student within its service area. Funding is provided by the consulting firm CH2M Hill. Recipients must attend a branch of the University of California or the California State University system on a full-time basis.

3800 ■ BULLETIN OF THE ATOMIC SCIENTISTS

Attn: Rieser Fellowship
6042 South Kimbark Avenue
Chicago, IL 60637-2806
Tel: (773)702-2555
Fax: (773)702-0725
Web Site: http://www.thebulletin.org/about_us/rieser_fellowships.htm
To provide funding to undergraduate students interested in developing a project, at home or abroad, that will enable them to investigate the role of scientists in formulating public policy and in addressing global security policy challenges.
Title of Award: Leonard M. Rieser Fellowship in Science, Technology, and Global Security **Area, Field, or Subject:** International affairs and relations; Public administration; Science; Technology **Level of Education for which Award is Granted:** Undergraduate **Number Awarded:** 3 to 5 each year. **Funds Available:** Stipends range from $2,500 to $5,000. **Duration:** 1 year; nonrenewable.
Eligibility Requirements: This program is open to students at U.S. colleges and universities who are interested in exploring the connections between science, technology, global security, and public policy. Applicants must be seeking funding to 1) provide a stipend for an otherwise unpaid full-time internship; 2) underwrite the cost of travel or transportation to support academic research; 3) participate in or travel to professional conferences where they present academic research; or 4) underwrite the production costs of a special project, ranging from laboratory work to the making of a documentary film. The proposed activity may take place in the United States or abroad. Along with their application, they must submit a narrative (from 800 to 1,000 words) describing the intended use of the fellowship; a 1-page personal essay explaining how they would benefit from the fellowship and the experience being proposed; a detail project budget; and 2 letters of recommendation. Selection is based on demonstrated interest in the fields of science, technology, and public policy, international affairs, or global security policy. Science students are especially encouraged to apply. **Deadline for Receipt:** March of each year. **Additional Information:** This program was established in 1999.

3801 ■ CALIFORNIA ADOLESCENT NUTRITION, PHYSICAL EDUCATION, AND CULINARY ARTS SCHOLARSHIPS

2140 Shattuck Avenue, Suite 610
Berkeley, CA 94704
Tel: (510)644-1533
Free: 800-200-3131
Fax: (510)644-1535
E-mail: info@canfit.org
Web Site: http://www.canfit.org/scholarships.html
To provide financial assistance to minority undergraduate and graduate students who are studying nutrition, physical education or culinary arts in California.
Title of Award: CANFit Program Scholarships **Area, Field, or Subject:** Culinary arts; Education, Physical; Nutrition; Public health; Youth **Level of Education for which Award is Granted:** Graduate, Undergraduate **Number Awarded:** 5 graduate scholarships and 10 undergraduate

scholarships are available each year. **Funds Available:** Graduate stipends are $1,000 each and undergraduate stipends are $500 per year. **Eligibility Requirements:** Eligible to apply are American Indians/Alaska Natives, African Americans, Asians/Pacific Islanders, and Latinos/Hispanics who are enrolled in either: 1) an approved master's or doctoral graduate program in nutrition, public health nutrition, or physical education or in a preprofessional practice program approved by the American Dietetic Association at an accredited university in California; or, 2) an approved bachelor's or professional certificate program in culinary arts, nutrition, or physical education at an accredited university or college in California. Graduate student applicants must have completed at least 12 units of graduate course work and have a cumulative GPA of 3.0 or higher; undergraduate applicants must have completed 50 semester units or the equivalent of college credits and have a cumulative GPA of 2.5 or higher. Selection is based on financial need, academic goals, and community nutrition or physical education activities. **Deadline for Receipt:** March of each year. **Additional Information:** A goal of the California Adolescent Nutrition and Fitness (CANFit) program is to improve the nutritional status and physical fitness of California's low-income multiethnic youth aged 10 to 14. By offering these scholarships, the program hopes to encourage more students to consider careers in adolescent nutrition and fitness.

3802 ■ CALIFORNIA ENVIRONMENTAL HEALTH ASSOCIATION

110 South Fairfax, A11-175
Los Angeles, CA 90036
Tel: (323)634-7698
Fax: (323)571-1889
E-mail: support@ceha.org
Web Site: http://www.ceha.org/awards.html
To provide financial assistance to undergraduates in California interested in preparing for a career in the sciences, especially environmental health.
Title of Award: Martin Smilo Undergraduate Scholarship **Area, Field, or Subject:** Environmental conservation; Environmental science; Public health; Science **Level of Education for which Award is Granted:** Four Year College **Number Awarded:** 1 each year. **Funds Available:** The stipend is $2,500. **Duration:** 1 year.
Eligibility Requirements: This program is open to California students who have completed at least 48 semester units of undergraduate study, including at least 12 semester units in science, with a GPA of 3.0 or higher. Applicants must be enrolled full time at an accredited 4-year college or university with an intention to work on a degree and prepare for a career in science. Preference is given to students in environmental health. Along with their application, they must submit a 3-page essay on 1 of 3 assigned topics related to public health and the role of professional organizations. Financial need is not considered in the selection process. **Deadline for Receipt:** February of each year. **Additional Information:** Information is also available from Matt Fore, CEHA Awards Committee, 160 Gibson Drive, Number 17, Hollister, CA 95023, (831) 636-4035, E-mail: matt@sanbenitoco.org.

3803 ■ CALIFORNIA STATE UNIVERSITY

Office of the Chancellor
Attn: Lori Redfearn, Vice President
401 Golden Shore, Sixth Floor
Long Beach, CA 90802-4210
Tel: (562)951-4815
E-mail: lredfearn@calstate.edu
Web Site: http://www.calstate.edu/foundation/scholarship.shtml
To provide financial assistance to graduate students majoring in designated fields at campuses of the California State University (CSU) system.
Title of Award: Glenn and Dorothy Dumke Fellowship **Area, Field, or Subject:** Economics; History, American; Library and archival sciences; Political science; Public administration **Level of Education for which Award is Granted:** Four Year College, Master's **Number Awarded:** 1 each year. **Funds Available:** The stipend is $1,000 per year. **Duration:** 1 year.

Eligibility Requirements: This program is open to students working on a graduate degree at CSU campuses in public policy, American history, economics, archival management, or government.

3804 ■ CALIFORNIA STATE UNIVERSITY

Office of the Chancellor
Attn: Lori Redfearn, Vice President
401 Golden Shore, Sixth Floor
Long Beach, CA 90802-4210
Tel: (562)951-4815
E-mail: lredfearn@calstate.edu
Web Site: http://www.calstate.edu/foundation/scholarship.shtml
To provide financial assistance to students majoring in public administration at campuses of the California State University (CSU) system.
Title of Award: Robert M. Odell Endowed Scholarship in Public Administration **Area, Field, or Subject:** Public administration **Level of Education for which Award is Granted:** Four Year College **Number Awarded:** 1 each year, alternating between the southern and northern regions of California **Funds Available:** The stipend is $1,500 per year. **Duration:** 1 year.
Eligibility Requirements: This program is open to students enrolled at the 16 CSU campuses that offer degree programs in public administration. **Additional Information:** This program was established in 1987 by the California Society of Municipal Finance Officers.

3805 ■ COMMUNITY FOUNDATION OF GREATER JACKSON

525 East Capitol Street, Suite 5B
Jackson, MS 39201
Tel: (601)974-6044
Fax: (601)974-6045
E-mail: info@cfgreaterjackson.org
Web Site: http://www.cfgreaterjackson.org
To provide financial assistance to undergraduate students in Mississippi who are preparing for a career in the field of public works.
Title of Award: APWA Scholarship Fund **Area, Field, or Subject:** Biological and clinical sciences; Chemistry; Engineering, Civil; Engineering, Electrical; Environmental science; Public administration **Level of Education for which Award is Granted:** Four Year College **Number Awarded:** 2 each year. **Funds Available:** The stipend is $1,000. **Duration:** 1 year.
Eligibility Requirements: This program is open to full-time juniors and seniors at public universities in Mississippi who are preparing to enter the field of public works. Applicants must have graduated from a high school in Mississippi. Eligible majors include civil engineering, electrical engineering, environmental engineering, public administration, biology, or chemistry. Selection is based on merit and need. **Deadline for Receipt:** April of each year. **Additional Information:** This program, established in 2000, is sponsored by the Mississippi chapter of the American Public Works Association (APWA).

3806 ■ CONFERENCE OF MINORITY TRANSPORTATION OFFICIALS-NEW JERSEY CHAPTER

Attn: Scholarship Committee
P.O. Box 22968
Newark, NJ 07101
E-mail: comtonj@mail.comtonj.org
Web Site: http://www.comtonj.org/scholarshipInfo.asp
To provide financial assistance to college students from New Jersey interested in working on a degree in a field related to transportation.
Title of Award: COMTO NJ Scholarships **Area, Field, or Subject:** Environmental conservation; Environmental science; Protective services; Public administration; Transportation; Urban affairs/design/planning **Level of Education for which Award is Granted:** Undergraduate **Number Awarded:** 4 each year: 1 at $1,000 and 3 at $500. **Funds Available:** Stipends are $1,000 or $500. **Duration:** 1 year.
Eligibility Requirements: This program is open to students entering or attending colleges and universities in New Jersey to major in a field related to transportation (e.g., environmental disciplines, public service, safety, transportation, urban planning). Applicants must have a GPA of 3.0 or higher. Along with their application, they must submit a 500-word essay on why they chose a career in transportation. Selection is based on the essay, academic achievement, extracurricular and community activities, and letters of recommendation. **Deadline for Receipt:** April of each year.

Additional Information: The sponsor is the New Jersey chapter of the Conference of Minority Transportation Officials (COMTO). The national organization was founded in 1971 to promote, strengthen, and expand the roles of minorities in all aspects of transportation. This program includes the Lewis R. Rosser Scholarship, the Paul Smith Scholarship, and the Garrett Morgan Scholarship. Recipients must attend the COMTO NJ Scholarship Gala to accept the award.

3807 ■ DEPARTMENT OF TRANSPORTATION

Federal Highway Administration
Attn: National Highway Institute, HNHI-20
4600 North Fairfax Drive, Suite 800
Arlington, VA 22203-1553
Tel: (703)235-0538
Fax: (703)235-0593
E-mail: transportationedu@fhwa.dot.gov
Web Site: http://www.nhi.fhwa.dot.gov/ddetfp.asp
To enable students to participate in research activities at facilities of the U.S. Department of Transportation (DOT) Federal Highway Administration in the Washington, D.C. area.
Title of Award: Eisenhower Grants for Research Fellowships **Area, Field, or Subject:** Chemistry; Economics; Engineering; Engineering, Civil; Geography; Information science and technology; Materials research/science; Operations research; Physics; Public administration; Statistics; Technology; Transportation; Urban affairs/design/planning **Level of Education for which Award is Granted:** Four Year College, Graduate **Number Awarded:** Varies each year; recently, 9 students participated in this program. **Funds Available:** Fellows receive full tuition and fees that relate to the academic credits for the approved research project and a monthly stipend of $1,450 for college seniors, $1,700 for master's students, or $2,000 for doctoral students. An allowance for travel to and from the DOT facility where the research is conducted is also provided, but selectees are responsible for their own housing accommodations. Faculty advisors are allowed 1 site review on projects over 6 months and 2 site reviews on projects over 9 months; travel and per diem are provided for those site reviews. **Duration:** Tenure is normally 3, 6, 9, or 12 months. **Eligibility Requirements:** This program is open to 1) students in their junior year of a baccalaureate program who will complete their junior year before being awarded a fellowship; 2) students in their senior year of a baccalaureate program; and 3) students who have completed their baccalaureate degree and are enrolled in a program leading to a master's, Ph.D., or equivalent degree. Applicants must be U.S. citizens enrolled in an accredited U.S. institution of higher education working on a degree full time and planning to enter the transportation profession after completing their higher education. They select 1 or more projects from a current list of research projects underway at various DOT facilities; the research will be conducted with academic supervision provided by a faculty advisor from their home university (which grants academic credit for the research project) and with technical direction provided by the DOT staff. Specific requirements for the target projects vary; most require engineering backgrounds, but others involve transportation planning, information management, public administration, physics, materials science, statistical analysis, operations research, chemistry, economics, technology transfer, urban studies, geography, and urban and regional planning. The DOT encourages students at Historically Black Colleges and Universities (HBCUs) and Hispanic Serving Institutions (HSIs) to apply for these grants. Selection is based on match of the student's qualifications with the proposed research project (including the student's ability to accomplish the project in the available time), recommendation letters regarding the nominee's qualifications to conduct the research, academic records (including class standing, GPA, and transcripts), and transportation work experience (if any) including the employer's endorsement. **Deadline for Receipt:** February of each year.

3808 ■ ELECTRONIC DOCUMENT SYSTEMS FOUNDATION

Attn: EDSF Scholarship Awards
24238 Hawthorne Boulevard
Torrance, CA 90505-6505
Tel: (310)541-1481
Fax: (310)541-4803
Web Site: http://www.edsf.org/scholarships.cfm

To provide financial assistance to upper-division and graduate students interested in working with electronic documents as a career.
Title of Award: David Hoods Memorial Scholarship **Area, Field, or Subject:** Computer and information sciences; Graphic art and design; Internet design and development; Marketing and distribution; Printing trades and industries; Public relations; Telecommunications systems **Level of Education for which Award is Granted:** Four Year College, Graduate **Number Awarded:** 1 each year. **Funds Available:** The stipend is $2,000. **Duration:** 1 year.
Eligibility Requirements: This program is open to full-time juniors, seniors, and graduate students who demonstrate a strong interest in working with electronic documents as a career (including graphic communications, document management, document content, and/or document distribution). Special consideration is given to students interested in marketing and public relations. Applicants must submit a statement of their career goals in the field of document communications, an essay on a topic related to their view of the future of the document management and production industry, a list of current professional and college extracurricular activities and achievements, college transcripts (GPA of 3.0 or higher), samples of their creative work, and 2 letters of recommendation. Financial need is not considered. **Deadline for Receipt:** May of each year.

3809 ■ ENVIRONMENTAL PROTECTION AGENCY

Attn: National Center for Environmental Research
Ariel Rios Building - 3500
1200 Pennsylvania Avenue, N.W.
Washington, DC 20460
Tel: (202)343-9862
E-mail: barnwell.thomas@epa.gov
Web Site: http://es.epa.gov/ncer/P3
To provide funding to teams of undergraduate and graduate students interested in conducting a research project related to environmental sustainability.
Title of Award: P3 Award Program **Area, Field, or Subject:** Agricultural sciences; Biological and clinical sciences; Chemistry; Energy-related areas; Environmental conservation; Environmental science; Information science and technology; Public health; Transportation; Water resources **Level of Education for which Award is Granted:** Graduate, Undergraduate **Number Awarded:** Varies each year. Recently, 42 Phase I grants were awarded, of which 10 were selected to receive Phase II grants. **Funds Available:** Phase I grants are $10,000. Phase II grants are $75,000. Grants cover all direct and indirect costs; cost-sharing is not required. **Duration:** 1 year for Phase I and 1 additional year for Phase II. **Eligibility Requirements:** This competition is open to teams of undergraduate and graduate students at U.S. colleges and universities who are interested in conducting a research project related to the 3 components of sustainability: people, prosperity, and the planet. Projects must address the causes, effects, extent, prevention, reduction, or elimination of air, water, or solid and hazardous waste pollution. Categories include agriculture (e.g., irrigation practices, reduction or elimination of pesticides); materials and chemicals (e.g., materials conservation, green engineering, green chemistry, biotechnology, recovery and reuse of materials); energy (e.g., reduction in air emissions, energy conservation); information technology (e.g., delivery of and access to environmental performance, technical, educational, or public health information related environmental decision making); water (e.g., quality, quantity, conservation, availability, and access); or the built environment (e.g., environmental benefits through innovative green buildings, transportation, and mobility strategies, and smart growth as it results in reduced vehicle miles traveled or reduces storm water runoff). Student teams, with a faculty advisor (who serves as the principal investigator on the grant), submit designs for Phase I of the competition. Selection of grantees is based on the extent to which the proposed project achieves the outcomes of minimizing the use and generation of hazardous substances; utilizes resources and energy effectively and efficiently; and advances the goals of economic competitiveness, human health, and environmental protection for societal benefit. Recipients of Phase I grants are then invited to apply for additional funding through a Phase I grant. **Deadline for Receipt:** February of each year. **Additional Information:** This program began in 2004. It is supported by a large number of organizations from industry, the nonprofit sector, and the federal government.

3810.■ FLORIDA STATE ASSOCIATION OF SUPERVISORS OF ELECTIONS

c/o David H. Stafford
Escambia County Supervisor of Elections
213 Palafox Place, Suite 4
P.O. Box 12601
Pensacola, FL 32591-2601
Tel: (850)595-3900
Fax: (850)595-3914
E-mail: soe@escambiavotes.com
Web Site: http://www.gotvflorida.com/scholarship.htm

To provide financial assistance to Florida residents who are interested in majoring in business, political science, or communications in college.

Title of Award: Florida State Association of Supervisors of Elections Scholarship **Area, Field, or Subject:** Business administration; Communications; Journalism; Political science; Public administration **Level of Education for which Award is Granted:** Four Year College **Number Awarded:** 3 each year. **Funds Available:** The stipend is $1,200 per year. **Duration:** 1 year; recipients may reapply.

Eligibility Requirements: This program is open to residents of Florida who have completed 2 years of undergraduate study and are enrolled or planning to enroll full time at a 4-year college or university in the state. Applicants must be majoring in business administration, political science/public administration, or journalism/mass communications and have a GPA of 2.0 or higher. They must be U.S. citizens registered to vote in Florida. Along with their application, they must submit 2 letters of recommendation, a resume of high school and/or college activities, and documentation of financial need. Applications should be submitted to the student's county Supervisor of Elections. Each county's supervisor will review the applications received and select 1 finalist to be sent to the association for consideration. **Deadline for Receipt:** March of each year.

Additional Information: This program includes the following named scholarships: the Joe Oldmixon Scholarship, the Jimmy Whitehouse Scholarship, and the Dorothy Walker Ruggles Scholarship.

3811 ■ INDIAN HEALTH SERVICE

Attn: Scholarship Program
801 Thompson Avenue, Suite 120
Rockville, MD 20852
Tel: (301)443-6197
Fax: (301)443-6048
E-mail: bmiller@na.ihs.gov
Web Site: http://www.ihs.gov

To provide loans-for-service to American Indian and Alaska Native students enrolled in health professions and allied health professions programs.

Title of Award: Health Professions Scholarship Program **Area, Field, or Subject:** Counseling/Guidance; Dental hygiene; Dentistry; Health care services; Medical assisting; Medical technology; Medicine; Medicine, Osteopathic; Nursing; Nutrition; Optometry; Pharmaceutical sciences; Physical therapy; Podiatry; Psychology; Public health; Radiology; Respiratory therapy; Social work; **Level of Education for which Award is Granted:** Graduate, Undergraduate **Number Awarded:** Varies each year. **Funds Available:** Awards provide a payment directly to the school for tuition and required fees; a stipend for living expenses of approximately $1,160 per month for 12 months; a lump sum to cover the costs of books, travel, and other necessary educational expenses; and up to $400 for approved tutorial costs. Upon completion of their program of study, recipients are required to provide payback service of 1 year for each year of scholarship support at the Indian Health Service, a tribal health programs, an urban Indian health program, or in private practice in a designated health professional shortage area serving a substantial number of Indians. Recipients who fail to complete their service obligation must repay all funds received (although no interest is charged). **Duration:** 1 year; may be renewed for up to 3 additional years.

Eligibility Requirements: This program is open to American Indians and Alaska Natives who are at least high school graduates and enrolled in a full-time study program leading to a degree in a health-related professions school within the United States. Priority is given to upper-division and graduate students. Qualifying fields of study include chemical dependency counseling (bachelor's or master's degree), clinical psychology (Ph.D. only), coding specialist (certificate), counseling psychology (Ph.D. only), dental hygiene (B.S.), dentistry (D.D.S.), diagnostic radiology technology

(certificate, associate, or B.S.), dietitian (B.S.), civil or environmental engineering (B.S.), environmental health (B.S.), health care administration (B.S. or M.S.), health education (B.S. or M.S.), health records (R.H.I.T. or R.H.I.A.), injury prevention specialist (certificate), medical technology (B.S.), allopathic and osteopathic medicine, nursing (A.D.N., B.S.N., or C.R.N.A), optometry, pharmacy (B.S. or Pharm.D.), physician assistant (B.S.), physical therapy (M.S. or D.P.T.), podiatry (D.P.M.), public health (M.P.H. only), public health nutrition (master's only), social work (master's only), respiratory therapy (associate), and ultrasonography. **Deadline for Receipt:** February of each year.

3812 ■ INTERNATIONAL FOODSERVICE EDITORIAL COUNCIL

P.O. Box 491
Hyde Park, NY 12538
Tel: (845)229-6973
Fax: (845)229-6993
E-mail: ifec@aol.com
Web Site: http://www.ifec-is-us.com

To provide financial assistance to undergraduate or graduate students who are interested in preparing for a career in communications in the food service industry.

Title of Award: IFEC Scholarships **Area, Field, or Subject:** Communications; Creative writing; Culinary arts; English language and literature; Food science and technology; Food service careers; Graphic art and design; Hotel, institutional, and restaurant management; Journalism; Management; Marketing and distribution; Nutrition; Photography; Photography, Journalistic; Public relations **Level of Education for which Award is Granted:** Master's, Undergraduate **Number Awarded:** Varies each year; recently, 5 of these scholarships were awarded. **Funds Available:** The stipend is $3,000 per year. **Duration:** 1 year.

Eligibility Requirements: This program is open to currently-enrolled college students who are working on an associate, bachelor's, or master's degree. They must be enrolled full time and planning on a career in editorial, public relations, photography, food styling, or a related aspect of communications in the food service industry. The following food service majors are considered appropriate for this program: culinary arts; hospitality management; hotel, restaurant, and institutional management; dietetics; food science and technology; and nutrition. Applicable communications areas include journalism, English, mass communications, public relations, marketing, broadcast journalism, creative writing, graphic arts, and photography. Selection is based on academic record, character references, and demonstrated financial need. **Deadline for Receipt:** March of each year.

3813 ■ KOSTER INSURANCE AGENCY

Attn: Scholarship
500 Victory Road
Quincy, MA 02171
Tel: (617)770-9889
Free: 800-457-5599
Fax: (617)479-0860
E-mail: Scholarship@kosterins.com
Web Site: http://www.kosterweb.com/about/scholarship_main.php

To provide financial assistance to undergraduate students working on a degree in a health-related field.

Title of Award: Koster Insurance Health Careers Scholarship Program **Area, Field, or Subject:** Biological and clinical sciences; Chemistry; Dentistry; Health care services; Nursing; Occupational therapy; Optometry; Pharmaceutical sciences; Physical therapy; Physiology; Public health; Social work **Level of Education for which Award is Granted:** Undergraduate **Number Awarded:** 5 each year. **Funds Available:** The stipend is $3,000 per year. **Duration:** 1 year; may be renewed 1 additional year.

Eligibility Requirements: This program is open to full-time undergraduates entering their second-to-last or final year of study in a health-related field, including (but not limited to) pre-medicine, nursing, public and community health, physical therapy, occupational therapy, pharmacy, biology, chemistry, physiology, social work, dentistry, and optometry. Applicants must have a GPA of 3.0 or higher and be able to demonstrate financial need. Along with their application, they must submit a 1-page essay describing their personal goals, including their reasons for preparing for a career in health care. Selection is based on motivation to pursue a career in health care, academic excellence, dedication to community service, and financial need. **Deadline for Receipt:** April of each year. **Additional Information:** This program began in 2001.

3814 ■ PAPA OLA LOKAHI, INC.
Attn: Native Hawaiian Health Scholarship Program
345 Queen Street, Suite 706
Honolulu, HI 96813
Tel: (808)585-8944
Fax: (808)585-8081
E-mail: nhhsp@hawaii.rr.com
Web Site: http://www.nhhsp.org
To provide scholarship/loans to Native Hawaiians for training in the health professions in exchange for service in a federally-designated health professional shortage area (HPSA) or other facility for Native Hawaiians.
Title of Award: Native Hawaiian Health Scholarship Program **Area, Field, or Subject:** Dental hygiene; Dentistry; Family/Marital therapy; Health care services; Medical assisting; Medicine; Medicine, Osteopathic; Midwifery; Nursing; Nursing, Psychiatric; Psychiatry; Psychology; Public health **Level of Education for which Award is Granted:** Graduate, Undergraduate **Number Awarded:** Varies each year, depending upon the funding available. Since the program began, 151 scholars have received support. **Funds Available:** Full coverage of tuition and fees is paid directly to the health professional school. A stipend, current set at $1,157 per month, is paid directly to the scholar. This is a scholarship/loan program. Participants are obligated to provide full-time clinical primary health care services to populations in 1) a Native Hawaiian Health Care System, or 2) an HPSA in Hawaii, medically underserved area (MUA), or another area or facility in Hawaii designated by the U.S. Department of Health and Human Services. Participants owe 1 year of service in the National Health Service Corps for each full or partial year of support received under this program. The minimum service obligation is 2 years.
Duration: 1 year; may be renewed for up to 3 additional years.
Eligibility Requirements: Applicants must be Native Hawaiians training in allopathic or osteopathic medicine, dentistry, clinical psychology, registered nursing, nurse midwifery, psychiatric nursing, public health/community nursing, social work, dental hygiene, physician assistant, public health, marriage and family therapy, or primary care nurse practitioner. They may be studying in any state. Recipients must agree to serve in a designated health-care facility in Hawaii upon completion of training. First priority is given to former scholars who have completed their previous service obligation and are seeking another year of support. Second priority is given to applicants who appear to have characteristics that increase the probability they will continue to serve underserved Native Hawaiians after the completion of their service obligations. **Deadline for Receipt:** March of each year. **Additional Information:** This program, which began in 1991, is administered by the U.S. Health Resources and Services Administration, Bureau of Health Professions, through a contract with Papa Ola Lokahi, Inc.

3815 ■ MARYLAND HIGHER EDUCATION COMMISSION
Attn: Office of Student Financial Assistance
839 Bestgate Road, Suite 400
Annapolis, MD 21401-3013
Tel: (410)260-4563
Free: 800-974-1024
Fax: (410)974-5376
E-mail: osfamail@mhec.state.md.us
Web Site: http://www.mhec.state.md.us/financialAid/ProgramDescriptions/prog_WDS.asp
To provide scholarship/loans to Maryland residents interested in a career in public service.
Title of Award: William Donald Schaefer Scholarship Program **Area, Field, or Subject:** General studies/Field of study not specified; Public administration **Level of Education for which Award is Granted:** Graduate, Undergraduate **Number Awarded:** Varies each year. **Funds Available:** The amount of the award is equal to tuition and fees at a Maryland postsecondary institution, to a maximum of $8,550. The total amount of all state awards may not exceed the cost of attendance as determined by the school's financial aid office or $17,800, whichever is less. Within 1 year of graduation, recipients must provide 1 year of public service in Maryland for each year of financial aid received under this program; failure to comply with that service obligation will require them to repay the scholarship money with interest. Public service is defined as employment in

government at any level, public interest organizations, public schools, and nonprofit organizations. **Duration:** 1 year; may be renewed up to 3 additional years provided the recipient continues to meet eligibility requirements.
Eligibility Requirements: This program is open to residents of Maryland who are high school seniors, full-time undergraduates, or full-time graduate students. Applicants must be enrolled or planning to enroll at a 2-year or 4-year Maryland college or university. They may major in any field, but they must enroll in courses of study, training, or other educational activities that are designed to prepare individuals for a career in public service. Financial need is considered. **Deadline for Receipt:** June of each year.

3816 ■ MISSOURI BUSINESS AND PROFESSIONAL WOMEN'S FOUNDATION, INC.
P.O. Box 338
Carthage, MO 64836-0338
Web Site: http://www.bpwmo.org/scholarship.htm
To provide financial assistance to members of the Missouri Federation of Business and Professional Women (BPW Missouri) who are interested in working on a college degree leading to public service.
Title of Award: Judge Hazel Palmer General Scholarship **Area, Field, or Subject:** Public service **Level of Education for which Award is Granted:** Undergraduate **Number Awarded:** 1 each year. **Funds Available:** A stipend is awarded (amount not specified). **Duration:** 1 year.
Eligibility Requirements: This program is open to BPW Missouri members who have been accepted into an accredited program or course of study to work on a degree leading to public service. Along with their application, they must submit brief statements on the following: their achievements and/or specific recognitions in their field of endeavor; professional and/or civic affiliations; present and long-range career goals; how they plan to participate in and contribute to their community upon completion of their program of study; why they feel they would make a good recipient; and any special circumstances that may have influenced their ability to continue or complete their education. They must also demonstrate financial need and U.S. citizenship. **Deadline for Receipt:** January of each year. **Additional Information:** Information is also available from Pat Henderson, Scholarship Committee Chair, P.O. Box 296, Hillsboro, MO 63050, (636) 789-2119.

3817 ■ NATIONAL DAIRY PROMOTION AND RESEARCH BOARD
c/o Dairy Management Inc.
10255 West Higgins Road, Suite 900
Rosemont, IL 60018-5616
Tel: (847)803-2000
Fax: (847)803-2077
E-mail: marykateg@rosedmi.com
Web Site: http://www.dairycheckoff.com/DairyCheckoff/about/scholarship.htm
To provide financial assistance to undergraduate students in fields related to the dairy industry.
Title of Award: NDPRB Undergraduate Scholarship Program **Area, Field, or Subject:** Business administration; Communications; Dairy science; Economics; Education; Food science and technology; Journalism; Marketing and distribution; Nutrition; Public relations **Level of Education for which Award is Granted:** Four Year College **Number Awarded:** 20 each year: the James H. Loper Jr. Memorial Scholarship at $2,500 and 19 other scholarships at $1,500. **Funds Available:** Stipends are $2,500 or $1,500. **Duration:** 1 year; may be renewed.
Eligibility Requirements: This program is open to sophomores, juniors, and seniors enrolled in college and university programs that emphasize dairy. Eligible majors include agricultural education, business, communications and/or public relations, economics, food science, journalism, marketing, and nutrition. Fields related to production (e.g., animal science) are not eligible. Selection is based on academic performance; interest in a career in dairy; involvement in extracurricular activities, especially those relating to dairy; and evidence of leadership ability, initiative, character, and integrity. The applicant who is judged most outstanding is awarded the James H. Loper Jr. Memorial Scholarship. **Deadline for**

Receipt: May of each year. **Additional Information:** Dairy Management Inc. manages this program on behalf of the National Dairy Promotion and Research Board (NDPRB).

3818 ■ NATIONAL FIRE PROTECTION ASSOCIATION

Attn: Fire Safety Educational Memorial Fund Committee
1 Batterymarch Park
Quincy, MA 02169-7471
Tel: (617)984-7244
Fax: (617)984-7222
E-mail: cellis@nfpa.org
Web Site: http://www.nfpa.org
To provide financial assistance to undergraduate and graduate students enrolled in fire service or public administration programs.
Title of Award: George D. Miller Scholarship **Area, Field, or Subject:** Fires and fire prevention; Public administration **Level of Education for which Award is Granted:** Graduate, Undergraduate **Number Awarded:** 1 each year. **Funds Available:** The stipend is at least $5,000. **Duration:** 1 year.
Eligibility Requirements: Colleges and universities in the United States and Canada are invited to nominate up to 2 undergraduate or graduate students enrolled in a fire service or public administration program. Nominees must exhibit scholastic achievement, leadership qualities, concern for others (volunteerism), and intent to prepare for a career in fire service or public administration **Deadline for Receipt:** March of each year. **Additional Information:** This fund was established in 2001.

3819 ■ NATIONAL NAVAL OFFICERS ASSOCIATION-WASHINGTON, D.C. CHAPTER

Attn: Scholarship Program
2701 Park Center Drive, B704
Alexandria, VA 22302
E-mail: williams.stephen@hq.navy.mil
Web Site: http://www.dcnnoa.org
To provide financial assistance to African American high school seniors from the Washington, D.C. area who are interested in majoring in designated fields in college.
Title of Award: DCNNOA/Advanced Concepts and Technologies Scholarship **Area, Field, or Subject:** Computer and information sciences; Political science; Public administration **Level of Education for which Award is Granted:** Undergraduate **Number Awarded:** 1 each year. **Funds Available:** The stipend is $1,000 per year. **Duration:** 1 year; nonrenewable.
Eligibility Requirements: This program is open to African American seniors at high schools in the Washington, D.C. metropolitan area who plan to enroll full time at an accredited 2-year or 4-year college or university. Applicants must be planning to major in governmental affairs, political science, or computer science. They must have a GPA of 2.5 or higher and be U.S. citizens or permanent residents. Selection is based on academic achievement, community involvement, interpersonal and leadership skills, creativity, drive, and maturity. **Deadline for Receipt:** April of each year. **Additional Information:** Recipients are not required to join or affiliate with the military in any way. This program is sponsored by Advanced Concepts and Technologies, Inc.

3820 ■ NEW JERSEY HOSPITAL ASSOCIATION

Attn: Health Research and Educational Trust
760 Alexander Road
P.O. Box 1
Princeton, NJ 08543-0001
Tel: (609)275-4224
Fax: (609)452-8097
Web Site: http://www.njha.com/hret/scholarship.aspx
To provide financial assistance to New Jersey residents working on an undergraduate or graduate degree in a health-related field.
Title of Award: Health Research and Educational Trust Scholarships **Area, Field, or Subject:** Health care services; Nursing; Public administration **Level of Education for which Award is Granted:** Graduate, Undergraduate **Number Awarded:** Varies each year; recently, 2 of these scholarships were awarded. **Funds Available:** The stipend is $2,000. **Duration:** 1 year.
Eligibility Requirements: This program is open to residents of New Jersey enrolled in an upper-division or graduate program in hospital or

health care administration, public administration, nursing, or other allied health profession. Applicants must have a GPA of 3.0 or higher and be able to demonstrate financial need. Along with their application, they must submit a 2-page essay (on which 50% of the selection is based) describing their academic plans for the future. Minorities and women are especially encouraged to apply. **Deadline for Receipt:** July of each year. **Additional Information:** This program began in 1983.

3821 ■ NEW YORK STATE LEGION PRESS ASSOCIATION

c/o Scholarship Chairman
American Legion (NYSLPA)
P.O. Box 650
East Aurora, NY 14052
To provide financial assistance to the children of members of the American Legion or American Legion Auxiliary in New York who are interested in careers in communications.
Title of Award: New York State Legion Press Association Scholarship **Area, Field, or Subject:** Communications; Graphic art and design; Journalism; Public relations **Level of Education for which Award is Granted:** Four Year College **Number Awarded:** 1 each year. **Funds Available:** The stipend is $1,000. **Duration:** 1 year.
Eligibility Requirements: This program is open to New York residents who are the children of members of the American Legion or American Legion Auxiliary, or members of the Sons of the American Legion, or junior members of the American Legion Auxiliary, or graduates of the New York Boys State or Girls State. Applicants must be entering or attending an accredited 4-year college or university, working on a degree in communications (including public relations, journalism, reprographics, newspaper design or management, or other related fields acceptable to the scholarship committee). Along with their application, they must submit a 500-word essay on why they chose the field of communications as a future vocation. Financial need and class standing are not considered. **Deadline for Receipt:** May of each year.

3822 ■ NORTH CAROLINA STATE EDUCATION ASSISTANCE AUTHORITY

Attn: Scholarship and Grant Services
10 T.W. Alexander Drive
P.O. Box 14223
Research Triangle Park, NC 27709-4223
Tel: (919)549-8614
Free: 800-700-1775
Fax: (919)549-8481
E-mail: information@ncseaa.edu
Web Site: http://www.ncseaa.edu
To provide loans and loans-for-service to North Carolina residents who are interested in preparing for a career in health, science, or mathematics.
Title of Award: North Carolina Student Loan Program for Health, Science, and Mathematics **Area, Field, or Subject:** Allied health; Dentistry; Medicine; Nursing; Optometry; Public health; Social work **Level of Education for which Award is Granted:** Graduate, Undergraduate **Number Awarded:** Varies each year; recently, a total of 497 students were receiving $3,238,569 in support through this program. **Funds Available:** Maximum loans are $3,000 per year for associate degree and certificate programs, $5,000 per year for baccalaureate degree/certificate programs, $6,500 per year for master's degree programs, or $8,500 per year for health/professional doctoral programs. The maximum amount that any student can borrow through this program is $58,000. The interest rate is 4% while the borrowers are attending school and from 10 to 15% after they leave school. Cash repayments must begin 90 days or less after completion of course work and training. Under specified conditions, certain loan recipients in qualifying disciplines may have their loans canceled through service in North Carolina. **Duration:** 1 year; renewable for 1 additional year for diploma, associate, certificate, and master's degree programs, for 2 additional years for baccalaureate degree programs, or for 3 additional years for doctoral programs.
Eligibility Requirements: North Carolina residents are eligible to apply for this program if they have been accepted as full-time students in an accredited associate, baccalaureate, master's, or doctoral program leading to a degree in 1 of the following areas: allied health (including audiology/communications assistant, cytotechnology, dental hygiene, diagnostic medical sonographer, imaging technologist, medical technology, nuclear medicine technologist, occupational therapy/assistant, physi-

cian assistant, physical therapy/assistant, radiation therapist, radiography, respiratory therapy, and speech language pathology); clinical psychology (Ph.D. level only); dentistry; dietetics and nutrition (graduate level only); mathematics education; medicine (including chiropractic medicine, emergency medicine, family medicine, geriatrics, internal medicine, obstetrics and gynecology, osteopathic medicine, pediatrics, podiatry, primary care medicine, and psychiatry); nursing (including anesthetist, family nurse practitioner, nursing administration, general nursing, and midwifery); optometry; pharmacy; public health (graduate level only); science education (including biology, chemistry, communications and technologies, computer and information sciences, engineering, and physical science); social work (graduate level only); and veterinary medicine. U.S. citizenship is required. Selection is based on academic progress, financial ability of sureties to repay all loans and accrued interest in case of applicant's default, applicant's willingness to work in underserved areas of the state or in disciplines for which there is a shortage of professionals, applicant's willingness to comply with all program regulations, and financial need. **Deadline for Receipt:** May of each year. **Additional Information:** Recipients may attend a North Carolina postsecondary institution or an eligible out-of-state institution. This program was formerly known as the North Carolina Medical Student Loan Program.

3823 ■ OAK RIDGE INSTITUTE FOR SCIENCE AND EDUCATION

Attn: Science and Engineering Education
P.O. Box 117
Oak Ridge, TN 37831-0117
Tel: (865)576-8239
Fax: (865)241-5219
E-mail: igrid.gregory@orau.gov
Web Site: http://www.orau.gov/orise.htm

To provide financial assistance and summer research experience to undergraduate students who are working on a degree in a field of interest to the Department of Homeland Security (DHS).

Title of Award: Department of Homeland Security Undergraduate Scholarships **Area, Field, or Subject:** Agricultural sciences; Biological and clinical sciences; Communications; Computer and information sciences; Engineering; Information science and technology; Mathematics and mathematical sciences; Physical sciences; Psychology; Public administration; Religion; Social sciences; Writing **Level of Education for which Award is Granted:** Undergraduate **Number Awarded:** Approximately 50 each year. **Funds Available:** This program provides a stipend of $1,000 per month during the academic year and $5,000 for the internship plus full payment of tuition and mandatory fees. **Duration:** 2 academic years plus 10 weeks during the intervening summer.

Eligibility Requirements: This program is open to 1) full-time students who are in their second year of college attendance as of the application deadline; and 2) part-time students who have completed at least 45 but no more than 60 semester hours as of the application deadline. Applicants must be majoring in the agricultural sciences, biological and life sciences, computer and information sciences, engineering, mathematics, physical sciences, psychology, social sciences, or selected humanities (religious studies, cultural studies, public policy, advocacy, communications, or science writing). They must have a GPA of 3.3 or higher. Along with their application, they must submit 2 statements on 1) their educational and professional goals, the kinds of research they are interested in conducting, specific questions that interest them, and how they became interested in them; and 2) how they think their interests, talents, and initiative would contribute to make the homeland safer and secure. Selection is based on those statements, academic record, references, and SAT or ACT scores. As part of their program, they must be interested in participating in summer research and development activities at a DHS-designated facility. U.S. citizenship is required. **Deadline for Receipt:** January of each year. **Additional Information:** This program, established in 2003, is funded by DHS and administered by Oak Ridge Institute for Science and Education (ORISE). Recipients must enroll full time.

3824 ■ OKLAHOMA STATE REGENTS FOR HIGHER EDUCATION

Attn: Director of Scholarship and Grant Programs
655 Research Parkway, Suite 200
P.O. Box 108850
Oklahoma City, OK 73101-8850
Tel: (405)225-9239
Free: 800-858-1840

Fax: (405)225-9230
E-mail: studentinfo@osrhe.edu
Web Site: http://www.okhighered.org/student-center/financial-aid/nigh.shtml

To provide financial assistance for college to residents in Oklahoma who are interested in a career in public service.

Title of Award: George and Donna Nigh Public Service Scholarship **Area, Field, or Subject:** Public administration **Level of Education for which Award is Granted:** Undergraduate **Number Awarded:** Varies each year. **Funds Available:** The stipend is $1,000 per year. **Duration:** 1 year; nonrenewable.

Eligibility Requirements: This program is open to residents of Oklahoma who are enrolled full time in an undergraduate program at a public or private college or university in the state. Applicants must be enrolled in a degree program leading to a career in public service (as determined by the institution). Selection is based on academic achievement, including GPA, class rank, national awards, scholastic achievement, honors, teachers' recommendations, and participation in extracurricular activities. Each participating college or university may nominate 1 student each year. **Additional Information:** This program, established in 1999, operates in conjunction with the George and Donna Nigh Institute, Downtown College Consortium, 120 North Robinson, Suite 500 C, Oklahoma City, OK 73102, (405) 319-3085, E-mail: mbigger@okc.cc.ok.us. Scholarship recipients participate in seminars on public service offered by the Institute.

3825 ■ OREGON STUDENT ASSISTANCE COMMISSION

Attn: Grants and Scholarships Division
1500 Valley River Drive, Suite 100
Eugene, OR 97401-2146
Tel: (541)687-7395
Free: 800-452-8807
Fax: (541)687-7419
E-mail: awardinfo@mercury.osac.state.or.us
Web Site: http://www.osac.state.or.us

To provide financial assistance for college or graduate school to residents of Oregon who are interested in preparing for a public health career.

Title of Award: Lawrence R. Foster Memorial Scholarship **Area, Field, or Subject:** Medical assisting; Medical technology; Nursing; Public health **Level of Education for which Award is Granted:** Four Year College, Graduate **Number Awarded:** Varies each year; recently, 6 of these scholarships were awarded. **Funds Available:** Stipend amounts vary; recently, they were at least $4,167. **Duration:** 1 year.

Eligibility Requirements: This program is open to residents of Oregon who are attending a 4-year college or university in any state to prepare for a career in public health (not private practice). First preference is given to applicants who are either working in public health or enrolled as graduate students in that field. Second preference is given to undergraduates entering the junior or senior year of a health program, including nursing, medical technology, and physician assistant. A general preference is given to applicants from diverse cultures. Along with their application, they must submit a 1- to 2-page essay on their interest, experience, and future plans for a public health career **Deadline for Receipt:** February of each year. **Additional Information:** This program is administered by the Oregon Student Assistance Commission (OSAC) with funds provided by the Oregon Community Foundation, 1221 S.W. Yamhill, Suite 100, Portland, OR 97205, (503) 227-6846, Fax: (503) 274-7771.

3826 ■ PACIFICARE FOUNDATION

3100 Lake Center Drive
P.O. Box 25186
Santa Ana, CA 92799
Tel: (714)825-5233
Web Site: http://www.pacificare.com

To provide financial assistance to Latino high school seniors in designated states planning to major in a health care field in college.

Title of Award: PacifiCare Latino Health Scholars Program **Area, Field, or Subject:** Health care services; Medical technology; Medicine; Nursing; Pharmaceutical sciences; Psychology; Public health **Level of Education for which Award is Granted:** Undergraduate **Number Awarded:** Approximately 50 each year. **Funds Available:** The stipend is $2,000. **Duration:** 1 year.

Eligibility Requirements: This program is open to seniors graduating from high schools in Arizona, California, Colorado, Nevada, Oklahoma,

Oregon, Texas, and Washington. Applicants must have a GPA of 3.0 or higher, be fluent in Spanish, and have been accepted as a full-time student at a university, community college, or accredited technical college. Their proposed field of study must relate to health care, including (but not limited to) nursing, medical interpretation, health claims examiner, health information technology programs, pharmacy technician, public health, psychology, or pre-medical studies. Along with their application, they must submit a 2-page essay (in both English and Spanish) on their personal and academic accomplishments, community involvement, volunteer and leadership activities, academic plans, and the reason they want a career in the health care field. **Deadline for Receipt:** June of each year. **Additional Information:** This program was established in 2003.

3827 ■ PUBLIC RELATIONS SOCIETY OF AMERICA-PUGET SOUND CHAPTER

c/o Diane Beins
1006 Industry Drive
Seattle, WA 98188-4801
Tel: (206)623-8632
E-mail: prsascholarship@asi-seattle.net
Web Site: http://www.prsapugetsound.org/cayton
To provide financial assistance to minority upper-classmen from Washington who are interested in preparing for a career in public relations.
Title of Award: Horace and Susie Revels Cayton Scholarship **Area, Field, or Subject:** Public relations **Level of Education for which Award is Granted:** Four Year College **Number Awarded:** 1 each year. **Funds Available:** The stipend is $2,500. **Duration:** 1 year.
Eligibility Requirements: This program is open to U.S. citizens who are members of minority groups, defined as African Americans, Asian Americans, Hispanic/Latino Americans, Native Americans, and Pacific Islanders. Applicants must be juniors or seniors attending a college in Washington or Washington students (who graduated from a Washington high school or whose parents live in the state year-round) attending college elsewhere. They must be able to demonstrate aptitude in public relations and related courses, activities, and/or internships. Along with their application, they must submit a description of their career goals and the skills that are most important in general to a public relations career (15 points in the selection process); a description of their activities in communications in class, on campus, in the community, or during internships, including 3 samples of their work (15 points); a statement on the value of public relations to an organization (10 points); a description of any barriers, financial or otherwise, they have encountered in pursuing their academic or personal goals and how they have addressed them (15 points); a discussion of their heritage, and how their cultural background and/or the discrimination they may have experienced has impacted them (15 points); a certified transcript (15 points); and 2 or more letters of recommendation (15 points). **Deadline for Receipt:** March of each year. **Additional Information:** This program was established in 1992.

3828 ■ PUBLIC RELATIONS SOCIETY OF AMERICA-PUGET SOUND CHAPTER

c/o Diane Beins
1006 Industry Drive
Seattle, WA 98188-4801
Tel: (206)623-8632
E-mail: prsascholarship@asi-seattle.net
Web Site: http://www.prsapugetsound.org/heet
To provide financial assistance to upper-classmen in Washington who are interested in preparing for a career in public relations.
Title of Award: Sally Heet Memorial Scholarship **Area, Field, or Subject:** Public relations **Level of Education for which Award is Granted:** Four Year College **Number Awarded:** 1 each year. **Funds Available:** The stipend is $2,500. **Duration:** 1 year.
Eligibility Requirements: This program is open to U.S. citizens who are enrolled as juniors or seniors at colleges and universities in Washington. Applicants must be preparing for a career in public relations. They must be able to demonstrate aptitude in public relations and related courses, activities, and/or internships. Along with their application, they must submit a description of their career goals and the skills that are most important in general to a public relations career (20 points in the selection process); a description of their activities in communications in class, on campus, in the community, or during internships, including 3 samples of

their work (30 points); a statement on the value of public relations to an organization (10 points); a certified transcript (20 points); and 2 or more letters of recommendation (20 points). **Deadline for Receipt:** March of each year. **Additional Information:** This program was established in 1986.

3829 ■ RHODE ISLAND FOUNDATION

Attn: Scholarship Coordinator
One Union Station
Providence, RI 02903
Tel: (401)274-4564
Fax: (401)331-8085
E-mail: libbym@rifoundation.org
Web Site: http://www.rifoundation.org
To provide financial assistance to residents of Rhode Island who are enrolled in college to prepare for a career in advertising.
Title of Award: J.D. Edsal Advertising Scholarship **Area, Field, or Subject:** Advertising; Broadcasting; Filmmaking; Graphic art and design; Marketing and distribution; Public relations; Radio and television **Level of Education for which Award is Granted:** Undergraduate **Number Awarded:** 2 each year. **Funds Available:** The stipend is $1,500. **Duration:** 1 year.
Eligibility Requirements: This program is open to residents of Rhode Island who are enrolled full time as undergraduates at the sophomore level or above. Applicants must be preparing for a career in advertising and majoring in a related field (e.g., broadcast production, graphic design, interactive film, marketing, public relations, television, or video). Along with their application, they must submit an essay (up to 300 words) on the impact they would like to have on the advertising industry. Financial need is also considered in the selection process. **Deadline for Receipt:** April of each year.

3830 ■ SURFRIDER FOUNDATION

Attn: Pratte Scholarship
P.O. Box 6010
San Clemente, CA 92674-6010
Tel: (949)492-8170
Fax: (949)492-8142
E-mail: prattescholarship@surfrider.org
Web Site: http://www.surfrider.org
To provide financial assistance to members of the Surfrider Foundation working on an undergraduate or graduate degree in an environmental field.
Title of Award: Thomas Pratte Memorial Scholarships **Area, Field, or Subject:** Environmental conservation; Environmental science; Marine biology; Natural resources; Oceanography; Public administration; Urban affairs/design/planning **Level of Education for which Award is Granted:** Four Year College, Graduate **Number Awarded:** 3 each year: 1 for a student at each academic level. **Funds Available:** The stipend is $2,000 for an undergraduate, $3,000 for a master's degree student, and $5,000 for a doctoral student. **Duration:** 1 year.
Eligibility Requirements: This program is open to members of the foundation working on an undergraduate, master's, or doctoral degree in a field consistent with the foundation's mission, including (but not limited to) oceanography, marine affairs, environmental sciences, public policy, community planning, or natural resources. Applicants must be enrolled at an accredited college or university in the United States or Puerto Rico as an upper-division or graduate student. Undergraduates must have a GPA of 3.4 or higher and graduate students 3.6 or higher. Along with their application, they must submit 1) a personal statement describing their career goals, volunteer activities, work, or summer plans as they pertain to the coastal environmental issues relevant to the foundation and its mission; and 2) a description of their current research and how it relates to the foundation's stated mission and environmental programs. Financial need is not considered in the selection process. **Deadline for Receipt:** March of each year. **Additional Information:** This foundation, established in 1984 by a group of surfers, is a nonprofit environmental grassroots

organization dedicated to the protection and preservation of the world's waves, oceans, and beaches. It currently has 50,000 members with 60 chapters in 22 states.

3831 ■ TEXAS FEDERATION OF BUSINESS AND PROFESSIONAL WOMEN'S FOUNDATION, INC.

Attn: TFBPW Foundation
803 Forest Ridge Drive, Suite 207
Bedford, TX 76022
Tel: (817)283-0862
Fax: (817)283-0872
E-mail: bpwtx@swbell.net
Web Site: http://www.bpwtx.org/foundation.asp
To provide financial assistance to women in Texas who are preparing to enter selected professions.
Title of Award: Hermine Dalkowitz Tobolowsky Scholarship **Area, Field, or Subject:** History; Law; Political science; Public administration; Women's studies **Level of Education for which Award is Granted:** Graduate, Undergraduate **Number Awarded:** 1 or more each year. **Funds Available:** A stipend is awarded (amount not specified). **Duration:** 1 year.
Eligibility Requirements: This program is open to women in Texas who are interested in attending school to prepare for a career in law, public service, government, political science, or women's history. Applicants must have completed at least 2 semesters of study at an accredited college or university in Texas, have a GPA of 3.0 or higher, and be U.S. citizens. Selection is based on academic achievement and financial need. **Deadline for Receipt:** April of each year. **Additional Information:** This program was established in 1995.

3832 ■ TEXAS HIGHER EDUCATION COORDINATING BOARD

Attn: Hinson-Hazlewood College Student Loan Program
1200 East Anderson Lane
P.O. Box 12788, Capitol Station
Austin, TX 78711-2788
Tel: (512)427-6340
Free: 800-242-3062
Fax: (512)427-6423
E-mail: loaninfo@thecb.state.tx.us
Web Site: http://www.hhloans.com
To provide educational loans to students in Texas in health-related degree programs.
Title of Award: Hinson-Hazlewood Health Education Loan Program **Area, Field, or Subject:** Dentistry; Health care services; Medicine; Medicine, Osteopathic; Nursing; Optometry; Pharmaceutical sciences; Podiatry; Public health; Veterinary science and medicine **Level of Education for which Award is Granted:** Four Year College, Graduate **Number Awarded:** Varies each year. **Funds Available:** The maximum annual loan is $12,500 for pharmacy, nursing, allied health, and public health students; or $20,000 for medicine, dentistry, optometry, osteopathy, podiatry, or veterinary medicine students. The origination fee is 3%. After a grace period of 9 months, repayment must be completed within 25 years at a minimum monthly payment of $50. The current interest rate is 5.25% which begins to accrue immediately, even while the student is in school. **Duration:** 1 year; may be renewed up to 3 additional years. The maximum total loan is $50,000 for pharmacy, nursing, allied health, and public health students or $80,000 for medicine, dentistry, optometry, osteopathy, podiatry, or veterinary medicine students.
Eligibility Requirements: This program is open to students who qualify as Texas residents and meet the academic requirements of a public or private college or university in the state. Applicants must be enrolled at least half time in a course of study leading to 1) a doctoral degree in medicine, dentistry, optometry, osteopathy, podiatry, or veterinary medicine; 2) a bachelor's or master's degree in pharmacy; 3) a graduate or equivalent degree in public health; or 4) an associate, bachelor's, or graduate degree in nursing or allied health fields. They must be able to demonstrate financial need and enroll full time. U.S. citizenship is required. **Additional Information:** Applications must be submitted through the financial aid office at the college or university attended. This program is part of the Hinton-Hazelwood College Student Loan Program (HHCSLP).

3833 ■ HARRY S. TRUMAN SCHOLARSHIP FOUNDATION

Attn: Executive Secretary
712 Jackson Place, N.W.
Washington, DC 20006
Tel: (202)395-4831
Fax: (202)395-6995
E-mail: office@truman.gov
Web Site: http://www.truman.gov
To provide grants-for-service for graduate school to current college juniors who are interested in preparing for a career in public service.
Title of Award: Harry S. Truman Scholarship Program **Area, Field, or Subject:** Agricultural sciences; Biological and clinical sciences; Economics; Education; Engineering; Environmental conservation; Environmental science; History; International affairs and relations; Law; Physical sciences; Political science; Public administration; Public health; Public service; Social sciences; Technology **Level of Education for which Award is Granted:** Four Year College, Graduate **Number Awarded:** 70 to 75 each year: a) 1 "state" scholarship is available to a qualified resident nominee in each of the 50 states, the District of Columbia, Puerto Rico, and the Islands (Guam, the Virgin Islands, American Samoa, and the Commonwealth of the Northern Mariana Islands); and b) up to 25 at-large scholars. **Funds Available:** The program provides up to $30,000, including up to $15,000 for the first year of graduate study and up to $15,000 for the final year of graduate study. **Duration:** Support is provided for the first and last year of graduate study.
Eligibility Requirements: Students must be nominated to be considered for this program. Nominees must be full-time students with junior standing at a 4-year institution, committed to a career in government or public service, in the upper quarter of their class, and U.S. citizens or nationals. Each participating institution may nominate up to 4 candidates (and up to 3 additional students who completed their first 2 years at a community college); community colleges and other 2-year institutions may nominate former students who are enrolled as full-time students with junior-level academic standing at accredited 4-year institutions. Selection is based on extent and quality of community service and government involvement, academic performance, leadership record, suitability of the nominee's proposed program of study for a career in public service, and writing and analytical skills. Priority is given to candidates who plan to enroll in a graduate program that specifically trains them for a career in public service, including government at any level, uniformed services, public interest organizations, nongovernmental research and/or educational organizations, public and private schools, and public service oriented nonprofit organizations. The fields of study may include agriculture, biology, engineering, environmental management, physical and social sciences, and technology policy, as well as such traditional fields as economics, education, government, history, international relations, law, nonprofit management, political science, public administration, public health, and public policy. Interviews are required. **Deadline for Receipt:** February of each year. **Additional Information:** Recipients may attend graduate school in the United States or in foreign countries. Scholars are required to work in public service for 3 of the 7 years following completion of a graduate degree program funded by this program. Scholars who do not meet this service requirement, or who fail to provide timely proof to the foundation of such employment, will be required to repay funds received, along with interest.

3834 ■ MORRIS K. UDALL FOUNDATION

130 South Scott Avenue
Tucson, AZ 85701-1922
Tel: (520)670-5529
Fax: (520)670-5530
Web Site: http://www.udall.gov/scholarship
To provide financial assistance to 1) college sophomores and juniors who intend to prepare for a career in environmental public policy and 2) Native American and Alaska Native students who intend to prepare for a career in health care or tribal public policy.
Title of Award: Morris K. Udall Scholarships **Area, Field, or Subject:** Business administration; Economics; Education; Environmental conservation; Environmental science; Health care services; Native American stud-

ies; Natural resources; Political science; Public administration; Public health; Urban affairs/design/planning **Level of Education for which Award is Granted:** Undergraduate **Number Awarded:** Approximately 80 scholarships and 50 honorable mentions are awarded each year. **Funds Available:** The maximum stipend for scholarship winners is $5,000 per year. Funds are to be used for tuition, fees, books, and room and board. Honorable mention stipends are $350. **Duration:** 1 year; recipients nominated as sophomores may be renominated in their junior year. **Eligibility Requirements:** Each 2-year and 4-year college and university in the United States and its possessions may nominate up to 6 sophomores or juniors from either or both categories of this program: 1) students who intend to prepare for a career in environmental public policy, and 2) Native American and Alaska Native students who intend to prepare for a career in health care or tribal public policy. For the first category, the program seeks future leaders across a wide spectrum of environmental fields, such as policy, engineering, science, education, urban planning and renewal, business, health, justice, and economics. For the second category, the program seeks future Native American and Alaska Native leaders in public and community health care, tribal government, and public policy affecting Native American communities, including land and resource management, economic development, and education. Nominees must be U.S. citizens, nationals, or permanent residents with a GPA of 3.0 or higher. Along with their application, they must submit an 800-word essay discussing a significant public speech, legislative act, or public policy statement by former Congressman Morris K. Udall and its impact on their field of study, interests, and career goals. Selection is based on demonstrated commitment to 1) environmental issues through substantial commitment to and participation in 1 or more of the following: campus activities, research, community service, or public service; or 2) tribal public policy or Native American health through substantial contributions to and participation in 1 or more of the following: campus activities, tribal involvement, community or public service, or research; a course of study and proposed career likely to lead to position where nominee can make significant contributions to the shaping of environmental, tribal public policy, or Native American health care issues, whether through scientific advances, public or political service, or community action; and leadership, character, desire to make a difference, and general well-roundedness. **Deadline for Receipt:** Faculty representatives must submit their nominations by early March of each year.

3835 ■ WATTS CHARITY ASSOCIATION, INC.

6245 Bristol Parkway, Suite 224
Culver City, CA 90230
Tel: (323)671-0394
Fax: (323)778-2613
E-mail: wattscharity@yahoo.com
Web Site: http://4watts.tripod.com/id5.html
To provide financial assistance to upper-division college students interested in health, civil rights, or administration.
Title of Award: Royce R. Watts Sr. Scholarship **Area, Field, or Subject:** Business administration; Civil rights; Health care services; Human rights; Medicine; Public administration **Level of Education for which Award is Granted:** Four Year College **Number Awarded:** 1 each year. **Funds Available:** A stipend is awarded (amount not specified). **Duration:** 1 year.
Eligibility Requirements: This program is open to U.S. citizens of African American descent who are enrolled full time as a college or university junior. Applicants must have an interest in health and pre-medicine, community activities and civil rights, or administration. They must have a GPA of 3.0 or higher, be between 17 and 24 years of age, and be able to demonstrate that they intend to continue their education for at least 2 years. Along with their application, they must submit 1) a 1-paragraph statement on why they should be awarded a Watts Foundation scholarship, and 2) a 1- to 2-page essay on a specific type of cancer, based either on how it has impacted their life or on researched information. **Deadline for Receipt:** May of each year. **Additional Information:** Royce R. Watts, Sr. established the Watts Charity Association after he learned he had cancer in 2001.

3836 ■ WESTERN INTERSTATE COMMISSION FOR HIGHER EDUCATION

Attn: Student Exchange Programs
3035 Center Green Drive
P.O. Box 9752
Boulder, CO 80301-9752

Tel: (303)541-0210
Fax: (303)541-0291
E-mail: info-sep@wiche.edu
Web Site: http://www.wiche.edu/sep/psep
To underwrite some of the cost of out-of-state professional schooling for students in selected western states.
Title of Award: Professional Student Exchange Program **Area, Field, or Subject:** Architecture; Dentistry; Library and archival sciences; Medical assisting; Medicine; Medicine, Osteopathic; Nursing; Occupational therapy; Optometry; Pharmaceutical sciences; Physical therapy; Podiatry; Public health; Veterinary science and medicine **Level of Education for which Award is Granted:** Graduate, Undergraduate **Number Awarded:** Varies each year. **Funds Available:** The assistance consists of reduced levels of tuition, usually resident tuition in public institutions or reduced standard tuition at private schools. The home state pays a support fee to the admitting school to help cover the cost of the recipient's education. **Duration:** 1 year; may be renewed.
Eligibility Requirements: This program is open to residents of 13 western states who are interested in pursuing professional study at selected out-of-state institutions, usually because those fields of study are not available in their home states. The eligible programs, and the states whose residents are eligible, presently include: 1) architecture (master's degree), for residents of Wyoming, to study at designated institutions in Arizona, California, Colorado, Idaho, Montana, New Mexico, Oregon, Utah, or Washington; 2) dentistry, for residents of Alaska, Arizona, Hawaii, Montana, New Mexico, North Dakota, and Wyoming, to study at designated institutions in Arizona, California, Colorado, Nevada, Oregon, or Washington; 3) library studies (master's degree), for residents of New Mexico and Wyoming, to study at designated institutions in Arizona, California, Hawaii, or Washington; 4) medicine, for residents of Montana and Wyoming, to study at designated institutions in Arizona, California, Colorado, Hawaii, Nevada, New Mexico, North Dakota, Oregon, or Utah; 5) nursing (graduate degree), for residents of Wyoming, to study at designated institutions in California, Hawaii, North Dakota, or Oregon; 6) occupational therapy (bachelors' or master's degree), for residents of Alaska, Arizona, Hawaii, Montana, and Wyoming, to study at designated institutions in Arizona, California, Idaho, New Mexico, North Dakota, Oregon, Utah, or Washington; 7) optometry, for residents of Alaska, Arizona, Colorado, Hawaii, Idaho, Montana, Nevada, New Mexico, North Dakota, Utah, Washington, and Wyoming, to study at designated institutions in California or Oregon; 8) osteopathic medicine, for residents of Arizona, Montana, New Mexico, Washington, and Wyoming, to study at designated institutions in Arizona or California; 9) pharmacy, for residents of Alaska, Hawaii, and Nevada, to study at designated institutions in Arizona, California, Colorado, Idaho, Montana, New Mexico, North Dakota, Oregon, Utah, Washington, or Wyoming; 10) physical therapy (master's or doctoral degree), for residents of Alaska, Hawaii, and Wyoming, to study at designated institutions in Arizona, California, Colorado, Idaho, Montana, New Mexico, North Dakota, Oregon, Utah, or Washington; 11) physician assistant, for residents of Alaska, Arizona, Nevada, and Wyoming, to study at designated institutions in Arizona, California, Colorado, Idaho, Oregon, Utah, or Washington; 12) podiatry, for residents of Alaska, Montana, New Mexico, Utah, and Wyoming, to study at a designated institution in California; 13) public health, for residents of Montana and New Mexico, to study at designated institutions in California, Colorado, or Washington; and 14) veterinary medicine, for residents of Arizona, Hawaii, Montana, Nevada, New Mexico, North Dakota, Utah, and Wyoming, to study at designated institutions in California, Colorado, Oregon, or Washington. The financial status of the applicants is not considered. Interested students must apply for admission and for PSEP assistance directly from the institution of their choice. They must be certified by their state of residence to become an exchange student and be seeking enrollment at the first professional degree level. **Deadline for Receipt:** In most states, the deadline for receiving completed applications for certification is in October. After obtaining certification, students must still apply to the school of their choice, which also sets its own deadline.

3837 ■ WISCONSIN FOUNDATION FOR INDEPENDENT COLLEGES, INC.

Attn: College-to-Work Program
735 North Water Street, Suite 600
Milwaukee, WI 53202-4100

Tel: (414)273-5980

Fax: (414)273-5995

E-mail: wfic@wficweb.org

Web Site: http://www.wficweb.org/work.html

To provide financial assistance and work experience to students majoring in fields related to communications at member institutions of the Wisconsin Foundation for Independent Colleges (WFIC).

Title of Award: Manitowoc American Red Cross College-to-Work Program **Area, Field, or Subject:** Communications; English language and literature; General studies/Field of study not specified; Graphic art and design; Public relations **Level of Education for which Award is Granted:** Four Year College **Number Awarded:** 1 each year. **Funds Available:** The stipends are $3,500 for the scholarship and $1,500 for the internship. **Duration:** 1 year for the scholarship; 10 weeks for the internship.

Eligibility Requirements: This program is open to full-time sophomores, juniors, and seniors at private colleges and universities in Wisconsin. Applicants must be interested in an internship at the Manitowoc/Calumet County Chapter of the American Red Cross in Manitowoc. Preference is given to 1) students attending Lakeland College or Silver Lake College; 2) residents of Manitowoc County attending another WFIC member institution; and 3) students majoring in communications, English, graphic design, or public relations. Along with their application, they must submit a 1-page essay that includes why they are applying for the internship, why they have selected their major and what interests them about it, why they are attending their chosen college or university, and their future career objectives. **Deadline for Receipt:** February of each year. **Additional Information:** The other WFIC schools are Alverno College, Beloit College, Cardinal Stritch University, Carroll College, Carthage College, Concordia University of Wisconsin, Edgewood College, Lawrence University, Marian College, Marquette University, Milwaukee Institute of Art & Design, Milwaukee School of Engineering, Mount Mary College, Northland College, Ripon College, St. Norbert College, Viterbo University, and Wisconsin Lutheran College. This program is sponsored by the Manitowoc/Calumet County Chapter of the American Red Cross. The WFIC's College-to-Work Program includes a number of other financial assistance and work experience programs aimed at eligible students interested in majoring in fields related to communications, journalism, media, and related fields, including the Post-Crescent College-to-Work Program and Reporter College-to-Work Program.

3838 ■ WOMEN'S OVERSEAS SERVICE LEAGUE

P.O. Box 7124

Washington, DC 20044-7124

To provide financial assistance for college to women who are planning a military or other public service career.

Title of Award: Women's Overseas Service League Scholarships for Women **Area, Field, or Subject:** General studies/Field of study not specified; Public service **Level of Education for which Award is Granted:** Undergraduate **Funds Available:** Stipends range from $500 to $1,000 per year. **Duration:** 1 year; may be renewed 1 additional year.

Eligibility Requirements: This program is open to women who are committed to a military or other public service career. Applicants must have completed at least 12 semester or 18 quarter hours of postsecondary study with at a GPA of 2.5 or higher. They must be working on an academic degree (the program may be professional or technical in nature) and must agree to enroll for at least 6 semester or 9 quarter hours of study each academic period. Along with their application, they must submit an official transcript, a 1-page description of career goals, 3 current letters of reference, and a brief statement describing sources of financial support and the need for scholarship assistance. They must also provide information on their educational background, employment experience, civic and volunteer activities, and expected degree completion date.

Deadline for Receipt: February of each year. **Additional Information:** The Women's Overseas Service League is a national organization of women who have served overseas in or with the armed forces.

Social Work

3839 ■ ALASKA COMMISSION ON POSTSECONDARY EDUCATION

Attn: AlaskAdvantage Programs

3030 Vintage Boulevard

Juneau, AK 99801-7109

Tel: (907)465-6779; (866)427-5683

Fax: (907)465-5316

E-mail: customer_service@acpe.ak.us

Web Site: http://alaskaadvantage.state.ak.us/page/276

To provide financial assistance to Alaska residents who attend college in the state to prepare for a career in designated fields with a workforce shortage.

Title of Award: AlaskAdvantage Educational Grants **Area, Field, or Subject:** Education; Health care services; Social work **Level of Education for which Award is Granted:** Undergraduate **Number Awarded:** Varies each year; students with the greatest financial need are awarded support until funds are exhausted. **Funds Available:** Grants range from $500 to $2,000 per year, depending on the need of the recipient. **Duration:** 1 year; may be renewed as long as the recipient remains enrolled at least half time, makes satisfactory academic progress, and continues to meet residency and financial need requirements.

Eligibility Requirements: This program is open to residents of Alaska who have been admitted to an undergraduate degree or vocational certificate program at a qualifying institution in the state. Applicants must be planning to work on a degree or certificate in a field that the state has designated as a workforce shortage area; currently, those are allied health sciences, community or social service, and teaching. They must be able to demonstrate financial need and SAT or ACT scores in the top quartile. U.S. citizenship or permanent resident status is required. **Deadline for Receipt:** April of each year.

3840 ■ CHRISTIAN LIFE RESOURCES

Attn: WELS Lutherans for Life

Scholarship Review Committee

2949 North Mayfair Road, Suite 309

Milwaukee, WI 53222-4304

Tel: (414)774-1331

Fax: (414)774-1360

Web Site: http://www.christianliferesources.com

To provide financial assistance to Lutheran high school seniors in Wisconsin who are interested in studying life-related issues in college.

Title of Award: WELS Lutherans for Life Scholarship Program **Area, Field, or Subject:** Biological and clinical sciences; Education, Special; Engineering, Biomedical; Journalism; Law; Medicine; Physical therapy; Political science; Psychology; Social work **Level of Education for which Award is Granted:** Four Year College **Number Awarded:** Varies each year; recently, 9 of these scholarships were awarded. **Funds Available:** Stipends up to $1,000 are available. **Duration:** 1 year.

Eligibility Requirements: This program is open to high school seniors who are active members of the Wisconsin Evangelical Lutheran Synod (WELS) or an affiliated church. Applicants must be planning to go to a 4-year school to prepare for a secular career in which pro-life values will be demonstrated. Acceptable fields include medicine, biotechnology/biological engineering, medical research/genetics, law/politics, journalism/media, psychology, physical therapy, social services, or special education. They must have a GPA of 3.25 or higher. Along with their application, they must submit essays on 1) the field of study they plan to enter and how it relates to pro-life issues; 2) why the scholarship should be awarded to them, including their future goals; and 3) how they have demonstrated a Christian, pro-life attitude in their life. **Deadline for Receipt:** February of each year. **Additional Information:** WELS Lutherans for Life was formerly a ministry of the Wisconsin Evangelical Lutheran Synod.

3841 ■ COMMUNITY FOUNDATION FOR GREATER ATLANTA, INC.

50 Hurt Plaza, Suite 449

Atlanta, GA 30303

Tel: (404)688-5525

Fax: (404)688-3060

E-mail: vweekes@atlcf.org

Web Site: http://www.atlcf.org/GrantsScholarships/Scholarships/SteveDearduff.aspx

To provide financial assistance to Georgia residents who are working on an undergraduate or graduate degree, especially in medicine or social work.

Title of Award: Steve Dearduff Scholarship **Area, Field, or Subject:** General studies/Field of study not specified; Medicine; Social work **Level of Education for which Award is Granted:** Graduate, Undergraduate **Number Awarded:** Varies each year; recently, 7 of these scholarships were awarded. **Funds Available:** Stipends range up to $2,500 per year. **Duration:** 1 year; recipients may reapply.

Eligibility Requirements: This program is open to legal residents of Georgia who are enrolled in or accepted at an accredited institution of higher learning on the undergraduate or graduate school level. Applicants must be able to demonstrate a history of outstanding community service and potential for success in their chosen field. They must have a GPA of 2.0 or higher. Preference is given to candidates entering the fields of medicine (research or clinical practice) or social work. **Deadline for Receipt:** March of each year.

3842 ■ COMMUNITY FOUNDATION FOR GREATER ATLANTA, INC.

50 Hurt Plaza, Suite 449
Atlanta, GA 30303
Tel: (404)688-5525
Fax: (404)688-3060
E-mail: vweekes@atlcf.org
Web Site: http://www.atlcf.org/GrantsScholarships/Scholarships/Smyth.aspx

To provide financial assistance for college to high school seniors, especially those from designated states.

Title of Award: James M. and Virginia M. Smyth Scholarship Fund **Area, Field, or Subject:** General studies/Field of study not specified; Music; Religion; Social work **Level of Education for which Award is Granted:** Undergraduate **Number Awarded:** Varies each year. **Funds Available:** Stipends range up to $2,500. **Duration:** 1 year; recipients may reapply.

Eligibility Requirements: This program is open to graduating high school seniors, with special consideration given to residents of Georgia, Illinois, Mississippi, Missouri, Oklahoma, Tennessee, and Texas. Applicants must have a GPA of 3.0 or higher and be interested in attending a college, university, or community college to work on a degree in the arts and sciences, human services, music, or ministry. They must be able to demonstrate financial need and a commitment to community service through school, community, or religious organizations. Adults returning to school to increase employability are also eligible. **Deadline for Receipt:** March of each year.

3843 ■ CONTINENTAL SOCIETY, DAUGHTERS OF INDIAN WARS

c/o Mrs. Donald C. Trolinger, Scholarship Chair
61300 East 110 Road
Miami, OK 74354-4726
E-mail: ottawahillpt@neok.com

To provide financial assistance to Native American college students who are interested in preparing for a career in education.

Title of Award: Continental Society, Daughters of Indian Wars Scholarship **Area, Field, or Subject:** Education; Social work **Level of Education for which Award is Granted:** Four Year College **Number Awarded:** 1 each year. **Funds Available:** The stipend is $1,000. **Duration:** 1 year; may be renewed.

Eligibility Requirements: Applicants must be certified tribal members of a federally-recognized tribe, plan to prepare for a career in education or social service, plan to work on a reservation, be a junior at an accredited college, have earned at least a 3.0 GPA, and carry at least 10 quarter hours or 8 semester hours. Selection is based primarily on academic achievement and commitment to the field of study; financial need is not necessary but is considered. **Deadline for Receipt:** June of each year.

3844 ■ DELTA SIGMA THETA SORORITY, INC.

1707 New Hampshire Avenue, N.W.
Washington, DC 20009
Tel: (202)986-2400
Fax: (202)986-2513
E-mail: dstemail@deltasigmatheta.org
Web Site: http://www.deltasigmatheta.org

To provide financial assistance to members of Delta Sigma Theta who are interested in preparing for a career in social work.

Title of Award: Juliette Derricotte Scholarship **Area, Field, or Subject:** Social work **Level of Education for which Award is Granted:** Four Year College, Graduate **Funds Available:** The stipends range from $1,000 to $2,000 per year. The funds may be used to cover tuition, school, and living expenses. **Duration:** 1 year; may be renewed for up to 2 additional years.

Eligibility Requirements: Applicants must be college seniors or graduate students who are interested in preparing for a career in social work and

who are active, dues-paying members of Delta Sigma Theta. **Deadline for Receipt:** March of each year. **Additional Information:** Winners may also receive financial assistance from other sources. Confirmation of registration must be received before stipends are paid.

3845 ■ EPILEPSY FOUNDATION

Attn: Research Department
4351 Garden City Drive
Landover, MD 20785-7223
Tel: (301)459-3700
Free: 800-EFA-1000
Fax: (301)577-2684
E-mail: grants@efa.org
Web Site: http://www.epilepsyfoundation.org/research/grants.cfm

To provide funding to undergraduate and graduate students interested in working on a summer research training project in a field relevant to epilepsy.

Title of Award: Behavioral Sciences Student Fellowships in Epilepsy **Area, Field, or Subject:** Anthropology; Behavioral sciences; Counseling/Guidance; Economics; Epilepsy; Nursing; Political science; Psychology; Rehabilitation, Physical/Psychological; Social work; Sociology **Level of Education for which Award is Granted:** Graduate, Undergraduate **Number Awarded:** Varies each year; recently, 4 of these fellowships were awarded. **Funds Available:** The grant is $3,000. **Duration:** 3 months during the summer.

Eligibility Requirements: This program is open to undergraduate and graduate students in a behavioral science program relevant to epilepsy research or clinical care, including, but not limited to, sociology, social work, psychology, anthropology, nursing, economics, vocational rehabilitation, counseling, and political science. Applicants must be interested in working on an epilepsy research project under the supervision of a qualified mentor. Because the program is designed as a training opportunity, the quality of the training plans and environment are considered in the selection process. Other selection criteria include the quality of the proposed project, the relevance of the proposed work to epilepsy, the applicant's interest in the field of epilepsy, the applicant's qualifications, and the mentor's qualifications, including his or her commitment to the student and the project. U.S. citizenship is not required, but the project must be conducted in the United States. Applications from women, members of minority groups, and people with disabilities are especially encouraged. The program is not intended for students working on a dissertation research project. **Deadline for Receipt:** March of each year. **Additional Information:** This program is supported by the American Epilepsy Society, Abbott Laboratories, Ortho-McNeil Pharmaceutical Corporation, and Pfizer Inc.

3846 ■ INDIAN HEALTH SERVICE

Attn: Scholarship Program
801 Thompson Avenue, Suite 120
Rockville, MD 20852
Tel: (301)443-6197
Fax: (301)443-6048
E-mail: bmiller@na.ihs.gov
Web Site: http://www.ihs.gov

To provide financial assistance to Native American students who need compensatory or preprofessional education to qualify for enrollment in a health professions school.

Title of Award: Health Professions Preparatory Scholarship Program **Area, Field, or Subject:** Engineering; Health care services; Medical technology; Nursing; Nutrition; Pharmaceutical sciences; Physical therapy; Social work **Level of Education for which Award is Granted:** Undergraduate **Number Awarded:** Varies each year. **Funds Available:** Awards provide a payment directly to the school for tuition and required fees; a stipend for living expenses of approximately $1,160 per month for 10 months; a lump sum to cover the costs of books, travel, and other necessary educational expenses; and up to $400 for approved tutorial costs. **Duration:** Up to 2 years of full-time study or up to 4 years of part-time study.

Eligibility Requirements: Applicants must be American Indians or Alaska Natives; be high school graduates or the equivalent; have the capacity to complete a health professions course of study; and be enrolled or accepted for enrollment in a compensatory or preprofessional general education course or curriculum. The qualifying fields of study include premedical technology, pre-dietetics, pre-nursing, pre-pharmacy, pre-physical therapy, pre-social work, and pre-engineering. Recipients must intend to serve Indian people upon completion of professional health care education as a health care provider in the discipline for which they are enrolled at the pregraduate level. **Deadline for Receipt:** February of each year.

3847 ■ INDIAN HEALTH SERVICE

Attn: Scholarship Program
801 Thompson Avenue, Suite 120
Rockville, MD 20852
Tel: (301)443-6197
Fax: (301)443-6048
E-mail: bmiller@na.IHS.gov
Web Site: http://www.ihs.gov
To provide loans-for-service to American Indian and Alaska Native students enrolled in health professions and allied health professions programs.
Title of Award: Health Professions Scholarship Program **Area, Field, or Subject:** Counseling/Guidance; Dental hygiene; Dentistry; Health care services; Medical assisting; Medical technology; Medicine; Medicine, Osteopathic; Nursing; Nutrition; Optometry; Pharmaceutical sciences; Physical therapy; Podiatry; Psychology; Public health; Radiology; Respiratory therapy; Social work; **Level of Education for which Award is Granted:** Graduate, Undergraduate **Number Awarded:** Varies each year. **Funds Available:** Awards provide a payment directly to the school for tuition and required fees; a stipend for living expenses of approximately $1,160 per month for 12 months; a lump sum to cover the costs of books, travel, and other necessary educational expenses; and up to $400 for approved tutorial costs. Upon completion of their program of study, recipients are required to provide payback service of 1 year for each year of scholarship support at the Indian Health Service, a tribal health programs, an urban Indian health program, or in private practice in a designated health professional shortage area serving a substantial number of Indians. Recipients who fail to complete their service obligation must repay all funds received (although no interest is charged). **Duration:** 1 year; may be renewed for up to 3 additional years.
Eligibility Requirements: This program is open to American Indians and Alaska Natives who are at least high school graduates and enrolled in a full-time study program leading to a degree in a health-related professions school within the United States. Priority is given to upper-division and graduate students. Qualifying fields of study include chemical dependency counseling (bachelor's or master's degree), clinical psychology (Ph.D. only), coding specialist (certificate), counseling psychology (Ph.D. only), dental hygiene (B.S.), dentistry (D.D.S.), diagnostic radiology technology (certificate, associate, or B.S.), dietitian (B.S.), civil or environmental engineering (B.S.), environmental health (B.S.), health care administration (B.S. or M.S.), health education (B.S. or M.S.), health records (R.H.I.T. or R.H.I.A.), injury prevention specialist (certificate), medical technology (B.S.), allopathic and osteopathic medicine, nursing (A.D.N., B.S.N., or C.R.N.A), optometry, pharmacy (B.S. or Pharm.D.), physician assistant (B.S.), physical therapy (M.S. or D.P.T.), podiatry (D.P.M.), public health (M.P.H. only), public health nutrition (master's only), social work (master's only), respiratory therapy (associate), and ultrasonography. **Deadline for Receipt:** February of each year.

3848 ■ INTERNATIONAL FOUNDATION FOR GENDER EDUCATION

Attn: Transgender Scholarship and Education Legacy Fund
P.O. Box 540229
Waltham, MA 02454-0229
Tel: (781)899-2212
Fax: (781)899-5703
E-mail: carrie@tself.org
Web Site: http://www.tself.org
To provide financial assistance to transgender students who are working on an undergraduate or graduate degree in the caring professions.
Title of Award: Transgender Scholarship and Education Legacy Fund Awards **Area, Field, or Subject:** Education; Health care services; Law; Religion; Social work **Level of Education for which Award is Granted:** Graduate, Undergraduate **Number Awarded:** Varies each year; recently, 4 of these scholarships were awarded. **Funds Available:** Stipends average $2,000. Funds are paid directly to the student. **Duration:** 1 year; nonrenewable.
Eligibility Requirements: This program is open to undergraduate and graduate students who are living full time in a gender or sex role that

differs from that assigned to them at birth and who are "out and proud" about their transgender identity. Applicants must be working on a degree in the helping and caring professions, including, but not limited to, social services, health care, religious instruction, education, and the law. They may be of any age or nationality, but they must be attending or planning to attend a college, university, trade school, or technical college in the United States or Canada. Selection is based on affirmation of transgender identity; demonstration of integrity and honesty; participation and leadership in community activities; service as role model, mentor, colleague, or advisor for the transgender communities; and service as transgender role model, mentor, colleague, or advisor to non-transpeople in the helping and caring professions. **Deadline for Receipt:** January of each year. **Additional Information:** This program includes the TSELF Youth Award (for applicants under 22 years of age entering their first or second year of postsecondary education); the TSELF Schools Education Award (for applicants working on a degree in education and teaching); the Lee Frances Heller Memorial Award (for Christian students or applicants who are or will be attending a college, university, or other institution for religious studies); the HIV/AIDS Prevention and Treatment Award (for applicants who have been involved in HIV/AIDS prevention, care, and treatment activities); and the Chicago Gender Society Leadership Award (for applicants who have been involved in community building activities).

3849 ■ KOSTER INSURANCE AGENCY

Attn: Scholarship
500 Victory Road
Quincy, MA 02171
Tel: (617)770-9889
Free: 800-457-5599
Fax: (617)479-0860
E-mail: Scholarship@kosterins.com
Web Site: http://www.kosterweb.com/about/scholarship_main.php
To provide financial assistance to undergraduate students working on a degree in a health-related field.
Title of Award: Koster Insurance Health Careers Scholarship Program **Area, Field, or Subject:** Biological and clinical sciences; Chemistry; Dentistry; Health care services; Nursing; Occupational therapy; Optometry; Pharmaceutical sciences; Physical therapy; Physiology; Public health; Social work **Level of Education for which Award is Granted:** Undergraduate **Number Awarded:** 5 each year. **Funds Available:** The stipend is $3,000 per year. **Duration:** 1 year; may be renewed 1 additional year.
Eligibility Requirements: This program is open to full-time undergraduates entering their second-to-last or final year of study in a health-related field, including (but not limited to) pre-medicine, nursing, public and community health, physical therapy, occupational therapy, pharmacy, biology, chemistry, physiology, social work, dentistry, and optometry. Applicants must have a GPA of 3.0 or higher and be able to demonstrate financial need. Along with their application, they must submit a 1-page essay describing their personal goals, including their reasons for preparing for a career in health care. Selection is based on motivation to pursue a career in health care, academic excellence, dedication to community service, and financial need. **Deadline for Receipt:** April of each year. **Additional Information:** This program began in 2001.

3850 ■ MAINE ROADS SCHOLARSHIP FUND

c/o University of Southern Maine, Muskie School
400 Congress Street
P.O. Box 15010
Portland, ME 04112
888-900-0055
Fax: (207)780-5817
E-mail: sturner@usm.maine.edu
Web Site: http://muskie.usm.maine.edu/maineroads/scholarship.html
To provide financial assistance to child care providers in Maine who are working on an undergraduate or graduate degree at an institution in the state.
Title of Award: Maine Roads Degree Scholarship **Area, Field, or Subject:** Child development; Education, Early childhood; Parks and recreation; Social work **Level of Education for which Award is Granted:** Graduate, Professional, Undergraduate **Number Awarded:** Varies each year. **Funds Available:** Stipends range up to $1,800 for undergraduate students or up to $2,400 for graduate students. **Duration:** 1 year.

Eligibility Requirements: This program is open to child care providers who are residents of Maine working on a bachelor's, master's, or doctoral degree at an institution of higher education in the state. Applicants must have a family income that does not exceed 300% of the federal poverty level (currently, that means an income of $26,940 for a family of 1, rising to $92,880 for a family of 8). They must have experience within the past 2 years working in the child care and early education field in licensed or certified child care facilities or resource development centers. Courses of study may include early childhood education, child development, recreation and leisure services with a special needs focus, social work with an emphasis on early childhood, or child care administration. Along with their application, they must submit brief statements on their plans to work directly with children after completing their degree and how earning their degree will impact their work in child care. **Deadline for Receipt:** June or October of each year.

3851 ■ MARYLAND HIGHER EDUCATION COMMISSION

Attn: Office of Student Financial Assistance
839 Bestgate Road, Suite 400
Annapolis, MD 21401-3013
Tel: (410)260-4594
Free: 800-974-1024
Fax: (410)974-5376
E-mail: osfamail@mhec.state.md.us
Web Site: http://www.mhec.state.md.us/financialAid/
ProgramDescriptions/prog_devdis.asp
To provide scholarship/loans to students in Maryland who are interested in working on a degree in a designated human services program.

Title of Award: Maryland Developmental Disabilities, Mental Health, Child Welfare, and Juvenile Justice Workforce Tuition Assistance Program **Area, Field, or Subject:** Counseling/Guidance; Criminal justice; Criminology; Disabilities; Education, Special; Gerontology; Law enforcement; Mental health; Nursing; Occupational therapy; Physical therapy; Psychology; Rehabilitation, Physical/Psychological; Social work **Level of Education for which Award is Granted:** Graduate, Undergraduate **Number Awarded:** Varies each year. **Funds Available:** The maximum stipend is $2,000 per year for students attending a 2-year institution or $3,000 per year for students at a 4-year institution. The total amount of all state awards may not exceed the cost of attendance as determined by the school's financial aid office or $17,800, whichever is less. Recipients must agree to work in a Maryland community-based program that is licensed by the Developmental Disabilities Administration or approved by the Mental Hygiene Administration, or in a residential program that is licensed by the Department of Human Resources or the Department of Juvenile Justice. The service obligation must begin within 6 months of graduation. The total service requirement is 2,000 hours if the award amount is $1,999 or less, 3,000 hours if the award amount is $2,000 to $3,999, or 4,000 hours if the award amount is $4,000 or more. If the service requirement is not completed, the award must be repaid with interest. **Duration:** 1 year; may be renewed if the recipient maintains satisfactory academic progress and remains enrolled in a human services degree program.
Eligibility Requirements: This program is open to high school seniors and full-time and part-time undergraduate and graduate students. Applicants and their parents must be Maryland residents attending a college or university in the state in 1 of the following human services degree programs: aging services, counseling, disability services, mental health, nursing, occupational therapy, physical therapy, psychology, rehabilitation, social work, special education, supported employment, vocational rehabilitation, or any other concentration in the healing arts or a program providing support services to individuals with special needs including child welfare and juvenile justice. Financial need is not considered in the selection process. **Deadline for Receipt:** June of each year.

3852 ■ MEMORIAL FOUNDATION FOR JEWISH CULTURE

50 Broadway, 34th Floor
New York, NY 10004
Tel: (212)425-6606
Fax: (212)425-6602
E-mail: office@mfjc.org
Web Site: http://www.mfjc.org
To assist well-qualified individuals to train for careers in a field related to Jewish community service.
Title of Award: International Scholarship Program for Community Service **Area, Field, or Subject:** Education; Jewish studies; Religion; Social work

Level of Education for which Award is Granted: Graduate, Undergraduate **Funds Available:** The amount of the grant varies, depending on the country in which the student will be trained and other considerations. **Duration:** 1 year; may be renewed.
Eligibility Requirements: The scholarship is open to any individual, regardless of country of origin, who is presently receiving or plans to undertake training in his/her chosen field at a recognized yeshiva, teacher training seminary, school of social work, university, or other educational institution. Applicants must be interested in pursuing professional training for careers in Jewish education, Jewish social service, the rabbinate, or as religious functionaries (e.g., shohatim, mohalim) in Diaspora Jewish communities in need of such personnel. Students planning to serve in the United States, Canada, or Israel are not eligible. **Deadline for Receipt:** November of each year. **Additional Information:** Recipients must agree to serve for at least 2 to 3 years in a Jewish-deprived Diaspora community where their skills are needed after completing their training.

3853 ■ NATIONAL ASSOCIATION OF BLACK SOCIAL WORKERS

Attn: National Student Coordinator
1220 11th Street, N.W., Suite 2
Washington, DC 20001
Tel: (202)589-1850
Fax: (202)589-1853
E-mail: nabsw.Harambee@verizon.net
Web Site: http://www.nabsw.org/mserver/
StudentAffairs.aspx?menuContext=770
To provide financial assistance for college or graduate school to members of the National Association of Black Social Workers (NABSW).
Title of Award: Cenie Jomo Williams Tuition Scholarship **Area, Field, or Subject:** Social work **Level of Education for which Award is Granted:** Graduate, Undergraduate **Number Awarded:** 1 or more each year. **Funds Available:** The stipend is $2,000. Funds are sent directly to the recipient's school. **Duration:** 1 year.
Eligibility Requirements: This program is open to African American members of NABSW enrolled full time at an accredited U.S. social work or social welfare program with a GPA of 2.5 or higher. Applicants must be able to demonstrate community service and a research interest in the Black community. Along with their application, they must submit an essay of 2 to 3 pages on their professional interests, future social work aspirations, previous social work experiences (volunteer and professional), honors and achievements (academic and community service), and research interests within the Black community (for master's and doctoral students). Recommendations are required. Financial need is considered in the selection process. **Deadline for Receipt:** December of each year.

3854 ■ NORTH CAROLINA STATE EDUCATION ASSISTANCE AUTHORITY

Attn: Scholarship and Grant Services
10 T.W. Alexander Drive
P.O. Box 14223
Research Triangle Park, NC 27709-4223
Tel: (919)549-8614
Free: 800-700-1775
Fax: (919)549-8481
E-mail: information@ncseaa.edu
Web Site: http://www.ncseaa.edu
To provide loans and loans-for-service to North Carolina residents who are interested in preparing for a career in health, science, or mathematics.
Title of Award: North Carolina Student Loan Program for Health, Science, and Mathematics **Area, Field, or Subject:** Allied health; Dentistry; Medicine; Nursing; Optometry; Public health; Social work **Level of Education for which Award is Granted:** Graduate, Undergraduate **Number Awarded:** Varies each year; recently, a total of 497 students were receiving $3,238,569 in support through this program. **Funds Available:** Maximum loans are $3,000 per year for associate degree and certificate programs, $5,000 per year for baccalaureate degree/certificate programs, $6,500 per year for master's degree programs, or $8,500 per year for health/professional doctoral programs. The maximum amount that any student can borrow through this program is $58,000. The interest rate is 4% while the borrowers are attending school and from 10 to 15% after they leave school. Cash repayments must begin 90 days or less after completion of course work and training. Under specified conditions, certain loan recipients in qualifying disciplines may have their loans

canceled through service in North Carolina. **Duration:** 1 year; renewable for 1 additional year for diploma, associate, certificate, and master's degree programs, for 2 additional years for baccalaureate degree programs, or for 3 additional years for doctoral programs.

Eligibility Requirements: North Carolina residents are eligible to apply for this program if they have been accepted as full-time students in an accredited associate, baccalaureate, master's, or doctoral program leading to a degree in 1 of the following areas: allied health (including audiology/communications assistant, cytotechnology, dental hygiene, diagnostic medical sonographer, imaging technologist, medical technology, nuclear medicine technologist, occupational therapy/assistant, physician assistant, physical therapy/assistant, radiation therapist, radiography, respiratory therapy, and speech language pathology); clinical psychology (Ph.D. level only); dentistry; dietetics and nutrition (graduate level only); mathematics education; medicine (including chiropractic medicine, emergency medicine, family medicine, geriatrics, internal medicine, obstetrics and gynecology, osteopathic medicine, pediatrics, podiatry, primary care medicine, and psychiatry); nursing (including anesthetist, family nurse practitioner, nursing administration, general nursing, and midwifery); optometry; pharmacy; public health (graduate level only); science education (including biology, chemistry, communications and technologies, computer and information sciences, engineering, and physical science); social work (graduate level only); and veterinary medicine. U.S. citizenship is required. Selection is based on academic progress, financial ability of sureties to repay all loans and accrued interest in case of applicant's default, applicant's willingness to work in underserved areas of the state or in disciplines for which there is a shortage of professionals, applicant's willingness to comply with all program regulations, and financial need. **Deadline for Receipt:** May of each year. **Additional Information:** Recipients may attend a North Carolina postsecondary institution or an eligible out-of-state institution. This program was formerly known as the North Carolina Medical Student Loan Program.

3855 ■ WATTS CHARITY ASSOCIATION, INC.

6245 Bristol Parkway, Suite 224
Culver City, CA 90230
Tel: (323)671-0394
Fax: (323)778-2613
E-mail: wattscharity@yahoo.com
Web Site: http://4watts.tripod.com/id5.html

To provide financial assistance to upper-division college students majoring in child development, teaching, or social services.

Title of Award: Joyce Washington Scholarship **Area, Field, or Subject:** Child development; Education; Social work **Level of Education for which Award is Granted:** Four Year College **Number Awarded:** 1 each year. **Funds Available:** A stipend is awarded (amount not specified). **Duration:** 1 year.

Eligibility Requirements: This program is open to U.S. citizens of African American descent who are enrolled full time as a college or university junior. Applicants must be majoring in child development, teaching, or the study of social services. They must have a GPA of 3.0 or higher, be between 17 and 24 years of age, and be able to demonstrate that they intend to continue their education for at least 2 years. Along with their application, they must submit 1) a 1-paragraph statement on why they should be awarded a Watts Foundation scholarship, and 2) a 1- to 2-page essay on a specific type of cancer, based either on how it has impacted their life or on researched information. **Deadline for Receipt:** May of each year. **Additional Information:** Royce R. Watts, Sr. established the Watts Charity Association after he learned he had cancer in 2001.

3856 ■ WISCONSIN FOUNDATION FOR INDEPENDENT COLLEGES, INC.

Attn: College-to-Work Program
735 North Water Street, Suite 600
Milwaukee, WI 53202-4100
Tel: (414)273-5980
Fax: (414)273-5995
E-mail: wfic@wficweb.org
Web Site: http://www.wficweb.org/work.html

To provide financial assistance and work experience to students majoring in fields related to social work at member institutions of the Wisconsin Foundation for Independent Colleges (WFIC).

Title of Award: Holiday House of Manitowoc County College-to-Work Program **Area, Field, or Subject:** Education; General studies/Field of study not specified; Occupational therapy; Social work **Level of Education for which Award is Granted:** Four Year College **Number Awarded:** 1 each year. **Funds Available:** The stipends are $3,500 for the scholarship and $1,500 for the internship. **Duration:** 1 year for the scholarship; 10 weeks for the internship.

Eligibility Requirements: This program is open to full-time sophomores, juniors, and seniors at private colleges and universities in Wisconsin. Applicants must be interested in an internship at Holiday House of Manitowoc County. Preference is given to 1) students attending Lakeland College or Silver Lake College; 2) residents of Manitowoc County attending another WFIC member institution; and 3) students majoring in education, occupational therapy, or social work. Along with their application, they must submit a 1-page essay that includes why they are applying for the internship, why they have selected their major and what interests them about it, why they are attending their chosen college or university, and their future career objectives. **Deadline for Receipt:** February of each year. **Additional Information:** The other WFIC schools are Alverno College, Beloit College, Cardinal Stritch University, Carroll College, Carthage College, Concordia University of Wisconsin, Edgewood College, Lawrence University, Marian College, Marquette University, Milwaukee Institute of Art & Design, Milwaukee School of Engineering, Mount Mary College, Northland College, Ripon College, St. Norbert College, Viterbo University, and Wisconsin Lutheran College. This program is sponsored by Holiday House of Manitowoc County, Inc. The WFIC's College-to-Work Program includes a number of other financial assistance and work experience programs aimed at eligible students interested in majoring in fields related to social work, including the Lutheran Social Services College-to-Work Program, Manitowoc County Domestic Violence Center College-to-Work Program, and YWCA of Rock County College-to-Work Program.

Urban Affairs

3857 ■ AMERICAN PLANNING ASSOCIATION

Attn: Federal Planning Division
122 South Michigan Avenue, Suite 1600
Chicago, IL 60603-6107
Tel: (312)431-9100
Fax: (312)431-9985
E-mail: fpd-info@list.planning.org
Web Site: http://www.FedPlan.org

To provide financial assistance to undergraduate and graduate students preparing for a career in planning, especially as it relates to activities of the federal government.

Title of Award: Federal Planning Division Annual Student Scholarship **Area, Field, or Subject:** Public administration; Urban affairs/design/planning **Level of Education for which Award is Granted:** Four Year College, Graduate **Number Awarded:** 1 or more each year. **Funds Available:** Stipends range from $500 to $2,500. **Duration:** 1 year.

Eligibility Requirements: This program is open to juniors, seniors, and graduate students at U.S. and Canadian accredited colleges and universities. Applicants must be preparing for a career in public service, especially at the federal level, as a planner. They must have a GPA of 3.0 or higher. Along with their application, they must submit an essay that addresses the federal government's role in managing its lands and resources in the best interests of the United States. Selection is based primarily on the essay, which is judged on clarity of message, freshness of idea, and potential for implementation. **Deadline for Receipt:** November of each year. **Additional Information:** This program began in 2004. Information is also available from Justin Hollander, U.S. General Services Administration, 26 Federal Plaza, Room 1609, New York, NY 10278, (212) 264-1622, E-mail: Justin.Hollander@gsa.gov.

3858 ■ AMERICAN PLANNING ASSOCIATION

Attn: Leadership Affairs Associate
122 South Michigan Avenue, Suite 1600
Chicago, IL 60603-6107
Tel: (312)431-9100
Fax: (312)431-9985
E-mail: fellowship@planning.org
Web Site: http://www.planning.org/institutions/scholarship.htm

To provide financial assistance to women and underrepresented minority students enrolled in undergraduate or graduate degree programs at recognized planning schools.

Title of Award: Judith McManus Price Scholarships **Area, Field, or Subject:** Urban affairs/design/planning **Level of Education for which Award is Granted:** Graduate, Undergraduate **Number Awarded:** Varies each year; recently, 3 of these scholarships were awarded. **Funds Available:** Stipends range from $2,000 to $4,000 per year. The money may be applied to tuition and living expenses only. Payment is made to the recipient's university and divided by terms in the school year. **Duration:** 1 year; recipients may reapply.

Eligibility Requirements: This program is open to undergraduate and graduate students in urban and regional planning who are women or members of the following minority groups: African American, Hispanic American, or Native American. Applicants must be citizens of the United States and able to document financial need. They must intend to work as practicing planners in the public sector. Along with their application, they must submit a 2- to 5-page personal statement describing how their education will be applied to career goals and why they chose planning as a career path. Selection is based (in order of importance) on 1) commitment to planning as reflected in the personal statement and resume; 2) academic achievement and/or improvement during the past 2 years; 3) letters of recommendation; 4) financial need; and 5) professional presentation. **Deadline for Receipt:** April of each year. **Additional Information:** This program was established in 2004.

3859 ■ AMERICAN PLANNING ASSOCIATION

Attn: Planning and the Black Community Division
122 South Michigan Avenue, Suite 1600
Chicago, IL 60603-6107
Tel: (312)431-9100
Fax: (312)431-9985
E-mail: info_pbcd@planning.org
Web Site: http://www.planning.org/blackcommunity/scholarship.htm
To provide financial assistance to African American undergraduate students interested in majoring in planning or a related field.

Title of Award: Planning and the Black Community Division Scholarship **Area, Field, or Subject:** Environmental conservation; Environmental science; Geography; Public administration; Transportation; Urban affairs/design/planning **Level of Education for which Award is Granted:** Four Year College **Number Awarded:** 1 each year. **Funds Available:** The stipend is $2,500. **Duration:** 1 year.

Eligibility Requirements: This program is open to full-time African American undergraduate students entering their junior or senior year. Applicants must be majoring in planning or a related field (e.g., geography, environmental sciences, public administration, transportation, or urban studies) with a GPA of 3.0 or higher. They must submit a 2-page personal statement on the importance of urban planning to the African American community and how they see themselves making a contribution to the urban planning profession. U.S. citizenship is required. **Deadline for Receipt:** October of each year. **Additional Information:** Information is also available from Sigmund Shipp, Hunter College, Department of Urban Affairs and Planning, 695 Park Avenue, New York, NY 10021.

3860 ■ AMERICAN PLANNING ASSOCIATION-CALIFORNIA CHAPTER

Attn: California Planning Foundation
c/o Paul Wack
P.O. Box 886
San Luis Obispo, CA 93406
Tel: (805)544-8282
Fax: (805)544-8286
E-mail: pwack@calpoly.edu
Web Site: http://www.californiaplanningfoundation.org/scholarships.html
To provide financial assistance to undergraduate and graduate students in accredited planning programs at California universities.

Title of Award: California Planning Foundation Outstanding Student Scholarships **Area, Field, or Subject:** Urban affairs/design/planning **Level of Education for which Award is Granted:** Master's, Undergraduate **Number Awarded:** 4 each year: 1 at $4,000 and 3 at $2,000. **Funds Available:** Stipends are $4,000 or $2,000. **Duration:** 1 year.

Eligibility Requirements: This program is open to students entering their final year for an undergraduate or master's degree in an accredited planning program at a university in California. Selection is based on academic performance, professional promise, financial need, and increasing diversity in the planning profession. **Deadline for Receipt:** April of each

year. **Additional Information:** The accredited planning programs are at 3 campuses of the California State University system (California State Polytechnic University at Pomona, California Polytechnic State University at San Luis Obispo, and San Jose State University), 3 campuses of the University of California (Berkeley, Irvine, and Los Angeles), and the University of Southern California.

3861 ■ AMERICAN PLANNING ASSOCIATION-CALIFORNIA CHAPTER

Attn: California Planning Foundation
c/o Paul Wack
P.O. Box 886
San Luis Obispo, CA 93406
Tel: (805)544-8282
Fax: (805)544-8286
E-mail: pwack@calpoly.edu
Web Site: http://www.californiaplanningfoundation.org/scholarships.html
To provide financial assistance to undergraduate and graduate students in accredited planning programs at California universities.

Title of Award: Ken Milam Scholarship **Area, Field, or Subject:** Urban affairs/design/planning **Level of Education for which Award is Granted:** Master's, Undergraduate **Number Awarded:** 1 each year. **Funds Available:** The stipend is $1,000. **Duration:** 1 year.

Eligibility Requirements: This program is open to students entering their final year for an undergraduate or master's degree in an accredited planning program at a university in California. Applicants must be interested in preparing for a career in public planning in California. Selection is based on academic excellence, financial need, and commitment to serve the planning profession in California. **Deadline for Receipt:** April of each year. **Additional Information:** This program is sponsored by the County Planning Director's Association. The accredited planning programs are at 3 campuses of the California State University system (California State Polytechnic University at Pomona, California Polytechnic State University at San Luis Obispo, and San Jose State University), 3 campuses of the University of California (Berkeley, Irvine, and Los Angeles), and the University of Southern California.

3862 ■ AMERICAN PLANNING ASSOCIATION-CALIFORNIA CHAPTER

Attn: California Planning Foundation
c/o Paul Wack
P.O. Box 886
San Luis Obispo, CA 93406
Tel: (805)544-8282
Fax: (805)544-8286
E-mail: pwack@calpoly.edu
Web Site: http://www.californiaplanningfoundation.org/scholarships.html
To provide financial assistance to undergraduate and graduate students in planning programs at California universities.

Title of Award: Richard G. Munsell/CPR Scholarship **Area, Field, or Subject:** Urban affairs/design/planning **Level of Education for which Award is Granted:** Master's, Undergraduate **Number Awarded:** 3 each year: 1 to an undergraduate at an accredited program, 1 to a graduate student at an accredited program, and 1 to a student at a non-accredited program. **Funds Available:** The stipend is $1,000. **Duration:** 1 year.

Eligibility Requirements: This program is open to students entering their final year for an undergraduate or master's degree in an accredited or non-accredited planning program at a university in California. Applicants must be interested in preparing for a career in public planning in California. Selection is based on academic excellence, financial need, and commitment to serve the planning profession in California. **Deadline for Receipt:** April of each year. **Additional Information:** This program is sponsored by the California Planning Roundtable (CPR). The accredited planning programs are at 3 campuses of the California State University system (California State Polytechnic University at Pomona, California Polytechnic State University at San Luis Obispo, and San Jose State University), 3 campuses of the University of California (Berkeley, Irvine, and Los Angeles), and the University of Southern California. The non-accredited programs are at 5 campuses of the California State University system (San Francisco, Sonoma, Northridge, Chico, and San Diego) and 3 campuses of the University of California (Davis, Santa Barbara, and San Diego).

3863 ■ ARIZONA PLANNING ASSOCIATION
10000 North 31st Avenue, Suite D400
Phoenix, AZ 85051
Tel: (602)866-7188
Fax: (602)789-9126
E-mail: arizonaplanning@eschelon.com
Web Site: http://www.azplanning.org
To provide financial assistance to undergraduate and graduate students in planning programs at selected Arizona universities.
Title of Award: Arizona APA Chapter Scholarships **Area, Field, or Subject:** Urban affairs/design/planning **Level of Education for which Award is Granted:** Graduate, Undergraduate **Number Awarded:** 4 each year: 1 to an undergraduate at ASU, 1 to a graduate student at ASU, 1 to a graduate student at UA, and 1 to a graduate student at NAU. **Funds Available:** The stipend is $2,000 per year. **Duration:** 1 year.
Eligibility Requirements: This program is open to undergraduate and graduate students at Arizona State University (ASU), graduate students at the University of Arizona (UA), and graduate students at Northern Arizona University (NAU). Applicants must be enrolled in the planning program at their university. **Additional Information:** Further information is available from Dennis Newcombe, (480) 503-6748, E-mail: dennis@senderlaw.com.

3864 ■ ASSOCIATION FOR WOMEN IN ARCHITECTURE
Attn: Scholarship Chair
22815 Frampton Avenue
Torrance, CA 90501-5034
Tel: (310)534-8466
Fax: (310)257-6885
E-mail: scholarship@awa-la.org
Web Site: http://www.awa-la.org/scholarships.php
To provide financial assistance to women undergraduates in California who are interested in careers in architecture.
Title of Award: Association for Women in Architecture Scholarships **Area, Field, or Subject:** Architecture; Engineering; Engineering, Civil; Engineering, Electrical; Engineering, Mechanical; Graphic art and design; Illustrators and illustrations; Interior design; Landscape architecture and design; Urban affairs/design/planning **Level of Education for which Award is Granted:** Undergraduate **Number Awarded:** 3 each year: 1 at $2,500, 1 at $1,500, and 1 at $1,000. **Funds Available:** Stipends are $2,500, $1,500, or $1,000. **Duration:** 1 year.
Eligibility Requirements: Eligible to apply are women students who have completed at least 1 full year of study in any of the following fields: architecture; civil, structural, mechanical, or electrical engineering as related to architecture; landscape architecture; urban and land planning; interior design; architectural rendering and illustration; or environmental design. They must be residents of California or attending school in California. Interviews are required for semifinalists. Selection is based on grades, a personal statement, financial need, recommendations, and the quality and organization of materials submitted. **Deadline for Receipt:** April of each year.

3865 ■ BEZEK-DURST-SEISER ARCHITECTS AND PLANNERS
Attn: Scholarship Program
3330 C Street, Suite 200
Anchorage, AK 99503
Tel: (907)562-6076
Fax: (907)562-6635
E-mail: bds@bdsak.com
Web Site: http://www.bdsak.com
To provide financial assistance to Alaska Native high school seniors interested in studying architecture, planning, or interior design in college.
Title of Award: Bezek-Durst-Seiser Scholarship Program **Area, Field, or Subject:** Architecture; Interior design; Urban affairs/design/planning **Level of Education for which Award is Granted:** Undergraduate **Number Awarded:** 1 each year. **Funds Available:** The stipend is $1,500 per year. **Duration:** 1 year; may be renewed.
Eligibility Requirements: This program is open to seniors graduating from high schools in Alaska who are Natives accepted into an architecture,

planning, or interior design program. Applications must be submitted through a school district or native corporation; direct applications from students are not accepted. Each school district and native corporation in the state may submit 2 applications. Students must include essays on what they are like, the school activities and interests that interest them, why they have chosen their career field, what they have done to prepare themselves to enter that field, why they chose the university or college they plan to attend, and if they plan to return to Alaska after college. **Deadline for Receipt:** April of each year. **Additional Information:** Recipients are also offered paid internships at the Bezek-Durst-Seiser office in Anchorage during summer breaks.

3866 ■ COMMUNITY FOUNDATION FOR THE FOX VALLEY REGION, INC.
Attn: Scholarships
4455 West Lawrence Street
P.O. Box 563
Appleton, WI 54912-0563
Tel: (920)830-1290
Fax: (920)830-1293
E-mail: cffvr@cffoxvalley.org
Web Site: http://www.cffoxvalley.org/scholarship_fundslist.html
To provide financial assistance to upper-division and graduate students in Wisconsin who are working on a degree related to gardening.
Title of Award: Wisconsin Garden Club Federation Scholarship **Area, Field, or Subject:** Agricultural sciences; Botany; Environmental conservation; Environmental science; Forestry; Horticulture; Landscape architecture and design; Urban affairs/design/planning **Level of Education for which Award is Granted:** Graduate, Four Year College **Number Awarded:** Varies each year; recently, 4 of these scholarships were awarded. **Funds Available:** The stipend is $1,000. **Duration:** 1 year.
Eligibility Requirements: This program is open to college juniors, seniors, and graduate students at colleges and universities in Wisconsin. Applicants must be majoring in horticulture, floriculture, landscape design/architecture, botany, forestry, agronomy, plant pathology, environmental studies, city planning, land management, or a related field. They must have a 3.0 GPA or higher. **Deadline for Receipt:** February of each year. **Additional Information:** This program is sponsored by the Wisconsin Garden Club Federation. Information is also available from Carolyn A. Craig, WGCF Scholarship Chair, 900 North Shore Drive, New Richmond, WI 54017-9466, (715) 246-6242, E-mail: cacraig@frontiernet.net.

3867 ■ CONFERENCE OF MINORITY TRANSPORTATION OFFICIALS-NEW JERSEY CHAPTER
Attn: Scholarship Committee
P.O. Box 22968
Newark, NJ 07101
E-mail: comtonj@mail.comtonj.org
Web Site: http://www.comtonj.org/scholarshipInfo.asp
To provide financial assistance to college students from New Jersey interested in working on a degree in a field related to transportation.
Title of Award: COMTO NJ Scholarships **Area, Field, or Subject:** Environmental conservation; Environmental science; Protective services; Public administration; Transportation; Urban affairs/design/planning **Level of Education for which Award is Granted:** Undergraduate **Number Awarded:** 4 each year: 1 at $1,000 and 3 at $500. **Funds Available:** Stipends are $1,000 or $500. **Duration:** 1 year.
Eligibility Requirements: This program is open to students entering or attending colleges and universities in New Jersey to major in a field related to transportation (e.g., environmental disciplines, public service, safety, transportation, urban planning). Applicants must have a GPA of 3.0 or higher. Along with their application, they must submit a 500-word essay on why they chose a career in transportation. Selection is based on the essay, academic achievement, extracurricular and community activities, and letters of recommendation. **Deadline for Receipt:** April of each year. **Additional Information:** The sponsor is the New Jersey chapter of the Conference of Minority Transportation Officials (COMTO). The national organization was founded in 1971 to promote, strengthen, and expand the roles of minorities in all aspects of transportation. This program includes the Lewis R. Rosser Scholarship, the Paul Smith Scholarship, and the

Garrett Morgan Scholarship. Recipients must attend the COMTO NJ Scholarship Gala to accept the award.

3868 ■ CONNECTICUT BUILDING CONGRESS

Attn: Scholarship Fund
2600 Dixwell Avenue, Suite 7
Hamden, CT 06514-1800
Tel: (203)281-3183
Fax: (203)281-8932
E-mail: info@cbc-ct.org
Web Site: http://www.cbc-ct.org/secondpage_folder/member.html
To provide financial assistance to high school seniors in Connecticut who are interested in studying a field related to the construction industry in college.
Title of Award: Connecticut Building Congress Scholarships **Area, Field, or Subject:** Architecture; Cartography/Surveying; Construction; Engineering; Management; Urban affairs/design/planning **Level of Education for which Award is Granted:** Undergraduate **Number Awarded:** Varies each year. **Funds Available:** Stipends range from $500 to $2,000 per year. **Duration:** Up to 4 years.
Eligibility Requirements: This program is open to graduating seniors at high schools in Connecticut. Applicants must be interested in attending a 2- or 4-year college or university to major in a field related to construction (e.g., architecture, engineering, construction management, surveying, planning, drafting). They must submit an essay (up to 500 words) that explains how their planned studies will relate to a career in the construction industry. Selection is based on academic merit, extracurricular activities, potential, and financial need. **Deadline for Receipt:** February of each year.

3869 ■ CONNECTICUT CHAPTER OF THE AMERICAN PLANNING ASSOCIATION

c/o Alan L. Weiner, Member Services Committee
City Planner, City of Bristol
111 North Main Street
Bristol, CT 06010
Tel: (860)584-6225
Fax: (860)584-3838
E-mail: alanweiner@ci.bristol.ct.us
Web Site: http://www.ccapa.org
To provide financial assistance to undergraduate students in planning or architecture at schools in New England and New York.
Title of Award: Sam Pine Scholarship **Area, Field, or Subject:** Architecture; Urban affairs/design/planning **Level of Education for which Award is Granted:** Undergraduate **Number Awarded:** 1 each year. **Funds Available:** The stipend is $2,000. **Duration:** 1 year.
Eligibility Requirements: This program is open to undergraduate students in planning, architecture, or a related field. Applicants must attend a college or university in New England or New York. Selection is based, first, on financial need and then on academic record. **Additional Information:** This program was established in 1997.

3870 ■ DEPARTMENT OF TRANSPORTATION

Federal Highway Administration
Attn: National Highway Institute, HNHI-20
4600 North Fairfax Drive, Suite 800
Arlington, VA 22203-1553
Tel: (703)235-0538
Fax: (703)235-0593
E-mail: transportationedu@fhwa.dot.gov
Web Site: http://www.nhi.fhwa.dot.gov/ddetfp.asp
To enable students to participate in research activities at facilities of the U.S. Department of Transportation (DOT) Federal Highway Administration in the Washington, D.C. area.
Title of Award: Eisenhower Grants for Research Fellowships **Area, Field, or Subject:** Chemistry; Economics; Engineering; Engineering, Civil; Geography; Information science and technology; Materials research/ science; Operations research; Physics; Public administration; Statistics; Technology; Transportation; Urban affairs/design/planning **Level of Education for which Award is Granted:** Four Year College, Graduate **Number Awarded:** Varies each year; recently, 9 students participated in this program. **Funds Available:** Fellows receive full tuition and fees that relate to the academic credits for the approved research project and a

monthly stipend of $1,450 for college seniors, $1,700 for master's students, or $2,000 for doctoral students. An allowance for travel to and from the DOT facility where the research is conducted is also provided, but selectees are responsible for their own housing accommodations. Faculty advisors are allowed 1 site review on projects over 6 months and 2 site reviews on projects over 9 months; travel and per diem are provided for those site reviews. **Duration:** Tenure is normally 3, 6, 9, or 12 months.
Eligibility Requirements: This program is open to 1) students in their junior year of a baccalaureate program who will complete their junior year before being awarded a fellowship; 2) students in their senior year of a baccalaureate program; and 3) students who have completed their baccalaureate degree and are enrolled in a program leading to a master's, Ph.D., or equivalent degree. Applicants must be U.S. citizens enrolled in an accredited U.S. institution of higher education working on a degree full time and planning to enter the transportation profession after completing their higher education. They select 1 or more projects from a current list of research projects underway at various DOT facilities; the research will be conducted with academic supervision provided by a faculty advisor from their home university (which grants academic credit for the research project) and with technical direction provided by the DOT staff. Specific requirements for the target projects vary; most require engineering backgrounds, but others involve transportation planning, information management, public administration, physics, materials science, statistical analysis, operations research, chemistry, economics, technology transfer, urban studies, geography, and urban and regional planning. The DOT encourages students at Historically Black Colleges and Universities (HBCUs) and Hispanic Serving Institutions (HSIs) to apply for these grants. Selection is based on match of the student's qualifications with the proposed research project (including the student's ability to accomplish the project in the available time), recommendation letters regarding the nominee's qualifications to conduct the research, academic records (including class standing, GPA, and transcripts), and transportation work experience (if any) including the employer's endorsement. **Deadline for Receipt:** February of each year.

3871 ■ FEDERATED GARDEN CLUBS OF CONNECTICUT, INC.

14 Business Park Drive
P.O. Box 854
Branford, CT 06405-0854
Tel: (203)488-5528
Fax: (203)488-5528
E-mail: gardenclubs@ctgardenclubs.org
Web Site: http://www.ctgardenclubs.org/scholarship.html
To provide financial assistance to Connecticut residents who are interested in majoring in horticulture-related fields at a Connecticut college or university.
Title of Award: Federated Garden Clubs of Connecticut Scholarship **Area, Field, or Subject:** Agricultural sciences; Botany; Environmental conservation; Environmental science; Forestry; Horticulture; Landscape architecture and design; Urban affairs/design/planning **Level of Education for which Award is Granted:** Four Year College, Graduate **Number Awarded:** Varies each year, depending upon the availability of funds. **Funds Available:** Stipends are generally about $1,000 each. Funds are sent to the recipient's school in 2 equal installments. **Duration:** 1 year.
Eligibility Requirements: Applicants must be legal residents of Connecticut who are studying at a college or university in the state in horticulture, floriculture, landscape design, conservation, forestry, botany, agronomy, plant pathology, environmental control, city planning, land management, or related subjects. They must be entering their junior or senior year of college or be a graduate student, have a GPA of 3.0 or higher, and be able to demonstrate financial need. **Deadline for Receipt:** June of each year. **Additional Information:** Information is also available from the Connecticut State Scholarship Chair, Mary Gray, 18 Long Hill Farm Road, Guilford, CT 06437, (203) 458-2784.

3872 ■ INSTITUTE OF TRANSPORTATION ENGINEERS-INDIANA SECTION

c/o Ann M. Sheidler, Scholarship Chair
Parsons Brinckerhoff Quade & Douglas, Inc.
300 North Meridian Street, Suite 990
Indianapolis, IN 46204
Tel: (317)972-1706
Fax: (317)972-1708

E-mail: sheidler@pbworld.com
Web Site: http://www.indianaite.org
To provide financial assistance to students in Indiana working on a degree related to transportation engineering.
Title of Award: Edward J. Cox Memorial Transportation Scholarship **Area, Field, or Subject:** Engineering, Civil; Transportation; Urban affairs/design/planning **Level of Education for which Award is Granted:** Graduate, Undergraduate **Number Awarded:** Varies each year; recently, 3 of these scholarships were awarded. **Funds Available:** The stipend is at least $2,500. **Duration:** 1 year.
Eligibility Requirements: This program is open to full-time undergraduate or graduate students who are attending a college or university in Indiana and are working on a degree related to transportation engineering or transportation planning. Applicants may be interested in any of the following areas: roadway or bridge design, pavement design, transportation-related environmental concerns, roadway safety, transit, traffic engineering and design, signal systems, ITS, transportation or urban planning, transportation facilities construction management, or related topics. Along with their application, they must submit a 2-page essay on their understanding of the profession of transportation engineering and planning and how they plan to contribute to the excellence of the profession. Selection is based on past academic performance, educational plans, career goals, extracurricular activities, work experience, and record of leadership. **Deadline for Receipt:** January of each year. **Additional Information:** This scholarship was first awarded in 1997.

3873 ■ NORTH CENTRAL TEXAS COUNCIL OF GOVERNMENTS

Attn: Transportation Department
616 Six Flags Drive, Centerpoint Two
P.O. Box 5888
Arlington, TX 76005-5888
Tel: (817)695-9242
Fax: (817)640-7806
Web Site: http://www.nctcog.org/trans/admin/fellowship
To provide financial assistance to ethnic minorities, women, and economically disadvantaged persons who are interested in obtaining an undergraduate or graduate degree and work experience in a transportation-related field in Texas.
Title of Award: Transportation Fellowship Program **Area, Field, or Subject:** Engineering, Civil; Environmental conservation; Environmental science; Geography; Law; Management; Transportation; Urban affairs/design/planning **Level of Education for which Award is Granted:** Graduate, Undergraduate **Funds Available:** The stipend is $2,000. **Duration:** 1 year; may be renewed if the recipient maintains a GPA of 3.0 or higher.
Eligibility Requirements: This program is open to ethnic minorities (African Americans, Hispanics, American Indians, Alaskan Natives, Asians, and Pacific Islanders), women, and those who are economically disadvantaged. Only U.S. citizens or permanent residents may apply. They must attend or be willing to attend a college or university within the 16-county North Central Texas region as an undergraduate or graduate student. Applicants must have a GPA of 2.5 or higher. They may be enrolled full or part time, but they must be majoring in a designated transportation-related field: transportation planning, transportation or civil engineering, urban and regional planning, transportation/environmental sciences, transportation law, urban or spatial geography, logistics, geographic information systems, or transportation management. Selection is based on financial need, interest in a professional career in transportation, and the ability to complete the program. **Deadline for Receipt:** March of each year. **Additional Information:** These fellowships are financed by the Federal Highway Administration, Federal Transit Administration, and the Texas Department of Transportation, in conjunction with local governments in north central Texas. An important part of the fellowship is an internship with a local agency (city or county), school, or transportation agency.

3874 ■ PENNSYLVANIA PLANNING ASSOCIATION

587 James Drive
Harrisburg, PA 17112-2273
Tel: (717)671-4510
Fax: (717)545-9247
E-mail: info@planningpa.org
Web Site: http://www.planningpa.org/education_scholarships.shtml

To provide financial assistance to undergraduate and graduate students from Pennsylvania who are working on a degree in planning.
Title of Award: Pennsylvania Planning Association Scholarships **Area, Field, or Subject:** Urban affairs/design/planning **Level of Education for which Award is Granted:** Four Year College, Graduate **Number Awarded:** 1 or more each year. **Funds Available:** A stipend is awarded (amount not specified). **Duration:** 1 year.
Eligibility Requirements: This program is open to residents of Pennsylvania and students at Pennsylvania institutions. Applicants must be enrolled as juniors, seniors, or graduate students in a planning curriculum that has a demonstrated record of preparing students to become planners. They must have a GPA of 3.0 or higher and be able to demonstrate financial need. **Additional Information:** This program is supported by the Pitkin Trust and the Spaulding Fund.

3875 ■ SURFRIDER FOUNDATION

Attn: Pratte Scholarship
P.O. Box 6010
San Clemente, CA 92674-6010
Tel: (949)492-8170
Fax: (949)492-8142
E-mail: prattescholarship@surfrider.org
Web Site: http://www.surfrider.org
To provide financial assistance to members of the Surfrider Foundation working on an undergraduate or graduate degree in an environmental field.
Title of Award: Thomas Pratte Memorial Scholarships **Area, Field, or Subject:** Environmental conservation; Environmental science; Marine biology; Natural resources; Oceanography; Public administration; Urban affairs/design/planning **Level of Education for which Award is Granted:** Four Year College, Graduate **Number Awarded:** 3 each year: 1 for a student at each academic level. **Funds Available:** The stipend is $2,000 for an undergraduate, $3,000 for a master's degree student, and $5,000 for a doctoral student. **Duration:** 1 year.
Eligibility Requirements: This program is open to members of the foundation working on an undergraduate, master's, or doctoral degree in a field consistent with the foundation's mission, including (but not limited to) oceanography, marine affairs, environmental sciences, public policy, community planning, or natural resources. Applicants must be enrolled at an accredited college or university in the United States or Puerto Rico as an upper-division or graduate student. Undergraduates must have a GPA of 3.4 or higher and graduate students 3.6 or higher. Along with their application, they must submit 1) a personal statement describing their career goals, volunteer activities, work, or summer plans as they pertain to the coastal environmental issues relevant to the foundation and its mission; and 2) a description of their current research and how it relates to the foundation's stated mission and environmental programs. Financial need is not considered in the selection process. **Deadline for Receipt:** March of each year. **Additional Information:** This foundation, established in 1984 by a group of surfers, is a nonprofit environmental grassroots organization dedicated to the protection and preservation of the world's waves, oceans, and beaches. It currently has 50,000 members with 60 chapters in 22 states.

3876 ■ MORRIS K. UDALL FOUNDATION

130 South Scott Avenue
Tucson, AZ 85701-1922
Tel: (520)670-5529
Fax: (520)670-5530
Web Site: http://www.udall.gov/scholarship
To provide financial assistance to 1) college sophomores and juniors who intend to prepare for a career in environmental public policy and 2) Native American and Alaska Native students who intend to prepare for a career in health care or tribal public policy.
Title of Award: Morris K. Udall Scholarships **Area, Field, or Subject:** Business administration; Economics; Education; Environmental conservation; Environmental science; Health care services; Native American studies; Natural resources; Political science; Public administration; Public health; Urban affairs/design/planning **Level of Education for which Award is Granted:** Undergraduate **Number Awarded:** Approximately 80 scholarships and 50 honorable mentions are awarded each year. **Funds Available:** The maximum stipend for scholarship winners is $5,000 per year. Funds are to be used for tuition, fees, books, and room and board.

Honorable mention stipends are $350. **Duration:** 1 year; recipients nominated as sophomores may be renominated in their junior year.

Eligibility Requirements: Each 2-year and 4-year college and university in the United States and its possessions may nominate up to 6 sophomores or juniors from either or both categories of this program: 1) students who intend to prepare for a career in environmental public policy, and 2) Native American and Alaska Native students who intend to prepare for a career in health care or tribal public policy. For the first category, the program seeks future leaders across a wide spectrum of environmental fields, such as policy, engineering, science, education, urban planning and renewal, business, health, justice, and economics. For the second category, the program seeks future Native American and Alaska Native leaders in public and community health care, tribal government, and public policy affecting Native American communities, including land and resource management, economic development, and education. Nominees must be U.S. citizens, nationals, or permanent residents with a GPA of 3.0 or higher. Along with their application, they must submit an 800-word essay discussing a significant public speech, legislative act, or public policy statement by former Congressman Morris K. Udall and its impact on their field of study, interests, and career goals. Selection is based on demonstrated commitment to 1) environmental issues through substantial commitment to and participation in 1 or more of the following: campus activities, research, community service, or public service; or 2) tribal public policy or Native American health through substantial contributions to and participation in 1 or more of the following: campus activities, tribal involvement, community or public service, or research; a course of study and proposed career likely to lead to position where nominee can make significant contributions to the shaping of environmental, tribal public policy, or Native American health care issues, whether through scientific advances, public or political service, or community action; and leadership, character, desire to make a difference, and general well-roundedness.

Deadline for Receipt: Faculty representatives must submit their nominations by early March of each year.

3877 ■ WORLDSTUDIO FOUNDATION
200 Varick Street, Suite 507
New York, NY 10014
Tel: (212)366-1317
Fax: (212)807-0024
E-mail: scholarshipcoordinator@worldstudio.org
Web Site: http://www.worldstudio.org/schol/index.html

To provide financial assistance to undergraduate and graduate students, especially minorities, who wish to study fine or commercial arts, design, or architecture.

Title of Award: Worldstudio Foundation Scholarships **Area, Field, or Subject:** Advertising; Architecture; Art; Art industries and trade; Crafts; Design; Fashion design; Filmmaking; Graphic art and design; Interior design; Landscape architecture and design; Photography; Urban affairs/design/planning **Level of Education for which Award is Granted:** Graduate, Undergraduate **Number Awarded:** Varies each year; recently, 24 scholarships and 7 honorable mentions were awarded. **Funds Available:** Basic scholarships range from $1,000 to $2,000, but awards between $3,000 and $5,000 are also presented at the discretion of the jury. Honorable mentions are $100. Funds are paid directly to the recipient's school. **Duration:** 1 academic year. Recipients may reapply.

Eligibility Requirements: This program is open to undergraduate and graduate students who are currently enrolled or planning to enroll at an accredited college or university and major in 1 of the following areas: advertising (art direction only), architecture, crafts, environmental graphics, fashion design, film/video (direction or cinematography only), film/theater design (including set, lighting, and costume design), fine arts, furniture design, graphic design, industrial/product design, interior design, landscape architecture, new media, photography, surface/textile design, or urban planning. Although not required, minority status is a significant factor in the selection process. International students may apply if they are enrolled at a U.S. college or university. Applicants must have a GPA of 2.0 or higher. Along with their application, they must submit a 600-word statement of purpose that includes a brief autobiography, an explanation of how their experiences have influenced their creative work and/or their career plans, and how they see themselves contributing to the community at large in the future. Selection is based on that statement, the quality of submitted work, financial need, minority status, and academic record.

Deadline for Receipt: March of each year. **Additional Information:** The foundation encourages the scholarship recipients to focus on ways that their work can address issues of social and environmental responsibility. This program includes the following named awards: the Sherry and Gary Baker Award, the Bobolink Foundation Award, the Bombay Sapphire Awards, the Richard and Jean Coyne Family Foundation Awards, the David A. Dechman Foundation Awards, the Philip and Edina Jennison Award, the Kraus Family Foundation Awards, the Dena McKelvey Award. the New York Design Center Award, the Rudin Foundation Awards, the Starr Foundation Awards, and the John F. Wright III Award.

General

3878 ■ AMERICAN FEDERATION OF TELEVISION AND RADIO ART-ISTS

Attn: AFTRA/Heller Memorial Foundation, Inc.
260 Madison Avenue, Seventh Floor
New York, NY 10016
Tel: (212)532-0800
Fax: (212)532-2242
E-mail: info@aftra.com
Web Site: http://www.aftra.org/benefits/scholarship.htm
To provide financial assistance to undergraduate and graduate students who are members or the dependent children of members of the American Federation of Television and Radio Artists (AFTRA).
Title of Award: AFTRA/Heller Memorial Foundation Scholarships **Area, Field, or Subject:** Communications; General studies/Field of study not specified; Industrial and labor relations; Journalism; Performing arts **Level of Education for which Award is Granted:** Graduate, Undergraduate **Number Awarded:** 12 to 15 each year. **Funds Available:** Stipends up to $2,500 per year are available. **Duration:** 1 year; nonrenewable.

Eligibility Requirements: This program is open to AFTRA members and the dependent children of AFTRA members (or deceased members) in good standing for at least 5 years. Applicants may be interested in working on a bachelor's or advanced degree in any field, including broadcast journalism and labor relations, or professional training in the performing arts. Selection is based on academic achievement and financial need. **Deadline for Receipt:** April of each year.

3879 ■ AMERICAN HEALTH INFORMATION MANAGEMENT AS-SOCIATION

Attn: Foundation of Research and Education
233 North Michigan Avenue, Suite 2150
Chicago, IL 60601-5806
Tel: (312)233-1168
Fax: (312)233-1090
E-mail: fore@ahima.org
Web Site: http://www.ahima.org/fore/programs.asp
To provide financial assistance to minority members of the American Health Information Management Association (AHIMA) who are interested in working on an undergraduate or graduate degree in health information administration or technology.
Title of Award: FORE Diversity Scholarships **Area, Field, or Subject:** Health care services; Information science and technology; Management; Technology **Level of Education for which Award is Granted:** Graduate, Undergraduate **Number Awarded:** Varies each year. Recently, 5 of these scholarships were awarded: 4 to undergraduates and 1 to a graduate student. **Funds Available:** Stipends range from $1,000 to $5,000. **Duration:** 1 year; nonrenewable.
Eligibility Requirements: This program is open to AHIMA members who are enrolled in a health information administration or health information technology program accredited by the Commission on Accreditation of Allied Health Education Programs. Applicants must be minorities, be working on an undergraduate or graduate degree on at least a half-time basis,

and have a GPA of 3.0 or higher. U.S. citizenship is required. Selection is based (in order of importance) on GPA and academic achievement, volunteer and work experience, commitment to the health information management profession, suitability to the health information management profession, quality and suitability of references provided, and clarity of application. **Deadline for Receipt:** May of each year.

3880 ■ AMERICAN HEALTH INFORMATION MANAGEMENT AS-SOCIATION

Attn: Foundation of Research and Education
233 North Michigan Avenue, Suite 2150
Chicago, IL 60601-5806
Tel: (312)233-1168
Fax: (312)233-1090
E-mail: fore@ahima.org
Web Site: http://www.ahima.org/fore/programs.asp
To provide financial assistance to members of the American Health Information Management Association (AHIMA) who are interested in working on an undergraduate degree in health information administration or technology.
Title of Award: FORE Undergraduate Merit Scholarships **Area, Field, or Subject:** Health care services; Information science and technology; Management; Technology **Level of Education for which Award is Granted:** Undergraduate **Number Awarded:** Varies each year; recently, 41 of these scholarships were awarded. **Funds Available:** Stipends range from $1,000 to $5,000. **Duration:** 1 year; nonrenewable.
Eligibility Requirements: This program is open to AHIMA members who are enrolled in a health information administration or health information technology program accredited by the Commission on Accreditation of Allied Health Education Programs. Applicants must be working on a degree on at least a half-time basis and have a GPA of 3.0 or higher. U.S. citizenship is required. Selection is based (in order of importance) on GPA and academic achievement, volunteer and work experience, commitment to the health information management profession, suitability to the health information management profession, quality and suitability of references provided, and clarity of application. **Deadline for Receipt:** May of each year. **Additional Information:** This program includes the following named scholarships (not all of which may be offered each year): the David A. Cohen Scholarship (established in 2004), the Jimmy Gamble Memorial Scholarship (established in 2001 and sponsored by 3M Health Information Systems), the Sanfra L. Key Memorial Scholarship (established in 2003 and sponsored by Healthcare Contract Resources), the Lucretia Spears Scholarship (established in 1998), the Julia LeBlond Memorial Undergraduate Scholarships (sponsored by St. Anthony Publishing/Medicode, Ingenix Companies), the Rita Finnegan Memorial Scholarship (established in 2001 and sponsored by MC Strategies, Inc.), the Annie Blaylock Memorial Scholarship (established in 2002), the Connie Marshall Memorial Scholarship (established in 2004 and sponsored by MedQuist Inc.), the Bright Future Scholarship (sponsored by previous Merit Scholarship recipients), the PricewaterhouseCoopers Scholarship, the Smart Corporation Scholarships, the Aspen Systems Corporation Scholarship, the Care

Communications, Inc. Scholarship, the Siemens Medical Solutions Scholarship, and the Precyse Solutions, Inc. Scholarship.

3881 ■ AMERICAN HEALTH INFORMATION MANAGEMENT AS-SOCIATION

Attn: Foundation of Research and Education
233 North Michigan Avenue, Suite 2150
Chicago, IL 60601-5806
Tel: (312)233-1168
Fax: (312)233-1090
E-mail: fore@ahima.org
Web Site: http://www.ahima.org/fore/programs.asp
To provide educational loans to undergraduate members of the American Health Information Management Association (AHIMA) who are interested in majoring in health information administration or technology.
Title of Award: FORE Undergraduate Student Loans **Area, Field, or Subject:** Health care services; Information science and technology; Management; Technology **Level of Education for which Award is Granted:** Undergraduate **Number Awarded:** Several each year. **Funds Available:** Loans are provided up to $1,000 for coding specialist programs, up to $2,000 for technology programs, and up to $5,000 for management programs. Repayment at 8% interest must be completed within 3 years after graduation. **Duration:** 1 year; may be renewed.
Eligibility Requirements: This program is open to 1) undergraduate students who are accepted for enrollment in a program for health information administration or health information technology that is approved by the Commission on Accreditation of Allied Health Education Programs or 2) students enrolled in a coding specialist program affiliated with a regionally accredited college or university. Applicants must be U.S. citizens making satisfactory progress toward a degree or certificate. Selection is based on demonstrated need and ability to repay a loan. **Deadline for Receipt:** May of each year.

3882 ■ AMERICAN HEALTH INFORMATION MANAGEMENT AS-SOCIATION

Attn: Foundation of Research and Education
233 North Michigan Avenue, Suite 2150
Chicago, IL 60601-5806
Tel: (312)233-1168
Fax: (312)233-1090
E-mail: fore@ahima.org
Web Site: http://www.ahima.org/fore/programs.asp
To provide financial assistance to members of the American Health Information Management Association (AHIMA) from Colorado who are interested in working on an undergraduate or graduate degree in health information administration or technology.
Title of Award: Viola M. Griffin Memorial Scholarship **Area, Field, or Subject:** Health care services; Information science and technology; Management; Technology **Level of Education for which Award is Granted:** Graduate, Undergraduate **Number Awarded:** 1 each year. **Funds Available:** The stipend ranges from $1,000 to $5,000. **Duration:** 1 year; nonrenewable.
Eligibility Requirements: This program is open to AHIMA members who are residents of Colorado and enrolled in a health information administration or health information technology program accredited by the Commission on Accreditation of Allied Health Education Programs. Applicants must be working on an undergraduate or graduate degree on at least a half-time basis and have a GPA of 3.0 or higher. U.S. citizenship is required. Selection is based on (in order of importance) GPA and academic achievement, volunteer and work experience, commitment to the health information management profession, suitability to the health information management profession, quality and suitability of references provided, and clarity of application. **Deadline for Receipt:** May of each year. **Additional Information:** Funding for this program, established in 2003, is provided by Craig Hospital.

3883 ■ AMERICAN HEALTH INFORMATION MANAGEMENT AS-SOCIATION

Attn: Foundation of Research and Education
233 North Michigan Avenue, Suite 2150
Chicago, IL 60601-5806
Tel: (312)233-1168
Fax: (312)233-1090

E-mail: fore@ahima.org
Web Site: http://www.ahima.org/fore/programs.asp
To provide financial assistance to members of the American Health Information Management Association (AHIMA) who are single parents interested in working on an undergraduate or graduate degree in health information administration or technology.
Title of Award: Redi-Tag Corporation Scholarship **Area, Field, or Subject:** Health care services; Information science and technology; Management; Technology **Level of Education for which Award is Granted:** Graduate, Undergraduate **Number Awarded:** 1 each year. **Funds Available:** The stipend ranges from $1,000 to $5,000. **Duration:** 1 year; nonrenewable.
Eligibility Requirements: This program is open to AHIMA members who are single parents enrolled in a health information administration or health information technology program accredited by the Commission on Accreditation of Allied Health Education Programs. Applicants must be working on an undergraduate or graduate degree on at least a half-time basis and have a GPA of 3.0 or higher. U.S. citizenship is required. Selection is based on (in order of importance) GPA and academic achievement, volunteer and work experience, commitment to the health information management profession, suitability to the health information management profession, quality and suitability of references provided, and clarity of application. **Deadline for Receipt:** May of each year. **Additional Information:** Funding for this program is provided by the Redi-Tag Corporation.

3884 ■ AMERICAN HEALTH INFORMATION MANAGEMENT AS-SOCIATION

Attn: Foundation of Research and Education
233 North Michigan Avenue, Suite 2150
Chicago, IL 60601-5806
Tel: (312)233-1168
Fax: (312)233-1090
E-mail: fore@ahima.org
Web Site: http://www.ahima.org/fore/programs.asp
To provide financial assistance to African American members of the American Health Information Management Association (AHIMA) who are interested in working on an undergraduate or graduate degree in health information administration or technology.
Title of Award: Esther Mayo Sherard Scholarship **Area, Field, or Subject:** Health care services; Information science and technology; Management; Technology **Level of Education for which Award is Granted:** Graduate, Undergraduate **Number Awarded:** 1 each year. **Funds Available:** The stipend ranges from $1,000 to $5,000. **Duration:** 1 year; nonrenewable.
Eligibility Requirements: This program is open to AHIMA members who are African Americans enrolled in a health information administration or health information technology program accredited by the Commission on Accreditation of Allied Health Education Programs. Applicants must be working on an undergraduate or graduate degree on at least a half-time basis and have a GPA of 3.0 or higher. U.S. citizenship is required. Selection is based on (in order of importance) on GPA and academic achievement, volunteer and work experience, commitment to the health information management profession, suitability to the health information management profession, quality and suitability of references provided, and clarity of application. **Deadline for Receipt:** May of each year. **Additional Information:** This program was established in 2000 by the Esther Mayo Sherard Foundation.

3885 ■ AMERICAN INDIAN COLLEGE FUND

Attn: Scholarship Department
8333 Greenwood Boulevard
Denver, CO 80221
Tel: (303)426-8900
Free: 800-776-FUND
Fax: (303)426-1200
E-mail: info@collegefund.org
Web Site: http://www.collegefund.org/scholarships/main.html
To provide financial assistance to American Indian students currently enrolled full time at a tribal college or university to prepare for a career in business and the financial services industry.
Title of Award: Morgan Stanley Tribal College Scholars Program **Area, Field, or Subject:** Accounting; Banking; Business administration; Finance; Information science and technology; Marketing and distribution

Level of Education for which Award is Granted: Undergraduate **Number Awarded:** 10 each year. **Funds Available:** The stipend is $2,500. **Duration:** 1 year.

Eligibility Requirements: Eligible to apply are American Indians or Alaska Natives who are enrolled full time in either an associate's or bachelor's degree program at an accredited tribal college or university. Applicants must be able to demonstrate exceptional academic achievement (GPA of 3.0 or higher), as well as leadership, service, and commitment to the American Indian community. They must be interested in a career in business and the financial services industry (e.g., information technology, investment banking, marketing, financial accounting). Along with their application, they must submit official college transcripts; personal essays (500 words or less) on their personal and academic background, a role model who has motivated them, and an experience or risk they have taken and its impact on them; 2 letters of recommendation; tribal enrollment information; a statement regarding any financial hardship they have; and a color photograph. **Deadline for Receipt:** April of each year. **Additional Information:** This scholarship is sponsored by Morgan Stanley, in partnership with the American Indian College Fund.

3886 ■ AMERICAN INSTITUTE OF CERTIFIED PUBLIC AC- COUNTANTS

Attn: Academic and Career Development Division
1211 Avenue of the Americas
New York, NY 10036-8775
Tel: (212)596-6224
Fax: (212)596-6292
E-mail: educat@aicpa.org
Web Site: http://www.aicpa.org/nolimits/become/ships/AICPA.htm
To provide financial assistance to student affiliate members of the American Institute of Certified Public Accountants (AICPA) who are working on an undergraduate or graduate degree in accounting, finance, or information systems.

Title of Award: Accountemps/AICPA Student Scholarship **Area, Field, or Subject:** Accounting; Finance; Information science and technology **Level of Education for which Award is Granted:** Four Year College, Graduate **Number Awarded:** 2 each year. **Funds Available:** The stipend is $2,500. **Duration:** 1 year.

Eligibility Requirements: This program is open to full-time undergraduate and graduate students who are AICPA student affiliate members with a declared major in accounting, finance, or information systems. Applicants must have completed at least 30 semester hours, including at least 6 semesters in accounting, with a GPA of 3.0 or higher and be a U.S. citizen. Students who will be transferring to a 4-year school must include an acceptance letter from that school. Selection is based on outstanding academic achievement, leadership, and future career interests. **Deadline for Receipt:** March of each year.

3887 ■ AMERICAN NUCLEAR SOCIETY

Attn: Scholarship Coordinator
555 North Kensington Avenue
La Grange Park, IL 60526-5592
Tel: (708)352-6611
Fax: (708)352-0499
E-mail: outreach@ans.org
Web Site: http://www.ans.org/honors/scholarships
To provide financial assistance to undergraduate and graduate students who are interested in preparing for a career in nuclear science.

Title of Award: James R. Vogt Radiochemistry Scholarship **Area, Field, or Subject:** Chemistry; Nuclear science **Level of Education for which Award is Granted:** Four Year College, Graduate **Number Awarded:** 1 each year. **Funds Available:** The stipend is $2,000 for undergraduate students or $3,000 for graduate students. **Duration:** 1 year; nonrenewable.

Eligibility Requirements: This program is open to juniors, seniors, and first-year graduate students who are enrolled in or proposing to undertake research in radio-analytical chemistry, analytical chemistry, or analytical applications of nuclear science. Applicants must be U.S. citizens or

permanent residents and able to demonstrate academic achievement. **Deadline for Receipt:** January of each year.

3888 ■ AMERICAN RADIO RELAY LEAGUE

Attn: ARRL Foundation
225 Main Street
Newington, CT 06111
Tel: (860)594-0397
Fax: (860)594-0259
E-mail: foundation@arrl.org
Web Site: http://www.arrl.org/arrlf/scholgen.html
To provide financial assistance to licensed radio amateurs who are interested in working on an undergraduate or graduate degree, especially in electronics or communications.

Title of Award: Irving W. Cook, WA0CGS, Scholarship **Area, Field, or Subject:** Communications; Electronics; General studies/Field of study not specified **Level of Education for which Award is Granted:** Graduate, Undergraduate **Number Awarded:** 1 each year. **Funds Available:** The stipend is $1,000. **Duration:** 1 year.

Eligibility Requirements: This program is open to undergraduate or graduate students at accredited institutions who are licensed radio amateurs (any class). Applicants must submit an essay on the role amateur radio has played in their lives and provide documentation of financial need. Preference is given to applicants from Kansas who are majoring in electronics, communications, or related fields. **Deadline for Receipt:** January of each year. **Additional Information:** Recipients may attend school in any state.

3889 ■ AMERICAN RADIO RELAY LEAGUE

Attn: ARRL Foundation
225 Main Street
Newington, CT 06111
Tel: (860)594-0397
Fax: (860)594-0259
E-mail: foundation@arrl.org
Web Site: http://www.arrl.org/arrlf/scholgen.html
To provide financial assistance to licensed radio amateurs, particularly from Arizona and selected counties in California, who are interested in working on an undergraduate or graduate degree, particularly in electronics, communications, or related fields.

Title of Award: Charles N. Fisher Memorial Scholarship **Area, Field, or Subject:** Communications; Electronics; General studies/Field of study not specified **Level of Education for which Award is Granted:** Graduate, Undergraduate **Number Awarded:** 1 each year. **Funds Available:** The stipend is $1,000. **Duration:** 1 year.

Eligibility Requirements: This program is open to undergraduate or graduate students at accredited institutions who are licensed radio amateurs (any class). Applicants must submit an essay on the role amateur radio has played in their lives and provide documentation of financial need. Preference is given to students who are 1) residents of Arizona or selected counties in California (Los Angeles, Orange, San Diego, Santa Barbara), and 2) majoring in electronics, communications, or related fields. **Deadline for Receipt:** January of each year.

3890 ■ AMERICAN RADIO RELAY LEAGUE

Attn: ARRL Foundation
225 Main Street
Newington, CT 06111
Tel: (860)594-0397
Fax: (860)594-0259
E-mail: foundation@arrl.org
Web Site: http://www.arrl.org/arrlf/scholgen.html
To provide financial assistance to licensed radio amateurs who are interested in working on an undergraduate or graduate degree, particularly in electronics or communications.

Title of Award: Paul and Helen L. Grauer Scholarship **Area, Field, or Subject:** Communications; Electronics; General studies/Field of study not specified **Level of Education for which Award is Granted:** Graduate, Undergraduate **Number Awarded:** 1 each year. **Funds Available:** The stipend is $1,000. **Duration:** 1 year.

Eligibility Requirements: This program is open to undergraduate or graduate students at accredited institutions who are licensed radio amateurs of the novice class or higher. Preference is given to students who are 1) residents of Iowa, Kansas, Missouri, or Nebraska and attending schools in those states, and 2) majoring in electronics, communications, or related fields. Applicants must submit an essay on the role amateur radio has played in their lives and provide documentation of financial need. **Deadline for Receipt:** January of each year.

3891 ■ AMERICAN RADIO RELAY LEAGUE

Attn: ARRL Foundation
225 Main Street
Newington, CT 06111
Tel: (860)594-0397
Fax: (860)594-0259
E-mail: foundation@arrl.org
Web Site: http://www.arrl.org/arrlf/scholgen.html
To provide financial assistance to licensed radio amateurs from designated states who are interested in working on an undergraduate or graduate degree, particularly in electronics or communications.
Title of Award: L. Phil Wicker Scholarship **Area, Field, or Subject:** Communications; Electronics; General studies/Field of study not specified **Level of Education for which Award is Granted:** Graduate, Undergraduate **Number Awarded:** 1 each year. **Funds Available:** The stipend is $1,000. **Duration:** 1 year.
Eligibility Requirements: This program is open to undergraduate or graduate students at accredited institutions who are licensed radio amateurs of general class. Preference is given to students who are 1) residents of North Carolina, South Carolina, Virginia, or West Virginia and attending school in those states, and 2) majoring in electronics, communications, or related fields. Applicants must submit an essay on the role amateur radio has played in their lives and provide documentation of financial need. **Deadline for Receipt:** January of each year.

3892 ■ ASSOCIATION OF INFORMATION TECHNOLOGY PROFESSIONALS

Attn: Foundation for Information Technology Education
401 North Michigan Avenue, Suite 2400
Chicago, IL 60611-4267
Tel: (312)245-1070
Free: 800-224-9371
Fax: (312)527-6636
E-mail: larry_schmitz@aitp.org
Web Site: http://www.edfoundation.org
To provide financial assistance to students working on a degree (at any level) in information technology.
Title of Award: Kevin Jetton Service Scholarship **Area, Field, or Subject:** Information science and technology **Level of Education for which Award is Granted:** Graduate, Undergraduate **Number Awarded:** 1 each year. **Funds Available:** A stipend is awarded (amount not specified). **Duration:** 1 year.
Eligibility Requirements: Eligible to apply are full-time students who are working on an associate, bachelor's, master's, or doctoral degree in information technology in the United States. Applicants must be members of the Association of Information Technology Professionals. Selection is based on scholastic ability, demonstrated record of service to fellow information technology students and professionals, leadership potential, and financial need. **Deadline for Receipt:** May of each year. **Additional Information:** This scholarship was first awarded in 2004.

3893 ■ ASSOCIATION OF INFORMATION TECHNOLOGY PROFESSIONALS

Attn: Foundation for Information Technology Education
401 North Michigan Avenue, Suite 2400
Chicago, IL 60611-4267
Tel: (312)245-1070
Free: 800-224-9371
Fax: (312)527-6636
E-mail: larry_schmitz@aitp.org
Web Site: http://www.edfoundation.org
To provide financial assistance to students working on a degree (at any level) in information technology.
Title of Award: Betty Stevens-Frecknall Scholarships **Area, Field, or Subject:** Information science and technology **Level of Education for which Award is Granted:** Graduate, Undergraduate **Number Awarded:** Varies each year; recently, 2 of these scholarships were awarded. **Funds Available:** The stipend is $2,000. **Duration:** 1 year.

Eligibility Requirements: Eligible to apply are full-time students who are working on an associate, bachelor's, master's, or doctoral degree in information technology in the United States. Applicants must be members of the Association of Information Technology Professionals. Selection is based on scholastic ability, leadership potential, and financial need. **Deadline for Receipt:** May of each year.

3894 ■ ASSOCIATION OF INFORMATION TECHNOLOGY PROFESSIONALS-OMAHA CHAPTER

Attn: Scholarship Committee
P.O. Box 583
Omaha, NE 68101
Tel: (402)449-2180
E-mail: aitp@novia.net
Web Site: http://www.aitpomaha.org/scholarship/Default.htm
To provide financial assistance to high school seniors and college students who either reside in or will be studying in Nebraska or western Iowa and who plan to major in information systems.
Title of Award: AITP Omaha Scholarship **Area, Field, or Subject:** Information science and technology **Level of Education for which Award is Granted:** Undergraduate **Number Awarded:** Several each year. **Funds Available:** The maximum stipend is $1,000. **Duration:** 1 year.
Eligibility Requirements: This program is open to 1) students who are enrolled or planning to enroll at a 4-year college or university, community college, or technical school in Nebraska or western Iowa and major in information systems or a related field, and 2) members of the Omaha or Lincoln chapters of the Association of Information Technology Professionals, their spouses, and their children who are interested in attending a college or university in any state and major in information systems Applicants must include an essay of 250 to 500 words on 1) what motivated them to choose the field of information technology, the goals they have set, and how they plan to achieve those goals; or 2) a challenge facing professionals entering the field today and what they have done to prepare for that challenge. Selection is based on the essay, 2 letters of recommendation, academic achievement, job experience, participation in local community organizations, participation in high school and/or college extracurricular activities, and leadership and other awards received. Financial need is not considered. **Deadline for Receipt:** April of each year.

3895 ■ BULLETIN OF THE ATOMIC SCIENTISTS

Attn: Rieser Fellowship
6042 South Kimbark Avenue
Chicago, IL 60637-2806
Tel: (773)702-2555
Fax: (773)702-0725
Web Site: http://www.thebulletin.org/about_us/rieser_fellowships.htm
To provide funding to undergraduate students interested in developing a project, at home or abroad, that will enable them to investigate the role of scientists in formulating public policy and in addressing global security policy challenges.
Title of Award: Leonard M. Rieser Fellowship in Science, Technology, and Global Security **Area, Field, or Subject:** International affairs and relations; Public administration; Science; Technology **Level of Education for which Award is Granted:** Undergraduate **Number Awarded:** 3 to 5 each year. **Funds Available:** Stipends range from $2,500 to $5,000. **Duration:** 1 year; nonrenewable.
Eligibility Requirements: This program is open to students at U.S. colleges and universities who are interested in exploring the connections between science, technology, global security, and public policy. Applicants must be seeking funding to 1) provide a stipend for an otherwise unpaid full-time internship; 2) underwrite the cost of travel or transportation to support academic research; 3) participate in or travel to professional conferences where they present academic research; or 4) underwrite the production costs of a special project, ranging from laboratory work to the making of a documentary film. The proposed activity may take place in the United States or abroad. Along with their application, they must submit a narrative (from 800 to 1,000 words) describing the intended use of the fellowship; a 1-page personal essay explaining how they would benefit from the fellowship and the experience being proposed; a detail project budget; and 2 letters of recommendation. Selection is based on demonstrated interest in the fields of science, technology, and public

policy, international affairs, or global security policy. Science students are especially encouraged to apply. **Deadline for Receipt:** March of each year. **Additional Information:** This program was established in 1999.

3896 ■ C I HOST

1901 Central Drive
Bedford, TX 76021
Tel: (817)868-9931; 888-565-1115
Fax: (817)868-7203
E-mail: pr@cihost.com
Web Site: http://www.cihost.com
To provide financial assistance to high school students planning to attend college and study a technology-based field.
Title of Award: C I Host Technology Scholarship **Area, Field, or Subject:** Technology **Level of Education for which Award is Granted:** Undergraduate **Number Awarded:** 1 each year. **Funds Available:** The stipend is $2,500. **Duration:** 1 year; nonrenewable.
Eligibility Requirements: This program is open to students currently enrolled as juniors or seniors in high school. Applicants must be planning to attend an accredited 2-year or 4-year college or university to study technology or major in a technology-based field as a full-time student. Along with their application, they must submit a written proposal for a new and innovative online service or product; the proposal must include an outline of the idea, a complete technical description and/or drawing for execution of the idea, and a business to sell the idea. **Additional Information:** This program began in 2003.

3897 ■ CALIFORNIA LABOR FEDERATION, AFL-CIO

Attn: Education Committee
600 Grand Avenue, Suite 410
Oakland, CA 94610-3561
Tel: (510)663-4024
Fax: (510)663-4099
E-mail: scholarships@calaborfed.org
Web Site: http://www.calaborfed.org/Scholarship.htm
To recognize and reward, with college scholarships, graduating high school seniors in California who submit outstanding essays on topics related to labor unions.
Title of Award: California Labor Federation Scholarships **Area, Field, or Subject:** General studies/Field of study not specified; Industrial and labor relations; Writing **Level of Education for which Award is Granted:** Undergraduate **Number Awarded:** Varies each year; recently, 22 of these awards were presented. **Funds Available:** The award is a $2,000 scholarship. **Duration:** The competition is held annually.
Eligibility Requirements: This competition is open to graduating high school students in public, private, or parochial schools in California who plan to enroll in an accredited college or technical school. Applicants must write an essay of up to 1,000 words on topics that change annually; recently, students were invited to write on an important event in the history of California's unions, why it was important when it happened, and what impact it has on working people in California today. Essays are submitted to high school principals who forward them for judging. **Deadline for Receipt:** April of each year. **Additional Information:** This program is administered by the University of California's Center for Labor Research and Education, 2521 Channing Way, Berkeley, CA 94720-5555, (510) 642-0323, Fax: (510) 642-6432, E-mail: osmer@uclink4.berkeley.edu.

3898 ■ DATATEL SCHOLARS FOUNDATION

4375 Fair Lakes Court
Fairfax, VA 22033
Tel: (703)968-9000
Free: 800-486-4332
Fax: (703)968-4573
E-mail: scholars@datatel.com
Web Site: http://www.datatel.com
To provide financial assistance to graduating high school seniors, continuing college students, or graduate students who will be majoring in a field related to information technology at a Datatel client school.
Title of Award: Nancy Goodhue Lynch Scholarship **Area, Field, or Subject:** Information science and technology **Level of Education for which Award is Granted:** Graduate, Undergraduate **Number Awarded:** 2 each year. **Funds Available:** The stipend is $2,500. Funds are paid directly to the institution. **Duration:** 1 year.

Eligibility Requirements: This program is open to students who will attend a Datatel client college or university during the upcoming school year. Applicants must be majoring or planning to major in a program related to information technology. They first apply to their institution, which selects 1 semifinalist and forwards the application to the sponsor. Along with their application, they must include a personal statement that explains why they chose to study in a technology-related field, the impact of technology and their future, and the importance of receiving this scholarship. Selection is based on the quality of the personal statement (40%), academic merit (30%), achievements and civic involvement (20%), and 2 letters of recommendation (10%). **Deadline for Receipt:** Students must submit online applications to their institution or organization by January of each year. **Additional Information:** Datatel, Inc. produces advanced information technology solutions for higher education. It has more than 470 client sites in the United States and Canada.

3899 ■ ENVIRONMENTAL PROTECTION AGENCY

Attn: National Center for Environmental Research
Ariel Rios Building - 3500
1200 Pennsylvania Avenue, N.W.
Washington, DC 20460
Tel: (202)343-9862
E-mail: barnwell.thomas@epa.gov
Web Site: http://es.epa.gov/ncer/P3
To provide funding to teams of undergraduate and graduate students interested in conducting a research project related to environmental sustainability.
Title of Award: P3 Award Program **Area, Field, or Subject:** Agricultural sciences; Biological and clinical sciences; Chemistry; Energy-related areas; Environmental conservation; Environmental science; Information science and technology; Public health; Transportation; Water resources **Level of Education for which Award is Granted:** Graduate, Undergraduate **Number Awarded:** Varies each year. Recently, 42 Phase I grants were awarded, of which 10 were selected to receive Phase II grants. **Funds Available:** Phase I grants are $10,000. Phase II grants are $75,000. Grants cover all direct and indirect costs; cost-sharing is not required. **Duration:** 1 year for Phase I and 1 additional year for Phase II.
Eligibility Requirements: This competition is open to teams of undergraduate and graduate students at U.S. colleges and universities who are interested in conducting a research project related to the 3 components of sustainability: people, prosperity, and the planet. Projects must address the causes, effects, extent, prevention, reduction, or elimination of air, water, or solid and hazardous waste pollution. Categories include agriculture (e.g., irrigation practices, reduction or elimination of pesticides); materials and chemicals (e.g., materials conservation, green engineering, green chemistry, biotechnology, recovery and reuse of materials); energy (e.g., reduction in air emissions, energy conservation); information technology (e.g., delivery of and access to environmental performance, technical, educational, or public health information related environmental decision making); water (e.g., quality, quantity, conservation, availability, and access); or the built environment (e.g., environmental benefits through innovative green buildings, transportation, and mobility strategies, and smart growth as it results in reduced vehicle miles traveled or reduces storm water runoff). Student teams, with a faculty advisor (who serves as the principal investigator on the grant), submit designs for Phase I of the competition. Selection of grantees is based on the extent to which the proposed project achieves the outcomes of minimizing the use and generation of hazardous substances; utilizes resources and energy effectively and efficiently; and advances the goals of economic competitiveness, human health, and environmental protection for societal benefit. Recipients of Phase I grants are then invited to apply for additional funding through a Phase I grant. **Deadline for Receipt:** February of each year. **Additional Information:** This program began in 2004. It is supported by a large number of organizations from industry, the nonprofit sector, and the federal government.

3900 ■ FOUNDATION FOR AMATEUR RADIO, INC.

Attn: Scholarship Committee
P.O. Box 831
Riverdale, MD 20738
E-mail: aa3of@arrl.net
Web Site: http://www.amateurradio-far.org/scholarships.php

To provide funding to licensed radio amateurs in Florida who are interested in studying electronics or other subjects in college.

Title of Award: Tropical Hamboree Scholarships **Area, Field, or Subject:** Electronics; General studies/Field of study not specified; Science **Level of Education for which Award is Granted:** Undergraduate **Number Awarded:** 1 each year. **Funds Available:** The stipend is $1,000. **Duration:** 1 year.

Eligibility Requirements: Applicants must be residents of Florida and intend to work on a bachelor's degree. There is no restriction on the course of study; however, preference is given to those studying electronics or science-related fields. The minimum license requirement is technician class. **Deadline for Receipt:** Requests for applications must be submitted by April of each year. **Additional Information:** This program, established in 1983, is sponsored by the Dade Radio Club of Miami. Recipients must attend an accredited school (university, college, or technical institute) on a full-time basis.

3901 ■ FOUNDRY EDUCATIONAL FOUNDATION

1695 North Penny Lane
Schaumburg, IL 60173
Tel: (847)490-9200
Fax: (847)890-6270
E-mail: info@fefoffice.org
Web Site: http://www.fefinc.org
To provide financial assistance to undergraduate students, especially those in Wisconsin, who are interested in preparing for a career in the die casting industry.

Title of Award: AFS Wisconsin Past President Fund **Area, Field, or Subject:** Business; Manufacturing **Level of Education for which Award is Granted:** Undergraduate **Number Awarded:** 1 each year. **Funds Available:** The stipends range from $500 to $2,000 per year. **Duration:** 1 year.

Eligibility Requirements: This program is open to full-time undergraduate and graduate students who are U.S. citizens, have taken or plan to take courses in the die-casting process, and can demonstrate their intention to prepare for a career in the die-casting industry. Preference is given first to residents of Wisconsin within the area of the American Foundrymen's Society (AFS) chapter, then to residents of Wisconsin outside the AFS area, then to residents of states adjacent to Wisconsin, then to residents of other states. Preference is also given to students attending a college or university with an agreement with the Foundry Educational Foundation (FEF), then to students attending school in Wisconsin, then to students attending school in an adjacent state. In addition, preference is given to applicants who are currently participating in a co-op program involving the cast metal industry, who have work experience in the cast metal industry, who have any manufacturing work experience, and who have any work experience. **Deadline for Receipt:** January of each year. **Additional Information:** This scholarship is provided by the Wisconsin Chapter of the American Foundrymen's Society (AFS).

3902 ■ FOUNDRY EDUCATIONAL FOUNDATION

1695 North Penny Lane
Schaumburg, IL 60173
Tel: (847)490-9200
Fax: (847)890-6270
E-mail: info@fefoffice.org
Web Site: http://www.fefinc.org
To provide financial assistance to undergraduate students who are interested in preparing for a career in the die casting industry.

Title of Award: David Laine Memorial Scholarship **Area, Field, or Subject:** Business; Manufacturing **Level of Education for which Award is Granted:** Undergraduate **Number Awarded:** 4 each year. **Funds Available:** The stipends range from $500 to $2,000 per year. **Duration:** 1 year.

Eligibility Requirements: This program is open to full-time undergraduate students who are h citizens of the United States, Canada, or Mexico, Applicants must have worked in the die casting industry for at least 3 months within the past year. Along with their application, they must submit a paper on their activities and results from their work in the die casing industry. **Deadline for Receipt:** September of each year. **Additional Information:** This scholarship, established in 1975, is jointly sponsored by the North American Die Casting Association and the Foundry Educational Foundation.

3903 ■ FOUNDRY EDUCATIONAL FOUNDATION

1695 North Penny Lane
Schaumburg, IL 60173
Tel: (847)490-9200
Fax: (847)890-6270
E-mail: info@fefoffice.org
Web Site: http://www.fefinc.org
To provide financial assistance to undergraduate and graduate students who are interested in preparing for a career in the ductile iron industry.

Title of Award: Keith Dwight Millis Scholarship **Area, Field, or Subject:** Business; Manufacturing **Level of Education for which Award is Granted:** Graduate, Undergraduate **Number Awarded:** 1 each year. **Funds Available:** The stipend is $2,000 per year. **Duration:** 1 year.

Eligibility Requirements: This program is open to full-time undergraduate and graduate students who are citizens of any country, are enrolled in a college or university in the United States, and have a demonstrated interest in ductile iron. Applicants must be registered with the Foundry Educational Foundation (FEF), but they are not required to attend FEF schools. As part of their application, they must explain their interest in ductile iron. **Deadline for Receipt:** October of each year. **Additional Information:** This scholarship is jointly sponsored by the Ductile Iron Society and the Foundry Educational Foundation.

3904 ■ FOUNDRY EDUCATIONAL FOUNDATION

1695 North Penny Lane
Schaumburg, IL 60173
Tel: (847)490-9200
Fax: (847)890-6270
E-mail: info@fefoffice.org
Web Site: http://www.fefinc.org
To provide financial assistance to college students in Indiana and adjoining states who are interested in preparing for a career in the die casting industry.

Title of Award: NADCA Indiana Chapter 25 Scholarship Fund **Area, Field, or Subject:** Business; Manufacturing **Level of Education for which Award is Granted:** Undergraduate **Number Awarded:** 1 each year. **Funds Available:** The stipends range from $500 to $2,000 per year. **Duration:** 1 year.

Eligibility Requirements: This program is open to full-time students who are U.S. citizens, have taken or plan to take courses in the die-casting process, and can demonstrate their intention to prepare for a career in the die-casting industry. Preference is given first to residents of central Indiana, then to residents of Indiana outside the central area, then to residents of states adjacent to Indiana. Preference is also given to students attending an Indiana college or university with an agreement with the Foundry Educational Foundation (FEF), then to students attending school in Indiana, then to students attending an FEF school in an adjacent state. Preference is also given to applicants pursuing programs deemed most useful to the die casting industry, then to candidates with the best scholastic record. In addition, preference is given (in order) to applicants who are currently participating in a co-op program involving the die casting industry, who have work experience in the die casting industry, who have work experience in the cast metal industry, and who have any manufacturing work experience. Finally, preference is given to applicants who know or have worked for or with a member of Indiana Chapter 25 of the North American Die Casting Association. **Deadline for Receipt:** May of each year.

3905 ■ FOUNDRY EDUCATIONAL FOUNDATION

1695 North Penny Lane
Schaumburg, IL 60173
Tel: (847)490-9200
Fax: (847)890-6270
E-mail: info@fefoffice.org
Web Site: http://www.fefinc.org
To provide financial assistance to college students in Illinois and adjacent states who are interested in preparing for a career in the metal-casting industry.

Title of Award: Roy W. Schroeder Scholarship **Area, Field, or Subject:** Business; Manufacturing **Level of Education for which Award is Granted:** Undergraduate **Number Awarded:** 1 each year. **Funds Available:** The stipends range from $500 to $2,000 per year. **Duration:** 1 year.

Eligibility Requirements: This program is open to full-time students who are U.S. citizens, have taken or plan to take courses in metal casting, and can demonstrate their intention to prepare for a career in the metal-casting industry. Preference is given first to residents within the area of the American Foundrymen's Society (AFS) Chicago chapter, then to residents of Illinois, then to residents of states adjacent to Illinois. Preference is also given to students attending a college or university with an agreement with the Foundry Educational Foundation (FEF), then to students attending school in Illinois, then to students attending a school that meets FEF guidelines. In addition, preference is given first to applicants who have expressed interest in metal casting through job experience, then to candidates with the best scholastic record. **Deadline for Receipt:** October of each year.

3906 ■ HANDWEAVERS GUILD OF AMERICA, INC.

Attn: Scholarship Chair
1255 Buford Highway, Suite 211
Suwanee, GA 30024
Tel: (678)730-0010
Fax: (678)730-0836
E-mail: hga@weavespindye.org
Web Site: http://www.weavespindye.org
To provide financial assistance to undergraduate and graduate students working on a degree in the field of fiber arts.
Title of Award: Dendel Scholarships **Area, Field, or Subject:** Art conservation; History; Textile science **Level of Education for which Award is Granted:** Graduate, Undergraduate **Number Awarded:** Varies; more than $4,000 is available for this program each year. **Funds Available:** The amount of the award depends on the availability of funds. Recipients may use the funds for tuition, materials (e.g., film for photographs), or travel. **Duration:** 1 year.
Eligibility Requirements: This program is open to undergraduate and graduate students enrolled in accredited colleges and universities in the United States, its possessions, and Canada. Applicants must be working on a degree in the field of fiber arts, including training for research, textile history, and conservation. Along with their application, they must submit 1) an essay on their study goals and how those fit into their future plans, and 2) 5 to 16 slides of their work. Selection is based on artistic and technical merit; financial need is not considered. **Deadline for Receipt:** March of each year.

3907 ■ HANDWEAVERS GUILD OF AMERICA, INC.

Attn: Scholarship Chair
1255 Buford Highway, Suite 211
Suwanee, GA 30024
Tel: (678)730-0010
Fax: (678)730-0836
E-mail: hga@weavespindye.org
Web Site: http://www.weavespindye.org
To provide financial assistance to undergraduate and graduate students working on a degree in the field of fiber arts.
Title of Award: HGA Scholarships **Area, Field, or Subject:** Art conservation; History; Textile science **Level of Education for which Award is Granted:** Graduate, Undergraduate **Number Awarded:** Varies; more than $4,000 is available for this program each year. **Funds Available:** The amount of the award depends on the availability of funds. Use of funds is restricted to tuition. **Duration:** 1 year.
Eligibility Requirements: This program is open to undergraduate and graduate students enrolled in accredited colleges and universities in the United States, its possessions, and Canada. Applicants must be working on a degree in the field of fiber arts, including training for research, textile history, and conservation. Along with their application, they must submit 1) an essay on their study goals and how they fit into their future plans, and 2) 5 to 16 slides of their work. Selection is based on artistic and technical merit; financial need is not considered. **Deadline for Receipt:** March of each year.

3908 ■ HEALTHCARE FINANCIAL MANAGEMENT ASSOCIATION-CONNECTICUT CHAPTER

Attn: Scholarship Committee Chair
110 Barnes Road
P.O. Box 90
Wallingford, CT 06492-0090
Tel: (203)949-6383
Fax: (203)949-6331

E-mail: jagorin@mmm.com
Web Site: http://www.cthfma.org
To recognize and reward, with scholarships, undergraduate and graduate students in fields related to health care financial management at colleges and universities in Connecticut who submit outstanding essays on topics in the field.
Title of Award: Connecticut Chapter HFMA Scholarships **Area, Field, or Subject:** Accounting; Business administration; Finance; Health care services; Information science and technology; Nursing; Writing **Level of Education for which Award is Granted:** Graduate, Undergraduate **Number Awarded:** 2 each year: 1 for an undergraduate and 1 for a graduate student. **Funds Available:** The winner receives a $2,000 fellowship, membership in the Connecticut chapter of HFMA, a 1-year subscription to *Healthcare Financial Management,* and waiver of chapter program fees for 1 year. **Duration:** 1 year.
Eligibility Requirements: This competition is open to undergraduate and graduate students at colleges and universities in Connecticut, children of members of the Connecticut chapter of the Healthcare Financial Management Association (HFMA) attending a school outside of Connecticut, and residents of Connecticut commuting to a college or university in a state that borders Connecticut. Applicants must be enrolled in a business, finance, accounting, or information systems program and have an interest in health care or be enrolled in a nursing or allied health program. They must submit an essay, up to 5 pages, on a topic that changes annually; recently, applicants were allowed to choose among the new Medicare prescription drug coverage and its impact on providers and beneficiaries, the impact of the "baby boomer" segment of the U.S. population on the health care system, the impact of health care spending accounts on employers and individuals, or the voluntary and required reporting of clinical and operational data by health care providers. Finalists may be interviewed. **Deadline for Receipt:** March of each year.

3909 ■ HEALTHCARE INFORMATION AND MANAGEMENT SYSTEMS SOCIETY

Attn: HIMSS Foundation Scholarship Program Coordinator
230 East Ohio Street, Suite 500
Chicago, IL 60611-3269
Tel: (312)664-4467
Fax: (312)664-6143
Web Site: http://www.himss.org/asp/scholarships.asp
To provide financial assistance to student members of the Healthcare Information and Management Systems Society (HIMSS) who are working on an undergraduate or graduate degree in health care informatics or nursing.
Title of Award: Midwest Alliance for Nursing Informatics Scholarship **Area, Field, or Subject:** Health care services; Information science and technology; Nursing **Level of Education for which Award is Granted:** Four Year College, Graduate **Number Awarded:** 1 each year. **Funds Available:** The stipend is $2,500. The award includes an all-expense paid trip to the annual HIMSS conference and exhibition. **Duration:** 1 year; nonrenewable.
Eligibility Requirements: This program is open to student members of the society, although an application for membership, including dues, may accompany the scholarship application. Applicants must be graduate students working on an undergraduate or graduate degree in health care informatics. They must submit a 1-page narrative that describes the integration of informatics in their professional practice, with emphasis on actual work responsibilities and how they would utilize the scholarship. Selection is based on that narrative; student, community, or professional activities in the workplace related to nursing and/or health care informatics; and involvement and participation in health care informatics professional organizations. **Deadline for Receipt:** October of each year.
Additional Information: This program was established in 2004.

3910 ■ INSTITUTE OF MANAGEMENT ACCOUNTANTS

Attn: Committee on Students
10 Paragon Drive
Montvale, NJ 07645-1718
Tel: (201)573-9000
Free: 800-638-4427
Fax: (201)474-1600
E-mail: students@imanet.org
Web Site: http://www.imanet.org

To provide financial assistance to student members of the Institute of Management Accountants (IMA) who are interested in preparing for a career in a field related to management accounting.

Title of Award: IMA Memorial Education Fund Scholarships **Area, Field, or Subject:** Accounting; Finance; Information science and technology; Management **Level of Education for which Award is Granted:** Graduate, Undergraduate **Number Awarded:** Varies each year; recently, 10 of these scholarships were awarded. **Funds Available:** Stipends range from $1,000 to $2,500 per year. **Duration:** 1 year.

Eligibility Requirements: This program is open to undergraduate and graduate student IMA members who have a GPA of 2.8 or higher. Applicants must be preparing for a career in management accounting, financial management, or information technology. They must submit a 2-page statement on their reasons for applying for the scholarship, reasons that they deserve the award, specific contributions to the IMA, ideas on how they will promote awareness and increase membership and certification within IMA, and their career goals and objectives. Selection is based on that statement, academic merit, IMA participation, the quality of the presentation, a resume, and letters of recommendation. **Deadline for Receipt:** February of each year. **Additional Information:** Up to 30 finalists in each category (including the scholarship winners) receive a scholarship to take 5 parts of the Certified Management Accountant (CMA) and/or Certified in Financial Management (CFM) examination within a year of graduation.

3911 ■ INSTITUTE OF MANAGEMENT ACCOUNTANTS

Attn: Committee on Students
10 Paragon Drive
Montvale, NJ 07645-1718
Tel: (201)573-9000
Free: 800-638-4427
Fax: (201)474-1600
E-mail: students@imanet.org
Web Site: http://www.imanet.org

To provide financial assistance to undergraduate or graduate student members of the Institute of Management Accountants (IMA) who are interested in preparing for a career in management accounting or financial management.

Title of Award: Stuart Cameron and Margaret McLeod Memorial Scholarship **Area, Field, or Subject:** Accounting; Finance; Information science and technology; Management **Level of Education for which Award is Granted:** Graduate, Undergraduate **Number Awarded:** 1 each year. **Funds Available:** The stipend is $5,000. **Duration:** 1 year.

Eligibility Requirements: This program is open to undergraduate and graduate student IMA members who have a GPA of 2.8 or higher. Applicants must be preparing for a career in management accounting, financial management, or information technology. They must submit a 2-page statement on their reasons for applying for the scholarship, reasons that they deserve the award, specific contributions to the IMA, ideas on how they will promote awareness and increase membership and certification within IMA, and their career goals and objectives. Selection is based on that statement, academic merit, IMA participation, the quality of the presentation, a resume, and letters of recommendation. **Deadline for Receipt:** February of each year. **Additional Information:** The recipient is required to participate in the parent chapter, at the council level, or at the national level.

3912 ■ INTERNATIONAL COMMUNICATIONS INDUSTRIES AS-SOCIATION, INC.

Attn: Director of Strategic Initiatives
11242 Waples Mill Road, Suite 200
Fairfax, VA 22030
Tel: (703)273-7200
Free: 800-659-7469
Fax: (703)278-8082
E-mail: dwilbert@infocomm.org
Web Site: http://www.infocomm.org/Foundation/Scholarships/College.cfm

To provide financial assistance to college students in their final year of study who are interested in preparing for a career in the audiovisual industry.

Title of Award: International Communications Industries Association College Scholarships **Area, Field, or Subject:** Electronics; Information science and technology; Journalism; Telecommunications systems **Level of**

Education for which Award is Granted: Graduate, Undergraduate **Number Awarded:** Varies each year; recently, 7 of these scholarships were awarded. **Funds Available:** The stipend is $2,500. **Duration:** 1 year.

Eligibility Requirements: This program is open to 1) college juniors completing their bachelor's degree in the following year; 2) college seniors who plan to enter graduate school; and 3) students in their final year of study for an associate degree. Applicants must have a GPA of 2.75 or higher in a program of audio, visual, audiovisual, electronics, telecommunications, technical theater, data networking, software development, or information technology. Students in other programs, such as journalism, may be eligible if they can demonstrate a relationship to career goals in the audiovisual industry. Along with their application, they must submit essays on why they are applying for this scholarship, why they are interested in the audiovisual industry, and their professional plans following graduation. Minority and women candidates are especially encouraged to apply. Selection is based on the essays, presentation of the application, GPA, work experience, and letters of recommendation. **Deadline for Receipt:** April of each year. **Additional Information:** Recipients are required to work during the summer as paid interns with a manufacturer, dealer, designer, or other firm that is a member of the International Communications Industries Association.

3913 ■ INTERNATIONAL COMMUNICATIONS INDUSTRIES AS-SOCIATION, INC.

Attn: Director of Strategic Initiatives
11242 Waples Mill Road, Suite 200
Fairfax, VA 22030
Tel: (703)273-7200
Free: 800-659-7469
Fax: (703)278-8082
E-mail: dwilbert@infocomm.org
Web Site: http://www.infocomm.org/Foundation/Scholarships

To provide financial assistance for college to dependents of members of the International Communications Industries Association (ICIA) interested in preparing for a career in the audiovisual industry.

Title of Award: Scholarships for Dependents of ICIA Members **Area, Field, or Subject:** Electronics; Information science and technology; Journalism; Telecommunications systems **Level of Education for which Award is Granted:** Undergraduate **Number Awarded:** Varies each year; recently, 3 of these scholarships were awarded. **Funds Available:** The stipend is $1,500. **Duration:** 1 year.

Eligibility Requirements: This program is open to graduating high school seniors and current college students who are the children, stepchildren, and spouses of employees at ICIA member companies. Applicants must have a GPA of 2.75 or higher and be majoring or planning to major in audio, visual, audiovisual, electronics, telecommunications, technical theater, data networking, software development, or information technology. Students in other programs, such as journalism, may be eligible if they can demonstrate a relationship to career goals in the audiovisual industry. Along with their application, they must submit 1) an essay of 150 to 200 words on the career path they see themselves pursuing in the next 5 years and why, and 2) an essay of 250 to 300 words on the experience or person that most influenced them in selecting the audiovisual industry as their career of choice. Minority and women candidates are especially encouraged to apply. Selection is based on the essays, presentation of the application, GPA, work experience, and letters of recommendation. **Deadline for Receipt:** April of each year.

3914 ■ IOWA FEDERATION OF LABOR, AFL-CIO

Attn: Scholarship Program
2000 Walker Street, Suite A
Des Moines, IA 50317-5290
Tel: (515)262-9571
Free: 800-372-4817
Fax: (515)262-9573
E-mail: ifl@iowaaflcio.org
Web Site: http://www.iowaaflcio.org

To recognize and reward outstanding essays on a labor-related topic written by high school seniors in Iowa.

Title of Award: Iowa Federation of Labor Scholarships **Area, Field, or Subject:** History, American; Industrial and labor relations; Writing **Level of Education for which Award is Granted:** Undergraduate **Number**

Awarded: 3 each year. **Funds Available:** First prize is $1,500, second prize is $1,000, and third prize is $500. Funds may be used as a scholarship at the college or university of the recipient's choice. **Duration:** The competition is held annually.

Eligibility Requirements: This competition is open to all seniors in accredited high schools in Iowa (public, private, and parochial). Students must write an essay (from 500 to 750 words) on the history of the labor movement in the United States. It is recommended that competitors read *A History of the Labor Movement in the United States* before writing the essay. **Deadline for Receipt:** March of each year.

3915 ■ KNIGHT RIDDER, INC.
Attn: Office of Diversity
50 West San Fernando Street, Suite 1200
San Jose, CA 95113
Tel: (408)938-7734
Fax: (408)938-7755
Web Site: http://www.knightridder.com/career/internships.html
To provide financial assistance and work experience to minority high school seniors who are interested in going to college to prepare for a career in journalism.

Title of Award: Knight Ridder Minority Scholars Program **Area, Field, or Subject:** Advertising; Graphic art and design; Information science and technology; Journalism; Marketing and distribution; Photography, Journalistic **Level of Education for which Award is Granted:** Undergraduate **Number Awarded:** Up to 5 each year: 2 for news, 2 for business, and 1 for either. **Funds Available:** The stipend is $5,000 per year for the freshman and sophomore year and $15,000 per year for the junior and senior year. **Duration:** 1 year; may be renewed for up to 3 additional years, if the recipient maintains a GPA of 3.0 or higher and satisfactory performance on internships.

Eligibility Requirements: This program is open to minority seniors graduating from high schools in areas served by Knight Ridder. Applicants must be interested in attending college to prepare for a career in the newspaper industry. They first apply to their local Knight Ridder newspaper and compete for local scholarships; selected winners are then nominated for this award. Both "news" and "business" students are eligible. **Additional Information:** Recipients are offered an internship opportunity at a Knight Ridder newspaper during the summer. News scholars work in the newsroom, writing and editing stories, taking photographs, crafting illustrations, and designing news pages. Business scholars complete internships in advertising, marketing, information technology, circulation, and other areas essential to the industry. At the end of the sophomore year, recipients must agree to work at a Knight Ridder newspaper for 1 year after graduation.

3916 ■ LOWE'S COMPANIES, INC.
Attn: Scholarship Program
P.O. Box 1111
North Wilkesboro, NC 28656
Tel: (336)658-4104
Free: 800-44-LOWES
Web Site: http://www.lowes.com/scholarships
To provide financial assistance to students at selected community and technical colleges who are preparing for a career in a business or technical field related to Lowe's stores.

Title of Award: Lowe's Educational Scholarship Program **Area, Field, or Subject:** Business; Construction; Drafting; Electronics; Heating, air conditioning, and refrigeration; Horticulture **Level of Education for which Award is Granted:** Two Year College, Vocational/Occupational **Number Awarded:** Varies each year; since the program was established, more than 150 of these scholarships have been awarded. **Funds Available:** Stipends are $2,000 for full-time students, $1,000 for three-quarter time students, or $800 for half-time students. **Duration:** 1 year; may be renewed if the recipient qualifies for employment at Lowe's.

Eligibility Requirements: This program is open to students who are at least 18 years of age and currently enrolled in a community or technical college that is cooperating with Lowe's stores. Applicants must intend to prepare for a career in an approved discipline within the business division (business management, business administration) or vocational/technical division (air conditioning, heating and refrigeration, construction, electrical or electronics, industrial maintenance, machining, mechanical drafting and design, plumbing, carpentry, or horticulture) of Lowe's. They must have

completed at least 1 semester with a GPA of 2.0 or higher. Applications are accepted from current Lowe's employees, but students working for another major retailer are not eligible. **Additional Information:** This program was established in 1999. Currently, 32 community and technical colleges are participating in the program. For a list, contact Lowe's.

3917 ■ MORGAN STANLEY
c/o Joyce Arencibia, IT College Recruiting
750 Seventh Avenue, 30th Floor
New York, NY 10019
Tel: (212)762-4000
E-mail: diversityrecruiting@morganstanley.com
Web Site: http://www.morganstanley.com/about/diversity/
recruit_programs.html?page=div
To provide financial assistance and work experience to members of minority groups who are preparing for a career in technology within the financial services industry.

Title of Award: Richard B. Fisher Scholarship **Area, Field, or Subject:** Technology **Level of Education for which Award is Granted:** Four Year College **Number Awarded:** 1 or more each year. **Funds Available:** The stipend is $5,000. **Duration:** 1 year.

Eligibility Requirements: This program is open to members of minority groups who are enrolled in their sophomore or junior year of college (or the third or fourth year of a 5-year program). Applicants must be enrolled full time and have a GPA of 3.0 or higher. They must be willing to commit to a paid summer internship in the Morgan Stanley Information Technology Division. All majors and disciplines are eligible, but preference is given to students preparing for a career in technology within the financial services industry. Along with their application, they must submit 1-page essays on 1) why they are applying for this scholarship and why they should be selected as a recipient; 2) a technical project on which they worked, either through a university course or previous work experience, their role in the project, and how they contributed to the end result; and 3) a software, hardware, or new innovative application of existing technology that they would create if they could and the impact it would have. Financial need is not considered in the selection process. **Deadline for Receipt:** February of each year. **Additional Information:** The program includes a paid summer internship in the Morgan Stanley Information Technology Division in the summer following the time of application.

3918 ■ NATIONAL FFA ORGANIZATION
Attn: Scholarship Office
6060 FFA Drive
P.O. Box 68960
Indianapolis, IN 46268-0960
Tel: (317)802-4321
Fax: (317)802-5321
E-mail: scholarships@ffa.org
Web Site: http://www.ffa.org
To provide financial assistance to FFA members who are interested in studying agricultural mechanics or engineering in college.

Title of Award: WIX Filters Scholarships **Area, Field, or Subject:** Agricultural sciences; Engineering, Agricultural; Technology **Level of Education for which Award is Granted:** Undergraduate **Number Awarded:** 4 each year. **Funds Available:** The stipend is $1,000. Funds are paid directly to the recipient. **Duration:** 1 year; nonrenewable.

Eligibility Requirements: This program is open to members who are graduating high school seniors planning to enroll full time in college. Applicants must be interested in working on a 2-year or 4-year degree in agricultural mechanics or agricultural engineering. Selection is based on academic achievement (10 points for GPA, 10 points for SAT or ACT score, 10 points for class rank), leadership in FFA activities (30 points), leadership in community activities (10 points), and participation in the Supervised Agricultural Experience (SAE) program (30 points). U.S. citizenship is required. **Deadline for Receipt:** February of each year. **Additional Information:** Funding for these scholarships is provided by WIX Filters.

3919 ■ NATIONAL SECURITY AGENCY
Attn: Office of Recruitment and Staffing (Roberts)
9800 Savage Road, Suite 6779
P.O. Box 1661, Suite 6779
Fort Meade, MD 20755-6779

Tel: (410)854-4725; (866)672-4473
Web Site: http://www.nsa.gov/careers/students_4.cfm
To provide financial assistance to college juniors interested in preparing for a career with the National Security Agency (NSA) as an intelligence analyst.
Title of Award: Pat Roberts Intelligence Scholars Program for Intelligence Analysts **Area, Field, or Subject:** Asian studies; Banking; Finance;. Foreign languages; Geography; Information science and technology; International affairs and relations; Library and archival sciences; Near Eastern studies; South Asian studies; Telecommunications systems **Level of Education for which Award is Granted:** Four Year College **Number Awarded:** Varies each year. **Funds Available:** The stipend is $25,000 per year. After graduation, recipients have an employment obligation to NSA equal to 1.5 times the length of educational support provided. **Duration:** 1 year (the senior year of college).
Eligibility Requirements: This program is open to college juniors whose academic program includes 1 of the following areas of emphasis: 1) regional studies (Middle East or south, east, or central Asia); 2) topical studies (terrorism, proliferation or related sciences, international banking and finance, or telecommunications and information systems networks); or 3) disciplines (intelligence analysis, philosophy, or international relations; familiarity with foreign languages, particularly Arabic, Chinese, Dari, Farsi, Hindi, Korean, Pashto, Urdu, or a central Asian language is desirable; highly qualified applicants studying social network analysis, library science, or geographic information systems may also be considered). Applicants must be enrolled full time with a GPA of 3.0 or higher. Along with their application, they must submit a 1-page essay describing how the proposed program of study will improve their ability to analyze information and to think and write critically. U.S. citizenship and eligibility to obtain a high-level security clearance are required **Deadline for Receipt:** October of each year. **Additional Information:** After graduation, participants enter NSA's Intelligence Analysis Development Program as a full-time employee.

3920 ■ NATIONAL URBAN LEAGUE
Attn: Scholarship Coordinator
120 Wall Street
New York, NY 10005
Tel: (212)558-5300; 888-839-0467
Fax: (212)344-5332
E-mail: info@nul.org
Web Site: http://www.nul.org/jerrybartowscholarship.html
To provide financial assistance to undergraduate students at Historically Black Colleges and Universities (HBCUs) that are participating in the Black Executive Exchange Program (BEEP).
Title of Award: Jerry Bartow Scholarship Fund **Area, Field, or Subject:** Business administration; Education; Management; Technology **Level of Education for which Award is Granted:** Undergraduate **Number Awarded:** 2 each year. **Funds Available:** The stipend is $1,500 per year. **Duration:** 1 year.
Eligibility Requirements: This program is open to African American sophomores, juniors, and seniors at HBCUs that are participating in the BEEP. Applicants must be majoring in business, management, technology, and/or education. **Deadline for Receipt:** January of each year. **Additional Information:** This program was established in 1997 by ITT Hartford Insurance Company. Recipients are required to attend the annual BEEP conference to accept the award. Travel and hotel arrangements are provided by BEEP.

3921 ■ NORTH CAROLINA COMMUNITY COLLEGE SYSTEM
Attn: Student Development Services
200 West Jones Street
5016 Mail Service Center
Raleigh, NC 27699-5016
Tel: (919)807-7106
Fax: (919)807-7164
E-mail: littlep@ncccs.cc.nc.us
Web Site: http://www.ncccs.cc.nc.us
To provide financial assistance to North Carolina residents studying fields related to air conditioning, heating, and refrigeration at publicly-supported community colleges in the state.
Title of Award: George W. Ballard Memorial Scholarship **Area, Field, or Subject:** Heating, air conditioning, and refrigeration; Technology **Level of**

Education for which Award is Granted: Two Year College **Number Awarded:** 1 each year. The scholarship rotates annually among North Carolina community colleges that offer the relevant program of study. **Funds Available:** The scholarship pays 90% of full-time tuition. **Duration:** 1 year; may be renewed if the recipient maintains a GPA at or above the level required for graduation.
Eligibility Requirements: This program is open to North Carolina residents enrolled or planning to enroll in the air conditioning, heating, and refrigeration program at a community college in the state. Applicants must submit documentation of financial need and an essay on why they have chosen the field of study and how the scholarship will help them attain their educational goal. Selection is based on academic achievement, participation in outside activities, and demonstrated interest in working in the field of study. **Deadline for Receipt:** September or February of each year.

3922 ■ NORTH CAROLINA COMMUNITY COLLEGE SYSTEM
Attn: Student Development Services
200 West Jones Street
5016 Mail Service Center
Raleigh, NC 27699-5016
Tel: (919)807-7106
Fax: (919)807-7164
E-mail: littlep@ncccs.cc.nc.us
Web Site: http://www.ncccs.cc.nc.us
To provide financial assistance to North Carolina residents studying or planning to study electrical and electronics technology at designated community colleges in the state.
Title of Award: Rodney E. Powell Memorial Scholarship **Area, Field, or Subject:** Electronics **Level of Education for which Award is Granted:** Two Year College **Number Awarded:** 1 or more each year. **Funds Available:** The scholarship provides full or partial payment of tuition. **Duration:** 1 year; may be renewed if the recipient maintains full-time enrollment and a GPA at or above the level required for graduation.
Eligibility Requirements: This program is open to North Carolina residents enrolled or planning to enroll full time in an associate in applied science degree program of study in electrical and electronics technology at a community college within the Progress Energy service area. Applicants must have a GPA of 3.0 or higher. Selection is based on academic achievement, financial need, participation in outside activities, and demonstrated interest in practicing the electrical and electronics trade in their community. **Additional Information:** There are no special application forms for the scholarship. Students apply to their local community college, not to the system office. Each eligible school selects its own recipients from applicants meeting the above criteria.

3923 ■ OFFICE OF PERSONNEL MANAGEMENT
Attn: Scholarship for Service Program Office
8610 Broadway, Suite 305
San Antonio, TX 78217-6352
Tel: (210)805-2423
E-mail: sfs@opm.gov
Web Site: http://www.sfs.opm.gov
To provide scholarship/loans and summer work experience to upper-division undergraduates and graduate students who are majoring in information assurance at designated universities.
Title of Award: Scholarship for Service **Area, Field, or Subject:** Information science and technology **Level of Education for which Award is Granted:** Four Year College, Graduate **Number Awarded:** Varies each year. **Funds Available:** Scholarships pay tuition, room and board, books, travel costs related to attendance at a required summer symposium, and a stipend that is $8,000 per year for undergraduates or $12,000 per year for graduate students. Recipients must serve at a federal agency in an information assurance position for a period equivalent to the length of the scholarship or 1 year, whichever is longer. If they fail to complete that service obligation, they must repay a prorated amount of the assistance received. **Duration:** Up to 2 years.
Eligibility Requirements: This program is open to rising juniors, seniors, and graduate students working full time on a bachelor's, master's, or doctoral degree in a field related to information assurance at a participating university. Students must be nominated by the principal investigator at the university. They must be U.S. citizens, eligible for federal employment, and able to obtain a security clearance. Selection is based on merit. **Ad-**

ditional Information: This program is funded by the National Science Foundation, through grants to the participating institutions. Those institutions recently included Carnegie Mellon University, Florida State University, George Washington University, Georgia Institute of Technology, University of Idaho, Idaho State University, Iowa State University, Johns Hopkins University, Mississippi State University, Naval Postgraduate School, University of Nebraska at Omaha, New Mexico Institute of Mining and Technology, University of North Carolina at Charlotte, Norwich University, Polytechnic University of New York, Purdue University, State University of New York at Stony Brook, Syracuse University, and University of Tulsa. Participants are required to serve an internship at a federal agency, usually the agency where they will ultimately work. The internship must be for at least 10 weeks, normally during the summer between the 2 years of their scholarship.

3924 ■ PRINCESS GRACE AWARDS

Attn: Executive Director
150 East 58th Street, 25th Floor
New York, NY 10155
Tel: (212)317-1470
Fax: (212)317-1473
E-mail: pgfusa@pgfusa.com
Web Site: http://www.pgfusa.com/awards/theater/index.html
To provide financial support to students and professionals interested in acting, directing, and scenic, lighting, sound, and costume design.
Title of Award: Theater Awards Area, Field, or Subject: Fashion design; Lighting science; Performing arts Level of Education for which Award is Granted: Four Year College, Master's, Professional Number Awarded: Varies each year. Recently, 6 of these grants were awarded: 2 as scholarships, 2 as apprenticeships, and 2 as fellowships. Funds Available: Grants range from $5,000 to $25,000. Companies receiving apprenticeships and fellowships are entitled to additional support equal to 15-20% of the award to be used for general operating expenses. Duration: Up to 1 year.
Eligibility Requirements: Nominations for these grants are invited from the artistic directors of theater companies and the deans and department chairs of professional schools of theater. Nominees may be actors, directors, or designers (costume, scenic, sound, and lighting). Grants are available as 1) scholarships for tuition for the last year of professional training at a nonprofit school in the United States; 2) apprenticeships for salary assistance for individual artists who are "learning the trade" under the supervision of a skilled staff person or mentor; and 3) fellowships for salary assistance for individual artists who are "advanced" members of a company and are ready to assume significant production responsibilities on 1 or more mainstage production(s). Professional companies must employ professional artistic and management staff, have been in continuous operation as a professional company for at least 3 years, provide a total of 20 weeks of research and performance for the current and previous 3 years, and have demonstrated the ability to raise public and other private funds. Artists must have been with the company for less than 5 years. All nominees must be U.S. citizens or permanent residents. Individuals may not submit an application independently. Deadline for Receipt: March of each year. Additional Information: This program includes the following named awards: the Robert and Gloria Hausman Theater Award, the Faberge Theater Award, the Gant Gaither Theater Award, the George C. Wolfe Theater Award, the Pierre Cardin Theater Award, and the Grace Le Vine Theater Award.

3925 ■ SIGMA ALPHA IOTA PHILANTHROPIES, INC.

One Tunnel Road
Asheville, NC 28805
Tel: (828)251-0606
Fax: (828)251-0644
E-mail: philonline@sai-national.org
Web Site: http://www.sai-national.org/phil/philmustech.html
To provide financial assistance for college to members of Sigma Alpha Iota (an organization of women musicians).
Title of Award: Dorothy Cooke Whinery Music Business/Technology Scholarship Area, Field, or Subject: Business; Business administration; Management; Marketing and distribution; Music; Performing arts; Technology Level of Education for which Award is Granted: Four Year College Number Awarded: 1 each year. Funds Available: The stipend is $2,000. Duration: 1 year.

Eligibility Requirements: This program is open to members of the organization entering their junior or senior year of college. Applicants must be working on a degree in the field of music business or music technology, including music marketing, music business administration, entertainment industry, commercial music, recording and production, music management, or other related fields. They must have a GPA of 3.0 or higher. Along with their application, they must submit a statement of purpose that includes their career goals. Deadline for Receipt: March of each year. Additional Information: This program was established in 2003. There is a $25 nonrefundable application fee.

3926 ■ SOCIETY OF BROADCAST ENGINEERS

Attn: Scholarship Committee
9102 North Meridian Street, Suite 150
Indianapolis, IN 46260
Tel: (317)846-9000
Fax: (317)846-9120
Web Site: http://www.sbe.org/edu_ennes_scholarships.php
To provide financial assistance for college to students interested in the technical aspects of broadcasting.
Title of Award: Harold E. Ennes Scholarship Area, Field, or Subject: Communications technologies Level of Education for which Award is Granted: Undergraduate Number Awarded: 1 each year. Funds Available: The stipend ranges from $1,000 to $3,000, depending on the availability of funds. Awards may be used for 1) tuition, room, board, or textbook costs at postsecondary educational institutions, or 2) other technical training programs approved by the sponsor. Duration: 1 year.
Eligibility Requirements: Applicants must have a career interest in the technical aspects of broadcasting and must be recommended by 2 members of the Society of Broadcast Engineers (SBE). They must submit 1) a brief autobiography that includes their interest and goals in broadcasting, and 2) a summary of the technical changes they anticipate in broadcasting within the next 5 years. Preference is given to members of the SBE and to students currently employed at least part time in broadcast engineering. Both new students just entering college and students already enrolled in college may apply. Financial need is not considered in the selection process. Deadline for Receipt: June of each year. Additional Information: This scholarship fund was established in 1980.

3927 ■ SOCIETY OF BROADCAST ENGINEERS

Attn: Scholarship Committee
9102 North Meridian Street, Suite 150
Indianapolis, IN 46260
Tel: (317)846-9000
Fax: (317)846-9120
Web Site: http://www.sbe.org/edu_ennes_scholarships.php
To provide financial assistance for college to students interested in the technical aspects of broadcasting.
Title of Award: Robert D. Greenberg Scholarship Area, Field, or Subject: Communications technologies Level of Education for which Award is Granted: Undergraduate Number Awarded: 1 each year. Funds Available: The stipend ranges from $1,000 to $3,000, depending on the availability of funds. Awards may be used for 1) tuition, room, board, or textbook costs at postsecondary educational institutions, or 2) other technical training programs approved by the sponsor. Duration: 1 year.
Eligibility Requirements: Applicants must have a career interest in the technical aspects of broadcasting and must be recommended by 2 members of the Society of Broadcast Engineers (SBE). They must submit 1) a brief autobiography that includes their interest and goals in broadcasting, and 2) a summary of the technical changes they anticipate in broadcasting within the next 5 years. Preference is given to members of the SBE and to students currently employed at least part time in broadcast engineering. Both new students just entering college and students already enrolled in college may apply. Financial need is not considered in the selection process. Deadline for Receipt: June of each year.

3928 ■ SOCIETY OF BROADCAST ENGINEERS

Attn: Scholarship Committee
9102 North Meridian Street, Suite 150
Indianapolis, IN 46260

Tel: (317)846-9000

Fax: (317)846-9120

Web Site: http://www.sbe.org/edu_ennes_scholarships.php

To provide financial assistance for college to high school seniors interested in the technical aspects of broadcasting.

Title of Award: Society of Broadcast Engineers Youth Scholarship **Area, Field, or Subject:** Communications technologies **Level of Education for which Award is Granted:** Undergraduate **Number Awarded:** 1 each year. **Funds Available:** The award ranges from $1,000 to $3,000, depending on the availability of funds. **Duration:** 1 year.

Eligibility Requirements: This program is open to graduating high school seniors who intend to enroll at a technical school, college, or university the following fall. Applicants must have a serious interest in preparing for a career in broadcast engineering or a closely-related field. Along with their application, they must submit a brief autobiography that includes their interests and goals in broadcasting, a brief written statement explaining their career goals and education plans after high school, and transcripts. Financial need is not considered in the selection process. **Deadline for Receipt:** June of each year. **Additional Information:** This scholarship was first offered in 1999.

3929 ■ UNITED AMERICAN NURSES

Attn: Labor Relations Specialist

8515 Georgia Avenue, Suite 400

Silver Spring, MD 20910

Tel: (301)628-5140

Fax: (301)628-5347

E-mail: Katrina.Blomdahl@uannurse.org

Web Site: http://www.uannurse.org/resources/scholarship.html

To provide financial assistance to members of United American Nurses (UAN) who are interested in working on an undergraduate or graduate degree in labor studies.

Title of Award: UAN National Labor Education Scholarship **Area, Field, or Subject:** Industrial and labor relations **Level of Education for which Award is Granted:** Master's, Undergraduate **Number Awarded:** 1 or more each year. **Funds Available:** The stipend is $1,000. **Duration:** 1 year; recipients may reapply.

Eligibility Requirements: This program is open to registered nurses who have been active members of UAN for at least 1 year. Applicants must have been accepted into a labor-oriented school or program to work on a certificate, bachelor's degree, or master's degree in labor studies or labor relations. **Deadline for Receipt:** May of each year.

3930 ■ VERMONT STUDENT ASSISTANCE CORPORATION

Champlain Mill

Attn: Scholarship Programs

P.O. Box 2000

Winooski, VT 05404-2601

Tel: (802)654-3798; 888-253-4819

Fax: (802)654-3765

E-mail: info@vsac.org

Web Site: http://www.vsac.org

To provide financial assistance to residents of Vermont who are interested in working on an undergraduate or graduate degree in a field related to design.

Title of Award: Alfred T. Granger Student Art Fund **Area, Field, or Subject:** Architecture; Art; Engineering, Architectural; Graphic art and design; Interior design; Lighting science **Level of Education for which Award is Granted:** Graduate, Undergraduate **Number Awarded:** 2 graduate scholarships and 4 undergraduate scholarships are awarded each year. **Funds Available:** The stipend is $5,000 per year for graduate students or $2,500 per year for undergraduates. **Duration:** 1 year; recipients may reapply.

Eligibility Requirements: This program is open to residents of Vermont who are graduating high school seniors, high school graduates, or GED recipients. Applicants must be interested in attending an accredited postsecondary institution to work on a degree in architecture, interior design, fine arts, architectural engineering, mechanical drawing, or light-

ing design. Selection is based on academic achievement, a portfolio, letters of recommendation, required essays, and financial need. **Deadline for Receipt:** May of each year.

3931 ■ VIRGINIA FUTURE BUSINESS LEADERS OF AMERICA-PHI BETA LAMBDA

c/o Sandy Mills, FBLA-PBL Specialist

Lord Fairfax Community College

173 Skirmisher Lane

Middletown, VA 22645

Tel: (540)868-7043

Fax: (540)868-7100

E-mail: smills@lfcc.edu

Web Site: http://www.vafbla-pbl.org

To provide financial assistance for college to members of Future Business Leaders of America (FBLA) in Virginia.

Title of Award: L. Marguerite Crumley/Frank Manning Peele Scholarships **Area, Field, or Subject:** Business administration; Information science and technology **Level of Education for which Award is Granted:** Undergraduate **Number Awarded:** 4 of these scholarships are awarded at the state level each year. **Funds Available:** The stipend is $1,000. Funds are paid directly to the educational institution. **Duration:** 1 year.

Eligibility Requirements: To program is open to seniors graduating from high schools in Virginia who have been active members of FBLA. Applicants must have completed acceptable programs in business and information technology and be planning to continue their education in the field of business and information technology at a college, junior or community college, technical institute, or other educational institute of higher learning. They first compete at the local chapter level; winners are referred to regional directors. Selection is based on leadership influence, personal initiative, appearance, contributions to school life, personal responsibility, maturity, personality, and academic promise. **Deadline for Receipt:** Applications must be submitted to the regional directors by February of each year. **Additional Information:** Local FBLA chapters in Virginia also give scholarships as part of this program.

Aerospace Sciences

3932 ■ AERO CLUB OF NEW ENGLAND

Attn: Education Committee

Civil Air Terminal

200 Hanscom Drive, Suite 322

Bedford, MA 01730

Tel: (617)277-0100

Fax: (617)232-7571

E-mail: scholarships@acone.org

Web Site: http://www.acone.org/scholarship/overview.html

To provide financial assistance for flight school to New England residents who intend to prepare for a professional aviation career.

Title of Award: ACONE Honored Member Scholarship **Area, Field, or Subject:** Aviation **Level of Education for which Award is Granted:** Undergraduate **Number Awarded:** 1 each year. **Funds Available:** The stipend is $2,000. **Duration:** 1 year.

Eligibility Requirements: This program is open to residents of New England who are interested in attending a flight school in the region. Applicants must intend to prepare for a professional aviation career, have a current Airman Certificate, have a current Medical Certificate, have accumulated 160 hours total flight time, be at least 16 years of age, be a U.S. citizen, have a current Biennial Flight Review, and be able to demonstrate financial need. Along with their application, they must submit academic transcripts, a personal letter giving their reasons for selecting a professional aviation career path and describing their aviation-related activities, a financial statement, 2 letters of recommendation, and their flight time record. Selection is based on ability to meet the planned aviation goals (as shown by recommendations and academic records), participation in aviation activities (as described in the personal letter and recommendations), and financial need. **Deadline for Receipt:** March of each year. **Additional Information:** This scholarship was established in 1995. Each year, it is designated to honor a living member of the Aero

Club of New England (ACONE). Information is also available from Anne B. Baddour, 96 Fletcher Road, Belmont, MA 02478.

3933 ■ AERO CLUB OF NEW ENGLAND
Attn: Education Committee
Civil Air Terminal
200 Hanscom Drive, Suite 322
Bedford, MA 01730
Tel: (617)277-0100
Fax: (617)232-7571
E-mail: scholarships@acone.org
Web Site: http://www.acone.org/scholarship/overview.html
To provide financial assistance for flight school to New England residents who intend to prepare for a professional aviation career.
Title of Award: Aero Club of New England Flight Scholarships **Area, Field, or Subject:** Aviation **Level of Education for which Award is Granted:** Undergraduate **Number Awarded:** 7 each year. **Funds Available:** Stipends range from $500 to $2,500. **Duration:** 1 year.
Eligibility Requirements: This program is open to residents of New England who are interested in attending a flight school in the region. Applicants must intend to prepare for a professional aviation career, have a current Airman Certificate, have a current Medical Certificate, have accumulated 160 hours total flight time, be at least 16 years of age, be a U.S. citizen, have a current Biennial Flight Review, and be able to demonstrate financial need. Along with their application, they must submit academic transcripts, a personal letter giving their reasons for selecting a professional aviation career path and describing their aviation-related activities, a financial statement, 2 letters of recommendation, and their flight time record. Selection is based on ability to meet the planned aviation goals (as shown by recommendations and academic records), participation in aviation activities (as described in the personal letter and recommendations), and financial need. **Deadline for Receipt:** March of each year. **Additional Information:** This program includes the following named scholarships: the Andrew Channing Cabot Memorial Scholarship (established in 1997), the Ann Wood Kelly Scholarship (established in 1987), the Anne Bridge Baddour Scholarship (established in 1999), the Bauer-Bisgeier Memorial Scholarship (established in 1997), the Bonita Connors Memorial Scholarship (established in 1995), the Edward D. Waters Memorial Scholarship (established in 1996), and the Florence M. Abely Memorial Scholarship (established in 1994).

3934 ■ AERO CLUB OF NEW ENGLAND
Attn: Education Committee
Civil Air Terminal
200 Hanscom Drive, Suite 322
Bedford, MA 01730
Tel: (617)277-0100
Fax: (617)232-7571
E-mail: scholarships@acone.org
Web Site: http://www.acone.org/scholarship/overview.html
To provide funding for instrument training to New England residents who intend to prepare for a professional aviation career.
Title of Award: Aero Club of New England Instrument Scholarships **Area, Field, or Subject:** Aviation **Level of Education for which Award is Granted:** Undergraduate **Number Awarded:** 2 each year. **Funds Available:** Stipends range from $1,000 to $2,000. **Duration:** 1 year.
Eligibility Requirements: This program is open to residents of New England who are interested in attending a flight school in the region for instrument training. Applicants must intend to prepare for a professional aviation career, have a current Airman Certificate, have a current Medical Certificate, have accumulated 100 hours total flight time, be at least 16 years of age, be a U.S. citizen, have a current Biennial Flight Review, and be able to demonstrate financial need. Along with their application, they must submit academic transcripts, a personal letter giving their reasons for selecting a professional aviation career path and describing their aviation-related activities, a financial statement, 2 letters of recommendation, and their flight time record. Selection is based on ability to meet the planned aviation goals (as shown by recommendations and academic records), participation in aviation activities (as described in the personal letter and recommendations), and financial need. **Deadline for Receipt:** March of each year. **Additional Information:** This program includes the Crocker Snow Instrument Scholarship and the Charles and Arlene Ehlers Memorial Scholarship.

3935 ■ AERO CLUB OF NEW ENGLAND
Attn: Education Committee
Civil Air Terminal
200 Hanscom Drive, Suite 322
Bedford, MA 01730
Tel: (617)277-0100
Fax: (617)232-7571
E-mail: scholarships@acone.org
Web Site: http://www.acone.org/scholarship/overview.html
To provide financial assistance for primary flight training to New England residents who intend to pursue a professional aviation career.
Title of Award: Michael T. Hadik Memorial Scholarship **Area, Field, or Subject:** Aviation **Level of Education for which Award is Granted:** Undergraduate **Number Awarded:** 1 each year. **Funds Available:** The stipend is $1,000. **Duration:** 1 year.
Eligibility Requirements: This program is open to residents of New England who are interested in attending a flight school in the region for primary training. Applicants must intend to prepare for a professional aviation career, have a current Airman Certificate, have a current Medical Certificate, have accumulated 20 hours total flight time plus a solo, be at least 16 years of age, be a U.S. citizen, have a current Biennial Flight Review, and be able to demonstrate financial need. Along with their application, they must submit academic transcripts, a personal letter giving their reasons for selecting a professional aviation career path and describing their aviation-related activities, a financial statement, 2 letters of recommendation, and their flight time record. Selection is based on ability to meet the planned aviation goals (as shown by recommendations and academic records), participation in aviation activities (as described in the personal letter and recommendations), and financial need. **Deadline for Receipt:** March of each year. **Additional Information:** This program was established in 2001.

3936 ■ AERO CLUB OF NEW ENGLAND
Attn: Education Committee
Civil Air Terminal
200 Hanscom Drive, Suite 322
Bedford, MA 01730
Tel: (617)277-0100
Fax: (617)232-7571
E-mail: scholarships@acone.org
Web Site: http://www.acone.org/scholarship/overview.html
To provide financial assistance for flight school to women in New England who intend to pursue a professional aviation career.
Title of Award: Leslie Wickfield Scholarship **Area, Field, or Subject:** Aviation **Level of Education for which Award is Granted:** Undergraduate **Number Awarded:** 1 each year. **Funds Available:** A stipend is awarded (amount not specified). **Duration:** 1 year.
Eligibility Requirements: This program is open to women in New England who are interested in attending a flight school in the region. Applicants must intend to pursue a professional aviation career, have a current Airman Certificate, have a current Medical Certificate, have accumulated 160 hours total flight time, be at least 16 years of age, be a U.S. citizen, have a current Biennial Flight Review, and be able to demonstrate financial need. Along with their application, they must submit academic transcripts, a personal letter giving their reasons for selecting a professional aviation career path and describing their aviation-related activities, a financial statement, 2 letters of recommendation, and their flight time record. Selection is based on ability to meet the planned aviation goals (as shown by recommendations and academic records), participation in aviation activities (as described in the personal letter and recommendations), and financial need. **Deadline for Receipt:** March of each year. **Additional Information:** This program was established in 1999.

3937 ■ AEROSPACE ILLINOIS SPACE GRANT CONSORTIUM
c/o University of Illinois at Urbana-Champaign
Department of Aeronautical and Astronomical Engineering
308 Talbot Lab
104 South Wright Street
Urbana, IL 61801-2935
Tel: (217)244-8048
Fax: (217)244-0720
E-mail: dejeffer@uiuc.edu

Web Site: http://www.ae.uiuc.edu/ISGC
To provide financial support to faculty, staff, and students at Aerospace Illinois member institutions who are interested in pursuing space-related academic activities.
Title of Award: Aerospace Illinois Space Grant Consortium Program **Area, Field, or Subject:** Aerospace sciences; Engineering, Aerospace/Aeronautical/Astronautical; Space and planetary sciences **Level of Education for which Award is Granted:** Graduate, Postdoctoral, Undergraduate **Number Awarded:** Varies each year. **Funds Available:** Awards depend on the availability of funds and the nature of the proposal. **Duration:** Depends on the program.
Eligibility Requirements: Aerospace Illinois has established 4 program elements: 1) undergraduate/high school teaching and research, to attract undergraduates and secondary school students to aerospace science and engineering; 2) training in graduate research, through research experiences focused on aerospace science and engineering; 3) outreach and public service, to employ the region's extensive existing public educational information networks and outreach programs to attract the highest quality student populations, especially underrepresented minorities, women, and persons with disabilities; and 4) fellowships with industry, to add substantially to the national aerospace science and engineering pool. Aerospace Illinois is a component of the U.S. National Aeronautics and Space Administration which encourages applications from women, minorities, and persons with disabilities. **Additional Information:** Aerospace Illinois includes 4 member institutions: the University of Illinois at Urbana-Champaign (UIUC), the University of Chicago (UC), Illinois Institute of Technology (IIT), and Northwestern University (NU). It also includes 3 affiliate institutions: Southern Illinois University (SIU), Western Illinois University (WIU), and the University of Illinois at Chicago. This program is funded by NASA.

3938 ■ AIR TRAFFIC CONTROL ASSOCIATION
Attn: Scholarship Fund
1101 King Street, Suite 300
Alexandria, VA 22314
Tel: (703)299-2430
Fax: (703)299-2437
E-mail: info@atca.org
Web Site: http://www.atca.org/activities/scholarships.asp
To provide financial assistance to students working on a bachelor's degree or higher in aviation.
Title of Award: Air Traffic Control Association Student Scholarship Program **Area, Field, or Subject:** Aviation **Level of Education for which Award is Granted:** Graduate, Four Year College **Number Awarded:** Varies each year, depending on the number, qualifications, and need of the applicants. **Funds Available:** Stipends range from $1,500 to $2,500. **Duration:** 1 year; may be renewed.
Eligibility Requirements: This program is open to half- or full-time students who are U.S. citizens, enrolled or accepted for enrollment in an accredited college or university, taking classes to prepare for an aviation-related career, working on a bachelor's or graduate degree, registered for at least 6 hours, and at least 30 semester or 45 quarter hours away from graduation. Applicants must submit an essay on "How My Educational Efforts Will Enhance My Potential Contribution to Aviation." The essay should address the applicant's financial need. **Deadline for Receipt:** April of each year.

3939 ■ AIR TRAFFIC CONTROL ASSOCIATION
Attn: Scholarship Fund
1101 King Street, Suite 300
Alexandria, VA 22314
Tel: (703)299-2430
Fax: (703)299-2437
E-mail: info@atca.org
Web Site: http://www.atca.org/activities/scholarships.asp
To provide financial assistance to students enrolled in an air traffic control program.
Title of Award: Gabriel A. Hartl Scholarship **Area, Field, or Subject:** Aviation **Level of Education for which Award is Granted:** Undergraduate **Number Awarded:** 1 or more each year. **Funds Available:** The amount of the award depends on the availability of funds and the number, qualifications, and need of the applicants. **Duration:** 1 year; may be renewed.

Eligibility Requirements: This program is open to half or full-time students who are U.S. citizens, enrolled in a 2- or 4-year air traffic control program at an institution approved and/or listed by the Federal Aviation Administration (FAA) as directly supporting its college and training initiative. Applicants must be registered for at least 6 hours and be at least 30 semester or 45 quarter hours away from graduation. They must submit an essay on "How My Educational Efforts Will Enhance My Potential Contribution to Aviation." The essay should address their financial need. **Deadline for Receipt:** April of each year.

3940 ■ AIRCRAFT ELECTRONICS ASSOCIATION
Attn: AEA Educational Foundation
4217 South Hocker Drive
Independence, MO 64055-4723
Tel: (816)373-6565
Fax: (816)478-3100
E-mail: info@aea.net
Web Site: http://www.aea.net
To provide financial assistance to students who are interested in studying avionics or aircraft repair in a midwestern school.
Title of Award: David Arver Memorial Scholarship **Area, Field, or Subject:** Aviation; Electronics **Level of Education for which Award is Granted:** Vocational/Occupational **Number Awarded:** 1 each year. **Funds Available:** The stipend is $1,000. **Duration:** 1 year.
Eligibility Requirements: This program is open to high school seniors and college students who plan to attend an accredited vocational or technical school in the Aircraft Electronics Association Region III; this includes the states of Illinois, Indiana, Iowa, Kansas, Michigan, Minnesota, Missouri, Nebraska, North Dakota, South Dakota, and Wisconsin. Applicants must be planning to enroll in an avionics or aircraft repair program. They must submit an official transcript (cumulative GPA of 2.5 or higher), a statement about their career plans, a description of their involvement in school and community activities, and a 300-word essay on how the job requirements of aviation technicians will change with advancements in technology. Selection is based on merit. **Deadline for Receipt:** February of each year.

3941 ■ AIRCRAFT ELECTRONICS ASSOCIATION
Attn: AEA Educational Foundation
4217 South Hocker Drive
Independence, MO 64055-4723
Tel: (816)373-6565
Fax: (816)478-3100
E-mail: info@aea.net
Web Site: http://www.aea.net
To provide financial assistance to students preparing for a career in avionics.
Title of Award: Dutch and Ginger Arver Scholarship **Area, Field, or Subject:** Aviation; Electronics **Level of Education for which Award is Granted:** Undergraduate **Number Awarded:** 1 each year. **Funds Available:** The stipend is $1,000. **Duration:** 1 year.
Eligibility Requirements: This program is open to high school seniors and currently-enrolled college students who are attending (or planning to attend) an accredited postsecondary institution in an avionics program. Applicants must submit an official transcript (cumulative GPA of 2.5 or higher), a statement about their career plans, a description of their involvement in school and community activities, and a 300-word essay on how the job requirements of aviation technicians will change with advancements in technology. Selection is based on merit. **Deadline for Receipt:** February of each year.

3942 ■ AIRCRAFT ELECTRONICS ASSOCIATION
Attn: AEA Educational Foundation
4217 South Hocker Drive
Independence, MO 64055-4723
Tel: (816)373-6565
Fax: (816)478-3100
E-mail: info@aea.net
Web Site: http://www.aea.net
To provide financial assistance to students preparing for a career in avionics or aircraft repair.
Title of Award: Avionics and Aircraft Repair Scholarships **Area, Field, or Subject:** Aviation; Electronics **Level of Education for which Award is**

Granted: Undergraduate **Number Awarded:** 1 each year. **Funds Available:** The stipend is $1,000. **Duration:** 1 year.

Eligibility Requirements: This program is open to high school seniors and currently-enrolled college students who are attending (or planning to attend) an accredited postsecondary institution in an avionics or aircraft repair program. Applicants must submit an official transcript (cumulative GPA of 2.5 or higher), a statement about their career plans, a description of their involvement in school and community activities, and a 300-word essay on how the job requirements of aviation technicians will change with advancements in technology. Selection is based on merit. **Deadline for Receipt:** February of each year. **Additional Information:** This program awards a number of named scholarships, including the Bud Glover Memorial Scholarship, GARMIN International Scholarship, Honeywell Avionics Scholarship, Johnny Davis Memorial Scholarship, L-3 Avionics Systems Scholarship, Les Tarbox Memorial Scholarship, and Lowell Gaylor Memorial Scholarship.

3943 ■ AIRCRAFT ELECTRONICS ASSOCIATION
Attn: AEA Educational Foundation
4217 South Hocker Drive
Independence, MO 64055-4723
Tel: (816)373-6565
Fax: (816)478-3100
E-mail: info@aea.net
Web Site: http://www.aea.net
To provide financial assistance to Canadian students who are interested in studying avionics or aircraft repair.
Title of Award: Field Aviation Company Scholarship **Area, Field, or Subject:** Aviation; Electronics **Level of Education for which Award is Granted:** Undergraduate **Number Awarded:** 1 each year. **Funds Available:** The stipend is $1,000. **Duration:** 1 year.
Eligibility Requirements: This program is open to Canadian high school seniors and currently-enrolled college students who are attending (or planning to attend) an accredited school in Canada to major in avionics or aircraft repair. Applicants must submit an official transcript (cumulative GPA of 2.5 or higher), a statement about their career plans, a description of their involvement in school and community activities, and a 300-word essay on how the job requirements of aviation technicians will change with advancements in technology. Selection is based on merit. **Deadline for Receipt:** February of each year.

3944 ■ AIRCRAFT ELECTRONICS ASSOCIATION
Attn: AEA Educational Foundation
4217 South Hocker Drive
Independence, MO 64055-4723
Tel: (816)373-6565
Fax: (816)478-3100
E-mail: info@aea.net
Web Site: http://www.aea.net
To provide financial assistance to students who are interested in studying avionics in college.
Title of Award: Mid-Continent Instrument Scholarship **Area, Field, or Subject:** Aviation; Electronics **Level of Education for which Award is Granted:** Undergraduate **Number Awarded:** 1 each year. **Funds Available:** The stipend is $1,000. **Duration:** 1 year.
Eligibility Requirements: This program is open to high school seniors and currently-enrolled college students who are attending (or planning to attend) an accredited school in an avionics program. Applicants must submit an official transcript (cumulative GPA of 2.5 or higher), a statement about their career plans, a description of their involvement in school and community activities, and a 300-word essay on how the job requirements of aviation technicians will change with advancements in technology. Selection is based on merit. **Deadline for Receipt:** February of each year.

3945 ■ AIRCRAFT ELECTRONICS ASSOCIATION
Attn: AEA Educational Foundation
4217 South Hocker Drive
Independence, MO 64055-4723
Tel: (816)373-6565
Fax: (816)478-3100
E-mail: info@aea.net
Web Site: http://www.aea.net

To provide financial assistance to students preparing for a career in aviation management.
Title of Award: Chuck Peacock Memorial Scholarship **Area, Field, or Subject:** Aviation; Management **Level of Education for which Award is Granted:** Undergraduate **Number Awarded:** 1 each year. **Funds Available:** The stipend is $1,000. **Duration:** 1 year.
Eligibility Requirements: This program is open to high school seniors and currently-enrolled college students who are attending (or planning to attend) an accredited postsecondary institution in an aviation management program. Applicants must submit an official transcript (cumulative GPA of 2.5 or higher), a statement about their career plans, a description of their involvement in school and community activities, and a 300-word essay on how the job requirements of aviation technicians will change with advancements in technology. Selection is based on merit. **Deadline for Receipt:** February of each year.

3946 ■ AIRCRAFT ELECTRONICS ASSOCIATION
Attn: AEA Educational Foundation
4217 South Hocker Drive
Independence, MO 64055-4723
Tel: (816)373-6565
Fax: (816)478-3100
E-mail: info@aea.net
Web Site: http://www.aea.net
To provide financial assistance for vocational school to students interested in preparing for a career in avionics or aircraft repair.
Title of Award: Plane and Pilot Magazine/GARMIN Scholarship **Area, Field, or Subject:** Aviation; Electronics **Level of Education for which Award is Granted:** Vocational/Occupational **Number Awarded:** 1 each year. **Funds Available:** The stipend is $2,000. **Duration:** 1 year.
Eligibility Requirements: This program is open to high school, college, or vocational/technical students who are attending (or planning to attend) an accredited vocational/technical school in an avionics or aircraft repair program. Applicants must submit an official transcript (cumulative GPA of 2.5 or higher), a statement about their career plans, a description of their involvement in school and community activities, and a 300-word essay on how the job requirements of aviation technicians will change with advancements in technology. Selection is based on merit. **Deadline for Receipt:** February of each year.

3947 ■ AIRCRAFT ELECTRONICS ASSOCIATION
Attn: AEA Educational Foundation
4217 South Hocker Drive
Independence, MO 64055-4723
Tel: (816)373-6565
Fax: (816)478-3100
E-mail: info@aea.net
Web Site: http://www.aea.net
To provide financial assistance to students who are interested in majoring in avionics in college.
Title of Award: Sporty's/Cincinnati Avionics Scholarship **Area, Field, or Subject:** Aviation; Electronics **Level of Education for which Award is Granted:** Undergraduate **Number Awarded:** 1 each year. **Funds Available:** The stipend is $2,000. **Duration:** 1 year.
Eligibility Requirements: This program is open to high school seniors and currently-enrolled college students who are attending (or planning to attend) an accredited school in an avionics program. Applicants must submit an official transcript (cumulative GPA of 2.5 or higher), a statement about their career plans, a description of their involvement in school and community activities, and a 300-word essay on how the job requirements of aviation technicians will change with advancements in technology. Selection is based on merit. **Deadline for Receipt:** February of each year.

3948 ■ ALABAMA SPACE GRANT CONSORTIUM
c/o University of Alabama in Huntsville
Materials Science Building, Room 205
Huntsville, AL 35899
Tel: (256)824-6800
Fax: (256)824-6061
E-mail: reasonj@uah.edu
Web Site: http://www.uah.edu/ASGC
To provide financial assistance to undergraduate students at universities participating in the Alabama Space Grant Consortium who wish to prepare

for a career as a teacher of science or mathematics.

Title of Award: Teacher Education Scholarship Program of the Alabama Space Grant Consortium **Area, Field, or Subject:** Aerospace sciences; Earth sciences; Education; Environmental conservation; Environmental science; Geosciences; Mathematics and mathematical sciences; Science; Space and planetary sciences **Level of Education for which Award is Granted:** Undergraduate **Number Awarded:** Varies each year; recently, 10 of these scholarships were awarded. **Funds Available:** The stipend is $1,000 per year. **Duration:** 1 year; nonrenewable.

Eligibility Requirements: This program is open to students enrolled in or accepted for enrollment as full-time undergraduates at universities in Alabama participating in the consortium. Applicants must intend to enter the teacher certification program and teach in a pre-college setting. Priority is given to those majoring in science, mathematics, or earth/space/ environmental science. Applicants should have a GPA of 3.0 or higher and must be U.S. citizens. Members of underrepresented groups in science and mathematics (minorities and women) are especially encouraged to apply. Along with their application, they must submit a 1- to 2-page statement on the reasons for their desire to enter the teaching profession, specifically the fields of science or mathematics education. **Deadline for Receipt:** February of each year. **Additional Information:** The member universities are University of Alabama in Huntsville, Alabama A&M University, University of Alabama, University of Alabama at Birmingham, University of South Alabama, Tuskegee University, and Auburn University. Funding for this program is provided by NASA.

3949 ■ ALABAMA SPACE GRANT CONSORTIUM

c/o University of Alabama in Huntsville
Materials Science Building, Room 205
Huntsville, AL 35899
Tel: (256)824-6800
Fax: (256)824-6061
E-mail: reasonj@uah.edu
Web Site: http://www.uah.edu/ASGC
To provide financial assistance to undergraduates who are studying the space sciences at universities participating in the Alabama Space Grant Consortium (ASGC).

Title of Award: Undergraduate Scholarship Program of the Alabama Space Grant Consortium **Area, Field, or Subject:** Aerospace sciences; Behavioral sciences; Biological and clinical sciences; Business administration; Communications; Computer and information sciences; Economics; Education; Engineering, Aerospace/Aeronautical/Astronautical; International affairs and relations; Law; Natural sciences; Physical sciences; Public administration; Sociology; Space and planetary sciences **Level of Education for which Award is Granted:** Four Year College **Number Awarded:** Varies each year; recently, 32 of these scholarships were awarded. **Funds Available:** The stipend is $1,000 per year. **Duration:** 1 year; may be renewed 1 additional year.

Eligibility Requirements: This program is open to full-time students entering their junior or senior year at universities participating in the ASGC. Applicants must be studying in a field related to space, including the physical, natural, and biological sciences; engineering, education; economics; business; sociology; behavioral sciences; computer science; communications; law; international affairs; and public administration. They must be U.S. citizens and have a GPA of 3.0 or higher. Individuals from underrepresented groups (African Americans, Hispanic, American Indians, Pacific Islanders, Asian Americans, and women) are especially encouraged to apply. Interested students should submit a completed application with a career goal statement, personal references, a brief resume, and transcripts. Selection is based on 1) academic qualifications, 2) quality of the career goal statement, and 3) assessment of the applicant's motivation for a career in aerospace. **Deadline for Receipt:** February of each year. **Additional Information:** The member universities are University of Alabama in Huntsville, Alabama A&M University, University of Alabama, University of Alabama at Birmingham, University of South Alabama, Tuskegee University, and Auburn University. Funding for this program is provided by NASA.

3950 ■ AMERICAN ASSOCIATION OF AIRPORT EXECUTIVES FOUNDATION

Attn: AAAE Foundation Scholarship Program
601 Madison Street, Suite 400
Alexandria, VA 22314

Tel: (703)824-0500
Fax: (703)820-1395
Web Site: http://www.aaae.org/members/275_AAAE_Foundation/ index.html
To provide financial assistance to upper-division college students who are majoring in aviation.

Title of Award: AAAE Foundation Scholarship **Area, Field, or Subject:** Aviation **Level of Education for which Award is Granted:** Four Year College **Number Awarded:** 3 to 5 each year. **Funds Available:** The stipend is $1,000. **Duration:** 1 year.

Eligibility Requirements: This program is open to full-time college juniors or seniors who are enrolled in an aviation program and have earned a GPA of 3.0 or higher. Selection is based on academic record, financial need, participation in school and community activities, work experience, and a personal statement. **Deadline for Receipt:** May of each year.

3951 ■ AMERICAN ASSOCIATION OF AIRPORT EXECUTIVES FOUNDATION

Attn: AAAE Foundation Scholarship Program
601 Madison Street, Suite 400
Alexandria, VA 22314
Tel: (703)824-0500
Fax: (703)820-1395
Web Site: http://www.aaae.org/members/275_AAAE_Foundation/ index.html
To provide financial assistance to Native American upper-division college students who are majoring in aviation.

Title of Award: AAAE Foundation Scholarship for Native Americans **Area, Field, or Subject:** Aviation **Level of Education for which Award is Granted:** Four Year College **Number Awarded:** 1 or more each year. **Funds Available:** The stipend is $1,000. **Duration:** 1 year.

Eligibility Requirements: This program is open to full-time Native American college juniors or seniors who are enrolled in an aviation program and have earned a GPA of 3.0 or higher. Each college or university may nominate only 1 student for this scholarship. Selection is based on academic record, financial need, participation in school and community activities, work experience, and a personal statement. **Deadline for Receipt:** May of each year.

3952 ■ AMERICAN ASSOCIATION OF AIRPORT EXECUTIVES FOUNDATION

Attn: AAAE Foundation Scholarship Program
601 Madison Street, Suite 400
Alexandria, VA 22314
Tel: (703)824-0500
Fax: (703)820-1395
Web Site: http://www.aaae.org/members/275_AAAE_Foundation/ index.html
To provide financial assistance to undergraduate and graduate students who are accredited airport executive (AAE) members (or the dependents of members) of the American Association of Airport Executives.

Title of Award: AAE Scholarship **Area, Field, or Subject:** Aviation; General studies/Field of study not specified **Level of Education for which Award is Granted:** Graduate, Undergraduate **Number Awarded:** Varies each year. **Funds Available:** Varies; generally, the stipend is $1,000. **Duration:** 1 year.

Eligibility Requirements: This program is open to accredited airport executive members of the association, along with their spouses and children. Applicants must be attending or planning to attend school (on the undergraduate or graduate school level) on a full-time basis. **Deadline for Receipt:** May of each year. **Additional Information:** Recipients must attend an accredited college or university.

3953 ■ AMERICAN ASSOCIATION OF AIRPORT EXECUTIVES- NORTHEAST CHAPTER

Attn: Executive Secretary
P.O. Box 8
West Milford, NJ 07480-0008
Tel: (973)728-6760
Fax: (973)728-6760
Web Site: http://www.necaaae.org/postnec.htm

To provide financial assistance to upper-division students majoring in airport management.

Title of Award: Post Scholarship **Area, Field, or Subject:** Aviation; Management **Level of Education for which Award is Granted:** Four Year College **Number Awarded:** 4 each year. **Funds Available:** The stipend is $1,000. **Duration:** 1 year.

Eligibility Requirements: This program is open to juniors and seniors in colleges and universities who are majoring in airport management. Preference is given to those with a permanent residence in the northeast region. Student preparing for a career as commercial pilots are not eligible. Applicants must indicate how they will benefit from the grant and provide documentation of financial need. **Deadline for Receipt:** February of each year. **Additional Information:** The northeast region covers Connecticut, Delaware, Maine, Maryland, Massachusetts, New Hampshire, New Jersey, New York, Pennsylvania, Rhode Island, Vermont, Washington D.C., and the Canadian provinces of New Brunswick, Newfoundland, Nova Scotia, Prince Edward Island, and Quebec.

3954 ■ AMERICAN ASSOCIATION OF AIRPORT EXECUTIVES-SOUTHWEST CHAPTER

P.O. Box 4228
Sparks, NV 89432
Tel: (775)353-2080
E-mail: swaaae@sbcglobal.net
Web Site: http://www.swaaae.org/scholarships.html
To provide financial assistance to students working on an undergraduate or graduate degree in airport management at a college or university in the Southwest.

Title of Award: Southwest Chapter Academic Scholarships **Area, Field, or Subject:** Aviation; Management **Level of Education for which Award is Granted:** Graduate, Undergraduate **Number Awarded:** 2 each year. **Funds Available:** The stipend is $1,000 plus a $500 travel allowance for recipients to attend the award ceremony. **Duration:** 1 year.

Eligibility Requirements: This program is open to students working on an undergraduate or graduate degree in airport management at colleges and universities in Arizona, California, Hawaii, Nevada, or Utah. Applicants must submit an autobiography (not to exceed 1 page) and a statement of their interest in aviation and airport management (not to exceed 1 page). Selection is based on academic record, extracurricular activities, and financial need. **Deadline for Receipt:** October of each year. **Additional Information:** Information is also available from Charles Mangum, SWAAAE Scholarship Committee, 8565 North Sand Dune Place, Tucson, AZ 85743, (520) 682-9565, E-mail: cmangum@marana.com.

3955 ■ AMERICAN SOCIETY FOR ENGINEERING EDUCATION

Attn: SMART Defense Scholarship Program
1818 N Street, N.W., Suite 600
Washington, DC 20036-2479
Tel: (202)331-3516
Fax: (202)265-8504
E-mail: smart@asee.org
Web Site: http://www.asee.org/resources/fellowships/smart/index.cfm
To provide scholarship/loans to upper-division and graduate students in areas of science, mathematics, and engineering that are of interest to the U.S. Department of Defense.

Title of Award: Science, Mathematics, and Research for Transformation (SMART) Defense Scholarship Program **Area, Field, or Subject:** Architecture, Naval; Behavioral sciences; Biological and clinical sciences; Chemistry; Computer and information sciences; Earth sciences; Engineering, Aerospace/Aeronautical/Astronautical; Engineering, Chemical; Engineering, Civil; Engineering, Electrical; Engineering, Materials; Engineering, Mechanical; Engineering, Ocean; Geosciences; Materials research/science; Mathematics and mathematical sciences; Oceanography; Physics **Level of Education for which Award is Granted:** Four Year College, Graduate **Number Awarded:** Varies each year; recently, 36 of these scholarships were awarded. **Funds Available:** The program provides full payment of tuition, fees, room, board, and other normal educational expenses at the recipient's institution. A book allowance of $1,000 per year is also provided. This is a scholarship/loan program; recipients must agree to serve as a civilian employee of the Department of Defense in a science and engineering position. If they fail to fulfill that service obligation, they must reimburse the federal government for all funds they received. **Duration:** Up to 24 months.

Eligibility Requirements: This program is open to upper-division and graduate students working on an undergraduate or graduate degree in any of the following fields: aeronautical and astronautical engineering; biosciences; chemical engineering; chemistry; civil engineering; cognitive, neural, and behavioral sciences; computer and computational sciences; electrical engineering; geosciences, including terrain, water, and air; materials science and engineering; mathematics; mechanical engineering; naval architecture and ocean engineering; oceanography; or physics. Applicants must be U.S. citizens who have a GPA of 3.0 or higher. Selection is based on academic records, personal statements, letters of recommendation, and GRE scores. **Deadline for Receipt:** March of each year. **Additional Information:** This program, established in 2005, is sponsored by the Army Research Laboratory, the Air Force Office of Scientific Research, the Office of Naval Research, the Air Force Research Laboratory, the Defense Advanced Research Projects Agency, the Defense Information Systems Agency, and the Defense Threat Reduction Agency.

3956 ■ ARMED FORCES COMMUNICATIONS AND ELECTRONICS ASSOCIATION

Attn: AFCEA Educational Foundation
4400 Fair Lakes Court
Fairfax, VA 22033-3899
Tel: (703)631-6149
Free: 800-336-4583
Fax: (703)631-4693
E-mail: scholarship@afcea.org
Web Site: http://www.afcea.org/education/scholarships/rotc/rotc1.asp
To provide financial assistance to ROTC cadets who are majoring in fields related to communications and electronics.

Title of Award: AFCEA ROTC Scholarships **Area, Field, or Subject:** Computer and information sciences; Electronics; Engineering, Aerospace/Aeronautical/Astronautical; Engineering, Chemical; Engineering, Computer; Engineering, Electrical; Mathematics and mathematical sciences; Physics; Systems engineering **Level of Education for which Award is Granted:** Four Year College **Number Awarded:** 36 each year, divided equally among Army, Navy/Marine Corps, and Air Force ROTC programs; for each service, 6 are awarded to rising juniors, 6 to rising seniors. **Funds Available:** The stipend is $2,000. **Duration:** 1 year; may be renewed.

Eligibility Requirements: This program is open to ROTC cadets majoring in electronics, engineering (aerospace, chemical, computer, electrical, or systems), mathematics, physics, or computer science. Applicants must be nominated by their ROTC professor, be entering their junior or senior year, be U.S. citizens, be of good moral character, have demonstrated academic excellence, be motivated to complete a college education and serve as officers in the U.S. armed forces, and be able to demonstrate financial need. **Deadline for Receipt:** March of each year.

3957 ■ ARMED FORCES COMMUNICATIONS AND ELECTRONICS ASSOCIATION

Attn: AFCEA Educational Foundation
4400 Fair Lakes Court
Fairfax, VA 22033-3899
Tel: (703)631-6149
Free: 800-336-4583
Fax: (703)631-4693
E-mail: scholarship@afcea.org
Web Site: http://www.afcea.org/education/scholarships/workingstudents/ws1.asp
To provide financial assistance to undergraduate students who are working part time on a degree in engineering or the sciences while already employed.

Title of Award: AFCEA Scholarship for Working Professionals **Area, Field, or Subject:** Computer and information sciences; Engineering, Aerospace/Aeronautical/Astronautical; Engineering, Chemical; Engineering, Electrical; Mathematics and mathematical sciences; Physics; Systems engineering **Level of Education for which Award is Granted:** Undergraduate **Number Awarded:** 1 each year. **Funds Available:** The stipend is $1,500. **Duration:** 1 year; may be renewed.

Eligibility Requirements: This program is open to part-time students entering their sophomore, junior, or senior year at an accredited 2-year or 4-year college or university in the United States while already employed in a science or technology field. Applicants must be U.S. citizens working toward a degree in engineering (aerospace, chemical, electrical, or systems), mathematics, physics, or computer science with a GPA of 3.4 or higher. They must be able to demonstrate academic achievement, patriotism, and potential to contribute to the American work force. **Deadline for Receipt:** September of each year. **Additional Information:** This program was established in 2002.

3958 ■ ARMED FORCES COMMUNICATIONS AND ELECTRONICS ASSOCIATION

Attn: AFCEA Educational Foundation
4400 Fair Lakes Court
Fairfax, VA 22033-3899
Tel: (703)631-6149
Free: 800-336-4583
Fax: (703)631-4693
E-mail: scholarship@afcea.org
Web Site: http://www.afcea.org/education/scholarships/undergraduate/genemm.asp
To provide funding to veterans, military personnel, and their family members who are majoring in specified scientific fields in college.
Title of Award: General Emmett Paige Scholarships **Area, Field, or Subject:** Computer and information sciences; Engineering, Aerospace/Aeronautical/Astronautical; Engineering, Chemical; Engineering, Computer; Engineering, Electrical; Mathematics and mathematical sciences; Physics **Level of Education for which Award is Granted:** Four Year College **Number Awarded:** Varies each year; recently, 11 of these scholarships were awarded. **Funds Available:** The stipend is $2,000. **Duration:** 1 year; may be renewed.
Eligibility Requirements: This program is open to veterans, persons on active duty in the uniformed military services, and their spouses or dependents who are currently enrolled full time in an accredited 4-year college or university in the United States. Graduating high school seniors are not eligible, but veterans entering college as freshmen may apply. Spouses or dependents must be sophomores or juniors. Applicants must be U.S. citizens, be of good moral character, have demonstrated academic excellence, be motivated to complete a college education, and be working toward a degree in engineering (aerospace, chemical, computer, or electrical), mathematics, physics, or computer science with a GPA of 3.4 or higher. They must provide a copy of Discharge Form DD214, Certificate of Service, or facsimile of their current Department of Defense or Coast Guard Identification Card. **Deadline for Receipt:** February of each year.

3959 ■ ARMED FORCES COMMUNICATIONS AND ELECTRONICS ASSOCIATION

Attn: AFCEA Educational Foundation
4400 Fair Lakes Court
Fairfax, VA 22033-3899
Tel: (703)631-6149
Free: 800-336-4583
Fax: (703)631-4693
E-mail: scholarship@afcea.org
Web Site: http://www.afcea.org/education/scholarships/undergraduate/veteran.asp
To provide financial assistance to veterans and military personnel who served in Afghanistan or Iraq and are working on an undergraduate degree in fields related to the support of U.S. intelligence enterprises.
Title of Award: Veterans of Enduring Freedom-Afghanistan and Iraqi Freedom Combat Operations Scholarship **Area, Field, or Subject:** Computer and information sciences; Engineering; Engineering, Aerospace/Aeronautical/Astronautical; Engineering, Computer; Engineering, Electrical; Mathematics and mathematical sciences; Physics; Systems engineering **Level of Education for which Award is Granted:** Undergraduate **Number Awarded:** 1 or more each year. **Funds Available:** The stipend is $2,000. **Duration:** 1 year.
Eligibility Requirements: This program is open to active-duty and honorably discharged U.S. military veterans, Reservists, and National Guard personnel who served in combat operations of Enduring Freedom-Afghanistan or Iraqi Freedom. Applicants must be enrolled at a 2- or 4-year institution in the United States and working on an undergraduate degree in computer engineering technology, computer information systems, electronics engineering technology, engineering (aerospace, computer, electrical, or systems), mathematics, physics, or computer sci-

ence. Along with their application, they must submit an essay that includes a brief synopsis of relevant work experience (including military assignments), a brief statement of career goals after graduation, and a explanation of how their academic and career goals will contribute to the areas related to communications, intelligence and/or information systems, and the mission of the Armed Forces Communications and Electronics Association (AFCEA). Financial need is also considered in the selection process. **Deadline for Receipt:** October of each year. **Additional Information:** This scholarship was first offered in 2005.

3960 ■ ARMED FORCES COMMUNICATIONS AND ELECTRONICS ASSOCIATION

Attn: AFCEA Educational Foundation
4400 Fair Lakes Court
Fairfax, VA 22033-3899
Tel: (703)631-6149
Free: 800-336-4583
Fax: (703)631-4693
E-mail: scholarship@afcea.org
Web Site: http://www.afcea.org/education/scholarships/undergraduate/pub2.asp
To provide financial assistance to undergraduate students who are working full time on a degree in engineering or the sciences.
Title of Award: General John A. Wickham Scholarships **Area, Field, or Subject:** Computer and information sciences; Engineering, Aerospace/Aeronautical/Astronautical; Engineering, Chemical; Engineering, Computer; Engineering, Electrical; Mathematics and mathematical sciences; Physics; Systems engineering **Level of Education for which Award is Granted:** Four Year College **Number Awarded:** Varies each year; recently, 11 of these scholarships were awarded. **Funds Available:** The stipend is $2,000. **Duration:** 1 year; may be renewed.
Eligibility Requirements: This program is open to full-time students entering their junior or senior year at an accredited degree-granting 4-year college or university in the United States. Applicants must be U.S. citizens working toward a degree in engineering (aerospace, chemical, computer, electrical, or systems), mathematics, physics, or computer science with a GPA of 3.5 or higher. They must be able to demonstrate academic achievement, patriotism, and potential to contribute to the American work force. **Deadline for Receipt:** April of each year.

3961 ■ ARMED FORCES COMMUNICATIONS AND ELECTRONICS ASSOCIATION

Attn: AFCEA Educational Foundation
4400 Fair Lakes Court
Fairfax, VA 22033-3899
Tel: (703)631-6149
Free: 800-336-4583
Fax: (703)631-4693
E-mail: scholarship@afcea.org
Web Site: http://www.afcea.org/education/scholarships/undergraduate/sgtjean.asp
To provide funding to members and veterans of the U.S. Marine Corps (USMC) who are majoring in specified fields in college.
Title of Award: Marine Sgt. Jeannette L. Winters Memorial Scholarship **Area, Field, or Subject:** Computer and information sciences; Engineering, Aerospace/Aeronautical/Astronautical; Engineering, Computer; Engineering, Electrical; Mathematics and mathematical sciences; Physics; Systems engineering **Level of Education for which Award is Granted:** Undergraduate **Number Awarded:** 1 each year. **Funds Available:** The stipend is $2,000. **Duration:** 1 year.
Eligibility Requirements: This program is open to USMC personnel currently on active duty, in the Reserves, or honorably-discharged veterans who are enrolled full or part time in an accredited college or university in the United States. Applicants must be U.S. citizens, be of good moral character, have demonstrated academic excellence, be motivated to complete a college education, and be working on a degree in engineering (aerospace, computer, electrical, or systems), mathematics, physics, or computer science with a GPA of 3.0 or higher. They must provide a copy of Discharge Form DD214, Certificate of Service, or facsimile of their current Department of Defense Identification Card. **Deadline for Receipt:** September of each year. **Additional Information:** This program was established in 2002 to honor a Marine who died when her KC-130 aircraft crashed in Pakistan.

**3962 ■ AVIATION DISTRIBUTORS AND MANUFACTURERS AS-
SOCIATION**
100 North 20th Street, Fourth Floor
Philadelphia, PA 19103-1443
Tel: (215)564-3484
Fax: (215)963-9784
E-mail: adma@fernley.com
Web Site: http://www.adma.org/aviation_scholarship.html
To provide financial assistance to students who are preparing for a career
in the aviation field.
Title of Award: Aviation Distributors and Manufacturers Association
Scholarship Program **Area, Field, or Subject:** Aviation; Management
Level of Education for which Award is Granted: Undergraduate
Number Awarded: Varies each year; recently, 4 of these scholarships
were awarded. **Funds Available:** The stipend is $1,000. **Duration:** 1
year.
Eligibility Requirements: This program is open to college students who
are either 1) a third- or fourth-year student enrolled at an accredited
institution in a bachelor's degree program preparing for a career in aviation management or as a professional pilot; or 2) a second-year student in
an aircraft and powerplant (A&P) mechanic program at a 2-year accredited institution. Applicants must submit 2 letters of recommendation, a
500-word essay describing their desire to prepare for a career in aviation,
and verification of a GPA of 3.0 or higher. Selection is based on academic
performance, recommendations, extracurricular activities, leadership
contributions, and financial need. **Deadline for Receipt:** March of each
year.

3963 ■ AVIATION INSURANCE ASSOCIATION
14 West Third Street, Suite 200
Kansas City, MO 64105
Tel: (816)221-8488
Fax: (816)472-7765
E-mail: info@aiaweb.org
Web Site: http://www.aiaweb.org
To provide financial assistance to college students preparing for a career
in aviation.
Title of Award: Aviation Insurance Association Scholarship **Area, Field,
or Subject:** Aviation **Level of Education for which Award is Granted:**
Undergraduate **Number Awarded:** 1 each year. **Funds Available:** The
stipend is $5,000. **Duration:** 1 year.
Eligibility Requirements: This program is open to students enrolled in
an undergraduate aviation degree program at a college or university that
is a member of the University Aviation Association (UAA). Applicants must
have completed at least 45 college credits, of which 15 must be in aviation, with a GPA of 2.5 or higher. Along with their application, they must
submit 1) a letter describing their activities, leadership qualities, goals,
and reasons for applying for these funds; 2) at least 1 letter of recommendation from an employer or instructor; 3) an official transcript; and 4)
any FAA certificates. **Deadline for Receipt:** February of each year. **Additional Information:** Further information is also available from Bernard
Wulle, Purdue University, Aviation Technology Department, 1 Purdue
Airport, West Lafayette, IN 47906-3393.

3964 ■ COMMUNITIES FOUNDATION OF TEXAS
Attn: Scholarship Department
5500 Caruth Haven Lane
Dallas, TX 75225-8146
Tel: (214)750-4222
Fax: (214)750-4210
E-mail: grants@cftexas.org
Web Site: http://www.cftexas.org
To provide financial assistance to upper-division and graduate students
who are working on a degree in aerospace science or aeronautical
engineering.
Title of Award: General James H. Doolittle Scholarship **Area, Field, or
Subject:** Aerospace sciences; Engineering, Aerospace/Aeronautical/
Astronautical; Space and planetary sciences **Level of Education for
which Award is Granted:** Four Year College, Graduate **Number
Awarded:** 1 each year. **Funds Available:** The stipend is $5,000 per year.
Duration: 1 year; nonrenewable.
Eligibility Requirements: This program is open to college juniors,
seniors, and graduate students who are working on a baccalaureate or

advanced degree in aerospace science or aeronautical engineering. Applicants must have completed at least 52 hours of college course work
with a GPA of 2.75 or higher. They must be able to demonstrate financial
need. Along with their application, they must submit an essay (up to 3
pages) describing their interest in the field of aerospace science or
aeronautical engineering, how that interest began, the course of studies
pursued as a result of the interest, any special projects or jobs they have
held that are related to the field, and their career goals. U.S. citizenship is
required. **Deadline for Receipt:** February of each year.

3965 ■ COMMUNITIES FOUNDATION OF TEXAS
Attn: Scholarship Department
5500 Caruth Haven Lane
Dallas, TX 75225-8146
Tel: (214)750-4222
Fax: (214)750-4210
E-mail: grants@cftexas.org
Web Site: http://www.cftexas.org
To provide financial assistance to upper-division and graduate students
who are working on a degree in journalism and have an interest in avia-
tion.
Title of Award: George E. Haddaway Scholarship **Area, Field, or
Subject:** Aviation; Communications; Journalism **Level of Education for
which Award is Granted:** Four Year College, Graduate **Number
Awarded:** 1 each year. **Funds Available:** The stipend is $2,500 per year.
Duration: 1 year; nonrenewable.
Eligibility Requirements: This program is open to college juniors,
seniors, and graduate students who can demonstrate interest in aviation
by such activities as 1) current or former membership in the aviation
program of a college or university, the Boy or Girl Scouts of America, the
Civil Air Patrol, or a similar organization; or 2) pursuit or completion of the
requirements for an aircraft license. Applicants must be working on a baccalaureate or advanced degree in print or electronic journalism and have
completed at least 52 hours of college course work with a GPA of 2.75 or
higher. They must be able to demonstrate financial need. Along with their
application, they must submit an essay (200 to 500 words) describing
their interest in aviation and how they might combine that interest with a
career in journalism. U.S. citizenship is required. **Deadline for Receipt:**
March of each year.

3966 ■ DAEDALIAN FOUNDATION
Attn: Scholarship Committee
55 Main Circle (Building 676)
P.O. Box 249
Randolph AFB, TX 78148-0249
Tel: (210)945-2113
Fax: (210)945-2112
E-mail: daedalus@daedalians.org
Web Site: http://www.daedalians.org
To provide financial assistance to ROTC and other college students who
wish to become military pilots.
Title of Award: Daedalian Academic Matching Scholarship Program
Area, Field, or Subject: Aviation **Level of Education for which Award
is Granted:** Four Year College **Number Awarded:** Up to 99 each year.
Funds Available: The amount awarded varies but is intended to serve as
matching funds for the Flight scholarship. Generally, the maximum
awarded is $2,000.
Eligibility Requirements: Eligible are students who are attending or
have been accepted at an accredited 4-year college or university and
have demonstrated the desire and potential to become a commissioned
military pilot. Usually, students in ROTC units of all services apply to local
chapters (Flights) of Daedalian; if the Flight awards a scholarship, the application is forwarded to the Daedalian Foundation for 1 of these matching
scholarships. College students not part of a ROTC program are eligible if
their undergraduate goals and performance are consistent with Daedalian
criteria. Selection is based on intention to pursue a career as a military
pilot, demonstrated moral character and patriotism, scholastic and military
standing and aptitude, and physical condition and aptitude for flight. Additional eligibility criteria may be set by a Flight Scholarship Selection
Board. **Deadline for Receipt:** Applications may be submitted at any time.

3967 ■ DAEDALIAN FOUNDATION
Attn: Scholarship Committee
55 Main Circle (Building 676)

P.O. Box 249
Randolph AFB, TX 78148-0249
Tel: (210)945-2113
Fax: (210)945-2112
E-mail: daedalus@daedalians.org
Web Site: http://www.daedalians.org
To provide financial assistance to descendants of members of the Order of Daedalians who wish to prepare for a career in military aviation or space.
Title of Award: Daedalian Foundation Descendants' Scholarship Program **Area, Field, or Subject:** Aeronautics; Astronautics; Aviation **Level of Education for which Award is Granted:** Four Year College, Graduate **Number Awarded:** Up to 3 each year. **Funds Available:** The stipend is $2,000.
Eligibility Requirements: This program is open to descendants of members of the order who are working on or planning to work on a baccalaureate or higher degree. Applicants must be interested in and willing to commit to a career as a commissioned military pilot, flight crew member, astronaut, or a commissioned officer in 1 of the armed forces of the United States in a discipline directly supporting aeronautics or astronautics. They must be physically and mentally qualified for flight and/or space; if they intend to pursue a non-flying career as a commissioned officer in a scientific or engineering discipline supporting aviation or space, they must pass a physical examination qualifying for active commissioned duty in the U.S. armed forces. Nominations must be submitted by a local chapter (Flight) of Daedalian. Selection is based on academic achievement and recognition, extracurricular activities, honors, and employment experience. Financial need may also be considered, but only if all other factors are equal. **Deadline for Receipt:** June of each year.
Additional Information: The Order of Daedalians was founded in 1934 as an organization of the nearly 14,000 aviators who served as military pilots during World War I and are still listed and designated as Founder Members. In the 1950s, the organization expanded eligibility to include 1) on a sponsorship basis, current and former commissioned military pilots from all services, and 2) on a hereditary basis, descendants of Founder Members.

3968 ■ DAEDALIAN FOUNDATION
Attn: Scholarship Committee
55 Main Circle (Building 676)
P.O. Box 249
Randolph AFB, TX 78148-0249
Tel: (210)945-2113
Fax: (210)945-2112
E-mail: daedalus@daedalians.org
Web Site: http://www.daedalians.org
To provide financial assistance to college students who are participating in a ROTC program and wish to become military pilots.
Title of Award: John and Alice Egan Multi-Year Mentoring Scholarship Program **Area, Field, or Subject:** Aviation **Level of Education for which Award is Granted:** Four Year College **Number Awarded:** Up to 11 each year. **Funds Available:** The stipend is $2,500 per year. **Duration:** 1 year; may be renewed up to 2 or 3 additional years, provided the recipient maintains a GPA of 3.0 or higher and is enrolled in an undergraduate program.
Eligibility Requirements: This program is open to students who have completed at least the freshman year at an accredited 4-year college or university and have a GPA of 3.0 or higher. Applicants must be participating in an ROTC program and be medically qualified for flight training. They must plan to apply for and be awarded a military pilot training allocation at the appropriate juncture in their ROTC program. Selection is based on intention to prepare for a career as a military pilot, demonstrated moral character and patriotism, scholastic and military standing and aptitude, and physical condition and aptitude for flight. **Deadline for Receipt:** July of each year. **Additional Information:** This program began in 2003. It includes a mentoring component.

3969 ■ DELTA ZETA SORORITY
Attn: Foundation Coordinator
202 East Church Street
Oxford, OH 45056
Tel: (513)523-7597
E-mail: DZFoundation@dzshq.com

Web Site: http://www.deltazeta.org/pages/content/scholarships.html
To provide financial assistance for continued undergraduate study to members of Delta Zeta Sorority.
Title of Award: Arlene Davis Scholarship **Area, Field, or Subject:** Aviation **Level of Education for which Award is Granted:** Undergraduate **Number Awarded:** 1 each year. **Funds Available:** The stipend ranges from $900 to $1,100, depending on the availability of funds. **Duration:** 1 year; nonrenewable.
Eligibility Requirements: This program is open to members of the sorority who have a GPA of 3.0 or higher. Applicants should be entering their sophomore or junior year and working on a degree closely related to aviation. They must submit an official transcript, a statement of their career goals, information on their service to the sorority, documentation of campus activities and/or community involvement, and a list of academic honors. Financial need is also considered in the selection process. **Deadline for Receipt:** February of each year.

3970 ■ E-PUBLISHING GROUP, LLC
Attn: COMM1 Radio Simulators
113A East Church Street
Frederick, MD 21701
Tel: (301)620-9500; 888-333-2855
Fax: (301)620-9501
E-mail: feedback@comm1radiosimulator.com
Web Site: http://www.comm1.com
To provide financial assistance to students attending college to prepare for a career in aviation.
Title of Award: COMM1 Radio Aviation Scholarship **Area, Field, or Subject:** Aviation **Level of Education for which Award is Granted:** Undergraduate **Number Awarded:** 1 each year. **Funds Available:** The stipend is $1,000. **Duration:** 1 year.
Eligibility Requirements: This program is open to undergraduates working on a degree as preparation for a career in aviation. Applicants must complete the statement, "Proper pilot communications are essential to aviation safety because..." Selection is based on aviation career aspirations, academic and flight training records, recommendations from mentor, and financial need. **Deadline for Receipt:** September of each year.
Additional Information: This program began in 2001.

3971 ■ FLEET RESERVE ASSOCIATION
Past Regional Presidents Club
c/o W. Ralph Holcombe, Secretary/Treasurer
4911 Fennell Court
Suffolk, VA 23435
Tel: (757)484-7403
Fax: (757)686-5952
E-mail: info@fraprpscholarships.org
Web Site: http://www.fraprpscholarships.org
To provide financial assistance to relatives of members of the Fleet Reserve Association (FRA) interested in studying aeronautical engineering or aviation in college.
Title of Award: Walter Beale Scholarship **Area, Field, or Subject:** Aviation; Engineering; Engineering, Aerospace/Aeronautical/Astronautical **Level of Education for which Award is Granted:** Undergraduate **Number Awarded:** 1 or more each year. **Funds Available:** The amounts of the awards depend on the availability of funds and the need of the recipients; they range from $2,000 to $5,000. **Duration:** 1 year; renewable.
Eligibility Requirements: This program is open to spouses, children, and grandchildren of active-duty, reserve, and retired personnel of the Navy, Marine Corps, or Coast Guard who are relatives of FRA members in good standing (or who were in good standing at the time of their death). Students in a reserve officer candidate program receiving aid are not eligible. Applicants must be enrolled at an accredited college, university, or technical institution in the United States in a program related to engineering, aviation, or aeronautical engineering. Selection is based on GPA, scholastic aptitude test scores, curriculum goals, interests, community activities, awards, and financial need. **Deadline for Receipt:** April of each year.

3972 ■ GENERAL AVIATION MANUFACTURERS ASSOCIATION
Attn: Director of Administration
1400 K Street, N.W., Suite 801
Washington, DC 20005-2485

Tel: (202)393-1500
Fax: (202)842-4063
E-mail: bbailey@GAMA.aero
Web Site: http://www.gama.aero/resources/AVEducation/index.php
To provide financial assistance to students at schools belonging to the National Intercollegiate Flying Association (NIFA).
Title of Award: Dr. Harold S. Wood Award for Excellence **Area, Field, or Subject:** Aviation **Level of Education for which Award is Granted:** Undergraduate **Number Awarded:** 11 district winners and 1 national winner. **Funds Available:** The national winner is presented with an engraved propeller trophy and a $1,000 cash award. **Duration:** 1 year; nonrenewable.
Eligibility Requirements: Nominations are solicited from NIFA-member schools in each of the 11 NIFA regions. There is no limit to the number of applications submitted by each school. Eligible to be nominated by these schools are currently-enrolled students who have at least a 3.0 GPA. Each NIFA region chooses 1 winning finalist from the entries. A national winner is then chosen from the 11 finalists. Selection, on both levels, is based on academic record (30%), aviation-related extracurricular activities (50%), and service and contributions to school and community (20%).
Deadline for Receipt: Nominations must be submitted in February of each year.

3973 ■ GEORGIA SPACE GRANT CONSORTIUM

c/o Georgia Institute of Technology
Aerospace Engineering
Space Science and Technology Building, Room 210
Atlanta, GA 30332-0150
Tel: (404)894-0521
Fax: (404)894-9313
E-mail: wanda.pierson@aerospace.gatech.edu
Web Site: http://www.ae.gatech.edu/organizations/gsgc/html/fellowship.htm
To provide financial assistance for undergraduate and graduate study of space-related fields to students at member institutions of the Georgia Space Grant Consortium (GSGC).
Title of Award: Georgia Space Grant Consortium Fellowships **Area, Field, or Subject:** Aerospace sciences; Computer and information sciences; Engineering, Aerospace/Aeronautical/Astronautical; Mathematics and mathematical sciences; Space and planetary sciences **Level of Education for which Award is Granted:** Graduate, Undergraduate **Number Awarded:** 1 each year. **Funds Available:** A stipend is awarded (amount not specified).
Eligibility Requirements: This program is open to U.S. citizens who are undergraduate and graduate students at member institutions of the GSGC. Applicants must be working on a degree in mathematics, science, engineering, computer science, or a technical discipline related to space. Selection is based on transcripts, 3 letters of reference, and an essay of 100 to 500 words on the applicant's professional interests and objectives and their relationship to the field of aerospace. Awards are provided as part of the Space Grant program of the U.S. National Aeronautics and Space Administration (NASA), which encourages participation by women, minorities, and people with disabilities. **Additional Information:** Institutions that are members of the GSGC include Albany State University, Clark Atlanta University, Columbus State University, Fort Valley State University, Georgia Institute of Technology, Georgia State University, Kennesaw State University, Mercer University, Morehouse College, Spelman College, State University of West Georgia, and the University of Georgia. This program is funded by NASA.

3974 ■ HANSCOM OFFICERS' WIVES' CLUB

Attn: Scholarship Chair
P.O. Box 557
Bedford, MA 01730
Tel: (781)275-1251
E-mail: scholarship@hanscomowd.org
Web Site: http://www.hanscomowc.org
To provide financial assistance to children of military personnel and veterans in New England who are interested in studying aeronautics and space in college.
Title of Award: COL Chuck Jones Memorial Award **Area, Field, or Subject:** Aeronautics; Aerospace sciences; Communications; Engineering; Meteorology; Space and planetary sciences **Level of Education for**

which **Award is Granted:** Undergraduate **Number Awarded:** 1 each year. **Funds Available:** The stipend is $2,000. **Duration:** 1 year; nonrenewable.
Eligibility Requirements: This program is open to college-bound high school seniors living in New England who are dependents of active-duty, retired, or deceased military members of any branch of service. Also eligible are dependents of military recruiters working in the New York area and students living elsewhere but whose military sponsor is stationed at Hanscom Air Force Base. Applicants must demonstrate qualities of responsibility, leadership, scholastics, citizenship, and diversity of interest. They must have a valid military identification card and be planning to work on a college degree in a field related to aeronautics and space (including communications, meteorology, air/space maintenance, manufacturing processing, engineering, and the astronaut program). Along with their application, they must submit a 2-page essay on their educational goals, how their educational experience will help prepare them to pursue future goals, and how they intend to apply their education to better their community. **Deadline for Receipt:** March of each year. **Additional Information:** This program was established to honor a victim of an airplane crash on September 11, 2001. It is sponsored by the Paul Revere Chapter of the Air Force Association.

3975 ■ HANSCOM OFFICERS' WIVES' CLUB

Attn: Scholarship Chair
P.O. Box 557
Bedford, MA 01730
Tel: (781)275-1251
E-mail: scholarship@hanscomowd.org
Web Site: http://www.hanscomowc.org
To provide financial assistance to children of military personnel and veterans in New England who are interested in studying aviation in college.
Title of Award: Brian Sweeney Memorial Award **Area, Field, or Subject:** Aviation; Engineering, Aerospace/Aeronautical/Astronautical; Engineering, Civil; Environmental science; Meteorology; Protective services **Level of Education for which Award is Granted:** Undergraduate **Number Awarded:** 1 each year. **Funds Available:** The stipend is $2,000. **Duration:** 1 year; nonrenewable.
Eligibility Requirements: This program is open to college-bound high school seniors living in New England who are dependents of active-duty, retired, or deceased military members of any branch of service. Also eligible are dependents of military recruiters working in the New York area and students living elsewhere but whose military sponsor is stationed at Hanscom Air Force Base. Applicants must demonstrate qualities of responsibility, leadership, scholastics, citizenship, and diversity of interest. They must have a valid military identification card and be planning to work on a college degree in a field related to aviation (including civil, aeronautical, and environmental engineering; maintenance; management; aviation safety and security; and meteorology). Along with their application, they must submit a 2-page essay on their educational goals, how their educational experience will help prepare them to pursue future goals, and how they intend to apply their education to better their community. **Deadline for Receipt:** March of each year. **Additional Information:** This program was established to honor a victim of an airplane crash on September 11, 2001. It is sponsored by the Paul Revere Chapter of the Air Force Association.

3976 ■ HAWAI'I COMMUNITY FOUNDATION

Attn: Scholarship Department
1164 Bishop Street, Suite 800
Honolulu, HI 96813
Tel: (808)566-5570; 888-731-3863
Fax: (808)521-6286
E-mail: scholarships@hcf-hawaii.org
Web Site: http://www.hawaiicommunityfoundation.org/scholar/scholar.php
To provide financial assistance to Hawaii residents who are interested in preparing for a career in aerospace.
Title of Award: Ellison Onizuka Memorial Scholarship **Area, Field, or Subject:** Aerospace sciences; Space and planetary sciences **Level of Education for which Award is Granted:** Undergraduate **Number Awarded:** Varies each year. **Funds Available:** The amounts of the awards depend on the availability of funds and the need of the recipient. **Duration:** 1 year.

Eligibility Requirements: This program is open to high school seniors in Hawaii who are interested in preparing for an aerospace career. No direct applications are accepted; candidates must be nominated by their high school principal. Nominees must be residents of the state of Hawaii; able to demonstrate financial need; interested in attending an accredited 2- or 4-year college or university; and able to demonstrate academic achievement (GPA of 2.7 or higher). **Deadline for Receipt:** April of each year. **Additional Information:** Recipients may attend school in Hawaii or on the mainland.

3977 ■ HISPANIC ENGINEER NATIONAL ACHIEVEMENT AWARDS CONFERENCE

3900 Whiteside Street
Los Angeles, CA 90063
Tel: (323)262-0997
Fax: (323)262-0946
E-mail: info@henaac.org
Web Site: http://www.henaac.org/scholarships
To provide financial assistance to Hispanic undergraduate students majoring in engineering and related fields.
Title of Award: Ford/HENAAC Scholars Program **Area, Field, or Subject:** Computer and information sciences; Engineering, Aerospace/Aeronautical/Astronautical; Engineering, Electrical; Engineering, Industrial; Engineering, Mechanical **Level of Education for which Award is Granted:** Undergraduate **Number Awarded:** 5 each year. **Funds Available:** The stipend is $5,000. **Duration:** 1 year; recipients may reapply.
Eligibility Requirements: This program is open to Hispanic undergraduate students who are enrolled full time in computer science or the following engineering fields: aeronautical, electrical, industrial, and, mechanical. Applicants must have a GPA of 3.0 or higher. U.S. citizenship is required. Academic achievement and campus community activities are considered in the selection process. **Deadline for Receipt:** April of each year. **Additional Information:** This program is sponsored by Ford Motor Company as part of its effort to support the mission of the Hispanic Engineer National Achievement Awards Conference (HENAAC) to promote technical excellence and leadership in the Hispanic community.

3978 ■ HISPANIC ENGINEER NATIONAL ACHIEVEMENT AWARDS CONFERENCE

3900 Whiteside Street
Los Angeles, CA 90063
Tel: (323)262-0997
Fax: (323)262-0946
E-mail: info@henaac.org
Web Site: http://www.henaac.org/scholarships
To provide financial assistance to Hispanic undergraduate students majoring in engineering and related fields.
Title of Award: Northrop Grumman/HENAAC Scholars Program **Area, Field, or Subject:** Architecture, Naval; Computer and information sciences; Engineering, Aerospace/Aeronautical/Astronautical; Engineering, Chemical; Engineering, Civil; Engineering, Computer; Engineering, Electrical; Engineering, Industrial; Engineering, Mechanical; Engineering, Ocean; Information science and technology; Mathematics and mathematical sciences; Physics **Level of Education for which Award is Granted:** Undergraduate **Number Awarded:** 5 each year. **Funds Available:** The stipend is $5,000. **Duration:** 1 year; recipients may reapply.
Eligibility Requirements: This program is open to Hispanic undergraduate students who are enrolled full time in the following engineering fields: aerospace, chemical, civil, computer, electrical, industrial, manufacturing, marine, mechanical, ocean, or structural. Students majoring in computer science, information science, mathematics, naval architecture, and physics are also eligible. Applicants must be U.S. citizens and have a GPA of 3.0 or higher. Academic achievement and campus community activities are considered in the selection process. **Deadline for Receipt:** April of each year. **Additional Information:** This program is sponsored by Northrop Grumman as part of its effort to support the mission of the Hispanic Engineer National Achievement Awards Conference (HENAAC) to promote technical excellence and leadership in the Hispanic community.

3979 ■ IDAHO SPACE GRANT CONSORTIUM

c/o University of Idaho
College of Engineering

P.O. Box 441011
Moscow, ID 83844-1011
Tel: (208)885-6438
Fax: (208)885-1399
E-mail: isgc@uidaho.edu
Web Site: http://isgc.uidaho.edu
To provide financial assistance for study in space-related fields to undergraduate students at institutions belonging to the Idaho Space Grant Consortium (ISGC).
Title of Award: Idaho Space Grant Consortium Scholarship Program **Area, Field, or Subject:** Aerospace sciences; Education; Engineering, Aerospace/Aeronautical/Astronautical; Mathematics and mathematical sciences; Science; Space and planetary sciences **Level of Education for which Award is Granted:** Undergraduate **Number Awarded:** Varies each year; recently, 24 of these scholarships were awarded. **Funds Available:** The stipend is up to $1,000 per year. Funds are to be used to pay for registration at colleges in the consortium. **Duration:** 1 year; may be renewed.
Eligibility Requirements: This program is open to full-time undergraduate students at ISGC member institutions. Applicants must be majoring in engineering, mathematics, science, or science/math education and have a cumulative GPA of 3.0 or higher. They should be planning to work on a 4-year degree in a space-related field. Along with their application, they must submit a 500-word essay on their future career and educational goals and why they believe the U.S. National Aeronautics and Space Administration (NASA) should support their education. U.S. citizenship is required. As a component of the NASA Space Grant program, the ISGC encourages participation by women, underrepresented minorities, and persons with disabilities. **Deadline for Receipt:** February of each year. **Additional Information:** Members of the consortium include Albertson College of Idaho, Boise State University, College of Southern Idaho, Idaho State University, Lewis Clark State College, North Idaho College, Northwest Nazarene College, Brigham Young University of Idaho, and the University of Idaho. This program is funded by NASA.

3980 ■ IDAHO SPACE GRANT CONSORTIUM

c/o University of Idaho
College of Engineering
P.O. Box 441011
Moscow, ID 83844-1011
Tel: (208)885-6438
Fax: (208)885-1399
E-mail: isgc@uidaho.edu
Web Site: http://isgc.uidaho.edu
To provide funding to faculty and students at member institutions of the Idaho Space Grant Consortium (ISGC) who are interested in traveling to meetings or conferences.
Title of Award: Idaho Space Grant Consortium Travel Grants **Area, Field, or Subject:** Aerospace sciences; Engineering, Aerospace/Aeronautical/Astronautical; Space and planetary sciences **Level of Education for which Award is Granted:** Graduate, Postdoctoral, Undergraduate **Number Awarded:** Varies each year. **Funds Available:** Grants up to half the total cost of the travel.
Eligibility Requirements: This program is open to faculty members and students at institutions affiliated with ISGC. Applicants must be interested in traveling to a field center of the U.S. National Aeronautics and Space Administration (NASA) or a NASA-related meeting or conference. Students may travel to summer internships at NASA centers; faculty may travel to establish contacts with out-of-state scientists or researchers. International travel is not supported. U.S. citizenship is required. **Deadline for Receipt:** Applications may be submitted at any time. **Additional Information:** Members of the consortium include Albertson College of Idaho, Boise State University, College of Southern Idaho, Idaho State University, Lewis Clark State College, North Idaho College, Northwest Nazarene College, Brigham Young University of Idaho, and the University of Idaho. This program is funded by NASA.

3981 ■ INTERNATIONAL SOCIETY OF EXPLOSIVES ENGINEERS

Attn: SEE Education Foundation
30325 Bainbridge Road
Cleveland, OH 44139
Tel: (440)349-4400
Fax: (440)349-3788

Web Site: http://www.isee.org/education/SEEFoundation.htm

To provide financial assistance to undergraduate and graduate engineering students interested in preparing for a career involving the use of explosives.

Title of Award: SEE Education Foundation Scholarships **Area, Field, or Subject:** Engineering; Engineering, Aerospace/Aeronautical/Astronautical; Engineering, Automotive; Engineering, Industrial; Engineering, Mining and Mineral **Level of Education for which Award is Granted:** Graduate, Undergraduate **Number Awarded:** 1 each year. **Funds Available:** A stipend is awarded (amount not specified). **Duration:** 1 year; may be renewed.

Eligibility Requirements: This program is open to students working on their first associate, undergraduate, or graduate degree as a full-time student at an accredited college or university. Applicants must show an interest in the use of explosives and intend to enter an explosives-related field, such as mining, construction, forestry, manufacturing, automotives, or aerospace. If they have already completed some college work, their GPA must be 2.9 or higher. Selection is based on career and personal ambition, academic potential, written communications, ability to overcome personal hardships and/or challenges, and financial need. **Deadline for Receipt:** April of each year.

3982 ■ IOWA SPACE GRANT CONSORTIUM

Attn: Director
Iowa State University
2271 Howe Hall, Room 2365
Ames, IA 50011-2271
Tel: (515)294-3106
Free: 800-854-1667
Fax: (515)294-3361
E-mail: isgc@iastate.edu
Web Site: http://www.ia.spacegrant.org

To provide financial assistance to undergraduate and graduate students majoring in science, technology, engineering, or mathematics (STEM) disciplines at member institutions of the Iowa Space Grant Consortium (ISGC).

Title of Award: Iowa Space Grant Scholarship Program **Area, Field, or Subject:** Aerospace sciences; Biological and clinical sciences; Engineering, Aerospace/Aeronautical/Astronautical; Mathematics and mathematical sciences; Science; Space and planetary sciences; Technology **Level of Education for which Award is Granted:** Four Year College, Graduate **Number Awarded:** Approximately 16 each year. **Funds Available:** The stipend is $6,000. **Duration:** 1 year.

Eligibility Requirements: This program is open to U.S. citizens enrolled full time as undergraduate or graduate students at ISGC member institutions. Applicants must be majoring in a STEM discipline of interest to the National Aeronautics and Space Administration. They must be interested in working on the base research program at their institution. Students from underrepresented groups (women, minorities, and persons with disabilities) are especially encouraged to apply. **Deadline for Receipt:** March of each year. **Additional Information:** Member institutions of ISGC, and their base programs, include Drake University (molecular biology and space life sciences), Iowa State University (the Spacecraft Systems and Operations Laboratory), the University of Iowa (the Operator Performance Laboratory), and the University of Northern Iowa (student research program on Iowa's lakes and wetlands). Funding for this program is provided by NASA.

3983 ■ KANSAS SPACE GRANT CONSORTIUM

c/o University of Kansas
Learned Hall
1530 West 15th
Lawrence, KS 66045-7609
Tel: (785)864-7401
Fax: (785)864-3361
E-mail: ksgc@nasainkansas.org
Web Site: http://nasainkansas.org/ksgc/kansas_space_grant_consortium_ksgc

To provide funding for space-related activities to students and faculty at member institutions of the Kansas Space Grant Consortium.

Title of Award: Kansas Space Grant Consortium Program **Area, Field, or Subject:** Aerospace sciences; Engineering, Aerospace/Aeronautical/Astronautical; Space and planetary sciences **Level of Education for** which Award is Granted: Graduate, Postdoctoral, Undergraduate **Number Awarded:** Varies each year. **Funds Available:** Each participating institution determines the amounts of its awards.

Eligibility Requirements: This program is open to faculty and students at member institutions. Support is provided for undergraduate research scholarships, graduate research assistantships, undergraduate and graduate student participation in activities sponsored by the U.S. National Aeronautics and Space Administration (NASA), faculty participation in NASA research projects, and other activities in fields of interest to NASA. The consortium is a component of NASA's Space Grant program, which encourages participation by women, underrepresented minorities, and persons with disabilities. **Deadline for Receipt:** Each participating institution establishes its own deadlines. **Additional Information:** The member institutions of the consortium are Emporia State University, Fort Hayes State University, Haskell Indian Nations University, Kansas State University, Pittsburg State University, University of Kansas, and Wichita State University. Funding for this program is provided by NASA.

3984 ■ KENTUCKY SPACE GRANT CONSORTIUM

c/o Western Kentucky University
Department of Physics and Astronomy, TCCW 246
1906 College Heights Boulevard 11077
Bowling Green, KY 42101-1077
Tel: (270)745-4156
Fax: (270)745-4255
E-mail: Richard.Hackney@wku.edu
Web Site: http://www.wku.edu/KSGC

To provide financial assistance to undergraduate students at member institutions of the Kentucky Space Grant Consortium (KSGC) interested in pursuing education and research in space-related fields.

Title of Award: Kentucky Space Grant Consortium Undergraduate Scholarships **Area, Field, or Subject:** Aerospace sciences; Engineering, Aerospace/Aeronautical/Astronautical; Space and planetary sciences **Level of Education for which Award is Granted:** Undergraduate **Number Awarded:** Varies each year. **Funds Available:** The grant is $5,000, including a stipend of $4,500 and an additional $500 to support the student's mentored research project. Matching grants of at least $4,000 are required. Preference is given to applicants from schools that agree to waive tuition for the scholar as part of the program. **Duration:** 1 year; may be renewed depending on the quality of the student's research and satisfactory performance in the program of study as evidenced by grades, presentation of research results, and evaluation of progress by the mentor.

Eligibility Requirements: This program is open to undergraduate students at member institutions of the KSGC. Applicants must be enrolled in a baccalaureate degree program in a space-related field or teaching specialization. As part of the program, a faculty member must agree to serve as a mentor on a research project. U.S. citizenship is required. Selection is based on academic qualifications of the applicant, quality of the proposed research program and its relevance to space-related science and technology, and applicant's motivation for a space-related career as expressed in an essay on interests and goals. Applications are especially encouraged from women, members of other underrepresented groups (including minorities and people with disabilities), and students involved in projects of the U.S. National Aeronautics and Space Administration (NASA) such as NASA EPSCoR and SHARP. **Deadline for Receipt:** February of each year. **Additional Information:** This program is funded by NASA. The KSGC member institutions are Bellarmine University, Centre College, Eastern Kentucky University, Kentucky State University, Morehead State University, Murray State University, Northern Kentucky University, Thomas More College, Transylvania University, University of Kentucky, University of Louisville, and Western Kentucky University.

3985 ■ CLARE BOOTHE LUCE FUND

c/o Henry Luce Foundation, Inc.
111 West 50th Street, Suite 4601
New York, NY 10020
Tel: (212)489-7700
Fax: (212)581-9541
E-mail: jdaniels@hluce.org
Web Site: http://www.hluce.org

To provide funding to women interested in studying science or engineering at the undergraduate level at designated universities.

Title of Award: Clare Boothe Luce Scholarships in Science and Engineering **Area, Field, or Subject:** Biological and clinical sciences; Chemistry; Computer and information sciences; Engineering; Engineering, Aerospace/Aeronautical/Astronautical; Engineering, Civil; Engineering, Electrical; Engineering, Mechanical; Engineering, Nuclear; Mathematics and mathematical sciences; Meteorology; Physics **Level of Education for which Award is Granted:** Undergraduate **Number Awarded:** Varies; since the program began, more than 800 of these scholarships have been awarded. **Funds Available:** The amount awarded is established individually by each of the participating institutions. The stipends are intended to augment rather than replace any existing institutional support in these fields. Each stipend is calculated to include the cost of room and board as well as tuition and other fees or expenses. **Duration:** 2 years; in certain special circumstances, awards for the full 4 years of undergraduate study may be offered.

Eligibility Requirements: This program is open to female undergraduate students (particularly juniors and seniors) majoring in biology, chemistry, computer science, engineering (aeronautical, civil, electrical, mechanical, nuclear, and others), mathematics, meteorology, and physics. Applicants must be U.S. citizens attending 1 of the 12 designated colleges and universities affiliated with this program; periodically, other institutions are invited to participate. Premedical science majors are ineligible for this competition. The participating institutions select the recipients without regard to race, age, religion, ethnic background, or need. All awards are made on the basis of merit. **Deadline for Receipt:** Varies; check with the participating institutions for their current schedule. **Additional Information:** The participating institutions are Boston University, Colby College, Creighton University, Fordham University, Georgetown University, Marymount University, Mount Holyoke College, St. John's University, Santa Clara University, Seton Hall University, Trinity College, and University of Notre Dame.

3986 ■ MAINE SPACE GRANT CONSORTIUM

Attn: Executive Director
87 Winthrop Street, Suite 200
Augusta, ME 04330
Tel: (207)622-4688; 877-397-7223
Fax: (207)622-4548
E-mail: shehata@msgc.org
Web Site: http://www.msgc.org/education_students.asp

To provide funding to undergraduate and graduate students at colleges and universities in Maine interested in working on projects related to space.

Title of Award: Maine Space Grant Consortium Scholarship and Fellowship Program **Area, Field, or Subject:** Aerospace sciences; Biological and clinical sciences; Computer and information sciences; Earth sciences; Engineering, Aerospace/Aeronautical/Astronautical; Geosciences; Physical sciences; Social sciences; Space and planetary sciences; Technology **Level of Education for which Award is Granted:** Graduate, Undergraduate **Number Awarded:** Varies each year. **Funds Available:** Stipends are $2,500 for undergraduates or $5,000 for graduate students. **Duration:** 1 year.

Eligibility Requirements: This program is open to U.S. citizens who are enrolled on a full-time basis in an undergraduate or graduate program at a 2- or 4-year college or university in Maine, including those not members of the Maine Space Grant Consortium. Applicants must be proposing to conduct a project on a topic of interest to the U.S. National Aeronautics and Space Administration (NASA) in biological, earth, physical, social, or space science; human exploration and development of space; or other related science, technology, computer, or engineering fields. Undergraduates must have a GPA of 3.0 or higher; graduate students must have a GPA of 3.2 or higher. Proposals may involve conducting research at their home institution, traveling to conduct research and/or to present finished project work at a NASA field center, or facilitating technology transfer from NASA to their institution and industry in Maine. Applications are especially encouraged from women, minorities, and persons with disabilities. Selection is based on the relevance of the project to NASA's mission and its strategic enterprises, collaboration with researchers at NASA space flight centers, qualifications of the student, technical content and quality of the

proposal, and recommendation from a faculty member. **Deadline for Receipt:** May or October of each year. **Additional Information:** This program is funded by NASA.

3987 ■ MAINE SPACE GRANT CONSORTIUM

Attn: Executive Director
87 Winthrop Street, Suite 200
Augusta, ME 04330
Tel: (207)622-4688; 877-397-7223
Fax: (207)622-4548
E-mail: shehata@msgc.org
Web Site: http://www.msgc.org/education_students.asp

To provide funding to undergraduate and graduate students at member institutions of the Maine Space Grant Consortium (MSGC) interested in working on projects related to space.

Title of Award: MSGC Undergraduate and Graduate Research Fellowships **Area, Field, or Subject:** Aerospace sciences; Biological and clinical sciences; Earth sciences; Engineering, Aerospace/Aeronautical/Astronautical; Geosciences; Physical sciences; Space and planetary sciences **Level of Education for which Award is Granted:** Graduate, Undergraduate **Number Awarded:** Varies each year. **Funds Available:** Stipends vary at participating institutions, ranging from $2,500 to $5,000 per year for undergraduates and from $5,000 to $15,000 per year for graduate students. **Duration:** 1 year; may be renewed.

Eligibility Requirements: This program is open to U.S. citizens who are enrolled on a full-time basis in an undergraduate or graduate program at a MSGC member institution. Applicants must be proposing to conduct a project on a topic of interest to the U.S. National Aeronautics and Space Administration (NASA) in aerospace technology, biological and physical research, space science, earth science, human exploration and development of space, and other related science or engineering fields. They may be proposing to conduct research at their home institution, spend time conducting research at a NASA flight center, facilitate the development of a liaison between researchers at their home institution and a NASA center, or facilitate technology transfer from their home institution to industry. Selection is based on the relevance of the proposed research project to NASA's mission. Applications are especially encouraged from women and minorities. **Deadline for Receipt:** Each participating institution sets its own deadline. **Additional Information:** The member institutions are the University of Maine, the University of Southern Maine, the University of New England, and Maine Maritime Academy. This program is funded by NASA.

3988 ■ MARYLAND HIGHER EDUCATION COMMISSION

Attn: Office of Student Financial Assistance
839 Bestgate Road, Suite 400
Annapolis, MD 21401-3013
Tel: (410)260-4545
Free: 800-974-1024
Fax: (410)974-5376
E-mail: osfamail@mhec.state.md.us
Web Site: http://www.mhec.state.md.us/financialAid/
ProgramDescriptions/prog_scm.asp

To provide scholarship/loans to Maryland residents who wish to prepare for a teaching career.

Title of Award: Sharon Christa McAuliffe Memorial Teacher Education Award **Area, Field, or Subject:** Chemistry; Classical studies; Computer and information sciences; Earth sciences; Education; Education, English as a second language; Education, Special; Education, Vocational-technical; Foreign languages; Geosciences; Health care services; Hearing and deafness; Mathematics and mathematical sciences; Physical sciences; Physics; Space and planetary sciences; Visual impairment **Level of Education for which Award is Granted:** Master's, Professional, Undergraduate **Number Awarded:** Varies each year. **Funds Available:** The amount of the award is based on the recipient's enrollment and housing status, to a maximum of $17,000 per year. The total amount of all state awards may not exceed the cost of attendance as determined by the school's financial aid office or $17,800, whichever is less. Following graduation, recipients must teach at a Maryland public school for 1 year for each year of financial aid received under this program. If they fail to meet that service obligation, they must repay all funds they received with interest. They must begin the service obligation within 12 months of graduation. **Duration:** 1 year; may be renewed for 1 additional year if the recipient maintains satisfactory academic progress with a cumulative GPA of 3.0 or higher and enrollment at a 2-year or 4-year Maryland college or university in an approved teacher education program.

Eligibility Requirements: This program is open to Maryland residents who are college students with at least 60 semester credit hours completed, college graduates, and teachers in a non-critical shortage area. Applicants must have a GPA of 3.0 or higher and plan to teach in a field identified as a critical shortage area. Selection is based on cumulative GPA, applicable work or volunteer experience, quality of academic background in certification field, and a writing sample. **Deadline for Receipt:** December of each year. **Additional Information:** Recently, the eligible critical shortage areas were business education, chemistry, computer science, earth and space science, English for speakers of other languages, family and consumer sciences, German, health occupations, Latin, mathematics, physical science, physics, Spanish, special education (generic infant-grade 3, generic grades 1-8, generic grades 6-adult, hearing impaired, severely and profoundly handicapped, visually impaired), and technology education.

3989 ■ MARYLAND SPACE GRANT CONSORTIUM

c/o Johns Hopkins University
203 Bloomberg Center for Physics and Astronomy
3400 North Charles Street
Baltimore, MD 21218-2686
Tel: (410)516-7351
Fax: (410)516-4109
E-mail: info@mdspacegrant.org
Web Site: http://www.mdspacegrant.org/scholars_about.html

To provide financial assistance to undergraduates who are interested in studying space-related fields at selected universities in Maryland that are members of the Maryland Space Grant Consortium.

Title of Award: Maryland Space Scholars Program **Area, Field, or Subject:** Aerospace sciences; Astronomy and astronomical sciences; Biological and clinical sciences; Chemistry; Computer and information sciences; Engineering; Geology; Mathematics and mathematical sciences; Physics; Space and planetary sciences **Level of Education for which Award is Granted:** Undergraduate **Number Awarded:** Varies each year; recently 16 of these scholarships were awarded (2 at Johns Hopkins University, 5 at Morgan State University, 2 at Hagerstown Community College, 2 at Towson University, and 5 at the University of Maryland at College Park). **Funds Available:** Scholars receive partial payment of tuition at the participating university they attend. **Duration:** 1 year; may be renewed if the recipient maintains a GPA of 3.0 or higher.

Eligibility Requirements: This program is open to residents of Maryland and graduates of Maryland high schools who are enrolled full time at a member institution. Applicants must be interested in preparing for a career in mathematics, science, engineering, technology, or a space-related field. They must be majoring in a relevant field, including (but not limited to) astronomy, the biological and life sciences, chemistry, computer science, engineering, geological sciences, or physics. U.S. citizenship is required. Along with their application, they must submit an essay of 200 to 500 words on how this scholarship will help them meet their educational and financial goals. This program is a component of the U.S. National Aeronautics and Space Administration (NASA) Space Grant program, which encourages participation by women, underrepresented minorities, and persons with disabilities. **Deadline for Receipt:** August of each year. **Additional Information:** The participating universities are Hagerstown Community College, Johns Hopkins University, Morgan State University, Towson University, the University of Maryland at College Park, and Washington College. Funding for this program is provided by NASA.

3990 ■ MICHIGAN SPACE GRANT CONSORTIUM

c/o University of Michigan
2106 Space Physics Research Laboratory
2455 Hayward Avenue
Ann Arbor, MI 48109-2143
Tel: (734)764-9508
Fax: (734)764-4585
E-mail: blbryant@umich.edu
Web Site: http://www.engin.umich.edu/dept/aero/msgc/fellow

To provide funding to students at member institutions of the Michigan Space Grant Consortium who wish to conduct space-related research.

Title of Award: Michigan Space Grant Consortium Fellowships **Area, Field, or Subject:** Aeronautics; Aerospace sciences; Engineering,

Aerospace/Aeronautical/Astronautical; Mathematics and mathematical sciences; Space and planetary sciences; Technology **Level of Education for which Award is Granted:** Graduate, Undergraduate **Number Awarded:** Varies each year; recently, 23 undergraduate fellowships and 13 graduate fellowships were awarded. **Funds Available:** The maximum grant is $2,500 for undergraduates or $5,000 for graduate students.

Eligibility Requirements: This program is open to undergraduate and graduate students at affiliates of the Michigan consortium who are proposing to conduct research in aerospace, space science, earth system science, and other related fields in science, engineering, or mathematics; students working on educational research topics in mathematics, science, or technology are also eligible. Applicants must identify a mentor in the faculty research, education, or public service communities with whom they intend to work and who is available to write a letter of recommendation for the student. U.S. citizenship is required. Women, underrepresented minorities, and persons with disabilities are especially encouraged to apply. **Deadline for Receipt:** November of each year. **Additional Information:** The consortium consists of Eastern Michigan University, Grand Valley State University, Hope College, Michigan State University, Michigan Technological University, Oakland University, Saginaw Valley State University, University of Michigan, Wayne State University, and Western Michigan University. This program is supported by the U.S. National Aeronautics and Space Administration (NASA).

3991 ■ MISSISSIPPI SPACE GRANT CONSORTIUM

c/o University of Mississippi
217 Vardaman Hall
P.O. Box 1848
University, MS 38677-1848
Tel: (662)915-1187
Fax: (662)915-3927
E-mail: mschaff@olemiss.edu
Web Site: http://www.olemiss.edu/programs/nasa

To provide funding to undergraduate and graduate students for space-related activities at colleges and universities that are members of the Mississippi Space Grant Consortium.

Title of Award: Mississippi Space Grant Consortium Scholarships and Fellowships **Area, Field, or Subject:** Aerospace sciences; Engineering; Engineering, Aerospace/Aeronautical/Astronautical; Mathematics and mathematical sciences; Science; Space and planetary sciences **Level of Education for which Award is Granted:** Graduate, Undergraduate **Number Awarded:** Varies each year; recently, a total of 47 students received support through this program. **Funds Available:** Each participating institution establishes the amounts of the awards. Recently, the average undergraduate award was $1,308 and the average graduate award was $2,975. A total of $96,350 was awarded.

Eligibility Requirements: This program is open to undergraduate and graduate students at member institutions of the Mississippi consortium. Each participating college or university establishes its own program and criteria for admission, but all activities are in engineering, mathematics, and science fields of interest to the U.S. National Aeronautics and Space Administration (NASA). U.S. citizenship is required. The consortium is a component of NASA's Space Grant program, which encourages participation by women, underrepresented minorities, and persons with disabilities. **Additional Information:** Consortium members include Alcorn State University, Coahoma Community College, Delta State University, Hinds Community College (Utica Campus), Itawamba Community College, Jackson State University, Meridian Community College, Mississippi Delta Community College, Mississippi Gulf Coast Community College, Mississippi State University, Mississippi University for Women, Mississippi Valley State University, Northeast Mississippi Community College, Pearl River Community College, the University of Mississippi, and the University of Southern Mississippi. This program is funded by NASA.

3992 ■ MONTANA SPACE GRANT CONSORTIUM

c/o Montana State University
416 Cobleigh Hall
P.O. Box 173835
Bozeman, MT 59717-3835
Tel: (406)994-4223
Fax: (406)994-4452
E-mail: msgc@montana.edu
Web Site: http://spacegrant.montana.edu/Text/ScholarProgram.html

To provide financial assistance to students in Montana who are interested in working on an undergraduate degree in the space sciences and/or engineering.

Title of Award: Montana Space Grant Consortium Undergraduate Scholarships **Area, Field, or Subject:** Aerospace sciences; Astronomy and astronomical sciences; Biological and clinical sciences; Chemistry; Computer and information sciences; Engineering, Aerospace/ Aeronautical/Astronautical; Engineering, Chemical; Engineering, Civil; Engineering, Electrical; Engineering, Mechanical; Geology; Physics; Space and planetary sciences **Level of Education for which Award is Granted:** Undergraduate **Number Awarded:** Varies each year; recently, 23 of these scholarships were awarded. **Funds Available:** The stipend is $1,000 per year. **Duration:** 1 year; may be renewed.

Eligibility Requirements: This program is open to full-time undergraduate students at member institutions of the Montana Space Grant Consortium (MSGC) majoring in fields related to space sciences and engineering. Those fields include, but are not limited to, astronomy, biological and life sciences, chemical engineering, chemistry, civil engineering, computer sciences, electrical engineering, geological sciences, mathematics, mechanical engineering, and physics. Priority is given to students who have been involved in aerospace-related research. U.S. citizenship is required. The MSGC is a component of the U.S. National Aeronautics and Space Administration (NASA) Space Grant program, which encourages participation by women, underrepresented minorities, and persons with disabilities. **Deadline for Receipt:** March of each year. **Additional Information:** The MSGC member institutions are Blackfeet Community College, Carroll College, Chief Dull Knife College, Fort Belknap College, Fort Peck Community College, Little Big Horn College, Montana State University at Billings, Montana State University at Bozeman, Montana State University Northern, Montana Tech, Rocky Mountain College, Salish Kootenai College, Stone Child College, University of Great Falls, University of Montana, and University of Montana Western. Funding for this program is provided by NASA.

3993 ■ NATIONAL AERONAUTICS AND SPACE ADMINISTRATION

Attn: Program Manager,
NASA Headquarters
Washington, DC 20546-0001
Tel: (202)358-1523
Fax: (202)358-3048
E-mail: jdasch@hq.nasa.gov
Web Site: http://www.nasa.gov/audience/forstudents/postsecondary/learning/Space_Grant.html
To provide financial assistance to undergraduate and graduate students interested in preparing for a career in a space-related field.

Title of Award: National Space Grant College and Fellowship Program **Area, Field, or Subject:** Aerospace sciences; Engineering, Aerospace/ Aeronautical/Astronautical; Mathematics and mathematical sciences; Space and planetary sciences; Technology **Level of Education for which Award is Granted:** Graduate, Undergraduate **Number Awarded:** Varies each year. **Funds Available:** Each consortium establishes the terms of the fellowship program in its state.

Eligibility Requirements: This program is open to undergraduate and graduate students at colleges and universities that participate in the National Space Grant program of the U.S. National Aeronautics and Space Administration (NASA) through their state consortium. Applicants must be interested in a program of study and/or research in a field of science, mathematics, engineering, or technology (SMET) related to space. A specific goal of the program is to increase preparation by members of underrepresented groups (minorities, women, and persons with disabilities) for SMET space-related careers. **Deadline for Receipt:** Each consortium sets its own deadlines. **Additional Information:** NASA established the Space Grant program in 1989. It operates through 52 consortia in each state, the District of Columbia, and Puerto Rico. Each consortium includes selected colleges and universities in that state as well as other affiliates from industry, museums, science centers, and state and local agencies.

3994 ■ NATIONAL AGRICULTURAL AVIATION ASSOCIATION

Attn: Women of the NAAA
1005 E Street, S.E.
Washington, DC 20003-2947
Tel: (202)546-5722

Fax: (202)546-5726
E-mail: information@agaviation.org
Web Site: http://www.agaviation.org/scholarship.htm
To recognize and reward outstanding student essays on agricultural aviation.

Title of Award: Women's National Agricultural Aviation Association Scholarship Essay Contest **Area, Field, or Subject:** Agricultural sciences; Aviation; General studies/Field of study not specified; Writing **Level of Education for which Award is Granted:** Undergraduate **Number Awarded:** 2 each year. **Funds Available:** First prize is $2,000; second prize is $1,000. **Duration:** The competition is held annually.

Eligibility Requirements: This competition is open to the children, grandchildren, sons-in-law, daughters-in-law, or spouses of any National Agricultural Aviation Association operator, pilot member, retired operator, or pilot who maintains an active membership in the association. The contest is also open to the children, grandchildren, sons-in-law, daughters-in-law, or spouses of an allied industry member. Entrants must be high school seniors, high school graduates, or college students. They may be of any age pursuing any area of education beyond high school. They are invited to submit an essay, up to 1,500 words, on a theme related to agricultural aviation that changes annually; recently, the topic was "Agricultural Aviation's Contribution to the World's Food Supply." A photograph of the entrant and a short biography should accompany the submission. Essays are judged on theme, development, clarity, and originality. **Deadline for Receipt:** August of each year.

3995 ■ NATIONAL AIR TRANSPORTATION FOUNDATION

Attn: Manager, Education and Training
4226 King Street
Alexandria, VA 22302
Tel: (703)845-9000
Free: 800-808-6282
Fax: (703)845-8176
E-mail: dhighsmith@nata.aero
Web Site: http://www.nata.aero/about/sch_meisinger.jsp
To provide financial assistance for flight training to college students.

Title of Award: Dan L. Meisinger, Sr. Memorial Learn to Fly Scholarship **Area, Field, or Subject:** Aviation **Level of Education for which Award is Granted:** Undergraduate **Number Awarded:** 1 each year. **Funds Available:** The stipend is $2,500. Funds may be used only for initial or primary flight training. Scholarship checks are made payable jointly to the recipient and the participating flight school. **Duration:** 1 year.

Eligibility Requirements: This program is open to college students currently enrolled in an aviation program with a GPA of 3.0 or higher. Preference is given to residents of Kansas, Missouri, and Illinois. Along with their application, they must submit a statement of their plans as they relate to their educational, flight training, and career objectives; future goals; and contributions and commitment to general aviation. Selection is based on academic record, potential to succeed, leadership and participation in school and community activities, and relevant work experience. **Deadline for Receipt:** November of each year. **Additional Information:** A $5 application fee is required.

3996 ■ NATIONAL AIR TRANSPORTATION FOUNDATION

Attn: Manager, Education and Training
4226 King Street
Alexandria, VA 22302
Tel: (703)845-9000
Free: 800-808-6282
Fax: (703)845-8176
E-mail: dhighsmith@nata.aero
Web Site: http://www.nata.aero/about/sch_business.jsp
To provide financial assistance for continuing education to employees of member companies of the National Air Transportation Association (NATA)

Title of Award: NATA Business Scholarship **Area, Field, or Subject:** Aviation **Level of Education for which Award is Granted:** Graduate, Professional, Undergraduate **Number Awarded:** 1 each year. **Funds Available:** The stipend is $2,500. Scholarship checks are made payable jointly to the recipient and the training institute. **Duration:** 1 year.

Eligibility Requirements: Applicants must be at least 18 years of age and possess a student pilot certificate (or higher) with a third class medical certificate. They must be nominated and endorsed by a regular or associate member of the National Air Transportation Association (NATA) and able to demonstrate a commitment to general aviation. Applicable training includes aviation maintenance programs, pilot certificate or rating, or aviation-related 2-year, 4-year, or graduate degree program at an accredited college or university. Along with their application, they must submit a 500-word essay on their aviation history and goals; educational scholarships, awards, and honors received; what they have done to achieve their goals; where they see themselves in 5 and 10 years; how the scholarship will help them achieve their objective, including their present financial need; the type of training or education for which they need assistance; and where they would obtain the training if granted this scholarship. **Deadline for Receipt:** December of each year. **Additional Information:** A $5 application fee is required.

3997 ■ NATIONAL AIR TRANSPORTATION FOUNDATION

Attn: Manager, Education and Training
4226 King Street
Alexandria, VA 22302
Tel: (703)845-9000
Free: 800-808-6282
Fax: (703)845-8176
E-mail: dhighsmith@nata.aero
Web Site: http://www.nata.aero/about/sch_pioneersofflight.jsp
To provide financial assistance for college to students planning careers in general aviation.
Title of Award: Pioneers of Flight Scholarship Program **Area, Field, or Subject:** Aviation **Level of Education for which Award is Granted:** Four Year College **Number Awarded:** 2 each year. **Funds Available:** The stipend is $1,000. **Duration:** 1 year; may be renewed 1 additional year if the recipient maintains a 3.0 GPA and full-time enrollment.
Eligibility Requirements: This program is open to students intending to enroll full time at an accredited 4-year college or university as juniors or seniors. Applicants must demonstrate an interest in a career in general aviation (not the major commercial airlines) and have a GPA of 3.0 or higher. Along with their application, they must submit a 250-word essay on their goals in general aviation. Selection is based on that essay, academic record, and letter of recommendation. **Deadline for Receipt:** December of each year. **Additional Information:** This program, established in 1989, is administered by the University Aviation Association (UAA), which selects the semifinalists. The National Air Transportation Foundation selects the final winners. Further information is available from the UAA, c/o Gregory Schwab, Indiana State University, Department of Aerospace Technology, TC 216, Terre Haute, IN 47809, E-mail: aeschwab@isugw.indstate.edu. A $5 application fee is required.

3998 ■ NATIONAL GAY PILOTS ASSOCIATION

Attn: NGPA Education Fund
P.O. Box 7271
Dallas, TX 75209-0271
Tel: (214)336-0873
Fax: (214)350-0447
E-mail: info@ngpa.org
Web Site: http://www.ngpa.org/education.html
To provide financial assistance to those affiliated with the gay and lesbian community who have expressed an interest in an aviation career as a professional pilot.
Title of Award: NGPA Education Fund **Area, Field, or Subject:** Aeronautics; Aerospace sciences; Aviation; Engineering; Space and planetary sciences **Level of Education for which Award is Granted:** Undergraduate **Number Awarded:** 1 or more each year. **Funds Available:** The stipend is $2,000 per year. Funds are paid directly to the educational institution and cannot be used to pay for the basic Private Certificate; they must be applied toward advanced flight training at a facility certified under FAR Part 141 or to college tuition if enrolled in an accredited aviation degree program. **Duration:** 1 year.
Eligibility Requirements: Applicants must be preparing for a career as a professional pilot. They must be 1) accepted at or currently enrolled in an accredited college or university with an aviation-related curriculum (aerospace, aerodynamics, engineering, airport management, etc.) or 2) accepted to or currently undergoing a course of study in a recognized professional pilot aviation training program in an institution of higher learning, aviation technical school, or school that provides advanced pilot training under FAR Part 141. They must have at least a Private Pilot Certificate. While scholarships are not awarded on the basis of an

individual's sexual orientation, applicants must provide evidence of their contribution to the gay and lesbian community. Selection is based on demonstrated personal excellence, aviation accomplishments, potential to become a successful professional pilot, and financial need. **Deadline for Receipt:** November of each year.

3999 ■ NATIONAL SOCIETY OF BLACK ENGINEERS

Attn: Programs Department
1454 Duke Street
Alexandria, VA 22314
Tel: (703)549-2207
Fax: (703)683-5312
E-mail: scholarships@nsbe.org
Web Site: http://www.nsbe.org/programs/schol_delta.php
To provide financial assistance to members of the National Society of Black Engineers (NSBE) who are majoring in designated science and engineering fields.
Title of Award: Delta Air Lines NSBE Corporate Scholarship **Area, Field, or Subject:** Computer and information sciences; Engineering, Aerospace/Aeronautical/Astronautical; Engineering, Chemical; Engineering, Electrical; Engineering, Materials; Engineering, Mechanical; Materials research/science **Level of Education for which Award is Granted:** Four Year College **Number Awarded:** 1 each year. **Funds Available:** The stipend is $3,000. **Duration:** 1 year.
Eligibility Requirements: This program is open to members of the society who are college juniors or seniors majoring in the following fields of study: aerospace/aeronautical engineering, chemical engineering, computer science, electrical engineering, materials engineering, materials science, or mechanical engineering. Applicants must have a GPA of 3.0 or higher and a demonstrated interest in employment with Delta Air Lines. They must submit essays of 100 to 150 words on each of the following topics: 1) how they personally define global diversity and why it is important for the airlines to value diversity; 2) how they have demonstrated their leadership ability in their school and community; 3) what influenced their decision to pursue their current course of study; and 4) the top 2 challenges facing Delta Air Lines today and how they would use their technical training and experience to help overcome those challenges. **Deadline for Receipt:** January of each year. **Additional Information:** The recipient also receives a round-trip airline ticket, paid registration, and 2 nights' hotel accommodations to the NSBE national convention.

4000 ■ NATIONAL SOCIETY OF BLACK ENGINEERS

Attn: Programs Department
1454 Duke Street
Alexandria, VA 22314
Tel: (703)549-2207
Fax: (703)683-5312
E-mail: scholarships@nsbe.org
Web Site: http://www.nsbe.org/programs/schol_lockheed.php
To provide financial assistance to members of the National Society of Black Engineers (NSBE) who are majoring in fields related to engineering.
Title of Award: Lockheed Martin NSBE Corporate Scholarship Program **Area, Field, or Subject:** Computer and information sciences; Engineering, Aerospace/Aeronautical/Astronautical; Engineering, Computer; Engineering, Electrical; Engineering, Mechanical; Mathematics and mathematical sciences; Systems engineering **Level of Education for which Award is Granted:** Four Year College **Number Awarded:** 5 each year. **Funds Available:** The stipend is $2,000. **Duration:** 1 year.
Eligibility Requirements: This program is open to members of the society who are entering their junior or senior year in college and majoring in computer science, mathematics, or the following fields of engineering: aerospace, computer, electrical, mechanical, or systems. Applicants must have a GPA of 3.0 or higher and a demonstrated interest in employment with Lockheed Martin Corporation. Along with their application, they must submit a 250-word essay describing their career goals and how they can make a community and professional impact as a Lockheed Martin employee. **Deadline for Receipt:** January of each year.

4001 ■ NATIONAL SOCIETY OF BLACK ENGINEERS

Attn: Programs Department
1454 Duke Street
Alexandria, VA 22314
Tel: (703)549-2207

Fax: (703)683-5312
E-mail: scholarships@nsbe.org
Web Site: http://www.nsbe.org/programs/schol_ng.php
To provide financial assistance to members of the National Society of Black Engineers (NSBE) who are working on an undergraduate degree in designated science and engineering fields.
Title of Award: Northrop Grumman NSBE Scholarships **Area, Field, or Subject:** Architecture, Naval; Computer and information sciences; Engineering, Aerospace/Aeronautical/Astronautical; Engineering, Chemical; Engineering, Civil; Engineering, Computer; Engineering, Electrical; Engineering, Industrial; Engineering, Mechanical; Engineering, Ocean; Mathematics and mathematical sciences; Physics **Level of Education for which Award is Granted:** Undergraduate **Number Awarded:** 5 each year. **Funds Available:** The stipend is $5,000. **Duration:** 1 year.
Eligibility Requirements: This program is open to members of the society who are U.S. citizens currently enrolled in college. Applicants must be majoring in computer science, information science, mathematics, naval architecture, physics, or the following engineering fields: aerospace, chemical, civil (structural), computer, electrical, industrial, manufacturing, marine, mechanical, or ocean. They must have a GPA of 3.0 or higher and demonstrate an interest in employment with Northrop Grumman Corporation. **Deadline for Receipt:** January of each year.

4002 ■ NATIONAL SPACE CLUB

2025 M Street, N.W., Suite 800
Washington, DC 20036
Tel: (202)973-8661
E-mail: info@spaceclub.org
Web Site: http://www.spaceclub.org/programs.html
To provide financial assistance to undergraduate and graduate students interested in preparing for a career in space research or exploration.
Title of Award: Dr. Robert H. Goddard Scholarship **Area, Field, or Subject:** Aerospace sciences; Engineering; Science; Space and planetary sciences **Level of Education for which Award is Granted:** Four Year College, Graduate **Number Awarded:** 1 each year. **Funds Available:** The stipend is $10,000. The winner's way is paid to the Goddard Memorial Dinner (usually held in March), where the winner is introduced to the nation's leaders in science, government, and industry. **Duration:** 1 year.
Eligibility Requirements: Applicants must be U.S. citizens, at least a junior in college, and intending to pursue undergraduate or graduate studies in science or engineering. Selection is based on official college transcript, letters of recommendation from faculty, accomplishments demonstrating creativity and leadership, plans to prepare for a career in aerospace sciences or technology, and past research and participation in space-related science and engineering; financial need is considered but is not a primary factor. **Deadline for Receipt:** January of each year. **Additional Information:** Upon completion of the scholarship, the winner may be asked to prepare and deliver a brief report to the National Space Club.

4003 ■ NAVAL WEATHER SERVICE ASSOCIATION

c/o Jim Stone, Secretary-Treasurer
600 East Fifth Street, Apartment 179
Waverly, OH 45690-1500
E-mail: jstone@navalweather.org
Web Site: http://www.navalweather.org/NWSA_Scholarships.htm
To provide financial assistance to high school seniors and currently-enrolled undergraduates who plan to work on a college degree in selected science or engineering fields.
Title of Award: Naval Weather Service Association Scholarship **Area, Field, or Subject:** Engineering, Aerospace/Aeronautical/Astronautical; Meteorology; Oceanography **Level of Education for which Award is Granted:** Undergraduate **Number Awarded:** 1 or more each year. **Funds Available:** Stipends range from $500 to $2,000. Funds may be used to pay for tuition, fees, books, supplies, equipment, or any other educational expenses. **Duration:** 1 year; recipients may reapply.
Eligibility Requirements: This program is open to students who are enrolled or planning to enroll in an undergraduate program in meteorology, oceanography, or aerospace engineering. Applicants must be U.S. citizens and sponsored by a member of the association. Priority is given to graduating high school seniors, but current undergraduates are also eligible. Students planning to attend junior or community colleges may ap-

ply when they intend to transfer to a 4-year college or university. Selection is based on academic record, leadership skills, character, all-around ability, and financial need. **Deadline for Receipt:** April of each year. **Additional Information:** The Naval Weather Service Association is a nonprofit organization open to retired and active-duty meteorological and oceanographic personnel of the Navy and Marine Corps.

4004 ■ NEW HAMPSHIRE SPACE GRANT CONSORTIUM

c/o University of New Hampshire
Institute for the Study of Earth, Oceans, and Space
Morse Hall
39 College Road
Durham, NH 03824-3525
Tel: (603)862-0094
Fax: (603)862-1915
E-mail: nhspacegrant@unh.edu
Web Site: http://www.nhsgc.sr.unh.edu
To provide financial assistance to students at member institutions of the New Hampshire Space Grant Consortium (NHSGC) who are interested in participating in space-related activities.
Title of Award: New Hampshire Space Grant Consortium Project Support **Area, Field, or Subject:** Aerospace sciences; Astronomy and astronomical sciences; Atmospheric science; Biological and clinical sciences; Computer and information sciences; Earth sciences; Engineering, Aerospace/Aeronautical/Astronautical; Geosciences; Oceanography; Physics; Space and planetary sciences **Level of Education for which Award is Granted:** Graduate, Undergraduate **Number Awarded:** Varies each year. **Funds Available:** The amount of the award depends on the nature of the project. **Duration:** From 1 quarter to 1 year.
Eligibility Requirements: This program is open to students at member institutions of the NHSGC. Applicants must be studying space physics, astrophysics, astronomy, or aspects of computer science, engineering, earth sciences, ocean sciences, atmospheric sciences, or life sciences that utilize space technology and/or adopt a planetary view of the global environment. U.S. citizenship is required. The New Hampshire Space Grant Consortium is a component of the U.S. National Aeronautics and Space Administration (NASA) Space Grant program, which encourages participation by women, underrepresented minorities, and persons with disabilities. **Deadline for Receipt:** Each participating college or university sets its own deadline. **Additional Information:** This program is funded by NASA. Currently, projects operating through this program include space grant fellowships at the University of New Hampshire, Agnes M. Lindsay Trust/NASA Challenge Scholars Initiative at the New Hampshire Community Technical College System, Presidential Scholars Research Assistantships at Dartmouth College, and Women in Science Internships at Dartmouth.

4005 ■ NINETY-NINES, INC.-EASTERN NEW ENGLAND CHAPTER

c/o Katharine Barr
278 Elm Street
North Reading, MA 01864
E-mail: KayBarr@Primushost.com
To provide financial assistance to residents of New England who are interested in preparing for a career in aviation.
Title of Award: "Honor" and Carla Carrol Memorial Scholarship **Area, Field, or Subject:** Aviation **Level of Education for which Award is Granted:** Undergraduate **Number Awarded:** 1 each year. **Funds Available:** The stipend is $1,000. Funds may be applied to academic tuition, technical school, or flight training. **Duration:** 1 year.
Eligibility Requirements: This program is open to high school seniors and current college students who are residents of or studying in Maine, New Hampshire, Rhode Island, Vermont, Massachusetts, or Connecticut. Applicants must be planning a career in aviation and need financial assistance to pursue appropriate education or flight training. Selection is based on aviation activities, science fair projects, aviation employment, recommendations, academic record, aviation goals, and financial need. **Deadline for Receipt:** January of each year.

4006 ■ NINETY-NINES, INC.-EASTERN NEW ENGLAND CHAPTER

c/o Katharine Barr
278 Elm Street
North Reading, MA 01864-2526
To provide financial assistance to residents of New England who are interested in preparing for a career in aviation.

Title of Award: Karla Carroll Memorial Scholarship **Area, Field, or Subject:** Aviation **Level of Education for which Award is Granted:** Undergraduate **Number Awarded:** 1 each year. **Funds Available:** The stipend is $1,000. Funds may be applied to academic tuition, technical school, or flight training. **Duration:** 1 year.

Eligibility Requirements: Eligible to apply are high school seniors or beyond who hold a private pilot license and reside or study in 1 of the following states: Maine, New Hampshire, Rhode Island, Vermont, Massachusetts, or Connecticut. They must be planning a career in aviation and need financial assistance to pursue appropriate education or flight training. Criteria for selecting recipients include: aviation activities, science fair projects, aviation employment, recommendations, academic record, aviation goals, and financial need. **Deadline for Receipt:** January of each year.

4007 ■ NINETY-NINES, INC.-EASTERN NEW ENGLAND CHAPTER

c/o Katharine Barr
278 Elm Street
North Reading, MA 01864-2526
To provide financial assistance to residents of New England who are interested in preparing for a career in aviation.

Title of Award: Billie M. Downing Honorary Scholarship **Area, Field, or Subject:** Aviation **Level of Education for which Award is Granted:** Undergraduate **Number Awarded:** 1 each year. **Funds Available:** The stipend is $1,000. Funds may be applied to academic tuition, technical school, or flight training. **Duration:** 1 year.

Eligibility Requirements: Eligible to apply are high school seniors or beyond who hold a private pilot license and reside or study in 1 of the following states: Maine, New Hampshire, Rhode Island, Vermont, Massachusetts, or Connecticut. They must be planning a career in aviation and need financial assistance to pursue appropriate education or flight training. Criteria for selecting recipients include: aviation activities, science fair projects, aviation employment, recommendations, academic record, aviation goals, and financial need. **Deadline for Receipt:** January of each year.

4008 ■ NINETY-NINES, INC.-EASTERN NEW ENGLAND CHAPTER

c/o Katharine Barr
278 Elm Street
North Reading, MA 01864-2526
To provide financial assistance to female residents of New England who are interested in preparing for a career in aviation.

Title of Award: William Bridge Scholarship **Area, Field, or Subject:** Aviation **Level of Education for which Award is Granted:** Undergraduate **Number Awarded:** 1 each year. **Funds Available:** The stipend is $1,000. Funds may be applied to academic tuition, technical school, or flight training. **Duration:** 1 year.

Eligibility Requirements: Eligible to apply are high school seniors or beyond who are female, hold a private pilot license, and reside or study in 1 of the following states: Maine, New Hampshire, Rhode Island, Vermont, Massachusetts, or Connecticut. They must be planning a career in aviation and need financial assistance to pursue appropriate education or flight training. Criteria for selecting recipients include: aviation activities, science fair projects, aviation employment, recommendations, academic record, aviation goals, and financial need. **Deadline for Receipt:** January of each year.

4009 ■ NORTH CAROLINA SPACE GRANT CONSORTIUM

c/o North Carolina State University
Mechanical and Aerospace Engineering
1009 Capability Drive, Suite 210
Box 7515
Raleigh, NC 27695-7515
Tel: (919)515-4240
Fax: (919)515-5934
E-mail: scholarships@ncspacegrant.org
Web Site: http://www.ncspacegrant.org
To provide funding to undergraduate students at institutions affiliated with the North Carolina Space Grant Consortium (NCSGC) interested in conducting space-related research.

Title of Award: North Carolina Space Grant Consortium Undergraduate Research Scholarships **Area, Field, or Subject:** Aeronautics; Aerospace sciences; Engineering, Aerospace/Aeronautical/Astronautical; Mathemat-

ics and mathematical sciences; Space and planetary sciences; Technology **Level of Education for which Award is Granted:** Undergraduate **Number Awarded:** Varies each year; recently, 8 of these scholarships were awarded. **Funds Available:** The maximum grant is $4,000 for a summer project on campus, $2,000 for an academic year project on campus, or $7,000 for a project at a NASA center or industrial contractor. **Duration:** 1 summer or 1 academic year.

Eligibility Requirements: This program is open to full-time undergraduate students at institutions affiliated with the NCSGC who are interested in working on a research project under the direct supervision of a faculty mentor. Applicants must be working on a degree in a science, technology, engineering, or mathematics (STEM) discipline of interest to the U.S. National Aeronautics and Space Administration (NASA). The research project must be space or aeronautics related or have a space or aeronautics application. Selection is based on the quality of the research proposal, the student's academic achievement, a letter of recommendation from the research mentor, and exhibited leadership qualities. U.S. citizenship is required. A primary goal of this program is the recruitment and retention of underrepresented minorities, women, and persons with disabilities into space-related fields. **Deadline for Receipt:** March of each year. **Additional Information:** The affiliated institutions are North Carolina State University, North Carolina A&T State University, Duke University, North Carolina Central University, the University of North Carolina at Charlotte, the University of North Carolina at Chapel Hill, the University of North Carolina at Pembroke, and Winston-Salem State University. This program is funded by NASA.

4010 ■ NORTH CAROLINA SPACE GRANT CONSORTIUM

c/o North Carolina State University
Mechanical and Aerospace Engineering
1009 Capability Drive, Suite 210
Box 7515
Raleigh, NC 27695-7515
Tel: (919)515-4240
Fax: (919)515-5934
E-mail: scholarships@ncspacegrant.org
Web Site: http://www.ncspacegrant.org
To provide funding to undergraduate students at institutions affiliated with the North Carolina Space Grant Consortium (NCSGC) interested in major in space-related fields.

Title of Award: North Carolina Space Grant Consortium Undergraduate Scholarships **Area, Field, or Subject:** Aerospace sciences; Engineering, Aerospace/Aeronautical/Astronautical; Mathematics and mathematical sciences; Space and planetary sciences; Technology **Level of Education for which Award is Granted:** Undergraduate **Number Awarded:** Varies each year. **Funds Available:** The stipend is $1,000 per year. **Duration:** 1 year; may be renewed 1 additional year.

Eligibility Requirements: This program is open to full-time undergraduate students at institutions affiliated with the NCSGC who are freshmen, sophomores, or recent transfers from a community or junior college. Applicants must be working on a degree in a science, technology, engineering, or mathematics (STEM) discipline of interest to the U.S. National Aeronautics and Space Administration (NASA). Selection is based on the student's academic achievement, a letter of recommendation, and exhibited leadership qualities. U.S. citizenship is required. A primary goal of this program is the recruitment and retention of underrepresented minorities, women, and persons with disabilities into space-related fields. **Deadline for Receipt:** March of each year. **Additional Information:** The affiliated institutions are North Carolina State University, North Carolina A&T State University, Duke University, North Carolina Central University, the University of North Carolina at Charlotte, the University of North Carolina at Chapel Hill, the University of North Carolina at Pembroke, and Winston-Salem State University. This program is funded by NASA.

4011 ■ OHIO SPACE GRANT CONSORTIUM

c/o Ohio Aerospace Institute
22800 Cedar Point Road
Cleveland, OH 44142
Tel: (440)962-3032
Free: 800-828-OSGC
Fax: (440)962-3057
E-mail: osgc@oai.org
Web Site: http://www.osgc.org/Scholarship.html

To provide financial assistance to students in their junior year at selected universities in Ohio who wish to working on a bachelor's degree in an aerospace-related field.

Title of Award: Ohio Space Grant Consortium Junior Scholarships **Area, Field, or Subject:** Astronomy and astronomical sciences; Biological and clinical sciences; Chemistry; Computer and information sciences; Engineering, Aerospace/Aeronautical/Astronautical; Engineering, Chemical; Engineering, Civil; Engineering, Computer; Engineering, Electrical; Engineering, Industrial; Engineering, Materials; Engineering, Mechanical; Engineering, Petroleum; Geography; Geology; Materials research/science; Mathematics and mathematical sciences; Physics; Space and planetary sciences **Level of Education for which Award is Granted:** Four Year College **Number Awarded:** Varies each year; recently, 20 of these scholarships were awarded. **Funds Available:** The stipend is $2,000. **Duration:** 1 year; recipients may apply for a senior scholarship if they maintain satisfactory academic performance and good progress on their research project.

Eligibility Requirements: These scholarships are available to U.S. citizens who expect to complete within 2 years the requirements for a bachelor of science degree in an aerospace-related discipline (aeronautical engineering, aerospace engineering, astronomy, biology, chemical engineering, chemistry, civil engineering, computer engineering and science, control engineering, electrical engineering, engineering mechanics, geography, geology, industrial engineering, manufacturing engineering, materials science and engineering, mathematics, mechanical engineering, petroleum engineering, physics, and systems engineering). Applicants must be attending a member university of the Ohio Space Grant Consortium (OSGC) or another participating university. They must propose and initiate a research project on campus under the guidance of a faculty member. Along with their application, they must submit a 1-page personal objective statement that discusses their career goals and anticipated benefits to be derived from this program. Women, underrepresented minorities, and persons with disabilities are particularly encouraged to apply. **Deadline for Receipt:** February of each year. **Additional Information:** These scholarships are funded through the National Space Grant College and Fellowship Program administered by the National Aeronautics and Space Administration (NASA), with matching funds provided by the member universities, the Ohio Aerospace Institute, and private industry. The OSGC member universities include the University of Akron, Case Western Reserve University, Central State University, University of Cincinnati, Cleveland State University, University of Dayton, Ohio State University, Ohio University, University of Toledo, Wilberforce University, and Wright State University. Other participating universities are Cedarville University, Marietta College (petroleum engineering), Miami University (manufacturing engineering), Ohio Northern University (mechanical engineering), and Youngstown State University (mechanical and industrial engineering). Recipients are required to attend the annual spring research symposium sponsored by the OSGC and present a poster on their research project.

4012 ■ OKLAHOMA NASA SPACE GRANT CONSORTIUM

c/o University of Oklahoma
Ditmars House, Suite 9
1623 Cross Center Drive
Norman, OK 73069
Tel: (405)325-6559
Fax: (405)325-5537
E-mail: vduca@ou.edu
Web Site: http://www.okspacegrant.ou.edu

To provide financial assistance to upper-division students at member institutions of the Oklahoma NASA Space Grant Consortium who are enrolled in aerospace-related studies.

Title of Award: Oklahoma NASA Space Grant Consortium Scholarships **Area, Field, or Subject:** Aeronautics; Aerospace sciences; Engineering, Aerospace/Aeronautical/Astronautical; Geography; Mathematics and mathematical sciences; Space and planetary sciences; Technology **Level of Education for which Award is Granted:** Four Year College **Number Awarded:** Approximately 40 each year. **Funds Available:** Stipends range from $500 to $1,000. **Duration:** 1 year.

Eligibility Requirements: This program is open to juniors and seniors at member institutions of the Oklahoma NASA Space Grant Consortium (OSGC). Applicants must be majoring in science, mathematics, engineering, technology, geography, or other aeronautics or space-related

disciplines. They must have a GPA of 2.5 or higher. U.S. citizenship is required. The OSGC is a component of the U.S. National Aeronautics and Space Administration (NASA) Space Grant program, which encourages participation by women, underrepresented minorities, and persons with disabilities. **Deadline for Receipt:** December of each year. **Additional Information:** Members of OSGC are Oklahoma State University, the University of Oklahoma, Cameron University, Langston University. Cameron University, East Central University, Southeastern Oklahoma State University, Southern Nazarene University, and Southwestern Oklahoma State University. This program is funded by NASA.

4013 ■ OREGON NASA SPACE GRANT CONSORTIUM

c/o Oregon State University
92 Kerr Administration Building
Corvallis, OR 97331-2103
Tel: (541)737-2414
Fax: (541)737-9946
E-mail: spacegrant@oregonstate.edu
Web Site: http://www.oregonspacegrant.orst.edu/programs/education/undergraduate.html

To provide financial assistance for study in space-related fields to undergraduate students at colleges and universities that are members of the Oregon Space Grant Consortium (OSGC).

Title of Award: Oregon Space Grant Undergraduate Scholarship Program **Area, Field, or Subject:** Aerospace sciences; Education; Engineering, Aerospace/Aeronautical/Astronautical; Mathematics and mathematical sciences; Space and planetary sciences; Technology **Level of Education for which Award is Granted:** Undergraduate **Number Awarded:** Varies each year. **Funds Available:** The stipend is $2,000. **Duration:** 1 year.

Eligibility Requirements: This program is open to U.S. citizens enrolled full time at OSGC member institutions. Applicants must be working on 1) a baccalaureate degree in a science, technology, engineering, or mathematics (STEM) field (including mathematics or science education) related to the mission of the U.S. National Aeronautics and Space Administration (NASA); or 2) an associate degree in applied science and planning to transfer to a 4-year institution to complete a baccalaureate in the same fields. Along with their application, they must submit a letter of intent of 250 to 300 words on their career goals as they relate to NASA and how this scholarship will contribute to those goals. Selection is based on scholastic achievement, aerospace-related career goals, and 2 letters of recommendation. Applications are especially encouraged from members of underrepresented groups (women, minorities, and people with disabilities). **Deadline for Receipt:** January of each year. **Additional Information:** Institutions that are members of OSG include Oregon State University, Portland State University, the University of Oregon, Southern Oregon University, Eastern Oregon University, Western Oregon University, George Fox University, Lane Community College, Linfield College, Portland Community College, and Oregon Institute of Technology. This program is funded by NASA.

4014 ■ PENNSYLVANIA SPACE GRANT CONSORTIUM

c/o Pennsylvania State University
2217 Earth-Engineering Sciences Building
University Park, PA 16802
Tel: (814)863-7687
Fax: (814)863-8286
E-mail: spacegrant@psu.edu
Web Site: http://www.psu.edu/spacegrant/highered/scholar.html

To provide financial assistance for space-related study to undergraduate students at universities affiliated with the Pennsylvania Space Grant Consortium.

Title of Award: Pennsylvania Space Grant Consortium Scholarships **Area, Field, or Subject:** Aerospace sciences; Biological and clinical sciences; Earth sciences; Engineering, Aerospace/Aeronautical/Astronautical; Geosciences; Physical sciences; Space and planetary sciences **Level of Education for which Award is Granted:** Undergraduate **Number Awarded:** Varies each year. **Funds Available:** The stipend is set by each participating university. At Pennsylvania State University, for instance, it is $4,000 per year. **Duration:** 1 year.

Eligibility Requirements: This program is open to full-time undergraduate students at participating universities. Applicants must be studying a field that does, or can, promote a strategic enterprise of the U.S. National

Aeronautics and Space Administration (NASA): aerospace technology, earth science, human exploration and development of space, biological and physical research, or space science. U.S. citizenship is required. Students from underrepresented groups (women, minorities, rural populations, and those with disabilities) are especially encouraged to apply. **Deadline for Receipt:** Each participating university sets its own deadline. **Additional Information:** Participating institutions include California University of Pennsylvania, Carnegie Mellon University, Clarion University, Lincoln University, Pennsylvania State University, University of Pittsburgh, Susquehanna University, Lincoln University, Temple University, West Chester University, and Pennsylvania State University at Abington. At Pennsylvania State University, the award is designated as the Sylvia Stein Memorial Space Grant Scholarship. This program is sponsored by the U.S. National Aeronautics and Space Administration (NASA).

4015 ■ PROFESSIONAL AVIATION MAINTENANCE ASSOCIATION

Attn: PAMA Scholarship Foundation
717 Princess Street
Alexandria, VA 22314
Tel: (703)683-3171; (866)865-PAMA
Fax: (703)683-0018
E-mail: hq@pama.org
Web Site: http://www.pama.org
To provide financial assistance to students interested in studying aviation maintenance on the undergraduate level.
Title of Award: Professional Aviation Maintenance Association Student Scholarship Program **Area, Field, or Subject:** Aviation **Level of Education for which Award is Granted:** Undergraduate **Number Awarded:** Varies each year; recently, 15 of these scholarships were awarded. **Funds Available:** The award is $1,000. Funds may be used for tuition, fees, books, or supplies. **Duration:** 1 year; recipients may reapply.
Eligibility Requirements: This program is open to students currently enrolled in an institution to obtain an airframe and powerplant (A&P) or avionics license. Applicants must have completed 25% of the required curriculum; have at least a 3.0 GPA; and need financial assistance. Selection is based on educational performance, work experience, participation in school and community activities, career commitment and future potential, financial need, and a recommendation by a counselor, advisor, aviation maintenance instructor, or current employer. **Deadline for Receipt:** November of each year.

4016 ■ RHODE ISLAND PILOTS ASSOCIATION

Attn: Scholarship Chair
644 Airport Road, Hangar One
Warwick, RI 02886
Tel: (401)568-3497
Fax: (401)568-5392
E-mail: ripaemail@aol.com
Web Site: http://www.ripilots.com/Scholarships.htm
To provide financial assistance to Rhode Island residents interested in obtaining pilot flight training or a college degree in an aviation-related field.
Title of Award: Rhode Island Pilots Association Scholarship **Area, Field, or Subject:** Aviation **Level of Education for which Award is Granted:** Undergraduate **Number Awarded:** 2 each year. **Funds Available:** The stipend is $1,000. **Duration:** 1 year.
Eligibility Requirements: This program is open to residents of Rhode Island who are at least 16 years of age. Applicants must be interested in a program of pilot flight training or a college degree program in a field that is related to aviation and approved by the sponsoring organization. Flight training candidates must be able to pass the FAA Class III physical. Along with their application, they must submit a 2-page personal letter describing how scholarship funds would be used to pursue goals in aviation or related areas; a list of extracurricular activities, hobbies, and personal interests; 2 letters of recommendation; details of school record; and documentation of financial need. **Deadline for Receipt:** February of each year. **Additional Information:** This program was established in 1996.

4017 ■ RHODE ISLAND SPACE GRANT

c/o Brown University
Lincoln Field Building
Box 1846
Providence, RI 02912-1846

Tel: (401)863-2889
Fax: (401)863-1292
E-mail: RISpaceGrant@brown.edu
Web Site: http://www.planetary.brown.edu/RI_Space_Grant
To provide financial assistance to undergraduate students at institutions that are members of the Rhode Island Space Grant Consortium (RISGC) who are interested in a career in a space-related field of science, mathematics, or engineering.
Title of Award: Rhode Island Space Grant Undergraduate Scholarship Program **Area, Field, or Subject:** Aerospace sciences; Engineering; Engineering, Aerospace/Aeronautical/Astronautical; Mathematics and mathematical sciences; Science; Space and planetary sciences **Level of Education for which Award is Granted:** Undergraduate **Number Awarded:** Varies each year; recently, 9 of these scholarships were awarded. **Funds Available:** The stipend is $4,000. **Duration:** 1 year.
Eligibility Requirements: This program is open to undergraduate students beyond their freshman year at RISGC-member universities. Applicants must be studying in science, mathematics, or engineering fields of interest to the National Aeronautics and Space Administration (NASA). U.S. citizenship is required. The sponsor is a component of NASA's Space Grant program, which encourages participation by women, underrepresented minorities, and persons with disabilities. **Deadline for Receipt:** February of each year. **Additional Information:** Members of the RISGC are Bryant College, Community College of Rhode Island, Providence College, Roger Williams University, Rhode Island College, Rhode Island School of Design, Salve Regina University, University of Rhode Island, and Wheaton College. This program is funded by NASA. Scholars are designated as research scholars (who are required to devote up to 4 hours per week to outreach activities in science education for K-12 children and teachers through Rhode Island), outreach scholars (who are required to devote up to 8 hours per week to outreach activities), or "Science En Espanol" scholars (who are required to devote up to 8 hours per week to curriculum support for K-12 children and teachers throughout Rhode Island).

4018 ■ RHODE ISLAND SPACE GRANT

c/o Brown University
Lincoln Field Building
Box 1846
Providence, RI 02912-1846
Tel: (401)863-2889
Fax: (401)863-1292
E-mail: RISpaceGrant@brown.edu
Web Site: http://www.planetary.brown.edu/RI_Space_Grant
To provide funding for summer research activities to undergraduate students at institutions that are members of the Rhode Island Space Grant Consortium (RISGC) who are interested in a career in a space-related field of science, mathematics, or engineering.
Title of Award: Rhode Island Space Grant Undergraduate Summer Scholar Program **Area, Field, or Subject:** Aerospace sciences; Engineering; Engineering, Aerospace/Aeronautical/Astronautical; Mathematics and mathematical sciences; Science; Space and planetary sciences **Level of Education for which Award is Granted:** Undergraduate **Number Awarded:** Varies each year; recently, 3 of these scholarships were awarded. **Funds Available:** The stipend is $4,000. **Duration:** 1 summer.
Eligibility Requirements: This program is open to undergraduate students at RISGC-member universities. Applicants must be studying in science, mathematics, or engineering fields of interest to the National Aeronautics and Space Administration (NASA). They must be interested in participating in a research project during the summer with an advisor in their own department. U.S. citizenship is required. The sponsor is a component of NASA's Space Grant program, which encourages participation by women, underrepresented minorities, and persons with disabilities. **Deadline for Receipt:** February of each year. **Additional Information:** Members of the RISGC are Bryant College, Community College of Rhode Island, Providence College, Roger Williams University, Rhode Island College, Rhode Island School of Design, Salve Regina University, University of Rhode Island, and Wheaton College. This program is funded by NASA. Scholars are required to devote 75% of their time to their research and

25% of their time to science education outreach activities organized and coordinated by Rhode Island Space Grant.

4019 ■ ROCKY MOUNTAIN NASA SPACE GRANT CONSORTIUM

c/o Utah State University
EL Building, Room 302
Logan, UT 84322-4140
Tel: (435)797-3666
Fax: (435)797-3382
E-mail: spacegrant@cc.usu.edu
Web Site: http://spacegrant.usu.edu
To provide financial support to undergraduate students at designated universities in Utah or Colorado who are working on a degree in fields of interest to the National Aeronautics and Space Administration (NASA).
Title of Award: Rocky Mountain NASA Space Grant Consortium Undergraduate Scholarships **Area, Field, or Subject:** Aerospace sciences; Engineering; Engineering, Aerospace/Aeronautical/Astronautical; Medicine; Science; Space and planetary sciences; Technology **Level of Education for which Award is Granted:** Undergraduate **Number Awarded:** Varies each year. **Funds Available:** The amount of the awards depends on the availability of funds. **Duration:** 1 year.
Eligibility Requirements: This program is open to undergraduate students at member institutions of the Rocky Mountain NASA Space Grant Consortium who are studying engineering, science, medicine, or technology. U.S. citizenship is required. Selection is based on academic performance to date and potential for the future, with emphasis on space-related research interests. This program is part of the NASA Space Grant program, which encourages participation by women, underrepresented minorities, and persons with disabilities. **Deadline for Receipt:** June of each year. **Additional Information:** Members of the consortium are Utah State University, the University of Utah, Brigham Young University, Dixie State College, Salt Lake Community College, Shoshone-Bannock School, Snow College, Southern Utah University, the University of Denver, and Weber State University. This program is funded by NASA.

4020 ■ SOUTH CAROLINA SPACE GRANT CONSORTIUM

c/o College of Charleston
Department of Geology and Environmental Sciences
66 George Street
Charleston, SC 29424
Tel: (843)953-5463
Fax: (843)953-5446
E-mail: scozzarot@cofc.edu
Web Site: http://www.cofc.edu/~scsgrant/scholar/overview.html
To provide financial assistance to upper-division and graduate students in South Carolina who are preparing for a career as a science and mathematics teacher.
Title of Award: South Carolina Space Grant Consortium Pre-Service Teacher Scholarships **Area, Field, or Subject:** Aerospace sciences; Astronomy and astronomical sciences; Education; Engineering; Engineering, Aerospace/Aeronautical/Astronautical; Environmental conservation; Environmental science; Science; Space and planetary sciences **Level of Education for which Award is Granted:** Four Year College, Graduate **Number Awarded:** Varies each year. **Funds Available:** The stipend is $2,000. Funds may be used for such expenses as 1) partial payment of tuition; 2) travel and registration for attending science and mathematics education workshops or conferences for the purpose of professional development; 3) purchase of supplies for student teaching activities; or 4) other supportive activities that lead to successful professional development and graduation as an educator in South Carolina. **Duration:** 1 year.
Eligibility Requirements: This program is open to juniors, seniors, and graduate students at member institutions of the South Carolina Space Grant Consortium. Applicants must be working on a teaching certificate in science, mathematics, or engineering. Their areas of interest may include, but are not limited to, the basic sciences, astronomy, science education, planetary science, environmental studies, or engineering. U.S. citizenship is required. Selection is based on academic qualifications of the applicant; 2 letters of recommendation; a description of past activities, current interests, and future plans concerning a space science or aerospace-related field; a sample lesson plan using curriculum materials available from the U.S. National Aeronautics and Space Administration (NASA); and faculty sponsorship. Women, minorities, and persons with disabilities are encouraged to apply. **Deadline for Receipt:** January of each year.

Additional Information: Members of the consortium are Benedict College, The Citadel, College of Charleston, Clemson University, Coastal Carolina University, Furman University, University of South Carolina, Wofford College, South Carolina State University, The Medical University of South Carolina, and University of the Virgin Islands. This program is funded by NASA.

4021 ■ SOUTH DAKOTA SPACE GRANT CONSORTIUM

Attn: Deputy Director and Outreach Coordinator
South Dakota School of Mines and Technology
Mineral Industries Building, Room 228
501 East St. Joseph Street
Rapid City, SD 57701-3995
Tel: (605)394-1975
Fax: (605)394-5360
E-mail: Thomas.Durkin@sdsmt.edu
Web Site: http://www.sdsmt.edu/space
To provide funding to undergraduate and graduate students for space-related activities in South Dakota.
Title of Award: South Dakota Space Grant Consortium Graduate Fellowships and Undergraduate Scholarships **Area, Field, or Subject:** Aerospace sciences; Earth sciences; Engineering, Aerospace/Aeronautical/Astronautical; Environmental conservation; Environmental science; Geology; Geosciences; Mathematics and mathematical sciences; Space and planetary sciences; Technology **Level of Education for which Award is Granted:** Graduate, Undergraduate **Number Awarded:** Varies each year. Approximately $70,000 is available for this program annually. **Funds Available:** Stipends range from $1,000 to $7,500. **Duration:** 1 academic year, semester, or summer.
Eligibility Requirements: This program is open to undergraduate and graduate students at member and affiliated institutions of the South Dakota Space Grant Consortium. Applicants must be interested in 1) earth- and space-science related educational and research projects in fields relevant to the goals of the U.S. National Aeronautics and Space Administration (NASA); or 2) eventual employment with NASA or in a NASA-related career field in science, technology, engineering, and mathematics (STEM) education. Activities may include student research and educational efforts in remote sensing, GIS, global and regional geoscience, environmental science, and K-12 educational outreach; exposure to NASA-relevant projects; and internship experiences at various NASA centers and the Earth Resources Observation and Science (EROS) Center in Sioux Falls. U.S. citizenship is required. Women, members of underrepresented groups (African Americans, Hispanics, Pacific Islanders, Asian Americans, Native Americans, and persons with disabilities), and Tribal College students are specifically encouraged to apply. Selection is based on academic qualifications of the application (preference is given to students with a GPA of 3.0 or higher), quality of the application and its career goal statement, and assessment of the applicant's motivation toward an earth science, aerospace, or engineering career or research. **Deadline for Receipt:** January of each year. **Additional Information:** Member institutions include South Dakota School of Mines and Technology, South Dakota State University, and Augustana College. Educational affiliates include Black Hills State University, the University of South Dakota, Dakota State University, Lower Brule Community College, Oglala Lakota College, Sinte Gleska University, and Lake Area Technical Institute.

4022 ■ TEXAS SPACE GRANT CONSORTIUM

Attn: Administrative Assistant
3925 West Braker Lane, Suite 200
Austin, TX 78759
Tel: (512)471-3583
Free: 800-248-8742
Fax: (512)471-3585
E-mail: scholarships@tsgc.utexas.edu
Web Site: http://www.tsgc.utexas.edu/grants
To provide financial assistance to upper-division and medical students at Texas universities working on degrees in the fields of space science and engineering.
Title of Award: Columbia Crew Memorial Undergraduate Scholarships **Area, Field, or Subject:** Aerospace sciences; Biological and clinical sciences; Chemistry; Engineering, Aerospace/Aeronautical/Astronautical; Engineering, Chemical; Engineering, Electrical; Engineering, Industrial;

Engineering, Mechanical; Geology; Mathematics and mathematical sciences; Physics; Space and planetary sciences **Level of Education for which Award is Granted:** Doctorate, Undergraduate **Number Awarded:** Varies each year; recently, 29 of these scholarships were awarded. **Funds Available:** The stipend is $1,000. **Duration:** 1 year; nonrenewable.

Eligibility Requirements: Applicants must be U.S. citizens, eligible for financial assistance, and registered for full-time study at a participating college or university. Applicants must be a sophomore at a 2-year institution, a junior or senior at a 4-year institution, or a first- or second-year student at a medical school. Supported fields of study have included aerospace engineering, biology, chemical engineering, chemistry, electrical engineering, geology, industrial engineering, mathematics, mechanical engineering, and physics. The program encourages participation by members of groups underrepresented in science and engineering (persons with disabilities, women, African Americans, Hispanic Americans, Native Americans, and Pacific Islanders). Selection is based on excellence in academics, participation in space education projects, participation in research projects, and exhibited leadership qualities. **Deadline for Receipt:** March of each year. **Additional Information:** In 2003, the Texas Space Grant Consortium renamed its undergraduate scholarship program in honor of the 7 Space Shuttle Columbia astronauts. The participating universities are Baylor University, Lamar University, Prairie View A&M University, Rice University, San Jacinto College, Southern Methodist University, Sul Ross State University, Texas A&M University (including Kingsville and Corpus Christi campuses), Texas Christian University, Texas Southern University, Texas Tech University, Trinity University, University of Houston (including Clear Lake and Downtown campuses), University of Texas at Arlington, University of Texas at Austin, University of Texas at Dallas, University of Texas at El Paso, University of Texas at San Antonio, and University of Texas/Pan American. This program is funded by the National Aeronautics and Space Administration (NASA).

4023 ■ TUSKEGEE AIRMEN, INC.

1501 Lee Highway, Suite 130
Arlington, VA 22209-1109
Tel: (703)522-8590
Fax: (703)522-8542
E-mail: hqtai@tuskegeeairmen.org
Web Site: http://www.tuskegeeairmen.org/youthinaviation/scholarships.html
To provide financial assistance for college to high school seniors and graduates who are interested in a career in aviation and submit an essay on the history of Tuskegee Airmen, a group of African Americans who served as pilots in World War II.

Title of Award: Golden Eagle Award **Area, Field, or Subject:** Aerospace sciences; Aviation; Space and planetary sciences **Level of Education for which Award is Granted:** Undergraduate **Number Awarded:** 1 each year. **Funds Available:** The stipend is $5,000 per year. **Duration:** 4 years, provided the recipient maintains a GPA of 2.0 or higher and continues in an aerospace or aviation career path.

Eligibility Requirements: This program is open to students who have graduated or will graduate from high school in the current year with a GPA of 3.0 or higher and plan to prepare for a career in aviation, aerospace technology, and research. Applicants must submit a 1-page essay entitled "The Tuskegee Airmen" that reflects an overview of their history. They must also submit documentation of financial need and a 2-page essay that includes a brief autobiographical sketch, educational aspirations, career goals, and an explanation of why financial assistance is essential. Applications must be submitted to individual chapters of Tuskegee Airmen, Inc. which verify them as appropriate, evaluate them, and forward those considered worthy of further consideration to the national competition. Selection is based on academic achievement, extracurricular and community activities, financial need, recommendations, and both essays. **Deadline for Receipt:** February of each year. **Additional Information:** Information is also available from the Tuskegee Airmen National Scholarship Fund, P.O. Box 78967, Los Angeles, CA 90016.

4024 ■ U.S. AIR FORCE

Attn: Headquarters AFROTC/RRUC
551 East Maxwell Boulevard
Maxwell AFB, AL 36112-5917
Tel: (334)953-2091; (866)423-7682

Fax: (334)953-6167
Web Site: http://www.afrotc.com/scholarships/incolschol/expressSchol.php
To provide financial assistance to students who are interested in joining Air Force ROTC and majoring in critical Air Force officer fields in college.

Title of Award: Air Force ROTC Express Scholarships **Area, Field, or Subject:** Atmospheric science; Engineering, Aerospace/Aeronautical/Astronautical; Engineering, Civil; Engineering, Computer; Engineering, Electrical; Engineering, Mechanical; Environmental science; Meteorology **Level of Education for which Award is Granted:** Undergraduate **Funds Available:** Awards are type 2 AFROTC scholarships that provide for payment of tuition and fees, to a maximum of $15,000 per year, plus an annual book allowance of $600. All recipients are also awarded a tax-free monthly subsistence allowance that is $250 for freshmen, $300 for sophomores, $350 for juniors, and $400 for seniors. **Duration:** 3 and a half years, until completion of a bachelor's degree.

Eligibility Requirements: This program is open to U.S. citizens who are completing at least their first year of college and are working on a degree in fields that may change annually but are of critical interest to the Air Force. Applicants must have a GPA of 2.5 or higher and meet all other academic and physical requirements for participation in AFROTC. At the time of their Air Force commissioning, they may be no more than 31 years of age. They must be able to pass the Air Force Officer Qualifying Test (AFOQT) and the Air Force ROTC Physical Fitness Test. years as active-duty Air Force officers following graduation from college. **Additional Information:** Recently, freshmen were eligible if they were majoring in computer, electrical, or environmental engineering. Sophomores and juniors were eligible if they were majoring in those fields, meteorology and atmospheric sciences, or in the following engineering disciplines: aeronautical, aerospace, astronautical, civil, or mechanical. Recipients must also complete 4 years of aerospace studies courses at 1 of the 144 colleges and universities that have an Air Force ROTC unit on campus or 1 of the approximately 900 colleges that have cross-enrollment agreements with those institutions. They must also attend a 4-week summer training camp at an Air Force base, usually between their sophomore and junior years. Following completion of their bachelor's degree, scholarship recipients earn a commission as a second lieutenant in the Air Force and serve at least 4 years.

4025 ■ U.S. AIR FORCE

Attn: Headquarters AFROTC/RRUC
551 East Maxwell Boulevard
Maxwell AFB, AL 36112-5917
Tel: (334)953-2091; (866)423-7682
Fax: (334)953-6167
Web Site: http://www.afrotc.com/scholarships/hsschol/types.php
To provide financial assistance to high school seniors or graduates who are interested in joining Air Force ROTC in college and are willing to serve as Air Force officers following completion of their bachelor's degree.

Title of Award: Air Force ROTC High School Scholarships **Area, Field, or Subject:** Architecture; Chemistry; Computer and information sciences; Engineering, Aerospace/Aeronautical/Astronautical; Engineering, Architectural; Engineering, Civil; Engineering, Computer; Engineering, Electrical; Engineering, Mechanical; Environmental science; General studies/Field of study not specified; Mathematics and mathematical sciences; Meteorology; Operations research; Physics **Level of Education for which Award is Granted:** Four Year College **Number Awarded:** Approximately 2,000 each year. **Funds Available:** Type 1 scholarships provide payment of full tuition and most laboratory fees, as well as $600 for books. Type 2 scholarships pay the same benefits except tuition is capped at $15,000 per year; students who attend an institution where tuition exceeds $15,000 must pay the difference. Type 7 scholarships pay full tuition and most laboratory fees, but students must attend a college or university where the tuition is less than $9,000 per year or a public college or university where they qualify for the in-state tuition rate; they may not attend an institution with higher tuition and pay the difference. Approximately 5% of scholarship offers are for Type 1, approximately 20% are for Type 2, and approximately 75% are for type 7. All recipients are also awarded a tax-free subsistence allowance for 10 months of each year that is $250 per month as a freshman, $300 per month as a sophomore, $350 per month as a junior, and $400 per month as a senior. **Duration:** 4 years.

Eligibility Requirements: This program is open to high school seniors who are U.S. citizens at least 17 of age and have been accepted at a college or university with an Air Force ROTC unit on campus or a college with a cross-enrollment agreement with such a college. Applicants must have a cumulative GPA of 3.0 or higher and an ACT composite score of 24 or higher or an SAT score of 1100 (mathematics and verbal portion only) or higher. At the time of their commissioning in the Air Force, they must be no more than 31 years of age. They must agree to serve for at least 4 years as active-duty Air Force officers following graduation from college. **Deadline for Receipt:** November of each year. **Additional Information:** Recently, approximately 70% of these scholarships were offered to students planning to major in the science and technical fields of architecture, chemistry, computer science, engineering (aeronautical, aerospace, astronautical, architectural, civil, computer, electrical, environmental, or mechanical), mathematics, meteorology and atmospheric sciences, operations research, or physics. Approximately 30% were offered to students in all other fields. While scholarship recipients can major in any subject, they must enroll in 4 years of aerospace studies courses at 1 of the 144 colleges and universities that have an Air Force ROTC unit on campus; students may also attend nearly 900 other colleges that have cross-enrollment agreements with the institutions that have an Air Force ROTC unit on campus. Recipients must attend a 4-week summer training camp at an Air Force base, usually between their sophomore and junior years. Most cadets incur a 4-year active-duty commitment. Pilots incur a 10-year active-duty service commitment after successfully completing Specialized Undergraduate Pilot Training and navigators incur a 6-year commitment after successfully completing Specialized Undergraduate Navigator Training. The minimum service obligation for intelligence and Air Battle Management career fields is 5 years.

4026 ■ U.S. AIR FORCE

Attn: Headquarters AFROTC/RRUC
551 East Maxwell Boulevard
Maxwell AFB, AL 36112-5917
Tel: (334)953-2091; (866)423-7682
Fax: (334)953-6167
Web Site: http://www.afrotc.com/scholarships/incolschol/incolProgram.php
To provide financial assistance to undergraduate students who are willing to join Air Force ROTC in college and serve as Air Force officers following completion of their bachelor's degree.
Title of Award: Air Force ROTC In-College Scholarship Program **Area, Field, or Subject:** Architecture; Chemistry; Computer and information sciences; Engineering, Aerospace/Aeronautical/Astronautical; Engineering, Architectural; Engineering, Civil; Engineering, Computer; Engineering, Electrical; Engineering, Mechanical; Environmental science; General studies/Field of study not specified; Mathematics and mathematical sciences; Meteorology; Operations research; Physics **Level of Education for which Award is Granted:** Undergraduate **Number Awarded:** Varies each year. **Funds Available:** Cadets selected in Phase 1 are awarded type 2 AFROTC scholarships that provide for payment of tuition and fees, to a maximum of $15,000 per year. A limited number of cadets selected in Phase 2 are also awarded type 2 AFROTC scholarships, but most are awarded type 3 AFROTC scholarships with tuition capped at $9,000 per year. Cadets selected in Phase 3 are awarded type 6 AFROTC scholarships with tuition capped at $3,000 per year. All recipients are also awarded a book allowance of $600 and a tax-free subsistence allowance for 10 months of each year that is $300 per month during the sophomore year, $350 during the junior year, and $400 during the senior year. **Duration:** 3 years for students selected as freshmen or 2 years for students selected as sophomores.
Eligibility Requirements: This program is open to U.S. citizens enrolled as freshmen or sophomores at 1 of the 144 colleges and universities that have an Air Force ROTC unit on campus. Applicants must have a cumulative GPA of 2.5 or higher and be able to pass the Air Force Officer Qualifying Test and the Air Force ROTC Physical Fitness Test. At the time of commissioning, they may be no more than 31 years of age. They must agree to serve for at least 4 years as active-duty Air Force officers following graduation from college. Phase 1 is open to students enrolled in the Air Force ROTC program who do not currently have a scholarship but now wish to apply. Phase 2 is open to Phase 1 nonselects and students not enrolled in Air Force ROTC. Phase 3 is open only to Phase 2 nonselects.

Recently, the program gave preference to students majoring in the science and technical fields of architecture, chemistry, computer science, engineering (aeronautical, aerospace, astronautical, architectural, civil, computer, electrical, environmental, or mechanical), mathematics, meteorology and atmospheric sciences, operations research, or physics. **Deadline for Receipt:** January of each year. **Additional Information:** While scholarship recipients can major in any subject, they must complete 4 years of aerospace studies courses at 1 of the 144 colleges or universities that have an Air Force ROTC unit on campus. Recipients must also attend a 4-week summer training camp at an Air Force base, usually between their sophomore and junior years; 2-year scholarship awardees attend in the summer after their junior year. Current military personnel are eligible for early release from active duty in order to enter the Air Force ROTC program. Following completion of their bachelor's degree, scholarship recipients earn a commission as a second lieutenant in the Air Force and serve at least 4 years.

4027 ■ U.S. AIR FORCE

Attn: Headquarters AFROTC/RRUC
551 East Maxwell Boulevard
Maxwell AFB, AL 36112-5917
Tel: (334)953-2091; (866)423-7682
Fax: (334)953-6167
Web Site: http://www.afrotc.com/overview/programs.php
To provide financial assistance for undergraduate and graduate education to individuals who have completed 2 years of college and who are willing to join Air Force ROTC and serve as Air Force officers following completion of their degree.
Title of Award: Air Force ROTC Professional Officer Corps Incentive **Area, Field, or Subject:** Aerospace sciences; General studies/Field of study not specified; Space and planetary sciences **Level of Education for which Award is Granted:** Four Year College, Graduate **Number Awarded:** Varies each year. **Funds Available:** This scholarship provides $3,000 per year for tuition and a monthly subsistence allowance of $350 as a junior or $400 as a senior. **Duration:** Until completion of a graduate degree.
Eligibility Requirements: Applicants must be U.S. citizens who have completed 2 years of the general military course at a college or university with an Air Force ROTC unit on campus or a college with a cross-enrollment agreement with such a college. They must be full-time students, have a GPA of 2.0 or higher both cumulatively and for the prior term, be enrolled in both Aerospace Studies class and Leadership Laboratory, pass the Air Force Officer Qualifying Test, meet Air Force physical fitness and weight requirements, and be able to be commissioned before they become 31 years of age. They must agree to serve for at least 4 years as active-duty Air Force officers following graduation from college with either a bachelor's or graduate degree. **Additional Information:** Scholarship recipients must complete 4 years of aerospace studies courses at 1 of the 144 colleges and universities that have an Air Force ROTC unit on campus; students may also attend other colleges that have cross-enrollment agreements with the institutions that have an Air Force ROTC unit on campus. Recipients must also attend a 4-week summer training camp at an Air Force base between their junior and senior year.

4028 ■ U.S. AIR FORCE

Attn: Headquarters AFROTC/RRUE
Enlisted Commissioning Section
551 East Maxwell Boulevard
Maxwell AFB, AL 36112-5917
Tel: (334)953-2091; (866)423-7682
Fax: (334)953-6167
E-mail: enlisted@afrotc.com
Web Site: http://www.afoats.af.mil/AFROTC/EnlistedComm/ASCP.asp
To allow selected enlisted Air Force personnel to earn a bachelor's degree in approved majors by providing financial assistance for full-time college study.
Title of Award: Airman Scholarship and Commissioning Program **Area, Field, or Subject:** Architecture; Atmospheric science; Chemistry; Computer and information sciences; Engineering; Engineering, Aerospace/Aeronautical/Astronautical; Engineering, Architectural; Engineering, Civil; Engineering, Computer; Engineering, Electrical; Engineering, Mechanical; Environmental science; General studies/Field of study not specified; Mathematics and mathematical sciences; Meteorol-

ogy; Operations research; Physics **Level of Education for which Award is Granted:** Undergraduate **Number Awarded:** Varies each year. **Funds Available:** Awards are type 2 AFROTC scholarships that provide for payment of tuition and fees, to a maximum of $15,000 per year, plus an annual book allowance of $600. All recipients are also awarded a tax-free subsistence allowance for 10 months of each year that is $300 per month during their sophomore year, $350 during their junior year, and $400 during their senior year. **Duration:** 2 to 4 years, until completion of a bachelor's degree.

Eligibility Requirements: This program is open to active-duty enlisted members of the Air Force who have completed at least 1 year of continuous active duty and at least 1 year on station. Applicants normally must have completed at least 24 semester hours of graded college credit with a cumulative college GPA of 2.5 or higher. If they have not completed 24 hours of graded college credit, they must have an ACT score of 24 or higher or an SAT combined verbal and mathematics score of 1100 or higher. They must also have scores on the Air Force Officer Qualifying Test (AFOQT) of 15 or more on the verbal scale and 10 or more on the quantitative scale and be able to pass the Air Force ROTC Physical Fitness Test. Applicants must have been accepted at a college or university (including crosstown schools) offering the AFROTC 4-year program. When they complete the program and receive their commission, they may not be 31 years of age or older. U.S. citizenship is required. Recently, awards were presented according to the following priorities: 1) computer, electrical, and environmental engineering; 2) aeronautical, aerospace, architectural, astronautical, civil, and mechanical engineering and meteorology and atmospheric sciences; 3) all other ABET-accredited engineering majors, architecture, chemistry, computer science, mathematics, operations research, and physics; 4) all other majors. **Deadline for Receipt:** October of each year. **Additional Information:** Selectees separate from the active-duty Air Force, join an AFROTC detachment, and become full-time students. Upon completing their degree, they are commissioned as officers and returned to active duty in the Air Force with a 4-year service obligation. Further information is available from base education service officers or an Air Force ROTC unit.

4029 ■ U.S. AIR FORCE
Attn: Headquarters AFROTC/RRUE
Enlisted Commissioning Section
551 East Maxwell Boulevard
Maxwell AFB, AL 36112-5917
Tel: (334)953-2091; (866)423-7682
Fax: (334)953-6167
E-mail: enlisted@afrotc.com
Web Site: http://www.afoats.af.mil/AFROTC/EnlistedComm/POC-ERP.asp
To allow selected enlisted Air Force personnel to earn a baccalaureate degree by providing financial assistance for full-time college study.

Title of Award: Professional Officer Course Early Release Program **Area, Field, or Subject:** Architecture; Atmospheric science; Chemistry; Computer and information sciences; Engineering; Engineering, Aerospace/Aeronautical/Astronautical; Engineering, Architectural; Engineering, Civil; Engineering, Computer; Engineering, Electrical; Engineering, Mechanical; Environmental science; General studies/Field of study not specified; Mathematics and mathematical sciences; Meteorology; Operations research; Physics **Level of Education for which Award is Granted:** Undergraduate **Number Awarded:** Varies each year. **Funds Available:** Participants receive a stipend for 10 months of the year that is $350 per month during the first year and $400 per month during the second year. Scholarship recipients earn the Professional Officer Course Incentive of $3,000 per year for tuition and $600 per year for books. **Duration:** 2 years (no more and no less).

Eligibility Requirements: Eligible to participate in this program are enlisted members of the Air Force under the age of 30 (or otherwise able to be commissioned before becoming 35 years of age) who have completed at least 1 year on continuous active duty, have served on station for at least 1 year, and have no more than 2 years remaining to complete their initial baccalaureate degree. Scholarship applicants must be younger than 31 years of age when they graduate and earn their commission. All applicants must have been accepted at a college or university offering the AFROTC 4-year program and must have a cumulative college GPA of 2.5 or higher. Their Air Force Officer Qualifying Test (AFOQT) scores must be at least 15 on the verbal and 10 on the quantitative. Ap-

plicants who have not completed 24 units of college work must have an ACT composite score of 24 or higher or an SAT combined verbal and mathematics score of 1100 or higher. U.S. citizenship is required. Recently, awards were presented according to the following priorities: 1) computer, electrical, and environmental engineering; 2) aeronautical, aerospace, architectural, astronautical, civil, and mechanical engineering and meteorology and atmospheric sciences; 3) all other ABET-accredited engineering majors, architecture, chemistry, computer science, mathematics, operations research, and physics; 4) all other majors. **Deadline for Receipt:** October of each year. **Additional Information:** Upon completing their degree, selectees are commissioned as officers in the Air Force with a 4-year service obligation. Further information is available from base education service officers or an Air Force ROTC unit.

4030 ■ UNIVERSITY AVIATION ASSOCIATION
3410 Skyway Drive
Auburn, AL 36830-6444
Tel: (334)844-2434
E-mail: uaa@auburn.edu
Web Site: http://www.uaa.aero
To provide financial assistance to upper-division college students majoring in aviation.

Title of Award: Joseph Frasca Excellence in Aviation Scholarship **Area, Field, or Subject:** Aviation **Level of Education for which Award is Granted:** Four Year College **Number Awarded:** 2 each year. **Funds Available:** The stipend is $1,000. **Duration:** 1 year.

Eligibility Requirements: This program is open to juniors or seniors who are currently enrolled at a school affiliated with the University Aviation Association (UAA). Applicants must have earned a GPA of 3.0 or higher in their college courses; have Federal Aviation Administration certification/qualifications in either aviation maintenance or flight; be a member of at least 1 aviation organization (e.g., Alpha Eta Rho, National Intercollegiate Flying Association's Flying Team, Experimental Aircraft Association, Warbirds of America); and have a record of aviation activities, projects, or events that demonstrates an interest and an enthusiasm for aviation. Preference is given to applicants who can document interest or experience in aviation simulation, work experience in aviation, interest or experience in aircraft restoration, work experience while in school, interest or experience in aerobatics, or financial need. They may also submit an optional 250-word essay on their personal philosophy of excellence in aviation, especially as it relates to flying, aerobatics, aircraft mechanics and restoration, and aviation simulation; completion of the essay enhances their application but non-completion does not eliminate them from consideration. **Deadline for Receipt:** April of each year. **Additional Information:** Information is also available from David A. NewMyer, Southern Illinois University at Carbondale, College of Applied Sciences and Arts, 1365 Douglas Drive, Carbondale, IL 62901-6623, (618) 453-8898, E-mail: newmyer@siu.edu.

4031 ■ UNIVERSITY AVIATION ASSOCIATION
3410 Skyway Drive
Auburn, AL 36830-6444
Tel: (334)844-2434
E-mail: uaa@auburn.edu
Web Site: http://www.uaa.aero
To provide financial assistance for college to students enrolled in an aviation-related curriculum at a college or university affiliated with the University Aviation Association (UAA).

Title of Award: Eugene S. Kropf Scholarship **Area, Field, or Subject:** Aviation **Level of Education for which Award is Granted:** Undergraduate **Number Awarded:** 1 each year. **Funds Available:** The stipend is $1,000. **Duration:** 1 year.

Eligibility Requirements: Applicants must be U.S. citizens, be enrolled in a 2-year or 4-year degree in the field of aviation at a UAA-member college or university, and have earned at least a 3.0 GPA. They must submit a 250-word essay on "How Can I Improve Aviation Education." **Deadline for Receipt:** April of each year. **Additional Information:** Information is also available from Bernard W. Wulle, Purdue University, Aviation Technology Department, 1 Airport Road, West Lafayette, IN 47906-3398, (765) 494-9973, E-mail: bwulle@purdue.tech.edu.

4032 ■ UNIVERSITY AVIATION ASSOCIATION
3410 Skyway Drive
Auburn, AL 36830-6444

Tel: (334)844-2434
E-mail: uaa@auburn.edu
Web Site: http://www.uaa.aero
To provide financial assistance to students working on an undergraduate or graduate degree in aviation or a space-related field.
Title of Award: Paul A. Whelan Aviation Scholarship **Area, Field, or Subject:** Aerospace sciences; Aviation; Engineering, Aerospace/Aeronautical/Astronautical; Space and planetary sciences **Level of Education for which Award is Granted:** Graduate, Undergraduate **Number Awarded:** 1 each year. **Funds Available:** The stipend is $2,000. **Duration:** 1 year.
Eligibility Requirements: This program is open to sophomore, juniors, seniors, and graduate students who are currently enrolled at a college, university, or community college affiliated with the University Aviation Association (UAA). Applicants must be majoring in aviation or a space-related field and have a GPA of 2.5 or higher overall and 3.0 in their aviation courses. They must be able to demonstrate a love of aviation, extracurricular and community involvement, and leadership. Preference is given to applicants who have Federal Aviation Administration certification as a pilot or mechanic; former or current military service through active duty, ROTC, Air National Guard, or Reserves while in school; or membership in an aviation-related association or professional group. **Deadline for Receipt:** August of each year. **Additional Information:** Information is also available from David A. NewMyer, Southern Illinois University at Carbondale, College of Applied Sciences and Arts, 1365 Douglas Drive, Carbondale, IL 62901-6623, (618) 453-8898, E-mail: newmyer@siu.edu.

4033 ■ VERTICAL FLIGHT FOUNDATION

Attn: Scholarship Coordinator
217 North Washington Street
Alexandria, VA 22314-2538
Tel: (703)684-6777
Fax: (703)739-9279
E-mail: Staff@vtol.org
Web Site: http://www.vtol.org/vff.html
To provide financial assistance for college to high school seniors in the area of the Federal City chapter of the American Helicopter Society (AHS).
Title of Award: Initiative 21 Frank Piasecki Scholarship **Area, Field, or Subject:** Aviation; Engineering, Aerospace/Aeronautical/Astronautical; General studies/Field of study not specified **Level of Education for which Award is Granted:** Undergraduate **Number Awarded:** 1 each year. **Funds Available:** The stipend is $1,500. **Duration:** 1 year.
Eligibility Requirements: This program is open to seniors graduating from high schools in the Federal City chapter area, which covers Washington, D.C., Maryland (except zip codes 20600-20699), and Virginia (except zip codes 22000-22499). Applicants must have been accepted as a freshman at an accredited college or university. They must submit a narrative covering their future academic interest, their future career interest, and other reasons why they should be considered for this scholarship. Selection is based only on merit. Preference is given to applicants with an interest in aeronautical engineering, rotocraft, or vertical flight, and/or entering a college or university in a field or discipline most closely related to the aeronautical engineering or vertical flight industry. **Deadline for Receipt:** May of each year. **Additional Information:** This program was established in 1983.

4034 ■ VIRGINIA AIRPORT OPERATORS COUNCIL

c/o Betty Wilson
Virginia Aviation and Space Education Forum
5702 Gulfstream Road
Richmond, VA 23250-2422
800-292-1034
To provide financial assistance to high school seniors in Virginia who are interested in preparing for a career in aviation.
Title of Award: John R. Lillard VAOC Scholarship **Area, Field, or Subject:** Aviation **Level of Education for which Award is Granted:** Undergraduate **Number Awarded:** 1 each year. **Funds Available:** The stipend is $1,500. **Duration:** 1 year.
Eligibility Requirements: This program is open to seniors graduating from high schools in Virginia who have a GPA of 3.75 or higher and are planning a career in the field of aviation. Applicants must have been accepted to an aviation-related program at an accredited college. They must

submit an essay of 350 to 500-words on why they wish to prepare for a career in aviation. Selection is based on the essay (30%), academic achievement (35%), accomplishment and leadership (20%), and financial need (15%). **Deadline for Receipt:** February of each year.

4035 ■ VIRGINIA SPACE GRANT CONSORTIUM

Attn: Fellowship Coordinator
Old Dominion University Peninsula Center
600 Butler Farm Road
Hampton, VA 23666
Tel: (757)766-5210
Fax: (757)766-5205
E-mail: vsgc@odu.edu
Web Site: http://www.vsgc.odu.edu/Menu3_1_1.htm
To provide financial assistance for research in space-related fields to undergraduate students in Virginia.
Title of Award: Virginia Space Grant Aerospace Undergraduate Research Scholarships **Area, Field, or Subject:** Aerospace sciences; Engineering, Aerospace/Aeronautical/Astronautical; Space and planetary sciences **Level of Education for which Award is Granted:** Four Year College **Number Awarded:** Varies each year. **Funds Available:** Grants provide a student stipend of $3,000 during the academic year and a $3,500 stipend during the summer (either before or after the academic year). Recipients may request an additional $1,000 research allocation for materials and travel to support research activities conducted during the academic year and/or a $1,000 research allocation during the summer. The maximum award per year cannot exceed $8,500. **Duration:** 1 year; renewable.
Eligibility Requirements: This program is open to undergraduate students who will be enrolled in a program of full-time study in an aerospace-related discipline at 1 of the Virginia Space Grant Consortium (VSGC) Colleges. Applicants must be U.S. citizens who have completed at least 2 years of an undergraduate program with a GPA of 3.0 or higher. They must be proposing to participate in an active, identified research activity that has aerospace applications. The research must be supervised by a faculty mentor and may be conducted on the home campus or at an industrial or government facility. It should be continuous and may be conducted any time during the academic year, summer, or both. Since an important purpose of this program is to increase the participation of underrepresented minorities, females, and persons with disabilities in aerospace-related careers, the VSGC especially encourages applications from those students. **Deadline for Receipt:** February of each year. **Additional Information:** The VSGC colleges are College of William and Mary, Hampton University, Old Dominion University, the University of Virginia, and Virginia Polytechnic Institute and State University. This program is funded by the U.S. National Aeronautics and Space Administration (NASA). Awardees are required to participate in the VSGC annual student research conference in late March or early April.

4036 ■ VIRGINIA SPACE GRANT CONSORTIUM

Attn: Fellowship Coordinator
Old Dominion University Peninsula Center
600 Butler Farm Road
Hampton, VA 23666
Tel: (757)766-5210
Fax: (757)766-5205
E-mail: vsgc@odu.edu
Web Site: http://www.vsgc.odu.edu/Menu3_1_1.htm
To provide financial assistance to students who are interested in pursuing space-related studies at community colleges in Virginia.
Title of Award: Virginia Space Grant Community College Scholarship Program **Area, Field, or Subject:** Aerospace sciences; Computer and information sciences; Electronics; Engineering; Mathematics and mathematical sciences; Space and planetary sciences; Technology **Level of Education for which Award is Granted:** Two Year College **Number Awarded:** Approximately 10 each year. **Funds Available:** The maximum stipend is $1,500. **Duration:** 1 year; nonrenewable.
Eligibility Requirements: This program is open to students currently enrolled in a Virginia community college who are U.S. citizens and have completed at least the first semester of their program with a GPA of 3.0 or higher. Awards are generally made to full-time students, but part-time students demonstrating academic merit are also eligible. Applicants can be enrolled in any program that includes course work related to an

understanding of or interest in technological fields supporting aerospace; that includes (but is not limited to) computers, electronics, engineering, industrial technology, and mathematics. Since a particular goal of the program is to increase the participation of underrepresented minorities, women, and persons with disabilities in aerospace-related, high technology careers, the sponsor especially encourages applications from those students. **Deadline for Receipt:** February of each year. **Additional Information:** This program is funded by the U.S. National Aeronautics and Space Administration (NASA).

4037 ■ VIRGINIA SPACE GRANT CONSORTIUM

Attn: Fellowship Coordinator
Old Dominion University Peninsula Center
600 Butler Farm Road
Hampton, VA 23666
Tel: (757)766-5210
Fax: (757)766-5205
E-mail: vsgc@odu.edu
Web Site: http://www.vsgc.odu.edu/Menu3_1_1.htm
To provide financial assistance for college or graduate school to students in Virginia planning a career as science, mathematics, or technology educators.
Title of Award: Virginia Space Grant Teacher Education Scholarship Program **Area, Field, or Subject:** Aerospace sciences; Earth sciences; Education; Environmental conservation; Environmental science; Geosciences; Mathematics and mathematical sciences; Science; Space and planetary sciences; Technology **Level of Education for which Award is Granted:** Four Year College, Master's **Number Awarded:** Approximately 10 each year. **Funds Available:** The maximum stipend is $1,000. **Duration:** 1 year; nonrenewable.
Eligibility Requirements: This program is open to full-time undergraduate students at the Virginia Space Grant Consortium (VSGC) colleges and universities in a track that will qualify them to teach in a pre-college setting. Priority is given to those majoring in technology education, mathematics, or science, particularly earth, space, or environmental science. Applicants may apply while seniors in high school or sophomores in a community college, with the award contingent on their enrollment at a VSGC college and entrance into a teacher certification program. They must submit a statement of academic goals and plan of study, explaining their reasons for desiring to enter the teaching profession, specifically the fields of science, mathematics, or technology education. Students currently enrolled in a VSGC college can apply when they declare their intent to enter the teacher certification program. Students enrolled in a master of education degree program leading to teacher certification in eligible fields are also eligible to apply. Applicants must be U.S. citizens with a GPA of 3.0 or higher. Since an important purpose of this program is to increase the participation of underrepresented minorities, women, and persons with disabilities in science, mathematics, and technology education, the VSGC especially encourages applications from those students. **Deadline for Receipt:** February of each year. **Additional Information:** The VSGC institutions are College of William and Mary, Hampton University, Old Dominion University, the University of Virginia, and Virginia Polytechnic Institute and State University. This program is funded by the U.S. National Aeronautics and Space Administration (NASA).

4038 ■ WASHINGTON NASA SPACE GRANT CONSORTIUM

c/o University of Washington
Johnson Hall, Room 141
Box 351310
Seattle, WA 98195-1310
Tel: (206)543-1943
Free: 800-659-1943
Fax: (206)543-0179
E-mail: nasa@u.washington.edu
Web Site: http://www.waspacegrant.org/undergr.html
To provide financial assistance for college to students in Washington who wish to study science, engineering, or mathematics with an emphasis on space.
Title of Award: Washington NASA Space Grant Consortium Undergraduate Scholarships **Area, Field, or Subject:** Aerospace sciences; Engineering; Engineering, Aerospace/Aeronautical/Astronautical; Mathematics and mathematical sciences; Science; Space and planetary sciences **Level of Education for which Award is Granted:** Undergraduate **Number**

Awarded: Varies each year. **Funds Available:** Stipends vary at participating institutions, but range from $1,000 to $5,000. **Duration:** 1 year; may be renewed.
Eligibility Requirements: This program is open to residents of Washington who are attending or planning to attend designated institutions that are members of the Washington NASA Space Grant Consortium. Applicants must be interested in majoring in space-related aspects of science, engineering, or mathematics. U.S. citizenship is required. The program values diversity and strongly encourages women and minorities to apply. **Deadline for Receipt:** Each participating institution sets its own deadline. **Additional Information:** This program is funded by the U.S. National Aeronautics and Space Administration (NASA). Members of the consortium that offer undergraduate scholarships are Northwest Indian College, Seattle Central Community College, University of Washington, and Washington State University.

4039 ■ CHARLIE WELLS MEMORIAL SCHOLARSHIP FUND

P.O. Box 262
Springfield, IL 62705-0262
E-mail: Rog@wellsscholarship.com
Web Site: http://www.wellsscholarship.com
To provide financial assistance to students preparing for an aviation-related program in college.
Title of Award: Charlie Wells Memorial Aviation Scholarships **Area, Field, or Subject:** Aviation **Level of Education for which Award is Granted:** Undergraduate **Number Awarded:** Varies each year; recently, 2 of these scholarships were awarded. **Funds Available:** Stipends vary, depending on the availability of funds. Recently, they were $1,150. Funds are sent directly to the recipient's school to help pay the costs of tuition. **Duration:** 1 year.
Eligibility Requirements: This program is open to students who are currently majoring full time in an aviation-oriented curriculum at a college or university in the United States. Applicants must submit information on their career interests, 2 letters of reference, an essay on why they deserve the scholarship (including their past accomplishments, future goals, and financial need), and a list of their extracurricular activities. **Deadline for Receipt:** March of each year. **Additional Information:** Requests for applications must be accompanied by a self-addressed stamped envelope.

4040 ■ WEST VIRGINIA SPACE GRANT CONSORTIUM

c/o West Virginia University
College of Engineering and Mineral Resources
G-68 Engineering Sciences Building
P.O. Box 6070
Morgantown, WV 26506-6070
Tel: (304)293-4099
Fax: (304)293-4970
E-mail: nasa@cemr.wvu.edu
Web Site: http://www.nasa.wvu.edu/scholarships.html
To provide financial assistance to undergraduates at academic institutions affiliated with the West Virginia Space Grant Consortium who wish to conduct a space-related science or engineering research project.
Title of Award: West Virginia Space Grant Consortium Undergraduate Research Fellowship Program **Area, Field, or Subject:** Aerospace sciences; Engineering, Aerospace/Aeronautical/Astronautical; Mathematics and mathematical sciences; Space and planetary sciences **Level of Education for which Award is Granted:** Undergraduate **Number Awarded:** Varies each year. **Funds Available:** Grants range from $1,000 to $5,000. **Duration:** 1 academic year or summer.
Eligibility Requirements: This program is open to full-time undergraduates enrolled in mathematics, science, or engineering programs at member institutions of the consortium. Applicants must be interested in conducting a space-related research project with a faculty member from their department who agrees to serve as a mentor and research advisor. Selection is based on soundness and technical merit of the proposed research (50 points), student's academic and extracurricular achievements (30 points), and budget and plans for dissemination and publicizing of the results (20 points). The consortium is a component of the Space Grant program of the U.S. National Aeronautics and Space Administration (NASA), which strongly encourages participation by members of underrepresented groups (minorities, women, and persons with disabilities). **Deadline for Receipt:** March of each year. **Additional Information:** Funding for this program is provided by NASA. The consortium

includes Bethany College, Bluefield College, Fairmont State College, Marshall University, Shepherd College, West Liberty State College, West Virginia Institute of Technology, West Virginia State College, West Virginia University, West Virginia Wesleyan College, and Wheeling-Jesuit University.

4041 ■ WISCONSIN SPACE GRANT CONSORTIUM
c/o University of Wisconsin at Green Bay
Department of Natural and Applied Sciences
2420 Nicolet Drive
Green Bay, WI 54311-7001
Tel: (920)465-2108
Fax: (920)465-2376
E-mail: wsgc@uwgb.edu
Web Site: http://www.uwgb.edu/wsgc/students/us.asp
To provide financial assistance to undergraduate students at colleges and universities participating in the Wisconsin Space Grant Consortium (WSGC).

Title of Award: Wisconsin Space Grant Consortium Undergraduate Scholarships **Area, Field, or Subject:** Aerospace sciences; Architecture; Business administration; Engineering; Engineering, Aerospace/Aeronautical/Astronautical; Law; Medicine; Nursing; Science; Space and planetary sciences **Level of Education for which Award is Granted:** Undergraduate **Number Awarded:** Varies each year; recently, 26 of these scholarships were awarded. **Funds Available:** Stipends up to $1,500 per year are available. **Duration:** 1 academic year.

Eligibility Requirements: This program is open to undergraduate students enrolled at universities participating in the WSGC. Applicants must be U.S. citizens; be working full time on a bachelor's degree in space science, aerospace, or interdisciplinary space studies (including, but not limited to, engineering, the sciences, architecture, law, business, nursing, and medicine); and have a GPA of 3.0 or higher. The consortium especially encourages applications from underrepresented minorities, women, and students with disabilities. Selection is based on academic performance and space-related promise. **Deadline for Receipt:** February of each year. **Additional Information:** Funding for this program is provided by the U.S. National Aeronautics and Space Administration (NASA). The schools participating in the consortium include the University of Wisconsin campuses at Fox Valley, Green Bay, La Crosse, Madison, Milwaukee, Oshkosh, Parkside, Superior, and Whitewater; Alverno College; Marquette University; College of the Menominee Nation; Carroll College; Lawrence University; Milwaukee School of Engineering; Ripon College; Medical College of Wisconsin; Western Wisconsin Technical College; and Wisconsin Lutheran College.

4042 ■ WOMEN IN AVIATION, INTERNATIONAL
Attn: Scholarships
101 Corsair Drive, Suite 101
P.O. Box 11287
Daytona Beach, FL 32120-1287
Tel: (386)226-7996
Fax: (386)226-7998
E-mail: scholarships@wai.org
Web Site: http://www.wai.org/education/scholarships.cfm
To provide financial assistance for college to members of Women in Aviation, International (WAI).

Title of Award: Airbus Leadership Grant **Area, Field, or Subject:** Aviation **Level of Education for which Award is Granted:** Undergraduate **Number Awarded:** Varies each year; recently, 2 of these scholarships were awarded. **Funds Available:** The stipend is $2,000 per year. **Duration:** 1 year.

Eligibility Requirements: This program is open to WAI members who are college sophomores or higher working on a degree in an aviation-related field. Applicants must have earned a GPA of 3.0 or higher and be able to demonstrate leadership potential. They must submit a 500-word essay addressing their career aspirations and how they have exhibited leadership skills, 3 letters of recommendation, a resume, copies of all aviation and medical certificates, and the last 3 pages of their pilot logbook, if applicable. Selection is based on achievements, attitude toward self and others, commitment to success, dedication to career, financial need, motivation, reliability, responsibility, and teamwork. **Deadline for Receipt:** December of each year. **Additional Information:** WAI is a nonprofit professional organization dedicated to encouraging

women to consider an aviation career, providing educational outreach activities, and networking resources to women active in the industry.

4043 ■ WOMEN IN AVIATION, INTERNATIONAL
Attn: Scholarships
101 Corsair Drive, Suite 101
P.O. Box 11287
Daytona Beach, FL 32120-1287
Tel: (386)226-7996
Fax: (386)226-7998
E-mail: scholarships@wai.org
Web Site: http://www.wai.org/education/scholarships.cfm
To provide financial assistance to members of Women in Aviation, International (WAI) who are studying aircraft maintenance.

Title of Award: Aircraft Electronics Association Aviation Maintenance Scholarship **Area, Field, or Subject:** Aviation **Level of Education for which Award is Granted:** Undergraduate **Number Awarded:** 1 each year. **Funds Available:** The stipend is $1,000. **Duration:** 1 year.

Eligibility Requirements: This program is open to WAI members who are seeking a degree in the aviation maintenance field at an accredited college or technical school. Preference is given to avionics majors. Applicants must have a GPA of 2.75 or higher. Selection is based on achievements, attitude toward self and others, commitment to success, dedication to career, financial need, motivation, reliability, responsibility, and teamwork. **Deadline for Receipt:** December of each year. **Additional Information:** WAI is a nonprofit professional organization dedicated to encouraging women to consider an aviation career, providing educational outreach activities, and networking resources to women active in the industry. This program is sponsored by the Aircraft Electronics Association (AEA).

4044 ■ WOMEN IN AVIATION, INTERNATIONAL
Attn: Scholarships
101 Corsair Drive, Suite 101
P.O. Box 11287
Daytona Beach, FL 32120-1287
Tel: (386)226-7996
Fax: (386)226-7998
E-mail: scholarships@wai.org
Web Site: http://www.wai.org/education/scholarships.cfm
To provide financial assistance to members of Women in Aviation, International (WAI) who are active in aerospace and need financial support to advance their career.

Title of Award: Boeing Career Enhancement Scholarship **Area, Field, or Subject:** Aerospace sciences; Aviation; Engineering, Aerospace/Aeronautical/Astronautical; Management; Space and planetary sciences; Technology **Level of Education for which Award is Granted:** Graduate, Professional, Undergraduate **Number Awarded:** 1 each year. **Funds Available:** A stipend is awarded (amount not specified). **Duration:** 1 year.

Eligibility Requirements: This program is open to WAI members who wish to advance their career in the aerospace industry in the fields of engineering, technology development, or management. Applicants may be 1) full-time or part-time employees working in the aerospace industry or a related field, or 2) students working on an aviation-related degree who are at least juniors and have a GPA of 2.5 or higher. They must submit an essay that addresses their career aspirations and goals, in addition to an application form, 3 letters of recommendation, a resume, copies of all aviation and medical certificates, and the last 3 pages of their pilot logbook, if applicable. Selection is based on achievements, attitude toward self and others, commitment to success, dedication to career, financial need, motivation, reliability, responsibility, and teamwork. **Deadline for Receipt:** December of each year. **Additional Information:** WAI is a nonprofit professional organization dedicated to encouraging women to consider an aviation career, providing educational outreach activities, and networking resources to women active in the industry.

4045 ■ WOMEN IN AVIATION, INTERNATIONAL
Attn: Scholarships
101 Corsair Drive, Suite 101
P.O. Box 11287
Daytona Beach, FL 32120-1287
Tel: (386)226-7996
Fax: (386)226-7998

E-mail: scholarships@wai.org

Web Site: http://www.wai.org/education/scholarships.cfm

To provide financial assistance to women who are working on an undergraduate or graduate degree in a field related to aviation.

Title of Award: Dassault Falcon Jet Corporation Scholarship **Area, Field, or Subject:** Aviation **Level of Education for which Award is Granted:** Graduate, Undergraduate **Number Awarded:** 1 each year. **Funds Available:** The stipend is $1,000. **Duration:** 1 year.

Eligibility Requirements: This program is open to women who are working on an undergraduate or graduate degree in an aviation-related field. Applicants must be U.S. citizens, be U.S. citizens, and have a GPA of 3.0 or higher. They must submit a 1-page essay describing their current status, what they hope to achieve with a degree in aviation, and their aspirations in the field. Selection is based on the essay, achievements, attitude toward self and others, commitment to success, dedication to career, financial need, motivation, reliability, responsibility, and teamwork.

Deadline for Receipt: December of each year. **Additional Information:** WAI is a nonprofit professional organization dedicated to encouraging women to consider an aviation career. This program is sponsored by Dassault Falcon Jet Corporation.

4046 ■ WOMEN IN AVIATION, INTERNATIONAL

Attn: Scholarships

101 Corsair Drive, Suite 101

P.O. Box 11287

Daytona Beach, FL 32120-1287

Tel: (386)226-7996

Fax: (386)226-7998

E-mail: scholarships@wai.org

Web Site: http://www.wai.org/education/scholarships.cfm

To provide financial assistance to members of Women in Aviation, International (WAI) who are interested in a career in aviation maintenance.

Title of Award: Delta Air Lines Aircraft Maintenance Technology Scholarships **Area, Field, or Subject:** Aviation **Level of Education for which Award is Granted:** Undergraduate **Number Awarded:** 1 each year. **Funds Available:** The stipend is $5,000. **Duration:** 1 year.

Eligibility Requirements: This program is open to WAI members who are full-time students with at least 2 semesters of study remaining. Applicants must be preparing for an aviation maintenance technician license (A&P) or a degree in aviation maintenance technology with a cumulative GPA of 3.0 or higher. U.S. citizenship or permanent resident status is required. As part of the selection process, applicants must submit an essay of 500 to 1,000 words that addresses such topics as who or what influenced them to prepare for a career in aviation maintenance technology, their greatest life challenge, their greatest strength and strongest characteristic, their most memorable academic experience, and why they are the best candidate for this scholarship. In addition to the essay, selection is based on achievements, attitude toward self and others, commitment to success, dedication to career, financial need, motivation, reliability, responsibility, and teamwork. **Deadline for Receipt:** December of each year. **Additional Information:** WAI is a nonprofit professional organization dedicated to encouraging women to consider an aviation career, providing educational outreach activities, and networking resources to women active in the industry. This program is sponsored by Delta Air Lines. In addition to the scholarship, recipients are reimbursed for up to $1,000 in travel and accommodations expenses to attend the WAIs annual conference.

4047 ■ WOMEN IN AVIATION, INTERNATIONAL

Attn: Scholarships

101 Corsair Drive, Suite 101

P.O. Box 11287

Daytona Beach, FL 32120-1287

Tel: (386)226-7996

Fax: (386)226-7998

E-mail: scholarships@wai.org

Web Site: http://www.wai.org/education/scholarships.cfm

To provide financial assistance to members of Women in Aviation, International (WAI) who are interested in a career in aviation management.

Title of Award: Delta Air Lines Aviation Maintenance Management/ Aviation Business Management Scholarships **Area, Field, or Subject:** Aviation; Business administration; Management **Level of Education for**

which **Award is Granted:** Undergraduate **Number Awarded:** 1 each year. **Funds Available:** The stipend is $5,000. **Duration:** 1 year.

Eligibility Requirements: This program is open to WAI members who are full-time students with at least 2 semesters of study remaining. Applicants must be working on an associate or baccalaureate degree in aviation maintenance management or aviation business management with a cumulative GPA of 3.0 or higher. U.S. citizenship or permanent resident status is required. As part of the selection process, applicants must submit an essay of 500 to 1,000 words that addresses such topics as who or what influenced them to prepare for a career in aviation maintenance management or aviation business management, their greatest strength and strongest characteristic, their most memorable academic experience, their greatest life challenge and how has it enriched their life, and why are they the best candidate for this scholarship. In addition to the essay, selection is based on achievements, attitude toward self and others, commitment to success, dedication to career, financial need, motivation, reliability, responsibility, and teamwork. **Deadline for Receipt:** December of each year. **Additional Information:** WAI is a nonprofit professional organization dedicated to encouraging women to consider an aviation career, providing educational outreach activities, and networking resources to women active in the industry. This program is sponsored by Delta Air Lines. In addition to the scholarship, recipients are reimbursed for up to $1,000 in travel and accommodations expenses to attend the WAI annual conference.

4048 ■ WOMEN IN AVIATION, INTERNATIONAL

Attn: Scholarships

101 Corsair Drive, Suite 101

P.O. Box 11287

Daytona Beach, FL 32120-1287

Tel: (386)226-7996

Fax: (386)226-7998

E-mail: scholarships@wai.org

Web Site: http://www.wai.org/education/scholarships.cfm

To provide financial assistance to members of Women in Aviation, International (WAI) who are studying engineering in college.

Title of Award: Delta Air Lines Engineering Scholarships **Area, Field, or Subject:** Engineering, Aerospace/Aeronautical/Astronautical; Engineering, Electrical; Engineering, Mechanical **Level of Education for which Award is Granted:** Undergraduate **Number Awarded:** 1 each year. **Funds Available:** The stipend is $5,000. **Duration:** 1 year.

Eligibility Requirements: This program is open to WAI members who are full-time juniors or seniors with at least 2 semesters of study remaining. Applicants must be working on a baccalaureate degree in aerospace, aeronautical, electrical, or mechanical engineering with a cumulative GPA of 3.0 or higher. U.S. citizenship is required. As part of the selection process, applicants must submit an essay of 500 to 1,000 words that addresses such questions as who or what influenced them to prepare for a career in engineering, their greatest strength and strongest characteristic, their most memorable academic experience, their greatest life challenge and how has it enriched their life, and why are they the best candidate for this scholarship. In addition to the essay, selection is based on achievements, attitude toward self and others, commitment to success, dedication to career, financial need, motivation, reliability, responsibility, and teamwork. **Deadline for Receipt:** December of each year. **Additional Information:** WAI is a nonprofit professional organization dedicated to encouraging women to consider an aviation career, providing educational outreach activities, and networking resources to women active in the industry. This program is sponsored by Delta Air Lines. In addition to the scholarship, recipients are reimbursed for up to $1,000 in travel and accommodations expenses to attend the WAI annual conference.

4049 ■ WOMEN IN AVIATION, INTERNATIONAL

Attn: Scholarships

101 Corsair Drive, Suite 101

P.O. Box 11287

Daytona Beach, FL 32120-1287

Tel: (386)226-7996

Fax: (386)226-7998

E-mail: scholarships@wai.org

Web Site: http://www.wai.org/education/scholarships.cfm

To provide financial assistance to members of Women in Aviation, International (WAI) who are active in aerospace and seeking financial support to enhance their aerospace career.

Title of Award: Amelia Earhart Society Career Enhancement Scholarship **Area, Field, or Subject:** Aerospace sciences; Aviation; Space and planetary sciences **Level of Education for which Award is Granted:** Graduate, Professional, Undergraduate **Number Awarded:** 1 each year. **Funds Available:** The stipend is $2,500. **Duration:** 1 year.
Eligibility Requirements: This program is open to 1) full-time and part-time employees in the aerospace industry, and 2) full-time students enrolled in an aerospace degree program or flight school. Applicants must be WAI members and able to demonstrate commitment as a community and/or care giver. They must submit a 500-word essay that addresses their career aspirations and goals, 3 letters of recommendation, a resume, copies of all aviation and medical certificates, and the last 3 pages of their pilot logbook, if applicable. Selection is based on achievements, attitude toward self and others, commitment to success, dedication to career, financial need, motivation, reliability, responsibility, and teamwork.
Deadline for Receipt: December of each year. **Additional Information:** WAI is a nonprofit professional organization dedicated to encouraging women to consider an aviation career, providing educational outreach activities, and networking resources to women active in the industry. The Amelia Earhart Society is a nonprofit organization for people who, like Amelia Earhart, provide a positive influence both at work and in the community; they are a diverse team of women and men who are Boeing employees, retirees, spouses, and contract hires from all areas of the company.

4050 ■ WOMEN IN AVIATION, INTERNATIONAL

Attn: Scholarships
101 Corsair Drive, Suite 101
P.O. Box 11287
Daytona Beach, FL 32120-1287
Tel: (386)226-7996
Fax: (386)226-7998
E-mail: scholarships@wai.org
Web Site: http://www.wai.org/education/scholarships.cfm
To provide financial assistance to members of Women in Aviation, International (WAI) who are interested in a career in aviation management.
Title of Award: GAT Wings to the Future Management Scholarship **Area, Field, or Subject:** Aviation; Business administration; Management **Level of Education for which Award is Granted:** Undergraduate **Number Awarded:** 1 each year. **Funds Available:** The stipend is $2,500. **Duration:** 1 year.
Eligibility Requirements: This program is open to WAI members who are enrolled in an aviation management or aviation business program at an accredited college or university. Applicants must be full-time students with a GPA of 3.0 or higher and interested in preparing for an aviation management career. Selection is based on achievements, attitude toward self and others, commitment to success, dedication to career, financial need, motivation, reliability, responsibility, and teamwork. **Deadline for Receipt:** December of each year. **Additional Information:** WAI is a nonprofit professional organization dedicated to encouraging women to consider an aviation career, providing educational outreach activities, and networking resources to women active in the industry. This program is sponsored by GAT Airline Ground Support. In addition to the scholarship, recipients are reimbursed for travel and lodging expenses to attend the WAI annual conference.

4051 ■ WOMEN IN AVIATION, INTERNATIONAL

Attn: Scholarships
101 Corsair Drive, Suite 101
P.O. Box 11287
Daytona Beach, FL 32120-1287
Tel: (386)226-7996
Fax: (386)226-7998
E-mail: scholarships@wai.org
Web Site: http://www.wai.org/education/scholarships.cfm
To provide financial assistance to members of Women in Aviation, International (WAI) who are interested in career development activities in corporate aviation.
Title of Award: Women in Corporate Aviation Career Scholarship **Area, Field, or Subject:** Aviation; Management **Level of Education for which Award is Granted:** Master's, Professional, Undergraduate **Number Awarded:** 1 each year. **Funds Available:** The stipend is $1,000.

Eligibility Requirements: This program is open to women interested in continued pursuit of a career in any job classification in corporate or business aviation. Applicants must be interested in participating in the NBAA Professional Development Program (PDP) courses, flight training, dispatcher training, upgrades in aviation education, or similar activities. General business course work is ineligible. Students currently enrolled in college should have an overall GPA of 3.25 or higher. Applicants should be actively working toward their goal and be able to show financial need.
Deadline for Receipt: December of each year. **Additional Information:** WAI is a nonprofit professional organization dedicated to encouraging women to consider an aviation career, providing educational outreach activities, and networking resources to women active in the industry.

4052 ■ WOMEN MILITARY AVIATORS, INC.

c/o Travel Soft, Inc.
24 West Mall Drive
Huntington, NY 11743
Tel: (631)423-7171
Fax: (631)423-9128
E-mail: ScholarshipCommittee@womenmilitaryaviators.org
Web Site: http://www.womenmilitaryaviators.org/Scholarship/sch_about.asp
To provide financial assistance to women interested in a career in aviation.
Title of Award: Dream of Flight Memorial Scholarship **Area, Field, or Subject:** Aviation **Level of Education for which Award is Granted:** Undergraduate **Number Awarded:** 1 each year. **Funds Available:** The stipend is $2,500. **Duration:** Recipients must complete flight training within 1 year.
Eligibility Requirements: This program is open to women interested in pursuing an FAA (or equivalent) private pilot or advanced rating. Applicants must be enrolled in an accredited college or university. Along with their application, they must submit an essay on why they believe they should be chosen for this scholarship, including why they learned to fly, what flying means to them, their career plans, and what they have already done to achieve those goals. Selection is based on ambition to advance women in aviation, past academic performance demonstrating persistence and determination toward achieving goals in aviation, and financial need.
Deadline for Receipt: Applications are accepted in May of each year. **Additional Information:** Each year, this scholarship is named in honor of a distinguished woman military aviator. Recently, it was designated the 1st Lt. Tamara L. Archuleta Scholarship.

4053 ■ WYOMING SPACE GRANT CONSORTIUM

c/o University of Wyoming
Physical Sciences Building, Room 210
1000 East University Avenue
P.O. Box 3905
Laramie, WY 82071-3905
Tel: (307)766-2862
Fax: (307)766-2652
E-mail: wy.spacegrant@uwyo.edu
Web Site: http://wyomingspacegrant.uwyo.edu/UGFellInfo.asp
To provide funding for space-related research to undergraduate students in Wyoming.
Title of Award: Wyoming Space Grant Consortium Undergraduate Research Fellowships **Area, Field, or Subject:** Aerospace sciences; Engineering, Aerospace/Aeronautical/Astronautical; General studies/Field of study not specified; Space and planetary sciences **Level of Education for which Award is Granted:** Undergraduate **Number Awarded:** Varies each year; recently, 8 of these fellowships were awarded. **Funds Available:** Grants range up to $5,000. Funds may be used only for undergraduate salary support, at the rate of $7.75 per hour. Tuition is not provided for the student's home institution, special institutes, or off-campus programs. Other expenditures not usually supported include travel, page charges, equipment, and supplies; applicants are encouraged to seek matching funds to cover those expenditures, and proposals that include matching by nonfederal funds are given priority. **Duration:** Research may be conducted during the academic year or summer.
Eligibility Requirements: This program is currently open to undergraduate students at the University of Wyoming and all community colleges in Wyoming. Applicants must be U.S. citizens who are interested in conducting a space-related research project under the mentorship of a faculty

member. A major in science or engineering is not required, because the program assumes that even non-science majors broaden their educations with a research experience. The faculty mentor must have active status and/or plan to be on-site and readily available to the student. Selection is based on the scientific merit of the proposed project, the pedagogical benefits to the student as a result of the overall research experience, and the quality of the proposal and recommendations. Wyoming Space Grant is a component of the Space Grant program of the U.S. National Aeronautics and Space Administration (NASA), which encourages participation by women, underrepresented minorities, and persons with disabilities. **Deadline for Receipt:** February of each year. **Additional Information:** This program is funded by NASA. Recipients are expected to keep the program informed of their progress, submit a final report in a timely manner, participate in publications of research results, and present a colloquium on their research.

Applied Science

4054 ■ ACADEMY OF APPLIED SCIENCE

Attn: JSHS National Office
24 Warren Street
Concord, NH 03301
Tel: (603)228-4520
Fax: (603)228-4730
E-mail: phampton@jshs.org
Web Site: http://www.jshs.org

To recognize and reward outstanding participants in the Army, Navy, and Air Force Junior Science and Humanities Symposia (JSHS).

Title of Award: JSHS Scholarships **Area, Field, or Subject:** Engineering; Mathematics and mathematical sciences; Science; Writing **Level of Education for which Award is Granted:** Undergraduate **Number Awarded:** Scholarships are awarded to 3 regional winners in each of the 48 regional symposia, to 6 first-place finalists in the national symposium, to 6 second-place national finalists, and to 6 third-place national finalists. Teacher awards are presented to 48 teachers, 1 in each of the regions. **Funds Available:** At each regional symposium, 5 finalists receive all-expense paid trips to the national symposium, the first and second place winners are invited to present their research investigation at the national symposium, and scholarships of $1,500, $1,000, and $500, are awarded. In the national competition, first-place finalists receive $16,000 scholarships, second-place finalists receive $6,000 scholarships, and third-place finalists receive $2,000 scholarships (all national scholarships are in addition to the regional scholarships). Top finalists are also awarded an all-expense paid trip to the International Youth Science Forum, held in London. The outstanding teacher in each region receives a $500 award. **Duration:** This competition is held annually. National scholarships are paid over a period of 4 years provided the recipients enroll full time and maintain a GPA of at least 3.0.

Eligibility Requirements: This program is open to students in grades 9-12, enrolled in public, private, or home schools, who have completed an original research investigation in the sciences, engineering, or mathematics. Investigations reporting on experimental, field, observational, or applied research are eligible. Students present their findings at a regional symposium, held on a university campus in their area. At each regional symposium, selected paper presenters are chosen to receive scholarships. From each of the 48 regional symposia, 5 students are selected to attend the national JSHS, where 1 of them presents his or her research paper in competition for further awards. **Additional Information:** The JSHS program was established by the Army in 1958 and since 1963 has been administered by the Academy of Applied Science. Since 1995, funding has also been provided by the Office of Naval Research and the Air Force Office of Scientific Research.

4055 ■ ALABAMA COUNCIL OF TEACHERS OF MATHEMATICS

c/o Lisa Miller, President
Hewitt-Trussville High School
5275 Trussville-Clay Road
Trussville, AL 35173
Tel: (205)379-3950
E-mail: mathnbct@yahoo.com
Web Site: http://www.dpo.uab.edu/%7Etsmith/scholar.html

To provide financial assistance to students majoring in mathematics at Alabama colleges and universities.

Title of Award: Alabama Council of Teachers of Mathematics Scholarships **Area, Field, or Subject:** Mathematics and mathematical sciences **Level of Education for which Award is Granted:** Four Year College **Number Awarded:** 5 each year. **Funds Available:** The stipend is $1,000. **Duration:** 1 year.

Eligibility Requirements: This program is open to students enrolled as juniors or seniors at colleges and universities in Alabama. Applicants must be majoring in mathematics and have a GPA of 3.0 or higher.

4056 ■ ALABAMA SPACE GRANT CONSORTIUM

c/o University of Alabama in Huntsville
Materials Science Building, Room 205
Huntsville, AL 35899
Tel: (256)824-6800
Fax: (256)824-6061
E-mail: reasonj@uah.edu
Web Site: http://www.uah.edu/ASGC

To provide financial assistance to undergraduate students at universities participating in the Alabama Space Grant Consortium who wish to prepare for a career as a teacher of science or mathematics.

Title of Award: Teacher Education Scholarship Program of the Alabama Space Grant Consortium **Area, Field, or Subject:** Aerospace sciences; Earth sciences; Education; Environmental conservation; Environmental science; Geosciences; Mathematics and mathematical sciences; Science; Space and planetary sciences **Level of Education for which Award is Granted:** Undergraduate **Number Awarded:** Varies each year; recently, 10 of these scholarships were awarded. **Funds Available:** The stipend is $1,000 per year. **Duration:** 1 year; nonrenewable.

Eligibility Requirements: This program is open to students enrolled in or accepted for enrollment as full-time undergraduates at universities in Alabama participating in the consortium. Applicants must intend to enter the teacher certification program and teach in a pre-college setting. Priority is given to those majoring in science, mathematics, or earth/space/environmental science. Applicants should have a GPA of 3.0 or higher and must be U.S. citizens. Members of underrepresented groups in science and mathematics (minorities and women) are especially encouraged to apply. Along with their application, they must submit a 1- to 2-page statement on the reasons for their desire to enter the teaching profession, specifically the fields of science or mathematics education. **Deadline for Receipt:** February of each year. **Additional Information:** The member universities are University of Alabama in Huntsville, Alabama A&M University, University of Alabama, University of Alabama at Birmingham, University of South Alabama, Tuskegee University, and Auburn University. Funding for this program is provided by NASA.

4057 ■ AMERICAN ASSOCIATION OF BLACKS IN ENERGY

Attn: Scholarship Committee
927 15th Street, N.W., Suite 200
Washington, DC 20005
Tel: (202)371-9530
Fax: (202)371-9218
E-mail: aabe@aabe.org
Web Site: http://aabe.org/taxonomy_menu/24/253

To provide financial assistance to underrepresented minority high school seniors who are interested in majoring in engineering, mathematics, or physical science in college.

Title of Award: American Association of Blacks in Energy Scholarship **Area, Field, or Subject:** Engineering; Mathematics and mathematical sciences; Physical sciences **Level of Education for which Award is Granted:** Undergraduate **Number Awarded:** 6 each year (1 in each of the organization's regions); of those 6 winners, 1 is chosen to receive the Premier Award. **Funds Available:** The stipends are $1,500. The Premier Award is an additional $3,000. All funds are paid directly to the students upon proof of enrollment at an accredited college or university. **Duration:** 1 year; nonrenewable.

Eligibility Requirements: This program is open to members of minority groups underrepresented in the energy industry (African Americans, Hispanics, and Native Americans) who are graduating high school seniors. Applicants must have a "B" academic average overall and a "B" average in mathematics and science courses. They must be planning to attend an accredited college or university to major in engineering, mathematics, or the physical sciences. Along with their application, they must submit a 350-word essay covering why they should receive this scholarship, their professional career objectives, and any other pertinent information. Financial need is also considered in the selection process. The applicant who demonstrates the most outstanding achievement and promise is presented with the Premier Award. All applications must be submitted to the local office of the sponsoring organization in the student's state. For a list of local offices, contact the scholarship committee at the national office. **Deadline for Receipt:** February of each year.

4058 ■ AMERICAN INDIAN SCIENCE AND ENGINEERING SOCIETY

Attn: Scholarship Coordinator
2305 Renard, S.E., Suite 200
P.O. Box 9828
Albuquerque, NM 87119-9828
Tel: (505)765-1052
Fax: (505)765-5608
E-mail: shirley@aises.org
Web Site: http://www.aises.org/highered/scholarships
To provide financial assistance to members of the American Indian Science and Engineering Society who are majoring in designated fields as undergraduate or graduate students.
Title of Award: A.T. Anderson Memorial Scholarship Program **Area, Field, or Subject:** Engineering; Mathematics and mathematical sciences; Medicine; Natural resources; Physical sciences; Science **Level of Education for which Award is Granted:** Graduate, Undergraduate **Number Awarded:** Varies; generally, 200 or more each year, depending upon the availability of funds from corporate and other sponsors. **Funds Available:** The annual stipend is $1,000 for undergraduates or $2,000 for graduate students. **Duration:** 1 year; nonrenewable.
Eligibility Requirements: This program is open to members of the society who can furnish proof of tribal enrollment or Certificate of Degree of Indian Blood. Applicants must be full-time students at the undergraduate or graduate school level attending an accredited 4-year college or university or a 2-year college leading to an academic degree in engineering, mathematics, medicine, natural resources, physical science, or the sciences. They must submit a 500-word essay that demonstrates their interest in and motivation to continue higher education, an understanding of the importance of college and a commitment to completion, their educational and/or career goals, and a commitment to learning and giving back to the community. Selection is based on the essay, academic achievement (GPA of 2.0 or higher), leadership potential, and commitment to helping other American Indians. Financial need is not considered. **Deadline for Receipt:** June of each year. **Additional Information:** This program was launched in 1983 in memory of A.T. Anderson, a Mohawk and a chemical engineer who worked with Albert Einstein. Anderson was 1 of the society's founders and was the society's first executive director. The program includes the following named awards: the Al Qoyawayma Award for an applicant who is majoring in science or engineering and also has a strong interest in the arts, the Norbert S. Hill, Jr. Leadership Award, the Polingaysi Qoyawayma Award for an applicant who is working on a teaching degree in order to teach mathematics or science in a Native community or an advanced degree for personal improvement or teaching at the college level, and the Robert W. Brocksbank Scholarship.

4059 ■ AMERICAN INDIAN SCIENCE AND ENGINEERING SOCIETY

Attn: Scholarship Coordinator
2305 Renard, S.E., Suite 200
P.O. Box 9828
Albuquerque, NM 87119-9828
Tel: (505)765-1052
Fax: (505)765-5608
E-mail: shirley@aises.org
Web Site: http://www.aises.org/highered/scholarships
To provide financial assistance for college to outstanding American Indian high school seniors from designated states who are members of American Indian Science and Engineering Society (AISES).
Title of Award: Burlington Northern Santa Fe Foundation Scholarship **Area, Field, or Subject:** Business administration; Engineering; Mathematics and mathematical sciences; Medicine; Natural resources; Physical sciences; Science; Technology **Level of Education for which Award is Granted:** Four Year College **Number Awarded:** 5 new awards are made each year. **Funds Available:** The stipend is $2,500 per year.

Duration: 4 years or until completion of a baccalaureate degree, whichever occurs first.
Eligibility Requirements: This program is open to AISES members who are high school seniors planning to attend an accredited 4-year college or university and major in business, engineering, mathematics, medicine, natural resources, physical science, science, or technology. Applicants must submit 1) proof of tribal enrollment or a Certificate of Degree of Indian Blood; 2) evidence of residence in the service area of the Burlington Northern and Santa Fe Corporation (Arizona, California, Colorado, Kansas, Minnesota, Montana, New Mexico, North Dakota, Oklahoma, Oregon, South Dakota, and Washington); 3) a statement of financial need; 4) a 500-word essay on why they chose their particular field of study, their career aspirations, an evaluation of past scholastic performance, obstacles faced as a student, and involvement in and commitment to tribal community life; and 5) high school transcripts showing a GPA of 2.0 or higher. **Deadline for Receipt:** April of each year. **Additional Information:** This program is funded by the Burlington Northern Santa Fe Foundation and administered by AISES.

4060 ■ AMERICAN METEOROLOGICAL SOCIETY

Attn: Fellowship/Scholarship Program
45 Beacon Street
Boston, MA 02108-3693
Tel: (617)227-2426
Fax: (617)742-8718
E-mail: scholar@ametsoc.org
Web Site: http://www.ametsoc.org/amsstudentinfo/scholfeldocs/index.html
To provide financial assistance to undergraduates majoring in meteorology or an aspect of atmospheric sciences with an interest in statistical meteorology.
Title of Award: Bob Glahn Scholarship in Statistical Meteorology **Area, Field, or Subject:** Atmospheric science; Hydrology; Meteorology; Oceanography; Statistics **Level of Education for which Award is Granted:** Four Year College **Number Awarded:** 1 each year. **Funds Available:** The stipend is $2,500 per year. **Duration:** 1 year.
Eligibility Requirements: This program is open to full-time students entering their final year of undergraduate study and majoring in meteorology or an aspect of the atmospheric or related oceanic and hydrologic sciences. Applicants must intend to make atmospheric or related sciences their career, with preference for students who have demonstrated a strong interest in statistical meteorology. They must be U.S. citizens or permanent residents enrolled at a U.S. institution and have a cumulative GPA of 3.25 or higher. Along with their application, they must submit 200-word essays on 1) their most important achievements that qualify them for this scholarship, and 2) their career goals in the atmospheric or related oceanic or hydrologic fields. Selection is based on academic excellence and achievement; financial need is not considered. The sponsor specifically encourages applications from women, minorities, and students with disabilities who are traditionally underrepresented in the atmospheric and related oceanic sciences. **Deadline for Receipt:** February of each year. **Additional Information:** Requests for an application must be accompanied by a self-addressed stamped envelope.

4061 ■ AMERICAN SOCIETY FOR ENGINEERING EDUCATION

Attn: SMART Defense Scholarship Program
1818 N Street, N.W., Suite 600
Washington, DC 20036-2479
Tel: (202)331-3516
Fax: (202)265-8504
E-mail: smart@asee.org
Web Site: http://www.asee.org/resources/fellowships/smart/index.cfm
To provide scholarship/loans to upper-division and graduate students in areas of science, mathematics, and engineering that are of interest to the U.S. Department of Defense.
Title of Award: Science, Mathematics, and Research for Transformation (SMART) Defense Scholarship Program **Area, Field, or Subject:** Architecture, Naval; Behavioral sciences; Biological and clinical sciences; Chemistry; Computer and information sciences; Earth sciences; Engineering, Aerospace/Aeronautical/Astronautical; Engineering, Chemical; Engineering, Civil; Engineering, Electrical; Engineering, Materials; Engineering, Mechanical; Engineering, Ocean; Geosciences; Materials research/science; Mathematics and mathematical sciences; Oceanogra-

phy; Physics **Level of Education for which Award is Granted:** Four Year College, Graduate **Number Awarded:** Varies each year; recently, 36 of these scholarships were awarded. **Funds Available:** The program provides full payment of tuition, fees, room, board, and other normal educational expenses at the recipient's institution. A book allowance of $1,000 per year is also provided. This is a scholarship/loan program; recipients must agree to serve as a civilian employee of the Department of Defense in a science and engineering position. If they fail to fulfill that service obligation, they must reimburse the federal government for all funds they received. **Duration:** Up to 24 months.

Eligibility Requirements: This program is open to upper-division and graduate students working on an undergraduate or graduate degree in any of the following fields: aeronautical and astronautical engineering; biosciences; chemical engineering; chemistry; civil engineering; cognitive, neural, and behavioral sciences; computer and computational sciences; electrical engineering; geosciences, including terrain, water, and air; materials science and engineering; mathematics; mechanical engineering; naval architecture and ocean engineering; oceanography; or physics. Applicants must be U.S. citizens who have a GPA of 3.0 or higher. Selection is based on academic records, personal statements, letters of recommendation, and GRE scores. **Deadline for Receipt:** March of each year. **Additional Information:** This program, established in 2005, is sponsored by the Army Research Laboratory, the Air Force Office of Scientific Research, the Office of Naval Research, the Air Force Research Laboratory, the Defense Advanced Research Projects Agency, the Defense Information Systems Agency, and the Defense Threat Reduction Agency.

4062 ■ APPALACHIAN COLLEGE ASSOCIATION

Attn: Director of Programs
210 Center Street
Berea, KY 40403
Tel: (859)986-4584
Fax: (859)986-9549
E-mail: kathrynb@acaweb.org
Web Site: http://www.acaweb.org
To provide financial assistance to students majoring in computer science, engineering, and mathematics (CSEM) at colleges and universities that are members of the Appalachian College Association (ACA).

Title of Award: Appalachian College Association Scholarships for Majoring in Computer Science, Engineering, Mathematics **Area, Field, or Subject:** Computer and information sciences; Engineering; Mathematics and mathematical sciences **Level of Education for which Award is Granted:** Four Year College **Number Awarded:** 30 each year. **Funds Available:** The stipend is $2,750 per year. **Duration:** 1 year; may be renewed 1 additional year.

Eligibility Requirements: This program is open to full-time students entering their junior or senior year at ACA member institutions. Applicants must be majoring in a CSEM discipline, have a GPA of 3.0 or higher, and be able to document financial need. Along with their application, they must submit a 500-word essay describing their career ambitions, their commitment to the Appalachian region, and the potential benefits to Appalachia of their degree choice. U.S. citizenship is required. Preference is given to graduates of high schools in the Appalachian region. **Deadline for Receipt:** March of each year. **Additional Information:** Funding for this program, which began in 2003, is provided by the National Science Foundation. The ACA includes member institutions in Kentucky (Alice Lloyd College, Berea College, Campbellsville University, University of the Cumberlands, Kentucky Christian University, Lindsey Wilson College, Pikeville College, and Union College), North Carolina (Brevard College, Lees-McRae College, Mars Hill College, Montreat College, and Warren Wilson College), Tennessee (Bryan College, Carson-Newman College, King College, Lee University, Lincoln Memorial University, Maryville College, Milligan College, Tennessee Wesleyan College, Tusculum College, and University of the South), Virginia (Bluefield College, Emery & Henry College, Ferrum College, and Virginia Intermont College), and West Virginia (Alderson-Broaddus College, Bethany College, Davis & Elkins College, Ohio Valley University, University of Charleston, West Virginia Wesleyan College, and Wheeling Jesuit University).

4063 ■ APPALACHIAN COLLEGE ASSOCIATION

Attn: Director of Programs
210 Center Street
Berea, KY 40403
Tel: (859)986-4584
Fax: (859)986-9549
E-mail: kathrynb@acaweb.org
Web Site: http://www.acaweb.org
To provide financial assistance to upper-division students majoring in biology, chemistry, or mathematics at colleges and universities that are members of the Appalachian College Association (ACA) who plan to become teachers.

Title of Award: Robert Noyce Scholarships **Area, Field, or Subject:** Biological and clinical sciences; Chemistry; Education; Mathematics and mathematical sciences **Level of Education for which Award is Granted:** Four Year College **Number Awarded:** 12 each year. **Funds Available:** The stipend is $7,500 per year. Recipients must be willing to sign a promissory note with a commitment to teach in a high-need middle or high school for 2 years for every year of the scholarship. **Duration:** 1 year; may be renewed 1 additional year.

Eligibility Requirements: This program is open to full-time students entering their junior or senior year at ACA member institutions with a major in biology, chemistry, or mathematics and plans to earn a teaching license. Applicants must have a GPA of 3.0 or higher and be able to document financial need. Along with their application, they must submit a 500-word essay describing their interest in becoming a 6-12 teacher; their commitment to the Appalachian region, including the impact they hope to have as a teacher; and actual and planned progress toward becoming certified. U.S. citizenship is required. Preference is given to graduates of high schools in the Appalachian region and to applicants who express a desire to teach in a high-need middle or high school, especially schools in central Appalachia. **Deadline for Receipt:** March of each year. **Additional Information:** Funding for this program is provided by the National Science Foundation. The ACA includes member institutions in Kentucky (Alice Lloyd College, Berea College, Campbellsville University, University of the Cumberlands, Kentucky Christian University, Lindsey Wilson College, Pikeville College, and Union College), North Carolina (Brevard College, Lees-McRae College, Mars Hill College, Montreat College, and Warren Wilson College), Tennessee (Bryan College, Carson-Newman College, King College, Lee University, Lincoln Memorial University, Maryville College, Milligan College, Tennessee Wesleyan College, Tusculum College, and University of the South), Virginia (Bluefield College, Emery & Henry College, Ferrum College, and Virginia Intermont College), and West Virginia (Alderson-Broaddus College, Bethany College, Davis & Elkins College, Ohio Valley University, University of Charleston, West Virginia Wesleyan College, and Wheeling Jesuit University).

4064 ■ ARKANSAS DEPARTMENT OF HIGHER EDUCATION

Attn: Financial Aid Division
114 East Capitol Avenue
Little Rock, AR 72201-3818
Tel: (501)371-2050
Free: 800-54-STUDY
Fax: (501)371-2001
E-mail: finaid@adhe.arknet.edu
Web Site: http://www.arkansashighered.com/mteachers.html
To provide scholarship/loans to minority undergraduates in Arkansas who want to become teachers.

Title of Award: Arkansas Minority Teacher Scholars Program **Area, Field, or Subject:** Counseling/Guidance; Education; Education, Elementary; Linguistics; Mathematics and mathematical sciences; Science **Level of Education for which Award is Granted:** Four Year College **Number Awarded:** Varies each year; recently, 97 of these scholarship/loans were approved. **Funds Available:** Awards up to $5,000 per year are available. This is a scholarship/loan program. The loan will be forgiven at the rate of 20% for each year the recipient teaches full time in an Arkansas public school (or 33% per year if the obligation is fulfilled in 3 years as described above). If the loan is not forgiven by service, it must be repaid with interest at a rate up to 5% points above the Federal Reserve discount rate. **Duration:** 1 year; may be renewed for 1 additional year if the recipient remains a full-time student with a GPA of 2.5 or higher.

Eligibility Requirements: Applicants must be minority (African American, Native American, Hispanic, or Asian American) residents of Arkansas who are U.S. citizens and enrolled as full-time juniors or seniors in an approved teacher certification program at an Arkansas public or independent 4-year institution. They must have a cumulative GPA of 2.5 or higher and be willing to teach in an Arkansas public school for at least 5 years after completion of their teaching certificate (3 years if the teaching is in 1 of the 42 counties of Arkansas designated as the Delta Region; or if the teaching is in mathematics, science, or foreign language; or if the recipient is an African American male and teaches at the elementary level; or if the service is as a guidance counselor). **Deadline for Receipt:** May of each year.

4065 ■ ARKANSAS DEPARTMENT OF HIGHER EDUCATION

Attn: Financial Aid Division
114 East Capitol Avenue
Little Rock, AR 72201-3818
Tel: (501)371-2050
Free: 800-54-STUDY
Fax: (501)371-2001
E-mail: finaid@adhe.arknet.edu
Web Site: http://www.starark.com

To provide scholarship/loans to college students in Arkansas who are interested in preparing for a teaching career in an approved subject or geographic shortage area.

Title of Award: Arkansas State Teacher Assistance Resource (STAR) Program **Area, Field, or Subject:** Biological and clinical sciences; Chemistry; Earth sciences; Education; Education, Secondary; Education, Special; Geosciences; Linguistics; Mathematics and mathematical sciences; Physical sciences; Physics **Level of Education for which Award is Granted:** Master's, Undergraduate **Number Awarded:** Varies each year; recently, 42 of these scholarship/loans were approved. **Funds Available:** The award is $3,000 per year for students who agree to teach in either a geographic teacher shortage area or a subject teacher shortage area. For students who agree to teach in both a geographic shortage area and a subject shortage area, the award is $6,000 per year. This is a scholarship/loan program. Recipients must teach in an Arkansas geographic or subject shortage area for 1 year for each year of support they receive. If they fail to complete that teaching obligation, they must repay all funds received. **Duration:** 1 year; may be renewed for 1 additional year if the recipient is enrolled in a 4-year teacher education program or 2 additional years if enrolled in a 5-year teacher education program. Renewal requires that the recipient maintain a GPA of 2.75 or higher and complete 24 semester hours as an undergraduate or 18 semester hours as a graduate student.

Eligibility Requirements: This program is open to Arkansas residents who are full-time students enrolled 1) at a 4-year public or private college or university in the state with an approved teacher education program; 2) in an associate of arts in teaching program; or 3) in an master of arts in teaching program. Applicants must have a GPA of 2.75 or higher and be entering their sophomore, junior, or senior year (or be in a master's degree program). They must be willing to teach in a public school located in a geographic area of Arkansas designated as having a critical shortage of teachers or in a subject matter area designated as having a critical shortage of teachers. Applicants must have completed their freshman year at an accredited Arkansas public or private college or university in a major field of study leading to secondary teacher certification in 1 of the shortage areas. U.S. citizenship is required. **Deadline for Receipt:** May of each year. **Additional Information:** This program was established in 2004 as a replacement for the former Arkansas Emergency Secondary Education Loan Program. Recently, the subject areas designated as having a critical shortage of teachers were foreign language, mathematics, chemistry, physics, biology, physical science, earth science, and special education. For a list of geographic areas of Arkansas that are designated as having a critical shortage of teachers, contact the Department of Higher Education. The State Teacher Assistance Resource (STAR) program also provides that teachers who received federal student loans may have those loans repaid 1) at the rate of $3,000 per year if they teach a subject area in Arkansas that is designated as a shortage area or if they teach in a geographic area of the state with a shortage of teachers, or 2) at the rate of $6,000 per year if they teach a shortage subject area in a shortage geographic area. Students may not, however, participate in both the scholarship/loan program and the federal loan repayment program.

4066 ■ ARMED FORCES COMMUNICATIONS AND ELECTRONICS ASSOCIATION

Attn: AFCEA Educational Foundation
4400 Fair Lakes Court
Fairfax, VA 22033-3899

Tel: (703)631-6149
Free: 800-336-4583
Fax: (703)631-4693
E-mail: scholarship@afcea.org
Web Site: http://www.afcea.org/education/scholarships/undergraduate/pub1.asp

To provide financial assistance to undergraduate students who are working full time on a degree by means of a distance-learning or on-line program.

Title of Award: AFCEA Distance-Learning/On-Line Scholarships **Area, Field, or Subject:** Computer and information sciences; Engineering, Chemical; Engineering, Computer; Engineering, Electrical; Mathematics and mathematical sciences; Physics; Systems engineering **Level of Education for which Award is Granted:** Four Year College **Number Awarded:** 1 each year. **Funds Available:** The stipend is $1,000. **Duration:** 1 year.

Eligibility Requirements: This program is open to U.S. citizens working full time on a bachelor's degree by means of a distance-learning or on-line program affiliated with a major, accredited 4-year college or university in the United States. Applicants must have completed at least 1 year of course work based on a 30-semester hour equivalent; classes in progress at the time of application cannot be used towards the 1-year minimum completion requirement. Completed courses must include at least 2 semesters of calculus (not pre-calculus). Majors are limited to the fields of engineering (chemical, computer, electrical, or systems), mathematics, physics, or computer science. Selection is based primarily on academic excellence. **Deadline for Receipt:** July of each year.

4067 ■ ARMED FORCES COMMUNICATIONS AND ELECTRONICS ASSOCIATION

Attn: AFCEA Educational Foundation
4400 Fair Lakes Court
Fairfax, VA 22033-3899
Tel: (703)631-6149
Free: 800-336-4583
Fax: (703)631-4693
E-mail: scholarship@afcea.org
Web Site: http://www.afcea.org/education/scholarships/rotc/rotc1.asp

To provide financial assistance to ROTC cadets who are majoring in fields related to communications and electronics.

Title of Award: AFCEA ROTC Scholarships **Area, Field, or Subject:** Computer and information sciences; Electronics; Engineering, Aerospace/Aeronautical/Astronautical; Engineering, Chemical; Engineering, Computer; Engineering, Electrical; Mathematics and mathematical sciences; Physics; Systems engineering **Level of Education for which Award is Granted:** Four Year College **Number Awarded:** 36 each year, divided equally among Army, Navy/Marine Corps, and Air Force ROTC programs; for each service, 6 are awarded to rising juniors, 6 to rising seniors. **Funds Available:** The stipend is $2,000. **Duration:** 1 year; may be renewed.

Eligibility Requirements: This program is open to ROTC cadets majoring in electronics, engineering (aerospace, chemical, computer, electrical, or systems), mathematics, physics, or computer science. Applicants must be nominated by their ROTC professor, be entering their junior or senior year, be U.S. citizens, be of good moral character, have demonstrated academic excellence, be motivated to complete a college education and serve as officers in the U.S. armed forces, and be able to demonstrate financial need. **Deadline for Receipt:** March of each year.

4068 ■ ARMED FORCES COMMUNICATIONS AND ELECTRONICS ASSOCIATION

Attn: AFCEA Educational Foundation
4400 Fair Lakes Court
Fairfax, VA 22033-3899
Tel: (703)631-6149
Free: 800-336-4583
Fax: (703)631-4693
E-mail: scholarship@afcea.org
Web Site: http://www.afcea.org/education/scholarships/workingstudents/ws1.asp

To provide financial assistance to undergraduate students who are working part time on a degree in engineering or the sciences while already employed.

Title of Award: AFCEA Scholarship for Working Professionals **Area, Field, or Subject:** Computer and information sciences; Engineering, Aerospace/Aeronautical/Astronautical; Engineering, Chemical; Engineering, Electrical; Mathematics and mathematical sciences; Physics; Systems engineering **Level of Education for which Award is Granted:** Undergraduate **Number Awarded:** 1 each year. **Funds Available:** The stipend is $1,500. **Duration:** 1 year; may be renewed.

Eligibility Requirements: This program is open to part-time students entering their sophomore, junior, or senior year at an accredited 2-year or 4-year college or university in the United States while already employed in a science or technology field. Applicants must be U.S. citizens working toward a degree in engineering (aerospace, chemical, electrical, or systems), mathematics, physics, or computer science with a GPA of 3.4 or higher. They must be able to demonstrate academic achievement, patriotism, and potential to contribute to the American work force. **Deadline for Receipt:** September of each year. **Additional Information:** This program was established in 2002.

4069 ■ ARMED FORCES COMMUNICATIONS AND ELECTRONICS ASSOCIATION

Attn: AFCEA Educational Foundation
4400 Fair Lakes Court
Fairfax, VA 22033-3899
Tel: (703)631-6149
Free: 800-336-4583
Fax: (703)631-4693
E-mail: scholarship@afcea.org
Web Site: http://www.afcea.org/education/scholarships/undergraduate/genemm.asp

To provide funding to veterans, military personnel, and their family members who are majoring in specified scientific fields in college.

Title of Award: General Emmett Paige Scholarships **Area, Field, or Subject:** Computer and information sciences; Engineering, Aerospace/Aeronautical/Astronautical; Engineering, Chemical; Engineering, Computer; Engineering, Electrical; Mathematics and mathematical sciences; Physics **Level of Education for which Award is Granted:** Four Year College **Number Awarded:** Varies each year; recently, 11 of these scholarships were awarded. **Funds Available:** The stipend is $2,000. **Duration:** 1 year; may be renewed.

Eligibility Requirements: This program is open to veterans, persons on active duty in the uniformed military services, and their spouses or dependents who are currently enrolled full time in an accredited 4-year college or university in the United States. Graduating high school seniors are not eligible, but veterans entering college as freshmen may apply. Spouses or dependents must be sophomores or juniors. Applicants must be U.S. citizens, be of good moral character, have demonstrated academic excellence, be motivated to complete a college education, and be working toward a degree in engineering (aerospace, chemical, computer, or electrical), mathematics, physics, or computer science with a GPA of 3.4 or higher. They must provide a copy of Discharge Form DD214, Certificate of Service, or facsimile of their current Department of Defense or Coast Guard Identification Card. **Deadline for Receipt:** February of each year.

4070 ■ ARMED FORCES COMMUNICATIONS AND ELECTRONICS ASSOCIATION

Attn: AFCEA Educational Foundation
4400 Fair Lakes Court
Fairfax, VA 22033-3899
Tel: (703)631-6149
Free: 800-336-4583
Fax: (703)631-4693
E-mail: scholarship@afcea.org
Web Site: http://www.afcea.org/education/scholarships/undergraduate/veteran.asp

To provide financial assistance to veterans and military personnel who served in Afghanistan or Iraq and are working on an undergraduate degree in fields related to the support of U.S. intelligence enterprises.

Title of Award: Veterans of Enduring Freedom-Afghanistan and Iraqi Freedom Combat Operations Scholarship **Area, Field, or Subject:** Computer and information sciences; Engineering; Engineering, Aerospace/Aeronautical/Astronautical; Engineering, Computer; Engineering, Electrical; Mathematics and mathematical sciences; Physics;

Systems engineering **Level of Education for which Award is Granted:** Undergraduate **Number Awarded:** 1 or more each year. **Funds Available:** The stipend is $2,000. **Duration:** 1 year.

Eligibility Requirements: This program is open to active-duty and honorably discharged U.S. military veterans, Reservists, and National Guard personnel who served in combat operations of Enduring Freedom-Afghanistan or Iraqi Freedom. Applicants must be enrolled at a 2- or 4-year institution in the United States and working on an undergraduate degree in computer engineering technology, computer information systems, electronics engineering technology, engineering (aerospace, computer, electrical, or systems), mathematics, physics, or computer science. Along with their application, they must submit an essay that includes a brief synopsis of relevant work experience (including military assignments), a brief statement of career goals after graduation, and an explanation of how their academic and career goals will contribute to the areas related to communications, intelligence and/or information systems, and the mission of the Armed Forces Communications and Electronics Association (AFCEA). Financial need is also considered in the selection process. **Deadline for Receipt:** October of each year. **Additional Information:** This scholarship was first offered in 2005.

4071 ■ ARMED FORCES COMMUNICATIONS AND ELECTRONICS ASSOCIATION

Attn: AFCEA Educational Foundation
4400 Fair Lakes Court
Fairfax, VA 22033-3899
Tel: (703)631-6149
Free: 800-336-4583
Fax: (703)631-4693
E-mail: scholarship@afcea.org
Web Site: http://www.afcea.org/education/scholarships/undergraduate/pub2.asp

To provide financial assistance to undergraduate students who are working full time on a degree in engineering or the sciences.

Title of Award: General John A. Wickham Scholarships **Area, Field, or Subject:** Computer and information sciences; Engineering, Aerospace/Aeronautical/Astronautical; Engineering, Chemical; Engineering, Computer; Engineering, Electrical; Mathematics and mathematical sciences; Physics; Systems engineering **Level of Education for which Award is Granted:** Four Year College **Number Awarded:** Varies each year; recently, 11 of these scholarships were awarded. **Funds Available:** The stipend is $2,000. **Duration:** 1 year; may be renewed.

Eligibility Requirements: This program is open to full-time students entering their junior or senior year at an accredited degree-granting 4-year college or university in the United States. Applicants must be U.S. citizens working toward a degree in engineering (aerospace, chemical, computer, electrical, or systems), mathematics, physics, or computer science with a GPA of 3.5 or higher. They must be able to demonstrate academic achievement, patriotism, and potential to contribute to the American work force. **Deadline for Receipt:** April of each year.

4072 ■ ARMED FORCES COMMUNICATIONS AND ELECTRONICS ASSOCIATION

Attn: AFCEA Educational Foundation
4400 Fair Lakes Court
Fairfax, VA 22033-3899
Tel: (703)631-6149
Free: 800-336-4583
Fax: (703)631-4693
E-mail: scholarship@afcea.org
Web Site: http://www.afcea.org/education/scholarships/undergraduate/sgtjean.asp

To provide funding to members and veterans of the U.S. Marine Corps (USMC) who are majoring in specified fields in college.

Title of Award: Marine Sgt. Jeannette L. Winters Memorial Scholarship **Area, Field, or Subject:** Computer and information sciences; Engineering, Aerospace/Aeronautical/Astronautical; Engineering, Computer; Engineering, Electrical; Mathematics and mathematical sciences; Physics; Systems engineering **Level of Education for which Award is Granted:** Undergraduate **Number Awarded:** 1 each year. **Funds Available:** The stipend is $2,000. **Duration:** 1 year.

Eligibility Requirements: This program is open to USMC personnel currently on active duty, in the Reserves, or honorably-discharged veterans who are enrolled full or part time in an accredited college or university in the United States. Applicants must be U.S. citizens, be of good moral character, have demonstrated academic excellence, be motivated to complete a college education, and be working on a degree in engineering (aerospace, computer, electrical, or systems), mathematics, physics, or computer science with a GPA of 3.0 or higher. They must provide a copy of Discharge Form DD214, Certificate of Service, or facsimile of their current Department of Defense Identification Card. **Deadline for Receipt:** September of each year. **Additional Information:** This program was established in 2002 to honor a Marine who died when her KC-130 aircraft crashed in Pakistan.

4073 ■ ASSOCIATION FOR IRON & STEEL TECHNOLOGY

Attn: AIST Foundation
186 Thorn Hill Road
Warrendale, PA 15086-7528
Tel: (724)776-6040
Fax: (724)776-1880
E-mail: lwharrey@aist.org
Web Site: http://www.aist.org/foundation/scholarships.htm
To provide financial assistance for college study of engineering to Canadians who are children of members of the Association for Iron & Steel Technology (AIST).
Title of Award: David H. Samson Canadian Scholarship **Area, Field, or Subject:** Chemistry; Engineering; Geology; Mathematics and mathematical sciences; Physics **Level of Education for which Award is Granted:** Undergraduate **Number Awarded:** 1 each year. **Funds Available:** The stipend is $US2,000. **Duration:** 1 year; may be renewed for up to 3 additional years.
Eligibility Requirements: This program is open to the children (natural, adopted, or ward) of Canadian citizens and landed immigrants who are members of the association. Applicants must have been accepted in an eligible full-time course of study of engineering at an accredited Canadian university. If no engineering student applies, the award may be made to an eligible student planning to major in chemistry, geology, mathematics, or physics. The scholarship may also be awarded to a student entering a community college if there is no eligible applicant entering an accredited university. The committee may also award the scholarship to a previous applicant entering the second or third year at a Canadian university or community college if there is no eligible applicant entering the first year. Selection is based on academic achievements, extracurricular activities, and the student's written statements; financial need is not considered. **Deadline for Receipt:** June of each year. **Additional Information:** The AIST was formed in 2004 by the merger of the Iron and Steel Society (ISS) and the Association of Iron and Steel Engineers (AISE). Information is also available from Robert Kneale, AIST Northern Member Chapter, P.O. Box 1734, Cambridge, Ontario N1R 7G8, Canada.

4074 ■ ASSOCIATION FOR IRON & STEEL TECHNOLOGY-NORTHWEST CHAPTER

c/o Gerardo L. Giraldo, Secretary-Treasurer
Nucor Steel Seattle, Inc.
Washington Steel Division
2424 S.W. Andover Street
Seattle, WA 98106-1100
Tel: (206)933-2245
Fax: (206)933-2207
E-mail: gerry.giraldo@nucor-seattle.com
Web Site: http://www.aist.org/chapters/
mc_pittsburgh_scholar_guidelines.htm
To provide financial assistance to family of members of the Northwest Chapter of the Association for Iron & Steel Technology (AIST) who are interested in studying engineering in college.
Title of Award: Northwest Chapter AIST Scholarships **Area, Field, or Subject:** Business; Chemistry; Engineering; Manufacturing; Mathematics and mathematical sciences; Metallurgy; Physics **Level of Education for which Award is Granted:** Four Year College **Number Awarded:** 2 each year. **Funds Available:** The stipend is $1,000. **Duration:** 1 year.
Eligibility Requirements: This program is open to children, grandchildren, spouses, or nieces/nephews of chapter members who are high school seniors planning to attend an accredited 4-year college or university. Applicants must intend to study engineering; if there are no applicants in engineering, the award may be given to a student majoring in

chemistry, mathematics, metallurgy, or physics, or to a student showing an interest in preparing for a career in the iron and steel industry. Along with their application, they must submit a 500-word essay on 1 of the following topics: 1) an accomplishment they have achieved while they have been a student, why they were successful, and how their success will influence their future plans as an engineer or an engineer in the steel industry; 2) their strengths and interests and how they will apply their skills to a career in the steel industry or as an engineer; or 3) the challenges that face the steel industry and the opportunities for graduates to improve the success of companies within the industry. Financial need is not considered in the selection process. **Deadline for Receipt:** June of each year. **Additional Information:** The AIST was formed in 2004 by the merger of the Iron and Steel Society (ISS) and the Association of Iron and Steel Engineers (AISE). The Northwest Chapter serves Alaska, Idaho, Montana, Oregon, Washington, and Wyoming.

4075 ■ ASSOCIATION OF OLD CROWS

Attn: AOC Educational Foundation
1000 North Payne Street
Alexandria, VA 22314-1652
Tel: (703)549-1600
Fax: (703)549-2589
Web Site: http://www.crows.org
To provide financial assistance to military enlisted personnel who are pursuing off-duty college-level education programs in fields related to electronics.
Title of Award: Association of Old Crows Enlisted Tuition Grants **Area, Field, or Subject:** Electronics; Engineering, Electrical; Mathematics and mathematical sciences; Physics **Level of Education for which Award is Granted:** Undergraduate **Number Awarded:** Varies each year; recently, a total of $160,000 per year was available for this program. **Funds Available:** Support is provided to supplement the funding available through the tuition assistance programs. **Duration:** 1 semester; may be renewed.
Eligibility Requirements: This program is open to military enlisted personnel (rank of E-4 and above) who are utilizing the tuition assistance programs of the services to study electrical engineering, physics, mathematics, and related areas during their off-duty hours. Selection is based on academic excellence and financial need. **Additional Information:** Funding is provided by local chapters of this organization, which was founded by World War II veterans who had engaged in electronic warfare to disrupt enemy communications and radars. The program was code-named "Raven" and its operators became known as Old Crows. For information on a chapter in your area, contact the AOC Educational Foundation.

4076 ■ ASSOCIATION FOR WOMEN IN SCIENCE-SEATTLE CHAPTER

c/o Fran Solomon, Scholarship Committee Chair
5805 16th Avenue, N.E.
Seattle, WA 98105
Tel: (206)522-6441
E-mail: fran.solomon@metrokc.gov
Web Site: http://www.scn.org/awis/undergraduate_scholarship.htm
To provide financial assistance to women undergraduates from any state majoring in science, mathematics, or engineering at colleges and universities in western Washington.
Title of Award: AWIS Seattle Scholarships **Area, Field, or Subject:** Biochemistry; Biological and clinical sciences; Chemistry; Engineering; Environmental conservation; Environmental science; Geology; Mathematics and mathematical sciences; Pharmaceutical sciences; Physics **Level of Education for which Award is Granted:** Four Year College **Number Awarded:** Varies each year; recently, 11 of these scholarships were awarded. **Funds Available:** Stipends range from $1,000 to $1,500. **Duration:** 1 year.
Eligibility Requirements: This program is open to women from any state entering their junior or senior year at a 4-year college or university in western Washington. Applicants must have a declared major in science (e.g., biological sciences, environmental science, biochemistry, chemistry, pharmacy, geology, computer science, physics), mathematics, or engineering. Along with their application, they must submit essays on the events that led to their choice of a major, their current career plans and long-term goals, and their volunteer and community activities. Financial need is considered in the selection process. At least 1 scholarship is

reserved for a woman from a group that is underrepresented in science, mathematics, and engineering careers, including Native American Indians and Alaska Natives, Black/African Americans, Mexican Americans/ Chicanas/Latinas, Native Pacific Islanders (Polynesians, Melanesians, and Micronesians), and women with disabilities. **Deadline for Receipt:** March of each year. **Additional Information:** This program includes the following named awards: the Virginia Badger Scholarship, the Angela Paez Memorial Scholarship, and the Fran Solomon Scholarship. Support for the program is provided by several sponsors, including the American Chemical Society, Iota Sigma Pi, Rosetta Inpharmatics, and ZymoGenetics, Inc.

4077 ■ BUSINESS AND PROFESSIONAL WOMEN OF VIRGINIA
Attn: Virginia BPW Foundation
P.O. Box 4842
McLean, VA 22103-4842
Web Site: http://www.bpwva.org/Foundation.shtml
To provide financial assistance to women in Virginia who are interested in working on a bachelor's or advanced degree in science or technology.
Title of Award: Women in Science and Technology Scholarship **Area, Field, or Subject:** Actuarial science; Biological and clinical sciences; Chemistry; Computer and information sciences; Dentistry; Engineering; Engineering, Biomedical; Insurance and insurance-related fields; Mathematics and mathematical sciences; Medicine; Physics; Science; Technology **Level of Education for which Award is Granted:** Graduate, Undergraduate **Number Awarded:** At least 1 each year. **Funds Available:** Stipends range from $500 to $1,000 per year, depending on the need of the recipient; funds may be used for tuition, fees, books, transportation, living expenses, and dependent care. **Duration:** 1 year; recipients may reapply (but prior recipients are not given priority).
Eligibility Requirements: This program is open to women who are at least 18 years of age, U.S. citizens, Virginia residents, accepted at or currently studying at a Virginia college or university, and working on a bachelor's, master's, or doctoral degree in 1 of the following fields: actuarial science, biology, bioengineering, chemistry, computer science, dentistry, engineering, mathematics, medicine, physics, or a similar scientific or technical field. Applicants must have a definite plan to use their education in a scientific or technical profession. They must be able to demonstrate financial need. **Deadline for Receipt:** March of each year. **Additional Information:** Recipients must complete their studies within 2 years.

4078 ■ CASUALTY ACTUARIAL SOCIETY
Attn: CAS Trust Scholarship Coordinator
1100 North Glebe Road, Suite 600
Arlington, VA 22201-4798
Tel: (703)276-3100
Fax: (703)276-3108
E-mail: office@casact.org
Web Site: http://www.casact.org/academ/scholarship.htm
To provide financial assistance to U.S. and Canadian students who are preparing for a career in the property and casualty actuarial profession.
Title of Award: CAS Trust Scholarship Program **Area, Field, or Subject:** Actuarial science; Insurance and insurance-related fields; Mathematics and mathematical sciences **Level of Education for which Award is Granted:** Undergraduate **Number Awarded:** Up to 3 each year. **Funds Available:** The stipend is $1,500. **Duration:** 1 year.
Eligibility Requirements: This program is open to U.S. and Canadian citizens who are enrolled full time at a college or university in the United States or Canada. Applicants must be preparing for a career in the property and casualty actuarial profession and pursuit of the Casualty Actuarial Society (CAS) designations. They must have demonstrated high scholastic achievement and strong interest in mathematics or a mathematics-related field. Preference is given to students who have passed an actuarial examination and who have not yet won this or another scholarship from this sponsor or the Society of Actuaries. Selection is based on individual merit. **Deadline for Receipt:** April of each year.

4079 ■ CATCHING THE DREAM
8200 Mountain Road, N.E., Suite 203
Albuquerque, NM 87110-7835
Tel: (505)262-2351
Fax: (505)262-0534

E-mail: NScholarsh@aol.com
Web Site: http://www.catchingthedream.org
To provide financial assistance to American Indian students who are interested in working on an undergraduate or graduate degree in selected fields.
Title of Award: MESBEC Program **Area, Field, or Subject:** Business administration; Computer and information sciences; Education; Engineering; Mathematics and mathematical sciences; Science **Level of Education for which Award is Granted:** Four Year College, Graduate **Number Awarded:** Varies; generally, 30 to 35 each year. **Funds Available:** Stipends range from $500 to $5,000. **Duration:** 1 year; may be renewed.
Eligibility Requirements: This program is open to American Indians who can provide proof that they are at least one-quarter Indian blood and a member of a U.S. tribe that is federally-recognized, state-recognized, or terminated. Applicants must be enrolled or planning to enroll full time and major in the 1 of the following fields: mathematics, engineering, science, business administration, education, or computer science. They may be entering freshmen, undergraduate students, graduate students, or Ph.D. candidates. Along with their application, they must submit documentation of financial need, 3 letters of recommendation, copies of applications and responses for at least 15 other sources of funding, official transcripts, standardized test scores (ACT, SAT, GRE, MCAT, LSAT, etc.), and an essay explaining their goals in life, college plans, and career plans (especially how those plans include working with and benefiting Indians). Selection is based on merit and potential for improving the lives of Indian people. **Deadline for Receipt:** April of each year for fall term; September of each year for spring and winter terms; March of each year for summer school. **Additional Information:** MESBEC is an acronym that stands for the priority areas of this program: mathematics, engineering, science, business, education, and computers. The sponsor was formerly known as the Native American Scholarship Fund.

4080 ■ COOK INLET REGION, INC.
Attn: CIRI Foundation
2600 Cordova Street, Suite 206
Anchorage, AK 99503
Tel: (907)263-5582
Free: 800-764-3382
Fax: (907)263-5588
E-mail: tcf@ciri.com
Web Site: http://www.thecirifoundation.org/scholarship.html
To provide financial assistance for undergraduate or graduate studies in selected fields to Alaska Natives who are original enrollees to Cook Inlet Region, Inc. (CIRI) and their lineal descendants.
Title of Award: CIRI Foundation Special Excellence Scholarships **Area, Field, or Subject:** Business administration; Education; Engineering; General studies/Field of study not specified; Health care services; Mathematics and mathematical sciences; Science **Level of Education for which Award is Granted:** Four Year College, Graduate **Number Awarded:** 1 or more each year. **Funds Available:** The stipend is $18,000 per year. **Duration:** 1 year; may be renewed.
Eligibility Requirements: This program is open to Alaska Native enrollees to CIRI under the Alaska Native Claims Settlement Act (ANCSA) of 1971 and their lineal descendants. There are no Alaska residency requirements or age limitations. Applicants must be accepted or enrolled full time in a 4-year undergraduate or a graduate degree program. They must have a GPA of 3.7 or higher. Preference is given to students working on a degree in business, education, mathematics, sciences, health services, or engineering. Selection is based on academic achievement, rigor of course work or degree program, quality of a statement of purpose, student financial contribution, financial need, grade level, previous work performance, education and community activities, letters of recommendation, seriousness of purpose, and practicality of educational and professional goals. **Deadline for Receipt:** May of each year. **Additional Information:** This program was established in 1997. Recipients must enroll in school on a full-time basis.

4081 ■ COUNCIL OF ENERGY RESOURCE TRIBES
Attn: Education Program Director
695 South Colorado Boulevard, Suite 10
Denver, CO 80246-8008
Tel: (303)282-7576
Fax: (303)282-7584

E-mail: info@CERTRedEarth.com

Web Site: http://www.certredearth.com

To provide financial assistance to American Indian high school seniors who are interested in studying fields related to mathematics, business, science, engineering, or other technical fields in college.

Title of Award: CERT Scholarships **Area, Field, or Subject:** Business administration; Engineering; Mathematics and mathematical sciences; Science **Level of Education for which Award is Granted:** Graduate, Undergraduate **Funds Available:** Costs of instruction, activities, and room and board for the summer institute are paid by the TRIBES program. The amount of the college scholarship is $1,000 per year. **Duration:** 1 year; may be renewed up to 4 additional years, provided the recipient maintains a GPA of 2.5 or higher.

Eligibility Requirements: This program is open to Indian high school seniors, college students, and graduates students who have participated in the Tribal Resource Institute in Business, Engineering, and Science (TRIBES) program, an intensive 7-week summer college-level program. CERT internship participants are also eligible. Applicants must be planning to enroll full time at an accredited 2- or 4-year tribal, public, or private college or university and major in business, engineering, science, mathematics, computer technology, or a related field. Along with their application, they must submit official tribal affiliation documents, university or college enrollment verification, and their most recent academic transcripts. Financial need is also considered in the selection process. **Deadline for Receipt:** Applications for the TRIBES program must be submitted by January of each year. Other students may apply by the end of August for the fall semester or January for the spring semester. **Additional Information:** The TRIBES program runs for 7 weeks during the summer at the University of New Mexico, Native American Studies, MSCO6 3740, Albuquerque, NM 87131-0001, (505) 277-1812, Fax: (505) 277-1818.

4082 ■ COUNCIL OF THE GREAT CITY SCHOOLS

1301 Pennsylvania Avenue, N.W., Suite 702

Washington, DC 20004

Tel: (202)393-2427

Fax: (202)393-2400

Web Site: http://www.cgcs.org

To provide financial assistance to African American women interested in studying engineering, mathematics, science, or technology in college.

Title of Award: Marcia Page Scholarship for Mathematics and Science Education **Area, Field, or Subject:** Engineering; Mathematics and mathematical sciences; Science; Technology **Level of Education for which Award is Granted:** Four Year College **Number Awarded:** 2 each year. **Funds Available:** The stipend is $5,000. **Duration:** 1 year; nonrenewable.

Eligibility Requirements: This program is open to African American women who are graduating from high school and have been accepted at a 4- or 5-year college or university as a full-time student. Applicants must be able to demonstrate academic achievement in high school, success in overcoming obstacles or achieving goals, and a commitment to a career in science, mathematics, engineering, or technology. They must be enrolled in a school district that is a member of the Council of the Great City Schools, a coalition of 64 of the nation's largest urban public school systems. **Deadline for Receipt:** April of each year. **Additional Information:** This scholarship, first awarded in 2005, is sponsored by Texas Instruments, Inc.

4083 ■ DELAWARE HIGHER EDUCATION COMMISSION

Carvel State Office Building

820 North French Street

Wilmington, DE 19801

Tel: (302)577-3240

Free: 800-292-7935

Fax: (302)577-6765

E-mail: dhec@doe.k12.de.us

Web Site: http://www.doe.state.de.us/high-ed/christa.htm

To provide scholarship/loans for teacher training to Delaware residents with outstanding academic records.

Title of Award: Christa McAuliffe Teacher Scholarship/Loan **Area, Field, or Subject:** Counseling/Guidance; Education; Education, Bilingual and cross-cultural; Education, English as a second language; Education, Special; English language and literature; Library and archival sciences; Linguistics; Mathematics and mathematical sciences; Reading; Technol-

ogy **Level of Education for which Award is Granted:** Undergraduate **Number Awarded:** Up to 50 each year. **Funds Available:** Funds up to the cost of tuition, fees, and other direct educational expenses are provided. This is a scholarship/loan program; if the recipient performs required service at a school in Delaware, the loan is forgiven at the rate of 1 year of assistance for each year of service. **Duration:** 1 year; may be renewed for up to 3 additional years.

Eligibility Requirements: This program is open to Delaware residents who are enrolled or accepted for enrollment at a Delaware college or university in a program leading to teacher qualification. Preference is given to applicants planning to teach in an area of critical need. High school seniors must rank in the top half of their class and have a combined score of at least 1570 on the SAT; applicants who are already enrolled in college must have a cumulative GPA of 2.75 or higher. Selection is based on academic achievement. U.S. citizenship or permanent resident status is required. **Deadline for Receipt:** March of each year. **Additional Information:** The areas of critical need recently included bilingual education, business education, English, foreign languages, English to speakers of other languages, mathematics, reading, science, school librarianship, special education, and technology education.

4084 ■ DELTA SIGMA THETA SORORITY, INC.-THE FEDERAL CITY ALUMNAE CHAPTER

Attn: Educational Development Committee

P.O. Box 1605

Washington, DC 20013

Tel: (202)545-1913

E-mail: thefcacdst@yahoo.com

Web Site: http://www.thefcacdst.org/html/chapterEvents.htm

To provide financial assistance to high school seniors in Washington, D.C. who plan to attend an Historically Black College or University (HBCU) to major in a field related to science and engineering.

Title of Award: Federal City Alumnae Chapter Scholarship for Excellence **Area, Field, or Subject:** Computer and information sciences; Engineering; Information science and technology; Mathematics and mathematical sciences; Science **Level of Education for which Award is Granted:** Undergraduate **Number Awarded:** 2 each year. **Funds Available:** The stipend is $5,000. **Duration:** 1 year; nonrenewable.

Eligibility Requirements: This program is open to seniors graduating from public and public charter high schools in the District of Columbia. Applicants must have been accepted to attend an HBCU to major in computer science, engineering, information technology, mathematics, science, or a related field. They must have a GPA of 3.0 or higher. Along with their application, they must submit a 2-page essay on why they decided to attend an HBCU to major in mathematics, science, or a related field. **Deadline for Receipt:** March of each year.

4085 ■ DEPARTMENT OF TRANSPORTATION

Federal Highway Administration

Attn: National Highway Institute, HNHI-20

4600 North Fairfax Drive, Suite 800

Arlington, VA 22203-1553

Tel: (703)235-0538

Fax: (703)235-0593

E-mail: transportationedu@fhwa.dot.gov

Web Site: http://www.nhi.fhwa.dot.gov/ddetfp.asp

To enable students to participate in research activities at facilities of the U.S. Department of Transportation (DOT) Federal Highway Administration in the Washington, D.C. area.

Title of Award: Eisenhower Grants for Research Fellowships **Area, Field, or Subject:** Chemistry; Economics; Engineering; Engineering, Civil; Geography; Information science and technology; Materials research/ science; Operations research; Physics; Public administration; Statistics; Technology; Transportation; Urban affairs/design/planning **Level of Education for which Award is Granted:** Four Year College, Graduate **Number Awarded:** Varies each year; recently, 9 students participated in this program. **Funds Available:** Fellows receive full tuition and fees that relate to the academic credits for the approved research project and a monthly stipend of $1,450 for college seniors, $1,700 for master's students, or $2,000 for doctoral students. An allowance for travel to and from the DOT facility where the research is conducted is also provided, but selectees are responsible for their own housing accommodations. Faculty advisors are allowed 1 site review on projects over 6 months and

2 site reviews on projects over 9 months; travel and per diem are provided for those site reviews. **Duration:** Tenure is normally 3, 6, 9, or 12 months. **Eligibility Requirements:** This program is open to 1) students in their junior year of a baccalaureate program who will complete their junior year before being awarded a fellowship; 2) students in their senior year of a baccalaureate program; and 3) students who have completed their baccalaureate degree and are enrolled in a program leading to a master's, Ph.D., or equivalent degree. Applicants must be U.S. citizens enrolled in an accredited U.S. institution of higher education working on a degree full time and planning to enter the transportation profession after completing their higher education. They select 1 or more projects from a current list of research projects underway at various DOT facilities; the research will be conducted with academic supervision provided by a faculty advisor from their home university (which grants academic credit for the research project) and with technical direction provided by the DOT staff. Specific requirements for the target projects vary; most require engineering backgrounds, but others involve transportation planning, information management, public administration, physics, materials science, statistical analysis, operations research, chemistry, economics, technology transfer, urban studies, geography, and urban and regional planning. The DOT encourages students at Historically Black Colleges and Universities (HBCUs) and Hispanic Serving Institutions (HSIs) to apply for these grants. Selection is based on match of the student's qualifications with the proposed research project (including the student's ability to accomplish the project in the available time), recommendation letters regarding the nominee's qualifications to conduct the research, academic records (including class standing, GPA, and transcripts), and transportation work experience (if any) including the employer's endorsement. **Deadline for Receipt:** February of each year.

4086 ■ THE DEVELOPMENT FUND FOR BLACK STUDENTS IN SCIENCE AND TECHNOLOGY

2705 Bladensburg Road, N.E.
Washington, DC 20018
Tel: (202)635-3604
E-mail: hattie.carwell@oak.doe.gov
Web Site: http://ourworld.compuserve.com/homepages/dlhinson/dfb_sch.htm
To provide scholarships to African American students who enroll in scientific or technical fields of study at Historically Black Colleges and Universities (HBCUs).
Title of Award: The Development Fund for Black Students in Science and Technology Scholarships **Area, Field, or Subject:** Engineering; Mathematics and mathematical sciences; Science **Level of Education for which Award is Granted:** Undergraduate **Number Awarded:** Several each year. **Funds Available:** The amount of the scholarship is based on merit and financial need. Awards up to $2,000 per year are available. **Duration:** 1 year; may be renewed for up to 4 years, as long as the recipient remains in good academic standing and enrolled full time in a science or engineering curriculum.
Eligibility Requirements: Deans and faculty members of the various engineering and science departments at predominantly Black colleges and universities are invited to identify students to be considered for these scholarships. To be eligible, nominated students must intend to enroll at a predominantly Black college or university or already be enrolled at such a college or university. They must intend to major in a technical field and be U.S. citizens or permanent residents who intend to remain in the United States after graduation. Selection is based on academic achievement (grades and SAT scores, especially in science and mathematics), a personal essay describing career goals and relevant extracurricular activities, recommendations, and financial need. **Deadline for Receipt:** June of each year. **Additional Information:** Prior to 1995, these scholarships were awarded solely or primarily through the National Merit Scholarship Corporation's National Achievement Scholarship Program. Scholarship applications are available only through the financial aid offices of prequalified schools. Currently, these are: Bennett College, Clark Atlanta University, Elizabeth City State University, Fisk University, Florida A&M University, Fort Valley State College, Hampton University, Howard University, Langston University, Lincoln University of Pennsylvania, Morehouse University, Morgan State University, North Carolina A&T State University, Prairie View A&M University, Southern University and A&M College, Spelman College, Tennessee State University, Tuskegee University, Wilberforce University, and Xavier University of Louisiana.

4087 ■ BILL AND MELINDA GATES FOUNDATION

P.O. Box 10500
Fairfax, VA 22031-8044
877-690-GMSP
Web Site: http://www.gmsp.org
To provide financial assistance to outstanding low-income minority students, particularly those interested in majoring in specific fields in college.
Title of Award: Gates Millennium Undergraduate Scholars Program **Area, Field, or Subject:** Education; Engineering; General studies/Field of study not specified; Mathematics and mathematical sciences; Science **Level of Education for which Award is Granted:** Undergraduate **Number Awarded:** Under the Gates Millennium Scholars Program, a total of 4,000 students receive support each year. **Funds Available:** The program covers the cost of tuition, fees, books, and living expenses not paid for by grants and scholarships already committed as part of the recipient's financial aid package. **Duration:** 4 years or the completion of the undergraduate degree, if the recipient maintains at least a 3.0 GPA.
Eligibility Requirements: This program is open to African Americans, Alaska Natives, American Indians, Hispanic Americans, and Asian Pacific Islander Americans who are graduating high school seniors with a GPA of 3.3 or higher. Principals, teachers, guidance counselors, tribal higher education representatives, and other professional educators are invited to nominate students with outstanding academic qualifications, especially those likely to succeed in the fields of mathematics, science, engineering, education, or library science. Nominees should have significant financial need and demonstrated leadership abilities through participation in community service, extracurricular, or other activities. U.S. citizenship or permanent resident status is required. Nominees must be planning to enter an accredited college or university as a full-time, degree-seeking freshman in the following fall. **Deadline for Receipt:** January of each year. **Additional Information:** This program, established in 1999, is funded by the Bill and Melinda Gates Foundation and administered by the United Negro College Fund with support from the American Indian Graduate Center, the Hispanic Scholarship Fund, and the Organization of Chinese Americans.

4088 ■ GEORGIA SPACE GRANT CONSORTIUM

c/o Georgia Institute of Technology
Aerospace Engineering
Space Science and Technology Building, Room 210
Atlanta, GA 30332-0150
Tel: (404)894-0521
Fax: (404)894-9313
E-mail: wanda.pierson@aerospace.gatech.edu
Web Site: http://www.ae.gatech.edu/organizations/gsgc/html/fellowship.htm
To provide financial assistance for undergraduate and graduate study of space-related fields to students at member institutions of the Georgia Space Grant Consortium (GSGC).
Title of Award: Georgia Space Grant Consortium Fellowships **Area, Field, or Subject:** Aerospace sciences; Computer and information sciences; Engineering, Aerospace/Aeronautical/Astronautical; Mathematics and mathematical sciences; Space and planetary sciences **Level of Education for which Award is Granted:** Graduate, Undergraduate **Number Awarded:** 1 each year. **Funds Available:** A stipend is awarded (amount not specified).
Eligibility Requirements: This program is open to U.S. citizens who are undergraduate and graduate students at member institutions of the GSGC. Applicants must be working on a degree in mathematics, science, engineering, computer science, or a technical discipline related to space. Selection is based on transcripts, 3 letters of reference, and an essay of 100 to 500 words on the applicant's professional interests and objectives and their relationship to the field of aerospace. Awards are provided as part of the Space Grant program of the U.S. National Aeronautics and Space Administration (NASA), which encourages participation by women, minorities, and people with disabilities. **Additional Information:** Institutions that are members of the GSGC include Albany State University, Clark Atlanta University, Columbus State University, Fort Valley State University, Georgia Institute of Technology, Georgia State University, Kennesaw State University, Mercer University, Morehouse College, Spelman College, State University of West Georgia, and the University of Georgia. This program is funded by NASA.

4089 ■ BARRY M. GOLDWATER SCHOLARSHIP AND EXCELLENCE IN EDUCATION FOUNDATION

Springfield Corporate Center
6225 Brandon Avenue, Suite 315
Springfield, VA 22150-2519
Tel: (703)756-6012
Fax: (703)756-6015
E-mail: goldh2o@vacoxmail.com
Web Site: http://www.act.org/goldwater
To provide financial assistance to outstanding college students planning careers in mathematics, engineering, or the natural sciences.
Title of Award: Barry M. Goldwater Scholarships **Area, Field, or Subject:** Engineering; Mathematics and mathematical sciences; Natural sciences **Level of Education for which Award is Granted:** Undergraduate **Number Awarded:** Up to 300 each year. **Funds Available:** Scholarships cover the cost of tuition, fees, books, and room and board up to a maximum of $7,500 per year. **Duration:** Students who receive scholarships as juniors are eligible for 2 years of support or until they complete their baccalaureate degree; students who receive scholarships as seniors are eligible for 1 year of support or until they complete their baccalaureate degree.
Eligibility Requirements: Eligible to be nominated are full-time students enrolled as sophomores or juniors who are in the top quarter of their class and majoring in the natural sciences, mathematics, or engineering with a GPA of at least 3.0. Students intending to enter medical school are eligible if they plan a career in research rather than private practice. Status as a U.S. citizen, national, or resident alien is also required. Students must be nominated by their institutions; 4-year colleges and universities may nominate up to 4 current sophomores or juniors and 2-year colleges may nominate up to 2 sophomores. Applicants must submit a 2-page essay on a significant issue or problem in their field of study that is of particular interest to them. Selection is based on academic performance and demonstrated potential for and commitment to a career in mathematics, engineering, or the natural sciences. **Deadline for Receipt:** Institutions set their own deadlines; they must submit nominations to the foundation by January of each year. **Additional Information:** This program was authorized by the U.S. Congress in 1986. Information is also available from the Goldwater Scholarship Review Committee, 2201 North Dodge Street, P.O. Box 4030, Iowa City, IA 52243-4030.

4090 ■ HAWAI'I COMMUNITY FOUNDATION

Attn: Scholarship Department
1164 Bishop Street, Suite 800
Honolulu, HI 96813
Tel: (808)566-5570; 888-731-3863
Fax: (808)521-6286
E-mail: scholarships@hcf-hawaii.org
Web Site: http://www.hawaiicommunityfoundation.org/scholar/scholar.php
To provide financial assistance for college to Hawaii residents who are interested in majoring in a scientific field.
Title of Award: Shuichi, Katsu and Itsuyo Suga Scholarship **Area, Field, or Subject:** Mathematics and mathematical sciences; Physics; Science; Technology **Level of Education for which Award is Granted:** Graduate, Undergraduate **Number Awarded:** Varies each year; recently, 9 of these scholarships were awarded. **Funds Available:** The amounts of the awards depend on the availability of funds and the need of the recipient; recently, stipends averaged $1,000. **Duration:** 1 year.
Eligibility Requirements: This program is open to Hawaii residents who plan to attend an accredited 2- or 4-year college or university as a full-time undergraduate or graduate student. Applicants must be planning to study mathematics, physics, science, or technology. They must be able to demonstrate academic achievement (GPA of 3.0 or higher), good moral character, and financial need. Along with their application, they must submit a short statement indicating their reasons for attending college, planned course of study, and career goals. **Deadline for Receipt:** February of each year. **Additional Information:** Recipients may attend college in Hawaii or on the mainland.

4091 ■ HEMOPHILIA HEALTH SERVICES

Attn: Scholarship Committee
6820 Charlotte Pike, Suite 100
Nashville, TN 37209-4234
Tel: (615)850-5175
Free: 800-800-6606
Fax: (615)352-2588
E-mail: scholarship@HemophiliaHealth.com
Web Site: http://www.HemophiliaHealth.com/consumers/products_services/scholarship.htm
To provide financial assistance to high school seniors and current college students who have hemophilia and are interested in working on a degree or certification in computer science and/or mathematics.
Title of Award: Scott Tarbell Scholarships **Area, Field, or Subject:** Computer and information sciences; Mathematics and mathematical sciences **Level of Education for which Award is Granted:** Undergraduate **Number Awarded:** Varies each year, depending on the availability of funds. **Funds Available:** The stipend is $1,500. Funds are issued payable to the recipient's school. **Duration:** 1 year; recipients may reapply.
Eligibility Requirements: This program is open to high school seniors and college freshmen, sophomores, and juniors who have hemophilia A or B severe. Applicants must be enrolled or planning to enroll at an accredited nonprofit college, university, or vocational/technical school in the United States or Puerto Rico. They must be interested in working on a degree or certification in computer science and/or mathematics. Along with their application, they must submit an essay, up to 250 words, on the following topic: "Upon receiving your education in math and/or computer science, how will you use the new technologies (i.e., computer, internet, etc.) to better mankind and what ethical issues will you need to address?" U.S. citizenship is required. Selection is based on academic achievement in relation to tested ability and dedication to the field of computer science or mathematics. Financial need is not considered. **Deadline for Receipt:** April of each year. **Additional Information:** This program, which started in 2003, is administered by Scholarship Program Administrators, Inc., 1201 Eighth Avenue South, P.O. Box 23737, Nashville, TN 27202-3737, (615) 320-3149, Fax: (615) 320-3151, E-mail: info@spaprog.com.

4092 ■ HISPANIC ENGINEER NATIONAL ACHIEVEMENT AWARDS CONFERENCE

3900 Whiteside Street
Los Angeles, CA 90063
Tel: (323)262-0997
Fax: (323)262-0946
E-mail: info@henaac.org
Web Site: http://www.henaac.org/scholarships
To provide financial assistance to Hispanic undergraduate students majoring in engineering and related fields.
Title of Award: Amerada Hess/HENAAC Scholars Program **Area, Field, or Subject:** Computer and information sciences; Engineering; Materials research/science; Mathematics and mathematical sciences; Science **Level of Education for which Award is Granted:** Undergraduate **Number Awarded:** 1 or more each year. **Funds Available:** Stipends range from $1,000 to $5,000. **Duration:** 1 year; recipients may reapply.
Eligibility Requirements: This program is open to Hispanic undergraduate students who are enrolled full time in computer science, engineering, material science, mathematics, or applied science. Applicants must have a GPA of 3.0 or higher. There is no citizenship requirement. Academic achievement and campus community activities are considered in the selection process. **Deadline for Receipt:** April of each year. **Additional Information:** This program is sponsored by the Amerada Hess Foundation as part of its effort to support the mission of the Hispanic Engineer National Achievement Awards Conference (HENAAC) to promote technical excellence and leadership in the Hispanic community.

4093 ■ HISPANIC ENGINEER NATIONAL ACHIEVEMENT AWARDS CONFERENCE

3900 Whiteside Street
Los Angeles, CA 90063
Tel: (323)262-0997
Fax: (323)262-0946
E-mail: info@henaac.org
Web Site: http://www.henaac.org/scholarships
To provide financial assistance to Hispanic undergraduate students majoring in engineering and related fields.
Title of Award: Future Electronics/HENAAC Scholars Program **Area, Field, or Subject:** Computer and information sciences; Engineering; Materials research/science; Mathematics and mathematical sciences; Science **Level of Education for which Award is Granted:** Undergraduate

Number Awarded: 1 or more each year. **Funds Available:** Stipends range from $1,000 to $5,000. **Duration:** 1 year; recipients may reapply. **Eligibility Requirements:** This program is open to Hispanic undergraduate students who are enrolled full time in computer science, engineering, material science, mathematics, or applied science. Applicants must have a GPA of 3.0 or higher. There is no citizenship requirement. Academic achievement and campus community activities are considered in the selection process. **Deadline for Receipt:** April of each year. **Additional Information:** This program is sponsored by the Future Electronics as part of its effort to support the mission of the Hispanic Engineer National Achievement Awards Conference (HENAAC) to promote technical excellence and leadership in the Hispanic community.

4094 ■ HISPANIC ENGINEER NATIONAL ACHIEVEMENT AWARDS CONFERENCE

3900 Whiteside Street
Los Angeles, CA 90063
Tel: (323)262-0997
Fax: (323)262-0946
E-mail: info@henaac.org
Web Site: http://www.henaac.org/scholarships
To provide financial assistance to Hispanic undergraduate and graduate students majoring in engineering and related fields.

Title of Award: HENAAC Student Leadership Awards **Area, Field, or Subject:** Computer and information sciences; Engineering; Materials research/science; Mathematics and mathematical sciences; Science **Level of Education for which Award is Granted:** Graduate, Undergraduate **Number Awarded:** 2 each year: 1 undergraduate and 1 graduate student. **Funds Available:** The stipend is $5,000. **Duration:** 1 year. **Eligibility Requirements:** This program is open to Hispanic undergraduate and graduate students who are enrolled full time in computer science, engineering, material science, mathematics, or applied science. Applicants must have a GPA of 3.0 or higher. There is no citizenship requirement. Academic achievement and campus community activities are considered in the selection process. **Deadline for Receipt:** April of each year. **Additional Information:** This program is sponsored by the Hispanic Engineer National Achievement Awards Conference (HENAAC) to promote technical excellence and leadership in the Hispanic community.

4095 ■ HISPANIC ENGINEER NATIONAL ACHIEVEMENT AWARDS CONFERENCE

3900 Whiteside Street
Los Angeles, CA 90063
Tel: (323)262-0997
Fax: (323)262-0946
E-mail: info@henaac.org
Web Site: http://www.henaac.org/scholarships
To provide financial assistance to Hispanic undergraduate students majoring in engineering and related fields.

Title of Award: Northrop Grumman/HENAAC Scholars Program **Area, Field, or Subject:** Architecture, Naval; Computer and information sciences; Engineering, Aerospace/Aeronautical/Astronautical; Engineering, Chemical; Engineering, Civil; Engineering, Computer; Engineering, Electrical; Engineering, Industrial; Engineering, Mechanical; Engineering, Ocean; Information science and technology; Mathematics and mathematical sciences; Physics **Level of Education for which Award is Granted:** Undergraduate **Number Awarded:** 5 each year. **Funds Available:** The stipend is $5,000. **Duration:** 1 year; recipients may reapply. **Eligibility Requirements:** This program is open to Hispanic undergraduate students who are enrolled full time in the following engineering fields: aerospace, chemical, civil, computer, electrical, industrial, manufacturing, marine, mechanical, ocean, or structural. Students majoring in computer science, information science, mathematics, naval architecture, and physics are also eligible. Applicants must be U.S. citizens and have a GPA of 3.0 or higher. Academic achievement and campus community activities are considered in the selection process. **Deadline for Receipt:** April of each year. **Additional Information:** This program is sponsored by Northrop Grumman as part of its effort to support the mission of the

Hispanic Engineer National Achievement Awards Conference (HENAAC) to promote technical excellence and leadership in the Hispanic community.

4096 ■ HISPANIC ENGINEER NATIONAL ACHIEVEMENT AWARDS CONFERENCE

3900 Whiteside Street
Los Angeles, CA 90063
Tel: (323)262-0997
Fax: (323)262-0946
E-mail: info@henaac.org
Web Site: http://www.henaac.org/scholarships
To provide financial assistance to Hispanic undergraduate students majoring in engineering and related fields.

Title of Award: NVIDIA Corporation/HENAAC Scholars Program **Area, Field, or Subject:** Computer and information sciences; Engineering; Materials research/science; Mathematics and mathematical sciences; Science **Level of Education for which Award is Granted:** Undergraduate **Number Awarded:** 1 or more each year. **Funds Available:** Stipends range from $1,000 to $5,000. **Duration:** 1 year; recipients may reapply. **Eligibility Requirements:** This program is open to Hispanic undergraduate students who are enrolled full time in computer science, engineering, material science, mathematics, or applied science. Applicants must have a GPA of 3.0 or higher. There is no citizenship requirement. Academic achievement and campus community activities are considered in the selection process. **Deadline for Receipt:** April of each year. **Additional Information:** This program is sponsored by the NVIDIA Corporation as part of its effort to support the mission of the Hispanic Engineer National Achievement Awards Conference (HENAAC) to promote technical excellence and leadership in the Hispanic community.

4097 ■ HISPANIC SCHOLARSHIP FUND

Attn: Selection Committee
55 Second Street, Suite 1500
San Francisco, CA 94105
Tel: (415)808-2350; 877-HSF-INFO
Fax: (415)808-2302
E-mail: highschool@hsf.net
Web Site: http://www.hsf.net/scholarship/programs/shpe.php
To provide financial assistance for college to Hispanic Americans who are interested in majoring in designated fields of science.

Title of Award: Society of Hispanic Professional Engineers Scholarship Program **Area, Field, or Subject:** Computer and information sciences; Engineering; Mathematics and mathematical sciences; Physical sciences **Level of Education for which Award is Granted:** Undergraduate **Number Awarded:** Varies each year; recently, 69 of these scholarships were awarded: 7 at $1,250, 2 at $1,307, and 60 at $2,500. **Funds Available:** Stipends range from $1,250 to $2,500 per year. **Duration:** 1 year. **Eligibility Requirements:** This program is open to U.S. citizens, permanent residents, and visitors with a passport stamped I-551 who are of Hispanic heritage. Applicants may be graduating high school seniors, community college students transferring to a 4-year institution, or continuing college students as long as they have a GPA of 3.0 or higher. They must be enrolled or planning to enroll full time at an accredited college or university in the United States to major in computer science, physical science, applied science, mathematics, or engineering. Along with their application, they must submit 600-word essays on 1) how their Hispanic heritage, family upbringing, and/or role models have influenced their personal long-term goals; 2) how they contribute to their community and what they have learned from their experiences; and 3) an academic challenge they have faced and how they have overcome it. Selection is based on academic achievement, personal strengths, leadership, and financial need. **Deadline for Receipt:** June of each year. **Additional Information:** This program is jointly sponsored by the Society of Hispanic Professional Engineers (SHPE) and the Hispanic Scholarship Fund (HSF).

4098 ■ HISPANIC SCHOLARSHIP FUND INSTITUTE

1001 Connecticut Avenue, N.W., Suite 632
Washington, DC 20036
Tel: (202)296-0009
Fax: (202)296-3633
E-mail: info@hsfi.org
Web Site: http://www.hsfi.org/scholarships/energy.asp

To provide financial assistance to Hispanic undergraduate students majoring in designated business, engineering, and science fields related to the U.S. Department of Energy (DOE) goals of environmental restoration and waste management.

Title of Award: Environmental Management Scholarship **Area, Field, or Subject:** Business administration; Chemistry; Computer and information sciences; Engineering, Agricultural; Engineering, Civil; Engineering, Electrical; Engineering, Industrial; Engineering, Mechanical; Engineering, Metallurgical; Engineering, Petroleum; Environmental science; Epidemiology; Geology; Hydrology; Management; Mathematics and mathematical sciences; Physics; Radiology; Toxicology **Level of Education for which Award is Granted:** Undergraduate **Number Awarded:** Varies each year. **Funds Available:** The stipend is $3,000 per year for 4-year university students or $2,000 per year for community college students. **Duration:** 1 year.

Eligibility Requirements: This program is open to U.S. citizens and permanent residents of Hispanic background who have completed at least 12 undergraduate credits with a GPA of 3.0 or higher. Applicants must be interested in preparing for a career supportive of the DOE goals of environmental restoration and waste management. Eligible academic majors are in the fields of business (management and system analysis), engineering (agricultural, chemical, civil, electrical, environmental, industrial, mechanical, metallurgical, nuclear, and petroleum), and science (applied math/physics, chemistry, computer science, ecology, environmental, epidemiology, geology, health physics, hydrology, radiochemistry, radio-ecology, and toxicology). Along with their application, they must submit a 2-page essay on 1) how their academic major, interests, and career goals correspond to environmental restoration and waste management issues; and 2) how their Hispanic background and family upbringing have influenced their academic and personal goals. Selection is based on the essay, academic record, academic plans and career goals, financial need, commitment to DOE's goal of environmental restoration and waste management, and a letter of recommendation. **Deadline for Receipt:** March of each year. **Additional Information:** This program, which began in 1990, is sponsored by DOE's Office of Environmental Management. Recipients must enroll full time at a college or university in the United States.

4099 ■ HISPANIC SCHOLARSHIP FUND INSTITUTE

1001 Connecticut Avenue, N.W., Suite 632
Washington, DC 20036
Tel: (202)296-0009
Fax: (202)296-3633
E-mail: info@hsfi.org
Web Site: http://www.hsfi.org/scholarships/generation.asp

To provide financial assistance to Hispanic and other students majoring in designated business, engineering, social science, and science fields who are interested in employment with the U.S. Department of Energy (DOE).

Title of Award: Next Generation of Public Servants Scholarship **Area, Field, or Subject:** Accounting; Biological and clinical sciences; Business administration; Computer and information sciences; Engineering; Environmental science; Finance; Geology; Information science and technology; Management; Mathematics and mathematical sciences; Physics; Political science; Psychology; Sociology **Level of Education for which Award is Granted:** Undergraduate **Number Awarded:** Varies each year. **Funds Available:** The stipend is $3,000 per year. **Duration:** 1 year; may be renewed up to 2 additional years if the recipient maintains full-time enrollment and a GPA of 2.8 or higher.

Eligibility Requirements: This program is open to U.S. citizens enrolled full time as sophomores with a GPA of 2.8 or higher. Applicants must be interested in preparing for a career with the DOE in an energy-related field. Eligible academic majors are in the fields of business (accounting, business administration, finance, and management), engineering (biomedical, chemical, civil, computer, electrical, environmental, industrial, materials, mechanical, metallurgical, nuclear, and petroleum), social science (economics, organizational psychology, political science, and sociology), and science (biological sciences, computer science, geology, information technology, mathematics, microbiology, and physics). They must be willing to participate in co-ops with the DOE. Along with their application, they must submit a 2-page essay on why a career in public service interests them, how their academic major connects with their stated DOE career goal, why the DOE should invest in them through this program, and how they believe the DOE will benefit from this investment.

Selection is based on academic achievement, financial need, demonstrated commitment to public service, and interest in federal employment with the DOE. **Deadline for Receipt:** February of each year. **Additional Information:** This program, sponsored by DOE's Office of Economic Impact and Diversity, is administered by the Hispanic Scholarship Fund Institute as part of its effort to increase Hispanic participation in federal service.

4100 ■ IDAHO SPACE GRANT CONSORTIUM

c/o University of Idaho
College of Engineering
P.O. Box 441011
Moscow, ID 83844-1011
Tel: (208)885-6438
Fax: (208)885-1399
E-mail: isgc@uidaho.edu
Web Site: http://isgc.uidaho.edu

To provide financial assistance for study in space-related fields to undergraduate students at institutions belonging to the Idaho Space Grant Consortium (ISGC).

Title of Award: Idaho Space Grant Consortium Scholarship Program **Area, Field, or Subject:** Aerospace sciences; Education; Engineering; Aerospace/Aeronautical/Astronautical; Mathematics and mathematical sciences; Science; Space and planetary sciences **Level of Education for which Award is Granted:** Undergraduate **Number Awarded:** Varies each year; recently, 24 of these scholarships were awarded. **Funds Available:** The stipend is up to $1,000 per year. Funds are to be used to pay for registration at colleges in the consortium. **Duration:** 1 year; may be renewed.

Eligibility Requirements: This program is open to full-time undergraduate students at ISGC member institutions. Applicants must be majoring in engineering, mathematics, science, or science/math education and have a cumulative GPA of 3.0 or higher. They should be planning to work on a 4-year degree in a space-related field. Along with their application, they must submit a 500-word essay on their future career and educational goals and why they believe the U.S. National Aeronautics and Space Administration (NASA) should support their education. U.S. citizenship is required. As a component of the NASA Space Grant program, the ISGC encourages participation by women, underrepresented minorities, and persons with disabilities. **Deadline for Receipt:** February of each year. **Additional Information:** Members of the consortium include Albertson College of Idaho, Boise State University, College of Southern Idaho, Idaho State University, Lewis Clark State College, North Idaho College, Northwest Nazarene College, Brigham Young University of Idaho, and the University of Idaho. This program is funded by NASA.

4101 ■ INSTITUTE OF INTERNATIONAL EDUCATION

Attn: Lucent Global Science Scholars Program
809 United Nations Plaza
New York, NY 10017-3580
Tel: (212)984-5419
Fax: (212)984-5452
E-mail: sciencescholars@iie.org
Web Site: http://www.iie.org/programs/lucent

To provide financial assistance for college to high school students in the United States and university students in other designated countries who are interested in preparing for careers in information technology.

Title of Award: Lucent Global Science Scholars Program **Area, Field, or Subject:** Chemistry; Computer and information sciences; Engineering; Information science and technology; Mathematics and mathematical sciences; Physics **Level of Education for which Award is Granted:** Undergraduate **Number Awarded:** Varies each year. Recently, 32 students from foreign countries (5 from China, 1 from Hong Kong, and 2 from each of the other countries) and 28 from the United States received these scholarships. **Funds Available:** The stipend is $5,000 per year. **Duration:** 1 year; nonrenewable.

Eligibility Requirements: This program is open to high school seniors in the United States and first-year university students in Brazil, Canada, China, France, Germany, Hong Kong, India, Korea, Mexico, the Netherlands, Philippines, Poland, Russia, Spain, and the United Kingdom. Students from the United States must have a GPA of 3.6 or higher. Eligible majors include applied physics, chemistry, computer science, engineering, information science and technology, mathematics and applied mathematics, and physics. Selection is based on a demonstrated record of distinction in science and mathematics and a desire to prepare for a career in information technology. **Deadline for Receipt:** February of each year for students from the United States; March of each year for students from other countries. **Additional Information:** This program, established in 1999, is funded by Lucent Technologies. Students are offered internships at Lucent's research and development and manufacturing facilities in their own countries during the summer following their freshman year in the United States or the sophomore year in other countries.

4102 ■ IOWA SPACE GRANT CONSORTIUM

Attn: Director
Iowa State University
2271 Howe Hall, Room 2365
Ames, IA 50011-2271
Tel: (515)294-3106
Free: 800-854-1667
Fax: (515)294-3361
E-mail: isgc@iastate.edu
Web Site: http://www.ia.spacegrant.org
To provide financial assistance to undergraduate and graduate students majoring in science, technology, engineering, or mathematics (STEM) disciplines at member institutions of the Iowa Space Grant Consortium (ISGC).
Title of Award: Iowa Space Grant Scholarship Program **Area, Field, or Subject:** Aerospace sciences; Biological and clinical sciences; Engineering, Aerospace/Aeronautical/Astronautical; Mathematics and mathematical sciences; Science; Space and planetary sciences; Technology **Level of Education for which Award is Granted:** Four Year College, Graduate **Number Awarded:** Approximately 16 each year. **Funds Available:** The stipend is $6,000. **Duration:** 1 year.
Eligibility Requirements: This program is open to U.S. citizens enrolled full time as undergraduate or graduate students at ISGC member institutions. Applicants must be majoring in a STEM discipline of interest to the National Aeronautics and Space Administration. They must be interested in working on the base research program at their institution. Students from underrepresented groups (women, minorities, and persons with disabilities) are especially encouraged to apply. **Deadline for Receipt:** March of each year. **Additional Information:** Member institutions of ISGC, and their base programs, include Drake University (molecular biology and space life sciences), Iowa State University (the Spacecraft Systems and Operations Laboratory), the University of Iowa (the Operator Performance Laboratory), and the University of Northern Iowa (student research program on Iowa's lakes and wetlands). Funding for this program is provided by NASA.

4103 ■ KANSAS INSURANCE DEPARTMENT

Attn: Scholarship Fund
420 S.W. Ninth Street
Topeka, KS 66612-2103
Tel: (785)296-3071
Free: 800-432-2484
Fax: (785)296-2283
Web Site: http://www.ksinsurance.org
To provide financial assistance to African American upper-division students who are majoring in business, computer science, or mathematics at a college or university in Kansas.
Title of Award: Kansas Insurance Department African American Scholarships **Area, Field, or Subject:** Business administration; Computer and information sciences; Mathematics and mathematical sciences **Level of Education for which Award is Granted:** Four Year College **Number Awarded:** 12 each year. **Funds Available:** The stipend is $1,000. **Duration:** 1 year.
Eligibility Requirements: This program is open to African American students enrolled as juniors or higher at 4-year accredited institutions of higher education in Kansas. Applicants must be majoring in business, computer science, or mathematics. **Deadline for Receipt:** May of each year. **Additional Information:** These scholarships were first awarded in

2005 with funds received in a settlement with Monumental Life as a result of the firm's race-based pricing of life insurance policies.

4104 ■ CLARE BOOTHE LUCE FUND

c/o Henry Luce Foundation, Inc.
111 West 50th Street, Suite 4601
New York, NY 10020
Tel: (212)489-7700
Fax: (212)581-9541
E-mail: jdaniels@hluce.org
Web Site: http://www.hluce.org
To provide funding to women interested in studying science or engineering at the undergraduate level at designated universities.
Title of Award: Clare Boothe Luce Scholarships in Science and Engineering **Area, Field, or Subject:** Biological and clinical sciences; Chemistry; Computer and information sciences; Engineering; Engineering, Aerospace/Aeronautical/Astronautical; Engineering, Civil; Engineering, Electrical; Engineering, Mechanical; Engineering, Nuclear; Mathematics and mathematical sciences; Meteorology; Physics **Level of Education for which Award is Granted:** Undergraduate **Number Awarded:** Varies; since the program began, more than 800 of these scholarships have been awarded. **Funds Available:** The amount awarded is established individually by each of the participating institutions. The stipends are intended to augment rather than replace any existing institutional support in these fields. Each stipend is calculated to include the cost of room and board as well as tuition and other fees or expenses. **Duration:** 2 years; in certain special circumstances, awards for the full 4 years of undergraduate study may be offered.
Eligibility Requirements: This program is open to female undergraduate students (particularly juniors and seniors) majoring in biology, chemistry, computer science, engineering (aeronautical, civil, electrical, mechanical, nuclear, and others), mathematics, meteorology, and physics. Applicants must be U.S. citizens attending 1 of the 12 designated colleges and universities affiliated with this program; periodically, other institutions are invited to participate. Premedical science majors are ineligible for this competition. The participating institutions select the recipients without regard to race, age, religion, ethnic background, or need. All awards are made on the basis of merit. **Deadline for Receipt:** Varies; check with the participating institutions for their current schedule. **Additional Information:** The participating institutions are Boston University, Colby College, Creighton University, Fordham University, Georgetown University, Marymount University, Mount Holyoke College, St. John's University, Santa Clara University, Seton Hall University, Trinity College, and University of Notre Dame.

4105 ■ MARYLAND ASSOCIATION OF PRIVATE COLLEGES AND CAREER SCHOOLS

Attn: Scholarship Committee
3100 Dunglow Road
Baltimore, MD 21222
Tel: (410)282-4012
Fax: (410)282-4133
E-mail: mdapcs@yahoo.com
Web Site: http://www.mapccs.org/scholarships.html
To provide financial assistance to students interested in attending selected private career schools in Maryland.
Title of Award: Maryland Association of Private Colleges and Career Schools Scholarships **Area, Field, or Subject:** Broadcasting; Cosmetology; Drafting; Health care services; Mechanics and repairs; Medicine, Holistic/alternative; Secretarial sciences **Level of Education for which Award is Granted:** Vocational/Occupational **Number Awarded:** Varies each year; since the program was established in 1983, more than $3 million in scholarships have been awarded. **Funds Available:** Individual awards range from $500 to more than $5,000. The H.R. Leslie Scholarship is $1,000. Funds must be applied for full or partial payment of tuition. Recently, a total of $164,000 was awarded. **Duration:** 1 year.
Eligibility Requirements: This program is open to high school seniors and graduates who are interested in attending a participating private career school in Maryland. Applicants should be interested in working on a degree in such business or technical areas as cosmetology, barbering, diesel mechanics, automotive technology, massage therapy, allied health, secretarial sciences, or drafting. The H.R. Leslie Scholarship is open to any student who applies to a member school. Selection is based on GPA,

involvement in school and community activities, recommendations from school officials, desire, and potential to succeed in their career field. Financial need is not considered in the selection process. **Deadline for Receipt:** March of each year. **Additional Information:** The participating schools are All State Career School (Baltimore) American Beauty Academy (Wheaton), Americare School of Allied Health (Silver Spring), Avara's Academy of Hair Design (Baltimore), Baltimore School of Massage, Baltimore Studio of Hair Design, Bladensburg Barber School (Bladensburg), Broadcasting Institute of Maryland (Baltimore), Diesel Institute of America (Grantsville), Frederick School of Cosmetology (Frederick), Hair Academy (New Carrollton), Holistic Massage Training Institute (Baltimore), International Beauty School (Bel Air), Lincoln Technical Institute (Columbia), Medix School (Towson), Savage Neon (Baltimore), and Von Lee School of Aesthetics (Pikesville). Scholarships can be used only to attend the schools listed above.

4106 ■ MARYLAND HIGHER EDUCATION COMMISSION

Attn: Office of Student Financial Assistance
839 Bestgate Road, Suite 400
Annapolis, MD 21401-3013
Tel: (410)260-4545
Free: 800-974-1024
Fax: (410)974-5376
E-mail: osfamail@mhec.state.md.us
Web Site: http://www.mhec.state.md.us/financialAid/
ProgramDescriptions/prog_scm.asp
To provide scholarship/loans to Maryland residents who wish to prepare for a teaching career.

Title of Award: Sharon Christa McAuliffe Memorial Teacher Education Award **Area, Field, or Subject:** Chemistry; Classical studies; Computer and information sciences; Earth sciences; Education; Education, English as a second language; Education, Special; Education, Vocational-technical; Foreign languages; Geosciences; Health care services; Hearing and deafness; Mathematics and mathematical sciences; Physical sciences; Physics; Space and planetary sciences; Visual impairment **Level of Education for which Award is Granted:** Master's, Professional, Undergraduate **Number Awarded:** Varies each year. **Funds Available:** The amount of the award is based on the recipient's enrollment and housing status, to a maximum of $17,000 per year. The total amount of all state awards may not exceed the cost of attendance as determined by the school's financial aid office or $17,800, whichever is less. Following graduation, recipients must teach at a Maryland public school for 1 year for each year of financial aid received under this program. If they fail to meet that service obligation, they must repay all funds they received with interest. They must begin the service obligation within 12 months of graduation. **Duration:** 1 year; may be renewed for 1 additional year if the recipient maintains satisfactory academic progress with a cumulative GPA of 3.0 or higher and enrollment at a 2-year or 4-year Maryland college or university in an approved teacher education program. **Eligibility Requirements:** This program is open to Maryland residents who are college students with at least 60 semester credit hours completed, college graduates, and teachers in a non-critical shortage area. Applicants must have a GPA of 3.0 or higher and plan to teach in a field identified as a critical shortage area. Selection is based on cumulative GPA, applicable work or volunteer experience, quality of academic background in certification field, and a writing sample. **Deadline for Receipt:** December of each year. **Additional Information:** Recently, the eligible critical shortage areas were business education, chemistry, computer science, earth and space science, English for speakers of other languages, family and consumer sciences, German, health occupations, Latin, mathematics, physical science, physics, Spanish, special education (generic infant-grade 3, generic grades 1-8, generic grades 6-adult, hearing impaired, severely and profoundly handicapped, visually impaired), and technology education.

4107 ■ MARYLAND SPACE GRANT CONSORTIUM

c/o Johns Hopkins University
203 Bloomberg Center for Physics and Astronomy
3400 North Charles Street
Baltimore, MD 21218-2686
Tel: (410)516-7351
Fax: (410)516-4109
E-mail: info@mdspacegrant.org

Web Site: http://www.mdspacegrant.org/scholars_about.html
To provide financial assistance to undergraduates who are interested in studying space-related fields at selected universities in Maryland that are members of the Maryland Space Grant Consortium.

Title of Award: Maryland Space Scholars Program **Area, Field, or Subject:** Aerospace sciences; Astronomy and astronomical sciences; Biological and clinical sciences; Chemistry; Computer and information sciences; Engineering; Geology; Mathematics and mathematical sciences; Physics; Space and planetary sciences **Level of Education for which Award is Granted:** Undergraduate **Number Awarded:** Varies each year; recently 16 of these scholarships were awarded (2 at Johns Hopkins University, 5 at Morgan State University, 2 at Hagerstown Community College, 2 at Towson University, and 5 at the University of Maryland at College Park). **Funds Available:** Scholars receive partial payment of tuition at the participating university they attend. **Duration:** 1 year; may be renewed if the recipient maintains a GPA of 3.0 or higher. **Eligibility Requirements:** This program is open to residents of Maryland and graduates of Maryland high schools who are enrolled full time at a member institution. Applicants must be interested in preparing for a career in mathematics, science, engineering, technology, or a space-related field. They must be majoring in a relevant field, including (but not limited to) astronomy, the biological and life sciences, chemistry, computer science, engineering, geological sciences, or physics. U.S. citizenship is required. Along with their application, they must submit an essay of 200 to 500 words on how this scholarship will help them meet their educational and financial goals. This program is a component of the U.S. National Aeronautics and Space Administration (NASA) Space Grant program, which encourages participation by women, underrepresented minorities, and persons with disabilities. **Deadline for Receipt:** August of each year. **Additional Information:** The participating universities are Hagerstown Community College, Johns Hopkins University, Morgan State University, Towson University, the University of Maryland at College Park, and Washington College. Funding for this program is provided by NASA.

4108 ■ MASSACHUSETTS OFFICE OF STUDENT FINANCIAL ASSISTANCE

454 Broadway, Suite 200
Revere, MA 02151
Tel: (617)727-9420
Fax: (617)727-0667
E-mail: osfa@osfa.mass.edu
Web Site: http://www.osfa.mass.edu
To provide scholarship/loans to educational paraprofessionals in Massachusetts who are interested in completing a college degree and becoming certified as teachers.

Title of Award: Massachusetts Paraprofessional Teacher Preparation Grant Program **Area, Field, or Subject:** Education; Education, Bilingual and cross-cultural; Education, Special; Linguistics; Mathematics and mathematical sciences; Science **Level of Education for which Award is Granted:** Undergraduate **Number Awarded:** Varies each year. **Funds Available:** Grants depend on the type of institution attended. At public universities, the maximum award is $625 per credit, to a total of $7,500 per academic year. At state colleges, the maximum award is $450 per credit, to a total of $6,000 per academic year. At community colleges, the maximum award is $250 per credit, to a total of $4,000 per academic year. This is a scholarship/loan program. Recipients must agree to teach in a Massachusetts public school 1 year for each year of full or partial grant received. If they fail to complete that teaching obligation, they must repay the amount of the grant received. **Duration:** Until completion of an undergraduate degree, provided the recipient maintains satisfactory academic progress. **Eligibility Requirements:** This program is open to Massachusetts residents who 1) have been employed as paraprofessionals in public schools in the state for at least 2 years, or 2) are working on a degree in an area of high need (recently defined as bilingual education, foreign languages, mathematics, science, and special education). Applicants must be enrolled full time in an undergraduate degree program leading to teacher certification at a Massachusetts public institution. U.S. citizenship or permanent resident status is required Applicants must submit a Free Application for Federal Student Aid (FAFSA), but financial need is not required.

4109 ■ MATHEMATICAL ASSOCIATION OF AMERICA

Attn: American Mathematical Competitions
University of Nebraska at Lincoln
1740 Vine Street
P.O. Box 880658
Lincoln, NE 68588-0658
Tel: (402)472-2257
Fax: (402)472-6087
E-mail: amcinfo@unl.edu
Web Site: http://www.unl.edu/amc

To recognize and reward (with college scholarships) the outstanding participants in the United States of America Mathematical Olympiad (USAMO).

Title of Award: USAMO Scholarships **Area, Field, or Subject:** Mathematics and mathematical sciences **Level of Education for which Award is Granted:** Undergraduate **Number Awarded:** 3 each year. **Funds Available:** Prizes are a $20,000 scholarship for first place, $15,000 for second place, and $10,000 for third place. **Duration:** The competition is held annually.

Eligibility Requirements: Each year, approximately 375 of the top scoring participants on the American Mathematical Competitions (the AMC 10 and AMC 12) and the American Invitational Mathematics Examination (AIME) are invited to participate in the USAMO. The AMC examination (begun in 2000) is for students in grades 10 and below (under 17.5 years of age). The AMC 12 examination (formerly the American High School Mathematics Examination, begun in 1950) is for students in grades 12 and below (under 19.5 years of age). Both examinations are 25-question, 75-minute multiple choice contests. The subject matter associated with AMC 10 is normally covered in grades 9 and 10. The AMC 12 covers the high school mathematics curriculum, excluding calculus. Students who score in the top 1% on the AMC 10 or achieve a score of 100 or higher on the AMC 12 are then invited to take the AIME (begun in 1983). The AIME is a 15-question, 3-hour examination on which all problems can be solved with pre-calculus methods. Selection for the USAMO is based on an index consisting of 10 times the student's AIME score plus the score on the AMC 10 or the AMC 12. Participation in the USAMO is limited to U.S. citizens and permanent residents of the United States and Canada. It is a 6-question, 2-day, 9-hour essay/proof examination. All problems can be solved with pre-calculus methods. The top scorers receive these scholarships. **Deadline for Receipt:** December of each year for early registration; mid-January of each year for regular registration; the end of January of each year for late registration for contest A; mid-February of each year for late registration for contest B. **Additional Information:** The AMC 10 and AMC 12 are taken on 2 dates (contest A and contest B) in February (so students in grades 10 and below can participate in both AMC 10A and AMC 12B). The AIME is administered in March. The USAMO (begun in 1972) takes place in April. The scholarships, sponsored by the Akamai Foundation of Boston, were first awarded in 2001. Entry fees for the AMC are $39 for early registration, $49 for regular registration, or $59 for late registration.

4110 ■ MICHIGAN SPACE GRANT CONSORTIUM

c/o University of Michigan
2106 Space Physics Research Laboratory
2455 Hayward Avenue
Ann Arbor, MI 48109-2143
Tel: (734)764-9508
Fax: (734)764-4585
E-mail: blbryant@umich.edu
Web Site: http://www.engin.umich.edu/dept/aero/msgc/fellow

To provide funding to students at member institutions of the Michigan Space Grant Consortium who wish to conduct space-related research.

Title of Award: Michigan Space Grant Consortium Fellowships **Area, Field, or Subject:** Aeronautics; Aerospace sciences; Engineering, Aerospace/Aeronautical/Astronautical; Mathematics and mathematical sciences; Space and planetary sciences; Technology **Level of Education for which Award is Granted:** Graduate, Undergraduate **Number Awarded:** Varies each year; recently, 23 undergraduate fellowships and 13 graduate fellowships were awarded. **Funds Available:** The maximum grant is $2,500 for undergraduates or $5,000 for graduate students.

Eligibility Requirements: This program is open to undergraduate and graduate students at affiliates of the Michigan consortium who are proposing to conduct research in aerospace, space science, earth system science, and other related fields in science, engineering, or mathematics; students working on educational research topics in mathematics, science, or technology are also eligible. Applicants must identify a mentor in the faculty research, education, or public service communities with whom they intend to work and who is available to write a letter of recommendation for the student. U.S. citizenship is required. Women, underrepresented minorities, and persons with disabilities are especially encouraged to apply. **Deadline for Receipt:** November of each year. **Additional Information:** The consortium consists of Eastern Michigan University, Grand Valley State University, Hope College, Michigan State University, Michigan Technological University, Oakland University, Saginaw Valley State University, University of Michigan, Wayne State University, and Western Michigan University. This program is supported by the U.S. National Aeronautics and Space Administration (NASA).

4111 ■ MICROSOFT CORPORATION

Attn: National Minority Technical Scholarship
One Microsoft Way
Redmond, WA 98052-8303
Tel: (425)882-8080
E-mail: scholars@microsoft.com
Web Site: http://www.microsoft.com/college/ss_overview.mspx

To provide financial assistance and summer work experience to undergraduate students, especially members of underrepresented groups, interested in preparing for a career in computer science or other related technical fields.

Title of Award: Microsoft National Scholarships **Area, Field, or Subject:** Computer and information sciences; Engineering, Computer; Engineering, Electrical; Mathematics and mathematical sciences; Physics; Technology **Level of Education for which Award is Granted:** Undergraduate **Number Awarded:** Varies. A total of $540,000 is available for this program each year. **Funds Available:** Scholarships cover 100% of the tuition as posted by the financial aid office of the university or college the recipient designates. Scholarships are made through that school and are not transferable to other academic institutions. Funds may be used for tuition only and may not be used for other costs on the recipient's bursar bill, such as room and board. **Duration:** 1 year.

Eligibility Requirements: This program is open to students who are enrolled full time and making satisfactory progress toward an undergraduate degree in computer science, computer engineering, or a related technical discipline (such as electrical engineering, mathematics, or physics) with a demonstrated interest in computer science. Applicants must be enrolled at a 4-year college or university in the United States, Canada, or Mexico. They must have a GPA of 3.0 or higher. Although all students who meet the eligibility criteria may apply, a large majority of scholarships are awarded to women, underrepresented minorities (African Americans, Hispanics, and Native Americans), and students with disabilities. Along with their application, students must submit an essay that describes the following 4 items: 1) how they demonstrate their passion for technology outside the classroom; 2) the toughest technical problem they have worked on, how they addressed the problem, their role in reaching the outcome if it was team-based, and the final outcome; 3) a situation that demonstrates initiative and their willingness to go above and beyond; and 4) how they are currently funding their college education. **Deadline for Receipt:** January of each year. **Additional Information:** Selected recipients are offered a paid summer internship where they will have a chance to develop Microsoft products.

4112 ■ MIKKELSON FOUNDATION

P.O. Box 768
Monument, CO 80132-9077
Web Site: http://www.mikkelson.com

To provide financial assistance to high school seniors in Colorado who plan to study science, engineering, or mathematics in college.

Title of Award: Mikkelson Foundation Student Scholarship Program **Area, Field, or Subject:** Engineering; Mathematics and mathematical sciences; Science **Level of Education for which Award is Granted:** Undergraduate **Number Awarded:** 2 each year. **Funds Available:** The stipend is $3,000 per year. **Duration:** 1 year; may be renewed up to 3 additional years.

Eligibility Requirements: This program is open to seniors graduating from high schools in Colorado. Applicants must be planning to attend an accredited college or university to major in science, engineering, or mathematics. Along with their application, they must submit a 2-page description of their strengths, accomplishments, and interests; their projected course of study in college; their plans following college graduation; how they plan to finance their education; and how this scholarship will help them achieve their goals. **Deadline for Receipt:** April of each year.

4113 ■ MINNESOTA HIGHER EDUCATION SERVICES OFFICE

1450 Energy Park Drive, Suite 350
St. Paul, MN 55108-5227
Tel: (651)642-0567
Free: 800-657-3866
Fax: (651)642-0675
E-mail: info@heso.state.mn.us
Web Site: http://www.mheso.state.mn.us

To provide financial assistance for college to outstanding high school seniors or graduates in Minnesota.
Title of Award: Minnesota Academic Excellence Scholarship **Area, Field, or Subject:** Art; Creative writing; English language and literature; Linguistics; Mathematics and mathematical sciences; Science; Social sciences **Level of Education for which Award is Granted:** Undergraduate **Number Awarded:** Varies each year. **Funds Available:** Scholarships at public institutions cover the cost of full-time attendance; scholarships at private institutions cover an amount equal to the lesser of the actual tuition and fees charged by the institution or the tuition and fees in comparable public institutions. **Duration:** 1 year; may be renewed up to 3 additional years.
Eligibility Requirements: This program is open to Minnesota residents who have demonstrated outstanding ability, achievement, and potential in English, creative writing, fine arts, foreign language, mathematics, science, or social science. Applicants must have been admitted as full-time students at a branch of the University of Minnesota, a Minnesota state university, or a private, baccalaureate degree-granting college or university in Minnesota. **Additional Information:** This program was established by the Minnesota Legislature in 1991. Funds for this program come from the sale of special collegiate license plates.

4114 ■ MISSISSIPPI SPACE GRANT CONSORTIUM

c/o University of Mississippi
217 Vardaman Hall
P.O. Box 1848
University, MS 38677-1848
Tel: (662)915-1187
Fax: (662)915-3927
E-mail: mschaff@olemiss.edu
Web Site: http://www.olemiss.edu/programs/nasa

To provide funding to undergraduate and graduate students for space-related activities at colleges and universities that are members of the Mississippi Space Grant Consortium.
Title of Award: Mississippi Space Grant Consortium Scholarships and Fellowships **Area, Field, or Subject:** Aerospace sciences; Engineering; Engineering, Aerospace/Aeronautical/Astronautical; Mathematics and mathematical sciences; Science; Space and planetary sciences **Level of Education for which Award is Granted:** Graduate, Undergraduate **Number Awarded:** Varies each year; recently, a total of 47 students received support through this program. **Funds Available:** Each participating institution establishes the amounts of the awards. Recently, the average undergraduate award was $1,308 and the average graduate award was $2,975. A total of $96,350 was awarded.
Eligibility Requirements: This program is open to undergraduate and graduate students at member institutions of the Mississippi consortium. Each participating college or university establishes its own program and criteria for admission, but all activities are in engineering, mathematics, and science fields of interest to the U.S. National Aeronautics and Space Administration (NASA). U.S. citizenship is required. The consortium is a component of NASA's Space Grant program, which encourages participation by women, underrepresented minorities, and persons with disabilities.
Additional Information: Consortium members include Alcorn State University, Coahoma Community College, Delta State University, Hinds Community College (Utica Campus), Itawamba Community College,

Jackson State University, Meridian Community College, Mississippi Delta Community College, Mississippi Gulf Coast Community College, Mississippi State University, Mississippi University for Women, Mississippi Valley State University, Northeast Mississippi Community College, Pearl River Community College, the University of Mississippi, and the University of Southern Mississippi. This program is funded by NASA.

4115 ■ NALS OF MICHIGAN

c/o Angela Head, Scholarship Chair
155 North 22nd Street
Battle Creek, MI 49015-1762
Tel: (269)964-9951
E-mail: angeenmad@yahoo.com
Web Site: http://www.nalsofmichigan.org/Scholarship.htm

To provide financial assistance to residents of Michigan interested in a career in the legal field.
Title of Award: NALS of Michigan Scholarships **Area, Field, or Subject:** Paralegal studies; Secretarial sciences **Level of Education for which Award is Granted:** Undergraduate **Number Awarded:** 2 each year. **Funds Available:** The stipend is $1,000. Funds are to be used for tuition or books. **Duration:** 1 year; nonrenewable.
Eligibility Requirements: This program is open to high school seniors, students currently enrolled in a school of higher education, and members of NALS of Michigan. Applicants must be interested in a career in the legal field (e.g., legal secretary) and have at least a "B" average or (if a percentile system is used) 90% or higher. Along with their application, they must submit an official transcript, 2 letters of recommendation, and a 1-page autobiographical statement that includes a description of their goals and desires. Selection is based on scholastic or legal career achievements, future career goals, leadership ability, and financial need. **Deadline for Receipt:** January of each year. **Additional Information:** NALS formerly stood for National Association of Legal Secretaries.

4116 ■ NATIONAL AERONAUTICS AND SPACE ADMINISTRATION

Attn: Program Manager,
NASA Headquarters
Washington, DC 20546-0001
Tel: (202)358-1523
Fax: (202)358-3048
E-mail: jdasch@hq.nasa.gov
Web Site: http://www.nasa.gov/audience/forstudents/postsecondary/learning/Space_Grant.html

To provide financial assistance to undergraduate and graduate students interested in preparing for a career in a space-related field.
Title of Award: National Space Grant College and Fellowship Program **Area, Field, or Subject:** Aerospace sciences; Engineering, Aerospace/Aeronautical/Astronautical; Mathematics and mathematical sciences; Space and planetary sciences; Technology **Level of Education for which Award is Granted:** Graduate, Undergraduate **Number Awarded:** Varies each year. **Funds Available:** Each consortium establishes the terms of the fellowship program in its state.
Eligibility Requirements: This program is open to undergraduate and graduate students at colleges and universities that participate in the National Space Grant program of the U.S. National Aeronautics and Space Administration (NASA) through their state consortium. Applicants must be interested in a program of study and/or research in a field of science, mathematics, engineering, or technology (SMET) related to space. A specific goal of the program is to increase preparation by members of underrepresented groups (minorities, women, and persons with disabilities) for SMET space-related careers. **Deadline for Receipt:** Each consortium sets its own deadlines. **Additional Information:** NASA established the Space Grant program in 1989. It operates through 52 consortia in each state, the District of Columbia, and Puerto Rico. Each consortium includes selected colleges and universities in that state as well as other affiliates from industry, museums, science centers, and state and local agencies.

4117 ■ NATIONAL ASSOCIATION OF EDUCATIONAL OFFICE PROFESSIONALS

Attn: NAEOP Foundation
P.O. Box 12619
Wichita, KS 67277-2619
Tel: (316)942-4822

Fax: (316)942-7100
E-mail: naeop@naeop.org
Web Site: http://www.naeop.org/foundation.htm
To provide financial assistance to students interested in preparing for an office-related career.
Title of Award: Marion T. Wood National Scholarships **Area, Field, or Subject:** Education; Secretarial sciences **Level of Education for which Award is Granted:** Undergraduate **Number Awarded:** Varies each year. **Funds Available:** The stipend is $1,000. **Duration:** 1 year.
Eligibility Requirements: This program is open to business education students preparing for an office-related career, preferably in the field of education. **Deadline for Receipt:** February of each year.

4118 ■ NATIONAL CONSORTIUM FOR GRADUATE DEGREES FOR MINORITIES IN ENGINEERING AND SCIENCE (GEM)

P.O. Box 537
Notre Dame, IN 46556
Tel: (574)631-7771
Fax: (574)287-1486
E-mail: gem.1@nd.edu
Web Site: http://www.gemfellowship.org
To provide financial assistance and summer work experience to underrepresented minority students interested in obtaining a Ph.D. degree in the life sciences, mathematics, or physical sciences.
Title of Award: GEM Ph.D. Science Fellowship Program **Area, Field, or Subject:** Biological and clinical sciences; Chemistry; Computer and information sciences; Earth sciences; Geosciences; Mathematics and mathematical sciences; Natural sciences; Physics **Level of Education for which Award is Granted:** Four Year College, Doctorate **Number Awarded:** Varies each year; recently, 40 of these fellowships were awarded. **Funds Available:** The stipend is $14,000 per year, plus tuition and fees. In addition, there is a summer internship program that provides a salary and reimbursement for travel expenses to and from the summer work site. The total value of the award is between $60,000 and $100,000, depending upon academic status at the time of application, summer employer, and graduate school attended. **Duration:** 3 to 5 years for the fellowship; 12 weeks during at least 1 summer for the internship. Fellows selected as juniors or seniors intern each summer until entrance to graduate school; fellows selected after college graduation intern at least 1 summer.
Eligibility Requirements: This program is open to U.S. citizens who are members of ethnic groups underrepresented in the natural sciences: Native Americans, African Americans, Latinos, Puerto Ricans, and other Hispanic Americans. Applicants must be juniors, seniors, or recent baccalaureate graduates in the life sciences, mathematics, or physical sciences (chemistry, computer science, earth sciences, and physics) with an academic record that indicates the ability to pursue doctoral studies (including a GPA of 3.0 or higher). **Deadline for Receipt:** October of each year. **Additional Information:** This program is valid only at 1 of 95 participating GEM member universities; write to GEM for a list. The fellowship award is designed to support the student in the first year of the doctoral program without working. Subsequent years are subsidized by the respective university and will usually include either a teaching or research assistantship. Recipients must participate in the GEM summer internship; failure to agree to accept the internship cancels the fellowship. Recipients must enroll in the same scientific discipline as their undergraduate major.

4119 ■ NATIONAL INSTITUTE OF GENERAL MEDICAL SCIENCES

Attn: Division of Minority Opportunities in Research
45 Center Drive, Suite 2AS37
Bethesda, MD 20892-6200
Tel: (301)594-3900
Fax: (301)480-2753
E-mail: at21z@nih.gov
Web Site: http://www.nih.gov/nigms
To enable faculty at minority and minority-serving institutions to complete a Ph.D. degree in the biomedical sciences.
Title of Award: Minority Access to Research Careers (MARC) Faculty Predoctoral Fellowships **Area, Field, or Subject:** Behavioral sciences; Biomedical sciences; Mathematics and mathematical sciences **Level of Education for which Award is Granted:** Four Year College, Professional, Doctorate **Funds Available:** The fellowships provide a stipend of

$32,820 per year and a supplement that offsets the cost of tuition, fees, and health insurance at a rate of 100% up to $3,000 and 60% of costs above $3,000. An institutional allowance of $2,750 per year is also provided. **Duration:** Up to 5 years.
Eligibility Requirements: This program is open to full-time faculty in a biomedical or behavioral science department (including mathematics) at minority and minority-serving institutions who lack a Ph.D. degree. The institution must be a college or university where the candidate has been employed for at least 3 years and that has substantial enrollments of students in biomedical and related sciences from minority groups underrepresented in those sciences. The candidate must have been accepted into the doctoral program at a research university, institution, or center with active biomedical and behavioral science research faculties. They must be sponsored by their home institution, which must have granted them a study leave and where they are expected to return after completing their doctoral degree. Only U.S. citizens, nationals, and permanent residents are eligible. **Deadline for Receipt:** April or December of each year.

4120 ■ NATIONAL INVENTORS HALL OF FAME

Attn: Collegiate Inventors Competition
221 South Broadway Street
Akron, OH 44308-1595
Tel: (330)849-6887
E-mail: collegiate@invent.org
Web Site: http://www.invent.org/collegiate
To recognize and reward outstanding inventions by college or university students in the fields of science, engineering, and technology.
Title of Award: Collegiate Inventors Competition **Area, Field, or Subject:** Biological and clinical sciences; Chemistry; Computer and information sciences; Engineering; Environmental conservation; Environmental science; Inventors; Mathematics and mathematical sciences; Medicine; Physics; Science; Technology; Veterinary science and medicine **Level of Education for which Award is Granted:** Graduate, Postdoctoral, Undergraduate **Number Awarded:** 15 semifinalists are selected each year; of those, 3 individuals or teams win prizes. **Funds Available:** Finalists receive an all-expense paid trip to Washington, D.C. to participate in a final round of judging and in the awards dinner and presentation. The Grand Prize winner or team receives $25,000. Other prizes are $10,000 for an undergraduate winner or team and $15,000 for a graduate winner or team. Academic advisors of the winning entries each receive a $3,000 cash prize. Awards are unrestricted cash gifts, not scholarships or grants. **Duration:** The competition is held annually.
Eligibility Requirements: This competition is open to undergraduate and graduate students who are (or have been) enrolled full time at least part of the 12-month period prior to entry in a college or university in the United States. Entries may also be submitted by teams, up to 4 members, of whom at least 1 must meet the full-time requirement and all others must have been enrolled at least half time sometime during the preceding 24-month period. Applicants must submit a description of their invention, including a patent search and summary of current literature that describes the state of the art and identifies the originality of the invention; test data demonstrating that the idea, invention, or design is workable; the societal, economic, and environmental benefits of the invention; and supplemental material that may include photos, slides, disks, videotapes, and even samples. Entries must be original ideas and the work of a student or team and a university advisor; the invention should be reproducible and may not have been 1) made available to the public as a commercial product or process, or 2) patented or published more than 1 year prior to the date of submission for this competition. Entries are first reviewed by a committee of judges that selects the finalists. The committee is comprised of mathematicians, engineers, biologists, chemists, environmentalists, physicists, computer specialists, members of the medical and veterinary profession, and specialists in invention and development of technology. Entries are judged on the basis of originality, inventiveness, potential value to society (socially, environmentally, and economically), and range or scope of use. **Deadline for Receipt:** May of each year. **Additional Information:** This program is co-sponsored by Abbott Laboratories and the United States Patent and Trademark Office. It was established in 1990 as the BFGoodrich Collegiate Inventors Program.

4121 ■ NATIONAL SECURITY AGENCY

Attn: Office of Recruitment and Staffing (Stokes)
9800 Savage Road, Suite 6779

P.O. Box 1661, Suite 6779
Fort Meade, MD 20755-6779
Tel: (410)854-4725; (866)672-4473
Web Site: http://www.nsa.gov/careers/students_4.cfm
To provide minority and other high school seniors and college sophomores with scholarship/loans and work experience at the National Security Agency (NSA).

Title of Award: Stokes Educational Scholarship Program **Area, Field, or Subject:** Asian studies; Computer and information sciences; Engineering, Computer; Engineering, Electrical; Finance; Foreign languages; International affairs and relations; Mathematics and mathematical sciences; Near Eastern studies; South Asian studies **Level of Education for which Award is Granted:** Undergraduate **Number Awarded:** Varies each year. **Funds Available:** Participants receive college tuition for up to 4 years, reimbursement for books and certain fees, a year-round salary, and a housing allowance and travel reimbursement during summer employment if the distance between the agency and school exceeds 75 miles. Following graduation, participants must work for the agency for 1 and a half times their length of study, usually 5 years. Students who leave agency employment earlier must repay the tuition cost. **Duration:** Up to 4 years, followed by employment at the agency for 5 years.

Eligibility Requirements: This program is open to graduating high school seniors, particularly minorities, who 1) are planning a college major in electrical or computer engineering, computer science, international affairs, international finance, mathematics, area studies (Middle East or south, east, or central Asia), foreign languages (recent language interests included Arabic, Chinese, Farsi, and Korean); 2) have minimum scores of 1600 on the SAT (1100 on critical reading and mathematics, 500 in writing) or 25 on the ACT; 3) have a GPA of 3.0 or higher; 4) are U.S. citizens; and 5) demonstrate leadership abilities. Also eligible are college sophomores who are U.S. citizens, have a GPA of 3.0 or higher, and are majoring in the eligible fields. Applicants must include a 1-page essay on why they want to have a career with the NSA. **Deadline for Receipt:** November of each year. **Additional Information:** Participants must attend classes full time and work at the agency during the summer in jobs tailored to their course of study. They must maintain at least a 3.0 GPA. This program, established in 1986, was formerly known as the National Security Agency Undergraduate Training Program.

4122 ■ NATIONAL SOCIETY OF BLACK ENGINEERS

Attn: Programs Department
1454 Duke Street
Alexandria, VA 22314
Tel: (703)549-2207
Fax: (703)683-5312
E-mail: scholarships@nsbe.org
Web Site: http://www.nsbe.org/programs/schol_pci_gta.php
To provide financial assistance to high school seniors who are junior members of the National Society of Black Engineers (NSBE) planning to major in a field related to engineering in college.

Title of Award: Golden Torch Awards **Area, Field, or Subject:** Computer and information sciences; Engineering; Mathematics and mathematical sciences; Technology **Level of Education for which Award is Granted:** Four Year College **Number Awarded:** Varies each year; recently, 7 of these awards were presented. **Funds Available:** The stipend is $1,000 per year. **Duration:** 1 year; may be renewed 3 additional years if the recipient maintains a GPA of 2.75 or higher in college.

Eligibility Requirements: This program is open to junior members of the society who are high school seniors. Applicants must have been accepted as a full-time student at a 4-year college or university to major in engineering, computer science, mathematics, or technology. They must have a GPA of 3.0 or higher. Along with their application, they must submit an essay, up to 500 words in length, on how they will continue the legacy of NSBE and how they will service as role models in their community after college. **Deadline for Receipt:** January of each year.

4123 ■ NATIONAL SOCIETY OF BLACK ENGINEERS

Attn: Programs Department
1454 Duke Street
Alexandria, VA 22314
Tel: (703)549-2207
Fax: (703)683-5312
E-mail: scholarships@nsbe.org

Web Site: http://www.nsbe.org/programs/schol_lockheed.php
To provide financial assistance to members of the National Society of Black Engineers (NSBE) who are majoring in fields related to engineering.

Title of Award: Lockheed Martin NSBE Corporate Scholarship Program **Area, Field, or Subject:** Computer and information sciences; Engineering, Aerospace/Aeronautical/Astronautical; Engineering, Computer; Engineering, Electrical; Engineering, Mechanical; Mathematics and mathematical sciences; Systems engineering **Level of Education for which Award is Granted:** Four Year College **Number Awarded:** 5 each year. **Funds Available:** The stipend is $2,000. **Duration:** 1 year.

Eligibility Requirements: This program is open to members of the society who are entering their junior or senior year in college and majoring in computer science, mathematics, or the following fields of engineering: aerospace, computer, electrical, mechanical, or systems. Applicants must have a GPA of 3.0 or higher and a demonstrated interest in employment with Lockheed Martin Corporation. Along with their application, they must submit a 250-word essay describing their career goals and how they can make a community and professional impact as a Lockheed Martin employee. **Deadline for Receipt:** January of each year.

4124 ■ NATIONAL SOCIETY OF BLACK ENGINEERS

Attn: Programs Department
1454 Duke Street
Alexandria, VA 22314
Tel: (703)549-2207
Fax: (703)683-5312
E-mail: scholarships@nsbe.org
Web Site: http://www.nsbe.org/programs/schol_micro.php
To provide financial assistance to members of the National Society of Black Engineers (NSBE) who are majoring in computer science or engineering.

Title of Award: Microsoft Corporation NSBE Scholarships **Area, Field, or Subject:** Computer and information sciences; Engineering, Computer; Mathematics and mathematical sciences; Physics **Level of Education for which Award is Granted:** Undergraduate **Number Awarded:** 3 each year. **Funds Available:** The stipend is $5,000. **Duration:** 1 year.

Eligibility Requirements: This program is open to members of the society who are undergraduate students majoring in computer engineering, computer science, or mathematics/physics with a demonstrated interest in computer science. Applicants must have a GPA of 3.0 or higher. They must submit a 300-word essay on their "passion for technology" outside of the classroom. **Deadline for Receipt:** January of each year. **Additional Information:** This program is supported by Microsoft Corporation.

4125 ■ NATIONAL SOCIETY OF BLACK ENGINEERS

Attn: Programs Department
1454 Duke Street
Alexandria, VA 22314
Tel: (703)549-2207
Fax: (703)683-5312
E-mail: scholarships@nsbe.org
Web Site: http://www.nsbe.org/programs/schol_ng.php
To provide financial assistance to members of the National Society of Black Engineers (NSBE) who are working on an undergraduate degree in designated science and engineering fields.

Title of Award: Northrop Grumman NSBE Scholarships **Area, Field, or Subject:** Architecture, Naval; Computer and information sciences; Engineering, Aerospace/Aeronautical/Astronautical; Engineering, Chemical; Engineering, Civil; Engineering, Computer; Engineering, Electrical; Engineering, Industrial; Engineering, Mechanical; Engineering, Ocean; Mathematics and mathematical sciences; Physics **Level of Education for which Award is Granted:** Undergraduate **Number Awarded:** 5 each year. **Funds Available:** The stipend is $5,000. **Duration:** 1 year.

Eligibility Requirements: This program is open to members of the society who are U.S. citizens currently enrolled in college. Applicants must be majoring in computer science, information science, mathematics, naval architecture, physics, or the following engineering fields: aerospace, chemical, civil (structural), computer, electrical, industrial, manufacturing, marine, mechanical, or ocean. They must have a GPA of 3.0 or higher and demonstrate an interest in employment with Northrop Grumman Corporation. **Deadline for Receipt:** January of each year.

4126 ■ NAVAL RESERVE ASSOCIATION

Attn: Educational Assistance Program
1619 King Street
Alexandria, VA 22314-2793
Tel: (703)548-5800; (866)672-4968
Fax: (866)683-3647
E-mail: admin@navy-reserve.org
Web Site: http://www.navy-reserve.org
To provide financial assistance for college to the children of members of the Naval Reserve Association.

Title of Award: Naval Reserve Association Scholarships **Area, Field, or Subject:** Engineering; General studies/Field of study not specified; Mathematics and mathematical sciences; Medicine **Level of Education for which Award is Granted:** Undergraduate **Number Awarded:** Varies each year; recently, 6 of these scholarships were awarded. **Funds Available:** The amounts of the stipends vary but recently averaged more than $4,000 per year. **Duration:** 1 year.

Eligibility Requirements: This program is open to the children of association members who are enrolled or accepted for enrollment at a college or university as a full-time student. Applicants must be U.S. citizens under 24 years of age. Preference is given to applicants who have demonstrated an interest in the "hard sciences" (e.g., mathematics, medicine, and engineering). **Deadline for Receipt:** April of each year.

4127 ■ NEBRASKA ACTUARIES CLUB

c/o Bob Jurgensmeier
Lincoln Beneficial Life
2940 South 84th Street, Suite 1A3
Lincoln, NE 68506
Fax: (402)328-6116
E-mail: bjurg@allstate.com
Web Site: http://www.n-a-c.org/Scholarships/Scholarships.PHP
To provide financial assistance to students in Nebraska who are preparing for an actuarial career.

Title of Award: Nebraska Actuaries Club Scholarships **Area, Field, or Subject:** Actuarial science; Economics; Insurance and insurance-related fields; Mathematics and mathematical sciences; Statistics **Level of Education for which Award is Granted:** Undergraduate **Number Awarded:** 3 each year: 2 to Nebraska high school graduates attending the University of Nebraska system (designated Madden Scholarships and supported by the Nebraska Insurance Federation) and 1 to graduates from other states attending a college or university in Nebraska (supported by the Nebraska Actuaries Club). **Funds Available:** The stipend is $1,000. **Duration:** 1 year.

Eligibility Requirements: This program is open to 1) seniors graduating from high schools in Nebraska and planning to attend a campus of the University of Nebraska; and 2) seniors graduating from high schools anywhere in the United States and planning to attend a college or university in Nebraska. Applicants must intend to major in actuarial science, mathematics, statistics, or economics and prepare for a career as an actuary. They must be able to demonstrate mathematical ability. Along with their application, they must submit an essay on their interest in actuarial science and why they would like to be an actuary. Financial need is not considered in the selection process. **Deadline for Receipt:** March of each year. **Additional Information:** This program is jointly sponsored by the Nebraska Actuaries Club and the Nebraska Insurance Federation.

4128 ■ NEBRASKA EDUCATIONAL OFFICE PROFESSIONALS ASSOCIATION

P.O. Box 83872
Lincoln, NE 68501-3872
Web Site: http://neopa.unl.edu/awards.html
To provide financial assistance to residents of Nebraska who are interested in preparing for an office-related career.

Title of Award: Nebraska Educational Office Professionals Association Student Scholarship **Area, Field, or Subject:** Accounting; Computer and information sciences; Law; Marketing and distribution; Publishing; Secretarial sciences **Level of Education for which Award is Granted:** Undergraduate **Number Awarded:** 1 each year. **Funds Available:** The stipend is $1,000. **Duration:** 1 year.

Eligibility Requirements: This program is open to residents of Nebraska who are graduating high school seniors or students currently enrolled in a postsecondary educational institution. Applicants must have completed 2 or more business education courses (in high school, college, or a combination) from among the following: computer classes, keyboarding/typing, marketing, accounting, office practices and procedures, bookkeeping, business communication, desktop publishing, and/or business law. They must submit a 1-page essay on why they are choosing an office-related career or vocation, 3 letters of recommendation, and high school or college transcripts. Selection is based on academic achievement, initiative of the student, and financial need. **Deadline for Receipt:** December of each year. **Additional Information:** Information is also available from Edie Schleiger, Scholarship Director, University of Nebraska at Lincoln, Office of Admissions, 1410 Q Street, Lincoln, NE 68588-0417.

4129 ■ NEBRASKA LEGAL PROFESSIONALS ASSOCIATION

c/o Diane Horak, Scholarship Chair
7111 Cedar Creek Circle
Lincoln, NE 68516-3056
Tel: (402)423-5077
Fax: (402)466-2288
To provide financial assistance to residents of Nebraska enrolled in a law-related program.

Title of Award: Nebraska Legal Professionals Scholarship **Area, Field, or Subject:** Law; Paralegal studies; Secretarial sciences **Level of Education for which Award is Granted:** Undergraduate **Number Awarded:** 2 each year. **Funds Available:** The stipend is $1,000 for first place and $500 for second. **Duration:** 1 year.

Eligibility Requirements: This program is open to residents of Nebraska enrolled full time in a pre-law, paralegal, legal secretary, or other law-related program. Applicants must submit a certified copy of their latest transcript; a resume covering their educational history, school and community activities, and work history for the last 5 years; a 1-page personal statement on why they wish to become a legal secretary/paralegal or why they wish to continue their formal legal secretarial/paralegal education; and a copy of their acceptance to the school of their choice. **Deadline for Receipt:** March of each year. **Additional Information:** This scholarship was first awarded in 2000.

4130 ■ NEVADA SPACE GRANT CONSORTIUM

c/o University of Nevada at Reno
Mackay School of Mines Building, Room 308
MS 168
Reno, NV 89557
Tel: (775)784-6261
Fax: (775)327-2235
E-mail: nvsg@mines.unr.edu
Web Site: http://www.unr.edu/spacegrant
To provide financial assistance for space-related study to undergraduate students at institutions that are members of the University and Community College System of Nevada (UCCSN) and participate in the Nevada Space Grant Consortium (NSGC).

Title of Award: Nevada Space Grant Consortium Undergraduate Scholarship Program **Area, Field, or Subject:** Engineering; Mathematics and mathematical sciences; Science; Technology **Level of Education for which Award is Granted:** Undergraduate **Number Awarded:** Varies each year; recently, 13 of these awards were granted. **Funds Available:** The stipend is $2,500 per year. Funds may be used for tuition or registration fees. Funds may not be regarded as payment for research work or any other work. **Duration:** 1 year; may be renewed.

Eligibility Requirements: This program is open to undergraduate students at UCCSN member institutions. Applicants must be working on a degree in an aerospace-related field, including any science, mathematics, engineering, or technology discipline that is concerned with or likely to improve the understanding, assessment, development, and utilization of space. They must be U.S. citizens and enrolled full time. This program is part of the Space Grant program of the U.S. National Aeronautics and Space Administration (NASA), which encourages participation by members of underrepresented groups (African Americans, Hispanics, American Indians, Pacific Islanders, people with physical disabilities, and women of all races). Selection is based on the academic qualifications of the applicant, the quality of a career goal statement, and an assessment of the applicant's motivation for an aerospace career. **Deadline for**

Receipt: March of each year. **Additional Information:** Funding for this program is provided by NASA.

4131 ■ NEW ENGLAND BOARD OF HIGHER EDUCATION

45 Temple Place
Boston, MA 02111
Tel: (617)357-9620
Fax: (617)338-1577
E-mail: pubinfo@nebhe.org
Web Site: http://www.nebhe.org/ETD/scholarship.html
To provide financial assistance to African Americans who are residents of New England and undergraduate students in science, mathematics, technology, or engineering.
Title of Award: Shaw's Coca-Cola Scholarship Grants for African-American Students **Area, Field, or Subject:** Engineering; Mathematics and mathematical sciences; Science; Technology **Level of Education for which Award is Granted:** Undergraduate **Number Awarded:** 12 each year. **Funds Available:** The stipend is $1,250. **Duration:** 1 year.
Eligibility Requirements: This program is open to African American residents of New England who are high school seniors or college freshmen or sophomores with a GPA of 3.0 or higher. Applicants must be attending or planning to attend a college or university in New England as a full-time student and major in science, mathematics, technology, or engineering. Both merit and need-based scholarships are available. U.S. citizenship or permanent resident status is required. **Additional Information:** This program was established in recognition of Black History Month by Shaw's Supermarkets and the Coca-Cola Company.

4132 ■ NEW HAMPSHIRE POSTSECONDARY EDUCATION COMMISSION

3 Barrell Court, Suite 300
Concord, NH 03301-8543
Tel: (603)271-2555
Fax: (603)271-2696
E-mail: pedes@pec.state.nh.us
Web Site: http://www.state.nh.us/postsecondary/finwork.html
To provide scholarship/loans to New Hampshire residents who are interested in attending college to prepare for careers in designated professions.
Title of Award: New Hampshire Workforce Incentive Program Forgivable Loans **Area, Field, or Subject:** Chemistry; Education; Education, Special; Linguistics; Mathematics and mathematical sciences; Nursing; Physical sciences; Physics; Science **Level of Education for which Award is Granted:** Graduate, Undergraduate **Number Awarded:** Varies each year. **Funds Available:** The stipend is $500 per semester ($1,000 per year). This is a scholarship/loan program; recipients must agree to pursue, within New Hampshire, the professional career for which they receive training. Recipients of loans for 1 year have their notes cancelled upon completion of 1 year of full-time service; repayment by service must be completed within 3 years from the date of licensure, certification, or completion of the program. Recipients of loans for more than 1 year have their notes cancelled upon completion of 2 years of full-time service; repayment by service must be completed within 5 years from the date of licensure, certification, or completion of the program. If the note is not cancelled because of service, the recipient must repay the loan within 2 years. **Duration:** 1 year; may be renewed.
Eligibility Requirements: This program is open to residents of New Hampshire who wish to prepare for careers in fields designated by the commission as shortage areas. Currently, the career shortage areas are chemistry, general science, mathematics, physical sciences, physics, special education, world languages, and nursing (L.P.N. through graduate). Applicants must be enrolled as a junior, senior, or graduate student at a college in New Hampshire and must be able to demonstrate financial need. **Deadline for Receipt:** May of each year for fall semester; December of each year for spring semester. **Additional Information:** The time for repayment of the loan, either in cash or through professional service, is extended while the recipient is 1) engaged in a course of study, at least on a half-time basis, at an institution of higher education; 2) serving on active duty as a member of the armed forces of the United States, or as a member of VISTA, the Peace Corps, or AmeriCorps, for a period up to 3 years; 3) temporarily totally disabled for a period up to 3 years; or 4) unable to secure employment because of the need to care for a disabled spouse, child, or parent for a period up to 12 months. The repay-

ment obligation is cancelled if the recipient is unable to work because of a permanent total disability, receives relief under federal bankruptcy laws, or dies. This program went into effect in 1999.

4133 ■ NORTH CAROLINA SPACE GRANT CONSORTIUM

c/o North Carolina State University
Mechanical and Aerospace Engineering
1009 Capability Drive, Suite 210
Box 7515
Raleigh, NC 27695-7515
Tel: (919)515-4240
Fax: (919)515-5934
E-mail: scholarships@ncspacegrant.org
Web Site: http://www.ncspacegrant.org
To provide funding to undergraduate students at institutions affiliated with the North Carolina Space Grant Consortium (NCSGC) interested in conducting space-related research.
Title of Award: North Carolina Space Grant Consortium Undergraduate Research Scholarships **Area, Field, or Subject:** Aeronautics; Aerospace sciences; Engineering, Aerospace/Aeronautical/Astronautical; Mathematics and mathematical sciences; Space and planetary sciences; Technology **Level of Education for which Award is Granted:** Undergraduate **Number Awarded:** Varies each year; recently, 8 of these scholarships were awarded. **Funds Available:** The maximum grant is $4,000 for a summer project on campus, $2,000 for an academic year project on campus, or $7,000 for a project at a NASA center or industrial contractor. **Duration:** 1 summer or 1 academic year.
Eligibility Requirements: This program is open to full-time undergraduate students at institutions affiliated with the NCSGC who are interested in working on a research project under the direct supervision of a faculty mentor. Applicants must be working on a degree in a science, technology, engineering, or mathematics (STEM) discipline of interest to the U.S. National Aeronautics and Space Administration (NASA). The research project must be space or aeronautics related or have a space or aeronautics application. Selection is based on the quality of the research proposal, the student's academic achievement, a letter of recommendation from the research mentor, and exhibited leadership qualities. U.S. citizenship is required. A primary goal of this program is the recruitment and retention of underrepresented minorities, women, and persons with disabilities into space-related fields. **Deadline for Receipt:** March of each year. **Additional Information:** The affiliated institutions are North Carolina State University, North Carolina A&T State University, Duke University, North Carolina Central University, the University of North Carolina at Charlotte, the University of North Carolina at Chapel Hill, the University of North Carolina at Pembroke, and Winston-Salem State University. This program is funded by NASA.

4134 ■ NORTH CAROLINA SPACE GRANT CONSORTIUM

c/o North Carolina State University
Mechanical and Aerospace Engineering
1009 Capability Drive, Suite 210
Box 7515
Raleigh, NC 27695-7515
Tel: (919)515-4240
Fax: (919)515-5934
E-mail: scholarships@ncspacegrant.org
Web Site: http://www.ncspacegrant.org
To provide funding to undergraduate students at institutions affiliated with the North Carolina Space Grant Consortium (NCSGC) interested in major in space-related fields.
Title of Award: North Carolina Space Grant Consortium Undergraduate Scholarships **Area, Field, or Subject:** Aerospace sciences; Engineering, Aerospace/Aeronautical/Astronautical; Mathematics and mathematical sciences; Space and planetary sciences; Technology **Level of Education for which Award is Granted:** Undergraduate **Number Awarded:** Varies each year. **Funds Available:** The stipend is $1,000 per year. **Duration:** 1 year; may be renewed 1 additional year.
Eligibility Requirements: This program is open to full-time undergraduate students at institutions affiliated with the NCSGC who are freshmen, sophomores, or recent transfers from a community or junior college. Applicants must be working on a degree in a science, technology, engineering, or mathematics (STEM) discipline of interest to the U.S. National Aeronautics and Space Administration (NASA). Selection is based on the

student's academic achievement, a letter of recommendation, and exhibited leadership qualities. U.S. citizenship is required. A primary goal of this program is the recruitment and retention of underrepresented minorities, women, and persons with disabilities into space-related fields. **Deadline for Receipt:** March of each year. **Additional Information:** The affiliated institutions are North Carolina State University, North Carolina A&T State University, Duke University, North Carolina Central University, the University of North Carolina at Charlotte, the University of North Carolina at Chapel Hill, the University of North Carolina at Pembroke, and Winston-Salem State University. This program is funded by NASA.

4135 ■ OAK RIDGE INSTITUTE FOR SCIENCE AND EDUCATION

Attn: Science and Engineering Education
P.O. Box 117
Oak Ridge, TN 37831-0117
Tel: (865)576-8239
Fax: (865)241-5219
E-mail: igrid.gregory@orau.gov
Web Site: http://www.orau.gov/orise.htm
To provide financial assistance and summer research experience to undergraduate students who are working on a degree in a field of interest to the Department of Homeland Security (DHS).
Title of Award: Department of Homeland Security Undergraduate Scholarships **Area, Field, or Subject:** Agricultural sciences; Biological and clinical sciences; Communications; Computer and information sciences; Engineering; Information science and technology; Mathematics and mathematical sciences; Physical sciences; Psychology; Public administration; Religion; Social sciences; Writing **Level of Education for which Award is Granted:** Undergraduate **Number Awarded:** Approximately 50 each year. **Funds Available:** This program provides a stipend of $1,000 per month during the academic year and $5,000 for the internship plus full payment of tuition and mandatory fees. **Duration:** 2 academic years plus 10 weeks during the intervening summer.
Eligibility Requirements: This program is open to 1) full-time students who are in their second year of college attendance as of the application deadline; and 2) part-time students who have completed at least 45 but no more than 60 semester hours as of the application deadline. Applicants must be majoring in the agricultural sciences, biological and life sciences, computer and information sciences, engineering, mathematics, physical sciences, psychology, social sciences, or selected humanities (religious studies, cultural studies, public policy, advocacy, communications, or science writing). They must have a GPA of 3.3 or higher. Along with their application, they must submit 2 statements on 1) their educational and professional goals, the kinds of research they are interested in conducting, specific questions that interest them, and how they became interested in them; and 2) how they think their interests, talents, and initiative would contribute to make the homeland safer and secure. Selection is based on those statements, academic record, references, and SAT or ACT scores. As part of their program, they must be interested in participating in summer research and development activities at a DHS-designated facility. U.S. citizenship is required. **Deadline for Receipt:** January of each year. **Additional Information:** This program, established in 2003, is funded by DHS and administered by Oak Ridge Institute for Science and Education (ORISE). Recipients must enroll full time.

4136 ■ OAK RIDGE INSTITUTE FOR SCIENCE AND EDUCATION

Attn: Science and Engineering Education
P.O. Box 117
Oak Ridge, TN 37831-0117
Tel: (865)241-8240
Fax: (865)241-5219
E-mail: hollingsscholarship@orau.gov
Web Site: http://www.orau.gov/orise.htm
To provide financial assistance and summer research experience to upper-division students who are working on a degree in a field of interest to the National Oceanic and Atmospheric Administration (NOAA).
Title of Award: Ernest F. Hollings Scholarship Program **Area, Field, or Subject:** Agricultural sciences; Behavioral sciences; Biological and clinical sciences; Computer and information sciences; Education; Engineering; Information science and technology; Mathematics and mathematical sciences; Physical sciences; Social sciences **Level of Education for which Award is Granted:** Four Year College **Number Awarded:** Approximately 100 each year. **Funds Available:** This program provides a

stipend of $8,000 per academic year and $650 per week during the internship, a housing subsidy and limited travel reimbursement for round-trip transportation to the internship site, and travel expenses to the scholarship program conference at the completion of the internship. **Duration:** 2 academic years plus 10 weeks during the intervening summer.
Eligibility Requirements: This program is open to full-time students entering their junior year at an accredited college or university in the United States or its territories. Applicants must be majoring in a discipline related to oceanic and atmospheric science, research, technology, and education, and supportive of the purposes of NOAA's programs and mission (e.g., biological, life, and agricultural sciences; computer and information sciences; engineering; mathematics; physical sciences; social and behavioral sciences; or teacher education). They must have a GPA of 3.0 or higher. As part of their program, they must be interested in participating in summer research and development activities at NOAA headquarters (Silver Spring, Maryland) or field centers. U.S. citizenship is required. **Deadline for Receipt:** May of each year. **Additional Information:** This program, established in 2005, is funded by NOAA and administered by Oak Ridge Institute for Science and Education (ORISE).

4137 ■ OAK RIDGE INSTITUTE FOR SCIENCE AND EDUCATION

Attn: Science and Engineering Education
P.O. Box 117
Oak Ridge, TN 37831-0117
Tel: (865)576-9279
Fax: (865)241-5220
E-mail: coxre@orau.gov
Web Site: http://www.orau.gov/orise.htm
To provide financial assistance and research experience to undergraduate students at minority serving institutions who are majoring in scientific fields of interest to the National Oceanic and Atmospheric Administration (NOAA).
Title of Award: National Oceanic and Atmospheric Administration Educational Partnership Program with Minority Serving Institutions Undergraduate Scholarships **Area, Field, or Subject:** Atmospheric science; Biological and clinical sciences; Cartography/Surveying; Chemistry; Computer and information sciences; Engineering; Environmental conservation; Environmental science; Geography; Mathematics and mathematical sciences; Meteorology; Photogrammetry; Physical sciences; Physics **Level of Education for which Award is Granted:** Four Year College **Number Awarded:** 10 each year. **Funds Available:** This program provides payment of tuition and fees (to a maximum of $4,000 per year) and a stipend during the internship of $650 per week. **Duration:** 1 academic year and 2 summers.
Eligibility Requirements: This program is open to juniors and seniors at minority serving institutions, including Hispanic Serving Institutions (HSIs), Historically Black Colleges and Universities (HBCUs), and Tribal Colleges and Universities (TCUs). Applicants must be majoring in atmospheric science, biology, cartography, chemistry, computer science, engineering, environmental science, geodesy, geography, marine science, mathematics, meteorology, photogrammetry, physical science, physics, or remote sensing. They must also be interested in participating in a research internship at a NOAA site. U.S. citizenship is required. **Deadline for Receipt:** January of each year. **Additional Information:** This program is funded by NOAA through an interagency agreement with the U.S. Department of Energy and administered by Oak Ridge Institute for Science and Education (ORISE).

4138 ■ OAK RIDGE INSTITUTE FOR SCIENCE AND EDUCATION

Attn: Science and Engineering Education
P.O. Box 117
Oak Ridge, TN 37831-0117
Tel: (865)576-9279
Fax: (865)241-5219
E-mail: coxre@orau.gov
Web Site: http://www.orau.gov/orise.htm
To provide scholarships and internship experience to students at Historically Black Colleges and Universities (HBCUs) working on undergraduate degrees in areas related to the Office of Civilian Radioactive Waste Management (OCRWM).
Title of Award: Office of Civilian Radioactive Waste Management Historically Black Colleges and Universities Undergraduate Scholarship Program **Area, Field, or Subject:** Energy-related areas; Engineering;

Mathematics and mathematical sciences; Nuclear science; Science; Social sciences **Level of Education for which Award is Granted:** Four Year College **Number Awarded:** 10 each year. **Funds Available:** The program provides for payment of tuition and fees (to a maximum of $8,000) plus a monthly stipend of $600. **Duration:** 2 years.

Eligibility Requirements: This program is open to juniors and seniors at HBCUs who are working on a degree in science, mathematics, engineering, engineering technology, or social sciences. As part of their program, they must be willing to participate in an internship at a U.S. Department of Energy (DOE) site conducting activities for the OCRWM. **Deadline for Receipt:** January of each year. **Additional Information:** This program is funded by DOE/OCRWM and administered by Oak Ridge Institute for Science and Education (ORISE).

4139 ■ OHIO SPACE GRANT CONSORTIUM

c/o Ohio Aerospace Institute
22800 Cedar Point Road
Cleveland, OH 44142
Tel: (440)962-3032
Free: 800-828-OSGC
Fax: (440)962-3057
E-mail: osgc@oai.org
Web Site: http://www.osgc.org/Scholarship.html

To provide financial assistance to students at selected community colleges in Ohio who are interested in continuing their studies at a 4-year university in the state that is a member of the Ohio Space Grant Consortium (OSGC).

Title of Award: Ohio Space Grant Consortium Community College Scholarship **Area, Field, or Subject:** Computer and information sciences; Electronics; Engineering; Mathematics and mathematical sciences; Science; Technology **Level of Education for which Award is Granted:** Two Year College **Number Awarded:** 2 each year. **Funds Available:** The stipend is $1,000. **Duration:** 1 year; nonrenewable.

Eligibility Requirements: This program is open to U.S. citizens who are students at designated community colleges in Ohio, normally enrolled full time in their freshman year (although applications are accepted from part-time students demonstrating academic merit and from students at any stage of their college career). Applicants must be enrolled in a program that includes course work related to an understanding of or interest in technological fields supporting aerospace, e.g. associate degrees related to mathematics, science, and such advanced technology fields as engineering, computers, electronics, and industrial technology. They must also have a GPA of 3.0 or higher and plans to continue their education in a 4-year program at an OSGC-member university. Along with their application, they must submit college transcripts, 2 letters of recommendation, and a brief resume of their education, significant accomplishments, work experience, educational and professional goals, and any other relevant information. Women, underrepresented minorities, and persons with disabilities are particularly encouraged to apply. **Deadline for Receipt:** October of each year. **Additional Information:** These scholarships are funded through the National Space Grant College and Fellowship Program administered by the National Aeronautics and Space Administration (NASA), with matching funds provided by the member colleges, the Ohio Aerospace Institute, and private industry. The participating institutions include Columbus State Community College, Cuyahoga Community College, Lorain County Community College, Owens Community College, Lakeland Community College, and Terra Community College. OSGC member institutions include the Air Force Institute of Technology, University of Akron, Case Western Reserve University, Central State University, University of Cincinnati, Cleveland State University, University of Dayton, Ohio State University, Ohio University, University of Toledo, Wilberforce University, and Wright State University.

4140 ■ OHIO SPACE GRANT CONSORTIUM

c/o Ohio Aerospace Institute
22800 Cedar Point Road
Cleveland, OH 44142
Tel: (440)962-3032
Free: 800-828-OSGC
Fax: (440)962-3057
E-mail: osgc@oai.org
Web Site: http://www.osgc.org/Scholarship.html

To provide financial assistance to students in their junior year at selected universities in Ohio who wish to working on a bachelor's degree in an aerospace-related field.

Title of Award: Ohio Space Grant Consortium Junior Scholarships **Area, Field, or Subject:** Astronomy and astronomical sciences; Biological and clinical sciences; Chemistry; Computer and information sciences; Engineering, Aerospace/Aeronautical/Astronautical; Engineering, Chemical; Engineering, Civil; Engineering, Computer; Engineering, Electrical; Engineering, Industrial; Engineering, Materials; Engineering, Mechanical; Engineering, Petroleum; Geography; Geology; Materials research/science; Mathematics and mathematical sciences; Physics; Space and planetary sciences **Level of Education for which Award is Granted:** Four Year College **Number Awarded:** Varies each year; recently, 20 of these scholarships were awarded. **Funds Available:** The stipend is $2,000. **Duration:** 1 year; recipients may apply for a senior scholarship if they maintain satisfactory academic performance and good progress on their research project.

Eligibility Requirements: These scholarships are available to U.S. citizens who expect to complete within 2 years the requirements for a bachelor of science degree in an aerospace-related discipline (aeronautical engineering, aerospace engineering, astronomy, biology, chemical engineering, chemistry, civil engineering, computer engineering and science, control engineering, electrical engineering, engineering mechanics, geography, geology, industrial engineering, manufacturing engineering, materials science and engineering, mathematics, mechanical engineering, petroleum engineering, physics, and systems engineering). Applicants must be attending a member university of the Ohio Space Grant Consortium (OSGC) or another participating university. They must propose and initiate a research project on campus under the guidance of a faculty member. Along with their application, they must submit a 1-page personal objective statement that discusses their career goals and anticipated benefits to be derived from this program. Women, underrepresented minorities, and persons with disabilities are particularly encouraged to apply. **Deadline for Receipt:** February of each year. **Additional Information:** These scholarships are funded through the National Space Grant College and Fellowship Program administered by the National Aeronautics and Space Administration (NASA), with matching funds provided by the member universities, the Ohio Aerospace Institute, and private industry. The OSGC member universities include the University of Akron, Case Western Reserve University, Central State University, University of Cincinnati, Cleveland State University, University of Dayton, Ohio State University, Ohio University, University of Toledo, Wilberforce University, and Wright State University. Other participating universities are Cedarville University, Marietta College (petroleum engineering), Miami University (manufacturing engineering), Ohio Northern University (mechanical engineering), and Youngstown State University (mechanical and industrial engineering). Recipients are required to attend the annual spring research symposium sponsored by the OSGC and present a poster on their research project.

4141 ■ OKLAHOMA NASA SPACE GRANT CONSORTIUM

c/o University of Oklahoma
Ditmars House, Suite 9
1623 Cross Center Drive
Norman, OK 73069
Tel: (405)325-6559
Fax: (405)325-5537
E-mail: vduca@ou.edu
Web Site: http://www.okspacegrant.ou.edu

To provide financial assistance to upper-division students at member institutions of the Oklahoma NASA Space Grant Consortium who are enrolled in aerospace-related studies.

Title of Award: Oklahoma NASA Space Grant Consortium Scholarships **Area, Field, or Subject:** Aeronautics; Aerospace sciences; Engineering, Aerospace/Aeronautical/Astronautical; Geography; Mathematics and mathematical sciences; Space and planetary sciences; Technology **Level of Education for which Award is Granted:** Four Year College **Number Awarded:** Approximately 40 each year. **Funds Available:** Stipends range from $500 to $1,000. **Duration:** 1 year.

Eligibility Requirements: This program is open to juniors and seniors at member institutions of the Oklahoma NASA Space Grant Consortium (OSGC). Applicants must be majoring in science, mathematics, engineering, technology, geography, or other aeronautics or space-related disciplines. They must have a GPA of 2.5 or higher. U.S. citizenship is required. The OSGC is a component of the U.S. National Aeronautics and Space Administration (NASA) Space Grant program, which encourages participation by women, underrepresented minorities, and persons with disabilities. **Deadline for Receipt:** December of each year. **Additional Information:** Members of OSGC are Oklahoma State University, the University of Oklahoma, Cameron University, Langston University. Cameron University, East Central University, Southeastern Oklahoma State University, Southern Nazarene University, and Southwestern Oklahoma State University. This program is funded by NASA.

4142 ■ OKLAHOMA STATE REGENTS FOR HIGHER EDUCATION
Attn: Director of Scholarship and Grant Programs
655 Research Parkway, Suite 200
P.O. Box 108850
Oklahoma City, OK 73101-8850
Tel: (405)225-9239
Free: 800-858-1840
Fax: (405)225-9230
E-mail: studentinfo@osrhe.edu
Web Site: http://www.okhighered.org/student-center/financial-aid/future-teach.shtml
To provide forgivable loans to Oklahoma residents who are interested in teaching (particularly in teacher shortage fields) in Oklahoma.
Title of Award: Oklahoma Future Teachers Scholarship Program **Area, Field, or Subject:** Education; Education, Special; English language and literature; Linguistics; Mathematics and mathematical sciences; Science **Level of Education for which Award is Granted:** Graduate, Undergraduate **Number Awarded:** Varies each year; recently, 136 students received support through this program. **Funds Available:** Full-time students receive up to $1,500 per year if they have completed 60 hours or more or up to $1,000 if they have completed fewer than 60 hours; part-time students receive up to $750 per year if they have completed 60 hours or more or up to $500 per year if they have completed fewer than 60 hours. Funds are paid directly to the institution on the student's behalf. This is a forgivable loan program; recipients must agree to teach in Oklahoma public schools for 3 years following graduation and licensure. **Duration:** 1 year; may be renewable for up to 3 additional years as long as the recipient maintains a GPA of 2.5 or higher.
Eligibility Requirements: Candidates for this program must be nominated by institutions of higher education in Oklahoma. Nominees may be high school seniors, high school graduates, or currently-enrolled undergraduate or graduate students. They must 1) rank in the top 15% of their high school graduating class; 2) have an ACT or SAT score ranking in the top 15% for high school graduates of the same year; 3) have been admitted into a professional education program at an accredited Oklahoma institution of higher education; or 4) have achieved an undergraduate record of outstanding success as defined by the institution. Both part-time and full-time students are eligible, but preference is given to full-time students. Applicants must be interested in teaching in critical shortage areas in the state upon graduation. These areas change periodically but recently have included special education, mathematics, science, English, and foreign languages. **Deadline for Receipt:** September of each year.

4143 ■ OREGON NASA SPACE GRANT CONSORTIUM
c/o Oregon State University
92 Kerr Administration Building
Corvallis, OR 97331-2103
Tel: (541)737-2414
Fax: (541)737-9946
E-mail: spacegrant@oregonstate.edu
Web Site: http://www.oregonspacegrant.orst.edu/programs/education/undergraduate.html
To provide financial assistance for study in space-related fields to undergraduate students at colleges and universities that are members of the Oregon Space Grant Consortium (OSGC).
Title of Award: Oregon Space Grant Undergraduate Scholarship Program **Area, Field, or Subject:** Aerospace sciences; Education; Engineering, Aerospace/Aeronautical/Astronautical; Mathematics and mathematical sciences; Space and planetary sciences; Technology **Level of Education for which Award is Granted:** Undergraduate **Number Awarded:** Varies each year. **Funds Available:** The stipend is $2,000. **Duration:** 1 year.

Eligibility Requirements: This program is open to U.S. citizens enrolled full time at OSGC member institutions. Applicants must be working on 1) a baccalaureate degree in a science, technology, engineering, or mathematics (STEM) field (including mathematics or science education) related to the mission of the U.S. National Aeronautics and Space Administration (NASA); or 2) an associate degree in applied science and planning to transfer to a 4-year institution to complete a baccalaureate in the same fields. Along with their application, they must submit a letter of intent of 250 to 300 words on their career goals as they relate to NASA and how this scholarship will contribute to those goals. Selection is based on scholastic achievement, aerospace-related career goals, and 2 letters of recommendation. Applications are especially encouraged from members of underrepresented groups (women, minorities, and people with disabilities). **Deadline for Receipt:** January of each year. **Additional Information:** Institutions that are members of OSG include Oregon State University, Portland State University, the University of Oregon, Southern Oregon University, Eastern Oregon University, Western Oregon University, George Fox University, Lane Community College, Linfield College, Portland Community College, and Oregon Institute of Technology. This program is funded by NASA.

4144 ■ OREGON UNIVERSITY SYSTEM
Attn: Chancellor's Office, Industry Affairs Division
Capital Center, Suite 1065
18640 N.W. Walker Road
Beaverton, OR 97006-8966
Tel: (503)725-2918
Fax: (503)775-2921
E-mail: aeaschol@ous.edu
Web Site: http://www.ous.edu/ecs/scholarships.html
To provide financial assistance to Oregon high school seniors interested in studying designated computer and engineering fields at selected public universities in the state.
Title of Award: AeA Technology Scholarship Program **Area, Field, or Subject:** Biochemistry; Chemistry; Computer and information sciences; Engineering; Engineering, Chemical; Engineering, Computer; Engineering, Electrical; Engineering, Industrial; Engineering, Mechanical; Mathematics and mathematical sciences; Physics **Level of Education for which Award is Granted:** Undergraduate **Number Awarded:** Varies each year; recently, this program awarded 25 new scholarships. **Funds Available:** The stipend is $2,500 per year. **Duration:** 1 year; may be renewed up to 3 additional years if the recipient maintains a GPA of 3.0 or higher.
Eligibility Requirements: This program is open to seniors graduating from high schools in Oregon who plan to attend Eastern Oregon University, Oregon Institute of Technology, Oregon State University, Portland State University, Southern Oregon University, Western Oregon University, or the University of Oregon. Applicants must be planning to major in biochemistry, chemical engineering, chemistry, computer engineering, computer science, electrical engineering, electronic engineering, engineering technology, industrial engineering, mathematics, mechanical engineering, or physics (not all majors are available at each institution). Women and ethnic minorities underrepresented in the technology industry (Black Americans, Hispanic Americans, and Native Americans) are strongly encouraged to apply. Selection is based on academic performance; college entrance examination scores; mathematics, science, and technology course work; achievements; leadership; civic participation; interests; employment; insight into and commitment to a career in technology; and communication skill. **Deadline for Receipt:** March of each year. **Additional Information:** This program was established in 1999 by Intel, which offered it to the Oregon Council of the AeA (formerly American Electronics Association) in the following year. Currently, Intel and other Oregon AeA member companies (such as Xerox and Hewlett Packard) provide ongoing support.

4145 ■ RHODE ISLAND SPACE GRANT
c/o Brown University
Lincoln Field Building
Box 1846
Providence, RI 02912-1846
Tel: (401)863-2889
Fax: (401)863-1292
E-mail: RISpaceGrant@brown.edu

Web Site: http://www.planetary.brown.edu/RI_Space_Grant
To provide financial assistance to undergraduate students at institutions that are members of the Rhode Island Space Grant Consortium (RISGC) who are interested in a career in a space-related field of science, mathematics, or engineering.

Title of Award: Rhode Island Space Grant Undergraduate Scholarship Program **Area, Field, or Subject:** Aerospace sciences; Engineering; Engineering, Aerospace/Aeronautical/Astronautical; Mathematics and mathematical sciences; Science; Space and planetary sciences **Level of Education for which Award is Granted:** Undergraduate **Number Awarded:** Varies each year; recently, 9 of these scholarships were awarded. **Funds Available:** The stipend is $4,000. **Duration:** 1 year.

Eligibility Requirements: This program is open to undergraduate students beyond their freshman year at RISGC-member universities. Applicants must be studying in science, mathematics, or engineering fields of interest to the National Aeronautics and Space Administration (NASA). U.S. citizenship is required. The sponsor is a component of NASA's Space Grant program, which encourages participation by women, underrepresented minorities, and persons with disabilities. **Deadline for Receipt:** February of each year. **Additional Information:** Members of the RISGC are Bryant College, Community College of Rhode Island, Providence College, Roger Williams University, Rhode Island College, Rhode Island School of Design, Salve Regina University, University of Rhode Island, and Wheaton College. This program is funded by NASA. Scholars are designated as research scholars (who are required to devote up to 4 hours per week to outreach activities in science education for K-12 children and teachers through Rhode Island), outreach scholars (who are required to devote up to 8 hours per week to outreach activities), or "Science En Espanol" scholars (who are required to devote up to 8 hours per week to curriculum support for K-12 children and teachers throughout Rhode Island).

4146 ■ RHODE ISLAND SPACE GRANT

c/o Brown University
Lincoln Field Building
Box 1846
Providence, RI 02912-1846
Tel: (401)863-2889
Fax: (401)863-1292
E-mail: RISpaceGrant@brown.edu
Web Site: http://www.planetary.brown.edu/RI_Space_Grant
To provide funding for summer research activities to undergraduate students at institutions that are members of the Rhode Island Space Grant Consortium (RISGC) who are interested in a career in a space-related field of science, mathematics, or engineering.

Title of Award: Rhode Island Space Grant Undergraduate Summer Scholar Program **Area, Field, or Subject:** Aerospace sciences; Engineering; Engineering, Aerospace/Aeronautical/Astronautical; Mathematics and mathematical sciences; Science; Space and planetary sciences **Level of Education for which Award is Granted:** Undergraduate **Number Awarded:** Varies each year; recently, 3 of these scholarships were awarded. **Funds Available:** The stipend is $4,000. **Duration:** 1 summer.

Eligibility Requirements: This program is open to undergraduate students at RISGC-member universities. Applicants must be studying in science, mathematics, or engineering fields of interest to the National Aeronautics and Space Administration (NASA). They must be interested in participating in a research project during the summer with an advisor in their own department. U.S. citizenship is required. The sponsor is a component of NASA's Space Grant program, which encourages participation by women, underrepresented minorities, and persons with disabilities. **Deadline for Receipt:** February of each year. **Additional Information:** Members of the RISGC are Bryant College, Community College of Rhode Island, Providence College, Roger Williams University, Rhode Island College, Rhode Island School of Design, Salve Regina University, University of Rhode Island, and Wheaton College. This program is funded by NASA. Scholars are required to devote 75% of their time to their research and 25% of their time to science education outreach activities organized and coordinated by Rhode Island Space Grant.

4147 ■ ROYAL NEIGHBORS OF AMERICA

Attn: Fraternal Services
230 16th Street
Rock Island, IL 61201-8645

Tel: (309)788-4561
Free: 800-627-4762
E-mail: contact@royalneighbors.org
Web Site: http://www.royalneighbors.org/MemberBenefits/scholarships.cfm
To provide financial assistance for college to women members of the Royal Neighbors of America who plan to enter nontraditional fields.

Title of Award: Eliza D. Watt Scholarships **Area, Field, or Subject:** Computer and information sciences; Engineering; Mathematics and mathematical sciences; Physical sciences **Level of Education for which Award is Granted:** Undergraduate **Number Awarded:** 5 each year. **Funds Available:** The stipend is $2,000 per year. **Duration:** 4 years.

Eligibility Requirements: This program is open to women members of the society who are graduating high school seniors. Applicants must be planning to enter a field considered nontraditional for women, including computer science, engineering, physical sciences, teaching of nontraditional women's fields, business writing, or mathematics. **Deadline for Receipt:** December of each year. **Additional Information:** This program was established in 2004.

4148 ■ SEALASKA CORPORATION

Attn: Sealaska Heritage Institute
One Sealaska Plaza, Suite 301
Juneau, AK 99801-1249
Tel: (907)586-9166; 888-311-4992
Fax: (907)586-9293
E-mail: scholarship@sealaska.com
Web Site: http://www.sealaskaheritage.org/programs/university_scholarships.htm
To provide financial assistance for undergraduate or graduate study to Native Alaskans who have a connection to Sealaska Corporation and are majoring in designated fields.

Title of Award: Sealaska Heritage Institute 7(i) Scholarships **Area, Field, or Subject:** Business administration; Chemistry; Engineering, Chemical; Health care services; Mathematics and mathematical sciences; Natural resources; Physics **Level of Education for which Award is Granted:** Graduate, Undergraduate **Number Awarded:** Varies each year. **Funds Available:** The amount of the award depends on the availability of funds, the number of qualified applicants, class standing, and cumulative GPA. **Duration:** 1 year; may be renewed up to 5 years for a bachelor's degree, up to 3 years for a master's degree, up to 2 years for a doctorate, or up to 3 years for vocational study. The maximum total support is limited to 9 years. Renewal depends on recipients' maintaining full-time enrollment and a GPA of 2.5 or higher.

Eligibility Requirements: This program is open to 1) Alaska Natives who are enrolled to Sealaska Corporation, and 2) Native lineal descendants of Alaska Natives enrolled to Sealaska Corporation, whether or not the applicant owns Sealaska Corporation stock. Applicants must be enrolled or accepted for enrollment as full-time undergraduate or graduate students. Along with their application, they must submit 2 essays: 1) their personal history and educational goals, and 2) their expected contributions to the Alaska Native or Native American community. Financial need is also considered in the selection process. The following areas of study qualify for these awards: natural resources (environmental sciences, engineering, conservation biology, environmental law, fisheries, geology, marine science/biology, forestry, wildlife management, and mining technology); business administration (accounting, finance, marketing, international business, international commerce and trade, management of information systems, human resources management, economics, computer information systems, and industrial management); and other special fields (cadastral surveys, chemistry, equipment/machinery operators, industrial safety specialists, health specialists, plastics engineers, trade specialists, physics, mathematics, and marine trades and occupations). **Deadline for Receipt:** February of each year. **Additional Information:** Funding for this program is provided from Alaska Native Claims Settlement Act (ANSCA) Section 7(i) revenue sharing provisions. Sealaska sponsors a number of other scholarships, including the Cape Fox Scholarships and the Sealaska Heritage Institute Scholarships.

4149 ■ SIEMENS FOUNDATION

170 Wood Avenue South
Iselin, NJ 08830
877-822-5233

Fax: (732)603-5890
E-mail: foundation@sc.siemens.com
Web Site: http://www.siemens-foundation.org/awards
To recognize and reward high school students with exceptional scores on the Advanced Placement (AP) examinations in mathematics and the sciences.

Title of Award: Siemens Awards for Advanced Placement **Area, Field, or Subject:** Biological and clinical sciences; Chemistry; Computer and information sciences; Environmental conservation; Environmental science; Mathematics and mathematical sciences; Physics; Statistics **Level of Education for which Award is Granted:** Professional, Undergraduate **Number Awarded:** 24 regional scholarships (2 females and 2 males in each of the 6 regions), 2 national scholarships (1 female and 1 male), 12 high school awards (in each region, 1 to a school for improvement in the number and percentage of students taking AP examinations, 1 to an urban school for providing access to AP mathematics and science to minorities), and 18 teacher awards (in each region, 2 for commitment to students and the AP program, 1 for teaching minorities) are awarded each year. **Funds Available:** Regional scholarships are $3,000; national winners receive additional $5,000 scholarships. Awards to teachers and to schools are $1,000. **Duration:** The awards are presented annually.
Eligibility Requirements: All students in U.S. high schools are eligible to be considered for these awards (including home-schooled students and those in U.S. territories). Each fall, the College Board identifies the male and female seniors in each of its regions who have earned the highest number of scores on 7 AP exams: biology, calculus BC, chemistry, computer science AB, environmental science, physics C (physics C: mechanics and physics C: electricity each count as half), and statistics. Males and females are considered separately. Regional winners receive all-expense paid trips to Washington, D.C., where national winners are announced. The program also recognizes and rewards monetarily 1) schools that have shown the greatest improvement in the number and percentage of students taking AP examinations in biology, calculus, chemistry, computer science, environmental science, physics, and statistics in the past year; and 2) non-magnet urban schools that provide access to AP mathematics and science to a significant number of underrepresented minority students. In addition, teachers are rewarded for their commitment to students and the AP program. Additional teachers are recognized because they have successfully taught AP mathematics and/or science to underrepresented minority students in non-magnet urban schools. **Deadline for Receipt:** There is no application or nomination process for these awards. The College Board identifies the students, teachers, and high schools for the Siemens Foundation. **Additional Information:** Information from the College Board is available at (703) 707-8999.

4150 ■ SIEMENS FOUNDATION

170 Wood Avenue South
Iselin, NJ 08830
877-822-5233
Fax: (732)603-5890
E-mail: foundation@sc.siemens.com
Web Site: http://www.siemens-foundation.org/scholarship
To recognize and reward outstanding high school seniors who have undertaken individual or team research projects in science, mathematics, and technology (or in combinations of those disciplines).

Title of Award: Siemens Westinghouse Competition Awards **Area, Field, or Subject:** Astronomy and astronomical sciences; Atmospheric science; Biochemistry; Biological and clinical sciences; Chemistry; Computer and information sciences; Earth sciences; Engineering, Civil; Engineering, Electrical; Engineering, Mechanical; Environmental science; Genetics; Geosciences; Materials research/science; Mathematics and mathematical sciences; Nutrition; Physics; Writing **Level of Education for which Award is Granted:** Undergraduate **Number Awarded:** In the initial round of judging, up to 300 regional semifinalists (up to 50 in each region) are selected. Of those, 60 are chosen as regional finalists (5 individuals and 5 teams in each of the 6 regions). Then 12 regional winners (1 individual and 1 team) are selected in the regional competitions, and they become the national finalists. **Funds Available:** At the regional level, finalists receive $1,000 scholarships, both as individuals and members of teams. Individual regional winners receive $3,000 scholarships. Winning regional teams receive $6,000 scholarships to be divided among the team members. Those regional winners then receive additional scholarships as

national finalists. In the national competition, first-place winners receive an additional $100,000 scholarship, second place an additional $50,000 scholarship, third place an additional $40,000 scholarship, fourth place an additional $30,000 scholarship, fifth place an additional $20,000 scholarship, and sixth place an additional $10,000 scholarship. Those national awards are provided both to individuals and to teams to be divided equally among team members. Scholarship money is sent directly to the recipient's college or university to cover undergraduate and/or graduate educational expenses. Schools with regional finalists receive a $2,000 award to be used to support science, mathematics, and technology programs in their schools. **Duration:** The competition is held annually.
Eligibility Requirements: This program is open to high school seniors who are legal or permanent U.S. residents. They must be enrolled in a high school in the United States, Puerto Rico, Guam, Virgin Islands, American Samoa, Wake and Midway Islands, or the Marianas. U.S. high school students enrolled in a Department of Defense dependents school, an accredited overseas American or international school, a foreign school as an exchange student, or a foreign school because their parent(s) live and work abroad are also eligible. Students being home-schooled qualify if they obtain the endorsement of the school district official responsible for such programs. Research projects may be submitted in mathematics and the biological and physical sciences, or involve combinations of disciplines, such as astrophysics, biochemistry, bioengineering, biology, biophysics, botany, chemistry, computer science, civil engineering, earth and atmospheric science engineering, electrical engineering, environmental sciences, fluid dynamics, genetics, geology, materials science, mathematics, mechanical engineering, nutritional science, physics, toxicology, and virology. Both individual and team projects (2 or 3 members) may be entered. All team members must meet the eligibility requirements. Team projects may include seniors, but that is not a requirement. Competition entrants must submit a detailed report on their research project, including a description of the purpose of the research, rationale for the research, pertinent scientific literature, methodology, results, discussion, and conclusion. All projects must be endorsed by a sponsoring high school (except home-schooled students, who obtain their endorsement from the district or state home-school official). Each project must have a project advisor or mentor who is a member of the instructional staff or a person approved by the endorsing high school. There are 3 judging phases to the competition. An initial review panel selects outstanding research projects from 6 different regions of the country. The students submitting these projects are identified as regional semifinalists. Out of those, the highest-rated projects from each region are selected and the students who submitted them are recognized as regional finalists. For the next phase, the regional finalists are offered all-expense paid trips to the regional competition on the campus of a regional university partner, where their projects are reviewed by a panel of judges appointed by the host institution. Regional finalists are required to prepare a poster display of their research project, make an oral presentation about the research and research findings, and respond to questions from the judges. The top-rated individual and the top-rated team project in each region are selected as regional winners to represent the region in the national competition as national finalists. At that competition, the national finalists again display their projects, make oral presentations, and respond to judges' questions. At each phase, selection is based on clarity of expression, comprehensiveness, creativity, field knowledge, future work, interpretation, literature review, presentation, scientific importance, and validity. **Deadline for Receipt:** September of each year. **Additional Information:** The program is offered by Siemens Foundation, in partnership with the College Board. Information is available from the College Board at (703) 707-8999, E-mail: spro@collegeboard.org. Students submitting the projects with the highest evaluations become part of a registry that is circulated to colleges and universities nationwide. To continue receiving scholarships, winners must attend an accredited academic institution on a full-time basis.

4151 ■ SOCIETY OF FLIGHT TEST ENGINEERS

44814 North Elm Avenue
P.O. Box 4037
Lancaster, CA 93539-4037
Tel: (661)949-2095
Fax: (661)949-2096
E-mail: sfte@sfte.org
Web Site: http://www.sfte.org

To provide financial assistance for college to student members and children of members of the Society of Flight Test Engineers (SFTE).

Title of Award: Society of Flight Test Engineers Scholarships **Area, Field, or Subject:** Computer and information sciences; Engineering; Mathematics and mathematical sciences; Physics **Level of Education for which Award is Granted:** Undergraduate **Number Awarded:** 1 or more each year. **Funds Available:** Stipends range from $200 to $2,000. **Duration:** 1 year; recipients may reapply.

Eligibility Requirements: This program is open to college students who have completed at least their freshman year. Applicants must be a student member of SFTE or the child of a member. They must be working on an undergraduate degree in engineering, computer sciences, mathematics, physics, or another technical discipline. Selection is based primarily on academic achievement; financial need is not considered. **Deadline for Receipt:** June of each year.

4152 ■ SOCIETY OF HISPANIC PROFESSIONAL ENGINEERS

5400 East Olympic Boulevard, Suite 210
Los Angeles, CA 90022
Tel: (323)725-3970
Fax: (323)725-0316
Web Site: http://oneshpe.shpe.org.

To provide financial assistance to Hispanic undergraduate and graduate students preparing for a career in science, technology, engineering, mathematics, or a related field.

Title of Award: Advancing Hispanic Excellence in Technology, Engineering, Math, and Science (AHETEMS) General Scholarships **Area, Field, or Subject:** Engineering; Mathematics and mathematical sciences; Science; Technology **Level of Education for which Award is Granted:** Graduate, Undergraduate **Number Awarded:** 1 or more each year. **Funds Available:** Stipends range from $1,000 to $3,000. **Duration:** 1 year.

Eligibility Requirements: This program is open to members of the Society of Hispanic Professional Engineers (SHPE) who are accepted into or attending an accredited 2-year or 4-year college or university in the United States or Puerto Rico. Applicants must be enrolled full time with a major in science, technology, engineering, mathematics, or a related field. High school seniors and undergraduates must have a GPA of 3.0 or higher; graduate students must have a GPA of 3.25 or higher. Along with their application, they must submit a 1-page personal statement covering their family background, community involvement, leadership, academic achievements, research internship and co-op experiences, and short-term and long-term goals and aspirations. Both merit-based and need-based scholarships are available. U.S. citizenship or permanent resident status is required. **Deadline for Receipt:** March of each year. **Additional Information:** Information is also available from the AHETEMS Scholarship Program, University of Texas at Arlington, College of Engineering, Box 19019, Arlington, TX 76019-0019, (817) 272-0776, E-mail: gary.cruz@shpe.org

4153 ■ SOUTH CAROLINA COMMISSION ON HIGHER EDUCATION

Attn: Director of Student Services
1333 Main Street, Suite 200
Columbia, SC 29201
Tel: (803)737-2260; 877-349-7183
Fax: (803)737-2297
E-mail: dbrown@che.sc.gov
Web Site: http://www.che.sc.gov

To provide scholarship/loans to teachers in South Carolina who wish to improve their content knowledge and degree programs.

Title of Award: South Carolina Teaching Scholarship Grants Program **Area, Field, or Subject:** Art; Dance; Economics; Education; Education, Early childhood; Education, Elementary; Education, Music; Education, Secondary; Education, Special; Geography; History; Linguistics; Mathematics and mathematical sciences; Music; Political science; Science **Level of Education for which Award is Granted:** Graduate, Professional, Undergraduate **Number Awarded:** Varies each year. **Funds Available:** The stipend is $1,000 per fiscal year. This is a scholarship/loan program. Recipients must sign a commitment to teach in South Carolina public schools for at least 1 year following completion of the scholarship grant year and agree to refund the scholarship amount if the 1-year teaching commitment is not honored. **Duration:** 1 year; may be renewed if recipients maintain a GPA of 3.0 or higher. They may receive up to 3 grants in a 5-year period.

Eligibility Requirements: This program is open to residents of South Carolina who have a professional teaching certificate and are under contract as a teacher in a public school in the state. Applicants must be 1) accepted as a degree-seeking graduate student in the teaching field at the master's level and enrolled at an eligible institution in the state; or 2) enrolled for graduate or undergraduate courses in their current teaching field or in a teaching field in which they wish to add on certification. Proposed fields of study must relate to core content areas of English, reading or language arts, mathematics, science, foreign languages, civics and government, economics, arts (advanced fine arts, art, dance, drama, music, and speech), history, or geography; early childhood, elementary education, middle level education, secondary education, and special education also qualify. Priority is given to classroom teachers (not administrators, counselors, media specialists, or other support personnel) whose teaching specialties are critical need subject areas. Continuing graduate students must have a GPA of 3.0 or higher. U.S. citizenship or permanent resident status is required. **Deadline for Receipt:** December of each year for second summer session and fall semester; June of each year for spring semester and first summer session. **Additional Information:** This program was established in 2001.

4154 ■ SOUTH CAROLINA STUDENT LOAN CORPORATION

Interstate Center
16 Berryhill Road, Suite 210
P.O. Box 21487
Columbia, SC 29221-1487
Tel: (803)798-0916
Free: 800-347-2752
Fax: (803)772-9410
Web Site: http://www.slc.sc.edu

To provide scholarship/loans to students in South Carolina who wish to teach certain subjects or in certain geographic areas.

Title of Award: South Carolina Teacher Loan Program **Area, Field, or Subject:** Agricultural sciences; Classical studies; Consumer affairs; Dance; Education, Elementary; Education, Music; Education, Special; English language and literature; Foreign languages; Library and archival sciences; Mathematics and mathematical sciences; Science; Speech and language pathology/audiology; Technology **Level of Education for which Award is Granted:** Graduate, Undergraduate **Number Awarded:** Varies each year. **Funds Available:** Freshmen and sophomores may borrow up to $2,500 per academic year; juniors, seniors, and graduate students may borrow up to $5,000 per academic year. This is a scholarship/loan program; loans are forgivable at the rate of 20% or $3,000, whichever is greater, for each full year of teaching in an area (either geographic or subject) of critical need; for students who teach in both critical subject and geographic areas, the rate of cancellation is 33% or $5,000, whichever is greater, per year. Borrowers who fail to teach in either a critical subject or geographic area must repay the loan at an annual interest rate that varies (currently, 5.37%) but is capped at 10.25%. **Duration:** 1 year; may be renewed for a total of 5 years of undergraduate and 5 years of graduate study.

Eligibility Requirements: Eligible to apply are residents of South Carolina who are planning to teach in certain critical geographic areas of the state, or to teach in critical subject areas. Entering freshmen must have ranked in the top 40% of their high school class and have an ACT or SAT score greater than the South Carolina average (recently 986 on the SAT or 19.3 on the ACT); enrolled undergraduates or entering graduate students must have at least a 2.75 cumulative GPA; graduate students who have completed at least 1 term must have a GPA of 3.5 or better. Undergraduate students at South Carolina colleges must have taken and passed the Education Entrance Exam; students at institutions outside South Carolina must have completed the necessary prerequisites required at that institution. Only U.S. citizens may apply. **Deadline for Receipt:** May of each year. **Additional Information:** Recently, the critical subject areas include mathematics, science (biology, chemistry, physics, and general science), media specialist, special education, industrial technology, foreign languages (Spanish, French, Latin, and German), family and consumer science, art, music, business education, English and language arts, dance, speech and drama/theater, and agriculture. For a list of critical geographic area, contact the sponsor.

4155 ■ SOUTH DAKOTA SPACE GRANT CONSORTIUM

Attn: Deputy Director and Outreach Coordinator
South Dakota School of Mines and Technology

Mineral Industries Building, Room 228
501 East St. Joseph Street
Rapid City, SD 57701-3995
Tel: (605)394-1975
Fax: (605)394-5360
E-mail: Thomas.Durkin@sdsmt.edu
Web Site: http://www.sdsmt.edu/space
To provide funding to undergraduate and graduate students for space-related activities in South Dakota.

Title of Award: South Dakota Space Grant Consortium Graduate Fellowships and Undergraduate Scholarships **Area, Field, or Subject:** Aerospace sciences; Earth sciences; Engineering, Aerospace/Aeronautical/Astronautical; Environmental conservation; Environmental science; Geology; Geosciences; Mathematics and mathematical sciences; Space and planetary sciences; Technology **Level of Education for which Award is Granted:** Graduate, Undergraduate **Number Awarded:** Varies each year. Approximately $70,000 is available for this program annually. **Funds Available:** Stipends range from $1,000 to $7,500. **Duration:** 1 academic year, semester, or summer.
Eligibility Requirements: This program is open to undergraduate and graduate students at member and affiliated institutions of the South Dakota Space Grant Consortium. Applicants must be interested in 1) earth- and space-science related educational and research projects in fields relevant to the goals of the U.S. National Aeronautics and Space Administration (NASA); or 2) eventual employment with NASA or in a NASA-related career field in science, technology, engineering, and mathematics (STEM) education. Activities may include student research and educational efforts in remote sensing, GIS, global and regional geoscience, environmental science, and K-12 educational outreach; exposure to NASA-relevant projects; and internship experiences at various NASA centers and the Earth Resources Observation and Science (EROS) Center in Sioux Falls. U.S. citizenship is required. Women, members of underrepresented groups (African Americans, Hispanics, Pacific Islanders, Asian Americans, Native Americans, and persons with disabilities), and Tribal College students are specifically encouraged to apply. Selection is based on academic qualifications of the application (preference is given to students with a GPA of 3.0 or higher), quality of the application and its career goal statement, and assessment of the applicant's motivation toward an earth science, aerospace, or engineering career or research. **Deadline for Receipt:** January of each year. **Additional Information:** Member institutions include South Dakota School of Mines and Technology, South Dakota State University, and Augustana College. Educational affiliates include Black Hills State University, the University of South Dakota, Dakota State University, Lower Brule Community College, Oglala Lakota College, Sinte Gleska University, and Lake Area Technical Institute.

4156 ■ TEXAS SPACE GRANT CONSORTIUM

Attn: Administrative Assistant
3925 West Braker Lane, Suite 200
Austin, TX 78759
Tel: (512)471-3583
Free: 800-248-8742
Fax: (512)471-3585
E-mail: scholarships@tsgc.utexas.edu
Web Site: http://www.tsgc.utexas.edu/grants
To provide financial assistance to upper-division and medical students at Texas universities working on degrees in the fields of space science and engineering.

Title of Award: Columbia Crew Memorial Undergraduate Scholarships **Area, Field, or Subject:** Aerospace sciences; Biological and clinical sciences; Chemistry; Engineering, Aerospace/Aeronautical/Astronautical; Engineering, Chemical; Engineering, Electrical; Engineering, Industrial; Engineering, Mechanical; Geology; Mathematics and mathematical sciences; Physics; Space and planetary sciences **Level of Education for which Award is Granted:** Doctorate, Undergraduate **Number Awarded:** Varies each year; recently, 29 of these scholarships were awarded. **Funds Available:** The stipend is $1,000. **Duration:** 1 year; nonrenewable.
Eligibility Requirements: Applicants must be U.S. citizens, eligible for financial assistance, and registered for full-time study at a participating college or university. Applicants must be a sophomore at a 2-year institution, a junior or senior at a 4-year institution, or a first- or second-year

student at a medical school. Supported fields of study have included aerospace engineering, biology, chemical engineering, chemistry, electrical engineering, geology, industrial engineering, mathematics, mechanical engineering, and physics. The program encourages participation by members of groups underrepresented in science and engineering (persons with disabilities, women, African Americans, Hispanic Americans, Native Americans, and Pacific Islanders). Selection is based on excellence in academics, participation in space education projects, participation in research projects, and exhibited leadership qualities. **Deadline for Receipt:** March of each year. **Additional Information:** In 2003, the Texas Space Grant Consortium renamed its undergraduate scholarship program in honor of the 7 Space Shuttle Columbia astronauts. The participating universities are Baylor University, Lamar University, Prairie View A&M University, Rice University, San Jacinto College, Southern Methodist University, Sul Ross State University, Texas A&M University (including Kingsville and Corpus Christi campuses), Texas Christian University, Texas Southern University, Texas Tech University, Trinity University, University of Houston (including Clear Lake and Downtown campuses), University of Texas at Arlington, University of Texas at Austin, University of Texas at Dallas, University of Texas at El Paso, University of Texas at San Antonio, and University of Texas/Pan American. This program is funded by the National Aeronautics and Space Administration (NASA).

4157 ■ U.S. AIR FORCE

Attn: Headquarters AFROTC/RRUC
551 East Maxwell Boulevard
Maxwell AFB, AL 36112-5917
Tel: (334)953-2091; (866)423-7682
Fax: (334)953-6167
Web Site: http://www.afrotc.com/scholarships/hsschol/types.php
To provide financial assistance to high school seniors or graduates who are interested in joining Air Force ROTC in college and are willing to serve as Air Force officers following completion of their bachelor's degree.

Title of Award: Air Force ROTC High School Scholarships **Area, Field, or Subject:** Architecture; Chemistry; Computer and information sciences; Engineering, Aerospace/Aeronautical/Astronautical; Engineering, Architectural; Engineering, Civil; Engineering, Computer; Engineering, Electrical; Engineering, Mechanical; Environmental science; General studies/Field of study not specified; Mathematics and mathematical sciences; Meteorology; Operations research; Physics **Level of Education for which Award is Granted:** Four Year College **Number Awarded:** Approximately 2,000 each year. **Funds Available:** Type 1 scholarships provide payment of full tuition and most laboratory fees, as well as $600 for books. Type 2 scholarships pay the same benefits except tuition is capped at $15,000 per year; students who attend an institution where tuition exceeds $15,000 must pay the difference. Type 7 scholarships pay full tuition and most laboratory fees, but students must attend a college or university where the tuition is less than $9,000 per year or a public college or university where they qualify for the in-state tuition rate; they may not attend an institution with higher tuition and pay the difference. Approximately 5% of scholarship offers are for Type 1, approximately 20% are for Type 2, and approximately 75% are for type 7. All recipients are also awarded a tax-free subsistence allowance for 10 months of each year that is $250 per month as a freshman, $300 per month as a sophomore, $350 per month as a junior, and $400 per month as a senior. **Duration:** 4 years.
Eligibility Requirements: This program is open to high school seniors who are U.S. citizens at least 17 of age and have been accepted at a college or university with an Air Force ROTC unit on campus or a college with a cross-enrollment agreement with such a college. Applicants must have a cumulative GPA of 3.0 or higher and an ACT composite score of 24 or higher or an SAT score of 1100 (mathematics and verbal portion only) or higher. At the time of their commissioning in the Air Force, they must be no more than 31 years of age. They must agree to serve for at least 4 years as active-duty Air Force officers following graduation from college. **Deadline for Receipt:** November of each year. **Additional Information:** Recently, approximately 70% of these scholarships were offered to students planning to major in the science and technical fields of architecture, chemistry, computer science, engineering (aeronautical, aerospace, astronautical, architectural, civil, computer, electrical, environmental, or mechanical), mathematics, meteorology and atmospheric sciences, operations research, or physics. Approximately 30% were offered to students in all other fields. While scholarship recipients

can major in any subject, they must enroll in 4 years of aerospace studies courses at 1 of the 144 colleges and universities that have an Air Force ROTC unit on campus; students may also attend nearly 900 other colleges that have cross-enrollment agreements with the institutions that have an Air Force ROTC unit on campus. Recipients must attend a 4-week summer training camp at an Air Force base, usually between their sophomore and junior years. Most cadets incur a 4-year active-duty commitment. Pilots incur a 10-year active-duty service commitment after successfully completing Specialized Undergraduate Pilot Training and navigators incur a 6-year commitment after successfully completing Specialized Undergraduate Navigator Training. The minimum service obligation for intelligence and Air Battle Management career fields is 5 years.

4158 ■ U.S. AIR FORCE

Attn: Headquarters AFROTC/RRUC
551 East Maxwell Boulevard
Maxwell AFB, AL 36112-5917
Tel: (334)953-2091; (866)423-7682
Fax: (334)953-6167
Web Site: http://www.afrotc.com/scholarships/incolschol/incolProgram.php
To provide financial assistance to undergraduate students who are willing to join Air Force ROTC in college and serve as Air Force officers following completion of their bachelor's degree.

Title of Award: Air Force ROTC In-College Scholarship Program **Area, Field, or Subject:** Architecture; Chemistry; Computer and information sciences; Engineering, Aerospace/Aeronautical/Astronautical; Engineering, Architectural; Engineering, Civil; Engineering, Computer; Engineering, Electrical; Engineering, Mechanical; Environmental science; General studies/Field of study not specified; Mathematics and mathematical sciences; Meteorology; Operations research; Physics **Level of Education for which Award is Granted:** Undergraduate **Number Awarded:** Varies each year. **Funds Available:** Cadets selected in Phase 1 are awarded type 2 AFROTC scholarships that provide for payment of tuition and fees, to a maximum of $15,000 per year. A limited number of cadets selected in Phase 2 are also awarded type 2 AFROTC scholarships, but most are awarded type 3 AFROTC scholarships with tuition capped at $9,000 per year. Cadets selected in Phase 3 are awarded type 6 AFROTC scholarships with tuition capped at $3,000 per year. All recipients are also awarded a book allowance of $600 and a tax-free subsistence allowance for 10 months of each year that is $300 per month during the sophomore year, $350 during the junior year, and $400 during the senior year. **Duration:** 3 years for students selected as freshmen or 2 years for students selected as sophomores.

Eligibility Requirements: This program is open to U.S. citizens enrolled as freshmen or sophomores at 1 of the 144 colleges and universities that have an Air Force ROTC unit on campus. Applicants must have a cumulative GPA of 2.5 or higher and be able to pass the Air Force Officer Qualifying Test and the Air Force ROTC Physical Fitness Test. At the time of commissioning, they may be no more than 31 years of age. They must agree to serve for at least 4 years as active-duty Air Force officers following graduation from college. Phase 1 is open to students enrolled in the Air Force ROTC program who do not currently have a scholarship but now wish to apply. Phase 2 is open to Phase 1 nonselects and students not enrolled in Air Force ROTC. Phase 3 is open only to Phase 2 nonselects. Recently, the program gave preference to students majoring in the science and technical fields of architecture, chemistry, computer science, engineering (aeronautical, aerospace, astronautical, architectural, civil, computer, electrical, environmental, or mechanical), mathematics, meteorology and atmospheric sciences, operations research, or physics. **Deadline for Receipt:** January of each year. **Additional Information:** While scholarship recipients can major in any subject, they must complete 4 years of aerospace studies courses at 1 of the 144 colleges or universities that have an Air Force ROTC unit on campus. Recipients must also attend a 4-week summer training camp at an Air Force base, usually between their sophomore and junior years; 2-year scholarship awardees attend in the summer after their junior year. Current military personnel are eligible for early release from active duty in order to enter the Air Force

ROTC program. Following completion of their bachelor's degree, scholarship recipients earn a commission as a second lieutenant in the Air Force and serve at least 4 years.

4159 ■ U.S. AIR FORCE

Attn: Headquarters AFROTC/RRUE
Enlisted Commissioning Section
551 East Maxwell Boulevard
Maxwell AFB, AL 36112-5917
Tel: (334)953-2091; (866)423-7682
Fax: (334)953-6167
E-mail: enlisted@afrotc.com
Web Site: http://www.afoats.af.mil/AFROTC/EnlistedComm/AECP.asp
To allow selected enlisted Air Force personnel to earn a bachelor's degree in approved majors by providing financial assistance for full-time college study.

Title of Award: Airman Education and Commissioning Program **Area, Field, or Subject:** African studies; Asian studies; Computer and information sciences; Engineering; Foreign languages; Mathematics and mathematical sciences; Meteorology; Near Eastern studies; Nursing; Physics; Russian studies **Level of Education for which Award is Granted:** Undergraduate **Number Awarded:** Approximately 60 each year. **Funds Available:** While participating in this program, cadets remain on active duty in the Air Force and receive their regular salary and benefits. They also receive payment of tuition and fees up to $15,000 per year and an annual textbook allowance of $600. **Duration:** 1 to 3 years, until completion of a bachelor's degree.

Eligibility Requirements: Eligible to participate in this program are enlisted members of the Air Force who have been accepted at a university or college (or approved crosstown institution) that is associated with AFROTC and that offers an approved major. The majors currently supported are computer science, all ABET-accredited engineering fields (not engineering technology), foreign area studies (limited to Middle East, Africa, Asia, Russia/Eurasia), foreign languages (limited to Arabic, Armenian, Azeri, Chinese, French, Georgian, Hebrew, Hindi, Indonesian, Kazakh, Pashto, Persian Farsi, Russian, Swahili, and Turkish), mathematics, meteorology, nursing, and physics. Applicants must have completed at least 1 year of time-in-service and 1 year of time-on-station. They must have scores on the Air Force Officer Qualifying Test of at least 15 on the verbal and 10 on the quantitative and be able to pass the Air Force ROTC Physical Fitness Test. Normally they should have completed at least 30 semester hours of college study with a GPA of 2.75 or higher. They must be younger than 31 years of age or otherwise able to be commissioned before they become 35 years of age. **Deadline for Receipt:** February of each year. **Additional Information:** While attending college, participants in this program attend ROTC classes at their college or university. Upon completing their degree, they are commissioned to serve in the Air Force in their area of specialization with an active-duty service commitment of at least 4 years. Further information is available from base education service officers or an Air Force ROTC unit. This program does not provide for undergraduate flying training.

4160 ■ U.S. AIR FORCE

Attn: Headquarters AFROTC/RRUE
Enlisted Commissioning Section
551 East Maxwell Boulevard
Maxwell AFB, AL 36112-5917
Tel: (334)953-2091; (866)423-7682
Fax: (334)953-6167
E-mail: enlisted@afrotc.com
Web Site: http://www.afoats.af.mil/AFROTC/EnlistedComm/ASCP.asp
To allow selected enlisted Air Force personnel to earn a bachelor's degree in approved majors by providing financial assistance for full-time college study.

Title of Award: Airman Scholarship and Commissioning Program **Area, Field, or Subject:** Architecture; Atmospheric science; Chemistry; Computer and information sciences; Engineering; Engineering, Aerospace/Aeronautical/Astronautical; Engineering, Architectural; Engineering, Civil; Engineering, Computer; Engineering, Electrical; Engineering, Mechanical; Environmental science; General studies/Field of study not specified; Mathematics and mathematical sciences; Meteorology; Operations research; Physics **Level of Education for which Award is Granted:** Undergraduate **Number Awarded:** Varies each year. **Funds**

Available: Awards are type 2 AFROTC scholarships that provide for payment of tuition and fees, to a maximum of $15,000 per year, plus an annual book allowance of $600. All recipients are also awarded a tax-free subsistence allowance for 10 months of each year that is $300 per month during their sophomore year, $350 during their junior year, and $400 during their senior year. **Duration:** 2 to 4 years, until completion of a bachelor's degree.

Eligibility Requirements: This program is open to active-duty enlisted members of the Air Force who have completed at least 1 year of continuous active duty and at least 1 year on station. Applicants normally must have completed at least 24 semester hours of graded college credit with a cumulative college GPA of 2.5 or higher. If they have not completed 24 hours of graded college credit, they must have an ACT score of 24 or higher or an SAT combined verbal and mathematics score of 1100 or higher. They must also have scores on the Air Force Officer Qualifying Test (AFOQT) of 15 or more on the verbal scale and 10 or more on the quantitative scale and be able to pass the Air Force ROTC Physical Fitness Test. Applicants must have been accepted at a college or university (including crosstown schools) offering the AFROTC 4-year program. When they complete the program and receive their commission, they may not be 31 years of age or older. U.S. citizenship is required. Recently, awards were presented according to the following priorities: 1) computer, electrical, and environmental engineering; 2) aeronautical, aerospace, architectural, astronautical, civil, and mechanical engineering and meteorology and atmospheric sciences; 3) all other ABET-accredited engineering majors, architecture, chemistry, computer science, mathematics, operations research, and physics; 4) all other majors. **Deadline for Receipt:** October of each year. **Additional Information:** Selectees separate from the active-duty Air Force, join an AFROTC detachment, and become full-time students. Upon completing their degree, they are commissioned as officers and returned to active duty in the Air Force with a 4-year service obligation. Further information is available from base education service officers or an Air Force ROTC unit.

4161 ■ U.S. AIR FORCE

Attn: Headquarters AFROTC/RRUE
Enlisted Commissioning Section
551 East Maxwell Boulevard
Maxwell AFB, AL 36112-5917
Tel: (334)953-2091; (866)423-7682
Fax: (334)953-6167
E-mail: enlisted@afrotc.com
Web Site: http://www.afoats.af.mil/AFROTC/EnlistedComm/POC-ERP.asp
To allow selected enlisted Air Force personnel to earn a baccalaureate degree by providing financial assistance for full-time college study.

Title of Award: Professional Officer Course Early Release Program **Area, Field, or Subject:** Architecture; Atmospheric science; Chemistry; Computer and information sciences; Engineering; Engineering, Aerospace/Aeronautical/Astronautical; Engineering, Architectural; Engineering, Civil; Engineering, Computer; Engineering, Electrical; Engineering, Mechanical; Environmental science; General studies/Field of study not specified; Mathematics and mathematical sciences; Meteorology; Operations research; Physics **Level of Education for which Award is Granted:** Undergraduate **Number Awarded:** Varies each year. **Funds Available:** Participants receive a stipend for 10 months of the year that is $350 per month during the first year and $400 per month during the second year. Scholarship recipients earn the Professional Officer Course Incentive of $3,000 per year for tuition and $600 per year for books. **Duration:** 2 years (no more and no less).

Eligibility Requirements: Eligible to participate in this program are enlisted members of the Air Force under the age of 30 (or otherwise able to be commissioned before becoming 35 years of age) who have completed at least 1 year on continuous active duty, have served on station for at least 1 year, and have no more than 2 years remaining to complete their initial baccalaureate degree. Scholarship applicants must be younger than 31 years of age when they graduate and earn their commission. All applicants must have been accepted at a college or university offering the AFROTC 4-year program and must have a cumulative college GPA of 2.5 or higher. Their Air Force Officer Qualifying Test (AFOQT) scores must be at least 15 on the verbal and 10 on the quantitative. Applicants who have not completed 24 units of college work must have an ACT composite score of 24 or higher or an SAT combined verbal and

mathematics score of 1100 or higher. U.S. citizenship is required. Recently, awards were presented according to the following priorities: 1) computer, electrical, and environmental engineering; 2) aeronautical, aerospace, architectural, astronautical, civil, and mechanical engineering and meteorology and atmospheric sciences; 3) all other ABET-accredited engineering majors, architecture, chemistry, computer science, mathematics, operations research, and physics; 4) all other majors. **Deadline for Receipt:** October of each year. **Additional Information:** Upon completing their degree, selectees are commissioned as officers in the Air Force with a 4-year service obligation. Further information is available from base education service officers or an Air Force ROTC unit.

4162 ■ U.S. NAVY

Attn: Navy Personnel Command
5722 Integrity Drive
Millington, TN 38054-5057
Tel: (901)874-3070; 888-633-9674
Fax: (901)874-2651
E-mail: nukeprograms@cnrc.navy.mil
Web Site: http://www.cnrc.navy.mil/nucfield/college/officer_options.htm
To provide financial assistance to college juniors and seniors who wish to serve in the Navy's nuclear propulsion training program following graduation.

Title of Award: Nuclear Propulsion Officer Candidate (NUPOC) Program **Area, Field, or Subject:** Chemistry; Engineering; General studies/Field of study not specified; Mathematics and mathematical sciences; Physics **Level of Education for which Award is Granted:** Four Year College **Number Awarded:** Varies each year. **Funds Available:** Participants become Active Reserve enlisted Navy personnel and receive a salary of up to $2,500 per month; the exact amount depends on the local cost of living and other factors. A bonus of $10,000 is also paid at the time of enlistment and another $2,000 upon completion of nuclear power training. **Duration:** Up to 30 months, until completion of a bachelor's degree.

Eligibility Requirements: This program is open to U.S. citizens who are entering their junior or senior year of college as a full-time student. Strong technical majors (mathematics, physics, chemistry, or an engineering field) are encouraged but not required. Applicants must have completed at least 1 year of calculus and 1 year of physics and must have earned a grade of "C" or better in all mathematics, science, and technical courses. Normally, they must be 26 years of age or younger at the expected date of commissioning, although applicants for the design and research specialty may be 29 years old. **Additional Information:** Following graduation, participants attend Officer Candidate School in Pensacola, Florida for 4 months and receive their commissions. They have a service obligation of 8 years (of which at least 5 years must be on active duty), beginning with 6 months at the Navy Nuclear Power Training Command in Charleston, South Carolina and 6 more months of hands-on training at a nuclear reactor facility. Further information on this program is available from a local Navy recruiter or the Navy Recruiting Command, 801 North Randolph Street, Arlington, VA 22203-1991.

4163 ■ U.S. NAVY

Attn: Commander, Naval Service Training Command
250 Dallas Street, Suite A
Pensacola, FL 32508-5268
Tel: (850)452-9563
Fax: (850)452-2486
E-mail: PNSC-STA21@navy.mil
Web Site: http://www.navy.com/careers/officerplanner/enlistedtoofficer
To allow outstanding enlisted Navy personnel to complete a bachelor's degree and receive a commission in the Supply Corps.

Title of Award: Supply Corps Option of the Seaman to Admiral-21 Program **Area, Field, or Subject:** Business administration; Engineering; Mathematics and mathematical sciences **Level of Education for which Award is Granted:** Four Year College **Number Awarded:** Varies each year. **Funds Available:** Awardees continue to receive their regular Navy pay and allowances while they attend college on a full-time basis. They also receive reimbursement for tuition, fees, and books up to $10,000 per year. If base housing is available, they are eligible to live there. Participants are not eligible to receive benefits under the Navy's Tuition Assistance Program (TA), the Montgomery GI Bill (MGIB), Navy College Fund, or the Veterans Educational Assistance Program (VEAP). **Duration:** Selectees are supported for up to 36 months of full-time, year-round study or completion of a bachelor's degree, as long as they maintain a GPA of 2.5 or higher.

Eligibility Requirements: This program is open to U.S. citizens who are currently serving on active duty in the U.S. Navy or Naval Reserve, including Training and Administration of the Reserves (TAR), Selected Reserves (SELRES), and Navy Reservists on active duty except for those on active for training (ACDUTRA). Applicants must be high school graduates (or GED recipients) who are able to complete requirements for a baccalaureate degree in a business, engineering, or mathematics related field in 36 months or less. When they complete their degree requirements, they must be younger than 27 years of age. Within the past 3 years, they must have taken the SAT test (and achieved scores of at least 500 on the mathematics section and 500 on the verbal or critical reading section) or the ACT test (and achieved a score of 41 or higher, including at least 21 on the mathematics portion and 20 on the English portion). **Deadline for Receipt:** July of each year. **Additional Information:** This program was established in 2001 as a replacement for the Seaman to Admiral Program (established in 1994), the Enlisted Commissioning Program, and other specialized programs for sailors to earn a commission. Upon acceptance into the program, selectees attend the Naval Science Institute (NSI) in Newport, Rhode Island for an 8-week program in the fundamental core concepts of being a naval officer (navigation, engineering, weapons, military history and justice, etc.). They then enter a college or university with an NROTC unit or affiliation and pursue full-time study for a bachelor's degree. They become members of and drill with the NROTC unit. When they complete their degree, they are commissioned as ensigns in the United States Naval Reserve and assigned to initial training as an officer in the Supply Corps. After commissioning, 5 years of active service are required.

4164 ■ VIRGINIA SPACE GRANT CONSORTIUM

Attn: Fellowship Coordinator
Old Dominion University Peninsula Center
600 Butler Farm Road
Hampton, VA 23666
Tel: (757)766-5210
Fax: (757)766-5205
E-mail: vsgc@odu.edu
Web Site: http://www.vsgc.odu.edu/Menu3_1_1.htm

To provide financial assistance to students who are interested in pursuing space-related studies at community colleges in Virginia.

Title of Award: Virginia Space Grant Community College Scholarship Program **Area, Field, or Subject:** Aerospace sciences; Computer and information sciences; Electronics; Engineering; Mathematics and mathematical sciences; Space and planetary sciences; Technology **Level of Education for which Award is Granted:** Two Year College **Number Awarded:** Approximately 10 each year. **Funds Available:** The maximum stipend is $1,500. **Duration:** 1 year; nonrenewable.

Eligibility Requirements: This program is open to students currently enrolled in a Virginia community college who are U.S. citizens and have completed at least the first semester of their program with a GPA of 3.0 or higher. Awards are generally made to full-time students, but part-time students demonstrating academic merit are also eligible. Applicants can be enrolled in any program that includes course work related to an understanding of or interest in technological fields supporting aerospace; that includes (but is not limited to) computers, electronics, engineering, industrial technology, and mathematics. Since a particular goal of the program is to increase the participation of underrepresented minorities, women, and persons with disabilities in aerospace-related, high technology careers, the sponsor especially encourages applications from those students. **Deadline for Receipt:** February of each year. **Additional Information:** This program is funded by the U.S. National Aeronautics and Space Administration (NASA).

4165 ■ VIRGINIA SPACE GRANT CONSORTIUM

Attn: Fellowship Coordinator
Old Dominion University Peninsula Center
600 Butler Farm Road
Hampton, VA 23666
Tel: (757)766-5210
Fax: (757)766-5205
E-mail: vsgc@odu.edu
Web Site: http://www.vsgc.odu.edu/Menu3_1_1.htm

To provide financial assistance for college or graduate school to students in Virginia planning a career as science, mathematics, or technology educators.

Title of Award: Virginia Space Grant Teacher Education Scholarship Program **Area, Field, or Subject:** Aerospace sciences; Earth sciences; Education; Environmental conservation; Environmental science; Geosciences; Mathematics and mathematical sciences; Science; Space and planetary sciences; Technology **Level of Education for which Award is Granted:** Four Year College, Master's **Number Awarded:** Approximately 10 each year. **Funds Available:** The maximum stipend is $1,000. **Duration:** 1 year; nonrenewable.

Eligibility Requirements: This program is open to full-time undergraduate students at the Virginia Space Grant Consortium (VSGC) colleges and universities in a track that will qualify them to teach in a pre-college setting. Priority is given to those majoring in technology education, mathematics, or science, particularly earth, space, or environmental science. Applicants may apply while seniors in high school or sophomores in a community college, with the award contingent on their enrollment at a VSGC college and entrance into a teacher certification program. They must submit a statement of academic goals and plan of study, explaining their reasons for desiring to enter the teaching profession, specifically the fields of science, mathematics, or technology education. Students currently enrolled in a VSGC college can apply when they declare their intent to enter the teacher certification program. Students enrolled in a master of education degree program leading to teacher certification in eligible fields are also eligible to apply. Applicants must be U.S. citizens with a GPA of 3.0 or higher. Since an important purpose of this program is to increase the participation of underrepresented minorities, women, and persons with disabilities in science, mathematics, and technology education, the VSGC especially encourages applications from those students. **Deadline for Receipt:** February of each year. **Additional Information:** The VSGC institutions are College of William and Mary, Hampton University, Old Dominion University, the University of Virginia, and Virginia Polytechnic Institute and State University. This program is funded by the U.S. National Aeronautics and Space Administration (NASA).

4166 ■ WASHINGTON HIGHER EDUCATION COORDINATING BOARD

917 Lakeridge Way
P.O. Box 43430
Olympia, WA 98504-3430
Tel: (360)753-7851; 888-535-0747
Fax: (360)753-7808
E-mail: futureteachers@hecb.wa.gov
Web Site: http://www.hecb.wa.gov/financialaid/other/alternative.asp

To provide forgivable loans to K-12 classified employees in Washington who are interested in attending a college or university in order to become a teacher.

Title of Award: Washington Conditional Scholarships for Alternative Teaching Certification **Area, Field, or Subject:** Chemistry; Education; Education, Bilingual and cross-cultural; Education, Elementary; Education, English as a second language; Education, Secondary; Education, Special; Foreign languages; Mathematics and mathematical sciences; Physics; Technology **Level of Education for which Award is Granted:** Professional, Undergraduate **Number Awarded:** Approximately 25 each year. **Funds Available:** The maximum award is $4,000 per academic year. These awards are in the form of loans that can be forgiven in exchange for teaching service. Each 2 years of eligible teaching service results in the forgiveness of 1 year of loan. **Duration:** 1 year; may be renewed up to 4 additional years.

Eligibility Requirements: This program is open to Washington residents who are currently employed as a classified instructional employee in a K-12 public school. Applicants must 1) have a transferable associate degree and be seeking residency teacher certification with endorsements in special education or English as a second language; or 2) have a bachelor's degree and subject matter expertise in a shortage area and be seeking residency teacher certification in a subject matter shortage area (currently defined as special education, English as a second language, chemistry, physics, Japanese, mathematics, and technology education). to enroll in an accredited Washington college or university and work as a teacher in a K-12 public school in the state after completing initial teacher certification. Selection is based on academic ability, a statement demonstrating commitment to the teaching profession, the applicant's ability to serve as a positive role model as a K-12 public school teacher, length and quality of contributions to the Washington K-12 public school, and recommendations from a current teacher or school official describing the applicant's potential as a future teacher. The priority in making awards is: 1) eligible renewal applicants who are within 2 years of completing their initial teacher certification requirements; 2) all other eligible renewable applicants; 3) eligible new applicants who are within 2 years of completing their initial teacher certification requirements; and 4) all other new eligible applicants. **Deadline for Receipt:** October of each year. **Additional Information:** This program was established by the Washington legislature in 2001. It is administered by the Washington Higher Education Coordinator Board, but the Washington State Professional Educator Standards Board selects the recipients.

4167 ■ WASHINGTON NASA SPACE GRANT CONSORTIUM

c/o University of Washington
Johnson Hall, Room 141
Box 351310
Seattle, WA 98195-1310
Tel: (206)543-1943
Free: 800-659-1943
Fax: (206)543-0179
E-mail: nasa@u.washington.edu
Web Site: http://www.waspacegrant.org/undergr.html
To provide financial assistance for college to students in Washington who wish to study science, engineering, or mathematics with an emphasis on space.
Title of Award: Washington NASA Space Grant Consortium Undergraduate Scholarships **Area, Field, or Subject:** Aerospace sciences; Engineering; Engineering, Aerospace/Aeronautical/Astronautical; Mathematics and mathematical sciences; Science; Space and planetary sciences **Level of Education for which Award is Granted:** Undergraduate **Number Awarded:** Varies each year. **Funds Available:** Stipends vary at participating institutions, but range from $1,000 to $5,000. **Duration:** 1 year; may be renewed.
Eligibility Requirements: This program is open to residents of Washington who are attending or planning to attend designated institutions that are members of the Washington NASA Space Grant Consortium. Applicants must be interested in majoring in space-related aspects of science, engineering, or mathematics. U.S. citizenship is required. The program values diversity and strongly encourages women and minorities to apply. **Deadline for Receipt:** Each participating institution sets its own deadline. **Additional Information:** This program is funded by the U.S. National Aeronautics and Space Administration (NASA). Members of the consortium that offer undergraduate scholarships are Northwest Indian College, Seattle Central Community College, University of Washington, and Washington State University.

4168 ■ WEST VIRGINIA SPACE GRANT CONSORTIUM

c/o West Virginia University
College of Engineering and Mineral Resources
G-68 Engineering Sciences Building
P.O. Box 6070
Morgantown, WV 26506-6070
Tel: (304)293-4099
Fax: (304)293-4970
E-mail: nasa@cemr.wvu.edu
Web Site: http://www.nasa.wvu.edu/scholarships.html
To provide financial assistance to undergraduates at academic institutions affiliated with the West Virginia Space Grant Consortium who wish to conduct a space-related science or engineering research project.
Title of Award: West Virginia Space Grant Consortium Undergraduate Research Fellowship Program **Area, Field, or Subject:** Aerospace sciences; Engineering, Aerospace/Aeronautical/Astronautical; Mathematics and mathematical sciences; Space and planetary sciences **Level of Education for which Award is Granted:** Undergraduate **Number Awarded:** Varies each year. **Funds Available:** Grants range from $1,000 to $5,000. **Duration:** 1 academic year or summer.
Eligibility Requirements: This program is open to full-time undergraduates enrolled in mathematics, science, or engineering programs at member institutions of the consortium. Applicants must be interested in conducting a space-related research project with a faculty member from their department who agrees to serve as a mentor and research advisor.

Selection is based on soundness and technical merit of the proposed research (50 points), student's academic and extracurricular achievements (30 points), and budget and plans for dissemination and publicizing of the results (20 points). The consortium is a component of the Space Grant program of the U.S. National Aeronautics and Space Administration (NASA), which strongly encourages participation by members of underrepresented groups (minorities, women, and persons with disabilities). **Deadline for Receipt:** March of each year. **Additional Information:** Funding for this program is provided by NASA. The consortium includes Bethany College, Bluefield College, Fairmont State College, Marshall University, Shepherd College, West Liberty State College, West Virginia Institute of Technology, West Virginia State College, West Virginia University, West Virginia Wesleyan College, and Wheeling-Jesuit University.

4169 ■ WISCONSIN FOUNDATION FOR INDEPENDENT COLLEGES, INC.

Attn: Program Manager
735 North Water Street, Suite 600
Milwaukee, WI 53202-4100
Tel: (414)273-5980
Fax: (414)273-5995
E-mail: wfic@wficweb.org
Web Site: http://www.wficweb.org/scholar.html
To provide financial assistance to students majoring in selected fields at member institutions of the Wisconsin Foundation for Independent Colleges (WFIC).
Title of Award: Sentry Insurance Foundation Scholarships **Area, Field, or Subject:** Architecture; Business administration; Design; Economics; Information science and technology; Interior design; Mathematics and mathematical sciences **Level of Education for which Award is Granted:** Four Year College **Number Awarded:** 20 each year: 1 at each of the participating schools. **Funds Available:** The stipend is $1,000. **Duration:** 1 year.
Eligibility Requirements: This program is open to student enrolled or planning to enroll at WFIC member colleges and universities. Applicants must have a declared major in 1 of the following fields: business, economics, mathematics, management information systems, industrial design, communication design, or interior architecture and design. They must have a GPA of 3.3 or higher; entering freshmen must rank in the top 25% of their high school class. Financial need is considered in the selection process. **Deadline for Receipt:** Each participating college sets its own deadline. **Additional Information:** The WFIC member schools are Alverno College, Beloit College, Cardinal Stritch University, Carroll College, Carthage College, Concordia University of Wisconsin, Edgewood College, Lakeland College, Lawrence University, Marian College, Marquette University, Milwaukee Institute of Art & Design, Milwaukee School of Engineering, Mount Mary College, Northland College, Ripon College, St. Norbert College, Silver Lake College, Viterbo University, and Wisconsin Lutheran College. This program is supported by the Sentry Insurance Foundation.

4170 ■ WYOMING TRUCKING ASSOCIATION, INC.

Attn: WTA Scholarship Trust Fund
555 North Poplar
P.O. Box 1909
Casper, WY 82602
Tel: (307)234-1579
Fax: (307)234-7082
E-mail: wytruck@aol.com
To provide financial assistance to high school seniors and currently-enrolled college students in Wyoming who are interested in preparing for a career in the highway transportation industry.
Title of Award: Wyoming Trucking Association Scholarships **Area, Field, or Subject:** Accounting; Business administration; Computer and information sciences; Management; Mechanics and repairs; Secretarial sciences; Transportation **Level of Education for which Award is Granted:** Undergraduate **Number Awarded:** 1 to 10 each year. **Funds Available:** Stipends range from $500 to $1,000. **Duration:** 1 year.
Eligibility Requirements: This program is open to high school seniors and graduates in Wyoming who are enrolled or planning to enroll in a community college in Wyoming, a trade school in the state, or the University of Wyoming. Applicants must be majoring or planning to major

in a course of study that could lead to a career in the transportation industry, including (but not limited to) business management, computer skills, accounting, office procedures and management, safety, diesel mechanics, and truck driving. Along with their application, they must submit a 1-page essay on "How is the trucking industry important to you and the State of Wyoming." Financial need is considered in the selection process. **Deadline for Receipt:** March of each year.

Computer Science

4171 ■ ALABAMA SPACE GRANT CONSORTIUM
c/o University of Alabama in Huntsville
Materials Science Building, Room 205
Huntsville, AL 35899
Tel: (256)824-6800
Fax: (256)824-6061
E-mail: reasonj@uah.edu
Web Site: http://www.uah.edu/ASGC
To provide financial assistance to undergraduates who are studying the space sciences at universities participating in the Alabama Space Grant Consortium (ASGC).
Title of Award: Undergraduate Scholarship Program of the Alabama Space Grant Consortium **Area, Field, or Subject:** Aerospace sciences; Behavioral sciences; Biological and clinical sciences; Business administration; Communications; Computer and information sciences; Economics; Education; Engineering, Aerospace/Aeronautical/Astronautical; International affairs and relations; Law; Natural sciences; Physical sciences; Public administration; Sociology; Space and planetary sciences **Level of Education for which Award is Granted:** Four Year College **Number Awarded:** Varies each year; recently, 32 of these scholarships were awarded. **Funds Available:** The stipend is $1,000 per year. **Duration:** 1 year; may be renewed 1 additional year.
Eligibility Requirements: This program is open to full-time students entering their junior or senior year at universities participating in the ASGC. Applicants must be studying in a field related to space, including the physical, natural, and biological sciences; engineering; education; economics; business; sociology; behavioral sciences; computer science; communications; law; international affairs; and public administration. They must be U.S. citizens and have a GPA of 3.0 or higher. Individuals from underrepresented groups (African Americans, Hispanic, American Indians, Pacific Islanders, Asian Americans, and women) are especially encouraged to apply. Interested students should submit a completed application with a career goal statement, personal references, a brief resume, and transcripts. Selection is based on 1) academic qualifications, 2) quality of the career goal statement, and 3) assessment of the applicant's motivation for a career in aerospace. **Deadline for Receipt:** February of each year. **Additional Information:** The member universities are University of Alabama in Huntsville, Alabama A&M University, University of Alabama, University of Alabama at Birmingham, University of South Alabama, Tuskegee University, and Auburn University. Funding for this program is provided by NASA.

4172 ■ AMERICAN COUNCIL OF THE BLIND
Attn: Coordinator, Scholarship Program
1155 15th Street, N.W., Suite 1004
Washington, DC 20005
Tel: (202)467-5081
Free: 800-424-8666
Fax: (202)467-5085
E-mail: info@acb.org
Web Site: http://www.acb.org
To provide financial assistance to students who are blind and interested in preparing for a career in the computer field.
Title of Award: Kellie Cannon Memorial Scholarship **Area, Field, or Subject:** Computer and information sciences **Level of Education for which Award is Granted:** Undergraduate **Number Awarded:** 1 each year. **Funds Available:** The stipend is $2,000. In addition, the winner receives a Kurzweil-1000 Reading System. **Duration:** 1 year.
Eligibility Requirements: Eligible to apply are high school seniors, high school graduates, and college students who are blind and are interested in majoring in college in computer information systems or data processing. In addition to letters of recommendation and copies of academic

transcripts, applications must include an autobiographical sketch. A cumulative GPA of 3.3 or higher is generally required. Selection is based on demonstrated academic record, involvement in extracurricular and civic activities, and academic objectives. The severity of the applicant's visual impairment and his/her study methods are also taken into account. **Deadline for Receipt:** February of each year. **Additional Information:** This program is sponsored by Blind Information Technology Specialist (BITS), Inc, a special interest affiliate of the American Council of the Blind. The scholarship winner is expected to be present at the council's annual national convention; the council will cover all reasonable costs connected with convention attendance.

4173 ■ AMERICAN FOUNDATION FOR THE BLIND
Attn: Scholarship Committee
11 Penn Plaza, Suite 300
New York, NY 10001
Tel: (212)502-7661
Free: 800-AFB-LINE
Fax: (212)502-7771
E-mail: afbinfo@afb.net
Web Site: http://www.afb.org/scholarships.asp
To provide financial assistance to visually impaired students who wish to work on a graduate or undergraduate degree in engineering or computer, physical, or life sciences.
Title of Award: Paul and Ellen Ruckes Scholarship **Area, Field, or Subject:** Biological and clinical sciences; Computer and information sciences; Engineering; Physical sciences **Level of Education for which Award is Granted:** Graduate, Undergraduate **Number Awarded:** 1 each year. **Funds Available:** The stipend is $1,000. **Duration:** 1 year.
Eligibility Requirements: This program is open to visually impaired undergraduate or graduate students who are U.S. citizens working on a degree in engineering or the computer, physical, or life sciences. Legal blindness is not required. Along with their application, they must submit an essay that includes the field of study they are pursuing and why they have chosen it; their educational and personal goals; their work experience; any extracurricular activities with which they have been involved, including those in school, religious organizations, and the community; and how they intend to use scholarship monies that may be awarded. **Deadline for Receipt:** April of each year.

4174 ■ AMERICAN INDIAN COLLEGE FUND
Attn: Scholarship Department
8333 Greenwood Boulevard
Denver, CO 80221
Tel: (303)426-8900
Free: 800-776-FUND
Fax: (303)426-1200
E-mail: info@collegefund.org
Web Site: http://www.collegefund.org/scholarships/main.html
To provide financial assistance to American Indian students who are attending designated tribal colleges in South Dakota.
Title of Award: Citigroup Scholarship and Career Exploration Program **Area, Field, or Subject:** Business administration; Computer and information sciences; General studies/Field of study not specified; Information science and technology **Level of Education for which Award is Granted:** Undergraduate **Number Awarded:** 1 or more each year. **Funds Available:** The stipend is $2,500. **Duration:** 1 year.
Eligibility Requirements: Eligible to apply are American Indians or Alaska Natives enrolled full time at Si Tanka University, Oglala Lakota College, Sinte Gleska University, or Sisseton Wahpeton College (all in South Dakota). Applicants must be able to demonstrate exceptional academic achievement (GPA of 3.0 or higher), as well as leadership, service, and commitment to the American Indian community. Along with their application, they must submit official college transcripts; a personal essay (500 words or less) on their personal and academic background, career goals, and how this scholarship will help them achieve those goals; a statement regarding any financial hardship they have; 2 letters of recommendation; tribal enrollment information; and a color photograph. All majors are eligible, but students interested in business and related fields, information technology, and computer science are especially encouraged to apply. **Deadline for Receipt:** April of each year. **Additional Information:** This scholarship is sponsored by Citigroup in partnership with the American Indian College Fund. Recipients assist with organizing a professional

development day called the Citigroup Career Exploration Day at their school.

4175 ■ AMERICAN INDIAN COLLEGE FUND

Attn: Scholarship Department
8333 Greenwood Boulevard
Denver, CO 80221
Tel: (303)426-8900
Free: 800-776-FUND
Fax: (303)426-1200
E-mail: info@collegefund.org
Web Site: http://www.collegefund.org/scholarships/main.html
To provide financial assistance to Native American college students who are majoring in designated fields at specified colleges and universities.
Title of Award: Ford Motor Company/American Indian College Fund Corporate Scholars Program **Area, Field, or Subject:** Accounting; Engineering, Computer; Engineering, Electrical; Engineering, Mechanical; Finance; Information science and technology; Marketing and distribution; Operations research **Level of Education for which Award is Granted:** Undergraduate **Number Awarded:** Varies each year. **Funds Available:** The stipend is $8,000 per year. **Duration:** 1 year; may be renewed.
Eligibility Requirements: This program is open to American Indians, Alaska Natives, and Hawaii Natives who have proof of enrollment or descendancy and have achieved at least sophomore status at 1 of 102 designated college and universities. Applicants must have a GPA of 3.0 or higher and be able to demonstrate financial need. They must have declared a major in accounting, computer engineering, electrical engineering, finance, information systems, marketing, mechanical engineering, or operations management. Along with their application, they must submit a 1-page personal essay on how they can become a role model and make a difference in their chosen field. Leadership and commitment to the American Indian community are also considered in the selection process. **Deadline for Receipt:** November of each year. **Additional Information:** This program is funded by the Ford Motor Company.

4176 ■ AMERICAN RADIO RELAY LEAGUE

Attn: ARRL Foundation
225 Main Street
Newington, CT 06111
Tel: (860)594-0397
Fax: (860)594-0259
E-mail: foundation@arrl.org
Web Site: http://www.arrl.org/arrlf/scholgen.html
To provide financial assistance to licensed radio amateurs who are interested in working on an undergraduate degree.
Title of Award: William R. Goldfarb Memorial Scholarship **Area, Field, or Subject:** Business administration; Computer and information sciences; Engineering; General studies/Field of study not specified; Medicine; Nursing; Science **Level of Education for which Award is Granted:** Undergraduate **Number Awarded:** 1 each year. **Funds Available:** The stipend is at least $10,000. **Duration:** 1 year.
Eligibility Requirements: This program is open to licensed radio amateurs of any class who have applied or been accepted for enrollment at an accredited institution of higher education. Preference is given to students planning to major in computers, medicine, nursing, engineering, science, or a business-related field. Applicants must submit an essay on the role amateur radio has played in their lives and provide documentation of financial need. **Deadline for Receipt:** January of each year.

4177 ■ AMERICAN RADIO RELAY LEAGUE

Attn: ARRL Foundation
225 Main Street
Newington, CT 06111
Tel: (860)594-0397
Fax: (860)594-0259
E-mail: foundation@arrl.org
Web Site: http://www.arrl.org/arrlf/scholgen.html
To provide financial assistance to licensed radio amateurs, particularly from designated midwestern states, who are interested in working on an undergraduate degree, particularly in journalism or the sciences.
Title of Award: PHD ARA Scholarship **Area, Field, or Subject:** Computer and information sciences; Engineering; General studies/Field of study not specified; Journalism **Level of Education for which Award is Granted:** Undergraduate **Number Awarded:** 1 each year. **Funds Available:** The stipend is $1,000. **Duration:** 1 year.
Eligibility Requirements: This program is open to licensed radio amateurs of any class who are pursuing postsecondary education. Preference is given to 1) residents of Iowa, Kansas, Missouri, and Nebraska; 2) students majoring in journalism, computer science, or electronic engineering; and 3) children of deceased radio amateurs. Applicants must submit an essay on the role amateur radio has played in their lives and provide documentation of financial need. **Deadline for Receipt:** January of each year.

4178 ■ AMERICAN SOCIETY FOR ENGINEERING EDUCATION

Attn: SMART Defense Scholarship Program
1818 N Street, N.W., Suite 600
Washington, DC 20036-2479
Tel: (202)331-3516
Fax: (202)265-8504
E-mail: smart@asee.org
Web Site: http://www.asee.org/resources/fellowships/smart/index.cfm
To provide scholarship/loans to upper-division and graduate students in areas of science, mathematics, and engineering that are of interest to the U.S. Department of Defense.
Title of Award: Science, Mathematics, and Research for Transformation (SMART) Defense Scholarship Program **Area, Field, or Subject:** Architecture, Naval; Behavioral sciences; Biological and clinical sciences; Chemistry; Computer and information sciences; Earth sciences; Engineering, Aerospace/Aeronautical/Astronautical; Engineering, Chemical; Engineering, Civil; Engineering, Electrical; Engineering, Materials; Engineering, Mechanical; Engineering, Ocean; Geosciences; Materials research/science; Mathematics and mathematical sciences; Oceanography; Physics **Level of Education for which Award is Granted:** Four Year College, Graduate **Number Awarded:** Varies each year; recently, 36 of these scholarships were awarded. **Funds Available:** The program provides full payment of tuition, fees, room, board, and other normal educational expenses at the recipient's institution. A book allowance of $1,000 per year is also provided. This is a scholarship/loan program; recipients must agree to serve as a civilian employee of the Department of Defense in a science and engineering position. If they fail to fulfill that service obligation, they must reimburse the federal government for all funds they received. **Duration:** Up to 24 months.
Eligibility Requirements: This program is open to upper-division and graduate students working on an undergraduate or graduate degree in any of the following fields: aeronautical and astronautical engineering; biosciences; chemical engineering; chemistry; civil engineering; cognitive, neural, and behavioral sciences; computer and computational sciences; electrical engineering; geosciences, including terrain, water, and air; materials science and engineering; mathematics; mechanical engineering; naval architecture and ocean engineering; oceanography; or physics. Applicants must be U.S. citizens who have a GPA of 3.0 or higher. Selection is based on academic records, personal statements, letters of recommendation, and GRE scores. **Deadline for Receipt:** March of each year. **Additional Information:** This program, established in 2005, is sponsored by the Army Research Laboratory, the Air Force Office of Scientific Research, the Office of Naval Research, the Air Force Research Laboratory, the Defense Advanced Research Projects Agency, the Defense Information Systems Agency, and the Defense Threat Reduction Agency.

4179 ■ AMERICAN SOCIETY OF ENGINEERS OF INDIAN ORIGIN

c/o Ramu Ramamurthy, Scholarship Committee Chair
47790 Pavillon Road
Canton, MI 48188
Tel: (248)226-6895
Fax: (248)226-7166
E-mail: awards@aseimichigan.org
Web Site: http://www.aseio.org
To provide financial assistance to undergraduate students of Indian origin (from India) who are majoring in architecture, engineering, or related areas.
Title of Award: ASEI Undergraduate Scholarships **Area, Field, or Subject:** Architecture; Computer and information sciences; Engineering **Level of Education for which Award is Granted:** Undergraduate **Number Awarded:** Several each year. **Funds Available:** The stipend is $1,000. **Duration:** 1 year.

Eligibility Requirements: This program is open to undergraduate students of Indian origin (by birth, ancestry, or relation). They must be enrolled full time at an accredited college or university in the United States and majoring in engineering, architecture, computer science, or allied science with a GPA of 3.2 or higher. Selection is based on demonstrated ability, academic achievement (including GPA, honors, and awards), career objectives, faculty recommendations, involvement in science fair and campus activities, and industrial exposure (including part-time work and internships). **Deadline for Receipt:** June of each year.

4180 ■ AMERICAN SOCIETY OF MILITARY COMPTROLLERS

Attn: National Awards Committee
415 North Alfred Street
Alexandria, VA 22314
Tel: (703)549-0360
Free: 800-462-5637
E-mail: asmchq@aol.com
Web Site: http://www.asmconline.org/national/nationalawards.shtml
To provide financial assistance for continuing education to members of the American Society of Military Comptrollers (ASMC).

Title of Award: ASMC Members' Continuing Education Program Award **Area, Field, or Subject:** Accounting; Business administration; Computer and information sciences; Economics; Finance; Operations research; Public administration **Level of Education for which Award is Granted:** Graduate, Professional, Undergraduate **Number Awarded:** 15 each year: 1 at $5,000 (the Dick Vincent Scholarship), 4 at $2,500, and 10 at $1,000. **Funds Available:** Stipends are $5,000, $2,500, or $1,000 per year. **Duration:** 1 year.

Eligibility Requirements: Applicants for this assistance must have been members of the society for at least 2 full years and must have been active in the local chapter at some level (board member, committee chair or member, volunteer for chapter events, etc.). They must be enrolled in or planning to enroll in an academic institution in a field of study directly related to financial resource management, including business administration, economics, public administration, computer science, or operations research related to financial management, accounting, and finance. As part of the selection process, they must submit an essay of up to 500 words on their academic and career goals and financial need. **Deadline for Receipt:** March of each year. **Additional Information:** The ASMC is open to all financial management professionals employed by the U.S. Department of Defense and Coast Guard, both civilian and military. The applicant whose service to the society is judged the most exceptional is designated the Dick Vincent Scholarship Winner.

4181 ■ AMERICAN SOCIETY OF MILITARY COMPTROLLERS

Attn: National Awards Committee
415 North Alfred Street
Alexandria, VA 22314
Tel: (703)549-0360
Free: 800-462-5637
E-mail: asmchq@aol.com
Web Site: http://www.asmconline.org/national/nationalawards.shtml
To provide financial assistance to high school seniors and recent graduates interested in preparing for a career in financial management.

Title of Award: ASMC National Scholarship Program **Area, Field, or Subject:** Accounting; Business administration; Computer and information sciences; Economics; Finance; Operations research; Public administration **Level of Education for which Award is Granted:** Undergraduate **Number Awarded:** 10 each year: 5 at $2,000 and 5 at $1,000. **Funds Available:** Stipends are $2,000 or $1,000 per year. **Duration:** 1 year.

Eligibility Requirements: This program is open to high school seniors and to people who graduated from high school during the preceding 6 months. Applicants must be planning to enter college in a field of study directly related to financial resource management, including business administration, economics, public administration, computer science, or operations research related to financial management, accounting, and finance. They must be endorsed by a chapter of the American Society of Military Comptrollers (ASMC). Selection is based on scholastic achievement, leadership ability, extracurricular activities, career and academic goals, and financial need. **Deadline for Receipt:** March of each year. **Additional Information:** The ASMC is open to all financial management professionals employed by the U.S. Department of Defense and Coast Guard, both civilian and military.

4182 ■ AMERICAN SOCIETY OF MILITARY COMPTROLLERS-MOUNT VERNON CHAPTER

Attn: Awards and Scholarships Director
P.O. Box 99
Fort Belvoir, VA 22060-0099
To provide financial assistance to high school seniors in the Washington, D.C. area who plan to work on an undergraduate degree related to financial management.

Title of Award: Mount Vernon Chapter Scholarships **Area, Field, or Subject:** Accounting; Business administration; Computer and information sciences; Economics; Finance; Operations research; Public administration **Level of Education for which Award is Granted:** Undergraduate **Number Awarded:** Several each year. **Funds Available:** The stipend is $1,000. **Duration:** 1 year.

Eligibility Requirements: This program is open to seniors graduating from high schools in Maryland, Virginia, and Washington, D.C. and to recent (within the past 6 months) graduates of those high schools. Applicants must be entering a field of study directly related to financial management (business administration, economics, public administration, computer science, operations research related to financial management, accounting, and finance). Along with their application, they must submit a 250-word essay on their career and academic goals and their financial need. Selection is based on academic achievement, leadership ability, extracurricular activities, career and academic goals, and financial need. **Deadline for Receipt:** March of each year.

4183 ■ APPALACHIAN COLLEGE ASSOCIATION

Attn: Director of Programs
210 Center Street
Berea, KY 40403
Tel: (859)986-4584
Fax: (859)986-9549
E-mail: kathrynb@acaweb.org
Web Site: http://www.acaweb.org
To provide financial assistance to students majoring in computer science, engineering, and mathematics (CSEM) at colleges and universities that are members of the Appalachian College Association (ACA).

Title of Award: Appalachian College Association Scholarships for Majoring in Computer Science, Engineering, Mathematics **Area, Field, or Subject:** Computer and information sciences; Engineering; Mathematics and mathematical sciences **Level of Education for which Award is Granted:** Four Year College **Number Awarded:** 30 each year. **Funds Available:** The stipend is $2,750 per year. **Duration:** 1 year; may be renewed 1 additional year.

Eligibility Requirements: This program is open to full-time students entering their junior or senior year at ACA member institutions. Applicants must be majoring in a CSEM discipline, have a GPA of 3.0 or higher, and be able to document financial need. Along with their application, they must submit a 500-word essay describing their career ambitions, their commitment to the Appalachian region, and the potential benefits to Appalachia of their degree choice. U.S. citizenship is required. Preference is given to graduates of high schools in the Appalachian region. **Deadline for Receipt:** March of each year. **Additional Information:** Funding for this program, which began in 2003, is provided by the National Science Foundation. The ACA includes member institutions in Kentucky (Alice Lloyd College, Berea College, Campbellsville University, University of the Cumberlands, Kentucky Christian University, Lindsey Wilson College, Pikeville College, and Union College), North Carolina (Brevard College, Lees-McRae College, Mars Hill College, Montreat College, and Warren Wilson College), Tennessee (Bryan College, Carson-Newman College, King College, Lee University, Lincoln Memorial University, Maryville College, Milligan College, Tennessee Wesleyan College, Tusculum College, and University of the South), Virginia (Bluefield College, Emery & Henry College, Ferrum College, and Virginia Intermont College), and West Virginia (Alderson-Broaddus College, Bethany College, Davis & Elkins College, Ohio Valley University, University of Charleston, West Virginia Wesleyan College, and Wheeling Jesuit University).

4184 ■ ARKANSAS DEPARTMENT OF WORKFORCE EDUCATION

Luther Hardin Building
Three Capitol Mall, Room 207
Little Rock, AR 72201-1083
Tel: (501)682-1500

Fax: (501)682-1509

Web Site: http://dwe.arkansas.gov/LoanForgiveness/atcslfp.htm

To provide forgivable loans to residents of Arkansas who are interested in pursuing technical education and working in the state.

Title of Award: Arkansas Technical Careers Student Loan Forgiveness Program **Area, Field, or Subject:** Biological and clinical sciences; Computer and information sciences; Engineering; Engineering, Biomedical; Engineering, Computer; Engineering, Electrical; Engineering, Industrial; Health care services; Physical sciences **Level of Education for which Award is Granted:** Undergraduate **Number Awarded:** Varies each year. **Funds Available:** The maximum loan is $2,500 per year. Loans are forgiven if the recipient works full time in the high demand technical field in Arkansas. Each year's loan may be forgiven with 1 year of full-time employment. Loan recipients who do not graduate from the program or work full time in the field in Arkansas must repay the loan in full. **Duration:** Up to 4 years.

Eligibility Requirements: This program is open to residents of Arkansas who are U.S. citizens or permanent residents admitted to an approved program resulting in a diploma, certificate, or degree in a high demand technical field. Applicants must indicate their intention to work in Arkansas in the field for which they receive the training. **Deadline for Receipt:** Applications must be submitted within 6 months of the completion of the program of study. **Additional Information:** The Arkansas General Assembly established this program in 1999. Recently, the designated career fields related to advanced manufacturing (including engineering and engineering technology, industrial electronics installers and repairers, machinist and machine technologies, and tool and die maker and technologist); computer and information technology (including computer engineering, computer and information sciences, electrical and electronic engineering and related technology, electromechanical instrumentation and maintenance technology, and computer installer and repairer); and biomedical and biotechnology (including biological and life sciences, physical sciences, science technologies, health professions and related sciences, bioengineering and biomedical engineering, and biomedical engineering technology and technician).

4185 ■ ARMED FORCES COMMUNICATIONS AND ELECTRONICS ASSOCIATION

Attn: AFCEA Educational Foundation

4400 Fair Lakes Court

Fairfax, VA 22033-3899

Tel: (703)631-6149

Free: 800-336-4583

Fax: (703)631-4693

E-mail: scholarship@afcea.org

Web Site: http://www.afcea.org/education/scholarships/undergraduate/pub1.asp

To provide financial assistance to undergraduate students who are working full time on a degree by means of a distance-learning or on-line program.

Title of Award: AFCEA Distance-Learning/On-Line Scholarships **Area, Field, or Subject:** Computer and information sciences; Engineering, Chemical; Engineering, Computer; Engineering, Electrical; Mathematics and mathematical sciences; Physics; Systems engineering **Level of Education for which Award is Granted:** Four Year College **Number Awarded:** 1 each year. **Funds Available:** The stipend is $1,000. **Duration:** 1 year.

Eligibility Requirements: This program is open to U.S. citizens working full time on a bachelor's degree by means of a distance-learning or on-line program affiliated with a major, accredited 4-year college or university in the United States. Applicants must have completed at least 1 year of course work based on a 30-semester hour equivalent; classes in progress at the time of application cannot be used towards the 1-year minimum completion requirement. Completed courses must include at least 2 semesters of calculus (not pre-calculus). Majors are limited to the fields of engineering (chemical, computer, electrical, or systems), mathematics, physics, or computer science. Selection is based primarily on academic excellence. **Deadline for Receipt:** July of each year.

4186 ■ ARMED FORCES COMMUNICATIONS AND ELECTRONICS ASSOCIATION

Attn: AFCEA Educational Foundation

4400 Fair Lakes Court

Fairfax, VA 22033-3899

Tel: (703)631-6149

Free: 800-336-4583

Fax: (703)631-4693

E-mail: scholarship@afcea.org

Web Site: http://www.afcea.org/education/scholarships/rotc/rotc1.asp

To provide financial assistance to ROTC cadets who are majoring in fields related to communications and electronics.

Title of Award: AFCEA ROTC Scholarships **Area, Field, or Subject:** Computer and information sciences; Electronics; Engineering, Aerospace/Aeronautical/Astronautical; Engineering, Chemical; Engineering, Computer; Engineering, Electrical; Mathematics and mathematical sciences; Physics; Systems engineering **Level of Education for which Award is Granted:** Four Year College **Number Awarded:** 36 each year, divided equally among Army, Navy/Marine Corps, and Air Force ROTC programs; for each service, 6 are awarded to rising juniors, 6 to rising seniors. **Funds Available:** The stipend is $2,000. **Duration:** 1 year; may be renewed.

Eligibility Requirements: This program is open to ROTC cadets majoring in electronics, engineering (aerospace, chemical, computer, electrical, or systems), mathematics, physics, or computer science. Applicants must be nominated by their ROTC professor, be entering their junior or senior year, be U.S. citizens, be of good moral character, have demonstrated academic excellence, be motivated to complete a college education and serve as officers in the U.S. armed forces, and be able to demonstrate financial need. **Deadline for Receipt:** March of each year.

4187 ■ ARMED FORCES COMMUNICATIONS AND ELECTRONICS ASSOCIATION

Attn: AFCEA Educational Foundation

4400 Fair Lakes Court

Fairfax, VA 22033-3899

Tel: (703)631-6149

Free: 800-336-4583

Fax: (703)631-4693

E-mail: scholarship@afcea.org

Web Site: http://www.afcea.org/education/scholarships/workingstudents/ws1.asp

To provide financial assistance to undergraduate students who are working part time on a degree in engineering or the sciences while already employed.

Title of Award: AFCEA Scholarship for Working Professionals **Area, Field, or Subject:** Computer and information sciences; Engineering, Aerospace/Aeronautical/Astronautical; Engineering, Chemical; Engineering, Electrical; Mathematics and mathematical sciences; Physics; Systems engineering **Level of Education for which Award is Granted:** Undergraduate **Number Awarded:** 1 each year. **Funds Available:** The stipend is $1,500. **Duration:** 1 year; may be renewed.

Eligibility Requirements: This program is open to part-time students entering their sophomore, junior, or senior year at an accredited 2-year or 4-year college or university in the United States while already employed in a science or technology field. Applicants must be U.S. citizens working toward a degree in engineering (aerospace, chemical, electrical, or systems), mathematics, physics, or computer science with a GPA of 3.4 or higher. They must be able to demonstrate academic achievement, patriotism, and potential to contribute to the American work force. **Deadline for Receipt:** September of each year. **Additional Information:** This program was established in 2002.

4188 ■ ARMED FORCES COMMUNICATIONS AND ELECTRONICS ASSOCIATION

Attn: AFCEA Educational Foundation

4400 Fair Lakes Court

Fairfax, VA 22033-3899

Tel: (703)631-6149

Free: 800-336-4583

Fax: (703)631-4693

E-mail: scholarship@afcea.org

Web Site: http://www.afcea.org/education/scholarships/undergraduate/graphicdes.asp

To provide financial assistance to students who are working on an undergraduate or graduate degree in computer graphic design.

Title of Award: Computer Graphic Design Scholarships **Area, Field, or Subject:** Computer and information sciences; Graphic art and design;

Internet design and development **Level of Education for which Award is Granted:** Four Year College, Graduate **Number Awarded:** 1 or more each year. **Funds Available:** The stipend is $2,000. **Duration:** 1 year; may be renewed.

Eligibility Requirements: This program is open to full-time students who are enrolled at an accredited college or university in the United States at least as a sophomore. Applicants must be U.S. citizens working on an undergraduate or graduate degree in computer graphic design or a related field. They must submit a sample of digital graphic artwork for intranets and internets, especially web-based graphics. Along with the artwork, include a textual statement of 100 to 200 words that describes the image submitted, how it was created, and what specific intent or purpose it represents. Selection is based on artistic creativity, mastery of web technology, a statement of career goals, school and community activities, and financial need. **Deadline for Receipt:** October of each year.

4189 ■ ARMED FORCES COMMUNICATIONS AND ELECTRONICS ASSOCIATION

Attn: AFCEA Educational Foundation
4400 Fair Lakes Court
Fairfax, VA 22033-3899
Tel: (703)631-6149
Free: 800-336-4583
Fax: (703)631-4693
E-mail: scholarship@afcea.org
Web Site: http://www.afcea.org/education/scholarships/undergraduate/genemm.asp

To provide funding to veterans, military personnel, and their family members who are majoring in specified scientific fields in college.

Title of Award: General Emmett Paige Scholarships **Area, Field, or Subject:** Computer and information sciences; Engineering, Aerospace/Aeronautical/Astronautical; Engineering, Chemical; Engineering, Computer; Engineering, Electrical; Mathematics and mathematical sciences; Physics **Level of Education for which Award is Granted:** Four Year College **Number Awarded:** Varies each year; recently, 11 of these scholarships were awarded. **Funds Available:** The stipend is $2,000. **Duration:** 1 year; may be renewed.

Eligibility Requirements: This program is open to veterans, persons on active duty in the uniformed military services, and their spouses or dependents who are currently enrolled full time in an accredited 4-year college or university in the United States. Graduating high school seniors are not eligible, but veterans entering college as freshmen may apply. Spouses or dependents must be sophomores or juniors. Applicants must be U.S. citizens, be of good moral character, have demonstrated academic excellence, be motivated to complete a college education, and be working toward a degree in engineering (aerospace, chemical, computer, or electrical), mathematics, physics, or computer science with a GPA of 3.4 or higher. They must provide a copy of Discharge Form DD214, Certificate of Service, or facsimile of their current Department of Defense or Coast Guard Identification Card. **Deadline for Receipt:** February of each year.

4190 ■ ARMED FORCES COMMUNICATIONS AND ELECTRONICS ASSOCIATION

Attn: AFCEA Educational Foundation
4400 Fair Lakes Court
Fairfax, VA 22033-3899
Tel: (703)631-6149
Free: 800-336-4583
Fax: (703)631-4693
E-mail: scholarship@afcea.org
Web Site: http://www.afcea.org/education/scholarships/undergraduate/vadmjerry.asp

To provide financial assistance to undergraduate students working on a degree in technology.

Title of Award: Vice Adm. Jerry O. Tuttle, USN (Ret.) and Mrs. Barbara A. Tuttle Science and Technology Scholarships **Area, Field, or Subject:** Computer and information sciences; Electronics; Engineering; Engineering, Computer **Level of Education for which Award is Granted:** Four Year College **Number Awarded:** Varies each year; recently, 2 of these scholarships were awarded. **Funds Available:** The stipend is $2,000. **Duration:** 1 year; may be renewed.

Eligibility Requirements: This program is open to full-time students entering their junior or senior year at an accredited 4-year technological institute in the United States. Applicants must be U.S. citizens working toward a degree in computer engineering technology, computer network systems, or electronics engineering technology. Primary consideration is given to candidates who are military enlisted personnel. Selection is based on a statement of career goals, school and community activities, and financial need. **Deadline for Receipt:** October of each year.

4191 ■ ARMED FORCES COMMUNICATIONS AND ELECTRONICS ASSOCIATION

Attn: AFCEA Educational Foundation
4400 Fair Lakes Court
Fairfax, VA 22033-3899
Tel: (703)631-6149
Free: 800-336-4583
Fax: (703)631-4693
E-mail: scholarship@afcea.org
Web Site: http://www.afcea.org/education/scholarships/undergraduate/veteran.asp

To provide financial assistance to veterans and military personnel who served in Afghanistan or Iraq and are working on an undergraduate degree in fields related to the support of U.S. intelligence enterprises.

Title of Award: Veterans of Enduring Freedom-Afghanistan and Iraqi Freedom Combat Operations Scholarship **Area, Field, or Subject:** Computer and information sciences; Engineering; Engineering, Aerospace/Aeronautical/Astronautical; Engineering, Computer; Engineering, Electrical; Mathematics and mathematical sciences; Physics; Systems engineering **Level of Education for which Award is Granted:** Undergraduate **Number Awarded:** 1 or more each year. **Funds Available:** The stipend is $2,000. **Duration:** 1 year.

Eligibility Requirements: This program is open to active-duty and honorably discharged U.S. military veterans, Reservists, and National Guard personnel who served in combat operations of Enduring Freedom-Afghanistan or Iraqi Freedom. Applicants must be enrolled at a 2- or 4-year institution in the United States and working on an undergraduate degree in computer engineering technology, computer information systems, electronics engineering technology, engineering (aerospace, computer, electrical, or systems), mathematics, physics, or computer science. Along with their application, they must submit an essay that includes a brief synopsis of relevant work experience (including military assignments), a brief statement of career goals after graduation, and a explanation of how their academic and career goals will contribute to the areas related to communications, intelligence and/or information systems, and the mission of the Armed Forces Communications and Electronics Association (AFCEA). Financial need is also considered in the selection process. **Deadline for Receipt:** October of each year. **Additional Information:** This scholarship was first offered in 2005.

4192 ■ ARMED FORCES COMMUNICATIONS AND ELECTRONICS ASSOCIATION

Attn: AFCEA Educational Foundation
4400 Fair Lakes Court
Fairfax, VA 22033-3899
Tel: (703)631-6149
Free: 800-336-4583
Fax: (703)631-4693
E-mail: scholarship@afcea.org
Web Site: http://www.afcea.org/education/scholarships/undergraduate/pub2.asp

To provide financial assistance to undergraduate students who are working full time on a degree in engineering or the sciences.

Title of Award: General John A. Wickham Scholarships **Area, Field, or Subject:** Computer and information sciences; Engineering, Aerospace/Aeronautical/Astronautical; Engineering, Chemical; Engineering, Computer; Engineering, Electrical; Mathematics and mathematical sciences; Physics; Systems engineering **Level of Education for which Award is Granted:** Four Year College **Number Awarded:** Varies each year; recently, 11 of these scholarships were awarded. **Funds Available:** The stipend is $2,000. **Duration:** 1 year; may be renewed.

Eligibility Requirements: This program is open to full-time students entering their junior or senior year at an accredited degree-granting 4-year college or university in the United States. Applicants must be U.S. citizens working toward a degree in engineering (aerospace, chemical, computer, electrical, or systems), mathematics, physics, or computer science with a GPA of 3.5 or higher. They must be able to demonstrate academic achievement, patriotism, and potential to contribute to the American work force. **Deadline for Receipt:** April of each year.

4193 ■ ARMED FORCES COMMUNICATIONS AND ELECTRONICS ASSOCIATION

Attn: AFCEA Educational Foundation
4400 Fair Lakes Court
Fairfax, VA 22033-3899
Tel: (703)631-6149
Free: 800-336-4583
Fax: (703)631-4693
E-mail: scholarship@afcea.org
Web Site: http://www.afcea.org/education/scholarships/undergraduate/sgtjean.asp

To provide funding to members and veterans of the U.S. Marine Corps (USMC) who are majoring in specified fields in college.
Title of Award: Marine Sgt. Jeannette L. Winters Memorial Scholarship **Area, Field, or Subject:** Computer and information sciences; Engineering, Aerospace/Aeronautical/Astronautical; Engineering, Computer; Engineering, Electrical; Mathematics and mathematical sciences; Physics; Systems engineering **Level of Education for which Award is Granted:** Undergraduate **Number Awarded:** 1 each year. **Funds Available:** The stipend is $2,000. **Duration:** 1 year.

Eligibility Requirements: This program is open to USMC personnel currently on active duty, in the Reserves, or honorably-discharged veterans who are enrolled full or part time in an accredited college or university in the United States. Applicants must be U.S. citizens, be of good moral character, have demonstrated academic excellence, be motivated to complete a college education, and be working on a degree in engineering (aerospace, computer, electrical, or systems), mathematics, physics, or computer science with a GPA of 3.0 or higher. They must provide a copy of Discharge Form DD214, Certificate of Service, or facsimile of their current Department of Defense Identification Card. **Deadline for Receipt:** September of each year. **Additional Information:** This program was established in 2002 to honor a Marine who died when her KC-130 aircraft crashed in Pakistan.

4194 ■ ASSOCIATION FOR IRON & STEEL TECHNOLOGY-OHIO VALLEY CHAPTER

c/o Jeff McKain, Scholarship Chair
Xtek, Inc.
11451 Reading Road
Cincinnati, OH 45241
Tel: (513)733-7843; (999)332-XTEK
Fax: (513)733-7939
E-mail: jeff.mckain@xtek.com
Web Site: http://www.aist.org/chapters/ohiovalley_scholarship.htm

To provide financial assistance for college to student members and children of members of the Ohio Valley Chapter of the Association for Iron & Steel Technology (AIST).
Title of Award: Ohio Valley Chapter AIST Scholarships **Area, Field, or Subject:** Biological and clinical sciences; Chemistry; Computer and information sciences; Earth sciences; Engineering; Engineering, Electrical; Engineering, Mechanical; Environmental conservation; Environmental science; Geosciences; Information science and technology; Metallurgy; Physical sciences; Physics **Level of Education for which Award is Granted:** Undergraduate **Number Awarded:** Up to 2 each year. **Funds Available:** The stipend is $1,000 per year. **Duration:** 1 year; may be renewed up to 3 additional years provided the recipient remains enrolled full time and maintains a GPA of 3.0 or higher.

Eligibility Requirements: This program is open to high school seniors and college students who are either 1) children of Ohio Valley Chapter AIST members, or 2) student AIST members. Applicants must be accepted at, planning to attend, or currently enrolled at an accredited college or university with a major in biology, chemistry, computer programming, computer technology, electrical engineering, engineering, engineering technology, environmental engineering, environmental science, information systems technology, mechanical engineering, metallurgy, microbiology, physical science, physics, or other field approved by the scholarship committee. Along with their application, they must submit

a 500-word essay on the reasons for their interests and reasons for working on a degree in their field of study, career goals and objectives, and extracurricular activities and their benefits. Selection is based on overall academic achievement (especially in mathematics and science), the essay, and extracurricular activities. **Deadline for Receipt:** February of each year. **Additional Information:** The AIST was formed in 2004 by the merger of the Iron and Steel Society (ISS) and the Association of Iron and Steel Engineers (AISE). This program was established by the former Ohio Valley District Section of AISE. The Ohio Valley Chapter covers Indiana (except for the northwestern portion), all of Kentucky, western Tennessee, and portions of southern Ohio.

4195 ■ ASSOCIATION FOR WOMEN IN COMPUTING-ANN ARBOR CHAPTER

Attn: Scholarship
P.O. Box 1864
Ann Arbor, MI 48106-1864
E-mail: awc@hvcn.org
Web Site: http://www.awc-aa.org/gala/scholarship.php

To provide financial assistance to women undergraduates working on a degree in a computer- or technology-related field at institutions in Michigan.
Title of Award: Ann Arbor AWC Scholarship for Women in Computing **Area, Field, or Subject:** Computer and information sciences; Technology **Level of Education for which Award is Granted:** Undergraduate **Number Awarded:** 1 or more each year. **Funds Available:** A stipend is awarded (amount not specified). **Duration:** 1 year.

Eligibility Requirements: This program is open to undergraduate women enrolled at institutions of higher education in Michigan. Applicants must be U.S. citizens or permanent residents preparing for a career in a field related to computers or technology. They must have at least 2 semesters of course work remaining. As part of the application, they must answer the following 3 questions: 1) "Why are you excited about working with computers and information technology?" 2) "Describe your most fulfilling computer-related project or experience;" and 3) "Identify a current trend in technology and describe how it might evolve over the next ten years." Based on those essays, awards are presented to applicants who demonstrate motivation, passion, thoughtfulness, creativity, skillful communication, and participation in the computing community. Financial need is not considered. **Deadline for Receipt:** March of each year.

4196 ■ BUSINESS AND PROFESSIONAL WOMEN OF VIRGINIA

Attn: Virginia BPW Foundation
P.O. Box 4842
McLean, VA 22103-4842
Web Site: http://www.bpwva.org/Foundation.shtml

To provide financial assistance to women in Virginia who are interested in working on a bachelor's or advanced degree in science or technology.
Title of Award: Women in Science and Technology Scholarship **Area, Field, or Subject:** Actuarial science; Biological and clinical sciences; Chemistry; Computer and information sciences; Dentistry; Engineering; Engineering, Biomedical; Insurance and insurance-related fields; Mathematics and mathematical sciences; Medicine; Physics; Science; Technology **Level of Education for which Award is Granted:** Graduate, Undergraduate **Number Awarded:** At least 1 each year. **Funds Available:** Stipends range from $500 to $1,000 per year, depending on the need of the recipient; funds may be used for tuition, fees, books, transportation, living expenses, and dependent care. **Duration:** 1 year; recipients may reapply (but prior recipients are not given priority).

Eligibility Requirements: This program is open to women who are at least 18 years of age, U.S. citizens, Virginia residents, accepted at or currently studying at a Virginia college or university, and working on a bachelor's, master's, or doctoral degree in 1 of the following fields: actuarial science, biology, bioengineering, chemistry, computer science, dentistry, engineering, mathematics, medicine, physics, or a similar scientific or technical field. Applicants must have a definite plan to use their education in a scientific or technical profession. They must be able to demonstrate financial need. **Deadline for Receipt:** March of each year. **Additional Information:** Recipients must complete their studies within 2 years.

4197 ■ CATCHING THE DREAM

8200 Mountain Road, N.E., Suite 203
Albuquerque, NM 87110-7835

Tel: (505)262-2351
Fax: (505)262-0534
E-mail: NScholarsh@aol.com
Web Site: http://www.catchingthedream.org
To provide financial assistance to American Indian students who are interested in working on an undergraduate or graduate degree in selected fields.
Title of Award: MESBEC Program **Area, Field, or Subject:** Business administration; Computer and information sciences; Education; Engineering; Mathematics and mathematical sciences; Science **Level of Education for which Award is Granted:** Four Year College, Graduate **Number Awarded:** Varies; generally, 30 to 35 each year. **Funds Available:** Stipends range from $500 to $5,000. **Duration:** 1 year; may be renewed. **Eligibility Requirements:** This program is open to American Indians who can provide proof that they are at least one-quarter Indian blood and a member of a U.S. tribe that is federally-recognized, state-recognized, or terminated. Applicants must be enrolled or planning to enroll full time and major in the 1 of the following fields: mathematics, engineering, science, business administration, education, or computer science. They may be entering freshmen, undergraduate students, graduate students, or Ph.D. candidates. Along with their application, they must submit documentation of financial need, 3 letters of recommendation, copies of applications and responses for at least 15 other sources of funding, official transcripts, standardized test scores (ACT, SAT, GRE, MCAT, LSAT, etc.), and an essay explaining their goals in life, college plans, and career plans (especially how those plans include working with and benefiting Indians). Selection is based on merit and potential for improving the lives of Indian people. **Deadline for Receipt:** April of each year for fall term; September of each year for spring and winter terms; March of each year for summer school. **Additional Information:** MESBEC is an acronym that stands for the priority areas of this program: mathematics, engineering, science, business, education, and computers. The sponsor was formerly known as the Native American Scholarship Fund.

4198 ■ CHICAGO URBAN LEAGUE

Attn: Education Department
4510 South Michigan Avenue
Chicago, IL 60653-3898
Tel: (773)451-3565
Fax: (773)285-7772
E-mail: info@cul-chicago.org
Web Site: http://www.cul-chicago.org
To provide financial assistance to Illinois residents of color interested in studying a field related to automotive technology in college.
Title of Award: Mercedes-Benz Scholarships **Area, Field, or Subject:** Accounting; Automotive technology; Business; Business administration; Computer and information sciences; Engineering, Automotive; Transportation **Level of Education for which Award is Granted:** Undergraduate **Number Awarded:** 4 each year. **Funds Available:** The stipend is $1,000 per year. **Duration:** 4 years.
Eligibility Requirements: This program is open to Illinois residents of color who are graduating high school seniors with a GPA of 2.5 or higher and planning to enroll as full-time undergraduate students at a 4-year college or university, Triton College, or 1 of the City Colleges of Chicago. Applicants must be planning to major in automotive technology or a field related to the automotive industry (e.g., engineering, computer science, business, or accounting). They must be able to demonstrate financial need. **Deadline for Receipt:** May of each year. **Additional Information:** This program is offered as part of the Chicago Urban League's Whitney M. Young, Jr. Memorial Scholarship Fund, established in 1970.

4199 ■ CHICKASAW FOUNDATION

P.O. Box 1726
Ada, OK 74821-1726
Tel: (580)421-9030
Fax: (580)421-9031
Web Site: http://www.cflink.org
To provide financial assistance to members of the Chickasaw Nation who are majoring in fields of interest to ComputerCraft Corporation.
Title of Award: ComputerCraft Corporation Scholarship **Area, Field, or Subject:** Biological and clinical sciences; Engineering, Computer; General studies/Field of study not specified; Graphic art and design; International affairs and relations **Level of Education for which Award is**

Granted: Undergraduate **Number Awarded:** 1 each year. **Funds Available:** The stipend is $1,500 per year. **Duration:** 1 year.
Eligibility Requirements: This program is open to Chickasaw students who are currently enrolled full time as an undergraduate student. The sponsor recruits computer engineers, graphic designers, biologists, conference managers, and international trade specialists. Preference may be given to those majors, but all fields of study are eligible. Applicants must have a GPA of 2.5 or higher. Along with their application, they must submit high school or college transcripts, 2 letters of recommendation, a copy of their Certificate of Degree of Indian Blood, a copy of their Chickasaw Nation citizenship card, and a 1-page essay on their long-term goals and plans for achieving them. Financial need is not considered in the selection process. **Deadline for Receipt:** May of each year.

4200 ■ DEFENSE INTELLIGENCE AGENCY

Attn: DAH-2
Bolling Air Force Base
Building 6000
Washington, DC 20340-5100
Tel: (202)231-4713
Fax: (202)231-4889
Web Site: http://www.dia.mil
To provide loans-for-service and work experience to women, minority, and disabled high school seniors interested in majoring in specified fields and working for the U.S. Defense Intelligence Agency (DIA).
Title of Award: Defense Intelligence Agency Undergraduate Training Assistance Program **Area, Field, or Subject:** Computer and information sciences; Geography; International affairs and relations; Political science **Level of Education for which Award is Granted:** Undergraduate **Number Awarded:** Only a few are awarded each year. **Funds Available:** Students accepted into this program receive tuition (up to $18,000 per year) at an accredited college or university selected by the student and endorsed by the sponsor; reimbursement for books and needed supplies; an annual salary to cover college room and board expenses and for summer employment; and a position at the sponsoring agency after graduation. Recipients must work for DIA after college graduation for at least 1 and a half times the length of study. For participants who leave DIA earlier than scheduled, the agency arranges for payments to reimburse DIA for the total cost of education (including the employee's pay and allowances). **Duration:** 4 years.
Eligibility Requirements: This program is open to women, minorities, and individuals with disabilities who are graduating high school seniors and interested in majoring in 1 of the following fields in college: geography, foreign area studies, international relations, or political science. Applicants must have a high school GPA of 3.0 or higher, have an SAT score of 1000 or higher or an ACT score of 21 or higher, be able to demonstrate financial need (household income ceiling of $65,000 for a family of 4 or $80,000 for a family of 5 or more), be U.S. citizens and from a family of U.S. citizens, and demonstrate leadership abilities through extracurricular activities, civic involvement, volunteer work, or part-time employment. **Deadline for Receipt:** November of each year. **Additional Information:** Recipients are provided a challenging summer internship and guaranteed a job at the agency in their field of study upon graduation. Recipients must attend school on a full-time basis.

4201 ■ DELTA SIGMA THETA SORORITY, INC.-THE FEDERAL CITY ALUMNAE CHAPTER

Attn: Educational Development Committee
P.O. Box 1605
Washington, DC 20013
Tel: (202)545-1913
E-mail: thefcacdst@yahoo.com
Web Site: http://www.thefcacdst.org/html/chapterEvents.htm
To provide financial assistance to high school seniors in Washington, D.C. who plan to attend an Historically Black College or University (HBCU) to major in a field related to science and engineering.
Title of Award: Federal City Alumnae Chapter Scholarship for Excellence **Area, Field, or Subject:** Computer and information sciences; Engineering; Information science and technology; Mathematics and mathematical sciences; Science **Level of Education for which Award is Granted:** Undergraduate **Number Awarded:** 2 each year. **Funds Available:** The stipend is $5,000. **Duration:** 1 year; nonrenewable.
Eligibility Requirements: This program is open to seniors graduating from public and public charter high schools in the District of Columbia.

Applicants must have been accepted to attend an HBCU to major in computer science, engineering, information technology, mathematics, science, or a related field. They must have a GPA of 3.0 or higher. Along with their application, they must submit a 2-page essay on why they decided to attend an HBCU to major in mathematics, science, or a related field. **Deadline for Receipt:** March of each year.

4202 ■ DESIGN AUTOMATION CONFERENCE

c/o Cherrice Traver
Union College
ECE Department
Schenectady, NY 12308
Tel: (518)388-6326
Fax: (518)388-6789
E-mail: traverc@union.edu
Web Site: http://doc.union.edu/acsee.html
To provide financial assistance to female, minority, or disabled high school seniors who are interested in preparing for a career in computer science or electrical engineering.

Title of Award: P.O. Pistilli Scholarships **Area, Field, or Subject:** Computer and information sciences; Engineering, Computer; Engineering, Electrical **Level of Education for which Award is Granted:** Undergraduate **Number Awarded:** 2 to 7 each year. **Funds Available:** Stipends are $4,000 each year. Awards are paid each year in 2 equal installments. **Duration:** 1 year; renewable for up to 4 additional years.

Eligibility Requirements: Eligible to apply are "underrepresented" high school seniors: women, African Americans, Hispanic Americans, Native Americans, and persons with disabilities. Applicants must be interested in preparing for a career in electrical engineering, computer engineering, or computer science. They must have at least a 3.0 GPA, have demonstrated high achievements in math and science courses, and be able to demonstrate significant financial need. U.S. citizenship is not required, but applicants must be U.S. residents when they apply and must plan to attend an accredited U.S. college or university. They must submit a completed application form, 3 letters of recommendation, official transcripts, ACT/SAT and/or PSAT scores, a personal statement outlining future goals, a copy of their latest income tax return, and a copy of the FAFSA form they submitted. **Deadline for Receipt:** January of each year. **Additional Information:** This program is funded by the Design Automation Conference and the IEEE Circuits and System Society. It is directed by the Association for Computing Machinery's Special Interest Group on Design Automation.

4203 ■ ELECTRONIC DOCUMENT SYSTEMS FOUNDATION

Attn: EDSF Scholarship Awards
24238 Hawthorne Boulevard
Torrance, CA 90505-6505
Tel: (310)541-1481
Fax: (310)541-4803
Web Site: http://www.edsf.org/scholarships.cfm
To provide financial assistance to college juniors, seniors, and graduate students interested in working with electronic documents as a career.

Title of Award: Wayne Alexander Memorial Scholarship **Area, Field, or Subject:** Computer and information sciences; Graphic art and design; Internet design and development; Marketing and distribution; Printing trades and industries; Telecommunications systems **Level of Education for which Award is Granted:** Four Year College, Graduate **Number Awarded:** 1 each year. **Funds Available:** The stipend is $2,000. **Duration:** 1 year.

Eligibility Requirements: This program is open to juniors, seniors, and graduate students who are working full time on a degree in the field of document communication, including marketing, graphic communication and arts, e-commerce, imaging science, printing, web authoring, electronic publishing, computer science, or telecommunications. Priority consideration is given to students at the University of Central Florida. Applicants must submit a statement of their career goals in the field of document communications, an essay on a topic related to their view of the future of the document management and production industry, a list of current professional and college extracurricular activities and achievements, college transcripts (GPA of 3.0 or higher), samples of their creative work, and 2 letters of recommendation. Financial need is not considered. **Deadline for Receipt:** May of each year. **Additional Information:** This program is sponsored by AXIS Inc.

4204 ■ ELECTRONIC DOCUMENT SYSTEMS FOUNDATION

Attn: EDSF Scholarship Awards
24238 Hawthorne Boulevard
Torrance, CA 90505-6505
Tel: (310)541-1481
Fax: (310)541-4803
Web Site: http://www.edsf.org/scholarships.cfm
To provide financial assistance to college juniors, seniors, and graduate students interested in working with electronic documents as a career.

Title of Award: EDSF Board of Directors Scholarships **Area, Field, or Subject:** Computer and information sciences; Graphic art and design; Internet design and development; Marketing and distribution; Printing trades and industries; Telecommunications systems **Level of Education for which Award is Granted:** Four Year College, Graduate **Number Awarded:** 20 each year. **Funds Available:** The stipend is $2,000. **Duration:** 1 year.

Eligibility Requirements: This program is open to juniors, seniors, and graduate students who are working full time on a degree in the field of document communication, including marketing, graphic communication and arts, e-commerce, imaging science, printing, web authoring, electronic publishing, computer science, or telecommunications. Applicants must submit a statement of their career goals in the field of document communications, an essay on a topic related to their view of the future of the document management and production industry, a list of current professional and college extracurricular activities and achievements, college transcripts (GPA of 3.0 or higher), samples of their creative work, and 2 letters of recommendation. Financial need is not considered. **Deadline for Receipt:** May of each year.

4205 ■ ELECTRONIC DOCUMENT SYSTEMS FOUNDATION

Attn: EDSF Scholarship Awards
24238 Hawthorne Boulevard
Torrance, CA 90505-6505
Tel: (310)541-1481
Fax: (310)541-4803
Web Site: http://www.edsf.org/scholarships.cfm
To provide financial assistance to students in technical schools and community colleges who are interested in working with electronic documents as a career.

Title of Award: EDSF Board of Directors Technical and Community College Scholarship **Area, Field, or Subject:** Computer and information sciences; Graphic art and design; Internet design and development; Marketing and distribution; Printing trades and industries; Telecommunications systems **Level of Education for which Award is Granted:** Two Year College, Vocational/Occupational **Number Awarded:** 5 each year. **Funds Available:** The stipend is $1,000. **Duration:** 1 year.

Eligibility Requirements: This program is open to first- and second-year students at technical and trade schools and community colleges. Applicants must be working on a degree in the field of electronic document communication, including marketing, graphic communication and arts, e-commerce, imaging science, printing, web authoring, electronic publishing, computer science, or telecommunications. They must submit a 1-page essay on 1 of the following topics: 1) a definition of their career goals in the field of document management and communications; 2) a recent technological change and how it has or will affect the document communication industry; or 3) a definition of the document communication industry. Selection is based on the essay, extracurricular activities and achievements, high school transcripts (GPA of 3.0 or higher), samples of creative work, and 2 letters of recommendation. Financial need is not considered. **Deadline for Receipt:** May of each year.

4206 ■ ELECTRONIC DOCUMENT SYSTEMS FOUNDATION

Attn: EDSF Scholarship Awards
24238 Hawthorne Boulevard
Torrance, CA 90505-6505
Tel: (310)541-1481
Fax: (310)541-4803
Web Site: http://www.edsf.org/scholarships.cfm
To provide financial assistance to upper-division and graduate students interested in working with electronic documents as a career.

Title of Award: David Hoods Memorial Scholarship **Area, Field, or Subject:** Computer and information sciences; Graphic art and design; Internet design and development; Marketing and distribution; Printing trades and industries; Public relations; Telecommunications systems **Level of Education for which Award is Granted:** Four Year College, Graduate **Number Awarded:** 1 each year. **Funds Available:** The stipend is $2,000. **Duration:** 1 year.

Eligibility Requirements: This program is open to full-time juniors, seniors, and graduate students who demonstrate a strong interest in working with electronic documents as a career (including graphic communications, document management, document content, and/or document distribution). Special consideration is given to students interested in marketing and public relations. Applicants must submit a statement of their career goals in the field of document communications, an essay on a topic related to their view of the future of the document management and production industry, a list of current professional and college extracurricular activities and achievements, college transcripts (GPA of 3.0 or higher), samples of their creative work, and 2 letters of recommendation. Financial need is not considered. **Deadline for Receipt:** May of each year.

4207 ■ ELECTRONIC DOCUMENT SYSTEMS FOUNDATION

Attn: EDSF Scholarship Awards
24238 Hawthorne Boulevard
Torrance, CA 90505-6505
Tel: (310)541-1481
Fax: (310)541-4803
Web Site: http://www.edsf.org/scholarships.cfm
To provide financial assistance to college juniors, seniors, and graduate students interested in working with electronic documents as a career.
Title of Award: John A. Lopiano Scholarship **Area, Field, or Subject:** Computer and information sciences; Graphic art and design; Internet design and development; Marketing and distribution; Printing trades and industries; Telecommunications systems **Level of Education for which Award is Granted:** Four Year College, Graduate **Number Awarded:** 1 each year. **Funds Available:** The stipend is $2,000. **Duration:** 1 year.

Eligibility Requirements: This program is open to juniors, seniors, and graduate students who are working full time on a degree in the field of document communication, including marketing, graphic communication and arts, e-commerce, imaging science, printing, web authoring, electronic publishing, computer science, or telecommunications. Priority consideration is given to students who work in or whose family member has worked or currently works in a segment of the high volume transaction output (HVTO) industry. Applicants must submit a statement of their career goals in the field of document communications, an essay on a topic related to their view of the future of the document management and production industry, a list of current professional and college extracurricular activities and achievements, college transcripts (GPA of 3.0 or higher), samples of their creative work, and 2 letters of recommendation. Financial need is not considered. **Deadline for Receipt:** May of each year. **Additional Information:** This program is sponsored by COPI/OutputLinks.

4208 ■ ELECTRONIC DOCUMENT SYSTEMS FOUNDATION

Attn: EDSF Scholarship Awards
24238 Hawthorne Boulevard
Torrance, CA 90505-6505
Tel: (310)541-1481
Fax: (310)541-4803
Web Site: http://www.edsf.org/scholarships.cfm
To provide financial assistance to upper-division and graduate students in Canada who are interested in working with electronic documents as a career.
Title of Award: Xplor Canada Scholarship **Area, Field, or Subject:** Computer and information sciences; Graphic art and design; Internet design and development; Printing trades and industries **Level of Education for which Award is Granted:** Four Year College, Graduate **Number Awarded:** 1 each year. **Funds Available:** The stipend is $C2,000. **Duration:** 1 year.

Eligibility Requirements: This program is open to third-year, fourth-year, and advanced-degree students who are working full time on a degree in the field of electronic documents, including content and design, print technologies, graphic communications, or computer science. Applicants must be Canadian citizens or landed immigrants and living in Canada, but they may be attending a course of study outside of Canada. They must submit a statement of their career goals in the field of document/

communication systems, an essay on a topic related to their view of the future of the document management and production industry, a list of current professional and college extracurricular activities and achievements, college transcripts (GPA of 3.0 or higher), samples of their creative work, and 2 letters of recommendation. Financial need is not considered. **Deadline for Receipt:** May of each year. **Additional Information:** This program is sponsored by Xplor Canada.

4209 ■ FLORIDA ASSOCIATION OF EDUCATIONAL DATA SYSTEMS

c/o Marsha Cole, FAEDS Scholarship Chair
Duval County Public Schools
4037 Boulevard Center Drive
Building B, Second Floor
Jacksonville, FL 32207
Tel: (904)348-5167
Fax: (904)348-5737
E-mail: colem@educationcentral.org
Web Site: http://www.faeds.org/Scholarships.htm
To provide financial assistance to high school seniors in Florida planning to attend a college or university in the state and major in computer science or information technology.
Title of Award: William J. English Memorial Scholarship **Area, Field, or Subject:** Computer and information sciences; Information science and technology. **Level of Education for which Award is Granted:** Undergraduate **Number Awarded:** Up to 3 each year. **Funds Available:** The stipend is $2,000. **Duration:** 1 year.

Eligibility Requirements: Any currently-enrolled college student who has at least a 2.5 GPA and is attending a Florida private or public college or university is eligible. Applicants must be enrolled full time and be majoring or planning to major in computer science or information technology. Along with their application, they must submit a 2-page essay indicating their interest in computer science and/or information technology and 3 letters of recommendation. Financial need is not considered in the selection process. **Deadline for Receipt:** February of each year. **Additional Information:** This scholarship was established in 1981.

4210 ■ FLORIDA ASSOCIATION OF EDUCATIONAL DATA SYSTEMS

c/o Marsha Cole, FAEDS Scholarship Chair
Duval County Public Schools
4037 Boulevard Center Drive
Building B, Second Floor
Jacksonville, FL 32207
Tel: (904)348-5167
Fax: (904)348-5737
E-mail: colem@educationcentral.org
Web Site: http://www.faeds.org/Scholarships.htm
To provide financial assistance to students attending a Florida college or university and majoring in computer science or information technology.
Title of Award: Dr. Robert W. Sims Memorial Scholarship **Area, Field, or Subject:** Computer and information sciences; Information science and technology **Level of Education for which Award is Granted:** Undergraduate **Number Awarded:** Up to 3 each year. **Funds Available:** The stipend is $2,000. **Duration:** 1 year.

Eligibility Requirements: Any currently-enrolled college student who has at least a 2.5 GPA and is attending a Florida private or public college or university is eligible. Applicants must be enrolled full time and be majoring or planning to major in computer science or information technology. Along with their application, they must submit a 2-page essay indicating their interest in computer science and/or information technology and 3 letters of recommendation. Financial need is not considered in the selection process. **Deadline for Receipt:** February of each year. **Additional Information:** This scholarship was established in 1969.

4211 ■ FOUNDATION FOR AMATEUR RADIO, INC.

Attn: Scholarship Committee
P.O. Box 831
Riverdale, MD 20738
E-mail: aa3of@arrl.net
Web Site: http://www.amateurradio-far.org/scholarships.php
To provide funding to licensed radio amateurs in Ohio who are interested in studying electrical engineering or other subjects in college.
Title of Award: Robert E. True Memorial Scholarship **Area, Field, or Subject:** Computer and information sciences; Electronics; Engineering, Electrical; General studies/Field of study not specified **Level of Educa-**

tion for which Award is Granted: Undergraduate **Number Awarded:** 1 each year. **Funds Available:** The stipend is $1,000. **Duration:** 1 year. **Eligibility Requirements:** Applicants must be residents of Ohio and have a valid amateur radio license of any class. They must intend to work on a bachelor's degree at an accredited college or university in the United States; preference is given to applicants pursuing courses in electrical engineering or electronic/computer technology. **Deadline for Receipt:** Requests for applications must be submitted by April of each year. **Additional Information:** Recipients must attend an accredited school (university, college, or technical institute) on a full-time basis.

4212 ■ FOUNDATION FOR THE CAROLINAS

Attn: Senior Vice President, Scholarships
217 South Tryon Street
P.O. Box 34769
Charlotte, NC 28234-4769
Tel: (704)973-4535
Free: 800-973-7244
Fax: (704)973-4935
E-mail: jseymour@fftc.org
Web Site: http://www.fftc.org/scholarships
To provide financial assistance to high school seniors from North and South Carolina who are interested in studying designed fields in college. **Title of Award:** Duke Energy Minority Professional Association Scholarship Fund **Area, Field, or Subject:** Accounting; Business administration; Computer and information sciences; Engineering; Finance; Science **Level of Education for which Award is Granted:** Four Year College **Number Awarded:** 1 or more each year. **Funds Available:** A stipend is awarded (amount not specified). **Duration:** 1 year. **Eligibility Requirements:** This program is open to seniors graduating from high schools in North and South Carolina. Applicants must be planning to attend a 4-year college or university in those states to major in accounting, business administration, computer science, engineering, finance, or the sciences. Selection is based on merit. **Deadline for Receipt:** February of each year. **Additional Information:** Information is also available from the Duke Energy Minority Professional Association Scholarship Committee, P.O. Box 30234, Charlotte, NC 28230.

4213 ■ GEORGIA SPACE GRANT CONSORTIUM

c/o Georgia Institute of Technology
Aerospace Engineering
Space Science and Technology Building, Room 210
Atlanta, GA 30332-0150
Tel: (404)894-0521
Fax: (404)894-9313
E-mail: wanda.pierson@aerospace.gatech.edu
Web Site: http://www.ae.gatech.edu/organizations/gsgc/html/fellowship.htm
To provide financial assistance for undergraduate and graduate study of space-related fields to students at member institutions of the Georgia Space Grant Consortium (GSGC). **Title of Award:** Georgia Space Grant Consortium Fellowships **Area, Field, or Subject:** Aerospace sciences; Computer and information sciences; Engineering, Aerospace/Aeronautical/Astronautical; Mathematics and mathematical sciences; Space and planetary sciences **Level of Education for which Award is Granted:** Graduate, Undergraduate **Number Awarded:** 1 each year. **Funds Available:** A stipend is awarded (amount not specified). **Eligibility Requirements:** This program is open to U.S. citizens who are undergraduate and graduate students at member institutions of the GSGC. Applicants must be working on a degree in mathematics, science, engineering, computer science, or a technical discipline related to space. Selection is based on transcripts, 3 letters of reference, and an essay of 100 to 500 words on the applicant's professional interests and objectives and their relationship to the field of aerospace. Awards are provided as part of the Space Grant program of the U.S. National Aeronautics and Space Administration (NASA), which encourages participation by women, minorities, and people with disabilities. **Additional Information:** Institutions that are members of the GSGC include Albany State University, Clark Atlanta University, Columbus State University, Fort Valley State University, Georgia Institute of Technology, Georgia State University, Kennesaw State University, Mercer University, Morehouse College, Spelman College, State University of West Georgia, and the University of

Georgia. This program is funded by NASA.

4214 ■ GOOGLE INC.

Attn: Scholarships
1600 Amphitheatre Parkway
Mountain View, CA 94043-8303
Tel: (650)623-4000
Fax: (650)618-1499
E-mail: anitaborgscholars@google.com
Web Site: http://www.google.com/anitaborg
To provide financial assistance to women working on a bachelor's or graduate degree in a computer-related field. **Title of Award:** Anita Borg Scholarships **Area, Field, or Subject:** Computer and information sciences; Engineering, Computer **Level of Education for which Award is Granted:** Four Year College, Graduate **Number Awarded:** Varies each year. Recently, 4 of these scholarships were awarded: 1 to an undergraduate, 2 to master's degree candidates, and 1 to a doctoral candidate. **Funds Available:** The stipend is $10,000. **Duration:** 1 year. **Eligibility Requirements:** This program is open to women who are entering their senior year of undergraduate study or are enrolled in a graduate program in computer science, computer engineering, or a related field. Applicants must be full-time students at a university in the United States with a GPA of 3.5 or higher. They must submit essays of 400 to 600 words on 1) a significant technical project on which they have worked; 2) examples of their leadership abilities; 3) what they would do if someone gave them the funding and resources for a 3- to 12-month project to investigate a technical topic of their choice; and 4) what they would do if someone gave them $1,000 to plan an event or project to benefit women in technical fields. Selection is based on academic background and demonstrated leadership. **Deadline for Receipt:** January of each year. **Additional Information:** These scholarships were first offered in 2004.

4215 ■ HANSCOM OFFICERS' WIVES' CLUB

Attn: Scholarship Chair
P.O. Box 557
Bedford, MA 01730
Tel: (781)275-1251
E-mail: scholarship@hanscomowd.org
Web Site: http://www.hanscomowc.org
To provide financial assistance to children of military personnel and veterans in New England who are interested in studying engineering or computer science in college. **Title of Award:** Lieutenant General Chubb Award **Area, Field, or Subject:** Computer and information sciences; Engineering **Level of Education for which Award is Granted:** Undergraduate **Number Awarded:** 1 each year. **Funds Available:** A stipend is awarded (amount not specified). **Duration:** 1 year; nonrenewable. **Eligibility Requirements:** This program is open to college-bound high school seniors living in New England who are dependents of active-duty, retired, or deceased military members of any branch of service. Also eligible are dependents of military recruiters working in the New York area and students living elsewhere but whose military sponsor is stationed at Hanscom Air Force Base. Applicants must demonstrate qualities of responsibility, leadership, scholastics, citizenship, and diversity of interest. They must have a valid military identification card and be planning to work on a college degree in engineering or computer science. Along with their application, they must submit a 2-page essay on their educational goals, how their educational experience will help prepare them to pursue future goals, and how they intend to apply their education to better their community. **Deadline for Receipt:** March of each year. **Additional Information:** This program is sponsored by the Military Affairs Council/North Suburban Chamber of Commerce.

4216 ■ HEMOPHILIA HEALTH SERVICES

Attn: Scholarship Committee
6820 Charlotte Pike, Suite 100
Nashville, TN 37209-4234
Tel: (615)850-5175
Free: 800-800-6606
Fax: (615)352-2588
E-mail: scholarship@HemophiliaHealth.com

Web Site: http://www.HemophiliaHealth.com/consumers/
products_services/scholarship.htm
To provide financial assistance to high school seniors and current college students who have hemophilia and are interested in working on a degree or certification in computer science and/or mathematics. **Title of Award:** Scott Tarbell Scholarships **Area, Field, or Subject:** Computer and information sciences; Mathematics and mathematical sciences **Level of Education for which Award is Granted:** Undergraduate **Number Awarded:** Varies each year, depending on the availability of funds. **Funds Available:** The stipend is $1,500. Funds are issued payable to the recipient's school. **Duration:** 1 year; recipients may reapply.

Eligibility Requirements: This program is open to high school seniors and college freshmen, sophomores, and juniors who have hemophilia A or B severe. Applicants must be enrolled or planning to enroll at an accredited nonprofit college, university, or vocational/technical school in the United States or Puerto Rico. They must be interested in working on a degree or certification in computer science and/or mathematics. Along with their application, they must submit an essay, up to 250 words, on the following topic: "Upon receiving your education in math and/or computer science, how will you use the new technologies (i.e., computer, internet, etc.) to better mankind and what ethical issues will you need to address?" U.S. citizenship is required. Selection is based on academic achievement in relation to tested ability and dedication to the field of computer science or mathematics. Financial need is not considered. **Deadline for Receipt:** April of each year. **Additional Information:** This program, which started in 2003, is administered by Scholarship Program Administrators, Inc., 1201 Eighth Avenue South, P.O. Box 23737, Nashville, TN 27202-3737, (615) 320-3149, Fax: (615) 320-3151, E-mail: info@spaprog.com.

4217 ■ HEWLETT-PACKARD COMPANY

Attn: Scholar Program Manager
8000 Foothills Boulevard
MS 5214
Roseville, CA 95747
Tel: (916)785-3809
E-mail: hpscholars@hp.com
Web Site: http://www.hp.com/go/hpscholars
To provide financial assistance and summer work experience to underrepresented minority high school seniors and community college transfer students who are interested in studying computer engineering, electrical engineering, or computer science at designated universities. **Title of Award:** HP Scholar Program **Area, Field, or Subject:** Computer and information sciences; Engineering, Computer; Engineering, Electrical **Level of Education for which Award is Granted:** Four Year College **Number Awarded:** Approximately 120 each year. **Funds Available:** The stipend is $3,000 per year. In addition, students receive a salary when they work at HP facilities during the summer. They also receive an HP laptop, printer, and PDA. The total value of the award exceeds $40,000 per student. **Duration:** 4 years of university study plus 3 summers of internships.

Eligibility Requirements: This program is open to graduating high school seniors and community college students who are members of an underrepresented minority group (African American, Latino, or American Indian). Applicants must be planning to major in electrical engineering, computer engineering, or computer science at the University of California at Los Angeles, San Jose State University, North Carolina A&T University, the University of Washington, or Morgan State University. They must be interested in working during the summer at a major Hewlett-Packard (HP) location in California, Colorado, Idaho, Oregon, Texas, or Washington. Selection is based on academic achievement, financial need, family's educational history (priority is given to first-generation students), letters of recommendation, a personal statement (communication skills, personal and professional qualities, community involvement), connections to HP Philanthropy and Education Partnerships, and demonstrated interest in math, science, and engineering. **Deadline for Receipt:** March of each year. **Additional Information:** Applications must be submitted to the school the student wishes to attend.

4218 ■ HISPANIC ENGINEER NATIONAL ACHIEVEMENT AWARDS CONFERENCE

3900 Whiteside Street
Los Angeles, CA 90063
Tel: (323)262-0997

Fax: (323)262-0946
E-mail: info@henaac.org
Web Site: http://www.henaac.org/scholarships
To provide financial assistance to Hispanic undergraduate students majoring in computer science. **Title of Award:** Adobe Systems/HENAAC Scholars Program **Area, Field, or Subject:** Computer and information sciences **Level of Education for which Award is Granted:** Four Year College **Number Awarded:** 1 or more each year. **Funds Available:** Stipends range from $1,000 to $5,000. **Duration:** 1 year; recipients may reapply.

Eligibility Requirements: This program is open to Hispanic undergraduate students who are enrolled full time in computer science. Applicants must be entering their junior or senior year and have a GPA of 3.0 or higher. Academic achievement and campus community activities are considered in the selection process. **Deadline for Receipt:** April of each year. **Additional Information:** This program is sponsored by Adobe Systems as part of its effort to support the mission of the Hispanic Engineer National Achievement Awards Conference (HENAAC) to promote technical excellence and leadership in the Hispanic community.

4219 ■ HISPANIC ENGINEER NATIONAL ACHIEVEMENT AWARDS CONFERENCE

3900 Whiteside Street
Los Angeles, CA 90063
Tel: (323)262-0997
Fax: (323)262-0946
E-mail: info@henaac.org
Web Site: http://www.henaac.org/scholarships
To provide financial assistance to Hispanic undergraduate students majoring in computer and electrical engineering. **Title of Award:** AMD/HENAAC Scholars Program **Area, Field, or Subject:** Engineering, Computer; Engineering, Electrical **Level of Education for which Award is Granted:** Undergraduate **Number Awarded:** 1 or more each year. **Funds Available:** Stipends range from $1,000 to $5,000. **Duration:** 1 year; recipients may reapply.

Eligibility Requirements: This program is open to Hispanic undergraduate students who are enrolled full time in computer or electrical engineering. Applicants must have a GPA of 3.5 or higher. Academic achievement and campus community activities are considered in the selection process. **Deadline for Receipt:** April of each year. **Additional Information:** This program is sponsored by AMD (Advanced Micro Devices, Inc.) as part of its effort to support the mission of the Hispanic Engineer National Achievement Awards Conference (HENAAC) to promote technical excellence and leadership in the Hispanic community.

4220 ■ HISPANIC ENGINEER NATIONAL ACHIEVEMENT AWARDS CONFERENCE

3900 Whiteside Street
Los Angeles, CA 90063
Tel: (323)262-0997
Fax: (323)262-0946
E-mail: info@henaac.org
Web Site: http://www.henaac.org/scholarships
To provide financial assistance to Hispanic undergraduate students majoring in engineering and related fields. **Title of Award:** Amerada Hess/HENAAC Scholars Program **Area, Field, or Subject:** Computer and information sciences; Engineering; Materials research/science; Mathematics and mathematical sciences; Science **Level of Education for which Award is Granted:** Undergraduate **Number Awarded:** 1 or more each year. **Funds Available:** Stipends range from $1,000 to $5,000. **Duration:** 1 year; recipients may reapply.

Eligibility Requirements: This program is open to Hispanic undergraduate students who are enrolled full time in computer science, engineering, material science, mathematics, or applied science. Applicants must have a GPA of 3.0 or higher. There is no citizenship requirement. Academic achievement and campus community activities are considered in the selection process. **Deadline for Receipt:** April of each year. **Additional Information:** This program is sponsored by the Amerada Hess Foundation as part of its effort to support the mission of the Hispanic Engineer

National Achievement Awards Conference (HENAAC) to promote technical excellence and leadership in the Hispanic community.

4221 ■ HISPANIC ENGINEER NATIONAL ACHIEVEMENT AWARDS CONFERENCE
3900 Whiteside Street
Los Angeles, CA 90063
Tel: (323)262-0997
Fax: (323)262-0946
E-mail: info@henaac.org
Web Site: http://www.henaac.org/scholarships
To provide financial assistance to Hispanic undergraduate students majoring in engineering and related fields.
Title of Award: Ford/HENAAC Scholars Program **Area, Field, or Subject:** Computer and information sciences; Engineering, Aerospace/Aeronautical/Astronautical; Engineering, Electrical; Engineering, Industrial; Engineering, Mechanical **Level of Education for which Award is Granted:** Undergraduate **Number Awarded:** 5 each year. **Funds Available:** The stipend is $5,000. **Duration:** 1 year; recipients may reapply.
Eligibility Requirements: This program is open to Hispanic undergraduate students who are enrolled full time in computer science or the following engineering fields: aeronautical, electrical, industrial, and, mechanical. Applicants must have a GPA of 3.0 or higher. U.S. citizenship is required. Academic achievement and campus community activities are considered in the selection process. **Deadline for Receipt:** April of each year. **Additional Information:** This program is sponsored by Ford Motor Company as part of its effort to support the mission of the Hispanic Engineer National Achievement Awards Conference (HENAAC) to promote technical excellence and leadership in the Hispanic community.

4222 ■ HISPANIC ENGINEER NATIONAL ACHIEVEMENT AWARDS CONFERENCE
3900 Whiteside Street
Los Angeles, CA 90063
Tel: (323)262-0997
Fax: (323)262-0946
E-mail: info@henaac.org
Web Site: http://www.henaac.org/scholarships
To provide financial assistance to Hispanic undergraduate students majoring in computer science or designated fields of engineering.
Title of Award: Freescale/HENAAC Scholars Program **Area, Field, or Subject:** Computer and information sciences; Engineering, Computer; Engineering, Electrical **Level of Education for which Award is Granted:** Undergraduate **Number Awarded:** 1 or more each year. **Funds Available:** The stipend is $5,000. **Duration:** 1 year; recipients may reapply.
Eligibility Requirements: This program is open to Hispanic undergraduate students who are enrolled full time in computer science or electrical or computer engineering. Applicants must be entering their sophomore, junior, or senior year and have a GPA of 3.0 or higher. Academic achievement and campus community activities are considered in the selection process. **Deadline for Receipt:** April of each year. **Additional Information:** This program is sponsored by Freescale Semiconductor as part of its effort to support the mission of the Hispanic Engineer National Achievement Awards Conference (HENAAC) to promote technical excellence and leadership in the Hispanic community. The recipient is required to accept a summer internship (where and when available) with Freescale Semiconductor.

4223 ■ HISPANIC ENGINEER NATIONAL ACHIEVEMENT AWARDS CONFERENCE
3900 Whiteside Street
Los Angeles, CA 90063
Tel: (323)262-0997
Fax: (323)262-0946
E-mail: info@henaac.org
Web Site: http://www.henaac.org/scholarships
To provide financial assistance to Hispanic undergraduate students majoring in engineering and related fields.
Title of Award: Future Electronics/HENAAC Scholars Program **Area, Field, or Subject:** Computer and information sciences; Engineering; Materials research/science; Mathematics and mathematical sciences; Science **Level of Education for which Award is Granted:** Undergraduate

Number Awarded: 1 or more each year. **Funds Available:** Stipends range from $1,000 to $5,000. **Duration:** 1 year; recipients may reapply.
Eligibility Requirements: This program is open to Hispanic undergraduate students who are enrolled full time in computer science, engineering, material science, mathematics, or applied science. Applicants must have a GPA of 3.0 or higher. There is no citizenship requirement. Academic achievement and campus community activities are considered in the selection process. **Deadline for Receipt:** April of each year. **Additional Information:** This program is sponsored by the Future Electronics as part of its effort to support the mission of the Hispanic Engineer National Achievement Awards Conference (HENAAC) to promote technical excellence and leadership in the Hispanic community.

4224 ■ HISPANIC ENGINEER NATIONAL ACHIEVEMENT AWARDS CONFERENCE
3900 Whiteside Street
Los Angeles, CA 90063
Tel: (323)262-0997
Fax: (323)262-0946
E-mail: info@henaac.org
Web Site: http://www.henaac.org/scholarships
To provide financial assistance to Hispanic undergraduate and graduate students majoring in engineering and related fields.
Title of Award: HENAAC Student Leadership Awards **Area, Field, or Subject:** Computer and information sciences; Engineering; Materials research/science; Mathematics and mathematical sciences; Science **Level of Education for which Award is Granted:** Graduate, Undergraduate **Number Awarded:** 2 each year: 1 undergraduate and 1 graduate student. **Funds Available:** The stipend is $5,000. **Duration:** 1 year.
Eligibility Requirements: This program is open to Hispanic undergraduate and graduate students who are enrolled full time in computer science, engineering, material science, mathematics, or applied science. Applicants must have a GPA of 3.0 or higher. There is no citizenship requirement. Academic achievement and campus community activities are considered in the selection process. **Deadline for Receipt:** April of each year. **Additional Information:** This program is sponsored by the Hispanic Engineer National Achievement Awards Conference (HENAAC) to promote technical excellence and leadership in the Hispanic community.

4225 ■ HISPANIC ENGINEER NATIONAL ACHIEVEMENT AWARDS CONFERENCE
3900 Whiteside Street
Los Angeles, CA 90063
Tel: (323)262-0997
Fax: (323)262-0946
E-mail: info@henaac.org
Web Site: http://www.henaac.org/scholarships
To provide financial assistance to Hispanic undergraduate students majoring in engineering and related fields.
Title of Award: Northrop Grumman/HENAAC Scholars Program **Area, Field, or Subject:** Architecture, Naval; Computer and information sciences; Engineering, Aerospace/Aeronautical/Astronautical; Engineering, Chemical; Engineering, Civil; Engineering, Computer; Engineering, Electrical; Engineering, Industrial; Engineering, Mechanical; Engineering, Ocean; Information science and technology; Mathematics and mathematical sciences; Physics **Level of Education for which Award is Granted:** Undergraduate **Number Awarded:** 5 each year. **Funds Available:** The stipend is $5,000. **Duration:** 1 year; recipients may reapply.
Eligibility Requirements: This program is open to Hispanic undergraduate students who are enrolled full time in the following engineering fields: aerospace, chemical, civil, computer, electrical, industrial, manufacturing, marine, mechanical, ocean, or structural. Students majoring in computer science, information science, mathematics, naval architecture, and physics are also eligible. Applicants must be U.S. citizens and have a GPA of 3.0 or higher. Academic achievement and campus community activities are considered in the selection process. **Deadline for Receipt:** April of each year. **Additional Information:** This program is sponsored by Northrop Grumman as part of its effort to support the mission of the

Hispanic Engineer National Achievement Awards Conference (HENAAC) to promote technical excellence and leadership in the Hispanic community.

4226 ■ HISPANIC ENGINEER NATIONAL ACHIEVEMENT AWARDS CONFERENCE

3900 Whiteside Street
Los Angeles, CA 90063
Tel: (323)262-0997
Fax: (323)262-0946
E-mail: info@henaac.org
Web Site: http://www.henaac.org/scholarships
To provide financial assistance to Hispanic undergraduate students majoring in engineering and related fields.
Title of Award: NVIDIA Corporation/HENAAC Scholars Program **Area, Field, or Subject:** Computer and information sciences; Engineering; Materials research/science; Mathematics and mathematical sciences; Science **Level of Education for which Award is Granted:** Undergraduate **Number Awarded:** 1 or more each year. **Funds Available:** Stipends range from $1,000 to $5,000. **Duration:** 1 year; recipients may reapply.
Eligibility Requirements: This program is open to Hispanic undergraduate students who are enrolled full time in computer science, engineering, material science, mathematics, or applied science. Applicants must have a GPA of 3.0 or higher. There is no citizenship requirement. Academic achievement and campus community activities are considered in the selection process. **Deadline for Receipt:** April of each year. **Additional Information:** This program is sponsored by the NVIDIA Corporation as part of its effort to support the mission of the Hispanic Engineer National Achievement Awards Conference (HENAAC) to promote technical excellence and leadership in the Hispanic community.

4227 ■ HISPANIC SCHOLARSHIP FUND

Attn: Selection Committee
55 Second Street, Suite 1500
San Francisco, CA 94105
Tel: (415)808-2350; 877-HSF-INFO
Fax: (415)808-2302
E-mail: highschool@hsf.net
Web Site: http://www.hsf.net/scholarship/programs/shpe.php
To provide financial assistance for college to Hispanic Americans who are interested in majoring in designated fields of science.
Title of Award: Society of Hispanic Professional Engineers Scholarship Program **Area, Field, or Subject:** Computer and information sciences; Engineering; Mathematics and mathematical sciences; Physical sciences **Level of Education for which Award is Granted:** Undergraduate **Number Awarded:** Varies each year; recently, 69 of these scholarships were awarded: 7 at $1,250, 2 at $1,307, and 60 at $2,500. **Funds Available:** Stipends range from $1,250 to $2,500 per year. **Duration:** 1 year.
Eligibility Requirements: This program is open to U.S. citizens, permanent residents, and visitors with a passport stamped I-551 who are of Hispanic heritage. Applicants may be graduating high school seniors, community college students transferring to a 4-year institution, or continuing college students as long as they have a GPA of 3.0 or higher. They must be enrolled or planning to enroll full time at an accredited college or university in the United States to major in computer science, physical science, applied science, mathematics, or engineering. Along with their application, they must submit 600-word essays on 1) how their Hispanic heritage, family upbringing, and/or role models have influenced their personal long-term goals; 2) how they contribute to their community and what they have learned from their experiences; and 3) an academic challenge they have faced and how they have overcome it. Selection is based on academic achievement, personal strengths, leadership, and financial need. **Deadline for Receipt:** June of each year. **Additional Information:** This program is jointly sponsored by the Society of Hispanic Professional Engineers (SHPE) and the Hispanic Scholarship Fund (HSF).

4228 ■ HISPANIC SCHOLARSHIP FUND INSTITUTE

1001 Connecticut Avenue, N.W., Suite 632
Washington, DC 20036
Tel: (202)296-0009
Fax: (202)296-3633
E-mail: info@hsfi.org
Web Site: http://www.hsfi.org/scholarships/energy.asp

To provide financial assistance to Hispanic undergraduate students majoring in designated business, engineering, and science fields related to the U.S. Department of Energy (DOE) goals of environmental restoration and waste management.
Title of Award: Environmental Management Scholarship **Area, Field, or Subject:** Business administration; Chemistry; Computer and information sciences; Engineering, Agricultural; Engineering, Civil; Engineering, Electrical; Engineering, Industrial; Engineering, Mechanical; Engineering, Metallurgical; Engineering, Petroleum; Environmental science; Epidemiology; Geology; Hydrology; Management; Mathematics and mathematical sciences; Physics; Radiology; Toxicology **Level of Education for which Award is Granted:** Undergraduate **Number Awarded:** Varies each year. **Funds Available:** The stipend is $3,000 per year for 4-year university students or $2,000 per year for community college students. **Duration:** 1 year.
Eligibility Requirements: This program is open to U.S. citizens and permanent residents of Hispanic background who have completed at least 12 undergraduate credits with a GPA of 3.0 or higher. Applicants must be interested in preparing for a career supportive of the DOE goals of environmental restoration and waste management. Eligible academic majors are in the fields of business (management and system analysis), engineering (agricultural, chemical, civil, electrical, environmental, industrial, mechanical, metallurgical, nuclear, and petroleum), and science (applied math/physics, chemistry, computer science, ecology, environmental, epidemiology, geology, health physics, hydrology, radiochemistry, radio-ecology, and toxicology). Along with their application, they must submit a 2-page essay on 1) how their academic major, interests, and career goals correspond to environmental restoration and waste management issues; and 2) how their Hispanic background and family upbringing have influenced their academic and personal goals. Selection is based on the essay, academic record, academic plans and career goals, financial need, commitment to DOE's goal of environmental restoration and waste management, and a letter of recommendation. **Deadline for Receipt:** March of each year. **Additional Information:** This program, which began in 1990, is sponsored by DOE's Office of Environmental Management. Recipients must enroll full time at a college or university in the United States.

4229 ■ HISPANIC SCHOLARSHIP FUND INSTITUTE

1001 Connecticut Avenue, N.W., Suite 632
Washington, DC 20036
Tel: (202)296-0009
Fax: (202)296-3633
E-mail: info@hsfi.org
Web Site: http://www.hsfi.org/scholarships/generation.asp
To provide financial assistance to Hispanic and other students majoring in designated business, engineering, social science, and science fields who are interested in employment with the U.S. Department of Energy (DOE).
Title of Award: Next Generation of Public Servants Scholarship **Area, Field, or Subject:** Accounting; Biological and clinical sciences; Business administration; Computer and information sciences; Engineering; Environmental science; Finance; Geology; Information science and technology; Management; Mathematics and mathematical sciences; Physics; Political science; Psychology; Sociology **Level of Education for which Award is Granted:** Undergraduate **Number Awarded:** Varies each year. **Funds Available:** The stipend is $3,000 per year. **Duration:** 1 year; may be renewed up to 2 additional years if the recipient maintains full-time enrollment and a GPA of 2.8 or higher.
Eligibility Requirements: This program is open to U.S. citizens enrolled full time as sophomores with a GPA of 2.8 or higher. Applicants must be interested in preparing for a career with the DOE in an energy-related field. Eligible academic majors are in the fields of business (accounting, business administration, finance, and management), engineering (biomedical, chemical, civil, computer, electrical, environmental, industrial, materials, mechanical, metallurgical, nuclear, and petroleum), social science (economics, organizational psychology, political science, and sociology), and science (biological sciences, computer science, geology, information technology, mathematics, microbiology, and physics). They must be willing to participate in co-ops with the DOE. Along with their application, they must submit a 2-page essay on why a career in public service interests them, how their academic major connects with their stated DOE career goal, why the DOE should invest in them through this program, and how they believe the DOE will benefit from this investment.

Selection is based on academic achievement, financial need, demonstrated commitment to public service, and interest in federal employment with the DOE. **Deadline for Receipt:** February of each year. **Additional Information:** This program, sponsored by DOE's Office of Economic Impact and Diversity, is administered by the Hispanic Scholarship Fund Institute as part of its effort to increase Hispanic participation in federal service.

4230 ■ IEEE COMPUTER SOCIETY
Attn: Student Awards
1730 Massachusetts Avenue, N.W.
Washington, DC 20036-1992
Tel: (202)371-1013
Fax: (202)778-0884
E-mail: csidc@computer.org
Web Site: http://www.computer.org/csidc
To recognize and reward undergraduate students who design and implement computer-based solutions to real-world problems

Title of Award: Computer Society International Design Competition **Area, Field, or Subject:** Computer and information sciences; Engineering, Computer **Level of Education for which Award is Granted:** Undergraduate **Number Awarded:** The competition is limited to 300 teams. If more teams apply, team selection is made at random. Of the entrants, 10 teams are selected as finalists and to receive prizes (including 7 honorable mentions). **Funds Available:** Prizes are $20,000 for first, $12,000 for second, $8,000 for third, and $4,000 for honorable mentions. Students determine how the prize money is distributed among the team. The 2 special Microsoft Prizes are each $2,000. **Duration:** The competition is held annually.

Eligibility Requirements: The competition is open to teams of undergraduate students in computer science, computer engineering, and related fields. Each team consists of 4 undergraduates plus a faculty mentor. Teams must design and implement a computer-based project on a topic that changes annually; a recent topic was "Preserving, Protecting, and Enhancing the Environment." They must submit a report that includes an abstract, a system overview (with a statement of what the system hardware and software are meant to accomplish, a statement of the performance requirements it is intended to meet, a summary of the design methodology used and why it was chosen, and a statement of what is unique or innovative about this project and any novel ideas that the design includes), a description of implementation and engineering considerations (with a detailed description of the system and the algorithms involved, the trade-offs considered and used, any tools that were developed in the context of the project, and verification and testing), and a summary. Based on those reports, finalists are chosen and invited to present their projects to the judging panel. Selection of winners is based on originality of the project, its relevance to the theme of being beneficial to society, the substance of the project, taking a systems approach, teamwork, quality and presentation of reports, creativity in design, plan for the project period, and practicality and feasibility of the project. The Microsoft Award for Software Engineering is awarded to the team that makes the best use of appropriate software engineering techniques in the planning, design, construction, testing, and documentation of their software. The Microsoft Multimedia Award is awarded to the team that makes best use of multimedia techniques in their formal presentation at the finals. **Deadline for Receipt:** Applications must be submitted by November of each year. Project reports are due in April, and the world finals are held at the end of June. **Additional Information:** This competition was first held in 2000. The 2 special Microsoft Prizes were first awarded in 2003.

4231 ■ IEEE COMPUTER SOCIETY
Attn: Student Awards
1730 Massachusetts Avenue, N.W.
Washington, DC 20036-1992
Tel: (202)371-1013
Fax: (202)778-0884
E-mail: hqofc@computer.org
Web Site: http://www.computer.org/students/schlrshp.htm
To recognize and reward students who are active leaders in the IEEE Computer Society student branch chapters.

Title of Award: Richard E. Merwin Student Scholarship **Area, Field, or Subject:** Computer and information sciences; Engineering, Computer;

Engineering, Electrical **Level of Education for which Award is Granted:** Four Year College, Graduate **Number Awarded:** Up to 10 each year. **Funds Available:** The stipend is $4,000, paid in 4 equal installments. **Duration:** 1 academic year.

Eligibility Requirements: Juniors, seniors, and graduate students in electrical engineering, computer engineering, computer science, or a well-defined computer-related field of engineering (e.g., biomedical computer engineering, design automation) are eligible to apply if they are full-time students and active members of the society's student branch chapter at their institution. Applicants must have a cumulative GPA of 2.5 or higher. Selection is based on involvement in chapter activities (40%), academic achievement (30%), other extracurricular activities in college (10%), and a letter of evaluation by the branch chapter advisor (20%). **Deadline for Receipt:** May of each year. **Additional Information:** A brief statement outlining accomplishments must be submitted by each recipient at the end of the academic year.

4232 ■ INSTITUTE OF INTERNATIONAL EDUCATION
Attn: Lucent Global Science Scholars Program
809 United Nations Plaza
New York, NY 10017-3580
Tel: (212)984-5419
Fax: (212)984-5452
E-mail: sciencescholars@iie.org
Web Site: http://www.iie.org/programs/lucent
To provide financial assistance for college to high school students in the United States and university students in other designated countries who are interested in preparing for careers in information technology.

Title of Award: Lucent Global Science Scholars Program **Area, Field, or Subject:** Chemistry; Computer and information sciences; Engineering; Information science and technology; Mathematics and mathematical sciences; Physics **Level of Education for which Award is Granted:** Undergraduate **Number Awarded:** Varies each year. Recently, 32 students from foreign countries (5 from China, 1 from Hong Kong, and 2 from each of the other countries) and 28 from the United States received these scholarships. **Funds Available:** The stipend is $5,000 per year. **Duration:** 1 year; nonrenewable.

Eligibility Requirements: This program is open to high school seniors in the United States and first-year university students in Brazil, Canada, China, France, Germany, Hong Kong, India, Korea, Mexico, the Netherlands, Philippines, Poland, Russia, Spain, and the United Kingdom. Students from the United States must have a GPA of 3.6 or higher. Eligible majors include applied physics, chemistry, computer science, engineering, information science and technology, mathematics and applied mathematics, and physics. Selection is based on a demonstrated record of distinction in science and mathematics and a desire to prepare for a career in information technology. **Deadline for Receipt:** February of each year for students from the United States; March of each year for students from other countries. **Additional Information:** This program, established in 1999, is funded by Lucent Technologies. Students are offered internships at Lucent's research and development and manufacturing facilities in their own countries during the summer following their freshman year in the United States or the sophomore year in other countries.

4233 ■ KANSAS INSURANCE DEPARTMENT
Attn: Scholarship Fund
420 S.W. Ninth Street
Topeka, KS 66612-2103
Tel: (785)296-3071
Free: 800-432-2484
Fax: (785)296-2283
Web Site: http://www.ksinsurance.org
To provide financial assistance to African American upper-division students who are majoring in business, computer science, or mathematics at a college or university in Kansas.

Title of Award: Kansas Insurance Department African American Scholarships **Area, Field, or Subject:** Business administration; Computer and information sciences; Mathematics and mathematical sciences **Level of Education for which Award is Granted:** Four Year College **Number Awarded:** 12 each year. **Funds Available:** The stipend is $1,000. **Duration:** 1 year.

Eligibility Requirements: This program is open to African American students enrolled as juniors or higher at 4-year accredited institutions of higher education in Kansas. Applicants must be majoring in business, computer science, or mathematics. **Deadline for Receipt:** May of each year. **Additional Information:** These scholarships were first awarded in 2005 with funds received in a settlement with Monumental Life as a result of the firm's race-based pricing of life insurance policies.

4234 ■ KNIGHT RIDDER NEWSPAPERS-WASHINGTON BUREAU

Attn: Anthony Pugh
700 12th Street, N.W., Suite 1000
Washington, DC 20005-3994
Tel: (202)383-6013
Fax: (202)383-3738
E-mail: tpugh@krwashington.com
Web Site: http://www.krwashington.com
To provide financial assistance to minority high school seniors from the Washington, D.C. area who are interested in attending college to prepare for a career in the newspaper industry.
Title of Award: Washington Bureau Minority Scholarships **Area, Field, or Subject:** Advertising; Business administration; Computer and information sciences; Graphic art and design; Journalism; Photography, Journalistic **Level of Education for which Award is Granted:** Undergraduate **Number Awarded:** 2 each year. **Funds Available:** The stipend is $1,000. **Duration:** 1 year.
Eligibility Requirements: This program is open to minority seniors graduating from high schools in the metropolitan area of Washington, D.C. Applicants must be able to demonstrate an interest in journalism, but they are not required to have been school newspaper reporters or editors. They may be photographers, graphic artists, computer experts, delivery workers with an interest in circulation, or business and advertising staff members. Along with their application, they must submit a transcript of grades (with a GPA of 3.0 or higher), SAT/ACT scores, 2 letters of recommendation, a list of journalism or business experience, information on extracurricular activities, up to 5 samples of work with bylines (for journalism applicants), and a 500-word essay on why they want to prepare for a career in journalism or communication business. **Deadline for Receipt:** January of each year. **Additional Information:** The recipients of these scholarships are entered into competition for the Knight Ridder Minority Scholarship Program of $40,000 over 4 years.

4235 ■ LEAGUE FOR INNOVATION IN THE COMMUNITY COLLEGE

Attn: Director, Membership Services
4505 East Chandler Boulevard, Suite 250
Phoenix, AZ 85048
Tel: (480)705-8200
Fax: (480)705-8201
E-mail: neil@league.org
Web Site: http://www.league.org/league/competitions/tob_awards.htm
To provide financial assistance to students at community colleges that are members of the League for Innovation in the Community College who are studying technology.
Title of Award: Terry O'Banion Student Technology Awards **Area, Field, or Subject:** Computer and information sciences; Technology **Level of Education for which Award is Granted:** Two Year College **Number Awarded:** 2 each year: 1 designated as the Student Technology Champion and 1 designated as the Student Developer Champion. **Funds Available:** The stipend is $5,000. **Duration:** 1 year.
Eligibility Requirements: Faculty and staff at institutions that are members of the League may nominate students for this award. Nominees must be preparing for a career in technology or software development. They must be able to demonstrate financial need. **Deadline for Receipt:** February of each year. **Additional Information:** This program is sponsored by Microsoft Corporation.

4236 ■ CLARE BOOTHE LUCE FUND

c/o Henry Luce Foundation, Inc.
111 West 50th Street, Suite 4601
New York, NY 10020
Tel: (212)489-7700
Fax: (212)581-9541
E-mail: jdaniels@hluce.org
Web Site: http://www.hluce.org
To provide funding to women interested in studying science or engineering at the undergraduate level at designated universities.

Title of Award: Clare Boothe Luce Scholarships in Science and Engineering **Area, Field, or Subject:** Biological and clinical sciences; Chemistry; Computer and information sciences; Engineering; Engineering, Aerospace/Aeronautical/Astronautical; Engineering, Civil; Engineering, Electrical; Engineering, Mechanical; Engineering, Nuclear; Mathematics and mathematical sciences; Meteorology; Physics **Level of Education for which Award is Granted:** Undergraduate **Number Awarded:** Varies; since the program began, more than 800 of these scholarships have been awarded. **Funds Available:** The amount awarded is established individually by each of the participating institutions. The stipends are intended to augment rather than replace any existing institutional support in these fields. Each stipend is calculated to include the cost of room and board as well as tuition and other fees or expenses. **Duration:** 2 years; in certain special circumstances, awards for the full 4 years of undergraduate study may be offered.
Eligibility Requirements: This program is open to female undergraduate students (particularly juniors and seniors) majoring in biology, chemistry, computer science, engineering (aeronautical, civil, electrical, mechanical, nuclear, and others), mathematics, meteorology, and physics. Applicants must be U.S. citizens attending 1 of the 12 designated colleges and universities affiliated with this program; periodically, other institutions are invited to participate. Premedical science majors are ineligible for this competition. The participating institutions select the recipients without regard to race, age, religion, ethnic background, or need. All awards are made on the basis of merit. **Deadline for Receipt:** Varies; check with the participating institutions for their current schedule. **Additional Information:** The participating institutions are Boston University, Colby College, Creighton University, Fordham University, Georgetown University, Marymount University, Mount Holyoke College, St. John's University, Santa Clara University, Seton Hall University, Trinity College, and University of Notre Dame.

4237 ■ MAINE SPACE GRANT CONSORTIUM

Attn: Executive Director
87 Winthrop Street, Suite 200
Augusta, ME 04330
Tel: (207)622-4688; 877-397-7223
Fax: (207)622-4548
E-mail: shehata@msgc.org
Web Site: http://www.msgc.org/education_students.asp
To provide funding to undergraduate and graduate students at colleges and universities in Maine interested in working on projects related to space.
Title of Award: Maine Space Grant Consortium Scholarship and Fellowship Program **Area, Field, or Subject:** Aerospace sciences; Biological and clinical sciences; Computer and information sciences; Earth sciences; Engineering, Aerospace/Aeronautical/Astronautical; Geosciences; Physical sciences; Social sciences; Space and planetary sciences; Technology **Level of Education for which Award is Granted:** Graduate, Undergraduate **Number Awarded:** Varies each year. **Funds Available:** Stipends are $2,500 for undergraduates or $5,000 for graduate students. **Duration:** 1 year.
Eligibility Requirements: This program is open to U.S. citizens who are enrolled on a full-time basis in an undergraduate or graduate program at a 2- or 4-year college or university in Maine, including those not members of the Maine Space Grant Consortium. Applicants must be proposing to conduct a project on a topic of interest to the U.S. National Aeronautics and Space Administration (NASA) in biological, earth, physical, social, or space science; human exploration and development of space; or other related science, technology, computer, or engineering fields. Undergraduates must have a GPA of 3.0 or higher; graduate students must have a GPA of 3.2 or higher. Proposals may involve conducting research at their home institution, traveling to conduct research and/or to present finished project work at a NASA field center, or facilitating technology transfer from NASA to their institution and industry in Maine. Applications are especially encouraged from women, minorities, and persons with disabilities. Selection is based on the relevance of the project to NASA's mission and its strategic enterprises, collaboration with researchers at NASA space flight centers, qualifications of the student, technical content and quality of the

proposal, and recommendation from a faculty member. **Deadline for Receipt:** May or October of each year. **Additional Information:** This program is funded by NASA.

4238 ■ MARYLAND HIGHER EDUCATION COMMISSION

Attn: Office of Student Financial Assistance
839 Bestgate Road, Suite 400
Annapolis, MD 21401-3013
Tel: (410)260-4545
Free: 800-974-1024
Fax: (410)974-5376
E-mail: osfamail@mhec.state.md.us
Web Site: http://www.mhec.state.md.us/financialAid/
ProgramDescriptions/prog_scm.asp
To provide scholarship/loans to Maryland residents who wish to prepare for a teaching career.

Title of Award: Sharon Christa McAuliffe Memorial Teacher Education Award **Area, Field, or Subject:** Chemistry; Classical studies; Computer and information sciences; Earth sciences; Education; Education, English as a second language; Education, Special; Education, Vocational-technical; Foreign languages; Geosciences; Health care services; Hearing and deafness; Mathematics and mathematical sciences; Physical sciences; Physics; Space and planetary sciences; Visual impairment **Level of Education for which Award is Granted:** Master's, Professional, Undergraduate **Number Awarded:** Varies each year. **Funds Available:** The amount of the award is based on the recipient's enrollment and housing status, to a maximum of $17,000 per year. The total amount of all state awards may not exceed the cost of attendance as determined by the school's financial aid office or $17,800, whichever is less. Following graduation, recipients must teach at a Maryland public school for 1 year for each year of financial aid received under this program. If they fail to meet that service obligation, they must repay all funds they received with interest. They must begin the service obligation within 12 months of graduation. **Duration:** 1 year; may be renewed for 1 additional year if the recipient maintains satisfactory academic progress with a cumulative GPA of 3.0 or higher and enrollment at a 2-year or 4-year Maryland college or university in an approved teacher education program.

Eligibility Requirements: This program is open to Maryland residents who are college students with at least 60 semester credit hours completed, college graduates, and teachers in a non-critical shortage area. Applicants must have a GPA of 3.0 or higher and plan to teach in a field identified as a critical shortage area. Selection is based on cumulative GPA, applicable work or volunteer experience, quality of academic background in certification field, and a writing sample. **Deadline for Receipt:** December of each year. **Additional Information:** Recently, the eligible critical shortage areas were business education, chemistry, computer science, earth and space science, English for speakers of other languages, family and consumer sciences, German, health occupations, Latin, mathematics, physical science, physics, Spanish, special education (generic infant-grade 3, generic grades 1-8, generic grades 6-adult, hearing impaired, severely and profoundly handicapped, visually impaired), and technology education.

4239 ■ MARYLAND SPACE GRANT CONSORTIUM

c/o Johns Hopkins University
203 Bloomberg Center for Physics and Astronomy
3400 North Charles Street
Baltimore, MD 21218-2686
Tel: (410)516-7351
Fax: (410)516-4109
E-mail: info@mdspacegrant.org
Web Site: http://www.mdspacegrant.org/scholars_about.html
To provide financial assistance to undergraduates who are interested in studying space-related fields at selected universities in Maryland that are members of the Maryland Space Grant Consortium.

Title of Award: Maryland Space Scholars Program **Area, Field, or Subject:** Aerospace sciences; Astronomy and astronomical sciences; Biological and clinical sciences; Chemistry; Computer and information sciences; Engineering; Geology; Mathematics and mathematical sciences; Physics; Space and planetary sciences **Level of Education for which Award is Granted:** Undergraduate **Number Awarded:** Varies each year; recently 16 of these scholarships were awarded (2 at Johns Hopkins University, 5 at Morgan State University, 2 at Hagerstown Community Col-

lege, 2 at Towson University, and 5 at the University of Maryland at College Park). **Funds Available:** Scholars receive partial payment of tuition at the participating university they attend. **Duration:** 1 year; may be renewed if the recipient maintains a GPA of 3.0 or higher.

Eligibility Requirements: This program is open to residents of Maryland and graduates of Maryland high schools who are enrolled full time at a member institution. Applicants must be interested in preparing for a career in mathematics, science, engineering, technology, or a space-related field. They must be majoring in a relevant field, including (but not limited to) astronomy, the biological and life sciences, chemistry, computer science, engineering, geological sciences, or physics. U.S. citizenship is required. Along with their application, they must submit an essay of 200 to 500 words on how this scholarship will help them meet their educational and financial goals. This program is a component of the U.S. National Aeronautics and Space Administration (NASA) Space Grant program, which encourages participation by women, underrepresented minorities, and persons with disabilities. **Deadline for Receipt:** August of each year. **Additional Information:** The participating universities are Hagerstown Community College, Johns Hopkins University, Morgan State University, Towson University, the University of Maryland at College Park, and Washington College. Funding for this program is provided by NASA.

4240 ■ MASSACHUSETTS OFFICE OF STUDENT FINANCIAL ASSISTANCE

454 Broadway, Suite 200
Revere, MA 02151
Tel: (617)727-9420
Fax: (617)727-0667
E-mail: osfa@osfa.mass.edu
Web Site: http://www.osfa.mass.edu
To provide financial assistance to students at Massachusetts public institutions of higher education who are participating in a high technology scholar/intern program.

Title of Award: Massachusetts High Technology Scholar/Intern Tuition Waiver Program **Area, Field, or Subject:** Computer and information sciences; Engineering, Computer; Information science and technology; Technology **Level of Education for which Award is Granted:** Undergraduate **Number Awarded:** Varies each year. **Funds Available:** The awards match industry scholarships up to the resident undergraduate tuition rate at the participating institution. **Duration:** Up to 4 academic years.

Eligibility Requirements: This program is open to students at Massachusetts public institutions who are participating as interns in a computer information science/technology and engineering program approved by the Massachusetts Board of Higher Education. Applicants must be U.S. citizens or permanent residents who are residents of Massachusetts. Their institution must have obtained scholarship funding from business and industry.

4241 ■ MATERIAL HANDLING INDUSTRY OF AMERICA

Attn: Material Handling Education Foundation, Inc.
8720 Red Oak Boulevard, Suite 201
Charlotte, NC 28217-3992
Tel: (704)676-1190
Free: 800-722-6832
Fax: (704)676-1199
E-mail: vwheeler@mhia.org
Web Site: http://www.mhia.org
To provide financial assistance to undergraduate or graduate students who are studying material handling.

Title of Award: MHEFI Scholarship Program **Area, Field, or Subject:** Business administration; Computer and information sciences; Engineering; Engineering, Civil; Engineering, Computer; Engineering, Electrical; Engineering, Industrial; Engineering, Mechanical; Logistics; Management **Level of Education for which Award is Granted:** Four Year College, Graduate **Number Awarded:** Varies each year; recently, 28 of these scholarships (with a total value of $73,500) were awarded. **Funds Available:** Awards range from $1,500 to $6,000. **Duration:** 1 year.

Eligibility Requirements: This program is open to 1) students at 4-year colleges and universities who have completed at least 2 years of undergraduate study; and 2) graduate students enrolled in a program leading to a master's or doctoral degree. Students from junior or community colleges are eligible if they have been accepted as a transfer student into a 4-year program. Applicants must be U.S. citizens; be attending an academic institution that has been prequalified for foundation funding; have earned a GPA of 3.0 or higher in college; and be enrolled in a course of study relevant to the material handling industry, including engineering (civil, computer, industrial, electrical, or mechanical), engineering technology, computer science, or business administration with an emphasis on production management, industrial distribution, and/or logistics. Along with their application, they must submit 3 letters of recommendation, official transcripts, documentation of financial need, and a 600-word essay on how their course of study, work experience, and career goals make them an appropriate candidate for this scholarship. **Deadline for Receipt:** February of each year. **Additional Information:** More than 60 colleges and universities have been prequalified for participation in this program. For a list, contact the Material Handling Education Foundation, Inc. (MHEFI).

4242 ■ MICRON TECHNOLOGY, INC.

Attn: Micron Technology Foundation
8000 South Federal Way
P.O. Box 6
Boise, ID 83707-0006
Tel: (208)368-3675
Web Site: http://www.micron.com/about/giving/foundation/
scholarships.html
To provide financial assistance to high school seniors in selected states who are interested in majoring in the physical sciences.
Title of Award: Micron Science and Technology Scholars **Area, Field, or Subject:** Chemistry; Computer and information sciences; Engineering, Chemical; Engineering, Computer; Engineering, Electrical; Engineering, Mechanical; Materials research/science; Physics **Level of Education for which Award is Granted:** Undergraduate **Number Awarded:** 13 each year: 1 at $55,000 and 12 at $16,500; 2 are awarded to students from each of 5 participating states, plus 3 floating scholarships are awarded within those states. **Funds Available:** Stipends are either $55,000 or $16,500. A cash grant of $1,000 is awarded to the high school of each winner.
Eligibility Requirements: This program is open to high school seniors who reside in and attend public or private schools in Colorado, Idaho, Texas, Utah, or Virginia. Applicants must have a combined SAT score of at least 1350 or a composite ACT score of at least 30; have at least a 3.5 GPA; have demonstrated leadership in school, work, and extracurricular activities; and plan to major in engineering (electrical, computer, chemical, or mechanical), computer science, chemistry, material sciences, or physics. Selection is based on merit (in academics and leadership). **Deadline for Receipt:** January of each year. **Additional Information:** This program began in 2000. Information is also available from Scholarship Management Services of Scholarship America, One Scholarship Way, P.O. Box 297, St. Peter, MN 56082, (507) 931-1682, (800) 537-4180, Fax: (507) 931-9168.

4243 ■ MICROSOFT CORPORATION

Attn: National Minority Technical Scholarship
One Microsoft Way
Redmond, WA 98052-8303
Tel: (425)882-8080
E-mail: scholars@microsoft.com
Web Site: http://www.microsoft.com/college/ss_overview.mspx
To provide financial assistance and summer work experience to undergraduate students, especially members of underrepresented groups, interested in preparing for a career in computer science or other related technical fields.
Title of Award: Microsoft National Scholarships **Area, Field, or Subject:** Computer and information sciences; Engineering, Computer; Engineering, Electrical; Mathematics and mathematical sciences; Physics; Technology **Level of Education for which Award is Granted:** Undergraduate **Number Awarded:** Varies. A total of $540,000 is available for this program each year. **Funds Available:** Scholarships cover 100% of the tuition as posted by the financial aid office of the university or college the recipient designates. Scholarships are made through that school and are not transferable to other academic institutions. Funds may be used for tuition only and may not be used for other costs on the recipient's bursar bill, such as room and board. **Duration:** 1 year.
Eligibility Requirements: This program is open to students who are enrolled full time and making satisfactory progress toward an undergradu-

ate degree in computer science, computer engineering, or a related technical discipline (such as electrical engineering, mathematics, or physics) with a demonstrated interest in computer science. Applicants must be enrolled at a 4-year college or university in the United States, Canada, or Mexico. They must have a GPA of 3.0 or higher. Although all students who meet the eligibility criteria may apply, a large majority of scholarships are awarded to women, underrepresented minorities (African Americans, Hispanics, and Native Americans), and students with disabilities. Along with their application, students must submit an essay that describes the following 4 items: 1) how they demonstrate their passion for technology outside the classroom; 2) the toughest technical problem they have worked on, how they addressed the problem, their role in reaching the outcome if it was team-based, and the final outcome; 3) a situation that demonstrates initiative and their willingness to go above and beyond; and 4) how they are currently funding their college education. **Deadline for Receipt:** January of each year. **Additional Information:** Selected recipients are offered a paid summer internship where they will have a chance to develop Microsoft products.

4244 ■ MONTANA SPACE GRANT CONSORTIUM

c/o Montana State University
416 Cobleigh Hall
P.O. Box 173835
Bozeman, MT 59717-3835
Tel: (406)994-4223
Fax: (406)994-4452
E-mail: msgc@montana.edu
Web Site: http://spacegrant.montana.edu/Text/ScholarProgram.html
To provide financial assistance to students in Montana who are interested in working on an undergraduate degree in the space sciences and/or engineering.
Title of Award: Montana Space Grant Consortium Undergraduate Scholarships **Area, Field, or Subject:** Aerospace sciences; Astronomy and astronomical sciences; Biological and clinical sciences; Chemistry; Computer and information sciences; Engineering, Aerospace/Aeronautical/Astronautical; Engineering, Chemical; Engineering, Civil; Engineering, Electrical; Engineering, Mechanical; Geology; Physics; Space and planetary sciences **Level of Education for which Award is Granted:** Undergraduate **Number Awarded:** Varies each year; recently, 23 of these scholarships were awarded. **Funds Available:** The stipend is $1,000 per year. **Duration:** 1 year; may be renewed.
Eligibility Requirements: This program is open to full-time undergraduate students at member institutions of the Montana Space Grant Consortium (MSGC) majoring in fields related to space sciences and engineering. Those fields include, but are not limited to, astronomy, biological and life sciences, chemical engineering, chemistry, civil engineering, computer sciences, electrical engineering, geological sciences, mathematics, mechanical engineering, and physics. Priority is given to students who have been involved in aerospace-related research. U.S. citizenship is required. The MSGC is a component of the U.S. National Aeronautics and Space Administration (NASA) Space Grant program, which encourages participation by women, underrepresented minorities, and persons with disabilities. **Deadline for Receipt:** March of each year. **Additional Information:** The MSGC member institutions are Blackfeet Community College, Carroll College, Chief Dull Knife College, Fort Belknap College, Fort Peck Community College, Little Big Horn College, Montana State University at Billings, Montana State University at Bozeman, Montana State University Northern, Montana Tech, Rocky Mountain College, Salish Kootenai College, Stone Child College, University of Great Falls, University of Montana, and University of Montana Western. Funding for this program is provided by NASA.

4245 ■ MORGAN STANLEY

c/o Joyce Arencibia, IT College Recruiting
750 Seventh Avenue, 30th Floor
New York, NY 10019
Tel: (212)762-4000
E-mail: diversityrecruiting@morganstanley.com
Web Site: http://www.morganstanley.com/about/diversity/
recruit_programs.html?page=div
To provide financial assistance and work experience to members of the National Society of Black Engineers (NSBE), Society of Hispanic Professional Engineers (SHPE), and Society of Women Engineers (SWE) who

are working on an undergraduate degree in computer science or engineering.

Title of Award: NSBE/SHPE/SWE Members Scholarship **Area, Field, or Subject:** Computer and information sciences; Engineering **Level of Education for which Award is Granted:** Four Year College **Number Awarded:** 1 or more each year. **Funds Available:** Students who receive a scholarship as juniors (or fourth-year students in a 5-year program) receive $10,000 for their final year of college. Students who receive a scholarship as sophomores (or third-year students in a 5-year program) receive $5,000 for their junior year (or fourth year of a 5-year program). **Duration:** 1 year; may be renewed for the final year for students who receive a scholarship as sophomores (or third-year students in a 5-year program).

Eligibility Requirements: This program is open to active members of NSBE, SHPE, and SWE who are enrolled in their sophomore or junior year of college (or the third or fourth year of a 5-year program). Applicants must be enrolled full time and have a GPA of 3.0 or higher. They must be willing to commit to a paid summer internship in the Morgan Stanley Information Technology Division. All majors and disciplines are eligible, but preference is given to students preparing for a career in computer science or engineering. Along with their application, they must submit 1-page essays on 1) why they are applying for this scholarship and why they should be selected as a recipient; 2) a technical project on which they worked, either through a university course or previous work experience, their role in the project, and how they contributed to the end result; and 3) a software, hardware, or new innovative application of existing technology that they would create if they could and the impact it would have. Financial need is not considered in the selection process. **Deadline for Receipt:** February of each year. **Additional Information:** The program includes a paid summer internship in the Morgan Stanley Information Technology Division in the summer following the time of application.

4246 ■ MORGAN STANLEY

c/o Joyce Arencibia, IT College Recruiting
750 Seventh Avenue, 30th Floor
New York, NY 10019
Tel: (212)762-4000
E-mail: diversityrecruiting@morganstanley.com
Web Site: http://www.morganstanley.com/about/diversity/
recruit_programs.html?page=div
To provide financial assistance and work experience to women who are working on an undergraduate degree in computer science or engineering.

Title of Award: Women in Technology Scholarship **Area, Field, or Subject:** Computer and information sciences; Engineering **Level of Education for which Award is Granted:** Four Year College **Number Awarded:** 1 or more each year. **Funds Available:** Students who receive a scholarship as juniors (or fourth-year students in a 5-year program) receive $10,000 for their final year of college. Students who receive a scholarship as sophomores (or third-year students in a 5-year program) receive $5,000 for their junior year (or fourth year of a 5-year program). **Duration:** 1 year; may be renewed for the final year for students who receive a scholarship as sophomores (or third-year students in a 5-year program).

Eligibility Requirements: This program is open to women who are enrolled in their sophomore or junior year of college (or the third or fourth year of a 5-year program). Applicants must be enrolled full time and have a GPA of 3.0 or higher. They must be willing to commit to a paid summer internship in the Morgan Stanley Information Technology Division. All majors and disciplines are eligible, but preference is given to students preparing for a career in computer science or engineering. Along with their application, they must submit 1-page essays on 1) why they are applying for this scholarship and why they should be selected as a recipient; 2) a technical project on which they worked, either through a university course or previous work experience, their role in the project, and how they contributed to the end result; and 3) a software, hardware, or new innovative application of existing technology that they would create if they could and the impact it would have. Financial need is not considered in the selection process. **Deadline for Receipt:** February of each year. **Ad-**ditional Information:** The program includes a paid summer internship in the Morgan Stanley Information Technology Division in the summer following the time of application.

4247 ■ NATIONAL ASSOCIATION OF BLACK TELECOMMUNICA-TIONS PROFESSIONALS, INC.

c/o Cynthia L. Newman
2020 Pennsylvania Avenue, N.W.
Box 735
Washington, DC 20006
800-946-6228
E-mail: office@nabtp.org
Web Site: http://www.nabtp.org/about/scholarships.shtml
To provide financial assistance to students who are working on a degree in telecommunications or a related field and are interested in participating in the activities of the National Association of Black Telecommunications Professionals (NABTP).

Title of Award: NABTP Collegian Scholarship **Area, Field, or Subject:** Business administration; Communications; Computer and information sciences; Engineering; Telecommunications systems **Level of Education for which Award is Granted:** Undergraduate **Number Awarded:** 1 each year. **Funds Available:** The stipend is $2,000 per year. **Duration:** 1 year; may be renewed for 2 or 3 additional years if the recipient maintains a GPA of 3.0 or higher and active involvement in NABTP.

Eligibility Requirements: This program is open to students majoring in telecommunications or a related field (e.g., computer science, business, engineering, mass communications) at an accredited college or university. Applicants must submit an essay on their educational and career goals, the skill sets and values they are able to bring to NABTP as a possible intern, and how they see active involvement in NABTP supportive to their career path and educational goals. As an option, they may also submit an essay in which they provide a profile of a majority owned African American telecommunications company, including CEO name, number of employees, percentage of minority ownership, annual revenue, address, phone number, web site address, company product and/or services, and company successes. Selection is based on the essays, GPA, notable achievements, and financial need. **Deadline for Receipt:** July of each year.

4248 ■ NATIONAL CONSORTIUM FOR GRADUATE DEGREES FOR MINORITIES IN ENGINEERING AND SCIENCE (GEM)

P.O. Box 537
Notre Dame, IN 46556
Tel: (574)631-7771
Fax: (574)287-1486
E-mail: gem.1@nd.edu
Web Site: http://www.gemfellowship.org
To provide financial assistance and summer work experience to underrepresented minority graduate students in engineering.

Title of Award: GEM M.S. Engineering Fellowship Program **Area, Field, or Subject:** Computer and information sciences; Engineering **Level of Education for which Award is Granted:** Four Year College, Master's **Number Awarded:** Varies each year; recently, 327 of these fellowships were awarded. **Funds Available:** The fellowship pays tuition, fees, and a stipend of $10,000 over its lifetime. In addition, each participant receives a salary during the summer work assignment as a GEM Summer Intern, making the value of the total award between $20,000 and $60,000. Employer members reimburse GEM participants for travel expenses to and from the summer work site. **Duration:** Up to 3 semesters or 4 quarters, plus a summer work internship lasting 10 to 14 weeks for up to 3 summers, depending on whether the student applies as a junior, senior, or college graduate; recipients begin their internship upon acceptance into the program and work each summer until completion of their master's degree.

Eligibility Requirements: This program is open to U.S. citizens who are members of ethnic groups underrepresented in engineering: Native Americans, African Americans, Latinos, Puerto Ricans, and other Hispanic Americans. Applicants must be enrolled as at least a junior in an ABET-accredited engineering discipline with an academic record that indicates the ability to pursue graduate studies in engineering (including a GPA of 2.8 or higher). Students in computer science and computer engineering may also apply, but engineering technology majors are not eligible. Applicants must be planning to attend 1 of the 95 GEM member universities that offer a master's degree. **Deadline for Receipt:** October of each year. **Additional Information:** During the summer internship, each fellow is assigned an engineering project in a research setting. Each project is based on the fellow's interest and background and is carried out under the supervision of an experienced engineer. At the conclusion of the internship, each fellow writes a project report. Recipients must seek the master's degree in the same engineering discipline as their baccalaureate degree.

4249 ■ NATIONAL CONSORTIUM FOR GRADUATE DEGREES FOR MINORITIES IN ENGINEERING AND SCIENCE (GEM)

P.O. Box 537
Notre Dame, IN 46556
Tel: (574)631-7771
Fax: (574)287-1486
E-mail: gem.1@nd.edu
Web Site: http://www.gemfellowship.org

To provide financial assistance and summer work experience to underrepresented minority students interested in obtaining a Ph.D. degree in the life sciences, mathematics, or physical sciences.
Title of Award: GEM Ph.D. Science Fellowship Program **Area, Field, or Subject:** Biological and clinical sciences; Chemistry; Computer and information sciences; Earth sciences; Geosciences; Mathematics and mathematical sciences; Natural sciences; Physics **Level of Education for which Award is Granted:** Four Year College, Doctorate **Number Awarded:** Varies each year; recently, 40 of these fellowships were awarded. **Funds Available:** The stipend is $14,000 per year, plus tuition and fees. In addition, there is a summer internship program that provides a salary and reimbursement for travel expenses to and from the summer work site. The total value of the award is between $60,000 and $100,000, depending upon academic status at the time of application, summer employer, and graduate school attended. **Duration:** 3 to 5 years for the fellowship; 12 weeks during at least 1 summer for the internship. Fellows selected as juniors or seniors intern each summer until entrance to graduate school; fellows selected after college graduation intern at least 1 summer.
Eligibility Requirements: This program is open to U.S. citizens who are members of ethnic groups underrepresented in the natural sciences: Native Americans, African Americans, Latinos, Puerto Ricans, and other Hispanic Americans. Applicants must be juniors, seniors, or recent baccalaureate graduates in the life sciences, mathematics, or physical sciences (chemistry, computer science, earth sciences, and physics) with an academic record that indicates the ability to pursue doctoral studies (including a GPA of 3.0 or higher). **Deadline for Receipt:** October of each year. **Additional Information:** This program is valid only at 1 of 95 participating GEM member universities; write to GEM for a list. The fellowship award is designed to support the student in the first year of the doctoral program without working. Subsequent years are subsidized by the respective university and will usually include either a teaching or research assistantship. Recipients must participate in the GEM summer internship; failure to agree to accept the internship cancels the fellowship. Recipients must enroll in the same scientific discipline as their undergraduate major.

4250 ■ NATIONAL FEDERATION OF THE BLIND

c/o Peggy Elliott, Scholarship Committee Chair
805 Fifth Avenue
Grinnell, IA 50112
Tel: (641)236-3366
Web Site: http://www.nfb.org/sch_intro.htm

To provide financial assistance to legally blind undergraduate and graduate students working on a degree in computer science.
Title of Award: National Federation of the Blind Computer Science Scholarship **Area, Field, or Subject:** Computer and information sciences **Level of Education for which Award is Granted:** Graduate, Undergraduate **Number Awarded:** 1 each year. **Funds Available:** The stipend is $3,000. **Duration:** 1 year; recipients may resubmit applications up to 2 additional years.
Eligibility Requirements: This program is open to legally blind students who are working on or planning to work full time on an undergraduate or graduate degree in computer science. Selection is based on academic excellence, service to the community, and financial need. **Deadline for Receipt:** March of each year. **Additional Information:** Scholarships are

awarded at the federation convention in July. Recipients attend the convention at federation expense; that funding is in addition to the scholarship grant.

4251 ■ NATIONAL FFA ORGANIZATION

Attn: Scholarship Office
6060 FFA Drive
P.O. Box 68960
Indianapolis, IN 46268-0960
Tel: (317)802-4321
Fax: (317)802-5321
E-mail: scholarships@ffa.org
Web Site: http://www.ffa.org

To provide financial assistance to FFA members who are interested in studying fields related to agriculture or agribusiness in college.
Title of Award: Rabo AgriFinance Scholarships **Area, Field, or Subject:** Agribusiness; Agricultural sciences; Agriculture, Economic aspects; Animal science and behavior; Computer and information sciences; Management **Level of Education for which Award is Granted:** Undergraduate **Number Awarded:** 3 each year. **Funds Available:** The stipend is $1,000 per year. Funds are paid directly to the recipient. **Duration:** 1 year; nonrenewable.
Eligibility Requirements: This program is open to members who are graduating high school seniors planning to enroll full time in college. Applicants must be interested in working on a 2- or 4-year degree in agronomy and crop science, farm and ranch management, livestock management, agricultural economics, agricultural power and equipment, or computer systems in agriculture. They must have a GPA of 30 or higher and rank in the upper 50% of their class. Selection is based on academic achievement (10 points for GPA, 10 points for SAT or ACT score, 10 points for class rank), leadership in FFA activities (30 points), leadership in community activities (10 points), and participation in the Supervised Agricultural Experience (SAE) program (30 points). U.S. citizenship is required. **Deadline for Receipt:** February of each year. **Additional Information:** Funding for this program is provided by Rabo AgriFinance.

4252 ■ NATIONAL FFA ORGANIZATION

Attn: Scholarship Office
6060 FFA Drive
P.O. Box 68960
Indianapolis, IN 46268-0960
Tel: (317)802-4321
Fax: (317)802-5321
E-mail: scholarships@ffa.org
Web Site: http://www.ffa.org

To provide financial assistance to FFA members from designated states who are interested in studying a field related to agriculture in college.
Title of Award: Wilbur-Ellis Company Scholarships **Area, Field, or Subject:** Agribusiness; Agricultural sciences; Agriculture, Economic aspects; Animal science and behavior; Biochemistry; Business administration; Computer and information sciences; Entomology; Finance; Forestry; Genetics; Horticulture; Management; Marketing and distribution; Poultry science; Soil science **Level of Education for which Award is Granted:** Four Year College **Number Awarded:** 13 each year: 1 at $5,000, 2 at $2,000, and 10 at $1,000. **Funds Available:** Stipends are $5,000, $2,000, or $1,000 per year. Funds are paid directly to the recipient. **Duration:** 1 year; nonrenewable.
Eligibility Requirements: This program is open to members who are graduating high school seniors planning to enroll or college students currently enrolled full time. Applicants must be residents of the following states: Arizona, California, Idaho, Indiana, Michigan, Minnesota, Montana, New Mexico, North Dakota, Ohio, Oregon, South Dakota, Texas, Utah, Washington, Wisconsin, or Wyoming. They must be planning to work on a 4-year degree in agricultural production, forest management, agronomy and crop science, animal nutrition, farm and ranch management, horticulture, nursery and landscape management, plant science, poultry science, general agriculture, business management, economics, international agriculture, finance, sales and marketing, biochemistry, biotechnology, computer systems in agriculture, entomology, plant breeding and genetics, plant pathology, range science, or soil science. Their combined SAT score must be 1000 or higher and their GPA must be 3.0 or higher. Selection is based on academic achievement (10 points for GPA, 10 points for SAT or ACT score, 10 points for class rank), leadership in

FFA activities (30 points), leadership in community activities (10 points), and participation in the Supervised Agricultural Experience (SAE) program (30 points). Financial need is also considered in the selection process. U.S. citizenship is required. **Deadline for Receipt:** February of each year. **Additional Information:** Funding for this scholarship is provided by the agriculture division of the Wilbur-Ellis Company.

4253 ■ NATIONAL INDIAN GAMING ASSOCIATION

Attn: Spirit of Sovereignty Foundation
224 Second Street, S.E.
Washington, DC 20003
Tel: (480)820-2464
E-mail: info@spiritfund.com
Web Site: http://www.spiritfund.com/student.htm
To provide financial assistance to Native American upper-division and graduate students who are working on a degree in a business-related field.
Title of Award: Spirit of Sovereignty Scholarships **Area, Field, or Subject:** Business administration; Computer and information sciences; Economics; Hotel, institutional, and restaurant management; Information science and technology **Level of Education for which Award is Granted:** Four Year College, Graduate **Number Awarded:** 1 or more each year. **Funds Available:** A stipend is awarded (amount not specified). **Duration:** 1 year.
Eligibility Requirements: This program is open to college juniors, seniors, and graduate students who are working on a degree in business or a related field (e.g., hotel management, information systems, computer science, economics, human resources). Applicants must submit a copy of their Certificate of Degree of Indian Blood (CDIB), current transcript, 2 letters of recommendation, and a 250-word essay that describes their extracurricular activities related to involvement of American Indian programs at their institution, volunteer and community work related to American Indian communities, potential for future interaction and support to Indian communities, tribal and community involvement, and potential to give strong representation to the American Indian community to non-Native constituents. **Deadline for Receipt:** February of each year.

4254 ■ NATIONAL INVENTORS HALL OF FAME

Attn: Collegiate Inventors Competition
221 South Broadway Street
Akron, OH 44308-1595
Tel: (330)849-6887
E-mail: collegiate@invent.org
Web Site: http://www.invent.org/collegiate
To recognize and reward outstanding inventions by college or university students in the fields of science, engineering, and technology.
Title of Award: Collegiate Inventors Competition **Area, Field, or Subject:** Biological and clinical sciences; Chemistry; Computer and information sciences; Engineering; Environmental conservation; Environmental science; Inventors; Mathematics and mathematical sciences; Medicine; Physics; Science; Technology; Veterinary science and medicine **Level of Education for which Award is Granted:** Graduate, Postdoctoral, Undergraduate **Number Awarded:** 15 semifinalists are selected each year; of those, 3 individuals or teams win prizes. **Funds Available:** Finalists receive an all-expense paid trip to Washington, D.C. to participate in a final round of judging and in the awards dinner and presentation. The Grand Prize winner or team receives $25,000. Other prizes are $10,000 for an undergraduate winner or team and $15,000 for a graduate winner or team. Academic advisors of the winning entries each receive a $3,000 cash prize. Awards are unrestricted cash gifts, not scholarships or grants. **Duration:** The competition is held annually.
Eligibility Requirements: This competition is open to undergraduate and graduate students who are (or have been) enrolled full time at least part of the 12-month period prior to entry in a college or university in the United States. Entries may also be submitted by teams, up to 4 members, of whom at least 1 must meet the full-time requirement and all others must have been enrolled at least half time sometime during the preceding 24-month period. Applicants must submit a description of their invention, including a patent search and summary of current literature that describes the state of the art and identifies the originality of the invention; test data demonstrating that the idea, invention, or design is workable; the societal, economic, and environmental benefits of the invention; and supplemental material that may include photos, slides, disks, videotapes, and even

samples. Entries must be original ideas and the work of a student or team and a university advisor; the invention should be reproducible and may not have been 1) made available to the public as a commercial product or process, or 2) patented or published more than 1 year prior to the date of submission for this competition. Entries are first reviewed by a committee of judges that selects the finalists. The committee is comprised of mathematicians, engineers, biologists, chemists, environmentalists, physicists, computer specialists, members of the medical and veterinary profession, and specialists in invention and development of technology. Entries are judged on the basis of originality, inventiveness, potential value to society (socially, environmentally, and economically), and range or scope of use. **Deadline for Receipt:** May of each year. **Additional Information:** This program is co-sponsored by Abbott Laboratories and the United States Patent and Trademark Office. It was established in 1990 as the BFGoodrich Collegiate Inventors Program.

4255 ■ NATIONAL NAVAL OFFICERS ASSOCIATION-WASHINGTON, D.C. CHAPTER

Attn: Scholarship Program
2701 Park Center Drive, B704
Alexandria, VA 22302
E-mail: williams.stephen@hq.navy.mil
Web Site: http://www.dcnnoa.org
To provide financial assistance to African American high school seniors from the Washington, D.C. area who are interested in majoring in designated fields in college.
Title of Award: DCNNOA/Advanced Concepts and Technologies Scholarship **Area, Field, or Subject:** Computer and information sciences; Political science; Public administration **Level of Education for which Award is Granted:** Undergraduate **Number Awarded:** 1 each year. **Funds Available:** The stipend is $1,000 per year. **Duration:** 1 year; nonrenewable.
Eligibility Requirements: This program is open to African American seniors at high schools in the Washington, D.C. metropolitan area who plan to enroll full time at an accredited 2-year or 4-year college or university. Applicants must be planning to major in governmental affairs, political science, or computer science. They must have a GPA of 2.5 or higher and be U.S. citizens or permanent residents. Selection is based on academic achievement, community involvement, interpersonal and leadership skills, creativity, drive, and maturity. **Deadline for Receipt:** April of each year. **Additional Information:** Recipients are not required to join or affiliate with the military in any way. This program is sponsored by Advanced Concepts and Technologies, Inc.

4256 ■ NATIONAL NAVAL OFFICERS ASSOCIATION-WASHINGTON, D.C. CHAPTER

Attn: Scholarship Program
2701 Park Center Drive, B704
Alexandria, VA 22302
E-mail: williams.stephen@hq.navy.mil
Web Site: http://www.dcnnoa.org
To provide financial assistance to African American high school seniors from the Washington, D.C. area who are interested in majoring in computer sciences in college.
Title of Award: NNOA/Booz Allen Hamilton Scholarship **Area, Field, or Subject:** Computer and information sciences **Level of Education for which Award is Granted:** Undergraduate **Number Awarded:** 1 each year. **Funds Available:** The stipend is $5,000 per year. **Duration:** 1 year; nonrenewable.
Eligibility Requirements: This program is open to African American seniors at high schools in the Washington, D.C. metropolitan area who plan to enroll full time in a computer science program at an accredited 2-year or 4-year college or university. Applicants must have a GPA of 3.0 or higher and be U.S. citizens or permanent residents. Selection is based on academic achievement, community involvement, interpersonal and leadership skills, creativity, drive, and maturity. **Deadline for Receipt:** April of each year. **Additional Information:** Recipients are not required to join or affiliate with the military in any way. This program is sponsored by Booz Allen Hamilton, and recipients have an option to work with the firm as a summer intern.

4257 ■ NATIONAL SECURITY AGENCY

Attn: Office of Recruitment and Staffing (Roberts)
9800 Savage Road, Suite 6779

P.O. Box 1661, Suite 6779
Fort Meade, MD 20755-6779
Tel: (410)854-4725; (866)672-4473
Web Site: http://www.nsa.gov/careers/students_4.cfm
To provide financial assistance and work experience to college sopho-
mores and juniors interested in preparing for a career with the National
Security Agency (NSA) as a global network analyst.
Title of Award: Pat Roberts Intelligence Scholars Program for Global
Network Analysts **Area, Field, or Subject:** Banking; Computer and
information sciences; Finance; Information science and technology;
International affairs and relations; Political science; Telecommunications
systems **Level of Education for which Award is Granted:** Undergraduate **Number Awarded:** Varies each year. **Funds Available:** The stipend
is $25,000 per year. During the summer after application, students
participate in a Global Network Analysis internship. After graduation, they
have an employment obligation to NSA equal to 1.5 times the length of
educational support provided. **Duration:** 1 year; may be renewed 1 additional year. The summer internship program is for 12 weeks.
Eligibility Requirements: This program is open to college sophomore
and juniors whose academic program includes 1 of the following areas of
emphasis: 1) technical studies (computer science major with a minor in
political science or international relations); 2) topical studies (terrorism,
proliferation or related sciences, international banking and finance, or
telecommunications and information systems networks); or 3) disciplines
(technical intelligence analysis, information assurance, networks, and
telecommunications). Applicants must be enrolled full time with a GPA of
3.0 or higher. Along with their application, they must submit a 1-page essay describing how the proposed program of study will improve their ability to analyze information and to think and write critically. U.S. citizenship
and eligibility to obtain a high-level security clearance are required
Deadline for Receipt: October of each year. **Additional Information:**
After graduation, participants enter NSA's Global Network Analysis Internship Program as a full-time employee.

4258 ■ NATIONAL SECURITY AGENCY
Attn: Office of Recruitment and Staffing (Stokes)
9800 Savage Road, Suite 6779
P.O. Box 1661, Suite 6779
Fort Meade, MD 20755-6779
Tel: (410)854-4725; (866)672-4473
Web Site: http://www.nsa.gov/careers/students_4.cfm
To provide minority and other high school seniors and college sophomores
with scholarship/loans and work experience at the National Security
Agency (NSA).
Title of Award: Stokes Educational Scholarship Program **Area, Field, or
Subject:** Asian studies; Computer and information sciences; Engineering,
Computer; Engineering, Electrical; Finance; Foreign languages;
International affairs and relations; Mathematics and mathematical sciences; Near Eastern studies; South Asian studies **Level of Education for
which Award is Granted:** Undergraduate **Number Awarded:** Varies
each year. **Funds Available:** Participants receive college tuition for up to
4 years, reimbursement for books and certain fees, a year-round salary,
and a housing allowance and travel reimbursement during summer
employment if the distance between the agency and school exceeds 75
miles. Following graduation, participants must work for the agency for 1
and a half times their length of study, usually 5 years. Students who leave
agency employment earlier must repay the tuition cost. **Duration:** Up to 4
years, followed by employment at the agency for 5 years.
Eligibility Requirements: This program is open to graduating high
school seniors, particularly minorities, who 1) are planning a college major
in electrical or computer engineering, computer science, international affairs, international finance, mathematics, area studies (Middle East or
south, east, or central Asia), foreign languages (recent language interests
included Arabic, Chinese, Farsi, and Korean); 2) have minimum scores of
1600 on the SAT (1100 on critical reading and mathematics, 500 in writing) or 25 on the ACT; 3) have a GPA of 3.0 or higher; 4) are U.S. citizens;
and 5) demonstrate leadership abilities. Also eligible are college
sophomores who are U.S. citizens, have a GPA of 3.0 or higher, and are
majoring in the eligible fields. Applicants must include a 1-page essay on
why they want to have a career with the NSA. **Deadline for Receipt:**
November of each year. **Additional Information:** Participants must attend classes full time and work at the agency during the summer in jobs
tailored to their course of study. They must maintain at least a 3.0 GPA.

This program, established in 1986, was formerly known as the National
Security Agency Undergraduate Training Program.

4259 ■ NATIONAL SOCIETY OF BLACK ENGINEERS
Attn: Programs Department
1454 Duke Street
Alexandria, VA 22314
Tel: (703)549-2207
Fax: (703)683-5312
E-mail: scholarships@nsbe.org
Web Site: http://www.nsbe.org/programs/schol_adobe.php
To provide financial assistance to members of the National Society of
Black Engineers (NSBE) who are majoring in computer science.
Title of Award: Adobe Systems Computer Science Corporate Scholar-
ships **Area, Field, or Subject:** Computer and information sciences **Level
of Education for which Award is Granted:** Four Year College **Number
Awarded:** 2 each year. **Funds Available:** The stipend is $1,500. **Dura-
tion:** 1 year.
Eligibility Requirements: This program is open to members of the
society who are entering their junior or senior year with a major in
computer science. Applicants must have a GPA of 3.0 or higher. Along
with their application, they must submit a resume and official transcript.
Deadline for Receipt: January of each year. **Additional Information:**
This program is supported by Adobe Systems Incorporated.

4260 ■ NATIONAL SOCIETY OF BLACK ENGINEERS
Attn: Programs Department
1454 Duke Street
Alexandria, VA 22314
Tel: (703)549-2207
Fax: (703)683-5312
E-mail: scholarships@nsbe.org
Web Site: http://www.nsbe.org/programs/schol_delta.php
To provide financial assistance to members of the National Society of
Black Engineers (NSBE) who are majoring in designated science and
engineering fields.
Title of Award: Delta Air Lines NSBE Corporate Scholarship **Area, Field,
or Subject:** Computer and information sciences; Engineering, Aerospace/
Aeronautical/Astronautical; Engineering, Chemical; Engineering, Electri-
cal; Engineering, Materials; Engineering, Mechanical; Materials research/
science **Level of Education for which Award is Granted:** Four Year
College **Number Awarded:** 1 each year. **Funds Available:** The stipend is
$3,000. **Duration:** 1 year.
Eligibility Requirements: This program is open to members of the
society who are college juniors or seniors majoring in the following fields
of study: aerospace/aeronautical engineering, chemical engineering,
computer science, electrical engineering, materials engineering, materials
science, or mechanical engineering. Applicants must have a GPA of 3.0 or
higher and a demonstrated interest in employment with Delta Air Lines.
They must submit essays of 100 to 150 words on each of the following
topics: 1) how they personally define global diversity and why it is
important for the airlines to value diversity; 2) how they have demonstrated
their leadership ability in their school and community; 3) what influenced
their decision to pursue their current course of study; and 4) the top 2
challenges facing Delta Air Lines today and how they would use their
technical training and experience to help overcome those challenges.
Deadline for Receipt: January of each year. **Additional Information:**
The recipient also receives a round-trip airline ticket, paid registration, and
2 nights' hotel accommodations to the NSBE national convention.

4261 ■ NATIONAL SOCIETY OF BLACK ENGINEERS
Attn: Programs Department
1454 Duke Street
Alexandria, VA 22314
Tel: (703)549-2207
Fax: (703)683-5312
E-mail: scholarships@nsbe.org
Web Site: http://www.nsbe.org/programs/schol_free.php
To provide financial assistance to members of the National Society of
Black Engineers (NSBE) who are majoring in computer science or
engineering or electrical engineering.
Title of Award: Freescale Conductor Scholarship **Area, Field, or
Subject:** Computer and information sciences; Engineering, Computer;

Engineering, Electrical **Level of Education for which Award is Granted:** Four Year College **Number Awarded:** 3 each year. **Funds Available:** The stipend is $5,000. **Duration:** 1 year.

Eligibility Requirements: This program is open to members of the society who are entering their sophomore, junior, or senior year in college and majoring in computer science, computer engineering, or electrical engineering. Applicants must have a GPA of 3.0 or higher and a demonstrated interest in employment with Freescale Semiconductor. Along with their application, they must submit a 250-word essay describing how they will use their education to make a positive impact on the African American community and how this scholarship opportunity will advance their career goals and benefit Freescale Semiconductor. **Deadline for Receipt:** January of each year.

4262 ■ NATIONAL SOCIETY OF BLACK ENGINEERS
Attn: Programs Department
1454 Duke Street
Alexandria, VA 22314
Tel: (703)549-2207
Fax: (703)683-5312
E-mail: scholarships@nsbe.org
Web Site: http://www.nsbe.org/programs/schol_pci_gta.php
To provide financial assistance to high school seniors who are junior members of the National Society of Black Engineers (NSBE) planning to major in a field related to engineering in college.

Title of Award: Golden Torch Awards **Area, Field, or Subject:** Computer and information sciences; Engineering; Mathematics and mathematical sciences; Technology **Level of Education for which Award is Granted:** Four Year College **Number Awarded:** Varies each year; recently, 7 of these awards were presented. **Funds Available:** The stipend is $1,000 per year. **Duration:** 1 year; may be renewed 3 additional years if the recipient maintains a GPA of 2.75 or higher in college.

Eligibility Requirements: This program is open to junior members of the society who are high school seniors. Applicants must have been accepted as a full-time student at a 4-year college or university to major in engineering, computer science, mathematics, or technology. They must have a GPA of 3.0 or higher. Along with their application, they must submit an essay, up to 500 words in length, on how they will continue the legacy of NSBE and how they will service as role models in their community after college. **Deadline for Receipt:** January of each year.

4263 ■ NATIONAL SOCIETY OF BLACK ENGINEERS
Attn: Programs Department
1454 Duke Street
Alexandria, VA 22314
Tel: (703)549-2207
Fax: (703)683-5312
E-mail: scholarships@nsbe.org
Web Site: http://www.nsbe.org/programs/schol_jnj.php
To provide financial assistance to members of the National Society of Black Engineers (NSBE) who are majoring in designated engineering fields.

Title of Award: Johnson & Johnson NSBE Corporate Scholarship Program **Area, Field, or Subject:** Biological and clinical sciences; Chemistry; Computer and information sciences; Engineering, Biomedical; Engineering, Chemical; Engineering, Computer; Engineering, Electrical; Engineering, Industrial; Engineering, Materials; Engineering, Mechanical; Logistics **Level of Education for which Award is Granted:** Four Year College **Number Awarded:** 13 each year: 1 national award and 12 regional awards (2 in each NSBE region). **Funds Available:** The national stipend is $2,000; the regional stipends are $1,500. **Duration:** 1 year.

Eligibility Requirements: This program is open to members of the society who are entering their junior or senior year in college and majoring in biology, chemistry, computer science, operations/logistics, or the following fields of engineering: biomedical, chemical, computer, electrical, industrial, material, or mechanical. Applicants must have a GPA of 3.2 or higher and a demonstrated interest in employment with Johnson & Johnson. Along with their application, they must submit a resume and official transcript. **Deadline for Receipt:** January of each year.

4264 ■ NATIONAL SOCIETY OF BLACK ENGINEERS
Attn: Programs Department
1454 Duke Street
Alexandria, VA 22314

Tel: (703)549-2207
Fax: (703)683-5312
E-mail: scholarships@nsbe.org
Web Site: http://www.nsbe.org/programs/schol_lockheed.php
To provide financial assistance to members of the National Society of Black Engineers (NSBE) who are majoring in fields related to engineering.

Title of Award: Lockheed Martin NSBE Corporate Scholarship Program **Area, Field, or Subject:** Computer and information sciences; Engineering, Aerospace/Aeronautical/Astronautical; Engineering, Computer; Engineering, Electrical; Engineering, Mechanical; Mathematics and mathematical sciences; Systems engineering **Level of Education for which Award is Granted:** Four Year College **Number Awarded:** 5 each year. **Funds Available:** The stipend is $2,000. **Duration:** 1 year.

Eligibility Requirements: This program is open to members of the society who are entering their junior or senior year in college and majoring in computer science, mathematics, or the following fields of engineering: aerospace, computer, electrical, mechanical, or systems. Applicants must have a GPA of 3.0 or higher and a demonstrated interest in employment with Lockheed Martin Corporation. Along with their application, they must submit a 250-word essay describing their career goals and how they can make a community and professional impact as a Lockheed Martin employee. **Deadline for Receipt:** January of each year.

4265 ■ NATIONAL SOCIETY OF BLACK ENGINEERS
Attn: Programs Department
1454 Duke Street
Alexandria, VA 22314
Tel: (703)549-2207
Fax: (703)683-5312
E-mail: scholarships@nsbe.org
Web Site: http://www.nsbe.org/programs/schol_micro.php
To provide financial assistance to members of the National Society of Black Engineers (NSBE) who are majoring in computer science or engineering.

Title of Award: Microsoft Corporation NSBE Scholarships **Area, Field, or Subject:** Computer and information sciences; Engineering, Computer; Mathematics and mathematical sciences; Physics **Level of Education for which Award is Granted:** Undergraduate **Number Awarded:** 3 each year. **Funds Available:** The stipend is $5,000. **Duration:** 1 year.

Eligibility Requirements: This program is open to members of the society who are undergraduate students majoring in computer engineering, computer science, or mathematics/physics with a demonstrated interest in computer science. Applicants must have a GPA of 3.0 or higher. They must submit a 300-word essay on their "passion for technology" outside of the classroom. **Deadline for Receipt:** January of each year. **Additional Information:** This program is supported by Microsoft Corporation.

4266 ■ NATIONAL SOCIETY OF BLACK ENGINEERS
Attn: Programs Department
1454 Duke Street
Alexandria, VA 22314
Tel: (703)549-2207
Fax: (703)683-5312
E-mail: scholarships@nsbe.org
Web Site: http://www.nsbe.org/programs/schol_ng.php
To provide financial assistance to members of the National Society of Black Engineers (NSBE) who are working on an undergraduate degree in designated science and engineering fields.

Title of Award: Northrop Grumman NSBE Scholarships **Area, Field, or Subject:** Architecture, Naval; Computer and information sciences; Engineering, Aerospace/Aeronautical/Astronautical; Engineering, Chemical; Engineering, Civil; Engineering, Computer; Engineering, Electrical; Engineering, Industrial; Engineering, Mechanical; Engineering, Ocean; Mathematics and mathematical sciences; Physics **Level of Education for which Award is Granted:** Undergraduate **Number Awarded:** 5 each year. **Funds Available:** The stipend is $5,000. **Duration:** 1 year.

Eligibility Requirements: This program is open to members of the society who are U.S. citizens currently enrolled in college. Applicants must be majoring in computer science, information science, mathematics, naval architecture, physics, or the following engineering fields: aerospace, chemical, civil (structural), computer, electrical, industrial, manufacturing, marine, mechanical, or ocean. They must have a GPA of 3.0 or higher and demonstrate an interest in employment with Northrop Grumman Corporation. **Deadline for Receipt:** January of each year.

4267 ■ NATIONAL SOCIETY OF BLACK ENGINEERS

Attn: Programs Department
1454 Duke Street
Alexandria, VA 22314
Tel: (703)549-2207
Fax: (703)683-5312
E-mail: scholarships@nsbe.org
Web Site: http://www.nsbe.org/programs/schol_praxair.php
To provide financial assistance and work experience to members of the National Society of Black Engineers (NSBE) who are majoring in designated engineering fields.
Title of Award: Praxair NSBE Partnership Scholarship Program **Area, Field, or Subject:** Computer and information sciences; Engineering, Chemical; Engineering, Electrical; Engineering, Mechanical **Level of Education for which Award is Granted:** Four Year College, Graduate **Number Awarded:** 5 each year: 1 for a graduate students and 4 for undergraduates. **Funds Available:** The stipend is $5,000 for graduate students or $2,500 for undergraduates. **Duration:** 1 year.
Eligibility Requirements: This program is open to members of the society who are juniors, seniors, or graduate students majoring in chemical engineering, computer science, electrical engineering, or mechanical engineering. Applicants must have a GPA of 3.0 or higher and a willingness to accept a summer internship at a Praxair location. They must demonstrate leadership involvement on campus and/or in the community. Along with their application, they must submit a 1-page statement describing how they demonstrate their "passion for technology" outside the classroom with examples of how they share their enthusiasm in the community. **Deadline for Receipt:** January of each year. **Additional Information:** The recipients also receive paid travel and accommodations to the NSBE national convention. Praxair, Inc., which sponsors this program, may also offer them a summer internship.

4268 ■ NATIONAL SOCIETY OF BLACK ENGINEERS

Attn: Programs Department
1454 Duke Street
Alexandria, VA 22314
Tel: (703)549-2207
Fax: (703)683-5312
E-mail: scholarships@nsbe.org
Web Site: http://www.nsbe.org/programs/schol_ge.php
To provide financial assistance to members of the National Society of Black Engineers (NSBE) who are studying engineering at a college or university east of the Mississippi River.
Title of Award: GE Lloyd Trotter African American Forum Scholarship **Area, Field, or Subject:** Computer and information sciences; Engineering, Electrical; Engineering, Industrial; Engineering, Mechanical; Information science and technology **Level of Education for which Award is Granted:** Four Year College **Number Awarded:** Varies each year, depending on the availability of funds. Recently, 16 of these scholarships were awarded. **Funds Available:** The stipend is $2,500. **Duration:** 1 year.
Eligibility Requirements: This program is open to members of the society who are undergraduate students majoring in computer science, electrical engineering, industrial engineering, information management/systems, or mechanical engineering at an accredited college or university located east of the Mississippi River. Applicants must be rising juniors or seniors with a GPA of 3.0 or higher. Selection is based on an essay; academic achievement; service to the society at the chapter, regional, and/or national level; and other professional, campus, and community activities. **Deadline for Receipt:** January of each year. **Additional Information:** This program is supported by General Electric employees with matching contributions from the GE Fund.

4269 ■ NEBRASKA EDUCATIONAL OFFICE PROFESSIONALS ASSOCIATION

P.O. Box 83872
Lincoln, NE 68501-3872
Web Site: http://neopa.unl.edu/awards.html
To provide financial assistance to residents of Nebraska who are interested in preparing for an office-related career.

Title of Award: Nebraska Educational Office Professionals Association Student Scholarship **Area, Field, or Subject:** Accounting; Computer and information sciences; Law; Marketing and distribution; Publishing; Secretarial sciences **Level of Education for which Award is Granted:** Undergraduate **Number Awarded:** 1 each year. **Funds Available:** The stipend is $1,000. **Duration:** 1 year.
Eligibility Requirements: This program is open to residents of Nebraska who are graduating high school seniors or students currently enrolled in a postsecondary educational institution. Applicants must have completed 2 or more business education courses (in high school, college, or a combination) from among the following: computer classes, keyboarding/typing, marketing, accounting, office practices and procedures, bookkeeping, business communication, desktop publishing, and/or business law. They must submit a 1-page essay on why they are choosing an office-related career or vocation, 3 letters of recommendation, and high school or college transcripts. Selection is based on academic achievement, initiative of the student, and financial need. **Deadline for Receipt:** December of each year. **Additional Information:** Information is also available from Edie Schleiger, Scholarship Director, University of Nebraska at Lincoln, Office of Admissions, 1410 Q Street, Lincoln, NE 68588-0417.

4270 ■ NEW HAMPSHIRE SPACE GRANT CONSORTIUM

c/o University of New Hampshire
Institute for the Study of Earth, Oceans, and Space
Morse Hall
39 College Road
Durham, NH 03824-3525
Tel: (603)862-0094
Fax: (603)862-1915
E-mail: nhspacegrant@unh.edu
Web Site: http://www.nhsgc.sr.unh.edu
To provide financial assistance to students at member institutions of the New Hampshire Space Grant Consortium (NHSGC) who are interested in participating in space-related activities.
Title of Award: New Hampshire Space Grant Consortium Project Support **Area, Field, or Subject:** Aerospace sciences; Astronomy and astronomical sciences; Atmospheric science; Biological and clinical sciences; Computer and information sciences; Earth sciences; Engineering, Aerospace/Aeronautical/Astronautical; Geosciences; Oceanography; Physics; Space and planetary sciences **Level of Education for which Award is Granted:** Graduate, Undergraduate **Number Awarded:** Varies each year. **Funds Available:** The amount of the award depends on the nature of the project. **Duration:** From 1 quarter to 1 year.
Eligibility Requirements: This program is open to students at member institutions of the NHSGC. Applicants must be studying space physics, astrophysics, astronomy, or aspects of computer science, engineering, earth sciences, ocean sciences, atmospheric sciences, or life sciences that utilize space technology and/or adopt a planetary view of the global environment. U.S. citizenship is required. The New Hampshire Space Grant Consortium is a component of the U.S. National Aeronautics and Space Administration (NASA) Space Grant program, which encourages participation by women, underrepresented minorities, and persons with disabilities. **Deadline for Receipt:** Each participating college or university sets its own deadline. **Additional Information:** This program is funded by NASA. Currently, projects operating through this program include space grant fellowships at the University of New Hampshire, Agnes M. Lindsay Trust/NASA Challenge Scholars Initiative at the New Hampshire Community Technical College System, Presidential Scholars Research Assistantships at Dartmouth College, and Women in Science Internships at Dartmouth.

4271 ■ OAK RIDGE INSTITUTE FOR SCIENCE AND EDUCATION

Attn: Science and Engineering Education
P.O. Box 117
Oak Ridge, TN 37831-0117
Tel: (865)576-8239
Fax: (865)241-5219
E-mail: igrid.gregory@orau.gov
Web Site: http://www.orau.gov/orise.htm
To provide financial assistance and summer research experience to undergraduate students who are working on a degree in a field of interest to the Department of Homeland Security (DHS).
Title of Award: Department of Homeland Security Undergraduate Scholarships **Area, Field, or Subject:** Agricultural sciences; Biological

and clinical sciences; Communications; Computer and information sciences; Engineering; Information science and technology; Mathematics and mathematical sciences; Physical sciences; Psychology; Public administration; Religion; Social sciences; Writing **Level of Education for which Award is Granted:** Undergraduate **Number Awarded:** Approximately 50 each year. **Funds Available:** This program provides a stipend of $1,000 per month during the academic year and $5,000 for the internship plus full payment of tuition and mandatory fees. **Duration:** 2 academic years plus 10 weeks during the intervening summer.

Eligibility Requirements: This program is open to 1) full-time students who are in their second year of college attendance as of the application deadline; and 2) part-time students who have completed at least 45 but no more than 60 semester hours as of the application deadline. Applicants must be majoring in the agricultural sciences, biological and life sciences, computer and information sciences, engineering, mathematics, physical sciences, psychology, social sciences, or selected humanities (religious studies, cultural studies, public policy, advocacy, communications, or science writing). They must have a GPA of 3.3 or higher. Along with their application, they must submit 2 statements on 1) their educational and professional goals, the kinds of research they are interested in conducting, specific questions that interest them, and how they became interested in them; and 2) how they think their interests, talents, and initiative would contribute to make the homeland safer and secure. Selection is based on those statements, academic record, references, and SAT or ACT scores. As part of their program, they must be interested in participating in summer research and development activities at a DHS-designated facility. U.S. citizenship is required. **Deadline for Receipt:** January of each year. **Additional Information:** This program, established in 2003, is funded by DHS and administered by Oak Ridge Institute for Science and Education (ORISE). Recipients must enroll full time.

4272 ■ OAK RIDGE INSTITUTE FOR SCIENCE AND EDUCATION
Attn: Science and Engineering Education
P.O. Box 117
Oak Ridge, TN 37831-0117
Tel: (865)241-8240
Fax: (865)241-5219
E-mail: hollingsscholarship@orau.gov
Web Site: http://www.orau.gov/orise.htm
To provide financial assistance and summer research experience to upper-division students who are working on a degree in a field of interest to the National Oceanic and Atmospheric Administration (NOAA).

Title of Award: Ernest F. Hollings Scholarship Program **Area, Field, or Subject:** Agricultural sciences; Behavioral sciences; Biological and clinical sciences; Computer and information sciences; Education; Engineering; Information science and technology; Mathematics and mathematical sciences; Physical sciences; Social sciences **Level of Education for which Award is Granted:** Four Year College **Number Awarded:** Approximately 100 each year. **Funds Available:** This program provides a stipend of $8,000 per academic year and $650 per week during the internship, a housing subsidy and limited travel reimbursement for round-trip transportation to the internship site, and travel expenses to the scholarship program conference at the completion of the internship. **Duration:** 2 academic years plus 10 weeks during the intervening summer.

Eligibility Requirements: This program is open to full-time students entering their junior year at an accredited college or university in the United States or its territories. Applicants must be majoring in a discipline related to oceanic and atmospheric science, research, technology, and education, and supportive of the purposes of NOAA's programs and mission (e.g., biological, life, and agricultural sciences; computer and information sciences; engineering; mathematics; physical sciences; social and behavioral sciences; or teacher education). They must have a GPA of 3.0 or higher. As part of their program, they must be interested in participating in summer research and development activities at NOAA headquarters (Silver Spring, Maryland) or field centers. U.S. citizenship is required. **Deadline for Receipt:** May of each year. **Additional Information:** This program, established in 2005, is funded by NOAA and administered by Oak Ridge Institute for Science and Education (ORISE).

4273 ■ OAK RIDGE INSTITUTE FOR SCIENCE AND EDUCATION
Attn: Science and Engineering Education
P.O. Box 117
Oak Ridge, TN 37831-0117

Tel: (865)576-9279
Fax: (865)241-5220
E-mail: coxre@orau.gov
Web Site: http://www.orau.gov/orise.htm
To provide financial assistance and research experience to undergraduate students at minority serving institutions who are majoring in scientific fields of interest to the National Oceanic and Atmospheric Administration (NOAA).

Title of Award: National Oceanic and Atmospheric Administration Educational Partnership Program with Minority Serving Institutions Undergraduate Scholarships **Area, Field, or Subject:** Atmospheric science; Biological and clinical sciences; Cartography/Surveying; Chemistry; Computer and information sciences; Engineering; Environmental conservation; Environmental science; Geography; Mathematics and mathematical sciences; Meteorology; Photogrammetry; Physical sciences; Physics **Level of Education for which Award is Granted:** Four Year College **Number Awarded:** 10 each year. **Funds Available:** This program provides payment of tuition and fees (to a maximum of $4,000 per year) and a stipend during the internship of $650 per week. **Duration:** 1 academic year and 2 summers.

Eligibility Requirements: This program is open to juniors and seniors at minority serving institutions, including Hispanic Serving Institutions (HSIs), Historically Black Colleges and Universities (HBCUs), and Tribal Colleges and Universities (TCUs). Applicants must be majoring in atmospheric science, biology, cartography, chemistry, computer science, engineering, environmental science, geodesy, geography, marine science, mathematics, meteorology, photogrammetry, physical science, physics, or remote sensing. They must also be interested in participating in a research internship at a NOAA site. U.S. citizenship is required. **Deadline for Receipt:** January of each year. **Additional Information:** This program is funded by NOAA through an interagency agreement with the U.S. Department of Energy and administered by Oak Ridge Institute for Science and Education (ORISE).

4274 ■ OHIO SPACE GRANT CONSORTIUM
c/o Ohio Aerospace Institute
22800 Cedar Point Road
Cleveland, OH 44142
Tel: (440)962-3032
Free: 800-828-OSGC
Fax: (440)962-3057
E-mail: osgc@oai.org
Web Site: http://www.osgc.org/Scholarship.html
To provide financial assistance to students at selected community colleges in Ohio who are interested in continuing their studies at a 4-year university in the state that is a member of the Ohio Space Grant Consortium (OSGC).

Title of Award: Ohio Space Grant Consortium Community College Scholarship **Area, Field, or Subject:** Computer and information sciences; Electronics; Engineering; Mathematics and mathematical sciences; Science; Technology **Level of Education for which Award is Granted:** Two Year College **Number Awarded:** 2 each year. **Funds Available:** The stipend is $1,000. **Duration:** 1 year; nonrenewable.

Eligibility Requirements: This program is open to U.S. citizens who are students at designated community colleges in Ohio, normally enrolled full time in their freshman year (although applications are accepted from part-time students demonstrating academic merit and from students at any stage of their college career). Applicants must be enrolled in a program that includes course work related to an understanding of or interest in technological fields supporting aerospace, e.g. associate degrees related to mathematics, science, and such advanced technology fields as engineering, computers, electronics, and industrial technology. They must also have a GPA of 3.0 or higher and plans to continue their education in a 4-year program at an OSGC-member university. Along with their application, they must submit college transcripts, 2 letters of recommendation, and a brief resume of their education, significant accomplishments, work experience, educational and professional goals, and any other relevant information. Women, underrepresented minorities, and persons with disabilities are particularly encouraged to apply. **Deadline for Receipt:** October of each year. **Additional Information:** These scholarships are funded through the National Space Grant College and Fellowship Program administered by the National Aeronautics and Space Administration (NASA), with matching funds provided by the member colleges, the Ohio Aerospace Institute, and private industry. The participating institutions include Columbus State Community College, Cuyahoga Community College, Lorain County Community College, Owens Community College, Lakeland Community College, and Terra Community College. OSGC member institutions include the Air Force Institute of Technology, University of Akron, Case Western Reserve University, Central State University, University of Cincinnati, Cleveland State University, University of Dayton, Ohio State University, Ohio University, University of Toledo, Wilberforce University, and Wright State University.

4275 ■ OHIO SPACE GRANT CONSORTIUM

c/o Ohio Aerospace Institute
22800 Cedar Point Road
Cleveland, OH 44142
Tel: (440)962-3032
Free: 800-828-OSGC
Fax: (440)962-3057
E-mail: osgc@oai.org
Web Site: http://www.osgc.org/Scholarship.html
To provide financial assistance to students in their junior year at selected universities in Ohio who wish to working on a bachelor's degree in an aerospace-related field.

Title of Award: Ohio Space Grant Consortium Junior Scholarships **Area, Field, or Subject:** Astronomy and astronomical sciences; Biological and clinical sciences; Chemistry; Computer and information sciences; Engineering, Aerospace/Aeronautical/Astronautical; Engineering, Chemical; Engineering, Civil; Engineering, Computer; Engineering, Electrical; Engineering, Industrial; Engineering, Materials; Engineering, Mechanical; Engineering, Petroleum; Geography; Geology; Materials research/science; Mathematics and mathematical sciences; Physics; Space and planetary sciences **Level of Education for which Award is Granted:** Four Year College **Number Awarded:** Varies each year; recently, 20 of these scholarships were awarded. **Funds Available:** The stipend is $2,000. **Duration:** 1 year; recipients may apply for a senior scholarship if they maintain satisfactory academic performance and good progress on their research project.

Eligibility Requirements: These scholarships are available to U.S. citizens who expect to complete within 2 years the requirements for a bachelor of science degree in an aerospace-related discipline (aeronautical engineering, aerospace engineering, astronomy, biology, chemical engineering, chemistry, civil engineering, computer engineering and science, control engineering, electrical engineering, engineering mechanics, geography, geology, industrial engineering, manufacturing engineering, materials science and engineering, mathematics, mechanical engineering, petroleum engineering, physics, and systems engineering). Applicants must be attending a member university of the Ohio Space Grant Consortium (OSGC) or another participating university. They must propose and initiate a research project on campus under the guidance of a faculty member. Along with their application, they must submit a 1-page personal objective statement that discusses their career goals and anticipated benefits to be derived from this program. Women, underrepresented minorities, and persons with disabilities are particularly encouraged to apply. **Deadline for Receipt:** February of each year. **Additional Information:** These scholarships are funded through the National Space Grant College and Fellowship Program administered by the National Aeronautics and Space Administration (NASA), with matching funds provided by the member universities, the Ohio Aerospace Institute, and private industry. The OSGC member universities include the University of Akron, Case Western Reserve University, Central State University, University of Cincinnati, Cleveland State University, University of Dayton, Ohio State University, Ohio University, University of Toledo, Wilberforce University, and Wright State University. Other participating universities are Cedarville University, Marietta College (petroleum engineering), Miami University (manufacturing engineering), Ohio Northern University (mechanical engineering), and Youngstown State University (mechanical and industrial engineering). Recipients are required to attend the annual spring research symposium sponsored by the OSGC and present a poster on their research project.

4276 ■ OREGON STUDENT ASSISTANCE COMMISSION

Attn: Grants and Scholarships Division
1500 Valley River Drive, Suite 100
Eugene, OR 97401-2146

Tel: (541)687-7395
Free: 800-452-8807
Fax: (541)687-7419
E-mail: awardinfo@mercury.osac.state.or.us
Web Site: http://www.osac.state.or.us
To provide financial assistance to Oregon residents who are working on a college degree in computer science or engineering.

Title of Award: Mentor Graphics Scholarships **Area, Field, or Subject:** Computer and information sciences; Engineering, Computer; Engineering, Electrical **Level of Education for which Award is Granted:** Four Year College **Number Awarded:** Varies each year; recently, 4 of these scholarships were awarded. **Funds Available:** The stipend is at least $2,000. **Duration:** 1 year.

Eligibility Requirements: This program is open to residents of Oregon who are U.S. citizens or permanent residents. Applicants must be full-time students in their junior or senior year of college and majoring in electrical engineering or computer science/engineering. Preference is given to female, African American, Native American, or Hispanic applicants. Financial need must be demonstrated. **Deadline for Receipt:** February of each year.

4277 ■ OREGON UNIVERSITY SYSTEM

Attn: Chancellor's Office, Industry Affairs Division
Capital Center, Suite 1065
18640 N.W. Walker Road
Beaverton, OR 97006-8966
Tel: (503)725-2918
Fax: (503)775-2921
E-mail: aeaschol@ous.edu
Web Site: http://www.ous.edu/ecs/scholarships.html
To provide financial assistance to Oregon high school seniors interested in studying designated computer and engineering fields at selected public universities in the state.

Title of Award: AeA Technology Scholarship Program **Area, Field, or Subject:** Biochemistry; Chemistry; Computer and information sciences; Engineering; Engineering, Chemical; Engineering, Computer; Engineering, Electrical; Engineering, Industrial; Engineering, Mechanical; Mathematics and mathematical sciences; Physics **Level of Education for which Award is Granted:** Undergraduate **Number Awarded:** Varies each year; recently, this program awarded 25 new scholarships. **Funds Available:** The stipend is $2,500 per year. **Duration:** 1 year; may be renewed up to 3 additional years if the recipient maintains a GPA of 3.0 or higher.

Eligibility Requirements: This program is open to seniors graduating from high schools in Oregon who plan to attend Eastern Oregon University, Oregon Institute of Technology, Oregon State University, Portland State University, Southern Oregon University, Western Oregon University, or the University of Oregon. Applicants must be planning to major in biochemistry, chemical engineering, chemistry, computer engineering, computer science, electrical engineering, electronic engineering, engineering technology, industrial engineering, mathematics, mechanical engineering, or physics (not all majors are available at each institution). Women and ethnic minorities underrepresented in the technology industry (Black Americans, Hispanic Americans, and Native Americans) are strongly encouraged to apply. Selection is based on academic performance; college entrance examination scores; mathematics, science, and technology course work; achievements; leadership; civic participation; interests; employment; insight into and commitment to a career in technology; and communication skill. **Deadline for Receipt:** March of each year. **Additional Information:** This program was established in 1999 by Intel, which offered it to the Oregon Council of the AeA (formerly American Electronics Association) in the following year. Currently, Intel and other Oregon AeA member companies (such as Xerox and Hewlett Packard) provide ongoing support.

4278 ■ ROYAL NEIGHBORS OF AMERICA

Attn: Fraternal Services
230 16th Street
Rock Island, IL 61201-8645
Tel: (309)788-4561
Free: 800-627-4762
E-mail: contact@royalneighbors.org

Web Site: http://www.royalneighbors.org/MemberBenefits/scholarships.cfm

To provide financial assistance for college to women members of the Royal Neighbors of America who plan to enter nontraditional fields.

Title of Award: Eliza D. Watt Scholarships **Area, Field, or Subject:** Computer and information sciences; Engineering; Mathematics and mathematical sciences; Physical sciences **Level of Education for which Award is Granted:** Undergraduate **Number Awarded:** 5 each year. **Funds Available:** The stipend is $2,000 per year. **Duration:** 4 years. **Eligibility Requirements:** This program is open to women members of the society who are graduating high school seniors. Applicants must be planning to enter a field considered nontraditional for women, including computer science, engineering, physical sciences, teaching of nontraditional women's fields, business writing, or mathematics. **Deadline for Receipt:** December of each year. **Additional Information:** This program was established in 2004.

4279 ■ SIEMENS FOUNDATION

170 Wood Avenue South
Iselin, NJ 08830
877-822-5233
Fax: (732)603-5890
E-mail: foundation@sc.siemens.com
Web Site: http://www.siemens-foundation.org/awards

To recognize and reward high school students with exceptional scores on the Advanced Placement (AP) examinations in mathematics and the sciences.

Title of Award: Siemens Awards for Advanced Placement **Area, Field, or Subject:** Biological and clinical sciences; Chemistry; Computer and information sciences; Environmental conservation; Environmental science; Mathematics and mathematical sciences; Physics; Statistics **Level of Education for which Award is Granted:** Professional, Undergraduate **Number Awarded:** 24 regional scholarships (2 females and 2 males in each of the 6 regions), 2 national scholarships (1 female and 1 male), 12 high school awards (in each region, 1 to a school for improvement in the number and percentage of students taking AP examinations, 1 to an urban school for providing access to AP mathematics and science to minorities), and 18 teacher awards (in each region, 2 for commitment to students and the AP program, 1 for teaching minorities) are awarded each year. **Funds Available:** Regional scholarships are $3,000; national winners receive additional $5,000 scholarships. Awards to teachers and to schools are $1,000. **Duration:** The awards are presented annually. **Eligibility Requirements:** All students in U.S. high schools are eligible to be considered for these awards (including home-schooled students and those in U.S. territories). Each fall, the College Board identifies the male and female seniors in each of its regions who have earned the highest number of scores on 7 AP exams: biology, calculus BC, chemistry, computer science AB, environmental science, physics C (physics C: mechanics and physics C: electricity each count as half), and statistics. Males and females are considered separately. Regional winners receive all-expense paid trips to Washington, D.C., where national winners are announced. The program also recognizes and rewards monetarily 1) schools that have shown the greatest improvement in the number and percentage of students taking AP examinations in biology, calculus, chemistry, computer science, environmental science, physics, and statistics in the past year; and 2) non-magnet urban schools that provide access to AP mathematics and science to a significant number of underrepresented minority students. In addition, teachers are rewarded for their commitment to students and the AP program. Additional teachers are recognized because they have successfully taught AP mathematics and/or science to underrepresented minority students in non-magnet urban schools. **Deadline for Receipt:** There is no application or nomination process for these awards. The College Board identifies the students, teachers, and high schools for the Siemens Foundation. **Additional Information:** Information from the College Board is available at (703) 707-8999.

4280 ■ SIEMENS FOUNDATION

170 Wood Avenue South
Iselin, NJ 08830
877-822-5233
Fax: (732)603-5890
E-mail: foundation@sc.siemens.com

Web Site: http://www.siemens-foundation.org/scholarship

To recognize and reward outstanding high school seniors who have undertaken individual or team research projects in science, mathematics, and technology (or in combinations of those disciplines).

Title of Award: Siemens Westinghouse Competition Awards **Area, Field, or Subject:** Astronomy and astronomical sciences; Atmospheric science; Biochemistry; Biological and clinical sciences; Chemistry; Computer and information sciences; Earth sciences; Engineering, Civil; Engineering, Electrical; Engineering, Mechanical; Environmental science; Genetics; Geosciences; Materials research/science; Mathematics and mathematical sciences; Nutrition; Physics; Writing **Level of Education for which Award is Granted:** Undergraduate **Number Awarded:** In the initial round of judging, up to 300 regional semifinalists (up to 50 in each region) are selected. Of those, 60 are chosen as regional finalists (5 individuals and 5 teams in each of the 6 regions). Then 12 regional winners (1 individual and 1 team) are selected in the regional competitions, and they become the national finalists. **Funds Available:** At the regional level, finalists receive $1,000 scholarships, both as individuals and members of teams. Individual regional winners receive $3,000 scholarships. Winning regional teams receive $6,000 scholarships to be divided among the team members. Those regional winners then receive additional scholarships as national finalists. In the national competition, first-place winners receive an additional $100,000 scholarship, second place an additional $50,000 scholarship, third place an additional $40,000 scholarship, fourth place an additional $30,000 scholarship, fifth place an additional $20,000 scholarship, and sixth place an additional $10,000 scholarship. Those national awards are provided both to individuals and to teams to be divided equally among team members. Scholarship money is sent directly to the recipient's college or university to cover undergraduate and/or graduate educational expenses. Schools with regional finalists receive a $2,000 award to be used to support science, mathematics, and technology programs in their schools. **Duration:** The competition is held annually. **Eligibility Requirements:** This program is open to high school seniors who are legal or permanent U.S. residents. They must be enrolled in a high school in the United States, Puerto Rico, Guam, Virgin Islands, American Samoa, Wake and Midway Islands, or the Marianas. U.S. high school students enrolled in a Department of Defense dependents school, an accredited overseas American or international school, a foreign school as an exchange student, or a foreign school because their parent(s) live and work abroad are also eligible. Students being home-schooled qualify if they obtain the endorsement of the school district official responsible for such programs. Research projects may be submitted in mathematics and the biological and physical sciences, or involve combinations of disciplines, such as astrophysics, biochemistry, bioengineering, biology, biophysics, botany, chemistry, computer science, civil engineering, earth and atmospheric science engineering, electrical engineering, environmental sciences, fluid dynamics, genetics, geology, materials science, mathematics, mechanical engineering, nutritional science, physics, toxicology, and virology. Both individual and team projects (2 or 3 members) may be entered. All team members must meet the eligibility requirements. Team projects may include seniors, but that is not a requirement. Competition entrants must submit a detailed report on their research project, including a description of the purpose of the research, rationale for the research, pertinent scientific literature, methodology, results, discussion, and conclusion. All projects must be endorsed by a sponsoring high school (except home-schooled students, who obtain their endorsement from the district or state home-school official). Each project must have a project advisor or mentor who is a member of the instructional staff or a person approved by the endorsing high school. There are 3 judging phases to the competition. An initial review panel selects outstanding research projects from 6 different regions of the country. The students submitting these projects are identified as regional semifinalists. Out of those, the highest-rated projects from each region are selected and the students who submitted them are recognized as regional finalists. For the next phase, the regional finalists are offered all-expense paid trips to the regional competition on the campus of a regional university partner, where their projects are reviewed by a panel of judges appointed by the host institution. Regional finalists are required to prepare a poster display of their research project, make an oral presentation about the research and research findings, and respond to questions from the judges. The top-rated individual and the top-rated team project in each region are selected as regional winners to represent the region in the national competition as national finalists. At that competition, the national finalists again display their projects, make oral presentations, and respond to judges' questions. At each phase, selection is based on clarity of expression, comprehensiveness, creativity, field knowledge, future work, interpretation, literature review, presentation, scientific importance, and validity. **Deadline for Receipt:** September of each year. **Additional Information:** The program is offered by Siemens Foundation, in partnership with the College Board. Information is available from the College Board at (703) 707-8999, E-mail: spro@collegeboard.org. Students submitting the projects with the highest evaluations become part of a registry that is circulated to colleges and universities nationwide. To continue receiving scholarships, winners must attend an accredited academic institution on a full-time basis.

4281 ■ SOCIETY OF FLIGHT TEST ENGINEERS

44814 North Elm Avenue
P.O. Box 4037
Lancaster, CA 93539-4037
Tel: (661)949-2095
Fax: (661)949-2096
E-mail: sfte@sfte.org
Web Site: http://www.sfte.org
To provide financial assistance for college to student members and children of members of the Society of Flight Test Engineers (SFTE).
Title of Award: Society of Flight Test Engineers Scholarships **Area, Field, or Subject:** Computer and information sciences; Engineering; Mathematics and mathematical sciences; Physics **Level of Education for which Award is Granted:** Undergraduate **Number Awarded:** 1 or more each year. **Funds Available:** Stipends range from $200 to $2,000. **Duration:** 1 year; recipients may reapply.
Eligibility Requirements: This program is open to college students who have completed at least their freshman year. Applicants must be a student member of SFTE or the child of a member. They must be working on an undergraduate degree in engineering, computer sciences, mathematics, physics, or another technical discipline. Selection is based primarily on academic achievement; financial need is not considered. **Deadline for Receipt:** June of each year.

4282 ■ SOCIETY OF WOMEN ENGINEERS-MINNESOTA SECTION

Attn: Scholarship Committee
P.O. Box 582813
Minneapolis, MN 55458-2813
E-mail: scholarships@swe-mn.org
Web Site: http://www.swe-mn.org
To provide financial assistance to upper-division women studying engineering or computer science at colleges and universities in Minnesota, North Dakota, and South Dakota.
Title of Award: Minnesota Section Scholarship **Area, Field, or Subject:** Computer and information sciences; Engineering **Level of Education for which Award is Granted:** Four Year College **Number Awarded:** At least 1 each year. Recently, 2 additional scholarships (1 at $1,500 and 1 at $1,000) were also awarded through the Corporate Partner Scholarship program. **Funds Available:** The stipend is at least $1,000. **Duration:** 1 year.
Eligibility Requirements: This program is open to women entering their junior or senior year at an accredited engineering program in Minnesota, North Dakota, or South Dakota. Applicants must be student members of the Society of Women Engineers (SWE) majoring in engineering or computer science. Selection is based on potential to succeed as an engineer (20 points), communication skills (10 points), extracurricular or community involvement and leadership skills (10 points), demonstration of work experience and successes (10 points), and academic success (5 points). **Deadline for Receipt:** March of each year. **Additional Information:** Through the Corporate Partner Scholarship program, additional scholarships may be funded by corporate sponsors. Recently, those sponsors included Ecolab and MTS Systems Corporation. Information is also

available from Leanne Knutson, Scholarship Co-Chair, Rosemount Inc., 8200 Market Boulevard, M/S PF17, Chanhassen, MN 55317, (952) 949-7578.

4283 ■ SOCIETY OF WOMEN ENGINEERS-ROCKY MOUNTAIN SECTION

Attn: Scholarship Committee Chair
P.O. Box 260692
Lakewood, CO 80226-0692
Tel: (303)893-0822
Web Site: http://www.swe.org/SWE/RegionI/Sections/RockyMtn/Scholarships.htm
To provide financial assistance to women who are working on an undergraduate or graduate degree in engineering at colleges and universities in Colorado and Wyoming.
Title of Award: Rocky Mountain Section College Scholarships **Area, Field, or Subject:** Computer and information sciences; Engineering **Level of Education for which Award is Granted:** Graduate, Undergraduate **Number Awarded:** 3 each year. **Funds Available:** The stipend is $1,000. **Duration:** 1 year.
Eligibility Requirements: This program is open to women who are enrolled as an undergraduate or graduate engineering student in an ABET-accredited engineering or computer science program in Colorado or Wyoming (excluding zip codes 80800-81599). Applicants must have a GPA of 3.0 or higher. They must include with their application an essay on why they have chosen an engineering major, what they will accomplish or how they believe they will make a difference as an engineer, and who or what influenced them to study engineering. Selection is based on merit. **Deadline for Receipt:** January of each year. **Additional Information:** Information is also available from Mary Ann Tavery, P.O. Box 12260, Denver, CO 80212. This program includes the following named scholarships: the Dorolyn Lines Scholarship, the Lottye Miner Scholarship, and the Rocky Mountain Section Pioneer Scholarship.

4284 ■ TEXAS BUSINESS AND TECHNOLOGY EDUCATORS ASSOCIATION

c/o Mona Fannon, Scholarship Committee Chair
Route 2 Box 8-14
Fritch, TX 79036
Tel: (806)857-9320
E-mail: mona.fannon@borgerisd.net
Web Site: http://www.tbtea.org
To provide financial assistance for college to members of Business Professionals of America (BPA) or Future Business Leaders of America (FBLA) in Texas.
Title of Award: Texas Business and Technology Educators Association Scholarships **Area, Field, or Subject:** Business administration; Computer and information sciences; Education; Information science and technology **Level of Education for which Award is Granted:** Undergraduate **Number Awarded:** 4 each year. **Funds Available:** The stipend is $1,000. **Duration:** 1 year.
Eligibility Requirements: This program is open to seniors graduating from high schools in Texas who are members of BPA or FBLA (or were members during their junior year). Applicants must have a GPA of 2.75 or higher and be nominated by a teacher who is a member of the Texas Business and Technology Educators Association. They must be planning to attend college to prepare for a career in business, business education, computer science, computer information systems, or a related field. Along with their application, they must submit a 1-page letter describing why they deserve this scholarship, defining their career goals, and including any information regarding financial need. **Deadline for Receipt:** February of each year.

4285 ■ UNITED DAUGHTERS OF THE CONFEDERACY

Attn: Education Director
328 North Boulevard
Richmond, VA 23220-4057
Tel: (804)355-1636
Fax: (804)353-1396
E-mail: hqudc@rcn.com
Web Site: http://www.hqudc.org/scholarships/scholarships.html
To provide financial assistance to mature women who are lineal descendants of Confederate veterans and plan to major in selected fields in college.

Title of Award: Walter Reed Smith Scholarship Program **Area, Field, or Subject:** Business administration; Computer and information sciences; Home Economics; Nursing; Nutrition **Level of Education for which Award is Granted:** Undergraduate **Number Awarded:** 1 each year. **Funds Available:** The amount of this scholarship depends on the availability of funds. **Duration:** 1 year; may be renewed.

Eligibility Requirements: Eligible to apply for these scholarships are women over the age of 30 who are lineal descendants of worthy Confederates or collateral descendants and members of the Children of the Confederacy or the United Daughters of the Confederacy. Applicants must intend to study business administration, computer science, home economics, nutrition, or nursing. They must submit certified proof of the Confederate record of 1 ancestor, with the company and regiment in which he served, and must have had at least a 3.0 GPA in high school. **Deadline for Receipt:** March of each year. **Additional Information:** Information is also available from Mrs. Robert C. Kraus, Second Vice President General, 239 Deerfield Lane, Franklin, NC 28734-0112. Members of the same family may not hold scholarships simultaneously, and only 1 application per family will be accepted within any 1 year. All requests for applications must be accompanied by a self-addressed stamped envelope.

4286 ■ U.S. AIR FORCE

Attn: Headquarters AFROTC/RRUC
551 East Maxwell Boulevard
Maxwell AFB, AL 36112-5917
Tel: (334)953-2091; (866)423-7682
Fax: (334)953-6167
Web Site: http://www.afrotc.com/scholarships/incolschol/
expressSchol.php

To provide financial assistance to students who are interested in joining Air Force ROTC and majoring in critical Air Force officer fields in college. **Title of Award:** Air Force ROTC Express Scholarships **Area, Field, or Subject:** Atmospheric science; Engineering, Aerospace/Aeronautical/Astronautical; Engineering, Civil; Engineering, Computer; Engineering, Electrical; Engineering, Mechanical; Environmental science; Meteorology **Level of Education for which Award is Granted:** Undergraduate **Funds Available:** Awards are type 2 AFROTC scholarships that provide for payment of tuition and fees, to a maximum of $15,000 per year, plus an annual book allowance of $600. All recipients are also awarded a tax-free monthly subsistence allowance that is $250 for freshmen, $300 for sophomores, $350 for juniors, and $400 for seniors. **Duration:** 3 and a half years, until completion of a bachelor's degree.

Eligibility Requirements: This program is open to U.S. citizens who are completing at least their first year of college and are working on a degree in fields that may change annually but are of critical interest to the Air Force. Applicants must have a GPA of 2.5 or higher and meet all other academic and physical requirements for participation in AFROTC. At the time of their Air Force commissioning, they may be no more than 31 years of age. They must be able to pass the Air Force Officer Qualifying Test (AFOQT) and the Air Force ROTC Physical Fitness Test. years as active-duty Air Force officers following graduation from college. **Additional Information:** Recently, freshmen were eligible if they were majoring in computer, electrical, or environmental engineering. Sophomores and juniors were eligible if they were majoring in those fields, meteorology and atmospheric sciences, or in the following engineering disciplines: aeronautical, aerospace, astronautical, civil, or mechanical. Recipients must also complete 4 years of aerospace studies courses at 1 of the 144 colleges and universities that have an Air Force ROTC unit on campus or 1 of the approximately 900 colleges that have cross-enrollment agreements with those institutions. They must also attend a 4-week summer training camp at an Air Force base, usually between their sophomore and junior years. Following completion of their bachelor's degree, scholarship recipients earn a commission as a second lieutenant in the Air Force and serve at least 4 years.

4287 ■ U.S. AIR FORCE

Attn: Headquarters AFROTC/RRUC
551 East Maxwell Boulevard
Maxwell AFB, AL 36112-5917
Tel: (334)953-2091; (866)423-7682
Fax: (334)953-6167
Web Site: http://www.afrotc.com/scholarships/hsschol/types.php

To provide financial assistance to high school seniors or graduates who are interested in joining Air Force ROTC in college and are willing to serve as Air Force officers following completion of their bachelor's degree. **Title of Award:** Air Force ROTC High School Scholarships **Area, Field, or Subject:** Architecture; Chemistry; Computer and information sciences; Engineering, Aerospace/Aeronautical/Astronautical; Engineering, Architectural; Engineering, Civil; Engineering, Computer; Engineering, Electrical; Engineering, Mechanical; Environmental science; General studies/Field of study not specified; Mathematics and mathematical sciences; Meteorology; Operations research; Physics **Level of Education for which Award is Granted:** Four Year College **Number Awarded:** Approximately 2,000 each year. **Funds Available:** Type 1 scholarships provide payment of full tuition and most laboratory fees, as well as $600 for books. Type 2 scholarships pay the same benefits except tuition is capped at $15,000 per year; students who attend an institution where tuition exceeds $15,000 must pay the difference. Type 7 scholarships pay full tuition and most laboratory fees, but students must attend a college or university where the tuition is less than $9,000 per year or a public college or university where they qualify for the in-state tuition rate; they may not attend an institution with higher tuition and pay the difference. Approximately 5% of scholarship offers are for Type 1, approximately 20% are for Type 2, and approximately 75% are for type 7. All recipients are also awarded a tax-free subsistence allowance for 10 months of each year that is $250 per month as a freshman, $300 per month as a sophomore, $350 per month as a junior, and $400 per month as a senior. **Duration:** 4 years.

Eligibility Requirements: This program is open to high school seniors who are U.S. citizens at least 17 of age and have been accepted at a college or university with an Air Force ROTC unit on campus or a college with a cross-enrollment agreement with such a college. Applicants must have a cumulative GPA of 3.0 or higher and an ACT composite score of 24 or higher or an SAT score of 1100 (mathematics and verbal portion only) or higher. At the time of their commissioning in the Air Force, they must be no more than 31 years of age. They must agree to serve for at least 4 years as active-duty Air Force officers following graduation from college. **Deadline for Receipt:** November of each year. **Additional Information:** Recently, approximately 70% of these scholarships were offered to students planning to major in the science and technical fields of architecture, chemistry, computer science, engineering (aeronautical, aerospace, astronautical, architectural, civil, computer, electrical, environmental, or mechanical), mathematics, meteorology and atmospheric sciences, operations research, or physics. Approximately 30% were offered to students in all other fields. While scholarship recipients can major in any subject, they must enroll in 4 years of aerospace studies courses at 1 of the 144 colleges and universities that have an Air Force ROTC unit on campus; students may also attend nearly 900 other colleges that have cross-enrollment agreements with the institutions that have an Air Force ROTC unit on campus. Recipients must attend a 4-week summer training camp at an Air Force base, usually between their sophomore and junior years. Most cadets incur a 4-year active-duty commitment. Pilots incur a 10-year active-duty service commitment after successfully completing Specialized Undergraduate Pilot Training and navigators incur a 6-year commitment after successfully completing Specialized Undergraduate Navigator Training. The minimum service obligation for intelligence and Air Battle Management career fields is 5 years.

4288 ■ U.S. AIR FORCE

Attn: Headquarters AFROTC/RRUC
551 East Maxwell Boulevard
Maxwell AFB, AL 36112-5917
Tel: (334)953-2091; (866)423-7682
Fax: (334)953-6167
Web Site: http://www.afrotc.com/scholarships/incolschol/
incolProgram.php

To provide financial assistance to undergraduate students who are willing to join Air Force ROTC in college and serve as Air Force officers following completion of their bachelor's degree. **Title of Award:** Air Force ROTC In-College Scholarship Program **Area, Field, or Subject:** Architecture; Chemistry; Computer and information sciences; Engineering, Aerospace/Aeronautical/Astronautical; Engineering, Architectural; Engineering, Civil; Engineering, Computer; Engineering, Electrical; Engineering, Mechanical; Environmental science; General studies/Field of study not specified; Mathematics and mathematical sciences; Meteorology; Operations research; Physics **Level of Education for which Award is Granted:** Undergraduate **Number Awarded:** Varies each year. **Funds Available:** Cadets selected in Phase 1 are awarded type 2 AFROTC scholarships that provide for payment of tuition and fees, to a maximum of $15,000 per year. A limited number of cadets selected in Phase 2 are also awarded type 2 AFROTC scholarships, but most are awarded type 3 AFROTC scholarships with tuition capped at $9,000 per year. Cadets selected in Phase 3 are awarded type 6 AFROTC scholarships with tuition capped at $3,000 per year. All recipients are also awarded a book allowance of $600 and a tax-free subsistence allowance for 10 months of each year that is $300 per month during the sophomore year, $350 during the junior year, and $400 during the senior year. **Duration:** 3 years for students selected as freshmen or 2 years for students selected as sophomores.

Eligibility Requirements: This program is open to U.S. citizens enrolled as freshmen or sophomores at 1 of the 144 colleges and universities that have an Air Force ROTC unit on campus. Applicants must have a cumulative GPA of 2.5 or higher and be able to pass the Air Force Officer Qualifying Test and the Air Force ROTC Physical Fitness Test. At the time of commissioning, they may be no more than 31 years of age. They must agree to serve for at least 4 years as active-duty Air Force officers following graduation from college. Phase 1 is open to students enrolled in the Air Force ROTC program who do not currently have a scholarship but now wish to apply. Phase 2 is open to Phase 1 nonselects and students not enrolled in Air Force ROTC. Phase 3 is open only to Phase 2 nonselects. Recently, the program gave preference to students majoring in the science and technical fields of architecture, chemistry, computer science, engineering (aeronautical, aerospace, astronautical, architectural, civil, computer, electrical, environmental, or mechanical), mathematics, meteorology and atmospheric sciences, operations research, or physics. **Deadline for Receipt:** January of each year. **Additional Information:** While scholarship recipients can major in any subject, they must complete 4 years of aerospace studies courses at 1 of the 144 colleges or universities that have an Air Force ROTC unit on campus. Recipients must also attend a 4-week summer training camp at an Air Force base, usually between their sophomore and junior years; 2-year scholarship awardees attend in the summer after their junior year. Current military personnel are eligible for early release from active duty in order to enter the Air Force ROTC program. Following completion of their bachelor's degree, scholarship recipients earn a commission as a second lieutenant in the Air Force and serve at least 4 years.

4289 ■ U.S. AIR FORCE
Attn: Headquarters AFROTC/RRUE
Enlisted Commissioning Section
551 East Maxwell Boulevard
Maxwell AFB, AL 36112-5917
Tel: (334)953-2091; (866)423-7682
Fax: (334)953-6167
E-mail: enlisted@afrotc.com
Web Site: http://www.afoats.af.mil/AFROTC/EnlistedComm/AECP.asp
To allow selected enlisted Air Force personnel to earn a bachelor's degree in approved majors by providing financial assistance for full-time college study.
Title of Award: Airman Education and Commissioning Program **Area, Field, or Subject:** African studies; Asian studies; Computer and information sciences; Engineering; Foreign languages; Mathematics and mathematical sciences; Meteorology; Near Eastern studies; Nursing; Physics; Russian studies **Level of Education for which Award is Granted:** Undergraduate **Number Awarded:** Approximately 60 each year. **Funds Available:** While participating in this program, cadets remain on active duty in the Air Force and receive their regular salary and benefits. They also receive payment of tuition and fees up to $15,000 per year and an annual textbook allowance of $600. **Duration:** 1 to 3 years, until completion of a bachelor's degree.
Eligibility Requirements: Eligible to participate in this program are enlisted members of the Air Force who have been accepted at a university or college (or approved crosstown institution) that is associated with AFROTC and that offers an approved major. The majors currently supported are computer science, all ABET-accredited engineering fields (not engineering technology), foreign area studies (limited to Middle East, Africa, Asia, Russia/Eurasia), foreign languages (limited to Arabic,

Armenian, Azeri, Chinese, French, Georgian, Hebrew, Hindi, Indonesian, Kazakh, Pashto, Persian Farsi, Russian, Swahili, and Turkish), mathematics, meteorology, nursing, and physics. Applicants must have completed at least 1 year of time-in-service and 1 year of time-on-station. They must have scores on the Air Force Officer Qualifying Test of at least 15 on the verbal and 10 on the quantitative and be able to pass the Air Force ROTC Physical Fitness Test. Normally they should have completed at least 30 semester hours of college study with a GPA of 2.75 or higher. They must be younger than 31 years of age or otherwise able to be commissioned before they become 35 years of age. **Deadline for Receipt:** February of each year. **Additional Information:** While attending college, participants in this program attend ROTC classes at their college or university. Upon completing their degree, they are commissioned to serve in the Air Force in their area of specialization with an active-duty service commitment of at least 4 years. Further information is available from base education service officers or an Air Force ROTC unit. This program does not provide for undergraduate flying training.

4290 ■ U.S. AIR FORCE
Attn: Headquarters AFROTC/RRUE
Enlisted Commissioning Section
551 East Maxwell Boulevard
Maxwell AFB, AL 36112-5917
Tel: (334)953-2091; (866)423-7682
Fax: (334)953-6167
E-mail: enlisted@afrotc.com
Web Site: http://www.afoats.af.mil/AFROTC/EnlistedComm/ASCP.asp
To allow selected enlisted Air Force personnel to earn a bachelor's degree in approved majors by providing financial assistance for full-time college study.
Title of Award: Airman Scholarship and Commissioning Program **Area, Field, or Subject:** Architecture; Atmospheric science; Chemistry; Computer and information sciences; Engineering; Engineering, Aerospace/Aeronautical/Astronautical; Engineering, Architectural; Engineering, Civil; Engineering, Computer; Engineering, Electrical; Engineering, Mechanical; Environmental science; General studies/Field of study not specified; Mathematics and mathematical sciences; Meteorology; Operations research; Physics **Level of Education for which Award is Granted:** Undergraduate **Number Awarded:** Varies each year. **Funds Available:** Awards are type 2 AFROTC scholarships that provide for payment of tuition and fees, to a maximum of $15,000 per year, plus an annual book allowance of $600. All recipients are also awarded a tax-free subsistence allowance for 10 months of each year that is $300 per month during their sophomore year, $350 during their junior year, and $400 during their senior year. **Duration:** 2 to 4 years, until completion of a bachelor's degree.
Eligibility Requirements: This program is open to active-duty enlisted members of the Air Force who have completed at least 1 year of continuous active duty and at least 1 year on station. Applicants normally must have completed at least 24 semester hours of graded college credit with a cumulative college GPA of 2.5 or higher. If they have not completed 24 hours of graded college credit, they must have an ACT score of 24 or higher or an SAT combined verbal and mathematics score of 1100 or higher. They must also have scores on the Air Force Officer Qualifying Test (AFOQT) of 15 or more on the verbal scale and 10 or more on the quantitative scale and be able to pass the Air Force ROTC Physical Fitness Test. Applicants must have been accepted at a college or university (including crosstown schools) offering the AFROTC 4-year program. When they complete the program and receive their commission, they may not be 31 years of age or older. U.S. citizenship is required. Recently, awards were presented according to the following priorities: 1) computer, electrical, and environmental engineering; 2) aeronautical, aerospace, architectural, astronautical, civil, and mechanical engineering and meteorology and atmospheric sciences; 3) all other ABET-accredited engineering majors, architecture, chemistry, computer science, mathematics, operations research, and physics; 4) all other majors. **Deadline for Receipt:** October of each year. **Additional Information:** Selectees separate from the active-duty Air Force, join an AFROTC detachment, and become full-time students. Upon completing their degree, they are commissioned as officers and returned to active duty in the Air Force with a

4-year service obligation. Further information is available from base education service officers or an Air Force ROTC unit.

4291 ■ U.S. AIR FORCE

Attn: Headquarters AFROTC/RRUE
Enlisted Commissioning Section
551 East Maxwell Boulevard
Maxwell AFB, AL 36112-5917
Tel: (334)953-2091; (866)423-7682
Fax: (334)953-6167
E-mail: enlisted@afrotc.com
Web Site: http://www.afoats.af.mil/AFROTC/EnlistedComm/POC-ERP.asp

To allow selected enlisted Air Force personnel to earn a baccalaureate degree by providing financial assistance for full-time college study.

Title of Award: Professional Officer Course Early Release Program **Area, Field, or Subject:** Architecture; Atmospheric science; Chemistry; Computer and information sciences; Engineering; Engineering, Aerospace/Aeronautical/Astronautical; Engineering, Architectural; Engineering, Civil; Engineering, Computer; Engineering, Electrical; Engineering, Mechanical; Environmental science; General studies/Field of study not specified; Mathematics and mathematical sciences; Meteorology; Operations research; Physics **Level of Education for which Award is Granted:** Undergraduate **Number Awarded:** Varies each year. **Funds Available:** Participants receive a stipend for 10 months of the year that is $350 per month during the first year and $400 per month during the second year. Scholarship recipients earn the Professional Officer Course Incentive of $3,000 per year for tuition and $600 per year for books. **Duration:** 2 years (no more and no less).

Eligibility Requirements: Eligible to participate in this program are enlisted members of the Air Force under the age of 30 (or otherwise able to be commissioned before becoming 35 years of age) who have completed at least 1 year on continuous active duty, have served on station for at least 1 year, and have no more than 2 years remaining to complete their initial baccalaureate degree. Scholarship applicants must be younger than 31 years of age when they graduate and earn their commission. All applicants must have been accepted at a college or university offering the AFROTC 4-year program and must have a cumulative college GPA of 2.5 or higher. Their Air Force Officer Qualifying Test (AFOQT) scores must be at least 15 on the verbal and 10 on the quantitative. Applicants who have not completed 24 units of college work must have an ACT composite score of 24 or higher or an SAT combined verbal and mathematics score of 1100 or higher. U.S. citizenship is required. Recently, awards were presented according to the following priorities: 1) computer, electrical, and environmental engineering; 2) aeronautical, aerospace, architectural, astronautical, civil, and mechanical engineering and meteorology and atmospheric sciences; 3) all other ABET-accredited engineering majors, architecture, chemistry, computer science, mathematics, operations research, and physics; 4) all other majors. **Deadline for Receipt:** October of each year. **Additional Information:** Upon completing their degree, selectees are commissioned as officers in the Air Force with a 4-year service obligation. Further information is available from base education service officers or an Air Force ROTC unit.

4292 ■ VIRGINIA SPACE GRANT CONSORTIUM

Attn: Fellowship Coordinator
Old Dominion University Peninsula Center
600 Butler Farm Road
Hampton, VA 23666
Tel: (757)766-5210
Fax: (757)766-5205
E-mail: vsgc@odu.edu
Web Site: http://www.vsgc.odu.edu/Menu3_1_1.htm

To provide financial assistance to students who are interested in pursuing space-related studies at community colleges in Virginia.

Title of Award: Virginia Space Grant Community College Scholarship Program **Area, Field, or Subject:** Aerospace sciences; Computer and information sciences; Electronics; Engineering; Mathematics and mathematical sciences; Space and planetary sciences; Technology **Level of Education for which Award is Granted:** Two Year College **Number Awarded:** Approximately 10 each year. **Funds Available:** The maximum stipend is $1,500. **Duration:** 1 year; nonrenewable.

Eligibility Requirements: This program is open to students currently enrolled in a Virginia community college who are U.S. citizens and have

completed at least the first semester of their program with a GPA of 3.0 or higher. Awards are generally made to full-time students, but part-time students demonstrating academic merit are also eligible. Applicants can be enrolled in any program that includes course work related to an understanding of or interest in technological fields supporting aerospace; that includes (but is not limited to) computers, electronics, engineering, industrial technology, and mathematics. Since a particular goal of the program is to increase the participation of underrepresented minorities, women, and persons with disabilities in aerospace-related, high technology careers, the sponsor especially encourages applications from those students. **Deadline for Receipt:** February of each year. **Additional Information:** This program is funded by the U.S. National Aeronautics and Space Administration (NASA).

4293 ■ WISCONSIN FOUNDATION FOR INDEPENDENT COLLEGES, INC.

Attn: College-to-Work Program
735 North Water Street, Suite 600
Milwaukee, WI 53202-4100
Tel: (414)273-5980
Fax: (414)273-5995
E-mail: wfic@wficweb.org
Web Site: http://www.wficweb.org/work.html

To provide financial assistance and work experience to students at member institutions of the Wisconsin Foundation for Independent Colleges (WFIC) who are interested in preparing for a career in a field related to Alzheimer's Disease.

Title of Award: Alzheimer's Support Center College-to-Work Program **Area, Field, or Subject:** Alzheimer's disease; Business administration; Computer and information sciences; Marketing and distribution; Psychology; Sociology **Level of Education for which Award is Granted:** Four Year College **Number Awarded:** 1 each year. **Funds Available:** The stipends are $3,500 for the scholarship and $1,500 for the internship. **Duration:** 1 year for the scholarship; 10 weeks during the summer for the internship.

Eligibility Requirements: This program is open to full-time sophomores, juniors, and seniors at WFIC member colleges and universities. Applicants should be majoring in psychology, sociology, business, marketing, or computers. They must be interested in an internship at the Alzheimer's Support Center in Janesville, Wisconsin. Along with their application, they must submit a 1-page essay that includes why they are applying for the internship, why they have selected their major and what interests them about it, why they are attending their chosen college or university, and their future career objectives. **Deadline for Receipt:** February of each year. **Additional Information:** The WFIC member schools are Alverno College, Beloit College, Cardinal Stritch University, Carroll College, Carthage College, Concordia University of Wisconsin, Edgewood College, Lakeland College, Lawrence University, Marian College, Marquette University, Milwaukee Institute of Art & Design, Milwaukee School of Engineering, Mount Mary College, Northland College, Ripon College, St. Norbert College, Silver Lake College, Viterbo University, and Wisconsin Lutheran College. This program is sponsored by the Alzheimer's Support Center of Janesville.

4294 ■ WISCONSIN FOUNDATION FOR INDEPENDENT COLLEGES, INC.

Attn: College-to-Work Program
735 North Water Street, Suite 600
Milwaukee, WI 53202-4100
Tel: (414)273-5980
Fax: (414)273-5995
E-mail: wfic@wficweb.org
Web Site: http://www.wficweb.org/work.html

To provide financial assistance and work experience to students majoring in fields related to technology at member institutions of the Wisconsin Foundation for Independent Colleges (WFIC).

Title of Award: Jefferson County Literacy Council College-to-Work Program **Area, Field, or Subject:** Computer and information sciences; Education; General studies/Field of study not specified; Internet design and development; Marketing and distribution **Level of Education for which Award is Granted:** Four Year College **Number Awarded:** 1 each year. **Funds Available:** The stipends are $3,500 for the scholarship and $1,500 for the internship. **Duration:** 1 year for the scholarship; 10 weeks during the summer for the internship.

Eligibility Requirements: This program is open to full-time sophomores, juniors, and seniors at WFIC member colleges and universities. Applicants may be studying any field, but preference is given to majors in computer technology, education, marketing, sales, or website design. They must be interested in an internship at the Jefferson County Literacy Council in Fort Atkinson, Wisconsin. Along with their application, they must submit a 1-page essay that includes why they are applying for the internship, why they have selected their major and what interests them about it, why they are attending their chosen college or university, and their future career objectives. **Deadline for Receipt:** February of each year. **Additional Information:** The WFIC member schools are Alverno College, Beloit College, Cardinal Stritch University, Carroll College, Carthage College, Concordia University of Wisconsin, Edgewood College, Lakeland College, Lawrence University, Marian College, Marquette University, Milwaukee Institute of Art & Design, Milwaukee School of Engineering, Mount Mary College, Northland College, Ripon College, St. Norbert College, Silver Lake College, Viterbo University, and Wisconsin Lutheran College. This program is sponsored by the Jefferson County Literacy Council.

4295 ■ WISCONSIN FOUNDATION FOR INDEPENDENT COLLEGES, INC.

Attn: College-to-Work Program
735 North Water Street, Suite 600
Milwaukee, WI 53202-4100
Tel: (414)273-5980
Fax: (414)273-5995
E-mail: wfic@wficweb.org
Web Site: http://www.wficweb.org/work.html
To provide financial assistance and work experience to minority students majoring in fields related to the fashion industry at member institutions of the Wisconsin Foundation for Independent Colleges (WFIC).
Title of Award: Jockey International College-to-Work Program **Area, Field, or Subject:** Art; Computer and information sciences; Fashion design; Finance; Graphic art and design; Marketing and distribution **Level of Education for which Award is Granted:** Four Year College **Number Awarded:** 1 each year. **Funds Available:** The stipend is $1,500 for the scholarship; the internship is paid hourly. **Duration:** 1 year for the scholarship; 10 weeks for the internship.
Eligibility Requirements: This program is open to minority students who are full-time juniors and seniors at WFIC member colleges or universities. Applicants may be majoring in any liberal arts field, but they must be preparing for or considering a career in art, computer science/MIS, fashion design, fashion merchandising, finance, graphic design, human resources, international business, or marketing. They must be interested in an internship at Jockey International in Kenosha, Wisconsin. Along with their application, they must submit a 1-page essay that includes why they are applying for the internship, why they have selected their major and what interests them about it, why they are attending their chosen college or university, and their future career objectives. **Deadline for Receipt:** February of each year. **Additional Information:** The WFIC member schools are Alverno College, Beloit College, Cardinal Stritch University, Carroll College, Carthage College, Concordia University of Wisconsin, Edgewood College, Lakeland College, Lawrence University, Marian College, Marquette University, Milwaukee Institute of Art & Design, Milwaukee School of Engineering, Mount Mary College, Northland College, Ripon College, St. Norbert College, Silver Lake College, Viterbo University, and Wisconsin Lutheran College. This program is sponsored by Jockey International, Inc.

4296 ■ WOMEN IN FEDERAL LAW ENFORCEMENT

Attn: Scholarship Coordinator
2200 Wilson Boulevard, Suite 102
PMB 204
Arlington, VA 22201-3324
Tel: (703)548-9211; (866)399-4353
Fax: (410)451-7373
E-mail: WIFLE@comcast.net
Web Site: http://www.wifle.com/scholarshipfund/wiflescholarship.htm
To provide financial assistance for college or graduate school to women interested in preparing for a career in law enforcement.
Title of Award: Women in Federal Law Enforcement Scholarship **Area, Field, or Subject:** Computer and information sciences; Criminal justice;

Criminology; Law enforcement **Level of Education for which Award is Granted:** Four Year College, Graduate **Number Awarded:** Several each year. **Funds Available:** Stipends range from $500 to $2,000. **Duration:** 1 year; may be renewed.
Eligibility Requirements: This program is open to women who are enrolled full time at an accredited 4-year college or university (or at a community college in the process of transferring to a 4-year school). Applicants must be preparing for a career in law enforcement (including special agents, forensic scientists, intelligence analysts, fingerprint and firearms examiners, bomb technicians, public information specialists, computer specialists, attorneys, and other related fields). They must have completed at least 1 year of college and have a GPA of 3.0 or higher. Students in graduate and postgraduate programs are also eligible, but those working on an associate degree are not. Along with their application, they must submit a 500-word essay describing a community project in which they have been involved and the results or impact to the community. Selection is based on academic potential, achievement, and commitment to serving communities in the field of law enforcement. **Deadline for Receipt:** April of each year. **Additional Information:** Information is also available from the WIFLE Scholarship Fund, P.O. Box 1480, Edgewater, MD 21037-7480.

4297 ■ WYOMING TRUCKING ASSOCIATION, INC.

Attn: WTA Scholarship Trust Fund
555 North Poplar
P.O. Box 1909
Casper, WY 82602
Tel: (307)234-1579
Fax: (307)234-7082
E-mail: wytruck@aol.com
To provide financial assistance to high school seniors and currently-enrolled college students in Wyoming who are interested in preparing for a career in the highway transportation industry.
Title of Award: Wyoming Trucking Association Scholarships **Area, Field, or Subject:** Accounting; Business administration; Computer and information sciences; Management; Mechanics and repairs; Secretarial sciences; Transportation **Level of Education for which Award is Granted:** Undergraduate **Number Awarded:** 1 to 10 each year. **Funds Available:** Stipends range from $500 to $1,000. **Duration:** 1 year.
Eligibility Requirements: This program is open to high school seniors and graduates in Wyoming who are enrolled or planning to enroll in a community college in Wyoming, a trade school in the state, or the University of Wyoming. Applicants must be majoring or planning to major in a course of study that could lead to a career in the transportation industry, including (but not limited to) business management, computer skills, accounting, office procedures and management, safety, diesel mechanics, and truck driving. Along with their application, they must submit a 1-page essay on "How is the trucking industry important to you and the State of Wyoming." Financial need is considered in the selection process. **Deadline for Receipt:** March of each year.

Engineering

4298 ■ ACADEMY OF APPLIED SCIENCE

Attn: JSHS National Office
24 Warren Street
Concord, NH 03301
Tel: (603)228-4520
Fax: (603)228-4730
E-mail: phampton@jshs.org
Web Site: http://www.jshs.org
To recognize and reward outstanding participants in the Army, Navy, and Air Force Junior Science and Humanities Symposia (JSHS).
Title of Award: JSHS Scholarships **Area, Field, or Subject:** Engineering; Mathematics and mathematical sciences; Science; Writing **Level of Education for which Award is Granted:** Undergraduate **Number Awarded:** Scholarships are awarded to 3 regional winners in each of the 48 regional symposia, to 6 first-place finalists in the national symposium, to 6 second-place national finalists, and to 6 third-place national finalists. Teacher awards are presented to 48 teachers, 1 in each of the regions. **Funds Available:** At each regional symposium, 5 finalists receive all-expense paid trips to the national symposium, the first and second place

winners are invited to present their research investigation at the national symposium, and scholarships of $1,500, $1,000, and $500, are awarded. In the national competition, first-place finalists receive $16,000 scholarships, second-place finalists receive $6,000 scholarships, and third-place finalists receive $2,000 scholarships (all national scholarships are in addition to the regional scholarships). Top finalists are also awarded an all-expense paid trip to the International Youth Science Forum, held in London. The outstanding teacher in each region receives a $500 award. **Duration:** This competition is held annually. National scholarships are paid over a period of 4 years provided the recipients enroll full time and maintain a GPA of at least 3.0.
Eligibility Requirements: This program is open to students in grades 9-12, enrolled in public, private, or home schools, who have completed an original research investigation in the sciences, engineering, or mathematics. Investigations reporting on experimental, field, observational, or applied research are eligible. Students present their findings at a regional symposium, held on a university campus in their area. At each regional symposium, selected paper presenters are chosen to receive scholarships. From each of the 48 regional symposia, 5 students are selected to attend the national JSHS, where 1 of them presents his or her research paper in competition for further awards. **Additional Information:** The JSHS program was established by the Army in 1958 and since 1963 has been administered by the Academy of Applied Science. Since 1995, funding has also been provided by the Office of Naval Research and the Air Force Office of Scientific Research.

4299 ■ AGGREGATE PRODUCERS OF WISCONSIN

P.O. Box 2157
Madison, WI 53701-2157
Tel: (608)283-2595
Fax: (608)283-2589
E-mail: admin@aggregateproducers.org
Web Site: http://www.aggregateproducers.org/apw_scholarship.htm
To provide financial assistance to members of the Aggregate Producers of Wisconsin (APW) and their families who plan to attend college to prepare for a career in the aggregate industry.
Title of Award: Aggregate Producers of Wisconsin Scholarships **Area, Field, or Subject:** Construction; Engineering; Engineering, Materials; Materials research/science **Level of Education for which Award is Granted:** Undergraduate **Number Awarded:** 1 or more each year. **Funds Available:** The stipend is $1,000. **Duration:** 1 year.
Eligibility Requirements: This program is open to APW members and their immediate family who are juniors or seniors in high school. Applicants must be planning to enroll at an accredited college, university, community college, or technical study to work on a degree in the study in aggregate production or a related field (e.g., engineering, construction, materials science). Along with their application, they must submit an essay of 250 to 350 words on their interest in the aggregate industry. **Deadline for Receipt:** July of each year. **Additional Information:** This program was established in 2002.

4300 ■ AIR & WASTE MANAGEMENT ASSOCIATION-CONNECTICUT CHAPTER

Attn: Ray Yarmac, Secretary
Sci-Tech, Inc.
185 Silas Deane Highway
Wethersfield, CT 06109
Tel: (860)257-0767
E-mail: ryarmac@sce-techinc.com
Web Site: http://www.awma-nes.org/connecticut_chapter.htm
To provide financial assistance to residents of Connecticut who are interested in studying fields related to air and waste management in college.
Title of Award: Connecticut Chapter Scholarship **Area, Field, or Subject:** Air pollution; Engineering; Environmental conservation; Environmental science; Science **Level of Education for which Award is Granted:** Undergraduate **Number Awarded:** 1 each year. **Funds Available:** The stipend is $1,000. **Duration:** 1 year; recipients may reapply.
Eligibility Requirements: This program is open to 1) seniors graduating from high schools in Connecticut who plan to enroll full time in college, and 2) Connecticut residents already enrolled full time in college. Applicants must be interested in working on a degree in science or engineering leading to careers in the environmental field, especially air pollution

control or waste management. Selection is based on their proposed plan of study, transcripts, work experience, and volunteer and extracurricular activities; financial need is not considered. **Deadline for Receipt:** April of each year.

4301 ■ ALABAMA CONCRETE INDUSTRIES ASSOCIATION

Attn: President
660 Adams Avenue, Suite 188
Montgomery, AL 36104
Tel: (334)265-0501
Free: 800-732-9118
Fax: (334)265-2250
E-mail: jsorrell@alconcrete.org
Web Site: http://www.alconcrete.org/scholarships
To provide financial assistance to students majoring in architecture, building sciences, or engineering in Alabama.
Title of Award: Alabama Concrete Industries Association Scholarships **Area, Field, or Subject:** Architecture; Construction; Engineering **Level of Education for which Award is Granted:** Four Year College **Number Awarded:** 2 each year. **Funds Available:** A stipend is awarded (amount not specified). **Duration:** 1 year.
Eligibility Requirements: This program is open to students completing their junior year at colleges and universities in Alabama. Applicants must be enrolled in an accredited program in architecture, engineering, or building sciences. Selection is based on academic and extracurricular activity record. **Additional Information:** This program was established in 1993.

4302 ■ ALABAMA ROAD BUILDERS ASSOCIATION

Attn: Scholarship Committee
630 Adams Avenue
Montgomery, AL 36104-4336
Tel: (334)832-4331
Free: 800-239-5828
Fax: (334)265-4931
Web Site: http://www.alrba.org/site/scholarship.html
To provide financial assistance to undergraduate and graduate students from Alabama working on a degree in civil engineering.
Title of Award: Ed and Charlotte Rodgers Scholarships **Area, Field, or Subject:** Engineering, Civil **Level of Education for which Award is Granted:** Graduate, Undergraduate **Number Awarded:** 3 to 5 each year. **Funds Available:** A stipend is awarded (amount not specified). **Duration:** 1 year.
Eligibility Requirements: This program is open to full-time undergraduate and graduate students in civil engineering in Alabama. Applicants must have completed their freshman year, have a satisfactory GPA, be in good academic standing, and be able to demonstrate financial need. Selection is based on accomplishments in student, community, honorary, or service organizations; excellence in academics; and demonstrated leadership qualities. **Deadline for Receipt:** March of each year. **Additional Information:** This program was established in 1978.

4303 ■ AMERICAN ASSOCIATION OF BLACKS IN ENERGY

Attn: Scholarship Committee
927 15th Street, N.W., Suite 200
Washington, DC 20005
Tel: (202)371-9530
Fax: (202)371-9218
E-mail: aabe@aabe.org
Web Site: http://aabe.org/taxonomy_menu/24/253
To provide financial assistance to underrepresented minority high school seniors who are interested in majoring in engineering, mathematics, or physical science in college.
Title of Award: American Association of Blacks in Energy Scholarship **Area, Field, or Subject:** Engineering; Mathematics and mathematical sciences; Physical sciences **Level of Education for which Award is Granted:** Undergraduate **Number Awarded:** 6 each year (1 in each of the organization's regions); of those 6 winners, 1 is chosen to receive the Premier Award. **Funds Available:** The stipends are $1,500. The Premier Award is an additional $3,000. All funds are paid directly to the students upon proof of enrollment at an accredited college or university. **Duration:** 1 year; nonrenewable.
Eligibility Requirements: This program is open to members of minority groups underrepresented in the energy industry (African Americans,

Hispanics, and Native Americans) who are graduating high school seniors. Applicants must have a "B" academic average overall and a "B" average in mathematics and science courses. They must be planning to attend an accredited college or university to major in engineering, mathematics, or the physical sciences. Along with their application, they must submit a 350-word essay covering why they should receive this scholarship, their professional career objectives, and any other pertinent information. Financial need is also considered in the selection process. The applicant who demonstrates the most outstanding achievement and promise is presented with the Premier Award. All applications must be submitted to the local office of the sponsoring organization in the student's state. For a list of local offices, contact the scholarship committee at the national office. **Deadline for Receipt:** February of each year.

4304 ■ AMERICAN CERAMIC SOCIETY

Attn: Electronics Division
735 Ceramic Place, Suite 100
Westerville, OH 43081
Tel: (614)890-4700
Fax: (614)899-6109
E-mail: info@ceramics.org
Web Site: http://www.ceramics.org
To provide financial assistance to undergraduate students in a field related to ceramic science.
Title of Award: Dr. Lewis C. Hoffman Scholarship **Area, Field, or Subject:** Crafts; Engineering, Materials; Materials research/science **Level of Education for which Award is Granted:** Four Year College **Number Awarded:** 1 each year. **Funds Available:** The stipend is $2,000. **Duration:** 1 year.
Eligibility Requirements: This program is open to juniors enrolled in a program related to ceramics/materials science and engineering. Applicants must submit a 500-word essay on a topic that changes annually; recently, the topic was "Electronic Ceramics in Clean Energy Technologies." Selection is based on the essay, extracurricular activities, a letter of recommendation from a faculty advisor, PSAT/SAT/ACT scores, and GPA (cumulative and in science courses). **Deadline for Receipt:** March of each year. **Additional Information:** Further information is also available from the Chair of the Awards and Scholarships Committee, Amit Goyal, Oak Ridge National Laboratory, Metals and Ceramics Division, Superconducting Materials Research, Oak Ridge, TN 37831-6116, (865) 574-1587, Fax: (865) 574-7659, E-mail: goyala@ornl.gov.

4305 ■ AMERICAN CERAMIC SOCIETY-NEW ENGLAND SECTION

c/o Lou Trostel, Counselor
Ceramics Concepts
P.O. Box 199
Princeton, MA 01541
Tel: (978)464-2469
Fax: (978)464-2755
E-mail: ljtjr@worldnet.att.net
Web Site: http://www.ceramics.org
To provide financial assistance to residents of the New England states who are working on a college degree in ceramics.
Title of Award: New England Section Scholarship **Area, Field, or Subject:** Crafts; Engineering, Materials **Level of Education for which Award is Granted:** Undergraduate **Number Awarded:** 1 or more each year. **Funds Available:** The stipend is $1,000. **Duration:** 1 year.
Eligibility Requirements: This program is open to undergraduates from New England who are working on a degree in ceramics in an accredited program in the United States.

4306 ■ AMERICAN CERAMIC SOCIETY-SOUTHWEST SECTION

c/o Felipe Lamilla, Scholarship Chair
Ferro Ceramics
1540 Selene Drive, Suite 110
Carrollton, TX 75006
Tel: (972)446-0459
E-mail: Felipe.lamilla@us.ferro.com
Web Site: http://www.ceramics.org
To provide financial assistance to college sophomores preparing for a career in the ceramic industry, particularly those from the Southwest.
Title of Award: Robert and Mary Buttle Scholarship **Area, Field, or Subject:** Engineering, Materials; Materials research/science **Level of**

Education for which Award is Granted: Undergraduate **Number Awarded:** 1 or more each year. **Funds Available:** Stipends range from $1,000 to $2,000. **Duration:** 1 year.
Eligibility Requirements: Students registered in recognized 2-year or 4-year programs of ceramic engineering or ceramic materials science are eligible to apply upon completion of their freshman year. Applicants must be able to demonstrate a commitment to ceramic sciences and the ceramic industry, a strong academic record, a well-rounded personal character, and financial need. Preference is given to applicants residing in the areas served by the Southwest Section: Arkansas, Kansas, Louisiana, Oklahoma, Texas, and the northern border states of Mexico. **Deadline for Receipt:** July or November of each year. **Additional Information:** This program was established in 1993.

4307 ■ AMERICAN CERAMIC SOCIETY-SOUTHWEST SECTION

c/o Felipe Lamilla, Scholarship Chair
Ferro Ceramics
1540 Selene Drive, Suite 110
Carrollton, TX 75006
Tel: (972)446-0459
E-mail: Felipe.lamilla@us.ferro.com
Web Site: http://www.ceramics.org
To provide financial assistance to students preparing for a career in the ceramic industry, particularly those from the Southwest.
Title of Award: Forrest K. Pence Memorial Scholarship **Area, Field, or Subject:** Engineering, Materials; Materials research/science **Level of Education for which Award is Granted:** Graduate, Undergraduate **Number Awarded:** 1 or more each year. **Funds Available:** Stipends range from $1,000 to $2,000. **Duration:** 1 year.
Eligibility Requirements: This program is open to students working towards an undergraduate or graduate degree in ceramic engineering. Applicants must be able to demonstrate a commitment to ceramic sciences and the ceramic industry, a strong academic record, a well-rounded personal character, and financial need. They must be sponsored or recommended by an active member of the Southwest Section of the American Ceramic Society (ACerS). Preference is given to applicants residing in the areas served by the Southwest Section: Arkansas, Kansas, Louisiana, Oklahoma, Texas, and the northern border states of Mexico. **Deadline for Receipt:** July or November of each year. **Additional Information:** This program was established in 1982.

4308 ■ AMERICAN CHEMICAL SOCIETY

Attn: Department of Diversity Programs
1155 16th Street, N.W.
Washington, DC 20036
Tel: (202)872-6250
Free: 800-227-5558
Fax: (202)776-8003
E-mail: scholars@acs.org
Web Site: http://www.chemistry.org/scholars
To provide financial assistance to underrepresented minority students with a strong interest in chemistry and a desire to prepare for a career in a chemically-related science.
Title of Award: American Chemical Society Scholars Program **Area, Field, or Subject:** Biochemistry; Chemistry; Engineering, Chemical; Environmental conservation; Environmental science; Materials research/science; Toxicology **Level of Education for which Award is Granted:** Undergraduate **Number Awarded:** Approximately 100 new awards are granted each year. **Funds Available:** The maximum stipend is $2,500 for the freshman year in college or $3,000 per year for sophomores, juniors, and seniors. **Duration:** 1 year; may be renewed.
Eligibility Requirements: This program is open to 1) college-bound high school seniors; 2) college freshmen, sophomores, and juniors enrolled full time at an accredited college or university; 3) community college graduates and transfer students who plan to study for a bachelor's degree; and 4) community college freshmen. Applicants must be African American, Hispanic/Latino, or American Indian. They must be majoring or planning to major in chemistry, biochemistry, chemical engineering, or other chemically-related fields, such as environmental science, materials science, or toxicology, and planning to prepare for a career in the chemical sciences or chemical technology. Students planning careers in medicine or pharmacy are not eligible. U.S. citizenship or permanent resident status is required. Selection is based on academic merit (GPA of 3.0 or higher)

and financial need. **Deadline for Receipt:** February of each year. **Additional Information:** This program was established in 1994.

4309 ■ AMERICAN CHEMICAL SOCIETY

Attn: Education Division
1155 16th Street, N.W.
Washington, DC 20036
Tel: (202)872-4380
Free: 800-227-5558
E-mail: r_rasheed@acs.org
Web Site: http://www.chemistry.org/education/SEED.html
To provide financial assistance for college to high school students who participated in the American Chemical Society's Project SEED: Summer Education Experience for the Disadvantaged.

Title of Award: Project SEED Scholarships **Area, Field, or Subject:** Biochemistry; Chemistry; Engineering, Chemical; Materials research/science **Level of Education for which Award is Granted:** Undergraduate **Number Awarded:** Varies each year; recently, 29 of these scholarships were awarded. **Funds Available:** Stipends up to $5,000 per year are available. **Duration:** 1 year; nonrenewable.

Eligibility Requirements: Applicants for Project SEED must have completed the junior or senior year in high school, live within commuting distance of a sponsoring institution, have completed a course in high school chemistry, and come from an economically disadvantaged family. The standards for economic disadvantage follow federal poverty guidelines for family size, but the maximum family income is $32,000 except in cases where other factors are present that may deter a student from considering a career in science; family income may be up to $44,000 if the student is a member of an ethnic group underrepresented in the sciences (African American, Hispanic, American Indian), if the parents have not attended college, or if the family is single-parent or very large. Participants in the Project SEED program are eligible to apply for these scholarships during their senior year in high school if they plan to major in college in a chemical science or engineering field, such as chemistry, chemical engineering, biochemistry, materials science, or another closely-related field. **Deadline for Receipt:** February of each year.

4310 ■ AMERICAN COMPOSITES MANUFACTURERS ASSOCIATION

Attn: Scholarship Office
1010 North Glebe Road, Suite 450
Arlington, VA 22201
Tel: (703)525-0511
Fax: (703)525-0743
E-mail: info@acmanet.org
Web Site: http://www.acmanet.org/scholarships/index.cfm
To recognize and reward, with college scholarships, students who submit outstanding reports on research related to composites.

Title of Award: Gary B. Multanen Applied Research Scholarship **Area, Field, or Subject:** Engineering, Materials **Level of Education for which Award is Granted:** Undergraduate **Number Awarded:** 1 each year. **Funds Available:** Winners receive a $1,000 scholarship and a trip to the Composites conference where they present their research. **Duration:** The competition is held annually.

Eligibility Requirements: This competition is open to students who submit reports of research they have conducted in the field of composites, including industrial technology and plastics engineering. **Additional Information:** This competition is sponsored by *Composites Manufacturing Magazine*, the official magazine of the American Composites Manufacturers Association.

4311 ■ AMERICAN CONCRETE INSTITUTE

Attn: Concrete Research and Education Foundation
38800 Country Club Drive
P.O. Box 9094
Farmington Hills, MI 48333-9094
Tel: (248)848-3700
Fax: (248)848-3701
E-mail: scholarships@concrete.org
Web Site: http://www.concrete.org/STUDENTS/STU_SCHOLAR.HTM
To provide funding to undergraduate and graduate students preparing for a career in the field of concrete.

Title of Award: ACI Student Fellowship Program **Area, Field, or Subject:** Business; Construction; Engineering **Level of Education for**

which **Award is Granted:** Graduate, Undergraduate **Number Awarded:** Varies each year; recently, 3 of these fellowships were awarded. **Funds Available:** The stipend is $10,000 per year; funds may be used for tuition, residence, books, and materials. Other financial benefits include reimbursement of expenses associated with attending the ACI convention and reimbursement of expenses associated with an internship. **Duration:** 2 years; may be renewed, including through graduate school for students who first receive an award as an undergraduate.

Eligibility Requirements: This program is open to full-time undergraduate and graduate students in engineering, construction management, and other appropriate fields. Applicants must first be nominated by a faculty member of the American Concrete Institute (ACI). They may be residing anywhere in the world, but graduate study must take place in the United States or Canada. **Deadline for Receipt:** November of each year.

4312 ■ AMERICAN CONCRETE INSTITUTE

Attn: Concrete Research and Education Foundation
38800 Country Club Drive
P.O. Box 9094
Farmington Hills, MI 48333-9094
Tel: (248)848-3700
Fax: (248)848-3701
E-mail: scholarships@concrete.org
Web Site: http://www.concrete.org/STUDENTS/STU_SCHOLAR.HTM
To provide funding to undergraduate students preparing for a career in the field of concrete construction.

Title of Award: Peter D. Courtois Concrete Construction Scholarships **Area, Field, or Subject:** Business; Construction; Engineering; Technology **Level of Education for which Award is Granted:** Four Year College **Number Awarded:** 1 each year. **Funds Available:** The stipend is $1,000. **Duration:** 1 year.

Eligibility Requirements: This program is open to undergraduate students in the United States or Canada who have achieved senior status in a 4-year or longer program in engineering, construction, or technology. Selection is based on demonstrated interest and ability to work in the field of concrete construction. **Deadline for Receipt:** November of each year.

4313 ■ AMERICAN CONCRETE INSTITUTE-GREATER MICHIGAN CHAPTER

c/o Ruben Ramos, President
Testing Engineers and Consultants
1343 Rochester Road
P.O. Box 249
Troy, MI 48099-0249
Tel: (248)588-6514
Fax: (248)588-6232
E-mail: rramos@tectest.com
Web Site: http://www.acigmc.org/Scholarship.html
To provide financial assistance to upper-division students from Michigan and Ontario who are working on a degree related to concrete.

Title of Award: Greater Michigan Chapter ACI Concrete Scholarship **Area, Field, or Subject:** Business; Construction; Engineering, Materials; Materials research/science **Level of Education for which Award is Granted:** Four Year College **Number Awarded:** 1 each year. **Funds Available:** The stipend is $2,000. **Duration:** 1 year.

Eligibility Requirements: This program is open to residents of Michigan and Ontario. Applicants must be enrolled full time at a designated university in the area and studying an engineering or technical field emphasizing concrete or masonry design, construction, or materials. **Deadline for Receipt:** March of each year. **Additional Information:** The participating universities are the University of Michigan, Wayne State University, Michigan State University, Michigan Technological University, Lawrence Technological University, University of Detroit-Mercy, and University of Windsor.

4314 ■ AMERICAN CONCRETE INSTITUTE-NEBRASKA CHAPTER

Attn: Scholarships
6901 Vine Street
Lincoln, NE 68505
Tel: (402)466-4233
E-mail: rdelorm@msn.com
Web Site: http://www.acinebraska.org/students/StudentsUGScholar2.html

To provide financial assistance to students entering their senior year at a college or university in Nebraska and majoring in a field related to the concrete industry.

Title of Award: Nebraska Chapter ACI Undergraduate Student Award **Area, Field, or Subject:** Business; Construction; Engineering; Technology **Level of Education for which Award is Granted:** Four Year College **Number Awarded:** 1 each year. **Funds Available:** The stipend is $1,000. **Duration:** 1 year.

Eligibility Requirements: This program is open to students entering their senior year at a 4-year college or university in Nebraska. Applicants must be majoring in a field of engineering, construction, or technology to prepare for a career in concrete construction. Along with their application, they must submit a 500-word essay explaining their interest, experience, ability, and career objectives as they relate to concrete construction. **Deadline for Receipt:** December of each year.

4315 ■ AMERICAN COUNCIL OF THE BLIND

Attn: Coordinator, Scholarship Program
1155 15th Street, N.W., Suite 1004
Washington, DC 20005
Tel: (202)467-5081
Free: 800-424-8666
Fax: (202)467-5085
E-mail: info@acb.org
Web Site: http://www.acb.org

To provide financial assistance to blind students who are working on an undergraduate or graduate degree in science at an accredited college or university.

Title of Award: Dr. S. Bradley Burson Memorial Scholarship **Area, Field, or Subject:** Biological and clinical sciences; Chemistry; Engineering; Physics **Level of Education for which Award is Granted:** Graduate, Undergraduate **Number Awarded:** 1 each year. **Funds Available:** The stipend is $1,000. In addition, the winner receives a Kurzweil-1000 Reading System. **Duration:** 1 year.

Eligibility Requirements: This program is open to legally blind undergraduate or graduate students majoring in the "hard" sciences (i.e., biology, chemistry, physics, and engineering, but not computer science) in college. They must be U.S. citizens. In addition to letters of recommendation and copies of academic transcripts, applications must include an autobiographical sketch. A cumulative GPA of 3.3 or higher is generally required. Selection is based on demonstrated academic record, involvement in extracurricular and civic activities, and academic objectives. The severity of the applicant's visual impairment and his/her study methods are also taken into account. **Deadline for Receipt:** February of each year. **Additional Information:** Scholarship winners are expected to be present at the council's annual conference; the council will cover all reasonable expenses connected with convention attendance.

4316 ■ AMERICAN COUNCIL OF ENGINEERING COMPANIES OF COLORADO

Attn: Scholarship Coordinator
899 Logan Street, Suite 109
Denver, CO 80203
Tel: (303)832-2200
E-mail: acec@acec-co.org
Web Site: http://www.acec-co.org/education/index.html

To provide financial assistance to students in Colorado currently working on a bachelor's degree in engineering.

Title of Award: ACEC Colorado Scholarship Program **Area, Field, or Subject:** Engineering **Level of Education for which Award is Granted:** Four Year College **Number Awarded:** 5 each year: the William Russell Stoneman Scholarship at $4,500, the Malcolm and Charles Meurer Scholarship at $4,000, the Fu Hua Chen Scholarship at $3,000, and 2 others at $2,000 each. **Funds Available:** Stipends are $4,500, $3,000, or $2,000. **Duration:** 1 year.

Eligibility Requirements: This program is open to students working on a bachelor's degree in an ABET-approved engineering program in Colorado. Applicants must be U.S. citizens entering their junior, senior, or fifth year. Along with their application, they must submit a 500-word essay on "What is the role or responsibility of the consulting engineer or land surveyor to shaping and protecting the natural environment." Selection is based on the essay (25 points), cumulative GPA (28 points), work experience (20 points), a letter of recommendation (17 points), and college

activities (10 points). **Deadline for Receipt:** October of each year. **Additional Information:** Recipients are nominated for national scholarships offered by the American Council of Engineering Companies (ACEC).

4317 ■ AMERICAN COUNCIL OF ENGINEERING COMPANIES OF COLORADO

Attn: Scholarship Coordinator
899 Logan Street, Suite 109
Denver, CO 80203
Tel: (303)832-2200
E-mail: acec@acec-co.org
Web Site: http://www.acec-co.org/education/index.html

To provide financial assistance to students in Colorado currently working on a bachelor's degree in engineering.

Title of Award: Jack Bruce Memorial Scholarship **Area, Field, or Subject:** Engineering **Level of Education for which Award is Granted:** Four Year College **Number Awarded:** 1 each year. **Funds Available:** The stipend is $2,000. **Duration:** 1 year.

Eligibility Requirements: This program is open to students working on a bachelor's degree in an ABET-approved engineering program in Colorado. Applicants must be U.S. citizens entering their junior, senior, or fifth year. Along with their application, they must submit a 500-word essay on "What is the role or responsibility of the consulting engineer or land surveyor to shaping and protecting the natural environment. Selection is based on the essay (25 points), cumulative GPA (28 points), work experience (20 points), a letter of recommendation (17 points), and college activities (10 points)." **Deadline for Receipt:** October of each year. **Additional Information:** This program is jointly sponsored by the Colorado Chapter of the American Public Works Association and American Council of Engineering Companies of Colorado.

4318 ■ AMERICAN FOUNDATION FOR THE BLIND

Attn: Scholarship Committee
11 Penn Plaza, Suite 300
New York, NY 10001
Tel: (212)502-7661
Free: 800-AFB-LINE
Fax: (212)502-7771
E-mail: afbinfo@afb.net
Web Site: http://www.afb.org/scholarships.asp

To provide financial assistance to visually impaired students who wish to work on a graduate or undergraduate degree in engineering or computer, physical, or life sciences.

Title of Award: Paul and Ellen Ruckes Scholarship **Area, Field, or Subject:** Biological and clinical sciences; Computer and information sciences; Engineering; Physical sciences **Level of Education for which Award is Granted:** Graduate, Undergraduate **Number Awarded:** 1 each year. **Funds Available:** The stipend is $1,000. **Duration:** 1 year.

Eligibility Requirements: This program is open to visually impaired undergraduate or graduate students who are U.S. citizens working on a degree in engineering or the computer, physical, or life sciences. Legal blindness is not required. Along with their application, they must submit an essay that includes the field of study they are pursuing and why they have chosen it; their educational and personal goals; their work experience; any extracurricular activities with which they have been involved, including those in school, religious organizations, and the community; and how they intend to use scholarship monies that may be awarded. **Deadline for Receipt:** April of each year.

4319 ■ AMERICAN INDIAN COLLEGE FUND

Attn: Scholarship Department
8333 Greenwood Boulevard
Denver, CO 80221
Tel: (303)426-8900
Free: 800-776-FUND
Fax: (303)426-1200
E-mail: info@collegefund.org
Web Site: http://www.collegefund.org/scholarships/main.html

To provide financial assistance to Native American college students who are majoring in designated fields at specified colleges and universities.

Title of Award: Ford Motor Company/American Indian College Fund Corporate Scholars Program **Area, Field, or Subject:** Accounting; Engineering, Computer; Engineering, Electrical; Engineering, Mechanical;

Finance; Information science and technology; Marketing and distribution; Operations research **Level of Education for which Award is Granted:** Undergraduate **Number Awarded:** Varies each year. **Funds Available:** The stipend is $8,000 per year. **Duration:** 1 year; may be renewed.

Eligibility Requirements: This program is open to American Indians, Alaska Natives, and Hawaii Natives who have proof of enrollment or descendancy and have achieved at least sophomore status at 1 of 102 designated college and universities. Applicants must have a GPA of 3.0 or higher and be able to demonstrate financial need. They must have declared a major in accounting, computer engineering, electrical engineering, finance, information systems, marketing, mechanical engineering, or operations management. Along with their application, they must submit a 1-page personal essay on how they can become a role model and make a difference in their chosen field. Leadership and commitment to the American Indian community are also considered in the selection process. **Deadline for Receipt:** November of each year. **Additional Information:** This program is funded by the Ford Motor Company.

4320 ■ AMERICAN INDIAN SCIENCE AND ENGINEERING SOCIETY

Attn: Scholarship Coordinator
2305 Renard, S.E., Suite 200
P.O. Box 9828
Albuquerque, NM 87119-9828
Tel: (505)765-1052
Fax: (505)765-5608
E-mail: shirley@aises.org
Web Site: http://www.aises.org/highered/scholarships

To provide financial assistance to members of the American Indian Science and Engineering Society who are majoring in designated fields as undergraduate or graduate students.

Title of Award: A.T. Anderson Memorial Scholarship Program **Area, Field, or Subject:** Engineering; Mathematics and mathematical sciences; Medicine; Natural resources; Physical sciences; Science **Level of Education for which Award is Granted:** Graduate, Undergraduate **Number Awarded:** Varies; generally, 200 or more each year, depending upon the availability of funds from corporate and other sponsors. **Funds Available:** The annual stipend is $1,000 for undergraduates or $2,000 for graduate students. **Duration:** 1 year; nonrenewable.

Eligibility Requirements: This program is open to members of the society who can furnish proof of tribal enrollment or Certificate of Degree of Indian Blood. Applicants must be full-time students at the undergraduate or graduate school level attending an accredited 4-year college or university or a 2-year college leading to an academic degree in engineering, mathematics, medicine, natural resources, physical science, or the sciences. They must submit a 500-word essay that demonstrates their interest in and motivation to continue higher education, an understanding of the importance of college and a commitment to completion, their educational and/or career goals, and a commitment to learning and giving back to the community. Selection is based on the essay, academic achievement (GPA of 2.0 or higher), leadership potential, and commitment to helping other American Indians. Financial need is not considered. **Deadline for Receipt:** June of each year. **Additional Information:** This program was launched in 1983 in memory of A.T. Anderson, a Mohawk and a chemical engineer who worked with Albert Einstein. Anderson was 1 of the society's founders and was the society's first executive director. The program includes the following named awards: the Al Qoyawayma Award for an applicant who is majoring in science or engineering and also has a strong interest in the arts, the Norbert S. Hill, Jr. Leadership Award, the Polingaysi Qoyawayma Award for an applicant who is working on a teaching degree in order to teach mathematics or science in a Native community or an advanced degree for personal improvement or teaching at the college level, and the Robert W. Brocksbank Scholarship.

4321 ■ AMERICAN INDIAN SCIENCE AND ENGINEERING SOCIETY

Attn: Scholarship Coordinator
2305 Renard, S.E., Suite 200
P.O. Box 9828
Albuquerque, NM 87119-9828
Tel: (505)765-1052
Fax: (505)765-5608
E-mail: shirley@aises.org
Web Site: http://www.aises.org/highered/scholarships

To provide financial assistance for college to outstanding American Indian high school seniors from designated states who are members of American Indian Science and Engineering Society (AISES).

Title of Award: Burlington Northern Santa Fe Foundation Scholarship **Area, Field, or Subject:** Business administration; Engineering; Mathematics and mathematical sciences; Medicine; Natural resources; Physical sciences; Science; Technology **Level of Education for which Award is Granted:** Four Year College **Number Awarded:** 5 new awards are made each year. **Funds Available:** The stipend is $2,500 per year. **Duration:** 4 years or until completion of a baccalaureate degree, whichever occurs first.

Eligibility Requirements: This program is open to AISES members who are high school seniors planning to attend an accredited 4-year college or university and major in business, engineering, mathematics, medicine, natural resources, physical science, science, or technology. Applicants must submit 1) proof of tribal enrollment or a Certificate of Degree of Indian Blood; 2) evidence of residence in the service area of the Burlington Northern and Santa Fe Corporation (Arizona, California, Colorado, Kansas, Minnesota, Montana, New Mexico, North Dakota, Oklahoma, Oregon, South Dakota, and Washington); 3) a statement of financial need; 4) a 500-word essay on why they chose their particular field of study, their career aspirations, an evaluation of past scholastic performance, obstacles faced as a student, and involvement in and commitment to tribal community life; and 5) high school transcripts showing a GPA of 2.0 or higher. **Deadline for Receipt:** April of each year. **Additional Information:** This program is funded by the Burlington Northern Santa Fe Foundation and administered by AISES.

4322 ■ AMERICAN INDIAN SCIENCE AND ENGINEERING SOCIETY

Attn: Scholarship Coordinator
2305 Renard, S.E., Suite 200
P.O. Box 9828
Albuquerque, NM 87119-9828
Tel: (505)765-1052
Fax: (505)765-5608
E-mail: shirley@aises.org
Web Site: http://www.aises.org/highered/scholarships

To provide financial assistance to members of the American Indian Science and Engineering Society (AISES) who are working on an undergraduate or graduate degree in engineering.

Title of Award: General Motors Engineering Scholarship **Area, Field, or Subject:** Engineering; Engineering, Electrical; Engineering, Industrial; Engineering, Mechanical **Level of Education for which Award is Granted:** Graduate, Undergraduate **Funds Available:** The stipend is $3,000 per year. **Duration:** 1 year; nonrenewable.

Eligibility Requirements: This program is open to AISES members who are full-time undergraduate or graduate students in engineering, with a preference for electrical, industrial, or mechanical engineering majors. Applicants must have a GPA of 3.0 or higher and be members of an American Indian tribe or Alaskan Native group or otherwise considered to be an American Indian or Alaskan Native by the tribe or group with which affiliation is claimed. They must submit an essay that explains their knowledge of and experiences with American Indian tribal culture, discusses their specific interests in engineering, and states how they will contribute their knowledge or professional experience to a Native American community. **Deadline for Receipt:** June of each year. **Additional Information:** This program, established in 2002, is funded by General Motors.

4323 ■ AMERICAN INDIAN SCIENCE AND ENGINEERING SOCIETY

Attn: Scholarship Coordinator
2305 Renard, S.E., Suite 200
P.O. Box 9828
Albuquerque, NM 87119-9828
Tel: (505)765-1052
Fax: (505)765-5608
E-mail: shirley@aises.org
Web Site: http://www.aises.org/highered/scholarships

To provide financial assistance and summer work experience to members of the American Indian Science and Engineering Society (AISES) who are working on an undergraduate degree in engineering or science related to water resources or environmental fields.

Title of Award: Henry Rodriguez Reclamation Scholarship **Area, Field, or Subject:** Engineering; Environmental conservation; Environmental science; Science; Water resources **Level of Education for which Award is Granted:** Undergraduate **Funds Available:** The stipend is $5,000 per year. **Duration:** 1 year; may be renewed up to 3 additional years.

Eligibility Requirements: This program is open to AISES members who are full-time undergraduate students in engineering or science related to water resources or environmental fields. Applicants must have a GPA of 2.5 or higher and be U.S. citizens or permanent residents. Non-Indians may apply, but all applicants must submit an essay on their first-hand knowledge of Indian tribal culture, their interest in engineering or environmental studies, how that interest relates to water resource issues and needs and concerns of Indian tribes, and how they will contribute their knowledge or professional experience to a Native American community. **Deadline for Receipt:** June of each year. **Additional Information:** This program, established in 2001, is funded by the U.S. Bureau of Reclamation and the National Water Research Institute and administered by AISES. Recipients must agree to serve an 8- to 10-week paid internship with the Bureau during the summer at a regional or area office located within the 17 western states served by the Bureau, at its Washington, D.C. headquarters, or at its Denver Technical Service Center.

4324 ■ AMERICAN LEGION

Attn: Department of Kansas
1314 S.W. Topeka Boulevard
Topeka, KS 66612-1886
Tel: (785)232-9315
Fax: (785)232-1399
Web Site: http://www.ksamlegion.org/programs.htm
To provide financial assistance for college to the children of members of the Kansas American Legion, particularly those interested in majoring in the sciences or business.

Title of Award: Charles W. and Annette Hill Scholarship Fund **Area, Field, or Subject:** Business administration; Engineering; General studies/ Field of study not specified; Science **Level of Education for which Award is Granted:** Undergraduate **Number Awarded:** 1 each year. **Funds Available:** The stipend is $1,000. **Duration:** 1 year; may be renewed if the recipient maintains a GPA of 3.0 or higher.

Eligibility Requirements: This program is open to graduating seniors at high schools in Kansas who have a GPA of 3.0 or higher. Applicants must be a descendant of a member of the American Legion. Preference is given to applicants planning to major in science, engineering, or business administration at a Kansas college, university, junior college, or trade school. Selection is based on high school transcripts, 3 letters of recommendation, an essay of 250 to 500 words on "Why I Want to Go to College," and financial need. **Deadline for Receipt:** February of each year.

4325 ■ AMERICAN NUCLEAR SOCIETY

Attn: Scholarship Coordinator
555 North Kensington Avenue
La Grange Park, IL 60526-5592
Tel: (708)352-6611
Fax: (708)352-0499
E-mail: outreach@ans.org
Web Site: http://www.ans.org/honors/scholarships
To provide financial assistance to students entering their freshman year of college and planning to prepare for a career in nuclear science or nuclear engineering.

Title of Award: ANS Incoming Freshman Scholarships **Area, Field, or Subject:** Engineering, Nuclear; Nuclear science **Level of Education for which Award is Granted:** Undergraduate **Number Awarded:** 5 each year. **Funds Available:** The stipend is $2,000. **Duration:** 1 year; nonrenewable.

Eligibility Requirements: This program is open to graduating high school seniors who have enrolled as a full-time college student. Applicants must be taking science, mathematics, or technical courses with an interest in working in nuclear science and technology. They must be U.S. citizens or permanent residents. Selection is based on high school academic achievement, freshmen college courses enrolled in, an essay, and letters of recommendation. **Deadline for Receipt:** March of each year. **Additional Information:** This program was established in 2005.

4326 ■ AMERICAN NUCLEAR SOCIETY

Attn: Scholarship Coordinator
555 North Kensington Avenue
La Grange Park, IL 60526-5592

Tel: (708)352-6611
Fax: (708)352-0499
E-mail: outreach@ans.org
Web Site: http://www.ans.org/honors/scholarships
To provide financial assistance to undergraduate students who are interested in preparing for a career in nuclear science or nuclear engineering.

Title of Award: ANS Undergraduate Scholarships **Area, Field, or Subject:** Engineering, Nuclear; Nuclear science **Level of Education for which Award is Granted:** Undergraduate **Number Awarded:** 31 each year: 4 for students entering their sophomore year and 27 (including the 6 named scholarships plus 21 others) for students entering their junior or senior year. **Funds Available:** The stipend is $2,000. **Duration:** 1 year; nonrenewable.

Eligibility Requirements: Eligible to apply are undergraduate students enrolled in nuclear science, nuclear engineering, or a nuclear-related field at an accredited institution in the United States. There are separate competitions for 1) students who have completed at least 1 academic year and who will be sophomores, and 2) students who have completed 2 or more years and will be entering as juniors or seniors. All applicants must be U.S. citizens or permanent residents and be able to demonstrate academic achievement. **Deadline for Receipt:** January of each year. **Additional Information:** This program includes the following named scholarships: the Angelo S. Bisesti Memorial Scholarship, the Joseph R. Dietrich Memorial Scholarship, the Raymond DiSalvo Memorial Scholarship, the Robert G. Lacy Memorial Scholarship, the John R. Lamarsh Memorial Scholarship, and the Robert T. Liner Memorial Scholarship.

4327 ■ AMERICAN NUCLEAR SOCIETY

Attn: Scholarship Coordinator
555 North Kensington Avenue
La Grange Park, IL 60526-5592
Tel: (708)352-6611
Fax: (708)352-0499
E-mail: outreach@ans.org
Web Site: http://www.ans.org/honors/scholarships
To provide financial assistance to undergraduate students who are working on a degree in engineering or science that is associated with decommissioning, decontamination, or environmental restoration aspects of nuclear power.

Title of Award: Decommissioning, Decontamination and Reutilization Scholarship **Area, Field, or Subject:** Engineering, Nuclear; Environmental conservation; Environmental science; Nuclear science **Level of Education for which Award is Granted:** Four Year College **Number Awarded:** 1 each year. **Funds Available:** The stipend is $2,000. **Duration:** 1 year; nonrenewable.

Eligibility Requirements: This program is open to students entering their junior or senior year in an engineering or science program at an accredited institution in the United States. The program must be associated with 1) decommissioning or decontamination of nuclear facilities; 2) management or characterization of nuclear waste; or 3) restoration of the environment. Applicants must be U.S. citizens and able to demonstrate academic achievement. Along with their application, they must submit a brief essay discussing the importance of an aspect of decommissioning, decontamination, and reutilization to the future of the nuclear field. **Deadline for Receipt:** January of each year. **Additional Information:** This program is offered by the Decommissioning, Decontamination and Reutilization (DD&R) Division of the ANS. Recipients must agree to join the ANS and designate the DD&R Division as 1 of their professional divisions. They must commit to participating in DD&R Division activities by attending the annual and winter meetings of the ANS and serving as a student representative at the DD&R executive committee meetings at both ANS meetings.

4328 ■ AMERICAN NUCLEAR SOCIETY

Attn: Scholarship Coordinator
555 North Kensington Avenue
La Grange Park, IL 60526-5592
Tel: (708)352-6611
Fax: (708)352-0499
E-mail: outreach@ans.org
Web Site: http://www.ans.org/honors/scholarships

To encourage mature women whose formal studies in nuclear science or nuclear engineering have been delayed or interrupted.

Title of Award: Delayed Education Scholarship for Women **Area, Field, or Subject:** Engineering, Nuclear; Nuclear science **Level of Education for which Award is Granted:** Graduate, Undergraduate **Number Awarded:** 1 each year. **Funds Available:** The stipend is $4,000. Funds may be used by the student to cover any bona fide education costs, including tuition, books, room, and board. **Duration:** 1 year; nonrenewable.

Eligibility Requirements: Applicants must be mature women who have experienced at least a 1-year delay or interruption of their undergraduate studies and are returning to school to work on an undergraduate or graduate degree in nuclear science or nuclear engineering. They must be U.S. citizens or permanent residents, have proven academic ability, and be able to demonstrate financial need. **Deadline for Receipt:** January of each year.

4329 ■ AMERICAN NUCLEAR SOCIETY
Attn: Scholarship Coordinator
555 North Kensington Avenue
La Grange Park, IL 60526-5592
Tel: (708)352-6611
Fax: (708)352-0499
E-mail: outreach@ans.org
Web Site: http://www.ans.org/honors/scholarships
To provide financial assistance to undergraduate students who are interested in preparing for a career in nuclear engineering.

Title of Award: William R. and Mila Kimel Scholarship **Area, Field, or Subject:** Engineering, Nuclear **Level of Education for which Award is Granted:** Four Year College **Number Awarded:** 1 each year. **Funds Available:** The stipend is $2,000. **Duration:** 1 year; nonrenewable.

Eligibility Requirements: This program is open to students entering their junior or senior year in nuclear engineering at an accredited institution in the United States. Applicants must be U.S. citizens or permanent residents and able to demonstrate academic achievement. **Deadline for Receipt:** January of each year. **Additional Information:** This program was established in 2003.

4330 ■ AMERICAN NUCLEAR SOCIETY
Attn: Scholarship Coordinator
555 North Kensington Avenue
La Grange Park, IL 60526-5592
Tel: (708)352-6611
Fax: (708)352-0499
E-mail: outreach@ans.org
Web Site: http://www.ans.org/honors/scholarships
To provide financial assistance to undergraduate or graduate students who are interested in preparing for a career in nuclear-related fields.

Title of Award: John and Muriel Landis Scholarships **Area, Field, or Subject:** Engineering, Nuclear; Nuclear science **Level of Education for which Award is Granted:** Graduate, Undergraduate **Number Awarded:** Up to 8 each year. **Funds Available:** The stipend is $4,000, to be used to cover tuition, books, fees, room, and board. **Duration:** 1 year; nonrenewable.

Eligibility Requirements: This program is open to undergraduate and graduate students at colleges or universities located in the United States who are preparing for, or planning to prepare for, a career in nuclear science, nuclear engineering, or a nuclear-related field. Qualified high school seniors are also eligible. Applicants must have greater than average financial need and have experienced circumstances that render them disadvantaged. U.S. citizenship or permanent resident status is required. Selection is primarily based on financial need and potential for academic and professional success. **Deadline for Receipt:** January of each year.

4331 ■ AMERICAN NUCLEAR SOCIETY
Attn: Scholarship Coordinator
555 North Kensington Avenue
La Grange Park, IL 60526-5592
Tel: (708)352-6611
Fax: (708)352-0499
E-mail: outreach@ans.org
Web Site: http://www.ans.org/honors/scholarships

To provide financial assistance to undergraduate students who are interested in preparing for a career dealing with operations and power aspects of nuclear science or nuclear engineering.

Title of Award: Operations and Power Division Walter A. Simon Scholarship **Area, Field, or Subject:** Engineering, Nuclear; Nuclear science **Level of Education for which Award is Granted:** Four Year College **Number Awarded:** 1 each year. **Funds Available:** The stipend is $2,500. **Duration:** 1 year; nonrenewable.

Eligibility Requirements: This program is open to students entering their junior or senior year in nuclear science, nuclear engineering, or a nuclear-related field at an accredited institution in the United States. Applicants must be interested in preparing for a career dealing with operations and power aspects of nuclear science or nuclear engineering. They must be U.S. citizens or permanent residents and able to demonstrate academic achievement. **Deadline for Receipt:** January of each year. **Additional Information:** This program is offered by the Operations and Power Division of the ANS.

4332 ■ AMERICAN NUCLEAR SOCIETY
Attn: Scholarship Coordinator
555 North Kensington Avenue
La Grange Park, IL 60526-5592
Tel: (708)352-6611
Fax: (708)352-0499
E-mail: outreach@ans.org
Web Site: http://www.ans.org/honors/scholarships
To provide financial assistance to upper-division students who are interested in preparing for a career dealing with the environmental aspects of nuclear science or nuclear engineering.

Title of Award: Charles (Tommy) Thomas Memorial Scholarship **Area, Field, or Subject:** Engineering, Nuclear; Environmental conservation; Environmental science; Nuclear science **Level of Education for which Award is Granted:** Four Year College **Number Awarded:** 1 each year. **Funds Available:** The stipend is $2,000. **Duration:** 1 year; nonrenewable.

Eligibility Requirements: This program is open to students entering their junior or senior year in nuclear science, nuclear engineering, or a nuclear-related field at an accredited institution in the United States. Applicants must be interested in preparing for a career dealing with the environmental aspects of nuclear science or nuclear engineering. They must be U.S. citizens or permanent residents and able to demonstrate academic achievement. **Deadline for Receipt:** January of each year. **Additional Information:** This program is offered by the Environmental Sciences Division of the ANS. It was formerly known as the Environmental Sciences Division Scholarship.

4333 ■ AMERICAN POLISH ENGINEERING ASSOCIATION
c/o Dr. Barbara R. Koscierzynski
53657 Kristin Court
Shelby Township, MI 48316-2239
Web Site: http://www.apea.us
To provide financial assistance to high school seniors of Polish origin who plan to study engineering in college.

Title of Award: American Polish Engineering Scholarship **Area, Field, or Subject:** Engineering **Level of Education for which Award is Granted:** Undergraduate **Number Awarded:** 2 each year: 1 to a woman and 1 to a man. **Funds Available:** The stipend is $1,000. **Duration:** 1 year.

Eligibility Requirements: This program is open to high school seniors who are of Polish origin or descent. Applicants must have a GPA of 3.0 or higher and plans to attend a college or university with an accredited engineering-related program. They must be available for an interview with the sponsor's scholarship committee. Women and men applicants are judged separately. **Deadline for Receipt:** March of each year.

4334 ■ AMERICAN RADIO RELAY LEAGUE
Attn: ARRL Foundation
225 Main Street
Newington, CT 06111
Tel: (860)594-0397
Fax: (860)594-0259
E-mail: foundation@arrl.org
Web Site: http://www.arrl.org/arrlf/scholgen.html

To provide financial assistance to members of the American Radio Relay League (ARRL), particularly from selected states, who are interested in working on an undergraduate degree.

Title of Award: Earl I. Anderson Scholarships **Area, Field, or Subject:** Engineering; General studies/Field of study not specified **Level of Education for which Award is Granted:** Undergraduate **Number Awarded:** 3 each year. **Funds Available:** The stipend is $1,250. **Duration:** 1 year.

Eligibility Requirements: This program is open to ARRL members who are licensed radio amateurs of any class. Preference is given to 1) residents of Florida, Illinois, Indiana, and Michigan who are attending school in any state, and 2) students majoring in electronic engineering or a related field. Applicants must submit an essay on the role amateur radio has played in their lives and provide documentation of financial need. **Deadline for Receipt:** January of each year.

4335 ■ AMERICAN RADIO RELAY LEAGUE

Attn: ARRL Foundation
225 Main Street
Newington, CT 06111
Tel: (860)594-0397
Fax: (860)594-0259
E-mail: foundation@arrl.org
Web Site: http://www.arrl.org/arrlf/scholgen.html

To provide financial assistance to licensed radio amateurs who are interested in working on a science-related undergraduate degree.

Title of Award: Henry Broughton, K2AE, Memorial Scholarship **Area, Field, or Subject:** Engineering; Science **Level of Education for which Award is Granted:** Four Year College **Number Awarded:** 1 or more each year. **Funds Available:** The stipend is $1,000. **Duration:** 1 year.

Eligibility Requirements: This program is open to students who are working on a bachelor's degree in engineering, science, or a related field at an accredited 4-year college or university. Applicants must be licensed radio amateurs of general class. They must submit an essay on the role amateur radio has played in their lives and provide documentation of financial need. Preference is given to students who reside within 70 miles of Schenectady, New York. **Deadline for Receipt:** January of each year.

4336 ■ AMERICAN RADIO RELAY LEAGUE

Attn: ARRL Foundation
225 Main Street
Newington, CT 06111
Tel: (860)594-0397
Fax: (860)594-0259
E-mail: foundation@arrl.org
Web Site: http://www.arrl.org/arrlf/scholgen.html

To provide financial assistance to licensed radio amateurs who are interested in working on an undergraduate degree.

Title of Award: William R. Goldfarb Memorial Scholarship **Area, Field, or Subject:** Business administration; Computer and information sciences; Engineering; General studies/Field of study not specified; Medicine; Nursing; Science **Level of Education for which Award is Granted:** Undergraduate **Number Awarded:** 1 each year. **Funds Available:** The stipend is at least $10,000. **Duration:** 1 year.

Eligibility Requirements: This program is open to licensed radio amateurs of any class who have applied or been accepted for enrollment at an accredited institution of higher education. Preference is given to students planning to major in computers, medicine, nursing, engineering, science, or a business-related field. Applicants must submit an essay on the role amateur radio has played in their lives and provide documentation of financial need. **Deadline for Receipt:** January of each year.

4337 ■ AMERICAN RADIO RELAY LEAGUE

Attn: ARRL Foundation
225 Main Street
Newington, CT 06111
Tel: (860)594-0397
Fax: (860)594-0259
E-mail: foundation@arrl.org
Web Site: http://www.arrl.org/arrlf/scholgen.html

To provide financial assistance to licensed radio amateurs from designated eastern states who are interested in working on an undergraduate or graduate degree in electrical or electronic engineering.

Title of Award: Perry F. Hadlock Memorial Scholarship **Area, Field, or Subject:** Engineering; Engineering, Electrical; Technology **Level of**

Education for which Award is Granted: Graduate, Undergraduate **Number Awarded:** 1 each year. **Funds Available:** The stipend is $2,000. **Duration:** 1 year.

Eligibility Requirements: This program is open to undergraduate or graduate students who are residents of the sponsor's Atlantic and Hudson divisions (Delaware, the District of Columbia, Maryland, New Jersey, New York, and Pennsylvania) and licensed radio amateurs of technician class. Applicants must be studying a technology-related field, preferably electrical or electronic engineering, at an accredited institution. They must submit an essay on the role amateur radio has played in their lives and provide documentation of financial need. Preference is given to students attending Clarkson University in Potsdam, New York. If no Clarkson student applies, the program is open to students at other universities in the Atlantic and Hudson division. **Deadline for Receipt:** January of each year.

4338 ■ AMERICAN RADIO RELAY LEAGUE

Attn: ARRL Foundation
225 Main Street
Newington, CT 06111
Tel: (860)594-0397
Fax: (860)594-0259
E-mail: foundation@arrl.org
Web Site: http://www.arrl.org/arrlf/scholgen.html

To provide financial assistance to licensed radio amateurs, particularly from designated midwestern states, who are interested in working on an undergraduate degree, particularly in journalism or the sciences.

Title of Award: PHD ARA Scholarship **Area, Field, or Subject:** Computer and information sciences; Engineering; General studies/Field of study not specified; Journalism **Level of Education for which Award is Granted:** Undergraduate **Number Awarded:** 1 each year. **Funds Available:** The stipend is $1,000. **Duration:** 1 year.

Eligibility Requirements: This program is open to licensed radio amateurs of any class who are pursuing postsecondary education. Preference is given to 1) residents of Iowa, Kansas, Missouri, and Nebraska; 2) students majoring in journalism, computer science, or electronic engineering; and 3) children of deceased radio amateurs. Applicants must submit an essay on the role amateur radio has played in their lives and provide documentation of financial need. **Deadline for Receipt:** January of each year.

4339 ■ AMERICAN RADIO RELAY LEAGUE

Attn: ARRL Foundation
225 Main Street
Newington, CT 06111
Tel: (860)594-0397
Fax: (860)594-0259
E-mail: foundation@arrl.org
Web Site: http://www.arrl.org/arrlf/scholgen.html

To provide financial assistance to licensed radio amateurs who are interested in working on an undergraduate degree in science or engineering.

Title of Award: Yasme Foundation Scholarships **Area, Field, or Subject:** Engineering; General studies/Field of study not specified **Level of Education for which Award is Granted:** Four Year College **Number Awarded:** 5 each year. **Funds Available:** The stipend is $2,000 per year. **Duration:** 1 year; the program includes 2 awards that may be renewed for up to 3 additional years or until successful completion of undergraduate study.

Eligibility Requirements: This program is open to undergraduate students who are licensed radio amateurs of any active class. Applicants must be enrolled or planning to enroll at an accredited 4-year college or university. They must submit an essay on the role amateur radio has played in their lives and provide documentation of financial need. Preference is given to 1) students majoring in science or engineering; 2) high school seniors ranked in the 5% to 10% of their class; 3) college students ranked in the top 10% of their class; and 4) students who have participated in a local amateur radio club and community service activities. **Deadline for Receipt:** January of each year.

4340 ■ AMERICAN SOCIETY OF CIVIL ENGINEERS-MAINE SECTION

c/o Leslie L. Corrow, Scholarship Chair
Kleinschmidt Associates
75 Main Street

P.O. Box 576
Pittsfield, ME 04967
Tel: (207)487-3328
To provide financial assistance to high school seniors in Maine who are interested in studying civil engineering in college.
Title of Award: ASCE Maine Section Scholarship **Area, Field, or Subject:** Engineering, Civil **Level of Education for which Award is Granted:** Undergraduate **Number Awarded:** 1 each year. **Funds Available:** The stipend is $2,000. **Duration:** 1 year; nonrenewable.
Eligibility Requirements: This program is open to graduating high school seniors who are Maine residents and who intend to study civil engineering in college. Women and minorities are especially encouraged to apply. Applicants must submit a 200-word statement describing why they have chosen civil engineering as a career and what they hope to accomplish by being a civil engineer. Selection is based on the statement, academic performance, extracurricular activities, and letters of recommendation. **Deadline for Receipt:** January of each year.

4341 ■ AMERICAN SOCIETY FOR ENGINEERING EDUCATION

Attn: SMART Defense Scholarship Program
1818 N Street, N.W., Suite 600
Washington, DC 20036-2479
Tel: (202)331-3516
Fax: (202)265-8504
E-mail: smart@asee.org
Web Site: http://www.asee.org/resources/fellowships/smart/index.cfm
To provide scholarship/loans to upper-division and graduate students in areas of science, mathematics, and engineering that are of interest to the U.S. Department of Defense.
Title of Award: Science, Mathematics, and Research for Transformation (SMART) Defense Scholarship Program **Area, Field, or Subject:** Architecture, Naval; Behavioral sciences; Biological and clinical sciences; Chemistry; Computer and information sciences; Earth sciences; Engineering, Aerospace/Aeronautical/Astronautical; Engineering, Chemical; Engineering, Civil; Engineering, Electrical; Engineering, Materials; Engineering, Mechanical; Engineering, Ocean; Geosciences; Materials research/science; Mathematics and mathematical sciences; Oceanography; Physics **Level of Education for which Award is Granted:** Four Year College, Graduate **Number Awarded:** Varies each year; recently, 36 of these scholarships were awarded. **Funds Available:** The program provides full payment of tuition, fees, room, board, and other normal educational expenses at the recipient's institution. A book allowance of $1,000 per year is also provided. This is a scholarship/loan program; recipients must agree to serve as a civilian employee of the Department of Defense in a science and engineering position. If they fail to fulfill that service obligation, they must reimburse the federal government for all funds they received. **Duration:** Up to 24 months.
Eligibility Requirements: This program is open to upper-division and graduate students working on an undergraduate or graduate degree in any of the following fields: aeronautical and astronautical engineering; biosciences; chemical engineering; chemistry; civil engineering; cognitive, neural, and behavioral sciences; computer and computational sciences; electrical engineering; geosciences, including terrain, water, and air; materials science and engineering; mathematics; mechanical engineering; naval architecture and ocean engineering; oceanography; or physics. Applicants must be U.S. citizens who have a GPA of 3.0 or higher. Selection is based on academic records, personal statements, letters of recommendation, and GRE scores. **Deadline for Receipt:** March of each year.
Additional Information: This program, established in 2005, is sponsored by the Army Research Laboratory, the Air Force Office of Scientific Research, the Office of Naval Research, the Air Force Research Laboratory, the Defense Advanced Research Projects Agency, the Defense Information Systems Agency, and the Defense Threat Reduction Agency.

4342 ■ AMERICAN SOCIETY OF ENGINEERS OF INDIAN ORIGIN

c/o Ramu Ramamurthy, Scholarship Committee Chair
47790 Pavillon Road
Canton, MI 48188
Tel: (248)226-6895
Fax: (248)226-7166
E-mail: awards@aseimichigan.org
Web Site: http://www.aseio.org

To provide financial assistance to undergraduate students of Indian origin (from India) who are majoring in architecture, engineering, or related areas.
Title of Award: ASEI Undergraduate Scholarships **Area, Field, or Subject:** Architecture; Computer and information sciences; Engineering **Level of Education for which Award is Granted:** Undergraduate **Number Awarded:** Several each year. **Funds Available:** The stipend is $1,000. **Duration:** 1 year.
Eligibility Requirements: This program is open to undergraduate students of Indian origin (by birth, ancestry, or relation). They must be enrolled full time at an accredited college or university in the United States and majoring in engineering, architecture, computer science, or allied science with a GPA of 3.2 or higher. Selection is based on demonstrated ability, academic achievement (including GPA, honors, and awards), career objectives, faculty recommendations, involvement in science fair and campus activities, and industrial exposure (including part-time work and internships). **Deadline for Receipt:** June of each year.

4343 ■ AMERICAN SOCIETY OF HEATING, REFRIGERATING AND AIR-CONDITIONING ENGINEERS, INC.

Attn: Scholarship Administrator
1791 Tullie Circle, N.E.
Atlanta, GA 30329-2305
Tel: (404)636-8400
Fax: (404)321-5478
E-mail: benedict@ashrae.org
Web Site: http://www.ashrae.org
To provide financial assistance to engineering technology students interested in heating, ventilating, air conditioning, and refrigeration (HVAC&R).
Title of Award: Associate Degree Engineering Technology Scholarship **Area, Field, or Subject:** Engineering; Heating, air conditioning, and refrigeration **Level of Education for which Award is Granted:** Vocational/Occupational **Number Awarded:** 2 each year. **Funds Available:** The stipend is $3,000 per year. **Duration:** 1 year.
Eligibility Requirements: This program is open to engineering technology students enrolled full time in a program leading to an associate degree. Applicants must be engaged in a course of study that traditionally has been preparatory for the profession of HVAC&R. They must have a GPA of 3.0 or higher and at least 1 full year of study remaining. Selection is based on potential service to the HVAC&R profession, financial need, leadership ability, recommendations from instructors, and character. **Deadline for Receipt:** April of each year.

4344 ■ AMERICAN SOCIETY OF HEATING, REFRIGERATING AND AIR-CONDITIONING ENGINEERS, INC.

Attn: Scholarship Administrator
1791 Tullie Circle, N.E.
Atlanta, GA 30329-2305
Tel: (404)636-8400
Fax: (404)321-5478
E-mail: benedict@ashrae.org
Web Site: http://www.ashrae.org
To provide financial assistance to engineering technology students interested in heating, ventilating, air conditioning, and refrigeration (HVAC&R).
Title of Award: Bachelor Degree Engineering Technology Scholarship **Area, Field, or Subject:** Engineering; Heating, air conditioning, and refrigeration **Level of Education for which Award is Granted:** Four Year College **Number Awarded:** 1 each year. **Funds Available:** The stipend is $3,000 per year. **Duration:** 1 year.
Eligibility Requirements: This program is open to engineering technology students enrolled full time in an ABET-accredited program leading to a bachelor's degree. Applicants must be engaged in a course of study that traditionally has been preparatory for the profession of HVAC&R. They must have a GPA of 3.0 or higher and at least 1 full year of study remaining. Selection is based on potential service to the HVAC&R profession, financial need, leadership ability, recommendations from instructors, and character. **Deadline for Receipt:** April of each year.

4345 ■ AMERICAN SOCIETY FOR NONDESTRUCTIVE TESTING, INC.

Attn: Executive Assistant
1711 Arlingate Lane

P.O. Box 28518
Columbus, OH 43228-0518
Tel: (614)274-6003
Free: 800-222-2768
Fax: (614)274-6899
E-mail: sthomas@asnt.org
Web Site: http://www.asnt.org

To provide financial assistance to undergraduate engineering students who are interested in nondestructive testing and evaluation.

Title of Award: ASNT Engineering Undergraduate Awards **Area, Field, or Subject:** Engineering; Materials research/science **Level of Education for which Award is Granted:** Undergraduate **Number Awarded:** Up to 3 each year. **Funds Available:** The stipend is $3,000. **Duration:** 1 year. **Eligibility Requirements:** This program is open to undergraduate students enrolled in an engineering program at an ABET-accredited university who show an active interest in the field of nondestructive testing and evaluation. Students must be nominated. Nominations must include the official transcript of the student, 3 letters of recommendation from faculty members, and an essay by the student describing the role nondestructive testing and evaluation will play in their career. **Deadline for Receipt:** December of each year.

4346 ■ AMERICAN SOCIETY OF PLUMBING ENGINEERS

Attn: Scholarship Selection Committee
8614 West Catalpa Avenue, Suite 1007
Chicago, IL 60656-1116
Tel: (773)693-ASPE
Fax: (773)695-9007
E-mail: info@aspc.org
Web Site: http://www.aspe.org

To provide financial assistance for the study of engineering to members of the American Society of Plumbing Engineers (ASPE) and their families.

Title of Award: Alfred Steele Engineering Scholarship **Area, Field, or Subject:** Engineering **Level of Education for which Award is Granted:** Undergraduate **Number Awarded:** Up to 5 each year. **Funds Available:** The stipend is $1,000 per year. Funds are paid directly to the recipient's tuition account at a college, university, or technical school. **Duration:** 1 year. **Eligibility Requirements:** This program is open to members of the society, their spouses, and children. Applicants who are already in college must be full-time students in a school or program of engineering and have a GPA of 3.0 or higher. Seniors in high school who will graduate in June of the application year are also eligible if they have a GPA of 3.0 or higher and have been accepted into a college, university, or technical school where they plan to enroll in a school or program of engineering as a full-time student. Selection is based on GPA (1 to 5 points), letters of recommendation (10 to 15 points), personal activities and community involvement (10 to 15 points), a statement of personal achievement (15 to 30 points), and an essay on interest in engineering that demonstrates the imaginative and creative nature of the applicant (20 to 35 points). **Deadline for Receipt:** August of each year.

4347 ■ AMERICAN SOCIETY FOR QUALITY

Attn: Biomedical Division
600 North Plankinton Avenue
P.O. Box 3005
Milwaukee, WI 53201-3005
Tel: (414)272-8575
Free: 800-248-1946
Fax: (414)272-1734
E-mail: cs@asqu.org
Web Site: http://www.asq.org/biomed/scholarship/index.html

To provide financial assistance to undergraduate and graduate students working on a degree in a field related to quality in the biomedical community.

Title of Award: William J. Feingold Scholarship **Area, Field, or Subject:** Biomedical sciences; Engineering, Biomedical **Level of Education for which Award is Granted:** Four Year College, Graduate **Number Awarded:** 1 or more each year. **Funds Available:** The stipend is $5,000 per year. **Duration:** 1 year; may be renewed 1 additional year. **Eligibility Requirements:** This program is open to students who have completed at least 2 years of study in a program that involves the use of quality principles, concepts, and technologies in the biomedical com-

munity. Applicants must have a GPA of 3.0 or higher. Along with their application, they must submit essays on 1) their career objectives and how they relate to quality issues within the biomedical community; and 2) why quality systems are important in the biomedical community. Graduate students are eligible, but preference is given to undergraduates. Priority is given to students who 1) are enrolled in a technical or scientific course of study; 2) have a demonstrated contribution or participation in activities related to quality in the biomedical community; and 3) have a higher GPA or more compelling essay. **Deadline for Receipt:** April of each year. **Additional Information:** This program was approved in 2004. Information is also available from Hal Greenberg, 6 Coe Road, Framingham, MA 01701.

4348 ■ AMERICAN SOCIETY FOR QUALITY

Attn: Measurement Quality Division
600 North Plankinton Avenue
P.O. Box 3005
Milwaukee, WI 53201-3005
Tel: (414)272-8575
Free: 800-248-1946
Fax: (414)272-1734
E-mail: cs@asqu.org
Web Site: http://www.asq.org/measure/scholarship/index.html

To provide financial assistance to undergraduate and graduate students working on a degree in a field related to metrology and quality.

Title of Award: Joe D. Simmons Memorial Scholarship **Area, Field, or Subject:** Engineering; Testing, educational/psychological **Level of Education for which Award is Granted:** Graduate, Undergraduate **Number Awarded:** 1 or more each year. **Funds Available:** The stipend is $1,500 per year. **Duration:** 1 year. **Eligibility Requirements:** This program is open to undergraduate and graduate students who are working on a degree in a field of study related to measurement science and quality. Applicants must submit a 1,000-word essay describing the metrology and quality concepts they have learned and applied in academic or work settings and their career aspirations. Financial need is also considered in the selection process. **Deadline for Receipt:** April of each year. **Additional Information:** Information is also available from the Joe D. Simmons Memorial Scholarship, 7413 Mill Run Drive, Derwood, MD 20855-1156. E-mail: simmons_scholar@comcast.net.

4349 ■ AMERICAN SOCIETY OF SAFETY ENGINEERS

Attn: ASSE Foundation
1800 East Oakton Street
Des Plaines, IL 60018
Tel: (847)768-3441
Fax: (847)296-9220
E-mail: mrosario@asse.org
Web Site: http://www.asse.org

To provide financial assistance to undergraduate student members of the American Society of Safety Engineers (ASSE).

Title of Award: America Responds Memorial Scholarship **Area, Field, or Subject:** Engineering; Environmental conservation; Environmental science; Fires and fire prevention; Industrial hygiene; Occupational safety and health; Protective services **Level of Education for which Award is Granted:** Four Year College **Number Awarded:** 1 each year. **Funds Available:** The stipend is $1,000 per year. **Duration:** 1 year; nonrenewable. **Eligibility Requirements:** This program is open to ASSE student members who are majoring in occupational safety and health or a closely-related field (e.g., safety engineering, safety management, systems safety, environmental science, industrial hygiene, ergonomics, fire science). Applicants must be full-time students who have completed at least 60 semester hours with a GPA of 3.0 or higher. As part of the selection process, they must submit 2 essays of 300 words or less: 1) why they are seeking a degree in safety, a brief description of their current activities, and how those relate to their career goals and objectives; and 2) why they should be awarded this scholarship (including career goals and financial need). **Deadline for Receipt:** November of each year.

4350 ■ AMERICAN SOCIETY OF SAFETY ENGINEERS

Attn: ASSE Foundation
1800 East Oakton Street
Des Plaines, IL 60018

Tel: (847)768-3441
Fax: (847)296-9220
E-mail: mrosario@asse.org
Web Site: http://www.asse.org

To provide financial assistance to undergraduate student members of the American Society of Safety Engineers (ASSE), particularly those interested in construction safety.

Title of Award: Bechtel Foundation Scholarship for Safety and Health **Area, Field, or Subject:** Construction; Engineering; Environmental conservation; Environmental science; Fires and fire prevention; Industrial hygiene; Occupational safety and health; Protective services **Level of Education for which Award is Granted:** Four Year College **Number Awarded:** 1 each year. **Funds Available:** The stipend is $3,000 per year. **Duration:** 1 year; nonrenewable.

Eligibility Requirements: This program is open to ASSE student members who are majoring in occupational safety and health or a closely-related field (e.g., safety engineering, safety management, systems safety, environmental science, industrial hygiene, ergonomics, fire science) with an emphasis on construction safety. Applicants must be full-time students who have completed at least 60 semester hours with a GPA of 3.0 or higher. As part of the selection process, they must submit 2 essays of 300 words or less: 1) why they are seeking a degree in safety, a brief description of their current activities, and how those relate to their career goals and objectives; and 2) why they should be awarded this scholarship (including career goals and financial need). **Deadline for Receipt:** November of each year. **Additional Information:** Funding for this program is provided by Bechtel Foundation.

4351 ■ AMERICAN SOCIETY OF SAFETY ENGINEERS

Attn: ASSE Foundation
1800 East Oakton Street
Des Plaines, IL 60018
Tel: (847)768-3441
Fax: (847)296-9220
E-mail: mrosario@asse.org
Web Site: http://www.asse.org

To provide financial assistance to undergraduate and graduate student members of the American Society of Safety Engineers (ASSE) from designated western states.

Title of Award: Scott Dominguez-Craters of the Moon Chapter Scholarship **Area, Field, or Subject:** Engineering; Environmental conservation; Environmental science; Fires and fire prevention; Industrial hygiene; Occupational safety and health; Protective services **Level of Education for which Award is Granted:** Four Year College, Graduate **Number Awarded:** 1 each year. **Funds Available:** The stipend is $1,000 per year. **Duration:** 1 year; nonrenewable.

Eligibility Requirements: This program is open to ASSE student members who are majoring in occupational safety and health or a closely-related field (e.g., safety engineering, safety management, systems safety, environmental science, industrial hygiene, ergonomics, fire science). First priority is given to residents within the service area of Craters of the Moon Chapter in Idaho; second priority is given to residents of ASSE Region II (Arizona, Colorado, Idaho, Montana, Nevada, New Mexico, Utah, and Wyoming). Special consideration is also given to 1) employees of a sponsoring organization or their dependents; 2) students who are serving their country through active duty in the armed forces or are honorably discharged; 3) former members of the Boy Scouts, Girl Scouts, FFA, or 4-H; 4) recipients of awards from service organizations; and 5) students who have provided volunteer service to an ASSE chapter in a leadership role. Undergraduates must have completed at least 60 semester hours with a GPA of 3.0 or higher. Graduate students must have completed at least 9 semester hours with a GPA of 3.5 or higher and have had a GPA of 3.0 or higher as an undergraduate. As part of the selection process, all applicants must submit 2 essays of 300 words or less: 1) why they are seeking a degree in safety, a brief description of their current activities, and how those relate to their career goals and objectives; and 2) why they should be awarded this scholarship (including career goals and financial need). **Deadline for Receipt:** November of each year.

4352 ■ AMERICAN SOCIETY OF SAFETY ENGINEERS

Attn: ASSE Foundation
1800 East Oakton Street
Des Plaines, IL 60018

Tel: (847)768-3441
Fax: (847)296-9220
E-mail: mrosario@asse.org
Web Site: http://www.asse.org

To provide financial assistance to undergraduate and graduate student members of the American Society of Safety Engineers (ASSE) from designated western states.

Title of Award: Gold Country Section and Region II Scholarship **Area, Field, or Subject:** Engineering; Environmental conservation; Environmental science; Fires and fire prevention; Industrial hygiene; Occupational safety and health; Protective services **Level of Education for which Award is Granted:** Four Year College, Graduate **Number Awarded:** 1 each year. **Funds Available:** The stipend is $1,000 per year. **Duration:** 1 year; nonrenewable.

Eligibility Requirements: This program is open to ASSE student members who are majoring in occupational safety and health or a closely-related field (e.g., safety engineering, safety management, systems safety, environmental science, industrial hygiene, ergonomics, fire science). Priority is given to residents of ASSE Region II (Arizona, Colorado, Idaho, Montana, Nevada, New Mexico, Utah, and Wyoming). Undergraduates must be full-time students who have completed at least 60 semester hours with a GPA of 3.0 or higher. Graduate students must also be enrolled full time, have completed at least 9 semester hours with a GPA of 3.5 or higher, and have had a GPA of 3.0 or higher as an undergraduate. As part of the selection process, all applicants must submit 2 essays of 300 words or less: 1) why they are seeking a degree in safety, a brief description of their current activities, and how those relate to their career goals and objectives; and 2) why they should be awarded this scholarship (including career goals and financial need). **Deadline for Receipt:** November of each year.

4353 ■ AMERICAN SOCIETY OF SAFETY ENGINEERS

Attn: ASSE Foundation
1800 East Oakton Street
Des Plaines, IL 60018
Tel: (847)768-3441
Fax: (847)296-9220
E-mail: mrosario@asse.org
Web Site: http://www.asse.org

To provide financial assistance to undergraduate student members of the American Society of Safety Engineers (ASSE) from designated southeastern states.

Title of Award: Region IV/Edwin P. Granberry, Jr. Scholarship **Area, Field, or Subject:** Engineering; Environmental conservation; Environmental science; Fires and fire prevention; Industrial hygiene; Occupational safety and health; Protective services **Level of Education for which Award is Granted:** Four Year College **Number Awarded:** 1 each year. **Funds Available:** The stipend is $1,000 per year. **Duration:** 1 year; nonrenewable.

Eligibility Requirements: This program is open to ASSE student members who are majoring in occupational safety and health or a closely-related field (e.g., safety engineering, safety management, systems safety, environmental science, industrial hygiene, ergonomics, fire science). Applicants must be residents of ASSE Region IV (Louisiana, Alabama, Mississippi, Georgia, Florida, Puerto Rico, and the U.S. Virgin Islands), although they may be attending school elsewhere. They must be full-time students who have completed at least 60 semester hours with a GPA of 3.0 or higher. As part of the selection process, they must submit 2 essays of 300 words or less: 1) why they are seeking a degree in safety, a brief description of their current activities, and how those relate to their career goals and objectives; and 2) why they should be awarded this scholarship (including career goals and financial need). **Deadline for Receipt:** November of each year.

4354 ■ AMERICAN SOCIETY OF SAFETY ENGINEERS

Attn: ASSE Foundation
1800 East Oakton Street
Des Plaines, IL 60018
Tel: (847)768-3441
Fax: (847)296-9220
E-mail: mrosario@asse.org
Web Site: http://www.asse.org

To provide financial assistance to upper-division and graduate students at colleges and universities in New England who are members or family of members of the American Society of Safety Engineers (ASSE).

Title of Award: Greater Boston Chapter Leadership Award **Area, Field, or Subject:** Engineering; Environmental conservation; Environmental science; Fires and fire prevention; Industrial hygiene; Occupational safety and health; Protective services **Level of Education for which Award is Granted:** Four Year College, Graduate **Number Awarded:** 1 each year. **Funds Available:** The stipend is $1,000 per year. **Duration:** 1 year; may be renewed.

Eligibility Requirements: This program is open to undergraduate and graduate students who are working on a degree in occupational safety and health or a closely-related field (e.g., safety engineering, safety management, systems safety, environmental science, industrial hygiene, ergonomics, fire science). Applicants must be 1) a member of an ASSE chapter in New England; 2) the spouse or child of an ASSE chapter member in New England; or 3) a member of an ASSE student section in New England. Undergraduates must be full-time students who have completed at least 60 semester hours with a GPA of 3.0 or higher. Graduate students must also be enrolled full time, have completed at least 9 semester hours with a GPA of 3.5 or higher, and have had a GPA of 3.0 or higher as an undergraduate. As part of the selection process, all applicants must submit 2 essays of 300 words or less: 1) why they are seeking a degree in safety, a brief description of their current activities, and how those relate to their career goals and objectives; and 2) why they should be awarded this scholarship (including career goals and financial need). **Deadline for Receipt:** November of each year.

4355 ■ AMERICAN SOCIETY OF SAFETY ENGINEERS

Attn: ASSE Foundation
1800 East Oakton Street
Des Plaines, IL 60018
Tel: (847)768-3441
Fax: (847)296-9220
E-mail: mrosario@asse.org
Web Site: http://www.asse.org

To provide financial assistance to undergraduate students majoring in fields related to occupational safety and health.

Title of Award: Gulf Coast Past Presidents Scholarship **Area, Field, or Subject:** Engineering; Environmental conservation; Environmental science; Fires and fire prevention; Industrial hygiene; Occupational safety and health; Protective services **Level of Education for which Award is Granted:** Four Year College **Number Awarded:** 1 each year. **Funds Available:** The stipend is $1,000 per year. **Duration:** 1 year; nonrenewable.

Eligibility Requirements: This program is open to undergraduate students who are majoring in occupational safety and health or a closely-related field (e.g., safety engineering, safety management, systems safety, environmental science, industrial hygiene, ergonomics, fire science). Although the program is sponsored by the Gulf Coast (Texas) chapter of the American Society of Safety Engineers (ASSE), there are no geographical restrictions on eligibility. Applicants must be full- or part-time students who have completed at least 60 semester hours with a GPA of 3.0 or higher. Part-time students must be ASSE members. As part of the selection process, all applicants must submit 2 essays of 300 words or less: 1) why they are seeking a degree in safety, a brief description of their current activities, and how those relate to their career goals and objectives; and 2) why they should be awarded this scholarship (including career goals and financial need). **Deadline for Receipt:** November of each year.

4356 ■ AMERICAN SOCIETY OF SAFETY ENGINEERS

Attn: ASSE Foundation
1800 East Oakton Street
Des Plaines, IL 60018
Tel: (847)768-3441
Fax: (847)296-9220
E-mail: mrosario@asse.org
Web Site: http://www.asse.org

To provide financial assistance to upper-division student members of the American Society of Safety Engineers (ASSE).

Title of Award: Liberty Mutual Scholarship **Area, Field, or Subject:** Engineering; Environmental conservation; Environmental science; Fires

and fire prevention; Industrial hygiene; Occupational safety and health; Protective services **Level of Education for which Award is Granted:** Four Year College **Number Awarded:** 1 each year. **Funds Available:** The stipend is $3,000 per year. **Duration:** 1 year; nonrenewable.

Eligibility Requirements: This program is open to ASSE student members who are majoring in occupational safety and health or a closely-related field (e.g., safety engineering, safety management, systems safety, environmental science, industrial hygiene, ergonomics, fire science). Applicants must be full-time students who have completed at least 60 semester hours with a GPA of 3.0 or higher. As part of the selection process, they must submit 2 essays of 300 words or less: 1) why they are seeking a degree in safety, a brief description of their current activities, and how those relate to their career goals and objectives; and 2) why they should be awarded this scholarship (including career goals and financial need). **Deadline for Receipt:** November of each year. **Additional Information:** This program is supported by Liberty Mutual.

4357 ■ AMERICAN SOCIETY OF SAFETY ENGINEERS

Attn: ASSE Foundation
1800 East Oakton Street
Des Plaines, IL 60018
Tel: (847)768-3441
Fax: (847)296-9220
E-mail: mrosario@asse.org
Web Site: http://www.asse.org

To provide financial assistance to upper-division student members of the American Society of Safety Engineers (ASSE).

Title of Award: Marsh Risk Consulting Scholarship **Area, Field, or Subject:** Engineering; Environmental conservation; Environmental science; Fires and fire prevention; Industrial hygiene; Occupational safety and health; Protective services **Level of Education for which Award is Granted:** Four Year College **Number Awarded:** 1 each year. **Funds Available:** The stipend is $5,000 per year. **Duration:** 1 year; nonrenewable.

Eligibility Requirements: This program is open to ASSE student members who are majoring in occupational safety and health or a closely-related field (e.g., safety engineering, safety management, systems safety, environmental science, industrial hygiene, ergonomics, fire science). Applicants must be full-time students who have completed at least 60 semester hours with a GPA of 3.0 or higher. As part of the selection process, they must submit 2 essays of 300 words or less: 1) why they are seeking a degree in safety, a brief description of their current activities, and how those relate to their career goals and objectives; and 2) why they should be awarded this scholarship (including career goals and financial need). **Deadline for Receipt:** November of each year. **Additional Information:** Funding for this program is provided by Marsh Risk Consulting.

4358 ■ AMERICAN SOCIETY OF SAFETY ENGINEERS

Attn: ASSE Foundation
1800 East Oakton Street
Des Plaines, IL 60018
Tel: (847)768-3441
Fax: (847)296-9220
E-mail: mrosario@asse.org
Web Site: http://www.asse.org

To provide financial assistance to undergraduate student members of the American Society of Safety Engineers (ASSE).

Title of Award: Marcella Thompson Distinguished Service Award Scholarship **Area, Field, or Subject:** Engineering; Environmental conservation; Environmental science; Fires and fire prevention; Industrial hygiene; Occupational safety and health; Protective services **Level of Education for which Award is Granted:** Four Year College **Number Awarded:** 1 each year. **Funds Available:** The stipend is $2,000 per year. **Duration:** 1 year; nonrenewable.

Eligibility Requirements: This program is open to ASSE student members who are majoring in occupational safety and health or a closely-related field (e.g., safety engineering, safety management, systems safety, environmental science, industrial hygiene, ergonomics, fire science). Applicants must be full-time students who have completed at least 60 semester hours with a GPA of 3.0 or higher. As part of the selection process, they must submit 2 essays of 300 words or less: 1) why they are seeking a degree in safety, a brief description of their current activities, and how those relate to their career goals and objectives; and 2) why they should be awarded this scholarship (including career goals and financial need). **Deadline for Receipt:** November of each year.

4359 ■ AMERICAN SOCIETY OF SAFETY ENGINEERS
Attn: ASSE Foundation
1800 East Oakton Street
Des Plaines, IL 60018
Tel: (847)768-3441
Fax: (847)296-9220
E-mail: mrosario@asse.org
Web Site: http://www.asse.org
To provide financial assistance to minority undergraduate student members of the American Society of Safety Engineers (ASSE).
Title of Award: UPS Diversity Scholarships **Area, Field, or Subject:** Engineering; Environmental conservation; Environmental science; Fires and fire prevention; Industrial hygiene; Occupational safety and health; Protective services **Level of Education for which Award is Granted:** Four Year College **Number Awarded:** Varies each year; recently, 2 of these scholarships at $5,250 each were awarded. **Funds Available:** Stipends range from $4,000 to $6,000 per year. **Duration:** 1 year; nonrenewable.
Eligibility Requirements: This program is open to ASSE student members who are enrolled in a 4-year degree program in occupational safety and health or a closely-related field (e.g., safety engineering, safety management, systems safety, environmental science, industrial hygiene, ergonomics, fire science). Applicants must be U.S. citizens and members of a minority ethnic or racial group. They must be full-time students who have completed at least 60 semester hours with a GPA of 3.0 or higher. As part of the selection process, they must submit 2 essays of 300 words or less: 1) why they are seeking a degree in safety, a brief description of their current activities, and how those relate to their career goals and objectives; and 2) why they should be awarded this scholarship (including career goals and financial need). **Deadline for Receipt:** November of each year. **Additional Information:** Funding for this program is provided by the UPS Foundation.

4360 ■ AMERICAN SOCIETY OF SAFETY ENGINEERS
Attn: ASSE Foundation
1800 East Oakton Street
Des Plaines, IL 60018
Tel: (847)768-3441
Fax: (847)296-9220
E-mail: mrosario@asse.org
Web Site: http://www.asse.org
To provide financial assistance to undergraduate student members of the American Society of Safety Engineers (ASSE).
Title of Award: UPS Scholarships **Area, Field, or Subject:** Engineering; Environmental conservation; Environmental science; Fires and fire prevention; Industrial hygiene; Occupational safety and health; Protective services **Level of Education for which Award is Granted:** Four Year College **Number Awarded:** Varies each year; recently, 4 of these scholarships at $5,250 each were awarded. **Funds Available:** Stipends range from $4,000 to $6,000 per year. **Duration:** 1 year; nonrenewable.
Eligibility Requirements: This program is open to ASSE student members who are enrolled in a 4-year degree program in occupational safety and health or a closely-related field (e.g., safety engineering, safety management, systems safety, environmental science, industrial hygiene, ergonomics, fire science). Applicants must be full-time students who have completed at least 60 semester hours with a GPA of 3.0 or higher. As part of the selection process, they must submit 2 essays of 300 words or less: 1) why they are seeking a degree in safety, a brief description of their current activities, and how those relate to their career goals and objectives; and 2) why they should be awarded this scholarship (including career goals and financial need). **Deadline for Receipt:** November of each year. **Additional Information:** Funding for this program is provided by the UPS Foundation.

4361 ■ APPALACHIAN COLLEGE ASSOCIATION
Attn: Director of Programs
210 Center Street
Berea, KY 40403
Tel: (859)986-4584

Fax: (859)986-9549
E-mail: kathrynb@acaweb.org
Web Site: http://www.acaweb.org
To provide financial assistance to students majoring in computer science, engineering, and mathematics (CSEM) at colleges and universities that are members of the Appalachian College Association (ACA).
Title of Award: Appalachian College Association Scholarships for Majoring in Computer Science, Engineering, Mathematics **Area, Field, or Subject:** Computer and information sciences; Engineering; Mathematics and mathematical sciences **Level of Education for which Award is Granted:** Four Year College **Number Awarded:** 30 each year. **Funds Available:** The stipend is $2,750 per year. **Duration:** 1 year; may be renewed 1 additional year.
Eligibility Requirements: This program is open to full-time students entering their junior or senior year at ACA member institutions. Applicants must be majoring in a CSEM discipline, have a GPA of 3.0 or higher, and be able to document financial need. Along with their application, they must submit a 500-word essay describing their career ambitions, their commitment to the Appalachian region, and the potential benefits to Appalachia of their degree choice. U.S. citizenship is required. Preference is given to graduates of high schools in the Appalachian region. **Deadline for Receipt:** March of each year. **Additional Information:** Funding for this program, which began in 2003, is provided by the National Science Foundation. The ACA includes member institutions in Kentucky (Alice Lloyd College, Berea College, Campbellsville University, University of the Cumberlands, Kentucky Christian University, Lindsey Wilson College, Pikeville College, and Union College), North Carolina (Brevard College, Lees-McRae College, Mars Hill College, Montreat College, and Warren Wilson College), Tennessee (Bryan College, Carson-Newman College, King College, Lee University, Lincoln Memorial University, Maryville College, Milligan College, Tennessee Wesleyan College, Tusculum College, and University of the South), Virginia (Bluefield College, Emery & Henry College, Ferrum College, and Virginia Intermont College), and West Virginia (Alderson-Broaddus College, Bethany College, Davis & Elkins College, Ohio Valley University, University of Charleston, West Virginia Wesleyan College, and Wheeling Jesuit University).

4362 ■ ARKANSAS DEPARTMENT OF WORKFORCE EDUCATION
Luther Hardin Building
Three Capitol Mall, Room 207
Little Rock, AR 72201-1083
Tel: (501)682-1500
Fax: (501)682-1509
Web Site: http://dwe.arkansas.gov/LoanForgiveness/atcslfp.htm
To provide forgivable loans to residents of Arkansas who are interested in pursuing technical education and working in the state.
Title of Award: Arkansas Technical Careers Student Loan Forgiveness Program **Area, Field, or Subject:** Biological and clinical sciences; Computer and information sciences; Engineering; Engineering, Biomedical; Engineering, Computer; Engineering, Electrical; Engineering, Industrial; Health care services; Physical sciences **Level of Education for which Award is Granted:** Undergraduate **Number Awarded:** Varies each year. **Funds Available:** The maximum loan is $2,500 per year. Loans are forgiven if the recipient works full time in the high demand technical field in Arkansas. Each year's loan may be forgiven with 1 year of full-time employment. Loan recipients who do not graduate from the program or work full time in the field in Arkansas must repay the loan in full. **Duration:** Up to 4 years.
Eligibility Requirements: This program is open to residents of Arkansas who are U.S. citizens or permanent residents admitted to an approved program resulting in a diploma, certificate, or degree in a high demand technical field. Applicants must indicate their intention to work in Arkansas in the field for which they receive the training. **Deadline for Receipt:** Applications must be submitted within 6 months of the completion of the program of study. **Additional Information:** The Arkansas General Assembly established this program in 1999. Recently, the designated career fields related to advanced manufacturing (including engineering and engineering technology, industrial electronics installers and repairers, machinist and machine technologies, and tool and die maker and technologist); computer and information technology (including computer engineering, computer and information sciences, electrical and electronic engineering and related technology, electromechanical instrumentation and maintenance technology, and computer installer and repairer); and

biomedical and biotechnology (including biological and life sciences, physical sciences, science technologies, health professions and related sciences, bioengineering and biomedical engineering, and biomedical engineering technology and technician).

4363 ■ ARMED FORCES COMMUNICATIONS AND ELECTRONICS ASSOCIATION

Attn: AFCEA Educational Foundation
4400 Fair Lakes Court
Fairfax, VA 22033-3899
Tel: (703)631-6149
Free: 800-336-4583
Fax: (703)631-4693
E-mail: scholarship@afcea.org
Web Site: http://www.afcea.org/education/scholarships/undergraduate/pub1.asp
To provide financial assistance to undergraduate students who are working full time on a degree by means of a distance-learning or on-line program.

Title of Award: AFCEA Distance-Learning/On-Line Scholarships **Area, Field, or Subject:** Computer and information sciences; Engineering, Chemical; Engineering, Computer; Engineering, Electrical; Mathematics and mathematical sciences; Physics; Systems engineering **Level of Education for which Award is Granted:** Four Year College **Number Awarded:** 1 each year. **Funds Available:** The stipend is $1,000. **Duration:** 1 year.

Eligibility Requirements: This program is open to U.S. citizens working full time on a bachelor's degree by means of a distance-learning or on-line program affiliated with a major, accredited 4-year college or university in the United States. Applicants must have completed at least 1 year of course work based on a 30-semester hour equivalent; classes in progress at the time of application cannot be used towards the 1-year minimum completion requirement. Completed courses must include at least 2 semesters of calculus (not pre-calculus). Majors are limited to the fields of engineering (chemical, computer, electrical, or systems), mathematics, physics, or computer science. Selection is based primarily on academic excellence. **Deadline for Receipt:** July of each year.

4364 ■ ARMED FORCES COMMUNICATIONS AND ELECTRONICS ASSOCIATION

Attn: AFCEA Educational Foundation
4400 Fair Lakes Court
Fairfax, VA 22033-3899
Tel: (703)631-6149
Free: 800-336-4583
Fax: (703)631-4693
E-mail: scholarship@afcea.org
Web Site: http://www.afcea.org/education/scholarships/rotc/rotc1.asp
To provide financial assistance to ROTC cadets who are majoring in fields related to communications and electronics.

Title of Award: AFCEA ROTC Scholarships **Area, Field, or Subject:** Computer and information sciences; Electronics; Engineering, Aerospace/Aeronautical/Astronautical; Engineering, Chemical; Engineering, Computer; Engineering, Electrical; Mathematics and mathematical sciences; Physics; Systems engineering **Level of Education for which Award is Granted:** Four Year College **Number Awarded:** 36 each year, divided equally among Army, Navy/Marine Corps, and Air Force ROTC programs; for each service, 6 are awarded to rising juniors, 6 to rising seniors. **Funds Available:** The stipend is $2,000. **Duration:** 1 year; may be renewed.

Eligibility Requirements: This program is open to ROTC cadets majoring in electronics, engineering (aerospace, chemical, computer, electrical, or systems); mathematics, physics, or computer science. Applicants must be nominated by their ROTC professor, be entering their junior or senior year, be U.S. citizens, be of good moral character, have demonstrated academic excellence, be motivated to complete a college education and serve as officers in the U.S. armed forces, and be able to demonstrate financial need. **Deadline for Receipt:** March of each year.

4365 ■ ARMED FORCES COMMUNICATIONS AND ELECTRONICS ASSOCIATION

Attn: AFCEA Educational Foundation
4400 Fair Lakes Court
Fairfax, VA 22033-3899

Tel: (703)631-6149
Free: 800-336-4583
Fax: (703)631-4693
E-mail: scholarship@afcea.org
Web Site: http://www.afcea.org/education/scholarships/workingstudents/ws1.asp
To provide financial assistance to undergraduate students who are working part time on a degree in engineering or the sciences while already employed.

Title of Award: AFCEA Scholarship for Working Professionals **Area, Field, or Subject:** Computer and information sciences; Engineering, Aerospace/Aeronautical/Astronautical; Engineering, Chemical; Engineering, Electrical; Mathematics and mathematical sciences; Physics; Systems engineering **Level of Education for which Award is Granted:** Undergraduate **Number Awarded:** 1 each year. **Funds Available:** The stipend is $1,500. **Duration:** 1 year; may be renewed.

Eligibility Requirements: This program is open to part-time students entering their sophomore, junior, or senior year at an accredited 2-year or 4-year college or university in the United States while already employed in a science or technology field. Applicants must be U.S. citizens working toward a degree in engineering (aerospace, chemical, electrical, or systems), mathematics, physics, or computer science with a GPA of 3.4 or higher. They must be able to demonstrate academic achievement, patriotism, and potential to contribute to the American work force. **Deadline for Receipt:** September of each year. **Additional Information:** This program was established in 2002.

4366 ■ ARMED FORCES COMMUNICATIONS AND ELECTRONICS ASSOCIATION

Attn: AFCEA Educational Foundation
4400 Fair Lakes Court
Fairfax, VA 22033-3899
Tel: (703)631-6149
Free: 800-336-4583
Fax: (703)631-4693
E-mail: scholarship@afcea.org
Web Site: http://www.afcea.org/education/scholarships/rotc/Boyes.asp
To provide financial assistance to Navy ROTC cadets who are majoring in electrical engineering.

Title of Award: Dr. Jon L. Boyes, Vice Admiral, USN (Ret.) Memorial Scholarship **Area, Field, or Subject:** Engineering, Electrical **Level of Education for which Award is Granted:** Four Year College **Number Awarded:** 1 each year. **Funds Available:** The stipend is $3,000. **Duration:** 1 year.

Eligibility Requirements: This program is open to Navy ROTC cadets enrolled full time at an accredited degree-granting 4-year college or university in the United States. Applicants must be sophomores or juniors at the time of application and have a GPA of 3.0 or higher with a major in electrical engineering. Their application must be endorsed by the professor of Naval Science at their institution. Selection is based on demonstrated dedication, superior performance, and potential to serve as an officer in the United States Navy. **Deadline for Receipt:** March of each year.

4367 ■ ARMED FORCES COMMUNICATIONS AND ELECTRONICS ASSOCIATION

Attn: AFCEA Educational Foundation
4400 Fair Lakes Court
Fairfax, VA 22033-3899
Tel: (703)631-6149
Free: 800-336-4583
Fax: (703)631-4693
E-mail: scholarship@afcea.org
Web Site: http://www.afcea.org/education/scholarships/undergraduate/graphicdes.asp
To provide financial assistance to students who are working on an undergraduate or graduate degree in computer graphic design.

Title of Award: Computer Graphic Design Scholarships **Area, Field, or Subject:** Computer and information sciences; Graphic art and design; Internet design and development **Level of Education for which Award is Granted:** Four Year College, Graduate **Number Awarded:** 1 or more each year. **Funds Available:** The stipend is $2,000. **Duration:** 1 year; may be renewed.

Eligibility Requirements: This program is open to full-time students who are enrolled at an accredited college or university in the United States at least as a sophomore. Applicants must be U.S. citizens working on an undergraduate or graduate degree in computer graphic design or a related field. They must submit a sample of digital graphic artwork for intranets and internets, especially web-based graphics. Along with the artwork, include a textual statement of 100 to 200 words that describes the image submitted, how it was created, and what specific intent or purpose it represents. Selection is based on artistic creativity, mastery of web technology, a statement of career goals, school and community activities, and financial need. **Deadline for Receipt:** October of each year.

4368 ■ ARMED FORCES COMMUNICATIONS AND ELECTRONICS ASSOCIATION

Attn: AFCEA Educational Foundation
4400 Fair Lakes Court
Fairfax, VA 22033-3899
Tel: (703)631-6149
Free: 800-336-4583
Fax: (703)631-4693
E-mail: scholarship@afcea.org
Web Site: http://www.afcea.org/education/scholarships/undergraduate/genemm.asp
To provide funding to veterans, military personnel, and their family members who are majoring in specified scientific fields in college.
Title of Award: General Emmett Paige Scholarships **Area, Field, or Subject:** Computer and information sciences; Engineering, Aerospace/Aeronautical/Astronautical; Engineering, Chemical; Engineering, Computer; Engineering, Electrical; Mathematics and mathematical sciences; Physics **Level of Education for which Award is Granted:** Four Year College **Number Awarded:** Varies each year; recently, 11 of these scholarships were awarded. **Funds Available:** The stipend is $2,000. **Duration:** 1 year; may be renewed.
Eligibility Requirements: This program is open to veterans, persons on active duty in the uniformed military services, and their spouses or dependents who are currently enrolled full time in an accredited 4-year college or university in the United States. Graduating high school seniors are not eligible, but veterans entering college as freshmen may apply. Spouses or dependents must be sophomores or juniors. Applicants must be U.S. citizens, be of good moral character, have demonstrated academic excellence, be motivated to complete a college education, and be working toward a degree in engineering (aerospace, chemical, computer, or electrical), mathematics, physics, or computer science with a GPA of 3.4 or higher. They must provide a copy of Discharge Form DD214, Certificate of Service, or facsimile of their current Department of Defense or Coast Guard Identification Card. **Deadline for Receipt:** February of each year.

4369 ■ ARMED FORCES COMMUNICATIONS AND ELECTRONICS ASSOCIATION

Attn: AFCEA Educational Foundation
4400 Fair Lakes Court
Fairfax, VA 22033-3899
Tel: (703)631-6149
Free: 800-336-4583
Fax: (703)631-4693
E-mail: scholarship@afcea.org
Web Site: http://www.afcea.org/education/scholarships/undergraduate/vadmjerry.asp
To provide financial assistance to undergraduate students working on a degree in technology.
Title of Award: Vice Adm. Jerry O. Tuttle, USN (Ret.) and Mrs. Barbara A. Tuttle Science and Technology Scholarships **Area, Field, or Subject:** Computer and information sciences; Electronics; Engineering; Engineering, Computer **Level of Education for which Award is Granted:** Four Year College **Number Awarded:** Varies each year; recently, 2 of these scholarships were awarded. **Funds Available:** The stipend is $2,000. **Duration:** 1 year; may be renewed.
Eligibility Requirements: This program is open to full-time students entering their junior or senior year at an accredited 4-year technological institute in the United States. Applicants must be U.S. citizens working toward a degree in computer engineering technology, computer network

systems, or electronics engineering technology. Primary consideration is given to candidates who are military enlisted personnel. Selection is based on a statement of career goals, school and community activities, and financial need. **Deadline for Receipt:** October of each year.

4370 ■ ARMED FORCES COMMUNICATIONS AND ELECTRONICS ASSOCIATION

Attn: AFCEA Educational Foundation
4400 Fair Lakes Court
Fairfax, VA 22033-3899
Tel: (703)631-6149
Free: 800-336-4583
Fax: (703)631-4693
E-mail: scholarship@afcea.org
Web Site: http://www.afcea.org/education/scholarships/undergraduate/veteran.asp
To provide financial assistance to veterans and military personnel who served in Afghanistan or Iraq and are working on an undergraduate degree in fields related to the support of U.S. intelligence enterprises.
Title of Award: Veterans of Enduring Freedom-Afghanistan and Iraqi Freedom Combat Operations Scholarship **Area, Field, or Subject:** Computer and information sciences; Engineering; Engineering, Aerospace/Aeronautical/Astronautical; Engineering, Computer; Engineering, Electrical; Mathematics and mathematical sciences; Physics; Systems engineering **Level of Education for which Award is Granted:** Undergraduate **Number Awarded:** 1 or more each year. **Funds Available:** The stipend is $2,000. **Duration:** 1 year.
Eligibility Requirements: This program is open to active-duty and honorably discharged U.S. military veterans, Reservists, and National Guard personnel who served in combat operations of Enduring Freedom-Afghanistan or Iraqi Freedom. Applicants must be enrolled at a 2- or 4-year institution in the United States and working on an undergraduate degree in computer engineering technology, computer information systems, electronics engineering technology, engineering (aerospace, computer, electrical, or systems), mathematics, physics, or computer science. Along with their application, they must submit an essay that includes a brief synopsis of relevant work experience (including military assignments), a brief statement of career goals after graduation, and a explanation of how their academic and career goals will contribute to the areas related to communications, intelligence and/or information systems, and the mission of the Armed Forces Communications and Electronics Association (AFCEA). Financial need is also considered in the selection process. **Deadline for Receipt:** October of each year. **Additional Information:** This scholarship was first offered in 2005.

4371 ■ ARMED FORCES COMMUNICATIONS AND ELECTRONICS ASSOCIATION

Attn: AFCEA Educational Foundation
4400 Fair Lakes Court
Fairfax, VA 22033-3899
Tel: (703)631-6149
Free: 800-336-4583
Fax: (703)631-4693
E-mail: scholarship@afcea.org
Web Site: http://www.afcea.org/education/scholarships/undergraduate/pub2.asp
To provide financial assistance to undergraduate students who are working full time on a degree in engineering or the sciences.
Title of Award: General John A. Wickham Scholarships **Area, Field, or Subject:** Computer and information sciences; Engineering, Aerospace/Aeronautical/Astronautical; Engineering, Chemical; Engineering, Computer; Engineering, Electrical; Mathematics and mathematical sciences; Physics; Systems engineering **Level of Education for which Award is Granted:** Four Year College **Number Awarded:** Varies each year; recently, 11 of these scholarships were awarded. **Funds Available:** The stipend is $2,000. **Duration:** 1 year; may be renewed.
Eligibility Requirements: This program is open to full-time students entering their junior or senior year at an accredited degree-granting 4-year college or university in the United States. Applicants must be U.S. citizens working toward a degree in engineering (aerospace, chemical, computer, electrical, or systems), mathematics, physics, or computer science with a GPA of 3.5 or higher. They must be able to demonstrate academic achievement, patriotism, and potential to contribute to the American work

force. **Deadline for Receipt:** April of each year.

4372 ■ ARMED FORCES COMMUNICATIONS AND ELECTRONICS ASSOCIATION

Attn: AFCEA Educational Foundation
4400 Fair Lakes Court
Fairfax, VA 22033-3899
Tel: (703)631-6149
Free: 800-336-4583
Fax: (703)631-4693
E-mail: scholarship@afcea.org
Web Site: http://www.afcea.org/education/scholarships/undergraduate/
sgtjean.asp
To provide funding to members and veterans of the U.S. Marine Corps (USMC) who are majoring in specified fields in college.
Title of Award: Marine Sgt. Jeannette L. Winters Memorial Scholarship **Area, Field, or Subject:** Computer and information sciences; Engineering, Aerospace/Aeronautical/Astronautical; Engineering, Computer; Engineering, Electrical; Mathematics and mathematical sciences; Physics; Systems engineering **Level of Education for which Award is Granted:** Undergraduate **Number Awarded:** 1 each year. **Funds Available:** The stipend is $2,000. **Duration:** 1 year.
Eligibility Requirements: This program is open to USMC personnel currently on active duty, in the Reserves, or honorably-discharged veterans who are enrolled full or part time in an accredited college or university in the United States. Applicants must be U.S. citizens, be of good moral character, have demonstrated academic excellence, be motivated to complete a college education, and be working on a degree in engineering (aerospace, computer, electrical, or systems), mathematics, physics, or computer science with a GPA of 3.0 or higher. They must provide a copy of Discharge Form DD214, Certificate of Service, or facsimile of their current Department of Defense Identification Card. **Deadline for Receipt:** September of each year. **Additional Information:** This program was established in 2002 to honor a Marine who died when her KC-130 aircraft crashed in Pakistan.

4373 ■ ASM INTERNATIONAL-MILWAUKEE CHAPTER

Attn: EGMF Committee
P.O. Box 370138
Milwaukee, WI 53237-1238
Web Site: http://www.asm-milwaukee.cjb.net
To provide financial assistance to students at colleges and universities in Wisconsin who are majoring in a field related to metals and materials.
Title of Award: Ernie Guenther Memorial Scholarship **Area, Field, or Subject:** Engineering, Materials; Engineering, Metallurgical; Materials research/science; Metallurgy **Level of Education for which Award is Granted:** Undergraduate **Number Awarded:** 4 to 6 each year. **Funds Available:** Stipends range from $500 to $1,000. **Duration:** 1 year.
Eligibility Requirements: This program is open to students at Wisconsin colleges and universities who are interested in metals and materials and are planning to make those technical areas part of their future career. Applicants must indicate 1) their reasons for their interest and pursuit of a career in the metals and materials field; 2) any projects or activities they have completed or are doing related to metals and materials; 3) their goals for work and/or further study in the metals and materials field; 4) their activities, jobs, and organizations both on and off campus; and 5) any other pertinent information. Financial need is not considered in the selection process. **Deadline for Receipt:** April of each year. **Additional Information:** This program began in 1974. Information is also available from Robb Denkenberger, Ladish Company, Inc., P.O. Box 8902, Cudahy, WI 53110-8902, (414) 747-3384, Fax: (414) 747-3036, E-mail: rdenkenberger@ladishco.com.

4374 ■ ASSOCIATED BUILDERS AND CONTRACTORS

Attn: Trimmer Education Foundation
4250 North Fairfax Drive, Ninth Floor
Arlington, VA 22203
Tel: (703)812-2000
Fax: (703)812-8235
E-mail: StudentChapters@abc.org
Web Site: http://www.abc.org
To provide financial assistance to undergraduate students who are associated with Associated Builders and Contractors (ABC) and preparing for a career in the construction industry.

Title of Award: Trimmer Education Foundation Scholarship **Area, Field, or Subject:** Construction; Engineering **Level of Education for which Award is Granted:** Undergraduate **Number Awarded:** 1 or more each year. **Funds Available:** Stipends range up to $1,000. **Duration:** 1 year; nonrenewable.
Eligibility Requirements: This program is open to members of ABC student chapters, children of ABC members, and chapter staff. Applicants must be planning to continue their education in fields related to construction. They must be able to demonstrate financial need. **Deadline for Receipt:** May of each year.

4375 ■ ASSOCIATED GENERAL CONTRACTORS OF CONNECTICUT, INC.

912 Silas Deane Highway
Wethersfield, CT 06109-3433
Tel: (860)529-6855
Fax: (860)563-0616
E-mail: info@ctconstruction.org
Web Site: http://www.ctconstruction.org
To provide financial assistance and work experience to high school seniors from Connecticut who are interested in entering a building technology, civil engineering, or construction course of study.
Title of Award: Associated General Contractors of Connecticut Scholarships **Area, Field, or Subject:** Construction; Engineering, Civil **Level of Education for which Award is Granted:** Undergraduate **Funds Available:** The stipend is $2,500 per year for both the freshman and sophomore years of college. In addition, recipients are awarded $2,500 each summer for student work experience with a qualified contractor. **Duration:** 2 years of college and 2 summer internships.
Eligibility Requirements: Eligible to apply are graduating high school seniors in Connecticut who are interested in 1) entering a 4-year building technology or civil engineering program as a freshman or 2) entering a 2-year technical school with a construction course of study, with the intent of entering a 4-year college upon completion of the technical school. All applicants must be U.S. citizens or documented permanent residents. Semifinalists are interviewed. Final selection is based on interest in construction as a career, grades, extracurricular activities, employment experience, recommendations, and financial status. **Deadline for Receipt:** October of each year. **Additional Information:** Recipients are offered summer internships with qualified contractors.

4376 ■ ASSOCIATED GENERAL CONTRACTORS OF MINNESOTA

Capitol Office Building
525 Park Street, Suite 110
St. Paul, MN 55103-2186
Tel: (651)632-8929
Free: 800-552-7670
Fax: (651)632-8928
E-mail: jsanem@agcmn.org
Web Site: http://www.agcmn.org
To provide financial assistance to students in Minnesota preparing for a career in the construction industry.
Title of Award: Associated General Contractors of Minnesota Scholarships **Area, Field, or Subject:** Architecture; Construction; Engineering, Civil; Engineering, Electrical; Heating, air conditioning, and refrigeration **Level of Education for which Award is Granted:** Undergraduate **Number Awarded:** Varies each year. Recently, 14 of these scholarships were awarded: 2 at $2,500, 2 at $2,000, 3 at $1,000, and 7 at $750. **Funds Available:** Stipends range from $750 to $2,500. **Duration:** 1 year.
Eligibility Requirements: This program is open to students enrolled in construction programs at colleges and universities in Minnesota. Fields of study include, but are not limited to, architecture, civil engineering, construction management, electrical engineering, and HVAC systems services. Applicants must submit a personal statement that includes information on their work-related experience, involvement in student or community organizations, honors or awards they have received, their financial situation, and other appropriate information. Selection is based on academic standing(20%), career objectives(20%), financial need

(20%), personal information (20%), and overall application clarity (20%).
Deadline for Receipt: May of each year.

4377 ■ ASSOCIATION OF CALIFORNIA WATER AGENCIES

Attn: Scholarship Program
910 K Street, Suite 100
Sacramento, CA 95814-3514
Tel: (916)441-4545
Fax: (916)325-4849
E-mail: lavonnew@acwa.com
Web Site: http://www.acwa.com/news_info/scholarships
To provide financial assistance to upper-division students in California
who are majoring in water resources-related fields of study.
Title of Award: Association of California Water Agencies Scholarships
Area, Field, or Subject: Agricultural sciences; Engineering; Environmental conservation; Environmental science; Public administration; Water resources **Level of Education for which Award is Granted:** Four Year College **Number Awarded:** At least 6 each year. **Funds Available:** The stipend is $1,500. Funds are paid directly to the recipient's school. **Duration:** 1 year.
Eligibility Requirements: This program is open to California residents attending selected colleges and universities in the state. Applicants must be full-time students in their junior or senior year at the time of the award and majoring in a field related to or identified with water resources, including engineering, agricultural and/or urban water supply, environmental sciences, or public administration. Along with their application, they must submit 2-page essay on key water-related issues they would address if given the opportunity, why they have chosen a career in the water resources field, and how their educational and career goals relate to a future in California water resources. Selection is based on scholastic achievement, commitment to a career in the field of water resources, and financial need. **Deadline for Receipt:** March of each year. **Additional Information:** Recipients must attend a college or university in California approved by the sponsor.

4378 ■ ASSOCIATION OF CALIFORNIA WATER AGENCIES

Attn: Scholarship Program
910 K Street, Suite 100
Sacramento, CA 95814-3514
Tel: (916)441-4545
Fax: (916)325-4849
E-mail: lavonnew@acwa.com
Web Site: http://www.acwa.com/news_info/scholarships
To provide financial assistance to upper-division students in California
who are majoring in water resources-related fields of study.
Title of Award: Clair A. Hill Scholarship **Area, Field, or Subject:** Agricultural sciences; Engineering; Environmental conservation; Environmental science; Public administration; Water resources **Level of Education for which Award is Granted:** Undergraduate **Number Awarded:** 1 each year. **Funds Available:** The stipend is $3,000. Funds are paid directly to the recipient's school. **Duration:** 1 year.
Eligibility Requirements: Applicants must be California residents attending public colleges or universities in the state. They should 1) have completed their sophomore work, 2) be full-time students in their junior or senior year at the time of the award, and 3) be majoring in a field related to or identified with water resources, including engineering, agricultural sciences, urban water supply, environmental sciences, and public administration. Selection is based on scholastic achievement, career plans, and financial need. **Deadline for Receipt:** March of each year. **Additional Information:** This program is administered each year by the current recipient of the Association of California Water Agencies Clair A. Hill Agency Award for Excellence, which is presented annually to a public water agency in recognition of outstanding and innovative water management programs. The winning agency generally selects a student within its service area. Funding is provided by the consulting firm CH2M Hill. Recipients must attend a branch of the University of California or the California State University system on a full-time basis.

4379 ■ ASSOCIATION OF CUBAN ENGINEERS

Attn: Selection Committee
P.O. Box 557575
Miami, FL 33255-7575
Tel: (305)649-7429
Web Site: http://www.a-i-c.org
To provide financial assistance to undergraduate and graduate students of Cuban American heritage who are interested in preparing for a career in engineering.
Title of Award: Association of Cuban Engineers Scholarships **Area, Field, or Subject:** Engineering **Level of Education for which Award is Granted:** Graduate, Undergraduate **Number Awarded:** Up to 20 each year. **Funds Available:** Stipends range from $500 to $1,000. **Duration:** 1 year.
Eligibility Requirements: This program is open to U.S. citizens and legal residents who have completed at least 30 units of college work in the United States and are majoring or planning to major in some aspect of engineering. Applicants must be attending an ABET-accredited college or university within the United States or Puerto Rico as a full-time student with a GPA of 3.0 or higher. They must be of Cuban or other Hispanic heritage (at least 1 grandparent Cuban or other Hispanic nationality). Along with their application, they must submit brief essays on their family history, professional goals, extracurricular activities, work experience, and how they will help other Cuban and Hispanic engineering students in the future. Financial need is not considered in the selection process.
Deadline for Receipt: November of each year. **Additional Information:** This program includes the Luciano Goicochea Award (for the top-rated Cuban American student at the University of Miami) and the Noel Betancourt Award (for the top-rated Cuban American student at Florida International University).

4380 ■ ASSOCIATION OF ENERGY ENGINEERS

Attn: Foundation
4025 Pleasantdale Road, Suite 420
Atlanta, GA 30340
Tel: (770)447-5083
Fax: (770)446-3969
E-mail: info@aeecenter.org
Web Site: http://www.aeecenter.org
To provide financial assistance to undergraduate and graduate students interested in taking courses directly related to energy engineering or energy management.
Title of Award: Association of Energy Engineers Scholarships **Area, Field, or Subject:** Energy-related areas; Engineering; Management **Level of Education for which Award is Granted:** Graduate, Undergraduate **Number Awarded:** Several each year, including 1 Victor Ottaviano Scholarship and 1 Al Thumann Scholarship. **Funds Available:** Stipends are $2,000, $1,000, or $500. In addition, the 2 most outstanding candidates receive the $1,000 Victor Ottaviano Scholarship and the $1,000 Al Thumann Scholarship. **Duration:** 1 year.
Eligibility Requirements: This program is open to undergraduate and graduate students who are enrolled in engineering or management programs at accredited colleges and universities and who would be interested in taking courses directly related to energy engineering or energy management (preferably within a curriculum leading to a major or minor in energy engineering). Qualified students are invited to submit their applications to the association's local chapter, along with transcripts and letters of recommendation. Each chapter may then submit up to 6 nominees, no more than 2 of whom may be graduate students. Selection is based on scholarship, character, and need. In awarding scholarships, preference is given to candidates needing aid their final year; second, to candidates needing aid for the last 2 years; third, to candidates needing aid for 3 years; and finally, to first-year students. **Deadline for Receipt:** April of each year. **Additional Information:** Since this program was established in 1983, it has awarded 771 scholarships worth $418,000. Information is also available from James P. Waltz, AEE Scholarship Committee Chair, c/o Energy Resource Associates, Inc., 1626 Holmes Street, Livermore, CA 94550-6010.

4381 ■ ASSOCIATION OF ENERGY ENGINEERS-GEORGIA CHAPTER

c/o Joseph Clements, Scholarship Chair
Fulton County Schools
Coordinator, Utilities Services
5270 Northfield Boulevard
College Park, GA 30349-3179
Tel: (404)669-8991
Fax: (404)765-7155

E-mail: clementsj@fulton.k12.ga.us

Web Site: http://www.aeegeorgia.org/scholarship.htm

To provide financial assistance to undergraduate and graduate students in Georgia interested in taking courses directly related to energy engineering or energy management.

Title of Award: Georgia AEE Chapter Scholarships **Area, Field, or Subject:** Energy-related areas; Engineering; Management **Level of Education for which Award is Granted:** Graduate, Undergraduate **Number Awarded:** Up to 2 each year. **Funds Available:** If a Georgia nominee wins an Association of Energy Engineers (AEE) national scholarship for $500, the Georgia chapter will match that award. If no Georgia nominee wins a national scholarship, the Georgia chapter will award a $1,000 scholarship. **Duration:** 1 year.

Eligibility Requirements: This program is open to undergraduate and graduate students who are enrolled in engineering or management programs at accredited colleges and universities in Georgia. Applicants must be interested in taking courses directly related to energy engineering or energy management (preferably within a curriculum leading to a major or minor in energy engineering). Selection is based on scholarship, character, and need. In awarding scholarships, preference is given to candidates needing aid their final year; second, to candidates needing aid for the last 2 years; third, to candidates needing aid for 3 years; and finally, to first-year students. **Deadline for Receipt:** April of each year.

4382 ■ ASSOCIATION OF ENERGY ENGINEERS-NEW ENGLAND CHAPTER

c/o Dan Wheatley, Scholarship Chair

Environmental Systems Corporation

750 Main Street

Winchester, MA 01890

Tel: (781)729-3760

Fax: (781)729-3778

E-mail: danw@esccontrols.com

Web Site: http://www.aeenewengland.org/Scholarships.html

To provide financial assistance to undergraduate and graduate students in New England interested in taking courses directly related to energy engineering or energy management.

Title of Award: New England AEE Academic Scholarships **Area, Field, or Subject:** Energy-related areas; Engineering; Management **Level of Education for which Award is Granted:** Graduate, Undergraduate **Number Awarded:** Varies each year; recently, 5 of these scholarships were awarded. **Funds Available:** The stipend is $1,000. **Duration:** 1 year.

Eligibility Requirements: This program is open to undergraduate and graduate students who are enrolled in engineering or management programs at accredited colleges and universities in New England. Applicants must be interested in taking courses directly related to energy engineering or energy management (preferably within a curriculum leading to a major or minor in energy engineering). Selection is based on scholarship, character, and need. In awarding scholarships, preference is given to candidates needing aid their final year; second, to candidates needing aid for the last 2 years; third, to candidates needing aid for 3 years; and finally, to first-year students. **Deadline for Receipt:** February of each year.

4383 ■ ASSOCIATION OF ENVIRONMENTAL AND ENGINEERING GEOLOGISTS

Attn: AEG Foundation

300 South Jackson Street, Suite 100

P.O. Box 460518

Denver, CO 80246

Tel: (303)757-2926

Fax: (303)757-2969

E-mail: aeg@aegweb.org

Web Site: http://www.aegfoundation.org/index2.php

To provide financial assistance for college or graduate school to student members of the Association of Environmental and Engineering Geologists.

Title of Award: Marliave Scholar Award **Area, Field, or Subject:** Engineering, Geological; Geology **Level of Education for which Award is Granted:** Four Year College, Graduate **Number Awarded:** 1 each year. **Funds Available:** The stipend is $1,000. **Duration:** 1 year.

Eligibility Requirements: Applicants must be college seniors or graduate students in engineering geology or geological engineering, must be

enrolled full time in a college or university offering a degree program directly applicable to engineering geology or geological engineering, and must be a student member of the association. Along with their application, they must submit official transcripts covering all undergraduate and graduate work, 3 letters of reference, copies of pertinent publications and abstracts, and a 2-page statement of career goals. Selection is based on demonstrated ability, academic record, potential for contributions to the profession, character, and activities in student/professional societies. Financial need is not considered. **Deadline for Receipt:** April of each year. **Additional Information:** This program was established in 1968. Information is also available from Paul M. Santi, Colorado School of Mines, Department of Geology and Geological Engineering, Berthoud Hall, Golden, CO 80401, (303) 273-3108, E-mail: psanti@mines.edu.

4384 ■ ASSOCIATION OF ENVIRONMENTAL AND ENGINEERING GEOLOGISTS

Attn: AEG Foundation

300 South Jackson Street, Suite 100

P.O. Box 460518

Denver, CO 80246

Tel: (303)757-2926

Fax: (303)757-2969

E-mail: aeg@aegweb.org

Web Site: http://www.aegfoundation.org/index2.php

To provide financial assistance to members of the Association of Environmental and Engineering Geologists (AEG) who are working on an undergraduate degree in geology or a graduate degree with an environmental or engineering geology emphasis.

Title of Award: Martin L. Stout Scholarship **Area, Field, or Subject:** Engineering, Geological; Geology **Level of Education for which Award is Granted:** Four Year College, Graduate **Number Awarded:** 1 each year. **Funds Available:** The stipend is $1,000. **Duration:** 1 year.

Eligibility Requirements: This program is open to student members of the association who are undergraduate geology majors in their sophomore through senior year or graduate students with an environmental or engineering geology emphasis. Applicants must submit a 500-word essay on either of the following questions: 1) how they intend to become a competent professional environmental and/or engineering geologist, or 2) why they need to become a competent field geologist. Selection is based on the essay and letters of recommendation. **Deadline for Receipt:** January of each year. **Additional Information:** This program was established in 1994 by the Southern California section of the Association of Engineering Geologists and transferred to the AEG Foundation in 2004. Information is also available from Robert A. Larson, 13376 Azores Avenue, Sylmar, CA 91342, (818) 362-0363, E-mail: ralarson@rampageusa.com.

4385 ■ ASSOCIATION OF INDEPENDENT COLLEGES AND UNIVERSITIES OF PENNSYLVANIA

101 North Front Street

Harrisburg, PA 17101-1405

Tel: (717)232-8649

Fax: (717)233-8574

E-mail: info@aicup.org

Web Site: http://www.aicup.org

To provide financial assistance to women and minority students at member institutions of the Association of Independent Colleges and Universities of Pennsylvania (AICUP) who are majoring in designated fields of engineering.

Title of Award: Air Products and Chemicals Scholarship for Diversity in Engineering **Area, Field, or Subject:** Engineering, Chemical; Engineering, Mechanical **Level of Education for which Award is Granted:** Four Year College **Number Awarded:** 2 each year. **Funds Available:** The stipend is $7,500 per year. **Duration:** 1 year; may be renewed 1 additional year if the recipient maintains appropriate academic standards.

Eligibility Requirements: This program is open to full-time undergraduate students at designated AICUP colleges and universities who are women and/or members of the following minority groups: American Indians, Alaska Natives, Asians, Blacks/African Americans, Hispanics/ Latinos, Native Hawaiians, or Pacific Islanders. Applicants must be juniors majoring in chemical or mechanical engineering with a GPA of 2.7 or higher. Along with their application, they must submit an essay on their characteristics, accomplishments, primary interests, plans, and goals, and what sets them apart. **Deadline for Receipt:** April of each year. **Ad-**

ditional Information: This program, sponsored by Air Products and Chemicals, Inc., is available at the following AICUP colleges and universities: Bucknell University, Carnegie Mellon University, Drexel University, Gannon University, Geneva College, Grove City College, Lafayette College, Lehigh University, Messiah College, Swarthmore College, Villanova University, Widener University, and Wilkes University.

4386 ■ ASSOCIATION OF INDEPENDENT COLLEGES AND UNIVERSITIES OF PENNSYLVANIA

101 North Front Street
Harrisburg, PA 17101-1405
Tel: (717)232-8649
Fax: (717)233-8574
E-mail: info@aicup.org
Web Site: http://www.aicup.org
To provide financial assistance to women and minority students at member institutions of the Association of Independent Colleges and Universities of Pennsylvania (AICUP) who are majoring in designated fields of engineering.
Title of Award: Michael Baker Corporation Scholarship Program for Diversity in Engineering **Area, Field, or Subject:** Engineering, Architectural; Engineering, Civil; Environmental science **Level of Education for which Award is Granted:** Four Year College **Number Awarded:** 1 each year. **Funds Available:** The stipend is $1,000 per year. **Duration:** 1 year; may be renewed 1 additional year if the recipient maintains appropriate academic standards.
Eligibility Requirements: This program is open to full-time undergraduate students at designated AICUP colleges and universities who are women and/or members of the following minority groups: American Indians, Alaska Natives, Asians, Blacks/African Americans, Hispanics/Latinos, Native Hawaiians, or Pacific Islanders. Applicants must be juniors majoring in architectural, civil, or environmental engineering with a GPA of 3.0 or higher. Along with their application, they must submit an essay on what they believe will be the greatest challenge facing the engineering profession over the next decade, and why. **Deadline for Receipt:** April of each year. **Additional Information:** This program, sponsored by the Michael Baker Corporation, is available at the following AICUP colleges and universities: Bucknell University, Carnegie Mellon University, Drexel University, Gannon University, Geneva College, Grove City College, Lafayette College, Lehigh University, Messiah College, Swarthmore College, Villanova University, Widener University, and Wilkes University.

4387 ■ ASSOCIATION FOR IRON & STEEL TECHNOLOGY

Attn: AIST Foundation
186 Thorn Hill Road
Warrendale, PA 15086-7528
Tel: (724)776-6040
Fax: (724)776-1880
E-mail: lwharrey@aist.org
Web Site: http://www.aist.org/foundation/scholarships.htm
To provide financial assistance for college to students interested in preparing for a career in the iron and steel or steel-related industries.
Title of Award: Association for Iron & Steel Technology Scholarships **Area, Field, or Subject:** Business; Engineering; Manufacturing; Materials research/science; Metallurgy **Level of Education for which Award is Granted:** Undergraduate **Number Awarded:** 7 each year, including 3 Willy Korf Memorial Fund Scholarships, 2 Ronald E. Lincoln Memorial Scholarship, and 2 Benjamin F. Fairless Scholarships. **Funds Available:** The stipend is $2,000. **Duration:** 1 year; recipients may reapply.
Eligibility Requirements: This program is open to full-time students majoring in metallurgy, materials science, or engineering at accredited universities in North America. Applicants must have a GPA of 3.0 or higher and a demonstrated interest in the iron and steel industry. Along with their application, they must submit 3 letters of recommendation; a resume with work experience and extracurricular activities, noting any leadership positions; a current academic transcript; and a 2-page essay on their professional goals, explaining why they are interested in a career in the steel industry and how their skills could be applied to enhance the industry. Financial need is not considered in the selection process. **Deadline for Receipt:** April of each year. **Additional Information:** The AIST was

formed in 2004 by the merger of the Iron and Steel Society (ISS) and the Association of Iron and Steel Engineers (AISE).

4388 ■ ASSOCIATION FOR IRON & STEEL TECHNOLOGY

Attn: AIST Foundation
186 Thorn Hill Road
Warrendale, PA 15086-7528
Tel: (724)776-6040
Fax: (724)776-1880
E-mail: lwharrey@aist.org
Web Site: http://www.aist.org/foundation/scholarships.htm
To provide financial assistance for college study of engineering to Canadians who are children of members of the Association for Iron & Steel Technology (AIST).
Title of Award: David H. Samson Canadian Scholarship **Area, Field, or Subject:** Chemistry; Engineering; Geology; Mathematics and mathematical sciences; Physics **Level of Education for which Award is Granted:** Undergraduate **Number Awarded:** 1 each year. **Funds Available:** The stipend is $US2,000. **Duration:** 1 year; may be renewed for up to 3 additional years.
Eligibility Requirements: This program is open to the children (natural, adopted, or ward) of Canadian citizens and landed immigrants who are members of the association. Applicants must have been accepted in an eligible full-time course of study of engineering at an accredited Canadian university. If no engineering student applies, the award may be made to an eligible student planning to major in chemistry, geology, mathematics, or physics. The scholarship may also be awarded to a student entering a community college if there is no eligible applicant entering an accredited university. The committee may also award the scholarship to a previous applicant entering the second or third year at a Canadian university or community college if there is no eligible applicant entering the first year. Selection is based on academic achievements, extracurricular activities, and the student's written statements; financial need is not considered. **Deadline for Receipt:** June of each year. **Additional Information:** The AIST was formed in 2004 by the merger of the Iron and Steel Society (ISS) and the Association of Iron and Steel Engineers (AISE). Information is also available from Robert Kneale, AIST Northern Member Chapter, P.O. Box 1734, Cambridge, Ontario N1R 7G8, Canada.

4389 ■ ASSOCIATION FOR IRON & STEEL TECHNOLOGY

Attn: AIST Foundation
186 Thorn Hill Road
Warrendale, PA 15086-7528
Tel: (724)776-6040
Fax: (724)776-1880
E-mail: lwharrey@aist.org
Web Site: http://www.aist.org/foundation/scholarships.htm
To provide financial assistance for college to students interested in preparing for a career in the iron and steel or steel-related industries.
Title of Award: William E. Schwabe Memorial Scholarship **Area, Field, or Subject:** Business; Engineering; Manufacturing; Materials research/science; Metallurgy **Level of Education for which Award is Granted:** Undergraduate **Number Awarded:** 1 each year. **Funds Available:** The stipend is $1,500. **Duration:** 1 year; recipients may reapply.
Eligibility Requirements: This program is open to full-time students majoring in metallurgy, materials science, or engineering at accredited universities in North America. Applicants must have a GPA of 3.0 or higher and a demonstrated interest in the iron and steel industry. Along with their application, they must submit 3 letters of recommendation; a resume with work experience and extracurricular activities, noting any leadership positions; a current academic transcript; and a 2-page essay on their professional goals, explaining why they are interested in a career in the steel industry and how their skills could be applied to enhance the industry. Financial need is not considered in the selection process. **Deadline for Receipt:** April of each year. **Additional Information:** The AIST was formed in 2004 by the merger of the Iron and Steel Society (ISS) and the Association of Iron and Steel Engineers (AISE). This scholarship was established in 2005 by the Steel Manufacturers Association.

4390 ■ ASSOCIATION FOR IRON & STEEL TECHNOLOGY-BALTIMORE CHAPTER

c/o Thomas J. Russo
Mittal Steel USA

5111 North Point Boulevard
Sparrows Point, MD 21219-1014
Tel: (410)388-6370
Fax: (410)388-3772
E-mail: tom.russo@mittalsteel.com
Web Site: http://www.aist.org/chapters/mc_baltimore_scholar.htm
To provide financial assistance to family of members of the Baltimore Chapter of the Association for Iron & Steel Technology (AIST) who are interested in studying engineering or metallurgy in college.

Title of Award: Baltimore Chapter AIST Scholarship **Area, Field, or Subject:** Business; Engineering; Manufacturing; Metallurgy **Level of Education for which Award is Granted:** Undergraduate **Number Awarded:** 1 each year. **Funds Available:** The stipend is $1,500. **Duration:** 1 year.

Eligibility Requirements: This program is open to children, grandchildren, and spouses of chapter members who are high school seniors or full-time undergraduates at an accredited college or university. Applicants must be studying or planning to study engineering or metallurgy with a demonstrated interest in a career in the iron and steel industry. Along with their application, they must submit 1) a 500-word essay on an accomplishment that they have achieved while they have been a student; 2) a 500-word essay on their interest and/or involvement in the iron and steel industry; 3) SAT/ACT scores; and 4) high school and/or college transcripts. Selection is based on academic achievement, extracurricular activities, and the essays; financial need is not considered. **Deadline for Receipt:** April of each year. **Additional Information:** The AIST was formed in 2004 by the merger of the Iron and Steel Society (ISS) and the Association of Iron and Steel Engineers (AISE). The Baltimore Chapter covers the District of Columbia, Maryland, and northern Virginia.

4391 ■ ASSOCIATION FOR IRON & STEEL TECHNOLOGY-DETROIT CHAPTER

c/o Judith A. Quinn, Secretary
14201 Robbe Road
Belleville, MI 48111
Tel: (313)319-2815
E-mail: judieqn@aol.com
Web Site: http://www.aist.org/chapters/detroit_scholarship.htm
To provide financial assistance to family of members of the Detroit Chapter of the Association for Iron & Steel Technology (AIST) who are interested in studying engineering, materials science, or metallurgy in college.

Title of Award: Detroit Chapter AIST Scholarship **Area, Field, or Subject:** Business; Engineering; Manufacturing; Materials research/science; Metallurgy **Level of Education for which Award is Granted:** Undergraduate **Number Awarded:** 1 each year. **Funds Available:** The stipend is $3,500. **Duration:** 1 year.

Eligibility Requirements: This program is open to children and grandchildren of chapter members who are high school seniors or full-time undergraduates at an accredited college or university. They must be studying or planning to study engineering, materials science, or metallurgy; if there are no applicants in those fields, the award may be given to a student majoring in another field relating to iron and steel production. Applicants must have a GPA of 3.0 or higher and a demonstrated interest in a career in the iron and steel industry. Along with their application, they must submit a 2-page essay on their professional goals, why they are interested in a career in the steel industry, and how their skills could be applied to enhance the industry. Financial need is not considered in the selection process. **Deadline for Receipt:** April of each year. **Additional Information:** The AIST was formed in 2004 by the merger of the Iron and Steel Society (ISS) and the Association of Iron and Steel Engineers (AISE). The Detroit Chapter serves Michigan and northwestern Ohio.

4392 ■ ASSOCIATION FOR IRON & STEEL TECHNOLOGY-MIDWEST CHAPTER

c/o Michael Heaney, Education Chair
Mittal Steel USA-East Chicago
3001 Dickey Road
East Chicago, IN 46312
Tel: (219)391-2026
Web Site: http://www.aist.org/chapters/midwest_scholarship.htm
To provide financial assistance to dependents of members of the Midwest Chapter of the Association for Iron & Steel Technology (AIST) who plan to study engineering in college.

Title of Award: Jack Gill Scholarship **Area, Field, or Subject:** Engineering **Level of Education for which Award is Granted:** Undergraduate **Number Awarded:** 1 each year. **Funds Available:** The stipend is $2,500. **Duration:** 1 year.

Eligibility Requirements: This program is open to dependents of the AIST Midwest Chapter who are graduating high school seniors or currently enrolled in the first, second, or third year at an accredited college or university. Applicants must be studying or planning to study engineering on a full-time basis. Along with their application, they must submit a letter of recommendation, a current transcript, and a 1- to 2-page essay describing their objectives for college and career. Selection is based on merit. **Deadline for Receipt:** May of each year. **Additional Information:** The AIST was formed in 2004 by the merger of the Iron and Steel Society (ISS) and the Association of Iron and Steel Engineers (AISE). The Midwest Chapter replaced the former AISE Chicago Section in northern Illinois and northwestern Indiana and also includes the states of Wisconsin, Minnesota, Iowa, Nebraska, South Dakota, and North Dakota.

4393 ■ ASSOCIATION FOR IRON & STEEL TECHNOLOGY-MIDWEST CHAPTER

c/o Michael Heaney, Education Chair
Mittal Steel USA-East Chicago
3001 Dickey Road
East Chicago, IN 46312
Tel: (219)391-2026
Web Site: http://www.aist.org/chapters/midwest_scholarship.htm
To provide financial assistance to female dependents of members of the Midwest Chapter of the Association for Iron & Steel Technology (AIST) who plan to study engineering in college.

Title of Award: Betty McKern Scholarship **Area, Field, or Subject:** Engineering **Level of Education for which Award is Granted:** Undergraduate **Number Awarded:** 1 each year. **Funds Available:** The stipend is $2,500. **Duration:** 1 year.

Eligibility Requirements: This program is open to female dependents of members of the AIST Midwest Chapter who are graduating high school seniors or currently enrolled in the first, second, or third year at an accredited college or university. Applicants must be studying or planning to study engineering on a full-time basis. Along with their application, they must submit a letter of recommendation, a current transcript, and a 1- to 2-page essay describing their objectives for college and career. Selection is based on merit. **Deadline for Receipt:** May of each year. **Additional Information:** The AIST was formed in 2004 by the merger of the Iron and Steel Society (ISS) and the Association of Iron and Steel Engineers (AISE). The Midwest Chapter replaced the former AISE Chicago Section in northern Illinois and northwestern Indiana and also includes the states of Wisconsin, Minnesota, Iowa, Nebraska, South Dakota, and North Dakota.

4394 ■ ASSOCIATION FOR IRON & STEEL TECHNOLOGY-MIDWEST CHAPTER

c/o Michael Heaney, Education Chair
Mittal Steel USA-East Chicago
3001 Dickey Road
East Chicago, IN 46312
Tel: (219)391-2026
Web Site: http://www.aist.org/chapters/midwest_scholarship.htm
To provide financial assistance to dependents of members of the Midwest Chapter of the Association for Iron & Steel Technology (AIST) who plan to study engineering in college.

Title of Award: Midwest Chapter AIST Engineering Scholarship **Area, Field, or Subject:** Engineering **Level of Education for which Award is Granted:** Undergraduate **Number Awarded:** 2 each year. **Funds Available:** The stipend is $1,000 per year. **Duration:** 4 years.

Eligibility Requirements: This program is open to dependents of the AIST Midwest Chapter who are graduating high school seniors or currently enrolled in the first, second, or third year at an accredited college or university. Applicants must be studying or planning to study engineering on a full-time basis. Along with their application, they must submit a letter of recommendation, a current transcript, and a 1- to 2-page essay describing their objectives for college and career. Selection is based on merit. **Deadline for Receipt:** May of each year. **Additional Information:** The AIST was formed in 2004 by the merger of the Iron and Steel Society (ISS) and the Association of Iron and Steel Engineers (AISE). The

Midwest Chapter replaced the former AISE Chicago Section in northern Illinois and northwestern Indiana and also includes the states of Wisconsin, Minnesota, Iowa, Nebraska, South Dakota, and North Dakota.

4395 ■ ASSOCIATION FOR IRON & STEEL TECHNOLOGY-MIDWEST CHAPTER

c/o Michael Heaney, Education Chair
Mittal Steel USA-East Chicago
3001 Dickey Road
East Chicago, IN 46312
Tel: (219)391-2026
Web Site: http://www.aist.org/chapters/midwest_scholarship.htm
To provide financial assistance to dependents of members of the Midwest Chapter of the Association for Iron & Steel Technology (AIST) who plan to study engineering in college.
Title of Award: Mel Nickel Scholarship **Area, Field, or Subject:** Engineering **Level of Education for which Award is Granted:** Undergraduate **Number Awarded:** 1 each year. **Funds Available:** The stipend is $2,500. **Duration:** 1 year.
Eligibility Requirements: This program is open to dependents of the AIST Midwest Chapter who are graduating high school seniors or currently enrolled in the first, second, or third year at an accredited college or university. Applicants must be studying or planning to study engineering on a full-time basis. Along with their application, they must submit a letter of recommendation, a current transcript, and a 1- to 2-page essay describing their objectives for college and career. Selection is based on merit. **Deadline for Receipt:** May of each year. **Additional Information:** The AIST was formed in 2004 by the merger of the Iron and Steel Society (ISS) and the Association of Iron and Steel Engineers (AISE). The Midwest Chapter replaced the former AISE Chicago Section in northern Illinois and northwestern Indiana and also includes the states of Wisconsin, Minnesota, Iowa, Nebraska, South Dakota, and North Dakota.

4396 ■ ASSOCIATION FOR IRON & STEEL TECHNOLOGY-NORTHWEST CHAPTER

c/o Gerardo L. Giraldo, Secretary-Treasurer
Nucor Steel Seattle, Inc.
Washington Steel Division
2424 S.W. Andover Street
Seattle, WA 98106-1100
Tel: (206)933-2245
Fax: (206)933-2207
E-mail: gerry.giraldo@nucor-seattle.com
Web Site: http://www.aist.org/chapters/
mc_pittsburgh_scholar_guidelines.htm
To provide financial assistance to family of members of the Northwest Chapter of the Association for Iron & Steel Technology (AIST) who are interested in studying engineering in college.
Title of Award: Northwest Chapter AIST Scholarships **Area, Field, or Subject:** Business; Chemistry; Engineering; Manufacturing; Mathematics and mathematical sciences; Metallurgy; Physics **Level of Education for which Award is Granted:** Four Year College **Number Awarded:** 2 each year. **Funds Available:** The stipend is $1,000. **Duration:** 1 year.
Eligibility Requirements: This program is open to children, grandchildren, spouses, or nieces/nephews of chapter members who are high school seniors planning to attend an accredited 4-year college or university. Applicants must intend to study engineering; if there are no applicants in engineering, the award may be given to a student majoring in chemistry, mathematics, metallurgy, or physics, or to a student showing an interest in preparing for a career in the iron and steel industry. Along with their application, they must submit a 500-word essay on 1 of the following topics: 1) an accomplishment they have achieved while they have been a student, why they were successful, and how their success will influence their future plans as an engineer or an engineer in the steel industry; 2) their strengths and interests and how they will apply their skills to a career in the steel industry or as an engineer; or 3) the challenges that face the steel industry and the opportunities for graduates to improve the success of companies within the industry. Financial need is not considered in the selection process. **Deadline for Receipt:** June of each year. **Additional Information:** The AIST was formed in 2004 by the merger of the Iron and Steel Society (ISS) and the Association of Iron and Steel Engineers (AISE). The Northwest Chapter serves Alaska, Idaho, Montana, Oregon, Washington, and Wyoming.

4397 ■ ASSOCIATION FOR IRON & STEEL TECHNOLOGY-OHIO VALLEY CHAPTER

c/o Jeff McKain, Scholarship Chair
Xtek, Inc.
11451 Reading Road
Cincinnati, OH 45241
Tel: (513)733-7843; (999)332-XTEK
Fax: (513)733-7939
E-mail: jeff.mckain@xtek.com
Web Site: http://www.aist.org/chapters/ohiovalley_scholarship.htm
To provide financial assistance for college to student members and children of members of the Ohio Valley Chapter of the Association for Iron & Steel Technology (AIST).
Title of Award: Ohio Valley Chapter AIST Scholarships **Area, Field, or Subject:** Biological and clinical sciences; Chemistry; Computer and information sciences; Earth sciences; Engineering; Engineering, Electrical; Engineering, Mechanical; Environmental conservation; Environmental science; Geosciences; Information science and technology; Metallurgy; Physical sciences; Physics **Level of Education for which Award is Granted:** Undergraduate **Number Awarded:** Up to 2 each year. **Funds Available:** The stipend is $1,000 per year. **Duration:** 1 year; may be renewed up to 3 additional years provided the recipient remains enrolled full time and maintains a GPA of 3.0 or higher.
Eligibility Requirements: This program is open to high school seniors and college students who are either 1) children of Ohio Valley Chapter AIST members, or 2) student AIST members. Applicants must be accepted at, planning to attend, or currently enrolled at an accredited college or university with a major in biology, chemistry, computer programming, computer technology, electrical engineering, engineering, engineering technology, environmental engineering, environmental science, information systems technology, mechanical engineering, metallurgy, microbiology, physical science, physics, or other field approved by the scholarship committee. Along with their application, they must submit a 500-word essay on the reasons for their interests and reasons for working on a degree in their field of study, career goals and objectives, and extracurricular activities and their benefits. Selection is based on overall academic achievement (especially in mathematics and science), the essay, and extracurricular activities. **Deadline for Receipt:** February of each year. **Additional Information:** The AIST was formed in 2004 by the merger of the Iron and Steel Society (ISS) and the Association of Iron and Steel Engineers (AISE). This program was established by the former Ohio Valley District Section of AISE. The Ohio Valley Chapter covers Indiana (except for the northwestern portion), all of Kentucky, western Tennessee, and portions of southern Ohio.

4398 ■ ASSOCIATION FOR IRON & STEEL TECHNOLOGY-PITTSBURGH CHAPTER

c/o Paul D. Conley
Allegheny Ludlum
100 River Road
Brackenridge, PA 15014-1597
Tel: (724)226-5000
Web Site: http://www.aist.org/chapters/
mc_pittsburgh_scholar_guidelines.htm
To provide financial assistance to family of members of the Pittsburgh Chapter of the Association for Iron & Steel Technology (AIST) who are interested in studying engineering or metallurgy in college.
Title of Award: Pittsburgh Chapter AIST Scholarships **Area, Field, or Subject:** Business; Engineering; Manufacturing; Metallurgy **Level of Education for which Award is Granted:** Undergraduate **Number Awarded:** Up to 2 each year. **Funds Available:** The stipend is $2,500. **Duration:** 1 year.
Eligibility Requirements: This program is open to children, grandchildren, or spouses of chapter members who are high school seniors or full-time undergraduates at an accredited college or university. Applicants must be studying or planning to study engineering or metallurgy; if there are no applicants in those fields, the award may be given to a student majoring in another field relating to iron and steel production. Along with their application, they must submit a 500-word essay on 1 of the following topics: 1) an accomplishment they have achieved while they have been a student, why they were successful, and how their success will influence their future plans as an engineer or an engineer in the steel industry; 2) their strengths and interests and how they will apply their skills to a career

in the steel industry or as an engineer; or 3) they challenges that face the steel industry and the opportunities for graduates to improve the success of companies within the industry. Financial need is not considered in the selection process. **Deadline for Receipt:** June of each year. **Additional Information:** The AIST was formed in 2004 by the merger of the Iron and Steel Society (ISS) and the Association of Iron and Steel Engineers (AISE). The Pittsburgh Chapter serves western Pennsylvania, West Virginia, and southeastern Ohio. This program includes the Lawrence G. Maloney Scholarship.

4399 ■ ASSOCIATION FOR IRON & STEEL TECHNOLOGY-SOUTHEAST CHAPTER

c/o Mike Hutson, Secretary
803 Floyd Street
Kings Mountain, NC 28086-3130
Tel: (704)730-8320
Fax: (704)730-8321
E-mail: Mike@johnhutsoncompany.com
Web Site: http://www.aist.org/chapters/
mc_southeast_scholar_guidelines.htm

To provide financial assistance to the families of members of the Southeast Chapter of the Association for Iron & Steel Technology (AIST) who are interested in studying engineering or science in college.

Title of Award: Gene Suave Scholarship **Area, Field, or Subject:** Business; Engineering; Manufacturing; Science **Level of Education for which Award is Granted:** Undergraduate **Number Awarded:** 1 each year. **Funds Available:** The stipend is $1,000. **Duration:** 1 year.

Eligibility Requirements: This program is open to high school seniors and undergraduate students who are the children, stepchildren, grandchildren, or spouses of active Southeast Chapter members for 2 consecutive years. Applicants must plan to work full or part time on a degree in engineering or the sciences. If no engineering or science student applies, the award may be presented to an applicant studying another major related to iron and steel production. Applicants must submit a 250-word essay on their extracurricular involvement in high school and why they should be the recipient of the scholarship. Financial need is not considered. **Deadline for Receipt:** June of each year. **Additional Information:** The AIST was formed in 2004 by the merger of the Iron and Steel Society (ISS) and the Association of Iron and Steel Engineers (AISE). The Southeast Chapter covers the states of North Carolina, South Carolina, Georgia, and Florida as well as portions of southern Virginia and eastern Tennessee.

4400 ■ ASSOCIATION OF OLD CROWS

Attn: AOC Educational Foundation
1000 North Payne Street
Alexandria, VA 22314-1652
Tel: (703)549-1600
Fax: (703)549-2589
Web Site: http://www.crows.org

To provide financial assistance to military enlisted personnel who are pursuing off-duty college-level education programs in fields related to electronics.

Title of Award: Association of Old Crows Enlisted Tuition Grants **Area, Field, or Subject:** Electronics; Engineering, Electrical; Mathematics and mathematical sciences; Physics **Level of Education for which Award is Granted:** Undergraduate **Number Awarded:** Varies each year; recently, a total of $160,000 per year was available for this program. **Funds Available:** Support is provided to supplement the funding available through the tuition assistance programs. **Duration:** 1 semester; may be renewed.

Eligibility Requirements: This program is open to military enlisted personnel (rank of E-4 and above) who are utilizing the tuition assistance programs of the services to study electrical engineering, physics, mathematics, and related areas during their off-duty hours. Selection is based on academic excellence and financial need. **Additional Information:** Funding is provided by local chapters of this organization, which was founded by World War II veterans who had engaged in electronic warfare to disrupt enemy communications and radars. The program was code-

named "Raven" and its operators became known as Old Crows. For information on a chapter in your area, contact the AOC Educational Foundation.

4401 ■ ASSOCIATION OF STATE DAM SAFETY OFFICIALS

Attn: Scholarship Coordinator
450 Old Vine Street, Second Floor
Lexington, KY 40507
Tel: (859)257-5140
Fax: (859)323-1958
E-mail: info@damsafety.org
Web Site: http://www.damsafety.org

To provide financial assistance for undergraduate education to students interested in fields related to dam safety.

Title of Award: Association of State Dam Safety Officials Scholarships **Area, Field, or Subject:** Engineering, Civil; Engineering, Hydraulic; Geology; Hydrology **Level of Education for which Award is Granted:** Four Year College **Number Awarded:** 2 or 3 each year. **Funds Available:** The stipend is $5,000 per year. **Duration:** 1 year; junior recipients may reapply for their senior year.

Eligibility Requirements: Applicants must be college seniors with a GPA of 2.5 or higher studying civil engineering or a related field. They must have a demonstrated interest in preparing for a career in hydraulics, hydrology, or geotechnical disciplines related to the design, construction, and operation of dams. U.S. citizenship is required. Selection is based on academic achievement, financial need, work experience and activities, and a 2-page essay on their proposed course of study and why dam safety is important. **Deadline for Receipt:** March of each year. **Additional Information:** This program was established in 1992.

4402 ■ ASSOCIATION OF THE UNITED STATES ARMY

Attn: National Secretary
2425 Wilson Boulevard
Arlington, VA 22201
Tel: (703)841-4300
Free: 800-336-4570
E-mail: ausa-info@ausa.org
Web Site: http://www.ausa.org

To provide financial assistance to active-duty and honorably-discharged soldiers interested in studying engineering in college.

Title of Award: Joseph P. and Helen T. Cribbins Scholarship **Area, Field, or Subject:** Engineering **Level of Education for which Award is Granted:** Undergraduate **Number Awarded:** 1 or more each year. **Funds Available:** The stipend is $2,000. **Duration:** 1 year.

Eligibility Requirements: This program is open to 1) soldiers currently serving in the active Army, Army Reserve, or Army National Guard of any rank; and 2) honorably-discharged soldiers from any component of the total Army. Applicants must have been accepted at an accredited college or university to work on a degree in engineering or a related field. Along with their application, they must submit a 1-page autobiography, 3 letters of recommendation, and a transcript of high school or college grades (depending on which they are currently attending). Selection is based on academic merit and personal achievement. Financial need is not normally a selection criterion, but in some cases of extreme need it may be used as a factor; the lack of financial need is never a cause for non-selection. **Deadline for Receipt:** June of each year.

4403 ■ ASSOCIATION OF THE WALL AND CEILING INDUSTRY

Attn: Foundation of the Wall and Ceiling Industry
803 West Broad Street, Suite 600
Falls Church, VA 22046
Tel: (703)538-1615
Fax: (703)534-8307
Web Site: http://www.awci.org/thefoundation.shtml

To provide financial assistance for undergraduate or graduate study in disciplines related to the wall and ceiling industry to employees of firms that are members of the Association of the Wall and Ceiling Industries-International (AWCI) and their dependents.

Title of Award: Foundation of the Wall and Ceiling Industry Scholarships **Area, Field, or Subject:** Architecture; Construction; Engineering **Level of Education for which Award is Granted:** Graduate, Undergraduate **Number Awarded:** 1 each year. **Funds Available:** The stipend is $10,000. **Duration:** 1 year.

Eligibility Requirements: This program is open to employees of AWCI member companies and their dependents. Applicants must be working on or planning to work on, as a full-time student, postsecondary education in the field of construction management, engineering, or architecture. They must have a GPA of 3.0 or higher during their last 2 semesters of study. Students in graduate schools, technical schools, associate degree programs, and 4-year colleges and universities are all eligible.

4404 ■ ASSOCIATION FOR WOMEN IN ARCHITECTURE

Attn: Scholarship Chair
22815 Frampton Avenue
Torrance, CA 90501-5034
Tel: (310)534-8466
Fax: (310)257-6885
E-mail: scholarship@awa-la.org
Web Site: http://www.awa-la.org/scholarships.php
To provide financial assistance to women undergraduates in California who are interested in careers in architecture.
Title of Award: Association for Women in Architecture Scholarships **Area, Field, or Subject:** Architecture; Engineering; Engineering, Civil; Engineering, Electrical; Engineering, Mechanical; Graphic art and design; Illustrators and illustrations; Interior design; Landscape architecture and design; Urban affairs/design/planning **Level of Education for which Award is Granted:** Undergraduate **Number Awarded:** 3 each year: 1 at $2,500, 1 at $1,500, and 1 at $1,000. **Funds Available:** Stipends are $2,500, $1,500, or $1,000. **Duration:** 1 year.
Eligibility Requirements: Eligible to apply are women students who have completed at least 1 full year of study in any of the following fields: architecture; civil, structural, mechanical, or electrical engineering as related to architecture; landscape architecture; urban and land planning; interior design; architectural rendering and illustration; or environmental design. They must be residents of California or attending school in California. Interviews are required for semifinalists. Selection is based on grades, a personal statement, financial need, recommendations, and the quality and organization of materials submitted. **Deadline for Receipt:** April of each year.

4405 ■ ASSOCIATION FOR WOMEN IN SCIENCE-SEATTLE CHAPTER

c/o Fran Solomon, Scholarship Committee Chair
5805 16th Avenue, N.E.
Seattle, WA 98105
Tel: (206)522-6441
E-mail: fran.solomon@metrokc.gov
Web Site: http://www.scn.org/awis/undergraduate_scholarship.htm
To provide financial assistance to women undergraduates from any state majoring in science, mathematics, or engineering at colleges and universities in western Washington.
Title of Award: AWIS Seattle Scholarships **Area, Field, or Subject:** Biochemistry; Biological and clinical sciences; Chemistry; Engineering; Environmental conservation; Environmental science; Geology; Mathematics and mathematical sciences; Pharmaceutical sciences; Physics **Level of Education for which Award is Granted:** Four Year College **Number Awarded:** Varies each year; recently, 11 of these scholarships were awarded. **Funds Available:** Stipends range from $1,000 to $1,500. **Duration:** 1 year.
Eligibility Requirements: This program is open to women from any state entering their junior or senior year at a 4-year college or university in western Washington. Applicants must have a declared major in science (e.g., biological sciences, environmental science, biochemistry, chemistry, pharmacy, geology, computer science, physics), mathematics, or engineering. Along with their application, they must submit essays on the events that led to their choice of a major, their current career plans and long-term goals, and their volunteer and community activities. Financial need is considered in the selection process. At least 1 scholarship is reserved for a woman from a group that is underrepresented in science, mathematics, and engineering careers, including Native American Indians and Alaska Natives, Black/African Americans, Mexican Americans/Chicanas/Latinas, Native Pacific Islanders (Polynesians, Melanesians, and Micronesians), and women with disabilities. **Deadline for Receipt:** March of each year. **Additional Information:** This program includes the following named awards: the Virginia Badger Scholarship, the Angela Paez Memorial Scholarship, and the Fran Solomon Scholarship. Support

for the program is provided by several sponsors, including the American Chemical Society, Iota Sigma Pi, Rosetta Inpharmatics, and ZymoGenetics, Inc.

4406 ■ ALEXANDER GRAHAM BELL ASSOCIATION FOR THE DEAF

Attn: Financial Aid Coordinator
3417 Volta Place, N.W.
Washington, DC 20007-2778
Tel: (202)337-5220
Fax: (202)337-8314
E-mail: financialaid@agbell.org
Web Site: http://www.agbell.org/
DesktopDefault.aspx?p=College_Scholarship_Awards
To provide financial assistance to undergraduate and graduate students with moderate to profound hearing loss, particularly those studying science or engineering.
Title of Award: Robert H. Weitbrecht Scholarship **Area, Field, or Subject:** Engineering; Science **Level of Education for which Award is Granted:** Graduate, Undergraduate **Number Awarded:** 1 each year. **Funds Available:** The stipend is $2,500 per year. **Duration:** 1 year; may be renewed 1 additional year.
Eligibility Requirements: This program is open to undergraduate and graduate students who have been diagnosed with a moderate to profound hearing loss prior to acquiring spoken language (hearing loss averages 60dB or greater in the better ear in the speech frequencies of 500, 1000, and 2000 Hz). Applicants must be able to demonstrate leadership potential and be committed to using spoken language as their primary mode of communication. They must be accepted or enrolled at a mainstream college or university as a full-time student. Along with their application, they must submit a 1-page essay discussing their career goals and how spoken communication is helping them to reach those goals as a person with a hearing loss. Financial need is considered in the selection process. Priority for this scholarship is given to applicants studying engineering or science. **Deadline for Receipt:** April of each year.

4407 ■ BOSTON SOCIETY OF CIVIL ENGINEERS

c/o The Engineering Center
One Walnut Street
Boston, MA 02108-3616
Tel: (617)227-5551
Fax: (617)227-6783
Web Site: http://www.bsces.org/sghscholarship.html
To provide financial assistance to undergraduate members of the American Society of Civil Engineers (ASCE) in Massachusetts.
Title of Award: Simpson, Gumpertz and Heger Scholarship **Area, Field, or Subject:** Engineering, Civil **Level of Education for which Award is Granted:** Four Year College **Number Awarded:** 1 each year. **Funds Available:** The stipend is $5,000. **Duration:** 1 year.
Eligibility Requirements: This program is open to undergraduate civil engineering majors who are members of an ASEC student chapter or club in Massachusetts. Applicants must have completed at least 2 and a half years of a 4-year program or the equivalent portion of a 5-year program and be planning to complete their degree in the following December or later. Along with their application, they must submit a 1-page letter of introduction that summarizes their qualifications; a resume that demonstrates their academic record, professional employment, other employment, professional activities, and personal items of interest; a 1-page essay on a topic that changes annually but relates to civil engineering problems; and transcripts. Financial need is not considered in the selection process. **Deadline for Receipt:** March of each year. **Additional Information:** This scholarship is sponsored by Simpson Gumperts and Heger Inc., 41 Seyon Street, Building 1, Suite 500, Waltham, MA 02453, (781) 907-9000, Fax: (781) 907-9009.

4408 ■ BOYS & GIRLS CLUBS OF GREATER SAN DIEGO

Attn: Scholarships
4635 Clairemont Mesa Boulevard
San Diego, CA 92117
Tel: (619)298-3520; (866)SD-YOUTH
Fax: (619)298-3615
Web Site: http://www.sdyouth.org/scholarships.htm
To provide financial assistance to graduating male high school seniors who plan to study designated fields in college.

Title of Award: Spence Reese Scholarships **Area, Field, or Subject:** Engineering; Law; Medicine; Political science **Level of Education for which Award is Granted:** Undergraduate **Number Awarded:** 4 each year: 1 in each of the designated fields. **Funds Available:** The stipend is $2,000 per year. **Duration:** 4 years.

Eligibility Requirements: Applicants must be graduating male high school seniors planning to study law, medicine, engineering, or political science in college. They may live anywhere in the United States, but must attend an interview in San Diego, California. Selection is based on academic standing, potential for good citizenship, academic ability, and financial need. **Deadline for Receipt:** April of each year. **Additional Information:** Travel expenses for the interview are reimbursed by the sponsor. A $10 processing fee must accompany all applications.

4409 ■ BROWN AND CALDWELL

Attn: Scholarship Program
201 North Civic Drive, Suite 115
P.O. Box 8045
Walnut Creek, CA 94596
Tel: (925)937-9010
Fax: (925)937-9026
E-mail: scholarships@brwncald.com
Web Site: http://www.brownandcaldwell.com
To provide financial assistance to minority students working on an undergraduate degree in an environmental or engineering field.

Title of Award: Brown and Caldwell Minority Scholarship **Area, Field, or Subject:** Biological and clinical sciences; Engineering, Chemical; Engineering, Civil; Environmental conservation; Environmental science; Geology; Hydrology; Industrial hygiene; Toxicology **Level of Education for which Award is Granted:** Four Year College **Number Awarded:** 1 each year. **Funds Available:** The stipend is $3,000. **Duration:** 1 year.

Eligibility Requirements: This program is open to members of minority groups (African Americans, Hispanics, Asians, Pacific Islanders, Native Americans, and Alaska Natives) who are full-time students in their junior year at an accredited 4-year college or university. Applicants must have a GPA of 3.0 or higher with a declared major in civil, chemical, or environmental engineering or an environmental science (e.g., biology, ecology, geology, hydrogeology, industrial hygiene, toxicology). Along with their application, they must submit an essay (up to 250 words) on why they chose to major in an environmental discipline. They must be U.S. citizens or permanent resident and available to participate in a summer internship at a Brown and Caldwell office. Financial need is not considered in the selection process. **Deadline for Receipt:** February of each year. **Additional Information:** As part of the paid summer internship at a Brown and Caldwell office at 1 of more than 40 cities in the country, the program provides a mentor to guide the intern through the company's information and communications resources.

4410 ■ BROWN AND CALDWELL

Attn: Scholarship Program
201 North Civic Drive, Suite 115
P.O. Box 8045
Walnut Creek, CA 94596
Tel: (925)937-9010
Fax: (925)937-9026
E-mail: scholarships@brwncald.com
Web Site: http://www.brownandcaldwell.com
To provide financial assistance to undergraduate students working on a degree in an environmental or engineering field.

Title of Award: Dr. W. Wesley Eckenfelder Scholarship **Area, Field, or Subject:** Biological and clinical sciences; Engineering, Chemical; Engineering, Civil; Environmental conservation; Environmental science; Geology; Hydrology; Industrial hygiene; Toxicology **Level of Education for which Award is Granted:** Four Year College **Number Awarded:** 1 each year. **Funds Available:** The stipend is $3,000. **Duration:** 1 year.

Eligibility Requirements: This program is open to U.S. citizens and permanent residents enrolled as full-time students in their junior year at an accredited 4-year college or university. Applicants must have a GPA of 3.0 or higher with a declared major in civil, chemical, or environmental engineering or an environmental science (e.g., biology, ecology, geology, hydrogeology, industrial hygiene, toxicology). Along with their application, they must submit an essay (up to 250 words) on why they chose to major in an environmental discipline. Financial need is not considered in the

selection process. **Deadline for Receipt:** February of each year. **Additional Information:** This scholarship was first awarded in 1999.

4411 ■ H. FLETCHER BROWN TRUST

PNC Bank Delaware
Attn: Donald W. Davis
222 Delaware Avenue, 16th Floor
Wilmington, DE 19899
Tel: (302)429-2827
Fax: (302)429-5658
E-mail: Robbie.testa@pncadvisors.com
To provide financial assistance to residents of Delaware who are interested in studying engineering, chemistry, medicine, dentistry, or law.

Title of Award: H. Fletcher Brown Scholarship **Area, Field, or Subject:** Chemistry; Dentistry; Engineering; Law; Medicine; Medicine, Osteopathic **Level of Education for which Award is Granted:** Graduate, Professional, Undergraduate **Funds Available:** The amount of the scholarship is determined by the scholarship committee and is awarded in installments over the length of study. **Duration:** 1 year; may be renewed if the recipient maintains a GPA of 2.5 or higher and continues to be worthy of and eligible for the award.

Eligibility Requirements: This program is open to Delaware residents who were born in Delaware, are either high school seniors entering the first year of college or college seniors entering the first year of graduate school, are of good moral character, and need financial assistance from sources outside their family. Applicants must have combined mathematics and verbal SAT scores of 1000 or higher, rank in the upper 20% of their class, and come from a family whose income is less than $75,000. Their proposed fields of study must be engineering, chemistry, medicine (for an M.D. or D.O. degree only), dentistry, or law. Finalists are interviewed. **Deadline for Receipt:** March of each year.

4412 ■ BUSINESS AND PROFESSIONAL WOMEN OF VIRGINIA

Attn: Virginia BPW Foundation
P.O. Box 4842
McLean, VA 22103-4842
Web Site: http://www.bpwva.org/Foundation.shtml
To provide financial assistance to women in Virginia who are interested in working on a bachelor's or advanced degree in science or technology.

Title of Award: Women in Science and Technology Scholarship **Area, Field, or Subject:** Actuarial science; Biological and clinical sciences; Chemistry; Computer and information sciences; Dentistry; Engineering; Engineering, Biomedical; Insurance and insurance-related fields; Mathematics and mathematical sciences; Medicine; Physics; Science; Technology **Level of Education for which Award is Granted:** Graduate, Undergraduate **Number Awarded:** At least 1 each year. **Funds Available:** Stipends range from $500 to $1,000 per year, depending on the need of the recipient; funds may be used for tuition, fees, books, transportation, living expenses, and dependent care. **Duration:** 1 year; recipients may reapply (but prior recipients are not given priority).

Eligibility Requirements: This program is open to women who are at least 18 years of age, U.S. citizens, Virginia residents, accepted at or currently studying at a Virginia college or university, and working on a bachelor's, master's, or doctoral degree in 1 of the following fields: actuarial science, biology, bioengineering, chemistry, computer science, dentistry, engineering, mathematics, medicine, physics, or a similar scientific or technical field. Applicants must have a definite plan to use their education in a scientific or technical profession. They must be able to demonstrate financial need. **Deadline for Receipt:** March of each year. **Additional Information:** Recipients must complete their studies within 2 years.

4413 ■ CALIFORNIA DEPARTMENT OF TRANSPORTATION

Attn: Division of Engineering Services
MS 9 5/2J
P.O. Box 168041
Sacramento, CA 95816-8041
Tel: (916)227-8126
E-mail: karen_bailey@dot.ca.gov
Web Site: http://www.dot.ca.gov/hq/esc/scholarships
To provide financial assistance to high school seniors in California who plan to study engineering or architecture at a college or university in the state.

Title of Award: Division of Engineering Services Engineering/Architectural Scholarship **Area, Field, or Subject:** Architecture; Engineering **Level of Education for which Award is Granted:** Undergraduate **Number Awarded:** At least 1 each year. **Funds Available:** The stipend is $1,000. **Duration:** 1 year.

Eligibility Requirements: This program is open to seniors graduating from high schools in California and planning to enroll in an engineering or architectural program at a community college, state college, or university in the state. Applicants must submit 1) a 100-word personal statement on their college and career plans and how they believe they can make a contribution to Caltrans; 2) a 500-word essay on how they would improve California's current transportation system; 3) a list of community and school activities; 4) information on work and/or volunteer experience; and 4) letters of recommendation. **Deadline for Receipt:** March **Additional Information:** This program is jointly sponsored by the California Department of Transportation (Caltrans) Division of Engineering Services and the California Transportation Foundation (CTF).

4414 ■ CALIFORNIA DEPARTMENT OF TRANSPORTATION

Attn: Division of Engineering Services
MS 9 5/2J
P.O. Box 168041
Sacramento, CA 95816-8041
Tel: (916)227-8126
E-mail: karen_bailey@dot.ca.gov
Web Site: http://www.dot.ca.gov/hq/esc/scholarships
To provide financial assistance to high school seniors in California who plan to study civil engineering at a college or university in the state in order to prepare for a career in transportation.

Title of Award: James E. Roberts Engineering Scholarship **Area, Field, or Subject:** Engineering, Civil; Transportation **Level of Education for which Award is Granted:** Undergraduate **Number Awarded:** 2 each year. **Funds Available:** The stipend is $1,000. **Duration:** 1 year.

Eligibility Requirements: This program is open to seniors graduating from high schools in California and planning to enroll in a civil engineering program at a community college, state college, or university in the state. Applicants must be planning to prepare for a career in transportation. Along with their application, they must submit a 100-word personal statement on their college and career plans and how they believe they can make a contribution to Caltrans as a civil engineer in the transportation field. Selection is based on that statement, community and school activities, work and/or volunteer experience, letters of recommendation, and financial need. **Deadline for Receipt:** March

4415 ■ JORGE MAS CANOSA FREEDOM FOUNDATION

c/o Cuban American National Foundation
1312 S.W. 27th Avenue
P.O. Box 440069
Miami, FL 33144-9926
Tel: (305)592-7768
Fax: (305)592-7889
Web Site: http://www.canf.org
To provide financial assistance to students of Cuban descent who are working on an undergraduate or graduate degree in selected subject areas.

Title of Award: Mas Family Scholarship Program **Area, Field, or Subject:** Business administration; Communications; Economics; Engineering; International affairs and relations; Journalism **Level of Education for which Award is Granted:** Graduate, Undergraduate **Funds Available:** The amount of the award depends on the cost of tuition at the recipient's selected institution, on the family's situation, and on the amount of funds received from other sources. The amount of the yearly award cannot exceed $10,000. Full scholarships are not awarded to students who will be receiving full tuition scholarships and/or stipendiary support from other sources. **Duration:** 1 year; recipients may reapply and are given preference over other candidates.

Eligibility Requirements: This program is open to students who are direct descendants of those who left Cuba or were born in Cuba themselves. Applicants must be or have been in the top 10% of their high school graduating class and have be able to meet federal standards of financial need. At least 1 parent or 2 grandparents must have been born in Cuba. Both undergraduate and graduate students may apply, provided they are majoring in 1 of the following subjects: engineering, business,

international relations, economics, communications, or journalism. Selection is based on academic performance, leadership qualities, financial need, potential to contribute to the advancement of a free society, and likelihood of succeeding in their chosen field. Finalists may be interviewed. **Deadline for Receipt:** March of each year. **Additional Information:** This program was previously offered by the Cuban American National Foundation.

4416 ■ CATCHING THE DREAM

8200 Mountain Road, N.E., Suite 203
Albuquerque, NM 87110-7835
Tel: (505)262-2351
Fax: (505)262-0534
E-mail: NScholarsh@aol.com
Web Site: http://www.catchingthedream.org
To provide financial assistance to American Indian students who are interested in working on an undergraduate or graduate degree in selected fields.

Title of Award: MESBEC Program **Area, Field, or Subject:** Business administration; Computer and information sciences; Education; Engineering; Mathematics and mathematical sciences; Science **Level of Education for which Award is Granted:** Four Year College, Graduate **Number Awarded:** Varies; generally, 30 to 35 each year. **Funds Available:** Stipends range from $500 to $5,000. **Duration:** 1 year; may be renewed.

Eligibility Requirements: This program is open to American Indians who can provide proof that they are at least one-quarter Indian blood and a member of a U.S. tribe that is federally-recognized, state-recognized, or terminated. Applicants must be enrolled or planning to enroll full time and major in the 1 of the following fields: mathematics, engineering, science, business administration, education, or computer science. They may be entering freshmen, undergraduate students, graduate students, or Ph.D. candidates. Along with their application, they must submit documentation of financial need, 3 letters of recommendation, copies of applications and responses for at least 15 other sources of funding, official transcripts, standardized test scores (ACT, SAT, GRE, MCAT, LSAT, etc.), and an essay explaining their goals in life, college plans, and career plans (especially how those plans include working with and benefiting Indians). Selection is based on merit and potential for improving the lives of Indian people. **Deadline for Receipt:** April of each year for fall term; September of each year for spring and winter terms; March of each year for summer school. **Additional Information:** MESBEC is an acronym that stands for the priority areas of this program: mathematics, engineering, science, business, education, and computers. The sponsor was formerly known as the Native American Scholarship Fund.

4417 ■ CHICAGO URBAN LEAGUE

Attn: Education Department
4510 South Michigan Avenue
Chicago, IL 60653-3898
Tel: (773)451-3565
Fax: (773)285-7772
E-mail: info@cul-chicago.org
Web Site: http://www.cul-chicago.org
To provide financial assistance to Illinois residents of color interested in studying a field related to automotive technology in college.

Title of Award: Mercedes-Benz Scholarships **Area, Field, or Subject:** Accounting; Automotive technology; Business; Business administration; Computer and information sciences; Engineering, Automotive; Transportation **Level of Education for which Award is Granted:** Undergraduate **Number Awarded:** 4 each year. **Funds Available:** The stipend is $1,000 per year. **Duration:** 4 years.

Eligibility Requirements: This program is open to Illinois residents of color who are graduating high school seniors with a GPA of 2.5 or higher and planning to enroll as full-time undergraduate students at a 4-year college or university, Triton College, or 1 of the City Colleges of Chicago. Applicants must be planning to major in automotive technology or a field related to the automotive industry (e.g., engineering, computer science, business, or accounting). They must be able to demonstrate financial need. **Deadline for Receipt:** May of each year. **Additional Information:**

This program is offered as part of the Chicago Urban League's Whitney M. Young, Jr. Memorial Scholarship Fund, established in 1970.

4418 ■ CHRISTIAN LIFE RESOURCES

Attn: WELS Lutherans for Life
Scholarship Review Committee
2949 North Mayfair Road, Suite 309
Milwaukee, WI 53222-4304
Tel: (414)774-1331
Fax: (414)774-1360
Web Site: http://www.christianliferesources.com
To provide financial assistance to Lutheran high school seniors in Wisconsin who are interested in studying life-related issues in college.
Title of Award: WELS Lutherans for Life Scholarship Program **Area, Field, or Subject:** Biological and clinical sciences; Education, Special; Engineering, Biomedical; Journalism; Law; Medicine; Physical therapy; Political science; Psychology; Social work **Level of Education for which Award is Granted:** Four Year College **Number Awarded:** Varies each year; recently, 9 of these scholarships were awarded. **Funds Available:** Stipends up to $1,000 are available. **Duration:** 1 year.
Eligibility Requirements: This program is open to high school seniors who are active members of the Wisconsin Evangelical Lutheran Synod (WELS) or an affiliated church. Applicants must be planning to go to a 4-year school to prepare for a secular career in which pro-life values will be demonstrated. Acceptable fields include medicine, biotechnology/ biological engineering, medical research/genetics, law/politics, journalism/ media, psychology, physical therapy, social services, or special education. They must have a GPA of 3.25 or higher. Along with their application, they must submit essays on 1) the field of study they plan to enter and how it relates to pro-life issues; 2) why the scholarship should be awarded to them, including their future goals; and 3) how they have demonstrated a Christian, pro-life attitude in their life. **Deadline for Receipt:** February of each year. **Additional Information:** WELS Lutherans for Life was formerly a ministry of the Wisconsin Evangelical Lutheran Synod.

4419 ■ COLORADO MOTOR CARRIERS ASSOCIATION

Attn: Scholarship Committee
4060 Elati Street
Denver, CO 80216
Tel: (303)433-3375
Fax: (303)477-6977
E-mail: meredith@cmca.com
Web Site: http://www.cmca.com/scholarship.htm
To provide financial assistance to Colorado residents preparing for a career in the trucking industry as diesel mechanics.
Title of Award: Colorado Motor Carriers Association Diesel Scholarship **Area, Field, or Subject:** Business; Mechanics and repairs; Transportation **Level of Education for which Award is Granted:** Undergraduate **Number Awarded:** Varies each year. **Funds Available:** A stipend is awarded (amount not specified). **Duration:** 1 year.
Eligibility Requirements: This program is open to Colorado residents currently enrolled in a diesel mechanic school with good standing in both GPA and attendance. Applicants must be preparing for a career in the trucking industry but need assistance to do so. Preference is given to students currently employed in the industry. Along with their application, they must submit a 300-word essay on themselves, their goals, what they imagine as their future, and why they chose this industry. **Deadline for Receipt:** March of each year.

4420 ■ COLORADO READY MIXED CONCRETE ASSOCIATION/ COLORADO ROCK PRODUCTS ASSOCIATION

Attn: Scholarship Fund
6855 South Havana Street, Suite 540
Centennial, CO 80112
Tel: (303)290-0303
Fax: (303)290-8008
E-mail: pschauer@crmca.org
Web Site: http://www.crmca.org/scholarships/default.php
To provide financial assistance to upper-division students from Colorado who are preparing for a career in areas of interest to the Colorado Ready Mixed Concrete Association (CRMCA) and the Colorado Rock Products Association (CRPA).
Title of Award: CRMCA/CRPA Scholarships **Area, Field, or Subject:** Architecture; Business; Construction; Engineering; Engineering, Materi-

als; Materials research/science **Level of Education for which Award is Granted:** Four Year College **Number Awarded:** 4 each year. **Funds Available:** The stipend is $1,000. Funds are paid directly to the student's institution. **Duration:** 1 year.
Eligibility Requirements: This program is open to full-time juniors and seniors at colleges and universities in Colorado who have a GPA of 3.0 or higher. Applicants must be preparing for a career in such fields as aggregate extraction, building construction, road building, municipal utility construction, building design, heavy equipment design, materials research or application, or other fields associated with the use of aggregates or concrete. Preference is given to students whose home residence is Colorado, have graduated from a high school in Colorado, and have a parent employed in concrete or aggregate production industries or associated or auxiliary industries. Along with their application, they must submit a brief resume of their current activities and work experience, 3 letters of character reference, and a 1-page statement on their plans for the future and career. Financial need is not considered in the selection process. **Deadline for Receipt:** July of each year.

4421 ■ COMMUNITY FOUNDATION OF GREATER JACKSON

525 East Capitol Street, Suite 5B
Jackson, MS 39201
Tel: (601)974-6044
Fax: (601)974-6045
E-mail: info@cfgreaterjackson.org
Web Site: http://www.cfgreaterjackson.org
To provide financial assistance to undergraduate students in Mississippi who are preparing for a career in the field of public works.
Title of Award: APWA Scholarship Fund **Area, Field, or Subject:** Biological and clinical sciences; Chemistry; Engineering, Civil; Engineering, Electrical; Environmental science; Public administration **Level of Education for which Award is Granted:** Four Year College **Number Awarded:** 2 each year. **Funds Available:** The stipend is $1,000. **Duration:** 1 year.
Eligibility Requirements: This program is open to full-time juniors and seniors at public universities in Mississippi who are preparing to enter the field of public works. Applicants must have graduated from a high school in Mississippi. Eligible majors include civil engineering, electrical engineering, environmental engineering, public administration, biology, or chemistry. Selection is based on merit and need. **Deadline for Receipt:** April of each year. **Additional Information:** This program, established in 2000, is sponsored by the Mississippi chapter of the American Public Works Association (APWA).

4422 ■ CONGRESSIONAL BLACK CAUCUS FOUNDATION, INC.

Attn: Director, Educational Programs
1720 Massachusetts Avenue, N.W.
Washington, DC 20036
Tel: (202)263-2836
Free: 800-784-2577
Fax: (202)775-0773
E-mail: spouses@cbcfinc.org
Web Site: http://www.cbcfinc.org
To provide financial assistance to minority and other undergraduate and graduate students who reside in a Congressional district represented by an African American and are interested in preparing for a health-related career.
Title of Award: Cheerios Brand Health Initiative Scholarship **Area, Field, or Subject:** Biological and clinical sciences; Chemistry; Education, Physical; Engineering; Food service careers; Health care services; Medicine; Nursing **Level of Education for which Award is Granted:** Graduate, Undergraduate **Number Awarded:** Varies each year. **Funds Available:** A stipend is awarded (amount not specified). **Duration:** 1 year.
Eligibility Requirements: This program is open to 1) minority and other graduating high school seniors planning to attend an accredited institution of higher education and 2) currently-enrolled full-time undergraduate, graduate, and doctoral students in good academic standing with a GPA of 2.5 or higher. Applicants must reside or attend school in a Congressional district represented by a member of the Congressional Black Caucus. They must be interested in preparing for a career in a medical, food services, or other health-related field, including pre-medicine, nursing, chemistry, biology, physical education, and engineering. Along with their application, they must submit a 500-word personal statement on 1) the

field of study they intend to pursue and why they have chosen that field; 2) their interests, involvement in school activities, community and public service, hobbies, special talents, sports, and other highlight areas; and 3) any other experiences, skills, or qualifications they feel should be considered. They must also be able to document financial need. **Deadline for Receipt:** April of each year. **Additional Information:** The program was established in 1998 with support from General Mills, Inc.

4423 ■ CONNECTICUT BUILDING CONGRESS

Attn: Scholarship Fund
2600 Dixwell Avenue, Suite 7
Hamden, CT 06514-1800
Tel: (203)281-3183
Fax: (203)281-8932
E-mail: info@cbc-ct.org
Web Site: http://www.cbc-ct.org/secondpage_folder/member.html
To provide financial assistance to high school seniors in Connecticut who are interested in studying a field related to the construction industry in college.
Title of Award: Connecticut Building Congress Scholarships **Area, Field, or Subject:** Architecture; Cartography/Surveying; Construction; Engineering; Management; Urban affairs/design/planning **Level of Education for which Award is Granted:** Undergraduate **Number Awarded:** Varies each year. **Funds Available:** Stipends range from $500 to $2,000 per year. **Duration:** Up to 4 years.
Eligibility Requirements: This program is open to graduating seniors at high schools in Connecticut. Applicants must be interested in attending a 2- or 4-year college or university to major in a field related to construction (e.g., architecture, engineering, construction management, surveying, planning, drafting). They must submit an essay (up to 500 words) that explains how their planned studies will relate to a career in the construction industry. Selection is based on academic merit, extracurricular activities, potential, and financial need. **Deadline for Receipt:** February of each year.

4424 ■ CONNECTICUT SOCIETY OF PROFESSIONAL ENGINEERS

Attn: Scholarship Program
2600 Dixwell Avenue, Suite 7
Hamden, CT 06514-1833
Tel: (203)281-4322
Fax: (203)248-8932
E-mail: info@ctspe.org
Web Site: http://www.ctspe.net
To provide financial assistance to high school seniors in Connecticut who are interested in preparing for a career in engineering.
Title of Award: Connecticut Society of Professional Engineers Scholarship **Area, Field, or Subject:** Engineering **Level of Education for which Award is Granted:** Undergraduate **Number Awarded:** Varies each year. **Funds Available:** A stipend is awarded (amount not specified). **Duration:** 1 year.
Eligibility Requirements: This program is open to Connecticut residents who are attending or planning to attend an ABET-accredited engineering program at a college or university anywhere in the United States. Applicants must submit a 500-word essay on their interest in engineering, their major area of study and area of specialization, and the occupation they plan to pursue after graduation. Selection is based on the essay, academic merit, extracurricular activities, potential, and financial need. **Deadline for Receipt:** October of each year.

4425 ■ CONSTRUCTION SPECIFICATIONS INSTITUTE-DC METROPOLITAN CHAPTER

c/o Dave Metzger, Academic Affairs Committee Chair
Heller & Metzger PC
11 Dupont Circle, N.W., Suite 601
Washington, DC 20036
Tel: (202)364-2222
Fax: (202)234-5502
E-mail: davem@hellerandmetzger.com
Web Site: http://www.csidcmetro.org/warner_fund.html
To provide financial assistance to members of student chapters of the Construction Specifications Institute (CSI) at colleges and universities in the Washington, D.C. metropolitan area.
Title of Award: Franklyn E. Warner Student Fellowship for Balanced Achievement **Area, Field, or Subject:** Architecture; Construction;

Engineering **Level of Education for which Award is Granted:** Four Year College **Number Awarded:** 1 each year. **Funds Available:** A stipend is awarded (amount not specified). **Duration:** 1 year.
Eligibility Requirements: This program is open to CSI student members at schools in the Washington, D.C. metropolitan area who are rising seniors or graduating seniors. Applicants must be majoring in architecture, engineering, or construction management. Along with their application, they must submit an essay of 500 to 750 words that demonstrates their understanding of the balanced relationships among the aesthetic, functional, technical, and managerial aspects of the built environment. Selection is based on the essay, potential as future leader in the design and construction industry, and letters of recommendation demonstrating the applicant's skills and abilities across a balanced and diversified range of professional areas. **Deadline for Receipt:** January of each year. **Additional Information:** This program was established in 2003.

4426 ■ CONSTRUCTION SPECIFICATIONS INSTITUTE-GRAND RAPIDS CHAPTER

c/o Lynn J. DePeal, Academic Affairs Committee Chair
IR SSC Michigan
2556 Albert Drive, S.E.
Grand Rapids, MI 49506
Tel: (616)285-8009
Fax: (616)285-8009
E-mail: lynn_depeal@irco.com
Web Site: http://www.csigrandrapids.org
To provide financial assistance to students at colleges and universities in Michigan who are preparing for a career in the construction industry.
Title of Award: Grand Rapids Chapter CSI Scholarship **Area, Field, or Subject:** Architecture; Construction; Engineering; Engineering, Electrical; Engineering, Mechanical **Level of Education for which Award is Granted:** Undergraduate **Number Awarded:** 1 or more each year. **Funds Available:** Stipends up to $1,500 are available. **Duration:** 1 year.
Eligibility Requirements: This program is open to students enrolled at an accredited college, university, or trade school in Michigan. Applicants must be working on a degree in a field directly related to the construction industry, including architecture, engineering (electrical, mechanical, construction), management technology, and facilities maintenance. Along with their application, they must submit brief essays about 1) the kinds of activities they participate in and enjoy, and the people who participate in those activities with them; 2) how they see their career in the construction-related industry and what they think they can offer the industry; and 3) their financial need and desire for assistance. Selection is based on scholastic ability, references, overall impression of the applicant as presented in the essays, and how the applicant will benefit from receiving this scholarship. Preference is given to applicants who are members of the Construction Specifics Institute (CSI) or related to a member. **Deadline for Receipt:** April of each year.

4427 ■ CONSTRUCTION SPECIFICATIONS INSTITUTE-MAINE CHAPTER

c/o James Beaulieu, Academic Affairs Committee Chair
Ledgewood Construction
27 Main Street
South Portland, ME 04106
Tel: (207)767-1866
Fax: (207)767-1869
Web Site: http://www.mecsi.org
To provide financial assistance to Maine residents preparing for a career in a field related to construction technology at a public university in the state.
Title of Award: Advancement of Construction Technology Scholarship **Area, Field, or Subject:** Architecture; Engineering **Level of Education for which Award is Granted:** Undergraduate **Number Awarded:** 1 each year. **Funds Available:** The stipend is at least $1,000. **Duration:** 1 year.
Eligibility Requirements: This program is open to residents of Maine who have completed at least 1 year of study at a campus of the University of Maine system. Applicants must be preparing for a career in architectural

or engineering technology. They must be able to demonstrate active involvement in a career or industry organization or association.

4428 ■ CONSTRUCTION SPECIFICATIONS INSTITUTE-RICHMOND CHAPTER

Attn: Richmond CSI Scholarship Fund Foundation
9016 Peaks Road
Ashland, VA 23005
Tel: (804)307-3282
Fax: (804)752-2670
E-mail: csirichmond@wans.net
Web Site: http://www.richmondcsi.org/scholarship.shtml

To provide financial assistance to undergraduate students in Virginia who are preparing for a construction-related career.

Title of Award: Norman F. Jacobs, Jr. Scholarship **Area, Field, or Subject:** Architecture; Construction; Engineering; Engineering, Civil; Engineering, Electrical; Engineering, Mechanical **Level of Education for which Award is Granted:** Four Year College **Number Awarded:** Up to 2 each year. **Funds Available:** The stipend is at least $1,000. Funds are sent directly to the recipient's institution. **Duration:** 1 year.
Eligibility Requirements: Eligible to apply are students who are enrolled full time at an accredited Virginia college or university and majoring in architecture, construction, or a construction-related field of engineering (civil, structural, mechanical, electrical). Applicants must have completed 1 year of a 2-year program or 2 full years of a 4- or 5-year bachelor's degree program. They must have a GPA of 2.5 or higher and be able to demonstrate financial need. **Deadline for Receipt:** April of each year.

4429 ■ CONSULTING ENGINEERS AND LAND SURVEYORS OF CALIFORNIA

Attn: Communications Director
1303 J Street, Suite 450
Sacramento, CA 95814
Tel: (916)441-7991
Fax: (916)441-6312
E-mail: staff@celsoc.org
Web Site: http://www.celsoc.org

To provide financial assistance to students working on a graduate degree at an approved engineering program in California.

Title of Award: Consulting Engineers and Land Surveyors of California Graduate Scholarships **Area, Field, or Subject:** Engineering, Civil; Environmental science **Level of Education for which Award is Granted:** Four Year College, Graduate **Number Awarded:** Varies each year. Recently, 2 of these scholarships were awarded: 1 at $5,000 and 1 at $1,000. **Funds Available:** The stipend is $5,000 or $1,000. **Duration:** 1 year; recipients may reapply for 1 additional year.
Eligibility Requirements: This program is open to U.S. citizens who are working full time on a graduate degree in an ABET-approved civil engineering (including environmental, geotechnical, structural, transportation, etc.) program in California. Applicants must be entering or continuing a graduate program to qualify; students graduating this academic year are not eligible. They must have a GPA of 3.0 or higher; to be considered for some scholarships, they must have a GPA in engineering and land surveying courses of 3.5 or higher and an overall GPA of 3.2 or higher. Along with their application, they must submit an essay, approximately 500 words in length, on "What is a consulting engineer or land surveyor and why should you consider it as a career?" Selection is based on GPA (28 points); the essay (25 points); work experience (20 points); recommendations (17 points); and college activities (10 points). Financial need is not considered in the selection process. **Deadline for Receipt:** January of each year.

4430 ■ CONSULTING ENGINEERS AND LAND SURVEYORS OF CALIFORNIA

Attn: Communications Director
1303 J Street, Suite 450
Sacramento, CA 95814
Tel: (916)441-7991
Fax: (916)441-6312
E-mail: staff@celsoc.org
Web Site: http://www.celsoc.org

To provide financial assistance to students working on a bachelor's degree at an approved engineering program or land surveying program in California.

Title of Award: Consulting Engineers and Land Surveyors of California Undergraduate Scholarships **Area, Field, or Subject:** Cartography/Surveying; Engineering **Level of Education for which Award is Granted:** Undergraduate **Number Awarded:** Varies each year. Recently, 4 of these scholarships were awarded: 1 at $7,500, 1 at $3,500, 1 at $2,000, and 1 at $1,000. **Funds Available:** Stipends range up to $7,500. **Duration:** 1 year; recipients may reapply for 1 additional year.
Eligibility Requirements: This program is open to U.S. citizens who are working full time on a bachelor's degree in an ABET-approved engineering program or an accredited land surveying program in California. Applicants must be entering their junior, senior, or fifth year to qualify; students graduating this academic year are not eligible. They must have a GPA of 3.0 or higher; to be considered for some scholarships, they must have a GPA in engineering and land surveying courses of 3.5 or higher and an overall GPA of 3.2 or higher. Along with their application, they must submit an essay, approximately 500 words in length, on "What is a consulting engineer or land surveyor and why should you consider it as a career?" Selection is based on GPA (28 points); the essay (25 points); work experience (20 points); recommendations (17 points); and college activities (10 points). Financial need is not considered in the selection process. **Deadline for Receipt:** January of each year.

4431 ■ COOK INLET REGION, INC.

Attn: CIRI Foundation
2600 Cordova Street, Suite 206
Anchorage, AK 99503
Tel: (907)263-5582
Free: 800-764-3382
Fax: (907)263-5588
E-mail: tcf@ciri.com
Web Site: http://www.thecirifoundation.org/scholarship.html

To provide financial assistance for undergraduate or graduate studies in selected fields to Alaska Natives who are original enrollees to Cook Inlet Region, Inc. (CIRI) and their lineal descendants.

Title of Award: CIRI Foundation Special Excellence Scholarships **Area, Field, or Subject:** Business administration; Education; Engineering; General studies/Field of study not specified; Health care services; Mathematics and mathematical sciences; Science **Level of Education for which Award is Granted:** Four Year College, Graduate **Number Awarded:** 1 or more each year. **Funds Available:** The stipend is $18,000 per year. **Duration:** 1 year; may be renewed.
Eligibility Requirements: This program is open to Alaska Native enrollees to CIRI under the Alaska Native Claims Settlement Act (ANCSA) of 1971 and their lineal descendants. There are no Alaska residency requirements or age limitations. Applicants must be accepted or enrolled full time in a 4-year undergraduate or a graduate degree program. They must have a GPA of 3.7 or higher. Preference is given to students working on a degree in business, education, mathematics, sciences, health services, or engineering. Selection is based on academic achievement, rigor of course work or degree program, quality of a statement of purpose, student financial contribution, financial need, grade level, previous work performance, education and community activities, letters of recommendation, seriousness of purpose, and practicality of educational and professional goals. **Deadline for Receipt:** May of each year. **Additional Information:** This program was established in 1997. Recipients must enroll in school on a full-time basis.

4432 ■ COOK INLET REGION, INC.

Attn: CIRI Foundation
2600 Cordova Street, Suite 206
Anchorage, AK 99503
Tel: (907)263-5582
Free: 800-764-3382
Fax: (907)263-5588
E-mail: tcf@ciri.com
Web Site: http://www.thecirifoundation.org/scholarship.html

To provide financial assistance for undergraduate or graduate studies to Alaska Natives who are original enrollees to Cook Inlet Region, Inc. (CIRI) and their lineal descendants.

Title of Award: Kirby McDonald Education Endowment Scholarship Fund **Area, Field, or Subject:** Business administration; Culinary arts; Engineering; General studies/Field of study not specified **Level of Education for which Award is Granted:** Four Year College, Graduate **Number**

Awarded: Varies each year; recently, 1 of these scholarships (at $2,000 per semester) was awarded. **Funds Available:** The stipend is $9,000 per year, $7,000 per year, or $2,000 per semester, depending on GPA. **Duration:** 1 year (2 semesters).
Eligibility Requirements: This program is open to Alaska Native enrollees to CIRI under the Alaska Native Claims Settlement Act (ANCSA) of 1971 and their lineal descendants. There are no Alaska residency requirements or age limitations. Applicants must be accepted or enrolled full time in a 4-year undergraduate or a graduate degree program. Preference is given to students in the culinary arts, but students in business administration and engineering are also eligible. They must have a GPA of 2.5 or higher. Selection is based on academic achievement, rigor of course work or degree program, quality of a statement of purpose, student financial contribution, financial need, grade level, previous work performance, education and community activities, letters of recommendation, seriousness of purpose, and practicality of educational and professional goals. **Deadline for Receipt:** May of each year. **Additional Information:** This program was established in 1991. Recipients must attend school on a full-time basis.

4433 ■ COOK INLET TRIBAL COUNCIL, INC.
Attn: Tribal Scholarships and Grants Program
2600 Cordova Street, Suite 206
Anchorage, AK 99503
Tel: (907)265-5904; 877-985-5900
Fax: (907)561-3755
E-mail: scholarships@citci.com
Web Site: http://www.thecirifoundation.org/scholarship.html
To provide financial assistance to Alaska Natives who are working on an undergraduate or graduate degree in information technology or engineering.
Title of Award: Alyeska Match Scholarships **Area, Field, or Subject:** Engineering; Information science and technology **Level of Education for which Award is Granted:** Graduate, Undergraduate **Number Awarded:** Varies each year. **Funds Available:** This program provides supplementary matching financial aid. The amount of the award depends on the availability of funds. Awards are intended to be applied to tuition, fees, course-required books and supplies, and on-campus housing and meal plans only. **Duration:** 1 year; may be renewed up to 4 additional years if the recipient maintains a GPA of 2.0 or higher.
Eligibility Requirements: This program is open to Alaska Natives who are enrolled in college, graduate school, or a vocational training program. Applicants must be studying information technology or engineering as a full-time student. They must be able to demonstrate unmet financial need even though they are receiving other funding. Awards are granted on a first-come, first-served basis. **Deadline for Receipt:** June or each year for fall; November of each year for spring. **Additional Information:** Funding for this program is provided by Alyeska Pipeline Service Company.

4434 ■ COUNCIL OF ENERGY RESOURCE TRIBES
Attn: Education Program Director
695 South Colorado Boulevard, Suite 10
Denver, CO 80246-8008
Tel: (303)282-7576
Fax: (303)282-7584
E-mail: info@CERTRedEarth.com
Web Site: http://www.certredearth.com
To provide financial assistance to American Indian high school seniors who are interested in studying fields related to mathematics, business, science, engineering, or other technical fields in college.
Title of Award: CERT Scholarships **Area, Field, or Subject:** Business administration; Engineering; Mathematics and mathematical sciences; Science **Level of Education for which Award is Granted:** Graduate, Undergraduate **Funds Available:** Costs of instruction, activities, and room and board for the summer institute are paid by the TRIBES program. The amount of the college scholarship is $1,000 per year. **Duration:** 1 year; may be renewed up to 4 additional years, provided the recipient maintains a GPA of 2.5 or higher.
Eligibility Requirements: This program is open to Indian high school seniors, college students, and graduates students who have participated in the Tribal Resource Institute in Business, Engineering, and Science (TRIBES) program, an intensive 7-week summer college-level program. CERT internship participants are also eligible. Applicants must be plan-

ning to enroll full time at an accredited 2- or 4-year tribal, public, or private college or university and major in business, engineering, science, mathematics, computer technology, or a related field. Along with their application, they must submit official tribal affiliation documents, university or college enrollment verification, and their most recent academic transcripts. Financial need is also considered in the selection process. **Deadline for Receipt:** Applications for the TRIBES program must be submitted by January of each year. Other students may apply by the end of August for the fall semester or January for the spring semester. **Additional Information:** The TRIBES program runs for 7 weeks during the summer at the University of New Mexico, Native American Studies, MSC06 3740, Albuquerque, NM 87131-0001, (505) 277-1812, Fax: (505) 277-1818.

4435 ■ COUNCIL OF THE GREAT CITY SCHOOLS
1301 Pennsylvania Avenue, N.W., Suite 702
Washington, DC 20004
Tel: (202)393-2427
Fax: (202)393-2400
Web Site: http://www.cgcs.org
To provide financial assistance to African American women interested in studying engineering, mathematics, science, or technology in college.
Title of Award: Marcia Page Scholarship for Mathematics and Science Education **Area, Field, or Subject:** Engineering; Mathematics and mathematical sciences; Science; Technology **Level of Education for which Award is Granted:** Four Year College **Number Awarded:** 2 each year. **Funds Available:** The stipend is $5,000. **Duration:** 1 year; nonrenewable.
Eligibility Requirements: This program is open to African American women who are graduating from high school and have been accepted at a 4- or 5-year college or university as a full-time student. Applicants must be able to demonstrate academic achievement in high school, success in overcoming obstacles or achieving goals, and a commitment to a career in science, mathematics, engineering, or technology. They must be enrolled in a school district that is a member of the Council of the Great City Schools, a coalition of 64 of the nation's largest urban public school systems. **Deadline for Receipt:** April of each year. **Additional Information:** This scholarship, first awarded in 2005, is sponsored by Texas Instruments, Inc.

4436 ■ DALLAS FOUNDATION
Attn: Scholarship Administrator
900 Jackson Street, Suite 150
Dallas, TX 75202
Tel: (214)741-9898
Fax: (214)741-9848
E-mail: cmcnally@dallasfoundation.org
Web Site: http://www.dallasfoundation.org/gs_schFundProfiles.cfm
To provide financial assistance and work experience to disadvantaged students who are majoring in civil engineering at public universities in Texas.
Title of Award: Jere W. Thompson, Jr. Scholarship **Area, Field, or Subject:** Engineering; Engineering, Civil **Level of Education for which Award is Granted:** Undergraduate **Number Awarded:** 1 each year. **Funds Available:** Stipends range up to $2,000 per semester, beginning in the recipient's junior year; the maximum award is $8,000 over 4 semesters. **Duration:** 1 semester; may be renewed for up to 3 additional semesters, provided the recipient remains a full-time student, maintains at least a 2.5 GPA, and submits a grade report within 45 days after the end of each semester.
Eligibility Requirements: This program is open to disadvantaged students in civil engineering or construction engineering at public colleges and universities in Texas; special consideration is given to residents of counties in the service area of the North Texas Tollway Authority: Collin, Dallas, Denton, or Tarrant. At the time of application, students must be full-time sophomores. Finalists may be interviewed. Financial need is considered in the selection process. **Deadline for Receipt:** March of each year. **Additional Information:** Recipients of the Thompson Scholarship are given an opportunity for a paid internship in the Dallas area during the summer between their junior and senior year. Assignments are available

at the scholarship's sponsors: North Texas Tollway Authority, Brown and Root Services, Carter & Burgess, Inc., and HNTB Companies.

4437 ■ DECA

1908 Association Drive
Reston, VA 20191-1594
Tel: (703)860-5000
Fax: (703)860-4013
E-mail: decainc@aol.com
Web Site: http://www.deca.org/student.html

To recognize and reward (with college scholarships) DECA members who develop outstanding advertising campaigns for display on the Internet.

Title of Award: 7 Up Challenge **Area, Field, or Subject:** Advertising; Internet design and development; Marketing and distribution **Level of Education for which Award is Granted:** Undergraduate **Number Awarded:** 4 finalists are selected in each category in each round (for a total of 16 finalists); from among those, 2 grand-prize winners (1 in each category) are selected. **Funds Available:** Each finalist receives a $500 award. The grand-prize winners receive $2,500 college scholarships. **Duration:** The competition is held annually.

Eligibility Requirements: This competition is open to high school DECA members who submit entries in either of 2 categories: 1) a web campaign of at least 400 x 400 pixels with up to 4 links and up to 500K in size; or 2) a banner ad of approximately 450 x 60 pixels, 72 dpi, and up to 20K. In either category, the campaign must promote brand awareness of lemon-lime and/or cherry-flavored soft drinks, involve the consumer, and utilize the themes of college basketball and/or music. Entries are received in 2 rounds, with finalists selected in each category in each round. Grand-prize winners are selected from among the finalists on the basis of how well and creatively the campaign or banner ad promotes the soft drinks, overall appearance, content of copy, ease of use, identification, layout, and impact. **Deadline for Receipt:** November of each year for the first round; February of each year for the second round. **Additional Information:** This program is sponsored by the Seven Up Division of Dr Pepper/ Seven Up, Inc.

4438 ■ DELAWARE VOLUNTEER FIREMEN'S ASSOCIATION

Attn: Executive Secretary
122A South Bradford Street
P.O. Box 1849
Dover, DE 19903-1849
Tel: (302)734-9390; 877-455-3832
Fax: (302)734-9404
E-mail: exsec@dvfassn.com
Web Site: http://www.dvfassn.com/html/schol.htm

To provide financial assistance for college to Delaware residents or members of fire departments or auxiliaries in the state.

Title of Award: Delaware Volunteer Firemen's Association Scholarship **Area, Field, or Subject:** Engineering; Fires and fire prevention; Medical technology **Level of Education for which Award is Granted:** Professional, Undergraduate **Number Awarded:** Varies each year; recently, 11 of these scholarships were awarded. **Funds Available:** The maximum stipend is $2,500. **Duration:** 1 year.

Eligibility Requirements: This program is open to 1) Delaware residents or 2) active members (for at least 1 year) of a fire department or auxiliary that is a member in good standing of the Delaware Volunteer Firemen's Association or DVFA Ladies Auxiliary. Applicants must have been accepted into an accredited fire service technology, medical technology, engineering, or related certificate, diploma, or degree program. Along with their application, they must submit 3 letters of recommendation, college and fire school transcripts, and a 250-word statement that covers their reasons for applying for financial assistance, why their course of study will be useful, and their career goals and objectives. **Deadline for Receipt:** March of each year. **Additional Information:** Information is also available from the DVFA Scholarship Committee, Delaware State Fire School, 1461 Chestnut Grove Road, Dover, DE 19904-1545, (302) 376-6393.

4439 ■ DELTA SIGMA THETA SORORITY, INC.-THE FEDERAL CITY ALUMNAE CHAPTER

Attn: Educational Development Committee
P.O. Box 1605
Washington, DC 20013
Tel: (202)545-1913

E-mail: thefcacdst@yahoo.com
Web Site: http://www.thefcacdst.org/html/chapterEvents.htm

To provide financial assistance to high school seniors in Washington, D.C. who plan to attend an Historically Black College or University (HBCU) to major in a field related to science and engineering.

Title of Award: Federal City Alumnae Chapter Scholarship for Excellence **Area, Field, or Subject:** Computer and information sciences; Engineering; Information science and technology; Mathematics and mathematical sciences; Science **Level of Education for which Award is Granted:** Undergraduate **Number Awarded:** 2 each year. **Funds Available:** The stipend is $5,000. **Duration:** 1 year; nonrenewable.

Eligibility Requirements: This program is open to seniors graduating from public and public charter high schools in the District of Columbia. Applicants must have been accepted to attend an HBCU to major in computer science, engineering, information technology, mathematics, science, or a related field. They must have a GPA of 3.0 or higher. Along with their application, they must submit a 2-page essay on why they decided to attend an HBCU to major in mathematics, science, or a related field. **Deadline for Receipt:** March of each year.

4440 ■ DEPARTMENT OF TRANSPORTATION

Federal Highway Administration
Attn: National Highway Institute, HNHI-20
4600 North Fairfax Drive, Suite 800
Arlington, VA 22203-1553
Tel: (703)235-0538
Fax: (703)235-0593
E-mail: transportationedu@fhwa.dot.gov
Web Site: http://www.nhi.fhwa.dot.gov/ddetfp.asp

To enable students to participate in research activities at facilities of the U.S. Department of Transportation (DOT) Federal Highway Administration in the Washington, D.C. area.

Title of Award: Eisenhower Grants for Research Fellowships **Area, Field, or Subject:** Chemistry; Economics; Engineering; Engineering, Civil; Geography; Information science and technology; Materials research/ science; Operations research; Physics; Public administration; Statistics; Technology; Transportation; Urban affairs/design/planning **Level of Education for which Award is Granted:** Four Year College, Graduate **Number Awarded:** Varies each year; recently, 9 students participated in this program. **Funds Available:** Fellows receive full tuition and fees that relate to the academic credits for the approved research project and a monthly stipend of $1,450 for college seniors, $1,700 for master's students, or $2,000 for doctoral students. An allowance for travel to and from the DOT facility where the research is conducted is also provided, but selectees are responsible for their own housing accommodations. Faculty advisors are allowed 1 site review on projects over 6 months and 2 site reviews on projects over 9 months; travel and per diem are provided for those site reviews. **Duration:** Tenure is normally 3, 6, 9, or 12 months.

Eligibility Requirements: This program is open to 1) students in their junior year of a baccalaureate program who will complete their junior year before being awarded a fellowship; 2) students in their senior year of a baccalaureate program; and 3) students who have completed their baccalaureate degree and are enrolled in a program leading to a master's, Ph.D., or equivalent degree. Applicants must be U.S. citizens enrolled in an accredited U.S. institution of higher education working on a degree full time and planning to enter the transportation profession after completing their higher education. They select 1 or more projects from a current list of research projects underway at various DOT facilities; the research will be conducted with academic supervision provided by a faculty advisor from their home university (which grants academic credit for the research project) and with technical direction provided by the DOT staff. Specific requirements for the target projects vary; most require engineering backgrounds, but others involve transportation planning, information management, public administration, physics, materials science, statistical analysis, operations research, chemistry, economics, technology transfer, urban studies, geography, and urban and regional planning. The DOT encourages students at Historically Black Colleges and Universities (HBCUs) and Hispanic Serving Institutions (HSIs) to apply for these grants. Selection is based on match of the student's qualifications with the proposed research project (including the student's ability to accomplish the project in the available time), recommendation letters regarding the nominee's qualifications to conduct the research, academic records (including class standing, GPA, and transcripts), and transportation work experience (if any) including the employer's endorsement. **Deadline for Receipt:** February of each year.

4441 ■ DEPARTMENT OF TRANSPORTATION
Federal Highway Administration
Attn: National Highway Institute, HNHI-20
4600 North Fairfax Drive, Suite 800
Arlington, VA 22203-1553
Tel: (703)235-0538
Fax: (703)235-0593
E-mail: transportationedu@fhwa.dot.gov
Web Site: http://www.nhi.fhwa.dot.gov/ddetfp.asp
To provide financial assistance for undergraduate study in transportation-related fields to students at Hispanic Serving Institutions.
Title of Award: Eisenhower Hispanic-Serving Institutions Fellowships **Area, Field, or Subject:** Accounting; Architecture; Business administration; Engineering, Civil; Environmental conservation; Environmental science; Transportation **Level of Education for which Award is Granted:** Four Year College **Number Awarded:** Varies each year; recently, 18 students received support from this program. **Funds Available:** The stipend covers the fellow's full cost of education, including tuition and fees. **Duration:** 1 year.
Eligibility Requirements: These fellowships are intended for students who are enrolled at federally-designated 4-year Hispanic Serving Institutions (HSIs) and who are working on a degree in a transportation-related field (i.e., engineering, accounting, business, architecture, environmental sciences, etc.). Applicants must have entered their junior year, have at least a 3.0 GPA, and have a faculty sponsor. **Deadline for Receipt:** February of each year.

4442 ■ DEPARTMENT OF TRANSPORTATION
Federal Highway Administration
Attn: National Highway Institute, HNHI-20
4600 North Fairfax Drive, Suite 800
Arlington, VA 22203-1553
Tel: (703)235-0538
Fax: (703)235-0593
E-mail: transportationedu@fhwa.dot.gov
Web Site: http://www.nhi.fhwa.dot.gov/ddetfp.asp
To provide financial assistance for undergraduate study in transportation-related fields to students at Historically Black Colleges and Universities.
Title of Award: Eisenhower Historically Black Colleges and Universities Fellowships **Area, Field, or Subject:** Accounting; Architecture; Business administration; Engineering, Civil; Environmental conservation; Environmental science; Transportation **Level of Education for which Award is Granted:** Four Year College **Number Awarded:** Varies each year; recently, 48 students received support from this program. **Funds Available:** The stipend covers the fellow's full cost of education, including tuition and fees. **Duration:** 1 year.
Eligibility Requirements: These fellowships are intended for students who are enrolled at federally-designated 4-year Historically Black Colleges and Universities (HBCUs) and working on a degree in a transportation-related field (i.e., engineering, accounting, business, architecture, environmental sciences, etc.). Applicants must have entered their junior year, have at least a 3.0 GPA, and have a faculty sponsor. **Deadline for Receipt:** February of each year.

4443 ■ DEPARTMENT OF TRANSPORTATION
Federal Highway Administration
Attn: National Highway Institute, HNHI-20
4600 North Fairfax Drive, Suite 800
Arlington, VA 22203-1553
Tel: (703)235-0538
Fax: (703)235-0593
E-mail: transportationedu@fhwa.dot.gov
Web Site: http://www.nhi.fhwa.dot.gov/ddetfp.asp
To provide financial assistance to Native American students and faculty in transportation-related fields at Tribal Colleges.
Title of Award: Eisenhower Tribal Colleges Initiatives **Area, Field, or Subject:** Engineering, Civil; Transportation **Level of Education for which Award is Granted:** Professional, Postdoctoral, Undergraduate **Number Awarded:** Varies each year; recently, 2 students participated in this program. **Funds Available:** Fellows receive the full cost of education, including tuition and fees. **Duration:** 1 year.

Eligibility Requirements: This program identifies transportation activities at Tribal Colleges in order to provide fellowships to Native American students and faculty for further study. **Deadline for Receipt:** February of each year.

4444 ■ DESIGN AUTOMATION CONFERENCE
c/o Cherrice Traver
Union College
ECE Department
Schenectady, NY 12308
Tel: (518)388-6326
Fax: (518)388-6789
E-mail: traverc@union.edu
Web Site: http://doc.union.edu/acsee.html
To provide financial assistance to female, minority, or disabled high school seniors who are interested in preparing for a career in computer science or electrical engineering.
Title of Award: P.O. Pistilli Scholarships **Area, Field, or Subject:** Computer and information sciences; Engineering, Computer; Engineering, Electrical **Level of Education for which Award is Granted:** Undergraduate **Number Awarded:** 2 to 7 each year. **Funds Available:** Stipends are $4,000 per year. Awards are paid each year in 2 equal installments. **Duration:** 1 year; renewable for up to 4 additional years.
Eligibility Requirements: Eligible to apply are "underrepresented" high school seniors: women, African Americans, Hispanic Americans, Native Americans, and persons with disabilities. Applicants must be interested in preparing for a career in electrical engineering, computer engineering, or computer science. They must have at least a 3.0 GPA, have demonstrated high achievements in math and science courses, and be able to demonstrate significant financial need. U.S. citizenship is not required, but applicants must be U.S. residents when they apply and must plan to attend an accredited U.S. college or university. They must submit a completed application form, 3 letters of recommendation, official transcripts, ACT/SAT and/or PSAT scores, a personal statement outlining future goals, a copy of their latest income tax return, and a copy of the FAFSA form they submitted. **Deadline for Receipt:** January of each year.
Additional Information: This program is funded by the Design Automation Conference and the IEEE Circuits and System Society. It is directed by the Association for Computing Machinery's Special Interest Group on Design Automation.

4445 ■ THE DEVELOPMENT FUND FOR BLACK STUDENTS IN SCIENCE AND TECHNOLOGY
2705 Bladensburg Road, N.E.
Washington, DC 20018
Tel: (202)635-3604
E-mail: hattie.carwell@oak.doe.gov
Web Site: http://ourworld.compuserve.com/homepages/dlhinson/dfb_sch.htm
To provide scholarships to African American students who enroll in scientific or technical fields of study at Historically Black Colleges and Universities (HBCUs).
Title of Award: The Development Fund for Black Students in Science and Technology Scholarships **Area, Field, or Subject:** Engineering; Mathematics and mathematical sciences; Science **Level of Education for which Award is Granted:** Undergraduate **Number Awarded:** Several each year. **Funds Available:** The amount of the scholarship is based on merit and financial need. Awards up to $2,000 per year are available. **Duration:** 1 year; may be renewed for up to 4 years, as long as the recipient remains in good academic standing and enrolled full time in a science or engineering curriculum.
Eligibility Requirements: Deans and faculty members of the various engineering and science departments at predominantly Black colleges and universities are invited to identify students to be considered for these scholarships. To be eligible, nominated students must intend to enroll at a predominantly Black college or university or already be enrolled at such a college or university. They must intend to major in a technical field and be U.S. citizens or permanent residents who intend to remain in the United States after graduation. Selection is based on academic achievement (grades and SAT scores, especially in science and mathematics), a personal essay describing career goals and relevant extracurricular activities, recommendations, and financial need. **Deadline for Receipt:** June of each year. **Additional Information:** Prior to 1995, these scholarships

were awarded solely or primarily through the National Merit Scholarship Corporation's National Achievement Scholarship Program. Scholarship applications are available only through the financial aid offices of prequalified schools. Currently, these are: Bennett College, Clark Atlanta University, Elizabeth City State University, Fisk University, Florida A&M University, Fort Valley State College, Hampton University, Howard University, Langston University, Lincoln University of Pennsylvania, Morehouse University, Morgan State University, North Carolina A&T State University, Prairie View A&M University, Southern University and A&M College, Spelman College, Tennessee State University, Tuskegee University, Wilberforce University, and Xavier University of Louisiana.

4446 ■ ELECTRONIC DOCUMENT SYSTEMS FOUNDATION

Attn: EDSF Scholarship Awards
24238 Hawthorne Boulevard
Torrance, CA 90505-6505
Tel: (310)541-1481
Fax: (310)541-4803
Web Site: http://www.edsf.org/scholarships.cfm
To provide financial assistance to college juniors, seniors, and graduate students interested in working with electronic documents as a career.
Title of Award: Wayne Alexander Memorial Scholarship **Area, Field, or Subject:** Computer and information sciences; Graphic art and design; Internet design and development; Marketing and distribution; Printing trades and industries; Telecommunications systems **Level of Education for which Award is Granted:** Four Year College, Graduate **Number Awarded:** 1 each year. **Funds Available:** The stipend is $2,000. **Duration:** 1 year.
Eligibility Requirements: This program is open to juniors, seniors, and graduate students who are working full time on a degree in the field of document communication, including marketing, graphic communication and arts, e-commerce, imaging science, printing, web authoring, electronic publishing, computer science, or telecommunications. Priority consideration is given to students at the University of Central Florida. Applicants must submit a statement of their career goals in the field of document communications, an essay on a topic related to their view of the future of the document management and production industry, a list of current professional and college extracurricular activities and achievements, college transcripts (GPA of 3.0 or higher), samples of their creative work, and 2 letters of recommendation. Financial need is not considered. **Deadline for Receipt:** May of each year. **Additional Information:** This program is sponsored by AXIS Inc.

4447 ■ ELECTRONIC DOCUMENT SYSTEMS FOUNDATION

Attn: EDSF Scholarship Awards
24238 Hawthorne Boulevard
Torrance, CA 90505-6505
Tel: (310)541-1481
Fax: (310)541-4803
Web Site: http://www.edsf.org/scholarships.cfm
To provide financial assistance to college juniors, seniors, and graduate students interested in working with electronic documents as a career.
Title of Award: EDSF Board of Directors Scholarships **Area, Field, or Subject:** Computer and information sciences; Graphic art and design; Internet design and development; Marketing and distribution; Printing trades and industries; Telecommunications systems **Level of Education for which Award is Granted:** Four Year College, Graduate **Number Awarded:** 20 each year. **Funds Available:** The stipend is $2,000. **Duration:** 1 year.
Eligibility Requirements: This program is open to juniors, seniors, and graduate students who are working full time on a degree in the field of document communication, including marketing, graphic communication and arts, e-commerce, imaging science, printing, web authoring, electronic publishing, computer science, or telecommunications. Applicants must submit a statement of their career goals in the field of document communications, an essay on a topic related to their view of the future of the document management and production industry, a list of current professional and college extracurricular activities and achievements, college transcripts (GPA of 3.0 or higher), samples of their creative work,

and 2 letters of recommendation. Financial need is not considered. **Deadline for Receipt:** May of each year.

4448 ■ ELECTRONIC DOCUMENT SYSTEMS FOUNDATION

Attn: EDSF Scholarship Awards
24238 Hawthorne Boulevard
Torrance, CA 90505-6505
Tel: (310)541-1481
Fax: (310)541-4803
Web Site: http://www.edsf.org/scholarships.cfm
To provide financial assistance to students in technical schools and community colleges who are interested in working with electronic documents as a career.
Title of Award: EDSF Board of Directors Technical and Community College Scholarship **Area, Field, or Subject:** Computer and information sciences; Graphic art and design; Internet design and development; Marketing and distribution; Printing trades and industries; Telecommunications systems **Level of Education for which Award is Granted:** Two Year College, Vocational/Occupational **Number Awarded:** 5 each year. **Funds Available:** The stipend is $1,000. **Duration:** 1 year.
Eligibility Requirements: This program is open to first- and second-year students at technical and trade schools and community colleges. Applicants must be working on a degree in the field of electronic document communication, including marketing, graphic communication and arts, e-commerce, imaging science, printing, web authoring, electronic publishing, computer science, or telecommunications. They must submit a 1-page essay on 1 of the following topics: 1) a definition of their career goals in the field of document management and communications; 2) a recent technological change and how it has or will affect the document communication industry; or 3) a definition of the document communication industry. Selection is based on the essay, extracurricular activities and achievements, high school transcripts (GPA of 3.0 or higher), samples of creative work, and 2 letters of recommendation. Financial need is not considered. **Deadline for Receipt:** May of each year.

4449 ■ ELECTRONIC DOCUMENT SYSTEMS FOUNDATION

Attn: EDSF Scholarship Awards
24238 Hawthorne Boulevard
Torrance, CA 90505-6505
Tel: (310)541-1481
Fax: (310)541-4803
Web Site: http://www.edsf.org/scholarships.cfm
To provide financial assistance to upper-division and graduate students interested in working with electronic documents as a career.
Title of Award: David Hoods Memorial Scholarship **Area, Field, or Subject:** Computer and information sciences; Graphic art and design; Internet design and development; Marketing and distribution; Printing trades and industries; Public relations; Telecommunications systems **Level of Education for which Award is Granted:** Four Year College, Graduate **Number Awarded:** 1 each year. **Funds Available:** The stipend is $2,000. **Duration:** 1 year.
Eligibility Requirements: This program is open to full-time juniors, seniors, and graduate students who demonstrate a strong interest in working with electronic documents as a career (including graphic communications, document management, document content, and/or document distribution). Special consideration is given to students interested in marketing and public relations. Applicants must submit a statement of their career goals in the field of document communications, an essay on a topic related to their view of the future of the document management and production industry, a list of current professional and college extracurricular activities and achievements, college transcripts (GPA of 3.0 or higher), samples of their creative work, and 2 letters of recommendation. Financial need is not considered. **Deadline for Receipt:** May of each year.

4450 ■ ELECTRONIC DOCUMENT SYSTEMS FOUNDATION

Attn: EDSF Scholarship Awards
24238 Hawthorne Boulevard
Torrance, CA 90505-6505
Tel: (310)541-1481
Fax: (310)541-4803
Web Site: http://www.edsf.org/scholarships.cfm

To provide financial assistance to college juniors, seniors, and graduate students interested in working with electronic documents as a career.

Title of Award: John A. Lopiano Scholarship **Area, Field, or Subject:** Computer and information sciences; Graphic art and design; Internet design and development; Marketing and distribution; Printing trades and industries; Telecommunications systems **Level of Education for which Award is Granted:** Four Year College, Graduate **Number Awarded:** 1 each year. **Funds Available:** The stipend is $2,000. **Duration:** 1 year.

Eligibility Requirements: This program is open to juniors, seniors, and graduate students who are working full time on a degree in the field of document communication, including marketing, graphic communication and arts, e-commerce, imaging science, printing, web authoring, electronic publishing, computer science, or telecommunications. Priority consideration is given to students who work in or whose family member has worked or currently works in a segment of the high volume transaction output (HVTO) industry. Applicants must submit a statement of their career goals in the field of document communications, an essay on a topic related to their view of the future of the document management and production industry, a list of current professional and college extracurricular activities and achievements, college transcripts (GPA of 3.0 or higher), samples of their creative work, and 2 letters of recommendation. Financial need is not considered. **Deadline for Receipt:** May of each year. **Additional Information:** This program is sponsored by COPI/OutputLinks.

4451 ■ ELECTRONIC DOCUMENT SYSTEMS FOUNDATION

Attn: EDSF Scholarship Awards
24238 Hawthorne Boulevard
Torrance, CA 90505-6505
Tel: (310)541-1481
Fax: (310)541-4803
Web Site: http://www.edsf.org/scholarships.cfm

To provide financial assistance to upper-division and graduate students in Canada who are interested in working with electronic documents as a career.

Title of Award: Xplor Canada Scholarship **Area, Field, or Subject:** Computer and information sciences; Graphic art and design; Internet design and development; Printing trades and industries **Level of Education for which Award is Granted:** Four Year College, Graduate **Number Awarded:** 1 each year. **Funds Available:** The stipend is $C2,000. **Duration:** 1 year.

Eligibility Requirements: This program is open to third-year, fourth-year, and advanced-degree students who are working full time on a degree in the field of electronic documents, including content and design, print technologies, graphic communications, or computer science. Applicants must be Canadian citizens or landed immigrants and living in Canada, but they may be attending a course of study outside of Canada. They must submit a statement of their career goals in the field of document/communication systems, an essay on a topic related to their view of the future of the document management and production industry, a list of current professional and college extracurricular activities and achievements, college transcripts (GPA of 3.0 or higher), samples of their creative work, and 2 letters of recommendation. Financial need is not considered. **Deadline for Receipt:** May of each year. **Additional Information:** This program is sponsored by Xplor Canada.

4452 ■ ENGINEERS' SOCIETY OF WESTERN PENNSYLVANIA

Attn: Scholarship Committee
Pittsburgh Engineers' Building
337 Fourth Avenue
Pittsburgh, PA 15222
Tel: (412)261-0710
Fax: (412)261-1606
E-mail: eswp@eswp.com
Web Site: http://www.eswp.com/water/student_scholarships.htm

To provide financial assistance to undergraduate students majoring in chemical or mechanical engineering and committed to a career in the field of water technology.

Title of Award: Joseph A. Levendusky Memorial Scholarship **Area, Field, or Subject:** Engineering, Chemical; Engineering, Mechanical; Water resources **Level of Education for which Award is Granted:** Professional, Undergraduate **Number Awarded:** 1 each year. **Funds Available:** The stipend is $7,000 per year. **Duration:** 1 year.

Eligibility Requirements: Eligible to apply for this program are undergraduate students majoring in chemical or mechanical engineering who are preparing for a career in water technology. They must have been employed in the field of water technology (excluding environmental wastewater, water pollution control, and water resource management) for at least 1 year. Along with their application, they must submit a 250-word essay on the occupation they want to prepare for by attending college and the reasons they have decided on the field of water technology. Financial need is considered in the selection process. **Deadline for Receipt:** August of each year.

4453 ■ FLEET RESERVE ASSOCIATION

Past Regional Presidents Club
c/o W. Ralph Holcombe, Secretary/Treasurer
4911 Fennell Court
Suffolk, VA 23435
Tel: (757)484-7403
Fax: (757)686-5952
E-mail: info@fraprpscholarships.org
Web Site: http://www.fraprpscholarships.org

To provide financial assistance to relatives of members of the Fleet Reserve Association (FRA) interested in studying aeronautical engineering or aviation in college.

Title of Award: Walter Beale Scholarship **Area, Field, or Subject:** Aviation; Engineering; Engineering, Aerospace/Aeronautical/Astronautical **Level of Education for which Award is Granted:** Undergraduate **Number Awarded:** 1 or more each year. **Funds Available:** The amounts of the awards depend on the availability of funds and the need of the recipients; they range from $2,000 to $5,000. **Duration:** 1 year; renewable.

Eligibility Requirements: This program is open to spouses, children, and grandchildren of active-duty, reserve, and retired personnel of the Navy, Marine Corps, or Coast Guard who are relatives of FRA members in good standing (or who were in good standing at the time of their death). Students in a reserve officer candidate program receiving aid are not eligible. Applicants must be enrolled at an accredited college, university, or technical institution in the United States in a program related to engineering, aviation, or aeronautical engineering. Selection is based on GPA, scholastic aptitude test scores, curriculum goals, interests, community activities, awards, and financial need. **Deadline for Receipt:** April of each year.

4454 ■ FLEXIBLE PAVEMENTS OF OHIO

Attn: Ohio Asphalt Scholarship Fund
37 West Broad Street, Suite 460
P.O. Box 16186
Columbus, OH 43216-6186
Tel: (614)221-5402; 888-4-HOTMIX
Fax: (614)221-0394
E-mail: info@flexiblepavements.org
Web Site: http://www.flexiblepavements.org/scholarship.cfm

To provide financial assistance to undergraduate and graduate students at colleges and universities in Ohio who are interested in preparing for a career in a field related to asphalt pavement technology.

Title of Award: Ohio Asphalt Scholarship Program **Area, Field, or Subject:** Construction; Engineering; Engineering, Civil **Level of Education for which Award is Granted:** Four Year College, Graduate **Number Awarded:** Varies each year; recently, 28 of these scholarships were awarded. **Funds Available:** The stipend is $1,000 per year. **Duration:** 1 year; may be renewed for up to 2 years or until graduation, whichever comes first.

Eligibility Requirements: This program is open to students entering their junior, senior, or fifth year of study in a civil engineering, construction management, or construction engineering curriculum at a participating university in Ohio. Preference is given to students who show an interest in the design and construction of Ohio's highways and transportation facilities. The university must offer, and the student must take, at least 1 course on hot mix asphalt technology. Graduate students with their major focus of study related to asphalt and attending an Ohio university or college are also considered. All applicants must be full-time students and U.S. citizens. Selection is based on academic performance and potential, leadership and participation in school and community activities, work experience, level of career and educational aspirations in the transportation industry, goals, and special personal or family circumstances. Although it is not a criterion, applicants should indicate if there is a need for financial assistance. **Deadline for Receipt:** January of each year. **Additional Information:** The following universities participate in this program: Bowling Green State University, Ohio Northern University, Ohio State University, Ohio University, University of Cincinnati, University of Dayton, Youngstown State University, University of Toledo, and University of Akron.

4455 ■ FLORIDA SEA GRANT COLLEGE PROGRAM

Attn: Director
University of Florida
Building 803 McCarty Drive
P.O. Box 110400
Gainesville, FL 32611-0400
Tel: (352)392-5870
Fax: (352)392-5113
Web Site: http://www.flseagrant.org/students/scholarships/index.htm
To provide financial assistance to undergraduate or graduate students working on a degree in a marine science-related field at any Florida university that participates in the Florida Sea Grant College Program.
Title of Award: Aylesworth Foundation for the Advancement of Marine Science Scholarships **Area, Field, or Subject:** Biological and clinical sciences; Economics; Engineering; Food science and technology; Marine biology **Level of Education for which Award is Granted:** Graduate, Undergraduate **Number Awarded:** Generally, 4 or more each year. **Funds Available:** The maximum stipend awarded is 65% of the annual official university or college cost of attendance or $4,000, whichever is less. **Duration:** 1 year; renewable until the recipient completes the degree.
Eligibility Requirements: Eligible to be nominated by their department chair are undergraduate or graduate students who are working on a degree in an academic discipline that has direct application in marine science (ranging from biology and engineering to economics and food science) at a university or college in Florida that participates in the Florida Sea Grant College Program. Financial need is the principal factor used in the selection process, although academic record, leadership, and personal character are also considered. Florida residents are given preference. **Deadline for Receipt:** November of each year. **Additional Information:** The Florida Sea Grant College Program, established in 1986, operates as a partnership between the Florida Board of Education and the U.S. National Oceanic and Atmospheric Administration. The participating institutions are Florida A&M University, Florida Gulf Coast University, Florida Atlantic University, Florida Institute of Technology, Florida International University, Florida State University, Harbor Branch Oceanographic Institution, Mote Marine Laboratory, New College of Florida, Nova Southeastern University, University of Central Florida, University of Florida, University of Miami, University of North Florida, University of South Florida, and University of West Florida. These scholarships are sponsored by the Aylesworth Foundation for the Advancement of Marine Science, the Southeastern Fisheries Association, and the Florida Sea Grant College Program.

4456 ■ FOUNDATION FOR AMATEUR RADIO, INC.

Attn: Scholarship Committee
P.O. Box 831
Riverdale, MD 20738
E-mail: aa3of@arrl.net
Web Site: http://www.amateurradio-far.org/scholarships.php
To provide funding to licensed radio amateurs from selected states who are interested in studying selected subjects in college.
Title of Award: Nanticoke Amateur Radio Club Scholarship **Area, Field, or Subject:** Architecture; Electronics; Engineering; Science **Level of Education for which Award is Granted:** Undergraduate **Number Awarded:** 1 each year. **Funds Available:** The stipend is $1,000. **Duration:** 1 year.
Eligibility Requirements: This program is open to college students who have an amateur radio license with HF privileges and are interested in majoring in architecture, engineering, electronics, science, or a related field at an institution of higher learning in the United States. They must be residents of Delaware, Maryland, Virginia, or the District of Columbia. **Deadline for Receipt:** Requests for applications must be submitted by April of each year. **Additional Information:** Recipients must attend an

accredited school (university, college, or technical institute) on a full-time basis.

4457 ■ FOUNDATION FOR AMATEUR RADIO, INC.

Attn: Scholarship Committee
P.O. Box 831
Riverdale, MD 20738
E-mail: aa3of@arrl.net
Web Site: http://www.amateurradio-far.org/scholarships.php
To provide funding to licensed radio amateurs who are interested in going to college or graduate school, particularly those majoring in engineering or the sciences.
Title of Award: Lawrence E. and Thelma J. Norrie Memorial Scholarship **Area, Field, or Subject:** Engineering; General studies/Field of study not specified; Science **Level of Education for which Award is Granted:** Graduate, Undergraduate **Number Awarded:** 1 each year. **Funds Available:** The stipend is $2,500. **Duration:** 1 year.
Eligibility Requirements: Applicants must be a resident of the United States and have an amateur radio license of any class with HF privileges. Special consideration is given to applicants who have demonstrated academic merit, financial need, and an interest in promoting the amateur radio service. Preference is given to juniors, seniors, and graduate students who have a GPA of 3.0 or higher and are working on a degree in science or engineering. **Deadline for Receipt:** Requests for applications must be submitted by April of each year. **Additional Information:** Recipients must attend an accredited school (university, college, or technical institute) on a full-time basis.

4458 ■ FOUNDATION FOR AMATEUR RADIO, INC.

Attn: Scholarship Committee
P.O. Box 831
Riverdale, MD 20738
E-mail: aa3of@arrl.net
Web Site: http://www.amateurradio-far.org/scholarships.php
To provide funding to licensed radio amateurs who are interested in studying electronic engineering or technology in college.
Title of Award: Radio Club of America Scholarships **Area, Field, or Subject:** Engineering; Technology **Level of Education for which Award is Granted:** Undergraduate **Number Awarded:** 3 each year. **Funds Available:** The stipend is $1,000. **Duration:** 1 year.
Eligibility Requirements: This program is open to students who have a general class amateur radio license and are enrolled or have been accepted for enrollment at a community college, college, or university. They must intend to study electronic engineering or technology and earn an associate or bachelor's degree. Preference is given to applicants taking courses in wireless communications. U.S. citizenship is required. **Deadline for Receipt:** Requests for applications must be submitted by April of each year. **Additional Information:** This program is sponsored by the Radio Club of America, Inc, 10 Drs. James Parker Boulevard, Suite 103, Red Bank, NJ 07701-1500, (732) 842-5070, Fax: (732) 219-1938. Recipients must attend an accredited school (university, college, or technical institute) on a full-time basis.

4459 ■ FOUNDATION FOR AMATEUR RADIO, INC.

Attn: Scholarship Committee
P.O. Box 831
Riverdale, MD 20738
E-mail: aa3of@arrl.net
Web Site: http://www.amateurradio-far.org/scholarships.php
To provide funding to licensed radio amateurs who are interested in studying engineering or the physical sciences in college.
Title of Award: Chuck Reville, K3FT, Memorial Scholarship **Area, Field, or Subject:** Engineering; Physical sciences **Level of Education for which Award is Granted:** Undergraduate **Number Awarded:** 1 each year. **Funds Available:** The stipend is $1,000. **Duration:** 1 year.
Eligibility Requirements: This program is open to radio amateurs who are interested in working on a bachelor's degree in a branch of engineering or the physical sciences. There are no restrictions on license class or residence area. **Deadline for Receipt:** Requests for applications must be

submitted by April of each year. **Additional Information:** Recipients must attend an accredited school (university, college, or technical institute) on a full-time basis.

4460 ■ FOUNDATION FOR AMATEUR RADIO, INC.
Attn: Scholarship Committee
P.O. Box 831
Riverdale, MD 20738
E-mail: aa3of@arrl.net
Web Site: http://www.amateurradio-far.org/scholarships.php
To provide funding to licensed radio amateurs in Wisconsin, Illinois, or Indiana who are interested in studying electrical engineering, technology, or other subjects in college.
Title of Award: South Milwaukee Amateur Radio Club Scholarships **Area, Field, or Subject:** Engineering, Electrical; General studies/Field of study not specified; Technology **Level of Education for which Award is Granted:** Undergraduate **Number Awarded:** 2 each year. **Funds Available:** The stipend is $1,000. **Duration:** 1 year.
Eligibility Requirements: Applicants must have an amateur radio license and intend to seek an associate or bachelor's degree from a college or university in the United States; preference is given to applicants studying electrical engineering or related technology. They must reside in Wisconsin. **Deadline for Receipt:** Requests for applications must be submitted by April of each year. **Additional Information:** Recipients must attend an accredited school (university, college, or technical institute) on a full-time basis.

4461 ■ FOUNDATION FOR AMATEUR RADIO, INC.
Attn: Scholarship Committee
P.O. Box 831
Riverdale, MD 20738
E-mail: aa3of@arrl.net
Web Site: http://www.amateurradio-far.org/scholarships.php
To provide funding to licensed radio amateurs in Ohio who are interested in studying electrical engineering or other subjects in college.
Title of Award: Robert E. True Memorial Scholarship **Area, Field, or Subject:** Computer and information sciences; Electronics; Engineering, Electrical; General studies/Field of study not specified **Level of Education for which Award is Granted:** Undergraduate **Number Awarded:** 1 each year. **Funds Available:** The stipend is $1,000. **Duration:** 1 year.
Eligibility Requirements: Applicants must be residents of Ohio and have a valid amateur radio license of any class. They must intend to work on a bachelor's degree at an accredited college or university in the United States; preference is given to applicants pursuing courses in electrical engineering or electronic/computer technology. **Deadline for Receipt:** Requests for applications must be submitted by April of each year. **Additional Information:** Recipients must attend an accredited school (university, college, or technical institute) on a full-time basis.

4462 ■ FOUNDATION FOR AMATEUR RADIO, INC.
Attn: Scholarship Committee
P.O. Box 831
Riverdale, MD 20738
E-mail: aa3of@arrl.net
Web Site: http://www.amateurradio-far.org/scholarships.php
To provide funding to licensed radio amateurs who are interested in studying engineering or the physical sciences in college.
Title of Award: Dwight Weller, KB3LA, Memorial Scholarship **Area, Field, or Subject:** Engineering; Physical sciences **Level of Education for which Award is Granted:** Undergraduate **Number Awarded:** 1 each year. **Funds Available:** The stipend is $1,000. **Duration:** 1 year.
Eligibility Requirements: This program is open to radio amateurs who are interested in working on a bachelor's degree in a branch of engineering or the physical sciences. There are no restrictions on license class or residence area. **Deadline for Receipt:** Requests for applications must be submitted by April of each year. **Additional Information:** Recipients must attend an accredited school (university, college, or technical institute) on a full-time basis.

4463 ■ FOUNDATION FOR THE CAROLINAS
Attn: Senior Vice President, Scholarships
217 South Tryon Street

P.O. Box 34769
Charlotte, NC 28234-4769
Tel: (704)973-4535
Free: 800-973-7244
Fax: (704)973-4935
E-mail: jseymour@fftc.org
Web Site: http://www.fftc.org/scholarships
To provide financial assistance to high school seniors from North and South Carolina who are interested in studying designed fields in college.
Title of Award: Duke Energy Minority Professional Association Scholarship Fund **Area, Field, or Subject:** Accounting; Business administration; Computer and information sciences; Engineering; Finance; Science **Level of Education for which Award is Granted:** Four Year College **Number Awarded:** 1 or more each year. **Funds Available:** A stipend is awarded (amount not specified). **Duration:** 1 year.
Eligibility Requirements: This program is open to seniors graduating from high schools in North and South Carolina. Applicants must be planning to attend a 4-year college or university in those states to major in accounting, business administration, computer science, engineering, finance, or the sciences. Selection is based on merit. **Deadline for Receipt:** February of each year. **Additional Information:** Information is also available from the Duke Energy Minority Professional Association Scholarship Committee, P.O. Box 30234, Charlotte, NC 28230.

4464 ■ FOUNDATION FOR THE CAROLINAS
Attn: Senior Vice President, Scholarships
217 South Tryon Street
P.O. Box 34769
Charlotte, NC 28234-4769
Tel: (704)973-4535
Free: 800-973-7244
Fax: (704)973-4935
E-mail: jseymour@fftc.org
Web Site: http://www.fftc.org/scholarships
To provide financial assistance to college students in North and South Carolina who are preparing for a career in the plastics industry.
Title of Award: Richard Goolsby Scholarship **Area, Field, or Subject:** Business administration; Chemistry; Engineering, Chemical; Engineering, Industrial; Engineering, Mechanical; Physics **Level of Education for which Award is Granted:** Undergraduate **Number Awarded:** 1 or more each year. **Funds Available:** Stipends range up to $4,000 per year; Funds are paid directly to the recipient's school to be used for tuition, required fees, books, and supplies. **Duration:** 1 year; may be renewed.
Eligibility Requirements: This program is open to residents of South Carolina, central North Carolina, or western North Carolina. Applicants must be entering their sophomore, junior, or senior year at a college or university in North or South Carolina and be majoring in a subject that will prepare them for a career in the plastics industry (e.g., chemistry, physics, chemical engineering, mechanical engineering, industrial engineering, business administration). They must be enrolled full time. Along with their application, they must submit a 1- to 2-page statement explaining why they are applying for the scholarship, their qualifications, and their educational and career goals in the plastics industry. Selection is based on academic performance, demonstrated interest in the plastics industry, financial need, school and community involvement, and personal achievements. **Deadline for Receipt:** February of each year.

4465 ■ FOUNDRY EDUCATIONAL FOUNDATION
1695 North Penny Lane
Schaumburg, IL 60173
Tel: (847)490-9200
Fax: (847)890-6270
E-mail: info@fefoffice.org
Web Site: http://www.fefinc.org
To provide financial assistance to undergraduate students from Minnesota, Wisconsin, and Iowa who are interested in preparing for a career in the die casting industry.
Title of Award: Twin City Chapter AFS Memorial Scholarship Fund **Area, Field, or Subject:** Business; Engineering, Metallurgical; Manufacturing **Level of Education for which Award is Granted:** Undergraduate **Number Awarded:** 1 each year. **Funds Available:** The stipends range from $500 to $2,000 per year. **Duration:** 1 year.
Eligibility Requirements: This program is open to full-time undergraduate students who are U.S. citizens, have taken or plan to take courses in

the die-casting process, and can demonstrate their intention to prepare for a career in the die-casting industry. Preference is given first to residents of Minnesota, then to residents of western Wisconsin, then to residents of northern Iowa. Preference is also given to students attending a college or university with an agreement with the Foundry Educational Foundation (FEF) and to students enrolled in foundry-related courses. **Deadline for Receipt:** October of each year. **Additional Information:** This scholarship is provided by the Twin City Chapter of the American Foundrymen's Society (AFS).

4466 ■ BILL AND MELINDA GATES FOUNDATION

P.O. Box 10500
Fairfax, VA 22031-8044
877-690 GMSP
Web Site: http://www.gmsp.org
To provide financial assistance to outstanding low-income minority students, particularly those interested in majoring in specific fields in college.
Title of Award: Gates Millennium Undergraduate Scholars Program **Area, Field, or Subject:** Education; Engineering; General studies/Field of study not specified; Mathematics and mathematical sciences; Science **Level of Education for which Award is Granted:** Undergraduate **Number Awarded:** Under the Gates Millennium Scholars Program, a total of 4,000 students receive support each year. **Funds Available:** The program covers the cost of tuition, fees, books, and living expenses not paid for by grants and scholarships already committed as part of the recipient's financial aid package. **Duration:** 4 years or the completion of the undergraduate degree, if the recipient maintains at least a 3.0 GPA **Eligibility Requirements:** This program is open to African Americans, Alaska Natives, American Indians, Hispanic Americans, and Asian Pacific Islander Americans who are graduating high school seniors with a GPA of 3.3 or higher. Principals, teachers, guidance counselors, tribal higher education representatives, and other professional educators are invited to nominate students with outstanding academic qualifications, especially those likely to succeed in the fields of mathematics, science, engineering, education, or library science. Nominees should have significant financial need and demonstrated leadership abilities through participation in community service, extracurricular, or other activities. U.S. citizenship or permanent resident status is required. Nominees must be planning to enter an accredited college or university as a full-time, degree-seeking freshman in the following fall. **Deadline for Receipt:** January of each year. **Additional Information:** This program, established in 1999, is funded by the Bill and Melinda Gates Foundation and administered by the United Negro College Fund with support from the American Indian Graduate Center, the Hispanic Scholarship Fund, and the Organization of Chinese Americans.

4467 ■ GENERAL MOTORS CORPORATION

Attn: GM Scholarship Administration Center
700 West Fifth Avenue
Naperville, IL 60563
888-377-5233
Fax: (630)428-2695
E-mail: scholarshipinfo@gmsac.com
Web Site: http://www.gm.com/company/careers/student/stu_scholar.html
To provide financial assistance to underrepresented minority college students interested in majoring in an engineering or science program of interest to General Motors.
Title of Award: General Motors Minority Engineering and Science Scholarship Program **Area, Field, or Subject:** Engineering; Engineering, Chemical; Engineering, Electrical; Engineering, Industrial; Engineering, Mechanical; Science **Level of Education for which Award is Granted:** Four Year College **Number Awarded:** A limited number are awarded each year. **Funds Available:** The stipend is $5,000 per year. **Duration:** 1 year.
Eligibility Requirements: This program is open to minority (African American, Hispanic, or Native American) students currently enrolled or planning to enroll full time at a 4-year college or university with sufficient credits to be classified as a sophomore or junior. Applicants must have a GPA of 3.0 or higher and plans to enroll in engineering or science; preference is given to students in chemical, electrical, industrial, manufacturing, or mechanical engineering or other closely related fields of science or engineering. They must be U.S. citizens or have eligibility to work

permanently in the United States. Along with their application, they must include a letter of recommendation from a college instructor or other representative, official transcripts from their college, and a personal statement (500 to 750 words) about how their college experiences (academics, extracurricular activities, outside activities, work experience) are shaping their educational and career goals. Selection is based on that statement, academic performance, proficiencies, and demonstrated skills in areas of interest to General Motors. Financial need is not considered. **Deadline for Receipt:** May of each year. **Additional Information:** Summer internships at a General Motors facility may also be available to recipients.

4468 ■ GEORGIA STUDENT FINANCE COMMISSION

Attn: Scholarships and Grants Division
2082 East Exchange Place, Suite 200
Tucker, GA 30084-5305
Tel: (770)724-9000
Free: 800-505-GSFC
Fax: (770)724-9089
E-mail: info@mail.gsfc.state.ga.us
Web Site: http://www.gsfc.org/gsfa/SCL/dsp_see.cfm
To provide scholarship/loans to Georgia residents who are enrolled or accepted for enrollment in an engineering program at a private university in the state.
Title of Award: Georgia Scholarship for Engineering Education **Area, Field, or Subject:** Engineering **Level of Education for which Award is Granted:** Undergraduate **Number Awarded:** Varies each year; recently, 195 of these grants were awarded. **Funds Available:** Awards up to $3,500 per year are available. This is a scholarship/loan program; recipients must either work in Georgia in an engineering-related field 1 year for each $3,000 received from the program or repay the full amount, plus interest, within 6 years. **Duration:** 1 year; may be renewed up to 4 additional years.
Eligibility Requirements: This program is open to full-time undergraduate engineering students at private colleges and universities in Georgia. Applicants currently enrolled in college must have a cumulative GPA of 2.5 or higher. All applicants must be in compliance with the Georgia Drug-Free Postsecondary Education Act. Georgia residency and U.S. citizenship or permanent resident status are required. **Deadline for Receipt:** Deadlines are established by the participating college or university in Georgia.

4469 ■ BARRY M. GOLDWATER SCHOLARSHIP AND EXCELLENCE IN EDUCATION FOUNDATION

Springfield Corporate Center
6225 Brandon Avenue, Suite 315
Springfield, VA 22150-2519
Tel: (703)756-6012
Fax: (703)756-6015
E-mail: goldh2o@vacoxmail.com
Web Site: http://www.act.org/goldwater
To provide financial assistance to outstanding college students planning careers in mathematics, engineering, or the natural sciences.
Title of Award: Barry M. Goldwater Scholarships **Area, Field, or Subject:** Engineering; Mathematics and mathematical sciences; Natural sciences **Level of Education for which Award is Granted:** Undergraduate **Number Awarded:** Up to 300 each year. **Funds Available:** Scholarships cover the cost of tuition, fees, books, and room and board up to a maximum of $7,500 per year. **Duration:** Students who receive scholarships as juniors are eligible for 2 years of support or until they complete their baccalaureate degree; students who receive scholarships as seniors are eligible for 1 year of support or until they complete their baccalaureate degree.
Eligibility Requirements: Eligible to be nominated are full-time students enrolled as sophomores or juniors who are in the top quarter of their class and majoring in the natural sciences, mathematics, or engineering with a GPA of at least 3.0. Students intending to enter medical school are eligible if they plan a career in research rather than private practice. Status as a U.S. citizen, national, or resident alien is also required. Students must be nominated by their institutions; 4-year colleges and universities may nominate up to 4 current sophomores or juniors and 2-year colleges may nominate up to 2 sophomores. Applicants must submit a 2-page essay on a significant issue or problem in their field of study that is of particular interest to them. Selection is based on academic performance and

demonstrated potential for and commitment to a career in mathematics, engineering, or the natural sciences. **Deadline for Receipt:** Institutions set their own deadlines; they must submit nominations to the foundation by January of each year. **Additional Information:** This program was authorized by the U.S. Congress in 1986. Information is also available from the Goldwater Scholarship Review Committee, 2201 North Dodge Street, P.O. Box 4030, Iowa City, IA 52243-4030.

4470 ■ HANSCOM OFFICERS' WIVES' CLUB

Attn: Scholarship Chair
P.O. Box 557
Bedford, MA 01730
Tel: (781)275-1251
E-mail: scholarship@hanscomowd.org
Web Site: http://www.hanscomowc.org
To provide financial assistance to children of military personnel and veterans in New England who are interested in studying aeronautics and space in college.
Title of Award: COL Chuck Jones Memorial Award **Area, Field, or Subject:** Aeronautics; Aerospace sciences; Communications; Engineering; Meteorology; Space and planetary sciences **Level of Education for which Award is Granted:** Undergraduate **Number Awarded:** 1 each year. **Funds Available:** The stipend is $2,000. **Duration:** 1 year; nonrenewable.
Eligibility Requirements: This program is open to college-bound high school seniors living in New England who are dependents of active-duty, retired, or deceased military members of any branch of service. Also eligible are dependents of military recruiters working in the New York area and students living elsewhere but whose military sponsor is stationed at Hanscom Air Force Base. Applicants must demonstrate qualities of responsibility, leadership, scholastics, citizenship, and diversity of interest. They must have a valid military identification card and be planning to work on a college degree in a field related to aeronautics and space (including communications, meteorology, air/space maintenance, manufacturing processing, engineering, and the astronaut program). Along with their application, they must submit a 2-page essay on their educational goals, how their educational experience will help prepare them to pursue future goals, and how they intend to apply their education to better their community. **Deadline for Receipt:** March of each year. **Additional Information:** This program was established to honor a victim of an airplane crash on September 11, 2001. It is sponsored by the Paul Revere Chapter of the Air Force Association.

4471 ■ HANSCOM OFFICERS' WIVES' CLUB

Attn: Scholarship Chair
P.O. Box 557
Bedford, MA 01730
Tel: (781)275-1251
E-mail: scholarship@hanscomowd.org
Web Site: http://www.hanscomowc.org
To provide financial assistance to children of military personnel and veterans in New England who are interested in studying engineering or computer science in college.
Title of Award: Lieutenant General Chubb Award **Area, Field, or Subject:** Computer and information sciences; Engineering **Level of Education for which Award is Granted:** Undergraduate **Number Awarded:** 1 each year. **Funds Available:** A stipend is awarded (amount not specified). **Duration:** 1 year; nonrenewable.
Eligibility Requirements: This program is open to college-bound high school seniors living in New England who are dependents of active-duty, retired, or deceased military members of any branch of service. Also eligible are dependents of military recruiters working in the New York area and students living elsewhere but whose military sponsor is stationed at Hanscom Air Force Base. Applicants must demonstrate qualities of responsibility, leadership, scholastics, citizenship, and diversity of interest. They must have a valid military identification card and be planning to work on a college degree in engineering or computer science. Along with their application, they must submit a 2-page essay on their educational goals, how their educational experience will help prepare them to pursue future goals, and how they intend to apply their education to better their community. **Deadline for Receipt:** March of each year. **Additional Information:** This program is sponsored by the Military Affairs Council/North Suburban Chamber of Commerce.

4472 ■ HANSCOM OFFICERS' WIVES' CLUB

Attn: Scholarship Chair
P.O. Box 557
Bedford, MA 01730
Tel: (781)275-1251
E-mail: scholarship@hanscomowd.org
Web Site: http://www.hanscomowc.org
To provide financial assistance to children of military personnel and veterans in New England who are interested in studying aviation in college.
Title of Award: Brian Sweeney Memorial Award **Area, Field, or Subject:** Aviation; Engineering, Aerospace/Aeronautical/Astronautical; Engineering, Civil; Environmental science; Meteorology; Protective services **Level of Education for which Award is Granted:** Undergraduate **Number Awarded:** 1 each year. **Funds Available:** The stipend is $2,000. **Duration:** 1 year; nonrenewable.
Eligibility Requirements: This program is open to college-bound high school seniors living in New England who are dependents of active-duty, retired, or deceased military members of any branch of service. Also eligible are dependents of military recruiters working in the New York area and students living elsewhere but whose military sponsor is stationed at Hanscom Air Force Base. Applicants must demonstrate qualities of responsibility, leadership, scholastics, citizenship, and diversity of interest. They must have a valid military identification card and be planning to work on a college degree in a field related to aviation (including civil, aeronautical, and environmental engineering; maintenance; management; aviation safety and security; and meteorology). Along with their application, they must submit a 2-page essay on their educational goals, how their educational experience will help prepare them to pursue future goals, and how they intend to apply their education to better their community. **Deadline for Receipt:** March of each year. **Additional Information:** This program was established to honor a victim of an airplane crash on September 11, 2001. It is sponsored by the Paul Revere Chapter of the Air Force Association.

4473 ■ HARVEST EDUCATION FOUNDATION

P.O. Box 100
Romeo, MI 48065-0100
Tel: (586)752-6066
Web Site: http://www.marvac.org/harvestapp.html
To provide financial assistance for college to Michigan residents interested in preparing for a career in the manufactured homes, recreational vehicles, or campground industries.
Title of Award: HARVEST Scholarships **Area, Field, or Subject:** Design; Engineering; Management; Marketing and distribution; Personnel administration/human resources **Level of Education for which Award is Granted:** Undergraduate **Number Awarded:** 1 or more each year. **Funds Available:** A stipend is awarded (amount not specified). **Duration:** 1 year; may be renewed.
Eligibility Requirements: This program is open to Michigan students enrolled or planning to enroll at an accredited college or university to prepare for a career in the manufactured homes, recreational vehicles, or campground industries. Fields of study may include engineering, marketing, management, service, design, human resources, or any other discipline that will serve the needs of the industries. Applicants must submit an essay of 200 to 300 words on their career goals and why they feel they deserve this scholarship. Selection is based on merit and/or financial need. **Deadline for Receipt:** March of each year. **Additional Information:** The HARVEST Education Foundation is a joint venture of the Michigan Manufactured Housing Association and the Michigan Association of Recreation Vehicles and Campgrounds, both at 2222 Association Drive, Okemos, MI 48864-5978, (517) 349-3300, E-mail: michhome@michhome.org and marvac@marvac.org.

4474 ■ HAWAI'I COMMUNITY FOUNDATION

Attn: Scholarship Department
1164 Bishop Street, Suite 800
Honolulu, HI 96813
Tel: (808)566-5570; 888-731-3863
Fax: (808)521-6286
E-mail: scholarships@hcf-hawaii.org
Web Site: http://www.hawaiicommunityfoundation.org/scholar/scholar.php

To provide financial assistance to Hawaiians who are interested in working on an undergraduate or graduate degree in engineering.
Title of Award: Earl Bakken Engineering Scholarships **Area, Field, or Subject:** Engineering **Level of Education for which Award is Granted:** Four Year College, Graduate **Number Awarded:** Varies each year; recently, 11 of these scholarships were awarded. **Funds Available:** The amounts of the awards depend on the availability of funds and the need of the recipient; recently, stipends averaged $5,000. **Duration:** 1 year.
Eligibility Requirements: Eligible to apply are residents of the island of Hawaii who are enrolled or planning to enroll in an undergraduate or graduate degree program in engineering. Applicants must demonstrate financial need and academic achievement (GPA of 2.7 or higher). Preference is given to applicants of Hawaiian ancestry. **Deadline for Receipt:** February of each year.

4475 ■ HAWAI'I COMMUNITY FOUNDATION

Attn: Scholarship Department
1164 Bishop Street, Suite 800
Honolulu, HI 96813
Tel: (808)566-5570; 888-731-3863
Fax: (808)521-6286
E-mail: scholarships@hcf-hawaii.org
Web Site: http://www.hawaiicommunityfoundation.org/scholar/scholar.php
To provide financial assistance for college to seniors at designated high schools in Hawaii.
Title of Award: Castle & Cooke Mililani Technology Park Scholarship **Area, Field, or Subject:** Engineering; General studies/Field of study not specified; Science **Level of Education for which Award is Granted:** Undergraduate **Number Awarded:** Varies each year; recently, 10 of these scholarships were awarded. **Funds Available:** The amounts of the awards depend on the availability of funds and the need of the recipient; recently, stipends averaged $1,000. **Duration:** 1 year.
Eligibility Requirements: This program is open to seniors at Leilehua, Mililani, and Waialua high schools who plan to attend an accredited college or university. Preference is given to students planning to major in a high technology field, such as science or engineering. Applicants must be able to demonstrate academic achievement (GPA of 2.7 or higher), good moral character, and financial need. In addition to filling out the standard application form, they must write a short statement indicating their reasons for attending college, their planned course of study, and their career goals. **Deadline for Receipt:** February of each year. **Additional Information:** Recipients may attend college in Hawaii or on the mainland.

4476 ■ HEWLETT-PACKARD COMPANY

Attn: Scholar Program Manager
8000 Foothills Boulevard
MS 5214
Roseville, CA 95747
Tel: (916)785-3809
E-mail: hpscholars@hp.com
Web Site: http://www.hp.com/go/hpscholars
To provide financial assistance and summer work experience to underrepresented minority high school seniors and community college transfer students who are interested in studying computer engineering, electrical engineering, or computer science at designated universities.
Title of Award: HP Scholar Program **Area, Field, or Subject:** Computer and information sciences; Engineering, Computer; Engineering, Electrical **Level of Education for which Award is Granted:** Four Year College **Number Awarded:** Approximately 120 each year. **Funds Available:** The stipend is $3,000 per year. In addition, students receive a salary when they work at HP facilities during the summer. They also receive an HP laptop, printer, and PDA. The total value of the award exceeds $40,000 per student. **Duration:** 4 years of university study plus 3 summers of internships.
Eligibility Requirements: This program is open to graduating high school seniors and community college students who are members of an underrepresented minority group (African American, Latino, or American Indian). Applicants must be planning to major in electrical engineering, computer engineering, or computer science at the University of California at Los Angeles, San Jose State University, North Carolina A&T University, the University of Washington, or Morgan State University. They must be interested in working during the summer at a major Hewlett-Packard (HP) location in California, Colorado, Idaho, Oregon, Texas, or Washington.

Selection is based on academic achievement, financial need, family's educational history (priority is given to first-generation students), letters of recommendation, a personal statement (communication skills, personal and professional qualities, community involvement), connections to HP Philanthropy and Education Partnerships, and demonstrated interest in math, science, and engineering. **Deadline for Receipt:** March of each year. **Additional Information:** Applications must be submitted to the school the student wishes to attend.

4477 ■ HISPANIC CONTRACTORS OF COLORADO

1114 West Seventh Avenue, Suite 210
Denver, CO 80204
Tel: (303)893-3893
Fax: (303)893-2877
Web Site: http://www.hispanic-contractors.org/html/scholarships.htm
To provide financial assistance for college to Hispanic residents of Colorado who are interested in preparing for a career in the construction industry.
Title of Award: Hispanic Contractors of Colorado Scholarships **Area, Field, or Subject:** Architecture; Construction; Engineering; Heating, air conditioning, and refrigeration **Level of Education for which Award is Granted:** Undergraduate **Number Awarded:** 1 or more each year. **Funds Available:** A stipend is awarded (amount not specified). **Duration:** 1 year.
Eligibility Requirements: This program is open to residents of Colorado of Hispanic heritage who have been accepted at or are attending an accredited college, university, or technical school. Applicants must have a cumulative GPA of 2.5 or higher and a declared major or certificate interest in a construction-related field (e.g., architecture, construction management, construction technology, engineering, HVAC certificate). Students in a 4-year college or university program must be juniors or above. Selection is based on a statement on career goals and why the applicant has chosen a career in construction, academic achievement, 2 letters of recommendation, community service and/or extracurricular activities, and financial need. **Deadline for Receipt:** March of each year.

4478 ■ HISPANIC ENGINEER NATIONAL ACHIEVEMENT AWARDS CONFERENCE

3900 Whiteside Street
Los Angeles, CA 90063
Tel: (323)262-0997
Fax: (323)262-0946
E-mail: info@henaac.org
Web Site: http://www.henaac.org/scholarships
To provide financial assistance to Hispanic undergraduate students majoring in computer and electrical engineering.
Title of Award: AMD/HENAAC Scholars Program **Area, Field, or Subject:** Engineering, Computer; Engineering, Electrical **Level of Education for which Award is Granted:** Undergraduate **Number Awarded:** 1 or more each year. **Funds Available:** Stipends range from $1,000 to $5,000. **Duration:** 1 year; recipients may reapply.
Eligibility Requirements: This program is open to Hispanic undergraduate students who are enrolled full time in computer or electrical engineering. Applicants must have a GPA of 3.5 or higher. Academic achievement and campus community activities are considered in the selection process. **Deadline for Receipt:** April of each year. **Additional Information:** This program is sponsored by AMD (Advanced Micro Devices, Inc.) as part of its effort to support the mission of the Hispanic Engineer National Achievement Awards Conference (HENAAC) to promote technical excellence and leadership in the Hispanic community.

4479 ■ HISPANIC ENGINEER NATIONAL ACHIEVEMENT AWARDS CONFERENCE

3900 Whiteside Street
Los Angeles, CA 90063
Tel: (323)262-0997
Fax: (323)262-0946
E-mail: info@henaac.org
Web Site: http://www.henaac.org/scholarships
To provide financial assistance to Hispanic undergraduate students majoring in engineering and related fields.
Title of Award: Amerada Hess/HENAAC Scholars Program **Area, Field, or Subject:** Computer and information sciences; Engineering; Materials research/science; Mathematics and mathematical sciences; Science

Level of Education for which Award is Granted: Undergraduate **Number Awarded:** 1 or more each year. **Funds Available:** Stipends range from $1,000 to $5,000. **Duration:** 1 year; recipients may reapply. **Eligibility Requirements:** This program is open to Hispanic undergraduate students who are enrolled full time in computer science, engineering, material science, mathematics, or applied science. Applicants must have a GPA of 3.0 or higher. There is no citizenship requirement. Academic achievement and campus community activities are considered in the selection process. **Deadline for Receipt:** April of each year. **Additional Information:** This program is sponsored by the Amerada Hess Foundation as part of its effort to support the mission of the Hispanic Engineer National Achievement Awards Conference (HENAAC) to promote technical excellence and leadership in the Hispanic community.

4480 ■ HISPANIC ENGINEER NATIONAL ACHIEVEMENT AWARDS CONFERENCE

3900 Whiteside Street
Los Angeles, CA 90063
Tel: (323)262-0997
Fax: (323)262-0946
E-mail: info@henaac.org
Web Site: http://www.henaac.org/scholarships
To provide financial assistance to Hispanic undergraduate students majoring in electrical or mechanical engineering.

Title of Award: DaimlerChrysler/HENAAC Scholars Program **Area, Field, or Subject:** Engineering, Electrical; Engineering, Mechanical **Level of Education for which Award is Granted:** Undergraduate **Number Awarded:** 1 or more each year. **Funds Available:** Stipends range from $1,000 to $5,000. **Duration:** 1 year; recipients may reapply. **Eligibility Requirements:** This program is open to Hispanic undergraduate students who are enrolled full time in electrical or mechanical engineering. Applicants must have a GPA of 3.0 or higher and be able to work in the United States. Academic achievement and campus community activities are considered in the selection process. **Deadline for Receipt:** April of each year. **Additional Information:** This program is sponsored by DaimlerChrysler as part of its effort to support the mission of the Hispanic Engineer National Achievement Awards Conference (HENAAC) to promote technical excellence and leadership in the Hispanic community.

4481 ■ HISPANIC ENGINEER NATIONAL ACHIEVEMENT AWARDS CONFERENCE

3900 Whiteside Street
Los Angeles, CA 90063
Tel: (323)262-0997
Fax: (323)262-0946
E-mail: info@henaac.org
Web Site: http://www.henaac.org/scholarships
To provide financial assistance to Hispanic undergraduate students majoring in engineering and related fields.

Title of Award: Ford/HENAAC Scholars Program **Area, Field, or Subject:** Computer and information sciences; Engineering, Aerospace/Aeronautical/Astronautical; Engineering, Electrical; Engineering, Industrial; Engineering, Mechanical **Level of Education for which Award is Granted:** Undergraduate **Number Awarded:** 5 each year. **Funds Available:** The stipend is $5,000. **Duration:** 1 year; recipients may reapply. **Eligibility Requirements:** This program is open to Hispanic undergraduate students who are enrolled full time in computer science or the following engineering fields: aeronautical, electrical, industrial, and, mechanical. Applicants must have a GPA of 3.0 or higher. U.S. citizenship is required. Academic achievement and campus community activities are considered in the selection process. **Deadline for Receipt:** April of each year. **Additional Information:** This program is sponsored by Ford Motor Company as part of its effort to support the mission of the Hispanic Engineer National Achievement Awards Conference (HENAAC) to promote technical excellence and leadership in the Hispanic community.

4482 ■ HISPANIC ENGINEER NATIONAL ACHIEVEMENT AWARDS CONFERENCE

3900 Whiteside Street
Los Angeles, CA 90063
Tel: (323)262-0997
Fax: (323)262-0946

E-mail: info@henaac.org
Web Site: http://www.henaac.org/scholarships
To provide financial assistance to Hispanic undergraduate students majoring in computer science or designated fields of engineering.

Title of Award: Freescale/HENAAC Scholars Program **Area, Field, or Subject:** Computer and information sciences; Engineering, Computer; Engineering, Electrical **Level of Education for which Award is Granted:** Undergraduate **Number Awarded:** 1 or more each year. **Funds Available:** The stipend is $5,000. **Duration:** 1 year; recipients may reapply. **Eligibility Requirements:** This program is open to Hispanic undergraduate students who are enrolled full time in computer science or electrical or computer engineering. Applicants must be entering their sophomore, junior, or senior year and have a GPA of 3.0 or higher. Academic achievement and campus community activities are considered in the selection process. **Deadline for Receipt:** April of each year. **Additional Information:** This program is sponsored by Freescale Semiconductor as part of its effort to support the mission of the Hispanic Engineer National Achievement Awards Conference (HENAAC) to promote technical excellence and leadership in the Hispanic community. The recipient is required to accept a summer internship (where and when available) with Freescale Semiconductor.

4483 ■ HISPANIC ENGINEER NATIONAL ACHIEVEMENT AWARDS CONFERENCE

3900 Whiteside Street
Los Angeles, CA 90063
Tel: (323)262-0997
Fax: (323)262-0946
E-mail: info@henaac.org
Web Site: http://www.henaac.org/scholarships
To provide financial assistance to Hispanic undergraduate students majoring in engineering and related fields.

Title of Award: Future Electronics/HENAAC Scholars Program **Area, Field, or Subject:** Computer and information sciences; Engineering; Materials research/science; Mathematics and mathematical sciences; Science **Level of Education for which Award is Granted:** Undergraduate **Number Awarded:** 1 or more each year. **Funds Available:** Stipends range from $1,000 to $5,000. **Duration:** 1 year; recipients may reapply. **Eligibility Requirements:** This program is open to Hispanic undergraduate students who are enrolled full time in computer science, engineering, material science, mathematics, or applied science. Applicants must have a GPA of 3.0 or higher. There is no citizenship requirement. Academic achievement and campus community activities are considered in the selection process. **Deadline for Receipt:** April of each year. **Additional Information:** This program is sponsored by the Future Electronics as part of its effort to support the mission of the Hispanic Engineer National Achievement Awards Conference (HENAAC) to promote technical excellence and leadership in the Hispanic community.

4484 ■ HISPANIC ENGINEER NATIONAL ACHIEVEMENT AWARDS CONFERENCE

3900 Whiteside Street
Los Angeles, CA 90063
Tel: (323)262-0997
Fax: (323)262-0946
E-mail: info@henaac.org
Web Site: http://www.henaac.org/scholarships
To provide financial assistance to Hispanic undergraduate and graduate students majoring in engineering and related fields.

Title of Award: HENAAC Student Leadership Awards **Area, Field, or Subject:** Computer and information sciences; Engineering; Materials research/science; Mathematics and mathematical sciences; Science **Level of Education for which Award is Granted:** Graduate, Undergraduate **Number Awarded:** 2 each year: 1 undergraduate and 1 graduate student. **Funds Available:** The stipend is $5,000. **Duration:** 1 year. **Eligibility Requirements:** This program is open to Hispanic undergraduate and graduate students who are enrolled full time in computer science, engineering, material science, mathematics, or applied science. Applicants must have a GPA of 3.0 or higher. There is no citizenship requirement. Academic achievement and campus community activities are considered in the selection process. **Deadline for Receipt:** April of each year. **Additional Information:** This program is sponsored by the Hispanic Engineer National Achievement Awards Conference (HENAAC) to promote technical excellence and leadership in the Hispanic community.

4485 ■ HISPANIC ENGINEER NATIONAL ACHIEVEMENT AWARDS CONFERENCE

3900 Whiteside Street
Los Angeles, CA 90063
Tel: (323)262-0997
Fax: (323)262-0946
E-mail: info@henaac.org
Web Site: http://www.henaac.org/scholarships
To provide financial assistance to Hispanic undergraduate students majoring in electrical engineering.
Title of Award: Motorola/HENAAC Scholars Program. **Area, Field, or Subject:** Engineering, Electrical **Level of Education for which Award is Granted:** Undergraduate **Number Awarded:** 1 or more each year. **Funds Available:** Stipends range from $1,000 to $5,000. **Duration:** 1 year; recipients may reapply.
Eligibility Requirements: This program is open to Hispanic undergraduate students who are enrolled full time in electrical engineering. Academic achievement and campus community activities are considered in the selection process. **Deadline for Receipt:** April of each year. **Additional Information:** This program is sponsored by Motorola as part of its effort to support the mission of the Hispanic Engineer National Achievement Awards Conference (HENAAC) to promote technical excellence and leadership in the Hispanic community.

4486 ■ HISPANIC ENGINEER NATIONAL ACHIEVEMENT AWARDS CONFERENCE

3900 Whiteside Street
Los Angeles, CA 90063
Tel: (323)262-0997
Fax: (323)262-0946
E-mail: info@henaac.org
Web Site: http://www.henaac.org/scholarships
To provide financial assistance to Hispanic undergraduate students majoring in engineering and related fields.
Title of Award: Northrop Grumman/HENAAC Scholars Program **Area, Field, or Subject:** Architecture, Naval; Computer and information sciences; Engineering, Aerospace/Aeronautical/Astronautical; Engineering, Chemical; Engineering, Civil; Engineering, Computer; Engineering, Electrical; Engineering, Industrial; Engineering, Mechanical; Engineering, Ocean; Information science and technology; Mathematics and mathematical sciences; Physics **Level of Education for which Award is Granted:** Undergraduate **Number Awarded:** 5 each year. **Funds Available:** The stipend is $5,000. **Duration:** 1 year; recipients may reapply.
Eligibility Requirements: This program is open to Hispanic undergraduate students who are enrolled full time in the following engineering fields: aerospace, chemical, civil, computer, electrical, industrial, manufacturing, marine, mechanical, ocean, or structural. Students majoring in computer science, information science, mathematics, naval architecture, and physics are also eligible. Applicants must be U.S. citizens and have a GPA of 3.0 or higher. Academic achievement and campus community activities are considered in the selection process. **Deadline for Receipt:** April of each year. **Additional Information:** This program is sponsored by Northrop Grumman as part of its effort to support the mission of the Hispanic Engineer National Achievement Awards Conference (HENAAC) to promote technical excellence and leadership in the Hispanic community.

4487 ■ HISPANIC ENGINEER NATIONAL ACHIEVEMENT AWARDS CONFERENCE

3900 Whiteside Street
Los Angeles, CA 90063
Tel: (323)262-0997
Fax: (323)262-0946
E-mail: info@henaac.org
Web Site: http://www.henaac.org/scholarships
To provide financial assistance to Hispanic undergraduate students majoring in engineering and related fields.
Title of Award: NVIDIA Corporation/HENAAC Scholars Program **Area, Field, or Subject:** Computer and information sciences; Engineering; Materials research/science; Mathematics and mathematical sciences; Science **Level of Education for which Award is Granted:** Undergraduate

Number Awarded: 1 or more each year. **Funds Available:** Stipends range from $1,000 to $5,000. **Duration:** 1 year; recipients may reapply.
Eligibility Requirements: This program is open to Hispanic undergraduate students who are enrolled full time in computer science, engineering, material science, mathematics, or applied science. Applicants must have a GPA of 3.0 or higher. There is no citizenship requirement. Academic achievement and campus community activities are considered in the selection process. **Deadline for Receipt:** April of each year. **Additional Information:** This program is sponsored by the NVIDIA Corporation as part of its effort to support the mission of the Hispanic Engineer National Achievement Awards Conference (HENAAC) to promote technical excellence and leadership in the Hispanic community.

4488 ■ HISPANIC ENGINEER NATIONAL ACHIEVEMENT AWARDS CONFERENCE

3900 Whiteside Street
Los Angeles, CA 90063
Tel: (323)262-0997
Fax: (323)262-0946
E-mail: info@henaac.org
Web Site: http://www.henaac.org/scholarships
To provide financial assistance to Hispanic undergraduate students majoring in designated fields of engineering at universities in the Southeast.
Title of Award: Shaw Industries/HENAAC Scholars Program **Area, Field, or Subject:** Engineering; Engineering, Chemical; Engineering, Electrical; Engineering, Industrial; Engineering, Mechanical **Level of Education for which Award is Granted:** Undergraduate **Number Awarded:** 1 or more each year. **Funds Available:** Stipends range from $1,000 to $5,000. **Duration:** 1 year; recipients may reapply.
Eligibility Requirements: This program is open to Hispanic undergraduate students who are enrolled full time in chemical, electrical, industrial, mechanical, or textile engineering. Applicants must be entering their junior or senior year at a university in the southeastern United States and have a GPA of 3.0 or higher. Academic achievement and campus community activities are considered in the selection process. **Deadline for Receipt:** April of each year. **Additional Information:** This program is sponsored by Shaw Industries as part of its effort to support the mission of the Hispanic Engineer National Achievement Awards Conference (HENAAC) to promote technical excellence and leadership in the Hispanic community.

4489 ■ HISPANIC SCHOLARSHIP FUND

Attn: Selection Committee
55 Second Street, Suite 1500
San Francisco, CA 94105
Tel: (415)808-2350; 877-HSF-INFO
Fax: (415)808-2302
E-mail: highschool@hsf.net
Web Site: http://www.hsf.net/scholarship/programs/gm.php
To provide financial assistance to Hispanic Americans who are interested in attending college to major in engineering or business.
Title of Award: General Motors Scholarship Program of the Hispanic Scholarship Fund **Area, Field, or Subject:** Business administration; Engineering **Level of Education for which Award is Granted:** Four Year College **Number Awarded:** 1 or more each year. **Funds Available:** The stipend is $2,500 per year. **Duration:** 1 year.
Eligibility Requirements: This program is open to U.S. citizens, permanent residents, and visitors with a passport stamped I-551 who are of Hispanic heritage. Applicants must have a GPA of 3.0 or higher and be enrolled or planning to enroll full time at an accredited 4-year college or university in the United States, Puerto Rico, or the U.S. Virgin Islands to major in business or engineering. Along with their application, they must submit 600-word essays on 1) how their Hispanic heritage, family upbringing, and/or role models have influenced their personal long-term goals; 2) how they contribute to their community and what they have learned from their experiences; and 3) an academic challenge they have faced and how they have overcome it. Selection is based on academic achievement, personal strengths, leadership, and financial need. **Deadline for Receipt:** June of each year. **Additional Information:** This program is jointly sponsored by General Motors and the Hispanic Scholarship Fund (HSF).

4490 ■ HISPANIC SCHOLARSHIP FUND

Attn: Selection Committee
55 Second Street, Suite 1500
San Francisco, CA 94105

Tel: (415)808-2350; 877-HSF-INFO
Fax: (415)808-2302
E-mail: highschool@hsf.net
Web Site: http://www.hsf.net/scholarship/programs/shpe.php
To provide financial assistance for college to Hispanic Americans who are interested in majoring in designated fields of science.
Title of Award: Society of Hispanic Professional Engineers Scholarship Program **Area, Field, or Subject:** Computer and information sciences; Engineering; Mathematics and mathematical sciences; Physical sciences **Level of Education for which Award is Granted:** Undergraduate **Number Awarded:** Varies each year; recently, 69 of these scholarships were awarded: 7 at $1,250, 2 at $1,307, and 60 at $2,500. **Funds Available:** Stipends range from $1,250 to $2,500 per year. **Duration:** 1 year.
Eligibility Requirements: This program is open to U.S. citizens, permanent residents, and visitors with a passport stamped I-551 who are of Hispanic heritage. Applicants may be graduating high school seniors, community college students transferring to a 4-year institution, or continuing college students as long as they have a GPA of 3.0 or higher. They must be enrolled or planning to enroll full time at an accredited college or university in the United States to major in computer science, physical science, applied science, mathematics, or engineering. Along with their application, they must submit 600-word essays on 1) how their Hispanic heritage, family upbringing, and/or role models have influenced their personal long-term goals; 2) how they contribute to their community and what they have learned from their experiences; and 3) an academic challenge they have faced and how they have overcome it. Selection is based on academic achievement, personal strengths, leadership, and financial need. **Deadline for Receipt:** June of each year. **Additional Information:** This program is jointly sponsored by the Society of Hispanic Professional Engineers (SHPE) and the Hispanic Scholarship Fund (HSF).

4491 ▪ HISPANIC SCHOLARSHIP FUND INSTITUTE
1001 Connecticut Avenue, N.W., Suite 632
Washington, DC 20036
Tel: (202)296-0009
Fax: (202)296-3633
E-mail: info@hsfi.org
Web Site: http://www.hsfi.org/scholarships/energy.asp
To provide financial assistance to Hispanic undergraduate students majoring in designated business, engineering, and science fields related to the U.S. Department of Energy (DOE) goals of environmental restoration and waste management.
Title of Award: Environmental Management Scholarship **Area, Field, or Subject:** Business administration; Chemistry; Computer and information sciences; Engineering, Agricultural; Engineering, Civil; Engineering, Electrical; Engineering, Industrial; Engineering, Mechanical; Engineering, Metallurgical; Engineering, Petroleum; Environmental science; Epidemiology; Geology; Hydrology; Management; Mathematics and mathematical sciences; Physics; Radiology; Toxicology **Level of Education for which Award is Granted:** Undergraduate **Number Awarded:** Varies each year. **Funds Available:** The stipend is $3,000 per year for 4-year university students or $2,000 per year for community college students. **Duration:** 1 year.
Eligibility Requirements: This program is open to U.S. citizens and permanent residents of Hispanic background who have completed at least 12 undergraduate credits with a GPA of 3.0 or higher. Applicants must be interested in preparing for a career supportive of the DOE goals of environmental restoration and waste management. Eligible academic majors are in the fields of business (management and system analysis), engineering (agricultural, chemical, civil, electrical, environmental, industrial, mechanical, metallurgical, nuclear, and petroleum), and science (applied math/physics, chemistry, computer science, ecology, environmental, epidemiology, geology, health physics, hydrology, radiochemistry, radio-ecology, and toxicology). Along with their application, they must submit a 2-page essay on 1) how their academic major, interests, and career goals correspond to environmental restoration and waste management issues; and 2) how their Hispanic background and family upbringing have influenced their academic and personal goals. Selection is based on the essay, academic record, academic plans and career goals, financial need, commitment to DOE's goal of environmental restoration and waste management, and a letter of recommendation. **Deadline for Receipt:** March of each year. **Additional Information:** This program, which began in 1990, is sponsored by DOE's Office of Environmental Management.

Recipients must enroll full time at a college or university in the United States.

4492 ▪ HISPANIC SCHOLARSHIP FUND INSTITUTE
1001 Connecticut Avenue, N.W., Suite 632
Washington, DC 20036
Tel: (202)296-0009
Fax: (202)296-3633
E-mail: info@hsfi.org
Web Site: http://www.hsfi.org/scholarships/generation.asp
To provide financial assistance to Hispanic and other students majoring in designated business, engineering, social science, and science fields who are interested in employment with the U.S. Department of Energy (DOE).
Title of Award: Next Generation of Public Servants Scholarship **Area, Field, or Subject:** Accounting; Biological and clinical sciences; Business administration; Computer and information sciences; Engineering; Environmental science; Finance; Geology; Information science and technology; Management; Mathematics and mathematical sciences; Physics; Political science; Psychology; Sociology **Level of Education for which Award is Granted:** Undergraduate **Number Awarded:** Varies each year. **Funds Available:** The stipend is $3,000 per year. **Duration:** 1 year; may be renewed up to 2 additional years if the recipient maintains full-time enrollment and a GPA of 2.8 or higher.
Eligibility Requirements: This program is open to U.S. citizens enrolled full time as sophomores with a GPA of 2.8 or higher. Applicants must be interested in preparing for a career with the DOE in an energy-related field. Eligible academic majors are in the fields of business (accounting, business administration, finance, and management), engineering (biomedical, chemical, civil, computer, electrical, environmental, industrial, materials, mechanical, metallurgical, nuclear, and petroleum), social science (economics, organizational psychology, political science, and sociology), and science (biological sciences, computer science, geology, information technology, mathematics, microbiology, and physics). They must be willing to participate in co-ops with the DOE. Along with their application, they must submit a 2-page essay on why a career in public service interests them, how their academic major connects with their stated DOE career goal, why the DOE should invest in them through this program, and how they believe the DOE will benefit from this investment. Selection is based on academic achievement, financial need, demonstrated commitment to public service, and interest in federal employment with the DOE. **Deadline for Receipt:** February of each year. **Additional Information:** This program, sponsored by DOE's Office of Economic Impact and Diversity, is administered by the Hispanic Scholarship Fund Institute as part of its effort to increase Hispanic participation in federal service.

4493 ▪ HOPI TRIBE
Attn: Office of Education
P.O. Box 123
Kykotsmovi, AZ 86039
Tel: (928)734-3533
Free: 800-762-9630
Fax: (928)734-9575
E-mail: IPolingyumptewa@hopi.nsn.us
Web Site: http://www.hopi.nsn.us/education_htgsp.asp
To encourage Hopi students to get an undergraduate or graduate degree in an area of interest to the Hopi Tribe.
Title of Award: Hopi Tribal Priority Scholarship **Area, Field, or Subject:** Business administration; Education; Engineering; Environmental conservation; Environmental science; Health care services; Law; Medicine **Level of Education for which Award is Granted:** Four Year College, Graduate **Number Awarded:** Varies each year. **Funds Available:** The stipend covers all educational expenses. **Duration:** 1 year; may be renewed.
Eligibility Requirements: This program is open to enrolled members of the Hopi Tribe. They must be college juniors, seniors, or graduate students whose degree is in a subject area that is of priority interest to the Hopi Tribe. Those areas are law, natural resources, education, medicine, health, engineering, or business. This is a highly competitive scholarship. Selection is based on academic merit and the likelihood that the applicants will use their training and expertise for tribal goals and objectives. **Deadline for Receipt:** July of each year. **Additional Information:** Recipients must attend school on a full-time basis.

4494 ■ IEEE COMPUTER SOCIETY

Attn: Student Awards
1730 Massachusetts Avenue, N.W.
Washington, DC 20036-1992
Tel: (202)371-1013
Fax: (202)778-0884
E-mail: hqofc@computer.org
Web Site: http://www.computer.org/students/schlrshp.htm
To recognize and reward students who are active leaders in the IEEE Computer Society student branch chapters.
Title of Award: Richard E. Merwin Student Scholarship **Area, Field, or Subject:** Computer and information sciences; Engineering, Computer; Engineering, Electrical **Level of Education for which Award is Granted:** Four Year College, Graduate **Number Awarded:** Up to 10 each year. **Funds Available:** The stipend is $4,000, paid in 4 equal installments. **Duration:** 1 academic year.
Eligibility Requirements: Juniors, seniors, and graduate students in electrical engineering, computer engineering, computer science, or a well-defined computer-related field of engineering (e.g., biomedical computer engineering, design automation) are eligible to apply if they are full-time students and active members of the society's student branch chapter at their institution. Applicants must have a cumulative GPA of 2.5 or higher. Selection is based on involvement in chapter activities (40%), academic achievement (30%), other extracurricular activities in college (10%), and a letter of evaluation by the branch chapter advisor (20%). **Deadline for Receipt:** May of each year. **Additional Information:** A brief statement outlining accomplishments must be submitted by each recipient at the end of the academic year.

4495 ■ ILLINOIS SOCIETY OF PROFESSIONAL ENGINEERS

Attn: ISPE Foundation, Inc.
600 South Second Street, Suite 403
Springfield, IL 62704
Tel: (217)544-7424
Fax: (217)528-6545
E-mail: info@IllinoisEngineer.com
Web Site: http://www.ilspe.com/StudentsAndYouth.asp
To provide financial assistance to college juniors and seniors in Illinois who are working on an engineering degree.
Title of Award: M.E. Amstutz Memorial Award **Area, Field, or Subject:** Engineering **Level of Education for which Award is Granted:** Four Year College **Number Awarded:** 1 each year. **Funds Available:** The stipend is $1,500 per year. **Duration:** 1 year.
Eligibility Requirements: Applicants must be Illinois residents who are juniors or seniors in college in the state, enrolled in an engineering program (not engineering technology) accredited by the Accreditation Board of Engineering and Technology (ABET). They must have at least a 3.0 GPA in those courses that count toward their engineering degree. Selection is based on financial need, scholastic achievement, activities, interest in engineering, and a 200-word essay on "Why I would like to become a professional engineer." **Deadline for Receipt:** January of each year.

4496 ■ ILLINOIS SOCIETY OF PROFESSIONAL ENGINEERS

Attn: ISPE Foundation, Inc.
600 South Second Street, Suite 403
Springfield, IL 62704
Tel: (217)544-7424
Fax: (217)528-6545
E-mail: info@IllinoisEngineer.com
Web Site: http://www.ilspe.com/StudentsAndYouth.asp
To provide financial assistance to college juniors and seniors in Illinois who are working on an engineering degree.
Title of Award: ISPE Advantage Award **Area, Field, or Subject:** Engineering **Level of Education for which Award is Granted:** Four Year College **Number Awarded:** 1 each year. **Funds Available:** The stipend is $1,200 per year. **Duration:** 1 year.
Eligibility Requirements: This program is open to Illinois residents who are juniors or seniors enrolled in an ABET-accredited engineering program (not engineering technology) program in the state. Applicants must have at least a 3.0 GPA in those courses that count toward their engineering degree. Selection is based on financial need, scholastic achievement, activities, interest in engineering, and a 200-word essay on

"Why I would like to become a professional engineer." This scholarship is reserved for the son or daughter of a member of the Illinois Society of Professional Engineers (ISPE), but if no applications are received from children of members, the scholarship is awarded to the most qualified applicant. **Deadline for Receipt:** January of each year.

4497 ■ ILLINOIS SOCIETY OF PROFESSIONAL ENGINEERS

Attn: ISPE Foundation, Inc.
600 South Second Street, Suite 403
Springfield, IL 62704
Tel: (217)544-7424
Fax: (217)528-6545
E-mail: info@IllinoisEngineer.com
Web Site: http://www.ilspe.com/StudentsAndYouth.asp
To provide financial assistance to college juniors and seniors in Illinois who are working on an engineering degree.
Title of Award: ISPE Foundation Scholarship **Area, Field, or Subject:** Engineering **Level of Education for which Award is Granted:** Four Year College **Number Awarded:** 1 each year. **Funds Available:** The stipend is $1,200 per year. **Duration:** 1 year.
Eligibility Requirements: This program is open to Illinois residents who are juniors or seniors enrolled in an ABET-accredited engineering program (not engineering technology) program in the state. Applicants must have at least a 3.0 GPA in those courses that count toward their engineering degree. Selection is based on financial need, scholastic achievement, activities, interest in engineering, and a 200-word essay on "Why I would like to become a professional engineer." **Deadline for Receipt:** January of each year.

4498 ■ ILLUMINATING ENGINEERING SOCIETY OF NORTH AMERICA-GOLDEN GATE SECTION

c/o Phil Hall
1514 Gibbons Drive
Alameda, CA 94501
Tel: (510)208-5005
Fax: (510)864-8511
E-mail: mrcatisbac@aol.com
Web Site: http://www.iesgg.org
To provide financial assistance to undergraduate or graduate students interested in studying or conducting research in lighting.
Title of Award: Robert W. Thunen Memorial Scholarships **Area, Field, or Subject:** Architecture; Engineering, Electrical; Filmmaking; Interior design; Lighting science; Radio and television **Level of Education for which Award is Granted:** Four Year College, Graduate **Number Awarded:** At least 2 each year. **Funds Available:** The stipend is $2,500. **Duration:** 1 year.
Eligibility Requirements: Applicants must be enrolled full time as an upper-division or graduate student at an accredited 4-year educational institution in northern California, northern Nevada, Oregon, or Washington and be studying architecture, electrical engineering, film/TV, lighting design, theater, or vision with an emphasis on lighting. Undergraduate students must be proposing course work related to potential employment in the lighting field. Graduate students must be proposing to conduct a research project that will further the lighting field or industry. Financial need is not considered in the selection process. **Deadline for Receipt:** March of each year. **Additional Information:** This program was established in 1986.

4499 ■ INDIAN HEALTH SERVICE

Attn: Scholarship Program
801 Thompson Avenue, Suite 120
Rockville, MD 20852
Tel: (301)443-6197
Fax: (301)443-6048
E-mail: bmiller@na.ihs.gov
Web Site: http://www.ihs.gov
To provide financial assistance to Native American students who need compensatory or preprofessional education to qualify for enrollment in a health professions school.
Title of Award: Health Professions Preparatory Scholarship Program **Area, Field, or Subject:** Engineering; Health care services; Medical technology; Nursing; Nutrition; Pharmaceutical sciences; Physical therapy; Social work **Level of Education for which Award is Granted:**

Undergraduate **Number Awarded:** Varies each year. **Funds Available:** Awards provide a payment directly to the school for tuition and required fees; a stipend for living expenses of approximately $1,160 per month for 10 months; a lump sum to cover the costs of books, travel, and other necessary educational expenses; and up to $400 for approved tutorial costs. **Duration:** Up to 2 years of full-time study or up to 4 years of part-time study.

Eligibility Requirements: Applicants must be American Indians or Alaska Natives; be high school graduates or the equivalent; have the capacity to complete a health professions course of study; and be enrolled or accepted for enrollment in a compensatory or preprofessional general education course or curriculum. The qualifying fields of study include pre-medical technology, pre-dietetics, pre-nursing, pre-pharmacy, pre-physical therapy, pre-social work, and pre-engineering. Recipients must intend to serve Indian people upon completion of professional health care education as a health care provider in the discipline for which they are enrolled at the pregraduate level. **Deadline for Receipt:** February of each year.

4500 ■ INDUSTRIAL DESIGNERS SOCIETY OF AMERICA

Attn: Design Foundation
Dulles, VA 20166-6717
Tel: (703)707-6000
Fax: (703)787-8501
E-mail: celiaw@idsa.org
Web Site: http://www.idsa.org
To provide financial assistance to upper-division students working on an undergraduate degree in industrial design.
Title of Award: IDSA Undergraduate Scholarships **Area, Field, or Subject:** Industrial design **Level of Education for which Award is Granted:** Four Year College **Number Awarded:** 2 each year. **Funds Available:** A stipend is awarded (amount not specified). **Duration:** 1 year.
Eligibility Requirements: Applicants must be enrolled as a full-time student in an industrial design program listed with the sponsor, be in their next-to-final year (juniors in a 4-year program, fourth-year students in a 5-year program), have earned at least a 3.0 GPA since entering the industrial design program, be a member of an Industrial Designers Society of America (IDSA) student chapter, and be a U.S. citizen or resident. Applicants are asked to send a letter of intent that indicates their goals, 3 letters of recommendation, 20 visual examples of their work (i.e., slides, photographs, laser printouts), a completed application form, and a current transcript. Financial need is not considered in the selection process. **Deadline for Receipt:** April of each year.

4501 ■ INSTITUTE OF ELECTRICAL AND ELECTRONICS ENGINEERS

c/o Gene Stuffle
Idaho State University
College of Engineering
833 South Eighth Avenue
Pocatello, ID 83209-8060
Tel: (208)282-2902
E-mail: gene.stuffle@isu.edu
Web Site: http://www.coe.isu.edu/ieee/wescon
To provide financial assistance for college to high school authors of outstanding papers on electronics.
Title of Award: Bruce Angwin Memorial Scholarships **Area, Field, or Subject:** Electronics; Engineering; Writing **Level of Education for which Award is Granted:** Four Year College **Number Awarded:** 2 scholarships are awarded each year. **Funds Available:** The first prize is $5,000 and second prize is $3,000; funds are sent directly to the winners' engineering schools of choice after they have started college classes with a defined major in electronics or a related field. Winners also receive transportation and 1 night's accommodations at the Wescon Electronics Show and Convention, held in alternating years in the San Francisco and Los Angeles areas. **Duration:** The competition is held annually.
Eligibility Requirements: This competition is open to students who are juniors in high school planning to attend 4-year colleges and major in electronics engineering or associated fields. They must be attending high school in Region 6 of the Institute of Electrical and Electronics Engineers, which covers the states of Alaska, Arizona, California, Hawaii, Idaho, Montana, Nevada, New Mexico, Oregon, Utah, and Washington. The competition requires entrants to write a 500- to 600-word essay explaining the importance of electronics technology, the future of electronics in the

United States, what electronics will offer to the next generation, how the students plan to prepare for a career in electronics, how they will contribute, and how they and others will benefit. **Deadline for Receipt:** April of each year. **Additional Information:** This program began in 1986 to honor the 7 astronauts who lost their lives aboard Space Shuttle Challenger. Originally named the Wescon Scholarships, its current name was adopted in 2004.

4502 ■ INSTITUTE OF ELECTRICAL AND ELECTRONICS ENGINEERS

Industry Applications Society
Attn: Administrative Secretary
799 North Beverly Glen
Los Angeles, CA 90077
Tel: (310)446-8360
Fax: (310)446-8390
E-mail: bob.myers@ieee.org
Web Site: http://www.energychallenge.org
To recognize and reward undergraduate engineering students who design and build prototype equipment to support fuel cell power systems.
Title of Award: International Future Energy Challenge Student Competition **Area, Field, or Subject:** Energy-related areas; Engineering **Level of Education for which Award is Granted:** Undergraduate **Number Awarded:** Varies each year. Recently, prizes for the motor topic included first place at $10,000, outstanding design innovation at $6,500, outstanding educational impact at $2,000, outstanding presentation at $2,000, and outstanding technical report at $2,500. For the inverter topic, prizes included first place at $10,000, second place at $8,000, third place at $5,000, outstanding presentation at $2,000, outstanding technical report at $2,000, outstanding educational impact at $1,500, innovative design at $1,500, innovative packaging at $1,000, and outstanding teamwork at $1,000. **Funds Available:** Prizes vary each year, depending on the funding available from sponsors. Recently, they ranged up to $10,000. **Duration:** The competition is held biennially, extending from mid-May of each even-numbered year to mid-August of the following odd-numbered year.
Eligibility Requirements: This program is open to teams of undergraduate students enrolled in an engineering program at a college or university that is ABET-accredited or equivalent. Applicants must have a faculty advisor and the support of the school's administration to design and build a prototype of a low-cost, manufacturable equipment that would accelerate deployment of distributed generation systems. They may submit an entry for 1 of the following topics: a single-phase adjustable speed motor drive, or a utility interactive inverter system for small distributed generation. Selection is based on cost effectiveness, performance, quality of the prototype and other results, engineering reports, adherence to rules and deadlines, innovation, future, and other criteria related to the specific topic. **Deadline for Receipt:** Initial proposals must be submitted by April of each even-numbered year. **Additional Information:** This program was established for 2001 by the U.S. Department of Energy (DOE), the U.S. Department of Defense, the National Association of State Energy Officials, and the following components of the Institute of Electrical and Electronics Engineers (IEEE): the Industry Applications Society, the Power Electronics Society, the Industrial Electronics Society, and the Power Engineering Society. Recent sponsors included the IEEE components, the DOE's National Renewable Energy Laboratory, and the European Power Electronics Association. The 2001 competition was limited to students at North American colleges and universities, but subsequent events have been open to students at any college or university.

4503 ■ INSTITUTE OF INTERNATIONAL EDUCATION

Attn: Lucent Global Science Scholars Program
809 United Nations Plaza
New York, NY 10017-3580
Tel: (212)984-5419
Fax: (212)984-5452
E-mail: sciencescholars@iie.org
Web Site: http://www.iie.org/programs/lucent
To provide financial assistance for college to high school students in the United States and university students in other designated countries who are interested in preparing for careers in information technology.
Title of Award: Lucent Global Science Scholars Program **Area, Field, or Subject:** Chemistry; Computer and information sciences; Engineering;

Information science and technology; Mathematics and mathematical sciences; Physics **Level of Education for which Award is Granted:** Undergraduate **Number Awarded:** Varies each year. Recently, 32 students from foreign countries (5 from China, 1 from Hong Kong, and 2 from each of the other countries) and 28 from the United States received these scholarships. **Funds Available:** The stipend is $5,000 per year. **Duration:** 1 year; nonrenewable.

Eligibility Requirements: This program is open to high school seniors in the United States and first-year university students in Brazil, Canada, China, France, Germany, Hong Kong, India, Korea, Mexico, the Netherlands, Philippines, Poland, Russia, Spain, and the United Kingdom. Students from the United States must have a GPA of 3.6 or higher. Eligible majors include applied physics, chemistry, computer science, engineering, information science and technology, mathematics and applied mathematics, and physics. Selection is based on a demonstrated record of distinction in science and mathematics and a desire to prepare for a career in information technology. **Deadline for Receipt:** February of each year for students from the United States; March of each year for students from other countries. **Additional Information:** This program, established in 1999, is funded by Lucent Technologies. Students are offered internships at Lucent's research and development and manufacturing facilities in their own countries during the summer following their freshman year in the United States or the sophomore year in other countries.

4504 ■ INSTITUTE OF TRANSPORTATION ENGINEERS-ALABAMA SECTION

c/o Robert Vecellio, ALSITE Scholarship
Auburn University
Civil Engineering Department
238 Harbert Engineering Center
Auburn, AL 36849-5337
Tel: (334)844-6286
E-mail: vecellio@engr.auburn.edu

To provide financial assistance to upper-division students in Alabama majoring in civil engineering.

Title of Award: Charles E. Alexander Transportation Engineering Scholarship **Area, Field, or Subject:** Engineering, Civil **Level of Education for which Award is Granted:** Four Year College **Number Awarded:** 1 each year. **Funds Available:** The stipend is $3,700. **Duration:** 1 year.

Eligibility Requirements: Applicants must be at least juniors in college, be majoring in civil engineering, and be attending an ABET-accredited university in Alabama. They must demonstrate a strong commitment to the discipline of transportation engineering and be recommended by a faculty member or a member of the Alabama Section of the Institute of Transportation Engineers (ALSITE). Selection is based on academic achievement, career objectives, leadership activities, employment history, and financial need. **Deadline for Receipt:** February of each year.

4505 ■ INSTITUTE OF TRANSPORTATION ENGINEERS-ALABAMA SECTION

c/o Robert Vecellio, ALSITE Scholarship
Auburn University
Civil Engineering Department
238 Harbert Engineering Center
Auburn, AL 36849-5337
Tel: (334)844-6286
E-mail: vecellio@engr.auburn.edu

To provide financial assistance to upper-division students in Alabama majoring in civil engineering.

Title of Award: Billy Jones Memorial Traffic Engineering Scholarship **Area, Field, or Subject:** Engineering, Civil **Level of Education for which Award is Granted:** Four Year College **Number Awarded:** 1 each year. **Funds Available:** The stipend is $2,500. **Duration:** 1 year.

Eligibility Requirements: Applicants must be at least juniors in college, be majoring in civil engineering, and be attending an ABET-accredited university in Alabama. They must demonstrate a strong commitment to the discipline of transportation engineering and be recommended by a faculty member or a member of the Alabama Section of the Institute of Transportation Engineers (ALSITE). Selection is based on academic

achievement, career objectives, leadership activities, employment history, and financial need. **Deadline for Receipt:** February of each year.

4506 ■ INSTITUTE OF TRANSPORTATION ENGINEERS-FLORIDA SECTION

c/o Philip Mann
City of Gainesville
5650 Enterprise Parkway
Fort Myers, FL 33905
Tel: (239)694-7600
Fax: (239)694-1332
E-mail: davisjad@leegov.com
Web Site: http://www.floridasectionite.org

To provide financial assistance to undergraduate and graduate students who are members of the Institute of Transportation Engineers' Florida Section.

Title of Award: Bill McGrath Transportation Scholarship **Area, Field, or Subject:** Engineering, Civil **Level of Education for which Award is Granted:** Graduate, Undergraduate **Number Awarded:** 1 each year. **Funds Available:** The stipend is at least $1,000. **Duration:** 1 year.

Eligibility Requirements: This program is open to undergraduate and graduate students at Florida universities who are members of the Florida Section. Applicants must submit a current transcript, a resume, 3 letters of recommendation, and an essay on their transportation career goals. Financial need is considered in the selection process. **Deadline for Receipt:** October of each year. **Additional Information:** This program was established in 1994.

4507 ■ INSTITUTE OF TRANSPORTATION ENGINEERS-GEORGIA SECTION

100 Peachtree Street, N.W., Suite 2150
Atlanta, GA 30303
Tel: (404)521-2324
Fax: (404)521-0238
Web Site: http://www.gaite.org

To provide financial assistance to students in Georgia who are members of the Georgia Section of the Institute of Transportation Engineers and interested in majoring in transportation.

Title of Award: Georgia Section Fellowship **Area, Field, or Subject:** Engineering, Civil; Transportation **Level of Education for which Award is Granted:** Undergraduate **Number Awarded:** 1 or more each year. **Funds Available:** The stipend is generally $3,000 per year. **Duration:** 1 year.

Eligibility Requirements: This program is open to members and students members of the Georgia Section who are working on a degree in transportation. **Additional Information:** Information is also available from Taylor Stukes, Scholarship Committee Chair, Gresham, Smith and Partners, 2325 Lakeview Parkway, Suite 400, Alpharetta, GA 30004, E-mail: taylor_stukes@gspnet.com.

4508 ■ INSTITUTE OF TRANSPORTATION ENGINEERS-ILLINOIS SECTION

c/o Timothy Sjogren, Scholarship Chair
Metro Transportation Group, Inc.
3100 West Higgins Road, Suite 100
Hoffman Estates, IL 60195-2093
Tel: (630)213-1000
Fax: (630)213-3227
E-mail: tps@metrotransportation.com
Web Site: http://www.ilite.org/studentaffairs/scholarshipinfo.htm

To provide financial assistance to college students in Illinois who are majoring in transportation planning or transportation engineering.

Title of Award: Illinois Section Scholarship **Area, Field, or Subject:** Engineering, Civil; Transportation **Level of Education for which Award is Granted:** Undergraduate **Number Awarded:** 1 each year. **Funds Available:** The stipend is $2,000. **Duration:** 1 year; nonrenewable.

Eligibility Requirements: Candidates must be full-time sophomores, juniors, or seniors at an Illinois college or university who are majoring in either transportation engineering or transportation planning. Selection is based on academic performance, education plans, career goals, activities, and record of leadership. **Deadline for Receipt:** December of each year.

4509 ■ INSTITUTE OF TRANSPORTATION ENGINEERS-INDIANA SECTION

c/o Ann M. Sheidler, Scholarship Chair
Parsons Brinckerhoff Quade & Douglas, Inc.
300 North Meridian Street, Suite 990
Indianapolis, IN 46204
Tel: (317)972-1706
Fax: (317)972-1708
E-mail: sheidler@pbworld.com
Web Site: http://www.indianaite.org
To provide financial assistance to students in Indiana working on a degree related to transportation engineering.
Title of Award: Edward J. Cox Memorial Transportation Scholarship **Area, Field, or Subject:** Engineering, Civil; Transportation; Urban affairs/design/planning **Level of Education for which Award is Granted:** Graduate, Undergraduate **Number Awarded:** Varies each year; recently, 3 of these scholarships were awarded. **Funds Available:** The stipend is at least $2,500. **Duration:** 1 year.
Eligibility Requirements: This program is open to full-time undergraduate or graduate students who are attending a college or university in Indiana and are working on a degree related to transportation engineering or transportation planning. Applicants may be interested in any of the following areas: roadway or bridge design, pavement design, transportation-related environmental concerns, roadway safety, transit, traffic engineering and design, signal systems, ITS, transportation or urban planning, transportation facilities construction management, or related topics. Along with their application, they must submit a 2-page essay on their understanding of the profession of transportation engineering and planning and how they plan to contribute to the excellence of the profession. Selection is based on past academic performance, educational plans, career goals, extracurricular activities, work experience, and record of leadership. **Deadline for Receipt:** January of each year. **Additional Information:** This scholarship was first awarded in 1997.

4510 ■ INSTITUTE OF TRANSPORTATION ENGINEERS-INTERMOUNTAIN SECTION

c/o Lee Cabell
Horrocks Engineering
One West Main Street
P.O. Box 377
American Fork, UT 84003
Tel: (801)763-5100
Fax: (801)756-2362
E-mail: lee@horrocks.com
To provide financial assistance to student members of the Institute of Transportation Engineers' Intermountain Section.
Title of Award: Ellis Mathes Scholarship **Area, Field, or Subject:** Engineering, Civil **Level of Education for which Award is Granted:** Four Year College, Graduate **Number Awarded:** 2 each year. **Funds Available:** The stipend is $1,000. **Duration:** 1 year.
Eligibility Requirements: This program is open to upper-division and graduate student members of the Intermountain Section. Applicants must be attending school in Idaho, Nevada, Montana, or Utah. Along with their application, they must submit an essay on their career and academic objectives, work experience (if any), academic record, and financial need. **Deadline for Receipt:** March of each year. **Additional Information:** This scholarship was first awarded in 1991.

4511 ■ INSTITUTE OF TRANSPORTATION ENGINEERS-NEW ENGLAND SECTION

c/o Rod Emery, Scholarship Committee
Edwards and Kelcey Engineers
529 Main Street, Suite 203
Charlestown, MA 02129-1114
Tel: (617)242-9222
Fax: (617)242-9824
E-mail: remery@ekmail.com
Web Site: http://www.neite.org/scholar.shtml

To provide financial assistance to engineering undergraduate and graduate students at colleges and universities in New England.
Title of Award: Thomas E. Desjardins Memorial Scholarship **Area, Field, or Subject:** Engineering; Engineering, Civil **Level of Education for which Award is Granted:** Graduate, Undergraduate **Number Awarded:** 2 each year: 1 to an undergraduate and 1 to a graduate student. **Funds Available:** A stipend is awarded (amount not specified). **Duration:** 1 year; nonrenewable.
Eligibility Requirements: This program is open to undergraduate and graduate students in engineering, especially those who demonstrate a strong commitment to transportation engineering in the course work and outside activities. Applicants may be residents of any state, but they must be attending an accredited engineering school in a New England state. Selection is based on moral character, academic achievement, participation in extracurricular activities, and financial need. **Deadline for Receipt:** July of each year. **Additional Information:** This scholarship was first awarded in 2000.

4512 ■ INSTITUTE OF TRANSPORTATION ENGINEERS-TENNESSEE SECTION

c/o Jeff Hammond
Neel-Schaffer, Inc.
210 25th Avenue North, Suite 800
Nashville, TN 37203
Tel: (615)383-8420
Fax: (615)383-9984
Web Site: http://www.tsite.org/scholarship/sscholarship.asp
To provide financial assistance to undergraduate and graduate students majoring in transportation engineering at colleges and universities in Tennessee.
Title of Award: Tennessee Section Institute of Transportation Engineers Transportation Engineering Scholarship **Area, Field, or Subject:** Engineering, Civil **Level of Education for which Award is Granted:** Graduate, Undergraduate **Number Awarded:** 2 each year. **Funds Available:** The stipend is $1,500. **Duration:** 1 year.
Eligibility Requirements: This program is open to undergraduate and graduate students enrolled in a transportation engineering program at colleges and universities in Tennessee. Applicants must submit a 1-page statement on their transportation engineering career objectives and commitment. Selection is based on that statement, academic record, leadership activities, and employment history. Financial need is not considered. **Deadline for Receipt:** January of each year. **Additional Information:** These scholarships were first awarded in 1991.

4513 ■ INSTITUTE OF TRANSPORTATION ENGINEERS-VIRGINIA SECTION

c/o Michael Martin, Scholarship Committee
Martin Enterprises and Associates, Inc.
2625 Steeplechase Drive
Reston, VA 20191
Tel: (703)391-7330
Fax: (703)391-0785
E-mail: mmartin-mea@verizon.net
Web Site: http://www.vasite.org/scholarship.php
To provide financial assistance for undergraduate or graduate studies in civil or transportation engineering to members of the Institute of Transportation Engineers' Virginia Section.
Title of Award: Kenneth E. Wilkinson Continued Engineering Studies Scholarship **Area, Field, or Subject:** Engineering, Civil **Level of Education for which Award is Granted:** Graduate, Undergraduate **Number Awarded:** 2 each year. **Funds Available:** The stipend is $1,000. **Duration:** 1 year.
Eligibility Requirements: Candidates must be enrolled in an undergraduate accredited civil or transportation engineering program within Virginia or enrolled in a master's degree program in civil or transportation engineering within Virginia for the year following nomination. They must be student members of the Virginia Section (membership applications may be submitted with the scholarship application) and should demonstrate a strong commitment to the discipline of transportation engineering. Selection is based on the applicant's justification for the award,

educational plans, potential for development within the transportation profession, leadership capacity, and demonstrated civic responsibility.

4514 ■ INSTRUMENTATION, SYSTEMS, AND AUTOMATION SOCIETY

Attn: ISA Educational Foundation
67 Alexander Drive
Research Triangle Park, NC 27709
Tel: (919)549-8411
Fax: (919)549-8288
E-mail: info@isa.org
Web Site: http://www.isa.org

To provide financial assistance to undergraduate and graduate students majoring in fields related to instrumentation, systems, and automation.

Title of Award: Chemical and Petroleum Industries Division Scholarship **Area, Field, or Subject:** Engineering; Engineering, Chemical; Engineering, Petroleum **Level of Education for which Award is Granted:** Graduate, Undergraduate **Number Awarded:** 1 each year. **Funds Available:** The stipend is $2,500. **Duration:** 1 year; may be renewed.

Eligibility Requirements: This program is open to full-time undergraduate and graduate students enrolled in a program in instrumentation, systems, automation, or a closely-related field. Applicants must have a GPA of 3.0 or higher. They may be from any country but must be attending an institution in their own country. Applicants in a 2-year program must have completed at least 1 academic semester of 12 hours or its equivalent. Applicants in a 4-year program must be in their sophomore year or higher. Along with their application, they must submit an essay (up to 400 words) on their ambitions and qualifications as an innovator or future leader in a career in instrumentation, systems, or automation; they should describe their career objectives, how the award of this scholarship will help them attain their objectives, why they want to enter this particular field of engineering, what they have achieved and learned through their studies and activities, and what this indicates about their character and determination. Preference is given to applicants studying technology related to chemical and petroleum industries. Financial need is not considered in the selection process. **Deadline for Receipt:** February of each year. **Additional Information:** This program was established in 2001.

4515 ■ INSTRUMENTATION, SYSTEMS, AND AUTOMATION SOCIETY

Attn: ISA Educational Foundation
67 Alexander Drive
Research Triangle Park, NC 27709
Tel: (919)549-8411
Fax: (919)549-8288
E-mail: info@isa.org
Web Site: http://www.isa.org

To provide financial assistance to undergraduate and graduate students majoring in fields related to instrumentation, systems, and automation.

Title of Award: Norman E. Huston Scholarship **Area, Field, or Subject:** Engineering **Level of Education for which Award is Granted:** Graduate, Undergraduate **Number Awarded:** 1 each year. **Funds Available:** The stipend is $4,000. **Duration:** 1 year; may be renewed.

Eligibility Requirements: This program is open to full-time undergraduate and graduate students enrolled in a program in instrumentation, systems, automation, or a closely-related field. Applicants must have a GPA of 3.0 or higher. They may be from any country but must be attending an institution in their own country. Applicants in a 2-year program must have completed at least 1 academic semester of 12 hours or its equivalent. Applicants in a 4-year program must be in their sophomore year or higher. Along with their application, they must submit an essay (up to 400 words) on their ambitions and qualifications as an innovator or future leader in a career in instrumentation, systems, or automation; they should describe their career objectives, how the award of this scholarship will help them attain their objectives, why they want to enter this particular field of engineering, what they have achieved and learned through their studies and activities, and what this indicates about their character and determination. Financial need is not considered in the selection process.

Deadline for Receipt: February of each year. **Additional Information:** This program was established in 2001.

4516 ■ INSTRUMENTATION, SYSTEMS, AND AUTOMATION SOCIETY

Attn: ISA Educational Foundation
67 Alexander Drive
Research Triangle Park, NC 27709
Tel: (919)549-8411
Fax: (919)549-8288
E-mail: info@isa.org
Web Site: http://www.isa.org

To provide financial assistance to undergraduate and graduate students majoring in fields related to instrumentation, systems, and automation.

Title of Award: ISA Educational Foundation Scholarships **Area, Field, or Subject:** Engineering **Level of Education for which Award is Granted:** Graduate, Undergraduate **Number Awarded:** Varies each year. Recently, 5 of these scholarships were awarded: 4 to undergraduates (at $700, $1,000, $3,000, and $3,500) and 1 to a graduate student (at $3,000). **Funds Available:** Stipends have ranged from $700 to $3,500. **Duration:** 1 year; may be renewed.

Eligibility Requirements: This program is open to full-time undergraduate and graduate students enrolled in a program in instrumentation, systems, automation, or a closely-related field. Applicants must have a GPA of 3.0 or higher. They may be from any country but must be attending an institution in their own country. Applicants in a 2-year program must have completed at least 1 academic semester of 12 hours or its equivalent. Applicants in a 4-year program must be in their sophomore year or higher. Along with their application, they must submit an essay (up to 400 words) on their ambitions and qualifications as an innovator or future leader in a career in instrumentation, systems, or automation; they should describe their career objectives, how the award of this scholarship will help them attain their objectives, why they want to enter this particular field of engineering, what they have achieved and learned through their studies and activities, and what this indicates about their character and determination. Financial need is not considered in the selection process. **Deadline for Receipt:** February of each year. **Additional Information:** This program was established in 2001.

4517 ■ INSTRUMENTATION, SYSTEMS, AND AUTOMATION SOCIETY

Attn: ISA Educational Foundation
67 Alexander Drive
Research Triangle Park, NC 27709
Tel: (919)549-8411
Fax: (919)549-8288
E-mail: info@isa.org
Web Site: http://www.isa.org

To provide financial assistance to undergraduate and graduate students majoring in fields related to instrumentation, systems, and automation.

Title of Award: ISA Executive Board Scholarship **Area, Field, or Subject:** Engineering **Level of Education for which Award is Granted:** Graduate, Undergraduate **Number Awarded:** 1 each year. **Funds Available:** The stipend is $1,800. **Duration:** 1 year; may be renewed.

Eligibility Requirements: This program is open to full-time undergraduate and graduate students enrolled in a program in instrumentation, systems, automation, or a closely-related field. Applicants must have a GPA of 3.0 or higher. They may be from any country but must be attending an institution in their own country. Applicants in a 2-year program must have completed at least 1 academic semester of 12 hours or its equivalent. Applicants in a 4-year program must be in their sophomore year or higher. Along with their application, they must submit an essay (up to 400 words) on their ambitions and qualifications as an innovator or future leader in a career in instrumentation, systems, or automation; they should describe their career objectives, how the award of this scholarship will help them attain their objectives, why they want to enter this particular field of engineering, what they have achieved and learned through their studies and activities, and what this indicates about their character and determination. Preference is given to applicants with demonstrated leadership capabilities. Financial need is not considered in the selection process. **Deadline for Receipt:** February of each year. **Additional Information:** This program was established in 2001.

4518 ■ INSTRUMENTATION, SYSTEMS, AND AUTOMATION SOCIETY

Attn: ISA Educational Foundation
67 Alexander Drive
Research Triangle Park, NC 27709
Tel: (919)549-8411
Fax: (919)549-8288
E-mail: info@isa.org
Web Site: http://www.isa.org
To provide financial assistance to undergraduate and graduate students majoring in fields related to instrumentation, systems, and automation.
Title of Award: Pulp and Paper Industry Division Scholarship **Area, Field, or Subject:** Engineering; Paper science; Science **Level of Education for which Award is Granted:** Four Year College, Master's **Number Awarded:** 1 each year. **Funds Available:** The stipend is $1,000. **Duration:** 1 year; may be renewed.
Eligibility Requirements: This program is open to full-time undergraduate and graduate students who are student members, or dependents of a member, of the Instrument Society of America. Applicants must be 1) juniors or seniors working on a bachelor's degree in an engineering, science, or pulp and paper program, or 2) graduate students working on a master's degree in a pulp and paper program. They must be able to demonstrate a significant interest in the instrumentation/process control component of the pulp and paper industry. Along with their application, they must submit official transcripts and 3 letters of recommendation from persons familiar with their character, interest in the pulp and paper industry, educational accomplishments, school activities, and leadership roles. Financial need is not considered in the selection process. **Deadline for Receipt:** February of each year. **Additional Information:** Information is also available from Michael H. Waller, Miami University, Paper Science and Engineering Department, Oxford, OH 45056, (513) 529-2205, Fax: (513) 529-2201, E-mail: wallermh@muohio.edu.

4519 ■ INTERNATIONAL SOCIETY OF EXPLOSIVES ENGINEERS

Attn: SEE Education Foundation
30325 Bainbridge Road
Cleveland, OH 44139
Tel: (440)349-4400
Fax: (440)349-3788
Web Site: http://www.isee.org/education/SEEFoundation.htm
To provide financial assistance to undergraduate and graduate engineering students interested in preparing for a career involving the use of explosives.
Title of Award: SEE Education Foundation Scholarships **Area, Field, or Subject:** Engineering; Engineering, Aerospace/Aeronautical/Astronautical; Engineering, Automotive; Engineering, Industrial; Engineering, Mining and Mineral **Level of Education for which Award is Granted:** Graduate, Undergraduate **Number Awarded:** 1 each year. **Funds Available:** A stipend is awarded (amount not specified). **Duration:** 1 year; may be renewed.
Eligibility Requirements: This program is open to students working on their first associate, undergraduate, or graduate degree as a full-time student at an accredited college or university. Applicants must show an interest in the use of explosives and intend to enter an explosives-related field, such as mining, construction, forestry, manufacturing, automotives, or aerospace. If they have already completed some college work, their GPA must be 2.9 or higher. Selection is based on career and personal ambition, academic potential, written communications, ability to overcome personal hardships and/or challenges, and financial need. **Deadline for Receipt:** April of each year.

4520 ■ INTERNATIONAL UNION OF ELECTRONIC, ELECTRICAL, SALARIED, MACHINE, AND FURNITURE WORKERS

Attn: IUE-CWA International Scholarship Program
501 Third Street, N.W., Suite 975
Washington, DC 20001
Tel: (202)434-1417
Fax: (202)434-1250
E-mail: bgray@iue-cwa.org
Web Site: http://www.iue-cwa.org/skills.html

To provide financial assistance children and grandchildren of members of the International Union of Electronic, Electrical, Salaried, Machine, and Furniture Workers (IUE)-Communications Workers of America (CWA) who are interested in majoring in engineering.
Title of Award: David J. Fitzmaurice Scholarship **Area, Field, or Subject:** Engineering **Level of Education for which Award is Granted:** Undergraduate **Number Awarded:** 1 each year. **Funds Available:** The stipend is $2,000 per year. **Duration:** 1 year.
Eligibility Requirements: This program is open to children and grandchildren of IUE-CWA members (including retired or deceased members). Applicants must be accepted for admission or already enrolled as full-time students at an accredited college, university, or technical school in an engineering program. Along with their application, they must submit an academic transcript (including rank in class, GPA, and SAT/ACT scores); a short statement of interests and civic activities; an essay (300 to 500 words) describing their career goals and aspirations, highlighting their relationship with the union and the labor movement, and explaining why they are deserving of a union scholarship. They must also have demonstrated a commitment to equality of opportunity for all, a concern for improving the quality of life for all people, an interest in service to the community, good character, leadership ability, and a desire to improve and move ahead. **Deadline for Receipt:** March of each year.

4521 ■ IOWA MOTOR TRUCK ASSOCIATION

Attn: Iowa Motor Carriers Foundation
717 East Court Avenue
Des Moines, IA 50309
Tel: (515)244-5193
Fax: (515)244-2204
E-mail: imta@iowamotortruck.com
Web Site: http://www.iowamotortruck.com/Scholarships/Foundation.asp
To provide financial assistance for college or the study of diesel technology to residents of Iowa.
Title of Award: Iowa Motor Carriers Foundation Scholarships **Area, Field, or Subject:** Automotive technology; General studies/Field of study not specified **Level of Education for which Award is Granted:** Undergraduate **Number Awarded:** 6 each year. **Funds Available:** The stipend is $1,000. **Duration:** 1 year.
Eligibility Requirements: This program is open to Iowa residents attending or planning to attend a college, university, trade school, or community college in the state. Applicants must submit a brief letter describing why they are applying for this scholarship, their intended career goal, its estimated cost, and their choices of educational institutions. Some scholarships are reserved for students in diesel technology. Selection is based on academic record, outside activities that pertain to school and community citizenship, and financial need. **Deadline for Receipt:** March of each year. **Additional Information:** This program, established in 1986, consists of the following named awards: the Cummins Great Plains Diesel Scholarship (reserved for a student in diesel technology), the Ziegler/Caterpillar Diesel Scholarship (reserved for a student in diesel technology), the Paul Crouse Memorial Scholarship (reserved for a student from western Iowa), the Harold Dickey Memorial Scholarship (reserved for a student from southeastern Iowa), the L.W. "Vern" Simpson Scholarship (awarded to the highest ranked applicants in the general category), and the Iowa Council of Safety Management Scholarship.

4522 ■ IOWA READY MIXED CONCRETE ASSOCIATION

Attn: Scholarship Committee
380 S.E. Delaware Avenue
Ankeny, IA 50021
Tel: (515)965-4575
Fax: (515)963-4010
Web Site: http://www.iowareadymix.org
To provide financial assistance to undergraduates at colleges and universities in Iowa who are preparing for a career in the concrete, construction, or engineering industries.
Title of Award: Iowa Ready Mixed Concrete Association Scholarship Program **Area, Field, or Subject:** Business; Construction; Engineering **Level of Education for which Award is Granted:** Four Year College **Number Awarded:** At least 3 scholarships at $1,000 and 4 at $500 are awarded each year. **Funds Available:** Stipends are $1,000 or $500. **Duration:** 1 year.
Eligibility Requirements: This program is open to students who have achieved at least sophomore status at a 4-year college or university in

Iowa. Applicants must be working on a degree in an area that will prepare them for a career in the ready mixed concrete or construction and engineering industries. Preference is given to applicants who are residents of Iowa, related to an employee of a member company of the Iowa Ready Mixed Concrete Association, and experienced in the ready mixed concrete industry. Along with their application, they must submit a 1-page essay explaining their career goals, why they are applying for a scholarship, and why they might consider employment in the ready mixed concrete, construction, or engineering fields. **Deadline for Receipt:** December of each year.

4523 ■ KOREAN-AMERICAN SCIENTISTS AND ENGINEERS ASSOCIATION

1952 Gallows Drive, Suite 300
Vienna, VA 22182
Tel: (703)748-1221
Fax: (703)748-1331
E-mail: sejong@ksea.org
Web Site: http://www.ksea.org
To provide financial assistance to undergraduate and graduate student members of the Korean-American Scientists and Engineers Association (KSEA).
Title of Award: KSEA Scholarships **Area, Field, or Subject:** Engineering; Science **Level of Education for which Award is Granted:** Graduate, Undergraduate **Number Awarded:** Varies each year. **Funds Available:** The stipend is $1,000. **Duration:** 1 year.
Eligibility Requirements: This program is open to Korean American undergraduate and graduate students who graduated from a high school in the United States, are KSEA members, and are majoring in science, engineering, or a related field. Along with their application, they must submit a 500-word essay on either of the following topics: 1) their career goals and intended contributions to society, or 2) the meaning of Korean heritage in their life. Selection is based on the essay (20%), work experience and extracurricular activities (20%), recommendation letters (30%), and academic performance (30%). **Deadline for Receipt:** February of each year. **Additional Information:** This program includes the following named scholarships: the Inyong Ham Scholarship, the Yohan and Rumie Cho Scholarship, the Shoon Kyung Kim Scholarship, the Nam Sook and Je Hyun Kim Scholarship, and the Hyundai Scholarships.

4524 ■ KOREAN-AMERICAN SCIENTISTS AND ENGINEERS ASSOCIATION

1952 Gallows Drive, Suite 300
Vienna, VA 22182
Tel: (703)748-1221
Fax: (703)748-1331
E-mail: sejong@ksea.org
Web Site: http://www.ksea.org
To provide financial assistance to women who are undergraduate or graduate student members of the Korean-American Scientists and Engineers Association (KSEA).
Title of Award: Chunghi Hong Park Scholarship **Area, Field, or Subject:** Engineering; Science **Level of Education for which Award is Granted:** Graduate, Undergraduate **Number Awarded:** 2 each year. **Funds Available:** The stipend is $1,000. **Duration:** 1 year.
Eligibility Requirements: This program is open to women who are Korean American undergraduate or graduate students, graduated from a high school in the United States, are KSEA members, and are majoring in science, engineering, or a related field. Along with their application, they must submit a 500-word essay on either of the following topics: 1) their career goals and intended contributions to society, or 2) the meaning of Korean heritage in their life. Selection is based on the essay (20%), work experience and extracurricular activities (20%), recommendation letters (30%), and academic performance (30%). **Deadline for Receipt:** February of each year.

4525 ■ LEAGUE OF UNITED LATIN AMERICAN CITIZENS

Attn: LULAC National Education Service Centers
2000 L Street, N.W., Suite 610
Washington, DC 20036
Tel: (202)835-9646
Fax: (202)835-9685
E-mail: scholarships@lnesc.org

Web Site: http://www.lnesc.org
To provide financial assistance to minority students who are studying engineering or business in college.
Title of Award: General Electric Fund/League of United Latin American Citizens Scholarships **Area, Field, or Subject:** Business administration; Engineering **Level of Education for which Award is Granted:** Undergraduate **Number Awarded:** Varies each year; recently, 6 of these scholarships were awarded. **Funds Available:** The stipends are $5,000 per year. The funds are to be used to pay for tuition, required fees, room and board, and required educational materials and books. The funds are sent directly to the college or university and deposited in the scholarship recipient's name. **Duration:** 1 year; may be renewed if the recipient maintains a GPA of 3.0 or higher.
Eligibility Requirements: Eligible to apply are minority students who will be enrolled as college sophomores pursuing full-time studies in a program leading to a baccalaureate degree in engineering or business at colleges or universities in the United States approved by the League of United Latin American Citizens (LULAC) and General Electric. They must have a GPA of 3.25 or higher and be U.S. citizens or legal residents. Selection is based on academic performance, likelihood of preparing for a career in business or engineering, performance in business or engineering subjects, writing ability, extracurricular activities, and community involvement. **Deadline for Receipt:** July of each year. **Additional Information:** Funding for this program is provided by the General Electric Fund. All requests for applications or information must include a self-addressed stamped envelope.

4526 ■ LEAGUE OF UNITED LATIN AMERICAN CITIZENS

Attn: LULAC National Education Service Centers
2000 L Street, N.W., Suite 610
Washington, DC 20036
Tel: (202)835-9646
Fax: (202)835-9685
E-mail: scholarships@lnesc.org
Web Site: http://www.lnesc.org
To provide financial assistance to Latino students interested in working on a degree in engineering in college.
Title of Award: General Motors/League of United Latin American Citizens Scholarships **Area, Field, or Subject:** Engineering **Level of Education for which Award is Granted:** Undergraduate **Number Awarded:** Varies each year; recently, 26 of these scholarships were awarded. **Funds Available:** The stipends are $2,000 per year. The funds are to be used to pay for tuition, required fees, room and board, and required educational materials and books. The funds are sent directly to the college or university and deposited in the scholarship recipient's name. **Duration:** 1 year.
Eligibility Requirements: Eligible to apply are Latino students who are enrolled or planning to enroll as full-time students in a program leading to a baccalaureate degree in engineering at colleges or universities in the United States approved by the League of United Latin American Citizens (LULAC) and General Motors. Continuing college students must have a GPA of 3.2 or better; entering college freshmen must have a high school GPA of 3.5 or higher and either an ACT composite score of at least 23 or an SAT combined score of at least 970. Selection is based on academic performance; likelihood of preparing for a career in engineering; performance in science, mathematics, and engineering subjects; writing ability; extracurricular activities; and community involvement. **Deadline for Receipt:** July of each year. **Additional Information:** All requests for applications or information must include a self-addressed stamped envelope.

4527 ■ CLARE BOOTHE LUCE FUND

c/o Henry Luce Foundation, Inc.
111 West 50th Street, Suite 4601
New York, NY 10020
Tel: (212)489-7700
Fax: (212)581-9541
E-mail: jdaniels@hluce.org
Web Site: http://www.hluce.org
To provide funding to women interested in studying science or engineering at the undergraduate level at designated universities.
Title of Award: Clare Boothe Luce Scholarships in Science and Engineering **Area, Field, or Subject:** Biological and clinical sciences;

Chemistry; Computer and information sciences; Engineering; Engineering, Aerospace/Aeronautical/Astronautical; Engineering, Civil; Engineering, Electrical; Engineering, Mechanical; Engineering, Nuclear; Mathematics and mathematical sciences; Meteorology; Physics **Level of Education for which Award is Granted:** Undergraduate **Number Awarded:** Varies; since the program began, more than 800 of these scholarships have been awarded. **Funds Available:** The amount awarded is established individually by each of the participating institutions. The stipends are intended to augment rather than replace any existing institutional support in these fields. Each stipend is calculated to include the cost of room and board as well as tuition and other fees or expenses. **Duration:** 2 years; in certain special circumstances, awards for the full 4 years of undergraduate study may be offered.

Eligibility Requirements: This program is open to female undergraduate students (particularly juniors and seniors) majoring in biology, chemistry, computer science, engineering (aeronautical, civil, electrical, mechanical, nuclear, and others), mathematics, meteorology, and physics. Applicants must be U.S. citizens attending 1 of the 12 designated colleges and universities affiliated with this program; periodically, other institutions are invited to participate. Premedical science majors are ineligible for this competition. The participating institutions select the recipients without regard to race, age, religion, ethnic background, or need. All awards are made on the basis of merit. **Deadline for Receipt:** Varies; check with the participating institutions for their current schedule. **Additional Information:** The participating institutions are Boston University, Colby College, Creighton University, Fordham University, Georgetown University, Marymount University, Mount Holyoke College, St. John's University, Santa Clara University, Seton Hall University, Trinity College, and University of Notre Dame.

4528 ■ MARYLAND ASSOCIATION OF PRIVATE COLLEGES AND CAREER SCHOOLS

Attn: Scholarship Committee
3100 Dunglow Road
Baltimore, MD 21222
Tel: (410)282-4012
Fax: (410)282-4133
E-mail: mdapcs@yahoo.com
Web Site: http://www.mapccs.org/scholarships.html
To provide financial assistance to students interested in attending selected private career schools in Maryland.

Title of Award: Maryland Association of Private Colleges and Career Schools Scholarships **Area, Field, or Subject:** Broadcasting; Cosmetology; Drafting; Health care services; Mechanics and repairs; Medicine, Holistic/alternative; Secretarial sciences **Level of Education for which Award is Granted:** Vocational/Occupational **Number Awarded:** Varies each year; since the program was established in 1983, more than $3 million in scholarships have been awarded. **Funds Available:** Individual awards range from $500 to more than $5,000. The H.R. Leslie Scholarship is $1,000. Funds must be applied for full or partial payment of tuition. Recently, a total of $164,000 was awarded. **Duration:** 1 year.

Eligibility Requirements: This program is open to high school seniors and graduates who are interested in attending a participating private career school in Maryland. Applicants should be interested in working on a degree in such business or technical areas as cosmetology, barbering, diesel mechanics, automotive technology, massage therapy, allied health, secretarial sciences, or drafting. The H.R. Leslie Scholarship is open to any student who applies to a member school. Selection is based on GPA, involvement in school and community activities, recommendations from school officials, desire, and potential to succeed in their career field. Financial need is not considered in the selection process. **Deadline for Receipt:** March of each year. **Additional Information:** The participating schools are All State Career School (Baltimore) American Beauty Academy (Wheaton), Americare School of Allied Health (Silver Spring), Avara's Academy of Hair Design (Baltimore), Baltimore School of Massage, Baltimore Studio of Hair Design, Bladensburg Barber School (Bladensburg), Broadcasting Institute of Maryland (Baltimore), Diesel Institute of America (Grantsville), Frederick School of Cosmetology (Frederick), Hair Academy (New Carrollton), Holistic Massage Training Institute (Baltimore), International Beauty School (Bel Air), Lincoln Technical Institute (Columbia), Medix School (Towson), Savage Neon (Baltimore), and Von Lee School of Aesthetics (Pikesville). Scholarships can be used only to attend the schools listed above.

4529 ■ MARYLAND SPACE GRANT CONSORTIUM

c/o Johns Hopkins University
203 Bloomberg Center for Physics and Astronomy
3400 North Charles Street
Baltimore, MD 21218-2686
Tel: (410)516-7351
Fax: (410)516-4109
E-mail: info@mdspacegrant.org
Web Site: http://www.mdspacegrant.org/scholars_about.html
To provide financial assistance to undergraduates who are interested in studying space-related fields at selected universities in Maryland that are members of the Maryland Space Grant Consortium.

Title of Award: Maryland Space Scholars Program **Area, Field, or Subject:** Aerospace sciences; Astronomy and astronomical sciences; Biological and clinical sciences; Chemistry; Computer and information sciences; Engineering; Geology; Mathematics and mathematical sciences; Physics; Space and planetary sciences **Level of Education for which Award is Granted:** Undergraduate **Number Awarded:** Varies each year; recently 16 of these scholarships were awarded (2 at Johns Hopkins University, 5 at Morgan State University, 2 at Hagerstown Community College, 2 at Towson University, and 5 at the University of Maryland at College Park). **Funds Available:** Scholars receive partial payment of tuition at the participating university they attend. **Duration:** 1 year; may be renewed if the recipient maintains a GPA of 3.0 or higher.

Eligibility Requirements: This program is open to residents of Maryland and graduates of Maryland high schools who are enrolled full time at a member institution. Applicants must be interested in preparing for a career in mathematics, science, engineering, technology, or a space-related field. They must be majoring in a relevant field, including (but not limited to) astronomy, the biological and life sciences, chemistry, computer science, engineering, geological sciences, or physics. U.S. citizenship is required. Along with their application, they must submit an essay of 200 to 500 words on how this scholarship will help them meet their educational and financial goals. This program is a component of the U.S. National Aeronautics and Space Administration (NASA) Space Grant program, which encourages participation by women, underrepresented minorities, and persons with disabilities. **Deadline for Receipt:** August of each year. **Additional Information:** The participating universities are Hagerstown Community College, Johns Hopkins University, Morgan State University, Towson University, the University of Maryland at College Park, and Washington College. Funding for this program is provided by NASA.

4530 ■ MATERIAL HANDLING INDUSTRY OF AMERICA

Attn: Material Handling Education Foundation, Inc.
8720 Red Oak Boulevard, Suite 201
Charlotte, NC 28217-3992
Tel: (704)676-1190
Free: 800-722-6832
Fax: (704)676-1199
E-mail: vwheeler@mhia.org
Web Site: http://www.mhia.org
To provide financial assistance to undergraduate or graduate students who are studying material handling.

Title of Award: MHEFI Scholarship Program **Area, Field, or Subject:** Business administration; Computer and information sciences; Engineering; Engineering, Civil; Engineering, Computer; Engineering, Electrical; Engineering, Industrial; Engineering, Mechanical; Logistics; Management **Level of Education for which Award is Granted:** Four Year College, Graduate **Number Awarded:** Varies each year; recently, 28 of these scholarships (with a total value of $73,500) were awarded. **Funds Available:** Awards range from $1,500 to $6,000. **Duration:** 1 year.

Eligibility Requirements: This program is open to 1) students at 4-year colleges and universities who have completed at least 2 years of undergraduate study; and 2) graduate students enrolled in a program leading to a master's or doctoral degree. Students from junior or community colleges are eligible if they have been accepted as a transfer student into a 4-year program. Applicants must be U.S. citizens; be attending an academic institution that has been prequalified for foundation funding; have earned a GPA of 3.0 or higher in college; and be enrolled in a course of study relevant to the material handling industry, including engineering (civil, computer, industrial, electrical, or mechanical), engineering technology, computer science, or business administration with an emphasis on production management, industrial distribution, and/or logistics. Along with their application, they must submit 3 letters of recommendation, official transcripts, documentation of financial need, and a 600-word essay on how their course of study, work experience, and career goals make them an appropriate candidate for this scholarship. **Deadline for Receipt:** February of each year. **Additional Information:** More than 60 colleges and universities have been prequalified for participation in this program. For a list, contact the Material Handling Education Foundation, Inc. (MHEFI).

4531 ■ MICRON TECHNOLOGY, INC.

Attn: Micron Technology Foundation
8000 South Federal Way
P.O. Box 6
Boise, ID 83707-0006
Tel: (208)368-3675
Web Site: http://www.micron.com/about/giving/foundation/scholarships.html
To provide financial assistance to high school seniors in selected states who are interested in majoring in the physical sciences.
Title of Award: Micron Science and Technology Scholars **Area, Field, or Subject:** Chemistry; Computer and information sciences; Engineering, Chemical; Engineering, Computer; Engineering, Electrical; Engineering, Mechanical; Materials research/science; Physics **Level of Education for which Award is Granted:** Undergraduate **Number Awarded:** 13 each year: 1 at $55,000 and 12 at $16,500; 2 are awarded to students from each of 5 participating states, plus 3 floating scholarships are awarded within those states. **Funds Available:** Stipends are either $55,000 or $16,500. A cash grant of $1,000 is awarded to the high school of each winner.
Eligibility Requirements: This program is open to high school seniors who reside in and attend public or private schools in Colorado, Idaho, Texas, Utah, or Virginia. Applicants must have a combined SAT score of at least 1350 or a composite ACT score of at least 30; have at least a 3.5 GPA; have demonstrated leadership in school, work, and extracurricular activities; and plan to major in engineering (electrical, computer, chemical, or mechanical), computer science, chemistry, material sciences, or physics. Selection is based on merit (in academics and leadership). **Deadline for Receipt:** January of each year. **Additional Information:** This program began in 2000. Information is also available from Scholarship Management Services of Scholarship America, One Scholarship Way, P.O. Box 297, St. Peter, MN 56082, (507) 931-1682, (800) 537-4180, Fax: (507) 931-9168.

4532 ■ MICROSOFT CORPORATION

Attn: National Minority Technical Scholarship
One Microsoft Way
Redmond, WA 98052-8303
Tel: (425)882-8080
E-mail: scholars@microsoft.com
Web Site: http://www.microsoft.com/college/ss_overview.mspx
To provide financial assistance and summer work experience to undergraduate students, especially members of underrepresented groups, interested in preparing for a career in computer science or other related technical fields.
Title of Award: Microsoft National Scholarships **Area, Field, or Subject:** Computer and information sciences; Engineering, Computer; Engineering, Electrical; Mathematics and mathematical sciences; Physics; Technology **Level of Education for which Award is Granted:** Undergraduate **Number Awarded:** Varies. A total of $540,000 is available for this program each year. **Funds Available:** Scholarships cover 100% of the tuition as posted by the financial aid office of the university or college the recipient designates. Scholarships are made through that school and are not transferable to other academic institutions. Funds may be used for tuition only and may not be used for other costs on the recipient's bursar bill, such as room and board. **Duration:** 1 year.
Eligibility Requirements: This program is open to students who are enrolled full time and making satisfactory progress toward an undergraduate degree in computer science, computer engineering, or a related technical discipline (such as electrical engineering, mathematics, or physics) with a demonstrated interest in computer science. Applicants must be enrolled at a 4-year college or university in the United States, Canada, or Mexico. They must have a GPA of 3.0 or higher. Although all students who meet the eligibility criteria may apply, a large majority of scholarships are

awarded to women, underrepresented minorities (African Americans, Hispanics, and Native Americans), and students with disabilities. Along with their application, students must submit an essay that describes the following 4 items: 1) how they demonstrate their passion for technology outside the classroom; 2) the toughest technical problem they have worked on, how they addressed the problem, their role in reaching the outcome if it was team-based, and the final outcome; 3) a situation that demonstrates initiative and their willingness to go above and beyond; and 4) how they are currently funding their college education. **Deadline for Receipt:** January of each year. **Additional Information:** Selected recipients are offered a paid summer internship where they will have a chance to develop Microsoft products.

4533 ■ MIKKELSON FOUNDATION

P.O. Box 768
Monument, CO 80132-9077
Web Site: http://www.mikkelson.com
To provide financial assistance to high school seniors in Colorado who plan to study science, engineering, or mathematics in college.
Title of Award: Mikkelson Foundation Student Scholarship Program **Area, Field, or Subject:** Engineering; Mathematics and mathematical sciences; Science **Level of Education for which Award is Granted:** Undergraduate **Number Awarded:** 2 each year. **Funds Available:** The stipend is $3,000 per year. **Duration:** 1 year; may be renewed up to 3 additional years.
Eligibility Requirements: This program is open to seniors graduating from high schools in Colorado. Applicants must be planning to attend an accredited college or university to major in science, engineering, or mathematics. Along with their application, they must submit a 2-page description of their strengths, accomplishments, and interests; their projected course of study in college; their plans following college graduation; how they plan to finance their education; and how this scholarship will help them achieve their goals. **Deadline for Receipt:** April of each year.

4534 ■ MINNESOTA ASSOCIATION OF ASPHALT PAVING TECHNOLOGISTS

c/o Associated General Contractors of Minnesota
Capitol Office Building
525 Park Street, Suite 110
St. Paul, MN 55103-2186
Tel: (651)632-8929
Free: 800-552-7670
Fax: (651)632-8928
E-mail: jsanem@agcmn.org
Web Site: http://www.agcmn.org
To provide financial assistance to students in Minnesota preparing for a career in asphalt pavement technology.
Title of Award: Minnesota Association of Asphalt Paving Technologists Scholarship **Area, Field, or Subject:** Construction; Engineering, Civil **Level of Education for which Award is Granted:** Undergraduate **Number Awarded:** 1 each year. **Funds Available:** The stipend is $2,000. **Duration:** 1 year.
Eligibility Requirements: This program is open to residents of Minnesota enrolled at colleges and universities in the state. Applicants must be studying civil engineering, construction management, or civil technology with an interest in asphalt pavement technology. Along with their application, they must submit a personal statement that includes information on their work-related experience, involvement in student or community organizations, honors or awards they have received, their financial situation, and other appropriate information. Selection is based on academic standing(20%), career objectives(20%), financial need (20%), personal information (20%), and overall application clarity (20%). **Deadline for Receipt:** May of each year.

4535 ■ MINNESOTA SPACE GRANT CONSORTIUM

c/o University of Minnesota
Department of Aerospace Engineering and Mechanics
107 Akerman Hall
110 Union Street S.E.
Minneapolis, MN 55455
Tel: (612)626-9295
Fax: (612)626-1558

E-mail: mnsgc@aem.umn.edu

Web Site: http://www.aem.umn.edu/msgc/Scholarships/sf.shtml

To provide financial assistance for space-related studies to undergraduate and graduate students in Minnesota.

Title of Award: Minnesota Space Grant Consortium Scholarships and Fellowships **Area, Field, or Subject:** Earth sciences; Engineering; Life sciences; Physical sciences; Social sciences **Level of Education for which Award is Granted:** Graduate, Undergraduate **Number Awarded:** 8 to 12 undergraduate scholarships and 2 to 3 graduate fellowships are awarded each year. **Funds Available:** This program awards approximately $125,000 in undergraduate scholarships and graduate fellowships each year. The amounts of the awards are set by each of the participating institutions, which augment funding from this program with institutional resources. **Duration:** 1 year; renewable.

Eligibility Requirements: This program is open to graduate and undergraduate full-time students at institutions that are affiliates of the Minnesota Space Grant Consortium. U.S. citizenship and a GPA of 3.2 or higher are required. Eligible fields of study include the physical sciences (astronomy, astrophysics, chemistry, computer science, mathematics, physics, planetary geoscience, and planetary science), life sciences (biology, biochemistry, botany, health science/nutrition, medicine, molecular/cellular biology, and zoology), social sciences (anthropology, architecture, art, economics, education, history, philosophy, political science/public policy, and psychology), earth sciences (atmospheric science, climatology/meteorology, environmental science, geography, geology, geophysics, and oceanography), and engineering (agricultural, aeronautical, aerospace, architectural, bioengineering, chemical, civil, computer, electrical, electronic, environmental, industrial, materials science, mechanical, mining, nuclear, petroleum, engineering science, and engineering mechanics). The Minnesota Space Grant Consortium is a component of the U.S. National Aeronautics and Space Administration (NASA) Space Grant program, which encourages participation by women, underrepresented minorities, and persons with disabilities. **Deadline for Receipt:** March of each year. **Additional Information:** This program is funded by NASA. The member institutions are: Augsburg College, Bethel College, Bemidji State University, College of St. Catherine, Carleton College, Concordia College, Fond du Lac Community College, Itasca Community College, Leech Lake Tribal College, Macalaster College, Normandale Community College, Southwest State University, University of Minnesota at Duluth, University of Minnesota at Twin Cities, and University of St. Thomas.

4536 ■ MISSISSIPPI SPACE GRANT CONSORTIUM

c/o University of Mississippi

217 Vardaman Hall

P.O. Box 1848

University, MS 38677-1848

Tel: (662)915-1187

Fax: (662)915-3927

E-mail: mschaff@olemiss.edu

Web Site: http://www.olemiss.edu/programs/nasa

To provide funding to undergraduate and graduate students for space-related activities at colleges and universities that are members of the Mississippi Space Grant Consortium.

Title of Award: Mississippi Space Grant Consortium Scholarships and Fellowships **Area, Field, or Subject:** Aerospace sciences; Engineering; Engineering, Aerospace/Aeronautical/Astronautical; Mathematics and mathematical sciences; Science; Space and planetary sciences **Level of Education for which Award is Granted:** Graduate, Undergraduate **Number Awarded:** Varies each year; recently, a total of 47 students received support through this program. **Funds Available:** Each participating institution establishes the amounts of the awards. Recently, the average undergraduate award was $1,308 and the average graduate award was $2,975. A total of $96,350 was awarded.

Eligibility Requirements: This program is open to undergraduate and graduate students at member institutions of the Mississippi consortium. Each participating college or university establishes its own program and criteria for admission, but all activities are in engineering, mathematics, and science fields of interest to the U.S. National Aeronautics and Space Administration (NASA). U.S. citizenship is required. The consortium is a component of NASA's Space Grant program, which encourages participation by women, underrepresented minorities, and persons with disabilities. **Additional Information:** Consortium members include Alcorn State

University, Coahoma Community College, Delta State University, Hinds Community College (Utica Campus), Itawamba Community College, Jackson State University, Meridian Community College, Mississippi Delta Community College, Mississippi Gulf Coast Community College, Mississippi State University, Mississippi University for Women, Mississippi Valley State University, Northeast Mississippi Community College, Pearl River Community College, the University of Mississippi, and the University of Southern Mississippi. This program is funded by NASA.

4537 ■ MONTANA SPACE GRANT CONSORTIUM

c/o Montana State University

416 Cobleigh Hall

P.O. Box 173835

Bozeman, MT 59717-3835

Tel: (406)994-4223

Fax: (406)994-4452

E-mail: msgc@montana.edu

Web Site: http://spacegrant.montana.edu/Text/ScholarProgram.html

To provide financial assistance to students in Montana who are interested in working on an undergraduate degree in the space sciences and/or engineering.

Title of Award: Montana Space Grant Consortium Undergraduate Scholarships **Area, Field, or Subject:** Aerospace sciences; Astronomy and astronomical sciences; Biological and clinical sciences; Chemistry; Computer and information sciences; Engineering, Aerospace/Aeronautical/Astronautical; Engineering, Chemical; Engineering, Civil; Engineering, Electrical; Engineering, Mechanical; Geology; Physics; Space and planetary sciences **Level of Education for which Award is Granted:** Undergraduate **Number Awarded:** Varies each year; recently, 23 of these scholarships were awarded. **Funds Available:** The stipend is $1,000 per year. **Duration:** 1 year; may be renewed.

Eligibility Requirements: This program is open to full-time undergraduate students at member institutions of the Montana Space Grant Consortium (MSGC) majoring in fields related to space sciences and engineering. Those fields include, but are not limited to, astronomy, biological and life sciences, chemical engineering, chemistry, civil engineering, computer sciences, electrical engineering, geological sciences, mathematics, mechanical engineering, and physics. Priority is given to students who have been involved in aerospace-related research. U.S. citizenship is required. The MSGC is a component of the U.S. National Aeronautics and Space Administration (NASA) Space Grant program, which encourages participation by women, underrepresented minorities, and persons with disabilities. **Deadline for Receipt:** March of each year. **Additional Information:** The MSGC member institutions are Blackfeet Community College, Carroll College, Chief Dull Knife College, Fort Belknap College, Fort Peck Community College, Little Big Horn College, Montana State University at Billings, Montana State University at Bozeman, Montana State University Northern, Montana Tech, Rocky Mountain College, Salish Kootenai College, Stone Child College, University of Great Falls, University of Montana, and University of Montana Western. Funding for this program is provided by NASA.

4538 ■ MORGAN STANLEY

c/o Joyce Arencibia, IT College Recruiting

750 Seventh Avenue, 30th Floor

New York, NY 10019

Tel: (212)762-4000

E-mail: diversityrecruiting@morganstanley.com

Web Site: http://www.morganstanley.com/about/diversity/recruit_programs.html?page=div

To provide financial assistance and work experience to members of the National Society of Black Engineers (NSBE), Society of Hispanic Professional Engineers (SHPE), and Society of Women Engineers (SWE) who are working on an undergraduate degree in computer science or engineering.

Title of Award: NSBE/SHPE/SWE Members Scholarship **Area, Field, or Subject:** Computer and information sciences; Engineering **Level of Education for which Award is Granted:** Four Year College **Number Awarded:** 1 or more each year. **Funds Available:** Students who receive a scholarship as juniors (or fourth-year students in a 5-year program) receive $10,000 for their final year of college. Students who receive a scholarship as sophomores (or third-year students in a 5-year program) receive $5,000 for their junior year (or fourth year of a 5-year program).

Duration: 1 year; may be renewed for the final year for students who receive a scholarship as sophomores (or third-year students in a 5-year program).
Eligibility Requirements: This program is open to active members of NSBE, SHPE, and SWE who are enrolled in their sophomore or junior year of college (or the third or fourth year of a 5-year program). Applicants must be enrolled full time and have a GPA of 3.0 or higher. They must be willing to commit to a paid summer internship in the Morgan Stanley Information Technology Division. All majors and disciplines are eligible, but preference is given to students preparing for a career in computer science or engineering. Along with their application, they must submit 1-page essays on 1) why they are applying for this scholarship and why they should be selected as a recipient; 2) a technical project on which they worked, either through a university course or previous work experience, their role in the project, and how they contributed to the end result; and 3) a software, hardware, or new innovative application of existing technology that they would create if they could and the impact it would have. Financial need is not considered in the selection process. **Deadline for Receipt:** February of each year. **Additional Information:** The program includes a paid summer internship in the Morgan Stanley Information Technology Division in the summer following the time of application.

4539 ■ MORGAN STANLEY

c/o Joyce Arencibia, IT College Recruiting
750 Seventh Avenue, 30th Floor
New York, NY 10019
Tel: (212)762-4000
E-mail: diversityrecruiting@morganstanley.com
Web Site: http://www.morganstanley.com/about/diversity/recruit_programs.html?page=div

To provide financial assistance and work experience to women who are working on an undergraduate degree in computer science or engineering.
Title of Award: Women in Technology Scholarship **Area, Field, or Subject:** Computer and information sciences; Engineering **Level of Education for which Award is Granted:** Four Year College **Number Awarded:** 1 or more each year. **Funds Available:** Students who receive a scholarship as juniors (or fourth-year students in a 5-year program) receive $10,000 for their final year of college. Students who receive a scholarship as sophomores (or third-year students in a 5-year program) receive $5,000 for their junior year (or fourth year of a 5-year program).
Duration: 1 year; may be renewed for the final year for students who receive a scholarship as sophomores (or third-year students in a 5-year program).
Eligibility Requirements: This program is open to women who are enrolled in their sophomore or junior year of college (or the third or fourth year of a 5-year program). Applicants must be enrolled full time and have a GPA of 3.0 or higher. They must be willing to commit to a paid summer internship in the Morgan Stanley Information Technology Division. All majors and disciplines are eligible, but preference is given to students preparing for a career in computer science or engineering. Along with their application, they must submit 1-page essays on 1) why they are applying for this scholarship and why they should be selected as a recipient; 2) a technical project on which they worked, either through a university course or previous work experience, their role in the project, and how they contributed to the end result; and 3) a software, hardware, or new innovative application of existing technology that they would create if they could and the impact it would have. Financial need is not considered in the selection process. **Deadline for Receipt:** February of each year. **Additional Information:** The program includes a paid summer internship in the Morgan Stanley Information Technology Division in the summer following the time of application.

4540 ■ NATIONAL ASPHALT PAVEMENT ASSOCIATION

Attn: NAPA Research and Education Foundation
5100 Forbes Boulevard
Lanham, MD 20706-4413
Tel: (301)731-4748; 888-HOT-MIXX
Fax: (301)731-4621
E-mail: cwilson@hotmix.org
Web Site: http://www.hotmix.org

To provide financial assistance to undergraduate and graduate engineering students interested in preparing for a career in the asphalt industry.

Title of Award: NAPA Research and Education Foundation Scholarship Program **Area, Field, or Subject:** Engineering; Engineering, Civil **Level of Education for which Award is Granted:** Graduate, Undergraduate **Number Awarded:** Varies each year; recently, more than 150 students received assistance through this program. **Funds Available:** Stipends range from $1,000 to $5,000 per year. **Duration:** 1 year; may be renewed for up to 2 years or graduation, whichever occurs first.
Eligibility Requirements: This program is open to undergraduate and graduate students interested in preparing for a career in the asphalt industry, especially the hot mix asphalt (HMA) industry. Applicants must be U.S. citizens and enrolled full time in a civil engineering, construction management, or construction engineering program at an accredited 4-year college or university or at a 2-year technical institution. The applicant's institution must offer at least 1 course in HMA technology. Financial need is not considered in the selection process; awards are based on academic performance, future potential, leadership and participation in school and community activities, work experience, career and educational aspirations, goals, unusual personal or family circumstances, and an outside appraisal.

4541 ■ NATIONAL ASSOCIATION OF BLACK TELECOMMUNICATIONS PROFESSIONALS, INC.

c/o Cynthia L. Newman
2020 Pennsylvania Avenue, N.W.
Box 735
Washington, DC 20006
800-946-6228
E-mail: office@nabtp.org
Web Site: http://www.nabtp.org/about/scholarships.shtml

To provide financial assistance to students who are working on a degree in telecommunications or a related field and are interested in participating in the activities of the National Association of Black Telecommunications Professionals (NABTP).
Title of Award: NABTP Collegian Scholarship **Area, Field, or Subject:** Business administration; Communications; Computer and information sciences; Engineering; Telecommunications systems **Level of Education for which Award is Granted:** Undergraduate **Number Awarded:** 1 each year. **Funds Available:** The stipend is $2,000 per year. **Duration:** 1 year; may be renewed for 2 or 3 additional years if the recipient maintains a GPA of 3.0 or higher and active involvement in NABTP.
Eligibility Requirements: This program is open to students majoring in telecommunications or a related field (e.g., computer science, business, engineering, mass communications) at an accredited college or university. Applicants must submit an essay on their educational and career goals, the skill sets and values they are able to bring to NABTP as a possible intern, and how they see active involvement in NABTP supportive to their career path and educational goals. As an option, they may also submit an essay in which they provide a profile of a majority owned African American telecommunications company, including CEO name, number of employees, percentage of minority ownership, annual revenue, address, phone number, web site address, company product and/or services, and company successes. Selection is based on the essays, GPA, notable achievements, and financial need. **Deadline for Receipt:** July of each year.

4542 ■ NATIONAL ASSOCIATION OF WOMEN IN CONSTRUCTION

Attn: NAWIC Founders' Scholarship Foundation
327 South Adams
Fort Worth, TX 76104-1081
Tel: (817)877-5551
Free: 800-552-3506
Fax: (817)877-0324
E-mail: nawic@nawic.org
Web Site: http://www.nawic.org/nfsf.htm

To provide financial assistance for college to students in construction-related degree programs.
Title of Award: National Association of Women in Construction Undergraduate Scholarships **Area, Field, or Subject:** Construction; Engineering **Level of Education for which Award is Granted:** Undergraduate **Number Awarded:** Varies; a total of $25,000 is available in scholarships each year. **Funds Available:** Stipends range from $1,000 to $2,000 per year. **Duration:** 1 year; recipients may reapply.
Eligibility Requirements: This program is open to full-time students who have completed at least 1 full year of course work and have a minimum of

1 year remaining in a course of study leading to a baccalaureate or associate degree in a construction-related degree program and a career in construction. Applicants must have a cumulative GPA of 3.0 or higher and be attending school in the United States or Canada. Along with their application, they must submit brief essays on 1) their ultimate goal in the construction industry; 2) their most important extracurricular activity, their most important contribution to it, and what their participation has meant to them as an individual; and 3) why they are interested in a construction industry career and what event or series of events has led them to this decision. Selection is based on GPA, interest in construction, extracurricular activities, employment experience, academic advisor evaluation, and financial need. **Deadline for Receipt:** March of each year. **Additional Information:** Information is also available from Marcia Rackley, NAWIC Founders' Scholarship Foundation Administrator, P.O. Box 410079, Kansas City, MO 64141, E-mail: mrackley@capitalelectric.com.

4543 ■ NATIONAL ASSOCIATION OF WOMEN IN CONSTRUCTION-BUFFALO CHAPTER 172

c/o Susan Zipp
Siemens Building Technologies
85 Northpointe Parkway, Suite 8
Amherst, NY 14228-1886
Tel: (716)568-0983
Web Site: http://buffalonawic.tripod.com/pr02.htm
To provide financial assistance to residents of New York attending college in the state to prepare for a career in construction.
Title of Award: Buffalo Chapter NAWIC Scholarship **Area, Field, or Subject:** Architecture; Construction; Design; Drafting; Engineering **Level of Education for which Award is Granted:** Undergraduate **Number Awarded:** 1 each year. **Funds Available:** The stipend is $1,000. **Duration:** 1 year.
Eligibility Requirements: This program is open to residents of New York entering the second, third, or fourth year at a 2- or 4-year college or university in the state. Applicants must be majoring in a construction-related program of study (e.g., architecture, construction technology, drafting and design, engineering, estimating). U.S. citizenship is required. **Deadline for Receipt:** June of each year.

4544 ■ NATIONAL ASSOCIATION OF WOMEN IN CONSTRUCTION-GRANITE STATE CHAPTER 218

c/o Bayview Construction Corporation
170 West Road, Suite 10
Portsmouth, NH 03801
Web Site: http://www.geocities.com/nawicnh/scholarship.htm
To provide financial assistance to New Hampshire residents who are majoring in a construction-related field.
Title of Award: Granite State Chapter NAWIC Scholarships **Area, Field, or Subject:** Business; Construction; Engineering; Engineering, Electrical **Level of Education for which Award is Granted:** Undergraduate **Number Awarded:** 1 each year. **Funds Available:** The stipend is $1,000. **Duration:** 1 year.
Eligibility Requirements: This program is open to New Hampshire residents (male or female) who are entering 1) the final year of a 2-year school or 2) the junior or senior year of a 4-year school. Applicants be majoring in a construction-related field (e.g., engineering, electrical, plumbing, carpentry, or general construction) and have a GPA of 2.0 or higher. Along with their application, they must submit a 150-word essay on why they have chosen the construction industry for their career. **Deadline for Receipt:** March of each year. **Additional Information:** The recipient's education institution may not utilize this scholarship as a reduction from previously granted financial aid of any form.

4545 ■ NATIONAL ASSOCIATION OF WOMEN IN CONSTRUCTION-GREATER OMAHA CHAPTER 116

Attn: Scholarship Committee
8712 West Dodge Road, Suite 200
Omaha, NE 68114
E-mail: nawicomaha@yahoo.com
Web Site: http://www.geocities.com/nawicomaha
To provide financial assistance to students in Nebraska who are preparing for a career in construction.
Title of Award: Greater Omaha Chapter NAWIC Scholarship **Area, Field, or Subject:** Architecture; Construction; Engineering **Level of Education**

for which **Award is Granted:** Undergraduate **Number Awarded:** 1 or more each year. **Funds Available:** A stipend is awarded (amount not specified). **Duration:** 1 year.
Eligibility Requirements: This program is open to graduating high school seniors and current college students in Nebraska. Applicants must be preparing for a career in the construction industry (e.g., architecture, engineering, construction management). They must have a GPA of 2.75 or higher and be enrolled or planning to enroll full time. **Deadline for Receipt:** March of each year.

4546 ■ NATIONAL ASSOCIATION OF WOMEN IN CONSTRUCTION-MAINE CHAPTER 276

P.O. Box 366
Hallowell, ME 04347
Tel: (207)623-4683
E-mail: nawicmaine@aol.com
Web Site: http://www.nawicmaine.org
To provide financial assistance to Maine residents who are working on a college degree in a field related to construction.
Title of Award: Maine Chapter 276 Scholarships **Area, Field, or Subject:** Architecture; Business; Construction; Engineering, Civil; Welding **Level of Education for which Award is Granted:** Undergraduate **Number Awarded:** Varies each year; recently, 7 of these scholarships were awarded. **Funds Available:** Stipends range from $500 to $1,000. **Duration:** 1 year.
Eligibility Requirements: This program is open to residents of Maine who are enrolled in a postsecondary educational program. Applicants must be preparing for a career in construction, including carpentry, civil engineering, architecture, welding, electrical, plumbing, or construction management. Along with their application, they must submit a 50-word statement on why they have chosen a career in construction. Selection is based on academic achievement and financial need. **Deadline for Receipt:** April of each year. **Additional Information:** Information is also available from Joyce Newman, 3 Hillcrest Street, Hallowell, ME 04347.

4547 ■ NATIONAL ASSOCIATION OF WOMEN IN CONSTRUCTION-METROPOLITAN DENVER CHAPTER 112

c/o Laruie Mullane
P.O. Box 40208
Denver, CO 80204-0204
Tel: (303)571-5377
To provide financial assistance to high school seniors in Colorado who are interested in preparing for a career in construction.
Title of Award: Vona J. Wagner Memorial Scholarship **Area, Field, or Subject:** Architecture; Construction; Engineering **Level of Education for which Award is Granted:** Undergraduate **Number Awarded:** Varies; generally, 3 to 4 each year. **Funds Available:** The stipend is $1,000. Money is not paid at the time of the award but only on a reimbursement basis after the recipient submits proof of enrollment at a Colorado institution and receipts for tuition, books, laboratory fees, and other school expenses; living expenses are not reimbursable. **Duration:** 1 year; nonrenewable.
Eligibility Requirements: This program is open to high school seniors who have applied to or been admitted to a college, university, or trade school in Colorado. Applicants must be interested in studying field related to construction (e.g., architecture, engineering, construction management) in college and planning to work on a bachelor's degree or certificate of completion. They must have a GPA of 2.5 or higher. Financial need is considered but it not an absolute requirement. **Deadline for Receipt:** March of each year.

4548 ■ NATIONAL ASSOCIATION OF WOMEN IN CONSTRUCTION-NASHVILLE CHAPTER 16

Attn: Scholarship Fund
P.O. Box 22246
Nashville, TN 37202-2246
E-mail: info@nawicnashville.com
Web Site: http://www.nawicnashville.com
To provide financial assistance to residents of Tennessee working on an undergraduate degree in a construction-related field.
Title of Award: Cordie Hughes Scholarship **Area, Field, or Subject:** Architecture; Construction; Engineering **Level of Education for which Award is Granted:** Undergraduate **Number Awarded:** Varies each year;

recently, a total of $2,000 was available for this program. **Funds Available:** A stipend is awarded (amount not specified). **Duration:** 1 year.
Eligibility Requirements: This program is open to residents of Tennessee attending a college or university in Alabama, Georgia, or Tennessee. Applicants must be working on a degree in a field related to construction (e.g., architecture, engineering, construction management). They must have a GPA of 2.8 or higher and be able to demonstrate financial need. Priority is given to applicants entering their junior or senior year at a 4-year institution. If no student at a 4-year school qualifies, students at 2-year colleges are considered.

4549 ■ NATIONAL ASSOCIATION OF WOMEN IN CONSTRUCTION-SAN ANTONIO CHAPTER 11

c/o Deborah L. Schievelbein, Scholarship Chair
405 North St. Mary's Street, Suite 150
San Antonio, TX 78205
Tel: (210)476-0400
E-mail: dbdrumm@world-net.net
Web Site: http://www.nawicsat.org
To provide financial assistance to students in Texas working on an undergraduate degree in a construction-related field.
Title of Award: San Antonio Chapter NAWIC Scholarship **Area, Field, or Subject:** Architecture; Construction; Engineering **Level of Education for which Award is Granted:** Undergraduate **Number Awarded:** 1 or more each year. **Funds Available:** A stipend is awarded (amount not specified). Funds are paid directly to the recipient's college or university. **Duration:** 1 year; may be renewed.
Eligibility Requirements: This program is open to full-time students who are residents of Texas and undergraduates attending a college or university in the state. Applicants must be majoring in a field related to construction (e.g., architecture, engineering, construction management). They must have a GPA of 3.0 or higher. Previous recipient are given priority in the selection process. **Deadline for Receipt:** January of each year.

4550 ■ NATIONAL ASSOCIATION OF WOMEN IN CONSTRUCTION-WILMINGTON CHAPTER 96

c/o Donna Myers
A.R. Myers Glass Building 31
1300 East Eighth Street
Wilmington, DE 19801
Tel: (302)652-3164
To provide financial assistance to students in Delaware who are interested in preparing for a career in construction.
Title of Award: Wilmington Chapter NAWIC Scholarship **Area, Field, or Subject:** Construction; Engineering **Level of Education for which Award is Granted:** Undergraduate **Number Awarded:** 1 or more each year. **Funds Available:** Stipends range from $500 to $1,000. **Duration:** 1 year.
Eligibility Requirements: This program is open to Delaware residents (both male and female) who are interested in working full time on an associate or bachelor's degree in a construction-related program, including engineering. Applicants may be high school seniors, high school graduates, or currently-enrolled college students. Selection is based on GPA, interest in construction, extracurricular activities, employment experience, academic advisor evaluation, and financial need. **Deadline for Receipt:** March of each year.

4551 ■ NATIONAL CONSORTIUM FOR GRADUATE DEGREES FOR MINORITIES IN ENGINEERING AND SCIENCE (GEM)

P.O. Box 537
Notre Dame, IN 46556
Tel: (574)631-7771
Fax: (574)287-1486
E-mail: gem.1@nd.edu
Web Site: http://www.gemfellowship.org
To provide financial assistance and summer work experience to underrepresented minority graduate students in engineering.
Title of Award: GEM M.S. Engineering Fellowship Program **Area, Field, or Subject:** Computer and information sciences; Engineering **Level of Education for which Award is Granted:** Four Year College, Master's **Number Awarded:** Varies each year; recently, 327 of these fellowships were awarded. **Funds Available:** The fellowship pays tuition, fees, and a stipend of $10,000 over its lifetime. In addition, each participant receives a

salary during the summer work assignment as a GEM Summer Intern, making the value of the total award between $20,000 and $60,000. Employer members reimburse GEM participants for travel expenses to and from the summer work site. **Duration:** Up to 3 semesters or 4 quarters, plus a summer work internship lasting 10 to 14 weeks for up to 3 summers, depending on whether the student applies as a junior, senior, or college graduate; recipients begin their internship upon acceptance into the program and work each summer until completion of their master's degree.
Eligibility Requirements: This program is open to U.S. citizens who are members of ethnic groups underrepresented in engineering: Native Americans, African Americans, Latinos, Puerto Ricans, and other Hispanic Americans. Applicants must be enrolled as at least a junior in an ABET-accredited engineering discipline with an academic record that indicates the ability to pursue graduate studies in engineering (including a GPA of 2.8 or higher). Students in computer science and computer engineering may also apply, but engineering technology majors are not eligible. Applicants must be planning to attend 1 of the 95 GEM member universities that offer a master's degree. **Deadline for Receipt:** October of each year.
Additional Information: During the summer internship, each fellow is assigned an engineering project in a research setting. Each project is based on the fellow's interest and background and is carried out under the supervision of an experienced engineer. At the conclusion of the internship, each fellow writes a project report. Recipients must seek the master's degree in the same engineering discipline as their baccalaureate degree.

4552 ■ NATIONAL FEDERATION OF THE BLIND

c/o Peggy Elliott, Scholarship Committee Chair
805 Fifth Avenue
Grinnell, IA 50112
Tel: (641)236-3366
Web Site: http://www.nfb.org/sch_intro.htm
To provide financial assistance for college or graduate school to blind students studying or planning to study law, medicine, engineering, architecture, or the natural sciences.
Title of Award: Howard Brown Rickard Scholarships **Area, Field, or Subject:** Architecture; Engineering; Law; Medicine; Natural sciences **Level of Education for which Award is Granted:** Graduate, Undergraduate **Number Awarded:** 1 each year. **Funds Available:** The stipend is $3,000. **Duration:** 1 year; recipients may resubmit applications up to 2 additional years.
Eligibility Requirements: This program is open to legally blind students who are enrolled in or planning to enroll in a full-time undergraduate or graduate course of study. Applicants must be studying or planning to study law, medicine, engineering, architecture, or the natural sciences. Selection is based on academic excellence, service to the community, and financial need. **Deadline for Receipt:** March of each year. **Additional Information:** Scholarships are awarded at the federation convention in July. Recipients attend the convention at federation expense; that funding is in addition to the scholarship grant.

4553 ■ NATIONAL FFA ORGANIZATION

Attn: Scholarship Office
6060 FFA Drive
P.O. Box 68960
Indianapolis, IN 46268-0960
Tel: (317)802-4321
Fax: (317)802-5321
E-mail: scholarships@ffa.org
Web Site: http://www.ffa.org
To provide financial assistance to FFA members who are interested in working on a postsecondary degree or automotive training.
Title of Award: CARQUEST Corporation Scholarships **Area, Field, or Subject:** Automotive technology; General studies/Field of study not specified **Level of Education for which Award is Granted:** Four Year College, Vocational/Occupational **Number Awarded:** 5 each year. **Funds Available:** The stipend is $1,000. Funds are paid directly to the recipient. **Duration:** 1 year; nonrenewable.
Eligibility Requirements: This program is open to members who are graduating high school seniors planning to enroll or college student currently enrolled full time. Applicants may be interested in studying any major at a 4-year college or an automotive degree at a postsecondary

NATEF-certified school. Their chapter must be located within a 25-mile radius of a CARQUEST store. Selection is based on academic achievement (10 points for GPA, 10 points for SAT or ACT score, 10 points for class rank), leadership in FFA activities (30 points), leadership in community activities (10 points), and participation in the Supervised Agricultural Experience (SAE) program (30 points). U.S. citizenship is required. **Deadline for Receipt:** February of each year. **Additional Information:** Funding for these scholarships is provided by CARQUEST Auto Parts Corporation.

4554 ■ NATIONAL FFA ORGANIZATION

Attn: Scholarship Office
6060 FFA Drive
P.O. Box 68960
Indianapolis, IN 46268-0960
Tel: (317)802-4321
Fax: (317)802-5321
E-mail: scholarships@ffa.org
Web Site: http://www.ffa.org
To provide financial assistance to current FFA members from selected states interested in studying engineering or finance in college.
Title of Award: International Truck and Engine Corporation Scholarships **Area, Field, or Subject:** Engineering; Finance **Level of Education for which Award is Granted:** Four Year College **Number Awarded:** 5 each year: 1 to a student from each of the selected states. **Funds Available:** The stipend is $1,000 per year. Funds are paid directly to the recipient. **Duration:** 1 year; nonrenewable.
Eligibility Requirements: This program is open to members from Alabama, Illinois, Indiana, Michigan, and Wisconsin. Applicants must be graduating high school seniors planning to enroll or college students currently enrolled full time. They must be planning to work on a 4-year degree in engineering or as a financial specialist at an institution in their home state. Selection is based on academic achievement (10 points for GPA, 10 points for SAT or ACT score, 10 points for class rank), leadership in FFA activities (30 points), leadership in community activities (10 points), and participation in the Supervised Agricultural Experience (SAE) program (30 points). U.S. citizenship is required. **Deadline for Receipt:** February of each year. **Additional Information:** Funding for these scholarships is provided by the International Truck and Engine Corporation.

4555 ■ NATIONAL FFA ORGANIZATION

Attn: Scholarship Office
6060 FFA Drive
P.O. Box 68960
Indianapolis, IN 46268-0960
Tel: (317)802-4321
Fax: (317)802-5321
E-mail: scholarships@ffa.org
Web Site: http://www.ffa.org
To provide financial assistance to FFA members who are interested in studying fields related to agriculture, business, engineering, or nursing in college.
Title of Award: Tyson Foods Scholarships **Area, Field, or Subject:** Agribusiness; Agricultural sciences; Business; Business administration; Engineering; Food science and technology; Management; Nursing; Packaging **Level of Education for which Award is Granted:** Undergraduate **Number Awarded:** 10 each year. **Funds Available:** The stipend is $1,000. Funds are paid directly to the recipient. **Duration:** 1 year; nonrenewable.
Eligibility Requirements: This program is open to members who are either high school seniors or already enrolled full time in college. Applicants must be working on or planning to work on a 2-year or 4-year degree in agriculture, food science, food technology, supply chain management, product development, product development, product packaging, nursing, engineering, or business. They must reside in a community in which a Tyson Foods processing facility is located. Selection is based on academic achievement (10 points for GPA, 10 points for SAT or ACT score, 10 points for class rank), leadership in FFA activities (30 points), leadership in community activities (10 points), and participation in the Supervised Agricultural Experience (SAE) program (30 points). U.S. citizenship is required. **Deadline for Receipt:** February of each year. **Additional Information:** Funding for these scholarships is provided by Tyson Foods, Inc.

4556 ■ NATIONAL GAY PILOTS ASSOCIATION

Attn: NGPA Education Fund
P.O. Box 7271
Dallas, TX 75209-0271
Tel: (214)336-0873
Fax: (214)350-0447
E-mail: info@ngpa.org
Web Site: http://www.ngpa.org/education.html
To provide financial assistance to those affiliated with the gay and lesbian community who have expressed an interest in an aviation career as a professional pilot.
Title of Award: NGPA Education Fund **Area, Field, or Subject:** Aeronautics; Aerospace sciences; Aviation; Engineering; Space and planetary sciences **Level of Education for which Award is Granted:** Undergraduate **Number Awarded:** 1 or more each year. **Funds Available:** The stipend is $2,000 per year. Funds are paid directly to the educational institution and cannot be used to pay for the basic Private Certificate; they must be applied toward advanced flight training at a facility certified under FAR Part 141 or to college tuition if enrolled in an accredited aviation degree program. **Duration:** 1 year.
Eligibility Requirements: Applicants must be preparing for a career as a professional pilot. They must be 1) accepted at or currently enrolled in an accredited college or university with an aviation-related curriculum (aerospace, aerodynamics, engineering, airport management, etc.) or 2) accepted to or currently undergoing a course of study in a recognized professional pilot aviation training program in an institution of higher learning, aviation technical school, or school that provides advanced pilot training under FAR Part 141. They must have at least a Private Pilot Certificate. While scholarships are not awarded on the basis of an individual's sexual orientation, applicants must provide evidence of their contribution to the gay and lesbian community. Selection is based on demonstrated personal excellence, aviation accomplishments, potential to become a successful professional pilot, and financial need. **Deadline for Receipt:** November of each year.

4557 ■ NATIONAL HOUSING ENDOWMENT

1201 15th Street, N.W.
Washington, DC 20005
Tel: (202)266-8483
Free: 800-368-5242
Fax: (202)266-8177
E-mail: nhe@nahb.com
Web Site: http://www.nationalhousingendowment.com/Scholarships.htm
To provide financial assistance to undergraduate students interested in preparing for a career in the building industry (particularly as a manager).
Title of Award: Centex Homes Build Your Future Scholarship **Area, Field, or Subject:** Architecture; Construction; Engineering, Civil **Level of Education for which Award is Granted:** Undergraduate **Number Awarded:** Varies each year; recently, 18 of these scholarships were awarded. **Funds Available:** Stipends range from $500 to $2,000. Funds are made payable to the recipient and sent to the recipient's school. **Duration:** 1 year; may be renewed.
Eligibility Requirements: This program is open to full-time undergraduate students working on a degree in a housing-related program, such as construction management, residential building, construction technology, civil engineering, architecture, or a trade specialty. Applicants must have at least a 2.5 GPA in all courses and at least a 3.0 GPA in core curriculum classes. Preference is given to applicants who would be unable to afford college without financial assistance and to applicants who demonstrate their interest in residential construction through 1 or more of the following activities: 1) experience/internships in the industry; 2) membership and participation in service organizations and activities related to the building industry; and 3) membership in a student chapter of the National Association of Home Builders. Along with their application, they must submit an essay on their reasons for becoming a professional in the housing industry and their career goals. Selection is based on financial need, career goals, academic achievement, employment history, extracurricular activities, and letters of recommendation. **Deadline for Receipt:** March of each year. **Additional Information:** The National Housing Endowment is

the philanthropic arm of the National Association of Home Builders. Centex Homes established this scholarship in 1999.

4558 ■ NATIONAL HOUSING ENDOWMENT

1201 15th Street, N.W.
Washington, DC 20005
Tel: (202)266-8483
Free: 800-368-5242
Fax: (202)266-8177
E-mail: nhe@nahb.com
Web Site: http://www.nationalhousingendowment.com/Scholarships.htm
To provide financial assistance to undergraduate students, especially women, interested in preparing for a career in the building industry.
Title of Award: NAHB Women's Council Strategies for Success Scholarship **Area, Field, or Subject:** Architecture; Construction; Engineering, Civil **Level of Education for which Award is Granted:** Undergraduate **Number Awarded:** Varies each year; recently, 2 of these scholarships were awarded. **Funds Available:** The stipend is $2,000. Funds are made payable to the recipient and sent to the recipient's school. **Duration:** 1 year; may be renewed.
Eligibility Requirements: This program is open to high school seniors and current undergraduates who are enrolled or planning to enroll full time at a 2- or 4-year college or university or vocational program. Applicants must be working on or planning to work on a degree in a housing-related program, such as construction management, building, construction technology, civil engineering, architecture, or a trade specialty. They must have at least a 2.5 GPA in all courses and at least a 3.0 GPA in core curriculum classes. Preference is given to 1) women; 2) applicants who would be unable to afford college without financial assistance; and 3) students who are current members (or will be members in the upcoming semester) of a student chapter of the National Association of Home Builders (NAHB). Along with their application, they must submit an essay on their reasons for becoming a professional in the housing industry and their career goals. Selection is based on financial need, career goals, academic achievement, employment history, extracurricular activities, and letters of recommendation. **Deadline for Receipt:** March of each year. **Additional Information:** The National Housing Endowment is the philanthropic arm of the National Association of Home Builders (NAHB). Its women's council established this scholarship in 2001.

4559 ■ NATIONAL INVENTORS HALL OF FAME

Attn: Collegiate Inventors Competition
221 South Broadway Street
Akron, OH 44308-1595
Tel: (330)849-6887
E-mail: collegiate@invent.org
Web Site: http://www.invent.org/collegiate
To recognize and reward outstanding inventions by college or university students in the fields of science, engineering, and technology.
Title of Award: Collegiate Inventors Competition **Area, Field, or Subject:** Biological and clinical sciences; Chemistry; Computer and information sciences; Engineering; Environmental conservation; Environmental science; Inventors; Mathematics and mathematical sciences; Medicine; Physics; Science; Technology; Veterinary science and medicine **Level of Education for which Award is Granted:** Graduate, Postdoctoral, Undergraduate **Number Awarded:** 15 semifinalists are selected each year; of those, 3 individuals or teams win prizes. **Funds Available:** Finalists receive an all-expense paid trip to Washington, D.C. to participate in a final round of judging and in the awards dinner and presentation. The Grand Prize winner or team receives $25,000. Other prizes are $10,000 for an undergraduate winner or team and $15,000 for a graduate winner or team. Academic advisors of the winning entries each receive a $3,000 cash prize. Awards are unrestricted cash gifts, not scholarships or grants. **Duration:** The competition is held annually.
Eligibility Requirements: This competition is open to undergraduate and graduate students who are (or have been) enrolled full time at least part of the 12-month period prior to entry in a college or university in the United States. Entries may also be submitted by teams, up to 4 members, of whom at least 1 must meet the full-time requirement and all others must have been enrolled at least half time sometime during the preceding 24-month period. Applicants must submit a description of their invention, including a patent search and summary of current literature that describes the state of the art and identifies the originality of the invention; test data

demonstrating that the idea, invention, or design is workable; the societal, economic, and environmental benefits of the invention; and supplemental material that may include photos, slides, disks, videotapes, and even samples. Entries must be original ideas and the work of a student or team and a university advisor; the invention should be reproducible and may not have been 1) made available to the public as a commercial product or process, or 2) patented or published more than 1 year prior to the date of submission for this competition. Entries are first reviewed by a committee of judges that selects the finalists. The committee is comprised of mathematicians, engineers, biologists, chemists, environmentalists, physicists, computer specialists, members of the medical and veterinary profession, and specialists in invention and development of technology. Entries are judged on the basis of originality, inventiveness, potential value to society (socially, environmentally, and economically), and range or scope of use. **Deadline for Receipt:** May of each year. **Additional Information:** This program is co-sponsored by Abbott Laboratories and the United States Patent and Trademark Office. It was established in 1990 as the BFGoodrich Collegiate Inventors Program.

4560 ■ NATIONAL NAVAL OFFICERS ASSOCIATION-WASHINGTON, D.C. CHAPTER

Attn: Scholarship Program
2701 Park Center Drive, B704
Alexandria, VA 22302
E-mail: williams.stephen@hq.navy.mil
Web Site: http://www.dcnnoa.org
To provide financial assistance to minority high school seniors from the Washington, D.C. area who are interested in majoring in engineering in college.
Title of Award: DCNNOA/General Dynamics Scholarship **Area, Field, or Subject:** Engineering **Level of Education for which Award is Granted:** Undergraduate **Number Awarded:** 1 each year. **Funds Available:** The stipend is $10,000 per year. **Duration:** 1 year; nonrenewable.
Eligibility Requirements: This program is open to minority seniors at high schools in the Washington, D.C. metropolitan area who plan to enroll full time in an engineering program at an accredited 2-year or 4-year college or university. Applicants must have a GPA of 3.0 or higher and be U.S. citizens or permanent residents. Selection is based on academic achievement, community involvement, and financial need. **Deadline for Receipt:** April of each year. **Additional Information:** Recipients are not required to join or affiliate with the military in any way. This program is sponsored by General Dynamics.

4561 ■ NATIONAL ORGANIZATION FOR THE PROFESSIONAL ADVANCEMENT OF BLACK CHEMISTS AND CHEMICAL ENGINEERS

c/o Howard University
P.O. Box 77040
Washington, DC 20013
Tel: (202)667-1699
Free: 800-776-1419
Fax: (267)200-0156
Web Site: http://www.nobcche.org
To provide financial assistance to African American undergraduates majoring in chemistry and chemical engineering.
Title of Award: NOBCChE Undergraduate Award **Area, Field, or Subject:** Chemistry; Engineering, Chemical **Level of Education for which Award is Granted:** Undergraduate **Number Awarded:** 1 each year. **Funds Available:** The stipend is $2,500. **Duration:** 1 year; nonrenewable.
Eligibility Requirements: This program is open to African American high school graduates and undergraduate students enrolled at a college or university and working on or planning to work on a bachelor's degree in chemistry or chemical engineering. Applicants must submit 3 letters of recommendation, an official transcript, and a resume. **Deadline for Receipt:** January of each year. **Additional Information:** This program is sponsored by the National Organization for the Professional Advancement of Black Chemists and Chemical Engineers (NOBCChE). Information is also available from Dr. Marlon L. Walker, Awards and Scholarships Com-

mittee Chair, National Institute of Standards and Technology, 100 Bureau Drive, Gaithersburg, MD 20899-8372, (301) 975-5593 E-mail: marlon. walker@nist.gov.

4562 ■ NATIONAL SCIENCE FOUNDATION
Directorate for Engineering
Attn: Division of Engineering Education and Centers
4201 Wilson Boulevard, Room 585
Arlington, VA 22230
Tel: (703)292-8380
Fax: (703)292-9051
Web Site: http://www.eng.nsf.gov/eec
To encourage principal investigators on projects funded by the National Science Foundation (NSF) to include in their research projects high school and/or undergraduate engineering research assistants who are members of groups underrepresented in the advanced levels of U.S. science and engineering.
Title of Award: Supplemental Funding for Support of Women, Minority, and Disabled Engineering Research Assistants **Area, Field, or Subject:** Engineering; Science **Level of Education for which Award is Granted:** Postdoctoral, Undergraduate **Number Awarded:** Varies each year. **Funds Available:** Supplemental funding of up to $5,000, including indirect costs, may be requested for each student to be added to the project. Funds provided by this program are limited to 2 students per grant. Up to 10% of this amount may be used for supplies and services. Additional funds in excess of $5,000 may be requested, if necessary, to provide special equipment, modify equipment, or provide other services required specifically for the participation of physically handicapped individuals. **Duration:** The support may be used for a summer, quarter, or academic year.
Eligibility Requirements: The supplemental funding is expected to support students from underrepresented groups who will contribute to the NSF project with meaningful research work under the supervision of the principal investigator. For the purposes of this program, "underrepresented groups" include 1) minority groups (i.e., Native American, African American, Hispanic, Alaskan Native, or Native Pacific Islander); 2) women; and 3) persons with disabilities. Students must be citizens or nationals of the United States at the time of proposal submission. **Additional Information:** Support may be requested in 2 ways: 1) requests for supplemental funding may be included in the initial proposal submission; or 2) current grantees may request supplemental funding of existing grants to add up to 2 students to the grant. Students interested in participating in this program should contact the sponsor to obtain a list of principal investigators in their area who have research grants from the Directorate for Engineering. The students are expected to be involved in an interesting and challenging aspect of the research, and the principal investigator should be available to participate in the research experience with the student.

4563 ■ NATIONAL SECURITY AGENCY
Attn: Office of Recruitment and Staffing (Stokes)
9800 Savage Road, Suite 6779
P.O. Box 1661, Suite 6779
Fort Meade, MD 20755-6779
Tel: (410)854-4725; (866)672-4473
Web Site: http://www.nsa.gov/careers/students_4.cfm
To provide minority and other high school seniors and college sophomores with scholarship/loans and work experience at the National Security Agency (NSA).
Title of Award: Stokes Educational Scholarship Program **Area, Field, or Subject:** Asian studies; Computer and information sciences; Engineering, Computer; Engineering, Electrical; Finance; Foreign languages; International affairs and relations; Mathematics and mathematical sciences; Near Eastern studies; South Asian studies **Level of Education for which Award is Granted:** Undergraduate **Number Awarded:** Varies each year. **Funds Available:** Participants receive college tuition for up to 4 years, reimbursement for books and certain fees, a year-round salary, and a housing allowance and travel reimbursement during summer employment if the distance between the agency and school exceeds 75 miles. Following graduation, participants must work for the agency for 1 and a half times their length of study, usually 5 years. Students who leave agency employment earlier must repay the tuition cost. **Duration:** Up to 4 years, followed by employment at the agency for 5 years.

Eligibility Requirements: This program is open to graduating high school seniors, particularly minorities, who 1) are planning a college major in electrical or computer engineering, computer science, international affairs, international finance, mathematics, area studies (Middle East or south, east, or central Asia), foreign languages (recent language interests included Arabic, Chinese, Farsi, and Korean); 2) have minimum scores of 1600 on the SAT (1100 on critical reading and mathematics, 500 in writing) or 25 on the ACT; 3) have a GPA of 3.0 or higher; 4) are U.S. citizens; and 5) demonstrate leadership abilities. Also eligible are college sophomores who are U.S. citizens, have a GPA of 3.0 or higher, and are majoring in the eligible fields. Applicants must include a 1-page essay on why they want to have a career with the NSA. **Deadline for Receipt:** November of each year. **Additional Information:** Participants must attend classes full time and work at the agency during the summer in jobs tailored to their course of study. They must maintain at least a 3.0 GPA. This program, established in 1986, was formerly known as the National Security Agency Undergraduate Training Program.

4564 ■ NATIONAL SOCIETY OF BLACK ENGINEERS
Attn: Programs Department
1454 Duke Street
Alexandria, VA 22314
Tel: (703)549-2207
Fax: (703)683-5312
E-mail: scholarships@nsbe.org
Web Site: http://www.nsbe.org/programs/schol_fellows.php
To provide financial assistance to members of the National Society of Black Engineers (NSBE) who are majoring in engineering.
Title of Award: Board of Corporate Affiliates Scholars Awards **Area, Field, or Subject:** Engineering **Level of Education for which Award is Granted:** Graduate, Undergraduate **Number Awarded:** Varies each year; recently, 42 of these scholarships were awarded. **Funds Available:** The stipend is $3,000. Travel, hotel accommodations, and registration to the national convention are also provided. **Duration:** 1 year.
Eligibility Requirements: This program is open to members of the society who are undergraduate or graduate engineering students. Applicants must have a GPA of 3.0 or higher. Selection is based on an essay; academic achievement; service to the society at the chapter, regional, and/or national level; and other professional, campus, and community activities. Applicants for the National Society of Black Engineers Fellows Scholarship Program who rank in the highest of 3 tiers receive these awards. **Deadline for Receipt:** January of each year.

4565 ■ NATIONAL SOCIETY OF BLACK ENGINEERS
Attn: Programs Department
1454 Duke Street
Alexandria, VA 22314
Tel: (703)549-2207
Fax: (703)683-5312
E-mail: scholarships@nsbe.org
Web Site: http://www.nsbe.org/programs/schol_delta.php
To provide financial assistance to members of the National Society of Black Engineers (NSBE) who are majoring in designated science and engineering fields.
Title of Award: Delta Air Lines NSBE Corporate Scholarship **Area, Field, or Subject:** Computer and information sciences; Engineering, Aerospace/Aeronautical/Astronautical; Engineering, Chemical; Engineering, Electrical; Engineering, Materials; Engineering, Mechanical; Materials research/science **Level of Education for which Award is Granted:** Four Year College **Number Awarded:** 1 each year. **Funds Available:** The stipend is $3,000. **Duration:** 1 year.
Eligibility Requirements: This program is open to members of the society who are college juniors or seniors majoring in the following fields of study: aerospace/aeronautical engineering, chemical engineering, computer science, electrical engineering, materials engineering, materials science, or mechanical engineering. Applicants must have a GPA of 3.0 or higher and a demonstrated interest in employment with Delta Air Lines. They must submit essays of 100 to 150 words on each of the following topics: 1) how they personally define global diversity and why it is important for the airlines to value diversity; 2) how they have demonstrated their leadership ability in their school and community; 3) what influenced their decision to pursue their current course of study; and 4) the top 2 challenges facing Delta Air Lines today and how they would use their

technical training and experience to help overcome those challenges. **Deadline for Receipt:** January of each year. **Additional Information:** The recipient also receives a round-trip airline ticket, paid registration, and 2 nights' hotel accommodations to the NSBE national convention.

4566 ■ NATIONAL SOCIETY OF BLACK ENGINEERS
Attn: Programs Department
1454 Duke Street
Alexandria, VA 22314
Tel: (703)549-2207
Fax: (703)683-5312
E-mail: scholarships@nsbe.org
Web Site: http://www.nsbe.org/programs/schol_exxon.php
To provide financial assistance to members of the National Society of Black Engineers (NSBE) who are majoring in designated engineering fields.
Title of Award: ExxonMobil Corporation NSBE Corporate Scholarships **Area, Field, or Subject:** Engineering, Chemical; Engineering, Civil; Engineering, Electrical; Engineering, Mechanical **Level of Education for which Award is Granted:** Undergraduate **Number Awarded:** 13 each year: 1 national award and 12 regional awards (2 in each NSBE region). **Funds Available:** The national stipend is $2,000; the regional stipends are $1,500. **Duration:** 1 year.
Eligibility Requirements: This program is open to members of the society who are college freshmen, sophomores, or juniors majoring in chemical, civil, electrical, or mechanical engineering. Applicants for regional awards must have a GPA of 3.3 or higher; applicants for the national award must have a GPA of 3.5 or higher. Along with their application, they must submit an essay of 150 words on the advice they would offer fellow engineering students to motivate them to make academic excellence a priority in their college career. **Deadline for Receipt:** January of each year. **Additional Information:** This program is sponsored by ExxonMobil Corporation.

4567 ■ NATIONAL SOCIETY OF BLACK ENGINEERS
Attn: Programs Department
1454 Duke Street
Alexandria, VA 22314
Tel: (703)549-2207
Fax: (703)683-5312
E-mail: scholarships@nsbe.org
Web Site: http://www.nsbe.org/programs/schol_free.php
To provide financial assistance to members of the National Society of Black Engineers (NSBE) who are majoring in computer science or engineering or electrical engineering.
Title of Award: Freescale Conductor Scholarship **Area, Field, or Subject:** Computer and information sciences; Engineering, Computer; Engineering, Electrical **Level of Education for which Award is Granted:** Four Year College **Number Awarded:** 3 each year. **Funds Available:** The stipend is $5,000. **Duration:** 1 year.
Eligibility Requirements: This program is open to members of the society who are entering their sophomore, junior, or senior year in college and majoring in computer science, computer engineering, or electrical engineering. Applicants must have a GPA of 3.0 or higher and a demonstrated interest in employment with Freescale Semiconductor. Along with their application, they must submit a 250-word essay describing how they will use their education to make a positive impact on the African American community and how this scholarship opportunity will advance their career goals and benefit Freescale Semiconductor. **Deadline for Receipt:** January of each year.

4568 ■ NATIONAL SOCIETY OF BLACK ENGINEERS
Attn: Programs Department
1454 Duke Street
Alexandria, VA 22314
Tel: (703)549-2207
Fax: (703)683-5312
E-mail: scholarships@nsbe.org
Web Site: http://www.nsbe.org/programs/schol_legacy.php
To provide financial assistance to members of the National Society of Black Engineers (NSBE) who are working on an undergraduate or graduate degree in engineering.
Title of Award: Fulfilling the Legacy Scholarships **Area, Field, or Subject:** Engineering **Level of Education for which Award is Granted:** Graduate, Undergraduate **Number Awarded:** Varies each year, depending on the availability of funds. Recently, 20 of these scholarships were awarded. **Funds Available:** The stipend depends on the availability of funds. **Duration:** 1 year; may be renewed.
Eligibility Requirements: This program is open to members of the society who are undergraduate or graduate engineering students. Selection is based on an essay; academic achievement; service to the society at the chapter, regional, and/or national level; and other professional, campus, and community activities. **Deadline for Receipt:** January of each year.

4569 ■ NATIONAL SOCIETY OF BLACK ENGINEERS
Attn: Programs Department
1454 Duke Street
Alexandria, VA 22314
Tel: (703)549-2207
Fax: (703)683-5312
E-mail: scholarships@nsbe.org
Web Site: http://www.nsbe.org/programs/schol_pci_gta.php
To provide financial assistance to high school seniors who are junior members of the National Society of Black Engineers (NSBE) planning to major in a field related to engineering in college.
Title of Award: Golden Torch Awards **Area, Field, or Subject:** Computer and information sciences; Engineering; Mathematics and mathematical sciences; Technology **Level of Education for which Award is Granted:** Four Year College **Number Awarded:** Varies each year; recently, 7 of these awards were presented. **Funds Available:** The stipend is $1,000 per year. **Duration:** 1 year; may be renewed 3 additional years if the recipient maintains a GPA of 2.75 or higher in college.
Eligibility Requirements: This program is open to junior members of the society who are high school seniors. Applicants must have been accepted as a full-time student at a 4-year college or university to major in engineering, computer science, mathematics, or technology. They must have a GPA of 3.0 or higher. Along with their application, they must submit an essay, up to 500 words in length, on how they will continue the legacy of NSBE and how they will service as role models in their community after college. **Deadline for Receipt:** January of each year.

4570 ■ NATIONAL SOCIETY OF BLACK ENGINEERS
Attn: Programs Department
1454 Duke Street
Alexandria, VA 22314
Tel: (703)549-2207
Fax: (703)683-5312
E-mail: scholarships@nsbe.org
Web Site: http://www.nsbe.org/programs/schol_jnj.php
To provide financial assistance to members of the National Society of Black Engineers (NSBE) who are majoring in designated engineering fields.
Title of Award: Johnson & Johnson NSBE Corporate Scholarship Program **Area, Field, or Subject:** Biological and clinical sciences; Chemistry; Computer and information sciences; Engineering, Biomedical; Engineering, Chemical; Engineering, Computer; Engineering, Electrical; Engineering, Industrial; Engineering, Materials; Engineering, Mechanical; Logistics **Level of Education for which Award is Granted:** Four Year College **Number Awarded:** 13 each year: 1 national award and 12 regional awards (2 in each NSBE region). **Funds Available:** The national stipend is $2,000; the regional stipends are $1,500. **Duration:** 1 year.
Eligibility Requirements: This program is open to members of the society who are entering their junior or senior year in college and majoring in biology, chemistry, computer science, operations/logistics, or the following fields of engineering: biomedical, chemical, computer, electrical, industrial, material, or mechanical. Applicants must have a GPA of 3.2 or higher and a demonstrated interest in employment with Johnson & Johnson. Along with their application, they must submit a resume and official transcript. **Deadline for Receipt:** January of each year.

4571 ■ NATIONAL SOCIETY OF BLACK ENGINEERS
Attn: Programs Department
1454 Duke Street
Alexandria, VA 22314
Tel: (703)549-2207
Fax: (703)683-5312

E-mail: scholarships@nsbe.org

Web Site: http://www.nsbe.org/programs/schol_elililly.php

To provide financial assistance to members of the National Society of Black Engineers (NSBE) from selected regions who are majoring in chemical or mechanical engineering.

Title of Award: Eli Lilly and Company NSBE Corporate Scholarship Program **Area, Field, or Subject:** Engineering, Chemical; Engineering, Mechanical **Level of Education for which Award is Granted:** Four Year College **Number Awarded:** 5 each year: 1 major award and 4 smaller awards. **Funds Available:** The stipend of the major award is $5,000; the stipend of the smaller awards is $2,500. **Duration:** 1 year.

Eligibility Requirements: This program is open to members of the society who are entering their sophomore, junior, or senior year in college and majoring in chemical or mechanical engineering. Applicants must be members in regions II, III, or IV. They must have a GPA of 3.5 or higher (for the major award) or 3.0 or higher (for the smaller awards) and a demonstrated interest in employment with Eli Lilly and Company. Along with their application, they must submit an official transcript and a resume. **Deadline for Receipt:** January of each year. **Additional Information:** The selected regions serve the mid-Atlantic, southeastern, and midwestern states.

4572 ■ NATIONAL SOCIETY OF BLACK ENGINEERS

Attn: Programs Department

1454 Duke Street

Alexandria, VA 22314

Tel: (703)549-2207

Fax: (703)683-5312

E-mail: scholarships@nsbe.org

Web Site: http://www.nsbe.org/programs/schol_lockheed.php

To provide financial assistance to members of the National Society of Black Engineers (NSBE) who are majoring in fields related to engineering.

Title of Award: Lockheed Martin NSBE Corporate Scholarship Program **Area, Field, or Subject:** Computer and information sciences; Engineering, Aerospace/Aeronautical/Astronautical; Engineering, Computer; Engineering, Electrical; Engineering, Mechanical; Mathematics and mathematical sciences; Systems engineering **Level of Education for which Award is Granted:** Four Year College **Number Awarded:** 5 each year. **Funds Available:** The stipend is $2,000. **Duration:** 1 year.

Eligibility Requirements: This program is open to members of the society who are entering their junior or senior year in college and majoring in computer science, mathematics, or the following fields of engineering: aerospace, computer, electrical, mechanical, or systems. Applicants must have a GPA of 3.0 or higher and a demonstrated interest in employment with Lockheed Martin Corporation. Along with their application, they must submit a 250-word essay describing their career goals and how they can make a community and professional impact as a Lockheed Martin employee. **Deadline for Receipt:** January of each year.

4573 ■ NATIONAL SOCIETY OF BLACK ENGINEERS

Attn: Programs Department

1454 Duke Street

Alexandria, VA 22314

Tel: (703)549-2207

Fax: (703)683-5312

E-mail: scholarships@nsbe.org

Web Site: http://www.nsbe.org/programs/schol_fellows.php

To provide financial assistance to members of the National Society of Black Engineers (NSBE) who are working on a degree in engineering.

Title of Award: National Society of Black Engineers Fellows Scholarship Program **Area, Field, or Subject:** Engineering **Level of Education for which Award is Granted:** Graduate, Undergraduate **Number Awarded:** Varies each year; recently, 10 of these scholarships were awarded. **Funds Available:** The stipend is $1,000. **Duration:** 1 year.

Eligibility Requirements: This program is open to members of the society who are undergraduate or graduate engineering students. Applicants must have a GPA of 2.7 or higher. Selection is based on an essay; academic achievement; service to the society at the chapter,

regional, and/or national level; and other professional, campus, and community activities. **Deadline for Receipt:** January of each year.

4574 ■ NATIONAL SOCIETY OF BLACK ENGINEERS

Attn: Programs Department

1454 Duke Street

Alexandria, VA 22314

Tel: (703)549-2207

Fax: (703)683-5312

E-mail: scholarships@nsbe.org

Web Site: http://www.nsbe.org/programs/schol_fellows.php

To provide financial assistance to members of the National Society of Black Engineers (NSBE) who are working on a degree in engineering.

Title of Award: National Society of Black Engineers Major Sponsors Scholars Awards **Area, Field, or Subject:** Engineering **Level of Education for which Award is Granted:** Graduate, Undergraduate **Number Awarded:** Varies each year; recently, 15 of these scholarships were awarded. **Funds Available:** The stipend is $1,500. Travel, hotel accommodations, and registration to the national convention are also provided. **Duration:** 1 year.

Eligibility Requirements: This program is open to members of the society who are undergraduate or graduate engineering students. Applicants must have a GPA of 3.0 or higher. Selection is based on an essay; academic achievement; service to the society at the chapter, regional, and/or national level; and other professional, campus, and community activities. Applicants for the National Society of Black Engineers Fellows Scholarship Program who rank in the second of 3 tiers receive these awards. **Deadline for Receipt:** January of each year.

4575 ■ NATIONAL SOCIETY OF BLACK ENGINEERS

Attn: Programs Department

1454 Duke Street

Alexandria, VA 22314

Tel: (703)549-2207

Fax: (703)683-5312

E-mail: scholarships@nsbe.org

Web Site: http://www.nsbe.org/programs/nsbescholarships.php

To provide financial assistance to members of the National Society of Black Engineers (NSBE) who are working on an undergraduate or graduate degree in engineering or related subjects.

Title of Award: National Society of Black Engineers Scholarship Program **Area, Field, or Subject:** Engineering **Level of Education for which Award is Granted:** Graduate, Undergraduate **Number Awarded:** Varies each year. **Funds Available:** Stipends range up to $7,500. **Duration:** 1 year.

Eligibility Requirements: These scholarships are available to members of the society who are undergraduate or graduate students of engineering or closely-related subjects. The program includes many designated awards with varying GPA and other requirements. Selection is based on an essay; academic achievement; service to the society at the chapter, regional, and/or national level; and other professional, campus, and community activities. The Mike Shinn Distinguished Member of the Year Awards are presented to the highest-ranked female and male applicants **Deadline for Receipt:** January of each year. **Additional Information:** This program includes the following named awards: the Adobe Systems Computer Science Corporate Scholarships, the Delta Air Lines NSBE Scholarship, the Eli Lilly and Company Corporate Scholarship, the ExxonMobil Corporation NSBE Scholarships, the Freescale Semiconductor NSBE scholarship, the Fulfilling the Legacy Scholarships, the GE Lloyd Trotter African American Forum Scholarship, the Golden Torch Awards, the Johnson & Johnson NSBE Corporate Scholarship Program, the Lockheed Martin NSBE Corporate Scholarship Program, the Microsoft Corporation NSBE Scholarships, the National Society of Black Engineers Alumni Extension Technical Scholarships, the National Society of Black Engineers Fellows Scholarship Program, the Northrop Grumman NSBE Scholarships, and the Praxair NSBE Partnership Scholarship Program. Corporate sponsors include Adobe Systems Incorporated, Delta Air Lines, Eli Lilly and Company, ExxonMobil Corporation, Freescale Semiconductor, GE Fund, Johnson & Johnson Medical, Inc., Lockheed Martin Corporation, Microsoft Corporation, Northrop Grumman Corporation, and Praxair, Inc.

4576 ■ NATIONAL SOCIETY OF BLACK ENGINEERS
Attn: Programs Department
1454 Duke Street
Alexandria, VA 22314
Tel: (703)549-2207
Fax: (703)683-5312
E-mail: scholarships@nsbe.org
Web Site: http://www.nsbe.org/programs/schol_ng.php
To provide financial assistance to members of the National Society of Black Engineers (NSBE) who are working on an undergraduate degree in designated science and engineering fields.
Title of Award: Northrop Grumman NSBE Scholarships **Area, Field, or Subject:** Architecture, Naval; Computer and information sciences; Engineering, Aerospace/Aeronautical/Astronautical; Engineering, Chemical; Engineering, Civil; Engineering, Computer; Engineering, Electrical; Engineering, Industrial; Engineering, Mechanical; Engineering, Ocean; Mathematics and mathematical sciences; Physics **Level of Education for which Award is Granted:** Undergraduate **Number Awarded:** 5 each year. **Funds Available:** The stipend is $5,000. **Duration:** 1 year.
Eligibility Requirements: This program is open to members of the society who are U.S. citizens currently enrolled in college. Applicants must be majoring in computer science, information science, mathematics, naval architecture, physics, or the following engineering fields: aerospace, chemical, civil (structural), computer, electrical, industrial, manufacturing, marine, mechanical, or ocean. They must have a GPA of 3.0 or higher and demonstrate an interest in employment with Northrop Grumman Corporation. **Deadline for Receipt:** January of each year.

4577 ■ NATIONAL SOCIETY OF BLACK ENGINEERS
Attn: Programs Department
1454 Duke Street
Alexandria, VA 22314
Tel: (703)549-2207
Fax: (703)683-5312
E-mail: scholarships@nsbe.org
Web Site: http://www.nsbe.org/programs/schol_praxair.php
To provide financial assistance and work experience to members of the National Society of Black Engineers (NSBE) who are majoring in designated engineering fields.
Title of Award: Praxair NSBE Partnership Scholarship Program **Area, Field, or Subject:** Computer and information sciences; Engineering, Chemical; Engineering, Electrical; Engineering, Mechanical **Level of Education for which Award is Granted:** Four Year College, Graduate **Number Awarded:** 5 each year: 1 for a graduate students and 4 for undergraduates. **Funds Available:** The stipend is $5,000 for graduate students or $2,500 for undergraduates. **Duration:** 1 year.
Eligibility Requirements: This program is open to members of the society who are juniors, seniors, or graduate students majoring in chemical engineering, computer science, electrical engineering, or mechanical engineering. Applicants must have a GPA of 3.0 or higher and a willingness to accept a summer internship at a Praxair location. They must demonstrate leadership involvement on campus and/or in the community. Along with their application, they must submit a 1-page statement describing how they demonstrate their "passion for technology" outside the classroom with examples of how they share their enthusiasm in the community. **Deadline for Receipt:** January of each year. **Additional Information:** The recipients also receive paid travel and accommodations to the NSBE national convention. Praxair, Inc., which sponsors this program, may also offer them a summer internship.

4578 ■ NATIONAL SOCIETY OF BLACK ENGINEERS
Attn: Programs Department
1454 Duke Street
Alexandria, VA 22314
Tel: (703)549-2207
Fax: (703)683-5312
E-mail: scholarships@nsbe.org
Web Site: http://www.nsbe.org/programs/schol_mshinn.php

To provide financial assistance to members of the National Society of Black Engineers (NSBE) who are majoring in engineering.
Title of Award: Mike Shinn Distinguished Member of the Year Awards **Area, Field, or Subject:** Engineering **Level of Education for which Award is Granted:** Graduate, Undergraduate **Number Awarded:** 2 each year: 1 male and 1 female. **Funds Available:** The stipend is $7,500. Travel, hotel accommodations, and registration to the national convention are also provided. **Duration:** 1 year.
Eligibility Requirements: This program is open to members of the society who are undergraduate or graduate engineering students. Applicants must have a GPA of 3.5 or higher. Selection is based on an essay; academic achievement; service to the society at the chapter, regional, and/or national level; and other professional, campus, and community activities. The male and female applicants for the NSBE Fellows Scholarship Program who are judged most outstanding receive these awards. **Deadline for Receipt:** January of each year.

4579 ■ NATIONAL SOCIETY OF BLACK ENGINEERS
Attn: Programs Department
1454 Duke Street
Alexandria, VA 22314
Tel: (703)549-2207
Fax: (703)683-5312
E-mail: scholarships@nsbe.org
Web Site: http://www.nsbe.org/programs/schol_ge.php
To provide financial assistance to members of the National Society of Black Engineers (NSBE) who are studying engineering at a college or university east of the Mississippi River.
Title of Award: GE Lloyd Trotter African American Forum Scholarship **Area, Field, or Subject:** Computer and information sciences; Engineering, Electrical; Engineering, Industrial; Engineering, Mechanical; Information science and technology **Level of Education for which Award is Granted:** Four Year College **Number Awarded:** Varies each year, depending on the availability of funds. Recently, 16 of these scholarships were awarded. **Funds Available:** The stipend is $2,500. **Duration:** 1 year.
Eligibility Requirements: This program is open to members of the society who are undergraduate students majoring in computer science, electrical engineering, industrial engineering, information management/systems, or mechanical engineering at an accredited college or university located east of the Mississippi River. Applicants must be rising juniors or seniors with a GPA of 3.0 or higher. Selection is based on an essay; academic achievement; service to the society at the chapter, regional, and/or national level; and other professional, campus, and community activities. **Deadline for Receipt:** January of each year. **Additional Information:** This program is supported by General Electric employees with matching contributions from the GE Fund.

4580 ■ NATIONAL SOCIETY OF PROFESSIONAL ENGINEERS
Attn: Education Services
1420 King Street
Alexandria, VA 22314-2794
Tel: (703)684-2833
Fax: (703)836-4875
E-mail: jiglesias@nspe.org
Web Site: http://www.nspe.org/scholarships/sc1-hs.asp
To provide financial assistance for college to women who are high school seniors and are interested in preparing for a career in engineering.
Title of Award: Auxiliary Scholarship **Area, Field, or Subject:** Engineering **Level of Education for which Award is Granted:** Undergraduate **Number Awarded:** 1 each year. **Funds Available:** The award is $1,000 per year; funds are paid directly to the recipient's institution. **Duration:** 4 years.
Eligibility Requirements: This program is open to women who are high school seniors planning to study engineering in an EAC-ABET accredited college program. Applicants must have a GPA of 3.5 or higher, verbal SAT score of 600 or higher, and math SAT score of 700 or higher (or English ACT score of 29 or higher and math ACT score of 29 or higher): They must submit an essay (up to 500 words) on their interest in engineering, their major area of study and area of specialization, and the occupation they propose to pursue after graduation. Selection is based on GPA (20 points), the essay (20 points), extracurricular activities, including work experience and volunteer activities (25 points), financial need (5 points),

SAT/ACT scores (20 points), and the composite application (10 points). U.S. citizenship is required. **Deadline for Receipt:** November of each year. **Additional Information:** Recipients may attend any college or university, as long as the engineering curriculum is accredited by EAC-ABET.

4581 ■ NATIONAL SOCIETY OF PROFESSIONAL ENGINEERS

Attn: Education Services
1420 King Street
Alexandria, VA 22314-2794
Tel: (703)684-2833
Fax: (703)836-4875
E-mail: jiglesias@nspe.org
Web Site: http://www.nspe.org/scholarships/sc1-hs.asp
To provide financial assistance for college to members of underrepresented ethnic minority groups interested in preparing for a career in engineering.

Title of Award: Maureen L. and Howard N. Blitman, P.E. Scholarship to Promote Diversity in Engineering **Area, Field, or Subject:** Engineering **Level of Education for which Award is Granted:** Four Year College **Number Awarded:** 1 each year. **Funds Available:** The stipend is $5,000 per year; funds are paid directly to the recipient's institution. **Duration:** 1 year; nonrenewable.

Eligibility Requirements: This program is open to members of underrepresented ethnic minorities (African Americans, Hispanics, or Native Americans) who are high school seniors accepted into an ABET-accredited engineering program at a 4-year college or university. Applicants must have a GPA of 3.5 or higher, verbal SAT score of 600 or higher, and math SAT score of 700 or higher (or English ACT score of 29 or higher and math ACT score of 29 or higher). They must submit brief essays on an experience they consider significant to their interest in engineering, how their study of engineering will contribute to their long-term career plans, how their ethnic background has influenced their personal development and perceptions, and anything special about them that they would like the selection committee to know. Financial need is not considered in the selection process. U.S. citizenship is required. **Deadline for Receipt:** February of each year.

4582 ■ NATIONAL SOCIETY OF PROFESSIONAL ENGINEERS

Attn: Education Services
1420 King Street
Alexandria, VA 22314-2794
Tel: (703)684-2833
Fax: (703)836-4875
E-mail: jiglesias@nspe.org
Web Site: http://www.nspe.org/scholarships/sc1-hs.asp
To provide financial assistance for college to women who are high school seniors and interested in preparing for a career in engineering.

Title of Award: Virginia D. Henry Scholarship **Area, Field, or Subject:** Engineering **Level of Education for which Award is Granted:** Undergraduate **Number Awarded:** 1 each year. **Funds Available:** The stipend is $1,000 per year; funds are paid directly to the institution. **Duration:** 1 year.

Eligibility Requirements: This program is open to women who are high school seniors planning to study engineering in an EAC-ABET accredited college program. Applicants must have earned a GPA of 3.5 or higher, verbal SAT score of 600 or higher, and math SAT score of 700 or higher (or English ACT score of 29 or higher and math ACT score of 29 or higher). They must submit an essay (up to 500 words) on their interest in engineering, their major area of study and area of specialization, and the occupation they propose to pursue after graduation. Selection is based on GPA (20 points), the essay (20 points), extracurricular activities, including work experience and volunteer activities (25 points), financial need (5 points), SAT/ACT scores (20 points), and the composite application (10 points). U.S. citizenship is required. **Deadline for Receipt:** November of each year. **Additional Information:** Recipients may attend any college or university, as long as the engineering curriculum is accredited by EAC-ABET.

4583 ■ NATIONAL SOCIETY OF PROFESSIONAL ENGINEERS

Attn: Practice Division Manager
1420 King Street
Alexandria, VA 22314-2794
Tel: (703)684-2884
Fax: (703)836-4875
E-mail: egarcia@nspe.org
Web Site: http://www.nspe.org/scholarships/sc1-pei.asp
To provide financial assistance to undergraduate engineering students in Kansas and Missouri.

Title of Award: William R. Kimel, P.E. Engineering Scholarship **Area, Field, or Subject:** Engineering **Level of Education for which Award is Granted:** Four Year College **Number Awarded:** 1 each year. **Funds Available:** The stipend is $2,500. **Duration:** 1 year.

Eligibility Requirements: This program is open to residents of Kansas and Missouri who are enrolled as juniors in an ABET-accredited engineering program at a college or university in either of those states. Applicants must submit a 500-word essay on "My Engineering Career Goals and Aspirations to Achieve Them." Selection is based on that essay, GPA, internship and co-op experience, involvement in other activities, 2 faculty recommendations, and honors and awards.

4584 ■ NATIONAL SOCIETY OF PROFESSIONAL ENGINEERS

Attn: Practice Division Manager
1420 King Street
Alexandria, VA 22314-2794
Tel: (703)684-2884
Fax: (703)836-4875
E-mail: egarcia@nspe.org
Web Site: http://www.nspe.org/scholarships/sc1-pei.asp
To provide financial assistance to engineering students sponsored by a member of the Professional Engineers in Industry (PEI) division of the National Society of Professional Engineers (NSPE).

Title of Award: PEI Scholarship **Area, Field, or Subject:** Engineering **Level of Education for which Award is Granted:** Graduate, Undergraduate **Number Awarded:** 1 or more each year. **Funds Available:** The stipend is $2,500. **Duration:** 1 year.

Eligibility Requirements: This program is open to students who 1) have completed at least 2 semesters or 3 quarters of undergraduate engineering studies, or 2) are enrolled in graduate engineering study. Applicants must be sponsored by a PEI member. Their program must be accredited by the Accreditation Board for Engineering and Technology (ABET). Preference is given to the children and grandchildren of PEI members. Students attending a community or junior college must have applied as an undergraduate engineering student at an ABET-accredited program. Along with their application, they must submit a 500-word essay discussing their interest in engineering, the specific field of engineering that is being pursued, and the occupation they propose to follow after graduation. Selection is based on work experience (25 points), professional and technical society membership and activities (25 points), the essay (25 points), and activities and honors (25 points). **Deadline for Receipt:** May of each year. **Additional Information:** Information is also available from Neal J. Illenberg, 35 Garden Lane, Rochester, NY 14626.

4585 ■ NATIONAL SOCIETY OF PROFESSIONAL ENGINEERS

Attn: Educational Foundation
1420 King Street
Alexandria, VA 22314-2794
Tel: (703)684-2833
Fax: (703)836-4875
E-mail: jiglesias@nspe.org
Web Site: http://www.nspe.org/scholarships/sc-home.asp
To provide financial assistance for college to high school seniors interested in preparing for a career in engineering.

Title of Award: Paul H. Robbins Scholarship **Area, Field, or Subject:** Engineering **Level of Education for which Award is Granted:** Undergraduate **Number Awarded:** 1 each year. **Funds Available:** The stipend is $1,000 per year; funds are paid directly to the recipient's institution. **Duration:** 2 years.

Eligibility Requirements: This program is open to high school seniors planning to study engineering in an EAC-ABET accredited college program. Applicants must have earned a GPA of 3.0 or higher, verbal SAT score of 500 or higher, and math SAT score of 600 or higher (or English ACT score of 25 or higher and math ACT score of 29 or higher). They must submit an essay (up to 500 words) on their interest in engineering, their major area of study and area of specialization, and the occupation they propose to pursue after graduation. Selection is based on GPA (20 points), the essay (20 points), extracurricular activities, including work experience and volunteer activities (25 points), financial need (5 points), SAT/ACT scores (20 points), and the composite application (10 points). U.S. citizenship is required. **Deadline for Receipt:** February of each year. **Additional Information:** Recipients may attend any college or university, as long as the engineering curriculum is accredited by EAC-ABET.

4586 ■ NATIONAL SPACE CLUB
2025 M Street, N.W., Suite 800
Washington, DC 20036
Tel: (202)973-8661
E-mail: info@spaceclub.org
Web Site: http://www.spaceclub.org/programs.html
To provide financial assistance to undergraduate and graduate students interested in preparing for a career in space research or exploration.
Title of Award: Dr. Robert H. Goddard Scholarship **Area, Field, or Subject:** Aerospace sciences; Engineering; Science; Space and planetary sciences **Level of Education for which Award is Granted:** Four Year College, Graduate **Number Awarded:** 1 each year. **Funds Available:** The stipend is $10,000. The winner's way is paid to the Goddard Memorial Dinner (usually held in March), where the winner is introduced to the nation's leaders in science, government, and industry. **Duration:** 1 year.
Eligibility Requirements: Applicants must be U.S. citizens, at least a junior in college, and intending to pursue undergraduate or graduate studies in science or engineering. Selection is based on official college transcript, letters of recommendation from faculty, accomplishments demonstrating creativity and leadership, plans to prepare for a career in aerospace sciences or technology, and past research and participation in space-related science and engineering; financial need is considered but is not a primary factor. **Deadline for Receipt:** January of each year. **Additional Information:** Upon completion of the scholarship, the winner may be asked to prepare and deliver a brief report to the National Space Club.

4587 ■ NAVAL RESERVE ASSOCIATION
Attn: Educational Assistance Program
1619 King Street
Alexandria, VA 22314-2793
Tel: (703)548-5800; (866)672-4968
Fax: (866)683-3647
E-mail: admin@navy-reserve.org
Web Site: http://www.navy-reserve.org
To provide financial assistance for college to the children of members of the Naval Reserve Association.
Title of Award: Naval Reserve Association Scholarships **Area, Field, or Subject:** Engineering; General studies/Field of study not specified; Mathematics and mathematical sciences; Medicine **Level of Education for which Award is Granted:** Undergraduate **Number Awarded:** Varies each year; recently, 6 of these scholarships were awarded. **Funds Available:** The amounts of the stipends vary but recently averaged more than $4,000 per year. **Duration:** 1 year.
Eligibility Requirements: This program is open to the children of association members who are enrolled or accepted for enrollment at a college or university as a full-time student. Applicants must be U.S. citizens under 24 years of age. Preference is given to applicants who have demonstrated an interest in the "hard sciences" (e.g., mathematics, medicine, and engineering). **Deadline for Receipt:** April of each year.

4588 ■ NAVY LEAGUE OF THE UNITED STATES
Attn: Scholarships
2300 Wilson Boulevard
Arlington, VA 22201-3308
Tel: (703)528-1775
Free: 800-356-5760
Fax: (703)528-2333
E-mail: cjarvis@navyleague.org
Web Site: http://www.navyleague.org/scholarship
To provide financial assistance to dependent children of sea service personnel or veterans who are interested in majoring in science or engineering in college.
Title of Award: Planning Systems Incorporated Science and Engineering Scholarship **Area, Field, or Subject:** Engineering; Science **Level of**

Education for which Award is Granted: Undergraduate **Number Awarded:** 1 each year. **Funds Available:** The stipend is $2,500 per year. **Duration:** 4 years, provided the recipient maintains a GPA of 3.0 or higher.
Eligibility Requirements: This program is open to U.S. citizens who are dependent children of active or honorably discharged members of the U.S. sea service (including the Navy, Marine Corps, or Coast Guard). Applicants must be entering their freshman year of college and planning to major in science or engineering. Along with their application, they must submit transcripts, 2 letters of recommendation, SAT/ACT scores, documentation of financial need, proof of qualifying sea service duty, and a 1-page personal statement on why they should be considered for this scholarship. **Deadline for Receipt:** February of each year.

4589 ■ NEVADA SPACE GRANT CONSORTIUM
c/o University of Nevada at Reno
Mackay School of Mines Building, Room 308
MS 168
Reno, NV 89557
Tel: (775)784-6261
Fax: (775)327-2235
E-mail: nvsg@mines.unr.edu
Web Site: http://www.unr.edu/spacegrant
To provide financial assistance for space-related study to undergraduate students at institutions that are members of the University and Community College System of Nevada (UCCSN) and participate in the Nevada Space Grant Consortium (NSGC).
Title of Award: Nevada Space Grant Consortium Undergraduate Scholarship Program **Area, Field, or Subject:** Engineering; Mathematics and mathematical sciences; Science; Technology **Level of Education for which Award is Granted:** Undergraduate **Number Awarded:** Varies each year; recently, 13 of these awards were granted. **Funds Available:** The stipend is $2,500 per year. Funds may be used for tuition or registration fees. Funds may not be regarded as payment for research work or any other work. **Duration:** 1 year; may be renewed.
Eligibility Requirements: This program is open to undergraduate students at UCCSN member institutions. Applicants must be working on a degree in an aerospace-related field, including any science, mathematics, engineering, or technology discipline that is concerned with or likely to improve the understanding, assessment, development, and utilization of space. They must be U.S. citizens and enrolled full time. This program is part of the Space Grant program of the U.S. National Aeronautics and Space Administration (NASA), which encourages participation by members of underrepresented groups (African Americans, Hispanics, American Indians, Pacific Islanders, people with physical disabilities, and women of all races). Selection is based on the academic qualifications of the applicant, the quality of a career goal statement, and an assessment of the applicant's motivation for an aerospace career. **Deadline for Receipt:** March of each year. **Additional Information:** Funding for this program is provided by NASA.

4590 ■ NEW ENGLAND BOARD OF HIGHER EDUCATION
45 Temple Place
Boston, MA 02111
Tel: (617)357-9620
Fax: (617)338-1577
E-mail: pubinfo@nebhe.org
Web Site: http://www.nebhe.org/ETD/scholarship.html
To provide financial assistance to African Americans who are residents of New England and undergraduate students in science, mathematics, technology, or engineering.
Title of Award: Shaw's Coca-Cola Scholarship Grants for African-American Students **Area, Field, or Subject:** Engineering; Mathematics and mathematical sciences; Science; Technology **Level of Education for which Award is Granted:** Undergraduate **Number Awarded:** 12 each year. **Funds Available:** The stipend is $1,250. **Duration:** 1 year.
Eligibility Requirements: This program is open to African American residents of New England who are high school seniors or college freshmen or sophomores with a GPA of 3.0 or higher. Applicants must be attending or planning to attend a college or university in New England as a full-time student and major in science, mathematics, technology, or engineering. Both merit and need-based scholarships are available. U.S. citizenship or permanent resident status is required. **Additional Informa-**

tion: This program was established in recognition of Black History Month by Shaw's Supermarkets and the Coca-Cola Company.

4591 ■ NEW ENGLAND WATER WORKS ASSOCIATION
125 Hopping Brook
Holliston, MA 01746
Tel: (508)893-7979
Fax: (508)893-9898
Web Site: http://www.newwa.org
To provide financial assistance to undergraduate or graduate students from New England interested in working on a degree in civil or environmental engineering or in business management.
Title of Award: Francis X. Crowley Scholarship **Area, Field, or Subject:** Business administration; Engineering, Civil; Environmental science; Management **Level of Education for which Award is Granted:** Graduate, Undergraduate **Funds Available:** The stipend is $3,000. **Duration:** 1 year.
Eligibility Requirements: This program is open to members and student members of the New England section of the American Water Works Association or the New England Water Works Association. Applicants must be high school seniors, currently-enrolled college students, or graduate students. They must be majoring or planning to major in civil or environmental engineering or in business management. Along with their application, they must submit a 100-word essay on why they have chosen their field of study and if it will improve the environment, public health, or the water industry. Financial need is also considered in the selection process. **Deadline for Receipt:** July of each year. **Additional Information:** Information is also available from Thomas J. MacElhaney, Scholarship Committee Chair, National Concrete Tanks, P.O. Box 1431, Concord, MA 01742, (617) 512-0203, Fax: (978) 418-9156, E-mail: Tmacelhaney@concretetank.com.

4592 ■ NEW ENGLAND WATER WORKS ASSOCIATION
125 Hopping Brook
Holliston, MA 01746
Tel: (508)893-7979
Fax: (508)893-9898
Web Site: http://www.newwa.org
To provide financial assistance to undergraduate or graduate students from New England interested in working on a degree in civil or environmental engineering.
Title of Award: Elson T. Killam Memorial Scholarship **Area, Field, or Subject:** Engineering, Civil; Environmental science **Level of Education for which Award is Granted:** Graduate, Undergraduate **Funds Available:** The stipend is $1,500. **Duration:** 1 year.
Eligibility Requirements: This program is open to members and student members of the New England section of the American Water Works Association or the New England Water Works Association. Applicants must be high school seniors, currently-enrolled college students, or graduate students. They must be majoring or planning to major in civil or environmental engineering. Along with their application, they must submit a 100-word essay on why they have chosen their field of study and if it will improve the environment, public health, or the water industry. Financial need is also considered in the selection process. **Deadline for Receipt:** July of each year. **Additional Information:** Information is also available from Thomas J. MacElhaney, Scholarship Committee Chair, National Concrete Tanks, P.O. Box 1431, Concord, MA 01742, (617) 512-0203, Fax: (978) 418-9156, E-mail: Tmacelhaney@concretetank.com.

4593 ■ NEW ENGLAND WATER WORKS ASSOCIATION
125 Hopping Brook
Holliston, MA 01746
Tel: (508)893-7979
Fax: (508)893-9898
Web Site: http://www.newwa.org
To provide financial assistance to undergraduate or graduate students from New England interested in working on a degree in civil or environmental engineering, business, or a related science field.
Title of Award: Joseph Murphy Scholarship **Area, Field, or Subject:** Business administration; Engineering, Civil; Environmental science; Science **Level of Education for which Award is Granted:** Graduate, Undergraduate **Funds Available:** The stipend is $1,500. **Duration:** 1 year.

Eligibility Requirements: This program is open to members and student members of the New England section of the American Water Works Association or the New England Water Works Association. Applicants must be high school seniors, currently-enrolled college students, or graduate students. They must be majoring or planning to major in civil or environmental engineering, business, or a related science field. Along with their application, they must submit a 100-word essay on why they have chosen their field of study and if it will improve the environment, public health, or the water industry. Financial need is also considered in the selection process. **Deadline for Receipt:** July of each year. **Additional Information:** Information is also available from Thomas J. MacElhaney, Scholarship Committee Chair, National Concrete Tanks, P.O. Box 1431, Concord, MA 01742, (617) 512-0203, Fax: (978) 418-9156, E-mail: Tmacelhaney@concretetank.com.

4594 ■ NEW ENGLAND WATER WORKS ASSOCIATION
125 Hopping Brook
Holliston, MA 01746
Tel: (508)893-7979
Fax: (508)893-9898
Web Site: http://www.newwa.org
To provide financial assistance to undergraduate or graduate students from New England interested in working on a degree in civil engineering.
Title of Award: George E. Watters Memorial Scholarship **Area, Field, or Subject:** Engineering, Civil **Level of Education for which Award is Granted:** Graduate, Undergraduate **Funds Available:** The stipend is $5,000. **Duration:** 1 year.
Eligibility Requirements: This program is open to members and student members of the New England section of the American Water Works Association or the New England Water Works Association. Applicants must be high school seniors, currently-enrolled college students, or graduate students. They must be majoring or planning to major in civil engineering. Along with their application, they must submit a 100-word essay on why they have chosen their field of study and if it will improve the environment, public health, or the water industry. Financial need is also considered in the selection process. **Deadline for Receipt:** July of each year. **Additional Information:** Information is also available from Thomas J. MacElhaney, Scholarship Committee Chair, National Concrete Tanks, P.O. Box 1431, Concord, MA 01742, (617) 512-0203, Fax: (978) 418-9156, E-mail: Tmacelhaney@concretetank.com.

4595 ■ NEW JERSEY UTILITIES ASSOCIATION
50 West State Street, Suite 1117
Trenton, NJ 08608
Tel: (609)392-1000
Fax: (609)396-4231
Web Site: http://www.njua.org
To provide financial assistance to minority, female, and disabled high school seniors in New Jersey interested in majoring in selected subjects in college.
Title of Award: New Jersey Utilities Association Scholarships **Area, Field, or Subject:** Accounting; Biological and clinical sciences; Business administration; Chemistry; Engineering; Environmental conservation; Environmental science **Level of Education for which Award is Granted:** Undergraduate **Number Awarded:** 2 each year. **Funds Available:** The stipend is $1,500 per year. **Duration:** 4 years.
Eligibility Requirements: Eligible to apply for this scholarship are women, minorities (Black, Hispanic, American Indian/Alaska Native, or Asian American/Pacific Islander), and persons with disabilities who are high school seniors in New Jersey. They must be able to demonstrate financial need, be planning to enroll on a full-time basis at an institute of higher education, and be planning to work on a bachelor's degree in engineering, environmental science, chemistry, biology, business administration, or accounting. Children of employees of any New Jersey Utilities Association-member company are ineligible. Selection is based on overall academic excellence and demonstrated financial need. **Deadline for Receipt:** March of each year.

4596 ■ NORTH CENTRAL TEXAS COUNCIL OF GOVERNMENTS
Attn: Transportation Department
616 Six Flags Drive, Centerpoint Two
P.O. Box 5888
Arlington, TX 76005-5888

Tel: (817)695-9242
Fax: (817)640-7806
Web Site: http://www.nctcog.org/trans/admin/fellowship
To provide financial assistance to ethnic minorities, women, and economically disadvantaged persons who are interested in obtaining an undergraduate or graduate degree and work experience in a transportation-related field in Texas.
Title of Award: Transportation Fellowship Program **Area, Field, or Subject:** Engineering, Civil; Environmental conservation; Environmental science; Geography; Law; Management; Transportation; Urban affairs/design/planning **Level of Education for which Award is Granted:** Graduate, Undergraduate **Funds Available:** The stipend is $2,000. **Duration:** 1 year; may be renewed if the recipient maintains a GPA of 3.0 or higher.
Eligibility Requirements: This program is open to ethnic minorities (African Americans, Hispanics, American Indians, Alaskan Natives, Asians, and Pacific Islanders), women, and those who are economically disadvantaged. Only U.S. citizens or permanent residents may apply. They must attend or be willing to attend a college or university within the 16-county North Central Texas region as an undergraduate or graduate student. Applicants must have a GPA of 2.5 or higher. They may be enrolled full or part time, but they must be majoring in a designated transportation-related field: transportation planning, transportation or civil engineering, urban and regional planning, transportation/environmental sciences, transportation law, urban or spatial geography, logistics, geographic information systems, or transportation management. Selection is based on financial need, interest in a professional career in transportation, and the ability to complete the program. **Deadline for Receipt:** March of each year. **Additional Information:** These fellowships are financed by the Federal Highway Administration, Federal Transit Administration, and the Texas Department of Transportation, in conjunction with local governments in north central Texas. An important part of the fellowship is an internship with a local agency (city or county), school, or transportation agency.

4597 ■ OAK RIDGE INSTITUTE FOR SCIENCE AND EDUCATION

Attn: Science and Engineering Education
P.O. Box 117
Oak Ridge, TN 37831-0117
Tel: (865)576-8239
Fax: (865)241-5219
E-mail: igrid.gregory@orau.gov
Web Site: http://www.orau.gov/orise.htm
To provide financial assistance and summer research experience to undergraduate students who are working on a degree in a field of interest to the Department of Homeland Security (DHS).
Title of Award: Department of Homeland Security Undergraduate Scholarships **Area, Field, or Subject:** Agricultural sciences; Biological and clinical sciences; Communications; Computer and information sciences; Engineering; Information science and technology; Mathematics and mathematical sciences; Physical sciences; Psychology; Public administration; Religion; Social sciences; Writing **Level of Education for which Award is Granted:** Undergraduate **Number Awarded:** Approximately 50 each year. **Funds Available:** This program provides a stipend of $1,000 per month during the academic year and $5,000 for the internship plus full payment of tuition and mandatory fees. **Duration:** 2 academic years plus 10 weeks during the intervening summer.
Eligibility Requirements: This program is open to 1) full-time students who are in their second year of college attendance as of the application deadline; and 2) part-time students who have completed at least 45 but no more than 60 semester hours as of the application deadline. Applicants must be majoring in the agricultural sciences, biological and life sciences, computer and information sciences, engineering, mathematics, physical sciences, psychology, social sciences, or selected humanities (religious studies, cultural studies, public policy, advocacy, communications, or science writing). They must have a GPA of 3.3 or higher. Along with their application, they must submit 2 statements on 1) their educational and professional goals, the kinds of research they are interested in conducting, specific questions that interest them, and how they became interested in them; and 2) how they think their interests, talents, and initiative would contribute to make the homeland safer and secure. Selection is based on those statements, academic record, references, and SAT or ACT scores. As part of their program, they must be interested in participating in sum-

mer research and development activities at a DHS-designated facility. U.S. citizenship is required. **Deadline for Receipt:** January of each year. **Additional Information:** This program, established in 2003, is funded by DHS and administered by Oak Ridge Institute for Science and Education (ORISE). Recipients must enroll full time.

4598 ■ OAK RIDGE INSTITUTE FOR SCIENCE AND EDUCATION

Attn: Science and Engineering Education
P.O. Box 117
Oak Ridge, TN 37831-0117
Tel: (865)241-8240
Fax: (865)241-5219
E-mail: hollingsscholarship@orau.gov
Web Site: http://www.orau.gov/orise.htm
To provide financial assistance and summer research experience to upper-division students who are working on a degree in a field of interest to the National Oceanic and Atmospheric Administration (NOAA).
Title of Award: Ernest F. Hollings Scholarship Program **Area, Field, or Subject:** Agricultural sciences; Behavioral sciences; Biological and clinical sciences; Computer and information sciences; Education; Engineering; Information science and technology; Mathematics and mathematical sciences; Physical sciences; Social sciences **Level of Education for which Award is Granted:** Four Year College **Number Awarded:** Approximately 100 each year. **Funds Available:** This program provides a stipend of $8,000 per academic year and $650 per week during the internship, a housing subsidy and limited travel reimbursement for round-trip transportation to the internship site, and travel expenses to the scholarship program conference at the completion of the internship. **Duration:** 2 academic years plus 10 weeks during the intervening summer.
Eligibility Requirements: This program is open to full-time students entering their junior year at an accredited college or university in the United States or its territories. Applicants must be majoring in a discipline related to oceanic and atmospheric science, research, technology, and education, and supportive of the purposes of NOAA's programs and mission (e.g., biological, life, and agricultural sciences; computer and information sciences; engineering; mathematics; physical sciences; social and behavioral sciences; or teacher education). They must have a GPA of 3.0 or higher. As part of their program, they must be interested in participating in summer research and development activities at NOAA headquarters (Silver Spring, Maryland) or field centers. U.S. citizenship is required. **Deadline for Receipt:** May of each year. **Additional Information:** This program, established in 2005, is funded by NOAA and administered by Oak Ridge Institute for Science and Education (ORISE).

4599 ■ OAK RIDGE INSTITUTE FOR SCIENCE AND EDUCATION

Attn: Science and Engineering Education
P.O. Box 117
Oak Ridge, TN 37831-0117
Tel: (865)576-9279
Fax: (865)241-5220
E-mail: coxre@orau.gov
Web Site: http://www.orau.gov/orise.htm
To provide financial assistance and research experience to undergraduate students at minority serving institutions who are majoring in scientific fields of interest to the National Oceanic and Atmospheric Administration (NOAA).
Title of Award: National Oceanic and Atmospheric Administration Educational Partnership Program with Minority Serving Institutions Undergraduate Scholarships **Area, Field, or Subject:** Atmospheric science; Biological and clinical sciences; Cartography/Surveying; Chemistry; Computer and information sciences; Engineering; Environmental conservation; Environmental science; Geography; Mathematics and mathematical sciences; Meteorology; Photogrammetry; Physical sciences; Physics **Level of Education for which Award is Granted:** Four Year College **Number Awarded:** 10 each year. **Funds Available:** This program provides payment of tuition and fees (to a maximum of $4,000 per year) and a stipend during the internship of $650 per week. **Duration:** 1 academic year and 2 summers.
Eligibility Requirements: This program is open to juniors and seniors at minority serving institutions, including Hispanic Serving Institutions (HSIs), Historically Black Colleges and Universities (HBCUs), and Tribal Colleges and Universities (TCUs). Applicants must be majoring in atmospheric science, biology, cartography, chemistry, computer science, engineering,

environmental science, geodesy, geography, marine science, mathematics, meteorology, photogrammetry, physical science, physics, or remote sensing. They must also be interested in participating in a research internship at a NOAA site. U.S. citizenship is required. **Deadline for Receipt:** January of each year. **Additional Information:** This program is funded by NOAA through an interagency agreement with the U.S. Department of Energy and administered by Oak Ridge Institute for Science and Education (ORISE).

4600 ■ OAK RIDGE INSTITUTE FOR SCIENCE AND EDUCATION

Attn: Science and Engineering Education
P.O. Box 117
Oak Ridge, TN 37831-0117
Tel: (865)576-9279
Fax: (865)241-5219
E-mail: coxre@orau.gov
Web Site: http://www.orau.gov/orise.htm

To provide scholarships and internship experience to students at Historically Black Colleges and Universities (HBCUs) working on undergraduate degrees in areas related to the Office of Civilian Radioactive Waste Management (OCRWM).

Title of Award: Office of Civilian Radioactive Waste Management Historically Black Colleges and Universities Undergraduate Scholarship Program **Area, Field, or Subject:** Energy-related areas; Engineering; Mathematics and mathematical sciences; Nuclear science; Science; Social sciences **Level of Education for which Award is Granted:** Four Year College **Number Awarded:** 10 each year. **Funds Available:** The program provides for payment of tuition and fees (to a maximum of $8,000) plus a monthly stipend of $600. **Duration:** 2 years.

Eligibility Requirements: This program is open to juniors and seniors at HBCUs who are working on a degree in science, mathematics, engineering, engineering technology, or social sciences. As part of their program, they must be willing to participate in an internship at a U.S. Department of Energy (DOE) site conducting activities for the OCRWM. **Deadline for Receipt:** January of each year. **Additional Information:** This program is funded by DOE/OCRWM and administered by Oak Ridge Institute for Science and Education (ORISE).

4601 ■ OHIO SPACE GRANT CONSORTIUM

c/o Ohio Aerospace Institute
22800 Cedar Point Road
Cleveland, OH 44142
Tel: (440)962-3032
Free: 800-828-OSGC
Fax: (440)962-3057
E-mail: osgc@oai.org
Web Site: http://www.osgc.org/Scholarship.html

To provide financial assistance to students at selected community colleges in Ohio who are interested in continuing their studies at a 4-year university in the state that is a member of the Ohio Space Grant Consortium (OSGC).

Title of Award: Ohio Space Grant Consortium Community College Scholarship **Area, Field, or Subject:** Computer and information sciences; Electronics; Engineering; Mathematics and mathematical sciences; Science; Technology **Level of Education for which Award is Granted:** Two Year College **Number Awarded:** 2 each year. **Funds Available:** The stipend is $1,000. **Duration:** 1 year; nonrenewable.

Eligibility Requirements: This program is open to U.S. citizens who are students at designated community colleges in Ohio, normally enrolled full time in their freshman year (although applications are accepted from part-time students demonstrating academic merit and from students at any stage of their college career). Applicants must be enrolled in a program that includes course work related to an understanding of or interest in technological fields supporting aerospace, e.g. associate degrees related to mathematics, science, and such advanced technology fields as engineering, computers, electronics, and industrial technology. They must also have a GPA of 3.0 or higher and plans to continue their education in a 4-year program at an OSGC-member university. Along with their application, they must submit college transcripts, 2 letters of recommendation, and a brief resume of their education, significant accomplishments, work experience, educational and professional goals, and any other relevant information. Women, underrepresented minorities, and persons with disabilities are particularly encouraged to apply. **Deadline for**

Receipt: October of each year. **Additional Information:** These scholarships are funded through the National Space Grant College and Fellowship Program administered by the National Aeronautics and Space Administration (NASA), with matching funds provided by the member colleges, the Ohio Aerospace Institute, and private industry. The participating institutions include Columbus State Community College, Cuyahoga Community College, Lorain County Community College, Owens Community College, Lakeland Community College, and Terra Community College. OSGC member institutions include the Air Force Institute of Technology, University of Akron, Case Western Reserve University, Central State University, University of Cincinnati, Cleveland State University, University of Dayton, Ohio State University, Ohio University, University of Toledo, Wilberforce University, and Wright State University.

4602 ■ OHIO SPACE GRANT CONSORTIUM

c/o Ohio Aerospace Institute
22800 Cedar Point Road
Cleveland, OH 44142
Tel: (440)962-3032
Free: 800-828-OSGC
Fax: (440)962-3057
E-mail: osgc@oai.org
Web Site: http://www.osgc.org/Scholarship.html

To provide financial assistance to students in their junior year at selected universities in Ohio who wish to working on a bachelor's degree in an aerospace-related field.

Title of Award: Ohio Space Grant Consortium Junior Scholarships **Area, Field, or Subject:** Astronomy and astronomical sciences; Biological and clinical sciences; Chemistry; Computer and information sciences; Engineering, Aerospace/Aeronautical/Astronautical; Engineering, Chemical; Engineering, Civil; Engineering, Computer; Engineering, Electrical; Engineering, Industrial; Engineering, Materials; Engineering, Mechanical; Engineering, Petroleum; Geography; Geology; Materials research/science; Mathematics and mathematical sciences; Physics; Space and planetary sciences **Level of Education for which Award is Granted:** Four Year College **Number Awarded:** Varies each year; recently, 20 of these scholarships were awarded. **Funds Available:** The stipend is $2,000. **Duration:** 1 year; recipients may apply for a senior scholarship if they maintain satisfactory academic performance and good progress on their research project.

Eligibility Requirements: These scholarships are available to U.S. citizens who expect to complete within 2 years the requirements for a bachelor of science degree in an aerospace-related discipline (aeronautical engineering, aerospace engineering, astronomy, biology, chemical engineering, chemistry, civil engineering, computer engineering and science, control engineering, electrical engineering, engineering mechanics, geography, geology, industrial engineering, manufacturing engineering, materials science and engineering, mathematics, mechanical engineering, petroleum engineering, physics, and systems engineering). Applicants must be attending a member university of the Ohio Space Grant Consortium (OSGC) or another participating university. They must propose and initiate a research project on campus under the guidance of a faculty member. Along with their application, they must submit a 1-page personal objective statement that discusses their career goals and anticipated benefits to be derived from this program. Women, underrepresented minorities, and persons with disabilities are particularly encouraged to apply. **Deadline for Receipt:** February of each year. **Additional Information:** These scholarships are funded through the National Space Grant College and Fellowship Program administered by the National Aeronautics and Space Administration (NASA), with matching funds provided by the member universities, the Ohio Aerospace Institute, and private industry. The OSGC member universities include the University of Akron, Case Western Reserve University, Central State University, University of Cincinnati, Cleveland State University, University of Dayton, Ohio State University, Ohio University, University of Toledo, Wilberforce University, and Wright State University. Other participating universities are Cedarville University, Marietta College (petroleum engineering), Miami University (manufacturing engineering), Ohio Northern University (mechanical engineering), and Youngstown State University (mechanical and industrial engineering). Recipients are required to attend the annual spring research symposium sponsored by the OSGC and present a poster on their research project.

4603 ■ OREGON STUDENT ASSISTANCE COMMISSION

Attn: Grants and Scholarships Division
1500 Valley River Drive, Suite 100
Eugene, OR 97401-2146
Tel: (541)687-7395
Free: 800-452-8807
Fax: (541)687-7419
E-mail: awardinfo@mercury.osac.state.or.us
Web Site: http://www.osac.state.or.us
To provide financial assistance to Oregon residents who are working on a college degree in computer science or engineering.
Title of Award: Mentor Graphics Scholarships **Area, Field, or Subject:** Computer and information sciences; Engineering, Computer; Engineering, Electrical **Level of Education for which Award is Granted:** Four Year College **Number Awarded:** Varies each year; recently, 4 of these scholarships were awarded. **Funds Available:** The stipend is at least $2,000. **Duration:** 1 year.

Eligibility Requirements: This program is open to residents of Oregon who are U.S. citizens or permanent residents. Applicants must be full-time students in their junior or senior year of college and majoring in electrical engineering or computer science/engineering. Preference is given to female, African American, Native American, or Hispanic applicants. Financial need must be demonstrated. **Deadline for Receipt:** February of each year.

4604 ■ OREGON UNIVERSITY SYSTEM

Attn: Chancellor's Office, Industry Affairs Division
Capital Center, Suite 1065
18640 N.W. Walker Road
Beaverton, OR 97006-8966
Tel: (503)725-2918
Fax: (503)775-2921
E-mail: aeaschol@ous.edu
Web Site: http://www.ous.edu/ecs/scholarships.html
To provide financial assistance to Oregon high school seniors interested in studying designated computer and engineering fields at selected public universities in the state.
Title of Award: AeA Technology Scholarship Program **Area, Field, or Subject:** Biochemistry; Chemistry; Computer and information sciences; Engineering; Engineering, Chemical; Engineering, Computer; Engineering, Electrical; Engineering, Industrial; Engineering, Mechanical; Mathematics and mathematical sciences; Physics **Level of Education for which Award is Granted:** Undergraduate **Number Awarded:** Varies each year; recently, this program awarded 25 new scholarships. **Funds Available:** The stipend is $2,500 per year. **Duration:** 1 year; may be renewed up to 3 additional years if the recipient maintains a GPA of 3.0 or higher.

Eligibility Requirements: This program is open to seniors graduating from high schools in Oregon who plan to attend Eastern Oregon University, Oregon Institute of Technology, Oregon State University, Portland State University, Southern Oregon University, Western Oregon University, or the University of Oregon. Applicants must be planning to major in biochemistry, chemical engineering, chemistry, computer engineering, computer science, electrical engineering, electronic engineering, engineering technology, industrial engineering, mathematics, mechanical engineering, or physics (not all majors are available at each institution). Women and ethnic minorities underrepresented in the technology industry (Black Americans, Hispanic Americans, and Native Americans) are strongly encouraged to apply. Selection is based on academic performance; college entrance examination scores; mathematics, science, and technology course work; achievements; leadership; civic participation; interests; employment; insight into and commitment to a career in technology; and communication skill. **Deadline for Receipt:** March of each year. **Additional Information:** This program was established in 1999 by Intel, which offered it to the Oregon Council of the AeA (formerly American Electronics Association) in the following year.

Currently, Intel and other Oregon AeA member companies (such as Xerox and Hewlett Packard) provide ongoing support.

4605 ■ PARENTS, FAMILIES AND FRIENDS OF LESBIANS AND GAYS

Attn: National Scholarships Program
1726 M Street, N.W., Suite 400
Washington, DC 20036
Tel: (202)467-8180
Fax: (202)467-8194
E-mail: schools@pflag.org
Web Site: http://www.pflag.org
To provide financial assistance for college to high school seniors and recent graduates interested in a business-related career who have a connection to Parents, Families and Friends of Lesbians and Gays (PFLAG).
Title of Award: PFLAG Scholarships for Science, Engineering, Business or Finance **Area, Field, or Subject:** Business administration; Engineering; Finance; Science **Level of Education for which Award is Granted:** Undergraduate **Number Awarded:** 13 each year. **Funds Available:** The stipend is $1,000. **Duration:** 1 year; nonrenewable.

Eligibility Requirements: This program is open to high school seniors and prior-year graduates who have not attended college. Applicants must have applied to an accredited high education institution to work on 1) an associate degree leading to transfer to complete a bachelor's degree in science, engineering, business, or finance, or 2) a bachelor's degree in science, engineering, business, or finance at a 4-year college or university. They must self-identify either as a gay, lesbian, bisexual, or transgender (GLBT) person or as a supporter of GLBT people. Along with their application, they must submit a high school transcript showing a GPA of 3.0 or higher, 2 letters of recommendation, and a 2-page essay discussing either their life as an LGBT student or how they have been involved with and supported the LGBT community. Financial need is also considered in the selection process. **Deadline for Receipt:** February of each year. **Additional Information:** This scholarship was first offered in 2004.

4606 ■ PENNSYLVANIA HIGHER EDUCATION ASSISTANCE AGENCY

Attn: State Grant and Special Programs Division
1200 North Seventh Street
Harrisburg, PA 17102-1444
Tel: (717)720-2800
Free: 800-692-7392
E-mail: info@pheaa.org
Web Site: http://www.pheaa.org/specialprograms/index.shtml
To provide scholarship/loans to residents of Pennsylvania who are interested in studying approved science or technology fields at a public or private college or university in the state and then working in the state after graduation.
Title of Award: Pennsylvania SciTech Scholarships **Area, Field, or Subject:** Engineering; Science; Technology **Level of Education for which Award is Granted:** Four Year College **Number Awarded:** Varies each year. **Funds Available:** Scholarships provide up to $3,000 per year based on total educational costs (tuition and mandatory fees, room and board, and an academic year allowance of $700 for books). **Duration:** Up to 3 years, as long as the recipient maintains a GPA of 3.0 or higher and full-time enrollment.

Eligibility Requirements: This program is open to residents of Pennsylvania who graduated from a high school in the state and are currently enrolled full time as at least a sophomore at an approved Pennsylvania public or private college or university. Applicants must be working on a bachelor's degree in an approved science or technology field with a GPA of 3.0 or higher. They must apply for a federal Pell Grant and a Pennsylvania State Grant, but financial need is not considered in the selection process. Funds are awarded on a first-come, first-served basis. **Deadline for Receipt:** December of each year. **Additional Information:** This program, established in 1999 as part of the New Economy Technology Scholarship (NETS) program, is administered jointly by the Pennsylvania Department of Education (PDE) and the Pennsylvania Higher Education Assistance Agency (PHEAA). The PDE designates the approved fields of study in consultation with the Team Pennsylvania State Workforce Investment Board. Recipients are required to 1) complete an approved internship or relevant work experience in a technology-intensive field with a Pennsylvania company prior to receiving a degree; and 2) begin full-time employment in the state within 1 year after completion of studies, 1 year for each year that the grant was awarded. If the student fails to satisfy both of those requirements, the scholarship grant reverts to a loan and must be repaid with interest.

4607 ■ PENNSYLVANIA HIGHER EDUCATION ASSISTANCE AGENCY

Attn: State Grant and Special Programs Division
1200 North Seventh Street
Harrisburg, PA 17102-1444
Tel: (717)720-2800
Free: 800-692-7392
E-mail: info@pheaa.org
Web Site: http://www.pheaa.org/specialprograms/index.shtml
To provide scholarship/loans to residents of Pennsylvania who are interested in studying approved science or technology fields at a community college in the state and then working in the state after graduation. **Title of Award:** Pennsylvania Technology Scholarships **Area, Field, or Subject:** Engineering; Science; Technology **Level of Education for which Award is Granted:** Two Year College, Vocational/Occupational **Number Awarded:** Varies each year. **Funds Available:** For full-time students, scholarships provide up to $1,000 per year based on total educational costs (tuition and mandatory fees, room and board, and an academic year allowance of $700 for books). Part-time students receive up to 20% of their tuition and mandatory fees or $1,000, whichever is less. **Duration:** 1 year; may be renewed for 1 additional year if the recipient maintains a GPA of 3.0 or higher. **Eligibility Requirements:** This program is open to residents of Pennsylvania who graduated from a high school in the state and are currently enrolled at an approved Pennsylvania community college, independent 2-year college, or licensed technical institute. Applicants must be enrolled in an approved science or technology field with a GPA of 3.0 or higher. They must apply for a federal Pell Grant and a Pennsylvania State Grant, but financial need is not considered in the selection process. Funds are awarded on a first-come, first-served basis. **Deadline for Receipt:** December of each year. **Additional Information:** This program, established in 1999 as part of the New Economy Technology Scholarship (NETS) program, is administered jointly by the Pennsylvania Department of Education (PDE) and the Pennsylvania Higher Education Assistance Agency (PHEAA). The PDE designates the approved fields of study in consultation with the Team Pennsylvania State Workforce Investment Board. Recipients are required to begin full-time employment in the state within 1 year after completion of studies, 1 year for each year that the grant was awarded. If the student fails to satisfy that requirement, the scholarship grant reverts to a loan and must be repaid with interest.

4608 ■ PENNSYLVANIA SOCIETY OF PROFESSIONAL ENGINEERS

Attn: Pennsylvania Engineering Foundation
908 North Second Street
Harrisburg, PA 17102
Tel: (717)441-6051
Fax: (717)236-2046
E-mail: pspeinfo@pspe.org
Web Site: http://www.pspe.org/scholarships.shtml
To provide financial assistance to Pennsylvania high school seniors who are interested in studying engineering at a college or university in the state. **Title of Award:** PEF Grant **Area, Field, or Subject:** Engineering **Level of Education for which Award is Granted:** Undergraduate **Number Awarded:** 1 each year. **Funds Available:** The stipend is $1,000. **Duration:** 1 year; nonrenewable. **Eligibility Requirements:** This program is open to graduating seniors at high schools in Pennsylvania. Applicants must be planning to enroll in an engineering program at an ABET-accredited college or university in the state. They must have a GPA of 3.6 or higher and minimum scores of 700 on SAT mathematics and 600 on SAT verbal. U.S. citizenship in required. Interviews are included in the selection process. **Deadline for Receipt:** Each local chapter sets its own deadline. Students who submit their application to the state PEF office must do so by April of each year. **Additional Information:** Scholarships are awarded by 22 local chapters of the Pennsylvania Engineering Foundation (PEF) in the state. Applications are available from the foundation, but they must be submitted to the local

chapter where the student lives. Students who live in counties with no local chairperson may submit their applications directly to the PEF.

4609 ■ PENNSYLVANIA SOCIETY OF PROFESSIONAL ENGINEERS

Attn: Pennsylvania Engineering Foundation
908 North Second Street
Harrisburg, PA 17102
Tel: (717)441-6051
Fax: (717)236-2046
E-mail: pspeinfo@pspe.org
Web Site: http://www.pspe.org/scholarships.shtml
To provide financial assistance to female Pennsylvania high school seniors who are interested in studying engineering at a college or university in the state. **Title of Award:** Pennsylvania State Council of Auxiliaries Grant **Area, Field, or Subject:** Engineering **Level of Education for which Award is Granted:** Undergraduate **Number Awarded:** 1 each year. **Funds Available:** The stipend is $1,000. **Duration:** 1 year; nonrenewable. **Eligibility Requirements:** This program is open to females graduating from high schools in Pennsylvania. Applicants must be planning to enroll in an engineering program at an ABET-accredited college or university in the state. They must have a GPA of 3.6 or higher and minimum scores of 700 on SAT mathematics and 600 on SAT verbal. U.S. citizenship in required. Interviews are included in the selection process. **Deadline for Receipt:** Each local chapter sets its own deadline. Students who submit their application to the state PEF office must do so by April of each year. **Additional Information:** Scholarships are awarded by 22 local chapters of the Pennsylvania Engineering Foundation (PEF) in the state. Applications are available from the sponsor, but they must be submitted to the local chapter where the student lives. Students who live in counties with no local chairperson may submit their applications directly to the PEF. This program is sponsored by the Pennsylvania State Council of Auxiliaries (PSCA).

4610 ■ PENNSYLVANIA SOCIETY OF PROFESSIONAL ENGINEERS

Attn: Pennsylvania Engineering Foundation
908 North Second Street
Harrisburg, PA 17102
Tel: (717)441-6051
Fax: (717)236-2046
E-mail: pspeinfo@pspe.org
Web Site: http://www.pspe.org/scholarships.shtml
To provide financial assistance to Pennsylvania high school seniors who are interested in studying engineering at a college or university in the state. **Title of Award:** Professional Engineers in Private Practice Grant **Area, Field, or Subject:** Engineering **Level of Education for which Award is Granted:** Undergraduate **Number Awarded:** 1 each year. **Funds Available:** The stipend is $1,000. **Duration:** 1 year; nonrenewable. **Eligibility Requirements:** This program is open to graduating seniors at high schools in Pennsylvania. Applicants must be planning to enroll in an engineering program at an ABET-accredited college or university in the state. They must have a GPA of 3.6 or higher and minimum scores of 700 on SAT mathematics and 600 on SAT verbal. U.S. citizenship in required. Interviews are included in the selection process. **Deadline for Receipt:** Each local chapter sets its own deadline. Students who submit their application to the state PEF office must do so by April of each year. **Additional Information:** Scholarships are awarded by 22 local chapters of the Pennsylvania Engineering Foundation (PEF) in the state. Applications are available from the foundation, but they must be submitted to the local chapter where the student lives. Students who live in counties with no local chairperson may submit their applications directly to the PEF.

4611 ■ PLASTICS INSTITUTE OF AMERICA

c/o University of Massachusetts at Lowell
Attn: Plastics Pioneers Association
333 Aiken Street
Lowell, MA 01854
Tel: (978)934-3130
Fax: (978)458-4141
E-mail: info@plasticsinstitute.org
Web Site: http://www.plasticsinstitute.org/scholarships.php

To provide financial assistance to college students taking courses related to plastics technology.
Title of Award: Plastics Pioneers Association Scholarships **Area, Field, or Subject:** Chemistry; Engineering, Materials; Technology **Level of Education for which Award is Granted:** Undergraduate **Number Awarded:** Varies each year; recently, 15 of these scholarships were awarded. **Funds Available:** The stipend is $1,500 per year. **Duration:** 1 year; may be renewed for 1 additional year.
Eligibility Requirements: This program is open to students enrolled in a 2-year, 4-year, or certificate program. Applicants must be studying plastics/polymer science, engineering, technology, and management. They must be U.S. citizens and interested in preparing for a career in the plastics industry. Selection is based on academic record. extracurricular activities, recommendations, and an essay on their interest in a career in plastics. **Deadline for Receipt:** March of each year. **Additional Information:** This program is funded by the Education Fund of the Plastics Pioneers Association and administered by the Plastics Institute of America.

4612 ■ PROFESSIONAL CONSTRUCTION ESTIMATORS ASSOCIATION

Attn: Wilson Memorial Scholarship Foundation
P.O. Box 680336
Charlotte, NC 28216-0336
Tel: (704)987-9978; 877-521-7232
E-mail: pcea@pcea.org
Web Site: http://www.pcea.org/scholarships.cfm
To provide financial assistance to high school seniors and currently-enrolled college students in selected states interested in working on a degree in construction or engineering.
Title of Award: Ted G. Wilson Memorial Scholarship **Area, Field, or Subject:** Construction; Engineering **Level of Education for which Award is Granted:** Undergraduate **Number Awarded:** 5 each year; 1 from each of the states with a PCEA chapter. **Funds Available:** The stipend is $1,500. **Duration:** 1 year.
Eligibility Requirements: This program is open to high school seniors, college freshmen, college sophomores, and college juniors who are attending or planning to attend a college or university full time and work on a bachelor's degree in construction or engineering (to prepare for a career in the construction industry). Applicants must reside or attend school in a state where the Professional Construction Estimators Association (PCEA) has an established chapter; currently, those are limited to Florida, Georgia, North Carolina, South Carolina, and Virginia. Along with their application, they must submit 2 recommendations, and an official transcript. Finalists may be interviewed. Selection is based on academic ability, financial need, and desire to enter the construction industry. **Deadline for Receipt:** March of each year.

4613 ■ PROFESSIONAL ENGINEERS OF COLORADO

11166 Huron Street, Suite 27
Denver, CO 80234
Tel: (303)480-1160
Fax: (303)458-0002
Web Site: http://www.pec.org/bridgebuild/contest.shtml
To recognize and reward, with college scholarships, high school students in Colorado who construct model bridges that meet technical specifications.
Title of Award: Colorado High School Bridge Building Contest **Area, Field, or Subject:** Engineering, Civil **Level of Education for which Award is Granted:** Undergraduate **Number Awarded:** Varies each year; recently, the prizes included 2 college scholarships. **Funds Available:** Prizes include $1,000 college scholarships. **Duration:** The competition is held annually.
Eligibility Requirements: This competition is open to students at high schools in Colorado. Entrants must construct a model bridge that conforms to the technical specifications of the contest. The bridges are then tested for efficiency and the highest scoring entries receive the prizes. **Deadline for Receipt:** The testing takes place in February of each year. Students may either travel to the testing site in Denver or mail in their models. **Additional Information:** Information is also available from the Project Manager, John J. Migliaccio, JR Engineering, LLC, 6020 Greenwood Plaza Boulevard, Greenwood Village, CO 80111, (303) 740-9393, E-mail: jmigliaccio@jrengineering.com. The competition is

sponsored by the Professional Engineers of Colorado, the Denver Office of the U.S. Bureau of Reclamation, and the American Council of Engineering Companies of Colorado (ACEC/CO).

4614 ■ RHODE ISLAND SPACE GRANT

c/o Brown University.
Lincoln Field Building
Box 1846
Providence, RI 02912-1846
Tel: (401)863-2889
Fax: (401)863-1292
E-mail: RISpaceGrant@brown.edu
Web Site: http://www.planetary.brown.edu/RI_Space_Grant
To provide financial assistance to undergraduate students at institutions that are members of the Rhode Island Space Grant Consortium (RISGC) who are interested in a career in a space-related field of science, mathematics, or engineering.
Title of Award: Rhode Island Space Grant Undergraduate Scholarship Program **Area, Field, or Subject:** Aerospace sciences; Engineering; Engineering, Aerospace/Aeronautical/Astronautical; Mathematics and mathematical sciences; Science; Space and planetary sciences **Level of Education for which Award is Granted:** Undergraduate **Number Awarded:** Varies each year; recently, 9 of these scholarships were awarded. **Funds Available:** The stipend is $4,000. **Duration:** 1 year.
Eligibility Requirements: This program is open to undergraduate students beyond their freshman year at RISGC-member universities. Applicants must be studying in science, mathematics, or engineering fields of interest to the National Aeronautics and Space Administration (NASA). U.S. citizenship is required. The sponsor is a component of NASA's Space Grant program, which encourages participation by women, underrepresented minorities, and persons with disabilities. **Deadline for Receipt:** February of each year. **Additional Information:** Members of the RISGC are Bryant College, Community College of Rhode Island, Providence College, Roger Williams University, Rhode Island College, Rhode Island School of Design, Salve Regina University, University of Rhode Island, and Wheaton College. This program is funded by NASA. Scholars are designated as research scholars (who are required to devote up to 4 hours per week to outreach activities in science education for K-12 children and teachers through Rhode Island), outreach scholars (who are required to devote up to 8 hours per week to outreach activities), or "Science En Espanol" scholars (who are required to devote up to 8 hours per week to curriculum support for K-12 children and teachers throughout Rhode Island).

4615 ■ RHODE ISLAND SPACE GRANT

c/o Brown University
Lincoln Field Building
Box 1846
Providence, RI 02912-1846
Tel: (401)863-2889
Fax: (401)863-1292
E-mail: RISpaceGrant@brown.edu
Web Site: http://www.planetary.brown.edu/RI_Space_Grant
To provide funding for summer research activities to undergraduate students at institutions that are members of the Rhode Island Space Grant Consortium (RISGC) who are interested in a career in a space-related field of science, mathematics, or engineering.
Title of Award: Rhode Island Space Grant Undergraduate Summer Scholar Program **Area, Field, or Subject:** Aerospace sciences; Engineering; Engineering, Aerospace/Aeronautical/Astronautical; Mathematics and mathematical sciences; Science; Space and planetary sciences **Level of Education for which Award is Granted:** Undergraduate **Number Awarded:** Varies each year; recently, 3 of these scholarships were awarded. **Funds Available:** The stipend is $4,000. **Duration:** 1 summer.
Eligibility Requirements: This program is open to undergraduate students at RISGC-member universities. Applicants must be studying in science, mathematics, or engineering fields of interest to the National Aeronautics and Space Administration (NASA). They must be interested in participating in a research project during the summer with an advisor in their own department. U.S. citizenship is required. The sponsor is a component of NASA's Space Grant program, which encourages participation by women, underrepresented minorities, and persons with disabilities. **Deadline for Receipt:** February of each year. **Additional Information:**

Members of the RISGC are Bryant College, Community College of Rhode Island, Providence College, Roger Williams University, Rhode Island College, Rhode Island College, Rhode Island School of Design, Salve Regina University, University of Rhode Island, and Wheaton College. This program is funded by NASA. Scholars are required to devote 75% of their time to their research and 25% of their time to science education outreach activities organized and coordinated by Rhode Island Space Grant.

4616 ■ ROCKY MOUNTAIN COAL MINING INSTITUTE

Attn: Executive Director
8057 South Yukon Way
Littleton, CO 80128-5510
Tel: (303)948-3300
Fax: (303)948-1132
E-mail: mail@rmcmi.org
Web Site: http://www.rmcmi.org
To provide financial assistance to college students from Rocky Mountain states who are preparing for a career in the mining industry.
Title of Award: Rocky Mountain Coal Mining Institute Scholarships **Area, Field, or Subject:** Business; Engineering, Electrical; Engineering, Geological; Engineering, Mechanical; Engineering, Metallurgical; Engineering, Mining and Mineral; Environmental science; Geology; Metallurgy; Mining **Level of Education for which Award is Granted:** Four Year College **Number Awarded:** 8 each year (1 from each of the participating states). **Funds Available:** The stipend is $2,000 per year. Funds are disbursed to the recipient's institution to be used as a tuition credit. during the junior, senior, and/or fifth year of undergraduate study. **Duration:** 2 years; renewable, if the recipient continues in school as a full-time student in good academic standing.
Eligibility Requirements: This program is open to full-time sophomores or juniors in college who are U.S. citizens and residents of Arizona, Colorado, Montana, New Mexico, North Dakota, Texas, Utah, or Wyoming. Applicants must be working on a degree in engineering (e.g., electrical, environmental, geological, mechanical, metallurgical, mining) or in a mining-related field (e.g., geology, mineral processing, metallurgy). They may be attending school in 1 of those states or another school approved by the sponsor (e.g., University of Missouri at Rolla, South Dakota School of Mines). Preference is given to students who are particularly interested in western coal as a career. Interviews are required. **Deadline for Receipt:** January of each year.

4617 ■ ROCKY MOUNTAIN ELECTRICAL LEAGUE

Attn: RMEL Foundation
2170 South Parker Road, Suite 225
Denver, CO 80231
Tel: (303)695-0089
Fax: (303)695-0704
E-mail: edblum@rmel.org
Web Site: http://www.rmel.org/foundation/foundationscholarships.cfm
To provide financial assistance to students sponsored by a member of the Rocky Mountain Electrical League (RMEL) who wish to study selected fields in college in order to prepare for a career in the electric energy industry.
Title of Award: RMEL Foundation Scholarships **Area, Field, or Subject:** Business administration; Energy-related areas; Engineering; Information science and technology **Level of Education for which Award is Granted:** Undergraduate **Number Awarded:** Varies each year; recently, 5 of these scholarships were awarded. **Funds Available:** The stipend is $1,000. **Duration:** 1 year.
Eligibility Requirements: This program is open to high school seniors, high school graduates, and college undergraduates who have an RMEL-member company as a sponsor. Applicants must be working on or planning to work on 1) an electric industry position certificate or associate degree, or 2) a full-time undergraduate degree. Their field of study must be engineering; business; information systems; plant, line, or distribution technology; line worker; or other program related to a career in the electric energy industry. U.S. citizenship is required. Selection is based on goals and aspirations in the electric energy industry, motivation to succeed, service to community and school, and academic ability. **Deadline for Receipt:** March of each year. **Additional Information:** The RMEL serves 17 states: Arizona, Colorado, Idaho, Iowa, Kansas, Minnesota, Missouri, Montana, Nebraska, Nevada, New Mexico, North Dakota, Oklahoma, South Dakota, Texas, Utah, and Wyoming.

4618 ■ ROCKY MOUNTAIN NASA SPACE GRANT CONSORTIUM

c/o Utah State University
EL Building, Room 302
Logan, UT 84322-4140
Tel: (435)797-3666
Fax: (435)797-3382
E-mail: spacegrant@cc.usu.edu
Web Site: http://spacegrant.usu.edu
To provide financial support to undergraduate students at designated universities in Utah or Colorado who are working on a degree in fields of interest to the National Aeronautics and Space Administration (NASA).
Title of Award: Rocky Mountain NASA Space Grant Consortium Undergraduate Scholarships **Area, Field, or Subject:** Aerospace sciences; Engineering; Engineering, Aerospace/Aeronautical/Astronautical; Medicine; Science; Space and planetary sciences; Technology **Level of Education for which Award is Granted:** Undergraduate **Number Awarded:** Varies each year. **Funds Available:** The amount of the awards depends on the availability of funds. **Duration:** 1 year.
Eligibility Requirements: This program is open to undergraduate students at member institutions of the Rocky Mountain NASA Space Grant Consortium who are studying engineering, science, medicine, or technology. U.S. citizenship is required. Selection is based on academic performance to date and potential for the future, with emphasis on space-related research interests. This program is part of the NASA Space Grant program, which encourages participation by women, underrepresented minorities, and persons with disabilities. **Deadline for Receipt:** June of each year. **Additional Information:** Members of the consortium are Utah State University, the University of Utah, Brigham Young University, Dixie State College, Salt Lake Community College, Shoshone-Bannock School, Snow College, Southern Utah University, the University of Denver, and Weber State University. This program is funded by NASA.

4619 ■ ROYAL NEIGHBORS OF AMERICA

Attn: Fraternal Services
230 16th Street
Rock Island, IL 61201-8645
Tel: (309)788-4561
Free: 800-627-4762
E-mail: contact@royalneighbors.org
Web Site: http://www.royalneighbors.org/MemberBenefits/scholarships.cfm
To provide financial assistance for college to women members of the Royal Neighbors of America who plan to enter nontraditional fields.
Title of Award: Eliza D. Watt Scholarships **Area, Field, or Subject:** Computer and information sciences; Engineering; Mathematics and mathematical sciences; Physical sciences **Level of Education for which Award is Granted:** Undergraduate **Number Awarded:** 5 each year. **Funds Available:** The stipend is $2,000 per year. **Duration:** 4 years.
Eligibility Requirements: This program is open to women members of the society who are graduating high school seniors. Applicants must be planning to enter a field considered nontraditional for women, including computer science, engineering, physical sciences, teaching of nontraditional women's fields, business writing, or mathematics. **Deadline for Receipt:** December of each year. **Additional Information:** This program was established in 2004.

4620 ■ SAGINAW COMMUNITY FOUNDATION

100 South Jefferson, Suite 201
Saginaw, MI 48607
Tel: (989)755-0545
Fax: (989)755-6524
E-mail: info@saginawfoundation.org
Web Site: http://www.saginawfoundation.org
To provide financial assistance to Michigan residents working on an undergraduate or graduate degree in civil engineering or land surveying.
Title of Award: Steve Wagner Scholarship **Area, Field, or Subject:** Cartography/Surveying; Engineering, Civil **Level of Education for which Award is Granted:** Graduate, Undergraduate **Number Awarded:** 1 or more each year. **Funds Available:** A stipend is awarded (amount not specified). **Duration:** 1 year.
Eligibility Requirements: This program is open to residents of Michigan working on an undergraduate or graduate degree at an ABET-accredited program in civil engineering or land surveying. Applicants must be

enrolled full time with a GPA of 2.5 or higher. They must have worked for a firm that is a member of the American Council of Engineering Companies (ACEC) in the last 24 months. Selection is based on academic record (10 points), community service (40 points), recommendations (20 points), and overall involvement in community, school, and work activities (30 points). **Deadline for Receipt:** February of each year. **Additional Information:** This program is sponsored by the American Council of Engineering Companies of Michigan.

4621 ■ SCHOLARSHIP ADMINISTRATIVE SERVICES, INC.

Attn: CEA Program
2000 Rock Street, Suite 3
Mountain View, CA 94043

To provide financial assistance to undergraduate and graduate students working on a degree in civil engineering.

Title of Award: Civil Engineers of America Scholarships **Area, Field, or Subject:** Engineering, Civil **Level of Education for which Award is Granted:** Graduate, Undergraduate **Number Awarded:** Up to 20 each year. **Funds Available:** The stipend is $5,000 per year. **Duration:** 1 year; may be renewed 1 additional year if the recipient maintains full-time enrollment and a GPA of 3.0 or higher.

Eligibility Requirements: This program is open to full-time students working on or planning to work on an undergraduate or graduate degree in civil engineering. Applicants must have a GPA of 3.0 or higher and be able to demonstrate a record of involvement in extracurricular and work activities related to civil engineering. Along with their application, they must submit a 1,000-word essay on their educational and career goals, how they became interested in civil engineering as a career, and what contributions they believe they can make to the civil engineering profession. Financial need is not considered in the selection process. **Deadline for Receipt:** April of each year. **Additional Information:** This program is sponsored by Civil Engineers of America (CEA) and administered by Scholarship Administrative Services, Inc. CEA was established in 2002 to encourage more American students to consider civil engineering as a career. Requests for applications should be accompanied by a self-addressed stamped envelope, the student's e-mail address, and the source where they found the scholarship information.

4622 ■ SEALASKA CORPORATION

Attn: Sealaska Heritage Institute
One Sealaska Plaza, Suite 301
Juneau, AK 99801-1249
Tel: (907)586-9166; 888-311-4992
Fax: (907)586-9293
E-mail: scholarship@sealaska.com
Web Site: http://www.sealaskaheritage.org/programs/university_scholarships.htm

To provide financial assistance for undergraduate or graduate study to Native Alaskans who have a connection to Sealaska Corporation and are majoring in designated fields.

Title of Award: Sealaska Heritage Institute 7(i) Scholarships **Area, Field, or Subject:** Business administration; Chemistry; Engineering, Chemical; Health care services; Mathematics and mathematical sciences; Natural resources; Physics **Level of Education for which Award is Granted:** Graduate, Undergraduate **Number Awarded:** Varies each year. **Funds Available:** The amount of the award depends on the availability of funds, the number of qualified applicants, class standing, and cumulative GPA. **Duration:** 1 year; may be renewed up to 5 years for a bachelor's degree, up to 3 years for a master's degree, up to 2 years for a doctorate, or up to 3 years for vocational study. The maximum total support is limited to 9 years. Renewal depends on recipients' maintaining full-time enrollment and a GPA of 2.5 or higher.

Eligibility Requirements: This program is open to 1) Alaska Natives who are enrolled to Sealaska Corporation, and 2) Native lineal descendants of Alaska Natives enrolled to Sealaska Corporation, whether or not the applicant owns Sealaska Corporation stock. Applicants must be enrolled or accepted for enrollment as full-time undergraduate or graduate students. Along with their application, they must submit 2 essays: 1) their personal history and educational goals, and 2) their expected contributions to the Alaska Native or Native American community. Financial need is also considered in the selection process. The following areas of study qualify for these awards: natural resources (environmental sciences, engineering, conservation biology, environmental law, fisheries, geology, marine science/biology, forestry, wildlife management, and mining technology); business administration (accounting, finance, marketing, international business, international commerce and trade, management of information systems, human resources management, economics, computer information systems, and industrial management); and other special fields (cadastral surveys, chemistry, equipment/machinery operators, industrial safety specialists, health specialists, plastics engineers, trade specialists, physics, mathematics, and marine trades and occupations). **Deadline for Receipt:** February of each year. **Additional Information:** Funding for this program is provided from Alaska Native Claims Settlement Act (ANSCA) Section 7(i) revenue sharing provisions. Sealaska sponsors a number of other scholarships, including the Cape Fox Scholarships and the Sealaska Heritage Institute Scholarships.

4623 ■ SIEMENS FOUNDATION

170 Wood Avenue South
Iselin, NJ 08830
877-822-5233
Fax: (732)603-5890
E-mail: foundation@sc.siemens.com
Web Site: http://www.siemens-foundation.org/scholarship

To recognize and reward outstanding high school seniors who have undertaken individual or team research projects in science, mathematics, and technology (or in combinations of those disciplines).

Title of Award: Siemens Westinghouse Competition Awards **Area, Field, or Subject:** Astronomy and astronomical sciences; Atmospheric science; Biochemistry; Biological and clinical sciences; Chemistry; Computer and information sciences; Earth sciences; Engineering, Civil; Engineering, Electrical; Engineering, Mechanical; Environmental science; Genetics; Geosciences; Materials research/science; Mathematics and mathematical sciences; Nutrition; Physics; Writing **Level of Education for which Award is Granted:** Undergraduate **Number Awarded:** In the initial round of judging, up to 300 regional semifinalists (up to 50 in each region) are selected. Of those, 60 are chosen as regional finalists (5 individuals and 5 teams in each of the 6 regions). Then 12 regional winners (1 individual and 1 team) are selected in the regional competitions, and they become the national finalists. **Funds Available:** At the regional level, finalists receive $1,000 scholarships, both as individuals and members of teams. Individual regional winners receive $3,000 scholarships. Winning regional teams receive $6,000 scholarships to be divided among the team members. Those regional winners then receive additional scholarships as national finalists. In the national competition: first-place winners receive an additional $100,000 scholarship, second place an additional $50,000 scholarship, third place an additional $40,000 scholarship, fourth place an additional $30,000 scholarship, fifth place an additional $20,000 scholarship, and sixth place an additional $10,000 scholarship. Those national awards are provided both to individuals and to teams to be divided equally among team members. Scholarship money is sent directly to the recipient's college or university to cover undergraduate and/or graduate educational expenses. Schools with regional finalists receive a $2,000 award to be used to support science, mathematics, and technology programs in their schools. **Duration:** The competition is held annually.

Eligibility Requirements: This program is open to high school seniors who are legal or permanent U.S. residents. They must be enrolled in a high school in the United States, Puerto Rico, Guam, Virgin Islands, American Samoa, Wake and Midway Islands, or the Marianas. U.S. high school students enrolled in a Department of Defense dependents school, an accredited overseas American or international school, a foreign school as an exchange student, or a foreign school because their parent(s) live and work abroad are also eligible. Students being home-schooled qualify if they obtain the endorsement of the school district official responsible for such programs. Research projects may be submitted in mathematics and the biological and physical sciences, or involve combinations of disciplines, such as astrophysics, biochemistry, bioengineering, biology, biophysics, botany, chemistry, computer science, civil engineering, earth and atmospheric science engineering, electrical engineering, environmental sciences, fluid dynamics, genetics, geology, materials science, mathematics, mechanical engineering, nutritional science, physics, toxicology, and virology. Both individual and team projects (2 or 3 members) may be entered. All team members must meet the eligibility requirements. Team projects may include seniors, but that is not a requirement. Competition entrants must submit a detailed report on their research project, including a description of the purpose of the research, rationale for the research, pertinent scientific literature, methodology, results, discussion, and conclusion. All projects must be endorsed by a sponsoring high school (except home-schooled students, who obtain their endorsement from the district or state home-school official). Each project must have a project advisor or mentor who is a member of the instructional staff or a person approved by the endorsing high school. There are 3 judging phases to the competition. An initial review panel selects outstanding research projects from 6 different regions of the country. The students submitting these projects are identified as regional semifinalists. Out of those, the highest-rated projects from each region are selected and the students who submitted them are recognized as regional finalists. For the next phase, the regional finalists are offered all-expense paid trips to the regional competition on the campus of a regional university partner, where their projects are reviewed by a panel of judges appointed by the host institution. Regional finalists are required to prepare a poster display of their research project, make an oral presentation about the research and research findings, and respond to questions from the judges. The top-rated individual and the top-rated team project in each region are selected as regional winners to represent the region in the national competition as national finalists. At that competition, the national finalists again display their projects, make oral presentations, and respond to judges' questions. At each phase, selection is based on clarity of expression, comprehensiveness, creativity, field knowledge, future work, interpretation, literature review, presentation, scientific importance, and validity. **Deadline for Receipt:** September of each year. **Additional Information:** The program is offered by Siemens Foundation, in partnership with the College Board. Information is available from the College Board at (703) 707-8999, E-mail: spro@collegeboard.org. Students submitting the projects with the highest evaluations become part of a registry that is circulated to colleges and universities nationwide. To continue receiving scholarships, winners must attend an accredited academic institution on a full-time basis.

4624 ■ HAROLD B. & DOROTHY A. SNYDER SCHOLARSHIP FUND
P.O. Box 671
Moorestown, NJ 08057-0671
Tel: (856)273-9745
To provide financial assistance to undergraduate and graduate students preparing for a career in the areas of Presbyterian ministry, nursing, building construction, or engineering.
Title of Award: Harold B. & Dorothy A. Snyder Scholarships **Area, Field, or Subject:** Construction; Engineering; Nursing; Religion **Level of Education for which Award is Granted:** Master's, Undergraduate **Number Awarded:** Varies each year. **Funds Available:** The amount awarded varies, depending upon the needs of the recipient. Funds are paid directly to the recipient's institution. **Duration:** 1 year; generally renewable until completion of the recipient's degree program.
Eligibility Requirements: This program is open to U.S. citizens who are attending or planning to attend institutions of higher learning. They must be preparing for a career in the areas of Presbyterian ministry (M.Div. degree), nursing (B.S.N.), building construction, or engineering. Applicants are evaluated on the basis of achievement, need, demonstrated commitment to community service, and character. Preference is given to applicants who are full-time students and who are New Jersey residents. In some instances, preference is also given to full-time enrollees of specific institutions and to members of certain denominations and congregations or residents of certain towns. There are no other preferences as to age, sex, religion (except when applicable), race, or country of origin. Personal interviews are required. **Deadline for Receipt:** March of each year. **Additional Information:** Snyder Scholars are required, by contract, to submit periodic reports and attend meetings. The foundation will withdraw scholarship aid from any recipient who, in its opinion, has engaged in activities detrimental to the school or college being attended or to the country. In addition, the foundation will withdraw aid from any recipient (other than a divinity student) who seeks to avoid service in the U.S. armed forces as a conscientious objector.

4625 ■ SOCIETY OF AMERICAN MILITARY ENGINEERS-ANCHORAGE POST
P.O. Box 6149
Elmendorf AFB, AK 99506-6149
E-mail: william_kontess@urscorp.com
Web Site: http://www.sameanchorage.org/h_about/scholinfo.html
To provide financial assistance to upper-division students from Alaska who are majoring in engineering or the natural sciences.
Title of Award: BG Benjamin B. Talley Scholarship **Area, Field, or Subject:** Engineering; Natural sciences **Level of Education for which Award is Granted:** Four Year College **Number Awarded:** Varies; recently, 6 were awarded. **Funds Available:** Varies; generally, stipends are $3,000, $2,000, or $1,000. **Duration:** 1 year.
Eligibility Requirements: Eligible to apply for this funding are juniors and seniors who are majoring in engineering or the natural sciences. Applicants must be U.S. citizens and either Alaska residents or attending school in Alaska. They must be 1) a member of the sponsoring organization, 2) the dependent of a member, 3) a member of the armed forces on active duty in Alaska, or 4) a dependent of a member of the armed forces on active duty in Alaska. Their GPA must be 2.5 or higher. Selection is based on academic achievement, participation in school and community activities, an essay on career goals (100 to 250 words), and work/family activities. Financial need is not considered in the selection process. **Deadline for Receipt:** November of each year. **Additional Information:** This program was established in 1997. Information is also available from Bruce Steely, Dihthaad Global Services, 10223 Stewart Drive, Eagle River, AK 99507, (907) 223-6339, Fax: (907) 694-3241, E-mail: Dihthaad_2@hotmail.com.

4626 ■ SOCIETY OF AMERICAN MILITARY ENGINEERS-ARKANSAS POST
P.O. Box 867
Little Rock, AR 72203-0867
Web Site: http://www.same.org/arkansas
To provide financial assistance to Arkansas high school seniors interested in studying architecture or engineering in college.
Title of Award: Arkansas Post Scholarships **Area, Field, or Subject:** Architecture; Engineering **Level of Education for which Award is Granted:** Undergraduate **Number Awarded:** 4 each year: 2 at $1,000 and 2 at $500. **Funds Available:** Stipends are $1,000 or $500. **Duration:** 1 year.
Eligibility Requirements: This program is open to seniors graduating from high schools in Arkansas. Applicants must be interested in studying architecture or engineering in college. **Additional Information:** Information is also available from Mike Callahan, Second Vice President, Cromwell Architects Engineers, (501) 372-2900, ext. 177, E-mail: macallahan@cromwell.com.

4627 ■ SOCIETY OF AMERICAN MILITARY ENGINEERS-BALTIMORE POST
c/o Al-Nisa Montague Aduwu
McDonough Bolyard Peck, Inc.
10440 Little Patuxent Parkway, Suite 530
Columbia, MD 21044
Tel: (410)715-9462
E-mail: aaduwu@mbpce.com
Web Site: http://www.same-balt.org/Scholarship/scholarship_home.htm
To provide financial assistance to high school seniors who plan to attend a college or university in the Baltimore area and major in engineering, architecture, or a related science.
Title of Award: Baltimore Post 4-Year Scholarships **Area, Field, or Subject:** Architecture; Engineering; Science **Level of Education for which Award is Granted:** Four Year College **Number Awarded:** 1 or more each year. **Funds Available:** The stipend is $2,000 per year. **Duration:** 4 years.
Eligibility Requirements: This program is open to high school seniors who plan to attend a designated university in the Baltimore area and major in engineering, architecture, or a related science. Applicants must plan to enroll on a full-time basis; be Maryland residents and U.S. citizens, and have a GPA of 3.0 or higher. Extracurricular activities and financial need are also considered in the selection process. **Deadline for Receipt:** September of each year. **Additional Information:** Recipients must enroll as full-time students at the following colleges and universities in the Baltimore area: Johns Hopkins University; Loyola College; University of

Maryland, College Park; University of Maryland, Baltimore County; or Morgan State University. Other schools may also be designated annually.

4628 ■ SOCIETY OF AMERICAN MILITARY ENGINEERS-BOSTON POST

c/o John M. Gerstenlauer
Perini Corporation
73 Mt. Wayte Avenue
Framingham, MA 01701-9160
Tel: (508)628-2442
Fax: (508)628-2537
Web Site: http://www.sameboston.org
To provide financial assistance to residents of New England majoring in a college program related to construction.
Title of Award: Boston Post Scholarships **Area, Field, or Subject:** Architecture; Construction; Engineering; Engineering, Civil; Environmental science **Level of Education for which Award is Granted:** Undergraduate **Number Awarded:** Approximately 25 each year. **Funds Available:** The stipend is approximately $2,000 per year. **Duration:** 1 year.
Eligibility Requirements: This program is open to residents of New England who are currently enrolled in an accepted engineering or architecture program, preferably in civil engineering, environmental engineering, architecture, or other construction-related program. Applicants must have completed at least 1 academic year and have at least 1 year remaining. Preference is given to applicants enrolled in ROTC (preferably not a recipient of an ROTC scholarship) or interested in or having prior U.S. military service. U.S. citizenship is required. Interested students are invited to submit an application form, transcripts, documentation of financial need, and a personal letter describing their qualifications and needs. An interview is required. Selection is based on academic achievements, financial need, extracurricular activities, and the interview. **Deadline for Receipt:** February of each year.

4629 ■ SOCIETY OF AMERICAN MILITARY ENGINEERS-GUAM POST

c/o Lt. Titania B. Cross
PSC 455. Box 175
FPO, AP 96540-2200
Tel: (671)339-3820
Fax: (671)339-4955
E-mail: crosstb@pwcguam.navy.mil
Web Site: http://www.same.org/guam
To provide financial assistance to residents of Guam who are interested in majoring in engineering or architecture in college.
Title of Award: Charlie Corn Scholarships **Area, Field, or Subject:** Architecture; Engineering **Level of Education for which Award is Granted:** Undergraduate **Number Awarded:** Varies each year. **Funds Available:** The stipend is $1,000 per year for high school seniors, $2,000 per year for students already in college, or $500 per year for students at Guam Community College. **Duration:** 1 year; may be renewed if the recipient maintains full-time enrollment and a GPA of 3.0 or higher.
Eligibility Requirements: This program is open to residents of Guam and the islands within the geographic area known as Micronesia. Applicants must be 1) high school seniors planning to attend their first year of college to work on a bachelor's degree in engineering or architecture; 2) upper-division students working on a bachelor's degree in engineering or architecture at an accredited college or university; and 3) students planning to attend Guam Community College to work on a 2-year engineering technology degree. They must demonstrate a sincere interest in returning to Guam or Micronesia after graduation to begin a professional career. Selection is based on that interest as well as scholastic achievement, aptitude, attitude, character, and financial need. **Deadline for Receipt:** May of each year.

4630 ■ SOCIETY OF AMERICAN MILITARY ENGINEERS-HONOLULU POST

Attn: LCDR Dustin Hamacher, Scholarship Committee Chair
USCG Naval Engineering Unit Honolulu
Sand Island Road
Honolulu, HI 96819-4398
Tel: (808)843-3871
Web Site: http://www.same.org/honolulu

To provide financial assistance to high school seniors from Hawaii who are interested in attending college to work on a degree in engineering or architecture.
Title of Award: Honolulu Post Scholarships **Area, Field, or Subject:** Architecture; Engineering **Level of Education for which Award is Granted:** Undergraduate **Number Awarded:** 2 each year. **Funds Available:** The stipend is $2,500. **Duration:** 1 year.
Eligibility Requirements: This program is open to seniors graduating from high schools in Hawaii who plan to work full time on an undergraduate degree in engineering or architecture at an accredited college or university. Applicants must be U.S. citizens with a GPA of 3.0 or higher. Military affiliation or experience (i.e., ROTC, member or dependent of a member of the Society of Military Engineers (SAME), military dependent, Junior ROTC) is not required but is given preference. Applicants must submit a transcript; a resume of work experience, academic activities, and extracurricular accomplishments; and an essay (1 page) written around an architecture or engineering theme and its impact on society and the nation's defense or homeland security. **Deadline for Receipt:** March of each year.

4631 ■ SOCIETY OF AMERICAN MILITARY ENGINEERS-KENTUCKIANA POST

Attn: Scholarship Committee
P.O. Box 59
Louisville, KY 40201-0059
Web Site: http://www.same.org/kentuckiana
To provide financial assistance to students in Indiana and Kentucky who are interested in majoring in engineering in college.
Title of Award: Kentuckiana Post Scholarship **Area, Field, or Subject:** Engineering **Level of Education for which Award is Granted:** Undergraduate **Number Awarded:** At least 5 each year. **Funds Available:** The stipend is $3,000 per year. **Duration:** 1 year; nonrenewable.
Eligibility Requirements: Applicants must be 1 of the following: a dependent of a current Society of American Military Engineers (SAME) Kentuckiana post member; an employee or dependent of an employee of a Kentuckiana post sustaining member firm; an employee or dependent of an employee of the Louisville District Corps of Engineers; a current student member of the Kentuckiana Post; a student whose permanent home address is within the Kentuckiana Post's geographic boundary (Kentucky and Indiana) and who is enrolled in an ROTC program or military academy; or an individual on active duty or the dependent of an individual on active duty who is assigned to an installation within the Kentuckiana post's geographic boundary. In addition, applicants must be U.S. citizens accepted to an undergraduate ABET-accredited engineering program; undergraduates enrolled in engineering technology programs are not eligible. Along with their application, they must submit an essay of 300 to 500 words on a topic that changes annually; recently, applicants were invited to write on the role of U.S. engineers in rebuilding war-torn countries. Financial need is not considered in the selection process. **Deadline for Receipt:** March of each year. **Additional Information:** Information is also available from D. Clay Kelly, Scholarship Co-Chair, Strand Associates, Waterfront Plaza, Suite 710, 325 West Main Street, Louisville, KY 40202, (502) 583-7020, E-mail: clay.kelly@strand.com. Recipients are required to attend the scholarship luncheon ceremony in Louisville in May.

4632 ■ SOCIETY OF AMERICAN MILITARY ENGINEERS-NEW JERSEY POST

c/o John Booth
CTSC
P.O. Box 60
Fort Monmouth, NJ 07703
Tel: (732)544-0995
E-mail: john.booth@mail1.monmouth.army.mil
Web Site: http://www.same.org/newjersey
To provide financial assistance to students in New Jersey working on an undergraduate degree in architecture, engineering, or a related field.
Title of Award: New Jersey Post SAME Scholarship **Area, Field, or Subject:** Architecture; Engineering **Level of Education for which Award is Granted:** Undergraduate **Number Awarded:** 1 each year. **Funds Available:** The stipend is $1,000. **Duration:** 1 year.
Eligibility Requirements: This program is open to undergraduate students working on a degree in architecture, engineering, or a related

field. Candidates must be nominated by a member of the New Jersey Post of the Society of American Military Engineers (SAME). Selection is based on school and community activities, educational goals, academics, recommendations, and employment. **Deadline for Receipt:** March of each year.

4633 ■ SOCIETY OF AMERICAN MILITARY ENGINEERS-VIRGINIA PENINSULA POST

c/o Jeffrey B. Merz, Scholarship Chair
HQ ACC/CEP
129 Andrews Street, Suite 102
Langley AFB, VA 23665-2769
Tel: (757)764-6579
E-mail: jeffrey.merz@langley.af.mil
To provide financial assistance to students at universities in Virginia and dependents of members of the Virginia Peninsula Post of the Society of American Military Engineers (SAME) who have a commitment to future military service and are majoring in engineering or architecture.
Title of Award: Virginia Peninsula Post Scholarship **Area, Field, or Subject:** Architecture; Engineering **Level of Education for which Award is Granted:** Four Year College **Number Awarded:** 3 each year. **Funds Available:** The stipend is $1,000 and 1-year's membership in the society. **Duration:** 1 year.
Eligibility Requirements: This program is open to students enrolled in an engineering or architecture program at the sophomore level or above. Applicants must be 1) attending a college or university in Virginia, or 2) the dependent of a SAME Virginia Peninsula Post member attending anywhere. They must have demonstrated commitment to future military service by enrolling in an ROTC program, a commissioning program, or an extended enlistment. Selection is based on financial need, academic standing, and involvement in university and community programs. **Deadline for Receipt:** March of each year.

4634 ■ SOCIETY OF AMERICAN MILITARY ENGINEERS-WASHINGTON DC POST

c/o Al O'Konski, Scholarship Committee Chair
URS Corporation
2020 K Street, N.W., Suite 300
Washington, DC 20006-1806
Tel: (202)872-0277
Fax: (202)872-0282
E-mail: Al_O'Konski@urscorp.com
Web Site: http://www.samedcpost.org/scholarship.html
To provide financial assistance to students interested in majoring in engineering, architecture, or environmental sciences.
Title of Award: Washington DC Post Scholarships **Area, Field, or Subject:** Architecture; Engineering; Environmental conservation; Environmental science **Level of Education for which Award is Granted:** Undergraduate **Number Awarded:** Varies each year; recently, 8 of these scholarships were awarded. **Funds Available:** The current stipend is $1,200. Funds are paid to the recipient's school after college enrollment is confirmed. **Duration:** 1 year.
Eligibility Requirements: This program is open to students who are enrolled full time at an accredited university as rising freshmen, sophomores, or juniors, are U.S. citizens, are of good character, and are majoring in engineering, architecture, or environmental science. Applicants must submit a 2-page narrative addressing the following topics: their academic performance, academic and professional goals, financial need, extracurricular activities, a summary of previous military service (if any), and a statement of why they should be considered for the award. Preference is given to applicants in the Washington, D.C. area. **Deadline for Receipt:** January of each year. **Additional Information:** This program includes the following named scholarships: the Paul Brott Scholarship, the Linda McCarthy Scholarship, the T-Bird/RPI Environmental Scholarship, and the Ronald Hubbard Scholarship.

4635 ■ SOCIETY OF AUTOMOTIVE ENGINEERS

Attn: Scholarship Administrator
400 Commonwealth Drive
Warrendale, PA 15096-0001
Tel: (724)772-4047
Fax: (724)776-3049
E-mail: scholarships@sae.org

Web Site: http://students.sae.org/awdscholar/scholarships/belfry
To provide financial support to college seniors in Canada who are majoring in engineering.
Title of Award: William G. Belfry/SAE Grants **Area, Field, or Subject:** Engineering **Level of Education for which Award is Granted:** Four Year College **Number Awarded:** 2 each year: 1 to a student at the University of Toronto and 1 to a student at any other Canadian university. **Funds Available:** The stipend is $C1,000 per year. **Duration:** 1 year.
Eligibility Requirements: Applicants must be entering their senior year of a full-time engineering program at a college or university in Canada. Separate competitions are held for students at the University of Toronto and for those at all other Canadian institutions. Canadian citizenship is required. Selection is based on academic and leadership achievement, intent to prepare for a career in mobility engineering, involvement in activities of the Society of Automotive Engineers (SAE) collegiate chapter, and a 300-word essay on the single experience that most strongly convinced or confirmed their decision to prepare for a career in engineering. Financial need is not considered. **Deadline for Receipt:** March of each year. **Additional Information:** Funding for this program is provided by the SAE Foundation Canada and the SAE Central Ontario Section.

4636 ■ SOCIETY OF AUTOMOTIVE ENGINEERS

Attn: Scholarship Administrator
400 Commonwealth Drive
Warrendale, PA 15096-0001
Tel: (724)772-4047
Fax: (724)776-3049
E-mail: scholarships@sae.org
Web Site: http://students.sae.org/awdscholar/scholarships/undesignated
To provide financial support for college to high school seniors interested in studying engineering.
Title of Award: BMW/SAE Engineering Scholarship **Area, Field, or Subject:** Engineering **Level of Education for which Award is Granted:** Undergraduate **Number Awarded:** 1 each year. **Funds Available:** The stipend is $6,000, paid at the rate of $1,500 per year. **Duration:** 4 years, provided the recipient maintains a GPA of 3.0 or higher.
Eligibility Requirements: This program is open to U.S. citizens who intend to earn an ABET-accredited degree in engineering. Applicants must be high school seniors with a GPA of 3.75 or higher and a rank in the 90th percentile in both mathematics and critical reading on the ACT or in the composite SAT. Selection is based on high school transcripts; SAT or ACT scores; school-related extracurricular activities; non-school related activities; academic honors, civic honors, and awards; and a 250-word essay on their goals, plans, experiences, and interests in mobility engineering. Financial need is not considered. **Deadline for Receipt:** November of each year. **Additional Information:** Funds for this scholarship are provided by BMW AG. Candidates must include a $5 processing fee with their applications.

4637 ■ SOCIETY OF AUTOMOTIVE ENGINEERS

Attn: Scholarship Administrator
400 Commonwealth Drive
Warrendale, PA 15096-0001
Tel: (724)772-4047
Fax: (724)776-3049
E-mail: scholarships@sae.org
Web Site: http://students.sae.org/awdscholar/scholarships/brubaker
To provide financial assistance to high school seniors who plan to major in engineering at a university in Maryland.
Title of Award: Bill Brubaker/Baltimore Section Scholarships **Area, Field, or Subject:** Engineering **Level of Education for which Award is Granted:** Undergraduate **Number Awarded:** 1 or more each year. **Funds Available:** The stipend is $1,000. **Duration:** 1 year; nonrenewable.
Eligibility Requirements: This program is open to high school seniors who are either 1) relatives of a member of the Baltimore section of the Society of Automotive Engineers (SAE), or 2) U.S. citizens accepted at a university in Maryland. Applicants must have a declared major in engineering. Selection is based on academic performance, school and non-school activities, awards and recognition, and a 300-word essay on their understanding of engineering and why they want to prepare for a career in the field. Financial need is not considered. **Deadline for Receipt:** May of each year. **Additional Information:** Funding for this program is provided by the SAE Baltimore Section. Information is also

available from Rich Bechtold, 5400 Thunder Hill Road, Columbia, MD 21045, (410) 997-1282, RLBechtold@aol.com.

4638 ■ SOCIETY OF AUTOMOTIVE ENGINEERS
Attn: Scholarship Administrator
400 Commonwealth Drive
Warrendale, PA 15096-0001
Tel: (724)772-4047
Fax: (724)776-3049
E-mail: scholarships@sae.org
Web Site: http://students.sae.org/awdscholar/scholarships/undesignated
To provide financial support to students working on a college degree in engineering.
Title of Award: TMC/SAE Donald D. Dawson Technical Scholarship **Area, Field, or Subject:** Engineering **Level of Education for which Award is Granted:** Undergraduate **Number Awarded:** 1 each year. **Funds Available:** The stipend is $1,500 per year. **Duration:** 1 year; may be renewed up to 3 additional years if the recipient maintains a GPA of 3.0 or higher.
Eligibility Requirements: This program is open to U.S. citizens who intend to earn an ABET-accredited degree in engineering. Applicants must be 1) high school seniors with a GPA of 3.25 or higher and minimum SAT scores of 600 in mathematics and 550 in critical reading or ACT score of 27 or higher; 2) transfer students from 4-year colleges or universities with a GPA of 3.0 or higher; or 3) transfer students from postsecondary technical or vocational schools with a GPA of 3.5 or higher. Selection is based on school transcripts; evidence of some type of hands-on technical experience or activity (e.g., rebuilding engines, working on cars or trucks); SAT or ACT scores; school-related extracurricular activities; non-school related activities; academic honors, civic honors, and awards; and a 250-word essay on their goals, plans, experiences, and interests in mobility engineering. Financial need is not considered. **Deadline for Receipt:** November of each year. **Additional Information:** The Society of Automotive Engineers (SAE) and The Maintenance Council (TMC) of American Trucking Associations established this scholarship to honor the leadership of Donald D. Dawson. Candidates must include a $5 processing fee with their applications.

4639 ■ SOCIETY OF AUTOMOTIVE ENGINEERS
Attn: Scholarship Administrator
400 Commonwealth Drive
Warrendale, PA 15096-0001
Tel: (724)772-4047
Fax: (724)776-3049
E-mail: scholarships@sae.org
Web Site: http://students.sae.org/awdscholar/scholarships/undesignated
To provide financial support for college to high school seniors interested in studying engineering.
Title of Award: Edward D. Hendrickson/SAE Engineering Scholarship **Area, Field, or Subject:** Engineering **Level of Education for which Award is Granted:** Undergraduate **Number Awarded:** 1 each year. **Funds Available:** The stipend is $4,000, paid at the rate of $1,000 per year. **Duration:** 4 years, provided the recipient maintains a GPA of 3.0 or higher.
Eligibility Requirements: This program is open to U.S. citizens who intend to earn an ABET-accredited degree in engineering. Applicants must be high school seniors with a GPA of 3.75 or higher and a rank in the 90th percentile in both mathematics and critical reading on the ACT or in the composite SAT. Selection is based on high school transcripts; SAT or ACT scores; school-related extracurricular activities; non-school related activities; academic honors, civic honors, and awards; and a 250-word essay on their goals, plans, experiences, and interests in mobility engineering. Financial need is not considered. **Deadline for Receipt:** November of each year. **Additional Information:** Hendrickson International, a Boler Company, established an endowment to underwrite this scholarship in memory of the late Edward D. Hendrickson. Candidates must include a $5 processing fee with their applications.

4640 ■ SOCIETY OF AUTOMOTIVE ENGINEERS
Attn: Scholarship Administrator
400 Commonwealth Drive
Warrendale, PA 15096-0001
Tel: (724)772-4047

Fax: (724)776-3049
E-mail: scholarships@sae.org
Web Site: http://students.sae.org/awdscholar/scholarships/hillquist
To provide financial assistance to college juniors who are majoring in mechanical or automotive engineering.
Title of Award: Ralph K. Hillquist Honorary SAE Scholarship **Area, Field, or Subject:** Engineering, Automotive; Engineering, Mechanical; Physics **Level of Education for which Award is Granted:** Four Year College **Number Awarded:** 1 each odd-numbered year. **Funds Available:** The stipend is $1,000. **Duration:** 1 year; nonrenewable.
Eligibility Requirements: This program is open to juniors enrolled full time at U.S. universities. Applicants must have a declared major in mechanical engineering or an automotive-related engineering discipline, with preference given to those who have completed studies or courses in the areas of expertise related to noise and vibration (e.g., statics, dynamics, physics, vibration). They must be U.S. citizens with a GPA of 3.0 or higher and significant academic and leadership achievements. along with their application, they must submit a 300-word essay on the single experience that most strongly convinced them or confirmed their decision to prepare for a career in engineering. Financial need is not considered in the selection process. **Deadline for Receipt:** January of each odd-numbered year. **Additional Information:** This scholarship, first awarded in 2005, is funded by the Noise & Vibration Conference of the Society of Automotive Engineers (SAE).

4641 ■ SOCIETY OF AUTOMOTIVE ENGINEERS
Attn: Award Program Staff
400 Commonwealth Drive
Warrendale, PA 15096-0001
Tel: (724)772-4047
Fax: (724)776-1830
E-mail: awards@sae.org
Web Site: http://students.sae.org/awdscholar/awards/rumbaugh
To recognize and reward undergraduate and graduate student members of the Society of Automotive Engineers (SAE) who provide outstanding leadership to the organization.
Title of Award: Rumbaugh Outstanding Student Leader Award **Area, Field, or Subject:** Engineering, Automotive **Level of Education for which Award is Granted:** Graduate, Undergraduate **Number Awarded:** 1 each year. **Funds Available:** The award consists of lifetime SAE membership, payment of travel expenses to an SAE meeting to receive the award, and a monetary stipend. **Duration:** The award is presented annually.
Eligibility Requirements: This program is open to undergraduate and graduate students who are current SAE student members or who recently transferred to SAE professional membership. They must be nominated by their SAE faculty advisor. Nominees must graduate between the preceding December and June from a university or college in a technical field related to mobility engineering and be employed in a mobility-related industry at the time of selection. Nominations are judged on the basis of SAE-related activities during the year of nomination and prospect of support of SAE and its activities. **Deadline for Receipt:** June of each year. **Additional Information:** This award was established in 2002.

4642 ■ SOCIETY OF AUTOMOTIVE ENGINEERS
Attn: Scholarship Administrator
400 Commonwealth Drive
Warrendale, PA 15096-0001
Tel: (724)772-4047
Fax: (724)776-3049
E-mail: scholarships@sae.org
Web Site: http://students.sae.org/awdscholar/scholarships/longtermmem
To provide financial support to engineering majors who are student members of the Society of Automotive Engineers (SAE).
Title of Award: SAE Long Term Member Sponsored Scholarships **Area, Field, or Subject:** Engineering **Level of Education for which Award is Granted:** Four Year College **Number Awarded:** Varies each year; recently, 6 of these scholarships were awarded. **Funds Available:** The stipend is $1,000. **Duration:** 1 year; nonrenewable.
Eligibility Requirements: This program is open to student members entering their senior year between August and February of the academic year following the award. Candidates must be nominated by the faculty advisor, the section chair, or the vice chair for student activities. Selection

is based on the nominee's involvement in the society, the collegiate chapter, or the local section and its programs. GPA and financial need are not considered. **Deadline for Receipt:** March of each year. **Additional Information:** Funding for this program is provided by long-term (25, 35, and 50 year) members of the society, many of whom have chosen to fund this scholarship program in lieu of receiving a Long Term Recognition Award. The program was established in 1994.

4643 ■ SOCIETY OF AUTOMOTIVE ENGINEERS

Attn: Scholarship Administrator
400 Commonwealth Drive
Warrendale, PA 15096-0001
Tel: (724)772-4047
Fax: (724)776-3049
E-mail: scholarships@sae.org
Web Site: http://students.sae.org/awdscholar/scholarships/undesignated
To provide financial support for college to high school seniors interested in studying engineering.
Title of Award: Tau Beta Pi/SAE Engineering Scholarship **Area, Field, or Subject:** Engineering **Level of Education for which Award is Granted:** Undergraduate **Number Awarded:** 6 each year. **Funds Available:** The stipend is $1,000. **Duration:** 1 year; nonrenewable.
Eligibility Requirements: This program is open to U.S. citizens who intend to earn an ABET-accredited degree in engineering. Applicants must be high school seniors with a GPA of 3.75 or higher and a rank in the 90th percentile in both mathematics and critical reading on the ACT or in the composite SAT. Selection is based on high school transcripts; SAT or ACT scores; school-related extracurricular activities; non-school related activities; academic honors, civic honors, and awards; and a 250-word essay on their goals, plans, experiences, and interests in mobility engineering. Financial need is not considered. **Deadline for Receipt:** November of each year. **Additional Information:** Funding for this program is provided by Tau Beta Pi, the national engineering society. Candidates must include a $5 processing fee with their applications.

4644 ■ SOCIETY OF AUTOMOTIVE ENGINEERS

Attn: Scholarship Administrator
400 Commonwealth Drive
Warrendale, PA 15096-0001
Tel: (724)772-4047
Fax: (724)776-3049
E-mail: scholarships@sae.org
Web Site: http://students.sae.org/awdscholar/scholarships/yanmar
To provide financial support to college seniors and graduate students majoring in engineering.
Title of Award: Yanmar/SAE Scholarship **Area, Field, or Subject:** Energy-related areas; Engineering; Transportation **Level of Education for which Award is Granted:** Four Year College, Graduate **Number Awarded:** 1 each year. **Funds Available:** The stipend is $1,000 per year. **Duration:** 2 years.
Eligibility Requirements: Applicants must be entering their senior year of an undergraduate engineering program or enrolled in a graduate engineering or related science program at a college or university in Canada, Mexico, or the United States. They must be pursuing a course of study or research related to the conservation of energy in transportation, agriculture, construction, and power generation. Emphasis is placed on research or study related to the internal combustion engine. Canadian, Mexican, or U.S. citizenship is required. Selection is based on academic and leadership achievement related to engineering or science, scholastic performance and special study or honors in the field of the award, and a 1-page essay on their study or research related to the field of their award. Financial need is not considered. **Deadline for Receipt:** March of each year. **Additional Information:** Funding for this program is provided by Yanmar Diesel American Corporation. Candidates must include a $5 processing fee with their application.

4645 ■ SOCIETY OF AUTOMOTIVE ENGINEERS

Attn: Scholarship Administrator
400 Commonwealth Drive
Warrendale, PA 15096-0001
Tel: (724)772-4047
Fax: (724)776-3049
E-mail: scholarships@sae.org

Web Site: http://students.sae.org/awdscholar/scholarships/undesignated
To provide financial support for college to high school seniors interested in studying engineering.
Title of Award: Fred M. Young Sr./SAE Engineering Scholarship **Area, Field, or Subject:** Engineering **Level of Education for which Award is Granted:** Undergraduate **Number Awarded:** 1 each year. **Funds Available:** The stipend is $4,000, paid at the rate of $1,000 per year. **Duration:** 4 years, provided the recipient maintains a GPA of 3.0 or higher.
Eligibility Requirements: This program is open to U.S. citizens who intend to earn an ABET-accredited degree in engineering. Applicants must be high school seniors with a GPA of 3.75 or higher and a rank in the 90th percentile in both mathematics and critical reading on the ACT or in the composite SAT. Selection is based on high school transcripts; SAT or ACT scores; school-related extracurricular activities; non-school related activities; academic honors, civic honors, and awards; and a 250-word essay on their goals, plans, experiences, and interests in mobility engineering. Financial need is not considered. **Deadline for Receipt:** November of each year. **Additional Information:** The Young Radiator Company established this scholarship in memory of the company's founder. Candidates must include a $5 processing fee with their applications.

4646 ■ SOCIETY OF EXPLORATION GEOPHYSICISTS

Attn: SEG Foundation
8801 South Yale, Suite 500
P.O. Box 702740
Tulsa, OK 74170-2740
Tel: (918)497-5513
Fax: (918)497-5557
E-mail: scholarships@seg.org
Web Site: http://seg.org/business/foundation/scholarships/index.shtml
To provide financial assistance to upper-division students working on a degree in geophysical engineering.
Title of Award: Ralph W. Baird Scholarship **Area, Field, or Subject:** Engineering; Geophysics **Level of Education for which Award is Granted:** Undergraduate **Number Awarded:** 1 each year. **Funds Available:** Stipends range from $1,000 to $3,000 per year. **Duration:** 1 academic year.
Eligibility Requirements: This program is open to juniors and seniors working on a degree in geophysical engineering. Along with their application, they must submit a 150-word essay on how they plan to use geophysics in their future. Financial need is not considered in the selection process. **Deadline for Receipt:** January of each year.

4647 ■ SOCIETY OF FIRE PROTECTION ENGINEERS

Attn: Educational and Scientific Foundation
7315 Wisconsin Avenue, Suite 1225 W
Bethesda, MD 20814
Tel: (301)718-2910
Fax: (301)718-2242
E-mail: sfpehqtrs@sfpe.org
Web Site: http://www.sfpe.org
To provide funding to students interested in conducting research that expands the art and science of fire protection engineering.
Title of Award: Society of Fire Protection Engineers Student Research Grants **Area, Field, or Subject:** Engineering; Fires and fire prevention **Level of Education for which Award is Granted:** Graduate, Undergraduate **Number Awarded:** Varies each year. **Funds Available:** Grants range from $3,000 to $25,000.
Eligibility Requirements: This program is open to bachelor's, master's, and doctoral students interested in conducting a research project in the fields of fire safety science or fire protection engineering. Selection is based on the quality of the research plan and the possibility that it will yield valid and broadly applicable result or contribute to knowledge in the profession (35%), potential impact of the research on the field of fire protection engineering (35%), qualifications of the fire protection engineering program (15%), and achievability of the proposed research plan within the stated time frame (15%). **Deadline for Receipt:** Applications may be submitted at any time. **Additional Information:** Recipients must deliver a publishable paper.

4648 ■ SOCIETY OF FIRE PROTECTION ENGINEERS-HAWAII CHAPTER

c/o Robert T. Bigtas, Vice President
S.S. Dannaway Associates, Inc.

720 Iwilei Road, Suite 412
Honolulu, HI 96817
Tel: (808)526-9019
Fax: (808)537-5385
E-mail: scholarship@sfpehawaii.org
Web Site: http://www.sfpehawaii.org
To provide financial assistance to members of the Society of Fire Protection Engineers (SFPE) in Hawaii.

Title of Award: Hawaii Chapter Society of Fire Protection Engineers Academic Scholarship **Area, Field, or Subject:** Engineering; Fires and fire prevention **Level of Education for which Award is Granted:** Graduate, Undergraduate **Number Awarded:** 1 each year. **Funds Available:** The stipend is $1,000 per year. **Duration:** 1 year.

Eligibility Requirements: This program is open to residents of Hawaii who are enrolled in a fire protection engineering undergraduate or graduate degree program at a college or university in Hawaii or a fire science curriculum in the state. Applicants must submit 1) a letter of introduction that explains when they first became interested in preparing for a career in the field of fire protection and why, their short-term and long-term career goals, and any past experience and/or accomplishments in the field of fire protection engineering; 2) transcripts of all undergraduate and graduate programs; 3) proof of permanent residence in Hawaii; 4) proof of membership in the local SFPE chapter; and 5) a 50-word statement on why they believe they should receive this scholarship. Financial need is not considered in the selection process. **Deadline for Receipt:** October of each year.

4649 ■ SOCIETY OF FIRE PROTECTION ENGINEERS-PACIFIC NORTHWEST CHAPTER
c/o Eric Tuazon, Scholarship Committee
4322 N.E. Seventh Street
Renton, WA 98059
Tel: (425)917-1683
Fax: (425)917-1705
E-mail: eric@tuazon.com
Web Site: http://www.sfpepnw.org
To provide financial assistance to upper-division students in fire protection engineering from the Pacific Northwest.

Title of Award: Kermit E. Gastfield Memorial Scholarship **Area, Field, or Subject:** Engineering **Level of Education for which Award is Granted:** Four Year College **Number Awarded:** 1 each year. **Funds Available:** The stipend is $1,200. **Duration:** 1 year.

Eligibility Requirements: This program is open to residents of the Pacific Northwest who are enrolled full time as junior or senior engineering students. Applicants must be preparing for a career in fire protection engineering. They must have a GPA of 2.5 or higher. Along with their application, they must submit a 1-page essay on their perception of the fire protection engineering profession and the role of the fire protection engineer in the overall design of a project or product. **Deadline for Receipt:** May of each year.

4650 ■ SOCIETY OF FIRE PROTECTION ENGINEERS-PHILADELPHIA-DELAWARE VALLEY CHAPTER
c/o Jeffrey LaSalle, Scholarship Committee
409 North Easton Road, Suite 1B
Willow Grove, PA 19090
Tel: (215)658-1770
E-mail: jlasalle@lasalleeng.com
Web Site: http://www.dtcc.edu/stanton/sfpe
To provide financial assistance to residents of the Philadelphia-Delaware Valley region who are studying fire protection engineering or a related field at the undergraduate or graduate level.

Title of Award: John D. Cook III Scholarship Award **Area, Field, or Subject:** Engineering; Fires and fire prevention **Level of Education for which Award is Granted:** Graduate, Undergraduate **Number Awarded:** 1 or more each year. **Funds Available:** Stipends range from $500 to $1,500. **Duration:** 1 year.

Eligibility Requirements: This program is open to residents of 1) the state of Delaware; 2) the following counties in Pennsylvania: Adams, Berks, Bradford, Bucks, Carbon, Centre, Chester, Clinton, Columbia, Cumberland, Dauphin, Delaware, Franklin, Juniata, Lackawanna, Lancaster, Lebanon, Lehigh, Luzerne, Lycoming, Mifflin, Monroe, Montgomery, Montour, Northampton, Northumberland, Perry, Philadel-

phia, Pike, Schuylkill, Snyder, Sullivan, Susquehanna, Tioga, Union, Wayne, Wyoming, and York; and 3) the following counties in New Jersey: Atlantic, Burlington, Camden, Cape May, Cumberland, Gloucester, Mercer, Ocean, and Salem. Applicants must be enrolled full time as juniors in an ABET-accredited fire protection engineering program, juniors in an ABET-accredited engineering program with a serious interest in a fire protection engineering career, graduate students in an engineering program with related studies in fire protection, second-year students in a 2-year fire engineering or fire science program with a serious interest in a fire protection engineering career, or juniors in a 4-year fire science program with a serious interest in a fire protection engineering career. They must be U.S. citizens or legal residents and have a GPA of 2.5 or higher. They may attend school in any state. Selection is based on demonstrated academic achievement and performance in the field of fire protection. **Deadline for Receipt:** February of each year.

4651 ■ SOCIETY OF FIRE PROTECTION ENGINEERS-TENNESSEE VALLEY CHAPTER
c/o Roger Rudy, President
Oak Ridge National Laboratory
P.O. Box 2008
Oak Ridge, TN 37831-6424
Tel: (865)241-8263
Fax: (865)241-5253
E-mail: rudyrb@ornl.gov
Web Site: http://www.tvsfpe.org
To provide financial assistance to fire protection engineering students from Tennessee.

Title of Award: John D. Hoogesteger Memorial Scholarship **Area, Field, or Subject:** Engineering **Level of Education for which Award is Granted:** Graduate, Undergraduate **Number Awarded:** Varies each year. Recently, 2 of these scholarships were awarded: 1 to an undergraduate and 1 to a graduate student. **Funds Available:** Stipends are $2,000 for graduate students or $1,000 for undergraduates. **Duration:** 1 year.

Eligibility Requirements: This program is open to undergraduate and graduate students from Tennessee who are preparing for a career in the field of fire protection engineering. **Deadline for Receipt:** April of each year.

4652 ■ SOCIETY OF FLIGHT TEST ENGINEERS
44814 North Elm Avenue
P.O. Box 4037
Lancaster, CA 93539-4037
Tel: (661)949-2095
Fax: (661)949-2096
E-mail: sfte@sfte.org
Web Site: http://www.sfte.org
To provide financial assistance for college to student members and children of members of the Society of Flight Test Engineers (SFTE).

Title of Award: Society of Flight Test Engineers Scholarships **Area, Field, or Subject:** Computer and information sciences; Engineering; Mathematics and mathematical sciences; Physics **Level of Education for which Award is Granted:** Undergraduate **Number Awarded:** 1 or more each year. **Funds Available:** Stipends range from $200 to $2,000. **Duration:** 1 year; recipients may reapply.

Eligibility Requirements: This program is open to college students who have completed at least their freshman year. Applicants must be a student member of SFTE or the child of a member. They must be working on an undergraduate degree in engineering, computer sciences, mathematics, physics, or another technical discipline. Selection is based primarily on academic achievement; financial need is not considered. **Deadline for Receipt:** June of each year.

4653 ■ SOCIETY OF HISPANIC PROFESSIONAL ENGINEERS
5400 East Olympic Boulevard, Suite 210
Los Angeles, CA 90022
Tel: (323)725-3970
Fax: (323)725-0316
Web Site: http://oneshpe.shpe.org
To provide financial assistance to Hispanic undergraduate and graduate students preparing for a career in science, technology, engineering, mathematics, or a related field.

Title of Award: Advancing Hispanic Excellence in Technology, Engineering, Math, and Science (AHETEMS) General Scholarships **Area, Field, or**

Subject: Engineering; Mathematics and mathematical sciences; Science; Technology **Level of Education for which Award is Granted:** Graduate, Undergraduate **Number Awarded:** 1 or more each year. **Funds Available:** Stipends range from $1,000 to $3,000. **Duration:** 1 year.
Eligibility Requirements: This program is open to members of the Society of Hispanic Professional Engineers (SHPE) who are accepted into or attending an accredited 2-year or 4-year college or university in the United States or Puerto Rico. Applicants must be enrolled full time with a major in science, technology, engineering, mathematics, or a related field. High school seniors and undergraduates must have a GPA of 3.0 or higher; graduate students must have a GPA of 3.25 or higher. Along with their application, they must submit a 1-page personal statement covering their family background, community involvement, leadership, academic achievements, research internship and co-op experiences, and short-term and long-term goals and aspirations. Both merit-based and need-based scholarships are available. U.S. citizenship or permanent resident status is required. **Deadline for Receipt:** March of each year. **Additional Information:** Information is also available from the AHETEMS Scholarship Program, University of Texas at Arlington, College of Engineering, Box 19019, Arlington, TX 76019-0019, (817) 272-0776, E-mail: gary. cruz@shpe.org

4654 ■ SOCIETY OF MANUFACTURING ENGINEERS
Attn: SME Education Foundation
One SME Drive
P.O. Box 930
Dearborn, MI 48121-0930
Tel: (313)425-3304
Free: 800-733-4763
Fax: (313)425-3411
E-mail: foundation@sme.org
Web Site: http://www.sme.org
To provide financial assistance to students from Arizona, New Mexico, and southern California who are working on a degree in manufacturing engineering or a closely-related field.
Title of Award: Walt Bartram Memorial Education Award **Area, Field, or Subject:** Engineering, Industrial **Level of Education for which Award is Granted:** Undergraduate **Number Awarded:** 1 each year. **Funds Available:** The stipend is $1,500 per year. Funds are paid to the recipient's institution. **Duration:** 1 year.
Eligibility Requirements: This program is open to graduating high seniors and currently-enrolled college and university students in Desert Pacific Region 12 (Arizona, New Mexico, and southern California) of the Society of Manufacturing Engineers (SME). Applicants must be interested in working on a degree in manufacturing engineering or a closely-related field as a full-time student. College and university applicants must be SME members. All applicants must have a GPA of 3.5 or higher for their senior year of high school. **Deadline for Receipt:** January of each year.

4655 ■ SOCIETY OF MANUFACTURING ENGINEERS
Attn: SME Education Foundation
One SME Drive
P.O. Box 930
Dearborn, MI 48121-0930
Tel: (313)425-3304
Free: 800-733-4763
Fax: (313)425-3411
E-mail: foundation@sme.org
Web Site: http://www.sme.org
To provide financial assistance to undergraduates enrolled in a degree program in manufacturing engineering or manufacturing engineering technology.
Title of Award: Caterpillar Scholars Award **Area, Field, or Subject:** Engineering; Engineering, Industrial **Level of Education for which Award is Granted:** Undergraduate **Number Awarded:** 5 each year. **Funds Available:** The stipend is $2,000. **Duration:** 1 year; may be renewed.
Eligibility Requirements: Applicants must be full-time students attending a degree-granting institution in North America and preparing for a career in manufacturing engineering. They must have completed at least 30 units in a manufacturing engineering or manufacturing engineering technology curriculum with a minimum GPA of 3.0. Minority applicants may apply as incoming freshmen. Need is not considered in awarding scholarships (un-

less 2 or more applicants have equal qualifications). **Deadline for Receipt:** January of each year. **Additional Information:** This program is sponsored by Caterpillar, Inc.

4656 ■ SOCIETY OF MANUFACTURING ENGINEERS
Attn: SME Education Foundation
One SME Drive
P.O. Box 930
Dearborn, MI 48121-0930
Tel: (313)425-3304
Free: 800-733-4763
Fax: (313)425-3411
E-mail: foundation@sme.org
Web Site: http://www.sme.org
To provide financial assistance to students enrolled in a degree program in manufacturing engineering or manufacturing engineering technology in Florida.
Title of Award: Arthur and Gladys Cervenka Scholarship **Area, Field, or Subject:** Engineering; Engineering, Industrial **Level of Education for which Award is Granted:** Undergraduate **Number Awarded:** 1 each year. **Funds Available:** The stipend is $1,250. **Duration:** 1 year; may be renewed.
Eligibility Requirements: This program is open to full-time undergraduate students enrolled in a manufacturing engineering or manufacturing engineering technology program. Applicants must have completed at least 30 units with a GPA of 3.0 or higher. Preference is given (but not limited) to students attending colleges or universities in Florida. Need is not considered in awarding scholarships (unless 2 or more applicants have equal qualifications). **Deadline for Receipt:** January of each year.

4657 ■ SOCIETY OF MANUFACTURING ENGINEERS
Attn: SME Education Foundation
One SME Drive
P.O. Box 930
Dearborn, MI 48121-0930
Tel: (313)425-3304
Free: 800-733-4763
Fax: (313)425-3411
E-mail: foundation@sme.org
Web Site: http://www.sme.org
To provide financial assistance to students working on an undergraduate or graduate degree in engineering in Michigan.
Title of Award: Downriver Detroit Scholarship **Area, Field, or Subject:** Engineering; Engineering, Industrial; Engineering, Mechanical **Level of Education for which Award is Granted:** Graduate, Undergraduate **Number Awarded:** 1 each year. **Funds Available:** The stipend is $1,200. **Duration:** 1 year; may be renewed.
Eligibility Requirements: This program is open to students working on an associate, bachelor's, or graduate degree in manufacturing engineering, mechanical engineering, industrial engineering, industrial technology, or engineering technology at a college or university in Michigan. Applicants must have a GPA of 2.5 or higher. Preference is given in the following order: first, children and grandchildren of current members of Downriver Detroit Chapter 198 of the Society of Manufacturing Engineers (SME); second, student members of chapters sponsored by SME Chapter 198; third, applicants who reside within Michigan; and fourth, applicants planning to attend a college or university in Michigan. **Deadline for Receipt:** January of each year. **Additional Information:** This program was established in 2003.

4658 ■ SOCIETY OF MANUFACTURING ENGINEERS
Attn: SME Education Foundation
One SME Drive
P.O. Box 930
Dearborn, MI 48121-0930
Tel: (313)425-3304
Free: 800-733-4763
Fax: (313)425-3411
E-mail: foundation@sme.org
Web Site: http://www.sme.org
To provide financial assistance to students, especially those from New Jersey, working on an undergraduate degree in engineering.
Title of Award: Fairfield County Scholarship **Area, Field, or Subject:** Engineering; Engineering, Industrial **Level of Education for which**

Award is Granted: Undergraduate **Number Awarded:** 1 each year. **Funds Available:** The stipend is $1,500. **Duration:** 1 year.

Eligibility Requirements: This program is open to students working full time on an undergraduate degree in manufacturing engineering, technology, or a closely-related field at a college or university in the United States or Canada. Applicants must have a GPA of 3.0 or higher. Preference is given to residents of New Jersey and students attending school in the state. **Deadline for Receipt:** January of each year. **Additional Information:** This program is supported by Chapter 6 of the Society of Manufacturing Engineers in Fairfield County, New Jersey.

4659 ■ SOCIETY OF MANUFACTURING ENGINEERS

Attn: SME Education Foundation
One SME Drive
P.O. Box 930
Dearborn, MI 48121-0930
Tel: (313)425-3304
Free: 800-733-4763
Fax: (313)425-3411
E-mail: foundation@sme.org
Web Site: http://www.sme.org

To provide financial assistance to students working on an undergraduate or graduate degree in engineering in Indiana.

Title of Award: Fort Wayne Scholarships **Area, Field, or Subject:** Engineering, Industrial; Engineering, Mechanical **Level of Education for which Award is Granted:** Graduate, Undergraduate **Number Awarded:** 3 each year. **Funds Available:** The stipend is $2,000. **Duration:** 1 year; may be renewed.

Eligibility Requirements: This program is open to students working on an associate, bachelor's, or graduate degree in manufacturing, mechanical, or industrial engineering at a college or university in Indiana. Applicants must have a GPA of 2.5 or higher. Preference is given in the following order: first, children and grandchildren of current members of Fort Wayne Chapter 56 of the Society of Manufacturing Engineers (SME); second, student members of chapters sponsored by SME Chapter 56; third, applicants who reside within Indiana; and fourth, applicants planning to attend a college or university in Indiana. **Deadline for Receipt:** January of each year. **Additional Information:** This program was established in 1989 by SME Chapter 56 in Fort Wayne, but limited to students at schools in northeast Indiana. In 2003, it was amended to support students anywhere in the state.

4660 ■ SOCIETY OF MANUFACTURING ENGINEERS

Attn: SME Education Foundation
One SME Drive
P.O. Box 930
Dearborn, MI 48121-0930
Tel: (313)425-3304
Free: 800-733-4763
Fax: (313)425-3411
E-mail: foundation@sme.org
Web Site: http://www.sme.org

To provide financial assistance to student members of the Society of Manufacturing Engineers (SME) who are working on an undergraduate or graduate degree in manufacturing engineering or a related field.

Title of Award: Future Leaders of Manufacturing Scholarship **Area, Field, or Subject:** Engineering; Engineering, Industrial **Level of Education for which Award is Granted:** Graduate, Undergraduate **Number Awarded:** 10 each year. **Funds Available:** The stipend is $1,000 per year. **Duration:** 1 year.

Eligibility Requirements: This program is open to undergraduate and graduate student members of SME who are working full time on a degree in manufacturing engineering, industrial technology, engineering technology, or a related field. They must be nominated by their SME faculty advisor; each advisor may nominate only 1 student. Letters of nomination must explain why the student should be selected, including participation in the student chapter, accomplishments, awards and honors, work experience, reasons for choosing a career in manufacturing, and how the scholarship will increase the student's leadership skills and career. **Deadline for Receipt:** January of each year.

4661 ■ SOCIETY OF MANUFACTURING ENGINEERS

Attn: SME Education Foundation
One SME Drive

P.O. Box 930
Dearborn, MI 48121-0930
Tel: (313)425-3304
Free: 800-733-4763
Fax: (313)425-3411
E-mail: foundation@sme.org
Web Site: http://www.sme.org

To provide financial assistance to students enrolled in a degree program at universities in Colorado in manufacturing engineering or manufacturing engineering technology.

Title of Award: Clinton J. Helton Manufacturing Scholarship **Area, Field, or Subject:** Engineering; Engineering, Industrial **Level of Education for which Award is Granted:** Undergraduate **Number Awarded:** 2 each year. **Funds Available:** The stipend is $3,000. **Duration:** 1 year; may be renewed.

Eligibility Requirements: Applicants must be full-time students attending Colorado State University or any campus of the University of Colorado and preparing for a career in manufacturing engineering. They must have completed at least 30 units in a manufacturing engineering or manufacturing engineering technology curriculum with a GPA of 3.0 or higher. Need is not considered in awarding scholarships (unless 2 or more applicants have equal qualifications). **Deadline for Receipt:** January of each year.

4662 ■ SOCIETY OF MANUFACTURING ENGINEERS

Attn: SME Education Foundation
One SME Drive
P.O. Box 930
Dearborn, MI 48121-0930
Tel: (313)425-3304
Free: 800-733-4763
Fax: (313)425-3411
E-mail: foundation@sme.org
Web Site: http://www.sme.org

To provide financial assistance to undergraduate women enrolled in a degree program in manufacturing engineering or manufacturing engineering technology.

Title of Award: Lucile B. Kaufman Women's Scholarships **Area, Field, or Subject:** Engineering; Engineering, Industrial **Level of Education for which Award is Granted:** Undergraduate **Number Awarded:** 2 each year. **Funds Available:** The stipend is $1,500. **Duration:** 1 year; may be renewed.

Eligibility Requirements: Applicants must be female students attending a degree-granting institution in North America on a full-time basis and preparing for a career in manufacturing engineering. They must have completed at least 30 units in a manufacturing engineering or manufacturing engineering technology curriculum with a GPA of 3.0 or higher. Need is not considered in awarding scholarships (unless 2 or more applicants have equal qualifications). **Deadline for Receipt:** January of each year.

4663 ■ SOCIETY OF MANUFACTURING ENGINEERS

Attn: SME Education Foundation
One SME Drive
P.O. Box 930
Dearborn, MI 48121-0930
Tel: (313)425-3304
Free: 800-733-4763
Fax: (313)425-3411
E-mail: foundation@sme.org
Web Site: http://www.sme.org

To provide financial assistance to undergraduate students enrolled in a co-op degree program in manufacturing engineering or manufacturing engineering technology.

Title of Award: E. Wayne Kay Co-op Scholarship **Area, Field, or Subject:** Engineering; Engineering, Industrial **Level of Education for which Award is Granted:** Undergraduate **Number Awarded:** 2 each year. **Funds Available:** The stipend is $2,500. **Duration:** 1 year; may be renewed.

Eligibility Requirements: This program is open to full-time undergraduate students enrolled in a manufacturing engineering or technology degree program in North America and working in a co-op program in a manufacturing-related environment. Applicants must have completed at least 30 units in a manufacturing engineering or manufacturing engineering technology curriculum with a GPA of 3.0 or higher. Need is not considered in awarding scholarships (unless 2 or more applicants have equal qualifications). **Deadline for Receipt:** January of each year.

4664 ■ SOCIETY OF MANUFACTURING ENGINEERS

Attn: SME Education Foundation
One SME Drive
P.O. Box 930
Dearborn, MI 48121-0930
Tel: (313)425-3304
Free: 800-733-4763
Fax: (313)425-3411
E-mail: foundation@sme.org
Web Site: http://www.sme.org
To provide financial assistance to students enrolled or planning to enroll in a community college program in manufacturing engineering or manufacturing engineering technology.
Title of Award: E. Wayne Kay Community College Scholarships **Area, Field, or Subject:** Engineering; Engineering, Industrial **Level of Education for which Award is Granted:** Two Year College, Vocational/Occupational **Number Awarded:** 2 each year. **Funds Available:** The stipend is $1,000. **Duration:** 1 year.
Eligibility Requirements: This program is open to entering freshmen and sophomores with less than 60 college credit hours at a community college, trade school, or other 2-year degree-granting institution in the United States or Canada. Applicants must be full-time students interested in preparing for a career in manufacturing engineering or technology and have a GPA of 3.0 or higher. Need is not considered in awarding scholarships (unless 2 or more applicants have equal qualifications). **Deadline for Receipt:** January of each year.

4665 ■ SOCIETY OF MANUFACTURING ENGINEERS

Attn: SME Education Foundation
One SME Drive
P.O. Box 930
Dearborn, MI 48121-0930
Tel: (313)425-3304
Free: 800-733-4763
Fax: (313)425-3411
E-mail: foundation@sme.org
Web Site: http://www.sme.org
To provide financial assistance to high school seniors planning to enroll in a degree program in manufacturing engineering or manufacturing engineering technology.
Title of Award: E. Wayne Kay High School Scholarships **Area, Field, or Subject:** Engineering; Engineering, Industrial **Level of Education for which Award is Granted:** Undergraduate **Number Awarded:** 2 each year. **Funds Available:** The stipend is $1,000 for the first year and $1,500 for the second year. **Duration:** 2 years.
Eligibility Requirements: This program is open to graduating high school seniors who plan to enroll full time in a manufacturing engineering or technology certificate or degree program at a North American institution. Applicants must have a GPA of 3.0 or higher for their senior year in high school. Need is not considered in awarding scholarships (unless 2 or more applicants have equal qualifications). **Deadline for Receipt:** January of each year.

4666 ■ SOCIETY OF MANUFACTURING ENGINEERS

Attn: SME Education Foundation
One SME Drive
P.O. Box 930
Dearborn, MI 48121-0930
Tel: (313)425-3304
Free: 800-733-4763
Fax: (313)425-3411
E-mail: foundation@sme.org
Web Site: http://www.sme.org
To provide financial assistance to undergraduate students enrolled in a degree program in manufacturing engineering or manufacturing engineering technology.
Title of Award: E. Wayne Kay Scholarships **Area, Field, or Subject:** Engineering; Engineering, Industrial **Level of Education for which Award is Granted:** Undergraduate **Number Awarded:** 10 each year. **Funds Available:** The stipend is $2,500. **Duration:** 1 year; may be renewed.

Eligibility Requirements: This program is open to full-time undergraduate students enrolled in a manufacturing engineering or technology degree program at a college or university in North America. Applicants must have completed at least 30 units in a manufacturing engineering or manufacturing engineering technology curriculum with a GPA of 3.0 or higher. Need is not considered in awarding scholarships (unless 2 or more applicants have equal qualifications). **Deadline for Receipt:** January of each year.

4667 ■ SOCIETY OF MANUFACTURING ENGINEERS

Attn: SME Education Foundation
One SME Drive
P.O. Box 930
Dearborn, MI 48121-0930
Tel: (313)425-3304
Free: 800-733-4763
Fax: (313)425-3411
E-mail: foundation@sme.org
Web Site: http://www.sme.org
To provide financial assistance to undergraduate students enrolled in a degree program in manufacturing engineering or manufacturing engineering technology.
Title of Award: Guiliano Mazzetti Scholarships **Area, Field, or Subject:** Engineering; Engineering, Industrial **Level of Education for which Award is Granted:** Undergraduate **Number Awarded:** 3 each year. **Funds Available:** The stipend is $2,000. **Duration:** 1 year.
Eligibility Requirements: This program is open to full-time undergraduate students enrolled in a manufacturing engineering or technology degree program at a college or university in North America. Applicants must have completed a minimum of 30 units in a manufacturing engineering or manufacturing engineering technology curriculum with a GPA of 3.0 or higher. Need is not considered in awarding scholarships (unless 2 or more applicants have equal qualifications). **Deadline for Receipt:** January of each year.

4668 ■ SOCIETY OF MANUFACTURING ENGINEERS

Attn: SME Education Foundation
One SME Drive
P.O. Box 930
Dearborn, MI 48121-0930
Tel: (313)425-3304
Free: 800-733-4763
Fax: (313)425-3411
E-mail: foundation@sme.org
Web Site: http://www.sme.org
To provide financial assistance to students working on an undergraduate or graduate degree in engineering in Indiana.
Title of Award: Clarence and Josephine Myers Scholarship **Area, Field, or Subject:** Engineering, Industrial; Engineering, Mechanical **Level of Education for which Award is Granted:** Graduate, Undergraduate **Number Awarded:** 1 each year. **Funds Available:** The stipend is $1,200. **Duration:** 1 year; may be renewed.
Eligibility Requirements: This program is open to students working on an associate, bachelor's, or graduate degree in manufacturing, mechanical, or industrial engineering at a college or university in Indiana. Applicants must have a GPA of 3.0 or higher. Preference is given to applicants who attending Arsenal Technological High School in Indianapolis, student members of chapters sponsored by Chapter 37 of the Society of Manufacturing Engineers in Indianapolis, and children and grandchildren of current Chapter 37 members. **Deadline for Receipt:** January of each year. **Additional Information:** This program was established in 2003.

4669 ■ SOCIETY OF MANUFACTURING ENGINEERS

Attn: SME Education Foundation
One SME Drive
P.O. Box 930
Dearborn, MI 48121-0930
Tel: (313)425-3304
Free: 800-733-4763
Fax: (313)425-3411
E-mail: foundation@sme.org
Web Site: http://www.sme.org

To provide financial assistance to students working on an undergraduate degree in engineering in North Central states.
Title of Award: North Central Region Scholarship **Area, Field, or Subject:** Engineering; Engineering, Industrial; Engineering, Mechanical **Level of Education for which Award is Granted:** Undergraduate **Number Awarded:** 1 each year. **Funds Available:** The stipend is $1,500. **Duration:** 1 year; may be renewed.
Eligibility Requirements: This program is open to students working on an associate or bachelor's degree in manufacturing engineering, mechanical engineering, industrial engineering, or industrial technology at a 2-year or 4-year college or university in Iowa, Minnesota, Nebraska, North Dakota, South Dakota, Wisconsin, or the upper peninsula of Michigan. Applicants must have a GPA of 3.0 or higher. Preference is given in the following order: first, applicants who are members of Region 9 of the Society of Manufacturing Engineers (SME), their spouses, children, or grandchildren; and second, residents of Iowa, Minnesota, Nebraska, North Dakota, South Dakota, Wisconsin, or the upper peninsula of Michigan. **Deadline for Receipt:** January of each year.

4670 ■ SOCIETY OF MANUFACTURING ENGINEERS

Attn: SME Education Foundation
One SME Drive
P.O. Box 930
Dearborn, MI 48121-0930
Tel: (313)425-3304
Free: 800-733-4763
Fax: (313)425-3411
E-mail: foundation@sme.org
Web Site: http://www.sme.org
To provide financial assistance to students enrolled or planning to enroll in a degree program in manufacturing or industrial technology in Arizona.
Title of Award: Phoenix Scholarships **Area, Field, or Subject:** Engineering; Engineering, Industrial **Level of Education for which Award is Granted:** Four Year College **Number Awarded:** 2 each year. **Funds Available:** The stipend is $2,000. **Duration:** 1 year; may be renewed if the recipient maintains a GPA of 2.5 or higher.
Eligibility Requirements: This program is open to graduating high school seniors and current full-time undergraduate students enrolled or planning to enrolled at an accredited college or university in Arizona. Applicants must be majoring in manufacturing engineering technology, manufacturing technology, industrial technology, or a closely-related field. They must have a GPA of 2.5 or higher. **Deadline for Receipt:** January of each year. **Additional Information:** This program is supported by Chapter 67 of the Society of Manufacturing Engineers.

4671 ■ SOCIETY OF MANUFACTURING ENGINEERS

Attn: SME Education Foundation
One SME Drive
P.O. Box 930
Dearborn, MI 48121-0930
Tel: (313)425-3304
Free: 800-733-4763
Fax: (313)425-3411
E-mail: foundation@sme.org
Web Site: http://www.sme.org
To provide financial assistance to high school seniors who are descendants of members of the Society of Manufacturing Engineers (SME) and plan to enroll in a degree program in manufacturing engineering or manufacturing engineering technology.
Title of Award: SME Education Foundation Family Scholarship **Area, Field, or Subject:** Engineering; Engineering, Industrial **Level of Education for which Award is Granted:** Undergraduate **Number Awarded:** 3 each year: 1 at $20,000 per year and 2 at $5,000. **Funds Available:** Annual stipends of $20,000 or $5,000 are offered. **Duration:** The scholarship of $20,000 per year is for 4 years, if the recipient maintains excellent performance and full-time enrollment. The $5,000 scholarships are for 1 year.
Eligibility Requirements: This program is open to graduating high seniors and undergraduate students with up to 30 credit hours completed who have at least 1 parent or grandparent who has been an SME member in good standing for at least the last 2 years. Applicants must work on a degree in manufacturing engineering, manufacturing engineering technology, or a closely-related engineering field of study at an accredited college

or university in 1 of SME's 14 regions in the United States or Canada. They must have a high school GPA of 3.0 or higher and a minimum score of 1000 on the SAT or 21 on the ACT. Selection is based on overall academic excellence, communication skills, interpersonal skills, demonstrated interest and aptitude for and potential future success in a manufacturing engineering or manufacturing engineering technology-related field, and extracurricular activities. **Deadline for Receipt:** January of each year. **Additional Information:** Recipients must enroll as full-time students.

4672 ■ SOCIETY OF MANUFACTURING ENGINEERS

Attn: SME Education Foundation
One SME Drive
P.O. Box 930
Dearborn, MI 48121-0930
Tel: (313)425-3304
Free: 800-733-4763
Fax: (313)425-3411
E-mail: foundation@sme.org
Web Site: http://www.sme.org
To provide financial assistance to undergraduate students enrolled in a degree program in manufacturing engineering or manufacturing engineering technology.
Title of Award: Society of Manufacturing Engineers Corporate Scholarships **Area, Field, or Subject:** Engineering; Engineering, Industrial **Level of Education for which Award is Granted:** Undergraduate **Number Awarded:** Varies each year. **Funds Available:** The stipend is $5,000. **Duration:** 1 year.
Eligibility Requirements: This program is open to full-time undergraduate students enrolled in a manufacturing engineering or technology degree program at a college or university in North America. Applicants must have a GPA of 3.0 or higher. **Deadline for Receipt:** January of each year.

4673 ■ SOCIETY OF MANUFACTURING ENGINEERS

Attn: SME Education Foundation
One SME Drive
P.O. Box 930
Dearborn, MI 48121-0930
Tel: (313)425-3304
Free: 800-733-4763
Fax: (313)425-3411
E-mail: foundation@sme.org
Web Site: http://www.sme.org
To provide financial assistance to undergraduate students enrolled in a degree program in manufacturing.
Title of Award: Society of Manufacturing Engineers Directors' Scholarships **Area, Field, or Subject:** Engineering, Industrial **Level of Education for which Award is Granted:** Undergraduate **Number Awarded:** 2 each year. **Funds Available:** The stipend is $5,000. **Duration:** 1 year; may be renewed.
Eligibility Requirements: This program is open to full-time undergraduate students enrolled in a manufacturing degree program at a college or university in North America. Applicants must have completed at least 30 units with a GPA of 3.5 or higher and be interested in preparing for a career in manufacturing. Preference is given to students who demonstrate leadership skills in a community, academic, or professional environment. Need is not considered in awarding scholarships (unless 2 or more applicants have equal qualifications). **Deadline for Receipt:** January of each year.

4674 ■ SOCIETY OF MANUFACTURING ENGINEERS

Attn: SME Education Foundation
One SME Drive
P.O. Box 930
Dearborn, MI 48121-0930
Tel: (313)425-3304
Free: 800-733-4763
Fax: (313)425-3411
E-mail: foundation@sme.org
Web Site: http://www.sme.org
To provide financial assistance to students enrolled or planning to enroll in a degree program in manufacturing, mechanical, or industrial engineering in Wisconsin.

Title of Award: Chapter 4 Lawrence A. Wacker Memorial Award **Area, Field, or Subject:** Engineering, Industrial; Engineering, Mechanical **Level of Education for which Award is Granted:** Four Year College **Number Awarded:** 2 each year: 1 to a graduating high school senior and 1 to a student currently enrolled as an undergraduate. **Funds Available:** The stipend is $1,500. **Duration:** 1 year; may be renewed.

Eligibility Requirements: This program is open to graduating high school seniors planning to enroll at a 4-year college or university in Wisconsin and current undergraduates already enrolled at such an institution. Applicants must be seeking a bachelor's degree in manufacturing, mechanical, or industrial engineering and have a GPA of 3.0 or higher. First preference is given to members of Chapter 4 (Milwaukee) of the Society of Manufacturing Engineers (SME), their spouses, children, and grandchildren. Second preference is given to residents of the following Wisconsin counties: Milwaukee, Ozaukee, Washington, and Waukesha. Third preference is given to residents of Wisconsin. Need is not considered in awarding scholarships (unless 2 or more applicants have equal qualifications). **Deadline for Receipt:** January of each year.

4675 ■ SOCIETY OF MANUFACTURING ENGINEERS

Attn: SME Education Foundation
One SME Drive
P.O. Box 930
Dearborn, MI 48121-0930
Tel: (313)425-3304
Free: 800-733-4763
Fax: (313)425-3411
E-mail: foundation@sme.org
Web Site: http://www.sme.org
To provide financial assistance to undergraduate students enrolled in a degree program in manufacturing engineering or manufacturing engineering technology.

Title of Award: Myrtle and Earl Walker Scholarships **Area, Field, or Subject:** Engineering; Engineering, Industrial **Level of Education for which Award is Granted:** Undergraduate **Number Awarded:** 20 each year. **Funds Available:** The scholarship is $2,000 per year. **Duration:** 1 year; may be renewed.

Eligibility Requirements: Applicants must be full-time students attending a North American degree-granting institution or accredited trade school to prepare for a career in manufacturing engineering. They must have completed at least 15 units in a manufacturing engineering or manufacturing engineering technology curriculum with a GPA of 3.0 or higher. Need is not considered (unless 2 or more applicants have equal qualifications). **Deadline for Receipt:** January of each year.

4676 ■ SOCIETY OF MANUFACTURING ENGINEERS

Attn: SME Education Foundation
One SME Drive
P.O. Box 930
Dearborn, MI 48121-0930
Tel: (313)425-3304
Free: 800-733-4763
Fax: (313)425-3411
E-mail: foundation@sme.org
Web Site: http://www.sme.org
To provide financial assistance to students preparing for a career in robotics or automated systems.

Title of Award: William E. Weisel Scholarship Award **Area, Field, or Subject:** Engineering; Engineering, Industrial; Robotics **Level of Education for which Award is Granted:** Undergraduate **Number Awarded:** 1 each year. **Funds Available:** This stipend is $2,000 per year; funds are paid directly to the recipient. **Duration:** 1 year; may be renewed.

Eligibility Requirements: Applicants must be U.S. or Canadian citizens who are full-time students attending a regionally accredited school in engineering or technology and preparing for a career in robotics or automated systems used in manufacturing or robotics used in the medical field. They must have completed at least 30 units with a GPA of 3.5 or higher. Need is not considered in awarding scholarships (unless 2 or more

applicants have identical qualifications). **Deadline for Receipt:** January of each year. **Additional Information:** The recipient will be asked to agree to contribute $1,000 to the William E. Weisel Scholarship Fund at some time in the future.

4677 ■ SOCIETY OF MANUFACTURING ENGINEERS

Attn: SME Education Foundation
One SME Drive
P.O. Box 930
Dearborn, MI 48121-0930
Tel: (313)425-3304
Free: 800-733-4763
Fax: (313)425-3411
E-mail: foundation@sme.org
Web Site: http://www.sme.org
To provide financial assistance to undergraduate and graduate students enrolled in a degree program in engineering in Kansas.

Title of Award: Wichita Scholarship **Area, Field, or Subject:** Engineering; Engineering, Industrial; Engineering, Mechanical **Level of Education for which Award is Granted:** Four Year College, Graduate **Number Awarded:** 1 each year. **Funds Available:** The stipend is $2,000. **Duration:** 1 year; may be renewed.

Eligibility Requirements: This program is open to students working on an associate, bachelor's, or graduate degree at an accredited college or university in Kansas. Applicants must be majoring in manufacturing engineering, mechanical engineering, industrial engineering, industrial technology, or mechanical technology. They must have a GPA of 2.5 or higher. Preference is given in the following order: first, children, grandchildren, and relatives of current members of Wichita Chapter 52 of the Society of Manufacturing Engineers (SME); second, residents of Kansas; and third, students attending a college or university in Kansas. **Deadline for Receipt:** January of each year. **Additional Information:** This program is supported by SME Chapter 52 in Wichita.

4678 ■ SOCIETY OF MEXICAN AMERICAN ENGINEERS AND SCIENTISTS

Attn: Scholarship Committee
711 West Bay Area Boulevard, Suite 206
Webster, TX 77598-4051
Tel: (281)557-3677
Fax: (281)557-3757
E-mail: maesscholars@maes-natl.org
Web Site: http://www.maes-natl.org
To provide financial assistance to undergraduate and graduate student members of the Society of Mexican American Engineers and Scientists (MAES).

Title of Award: Mexican American Engineers and Scientists Scholarship Program **Area, Field, or Subject:** Engineering; Science **Level of Education for which Award is Granted:** Graduate, Undergraduate **Number Awarded:** Varies each year. Recently, 32 of these scholarships were awarded: 3 Padrino/Madrina Scholarships at $4,000, 1 graduate scholarship at $3,000, 2 (the Founder's Scholarship and the President's Scholarship) at $2,500, 1 (the Pipeline Scholarship) at $2,000, 12 general scholarships at $2,000 each, and 13 general scholarships at $1,000 each. **Funds Available:** Stipends are $3,000, $2,000, or $1,000. **Duration:** 1 year.

Eligibility Requirements: This program is open to MAES student members who are full-time undergraduate or graduate students at a college or university in the United States. Community college students must be enrolled in majors that can transfer to a 4-year institution offering a baccalaureate degree. All applicants must be majoring in a field of science or engineering. U.S. citizenship or permanent resident status is required. Selection is based on financial need; academic achievement; personal qualities, strengths, and leadership abilities; and timeliness and completeness of the application. **Deadline for Receipt:** October of each year. **Additional Information:** This program includes Padrino/Madrina Scholarships at $4,000, graduate student scholarships at $3,000, the Founder's Scholarship at $2,500, the President's Scholarship at $2,500, the Pipeline

Scholarship at $2,000, and general scholarships at $2,000 and $1,000. Recipients must attend the MAES International Symposium's Medalla de Oro Banquet in December.

4679 ■ SOCIETY OF NAVAL ARCHITECTS AND MARINE ENGINEERS

Attn: Scholarships Coordinator
601 Pavonia Avenue, Suite 400
Jersey City, NJ 07306
Tel: (201)798-4800
Free: 800-798-2188
Fax: (201)798-4975
E-mail: efaustino@sname.org
Web Site: http://www.sname.org/scholarships_undergraduate.htm
To provide financial assistance for undergraduate study to members of the Society of Naval Architects and Marine Engineers.
Title of Award: Society of Naval Architects and Marine Engineers Undergraduate Scholarships **Area, Field, or Subject:** Architecture, Naval; Engineering, Ocean; Oceanography **Level of Education for which Award is Granted:** Four Year College **Number Awarded:** Varies each year; recently, 24 of these scholarships were awarded. **Funds Available:** Scholarships up to $2,000 per year are available. **Duration:** 1 year; may be renewed 1 additional year.
Eligibility Requirements: Applicants for these scholarships must have been accepted to study naval architecture, marine engineering, ocean engineering, or another field directly related to the marine industry at a participating university. They must be members of the society entering their junior or senior year. **Deadline for Receipt:** Participating universities must submit their nominations to the society by the end of April of each year. **Additional Information:** Applications for these scholarships should be submitted directly to the participating universities: California Maritime Academy, Florida Atlantic University, Florida Institute of Technology, Maine Maritime Academy, Massachusetts Institute of Technology, Memorial University of Newfoundland, Texas A&M University, University of British Columbia, University of California at Berkeley, University of Michigan, University of New Orleans, State University of New York Maritime College, Virginia Polytechnic Institute, or Webb Institute.

4680 ■ SOCIETY OF PETROLEUM ENGINEERS

Attn: Student Activities Manager
222 Palisades Creek Drive
P.O. Box 833836
Richardson, TX 75083-3836
Tel: (972)952-9452
Free: 800-456-6863
Fax: (972)952-9435
E-mail: twhipple@spelink.spe.org
Web Site: http://www.spe.org
To provide financial assistance to high school seniors interested in preparing for a career in petroleum engineering.
Title of Award: Gus Archie Memorial Scholarships **Area, Field, or Subject:** Engineering, Petroleum **Level of Education for which Award is Granted:** Undergraduate **Number Awarded:** 1 or more each year. **Funds Available:** The stipend is $5,000 per year. **Duration:** 1 year; may be renewed for up to 3 additional years, provided the recipient maintains full-time enrollment and a GPA of 3.0 or higher both cumulatively and for the current semester.
Eligibility Requirements: This program is open to graduating high school seniors who have a score of at least 1200 on the SAT or 27 on the ACT and are planning to enroll in a petroleum engineering program at an accredited college or university. Selection is based on academic record, career plans, and financial need. **Deadline for Receipt:** April of each year.

4681 ■ SOCIETY OF PETROLEUM ENGINEERS-ALASKA SECTION

c/o Lara D. Bennett
ConocoPhillips Alaska, Inc.
P.O. Box 100360
Anchorage, AK 99510-0360
Tel: (907)265-6427
E-mail: Lara.D.Bennett@conocophilips.com
Web Site: http://alaska.spe.org/section.cfm?id=17

To provide financial assistance to college students from Alaska who are majoring in engineering in college.
Title of Award: Alaska Section SPE Scholarships **Area, Field, or Subject:** Business; Energy-related areas; Engineering, Petroleum **Level of Education for which Award is Granted:** Undergraduate **Number Awarded:** 8 each year. **Funds Available:** Stipends range from $1,500 to $2,500. **Duration:** 1 year.
Eligibility Requirements: This program is open to students entering or attending an accredited university to work on an undergraduate degree in petroleum engineering, a related discipline, or a career in the petroleum exploration and production industry. Applicants must meet 1 of the following requirements: 1) graduating or graduated from a high school in Alaska; 2) currently enrolled in a college in Alaska; or 3) a dependent of a member of the Society of Petroleum Engineers (SPE) Alaska Section. Along with their application, they must submit essay on their continuing goals in college, eventual career plans, and what role they think the petroleum industry will play in their personal life and the future of Alaska. Financial need is not considered in the selection process. **Deadline for Receipt:** January of each year.

4682 ■ SOCIETY OF PETROLEUM ENGINEERS-POWDER RIVER BASIN SECTION

P.O. Box 3977
Gillette, WY 82717-3977
To provide financial assistance to Wyoming students interested in preparing for a career in the oil and gas industry.
Title of Award: Powder River Basin Section Annual Scholarship Awards **Area, Field, or Subject:** Business; Energy-related areas; Engineering, Petroleum **Level of Education for which Award is Granted:** Undergraduate **Number Awarded:** 5 to 15 each year. **Funds Available:** Stipends range from $250 to $1,000. **Duration:** 1 year.
Eligibility Requirements: This program is open to Wyoming students preparing for a career in the oil and gas industry. Applicants should be majoring in engineering (especially petroleum engineering and petroleum technology), although some of the scholarships may go to non-engineering students. They must be enrolled full time as entering freshmen, sophomores, juniors, or seniors in a 4-year program or freshmen or sophomores in a 2-year program and have a GPA of 2.75 or higher. Along with their application, they must submit a letter that covers their academic qualifications, primary career interests, extracurricular activities, and names of 2 references. Financial need is not considered in the selection process. **Deadline for Receipt:** March of each year. **Additional Information:** Information is also available from Bob Christofferson, Citation Oil and Gas Corporation, 1016 East Lincoln, Gillette, WY 82716, (307) 682-4853, E-mail: bchristofferson@cogc.com.

4683 ■ SOCIETY OF PETROLEUM ENGINEERS-SALT LAKE PETROLEUM SECTION

c/o Roberto Suarez-Rivera
TerraTek
1935 South Fremont Drive
Salt Lake City, UT 84104
Tel: (801)584-2432
Free: 800-372-2522
Fax: (801)584-2406
E-mail: rsuarez@terratek.com
Web Site: http://saltlake.spe.org
To provide financial assistance to engineering students in Utah who are preparing for a career in the petroleum industry.
Title of Award: Richard E. Wyman Scholarship Awards **Area, Field, or Subject:** Business; Energy-related areas; Engineering **Level of Education for which Award is Granted:** Undergraduate **Number Awarded:** 2 each year. **Funds Available:** The stipend is $1,000. **Duration:** 1 year.
Eligibility Requirements: This program is open to students enrolled or planning to enroll at an accredited college or university in Utah in a program leading to a degree in engineering. Applicants must be interested in preparing for a career in the petroleum industry. College students must be recommended by a member of the faculty at their school. High school

seniors must be recommended by a member of the Society of Petroleum Engineers (SPE). **Deadline for Receipt:** February of each year.

4684 ■ SOCIETY OF PLASTICS ENGINEERS

Attn: SPE Foundation
14 Fairfield Drive
Brookfield, CT 06804-0403
Tel: (203)740-5447
Fax: (203)775-1157
E-mail: foundation@4spe.org
Web Site: http://www.4spe.org/foundation/scholarships.php
To provide financial assistance to undergraduate students who have a career interest in the plastics industry.
Title of Award: American Plastics Council (APC)/SPE Plastics Environmental Division Scholarship **Area, Field, or Subject:** Chemistry; Engineering, Chemical; Engineering, Industrial; Engineering, Materials; Engineering, Mechanical; Physics **Level of Education for which Award is Granted:** Undergraduate **Number Awarded:** 1 each year. **Funds Available:** The stipend is $2,500 per year. Funds are paid directly to the recipient's school. **Duration:** 1 year.
Eligibility Requirements: This program is open to full-time undergraduate students at 4-year colleges or in 2-year technical programs. Applicants must 1) have a demonstrated or expressed interest in the plastics industry; 2) be majoring in or taking courses that would be beneficial to a career in the plastics or polymer industry (e.g., plastics engineering, polymer sciences, chemistry, physics, chemical engineering, mechanical engineering, or industrial engineering); 3) be in good academic standing at their school; and 4) be able to document financial need. Along with their application, they must submit 3 letters of recommendation; a high school and/or college transcript; and a 1- to 2-page statement telling why they are interested in the scholarship, their qualifications, and their educational and career goals in the plastics industry. **Deadline for Receipt:** January of each year. **Additional Information:** This scholarship is awarded annually in the names of corporations cited as the *Excellence in Plastics Impact on the Environment* by the Plastics Environmental Division of the Society of Plastics Engineers (SPE).

4685 ■ SOCIETY OF PLASTICS ENGINEERS

Attn: SPE Foundation
14 Fairfield Drive
Brookfield, CT 06804-0403
Tel: (203)740-5447
Fax: (203)775-1157
E-mail: foundation@4spe.org
Web Site: http://www.4spe.org/foundation/scholarships.php
To provide financial assistance to undergraduate student members of the Society of Plastics Engineers (SPE) who have a career interest in the plastics industry.
Title of Award: Blow Molding Division Memorial Scholarships **Area, Field, or Subject:** Engineering, Materials **Level of Education for which Award is Granted:** Four Year College **Number Awarded:** 2 each year. **Funds Available:** The stipend is $4,000 per year. Funds are paid directly to the recipient's school. **Duration:** 2 years.
Eligibility Requirements: This program is open to full-time students completing the second year of a 4-year undergraduate program in plastics engineering. Applicants must 1) have a demonstrated or expressed interest in the plastics industry; 2) be a member of an SPE student chapter; 3) be in good academic standing at their school; and 4) be able to document financial need. Along with their application, they must submit 3 letters of recommendation; a high school and/or college transcript; and a 1- to 2-page statement telling why they are interested in the scholarship, their qualifications, and their educational and career goals in the plastics industry. **Deadline for Receipt:** January of each year.

4686 ■ SOCIETY OF PLASTICS ENGINEERS

Attn: SPE Foundation
14 Fairfield Drive
Brookfield, CT 06804-0403
Tel: (203)740-5447
Fax: (203)775-1157
E-mail: foundation@4spe.org
Web Site: http://www.4spe.org/foundation/scholarships.php

To provide financial assistance to undergraduate and graduate students who have a career interest in the plastics industry.
Title of Award: Composites Division/Harold Giles Scholarship **Area, Field, or Subject:** Chemistry; Engineering, Chemical; Engineering, Industrial; Engineering, Materials; Engineering, Mechanical; Physics **Level of Education for which Award is Granted:** Graduate, Undergraduate **Number Awarded:** 1 each year. **Funds Available:** The stipend is $1,000 per year. Funds are paid directly to the recipient's school. **Duration:** 1 year.
Eligibility Requirements: This program is open to full-time undergraduate and graduate students at 4-year colleges or in 2-year technical programs. Applicants must 1) have a demonstrated or expressed interest in the plastics industry; 2) be majoring in or taking courses that would be beneficial to a career in the plastics or polymer industry (e.g., plastics engineering, polymer sciences, chemistry, physics, chemical engineering, mechanical engineering, or industrial engineering); 3) be in good academic standing at their school; and 4) be able to document financial need. Along with their application, they must submit 3 letters of recommendation; a high school and/or college transcript; and a 1- to 2-page statement telling why they are interested in the scholarship, their qualifications, and their educational and career goals in the plastics industry. **Deadline for Receipt:** January of each year.

4687 ■ SOCIETY OF PLASTICS ENGINEERS

Attn: SPE Foundation
14 Fairfield Drive
Brookfield, CT 06804-0403
Tel: (203)740-5447
Fax: (203)775-1157
E-mail: foundation@4spe.org
Web Site: http://www.4spe.org/foundation/scholarships.php
To provide financial assistance to undergraduate students who have a career interest in the plastics industry.
Title of Award: Robert E. Cramer/Product Design and Development Division/Mid-Michigan Section Scholarship **Area, Field, or Subject:** Chemistry; Engineering, Chemical; Engineering, Industrial; Engineering, Materials; Engineering, Mechanical; Physics **Level of Education for which Award is Granted:** Undergraduate **Number Awarded:** 1 each year. **Funds Available:** The stipend is $1,000 per year. Funds are paid directly to the recipient's school. **Duration:** 1 year.
Eligibility Requirements: This program is open to full-time undergraduate students at 4-year colleges or in 2-year technical programs. Applicants must 1) have a demonstrated or expressed interest in the plastics industry; 2) be majoring in or taking courses that would be beneficial to a career in the plastics or polymer industry (e.g., plastics engineering, polymer sciences, chemistry, physics, chemical engineering, mechanical engineering, or industrial engineering); 3) be in good academic standing at their school; and 4) be able to document financial need. Along with their application, they must submit 3 letters of recommendation; a high school and/or college transcript; and a 1- to 2-page statement telling why they are interested in the scholarship, their qualifications, and their educational and career goals in the plastics industry. **Deadline for Receipt:** January of each year.

4688 ■ SOCIETY OF PLASTICS ENGINEERS

Attn: SPE Foundation
14 Fairfield Drive
Brookfield, CT 06804-0403
Tel: (203)740-5447
Fax: (203)775-1157
E-mail: foundation@4spe.org
Web Site: http://www.4spe.org/foundation/scholarships.php
To provide financial assistance to undergraduate students who have a career interest in the plastics industry.
Title of Award: Robert G. Dailey/Detroit Section Scholarship **Area, Field, or Subject:** Chemistry; Engineering, Chemical; Engineering, Industrial; Engineering, Materials; Engineering, Mechanical; Physics **Level of Education for which Award is Granted:** Undergraduate **Number Awarded:** 1 each year. **Funds Available:** The stipend is $4,000 per year. Funds are paid directly to the recipient's school. **Duration:** 1 year.
Eligibility Requirements: This program is open to full-time undergraduate students at 4-year colleges or in 2-year technical programs. Applicants must 1) have a demonstrated or expressed interest in the plastics

industry; 2) be majoring in or taking courses that would be beneficial to a career in the plastics or polymer industry (e.g., plastics engineering, polymer sciences, chemistry, physics, chemical engineering, mechanical engineering, or industrial engineering); 3) be in good academic standing at their school; and 4) be able to document financial need. Along with their application, they must submit 3 letters of recommendation; a high school and/or college transcript; and a 1- to 2-page statement telling why they are interested in the scholarship, their qualifications, and their educational and career goals in the plastics industry. **Deadline for Receipt:** January of each year.

4689 ■ SOCIETY OF PLASTICS ENGINEERS

Attn: SPE Foundation
14 Fairfield Drive
Brookfield, CT 06804-0403
Tel: (203)740-5447
Fax: (203)775-1157
E-mail: foundation@4spe.org
Web Site: http://www.4spe.org/foundation/scholarships.php
To provide financial assistance to Mexican American undergraduate and graduate students who have a career interest in the plastics industry.
Title of Award: Fleming/Blaszcak Scholarship **Area, Field, or Subject:** Chemistry; Engineering, Chemical; Engineering, Industrial; Engineering, Materials; Engineering, Mechanical; Physics **Level of Education for which Award is Granted:** Four Year College, Graduate **Number Awarded:** 1 each year. **Funds Available:** The stipend is $2,000 per year. Funds are paid directly to the recipient's school. **Duration:** 1 year.
Eligibility Requirements: This program is open to full-time undergraduate and graduate students of Mexican descent who are enrolled in a 4-year college or university. Applicants must be U.S. citizens or legal residents. They must 1) have a demonstrated or expressed interest in the plastics industry; 2) be majoring in or taking courses that would be beneficial to a career in the plastics or polymer industry (e.g., plastics engineering, polymer sciences, chemistry, physics, chemical engineering, mechanical engineering, or industrial engineering); 3) be in good academic standing at their school; and 4) be able to document financial need. Along with their application, they must submit 3 letters of recommendation; a high school and/or college transcript; a 1- to 2-page statement telling why they are interested in the scholarship, their qualifications, and their educational and career goals in the plastics industry; and documentation of their Mexican heritage. **Deadline for Receipt:** January of each year. **Additional Information:** This program is sponsored by Cal Mold Inc. and Formula Plastics.

4690 ■ SOCIETY OF PLASTICS ENGINEERS

Attn: SPE Foundation
14 Fairfield Drive
Brookfield, CT 06804-0403
Tel: (203)740-5447
Fax: (203)775-1157
E-mail: foundation@4spe.org
Web Site: http://www.4spe.org/foundation/scholarships.php
To provide financial assistance to undergraduate and graduate students who have a career interest in the plastics industry and experience in the thermoset industry.
Title of Award: Thermoset Division/James I. MacKenzie Scholarship **Area, Field, or Subject:** Chemistry; Engineering, Chemical; Engineering, Industrial; Engineering, Materials; Engineering, Mechanical; Physics **Level of Education for which Award is Granted:** Graduate, Undergraduate **Number Awarded:** 2 each year: 1 to an undergraduate and 1 to a graduate student. **Funds Available:** The stipend is $1,000 per year. Funds are paid directly to the recipient's school. **Duration:** 1 year.
Eligibility Requirements: This program is open to full-time undergraduate and graduate students at either a 4-year college or in a 2-year technical program. Applicants must have experience in the thermoset industry, such as courses taken, research conducted, or jobs held. They must 1) have a demonstrated or expressed interest in the plastics industry; 2) be majoring in or taking courses that would be beneficial to a career in the plastics or polymer industry (e.g., plastics engineering, polymer sciences, chemistry, physics, chemical engineering, mechanical engineering, or industrial engineering); 3) be in good academic standing at their school; and 4) be able to document financial need. Along with their application, they must submit 3 letters of recommendation; a high school and/or col-

lege transcript; a 1- to 2-page statement telling why they are interested in the scholarship, their qualifications, and their educational and career goals in the plastics industry; and a statement detailing their exposure to the thermoset industry. **Deadline for Receipt:** January of each year.

4691 ■ SOCIETY OF PLASTICS ENGINEERS

Attn: SPE Foundation
14 Fairfield Drive
Brookfield, CT 06804-0403
Tel: (203)740-5447
Fax: (203)775-1157
E-mail: foundation@4spe.org
Web Site: http://www.4spe.org/foundation/scholarships.php
To provide financial assistance to undergraduate and graduate students who have a career interest in the plastics industry.
Title of Award: Ted Neward Scholarships **Area, Field, or Subject:** Chemistry; Engineering, Chemical; Engineering, Industrial; Engineering, Materials; Engineering, Mechanical; Physics **Level of Education for which Award is Granted:** Graduate, Undergraduate **Number Awarded:** 3 each year. **Funds Available:** The stipend is $3,000 per year. Funds are paid directly to the recipient's school. **Duration:** 1 year.
Eligibility Requirements: This program is open to full-time undergraduate and graduate students at 4-year colleges or in 2-year technical programs. Applicants must 1) have a demonstrated or expressed interest in the plastics industry; 2) be majoring in or taking courses that would be beneficial to a career in the plastics or polymer industry (e.g., plastics engineering, polymer sciences, chemistry, physics, chemical engineering, mechanical engineering, or industrial engineering); 3) be in good academic standing at their school; and 4) be able to document financial need. U.S. citizenship is required. Along with their application, they must submit 3 letters of recommendation; a high school and/or college transcript; and a 1- to 2-page statement telling why they are interested in the scholarship, their qualifications, and their educational and career goals in the plastics industry. **Deadline for Receipt:** January of each year.

4692 ■ SOCIETY OF PLASTICS ENGINEERS

Attn: SPE Foundation
14 Fairfield Drive
Brookfield, CT 06804-0403
Tel: (203)740-5447
Fax: (203)775-1157
E-mail: foundation@4spe.org
Web Site: http://www.4spe.org/foundation/scholarships.php
To provide financial assistance to undergraduate students who have a career interest in the plastics industry.
Title of Award: Polymer Modifiers and Additives Division Scholarships **Area, Field, or Subject:** Chemistry; Engineering, Chemical; Engineering, Industrial; Engineering, Materials; Engineering, Mechanical; Physics **Level of Education for which Award is Granted:** Undergraduate **Number Awarded:** 4 each year. **Funds Available:** The stipend is $4,000 per year. Funds are paid directly to the recipient's school. **Duration:** 1 year.
Eligibility Requirements: This program is open to full-time undergraduate students at 4-year colleges or in 2-year technical programs. Applicants must 1) have a demonstrated or expressed interest in the plastics industry; 2) be majoring in or taking courses that would be beneficial to a career in the plastics or polymer industry (e.g., plastics engineering, polymer sciences, chemistry, physics, chemical engineering, mechanical engineering, or industrial engineering); 3) be in good academic standing at their school; and 4) be able to document financial need. Along with their application, they must submit 3 letters of recommendation; a high school and/or college transcript; and a 1- to 2-page statement telling why they are interested in the scholarship, their qualifications, and their educational and career goals in the plastics industry. **Deadline for Receipt:** January of each year.

4693 ■ SOCIETY OF PLASTICS ENGINEERS

Attn: SPE Foundation
14 Fairfield Drive
Brookfield, CT 06804-0403
Tel: (203)740-5447
Fax: (203)775-1157
E-mail: foundation@4spe.org

Web Site: http://www.4spe.org/foundation/scholarships.php
To provide financial assistance to undergraduate and graduate students who have a career interest in the plastics industry.
Title of Award: Society of Plastics Engineers Foundation Scholarships **Area, Field, or Subject:** Chemistry; Engineering, Chemical; Engineering, Industrial; Engineering, Materials; Engineering, Mechanical; Physics **Level of Education for which Award is Granted:** Graduate, Undergraduate **Number Awarded:** 10 to 12 each year. **Funds Available:** Stipends range up to $4,000 per year. Funds are paid directly to the recipient's school. **Duration:** 1 year; may be renewed for up to 3 additional years.
Eligibility Requirements: This program is open to full-time undergraduate and graduate students at 4-year colleges or in 2-year technical programs. Applicants must 1) have a demonstrated or expressed interest in the plastics industry; 2) be majoring in or taking courses that would be beneficial to a career in the plastics or polymer industry (e.g., plastics engineering, polymer sciences, chemistry, physics, chemical engineering, mechanical engineering, or industrial engineering); 3) be in good academic standing at their school; and 4) be able to document financial need. Along with their application, they must submit 3 letters of recommendation; a high school and/or college transcript; and a 1- to 2-page statement telling why they are interested in the scholarship, their qualifications, and their educational and career goals in the plastics industry. **Deadline for Receipt:** January of each year.

4694 ■ SOCIETY OF PLASTICS ENGINEERS

Attn: SPE Foundation
14 Fairfield Drive
Brookfield, CT 06804-0403
Tel: (203)740-5447
Fax: (203)775-1157
E-mail: foundation@4spe.org
Web Site: http://www.4spe.org/foundation/scholarships.php
To provide college scholarships to students who have a career interest in the plastics industry and experience in the thermoforming industry.
Title of Award: Thermoforming Division Memorial Scholarships **Area, Field, or Subject:** Chemistry; Engineering, Chemical; Engineering, Industrial; Engineering, Materials; Engineering, Mechanical; Physics **Level of Education for which Award is Granted:** Graduate, Undergraduate **Number Awarded:** 2 each year. **Funds Available:** The stipend is $5,000 per year. Funds are paid directly to the recipient's school. **Duration:** 1 year.
Eligibility Requirements: This program is open to full-time undergraduate and graduate students at either a 4-year college or in a 2-year technical program. Applicants must have experience in the thermoforming industry, such as courses taken, research conducted, or jobs held. They must 1) have a demonstrated or expressed interest in the plastics industry; 2) be majoring in or taking courses that would be beneficial to a career in the plastics or polymer industry (e.g., plastics engineering, polymer sciences, chemistry, physics, chemical engineering, mechanical engineering, or industrial engineering); 3) be in good academic standing at their school; and 4) be able to document financial need. Along with their application, they must submit 3 letters of recommendation; a high school and/or college transcript; a 1to 2-page statement telling why they are interested in the scholarship, their qualifications, and their educational and career goals in the plastics industry; and a statement detailing their exposure to the thermoforming industry. **Deadline for Receipt:** January of each year.

4695 ■ SOCIETY OF PLASTICS ENGINEERS

Attn: SPE Foundation
14 Fairfield Drive
Brookfield, CT 06804-0403
Tel: (203)740-5447
Fax: (203)775-1157
E-mail: foundation@4spe.org
Web Site: http://www.4spe.org/foundation/scholarships.php
To provide financial assistance to undergraduate students who have a career interest in the plastics industry.
Title of Award: Thermoplastic Materials and Foams Division Scholarship **Area, Field, or Subject:** Engineering; Science **Level of Education for which Award is Granted:** Undergraduate **Number Awarded:** 1 each year. **Funds Available:** The stipend is $1,000 per year. Funds are paid directly to the recipient's school. **Duration:** 1 year.

Eligibility Requirements: This program is open to full-time undergraduate students at 4-year colleges or in 2-year technical programs. Applicants must 1) have a demonstrated or expressed interest in the plastics industry; 2) be majoring in a science or engineering program; 3) be in good academic standing at their school; and 4) be able to document financial need. Along with their application, they must submit 3 letters of recommendation; a high school and/or college transcript; and a 1- to 2-page statement telling why they are interested in the scholarship, their qualifications, and their educational and career goals in the plastics industry. **Deadline for Receipt:** January of each year.

4696 ■ SOCIETY OF PLASTICS ENGINEERS

Attn: SPE Foundation
14 Fairfield Drive
Brookfield, CT 06804-0403
Tel: (203)740-5447
Fax: (203)775-1157
E-mail: foundation@4spe.org
Web Site: http://www.4spe.org/foundation/scholarships.php
To provide financial assistance to undergraduate students who have a career interest in the plastics industry.
Title of Award: Vinyl Plastics Division Scholarship **Area, Field, or Subject:** Chemistry; Engineering, Chemical; Engineering, Industrial; Engineering, Materials; Engineering, Mechanical; Physics **Level of Education for which Award is Granted:** Undergraduate **Number Awarded:** 1 each year. **Funds Available:** The stipend is $1,000 per year. Funds are paid directly to the recipient's school. **Duration:** 1 year.
Eligibility Requirements: This program is open to full-time undergraduate students at 4-year colleges or in 2-year technical programs. Applicants must 1) have a demonstrated or expressed interest in the plastics industry; 2) be majoring in or taking courses that would be beneficial to a career in the plastics or polymer industry (e.g., plastics engineering, polymer sciences, chemistry, physics, chemical engineering, mechanical engineering, or industrial engineering); 3) be in good academic standing at their school; and 4) be able to document financial need. Along with their application, they must submit 3 letters of recommendation; a high school and/or college transcript; and a 1- to 2-page statement telling why they are interested in the scholarship, their qualifications, and their educational and career goals in the plastics industry. Preference is given to applicants with experience in the vinyl industry, such as courses taken, research conducted, or jobs held. **Deadline for Receipt:** January of each year.

4697 ■ SOCIETY OF WOMEN ENGINEERS-BALTIMORE-WASHINGTON SECTION

c/o Kathleen Hufnagel, Scholarship Chair
1601 Barnstead Drive
Reston, VA 20194
E-mail: Kphufnagel@cs.com
Web Site: http://www.swe-bws.org
To provide financial assistance to women who reside or attend school in the Washington, D.C. area and are interested in studying engineering in college or graduate school.
Title of Award: Baltimore-Washington Section Scholarships **Area, Field, or Subject:** Engineering **Level of Education for which Award is Granted:** Graduate, Undergraduate **Number Awarded:** Varies each year; recently, 4 of these scholarships (2 at $1,500 and 2 at $1,000) were awarded. **Funds Available:** Stipends are $1,500 or $1,000. **Duration:** 1 year.
Eligibility Requirements: This program is open to women who reside in northern Virginia, Washington, D.C., or Maryland or who are or will be students at universities or colleges in that area. Student members of the Society of Women Engineers (SWE) are given preference. Applicants must be enrolled or accepted for enrollment in an ABET-accredited or SWE-approved engineering degree program. They may be entering freshmen, current college students, reentry women, or graduate students, but they must have a GPA of 3.0 or higher. U.S. citizenship is required. Students who receive tuition reimbursement from an employer are not eligible. Selection is based on merit and an essay on what influenced the applicant to select her current course of study, why she would like to be

an engineer, and/or how she believes she will make a difference as an engineer. **Deadline for Receipt:** February of each year.

4698 ■ SOCIETY OF WOMEN ENGINEERS-BIRMINGHAM SECTION
P.O. Box 361311
Birmingham, AL 35236
Web Site: http://www.swebham.org
To provide financial assistance to female high school seniors entering a college or university in Alabama to study engineering.
Title of Award: Birmingham Section Scholarships **Area, Field, or Subject:** Engineering **Level of Education for which Award is Granted:** Undergraduate **Number Awarded:** 1 or more each year. **Funds Available:** A stipend is awarded (amount not specified). **Duration:** 1 year.
Eligibility Requirements: This program is open to female high school graduating seniors entering their freshman year at a college or university in Alabama that is accredited by the Accreditation Board for Engineering and Technology (ABET). Applicants must be U.S. citizens or permanent residents. Selection is based on national test scores (10 points); overall GPA, early college courses, and awards and honors (15 points); completion of high school mathematics and science courses (15 points); school leadership and extracurricular activities (15 points); community and civic activities (15 points); communication skills (10 points); financial need (5 points); and an essay on career goals and need for the scholarship (15 points). **Deadline for Receipt:** April of each year. **Additional Information:** Information is also available from Stephanie Swindle, 164 Belvedere Place, Alabaster, AL 35007, E-mail: Stephanie.Swindle@swe.org.

4699 ■ SOCIETY OF WOMEN ENGINEERS-CENTRAL NEW MEXICO SECTION
Attn: Georgianne Peek, Scholarship Chair
Sandia National Laboratories
Energy Storage Systems
P.O. Box 5800
Albuquerque, NM 87185-0710
Tel: (505)844-9855
Fax: (505)844-0968
E-mail: ghpeek@sandia.gov
Web Site: http://www.swecnm.org/scholarship.html
To provide financial assistance to female high school seniors in New Mexico who are interested in studying science or engineering in college.
Title of Award: Colleen Conley Memorial Scholarship **Area, Field, or Subject:** Engineering; Science **Level of Education for which Award is Granted:** Undergraduate **Number Awarded:** 1 each year. **Funds Available:** The stipend is $1,000 per year. **Duration:** 1 year; may be renewed up to 3 additional years as long as the recipient remains enrolled at least half time, makes minimum progress toward a degree, and maintains a GPA of 2.5 or higher.
Eligibility Requirements: This program is open to women graduating from high schools in New Mexico with a GPA of 3.0 or higher. Applicants must be interested in majoring in science, engineering technology, or engineering in college. Preference is given to students who are the first person in their immediate family within their generation to attend college. **Deadline for Receipt:** March of each year.

4700 ■ SOCIETY OF WOMEN ENGINEERS-DETROIT SECTION
Student Services Committee (Scholarships)
Attn: Scholarship Chair
P.O. Box 2978
Southfield, MI 48037-2978
Tel: (248)576-9703
E-mail: LLG2@dcx.com
Web Site: http://www.swe.org/SWE/RegionH/Detroit/HSscholarships.html
To provide financial assistance to female high school seniors in Michigan who are interested in studying engineering in college.
Title of Award: Detroit Section Scholarships **Area, Field, or Subject:** Engineering **Level of Education for which Award is Granted:** Undergraduate **Number Awarded:** Varies each year; recently, 2 of these scholarships were awarded. **Funds Available:** The stipend is $3,000. **Duration:** 1 year.
Eligibility Requirements: This program is open to female seniors at high schools in Michigan who are planning to enroll the following fall at a university or college with an ABET-accredited engineering program. Selection is based on an essay on why the applicant wants to be an

engineer (30%); awards, honors, and scholarships received in high school (25%); leadership, activities (community, church, school, etc.), and employment (35%); and academic performance (10%). Students in the top 10% of their class receive an additional 5%. **Deadline for Receipt:** March of each year.

4701 ■ SOCIETY OF WOMEN ENGINEERS-EASTERN WASHINGTON SECTION
Attn: Sandy Brower, Scholarship Committee Chair
P.O. Box 364
Richland, WA 99352
Tel: (509)375-3112
E-mail: embrower@aol.com
Web Site: http://www.eastwashingtonswe.org/scholarship.htm
To provide financial assistance to nontraditional women engineering students who live in the northwestern United States.
Title of Award: Wanda Munn Scholarship **Area, Field, or Subject:** Engineering **Level of Education for which Award is Granted:** Graduate, Undergraduate **Number Awarded:** 1 each year. **Funds Available:** The stipend is $1,000. **Duration:** 1 year.
Eligibility Requirements: This program is open to women residents of Alaska, Idaho, Montana, Oregon, and Washington who are nontraditional students attempting to reenter the work force or to assist in career growth and potential. Applicants must have completed at least 2 years of full-time study at an ABET-accredited college or university (do not have to be in an engineering curriculum) and be able to enter an undergraduate or graduate engineering program in the following year. Along with their application, they must submit 2 essays of 100 to 300 words: 1) their short-term and long-term career goals and their plan to reach those goals; and 2) a major obstacle they have encountered in their life, how they responded to it, and how they overcame it. Financial need and academic success are considered in the selection process, but greater weight is given to the applicant's motivation, leadership potential, and ability to follow projects through to completion. All other factors being equal, preference is given to residents of eastern Washington. **Deadline for Receipt:** March of each year.

4702 ■ SOCIETY OF WOMEN ENGINEERS-MINNESOTA SECTION
Attn: Scholarship Committee
P.O. Box 582813
Minneapolis, MN 55458-2813
E-mail: scholarships@swe-mn.org
Web Site: http://www.swe-mn.org
To provide financial assistance to upper-division women studying engineering or computer science at colleges and universities in Minnesota, North Dakota, and South Dakota.
Title of Award: Minnesota Section Scholarship **Area, Field, or Subject:** Computer and information sciences; Engineering **Level of Education for which Award is Granted:** Four Year College **Number Awarded:** At least 1 each year. Recently, 2 additional scholarships (1 at $1,500 and 1 at $1,000) were also awarded through the Corporate Partner Scholarship program. **Funds Available:** The stipend is at least $1,000. **Duration:** 1 year.
Eligibility Requirements: This program is open to women entering their junior or senior year at an accredited engineering program in Minnesota, North Dakota, or South Dakota. Applicants must be student members of the Society of Women Engineers (SWE) majoring in engineering or computer science. Selection is based on potential to succeed as an engineer (20 points), communication skills (10 points), extracurricular or community involvement and leadership skills (10 points), demonstration of work experience and successes (10 points), and academic success (5 points). **Deadline for Receipt:** March of each year. **Additional Information:** Through the Corporate Partner Scholarship program, additional scholarships may be funded by corporate sponsors. Recently, those sponsors included Ecolab and MTS Systems Corporation. Information is also available from Leanne Knutson, Scholarship Co-Chair, Rosemount Inc., 8200 Market Boulevard, M/S PF17, Chanhassen, MN 55317, (952) 949-7578.

4703 ■ SOCIETY OF WOMEN ENGINEERS-ROCKY MOUNTAIN SECTION
Attn: Scholarship Committee Chair
P.O. Box 260692
Lakewood, CO 80226-0692

Tel: (303)893-0822
Web Site: http://www.swe.org/SWE/Region1/Sections/RockyMtn/Scholarships.htm
To provide financial assistance to women who are working on an undergraduate or graduate degree in engineering at colleges and universities in Colorado and Wyoming.
Title of Award: Rocky Mountain Section College Scholarships **Area, Field, or Subject:** Computer and information sciences; Engineering **Level of Education for which Award is Granted:** Graduate, Undergraduate **Number Awarded:** 3 each year. **Funds Available:** The stipend is $1,000. **Duration:** 1 year.
Eligibility Requirements: This program is open to women who are enrolled as an undergraduate or graduate engineering student in an ABET-accredited engineering or computer science program in Colorado or Wyoming (excluding zip codes 80800-81599). Applicants must have a GPA of 3.0 or higher. They must include with their application an essay on why they have chosen an engineering major, what they will accomplish or how they believe they will make a difference as an engineer, and who or what influenced them to study engineering. Selection is based on merit.
Deadline for Receipt: January of each year. **Additional Information:** Information is also available from Mary Ann Tavery, P.O. Box 12260, Denver, CO 80212. This program includes the following named scholarships: the Dorolyn Lines Scholarship, the Lottye Miner Scholarship, and the Rocky Mountain Section Pioneer Scholarship.

4704 ■ SOUTH CAROLINA SPACE GRANT CONSORTIUM

c/o College of Charleston
Department of Geology and Environmental Sciences
66 George Street
Charleston, SC 29424
Tel: (843)953-5463
Fax: (843)953-5446
E-mail: scozzarot@cofc.edu
Web Site: http://www.cofc.edu/~scsgrant/scholar/overview.html
To provide financial assistance to upper-division and graduate students in South Carolina who are preparing for a career as a science and mathematics teacher.
Title of Award: South Carolina Space Grant Consortium Pre-Service Teacher Scholarships **Area, Field, or Subject:** Aerospace sciences; Astronomy and astronomical sciences; Education; Engineering; Engineering, Aerospace/Aeronautical/Astronautical; Environmental conservation; Environmental science; Science; Space and planetary sciences **Level of Education for which Award is Granted:** Four Year College, Graduate **Number Awarded:** Varies each year. **Funds Available:** The stipend is $2,000. Funds may be used for such expenses as 1) partial payment of tuition; 2) travel and registration for attending science and mathematics education workshops or conferences for the purpose of professional development; 3) purchase of supplies for student teaching activities; or 4) other supportive activities that lead to successful professional development and graduation as an educator in South Carolina. **Duration:** 1 year.
Eligibility Requirements: This program is open to juniors, seniors, and graduate students at member institutions of the South Carolina Space Grant Consortium. Applicants must be working on a teaching certificate in science, mathematics, or engineering. Their areas of interest may include, but are not limited to, the basic sciences, astronomy, science education, planetary science, environmental studies, or engineering. U.S. citizenship is required. Selection is based on academic qualifications of the applicant; 2 letters of recommendation; a description of past activities, current interests, and future plans concerning a space science or aerospace-related field; a sample lesson plan using curriculum materials available from the U.S. National Aeronautics and Space Administration (NASA); and faculty sponsorship. Women, minorities, and persons with disabilities are encouraged to apply. **Deadline for Receipt:** January of each year.
Additional Information: Members of the consortium are Benedict College, The Citadel, College of Charleston, Clemson University, Coastal Carolina University, Furman University, University of South Carolina, Wofford College, South Carolina State University, The Medical University of South Carolina, and University of the Virgin Islands. This program is funded by NASA.

4705 ■ SOUTH CAROLINA SPACE GRANT CONSORTIUM

c/o College of Charleston
Department of Geology and Environmental Sciences

66 George Street
Charleston, SC 29424
Tel: (843)953-5463
Fax: (843)953-5446
E-mail: scozzarot@cofc.edu
Web Site: http://www.cofc.edu/~scsgrant/scholar/overview.html
To provide financial assistance to outstanding science students in South Carolina.
Title of Award: Kathryn D. Sullivan Science and Engineering Fellowship **Area, Field, or Subject:** Engineering; Natural sciences **Level of Education for which Award is Granted:** Four Year College **Number Awarded:** 1 each year. **Funds Available:** The stipend is $7,000 per year. **Duration:** 1 year.
Eligibility Requirements: This program is open to students entering their senior year at a college or university in South Carolina or at the University of the Virgin Islands. Applicants must be studying natural science or engineering. Selection is based on academic qualifications of the applicant; 2 letters of recommendation; a description of past activities, current interests, and future plans concerning natural science-related and engineering-related studies; and faculty sponsorship. U.S. citizenship is required. **Deadline for Receipt:** January of each year. **Additional Information:** This program is funded by the National Aeronautics and Space Administration (NASA) through its Space Grant program and the National Oceanic and Atmospheric Administration (NOAA) through its Sea Grant program.

4706 ■ TANANA CHIEFS COUNCIL, LLC

Attn: Scholarship Program
P.O. Box 1643
Valdez, AK 99686
Tel: (907)835-2563
To provide financial assistance for college or graduate school to Native Americans interested in preparing for a career on the Trans Alaska Pipeline System (TAPS).
Title of Award: TCC Scholarship Program **Area, Field, or Subject:** Business administration; Engineering, Electrical; Engineering, Mechanical; Information science and technology; Personnel administration/human resources; Protective services **Level of Education for which Award is Granted:** Graduate, Undergraduate **Number Awarded:** Varies each year. **Funds Available:** A stipend is awarded (amount not specified). **Duration:** 1 year.
Eligibility Requirements: This program is open to Alaska Natives who are enrolled or planning to enroll in an accredited college, university, graduate school, or vocational training program. Applicants must be interested in preparing for a career as an electrical or mechanical engineer, quality assurance or inspection professional, safety professional, planner or scheduler, project manager, or instrument technician. Other fields of study that may qualify include business, information technology, process industry environment, human resources, and security planning. They must be interested in seeking employment after graduation with Alyeska Pipeline Service Company and its contractors on the TAPS. Undergraduate students must have a GPA of 2.0 or higher; graduate students must have a GPA of 3.0 or higher. Along with their application, they must submit a copy of their Certificate of Degree of Indian Blood, transcripts, 2 letters of recommendation, a resume, and documentation of financial need. Selection is based on GPA (20 points), academic standing (20 points), letters of recommendation (20 points), a personal essay (30 points), and the resume (10 points). **Deadline for Receipt:** May of each year. **Additional Information:** Funding for this program is provided by Alyeska.

4707 ■ TAU BETA PI

c/o University of Tennessee at Knoxville
508 Dougherty Engineering Building
1512 Middle Drive
P.O. Box 2697
Knoxville, TN 37901-2697
Tel: (865)546-4578
Fax: (865)546-4579
E-mail: Fellowships@tbp.org
Web Site: http://www.tbp.org/pages/Publications/InformationBook/Programs/StudentLoans.cfm

To provide educational loans to undergraduate and graduate members of Tau Beta Pi, the engineering honor society.

Title of Award: Tau Beta Pi Student Loan Fund **Area, Field, or Subject:** Engineering **Level of Education for which Award is Granted:** Graduate, Undergraduate **Number Awarded:** Varies each year; since the program was established, 1,760 loans worth more than $809,000 have been approved. **Funds Available:** Loans range from $25 to $2,500. The rate of interest is 6% per year. **Duration:** Up to 3 years.

Eligibility Requirements: This program is open to undergraduate and graduate members of the society who need assistance to remain in school. Undergraduate applications must be approved by the president, recording secretary, and treasurer of the members' chapter and by the head of the department in which they are studying; graduate applications must be approved by the students' department head. **Deadline for Receipt:** Applications may be submitted at any time. **Additional Information:** This program was established in 1935.

4708 ■ TAU BETA PI

c/o University of Tennessee at Knoxville
508 Dougherty Engineering Building
1512 Middle Drive
P.O. Box 2697
Knoxville, TN 37901-2697
Tel: (865)546-4578
Fax: (865)546-4579
E-mail: Fellowships@tbp.org
Web Site: http://www.tbp.org/pages/Publications/InformationBook/Programs/Scholarships.cfm

To provide financial assistance to undergraduate members of Tau Beta Pi, the engineering honor society, who are entering their senior year.

Title of Award: Tau Beta Pi Undergraduate Scholarships **Area, Field, or Subject:** Engineering **Level of Education for which Award is Granted:** Four Year College **Number Awarded:** Varies each year; recently, 69 of these scholarships were awarded. Of those, 50 were Leroy A. Record Scholarships, which include financial need as a selection criterion. **Funds Available:** The stipend is $2,000, payable in 2 increments (in September and January). **Duration:** 1 year.

Eligibility Requirements: This program is open to members of the society who are entering their senior year of full-time undergraduate engineering study. Applicants must submit statements on 1) their plan or purpose for the next 3 years, and 2) how this scholarship will help them meet a financial need in attaining their college education that cannot be met through other sources of financial aid. Selection is based on academic standing, contribution to campus or community activities, and 2 letters of reference; financial need is also considered for some of the scholarships. **Deadline for Receipt:** February of each year. **Additional Information:** This program, established in 1998, includes the following named scholarships: the R.H. Nagel Scholarship (awarded to the applicant judged most outstanding), the Charles R. Dodson Scholarship (preference given to members of Maryland Beta chapter), the Vincent A. Stabile Scholarship (established in 1999), the Leroy E. Record Scholarships (consideration also given to financial need), the Ruth M. and Cleveland L. Campbell Scholarship (consideration also given to community service and ethical standards), the Elsa and Peter Soderberg Scholarship (first awarded in 1998), the Tau Beta Pi Distinguished Alumnus Scholarship (established in 2002), the A.C. Scribner Scholarship (established in 2003), the Tau Beta Pi Mentor Scholarship (established in 2003), and the Albert H. Winkler Scholarship (established in 2004). Other scholarships are provided by the Alabama Power Foundation, Fluor, and General Motors. Information is also available from D. Stephen Pierre, Jr., Director of Fellowships, Alabama Power Company, 150 St. Joseph Street, P.O. Box 2247, Mobile, AL 36652-2247, (251) 694-2512, Fax: (251) 694-2310.

4709 ■ TEXAS ASPHALT PAVEMENT ASSOCIATION

Attn: Scholarships
149 Commercial Drive
Buda, TX 78610
Tel: (512)312-2099
E-mail: info@txhotmix.org
Web Site: http://www.txhotmix.org

To provide financial assistance to undergraduate and graduate students in Texas who are preparing for a career in the hot mix asphalt (HMA) field.

Title of Award: Texas Asphalt Pavement Association Scholarships **Area, Field, or Subject:** Construction; Engineering, Civil **Level of Education for which Award is Granted:** Graduate, Undergraduate **Number Awarded:** 8 each year. **Funds Available:** The stipend is $1,500. **Duration:** 1 year; sophomores and juniors may reapply.

Eligibility Requirements: This program is open to residents of Texas who are enrolled as sophomores, juniors, seniors, and graduate students at a college or university. Applicants must be working full time on a baccalaureate or graduate degree in civil engineering or construction science, management, or technology with a strong interest in the HMA filed. Preference is given to students who have demonstrated their interest in HMA through summer or part-time employment. Selection is based on academic record and demonstrated interest in the HMA field. **Deadline for Receipt:** May of each year.

4710 ■ TEXAS SPACE GRANT CONSORTIUM

Attn: Administrative Assistant
3925 West Braker Lane, Suite 200
Austin, TX 78759
Tel: (512)471-3583
Free: 800-248-8742
Fax: (512)471-3585
E-mail: scholarships@tsgc.utexas.edu
Web Site: http://www.tsgc.utexas.edu/grants

To provide financial assistance to upper-division and medical students at Texas universities working on degrees in the fields of space science and engineering.

Title of Award: Columbia Crew Memorial Undergraduate Scholarships **Area, Field, or Subject:** Aerospace sciences; Biological and clinical sciences; Chemistry; Engineering, Aerospace/Aeronautical/Astronautical; Engineering, Chemical; Engineering, Electrical; Engineering, Industrial; Engineering, Mechanical; Geology; Mathematics and mathematical sciences; Physics; Space and planetary sciences **Level of Education for which Award is Granted:** Doctorate, Undergraduate **Number Awarded:** Varies each year; recently, 29 of these scholarships were awarded. **Funds Available:** The stipend is $1,000. **Duration:** 1 year; nonrenewable.

Eligibility Requirements: Applicants must be U.S. citizens, eligible for financial assistance, and registered for full-time study at a participating college or university. Applicants must be a sophomore at a 2-year institution, a junior or senior at a 4-year institution, or a first- or second-year student at a medical school. Supported fields of study have included aerospace engineering, biology, chemical engineering, chemistry, electrical engineering, geology, industrial engineering, mathematics, mechanical engineering, and physics. The program encourages participation by members of groups underrepresented in science and engineering (persons with disabilities, women, African Americans, Hispanic Americans, Native Americans, and Pacific Islanders). Selection is based on excellence in academics, participation in space education projects, participation in research projects, and exhibited leadership qualities. **Deadline for Receipt:** March of each year. **Additional Information:** In 2003, the Texas Space Grant Consortium renamed its undergraduate scholarship program in honor of the 7 Space Shuttle Columbia astronauts. The participating universities are Baylor University, Lamar University, Prairie View A&M University, Rice University, San Jacinto College, Southern Methodist University, Sul Ross State University, Texas A&M University (including Kingsville and Corpus Christi campuses), Texas Christian University, Texas Southern University, Texas Tech University, Trinity University, University of Houston (including Clear Lake and Downtown campuses), University of Texas at Arlington, University of Texas at Austin, University of Texas at Dallas, University of Texas at El Paso, University of Texas at San Antonio, and University of Texas/Pan American. This program is funded by the National Aeronautics and Space Administration (NASA).

4711 ■ HARRY S. TRUMAN SCHOLARSHIP FOUNDATION

Attn: Executive Secretary
712 Jackson Place, N.W.
Washington, DC 20006
Tel: (202)395-4831
Fax: (202)395-6995
E-mail: office@truman.gov
Web Site: http://www.truman.gov

To provide grants-for-service for graduate school to current college juniors who are interested in preparing for a career in public service.

Title of Award: Harry S. Truman Scholarship Program **Area, Field, or Subject:** Agricultural sciences; Biological and clinical sciences; Economics; Education; Engineering; Environmental conservation; Environmental science; History; International affairs and relations; Law; Physical sciences; Political science; Public administration; Public health; Public service; Social sciences; Technology **Level of Education for which Award is Granted:** Four Year College, Graduate **Number Awarded:** 70 to 75 each year: a) 1 "state" scholarship is available to a qualified resident nominee in each of the 50 states, the District of Columbia, Puerto Rico, and the Islands (Guam, the Virgin Islands, American Samoa, and the Commonwealth of the Northern Mariana Islands); and b) up to 25 at-large scholars. **Funds Available:** The program provides up to $30,000, including up to $15,000 for the first year of graduate study and up to $15,000 for the final year of graduate study. **Duration:** Support is provided for the first and last year of graduate study.

Eligibility Requirements: Students must be nominated to be considered for this program. Nominees must be full-time students with junior standing at a 4-year institution, committed to a career in government or public service, in the upper quarter of their class, and U.S. citizens or nationals. Each participating institution may nominate up to 4 candidates (and up to 3 additional students who completed their first 2 years at a community college); community colleges and other 2-year institutions may nominate former students who are enrolled as full-time students with junior-level academic standing at accredited 4-year institutions. Selection is based on extent and quality of community service and government involvement, academic performance, leadership record, suitability of the nominee's proposed program of study for a career in public service, and writing and analytical skills. Priority is given to candidates who plan to enroll in a graduate program that specifically trains them for a career in public service, including government at any level, uniformed services, public interest organizations, nongovernmental research and/or educational organizations, public and private schools, and public service oriented nonprofit organizations. The fields of study may include agriculture, biology, engineering, environmental management, physical and social sciences, and technology policy, as well as such traditional fields as economics, education, government, history, international relations, law, nonprofit management, political science, public administration, public health, and public policy. Interviews are required. **Deadline for Receipt:** February of each year. **Additional Information:** Recipients may attend graduate school in the United States or in foreign countries. Scholars are required to work in public service for 3 of the 7 years following completion of a graduate degree program funded by this program. Scholars who do not meet this service requirement, or who fail to provide timely proof to the foundation of such employment, will be required to repay funds received, along with interest.

4712 ■ UNITED DAUGHTERS OF THE CONFEDERACY-VIRGINIA DIVISION

c/o Suzie Snyder, Education Committee Chair
8440 Bradshaw Road
Salem, VA 24153-2246
Tel: (540)384-6884
E-mail: Suzienotes@aol.com
Web Site: http://users.erols.com/va-udc/scholarships.html

To provide financial assistance for undergraduate or graduate study in medicine or engineering to Confederate descendants from Virginia.

Title of Award: Mary Anne Williams Scholarship **Area, Field, or Subject:** Engineering; Medicine **Level of Education for which Award is Granted:** Graduate, Undergraduate **Number Awarded:** This scholarship is offered whenever a prior recipient graduates or is no longer eligible. **Funds Available:** The amount of the stipend depends on the availability of funds. Payment is made directly to the college or university the recipient attends. **Duration:** 1 year; may be renewed up to 3 additional years if the recipient maintains a GPA of 3.0 or higher.

Eligibility Requirements: This program is open to residents of Virginia who are 1) lineal descendants of Confederates, or 2) collateral descendants and also members of the Children of the Confederacy or the United Daughters of the Confederacy. Applicants must be interested in working on an undergraduate or graduate degree in medicine or engineering. They must submit proof of the Confederate military record of at least 1 ancestor, with the company and regiment in which he served. They must

also submit a personal letter pledging to make the best possible use of the scholarship; describing their health, social, family, religious, and fraternal connections within the community; and reflecting on what a Southern heritage means to them (using the term "War Between the States" in lieu of "Civil War"). They must have a GPA of 3.0 or higher and be able to demonstrate financial need. **Deadline for Receipt:** May of years in which the scholarship is available. **Additional Information:** Information is also available from Mrs. George W. Bryson, 10103 Rixeyville Road, Culpeper, VA 22701-4422, E-mail: brysdale@aol.com.

4713 ■ U.S. AIR FORCE

Attn: Headquarters AFROTC/RRUC
551 East Maxwell Boulevard
Maxwell AFB, AL 36112-5917
Tel: (334)953-2091; (866)423-7682
Fax: (334)953-6167
Web Site: http://www.afrotc.com/scholarships/incolschol/expressSchol.php

To provide financial assistance to students who are interested in joining Air Force ROTC and majoring in critical Air Force officer fields in college.

Title of Award: Air Force ROTC Express Scholarships **Area, Field, or Subject:** Atmospheric science; Engineering, Aerospace/Aeronautical/Astronautical; Engineering, Civil; Engineering, Computer; Engineering, Electrical; Engineering, Mechanical; Environmental science; Meteorology **Level of Education for which Award is Granted:** Undergraduate **Funds Available:** Awards are type 2 AFROTC scholarships that provide for payment of tuition and fees, to a maximum of $15,000 per year, plus an annual book allowance of $600. All recipients are also awarded a tax-free monthly subsistence allowance that is $250 for freshmen, $300 for sophomores, $350 for juniors, and $400 for seniors. **Duration:** 3 and a half years, until completion of a bachelor's degree.

Eligibility Requirements: This program is open to U.S. citizens who are completing at least their first year of college and are working on a degree in fields that may change annually but are of critical interest to the Air Force. Applicants must have a GPA of 2.5 or higher and meet all other academic and physical requirements for participation in AFROTC. At the time of their Air Force commissioning, they may be no more than 31 years of age. They must be able to pass the Air Force Officer Qualifying Test (AFOQT) and the Air Force ROTC Physical Fitness Test. years as active-duty Air Force officers following graduation from college. **Additional Information:** Recently, freshmen were eligible if they were majoring in computer, electrical, or environmental engineering. Sophomores and juniors were eligible if they were majoring in those fields, meteorology and atmospheric sciences, or in the following engineering disciplines: aeronautical, aerospace, astronautical, civil, or mechanical. Recipients must also complete 4 years of aerospace studies courses at 1 of the 144 colleges and universities that have an Air Force ROTC unit on campus or 1 of the approximately 900 colleges that have cross-enrollment agreements with those institutions. They must also attend a 4-week summer training camp at an Air Force base, usually between their sophomore and junior years. Following completion of their bachelor's degree, scholarship recipients earn a commission as a second lieutenant in the Air Force and serve at least 4 years.

4714 ■ U.S. AIR FORCE

Attn: Headquarters AFROTC/RRUC
551 East Maxwell Boulevard
Maxwell AFB, AL 36112-5917
Tel: (334)953-2091; (866)423-7682
Fax: (334)953-6167
Web Site: http://www.afrotc.com/scholarships/hsschol/types.php

To provide financial assistance to high school seniors or graduates who are interested in joining Air Force ROTC in college and are willing to serve as Air Force officers following completion of their bachelor's degree.

Title of Award: Air Force ROTC High School Scholarships **Area, Field, or Subject:** Architecture; Chemistry; Computer and information sciences; Engineering, Aerospace/Aeronautical/Astronautical; Engineering, Architectural; Engineering, Civil; Engineering, Computer; Engineering, Electrical; Engineering, Mechanical; Environmental science; General studies/Field of study not specified; Mathematics and mathematical sciences; Meteorology; Operations research; Physics **Level of Education for which Award is Granted:** Four Year College **Number Awarded:** Approximately 2,000 each year. **Funds Available:** Type 1 scholarships

provide payment of full tuition and most laboratory fees, as well as $600 for books. Type 2 scholarships pay the same benefits except tuition is capped at $15,000 per year; students who attend an institution where tuition exceeds $15,000 must pay the difference. Type 7 scholarships pay full tuition and most laboratory fees, but students must attend a college or university where the tuition is less than $9,000 per year or a public college or university where they qualify for the in-state tuition rate; they may not attend an institution with higher tuition and pay the difference. Approximately 5% of scholarship offers are for Type 1, approximately 20% are for Type 2, and approximately 75% are for type 7. All recipients are also awarded a tax-free subsistence allowance for 10 months of each year that is $250 per month as a freshman, $300 per month as a sophomore, $350 per month as a junior, and $400 per month as a senior. **Duration:** 4 years.
Eligibility Requirements: This program is open to high school seniors who are U.S. citizens at least 17 of age and have been accepted at a college or university with an Air Force ROTC unit on campus or a college with a cross-enrollment agreement with such a college. Applicants must have a cumulative GPA of 3.0 or higher and an ACT composite score of 24 or higher or an SAT score of 1100 (mathematics and verbal portion only) or higher. At the time of their commissioning in the Air Force, they must be no more than 31 years of age. They must agree to serve for at least 4 years as active-duty Air Force officers following graduation from college. **Deadline for Receipt:** November of each year. **Additional Information:** Recently, approximately 70% of these scholarships were offered to students planning to major in the science and technical fields of architecture, chemistry, computer science, engineering (aeronautical, aerospace, astronautical, architectural, civil, computer, electrical, environmental, or mechanical), mathematics, meteorology and atmospheric sciences, operations research, or physics. Approximately 30% were offered to students in all other fields. While scholarship recipients can major in any subject, they must enroll in 4 years of aerospace studies courses at 1 of the 144 colleges and universities that have an Air Force ROTC unit on campus; students may also attend nearly 900 other colleges that have cross-enrollment agreements with the institutions that have an Air Force ROTC unit on campus. Recipients must attend a 4-week summer training camp at an Air Force base, usually between their sophomore and junior years. Most cadets incur a 4-year active-duty commitment. Pilots incur a 10-year active-duty service commitment after successfully completing Specialized Undergraduate Pilot Training and navigators incur a 6-year commitment after successfully completing Specialized Undergraduate Navigator Training. The minimum service obligation for intelligence and Air Battle Management career fields is 5 years.

4715 ■ U.S. AIR FORCE

Attn: Headquarters AFROTC/RRUC
551 East Maxwell Boulevard
Maxwell AFB, AL 36112-5917
Tel: (334)953-2091; (866)423-7682
Fax: (334)953-6167
Web Site: http://www.afrotc.com/scholarships/incolschol/incolProgram.php
To provide financial assistance to undergraduate students who are willing to join Air Force ROTC in college and serve as Air Force officers following completion of their bachelor's degree.
Title of Award: Air Force ROTC In-College Scholarship Program **Area, Field, or Subject:** Architecture; Chemistry; Computer and information sciences; Engineering, Aerospace/Aeronautical/Astronautical; Engineering, Architectural; Engineering, Civil; Engineering, Computer; Engineering, Electrical; Engineering, Mechanical; Environmental science; General studies/Field of study not specified; Mathematics and mathematical sciences; Meteorology; Operations research; Physics **Level of Education for which Award is Granted:** Undergraduate **Number Awarded:** Varies each year. **Funds Available:** Cadets selected in Phase 1 are awarded type 2 AFROTC scholarships that provide for payment of tuition and fees, to a maximum of $15,000 per year. A limited number of cadets selected in Phase 2 are also awarded type 2 AFROTC scholarships, but most are awarded type 3 AFROTC scholarships with tuition capped at $9,000 per year. Cadets selected in Phase 3 are awarded type 6 AFROTC scholarships with tuition capped at $3,000 per year. All recipients are also awarded a book allowance of $600 and a tax-free subsistence allowance for 10 months of each year that is $300 per month during the sophomore

year, $350 during the junior year, and $400 during the senior year. **Duration:** 3 years for students selected as freshmen or 2 years for students selected as sophomores.
Eligibility Requirements: This program is open to U.S. citizens enrolled as freshmen or sophomores at 1 of the 144 colleges and universities that have an Air Force ROTC unit on campus. Applicants must have a cumulative GPA of 2.5 or higher and be able to pass the Air Force Officer Qualifying Test and the Air Force ROTC Physical Fitness Test. At the time of commissioning, they may be no more than 31 years of age. They must agree to serve for at least 4 years as active-duty Air Force officers following graduation from college. Phase 1 is open to students enrolled in the Air Force ROTC program who do not currently have a scholarship but now wish to apply. Phase 2 is open to Phase 1 nonselects and students not enrolled in Air Force ROTC. Phase 3 is open only to Phase 2 nonselects. Recently, the program gave preference to students majoring in the science and technical fields of architecture, chemistry, computer science, engineering (aeronautical, aerospace, astronautical, architectural, civil, computer, electrical, environmental, or mechanical), mathematics, meteorology and atmospheric sciences, operations research, or physics. **Deadline for Receipt:** January of each year. **Additional Information:** While scholarship recipients can major in any subject, they must complete 4 years of aerospace studies courses at 1 of the 144 colleges or universities that have an Air Force ROTC unit on campus. Recipients must also attend a 4-week summer training camp at an Air Force base, usually between their sophomore and junior years; 2-year scholarship awardees attend in the summer after their junior year. Current military personnel are eligible for early release from active duty in order to enter the Air Force ROTC program. Following completion of their bachelor's degree, scholarship recipients earn a commission as a second lieutenant in the Air Force and serve at least 4 years.

4716 ■ U.S. AIR FORCE

Attn: Headquarters AFROTC/RRUE
Enlisted Commissioning Section
551 East Maxwell Boulevard
Maxwell AFB, AL 36112-5917
Tel: (334)953-2091; (866)423-7682
Fax: (334)953-6167
E-mail: enlisted@afrotc.com
Web Site: http://www.afoats.af.mil/AFROTC/EnlistedComm/AECP.asp
To allow selected enlisted Air Force personnel to earn a bachelor's degree in approved majors by providing financial assistance for full-time college study.
Title of Award: Airman Education and Commissioning Program **Area, Field, or Subject:** African studies; Asian studies; Computer and information sciences; Engineering; Foreign languages; Mathematics and mathematical sciences; Meteorology; Near Eastern studies; Nursing; Physics; Russian studies **Level of Education for which Award is Granted:** Undergraduate **Number Awarded:** Approximately 60 each year. **Funds Available:** While participating in this program, cadets remain on active duty in the Air Force and receive their regular salary and benefits. They also receive payment of tuition and fees up to $15,000 per year and an annual textbook allowance of $600. **Duration:** 1 to 3 years, until completion of a bachelor's degree.
Eligibility Requirements: Eligible to participate in this program are enlisted members of the Air Force who have been accepted at a university or college (or approved crosstown institution) that is associated with AFROTC and that offers an approved major. The majors currently supported are computer science, all ABET-accredited engineering fields (not engineering technology), foreign area studies (limited to Middle East, Africa, Asia, Russia/Eurasia), foreign languages (limited to Arabic, Armenian, Azeri, Chinese, French, Georgian, Hebrew, Hindi, Indonesian, Kazakh, Pashto, Persian Farsi, Russian, Swahili, and Turkish), mathematics, meteorology, nursing, and physics. Applicants must have completed at least 1 year of time-in-service and 1 year of time-on-station. They must have scores on the Air Force Officer Qualifying Test of at least 15 on the verbal and 10 on the quantitative and be able to pass the Air Force ROTC Physical Fitness Test. Normally they should have completed at least 30 semester hours of college study with a GPA of 2.75 or higher. They must be younger than 31 years of age or otherwise able to be commissioned before they become 35 years of age. **Deadline for Receipt:** February of each year. **Additional Information:** While attending college, participants in this program attend ROTC classes at their college or university. Upon

completing their degree, they are commissioned to serve in the Air Force in their area of specialization with an active-duty service commitment of at least 4 years. Further information is available from base education service officers or an Air Force ROTC unit. This program does not provide for undergraduate flying training.

4717 ■ U.S. AIR FORCE
Attn: Headquarters AFROTC/RRUE
Enlisted Commissioning Section
551 East Maxwell Boulevard
Maxwell AFB, AL 36112-5917
Tel: (334)953-2091; (866)423-7682
Fax: (334)953-6167
E-mail: enlisted@afrotc.com
Web Site: http://www.afoats.af.mil/AFROTC/EnlistedComm/ASCP.asp
To allow selected enlisted Air Force personnel to earn a bachelor's degree in approved majors by providing financial assistance for full-time college study.

Title of Award: Airman Scholarship and Commissioning Program **Area, Field, or Subject:** Architecture; Atmospheric science; Chemistry; Computer and information sciences; Engineering; Engineering, Aerospace/Aeronautical/Astronautical; Engineering, Architectural; Engineering, Civil; Engineering, Computer; Engineering, Electrical; Engineering, Mechanical; Environmental science; General studies/Field of study not specified; Mathematics and mathematical sciences; Meteorology; Operations research; Physics **Level of Education for which Award is Granted:** Undergraduate **Number Awarded:** Varies each year. **Funds Available:** Awards are type 2 AFROTC scholarships that provide for payment of tuition and fees, to a maximum of $15,000 per year, plus an annual book allowance of $600. All recipients are also awarded a tax-free subsistence allowance for 10 months of each year that is $300 per month during their sophomore year, $350 during their junior year, and $400 during their senior year. **Duration:** 2 to 4 years, until completion of a bachelor's degree.
Eligibility Requirements: This program is open to active-duty enlisted members of the Air Force who have completed at least 1 year of continuous active duty and at least 1 year on station. Applicants normally must have completed at least 24 semester hours of graded college credit with a cumulative college GPA of 2.5 or higher. If they have not completed 24 hours of graded college credit, they must have an ACT score of 24 or higher or an SAT combined verbal and mathematics score of 1100 or higher. They must also have scores on the Air Force Officer Qualifying Test (AFOQT) of 15 or more on the verbal scale and 10 or more on the quantitative scale and be able to pass the Air Force ROTC Physical Fitness Test. Applicants must have been accepted at a college or university (including crosstown schools) offering the AFROTC 4-year program. When they complete the program and receive their commission, they may not be 31 years of age or older. U.S. citizenship is required. Recently, awards were presented according to the following priorities: 1) computer, electrical, and environmental engineering; 2) aeronautical, aerospace, architectural, astronautical, civil, and mechanical engineering and meteorology and atmospheric sciences; 3) all other ABET-accredited engineering majors, architecture, chemistry, computer science, mathematics, operations research, and physics; 4) all other majors. **Deadline for Receipt:** October of each year. **Additional Information:** Selectees separate from the active-duty Air Force, join an AFROTC detachment, and become full-time students. Upon completing their degree, they are commissioned as officers and returned to active duty in the Air Force with a 4-year service obligation. Further information is available from base education service officers or an Air Force ROTC unit.

4718 ■ U.S. AIR FORCE
Attn: Headquarters AFROTC/RRUE
Enlisted Commissioning Section
551 East Maxwell Boulevard
Maxwell AFB, AL 36112-5917
Tel: (334)953-2091; (866)423-7682
Fax: (334)953-6167
E-mail: enlisted@afrotc.com
Web Site: http://www.afoats.af.mil/AFROTC/EnlistedComm/POC-ERP.asp
To allow selected enlisted Air Force personnel to earn a baccalaureate degree by providing financial assistance for full-time college study.

Title of Award: Professional Officer Course Early Release Program **Area, Field, or Subject:** Architecture; Atmospheric science; Chemistry; Computer and information sciences; Engineering; Engineering, Aerospace/Aeronautical/Astronautical; Engineering, Architectural; Engineering, Civil; Engineering, Computer; Engineering, Electrical; Engineering, Mechanical; Environmental science; General studies/Field of study not specified; Mathematics and mathematical sciences; Meteorology; Operations research; Physics **Level of Education for which Award is Granted:** Undergraduate **Number Awarded:** Varies each year. **Funds Available:** Participants receive a stipend for 10 months of the year that is $350 per month during the first year and $400 per month during the second year. Scholarship recipients earn the Professional Officer Course Incentive of $3,000 per year for tuition and $600 per year for books. **Duration:** 2 years (no more and no less).
Eligibility Requirements: Eligible to participate in this program are enlisted members of the Air Force under the age of 30 (or otherwise able to be commissioned before becoming 35 years of age) who have completed at least 1 year on continuous active duty, have served on station for at least 1 year, and have no more than 2 years remaining to complete their initial baccalaureate degree. Scholarship applicants must be younger than 31 years of age when they graduate and earn their commission. All applicants must have been accepted at a college or university offering the AFROTC 4-year program and must have a cumulative college GPA of 2.5 or higher. Their Air Force Officer Qualifying Test (AFOQT) scores must be at least 15 on the verbal and 10 on the quantitative. Applicants who have not completed 24 units of college work must have an ACT composite score of 24 or higher or an SAT combined verbal and mathematics score of 1100 or higher. U.S. citizenship is required. Recently, awards were presented according to the following priorities: 1) computer, electrical, and environmental engineering; 2) aeronautical, aerospace, architectural, astronautical, civil, and mechanical engineering and meteorology and atmospheric sciences; 3) all other ABET-accredited engineering majors, architecture, chemistry, computer science, mathematics, operations research, and physics; 4) all other majors. **Deadline for Receipt:** October of each year. **Additional Information:** Upon completing their degree, selectees are commissioned as officers in the Air Force with a 4-year service obligation. Further information is available from base education service officers or an Air Force ROTC unit.

4719 ■ U.S. NAVY
Attn: Commander, Naval Service Training Command
250 Dallas Street, Suite A
Pensacola, FL 32508-5268
Tel: (850)452-9563
Fax: (850)452-2486
E-mail: PNSC-STA21@navy.mil
Web Site: http://www.navy.com/careers/officerplanner/enlistedtoofficer
To allow outstanding enlisted Navy personnel to complete a bachelor's degree and receive a commission in the Civil Engineer Corps (CEC).
Title of Award: Civil Engineer Corps Option of the Seaman to Admiral-21 Program **Area, Field, or Subject:** Architecture; Engineering; Engineering, Civil; Engineering, Electrical; Engineering, Mechanical **Level of Education for which Award is Granted:** Four Year College **Number Awarded:** Varies each year. **Funds Available:** Awardees continue to receive their regular Navy pay and allowances while they attend college on a full-time basis. They also receive reimbursement for tuition, fees, and books up to $10,000 per year. If base housing is available, they are eligible to live there. Participants are not eligible to receive benefits under the Navy's Tuition Assistance Program (TA), the Montgomery GI Bill (MGIB), Navy College Fund, or the Veterans Educational Assistance Program (VEAP). **Duration:** Selectees are supported for up to 36 months of full-time, year-round study or completion of a bachelor's degree, as long as they maintain a GPA of 3.0 or higher.
Eligibility Requirements: This program is open to U.S. citizens who are currently serving on active duty in the Navy as enlisted personnel of occupational field 13 (Seabees). Applicants must have completed at least 4 years of active duty, of which at least 3 years were in an other than formal training environment. They must be high school graduates (or GED recipients) who are able to complete requirements for a professional Accreditation Board for Engineering and Technology (ABET) engineering degree or National Architectural Accrediting Board (NAAB) architectural degree within 36 months or less. Preferred specialties are for civil, electrical, and mechanical engineering. When applicants complete their degree

requirements, they must be younger than 35 years of age. Within the past 3 years, they must have taken the SAT test (and achieved scores of at least 500 on the mathematics section and 500 on the verbal or critical reading section) or the ACT test (and achieved a score of 41 or higher, including at least 21 on the mathematics portion and 20 on the English portion). **Deadline for Receipt:** July of each year. **Additional Information:** This program was established in 2001 as a replacement for the Civil Engineer Corps Enlisted Commissioning Program (CECECP). Upon acceptance into the program, selectees attend the Naval Science Institute (NSI) in Newport, Rhode Island for an 8-week program in the fundamental core concepts of being a naval officer (navigation, engineering, weapons, military history and justice, etc.). They then enter a college or university with an NROTC unit that is designated for the CEC and pursue full-time study for a bachelor's degree. They become members of and drill with the NROTC unit. When they complete their degree, they are commissioned as ensigns in the United States Naval Reserve and assigned to initial training as an officer in the CEC. After commissioning, 5 years of active service are required.

4720 ■ U.S. NAVY

Attn: Navy Personnel Command
5722 Integrity Drive
Millington, TN 38055-5057
Tel: (901)874-4034; (866)CEC-NAVY
Fax: (901)874-2681
E-mail: p4413d@persnet.navy.mil
Web Site: http://www.cec.navy.mil/scholarships.html
To provide financial assistance to undergraduate and graduate students in architecture and engineering who are interested in serving in the Navy's Civil Engineer Corps (CEC) following graduation.
Title of Award: Civil Engineer Corps Scholarships **Area, Field, or Subject:** Architecture; Engineering, Civil; Engineering, Electrical; Engineering, Mechanical; Engineering, Ocean **Level of Education for which Award is Granted:** Master's, Undergraduate **Number Awarded:** Varies each year. **Funds Available:** Students accepted as undergraduates receive E-3 pay (approximately $2,000 per month), allowance, and benefits; after completing 12 months of the program or being referred to other specified programs, they may be advanced to E-4 or E-5 levels. Graduate students receive payment of tuition and fees plus full officers' salary and allowances. **Duration:** Up to 24 months for the Exceptional Student Program, up to 12 months for the Collegiate Program, and up to 18 months (6 months of undergraduate school plus 12 months of graduate school) for the Graduate Program.
Eligibility Requirements: This program is open to undergraduate and master's degree students who are U.S. citizens between 19 and 35 years of age. Applicants must be enrolled in an engineering program accredited by the Accreditation Board for Engineering and Technology (ABET) or an architecture program accredited by the National Architectural Accrediting Board (NAAB) with a GPA of 3.0 or higher. Eligible majors include civil engineering, electrical engineering, mechanical engineering, ocean engineering, or architecture. For the Exceptional Student Program, they must apply at the end of their sophomore year. For the Collegiate Program, they must apply at the end of their junior year. For the Graduate Program, they must apply upon acceptance to an accredited graduate school and when they are within 6 months of completing a bachelor's degree in engineering. Preference is given to applicants who have engineering or architecture work experience and registration as a Professional Engineer (P.E.) or Engineer-in-Training (EIT). Students majoring in mathematics, physics, non-engineering programs, and engineering or architectural technology are not eligible. Applicants must also be able to meet the Navy's physical fitness requirements. **Additional Information:** While in college, selectees have no uniforms, drills, or military duties. After graduation with a bachelor's or master's degree, they enter the Navy and attend 13 weeks at Officer Candidate School (OCS) in Pensacola, Florida, followed by 15 weeks at Civil Engineer Corps Officers School (CECOS) in Port Hueneme, California. They then serve 4 years in the CEC, rotating among public works, contract management, and the Naval Construction Force (Seabees).

4721 ■ U.S. NAVY

Naval Education and Training Center
Attn: AEV Program Office
6490 Saufley Field Road
Pensacola, FL 32509-5204
Tel: (850)452-1001
Fax: (850)452-1357
E-mail: rick.cusimano@navy.mil
Web Site: http://www.npc.navy.mil/CareerInfo/Education
To provide financial assistance to Navy enlisted personnel who are interested in earning an undergraduate or graduate degree during off-duty hours.
Title of Award: Navy Advanced Education Voucher Program **Area, Field, or Subject:** Accounting; Business administration; Educational administration; Engineering; Engineering, Civil; Engineering, Electrical; Finance; Information science and technology; Leadership, Institutional and community; Management; Nursing; Personnel administration/human resources; Systems engineering; Technology **Level of Education for which Award is Granted:** Master's, Undergraduate **Number Awarded:** Varies each year. Recently, 30 of these positions were available: 25 for bachelor's degrees and 5 for master's degrees. **Funds Available:** This program covers 100% of graduate education costs (tuition, books, and fees), up to a maximum of $6,700 per year for a bachelor's degree or $20,000 per year for a master's degree. **Duration:** Up to 36 months from the time of enrollment for a bachelor's degree; up to 24 months from the time of enrollment for a master's degree.
Eligibility Requirements: This program is open to senior enlisted Navy personnel in ranks E-7 through E-9. Applicants should be transferring to, or currently on, shore duty with sufficient time ashore to complete a bachelor's or master's degree. Personnel at rank E-7 may have no more than 17 years time in service, E-8 no more than 20 years, or E-9 no more than 22 years. The area of study must be certified by the Naval Postgraduate School as Navy-relevant. **Deadline for Receipt:** March of each year. **Additional Information:** Recently approved majors for bachelor's degrees included accounting and finances, civil engineering, electrical engineering technology, engineering propulsion systems, human performance system integration, human resources, industrial management, information technology, leadership and management, nursing, and systems engineering and analysis. Approved fields of study for master's degrees included business administration, education and training management, emergency and disaster management, engineering and technology, homeland defense and security, human resources, information technology, leadership and management, project management, and systems engineering and analysis. Recipients of this assistance incur an obligation to remain on active duty following completion of the program for a period equal to 3 times the number of months of education completed, to a maximum obligation of 36 months.

4722 ■ U.S. NAVY

Attn: Navy Personnel Command
5722 Integrity Drive
Millington, TN 38054-5057
Tel: (901)874-3070; 888-633-9674
Fax: (901)874-2651
E-mail: nukeprograms@cnrc.navy.mil
Web Site: http://www.cnrc.navy.mil/nucfield/college/enlisted_options.htm
To provide financial assistance to high school seniors and current college students interested in attending college for a year and then entering the Navy's nuclear program.
Title of Award: Navy College Assistance/Student Headstart (Navy-CASH) Program **Area, Field, or Subject:** Engineering, Nuclear **Level of Education for which Award is Granted:** Undergraduate **Number Awarded:** Varies each year. **Funds Available:** While they attend school, participants are paid a regular Navy salary at a pay grade up to E-3 (starting at $1,303.50 per month). They are also eligible for all of the Navy's enlistment incentives, including the Navy College Fund, the Loan Repayment Program, and an enlistment bonus up to $12,000. **Duration:** 12 months.
Eligibility Requirements: Applicants must be able to meet the specific requirements of the Navy's Enlisted Nuclear Field Program. They must be enrolled or accepted for enrollment at an accredited 2-year community or junior college or 4-year college or university. **Additional Information:**

After 1 year of college, participants report for enlisted recruit training in the Navy's nuclear field. Further information on this program is available from a local Navy recruiter.

4723 ■ U.S. NAVY
Attn: Navy Personnel Command
5722 Integrity Drive
Millington, TN 38054-5057
Tel: (901)874-3070; 888-633-9674
Fax: (901)874-2651
E-mail: nukeprograms@cnrc.navy.mil
Web Site: http://www.cnrc.navy.mil/nucfield/college/officer_options.htm
To provide financial assistance to college juniors and seniors who wish to serve in the Navy's nuclear propulsion training program following graduation.
Title of Award: Nuclear Propulsion Officer Candidate (NUPOC) Program **Area, Field, or Subject:** Chemistry; Engineering; General studies/Field of study not specified; Mathematics and mathematical sciences; Physics **Level of Education for which Award is Granted:** Four Year College **Number Awarded:** Varies each year. **Funds Available:** Participants become Active Reserve enlisted Navy personnel and receive a salary of up to $2,500 per month; the exact amount depends on the local cost of living and other factors. A bonus of $10,000 is also paid at the time of enlistment and another $2,000 upon completion of nuclear power training. **Duration:** Up to 30 months, until completion of a bachelor's degree. **Eligibility Requirements:** This program is open to U.S. citizens who are entering their junior or senior year of college as a full-time student. Strong technical majors (mathematics, physics, chemistry, or an engineering field) are encouraged but not required. Applicants must have completed at least 1 year of calculus and 1 year of physics and must have earned a grade of "C" or better in all mathematics, science, and technical courses. Normally, they must be 26 years of age or younger at the expected date of commissioning, although applicants for the design and research specialty may be 29 years old. **Additional Information:** Following graduation, participants attend Officer Candidate School in Pensacola, Florida for 4 months and receive their commissions. They have a service obligation of 8 years (of which at least 5 years must be on active duty), beginning with 6 months at the Navy Nuclear Power Training Command in Charleston, South Carolina and 6 more months of hands-on training at a nuclear reactor facility. Further information on this program is available from a local Navy recruiter or the Navy Recruiting Command, 801 North Randolph Street, Arlington, VA 22203-1991.

4724 ■ U.S. NAVY
Attn: Commander, Naval Service Training Command
250 Dallas Street, Suite A
Pensacola, FL 32508-5268
Tel: (850)452-9563
Fax: (850)452-2486
E-mail: PNSC-STA21@navy.mil
Web Site: http://www.navy.com/careers/officerplanner/enlistedtoofficer
To allow outstanding enlisted Navy personnel to complete a bachelor's degree and receive a commission in the Supply Corps.
Title of Award: Supply Corps Option of the Seaman to Admiral-21 Program **Area, Field, or Subject:** Business administration; Engineering; Mathematics and mathematical sciences **Level of Education for which Award is Granted:** Four Year College **Number Awarded:** Varies each year. **Funds Available:** Awardees continue to receive their regular Navy pay and allowances while they attend college on a full-time basis. They also receive reimbursement for tuition, fees, and books up to $10,000 per year. If base housing is available, they are eligible to live there. Participants are not eligible to receive benefits under the Navy's Tuition Assistance Program (TA), the Montgomery GI Bill (MGIB), Navy College Fund, or the Veterans Educational Assistance Program (VEAP). **Duration:** Selectees are supported for up to 36 months of full-time, year-round study or completion of a bachelor's degree, as long as they maintain a GPA of 2.5 or higher.
Eligibility Requirements: This program is open to U.S. citizens who are currently serving on active duty in the U.S. Navy or Naval Reserve, including Training and Administration of the Reserves (TAR), Selected Reserves (SELRES), and Navy Reservists on active duty except for those on active for training (ACDUTRA). Applicants must be high school graduates (or GED recipients) who are able to complete requirements for a baccalaureate degree in a business, engineering, or mathematics related field in 36 months or less. When they complete their degree requirements, they must be younger than 27 years of age. Within the past 3 years, they must have taken the SAT test (and achieved scores of at least 500 on the mathematics section and 500 on the verbal or critical reading section) or the ACT test (and achieved a score of 41 or higher, including at least 21 on the mathematics portion and 20 on the English portion). **Deadline for Receipt:** July of each year. **Additional Information:** This program was established in 2001 as a replacement for the Seaman to Admiral Program (established in 1994), the Enlisted Commissioning Program, and other specialized programs for sailors to earn a commission. Upon acceptance into the program, selectees attend the Naval Science Institute (NSI) in Newport, Rhode Island for an 8-week program in the fundamental core concepts of being a naval officer (navigation, engineering, weapons, military history and justice, etc.). They then enter a college or university with an NROTC unit or affiliation and pursue full-time study for a bachelor's degree. They become members of and drill with the NROTC unit. When they complete their degree, they are commissioned as ensigns in the United States Naval Reserve and assigned to initial training as an officer in the Supply Corps. After commissioning, 5 years of active service are required.

4725 ■ UNIVERSITY INTERSCHOLASTIC LEAGUE
Attn: Texas Interscholastic League Foundation
1701 Manor Road
P.O. Box 8028
Austin, TX 78713
Tel: (512)232-4938
Fax: (512)471-5908
E-mail: carolyn.scott@mail.utexas.edu
Web Site: http://www.uil.utexas.edu/tilf/scholarships.html
To provide financial assistance to students who participate in programs of the Texas Interscholastic League Foundation (TILF) and plan to major in chemistry, biochemistry, or chemical engineering.
Title of Award: Welch Foundation Scholarships **Area, Field, or Subject:** Biochemistry; Chemistry; Engineering, Chemical **Level of Education for which Award is Granted:** Undergraduate **Number Awarded:** 20 each year. **Funds Available:** The stipend is $3,500 per year. **Duration:** 4 years.
Eligibility Requirements: This program is open to students who meet the 5 basic requirements of the TILF: 1) graduate from high school during the current year and begin college or university in Texas by the following fall; 2) enroll full time at an approved institution and maintain a GPA of 2.5 or higher during the first semester; 3) compete in a University Interscholastic League (UIL) academic state meet contest in accounting, calculator applications, computer applications, computer science, current issues and events, debate (cross-examination and Lincoln-Douglas), journalism (editorial writing, feature writing, headline writing, and news writing), literary criticism, mathematics, number sense, 1-act play, ready writing, science, social studies, speech (prose interpretation, poetry interpretation, informative speaking, and persuasive speaking), or spelling and vocabulary; 4) submit high school transcripts that include SAT and/or ACT scores; and 5) submit parents' latest income tax returns. Applicants for this scholarship must major in chemistry, biochemistry, or chemical engineering and be interested in engaging in chemical research at the graduate level. Along with their application, they must submit a 50-word essay on why they desire to major in chemistry, biochemistry, or chemical engineering. **Deadline for Receipt:** May of each year. **Additional Information:** This scholarships may be used at 56 approved colleges and universities in Texas. For a list, contact UIL.

4726 ■ UTAH SOCIETY OF PROFESSIONAL ENGINEERS
Attn: Dan Church, Scholarship Chair
488 East Winchester Street, Suite 400
Murray, UT 84107
Tel: (801)288-3224
E-mail: churchd@pbworld.com
Web Site: http://www.uspeonline.com
To provide financial assistance to high school seniors in Utah interested in studying engineering at a college or university in the state.
Title of Award: Utah Society of Professional Engineers Scholarship **Area, Field, or Subject:** Engineering **Level of Education for which Award is Granted:** Undergraduate **Number Awarded:** 1 or more each year. **Funds Available:** The stipend is $1,000. **Duration:** 1 year.

Eligibility Requirements: This program is open to seniors at high schools in Utah who have a cumulative GPA of 3.5 or higher and ACT scores of at least 30 in mathematics and 26 in English. Applicants must be U.S. citizens interested in attending a college or university in Utah that has been accredited by the Engineering Accreditation Commission of the Accreditation Board for Engineering and Technology (ABET-EAC). Along with their application they must submit an essay of 850 to 1,000 words on their interest in engineering. Selection is based on the essay (20 points), GPA (20 points), recommendations from at least 2 teachers (10 points), a resume (20 points), composite application (10 points), and ACT scores (20 points). **Deadline for Receipt:** March of each year.

4727 ■ VERMONT STUDENT ASSISTANCE CORPORATION
Champlain Mill
Attn: Scholarship Programs
P.O. Box 2000
Winooski, VT 05404-2601
Tel: (802)654-3798; 888-253-4819
Fax: (802)654-3765
E-mail: info@vsac.org
Web Site: http://www.vsac.org
To provide financial assistance to high school seniors in Vermont who are interested in working on a college degree in construction or engineering.
Title of Award: Kilbourn-Sawyer Memorial Scholarship **Area, Field, or Subject:** Construction; Engineering **Level of Education for which Award is Granted:** Undergraduate **Number Awarded:** 1 each year. **Funds Available:** The stipend is $1,000. **Duration:** 1 year; nonrenewable.
Eligibility Requirements: This scholarship is available to the residents of Vermont who are seniors in high school. Applicants must be planning to enroll in a 2-year or 4-year postsecondary degree program in engineering or construction. Selection is based on letters of recommendation, required essays, academic achievement, and financial need. **Deadline for Receipt:** April of each year. **Additional Information:** This program is funded by Pizzagalli Construction Company.

4728 ■ VIRGINIA SPACE GRANT CONSORTIUM
Attn: Fellowship Coordinator
Old Dominion University Peninsula Center
600 Butler Farm Road
Hampton, VA 23666
Tel: (757)766-5210
Fax: (757)766-5205
E-mail: vsgc@odu.edu
Web Site: http://www.vsgc.odu.edu/Menu3_1_1.htm
To provide financial assistance to students who are interested in pursuing space-related studies at community colleges in Virginia.
Title of Award: Virginia Space Grant Community College Scholarship Program **Area, Field, or Subject:** Aerospace sciences; Computer and information sciences; Electronics; Engineering; Mathematics and mathematical sciences; Space and planetary sciences; Technology **Level of Education for which Award is Granted:** Two Year College **Number Awarded:** Approximately 10 each year. **Funds Available:** The maximum stipend is $1,500. **Duration:** 1 year; nonrenewable.
Eligibility Requirements: This program is open to students currently enrolled in a Virginia community college who are U.S. citizens and have completed at least the first semester of their program with a GPA of 3.0 or higher. Awards are generally made to full-time students, but part-time students demonstrating academic merit are also eligible. Applicants can be enrolled in any program that includes course work related to an understanding of or interest in technological fields supporting aerospace; that includes (but is not limited to) computers, electronics, engineering, industrial technology, and mathematics. Since a particular goal of the program is to increase the participation of underrepresented minorities, women, and persons with disabilities in aerospace-related, high technology careers, the sponsor especially encourages applications from those students. **Deadline for Receipt:** February of each year. **Additional Information:** This program is funded by the U.S. National Aeronautics and Space Administration (NASA).

4729 ■ WASHINGTON NASA SPACE GRANT CONSORTIUM
c/o University of Washington
Johnson Hall, Room 141

Box 351310
Seattle, WA 98195-1310
Tel: (206)543-1943
Free: 800-659-1943
Fax: (206)543-0179
E-mail: nasa@u.washington.edu
Web Site: http://www.waspacegrant.org/undergr.html
To provide financial assistance for college to students in Washington who wish to study science, engineering, or mathematics with an emphasis on space.
Title of Award: Washington NASA Space Grant Consortium Undergraduate Scholarships **Area, Field, or Subject:** Aerospace sciences; Engineering; Engineering, Aerospace/Aeronautical/Astronautical; Mathematics and mathematical sciences; Science; Space and planetary sciences **Level of Education for which Award is Granted:** Undergraduate **Number Awarded:** Varies each year. **Funds Available:** Stipends vary at participating institutions, but range from $1,000 to $5,000. **Duration:** 1 year; may be renewed.
Eligibility Requirements: This program is open to residents of Washington who are attending or planning to attend designated institutions that are members of the Washington NASA Space Grant Consortium. Applicants must be interested in majoring in space-related aspects of science, engineering, or mathematics. U.S. citizenship is required. The program values diversity and strongly encourages women and minorities to apply. **Deadline for Receipt:** Each participating institution sets its own deadline. **Additional Information:** This program is funded by the U.S. National Aeronautics and Space Administration (NASA). Members of the consortium that offer undergraduate scholarships are Northwest Indian College, Seattle Central Community College, University of Washington, and Washington State University.

4730 ■ WEST VIRGINIA HIGHER EDUCATION POLICY COMMISSION
Attn: Office of Financial Aid and Outreach Services
1018 Kanawha Boulevard, East, Suite 700
Charleston, WV 25301-2827
Tel: (304)558-4614; 888-825-5707
Fax: (304)558-4622
E-mail: wicks@hepc.wvnet.edu
Web Site: http://www.hepc.wvnet.edu/students/estsp.html
To provide scholarship/loans to West Virginia residents who are interested in studying engineering, science, or technology and work in the state following graduation.
Title of Award: West Virginia Engineering, Science and Technology Scholarship Program **Area, Field, or Subject:** Engineering; Science; Technology **Level of Education for which Award is Granted:** Undergraduate **Number Awarded:** Varies each year; recently, a total of $500,000 in state funds was allocated for this program. **Funds Available:** The maximum stipend is $3,000 per year. Within 1 year after ceasing to be a full-time student, recipients must begin working full time in an engineering, science, or technology field in West Virginia for 1 year for each year the scholarship was received or being a program of community service relating to engineering, science, or technology in West Virginia for 1 year for each year the scholarship was received. If they fail to fulfill the work requirement, they must repay all scholarship funds received plus interest and any required collection fees. **Duration:** 1 year; may be renewed.
Eligibility Requirements: This program is open to West Virginia residents who are U.S. citizens or permanent residents. Applicants must be enrolled or accepted for enrollment in an engineering, science, or technology program leading to a certificate, associate, or baccalaureate degree at an eligible institution of higher education in West Virginia. They must have a cumulative GPA of 3.0 or higher either upon graduation from high school or after completing 2 semesters of course work in college. Selection is based on academic qualifications and interest in the fields of engineering, science, and technology. **Deadline for Receipt:** March of each year.

4731 ■ WISCONSIN FOUNDATION FOR INDEPENDENT COLLEGES, INC.
Attn: College-to-Work Program
735 North Water Street, Suite 600
Milwaukee, WI 53202-4100
Tel: (414)273-5980

Fax: (414)273-5995
E-mail: wfic@wficweb.org
Web Site: http://www.wficweb.org/work.html
To provide financial assistance and work experience to students majoring in fields related to technology at member institutions of the Wisconsin Foundation for Independent Colleges (WFIC).

Title of Award: Jefferson County Literacy Council College-to-Work Program **Area, Field, or Subject:** Computer and information sciences; Education; General studies/Field of study not specified; Internet design and development; Marketing and distribution **Level of Education for which Award is Granted:** Four Year College **Number Awarded:** 1 each year. **Funds Available:** The stipends are $3,500 for the scholarship and $1,500 for the internship. **Duration:** 1 year for the scholarship; 10 weeks during the summer for the internship.

Eligibility Requirements: This program is open to full-time sophomores, juniors, and seniors at WFIC member colleges and universities. Applicants may be studying any field, but preference is given to majors in computer technology, education, marketing, sales, or website design. They must be interested in an internship at the Jefferson County Literacy Council in Fort Atkinson, Wisconsin. Along with their application, they must submit a 1-page essay that includes why they are applying for the internship, why they have selected their major and what interests them about it, why they are attending their chosen college or university, and their future career objectives. **Deadline for Receipt:** February of each year. **Additional Information:** The WFIC member schools are Alverno College, Beloit College, Cardinal Stritch University, Carroll College, Carthage College, Concordia University of Wisconsin, Edgewood College, Lakeland College, Lawrence University, Marian College, Marquette University, Milwaukee Institute of Art & Design, Milwaukee School of Engineering, Mount Mary College, Northland College, Ripon College, St. Norbert College, Silver Lake College, Viterbo University, and Wisconsin Lutheran College. This program is sponsored by the Jefferson County Literacy Council.

4732 ■ WISCONSIN SPACE GRANT CONSORTIUM
c/o University of Wisconsin at Green Bay
Department of Natural and Applied Sciences
2420 Nicolet Drive
Green Bay, WI 54311-7001
Tel: (920)465-2108
Fax: (920)465-2376
E-mail: wsgc@uwgb.edu
Web Site: http://www.uwgb.edu/wsgc/students/us.asp
To provide financial assistance to undergraduate students at colleges and universities participating in the Wisconsin Space Grant Consortium (WSGC).

Title of Award: Wisconsin Space Grant Consortium Undergraduate Scholarships **Area, Field, or Subject:** Aerospace sciences; Architecture; Business administration; Engineering; Engineering, Aerospace/Aeronautical/Astronautical; Law; Medicine; Nursing; Science; Space and planetary sciences **Level of Education for which Award is Granted:** Undergraduate **Number Awarded:** Varies each year; recently, 26 of these scholarships were awarded. **Funds Available:** Stipends up to $1,500 per year are available. **Duration:** 1 academic year.

Eligibility Requirements: This program is open to undergraduate students enrolled at universities participating in the WSGC. Applicants must be U.S. citizens; be working full time on a bachelor's degree in space science, aerospace, or interdisciplinary space studies (including, but not limited to, engineering, the sciences, architecture, law, business, nursing, and medicine); and have a GPA of 3.0 or higher. The consortium especially encourages applications from underrepresented minorities, women, and students with disabilities. Selection is based on academic performance and space-related promise. **Deadline for Receipt:** February of each year. **Additional Information:** Funding for this program is provided by the U.S. National Aeronautics and Space Administration (NASA). The schools participating in the consortium include the University of Wisconsin campuses at Fox Valley, Green Bay, La Crosse, Madison, Milwaukee, Oshkosh, Parkside, Superior, and Whitewater; Alverno Col-

lege; Marquette University; College of the Menominee Nation; Carroll College; Lawrence University; Milwaukee School of Engineering; Ripon College; Medical College of Wisconsin; Western Wisconsin Technical College; and Wisconsin Lutheran College.

4733 ■ WOMEN IN AVIATION, INTERNATIONAL
Attn: Scholarships
101 Corsair Drive, Suite 101
P.O. Box 11287
Daytona Beach, FL 32120-1287
Tel: (386)226-7996
Fax: (386)226-7998
E-mail: scholarships@wai.org
Web Site: http://www.wai.org/education/scholarships.cfm
To provide financial assistance to members of Women in Aviation, International (WAI) who are studying engineering in college.

Title of Award: Delta Air Lines Engineering Scholarships **Area, Field, or Subject:** Engineering, Aerospace/Aeronautical/Astronautical; Engineering, Electrical; Engineering, Mechanical **Level of Education for which Award is Granted:** Undergraduate **Number Awarded:** 1 each year. **Funds Available:** The stipend is $5,000. **Duration:** 1 year.

Eligibility Requirements: This program is open to WAI members who are full-time juniors or seniors with at least 2 semesters of study remaining. Applicants must be working on a baccalaureate degree in aerospace, aeronautical, electrical, or mechanical engineering with a cumulative GPA of 3.0 or higher. U.S. citizenship is required. As part of the selection process, applicants must submit an essay of 500 to 1,000 words that addresses such questions as who or what influenced them to prepare for a career in engineering, their greatest strength and strongest characteristic, their most memorable academic experience, their greatest life challenge and how has it enriched their life, and why are they the best candidate for this scholarship. In addition to the essay, selection is based on achievements, attitude toward self and others, commitment to success, dedication to career, financial need, motivation, reliability, responsibility, and teamwork. **Deadline for Receipt:** December of each year. **Additional Information:** WAI is a nonprofit professional organization dedicated to encouraging women to consider an aviation career, providing educational outreach activities, and networking resources to women active in the industry. This program is sponsored by Delta Air Lines. In addition to the scholarship, recipients are reimbursed for up to $1,000 in travel and accommodations expenses to attend the WAI annual conference.

4734 ■ WYOMING TRUCKING ASSOCIATION, INC.
Attn: WTA Scholarship Trust Fund
555 North Poplar
P.O. Box 1909
Casper, WY 82602
Tel: (307)234-1579
Fax: (307)234-7082
E-mail: wytruck@aol.com
To provide financial assistance to high school seniors and currently-enrolled college students in Wyoming who are interested in preparing for a career in the highway transportation industry.

Title of Award: Wyoming Trucking Association Scholarships **Area, Field, or Subject:** Accounting; Business administration; Computer and information sciences; Management; Mechanics and repairs; Secretarial sciences; Transportation **Level of Education for which Award is Granted:** Undergraduate **Number Awarded:** 1 to 10 each year. **Funds Available:** Stipends range from $500 to $1,000. **Duration:** 1 year.

Eligibility Requirements: This program is open to high school seniors and graduates in Wyoming who are enrolled or planning to enroll in a community college in Wyoming, a trade school in the state, or the University of Wyoming. Applicants must be majoring or planning to major in a course of study that could lead to a career in the transportation industry, including (but not limited to) business management, computer skills, accounting, office procedures and management, safety, diesel mechanics, and truck driving. Along with their application, they must submit a 1-page essay on "How is the trucking industry important to you and the State of Wyoming." Financial need is considered in the selection process. **Deadline for Receipt:** March of each year.

Fire Science

4735 ■ AMERICAN SOCIETY OF SAFETY ENGINEERS

Attn: ASSE Foundation
1800 East Oakton Street
Des Plaines, IL 60018
Tel: (847)768-3441
Fax: (847)296-9220
E-mail: mrosario@asse.org
Web Site: http://www.asse.org
To provide financial assistance to undergraduate student members of the American Society of Safety Engineers (ASSE).
Title of Award: America Responds Memorial Scholarship **Area, Field, or Subject:** Engineering; Environmental conservation; Environmental science; Fires and fire prevention; Industrial hygiene; Occupational safety and health; Protective services **Level of Education for which Award is Granted:** Four Year College **Number Awarded:** 1 each year. **Funds Available:** The stipend is $1,000 per year. **Duration:** 1 year; nonrenewable.
Eligibility Requirements: This program is open to ASSE student members who are majoring in occupational safety and health or a closely-related field (e.g., safety engineering, safety management, systems safety, environmental science, industrial hygiene, ergonomics, fire science). Applicants must be full-time students who have completed at least 60 semester hours with a GPA of 3.0 or higher. As part of the selection process, they must submit 2 essays of 300 words or less: 1) why they are seeking a degree in safety, a brief description of their current activities, and how those relate to their career goals and objectives; and 2) why they should be awarded this scholarship (including career goals and financial need). **Deadline for Receipt:** November of each year.

4736 ■ AMERICAN SOCIETY OF SAFETY ENGINEERS

Attn: ASSE Foundation
1800 East Oakton Street
Des Plaines, IL 60018
Tel: (847)768-3441
Fax: (847)296-9220
E-mail: mrosario@asse.org
Web Site: http://www.asse.org
To provide financial assistance to undergraduate student members of the American Society of Safety Engineers (ASSE), particularly those interested in construction safety.
Title of Award: Bechtel Foundation Scholarship for Safety and Health **Area, Field, or Subject:** Construction; Engineering; Environmental conservation; Environmental science; Fires and fire prevention; Industrial hygiene; Occupational safety and health; Protective services **Level of Education for which Award is Granted:** Four Year College **Number Awarded:** 1 each year. **Funds Available:** The stipend is $3,000 per year. **Duration:** 1 year; nonrenewable.
Eligibility Requirements: This program is open to ASSE student members who are majoring in occupational safety and health or a closely-related field (e.g., safety engineering, safety management, systems safety, environmental science, industrial hygiene, ergonomics, fire science) with an emphasis on construction safety. Applicants must be full-time students who have completed at least 60 semester hours with a GPA of 3.0 or higher. As part of the selection process, they must submit 2 essays of 300 words or less: 1) why they are seeking a degree in safety, a brief description of their current activities, and how those relate to their career goals and objectives; and 2) why they should be awarded this scholarship (including career goals and financial need). **Deadline for Receipt:** November of each year. **Additional Information:** Funding for this program is provided by Bechtel Foundation.

4737 ■ AMERICAN SOCIETY OF SAFETY ENGINEERS

Attn: ASSE Foundation
1800 East Oakton Street
Des Plaines, IL 60018
Tel: (847)768-3441
Fax: (847)296-9220

E-mail: mrosario@asse.org
Web Site: http://www.asse.org
To provide financial assistance to undergraduate and graduate student members of the American Society of Safety Engineers (ASSE) from designated western states.
Title of Award: Scott Dominguez-Craters of the Moon Chapter Scholarship **Area, Field, or Subject:** Engineering; Environmental conservation; Environmental science; Fires and fire prevention; Industrial hygiene; Occupational safety and health; Protective services **Level of Education for which Award is Granted:** Four Year College, Graduate **Number Awarded:** 1 each year. **Funds Available:** The stipend is $1,000 per year. **Duration:** 1 year; nonrenewable.
Eligibility Requirements: This program is open to ASSE student members who are majoring in occupational safety and health or a closely-related field (e.g., safety engineering, safety management, systems safety, environmental science, industrial hygiene, ergonomics, fire science). First priority is given to residents within the service area of Craters of the Moon Chapter in Idaho; second priority is given to residents of ASSE Region II (Arizona, Colorado, Idaho, Montana, Nevada, New Mexico, Utah, and Wyoming). Special consideration is also given to 1) employees of a sponsoring organization or their dependents; 2) students who are serving their country through active duty in the armed forces or are honorably discharged; 3) former members of the Boy Scouts, Girl Scouts, FFA, or 4-H; 4) recipients of awards from service organizations; and 5) students who have provided volunteer service to an ASSE chapter in a leadership role. Undergraduates must have completed at least 60 semester hours with a GPA of 3.0 or higher. Graduate students must have completed at least 9 semester hours with a GPA of 3.5 or higher and have had a GPA of 3.0 or higher as an undergraduate. As part of the selection process, all applicants must submit 2 essays of 300 words or less: 1) why they are seeking a degree in safety, a brief description of their current activities, and how those relate to their career goals and objectives; and 2) why they should be awarded this scholarship (including career goals and financial need). **Deadline for Receipt:** November of each year.

4738 ■ AMERICAN SOCIETY OF SAFETY ENGINEERS

Attn: ASSE Foundation
1800 East Oakton Street
Des Plaines, IL 60018
Tel: (847)768-3441
Fax: (847)296-9220
E-mail: mrosario@asse.org
Web Site: http://www.asse.org
To provide financial assistance to undergraduate and graduate student members of the American Society of Safety Engineers (ASSE) from designated western states.
Title of Award: Gold Country Section and Region II Scholarship **Area, Field, or Subject:** Engineering; Environmental conservation; Environmental science; Fires and fire prevention; Industrial hygiene; Occupational safety and health; Protective services **Level of Education for which Award is Granted:** Four Year College, Graduate **Number Awarded:** 1 each year. **Funds Available:** The stipend is $1,000 per year. **Duration:** 1 year; nonrenewable.
Eligibility Requirements: This program is open to ASSE student members who are majoring in occupational safety and health or a closely-related field (e.g., safety engineering, safety management, systems safety, environmental science, industrial hygiene, ergonomics, fire science). Priority is given to residents of ASSE Region II (Arizona, Colorado, Idaho, Montana, Nevada, New Mexico, Utah, and Wyoming). Undergraduates must be full-time students who have completed at least 60 semester hours with a GPA of 3.0 or higher. Graduate students must also be enrolled full time, have completed at least 9 semester hours with a GPA of 3.5 or higher, and have had a GPA of 3.0 or higher as an undergraduate. As part of the selection process, all applicants must submit 2 essays of 300 words or less: 1) why they are seeking a degree in safety, a brief description of their current activities, and how those relate to their career goals and objectives; and 2) why they should be awarded this scholarship (including career goals and financial need). **Deadline for Receipt:** November of each year.

4739 ■ AMERICAN SOCIETY OF SAFETY ENGINEERS

Attn: ASSE Foundation
1800 East Oakton Street
Des Plaines, IL 60018

Tel: (847)768-3441
Fax: (847)296-9220
E-mail: mrosario@asse.org
Web Site: http://www.asse.org
To provide financial assistance to undergraduate student members of the American Society of Safety Engineers (ASSE) from designated southeastern states.
Title of Award: Region IV/Edwin P. Granberry, Jr. Scholarship **Area, Field, or Subject:** Engineering; Environmental conservation; Environmental science; Fires and fire prevention; Industrial hygiene; Occupational safety and health; Protective services **Level of Education for which Award is Granted:** Four Year College **Number Awarded:** 1 each year. **Funds Available:** The stipend is $1,000 per year. **Duration:** 1 year; nonrenewable.
Eligibility Requirements: This program is open to ASSE student members who are majoring in occupational safety and health or a closely-related field (e.g., safety engineering, safety management, systems safety, environmental science, industrial hygiene, ergonomics, fire science). Applicants must be residents of ASSE Region IV (Louisiana, Alabama, Mississippi, Georgia, Florida, Puerto Rico, and the U.S. Virgin Islands), although they may be attending school elsewhere. They must be full-time students who have completed at least 60 semester hours with a GPA of 3.0 or higher. As part of the selection process, they must submit 2 essays of 300 words or less: 1) why they are seeking a degree in safety, a brief description of their current activities, and how those relate to their career goals and objectives; and 2) why they should be awarded this scholarship (including career goals and financial need). **Deadline for Receipt:** November of each year.

4740 ■ AMERICAN SOCIETY OF SAFETY ENGINEERS

Attn: ASSE Foundation
1800 East Oakton Street
Des Plaines, IL 60018
Tel: (847)768-3441
Fax: (847)296-9220
E-mail: mrosario@asse.org
Web Site: http://www.asse.org
To provide financial assistance to upper-division and graduate students at colleges and universities in New England who are members or family of members of the American Society of Safety Engineers (ASSE).
Title of Award: Greater Boston Chapter Leadership Award **Area, Field, or Subject:** Engineering; Environmental conservation; Environmental science; Fires and fire prevention; Industrial hygiene; Occupational safety and health; Protective services **Level of Education for which Award is Granted:** Four Year College, Graduate **Number Awarded:** 1 each year. **Funds Available:** The stipend is $1,000 per year. **Duration:** 1 year; may be renewed.
Eligibility Requirements: This program is open to undergraduate and graduate students who are working on a degree in occupational safety and health or a closely-related field (e.g., safety engineering, safety management, systems safety, environmental science, industrial hygiene, ergonomics, fire science). Applicants must be 1) a member of an ASSE chapter in New England; 2) the spouse or child of an ASSE chapter member in New England; or 3) a member of an ASSE student section in New England. Undergraduates must be full-time students who have completed at least 60 semester hours with a GPA of 3.0 or higher. Graduate students must also be enrolled full time, have completed at least 9 semester hours with a GPA of 3.5 or higher, and have had a GPA of 3.0 or higher as an undergraduate. As part of the selection process, all applicants must submit 2 essays of 300 words or less: 1) why they are seeking a degree in safety, a brief description of their current activities, and how those relate to their career goals and objectives; and 2) why they should be awarded this scholarship (including career goals and financial need). **Deadline for Receipt:** November of each year.

4741 ■ AMERICAN SOCIETY OF SAFETY ENGINEERS

Attn: ASSE Foundation
1800 East Oakton Street
Des Plaines, IL 60018
Tel: (847)768-3441
Fax: (847)296-9220
E-mail: mrosario@asse.org
Web Site: http://www.asse.org

To provide financial assistance to undergraduate students majoring in fields related to occupational safety and health.
Title of Award: Gulf Coast Past Presidents Scholarship **Area, Field, or Subject:** Engineering; Environmental conservation; Environmental science; Fires and fire prevention; Industrial hygiene; Occupational safety and health; Protective services **Level of Education for which Award is Granted:** Four Year College **Number Awarded:** 1 each year. **Funds Available:** The stipend is $1,000 per year. **Duration:** 1 year; nonrenewable.
Eligibility Requirements: This program is open to undergraduate students who are majoring in occupational safety and health or a closely-related field (e.g., safety engineering, safety management, systems safety, environmental science, industrial hygiene, ergonomics, fire science). Although the program is sponsored by the Gulf Coast (Texas) chapter of the American Society of Safety Engineers (ASSE), there are no geographical restrictions on eligibility. Applicants must be full- or part-time students who have completed at least 60 semester hours with a GPA of 3.0 or higher. Part-time students must be ASSE members. As part of the selection process, all applicants must submit 2 essays of 300 words or less: 1) why they are seeking a degree in safety, a brief description of their current activities, and how those relate to their career goals and objectives; and 2) why they should be awarded this scholarship (including career goals and financial need). **Deadline for Receipt:** November of each year.

4742 ■ AMERICAN SOCIETY OF SAFETY ENGINEERS

Attn: ASSE Foundation
1800 East Oakton Street
Des Plaines, IL 60018
Tel: (847)768-3441
Fax: (847)296-9220
E-mail: mrosario@asse.org
Web Site: http://www.asse.org
To provide financial assistance to upper-division student members of the American Society of Safety Engineers (ASSE).
Title of Award: Liberty Mutual Scholarship **Area, Field, or Subject:** Engineering; Environmental conservation; Environmental science; Fires and fire prevention; Industrial hygiene; Occupational safety and health; Protective services **Level of Education for which Award is Granted:** Four Year College **Number Awarded:** 1 each year. **Funds Available:** The stipend is $3,000 per year. **Duration:** 1 year; nonrenewable.
Eligibility Requirements: This program is open to ASSE student members who are majoring in occupational safety and health or a closely-related field (e.g., safety engineering, safety management, systems safety, environmental science, industrial hygiene, ergonomics, fire science). Applicants must be full-time students who have completed at least 60 semester hours with a GPA of 3.0 or higher. As part of the selection process, they must submit 2 essays of 300 words or less: 1) why they are seeking a degree in safety, a brief description of their current activities, and how those relate to their career goals and objectives; and 2) why they should be awarded this scholarship (including career goals and financial need). **Deadline for Receipt:** November of each year. **Additional Information:** This program is supported by Liberty Mutual.

4743 ■ AMERICAN SOCIETY OF SAFETY ENGINEERS

Attn: ASSE Foundation
1800 East Oakton Street
Des Plaines, IL 60018
Tel: (847)768-3441
Fax: (847)296-9220
E-mail: mrosario@asse.org
Web Site: http://www.asse.org
To provide financial assistance to upper-division student members of the American Society of Safety Engineers (ASSE).
Title of Award: Marsh Risk Consulting Scholarship **Area, Field, or Subject:** Engineering; Environmental conservation; Environmental science; Fires and fire prevention; Industrial hygiene; Occupational safety and health; Protective services **Level of Education for which Award is Granted:** Four Year College **Number Awarded:** 1 each year. **Funds Available:** The stipend is $5,000 per year. **Duration:** 1 year; nonrenewable.
Eligibility Requirements: This program is open to ASSE student members who are majoring in occupational safety and health or a closely-

related field (e.g., safety engineering, safety management, systems safety, environmental science, industrial hygiene, ergonomics, fire science). Applicants must be full-time students who have completed at least 60 semester hours with a GPA of 3.0 or higher. As part of the selection process, they must submit 2 essays of 300 words or less: 1) why they are seeking a degree in safety, a brief description of their current activities, and how those relate to their career goals and objectives; and 2) why they should be awarded this scholarship (including career goals and financial need). **Deadline for Receipt:** November of each year. **Additional Information:** Funding for this program is provided by Marsh Risk Consulting.

4744 ■ AMERICAN SOCIETY OF SAFETY ENGINEERS
Attn: ASSE Foundation
1800 East Oakton Street
Des Plaines, IL 60018
Tel: (847)768-3441
Fax: (847)296-9220
E-mail: mrosario@asse.org
Web Site: http://www.asse.org
To provide financial assistance to undergraduate student members of the American Society of Safety Engineers (ASSE).
Title of Award: Marcella Thompson Distinguished Service Award Scholarship **Area, Field, or Subject:** Engineering; Environmental conservation; Environmental science; Fires and fire prevention; Industrial hygiene; Occupational safety and health; Protective services **Level of Education for which Award is Granted:** Four Year College **Number Awarded:** 1 each year. **Funds Available:** The stipend is $2,000 per year. **Duration:** 1 year; nonrenewable.
Eligibility Requirements: This program is open to ASSE student members who are majoring in occupational safety and health or a closely-related field (e.g., safety engineering, safety management, systems safety, environmental science, industrial hygiene, ergonomics, fire science). Applicants must be full-time students who have completed at least 60 semester hours with a GPA of 3.0 or higher. As part of the selection process, they must submit 2 essays of 300 words or less: 1) why they are seeking a degree in safety, a brief description of their current activities, and how those relate to their career goals and objectives; and 2) why they should be awarded this scholarship (including career goals and financial need). **Deadline for Receipt:** November of each year.

4745 ■ AMERICAN SOCIETY OF SAFETY ENGINEERS
Attn: ASSE Foundation
1800 East Oakton Street
Des Plaines, IL 60018
Tel: (847)768-3441
Fax: (847)296-9220
E-mail: mrosario@asse.org
Web Site: http://www.asse.org
To provide financial assistance to minority undergraduate student members of the American Society of Safety Engineers (ASSE).
Title of Award: UPS Diversity Scholarships **Area, Field, or Subject:** Engineering; Environmental conservation; Environmental science; Fires and fire prevention; Industrial hygiene; Occupational safety and health; Protective services **Level of Education for which Award is Granted:** Four Year College **Number Awarded:** Varies each year; recently, 2 of these scholarships at $5,250 each were awarded. **Funds Available:** Stipends range from $4,000 to $6,000 per year. **Duration:** 1 year; nonrenewable.
Eligibility Requirements: This program is open to ASSE student members who are enrolled in a 4-year degree program in occupational safety and health or a closely-related field (e.g., safety engineering, safety management, systems safety, environmental science, industrial hygiene, ergonomics, fire science). Applicants must be U.S. citizens and members of a minority ethnic or racial group. They must be full-time students who have completed at least 60 semester hours with a GPA of 3.0 or higher. As part of the selection process, they must submit 2 essays of 300 words or less: 1) why they are seeking a degree in safety, a brief description of their current activities, and how those relate to their career goals and objectives; and 2) why they should be awarded this scholarship (including career goals and financial need). **Deadline for Receipt:** November of each year. **Additional Information:** Funding for this program is provided by the UPS Foundation.

4746 ■ AMERICAN SOCIETY OF SAFETY ENGINEERS
Attn: ASSE Foundation
1800 East Oakton Street
Des Plaines, IL 60018
Tel: (847)768-3441
Fax: (847)296-9220
E-mail: mrosario@asse.org
Web Site: http://www.asse.org
To provide financial assistance to undergraduate student members of the American Society of Safety Engineers (ASSE).
Title of Award: UPS Scholarships **Area, Field, or Subject:** Engineering; Environmental conservation; Environmental science; Fires and fire prevention; Industrial hygiene; Occupational safety and health; Protective services **Level of Education for which Award is Granted:** Four Year College **Number Awarded:** Varies each year; recently, 4 of these scholarships at $5,250 each were awarded. **Funds Available:** Stipends range from $4,000 to $6,000 per year. **Duration:** 1 year; nonrenewable.
Eligibility Requirements: This program is open to ASSE student members who are enrolled in a 4-year degree program in occupational safety and health or a closely-related field (e.g., safety engineering, safety management, systems safety, environmental science, industrial hygiene, ergonomics, fire science). Applicants must be full-time students who have completed at least 60 semester hours with a GPA of 3.0 or higher. As part of the selection process, they must submit 2 essays of 300 words or less: 1) why they are seeking a degree in safety, a brief description of their current activities, and how those relate to their career goals and objectives; and 2) why they should be awarded this scholarship (including career goals and financial need). **Deadline for Receipt:** November of each year. **Additional Information:** Funding for this program is provided by the UPS Foundation.

4747 ■ CUMBERLAND VALLEY VOLUNTEER FIREMEN'S ASSOCIATION
Attn: Home Office Manager
11018 Clinton Street
Hagerstown, MD 21740-7701
Tel: (301)582-2345
E-mail: info@respondersafety.com
Web Site: http://cvvfa.org/scholarship.html
To provide financial assistance to residents of designated eastern states who are interested in working on a degree in fire science.
Title of Award: J.R. Haines Memorial Scholarship **Area, Field, or Subject:** Fires and fire prevention **Level of Education for which Award is Granted:** Undergraduate **Number Awarded:** 1 each year. **Funds Available:** The stipend is $1,000 per year. **Duration:** 1 year.
Eligibility Requirements: This program is open to residents of Delaware, Maryland, New Jersey, New York, North Carolina, Pennsylvania, Virginia, and West Virginia. Applicants must be enrolled or planning to enroll at a 2- or 4-year accredited college or university to work on a degree in fire science, including fire, fire investigation, and related subjects. Along with their application, they must submit a 250-word essay on why they are interested in a fire science-related career. **Deadline for Receipt:** February of each year.

4748 ■ DELAWARE VOLUNTEER FIREMEN'S ASSOCIATION
Attn: Executive Secretary
122A South Bradford Street
P.O. Box 1849
Dover, DE 19903-1849
Tel: (302)734-9390; 877-455-3832
Fax: (302)734-9404
E-mail: exsec@dvfassn.com
Web Site: http://www.dvfassn.com/html/schol.htm
To provide financial assistance for college to Delaware residents or members of fire departments or auxiliaries in the state.
Title of Award: Delaware Volunteer Firemen's Association Scholarship **Area, Field, or Subject:** Engineering; Fires and fire prevention; Medical technology **Level of Education for which Award is Granted:** Professional, Undergraduate **Number Awarded:** Varies each year; recently, 11 of these scholarships were awarded. **Funds Available:** The maximum stipend is $2,500. **Duration:** 1 year.
Eligibility Requirements: This program is open to 1) Delaware residents or 2) active members (for at least 1 year) of a fire department or auxiliary

that is a member in good standing of the Delaware Volunteer Firemen's Association or DVFA Ladies Auxiliary. Applicants must have been accepted into an accredited fire service technology, medical technology, engineering, or related certificate, diploma, or degree program. Along with their application, they must submit 3 letters of recommendation, college and fire school transcripts, and a 250-word statement that covers their reasons for applying for financial assistance, why their course of study will be useful, and their career goals and objectives. **Deadline for Receipt:** March of each year. **Additional Information:** Information is also available from the DVFA Scholarship Committee, Delaware State Fire School, 1461 Chestnut Grove Road, Dover, DE 19904-1545, (302) 376-6393.

4749 ■ MARYLAND HIGHER EDUCATION COMMISSION

Attn: Office of Student Financial Assistance
839 Bestgate Road, Suite 400
Annapolis, MD 21401-3013
Tel: (410)260-4574
Free: 800-974-1024
Fax: (410)974-5376
E-mail: osfamail@mhec.state.md.us
Web Site: http://www.mhec.state.md.us/financialAid/
ProgramDescriptions/prog_fire.asp
To provide financial assistance for college and graduate school to fire fighters, ambulance, and rescue squad members in Maryland.
Title of Award: Maryland Fire Fighter, Ambulance, and Rescue Squad Member Tuition Reimbursement Program **Area, Field, or Subject:** Fires and fire prevention; Medical technology **Level of Education for which Award is Granted:** Graduate, Professional, Undergraduate **Number Awarded:** Varies each year. **Funds Available:** Awards provide full reimbursement of tuition charges the student has paid. **Duration:** 1 year; may be renewed if the recipient maintains satisfactory academic progress and remains enrolled in an eligible program.
Eligibility Requirements: Eligible for this support are fire fighters, ambulance, and rescue squad members who are enrolled as full-time or part-time undergraduate or graduate students at an accredited institution of higher education in Maryland in a degree or certificate program for fire service technology or emergency medical technology. Applicants must have received at least a grade of "C" in any course required for completion of their program. They must be serving a Maryland community while they are taking college courses. **Deadline for Receipt:** June of each year. **Additional Information:** Recipients must continue to serve a Maryland community for an additional year following completion of the courses.

4750 ■ MICHIGAN LAW ENFORCEMENT EDUCATION PROGRAM

c/o Scholarship Committee
667 East Big Beaver Road, Suite 205
Troy, MI 48083
800-451-1220
To provide financial assistance for college to high school students in Michigan who are interested in preparing for a career in a field related to public safety.
Title of Award: LEEP Dream Scholarship **Area, Field, or Subject:** Criminal justice; Criminology; Emergency and disaster services; Fires and fire prevention; Law enforcement **Level of Education for which Award is Granted:** Undergraduate **Number Awarded:** Several each year. **Funds Available:** The stipend is $1,000. **Duration:** 1 year.
Eligibility Requirements: This program is open to seniors graduating from high schools in Michigan who are interested in preparing for a career as a law enforcement officer, police-fire dispatcher, corrections officer, fire fighter, or emergency medical technician. Applicants must be planning to attend a Michigan 4-year university, community college, or vocational training institution that grants a degree, certificate, or license in public safety or related field. **Deadline for Receipt:** May of each year.

4751 ■ NATIONAL FIRE PROTECTION ASSOCIATION

Attn: Fire Safety Educational Memorial Fund Committee
1 Batterymarch Park
Quincy, MA 02169-7471
Tel: (617)984-7244
Fax: (617)984-7222
E-mail: cellis@nfpa.org
Web Site: http://www.nfpa.org

To provide financial assistance to undergraduate and graduate students enrolled in fire service or public administration programs.
Title of Award: George D. Miller Scholarship **Area, Field, or Subject:** Fires and fire prevention; Public administration **Level of Education for which Award is Granted:** Graduate, Undergraduate **Number Awarded:** 1 each year. **Funds Available:** The stipend is at least $5,000. **Duration:** 1 year.
Eligibility Requirements: Colleges and universities in the United States and Canada are invited to nominate up to 2 undergraduate or graduate students enrolled in a fire service or public administration program. Nominees must exhibit scholastic achievement, leadership qualities, concern for others (volunteerism), and intent to prepare for a career in fire service or public administration **Deadline for Receipt:** March of each year. **Additional Information:** This fund was established in 2001.

4752 ■ SOCIETY OF FIRE PROTECTION ENGINEERS

Attn: Educational and Scientific Foundation
7315 Wisconsin Avenue, Suite 1225 W
Bethesda, MD 20814
Tel: (301)718-2910
Fax: (301)718-2242
E-mail: sfpehqtrs@sfpe.org
Web Site: http://www.sfpe.org
To provide funding to students interested in conducting research that expands the art and science of fire protection engineering.
Title of Award: Society of Fire Protection Engineers Student Research Grants **Area, Field, or Subject:** Engineering; Fires and fire prevention **Level of Education for which Award is Granted:** Graduate, Undergraduate **Number Awarded:** Varies each year. **Funds Available:** Grants range from $3,000 to $25,000.
Eligibility Requirements: This program is open to bachelor's, master's, and doctoral students interested in conducting a research project in the fields of fire safety science or fire protection engineering. Selection is based on the quality of the research plan and the possibility that it will yield valid and broadly applicable result or contribute to knowledge in the profession (35%), potential impact of the research on the field of fire protection engineering (35%), qualifications of the fire protection engineering program (15%), and achievability of the proposed research plan within the stated time frame (15%). **Deadline for Receipt:** Applications may be submitted at any time. **Additional Information:** Recipients must deliver a publishable paper.

4753 ■ SOCIETY OF FIRE PROTECTION ENGINEERS-HAWAII CHAPTER

c/o Robert T. Bigtas, Vice President
S.S. Dannaway Associates, Inc.
720 Iwilei Road, Suite 412
Honolulu, HI 96817
Tel: (808)526-9019
Fax: (808)537-5385
E-mail: scholarship@sfpehawaii.org
Web Site: http://www.sfpehawaii.org
To provide financial assistance to members of the Society of Fire Protection Engineers (SFPE) in Hawaii.
Title of Award: Hawaii Chapter Society of Fire Protection Engineers Academic Scholarship **Area, Field, or Subject:** Engineering; Fires and fire prevention **Level of Education for which Award is Granted:** Graduate, Undergraduate **Number Awarded:** 1 each year. **Funds Available:** The stipend is $1,000 per year. **Duration:** 1 year.
Eligibility Requirements: This program is open to residents of Hawaii who are enrolled in a fire protection engineering undergraduate or graduate degree program at a college or university in Hawaii or a fire science curriculum in the state. Applicants must submit 1) a letter of introduction that explains when they first became interested in preparing for a career in the field of fire protection and why, their short-term and long-term career goals, and any past experience and/or accomplishments in the field of fire protection engineering; 2) transcripts of all undergraduate and graduate programs; 3) proof of permanent residence in Hawaii; 4) proof of membership in the local SFPE chapter; and 5) a 50-word statement on why they

believe they should receive this scholarship. Financial need is not considered in the selection process. **Deadline for Receipt:** October of each year.

4754 ■ SOCIETY OF FIRE PROTECTION ENGINEERS-PHILADELPHIA-DELAWARE VALLEY CHAPTER

c/o Jeffrey LaSalle, Scholarship Committee
409 North Easton Road, Suite 1B
Willow Grove, PA 19090
Tel: (215)658-1770
E-mail: jlasalle@lasalleeng.com
Web Site: http://www.dtcc.edu/stanton/sfpe
To provide financial assistance to residents of the Philadelphia-Delaware Valley region who are studying fire protection engineering or a related field at the undergraduate or graduate level.
Title of Award: John D. Cook III Scholarship Award **Area, Field, or Subject:** Engineering; Fires and fire prevention **Level of Education for which Award is Granted:** Graduate, Undergraduate **Number Awarded:** 1 or more each year. **Funds Available:** Stipends range from $500 to $1,500. **Duration:** 1 year.
Eligibility Requirements: This program is open to residents of 1) the state of Delaware; 2) the following counties in Pennsylvania: Adams, Berks, Bradford, Bucks, Carbon, Centre, Chester, Clinton, Columbia, Cumberland, Dauphin, Delaware, Franklin, Juniata, Lackawanna, Lancaster, Lebanon, Lehigh, Luzerne, Lycoming, Mifflin, Monroe, Montgomery, Montour, Northampton, Northumberland, Perry, Philadelphia, Pike, Schuylkill, Snyder, Sullivan, Susquehanna, Tioga, Union, Wayne, Wyoming, and York; and 3) the following counties in New Jersey: Atlantic, Burlington, Camden, Cape May, Cumberland, Gloucester, Mercer, Ocean, and Salem. Applicants must be enrolled full time as juniors in an ABET-accredited fire protection engineering program, juniors in an ABET-accredited engineering program with a serious interest in a fire protection engineering career, graduate students in an engineering program with related studies in fire protection, second-year students in a 2-year fire engineering or fire science program with a serious interest in a fire protection engineering career, or juniors in a 4-year fire science program with a serious interest in a fire protection engineering career. They must be U.S. citizens or legal residents and have a GPA of 2.5 or higher. They may attend school in any state. Selection is based on demonstrated academic achievement and performance in the field of fire protection. **Deadline for Receipt:** February of each year.

Food Service and Food Science

4755 ■ ALASKA COMMISSION ON POSTSECONDARY EDUCATION

Attn: AlaskAdvantage Programs
3030 Vintage Boulevard
Juneau, AK 99801-7109
Tel: (907)465-2962
Free: 800-441-2962
Fax: (907)465-5316
E-mail: customer_service@acpe.ak.us
Web Site: http://alaskaadvantage.state.ak.us/page/257
To provide financial assistance to Alaska residents who are interested in working on an undergraduate or graduate degree in fisheries or related fields.
Title of Award: A.W. "Winn" Brindle Memorial Education Loan Program **Area, Field, or Subject:** Business; Fisheries sciences/management; Food science and technology **Level of Education for which Award is Granted:** Graduate, Undergraduate **Number Awarded:** Varies each year, depending upon the amount of contributions made to the fund by private donors and fisheries businesses. **Funds Available:** Loans are awarded to cover the cost of tuition, fees, books, supplies, room, board, and transportation costs. An origination fee of 3% is deducted from the eligible loan amount. The interest rate charged is 5%. This is a partial scholarship/loan program; recipients are eligible for up to 50% forgiveness upon graduation if they return to Alaska to secure employment in a fisheries-related field. **Duration:** Up to 5 years of undergraduate study and up to 5 years of graduate study, or a combined maximum of 8 years of study. Recipients have up to 15 years to repay the loans.
Eligibility Requirements: This program is open to full-time undergraduate and graduate students in Alaska who are interested in working on a

degree at an accredited college or university that will lead to a career in fisheries, fishery science, fishery management, seafood processing, food technology, or other fishery-related fields. Applicants who have been nominated by program donors are given preference for receipt of funds. **Additional Information:** This program is funded by private donations and contributions from fisheries businesses in exchange for tax credits. A fisheries business is entitled to a tax credit of up to 5% of its business tax liability for contributions made during the tax year to this scholarship/loan fund. Businesses and other donors are encouraged to nominate individuals for receipt of these funds.

4756 ■ AMERICAN HOTEL & LODGING EDUCATIONAL FOUNDATION

Attn: Manager of Foundation Programs
1201 New York Avenue, N.W., Suite 600
Washington, DC 20005-3931
Tel: (202)289-3188
Fax: (202)289-3199
E-mail: ahlef@ahlef.org
Web Site: http://www.ahlef.org/scholarships_american_express.asp
To provide financial assistance to undergraduate students interested in majoring in hospitality management in college.
Title of Award: American Express Academic Scholarships **Area, Field, or Subject:** Food service careers; Hotel, institutional, and restaurant management **Level of Education for which Award is Granted:** Undergraduate **Number Awarded:** Varies each year; recently, this program awarded 7 Academic Scholarships. **Funds Available:** Full-time students at 4-year institutions receive $2,000; part-time students at 4-year institutions receive $1,000; full- or part-time students at 2-year institutions receive $500. Funds are paid in 2 equal installments. Checks are made out jointly to the recipient and the academic institution and must be endorsed by both. Funds may be used only for tuition, fees, and books. **Duration:** 1 year.
Eligibility Requirements: Applicants must 1) be actively employed (at least 20 hours per week) at a hotel or motel that is a member of the American Hotel & Lodging Association (AH&LA) and have been employed at least 12 months by a hotel or 2) be the dependent of an employee who meets the requirements above and has been employed in the hospitality industry in some capacity in the past. In addition, applicants must be enrolled or planning to enroll as an undergraduate student in a hospitality management program offered by a university or college. Along with their application, they must submit a 500-word essay on their personal background, including when and why they became interested in the hospitality field, what characteristics will allow them to succeed, and how their education will help them to achieve their career objectives and future goals. Selection is based on financial need, industry-related work experience, academic record, extracurricular activities, career goals, the essay, and neatness and completeness of the application. **Deadline for Receipt:** April of each year. **Additional Information:** The American Hotel & Lodging Educational Institute (EI) offers a parallel program for students who meet the same eligibility requirements: the American Express EI Professional Development Scholarship, which provides funding for EI distance learning courses and professional certification programs. Information on those scholarships is available from the EI at 2113 North High Street, Lansing, MI 48906, (517) 372-8800, (800) 752-4567, Fax; (517) 372-5141, E-mail: academics@ei-ahla.org.

4757 ■ AMERICAN HOTEL & LODGING EDUCATIONAL FOUNDATION

Attn: Manager of Foundation Programs
1201 New York Avenue, N.W., Suite 600
Washington, DC 20005-3931
Tel: (202)289-3181
Fax: (202)289-3199
E-mail: ahlef@ahlef.org
Web Site: http://www.ahlef.org/scholarships_annual_grant.asp
To provide financial assistance to students working on an undergraduate degree in hospitality management at participating schools.
Title of Award: American Hotel & Lodging Educational Foundation Annual Scholarship Grant Program **Area, Field, or Subject:** Food service careers; Hotel, institutional, and restaurant management **Level of Education for which Award is Granted:** Undergraduate **Number Awarded:** Varies each year; recently, 212 students received support from this

program. **Funds Available:** The amount awarded varies by school. **Duration:** 1 year.

Eligibility Requirements: Applicants must be attending a 2-year or 4-year college in the United States or Canada that is preapproved and participating in the foundation's scholarship program (for a list of schools, write to the foundation). They must be majoring in hospitality management (including hotel and restaurant management) as full-time students with a GPA of 3.0 or higher. Individual schools select the final recipients. **Deadline for Receipt:** Schools must submit their nominations by April of each year. **Additional Information:** Nearly 80 schools are preapproved to participate in this program. This program includes the following named scholarships: the American Hotel and Lodging Association Allied Member Scholarships, the American Hotel and Lodging Foundation Annual Giving Campaign Scholarships, the American Hotel and Lodging Foundation General Scholarships, the Bill Fisher Scholarships, the Cecil B. Day Memorial Scholarships, the Steven Belmonte Scholarships, the Conrad N. Hilton Memorial Scholarships, the J. Willard Marriott Memorial Scholarships, the John Clifford Memorial Scholarships, the Karl Mehlmann Memorial Scholarships, the Richard Kessler Scholarships, the Curtis C. Nelson Scholarships, and the Handlery Scholarships.

4758 ■ AMERICAN HOTEL & LODGING EDUCATIONAL FOUNDATION

Attn: Manager of Foundation Programs
1201 New York Avenue, N.W., Suite 600
Washington, DC 20005-3931
Tel: (202)289-3181
Fax: (202)289-3199
E-mail: ahlef@ahlef.org
Web Site: http://www.ahlef.org/scholarships_ecolab.asp
To provide financial assistance to students working on a college degree in hospitality management.

Title of Award: Ecolab Academic Scholarship Program **Area, Field, or Subject:** Food service careers; Hotel, institutional, and restaurant management **Level of Education for which Award is Granted:** Professional, Undergraduate **Number Awarded:** Varies each year; recently, 22 of these scholarships were awarded. **Funds Available:** The stipend is $2,000 for students in 4-year baccalaureate programs or $1,000 for students in 2-year associate programs. Funds are distributed in 2 equal installments (in August and December). Checks are made out jointly to the recipient and the recipient's academic institution. Funds may be used only for tuition, fees, and books. **Duration:** 1 year.

Eligibility Requirements: This program is open to students working on an associate or baccalaureate degree in hospitality management. They must be enrolled or intending to enroll full time. Along with their application, they must submit a 500-word personal essay on when and why they became interested in the hospitality field, the characteristics or qualifications that will allow them to succeed, and how their education will help them to achieve their career objectives and future goals. Selection is based on industry-related work experience; financial need; academic record and educational qualifications; professional, community, and extracurricular activities; personal attributes, including career goals; the essay; and neatness and completeness of the application. **Deadline for Receipt:** May of each year. **Additional Information:** In addition to these academic scholarships, the program also provides support to hospitality professionals seeking certification in the following operational areas: certified hotel administrator, certified lodging manager, certified engineering operations executive, and certified hospitality housekeeping executive. This program is known as EI Certification Scholarship Program. Funds are available to cover the cost of the certification study guide, examination fee, and certification fee. Information on that program is available from the EI at 2113 North High Street, Lansing, MI 48906, (517) 372-8800, (800) 752-4567, Fax; (517) 372-5141, E-mail: academics@ei-ahla.org. Both academic and certification programs are supported by Ecolab.

4759 ■ AMERICAN HOTEL & LODGING EDUCATIONAL FOUNDATION

Attn: Manager of Foundation Programs
1201 New York Avenue, N.W., Suite 600
Washington, DC 20005-3931
Tel: (202)289-3181
Fax: (202)289-3199
E-mail: ahlef@ahlef.org

Web Site: http://www.ahlef.org/scholarships_packard_memorial.asp
To recognize and reward outstanding students working on an undergraduate degree in lodging management at participating universities.

Title of Award: Arthur J. Packard Memorial Scholarship Competition **Area, Field, or Subject:** Food service careers; Hotel, institutional, and restaurant management **Level of Education for which Award is Granted:** Four Year College **Number Awarded:** 1 winner and 2 runners-up each year. **Funds Available:** The national winner receives $5,000, the second-place runner-up receives $3,000, and the third-place runner-up receives $2,000. **Duration:** The competition is held annually.

Eligibility Requirements: Applicants must be attending a 4-year college or university that is preapproved and participating in the foundation's scholarship program (for a list of schools, write to the foundation). They must be enrolled full time in a hospitality-related degree-granting program, be a sophomore or junior at the time of application, have a GPA of 3.5 or higher, be a U.S. citizen or permanent resident, and be nominated by their school. Selection is based on academic performance, hospitality work experience, financial need, extracurricular involvement (activities and honors), and personal attributes. **Deadline for Receipt:** March of each year. **Additional Information:** Nearly 80 schools are preapproved to participate in this program.

4760 ■ CALIFORNIA STATE FAIR

Attn: Friends of the Fair Scholarship Program
1600 Exposition Boulevard
P.O. Box 15649
Sacramento, CA 95852
Tel: (916)274-5969
E-mail: wross@calexpo.com
Web Site: http://www.bigfun.org
To provide financial assistance to residents of California who are studying culinary cooking or hospitality management.

Title of Award: California State Fair Culinary Cooking and Hospitality Management Scholarships **Area, Field, or Subject:** Culinary arts; Food service careers; Hotel, institutional, and restaurant management **Level of Education for which Award is Granted:** Vocational/Occupational **Number Awarded:** 2 each year: 1 at $1,500 and 1 at $500. **Funds Available:** Stipends are $1,500 or $500. **Duration:** 1 year.

Eligibility Requirements: This program is open to residents of California currently working on an associate degree at a culinary specialty school in the state. Applicants must be enrolled in a culinary cooking or hospitality management program. They must have a GPA of 3.0 or higher. Along with their application, they must submit a 2-page essay on why they are pursuing their desired career and life goals. Selection is based on personal commitment, goals established for their chosen field, leadership potential, and civic accomplishments. field, leadership potential, and civic accomplishments. **Deadline for Receipt:** March of each year. **Additional Information:** The Friends of the Fair Scholarship Program was established in 1993.

4761 ■ CHOICE HOTELS INTERNATIONAL

Attn: Foundation
10750 Columbia Pike
Silver Spring, MD 20901
Tel: (301)592-6258
Web Site: http://www6.choicehotels.com
To provide financial assistance to women interested in preparing for a career in the hospitality industry.

Title of Award: Women's Business Alliance Scholarship Program **Area, Field, or Subject:** Food service careers; Hotel, institutional, and restaurant management **Level of Education for which Award is Granted:** Graduate, Undergraduate **Number Awarded:** 1 each year. **Funds Available:** The stipend is $2,000. **Duration:** 1 year; recipients may reapply.

Eligibility Requirements: This program is open to female high school seniors, undergraduates, and graduate students. Applicants must be U.S. citizens or permanent residents interested in preparing for a career in the hospitality industry. They must submit an essay of 500 words or less on their experience or interest in the hospitality industry and how it relates to their career goals, including any community service experience that has impacted their career goals or their interest in the industry. Financial need is not considered in the selection process. **Deadline for Receipt:** July of each year.

4762 ■ CLUB FOUNDATION

Attn: Scholarship Coordinator
1733 King Street
Alexandria, VA 22314-2720
Tel: (703)739-9500
Fax: (703)739-0124
E-mail: schaverr@clubfoundation.org
Web Site: http://www.clubfoundation.org/stuscholar.html
To provide financial assistance for college to students planning a career in private club management.
Title of Award: Joe Perdue Scholarships **Area, Field, or Subject:** Food service careers; Hotel, institutional, and restaurant management; Management **Level of Education for which Award is Granted:** Four Year College **Number Awarded:** Varies each year; recently, 7 of these scholarships were awarded. **Funds Available:** The stipend is $2,500 per year. Funds are paid directly to the recipient's college or university. **Duration:** 1 year.
Eligibility Requirements: This program is open to students who are currently attending an accredited 4-year college or university and are actively preparing for a managerial career in the private club industry. Applicants must have completed their freshman year with a GPA of 2.5 or higher. Along with their application, they must submit an essay of 500 to 1,000 words on their career objectives and goals, the characteristics they possess that will allow them to succeed as a club manager, how their experiences with the Club Management Association of American (CMAA) shaped their perception of the association and the private club management industry, their specified interests within the private club management field, and why they feel the Club Foundation should select them as a scholarship recipient. Selection is based on academic record (20 points), extracurricular activities (15 points), the essay (20 points), and employment record (15 points). **Deadline for Receipt:** April of each year. **Additional Information:** The Club Foundation was formerly the Club Management Institute Foundation. It is the nonprofit foundation affiliated with the CMAA.

4763 ■ CLUB MANAGERS ASSOCIATION OF AMERICA-GEORGIA CHAPTER

c/o Jeff Orkus, Chapter Scholarship Chair
Idle Hour Golf and Country Club
251 Idle Hour Drive
Macon, GA 31210
Tel: (478)477-1724
Fax: (478)757-2405
E-mail: jorkus@idlehourclub.com
Web Site: http://www.gacmaa.org
To provide financial assistance for college or graduate school to members of the Georgia Chapter of the Club Managers Association of America (CMAA) and their families, especially those interested in a career in club management.
Title of Award: Georgia Chapter Scholarship Program **Area, Field, or Subject:** Food service careers; General studies/Field of study not specified; Hotel, institutional, and restaurant management **Level of Education for which Award is Granted:** Graduate, Undergraduate **Number Awarded:** 3 each year. **Funds Available:** The stipend is $1,000. **Duration:** 1 year.
Eligibility Requirements: This program is open to students in the following priority order: 1) Georgia CMAA members and the children, stepchildren, grandchildren, and adopted children of Georgia CMAA members who are working on a hospitality degree; 2) children, stepchildren, grandchildren, and adopted children of Georgia CMAA members working on a liberal arts degree; and 3) CMAA student chapter members working on a hospitality degree. Both undergraduate and graduate students are eligible. Georgia chapter members must have completed their freshman year and be enrolled full time and CMAA student chapter member applicants must have completed their sophomore year and be full-time students in a hospitality management program. All applicants must have a GPA of 2.75 or higher. Along with their application, they must submit an essay of 250 to 500 words on their career objectives, their interest in club management, and why they should be a scholarship recipient. Selection is based on the essay, class ranking, GPA, extracurricular activities, and work experience; financial need is not considered. **Deadline for Receipt:** September of each year. **Additional Information:** Recipients may study at a college or university anywhere in the United States.

4764 ■ CLUB MANAGERS ASSOCIATION OF AMERICA-LONE STAR CHAPTER

c/o Mary P. Miller, Executive Secretary
6405 Kentucky Court
Colleyville, TX 76034
Tel: (817)849-8532
Free: 800-689-2622
Fax: (817)656-9769
E-mail: tlsc@sbcglobal.net
Web Site: http://www.texascmaa.org
To provide financial assistance to undergraduate and graduate students majoring in the hospitality program at selected universities in Texas.
Title of Award: James B. "Sam" Bass Scholarship **Area, Field, or Subject:** Food service careers; Hotel, institutional, and restaurant management **Level of Education for which Award is Granted:** Graduate, Undergraduate **Number Awarded:** Up to 3 each year. **Funds Available:** The stipend is $2,000 per year. Funds are paid directly to the recipient's university. **Duration:** 1 year.
Eligibility Requirements: This program is open to active members of the Club Managers Association of America (CMAA) in chapters at the University of Houston, Texas Tech University, or the University of North Texas. Applicants must be full-time students majoring in the hospitality program with a GPA of 3.0 or higher. Along with their application, they must submit an essay of 500 to 750 words on their club employment history, reason for application, local chapter involvement and contributions, goals in CMAA, and why they deserve the scholarship. Financial need is not considered in the selection process. **Deadline for Receipt:** February of each year. **Additional Information:** Information is also available from Christina Toups, Texas Lone Star Chapter Past President, Ridglea Country Club, 3700 Bernie Anderson, Fort Worth, TX 76116-2526, E-mail: cat@ridgleacountryclub.com.

4765 ■ CONGRESSIONAL BLACK CAUCUS FOUNDATION, INC.

Attn: Director, Educational Programs
1720 Massachusetts Avenue, N.W.
Washington, DC 20036
Tel: (202)263-2836
Free: 800-784-2577
Fax: (202)775-0773
E-mail: spouses@cbcfinc.org
Web Site: http://www.cbcfinc.org
To provide financial assistance to minority and other undergraduate and graduate students who reside in a Congressional district represented by an African American and are interested in preparing for a health-related career.
Title of Award: Cheerios Brand Health Initiative Scholarship **Area, Field, or Subject:** Biological and clinical sciences; Chemistry; Education, Physical; Engineering; Food service careers; Health care services; Medicine; Nursing **Level of Education for which Award is Granted:** Graduate, Undergraduate **Number Awarded:** Varies each year. **Funds Available:** A stipend is awarded (amount not specified). **Duration:** 1 year.
Eligibility Requirements: This program is open to 1) minority and other graduating high school seniors planning to attend an accredited institution of higher education and 2) currently-enrolled full-time undergraduate, graduate, and doctoral students in good academic standing with a GPA of 2.5 or higher. Applicants must reside or attend school in a Congressional district represented by a member of the Congressional Black Caucus. They must be interested in preparing for a career in a medical, food services, or other health-related field, including pre-medicine, nursing, chemistry, biology, physical education, and engineering. Along with their application, they must submit a 500-word personal statement on 1) the field of study they intend to pursue and why they have chosen that field; 2) their interests, involvement in school activities, community and public service, hobbies, special talents, sports, and other highlight areas; and 3) any other experiences, skills, or qualifications they feel should be considered. They must also be able to document financial need. **Deadline for Receipt:** April of each year. **Additional Information:** The program was established in 1998 with support from General Mills, Inc.

4766 ■ CONNECTICUT COMMISSION ON CULTURE AND TOURISM

Attn: Tourism Division
505 Hudson Street, Second Floor
Hartford, CT 06106

Tel: (860)270-8089
Fax: (860)270-8077
E-mail: joyce.fredericks@po.state.ct.us
Web Site: http://www.tourism.state.ct.us/tourism.asp
To provide financial assistance to undergraduate and graduate students from Connecticut who are preparing for a career in the hospitality industry.
Title of Award: Richard B. Combs Hospitality Scholarship **Area, Field, or Subject:** Food service careers; Hotel, institutional, and restaurant management **Level of Education for which Award is Granted:** Master's, Undergraduate **Number Awarded:** 1 each year. **Funds Available:** The stipend is $1,000. **Duration:** 1 year.
Eligibility Requirements: This program is open to residents of Connecticut who are high school seniors, high school graduates who have not yet enrolled in college, or enrolled undergraduate or graduate students at an accredited college or university. Applicants must be preparing for a career in the hospitality industry. Along with their application, they must submit an essay on a topic about hospitality as it relates to Connecticut tourism, 2 letters of recommendation, a current transcript, a personal letter of intent explaining how this scholarship will help them to achieve their academic goals, and a personal resume. Selection is based on personal achievement and demonstrated interest in the hospitality industry. **Deadline for Receipt:** September of each year.

4767 ■ DECA

1908 Association Drive
Reston, VA 20191-1594
Tel: (703)860-5000
Fax: (703)860-4013
E-mail: decainc@aol.com
Web Site: http://www.deca.org/student.html
To provide financial assistance for college to DECA members who are also members of an academy of hospitality and tourism affiliated with the National Academy Foundation.
Title of Award: American Express Foundation of Hospitality and Tourism Academy Scholarships **Area, Field, or Subject:** Food service careers; Hotel, institutional, and restaurant management; Management; Marketing and distribution; Travel and tourism **Level of Education for which Award is Granted:** Undergraduate **Number Awarded:** 2 each year. **Funds Available:** The stipend is $1,000. **Duration:** 1 year.
Eligibility Requirements: This program is open to DECA members who are high school seniors and also members of an academy of hospitality and tourism affiliated with the National Academy Foundation. Applicants must be interested in enrolling in a 2-year or 4-year course of study in marketing, merchandising, or management at an accredited institution or university. Selection based on DECA involvement, leadership, and grades. Applicants may also include a statement in support of financial need and it will be reviewed. **Deadline for Receipt:** February of each year. **Additional Information:** This program is sponsored by American Express.

4768 ■ DECA

1908 Association Drive
Reston, VA 20191-1594
Tel: (703)860-5000
Fax: (703)860-4013
E-mail: decainc@aol.com
Web Site: http://www.deca.org/student.html
To provide financial assistance for college to DECA members interested in the hospitality industry.
Title of Award: Marriott International Scholarships **Area, Field, or Subject:** Business administration; Food service careers; Hotel, institutional, and restaurant management; Marketing and distribution **Level of Education for which Award is Granted:** Undergraduate **Number Awarded:** Up to 6 each year. **Funds Available:** The stipend is $1,000. **Duration:** 1 year.
Eligibility Requirements: This program is open to DECA members who are interested in working full time on a 2-year or 4-year degree in business or marketing to prepare for a career in the hospitality industry. Applicants must be able to demonstrate evidence of DECA activities, academic achievement, leadership ability, and interest or experience in the hospitality industry. Selection is based on merit, not financial need. **Deadline for Receipt:** February of each year. **Additional Information:** This program is sponsored by Marriott International, Inc.

4769 ■ FLORIDA SEA GRANT COLLEGE PROGRAM

Attn: Director
University of Florida
Building 803 McCarty Drive
P.O. Box 110400
Gainesville, FL 32611-0400
Tel: (352)392-5870
Fax: (352)392-5113
Web Site: http://www.flseagrant.org/students/scholarships/index.htm
To provide financial assistance to undergraduate or graduate students working on a degree in a marine science-related field at any Florida university that participates in the Florida Sea Grant College Program.
Title of Award: Aylesworth Foundation for the Advancement of Marine Science Scholarships **Area, Field, or Subject:** Biological and clinical sciences; Economics; Engineering; Food science and technology; Marine biology **Level of Education for which Award is Granted:** Graduate, Undergraduate **Number Awarded:** Generally, 4 or more each year. **Funds Available:** The maximum stipend awarded is 65% of the annual official university or college cost of attendance or $4,000, whichever is less. **Duration:** 1 year; renewable until the recipient completes the degree.
Eligibility Requirements: Eligible to be nominated by their department chair are undergraduate or graduate students who are working on a degree in an academic discipline that has direct application in marine science (ranging from biology and engineering to economics and food science) at a university or college in Florida that participates in the Florida Sea Grant College Program. Financial need is the principal factor used in the selection process, although academic record, leadership, and personal character are also considered. Florida residents are given preference. **Deadline for Receipt:** November of each year. **Additional Information:** The Florida Sea Grant College Program, established in 1986, operates as a partnership between the Florida Board of Education and the U.S. National Oceanic and Atmospheric Administration. The participating institutions are Florida A&M University, Florida Gulf Coast University, Florida Atlantic University, Florida Institute of Technology, Florida International University, Florida State University, Harbor Branch Oceanographic Institution, Mote Marine Laboratory, New College of Florida, Nova Southeastern University, University of Central Florida, University of Florida, University of Miami, University of North Florida, University of South Florida, and University of West Florida. These scholarships are sponsored by the Aylesworth Foundation for the Advancement of Marine Science, the Southeastern Fisheries Association, and the Florida Sea Grant College Program.

4770 ■ INTERNATIONAL ASSOCIATION OF FOOD INDUSTRY SUPPLIERS

Attn: IAFIS Foundation
1451 Dolley Madison Boulevard
McLean, VA 22101-3850
Tel: (703)761-2600
Fax: (703)761-4334
E-mail: info@iafis.org
Web Site: http://www.iafis.org
To provide financial assistance to outstanding undergraduate students who are interested in working on a degree in food engineering.
Title of Award: Food Engineering Scholarship Program **Area, Field, or Subject:** Food science and technology; Food service careers **Level of Education for which Award is Granted:** Undergraduate **Number Awarded:** 2 each year. **Funds Available:** The stipend of $2,500 is paid to the student in equal installments throughout the junior or senior academic year. In addition, a $500 travel grant is given to each recipient to attend Worldwide Food EXPO. **Duration:** 1 year; nonrenewable.
Eligibility Requirements: This program is open to sophomores and juniors majoring in food engineering at accredited institutions in the United States or Canada. Applicants must be U.S. or Canadian citizens, have an outstanding academic record, have a well-rounded personality, and be able to demonstrate an intent to prepare for a career in the food industry. Along with their application, they must include a 250-word essay on their rationale for choosing the food industry as a career. Age, sex, race, and financial need are not considered in the selection process. **Deadline for Receipt:** February of each year. **Additional Information:** This program, established in 1983, includes the Paul Girton Food Engineering Scholarship and the Gordon Houran Food Engineering Scholarship.

4771 ■ INTERNATIONAL FOODSERVICE EDITORIAL COUNCIL
P.O. Box 491
Hyde Park, NY 12538
Tel: (845)229-6973
Fax: (845)229-6993
E-mail: ifec@aol.com
Web Site: http://www.ifec-is-us.com
To provide financial assistance to undergraduate or graduate students who are interested in preparing for a career in communications in the food service industry.
Title of Award: IFEC Scholarships **Area, Field, or Subject:** Communications; Creative writing; Culinary arts; English language and literature; Food science and technology; Food service careers; Graphic art and design; Hotel, institutional, and restaurant management; Journalism; Management; Marketing and distribution; Nutrition; Photography; Photography, Journalistic; Public relations **Level of Education for which Award is Granted:** Master's, Undergraduate **Number Awarded:** Varies each year; recently, 5 of these scholarships were awarded. **Funds Available:** The stipend is $3,000 per year. **Duration:** 1 year.
Eligibility Requirements: This program is open to currently-enrolled college students who are working on an associate, bachelor's, or master's degree. They must be enrolled full time and planning on a career in editorial, public relations, photography, food styling, or a related aspect of communications in the food service industry. The following food service majors are considered appropriate for this program: culinary arts; hospitality management; hotel, restaurant, and institutional management; dietetics; food science and technology; and nutrition. Applicable communications areas include journalism, English, mass communications, public relations, marketing, broadcast journalism, creative writing, graphic arts, and photography. Selection is based on academic record, character references, and demonstrated financial need. **Deadline for Receipt:** March of each year.

4772 ■ KENTUCKY RESTAURANT ASSOCIATION
Attn: Educational Foundation
133 Evergreen Road, suite 201
Louisville, KY 40243
Tel: (502)896-0464
Free: 800-896-0414
Fax: (502)896-0465
E-mail: info@kyra.org
Web Site: http://www.kyra.org
To provide financial assistance to students in Kentucky who are preparing for a career in the food service industry.
Title of Award: Kentucky Restaurant Association Academic Scholarships **Area, Field, or Subject:** Food service careers **Level of Education for which Award is Granted:** Master's, Undergraduate **Number Awarded:** Varies; generally, up to 25 each year. **Funds Available:** Stipend amounts vary, depending on tuition and fees at the school the recipient attends. **Duration:** 1 year; may be renewed.
Eligibility Requirements: Applicants must have been Kentucky residents (or residing within 25 miles of Kentucky's borders) for the past 18 months. They must be enrolled or planning to enroll at an accredited college to work on an associate, bachelor's, or master's degree in food service. Work experience in food service is required. Financial need is considered in the selection process. **Deadline for Receipt:** June or December of each year.

4773 ■ MASSACHUSETTS RESTAURANT ASSOCIATION
Attn: Hospitality Institute
333 Turnpike Road, Suite 102
Southborough, MA 01772-1775
Tel: (508)303-9905
Free: 800-852-3042
Fax: (508)303-9985
E-mail: pchristie@massrestaurantassoc.org
Web Site: http://www.marestaurantassoc.org/educationscholarships.htm
To provide financial assistance to Massachusetts residents interested in preparing for a career in the restaurant and food service industry.
Title of Award: Massachusetts Restaurant Association Hospitality Institute Scholarships **Area, Field, or Subject:** Food service careers **Level of Education for which Award is Granted:** Undergraduate **Number Awarded:** Varies each year; recently, 32 of these scholarships

were awarded. **Funds Available:** The stipend is $2,000. Several cooperating colleges and culinary institutes provide matching funds. **Duration:** 1 year.
Eligibility Requirements: This program is open to graduating high school seniors, high school graduates, and undergraduate college students who are residents of Massachusetts. Applicants must have been accepted as full-time or substantial part-time students in a restaurant or food service-related postsecondary program. They must have a GPA of 2.75 or higher. High school seniors must have at least 250 hours of restaurant or food service work experience; high school graduates and college students must have at least 750 hours of such experience. **Additional Information:** This program was established in 2001.

4774 ■ NATIONAL ASSOCIATION OF COLLEGES AND UNIVERSITY FOOD SERVICES
c/o Michigan State University
Manly Miles Building
1405 South Harrison Road, Suite 305
East Lansing, MI 48824-5242
Tel: (517)332-2494
Fax: (517)332-8144
Web Site: http://www.nacufs.org
To provide financial assistance to college students preparing for a career in the food service industry.
Title of Award: Clark E. DeHaven Scholarships **Area, Field, or Subject:** Food service careers **Level of Education for which Award is Granted:** Undergraduate **Number Awarded:** 4 each year. **Funds Available:** The stipend is $4,000. **Duration:** 1 year.
Eligibility Requirements: This program is open to U.S. or Canadian citizens currently enrolled full time as sophomores, juniors, or seniors in an accredited program that will lead to an undergraduate degree in food service or a related field. Applicants must be enrolled at institutions that are members of the National Association of Colleges and University Food Services. They must have a GPA of 2.75 or higher. Along with their application, they must submit an official transcript, 2 letters of recommendation, a letter of personal evaluation, and a resume. Selection is based on academic record, financial need, commitment to a career in food service professions, character, campus citizenship, volunteer activities, and campus involvement. **Deadline for Receipt:** February of each year. **Additional Information:** These scholarships were first awarded in 1990. Information is also available from H. Michael Rice, Michigan State University, Food Stores, 171 Service Road, East Lansing, MI 48824.

4775 ■ NATIONAL DAIRY PROMOTION AND RESEARCH BOARD
c/o Dairy Management Inc.
10255 West Higgins Road, Suite 900
Rosemont, IL 60018-5616
Tel: (847)803-2000
Fax: (847)803-2077
E-mail: marykateg@rosedmi.com
Web Site: http://www.dairycheckoff.com/DairyCheckoff/about/scholarship.htm
To provide financial assistance to undergraduate students in fields related to the dairy industry.
Title of Award: NDPRB Undergraduate Scholarship Program **Area, Field, or Subject:** Business administration; Communications; Dairy science; Economics; Education; Food science and technology; Journalism; Marketing and distribution; Nutrition; Public relations **Level of Education for which Award is Granted:** Four Year College **Number Awarded:** 20 each year: the James H. Loper Jr. Memorial Scholarship at $2,500 and 19 other scholarships at $1,500. **Funds Available:** Stipends are $2,500 or $1,500. **Duration:** 1 year; may be renewed.
Eligibility Requirements: This program is open to sophomores, juniors, and seniors enrolled in college and university programs that emphasize dairy. Eligible majors include agricultural education, business, communications and/or public relations, economics, food science, journalism, marketing, and nutrition. Fields related to production (e.g., animal science) are not eligible. Selection is based on academic performance; interest in a career in dairy; involvement in extracurricular activities, especially those relating to dairy; and evidence of leadership ability, initiative, character, and integrity. The applicant who is judged most outstanding is awarded the James H. Loper Jr. Memorial Scholarship. **Deadline for Receipt:** May of each year. **Additional Information:** Dairy Management

Inc. manages this program on behalf of the National Dairy Promotion and Research Board (NDPRB).

4776 ■ NATIONAL FFA ORGANIZATION

Attn: Scholarship Office
6060 FFA Drive
P.O. Box 68960
Indianapolis, IN 46268-0960
Tel: (317)802-4321
Fax: (317)802-5321
E-mail: scholarships@ffa.org
Web Site: http://www.ffa.org
To provide financial assistance to FFA members from designated states who are interested in studying agriculture or food science in college.
Title of Award: Bunge North America Scholarship **Area, Field, or Subject:** Agricultural sciences; Food science and technology **Level of Education for which Award is Granted:** Four Year College **Number Awarded:** 1 each year. **Funds Available:** The stipend is $2,000. Funds are paid directly to the recipient. **Duration:** 1 year; nonrenewable.
Eligibility Requirements: This program is open to members who are graduating high school seniors planning to enroll full time in college. Applicants must be residents of Alabama, Arkansas, California, Illinois, Indiana, Iowa, Kansas, Kentucky, Louisiana, Minnesota, Mississippi, Missouri, Nebraska, Ohio, Rhode Island, Tennessee, or Texas and interested in working on a 4-year degree in agriculture or food science. They must have a GPA of 3.0 or higher and be able to demonstrate active community involvement and strong leadership skills. Selection is based on academic achievement (10 points for GPA, 10 points for SAT or ACT score, 10 points for class rank), leadership in FFA activities (30 points), leadership in community activities (10 points), and participation in the Supervised Agricultural Experience (SAE) program (30 points). U.S. citizenship is required. **Deadline for Receipt:** February of each year. **Additional Information:** Funding for this scholarship is provided by Bunge North America, Inc. of St. Louis.

4777 ■ NATIONAL FFA ORGANIZATION

Attn: Scholarship Office
6060 FFA Drive
P.O. Box 68960
Indianapolis, IN 46268-0960
Tel: (317)802-4321
Fax: (317)802-5321
E-mail: scholarships@ffa.org
Web Site: http://www.ffa.org
To provide financial assistance to FFA members from Minnesota interested in studying food-related fields at a college or university in the state.
Title of Award: Malt-O-Meal Company Scholarship **Area, Field, or Subject:** Agricultural sciences; Business administration; Food science and technology **Level of Education for which Award is Granted:** Undergraduate **Number Awarded:** 2 each year. **Funds Available:** The stipend is $1,000 per year. Funds are paid directly to the recipient. **Duration:** 1 year; nonrenewable.
Eligibility Requirements: This program is open to members who are graduating high school seniors planning to enroll full time in college. Applicants must be residents of Minnesota interested in working on a 2- or 4-year degree in agriculture, food science, food technology, or business at a college or university in the state. Selection is based on academic achievement (10 points for GPA, 10 points for SAT or ACT score, 10 points for class rank), leadership in FFA activities (30 points), leadership in community activities (10 points), and participation in the Supervised Agricultural Experience (SAE) program (30 points). U.S. citizenship is required. **Deadline for Receipt:** February of each year. **Additional Information:** Funding for this scholarship is provided by Malt-O-Meal Company.

4778 ■ NATIONAL FFA ORGANIZATION

Attn: Scholarship Office
6060 FFA Drive
P.O. Box 68960
Indianapolis, IN 46268-0960
Tel: (317)802-4321
Fax: (317)802-5321

E-mail: scholarships@ffa.org
Web Site: http://www.ffa.org
To provide financial assistance to FFA members who wish to study agriculture and related fields in college.
Title of Award: National FFA Scholarships for Undergraduates in the Sciences **Area, Field, or Subject:** Agricultural sciences; Animal science and behavior; Dairy science; Engineering, Agricultural; Environmental conservation; Environmental science; Equine studies; Food science and technology; Horticulture; Natural resources; Technology **Level of Education for which Award is Granted:** Undergraduate **Number Awarded:** Varies; generally, a total of approximately 1,000 scholarships are awarded annually by the association. **Funds Available:** Stipends vary, but most are at least $1,000. **Duration:** 1 year or more.
Eligibility Requirements: This program is open to current and former members of the organization who are working or planning to work full time on a degree in fields related to agriculture; this includes: agricultural mechanics and engineering, agricultural technology, animal science, conservation, dairy science, equine science, floriculture, food science, horticulture, irrigation, lawn and landscaping, and natural resources. For most of the scholarships, applicants must be high school seniors; others are open to students currently enrolled in college. The program includes a large number of designated scholarships that specify the locations where the members must live, the schools they must attend, the fields of study they must pursue, or other requirements. Some consider family income in the selection process, but most do not. Selection is based on academic achievement (10 points for GPA, 10 points for SAT or ACT score, 10 points for class rank), leadership in FFA activities (30 points), leadership in community activities (10 points), and participation in the Supervised Agricultural Experience (SAE) program (30 points). U.S. citizenship is required. **Deadline for Receipt:** February of each year. **Additional Information:** Funding for these scholarships is provided by many different corporate sponsors.

4779 ■ NATIONAL FFA ORGANIZATION

Attn: Scholarship Office
6060 FFA Drive
P.O. Box 68960
Indianapolis, IN 46268-0960
Tel: (317)802-4321
Fax: (317)802-5321
E-mail: scholarships@ffa.org
Web Site: http://www.ffa.org
To provide financial assistance to FFA members from Indiana, Kentucky, and Ohio who are interested in studying food science in college.
Title of Award: Paradise Tomato Kitchens Scholarship **Area, Field, or Subject:** Food science and technology **Level of Education for which Award is Granted:** Four Year College **Number Awarded:** 2 each year. **Funds Available:** The stipend is $1,000 per year. Funds are paid directly to the recipient. **Duration:** 1 year; nonrenewable.
Eligibility Requirements: This program is open to members who are graduating high school seniors planning to enroll full time in college. Applicants must be residents of Indiana, Kentucky, or Ohio interested in majoring in food science at a 4-year institution in 1 of those states. Preference is given to applicants who have competed in state or national FFA sponsored events. Selection is based on academic achievement (10 points for GPA, 10 points for SAT or ACT score, 10 points for class rank), leadership in FFA activities (30 points), leadership in community activities (10 points), and participation in the Supervised Agricultural Experience (SAE) program (30 points). U.S. citizenship is required. **Deadline for Receipt:** February of each year. **Additional Information:** Funding for these scholarships is provided by Paradise Tomato Kitchens, Inc.

4780 ■ NATIONAL FFA ORGANIZATION

Attn: Scholarship Office
6060 FFA Drive
P.O. Box 68960
Indianapolis, IN 46268-0960
Tel: (317)802-4321
Fax: (317)802-5321
E-mail: scholarships@ffa.org
Web Site: http://www.ffa.org
To provide financial assistance to FFA members who are interested in studying fields related to agriculture, business, engineering, or nursing in college.

Title of Award: Tyson Foods Scholarships **Area, Field, or Subject:** Agribusiness; Agricultural sciences; Business; Business administration; Engineering; Food science and technology; Management; Nursing; Packaging **Level of Education for which Award is Granted:** Undergraduate **Number Awarded:** 10 each year. **Funds Available:** The stipend is $1,000. Funds are paid directly to the recipient. **Duration:** 1 year; nonrenewable.

Eligibility Requirements: This program is open to members who are either high school seniors or already enrolled full time in college. Applicants must be working on or planning to work on a 2-year or 4-year degree in agriculture, food science, food technology, supply chain management, product development, product development, product packaging, nursing, engineering, or business. They must reside in a community in which a Tyson Foods processing facility is located. Selection is based on academic achievement (10 points for GPA, 10 points for SAT or ACT score, 10 points for class rank), leadership in FFA activities (30 points), leadership in community activities (10 points), and participation in the Supervised Agricultural Experience (SAE) program (30 points). U.S. citizenship is required. **Deadline for Receipt:** February of each year. **Additional Information:** Funding for these scholarships is provided by Tyson Foods, Inc.

4781 ■ NATIONAL POULTRY AND FOOD DISTRIBUTORS ASSOCIATION

Attn: NPFDA Scholarship Foundation
958 McEver Road Extension, Unit B-8
Gainesville, GA 30504
Tel: (770)535-9901; 877-845-1545
Fax: (770)535-7385
E-mail: info@npfda.org
Web Site: http://www.npfda.org
To provide financial assistance to students enrolled in fields related to the poultry and food industries.

Title of Award: NPFDA Scholarships **Area, Field, or Subject:** Agriculture, Economic aspects; Food science and technology; Nutrition; Poultry science **Level of Education for which Award is Granted:** Four Year College **Number Awarded:** 4 each year. **Funds Available:** Stipends range from $1,500 to $2,000. **Duration:** 1 year.

Eligibility Requirements: This program is open to full-time students entering their junior or senior year of college. Applicants must be studying poultry science, food science, agricultural economics or marketing, nutrition, or another area related to the poultry industry. Along with their application, they must submit a 1-page narrative on their goals and ambitions and their transcripts. Selection is based on academic excellence, past and current involvement in poultry and food-related activities, and professional objectives. **Deadline for Receipt:** May of each year. **Additional Information:** The National Poultry and Food Distributors Association (NPFDA) established its Scholarship Foundation in 1979. The following named scholarships are included in the program: the Albin S. Johnson Memorial Scholarship, the William Manson Family Memorial Scholarship, and the Alfred Schwartz Memorial Scholarship.

4782 ■ TOURISM CARES FOR TOMORROW

Attn: Program Manager
585 Washington Street
Canton, MA 02021
Tel: (781)821-5990
Fax: (781)821-8949
E-mail: info@tourismcares.org
Web Site: http://www.tourismcares.org
To provide financial assistance to high school seniors planning to major in tourism in college.

Title of Award: Academy of Hospitality and Tourism Scholarship **Area, Field, or Subject:** Food service careers; Hotel, institutional, and restaurant management; Travel and tourism **Level of Education for which Award is Granted:** Undergraduate **Number Awarded:** 1 each year. **Funds Available:** The stipend is $1,000. **Duration:** 1 year.

Eligibility Requirements: This program is open to seniors at high schools with an Academy of Hospitality and Tourism program affiliated with the National Academy Foundation (NAF). Applicants must have a GPA of 3.0 or higher and be interested in majoring in a travel or tourism-related field (e.g., hotel management, restaurant management, tourism) in college. Along with their application, they must submit a 2-page essay on

the following question: "In your future career in tourism, what responsibility will you have for preservation and conservation of tourism sites around the globe? How will you meet those challenges?" **Deadline for Receipt:** March of each year. **Additional Information:** This program was established in 1995 as a partnership between NAF and National Tourism Foundation (now a part of Tourism Cares for Tomorrow).

4783 ■ TOURISM CARES FOR TOMORROW

Attn: Program Manager
585 Washington Street
Canton, MA 02021
Tel: (781)821-5990
Fax: (781)821-8949
E-mail: info@tourismcares.org
Web Site: http://www.tourismcares.org
To provide financial assistance to upper-division students from North Carolina who are majoring in tourism.

Title of Award: Rene Campbell Memorial Scholarship **Area, Field, or Subject:** Food service careers; Hotel, institutional, and restaurant management; Travel and tourism **Level of Education for which Award is Granted:** Four Year College **Number Awarded:** 1 each year. **Funds Available:** The stipend is $1,000. **Duration:** 1 year.

Eligibility Requirements: This program is open to residents of North Carolina entering their junior or senior year at an accredited 4-year college or university in the United States or Canada. Applicants must be working on a degree in a travel and tourism-related program and have a GPA of 3.0 or higher. Along with their application, they must submit a resume, a letter of recommendation, and a copy of their transcript. Financial need is not considered in the selection process. **Deadline for Receipt:** March of each year.

4784 ■ TOURISM CARES FOR TOMORROW

Attn: Program Manager
585 Washington Street
Canton, MA 02021
Tel: (781)821-5990
Fax: (781)821-8949
E-mail: info@tourismcares.org
Web Site: http://www.tourismcares.org
To provide financial assistance to college students in Kentucky who are majoring in tourism.

Title of Award: Pat and Jim Host Scholarship **Area, Field, or Subject:** Food service careers; Hotel, institutional, and restaurant management; Travel and tourism **Level of Education for which Award is Granted:** Four Year College **Number Awarded:** 1 each year. **Funds Available:** The stipend is $2,500 per year. **Duration:** 1 year.

Eligibility Requirements: This program is open to full-time students enrolled in a 4-year college or university in Kentucky. Applicants must be Kentucky residents, have at least a 3.0 GPA, and be majoring in a travel or tourism-related field (e.g., hotel management, restaurant management, tourism). Along with their application, they must submit an essay of 2 to 5 pages outlining how they perceive the changing role of the group tour industry. **Deadline for Receipt:** March of each year.

4785 ■ TOURISM CARES FOR TOMORROW

Attn: Program Manager
585 Washington Street
Canton, MA 02021
Tel: (781)821-5990
Fax: (781)821-8949
E-mail: info@tourismcares.org
Web Site: http://www.tourismcares.org
To provide financial assistance to college students in Wisconsin who are majoring in tourism.

Title of Award: LaMacchia Family Scholarship **Area, Field, or Subject:** Food service careers; Hotel, institutional, and restaurant management; Travel and tourism **Level of Education for which Award is Granted:** Four Year College **Number Awarded:** 1 each year. **Funds Available:** The stipend is $1,000 per year. **Duration:** 1 year.

Eligibility Requirements: This program is open to full-time students enrolled at a 4-year college or university in Wisconsin. Applicants must be entering their junior or senior year, have at least a 3.0 GPA, and be majoring in a travel or tourism-related field (e.g., hotel management, restaurant management, tourism). **Deadline for Receipt:** March of each year. **Additional Information:** This program was established in 2005.

4786 ■ TOURISM CARES FOR TOMORROW
Attn: Program Manager
585 Washington Street
Canton, MA 02021
Tel: (781)821-5990
Fax: (781)821-8949
E-mail: info@tourismcares.org
Web Site: http://www.tourismcares.org
To provide financial assistance to upper-division students from Michigan who are majoring in tourism.
Title of Award: New Horizons Kathy LeTarte Scholarship **Area, Field, or Subject:** Food service careers; Hotel, institutional, and restaurant management; Travel and tourism **Level of Education for which Award is Granted:** Four Year College **Number Awarded:** 1 each year. **Funds Available:** The stipend is $1,000. **Duration:** 1 year.
Eligibility Requirements: This program is open to residents of Michigan entering their junior year at an accredited 4-year college or university in the United States or Canada. Applicants must be working on a degree in a travel and tourism-related program and have a GPA of 3.0 or higher. Along with their application, they must submit a 2-page essay on niche markets with an emphasis of student markets. Financial need is not considered in the selection process. **Deadline for Receipt:** March of each year. **Additional Information:** This program was established in 2000.

4787 ■ TOURISM CARES FOR TOMORROW
Attn: Program Manager
585 Washington Street
Canton, MA 02021
Tel: (781)821-5990
Fax: (781)821-8949
E-mail: info@tourismcares.org
Web Site: http://www.tourismcares.org
To provide financial assistance to upper-division students who are majoring in tourism.
Title of Award: National Tour Association Scholarship **Area, Field, or Subject:** Food service careers; Hotel, institutional, and restaurant management; Travel and tourism **Level of Education for which Award is Granted:** Four Year College **Number Awarded:** 1 each year. **Funds Available:** The stipend is $2,500. **Duration:** 1 year.
Eligibility Requirements: This program is open to students entering their junior or senior year at an accredited 4-year college or university in the United States or Canada. Applicants must be working on a degree in a travel and tourism-related program and have a GPA of 3.0 or higher. Along with their application, they must submit a 2-page essay on why they have chosen to prepare for a career in the hospitality and tourism industry. Financial need is not considered in the selection process. **Deadline for Receipt:** March of each year. **Additional Information:** This program is sponsored by the National Tour Association (NTA).

4788 ■ TOURISM CARES FOR TOMORROW
Attn: Program Manager
585 Washington Street
Canton, MA 02021
Tel: (781)821-5990
Fax: (781)821-8949
E-mail: info@tourismcares.org
Web Site: http://www.tourismcares.org
To provide financial assistance to upper-division students who are majoring in tourism.
Title of Award: NTA State and Provincial Scholarship **Area, Field, or Subject:** Food service careers; Hotel, institutional, and restaurant management; Travel and tourism **Level of Education for which Award is Granted:** Four Year College **Number Awarded:** 1 each year. **Funds Available:** The stipend is $1,000. **Duration:** 1 year.
Eligibility Requirements: This program is open to students entering their junior or senior year at an accredited 4-year college or university in the United States or Canada. Applicants must be working on a degree in a travel and tourism-related program and have a GPA of 3.0 or higher. Along with their application, they must submit a 2-page essay on why they have chosen to prepare for a career in the hospitality and tourism industry.

Financial need is not considered in the selection process. **Deadline for Receipt:** March of each year. **Additional Information:** This program is sponsored by the National Tour Association (NTA).

4789 ■ TOURISM CARES FOR TOMORROW
Attn: Program Manager
585 Washington Street
Canton, MA 02021
Tel: (781)821-5990
Fax: (781)821-8949
E-mail: info@tourismcares.org
Web Site: http://www.tourismcares.org
To provide financial assistance to upper-division students in selected states who are majoring in tourism.
Title of Award: Tourism Cares for Tomorrow State Scholarships **Area, Field, or Subject:** Food service careers; Hotel, institutional, and restaurant management; Travel and tourism **Level of Education for which Award is Granted:** Four Year College **Number Awarded:** 20 each year: 1 in each of the participating states. **Funds Available:** Stipends range from $500 to $1,500. **Duration:** 1 year.
Eligibility Requirements: This program is open to students entering their junior or senior year at a designated 4-year college or university in 20 states. Applicants must be residents of 1 of the following states: Alabama, California, Connecticut, Florida, Hawaii, Illinois, Massachusetts, Michigan, Minnesota, Missouri, Montana, Nebraska, Nevada, New Jersey, New York, North Carolina, Ohio, Texas, Utah, or Virginia. They must be attending the designated institution in their state with a major in a field related to travel and tourism and a GPA of 3.0 or higher. **Deadline for Receipt:** March of each year. **Additional Information:** Information is also available from a faculty member at each of the 20 colleges and universities participating in this program. For a list of their names and addresses, contact Tourism Cares for Tomorrow.

4790 ■ TOURISM CARES FOR TOMORROW
Attn: Program Manager
585 Washington Street
Canton, MA 02021
Tel: (781)821-5990
Fax: (781)821-8949
E-mail: info@tourismcares.org
Web Site: http://www.tourismcares.org
To provide financial assistance to upper-division students who are majoring in tourism.
Title of Award: United States Tour Operators Association Scholarship **Area, Field, or Subject:** Food service careers; Hotel, institutional, and restaurant management; Travel and tourism **Level of Education for which Award is Granted:** Four Year College **Number Awarded:** 1 each year. **Funds Available:** The stipend is $2,500. **Duration:** 1 year.
Eligibility Requirements: This program is open to students entering their junior or senior year at an accredited 4-year college or university in the United States or Canada. Applicants must be working on a degree in a travel and tourism-related program and have a GPA of 3.0 or higher. Along with their application, they must submit a 2-page essay on why they have chosen to prepare for a career in the hospitality and tourism industry. Financial need is not considered in the selection process. **Deadline for Receipt:** March of each year. **Additional Information:** This program is sponsored by the United States Tour Operators Association.

4791 ■ TOURISM CARES FOR TOMORROW
Attn: Program Manager
585 Washington Street
Canton, MA 02021
Tel: (781)821-5990
Fax: (781)821-8949
E-mail: info@tourismcares.org
Web Site: http://www.tourismcares.org
To provide financial assistance for college to students with disabilities who are planning a career in the travel and tourism industry.
Title of Award: Yellow Ribbon Scholarship **Area, Field, or Subject:** Food service careers; Hotel, institutional, and restaurant management; Travel and tourism **Level of Education for which Award is Granted:** Undergraduate **Number Awarded:** 1 each year. **Funds Available:** The stipend is $3,500. **Duration:** 1 year.

Eligibility Requirements: This program is open to students with a physical or sensory disability (verified by an accredited physician) who are entering or attending an accredited 2- or 4-year college or university in the United States or Canada. Applicants must be working on or planning to work on a degree in a field related to travel and tourism. High school seniors must have a GPA of 3.0 or higher; college students must have at least a 2.5. Along with their application, they must submit a 2-page essay on how they intend to use their education in making a career in travel and tourism. **Deadline for Receipt:** March of each year. **Additional Information:** This program was established in 1993.

Home Economics

4792 ■ NORTH CAROLINA 4-H DEVELOPMENT FUND

c/o North Carolina State University
Department of 4-H Youth Development
202 Ricks Hall
P.O. Box 7606
Raleigh, NC 27695-7606
Tel: (919)515-8486
Fax: (919)515-7812
Web Site: http://www.nc4h.org
To provide financial assistance to high school seniors in North Carolina who are members of 4-H and interested in studying home economics in college.
Title of Award: Lorna Langley 4-H Scholarship **Area, Field, or Subject:** Home Economics **Level of Education for which Award is Granted:** Undergraduate **Number Awarded:** 1 each year. **Funds Available:** The stipend is $1,000 per year. **Duration:** 1 year.
Eligibility Requirements: This program is open to 4-H members who are graduating from high schools in North Carolina with a GPA of 3.0 or higher. Applicants must be planning to major in home economics at a college or university in the state. Selection is based on accomplishments in 4-H (50%), academic achievement as indicated by GPA and class rank (25%), and aptitude for college as indicated by grades and SAT or ACT scores (25%). **Deadline for Receipt:** January of each year.

4793 ■ TEXAS ELECTRIC COOPERATIVES, INC.

Attn: Vice President of Member Services
2550 South IH-35
Austin, TX 78704
Tel: (512)454-0311
E-mail: twortham@texas-ec.org
Web Site: http://www.texas-ec.org
To provide financial assistance to members of the Texas Association Family, Career and Community Leaders of America (FCCLA) interested in majoring in home economics in college.
Title of Award: Ann Lane Family and Consumer Science Scholarship **Area, Field, or Subject:** Home Economics **Level of Education for which Award is Granted:** Undergraduate **Funds Available:** The stipend is $1,000. It can be used at a Texas college or university only. **Duration:** 1 year.
Eligibility Requirements: Applicants need not necessarily be planning a career, but they must intend to major in home economics as preparation for home and family living. They must be graduating high school seniors and members in good standing of an affiliated chapter of the association. Only 1 member from each chapter may apply. Applicants must have earned at least a "B" average in homemaking and English courses and have completed 2 or more years of homemaking in high school. Selection is based on desire to continue educational activities, degree of involvement with FCCLA, community activities, financial need, and quality of the 250-word essay on "The Role of the Homemaker" that each applicant must submit. **Deadline for Receipt:** February of each year. **Additional Information:** This scholarship is sponsored by the Texas chapter of FCCLA and administered by Texas Electric Cooperatives, Inc.

4794 ■ TEXAS EXTENSION EDUCATION ASSOCIATION, INC.

c/o Texas Cooperative Extension
Texas A&M University
Jack K. Williams Administration Building, Room 112
College Station, TX 77843-7101
Tel: (979)845-7800

Fax: (979)845-9542
E-mail: agextension@tamu.edu
To provide financial assistance for college to members of 4-H in Texas.
Title of Award: Texas Extension Education Association Scholarships **Area, Field, or Subject:** General studies/Field of study not specified; Home Economics **Level of Education for which Award is Granted:** Undergraduate **Number Awarded:** 7 each year. **Funds Available:** The stipend is $1,000. **Duration:** 1 year; nonrenewable.
Eligibility Requirements: This program is open to students under 19 years of age at high schools in Texas who have completed or are in the third year of 4-H. Applicants must complete a 4-H Awards Program Recordbook and be able to demonstrate excellence in home economics, leadership, and personal development through 4-H. They must be planning to attend a college of their choice in the fall or spring following judging. **Deadline for Receipt:** Applications must be submitted to the county chairman of the organization by February of each year.

4795 ■ UNITED DAUGHTERS OF THE CONFEDERACY

Attn: Education Director
328 North Boulevard
Richmond, VA 23220-4057
Tel: (804)355-1636
Fax: (804)353-1396
E-mail: hqudc@rcn.com
Web Site: http://www.hqudc.org/scholarships/scholarships.html
To provide financial assistance to mature women who are lineal descendants of Confederate veterans and plan to major in selected fields in college.
Title of Award: Walter Reed Smith Scholarship Program **Area, Field, or Subject:** Business administration; Computer and information sciences; Home Economics; Nursing; Nutrition **Level of Education for which Award is Granted:** Undergraduate **Number Awarded:** 1 each year. **Funds Available:** The amount of this scholarship depends on the availability of funds. **Duration:** 1 year; may be renewed.
Eligibility Requirements: Eligible to apply for these scholarships are women over the age of 30 who are lineal descendants of worthy Confederates or collateral descendants and members of the Children of the Confederacy or the United Daughters of the Confederacy. Applicants must intend to study business administration, computer science, home economics, nutrition, or nursing. They must submit certified proof of the Confederate record of 1 ancestor, with the company and regiment in which he served, and must have had at least a 3.0 GPA in high school. **Deadline for Receipt:** March of each year. **Additional Information:** Information is also available from Mrs. Robert C. Kraus, Second Vice President General, 239 Deerfield Lane, Franklin, NC 28734-0112. Members of the same family may not hold scholarships simultaneously, and only 1 application per family will be accepted within any 1 year. All requests for applications must be accompanied by a self-addressed stamped envelope.

4796 ■ VIRGINIA DAUGHTERS OF THE AMERICAN REVOLUTION

c/o Catherine Rafferty, Scholarship Chair
10101 Sanders Court
Great Falls, VA 22066-2526
Web Site: http://www.vadar.org/vadarscholarships.htm
To provide financial assistance to high school seniors in Virginia who wish to study designated fields in college.
Title of Award: Virginia DAR Scholarships **Area, Field, or Subject:** Environmental conservation; Environmental science; Forestry; Genealogy; History, American; Home Economics; Medicine; Science **Level of Education for which Award is Granted:** Undergraduate **Number Awarded:** 2 each year: 1 at $1,000 and 1 at $500. **Funds Available:** Stipends are $1,000 or $500. **Duration:** 1 year.
Eligibility Requirements: This program is open to seniors graduating from high schools in Virginia who plan to attend a Virginia college or university. Applicants must be planning to work on a degree in the field of science, medicine, conservation, ecology, forestry, home arts, genealogical research, or American history. Along with their application, they must submit a 1,000-word letter giving their reasons for interest in the scholar-

ship, a transcript of grades, a letter of recommendation from a teacher in their chosen field, and documentation of financial need. **Deadline for Receipt:** January of each year.

Military Science

4797 ■ TEXAS HIGHER EDUCATION COORDINATING BOARD

Attn: Grants and Special Programs
1200 East Anderson Lane
P.O. Box 12788, Capitol Station
Austin, TX 78711-2788
Tel: (512)427-6101
Free: 800-242-3062
Fax: (512)427-6127
E-mail: grantinfo@thecb.state.tx.us
Web Site: http://www.collegefortexans.com
To provide educational assistance to students from outside Texas who will be attending a Texas public university under contract with the U.S. armed forces as a Reserve Officers Training Candidate (ROTC).
Title of Award: Texas ROTC Student Waiver **Area, Field, or Subject:** General studies/Field of study not specified; Military science and education **Level of Education for which Award is Granted:** Undergraduate **Number Awarded:** Varies each year. **Funds Available:** This program permits nonresident students to pay tuition and fees at the Texas resident rate. **Duration:** Up to 4 years, as long as the recipient enrolls in at least 12 credit hours per semester, including military science classes.
Eligibility Requirements: Eligible are students who are enrolled in or accepted for enrollment in the ROTC program at public colleges and universities in Texas and who are residents of other states. Applicants must have signed a contract that cannot be terminated and that obligates them to serve a period of active military duty. **Additional Information:** Further information is available from the military science department at the institution the student attends.

Mining and Metallurgy

4798 ■ AMERICAN INSTITUTE OF MINING, METALLURGICAL, AND PETROLEUM ENGINEERS

8307 Shaffer Parkway
P.O. Box 270728
Littleton, CO 80127-0013
Tel: (303)948-4255
Fax: (303)948-4260
E-mail: aime@aimehq.org
Web Site: http://www.aimehq.org/awards/awardlist.cfm
To provide financial assistance to student members of the Society for Mining, Metallurgy and Exploration (SME) working on an undergraduate degree in mining engineering.
Title of Award: John S. Marshall Memorial Scholarship **Area, Field, or Subject:** Engineering, Mining and Mineral **Level of Education for which Award is Granted:** Four Year College **Number Awarded:** 1 each year. **Funds Available:** The stipend is $8,000. **Duration:** 1 year.
Eligibility Requirements: This program is open to SME student members enrolled full time in an ABET-accredited mining engineering program. Applicants must be entering their junior or senior year of college. They must be able to demonstrate financial need and an interest in preparing for a career in the mining industry. **Deadline for Receipt:** June of each year. **Additional Information:** This program began in 2004.

4799 ■ ASM INTERNATIONAL-MILWAUKEE CHAPTER

Attn: EGMF Committee
P.O. Box 370138
Milwaukee, WI 53237-1238
Web Site: http://www.asm-milwaukee.cjb.net
To provide financial assistance to students at colleges and universities in Wisconsin who are majoring in a field related to metals and materials.
Title of Award: Ernie Guenther Memorial Scholarship **Area, Field, or Subject:** Engineering, Materials; Engineering, Metallurgical; Materials research/science; Metallurgy **Level of Education for which Award is Granted:** Undergraduate **Number Awarded:** 4 to 6 each year. **Funds Available:** Stipends range from $500 to $1,000. **Duration:** 1 year.

Eligibility Requirements: This program is open to students at Wisconsin colleges and universities who are interested in metals and materials and are planning to make those technical areas part of their future career. Applicants must indicate 1) their reasons for their interest and pursuit of a career in the metals and materials field; 2) any projects or activities they have completed or are doing related to metals and materials; 3) their goals for work and/or further study in the metals and materials field; 4) their activities, jobs, and organizations both on and off campus; and 5) any other pertinent information. Financial need is not considered in the selection process. **Deadline for Receipt:** April of each year. **Additional Information:** This program began in 1974. Information is also available from Robb Denkenberger, Ladish Company, Inc., P.O. Box 8902, Cudahy, WI 53110-8902, (414) 747-3384, Fax: (414) 747-3036, E-mail: rdendenberger@ladishco.com.

4800 ■ ASSOCIATION FOR IRON & STEEL TECHNOLOGY

Attn: AIST Foundation
186 Thorn Hill Road
Warrendale, PA 15086-7528
Tel: (724)776-6040
Fax: (724)776-1880
E-mail: lwharrey@aist.org
Web Site: http://www.aist.org/foundation/scholarships.htm
To provide financial assistance for college to students interested in preparing for a career in the iron and steel or steel-related industries.
Title of Award: Association for Iron & Steel Technology Scholarships **Area, Field, or Subject:** Business; Engineering; Manufacturing; Materials research/science; Metallurgy **Level of Education for which Award is Granted:** Undergraduate **Number Awarded:** 7 each year, including 3 Willy Korf Memorial Fund Scholarships, 2 Ronald E. Lincoln Memorial Scholarship, and 2 Benjamin F. Fairless Scholarships. **Funds Available:** The stipend is $2,000. **Duration:** 1 year; recipients may reapply.
Eligibility Requirements: This program is open to full-time students majoring in metallurgy, materials science, or engineering at accredited universities in North America. Applicants must have a GPA of 3.0 or higher and a demonstrated interest in the iron and steel industry. Along with their application, they must submit 3 letters of recommendation; a resume with work experience and extracurricular activities, noting any leadership positions; a current academic transcript; and a 2-page essay on their professional goals, explaining why they are interested in a career in the steel industry and how their skills could be applied to enhance the industry. Financial need is not considered in the selection process. **Deadline for Receipt:** April of each year. **Additional Information:** The AIST was formed in 2004 by the merger of the Iron and Steel Society (ISS) and the Association of Iron and Steel Engineers (AISE).

4801 ■ ASSOCIATION FOR IRON & STEEL TECHNOLOGY

Attn: AIST Foundation
186 Thorn Hill Road
Warrendale, PA 15086-7528
Tel: (724)776-6040
Fax: (724)776-1880
E-mail: lwharrey@aist.org
Web Site: http://www.aist.org/femet/femet_scholarship.htm
To provide financial assistance and work experience to college juniors working on a degree in metallurgy or materials sciences.
Title of Award: Ferrous Metallurgy Education Today (FeMET) Scholarships **Area, Field, or Subject:** Business; Manufacturing; Materials research/science; Metallurgy **Level of Education for which Award is Granted:** Four Year College **Number Awarded:** 10 each year. **Funds Available:** The program provides a stipend of $5,000 for the junior year, a paid internship during the following summer, and a stipend of $5,000 for the senior year. **Duration:** 2 years.
Eligibility Requirements: This program is open to full-time students entering their junior year in a metallurgy or materials science program at a college or university in North America (Canada, Mexico, and the United States). Applicants must have a GPA of 3.0 or higher and a demonstrated interest in the iron and steel industry. They must be available for employment at a steel company during the summer after their junior year; students unable to accept an internship will not be considered. Along with their application, they must submit a 2-page essay on their professional goals, why they are interested in a career in the steel industry, and how their skills could be applied to enhance the industry. Selection is based on

the essay; a resume with work experience and extracurricular activities, noting any leadership positions; letters of recommendation; a current academic transcript; and a list of the source and amount of other grants and scholarships. **Deadline for Receipt:** April of each year. **Additional Information:** The AIST was formed in 2004 by the merger of the Iron and Steel Society (ISS) and the Association of Iron and Steel Engineers (AISE). This program was established in 2005 by the AIST Foundation and the American Iron and Steel Institute, (202) 452-7143, E-mail: blakshmi@steel.org.

4802 ■ ASSOCIATION FOR IRON & STEEL TECHNOLOGY

Attn: AIST Foundation
186 Thorn Hill Road
Warrendale, PA 15086-7528
Tel: (724)776-6040
Fax: (724)776-1880
E-mail: lwharrey@aist.org
Web Site: http://www.aist.org/foundation/scholarships.htm
To provide financial assistance for college to students interested in preparing for a career in the iron and steel or steel-related industries.
Title of Award: William E. Schwabe Memorial Scholarship **Area, Field, or Subject:** Business; Engineering; Manufacturing; Materials research/ science; Metallurgy **Level of Education for which Award is Granted:** Undergraduate **Number Awarded:** 1 each year. **Funds Available:** The stipend is $1,500. **Duration:** 1 year; recipients may reapply.
Eligibility Requirements: This program is open to full-time students majoring in metallurgy, materials science, or engineering at accredited universities in North America. Applicants must have a GPA of 3.0 or higher and a demonstrated interest in the iron and steel industry. Along with their application, they must submit 3 letters of recommendation; a resume with work experience and extracurricular activities, noting any leadership positions; a current academic transcript; and a 2-page essay on their professional goals, explaining why they are interested in a career in the steel industry and how their skills could be applied to enhance the industry. Financial need is not considered in the selection process. **Deadline for Receipt:** April of each year. **Additional Information:** The AIST was formed in 2004 by the merger of the Iron and Steel Society (ISS) and the Association of Iron and Steel Engineers (AISE). This scholarship was established in 2005 by the Steel Manufacturers Association.

4803 ■ ASSOCIATION FOR IRON & STEEL TECHNOLOGY-BALTIMORE CHAPTER

c/o Thomas J. Russo
Mittal Steel USA
5111 North Point Boulevard
Sparrows Point, MD 21219-1014
Tel: (410)388-6370
Fax: (410)388-3772
E-mail: tom.russo@mittalsteel.com
Web Site: http://www.aist.org/chapters/mc_baltimore_scholar.htm
To provide financial assistance to family of members of the Baltimore Chapter of the Association for Iron & Steel Technology (AIST) who are interested in studying engineering or metallurgy in college.
Title of Award: Baltimore Chapter AIST Scholarship **Area, Field, or Subject:** Business; Engineering; Manufacturing; Metallurgy **Level of Education for which Award is Granted:** Undergraduate **Number Awarded:** 1 each year. **Funds Available:** The stipend is $1,500. **Duration:** 1 year.
Eligibility Requirements: This program is open to children, grandchildren, and spouses of chapter members who are high school seniors or full-time undergraduates at an accredited college or university. Applicants must be studying or planning to study engineering or metallurgy with a demonstrated interest in a career in the iron and steel industry. Along with their application, they must submit 1) a 500-word essay on an accomplishment that they have achieved while they have been a student; 2) a 500-word essay on their interest and/or involvement in the iron and steel industry; 3) SAT/ACT scores; and 4) high school and/or college transcripts. Selection is based on academic achievement, extracurricular activities, and the essays; financial need is not considered. **Deadline for Receipt:** April of each year. **Additional Information:** The AIST was formed in 2004 by the merger of the Iron and Steel Society (ISS) and the Association of Iron and Steel Engineers (AISE). The Baltimore Chapter covers the District of Columbia, Maryland, and northern Virginia.

4804 ■ ASSOCIATION FOR IRON & STEEL TECHNOLOGY-DETROIT CHAPTER

c/o Judith A. Quinn, Secretary
14201 Robbe Road
Belleville, MI 48111
Tel: (313)319-2815
E-mail: judieqn@aol.com
Web Site: http://www.aist.org/chapters/detroit_scholarship.htm
To provide financial assistance to family of members of the Detroit Chapter of the Association for Iron & Steel Technology (AIST) who are interested in studying engineering, materials science, or metallurgy in college.
Title of Award: Detroit Chapter AIST Scholarship **Area, Field, or Subject:** Business; Engineering; Manufacturing; Materials research/ science; Metallurgy **Level of Education for which Award is Granted:** Undergraduate **Number Awarded:** 1 each year. **Funds Available:** The stipend is $3,500. **Duration:** 1 year.
Eligibility Requirements: This program is open to children and grandchildren of chapter members who are high school seniors or full-time undergraduates at an accredited college or university. They must be studying or planning to study engineering, materials science, or metallurgy; if there are no applicants in those fields, the award may be given to a student majoring in another field relating to iron and steel production. Applicants must have a GPA of 3.0 or higher and a demonstrated interest in a career in the iron and steel industry. Along with their application, they must submit a 2-page essay on their professional goals, why they are interested in a career in the steel industry, and how their skills could be applied to enhance the industry. Financial need is not considered in the selection process. **Deadline for Receipt:** April of each year. **Additional Information:** The AIST was formed in 2004 by the merger of the Iron and Steel Society (ISS) and the Association of Iron and Steel Engineers (AISE). The Detroit Chapter serves Michigan and northwestern Ohio.

4805 ■ ASSOCIATION FOR IRON & STEEL TECHNOLOGY-NORTHWEST CHAPTER

c/o Gerardo L. Giraldo, Secretary-Treasurer
Nucor Steel Seattle, Inc.
Washington Steel Division
2424 S.W. Andover Street
Seattle, WA 98106-1100
Tel: (206)933-2245
Fax: (206)933-2207
E-mail: gerry.giraldo@nucor-seattle.com
Web Site: http://www.aist.org/chapters/
mc_pittsburgh_scholar_guidelines.htm
To provide financial assistance to family of members of the Northwest Chapter of the Association for Iron & Steel Technology (AIST) who are interested in studying engineering in college.
Title of Award: Northwest Chapter AIST Scholarships **Area, Field, or Subject:** Business; Chemistry; Engineering; Manufacturing; Mathematics and mathematical sciences; Metallurgy; Physics **Level of Education for which Award is Granted:** Four Year College **Number Awarded:** 2 each year. **Funds Available:** The stipend is $1,000. **Duration:** 1 year.
Eligibility Requirements: This program is open to children, grandchildren, spouses, or nieces/nephews of chapter members who are high school seniors planning to attend an accredited 4-year college or university. Applicants must intend to study engineering; if there are no applicants in engineering, the award may be given to a student majoring in chemistry, mathematics, metallurgy, or physics, or to a student showing an interest in preparing for a career in the iron and steel industry. Along with their application, they must submit a 500-word essay on 1 of the following topics: 1) an accomplishment they have achieved while they have been a student, why they were successful, and how their success will influence their future plans as an engineer or an engineer in the steel industry; 2) their strengths and interests and how they will apply their skills to a career in the steel industry or as an engineer; or 3) the challenges that face the steel industry and the opportunities for graduates to improve the success of companies within the industry. Financial need is not considered in the selection process. **Deadline for Receipt:** June of each year. **Additional Information:** The AIST was formed in 2004 by the merger of the Iron and Steel Society (ISS) and the Association of Iron and Steel Engineers (AISE). The Northwest Chapter serves Alaska, Idaho, Montana, Oregon, Washington, and Wyoming.

4806 ■ ASSOCIATION FOR IRON & STEEL TECHNOLOGY-OHIO VALLEY CHAPTER

c/o Jeff McKain, Scholarship Chair
Xtek, Inc.
11451 Reading Road
Cincinnati, OH 45241
Tel: (513)733-7843; (999)332-XTEK
Fax: (513)733-7939
E-mail: jeff.mckain@xtek.com
Web Site: http://www.aist.org/chapters/ohiovalley_scholarship.htm
To provide financial assistance for college to student members and children of members of the Ohio Valley Chapter of the Association for Iron & Steel Technology (AIST).

Title of Award: Ohio Valley Chapter AIST Scholarships **Area, Field, or Subject:** Biological and clinical sciences; Chemistry; Computer and information sciences; Earth sciences; Engineering; Engineering, Electrical; Engineering, Mechanical; Environmental conservation; Environmental science; Geosciences; Information science and technology; Metallurgy; Physical sciences; Physics **Level of Education for which Award is Granted:** Undergraduate **Number Awarded:** Up to 2 each year. **Funds Available:** The stipend is $1,000 per year. **Duration:** 1 year; may be renewed up to 3 additional years provided the recipient remains enrolled full time and maintains a GPA of 3.0 or higher.

Eligibility Requirements: This program is open to high school seniors and college students who are either 1) children of Ohio Valley Chapter AIST members, or 2) student AIST members. Applicants must be accepted at, planning to attend, or currently enrolled at an accredited college or university with a major in biology, chemistry, computer programming, computer technology, electrical engineering, engineering, engineering technology, environmental engineering, environmental science, information systems technology, mechanical engineering, metallurgy, microbiology, physical science, physics, or other field approved by the scholarship committee. Along with their application, they must submit a 500-word essay on the reasons for their interests and reasons for working on a degree in their field of study, career goals and objectives, and extracurricular activities and their benefits. Selection is based on overall academic achievement (especially in mathematics and science), the essay, and extracurricular activities. **Deadline for Receipt:** February of each year. **Additional Information:** The AIST was formed in 2004 by the merger of the Iron and Steel Society (ISS) and the Association of Iron and Steel Engineers (AISE). This program was established by the former Ohio Valley District Section of AISE. The Ohio Valley Chapter covers Indiana (except for the northwestern portion), all of Kentucky, western Tennessee, and portions of southern Ohio.

4807 ■ ASSOCIATION FOR IRON & STEEL TECHNOLOGY-PITTSBURGH CHAPTER

c/o Paul D. Conley
Allegheny Ludlum
100 River Road
Brackenridge, PA 15014-1597
Tel: (724)226-5000
Web Site: http://www.aist.org/chapters/
mc_pittsburgh_scholar_guidelines.htm
To provide financial assistance to family of members of the Pittsburgh Chapter of the Association for Iron & Steel Technology (AIST) who are interested in studying engineering or metallurgy in college.

Title of Award: Pittsburgh Chapter AIST Scholarships **Area, Field, or Subject:** Business; Engineering; Manufacturing; Metallurgy **Level of Education for which Award is Granted:** Undergraduate **Number Awarded:** Up to 2 each year. **Funds Available:** The stipend is $2,500. **Duration:** 1 year.

Eligibility Requirements: This program is open to children, grandchildren, or spouses of chapter members who are high school seniors or full-time undergraduates at an accredited college or university. Applicants must be studying or planning to study engineering or metallurgy; if there are no applicants in those fields, the award may be given to a student majoring in another field relating to iron and steel production. Along with their application, they must submit a 500-word essay on 1 of the following topics: 1) an accomplishment they have achieved while they have been a student, why they were successful, and how their success will influence their future plans as an engineer or an engineer in the steel industry; 2) their strengths and interests and how they will apply their skills to a career

in the steel industry or as an engineer; or 3) they challenges that face the steel industry and the opportunities for graduates to improve the success of companies within the industry. Financial need is not considered in the selection process. **Deadline for Receipt:** June of each year. **Additional Information:** The AIST was formed in 2004 by the merger of the Iron and Steel Society (ISS) and the Association of Iron and Steel Engineers (AISE). The Pittsburgh Chapter serves western Pennsylvania, West Virginia, and southeastern Ohio. This program includes the Lawrence G. Maloney Scholarship.

4808 ■ H.H. HARRIS FOUNDATION

Attn: Trustee
30 South Wacker Drive, Suite 2300
Chicago, IL 60606
Tel: (312)346-7900
Fax: (312)346-0904
E-mail: JohnHH@aol.com
Web Site: http://www.afsinc.org/Harris.htm
To provide financial assistance to students and professionals in the metallurgical and casting of metals field.

Title of Award: H.H. Harris Foundation Scholarships **Area, Field, or Subject:** Business; Manufacturing; Metallurgy **Level of Education for which Award is Granted:** Graduate, Professional, Undergraduate **Number Awarded:** Varies each year. **Funds Available:** Stipends are at least $1,000. **Duration:** 1 year.

Eligibility Requirements: This program is open to U.S. citizens who are enrolled in an undergraduate or graduate program in the metallurgical and casting of metals field. Preference is given to undergraduates. Along with their application, they must submit documentation of financial need and a statement of purpose that summarizes their career plans and goals with regard to the cast metal and/or metallurgical fields. **Deadline for Receipt:** June of each year.

4809 ■ INTERNATIONAL SOCIETY OF EXPLOSIVES ENGINEERS

Attn: SEE Education Foundation
30325 Bainbridge Road
Cleveland, OH 44139
Tel: (440)349-4400
Fax: (440)349-3788
Web Site: http://www.isee.org/education/SEEFoundation.htm
To provide financial assistance to undergraduate and graduate engineering students interested in preparing for a career involving the use of explosives.

Title of Award: SEE Education Foundation Scholarships **Area, Field, or Subject:** Engineering; Engineering, Aerospace/Aeronautical/Astronautical; Engineering, Automotive; Engineering, Industrial; Engineering, Mining and Mineral **Level of Education for which Award is Granted:** Graduate, Undergraduate **Number Awarded:** 1 each year. **Funds Available:** A stipend is awarded (amount not specified). **Duration:** 1 year; may be renewed.

Eligibility Requirements: This program is open to students working on their first associate, undergraduate, or graduate degree as a full-time student at an accredited college or university. Applicants must show an interest in the use of explosives and intend to enter an explosives-related field, such as mining, construction, forestry, manufacturing, automotives, or aerospace. If they have already completed some college work, their GPA must be 2.9 or higher. Selection is based on career and personal ambition, academic potential, written communications, ability to overcome personal hardships and/or challenges, and financial need. **Deadline for Receipt:** April of each year.

4810 ■ MICHIGAN AGGREGATES ASSOCIATION

3474 Alaiedon Parkway, Suite 700
Okemos, MI 48864
Tel: (517)381-1732
Fax: (517)381-1796
E-mail: contactmaa@miagg.org
Web Site: http://www.miagg.org
To provide financial assistance to undergraduate and graduate students affiliated with the Michigan Aggregates Association (MAA).

Title of Award: Michigan Aggregates Association Scholarships **Area, Field, or Subject:** Business; Engineering, Mining and Mineral; Mining **Level of Education for which Award is Granted:** Graduate, Undergraduate **Number Awarded:** 1 or more each year. **Funds Available:** The stipend is $1,000. **Duration:** 1 year; nonrenewable.

Eligibility Requirements: This program is open to students entering or attending an accredited institution of higher education who are immediate relatives of an MAA member or an MAA member employee or relative. Applicants must be working on an undergraduate or graduate degree in a field related to the extraction of mineral resources. Along with their application, they must submit an essay (up to 250 words) on their interest in the aggregate/mineral extraction industry. Financial need is not considered in the selection process. **Deadline for Receipt:** April of each year.

4811 ■ ROCKY MOUNTAIN COAL MINING INSTITUTE

Attn: Executive Director
8057 South Yukon Way
Littleton, CO 80128-5510
Tel: (303)948-3300
Fax: (303)948-1132
E-mail: mail@rmcmi.org
Web Site: http://www.rmcmi.org

To provide financial assistance to college students from Rocky Mountain states who are preparing for a career in the mining industry.

Title of Award: Rocky Mountain Coal Mining Institute Scholarships **Area, Field, or Subject:** Business; Engineering, Electrical; Engineering, Geological; Engineering, Mechanical; Engineering, Metallurgical; Engineering, Mining and Mineral; Environmental science; Geology; Metallurgy; Mining **Level of Education for which Award is Granted:** Four Year College **Number Awarded:** 8 each year (1 from each of the participating states). **Funds Available:** The stipend is $2,000 per year. Funds are disbursed to the recipient's institution to be used as a tuition credit during the junior, senior, and/or fifth year of undergraduate study. **Duration:** 2 years; renewable, if the recipient continues in school as a full-time student in good academic standing.

Eligibility Requirements: This program is open to full-time sophomores or juniors in college who are U.S. citizens and residents of Arizona, Colorado, Montana, New Mexico, North Dakota, Texas, Utah, or Wyoming. Applicants must be working on a degree in engineering (e.g., electrical, environmental, geological, mechanical, metallurgical, mining) or in a mining-related field (e.g., geology, mineral processing, metallurgy). They may be attending school in 1 of those states or another school approved by the sponsor (e.g., University of Missouri at Rolla, South Dakota School of Mines). Preference is given to students who are particularly interested in western coal as a career. Interviews are required. **Deadline for Receipt:** January of each year.

4812 ■ SOCIETY OF EXPLORATION GEOPHYSICISTS

Attn: SEG Foundation
8801 South Yale, Suite 500
P.O. Box 702740
Tulsa, OK 74170-2740
Tel: (918)497-5513
Fax: (918)497-5557
E-mail: scholarships@seg.org
Web Site: http://seg.org/business/foundation/scholarships/index.shtml

To provide financial assistance to undergraduate and graduate students who are interested in the field of applied geophysics related to mining or electrical methods.

Title of Award: G.W. Hohmann Scholarships **Area, Field, or Subject:** Business; Geophysics; Mining **Level of Education for which Award is Granted:** Graduate, Undergraduate **Number Awarded:** 2 each year: 1 for an undergraduate and 1 for a graduate student. **Funds Available:** The stipend is $3,000 per year for graduate students or $1,000 per year for undergraduates. **Duration:** 1 academic year; may be renewable, based on scholastic standing, availability of funds, and continuance of a course of study leading to a career in applied geophysics.

Eligibility Requirements: This program is open to 1) high school students planning to enter college in the fall, and 2) undergraduate or graduate students whose grades are above average. Applicants must intend to work on a degree directed toward a career in applied geophysics with an emphasis on mining or electrical methods. Along with their application, they must submit a 150-word essay on how they plan to use geophysics in their future. Financial need is not considered in the selection process. **Deadline for Receipt:** January of each year.

4813 ■ SOCIETY FOR MINING, METALLURGY, AND EXPLORATION, INC.

Attn: Student Center
8307 Shaffer Parkway
Littleton, CO 80127-4102
Tel: (303)973-9550
Free: 800-763-3132
Fax: (303)973-3845
E-mail: sme@smenet.org
Web Site: http://www.smenet.org/education/students/
sme_scholarships.cfm

To provide financial assistance to student members of the Society for Mining, Metallurgy, and Exploration (SME) who are majoring in mining engineering with an emphasis on coal.

Title of Award: Coal and Energy Division Scholarships **Area, Field, or Subject:** Engineering, Mining and Mineral **Level of Education for which Award is Granted:** Four Year College **Number Awarded:** Approximately 15 each year. **Funds Available:** The stipends are approximately $1,500 per year. **Duration:** 1 year.

Eligibility Requirements: This program is open to student members who have completed their sophomore year in college and are majoring in mining or mineral engineering at an ABET-accredited college. Applicants must be U.S. citizens engaged in coal-related activities. Financial need is considered in the selection process. **Deadline for Receipt:** October of each year.

4814 ■ SOCIETY FOR MINING, METALLURGY, AND EXPLORATION, INC.

Attn: Student Center
8307 Shaffer Parkway
Littleton, CO 80127-4102
Tel: (303)973-9550
Free: 800-763-3132
Fax: (303)973-3845
E-mail: sme@smenet.org
Web Site: http://www.smenet.org/education/students/
sme_scholarships.cfm

To provide financial assistance to upper-division student members of the Society for Mining, Metallurgy, and Exploration (SME) who are majoring in fields that will develop their skills related to mining and the environment.

Title of Award: Environmental Division Scholarship **Area, Field, or Subject:** Economics; Engineering, Mining and Mineral; Environmental conservation; Environmental science; Geology; Metallurgy **Level of Education for which Award is Granted:** Four Year College **Number Awarded:** 1 or more each year. **Funds Available:** A total of $2,000 is awarded each year. **Duration:** 1 year.

Eligibility Requirements: Applicants must 1) be majoring in a field related to the minerals industry (e.g., geology, minerals engineering, mining engineering, or mineral economics) at a 4-year college or university, 2) have completed at least their sophomore year in college, 3) be a U.S. citizen, and 4) be a student member of the society. They must be of good character, be of sound health, have demonstrated scholastic aptitude (GPA of 3.0 or higher), and be able to demonstrate financial need. Candidates for these scholarships must be working on an undergraduate degree related to mining and the environment with a faculty advisor who has special interests in an environmentally-oriented program. **Deadline for Receipt:** October of each year.

4815 ■ SOCIETY FOR MINING, METALLURGY, AND EXPLORATION, INC.

Attn: Student Center
8307 Shaffer Parkway
Littleton, CO 80127-4102
Tel: (303)973-9550
Free: 800-763-3132
Fax: (303)973-3845
E-mail: sme@smenet.org
Web Site: http://www.smenet.org/education/students/
sme_scholarships.cfm

To provide financial assistance to upper-division and graduate student members of the Society for Mining, Metallurgy, and Exploration (SME) who are majoring in fields that will prepare them for a career in industrial minerals.

Title of Award: Gerald V. Henderson Industrial Minerals Memorial Scholarship **Area, Field, or Subject:** Economics; Engineering, Mining and Mineral; Geology; Metallurgy **Level of Education for which Award is Granted:** Four Year College, Graduate **Number Awarded:** 1 or more each year. **Funds Available:** A total of $2,000 is awarded each year. **Duration:** 1 year.
Eligibility Requirements: Applicants must 1) be majoring in a field related to the minerals industry (e.g., geology, minerals engineering, mining engineering, or mineral economics) at a 4-year college or university, 2) have completed at least their sophomore year in college, 3) be a U.S. citizen, and 4) be a student member of the society. They must be of good character, be of sound health, have demonstrated scholastic aptitude (GPA of 3.0 or higher), and be able to demonstrate financial need. Candidates for these scholarships may be proposed by any of the following: mining and minerals companies; local sections of the society; state mining institutes; high school principals; industrial minerals associations; manufacturers of mining and processing equipment; minerals research organizations; or geology and mining engineering departments at colleges or universities. An interview may be required. **Deadline for Receipt:** October of each year.

4816 ■ SOCIETY FOR MINING, METALLURGY, AND EXPLORATION, INC.

Attn: Student Center
8307 Shaffer Parkway
Littleton, CO 80127-4102
Tel: (303)973-9550
Free: 800-763-3132
Fax: (303)973-3845
E-mail: sme@smenet.org
Web Site: http://www.smenet.org/education/students/sme_scholarships.cfm
To provide financial assistance to student members of the Society for Mining, Metallurgy, and Exploration (SME) who are preparing for a career in minerals processing.
Title of Award: Mineral and Metallurgical Processing Division Scholarship **Area, Field, or Subject:** Engineering, Mining and Mineral; Metallurgy **Level of Education for which Award is Granted:** Four Year College **Number Awarded:** Up to 6 each year. **Funds Available:** The first-place recipient is given $2,000 (plus travel to the society's annual meeting). The other winners each receive a $1,000 scholarship. **Duration:** 1 year.
Eligibility Requirements: This program is open to student members of the society who have completed their sophomore year in college; are enrolled full time in an undergraduate degree program that has required course work in minerals processing, hydrometallurgy, and/or metallurgical engineering; are U.S. citizens; and have a GPA of 2.5 or higher. Only 1 candidate from each eligible department may be nominated each academic year. Applicants must demonstrate an interest in preparing for a career in mineral processing or metallurgical engineering in the mining industry. **Deadline for Receipt:** October of each year.

4817 ■ SOCIETY FOR MINING, METALLURGY, AND EXPLORATION, INC.

Attn: Student Center
8307 Shaffer Parkway
Littleton, CO 80127-4102
Tel: (303)973-9550
Free: 800-763-3132
Fax: (303)973-3845
E-mail: sme@smenet.org
Web Site: http://www.smenet.org/education/students/sme_scholarships.cfm
To provide financial assistance to student members of the Society for Mining, Metallurgy, and Exploration (SME) who are preparing for a career in the minerals industry.
Title of Award: Mining and Exploration Division Scholarships **Area, Field, or Subject:** Engineering, Mining and Mineral; Geology; Metallurgy **Level of Education for which Award is Granted:** Four Year College **Number Awarded:** Up to 4 each year. **Funds Available:** The stipend is $1,500. **Duration:** 1 year.
Eligibility Requirements: Applicants must have completed their sophomore year in college and be majoring in mining, geology, or a related field of specialization at an ABET-accredited college or university.

They must be U.S. citizens or permanent residents, be able to demonstrate financial need, have a strong academic record, and be a student member of the society. Only 1 candidate from each eligible department may be nominated each academic year. **Deadline for Receipt:** November of each year.

4818 ■ SOCIETY FOR MINING, METALLURGY, AND EXPLORATION, INC.

Attn: Student Center
8307 Shaffer Parkway
Littleton, CO 80127-4102
Tel: (303)973-9550
Free: 800-763-3132
Fax: (303)973-3845
E-mail: sme@smenet.org
Web Site: http://www.smenet.org/education/students/sme_scholarships.cfm
To provide financial assistance to student members of the Society for Mining, Metallurgy, and Exploration (SME) who are majoring in mining engineering.
Title of Award: Eugene P. Pfleider Memorial Scholarship **Area, Field, or Subject:** Engineering, Mining and Mineral **Level of Education for which Award is Granted:** Four Year College **Number Awarded:** 1 each year. **Funds Available:** The stipend is $1,000. **Duration:** 1 year.
Eligibility Requirements: This program is open to student members who have completed their sophomore year in college and are majoring in mining engineering. Applicants must be U.S. citizens, be able to demonstrate financial need, have a strong academic record, and be committed to a career in mining engineering. Only 1 candidate from each eligible department may be nominated each academic year. **Deadline for Receipt:** November of each year.

4819 ■ WOMEN'S JEWELRY ASSOCIATION

Attn: Scholarship Committee
373 B Route 46 West, Building E, Suite 215
Fairfield, NJ 07004
Tel: (973)575-7190
Fax: (973)575-1445
E-mail: info@womensjewelry.org
Web Site: http://www.womensjewelry.org/scholarships.html
To provide financial assistance for college to women who are interested in careers in jewelry.
Title of Award: Women's Jewelry Association Scholarship **Area, Field, or Subject:** Business administration; Crafts; Finance; Marketing and distribution; Metallurgy **Level of Education for which Award is Granted:** Undergraduate **Number Awarded:** Varies each year. Recently, 12 of these scholarships were awarded: 1 at $5,000, 2 at $3,000, 1 at $2,500, 1 at $1,500 and 7 at $1,000. **Funds Available:** Stipends range from $500 to $5,000 per year. **Duration:** 1 year.
Eligibility Requirements: Women who are enrolled in a jewelry-related curriculum at an institution of higher learning located anywhere in the United States are eligible to apply. Eligible fields of study range from design to gemological analysis and include metalsmithing, finance, business, and marketing. Applicants must submit 2 letters of recommendation, a short essay explaining why they wish to prepare for a career in jewelry/toolmaking and their aspirations for the future, 3 slides showing examples of their work, and a list of 3 courses related to jewelry that have been most important to them. Financial need is considered in the selection process. **Deadline for Receipt:** April of each year. **Additional Information:** This program includes the June Herman Scholarship of $5,000, awarded for the first time in 2001.

Naval Science

4820 ■ AMERICAN SOCIETY FOR ENGINEERING EDUCATION

Attn: SMART Defense Scholarship Program
1818 N Street, N.W., Suite 600
Washington, DC 20036-2479
Tel: (202)331-3516
Fax: (202)265-8504

E-mail: smart@asee.org

Web Site: http://www.asee.org/resources/fellowships/smart/index.cfm

To provide scholarship/loans to upper-division and graduate students in areas of science, mathematics, and engineering that are of interest to the U.S. Department of Defense.

Title of Award: Science, Mathematics, and Research for Transformation (SMART) Defense Scholarship Program **Area, Field, or Subject:** Architecture, Naval; Behavioral sciences; Biological and clinical sciences; Chemistry; Computer and information sciences; Earth sciences; Engineering, Aerospace/Aeronautical/Astronautical; Engineering, Chemical; Engineering, Civil; Engineering, Electrical; Engineering, Materials; Engineering, Mechanical; Engineering, Ocean; Geosciences; Materials research/science; Mathematics and mathematical sciences; Oceanography; Physics **Level of Education for which Award is Granted:** Four Year College, Graduate **Number Awarded:** Varies each year; recently, 36 of these scholarships were awarded. **Funds Available:** The program provides full payment of tuition, fees, room, board, and other normal educational expenses at the recipient's institution. A book allowance of $1,000 per year is also provided. This is a scholarship/loan program; recipients must agree to serve as a civilian employee of the Department of Defense in a science and engineering position. If they fail to fulfill that service obligation, they must reimburse the federal government for all funds they received. **Duration:** Up to 24 months.

Eligibility Requirements: This program is open to upper-division and graduate students working on an undergraduate or graduate degree in any of the following fields: aeronautical and astronautical engineering; biosciences; chemical engineering; chemistry; civil engineering; cognitive, neural, and behavioral sciences; computer and computational sciences; electrical engineering; geosciences, including terrain, water, and air; materials science and engineering; mathematics; mechanical engineering; naval architecture and ocean engineering; oceanography; or physics. Applicants must be U.S. citizens who have a GPA of 3.0 or higher. Selection is based on academic records, personal statements, letters of recommendation, and GRE scores. **Deadline for Receipt:** March of each year.

Additional Information: This program, established in 2005, is sponsored by the Army Research Laboratory, the Air Force Office of Scientific Research, the Office of Naval Research, the Air Force Research Laboratory, the Defense Advanced Research Projects Agency, the Defense Information Systems Agency, and the Defense Threat Reduction Agency.

4821 ■ HISPANIC ENGINEER NATIONAL ACHIEVEMENT AWARDS CONFERENCE

3900 Whiteside Street

Los Angeles, CA 90063

Tel: (323)262-0997

Fax: (323)262-0946

E-mail: info@henaac.org

Web Site: http://www.henaac.org/scholarships

To provide financial assistance to Hispanic undergraduate students majoring in engineering and related fields.

Title of Award: Northrop Grumman/HENAAC Scholars Program **Area, Field, or Subject:** Architecture, Naval; Computer and information sciences; Engineering, Aerospace/Aeronautical/Astronautical; Engineering, Chemical; Engineering, Civil; Engineering, Computer; Engineering, Electrical; Engineering, Industrial; Engineering, Mechanical; Engineering, Ocean; Information science and technology; Mathematics and mathematical sciences; Physics **Level of Education for which Award is Granted:** Undergraduate **Number Awarded:** 5 each year. **Funds Available:** The stipend is $5,000. **Duration:** 1 year; recipients may reapply.

Eligibility Requirements: This program is open to Hispanic undergraduate students who are enrolled full time in the following engineering fields: aerospace, chemical, civil, computer, electrical, industrial, manufacturing, marine, mechanical, ocean, or structural. Students majoring in computer science, information science, mathematics, naval architecture, and physics are also eligible. Applicants must be U.S. citizens and have a GPA of 3.0 or higher. Academic achievement and campus community activities are considered in the selection process. **Deadline for Receipt:** April of each year. **Additional Information:** This program is sponsored by Northrop Grumman as part of its effort to support the mission of the

Hispanic Engineer National Achievement Awards Conference (HENAAC) to promote technical excellence and leadership in the Hispanic community.

4822 ■ NATIONAL SOCIETY OF BLACK ENGINEERS

Attn: Programs Department

1454 Duke Street

Alexandria, VA 22314

Tel: (703)549-2207

Fax: (703)683-5312

E-mail: scholarships@nsbe.org

Web Site: http://www.nsbe.org/programs/schol_ng.php

To provide financial assistance to members of the National Society of Black Engineers (NSBE) who are working on an undergraduate degree in designated science and engineering fields.

Title of Award: Northrop Grumman NSBE Scholarships **Area, Field, or Subject:** Architecture, Naval; Computer and information sciences; Engineering, Aerospace/Aeronautical/Astronautical; Engineering, Chemical; Engineering, Civil; Engineering, Computer; Engineering, Electrical; Engineering, Industrial; Engineering, Mechanical; Engineering, Ocean; Mathematics and mathematical sciences; Physics **Level of Education for which Award is Granted:** Undergraduate **Number Awarded:** 5 each year. **Funds Available:** The stipend is $5,000. **Duration:** 1 year.

Eligibility Requirements: This program is open to members of the society who are U.S. citizens currently enrolled in college. Applicants must be majoring in computer science, information science, mathematics, naval architecture, physics, or the following engineering fields: aerospace, chemical, civil (structural), computer, electrical, industrial, manufacturing, marine, mechanical, or ocean. They must have a GPA of 3.0 or higher and demonstrate an interest in employment with Northrop Grumman Corporation. **Deadline for Receipt:** January of each year.

4823 ■ SOCIETY OF NAVAL ARCHITECTS AND MARINE ENGINEERS

Attn: Scholarships Coordinator

601 Pavonia Avenue, Suite 400

Jersey City, NJ 07306

Tel: (201)798-4800

Free: 800-798-2188

Fax: (201)798-4975

E-mail: efaustino@sname.org

Web Site: http://www.sname.org/scholarships_undergraduate.htm

To provide financial assistance for undergraduate study to members of the Society of Naval Architects and Marine Engineers.

Title of Award: Society of Naval Architects and Marine Engineers Undergraduate Scholarships **Area, Field, or Subject:** Architecture, Naval; Engineering, Ocean; Oceanography **Level of Education for which Award is Granted:** Four Year College **Number Awarded:** Varies each year; recently, 24 of these scholarships were awarded. **Funds Available:** Scholarships up to $2,000 per year are available. **Duration:** 1 year; may be renewed 1 additional year.

Eligibility Requirements: Applicants for these scholarships must have been accepted to study naval architecture, marine engineering, ocean engineering, or another field directly related to the marine industry at a participating university. They must be members of the society entering their junior or senior year. **Deadline for Receipt:** Participating universities must submit their nominations to the society by the end of April of each year. **Additional Information:** Applications for these scholarships should be submitted directly to the participating universities: California Maritime Academy, Florida Atlantic University, Florida Institute of Technology, Maine Maritime Academy, Massachusetts Institute of Technology, Memorial University of Newfoundland, Texas A&M University, University of British Columbia, University of California at Berkeley, University of Michigan, University of New Orleans, State University of New York Maritime College, Virginia Polytechnic Institute, or Webb Institute.

4824 ■ U.S. NAVY

Attn: Chief of Naval Education and Training

Code N79A2

250 Dallas Street

Pensacola, FL 32508-5220

Tel: (850)452-4941

Free: 800-NAV-ROTC

Fax: (850)452-2486
E-mail: PNSC_NROTC.scholarship@navy.mil
Web Site: http://www.nrotc.navy.mil
To provide financial assistance to upper-division students who are interested in joining Navy ROTC in college.
Title of Award: Navy-Marine Corps ROTC 2-Year Scholarships **Area, Field, or Subject:** General studies/Field of study not specified; Naval art and science **Level of Education for which Award is Granted:** Undergraduate **Number Awarded:** Approximately 800 each year. **Funds Available:** These scholarships provide payment of full tuition and required educational fees, as well as a specified amount for textbooks, supplies, and equipment. The program also provides a stipend for 10 months of the year that is $350 per month as a junior and $400 per month as a senior. **Duration:** 2 years, until the recipient completes the bachelor's degree.
Eligibility Requirements: This program is open to students who have completed at least 2 years of college (or 3 years if enrolled in a 5-year program) with a GPA of 2.5 or higher overall and 2.0 or higher in calculus and physics. Preference is given to students at colleges with a Navy ROTC unit on campus or at colleges with a cross-enrollment agreement with a college with an NROTC unit. Applicants must be U.S. citizens between the ages of 17 and 21 who plan to pursue an approved course of study in college and complete their degree before they reach the age of 27. Former and current enlisted military personnel are also eligible if they will complete the program by the age of 30. **Deadline for Receipt:** March of each year. **Additional Information:** Applications must be made through professors of naval science at 1 of the schools hosting the Navy ROTC program. Prior to final selection, applicants must attend, at Navy expense, a 6-week summer training course at the Naval Science Institute at Newport, Rhode Island. Recipients must also complete 4 years of study in naval science classes as students either at 1 of the 70 colleges with NROTC units or at 1 of the more than 100 institutions with cross-enrollment agreements (in which case they attend their home college for their regular academic courses but attend naval science classes at a nearby school with an NROTC unit). After completing the program, all participants are commissioned as ensigns in the Naval Reserve or second lieutenants in the Marine Corps Reserve with an 8-year service obligation, including 4 years of active duty.

4825 ■ U.S. NAVY
Attn: Chief of Naval Education and Training
Code N79A2
250 Dallas Street
Pensacola, FL 32508-5220
Tel: (850)452-4941
Free: 800-NAV-ROTC
Fax: (850)452-2486
E-mail: PNSC_NROTC.scholarship@navy.mil
Web Site: http://www.nrotc.navy.mil
To provide financial assistance to graduating high school seniors who are interested in joining Navy ROTC in college.
Title of Award: Navy-Marine Corps ROTC 4-Year Scholarships **Area, Field, or Subject:** General studies/Field of study not specified; Naval art and science **Level of Education for which Award is Granted:** Undergraduate **Number Awarded:** Approximately 2,200 each year. **Funds Available:** These scholarships provide payment of full tuition and required educational fees, as well as a specified amount for textbooks, supplies, and equipment. The program also provides a stipend for 10 months of the year that is $250 per month as a freshman, $300 per month as a sophomore, $350 per month as a junior, and $400 per month as a senior. **Duration:** 4 years.
Eligibility Requirements: This program is open to graduating high school seniors who have been accepted at a college with a Navy ROTC unit on campus or a college with a cross-enrollment agreement with such a college. Applicants must be U.S. citizens between 17 and 23 years of age who are willing to serve for 4 years as active-duty Navy officers following graduation from college. They must not have reached their 27th birthday by the time of college graduation and commissioning; applicants who have prior active-duty military service may be eligible for age adjustments for the amount of time equal to their prior service, up to a maximum of 36 months. The qualifying scores for the Navy option are 530 critical reading and 520 mathematics on the SAT or 22 on both English and mathematics on the ACT; for the Marine Corps option they are 1000 composite on the SAT or 22 composite on the ACT. Current enlisted and former military personnel are also eligible if they will complete the program by the age of 30. **Deadline for Receipt:** January of each year. **Additional Information:** Students may apply for either a Navy or Marine Corps option scholarship but not for both. Navy option applicants apply through Navy recruiting offices; Marine Corps applicants apply through Marine Corps recruiting offices. Recipients must complete 4 years of study in naval science classes as students either at 1 of the 70 colleges, universities, and maritime institutes with NROTC units or at 1 of the more than 100 institutions with cross-enrollment agreements (in which case they attend their home college for their regular academic courses but attend naval science classes at a nearby school with an NROTC unit). After completing the program, all participants are commissioned as ensigns in the Naval Reserve or second lieutenants in the Marine Corps Reserve with an 8-year service obligation, including 4 years of active duty. Current military personnel who are accepted into this program are released from active duty and are not eligible for active-duty pay and allowances, medical benefits, or other active-duty entitlements.

4826 ■ U.S. NAVY
Attn: Chief of Naval Education and Training
Code N79A2
250 Dallas Street
Pensacola, FL 32508-5220
Tel: (850)452-4941
Free: 800-NAV-ROTC
Fax: (850)452-2486
E-mail: PNSC_NROTC.scholarship@navy.mil
Web Site: http://www.nrotc.navy.mil
To provide financial assistance to lower-division students who are interested in joining Navy ROTC in college.
Title of Award: Navy-Marine Corps ROTC College Program **Area, Field, or Subject:** General studies/Field of study not specified; Naval art and science **Level of Education for which Award is Granted:** Four Year College **Funds Available:** Participants in this program receive free naval science textbooks, all required uniforms, and a stipend for 10 months of the year that is $250 per month as a freshman, $300 per month as a sophomore, $350 per month as a junior and $400 per month as a senior. **Duration:** 2 or 4 years.
Eligibility Requirements: Applicants must be U.S. citizens between the ages of 17 and 21 who are already enrolled as non-scholarship students in naval science courses at a college or university with a Navy ROTC program on campus. They must apply before the spring of their sophomore year. All applications must be submitted through the professors of naval science at the college or university attended. **Deadline for Receipt:** March of each year. **Additional Information:** Following acceptance into the program, participants attend the 6-week Naval Science Institute in Newport, Rhode Island (or in Quantico, Virginia for Marine-option students). After graduation from college, they are commissioned ensigns in the Naval Reserve or second lieutenants in the Marine Corps Reserve with an 8-year service obligation, including 3 years of active duty.

4827 ■ U.S. NAVY
Attn: Chief of Naval Education and Training
Code N79A2
250 Dallas Street
Pensacola, FL 32508-5220
Tel: (850)452-4941
Free: 800-NAV-ROTC
Fax: (850)452-2486
E-mail: PNSC_NROTC.scholarship@navy.mil
Web Site: http://www.nrotc.navy.mil/scholarships.cfm
To provide financial assistance to currently-enrolled college students who are interested in joining Navy ROTC and majoring in a technical field in college.
Title of Award: Tweedale Scholarships **Area, Field, or Subject:** General studies/Field of study not specified; Naval art and science **Level of Education for which Award is Granted:** Undergraduate **Number Awarded:** Approximately 140 each year: 2 at each college and university with a Navy ROTC unit. **Funds Available:** These scholarships provide payment of full tuition and required educational fees, as well as a specified amount for textbooks, supplies, and equipment. The program also provides a stipend for 10 months of the year that is $300 per month as a sophomore, $350 per month as a junior, and $400 per month as a senior.

Duration: 2 or 3 years, until the recipient completes the bachelor's degree.
Eligibility Requirements: This program is open to students who have completed at least 1 but not more than 4 academic terms with a cumulative GPA that places them above their peer mean or 3.0, whichever is higher, and a grade of "C" or better in all classes attempted. They must have a strong mathematics and science background in high school (with a grade of "B" or higher in calculus, if taken) and completed at least 1 academic term of college-level mathematics or science. They must be majoring in specified technical fields (recently, those were chemistry, computer science, engineering, mathematics, and physics). Students must be interviewed by the Professor of Naval Science (PNS) at their college or university and must comply with standards of leadership potential and military/physical fitness. They must submit a plan indicating that they will complete the introductory naval science course as soon as possible and be able to complete all naval science requirements and graduate on time with their class. **Deadline for Receipt:** March of each year. **Additional Information:** Applications must be made through the PNS at 1 of the 70 schools hosting the Navy ROTC program. Prior to final selection, applicants must attend, at Navy expense, a 6-week summer training course at the Naval Science Institute at Newport, Rhode Island. After completing the program, all participants are commissioned as ensigns in the Naval Reserve or second lieutenants in the Marine Corps Reserve with an 8-year service obligation, including 4 years of active duty.

Photography

4828 ■ AMERICAN SOCIETY FOR PHOTOGRAMMETRY AND REMOTE SENSING

Attn: Scholarship Administrator
5410 Grosvenor Lane, Suite 210
Bethesda, MD 20814-2160
Tel: (301)493-0290
Fax: (301)493-0208
E-mail: scholarships@asprs.org
Web Site: http://www.asprs.org/membership/scholar.html
To provide financial assistance for undergraduate or graduate education to members of the American Society for Photogrammetry and Remote Sensing (ASPRS).
Title of Award: Robert E. Altenhofen Memorial Scholarship **Area, Field, or Subject:** Photogrammetry **Level of Education for which Award is Granted:** Graduate, Undergraduate **Number Awarded:** 1 each year. **Funds Available:** The stipend is $2,000. **Duration:** 1 year.
Eligibility Requirements: This program is open to both undergraduate and graduate students enrolled at accredited colleges or universities in the United States. Applicants must be either a student member or active member of the society. Selection is based on academic record, letters of recommendation, samples of the applicant's papers or research reports, and a 2-page statement about the applicant's plans for continuing studies in theoretical photogrammetry. **Deadline for Receipt:** September of each year. **Additional Information:** This program, established in 1986, is named for a past president of the ASPRS. It is administered by the International Geographic Information Foundation with funds provided by the estate of his widow.

4829 ■ FASHION GROUP INTERNATIONAL OF WASHINGTON

Attn: Julie Caine Brooks, Scholarship Chair
P.O. Box 1288
Great Falls, VA 22066
To provide financial assistance for college or graduate school to residents of Maryland, Virginia, and Washington, D. C. interested in preparing for a career in fashion or a fashion-related field.
Title of Award: Washington Fashion Group International Scholarship **Area, Field, or Subject:** Fashion design; Interior design; Journalism; Marketing and distribution; Photography; Textile science **Level of Education for which Award is Granted:** Graduate, Undergraduate **Number Awarded:** 1 each year. **Funds Available:** The maximum stipend is $5,000. **Duration:** 1 year; nonrenewable
Eligibility Requirements: This program is open to residents of Washington, D.C. and all cities and counties in Maryland and Virginia. Applicants must be graduating high school seniors or current undergraduate or graduate students enrolled in a fashion or fashion-related degree

program (commercial arts, textiles and clothing design, interior design, journalism, merchandising, or photography). They must submit a 200-word personal statement on their career goals and motivation for entering a fashion-related career. Selection is based on that statement, academic achievement, creative ability, related work activity (paid or unpaid), extracurricular activities and awards, and 3 letters of reference. Finalists are interviewed and asked to submit portfolio material of their work. **Deadline for Receipt:** April of each year.

4830 ■ HAWAI'I COMMUNITY FOUNDATION

Attn: Scholarship Department
1164 Bishop Street, Suite 800
Honolulu, HI 96813
Tel: (808)566-5570; 888-731-3863
Fax: (808)521-6286
E-mail: scholarships@hcf-hawaii.org
Web Site: http://www.hawaiicommunityfoundation.org/scholar/scholar.php
To provide financial assistance to residents of Hawaii who are interested in working on a degree in fine art.
Title of Award: Esther Kanagawa Memorial Art Scholarship **Area, Field, or Subject:** Crafts; Painting; Photography; Sculpture **Level of Education for which Award is Granted:** Graduate, Undergraduate **Number Awarded:** Varies each year; recently, 1 of these scholarships was awarded. **Funds Available:** The amount of the award depends on the availability of funds and the need of the recipient; recently, stipends averaged $1,000. **Duration:** 1 year.
Eligibility Requirements: This program is open to residents of Hawaii who are planning to study fine art (drawing, painting, sculpture, ceramics, or photography) as full-time students on the undergraduate or graduate level. Students majoring in video, film, performing arts, or the culinary arts are not eligible. Applicants must be able to demonstrate academic achievement (GPA of 2.7 or higher), good moral character, and financial need. **Deadline for Receipt:** February of each year. **Additional Information:** Recipients may attend college in Hawaii or on the mainland.

4831 ■ INTERNATIONAL FOODSERVICE EDITORIAL COUNCIL

P.O. Box 491
Hyde Park, NY 12538
Tel: (845)229-6973
Fax: (845)229-6993
E-mail: ifec@aol.com
Web Site: http://www.ifec-is-us.com
To provide financial assistance to undergraduate or graduate students who are interested in preparing for a career in communications in the food service industry.
Title of Award: IFEC Scholarships **Area, Field, or Subject:** Communications; Creative writing; Culinary arts; English language and literature; Food science and technology; Food service careers; Graphic art and design; Hotel, institutional, and restaurant management; Journalism; Management; Marketing and distribution; Nutrition; Photography; Photography, Journalistic; Public relations **Level of Education for which Award is Granted:** Master's, Undergraduate **Number Awarded:** Varies each year; recently, 5 of these scholarships were awarded. **Funds Available:** The stipend is $3,000 per year. **Duration:** 1 year.
Eligibility Requirements: This program is open to currently-enrolled college students who are working on an associate, bachelor's, or master's degree. They must be enrolled full time and planning on a career in editorial, public relations, photography, food styling, or a related aspect of communications in the food service industry. The following food service majors are considered appropriate for this program: culinary arts; hospitality management; hotel, restaurant, and institutional management; dietetics; food science and technology; and nutrition. Applicable communications areas include journalism, English, mass communications, public relations, marketing, broadcast journalism, creative writing, graphic arts, and photography. Selection is based on academic record, character references, and demonstrated financial need. **Deadline for Receipt:** March of each year.

4832 ■ KANSAS WILDSCAPE FOUNDATION, INC.

1 Riverfront Plaza, Suite 311
Lawrence, KS 66044
Tel: (785)843-9453; (866)455-6377
Fax: (785)843-6379

E-mail: wildscape@sunflower.com
Web Site: http://www.kansaswildscape.org
To provide financial assistance to high school seniors in Kansas who plan to attend a college or university in the state to major in natural resources or photography.
Title of Award: Steve Harper Memorial Scholarship **Area, Field, or Subject:** Natural resources; Photography **Level of Education for which Award is Granted:** Four Year College **Number Awarded:** 1 each year. **Funds Available:** The stipend is $1,000. **Duration:** 1 year.
Eligibility Requirements: This program is open to seniors graduating from high schools and planning to attend a 4-year college or university in the state. Applicants must be planning to study photography or natural resources. Selection is based on past or current involvement in the natural resources or photography area, strength of application, academic performance, and financial need. **Deadline for Receipt:** April of each year. **Additional Information:** This program was established following the death in 2000 of Steve Harper, a photojournalism instructor at Wichita State University and outdoor writer and photographer for the *Wichita Eagle.*

4833 ■ OAK RIDGE INSTITUTE FOR SCIENCE AND EDUCATION

Attn: Science and Engineering Education
P.O. Box 117
Oak Ridge, TN 37831-0117
Tel: (865)576-9279
Fax: (865)241-5220
E-mail: coxre@orau.gov
Web Site: http://www.orau.gov/orise.htm
To provide financial assistance and research experience to undergraduate students at minority serving institutions who are majoring in scientific fields of interest to the National Oceanic and Atmospheric Administration (NOAA).
Title of Award: National Oceanic and Atmospheric Administration Educational Partnership Program with Minority Serving Institutions Undergraduate Scholarships **Area, Field, or Subject:** Atmospheric science; Biological and clinical sciences; Cartography/Surveying; Chemistry; Computer and information sciences; Engineering; Environmental conservation; Environmental science; Geography; Mathematics and mathematical sciences; Meteorology; Photogrammetry; Physical sciences; Physics **Level of Education for which Award is Granted:** Four Year College **Number Awarded:** 10 each year. **Funds Available:** This program provides payment of tuition and fees (to a maximum of $4,000 per year) and a stipend during the internship of $650 per week. **Duration:** 1 academic year and 2 summers.
Eligibility Requirements: This program is open to juniors and seniors at minority serving institutions, including Hispanic Serving Institutions (HSIs), Historically Black Colleges and Universities (HBCUs), and Tribal Colleges and Universities (TCUs). Applicants must be majoring in atmospheric science, biology, cartography, chemistry, computer science, engineering, environmental science, geodesy, geography, marine science, mathematics, meteorology, photogrammetry, physical science, physics, or remote sensing. They must also be interested in participating in a research internship at a NOAA site. U.S. citizenship is required. **Deadline for Receipt:** January of each year. **Additional Information:** This program is funded by NOAA through an interagency agreement with the U.S. Department of Energy and administered by Oak Ridge Institute for Science and Education (ORISE).

4834 ■ VSA ARTS

Attn: VOA Awards
P.O. Box 33699
Washington, DC 20033-3699
Tel: (202)628-2800
Free: 800-933-8721
Fax: (202)737-0725
E-mail: voa@vsarts.org
Web Site: http://www.vsarts.org/x267.xml
To recognize and reward young artists with disabilities.
Title of Award: VSA arts/Volkswagen Art Awards **Area, Field, or Subject:** Art; Graphic art and design; Painting; Photography **Level of Education for which Award is Granted:** Graduate, Undergraduate **Number Awarded:** A total of 15 cash prizes are awarded each year: 1 grand prize, 1 first prize, 1 second prize, and 12 awards of excellence.

Funds Available: The grand prize is $20,000, first prize is $10,000, second prize is $6,000, and awards of excellence are $2,000. **Duration:** The competition is held annually.
Eligibility Requirements: This program is open to artists between 16 and 25 years of age who have a physical, cognitive, or mental disability. Applicants are invited to submit artwork that they have created in the last 3 years on a theme that changes annually. Recently, the theme was "Shifting Gears," in which artists were invited to reflect on a pivotal moment or event in their life that led them to a greater understanding of themselves in relation to their art and/or their disability. Both representational and abstract art may be submitted. Eligible media include paintings and drawings (oil, watercolor, acrylic, pencil, or charcoal), fine art prints (lithographs, etching, intaglio, or woodcuts), photography, computer generated prints, and 2-dimensional mixed media. Up to 5 slides may be submitted, along with a 400-word essay covering their artistic background and answers to questions on when they started creating artwork, what motivated them to begin, the techniques and media they use, the role their art plays in living with their disability, how their disability affects their artwork, a significant experience during their education where the arts played an important part, and when the arts were most effective in their education. **Deadline for Receipt:** July of each year. **Additional Information:** This program, which began in 2002, is sponsored by Volkswagen of America, Inc.

4835 ■ WORLDSTUDIO FOUNDATION

200 Varick Street, Suite 507
New York, NY 10014
Tel: (212)366-1317
Fax: (212)807-0024
E-mail: scholarshipcoordinator@worldstudio.org
Web Site: http://www.worldstudio.org/schol/index.html
To provide financial assistance to undergraduate and graduate students, especially minorities, who wish to study fine or commercial arts, design, or architecture.
Title of Award: Worldstudio Foundation Scholarships **Area, Field, or Subject:** Advertising; Architecture; Art; Art industries and trade; Crafts; Design; Fashion design; Filmmaking; Graphic art and design; Interior design; Landscape architecture and design; Photography; Urban affairs/design/planning **Level of Education for which Award is Granted:** Graduate, Undergraduate **Number Awarded:** Varies each year; recently, 24 scholarships and 7 honorable mentions were awarded. **Funds Available:** Basic scholarships range from $1,000 to $2,000, but awards between $3,000 and $5,000 are also presented at the discretion of the jury. Honorable mentions are $100. Funds are paid directly to the recipient's school. **Duration:** 1 academic year. Recipients may reapply.
Eligibility Requirements: This program is open to undergraduate and graduate students who are currently enrolled or planning to enroll at an accredited college or university and major in 1 of the following areas: advertising (art direction only), architecture, crafts, environmental graphics, fashion design, film/video (direction or cinematography only), film/theater design (including set, lighting, and costume design), fine arts, furniture design, graphic design, industrial/product design, interior design, landscape architecture, new media, photography, surface/textile design, or urban planning. Although not required, minority status is a significant factor in the selection process. International students may apply if they are enrolled at a U.S. college or university. Applicants must have a GPA of 2.0 or higher. Along with their application, they must submit a 600-word statement of purpose that includes a brief autobiography, an explanation of how their experiences have influenced their creative work and/or their career plans, and how they see themselves contributing to the community at large in the future. Selection is based on that statement, the quality of submitted work, financial need, minority status, and academic record. **Deadline for Receipt:** March of each year. **Additional Information:** The foundation encourages the scholarship recipients to focus on ways that their work can address issues of social and environmental responsibility. This program includes the following named awards: the Sherry and Gary Baker Award, the Bobolink Foundation Award, the Bombay Sapphire Awards, the Richard and Jean Coyne Family Foundation Awards, the David A. Dechman Foundation Awards, the Philip and Edina Jennison Award, the Kraus Family Foundation Awards, the Dena McKelvey Award, the New York Design Center Award, the Rudin Foundation Awards, the Starr Foundation Awards, and the John F. Wright III Award.

2440, 2447, 2448, 2449, 2450, 2461, 2465, 2466, 2552, 2553, 2558, 2599, 2600, 2663, 2665, 2666, 2716, 2747, 2753, 2791, 2796, 2846, 2876, 2953, 2959, 2973, 2977, 2987, 2990, 2995, 3009, 3011, 3015, 3021, 3022, 3025, 3027, 3028, 3030, 3034, 3036, 3037, 3038, 3041, 3043, 3045, 3046, 3047, 3049, 3054, 3055, 3057, 3059, 3060, 3061, 3063, 3064, 3066, 3067, 3068, 3072, 3073, 3085, 3100, 3101, 3102, 3107, 3108, 3109, 3111, 3112, 3118, 3142, 3144, 3152, 3155, 3156, 3166, 3168, 3169, 3175, 3177, 3179, 3182, 3183, 3184, 3187, 3189, 3190, 3191, 3194, 3195, 3214, 3226, 3239, 3242, 3261, 3267, 3320, 3386, 3399, 3408, 3468, 3493, 3505, 3508, 3522, 3526, 3607, 3632, 3664, 3669, 3680, 3699, 3701, 3710, 3734, 3762, 3770, 3777, 3781, 3805, 3809, 3813, 3823, 3833, 3840, 3849, 3899, 3949, 3955, 3982, 3985, 3986, 3987, 3989, 3992, 4004, 4011, 4014, 4022, 4061, 4063, 4065, 4076, 4077, 4099, 4102, 4104, 4107, 4118, 4120, 4135, 4136, 4137, 4140, 4149, 4150, 4156, 4171, 4173, 4178, 4184, 4194, 4196, 4199, 4229, 4236, 4237, 4239, 4244, 4249, 4254, 4263, 4270, 4271, 4272, 4273, 4275, 4279, 4280, 4315, 4318, 4341, 4362, 4397, 4405, 4409, 4410, 4412, 4418, 4421, 4422, 4455, 4492, 4527, 4529, 4537, 4559, 4570, 4595, 4597, 4598, 4599, 4602, 4623, 4710, 4711, 4765, 4769, 4806, 4820, 4833

Biomedical sciences – 2657, 2680, 2713, 2714, 2715, 3259, 3260, 4119, 4347

Botany – 1977, 1981, 1986, 2060, 2070, 2459, 2460, 2465, 2467, 2560, 2581, 2582, 2583, 2589, 2597, 2598, 2600, 2601, 2614, 2737, 3866, 3871

British studies – 1917, 2138, 2239, 3686, 3766

Broadcasting – 2039, 2174, 2242, 2280, 2699, 3319, 3370, 3430, 3445, 3473, 3476, 3829, 4105, 4528

Business – 1940, 2038, 2059, 2079, 2329, 2360, 2515, 2541, 2604, 2887, 3040, 3113, 3127, 3165, 3268, 3269, 3270, 3271, 3272, 3273, 3274, 3281, 3282, 3283, 3284, 3285, 3286, 3287, 3288, 3294, 3297, 3298, 3299, 3301, 3303, 3321, 3322, 3323, 3324, 3325, 3326, 3327, 3328, 3337, 3342, 3343, 3344, 3346, 3347, 3353, 3358, 3373, 3374, 3375, 3378, 3379, 3380, 3382, 3681, 3698, 3901, 3902, 3903, 3904, 3905, 3916, 3925, 4074, 4198, 4311, 4312, 4313, 4314, 4387, 4389, 4390, 4391, 4396, 4398, 4399, 4417, 4419, 4420, 4465, 4522, 4544, 4546, 4555, 4616, 4681, 4682, 4683, 4755, 4780, 4800, 4801, 4802, 4803, 4804, 4805, 4807, 4808, 4810, 4811, 4812

Business administration – 112, 137, 353, 360, 590, 728, 748, 754, 953, 967, 1130, 1135, 1173, 1594, 1763, 1900, 1935, 1936, 1937, 1939, 1982, 1983, 1987, 1996, 2013, 2014, 2068, 2069, 2108, 2109, 2124, 2162, 2164, 2188, 2190, 2218, 2221, 2234, 2244, 2248, 2255, 2257, 2266, 2309, 2360, 2372, 2380, 2384, 2404, 2425, 2431, 2441, 2470, 2505, 2512, 2541, 2545, 2577, 2587, 2592, 2610, 2627, 2628, 2629, 2630, 2631, 2632, 2633, 2634, 2644, 2645, 2676, 2693, 2694, 2712, 2725, 2732, 2742, 2826, 2864, 2887, 2923, 2930, 2945, 2950, 2954, 2990, 2997, 2998, 2999, 3009, 3013, 3024, 3050, 3051, 3066, 3071, 3106, 3107, 3171, 3174, 3175, 3193, 3239, 3263, 3266, 3267, 3276, 3277, 3278, 3279, 3280, 3291, 3292, 3293, 3294, 3295, 3296, 3302, 3306, 3307, 3308, 3310, 3327, 3333, 3334, 3338, 3340, 3341, 3348, 3358, 3361, 3362, 3366, 3374, 3382, 3383, 3387, 3390, 3391, 3394, 3395, 3399, 3415, 3423, 3431, 3449, 3450, 3487, 3493, 3504, 3518, 3530, 3532, 3534, 3537, 3553, 3583, 3599, 3604, 3608, 3631, 3633, 3634, 3640, 3669, 3679, 3690, 3698, 3700, 3701, 3717, 3740, 3758, 3768, 3770, 3778, 3779, 3781, 3782, 3783, 3784, 3785, 3786, 3787, 3788, 3789, 3791, 3794, 3795, 3796, 3797, 3810, 3817, 3834, 3835, 3876, 3885, 3908, 3920, 3925, 3931, 3949, 4041, 4047, 4050, 4059, 4079, 4080, 4081, 4098, 4099, 4103, 4148, 4163, 4169, 4170, 4171, 4174, 4176, 4180, 4181, 4182, 4197, 4198, 4212, 4228, 4229, 4233, 4234, 4241, 4247, 4252, 4253, 4284, 4285, 4293, 4297, 4321, 4324, 4336, 4415, 4416, 4417, 4431, 4432, 4434, 4441, 4442, 4463, 4464, 4489, 4491, 4492, 4493, 4525, 4530, 4541, 4555, 4591, 4593, 4595, 4605, 4617, 4622, 4706, 4721, 4724, 4732, 4734, 4768, 4775, 4777, 4780, 4795, 4819

Canadian studies – 1910, 1913, 1915, 2031, 3517

Cartography/Surveying – 1404, 1999, 2062, 2427, 3067, 3144, 3190, 3868, 4137, 4273, 4423, 4430, 4599, 4620, 4833

Cave studies – 3110

Chemistry – 1932, 1935, 1941, 1944, 1945, 1946, 1947, 1950, 1971, 1972, 1984, 1995, 1996, 1999, 2004, 2100, 2101, 2102, 2103, 2114, 2288, 2381, 2385, 2386, 2387, 2389, 2390, 2393, 2397, 2400, 2401, 2407, 2408, 2411, 2412, 2415, 2416, 2421, 2422, 2423, 2425, 2427, 2428, 2431, 2432, 2433, 2440, 2466, 2470, 2626, 2693, 2701, 2716, 2725, 2753, 2790, 2791, 2796, 2846, 2876, 2894, 2953, 2959, 2965, 2973, 2977, 3032, 3033, 3034, 3035, 3036, 3037, 3038, 3039, 3040, 3041, 3042, 3043, 3044, 3045, 3046, 3047, 3048, 3049, 3050, 3051, 3052, 3053, 3054, 3055, 3056, 3057, 3058, 3059, 3060, 3061, 3062, 3063, 3064, 3065, 3066, 3067, 3068, 3069, 3070, 3071, 3072, 3073, 3074, 3075, 3076, 3077, 3078, 3079, 3080, 3081, 3082, 3083, 3084, 3085, 3086, 3087, 3088, 3089, 3090, 3091, 3092, 3096, 3098, 3100, 3106, 3108, 3109, 3111, 3112, 3118, 3139, 3142, 3144, 3146, 3147, 3149, 3150, 3152, 3155, 3156, 3164, 3165, 3166, 3168, 3169, 3170, 3171, 3174, 3176, 3177, 3178, 3179, 3180, 3182, 3183, 3184, 3187, 3188, 3190, 3191, 3192, 3193, 3194, 3195, 3203, 3204, 3205, 3206, 3207, 3208, 3209, 3210, 3211, 3212, 3213, 3214, 3215, 3216, 3218, 3219, 3220, 3221, 3242, 3286, 3311, 3408, 3446, 3465, 3486, 3505, 3508, 3513, 3526, 3569, 3601, 3644, 3707, 3805, 3807, 3809, 3813, 3849, 3870, 3887, 3899, 3955, 3985, 3988, 3989, 3992, 4011, 4022, 4025, 4026, 4028, 4029, 4061, 4063, 4065, 4073, 4074, 4076, 4077, 4085, 4098, 4101, 4104, 4106, 4107, 4118, 4120, 4132, 4137, 4140, 4144, 4148, 4149, 4150, 4156, 4157, 4158, 4160, 4161, 4162, 4166, 4178, 4194, 4196, 4228, 4232, 4236, 4238, 4239, 4242, 4244, 4249, 4254, 4263, 4273, 4275, 4277, 4279, 4280, 4287, 4288, 4290, 4291, 4308, 4309, 4315, 4341, 4388, 4396, 4397, 4405, 4411, 4412, 4421, 4422, 4440, 4464, 4491, 4503, 4527, 4529, 4531, 4537, 4559, 4561, 4570, 4595, 4599, 4602, 4604, 4611, 4622, 4623, 4684, 4686, 4687, 4688, 4689, 4690, 4691, 4692, 4693, 4694, 4696, 4710, 4714, 4715, 4717, 4718, 4723, 4725, 4765, 4805, 4806, 4820, 4833

Child care – 3234, 3237, 3257, 3549, 3566

Child development – 2034, 2120, 2312, 2985, 3237, 3238, 3249, 3250, 3256, 3257, 3265, 3398, 3490, 3538, 3565, 3566, 3647, 3850, 3855

Chinese studies – 1911, 3484

Cinema – 2133, 2305, 2323, 3677

Civil rights – 2742, 3779, 3835

Classical studies – 2111, 2112, 2113, 2114, 2115, 2116, 2117, 2118, 2119, 2291, 2369, 2411, 2555, 2701, 3056, 3178, 3416, 3417, 3446, 3469, 3470, 3479, 3481, 3482, 3523, 3569, 3609, 3624, 3988, 4106, 4154, 4238

Communications – 1990, 2021, 2085, 2126, 2136, 2157, 2159, 2161, 2169, 2176, 2183, 2187, 2198, 2207, 2209, 2212, 2214, 2215, 2216, 2217, 2221, 2227, 2233, 2234, 2240, 2244, 2247, 2252, 2261, 2266, 2267, 2268, 2275, 2276, 2280, 2283, 2285, 2302, 2380, 2494, 2499, 2507, 2519, 2527, 2529, 2530, 2535, 2543, 2552, 2586, 2606, 2739, 2949, 2950, 2995, 3009, 3025, 3140, 3239, 3267, 3291, 3335, 3336, 3348, 3352, 3355, 3356, 3357, 3371, 3391, 3399, 3400, 3402, 3403, 3404, 3405, 3406, 3409, 3410, 3411, 3412, 3413, 3414, 3415, 3418, 3419, 3420, 3422, 3423, 3429, 3431, 3432, 3433, 3434, 3436, 3439, 3440, 3441, 3444, 3449, 3450, 3451, 3452, 3453, 3454, 3455, 3456, 3457, 3458, 3459, 3466, 3467, 3468, 3473, 3474, 3475, 3477, 3485, 3487, 3488, 3493, 3531, 3583, 3587, 3588, 3594, 3596, 3666, 3669, 3679, 3689, 3701, 3714, 3768, 3771, 3781, 3810, 3812, 3817, 3821, 3823, 3837, 3878, 3888, 3889, 3890, 3891, 3949, 3965, 3974, 4135, 4171, 4247, 4271, 4415, 4470, 4541, 4597, 4771, 4775, 4831

Communications technologies – 3926, 3927, 3928

Computer and information sciences – 1887, 1908, 1909, 1914, 1926, 1927, 1929, 1935, 1936, 1941, 1944, 1945, 1946, 1947, 1971, 1995, 1999, 2004, 2050, 2100, 2101, 2102, 2103, 2114, 2125, 2139, 2140, 2141, 2142, 2143, 2144, 2164, 2186, 2205, 2257, 2276, 2288, 2380, 2382, 2385, 2388, 2389, 2397, 2404, 2408, 2409, 2411, 2412, 2415, 2416,

2421, 2422, 2424, 2427, 2428, 2432, 2433, 2470, 2532, 2545, 2552, 2553, 2574, 2577, 2587, 2610, 2663, 2693, 2701, 2712, 2716, 2791, 2826, 2923, 2926, 2953, 2954, 2990, 2995, 2999, 3009, 3011, 3015, 3020, 3021, 3024, 3025, 3027, 3029, 3036, 3041, 3045, 3051, 3052, 3055, 3056, 3057, 3058, 3059, 3060, 3061, 3063, 3067, 3068, 3069, 3072, 3073, 3086, 3087, 3088, 3089, 3106, 3107, 3108, 3109, 3112, 3142, 3144, 3146, 3147, 3148, 3149, 3150, 3155, 3157, 3158, 3159, 3160, 3161, 3162, 3163, 3166, 3169, 3173, 3174, 3175, 3176, 3177, 3178, 3179, 3180, 3181, 3182, 3183, 3184, 3185, 3186, 3189, 3190, 3191, 3192, 3194, 3195, 3197, 3215, 3216, 3217, 3218, 3219, 3226, 3239, 3242, 3261, 3267, 3277, 3278, 3279, 3294, 3312, 3313, 3314, 3315, 3316, 3340, 3361, 3362, 3363, 3367, 3390, 3392, 3393, 3399, 3424, 3425, 3426, 3427, 3428, 3446, 3449, 3461, 3464, 3468, 3483, 3493, 3518, 3569, 3607, 3631, 3650, 3669, 3684, 3691, 3693, 3701, 3725, 3741, 3756, 3765, 3770, 3773, 3774, 3781, 3794, 3795, 3796, 3808, 3819, 3823, 3949, 3955, 3956, 3957, 3958, 3959, 3960, 3961, 3973, 3977, 3978, 3985, 3986, 3988, 3989, 3992, 3999, 4000, 4001, 4004, 4011, 4025, 4026, 4028, 4029, 4036, 4061, 4062, 4066, 4067, 4068, 4069, 4070, 4071, 4072, 4077, 4079, 4084, 4088, 4091, 4092, 4093, 4094, 4095, 4096, 4097, 4098, 4099, 4101, 4103, 4104, 4106, 4107, 4111, 4118, 4120, 4121, 4122, 4123, 4124, 4125, 4128, 4135, 4136, 4137, 4139, 4140, 4144, 4147, 4149, 4150, 4151, 4157, 4158, 4159, 4160, 4161, 4164, 4170, 4171, 4172, 4173, 4174, 4176, 4177, 4178, 4179, 4180, 4181, 4182, 4183, 4184, 4185, 4186, 4187, 4188, 4189, 4190, 4191, 4192, 4193, 4194, 4195, 4196, 4197, 4198, 4200, 4201, 4202, 4203, 4204, 4205, 4206, 4207, 4208, 4209, 4210, 4211, 4212, 4213, 4214, 4215, 4216, 4217, 4218, 4220, 4221, 4222, 4223, 4224, 4225, 4226, 4227, 4228, 4229, 4230, 4231, 4232, 4233, 4234, 4235, 4236, 4237, 4238, 4239, 4240, 4241, 4242, 4243, 4244, 4245, 4246, 4247, 4248, 4249, 4250, 4251, 4252, 4253, 4254, 4255, 4256, 4257, 4258, 4259, 4260, 4261, 4262, 4263, 4264, 4265, 4266, 4267, 4268, 4269, 4270, 4271, 4272, 4273, 4274, 4275, 4276, 4277, 4278, 4279, 4280, 4281, 4282, 4283, 4284, 4285, 4287, 4288, 4289, 4290, 4291, 4292, 4293, 4294, 4295, 4296, 4297, 4318, 4336, 4338, 4341, 4342, 4361, 4371, 4372, 4397, 4412, 4416, 4417, 4439, 4444, 4446, 4447, 4448, 4449, 4450, 4451, 4461, 4463, 4471, 4476, 4479, 4481, 4482, 4483, 4484, 4486, 4487, 4490, 4491, 4492, 4494, 4503, 4527, 4529, 4530, 4531, 4532, 4537, 4538, 4539, 4541, 4551, 4559, 4563, 4565, 4567, 4569, 4570, 4572, 4576, 4577, 4579, 4597, 4598, 4599, 4601, 4602, 4603, 4604, 4619, 4623, 4652, 4702, 4703, 4714, 4715, 4716, 4717, 4718, 4728, 4731, 4734, 4795, 4806, 4820, 4821, 4822, 4833

Construction – 307, 308, 508, 786, 1133, 1217, 1218, 1942, 1956, 2038, 2045, 2052, 2054, 2057, 2059, 2062, 2064, 2065, 2067, 2074, 2075, 2077, 2078, 2079, 2080, 2081, 2082, 2088, 2089, 2093, 2604, 2916, 3269, 3270, 3271, 3272, 3273, 3274, 3299, 3327, 3337, 3342, 3346, 3347, 3382, 3868, 3916, 4299, 4301, 4311, 4312, 4313, 4314, 4350, 4374, 4375, 4376, 4403, 4420, 4423, 4425, 4426, 4428, 4454, 4477, 4522, 4534, 4542, 4543, 4544, 4545, 4546, 4547, 4548, 4549, 4550, 4557, 4558, 4612, 4624, 4628, 4709, 4727, 4736

Consumer affairs – 2117, 2291, 2369, 2555, 3229, 3230, 3232, 3479, 3624, 4154

Cosmetology – 2039, 2699, 3445, 4105, 4528

Counseling/Guidance – 2232, 2751, 2754, 2795, 2806, 2856, 2871, 2878, 2948, 2958, 2967, 2976, 2988, 2991, 2993, 2997, 3003, 3005, 3006, 3233, 3243, 3244, 3245, 3246, 3247, 3248, 3253, 3258, 3263, 3317, 3407, 3421, 3507, 3509, 3519, 3535, 3567, 3711, 3719, 3745, 3747, 3763, 3767, 3811, 3845, 3847, 3851, 4064, 4083

Crafts – 1905, 1920, 2011, 2110, 2121, 2122, 2135, 2155, 2156, 2175, 2180, 2182, 2190, 2191, 2192, 2295, 2311, 2371, 3331, 3384, 3388, 3395, 3396, 3397, 3480, 3877, 4304, 4305, 4819, 4830, 4835

Creative writing – 1899, 2123, 2149, 2157, 2161, 2167, 2168, 2171, 2179, 2252, 2263, 2274, 2284, 2290, 2303, 2310, 2334, 2368, 2949, 3336, 3434,

4629, 4630, 4631, 4632, 4633, 4634, 4635, 4636,
4637, 4638, 4639, 4642, 4643, 4644, 4645, 4646,
4647, 4648, 4649, 4650, 4651, 4652, 4653, 4655,
4656, 4657, 4658, 4660, 4661, 4662, 4663, 4664,
4665, 4666, 4667, 4669, 4670, 4671, 4672, 4675,
4676, 4677, 4678, 4683, 4695, 4697, 4698, 4699,
4700, 4701, 4702, 4703, 4704, 4705, 4707, 4708,
4711, 4712, 4716, 4717, 4718, 4719, 4721, 4723,
4724, 4726, 4727, 4728, 4729, 4730, 4732, 4735,
4736, 4737, 4738, 4739, 4740, 4741, 4742, 4743,
4744, 4745, 4746, 4748, 4752, 4753, 4754, 4765,
4769, 4780, 4800, 4802, 4803, 4804, 4805, 4806,
4807, 4809, 4833

Engineering, Aerospace/Aeronautical/Astronautical –
1934, 1943, 1944, 1945, 1946, 1947, 2008, 2009,
2100, 2101, 2102, 2103, 2109, 2380, 2385, 2405,
2408, 2409, 2410, 2415, 2424, 2428, 2429, 2438,
2440, 2724, 2945, 3009, 3021, 3022, 3028, 3036,
3055, 3059, 3068, 3085, 3086, 3087, 3088, 3089,
3109, 3112, 3117, 3118, 3141, 3142, 3143, 3145,
3146, 3147, 3149, 3150, 3155, 3158, 3159, 3160,
3161, 3162, 3163, 3173, 3177, 3182, 3186, 3189,
3191, 3214, 3215, 3216, 3218, 3219, 3226, 3239,
3242, 3267, 3399, 3493, 3554, 3612, 3623, 3669,
3701, 3740, 3781, 3937, 3949, 3955, 3956, 3957,
3958, 3959, 3960, 3961, 3964, 3971, 3973, 3975,
3977, 3978, 3979, 3980, 3981, 3982, 3983, 3984,
3985, 3986, 3987, 3990, 3991, 3992, 3993, 3999,
4000, 4001, 4003, 4004, 4009, 4010, 4011, 4012,
4013, 4014, 4017, 4018, 4019, 4020, 4021, 4022,
4024, 4025, 4026, 4028, 4029, 4032, 4033, 4035,
4038, 4040, 4041, 4044, 4048, 4053, 4061, 4067,
4068, 4069, 4070, 4071, 4072, 4088, 4095, 4100,
4102, 4104, 4110, 4114, 4116, 4123, 4125, 4133,
4134, 4140, 4141, 4143, 4145, 4146, 4155, 4156,
4157, 4158, 4160, 4161, 4167, 4168, 4171, 4178,
4186, 4187, 4189, 4191, 4192, 4193, 4213, 4221,
4225, 4236, 4237, 4244, 4260, 4264, 4266, 4270,
4275, 4286, 4287, 4288, 4290, 4291, 4341, 4364,
4365, 4368, 4370, 4371, 4372, 4453, 4472, 4481,
4486, 4519, 4527, 4536, 4537, 4565, 4572, 4576,
4602, 4614, 4615, 4618, 4704, 4710, 4713, 4714,
4715, 4717, 4718, 4729, 4732, 4733, 4809, 4820,
4821, 4822

Engineering, Agricultural – 1935, 1992, 2020, 2087,
2447, 2448, 2449, 2450, 2470, 2473, 2478, 2483,
2487, 2520, 2527, 2537, 2539, 2546, 2570, 2584,
2586, 2607, 2609, 2693, 2704, 3051, 3106, 3174,
3355, 3455, 3594, 3918, 4098, 4228, 4491, 4778

Engineering, Architectural – 1931, 1944, 1945,
1946, 1947, 2053, 2100, 2101, 2102, 2103, 2106,
2181, 3086, 3087, 3088, 3089, 3146, 3147, 3149,
3150, 3215, 3216, 3218, 3219, 3930, 4025, 4026,
4028, 4029, 4157, 4158, 4160, 4161, 4287, 4288,
4290, 4291, 4386, 4714, 4715, 4717, 4718

Engineering, Automotive – 3196, 3294, 3981, 4198,
4417, 4519, 4640, 4641, 4809

Engineering, Biomedical – 2226, 2388, 2397, 2399,
2422, 2657, 2663, 2747, 2791, 2987, 3015, 3045,
3063, 3169, 3522, 3710, 3762, 3840, 4077, 4184,
4196, 4263, 4347, 4362, 4412, 4418, 4570

Engineering, Chemical – 1950, 1974, 1975, 2385,
2395, 2396, 2415, 2422, 2428, 2431, 2440, 2626,
2665, 2666, 2725, 3032, 3033, 3036, 3050, 3058,
3059, 3062, 3063, 3068, 3069, 3071, 3074, 3075,
3076, 3077, 3078, 3079, 3080, 3081, 3082, 3083,
3084, 3085, 3091, 3101, 3102, 3109, 3112, 3118,
3155, 3157, 3158, 3159, 3160, 3162, 3171, 3173,
3180, 3182, 3186, 3191, 3192, 3193, 3203, 3204,
3205, 3206, 3207, 3208, 3209, 3210, 3211, 3212,
3213, 3214, 3242, 3955, 3956, 3957, 3958, 3960,
3978, 3992, 3999, 4001, 4011, 4022, 4061, 4066,
4067, 4068, 4069, 4071, 4095, 4125, 4140, 4144,
4148, 4156, 4178, 4185, 4186, 4187, 4189, 4192,
4225, 4242, 4244, 4260, 4263, 4266, 4267, 4275,
4277, 4308, 4309, 4341, 4363, 4364, 4365, 4368,
4371, 4385, 4409, 4410, 4452, 4464, 4467, 4486,
4488, 4514, 4531, 4537, 4561, 4565, 4566, 4570,
4571, 4576, 4577, 4602, 4604, 4622, 4684, 4686,
4687, 4688, 4689, 4690, 4691, 4692, 4693, 4694,
4696, 4710, 4725, 4820, 4821, 4822

Engineering, Civil – 1931, 1932, 1933, 1934, 1935,
1937, 1938, 1939, 1941, 1942, 1943, 1944, 1945,
1946, 1947, 1974, 1975, 1982, 1983, 1997, 2052,
2053, 2055, 2067, 2068, 2069, 2079, 2088, 2089,
2093, 2100, 2101, 2102, 2103, 2104, 2105, 2128,

2288, 2385, 2395, 2396, 2400, 2408, 2415, 2428,
2433, 2470, 2665, 2666, 2693, 2930, 2953, 3036,
3046, 3048, 3051, 3055, 3059, 3068, 3073, 3086,
3087, 3088, 3089, 3097, 3101, 3102, 3106, 3109,
3112, 3141, 3142, 3145, 3146, 3147, 3149, 3150,
3155, 3170, 3173, 3174, 3177, 3182, 3186, 3191,
3195, 3215, 3216, 3218, 3219, 3242, 3311, 3347,
3728, 3805, 3807, 3864, 3870, 3872, 3873, 3955,
3975, 3978, 3985, 3992, 4001, 4011, 4024, 4025,
4026, 4028, 4029, 4061, 4085, 4095, 4098, 4104,
4125, 4140, 4150, 4157, 4158, 4160, 4161, 4178,
4225, 4228, 4236, 4241, 4244, 4266, 4275, 4280,
4286, 4287, 4288, 4290, 4291, 4302, 4340, 4341,
4375, 4376, 4386, 4401, 4404, 4407, 4409, 4410,
4414, 4421, 4428, 4429, 4436, 4440, 4441, 4442,
4443, 4454, 4472, 4486, 4491, 4504, 4505, 4506,
4507, 4508, 4509, 4510, 4511, 4512, 4513, 4527,
4530, 4534, 4537, 4540, 4546, 4557, 4558, 4566,
4576, 4591, 4592, 4593, 4594, 4596, 4602, 4613,
4620, 4621, 4623, 4628, 4709, 4713, 4714, 4715,
4717, 4718, 4719, 4720, 4721, 4820, 4821, 4822

Engineering, Computer – 1908, 1926, 1929, 1943,
1944, 1945, 1946, 1947, 2100, 2101, 2102, 2103,
2134, 2388, 2398, 2422, 2428, 2663, 3015, 3058,
3063, 3068, 3069, 3086, 3087, 3088, 3089, 3112,
3145, 3146, 3147, 3149, 3150, 3157, 3158, 3160,
3161, 3162, 3163, 3173, 3180, 3181, 3185, 3186,
3191, 3192, 3215, 3216, 3218, 3219, 3275, 3464,
3680, 3693, 3956, 3958, 3959, 3960, 3961, 3978,
4000, 4001, 4011, 4024, 4025, 4026, 4028, 4029,
4066, 4067, 4069, 4070, 4071, 4072, 4095, 4111,
4121, 4123, 4124, 4125, 4140, 4144, 4157, 4158,
4160, 4161, 4175, 4184, 4185, 4186, 4189, 4190,
4191, 4192, 4193, 4199, 4202, 4214, 4217, 4219,
4222, 4225, 4230, 4231, 4240, 4241, 4242, 4243,
4258, 4261, 4263, 4264, 4265, 4266, 4275, 4276,
4277, 4286, 4287, 4288, 4290, 4291, 4319, 4362,
4363, 4364, 4368, 4369, 4370, 4371, 4372, 4444,
4476, 4478, 4482, 4486, 4494, 4530, 4531, 4532,
4563, 4567, 4570, 4572, 4576, 4602, 4603, 4604,
4713, 4714, 4715, 4717, 4718, 4821, 4822

Engineering, Electrical – 1908, 1926, 1929, 1932,
1935, 1940, 1941, 1943, 1944, 1945, 1946, 1947,
1971, 2052, 2055, 2065, 2067, 2076, 2100, 2101,
2102, 2103, 2104, 2105, 2128, 2158, 2288, 2385,
2388, 2389, 2400, 2408, 2415, 2422, 2428, 2433,
2440, 2470, 2663, 2693, 2930, 2953, 3015, 3036,
3041, 3046, 3051, 3055, 3058, 3059, 3063, 3068,
3069, 3073, 3085, 3086, 3087, 3088, 3089, 3106,
3109, 3112, 3113, 3118, 3142, 3145, 3146, 3147,
3149, 3150, 3155, 3157, 3158, 3159, 3160, 3161,
3162, 3163, 3166, 3167, 3173, 3174, 3177, 3180,
3181, 3182, 3186, 3191, 3192, 3195, 3214, 3215,
3216, 3218, 3219, 3242, 3275, 3346, 3373, 3435,
3464, 3693, 3805, 3864, 3955, 3956, 3957, 3958,
3959, 3960, 3961, 3977, 3978, 3985, 3992, 3999,
4000, 4001, 4011, 4022, 4024, 4025, 4026, 4028,
4029, 4048, 4061, 4066, 4067, 4068, 4069, 4070,
4071, 4072, 4075, 4095, 4098, 4104, 4111, 4121,
4123, 4125, 4140, 4144, 4150, 4156, 4157, 4158,
4160, 4161, 4175, 4178, 4184, 4185, 4186, 4187,
4189, 4191, 4192, 4193, 4194, 4202, 4211, 4217,
4219, 4221, 4222, 4225, 4228, 4231, 4236, 4241,
4242, 4243, 4244, 4258, 4260, 4261, 4263, 4264,
4266, 4267, 4268, 4275, 4276, 4277, 4280, 4286,
4287, 4288, 4290, 4291, 4319, 4322, 4337, 4341,
4362, 4363, 4364, 4365, 4366, 4368, 4370, 4371,
4372, 4376, 4397, 4400, 4404, 4421, 4426, 4428,
4444, 4460, 4461, 4467, 4476, 4478, 4480, 4481,
4482, 4485, 4486, 4488, 4491, 4494, 4498, 4527,
4530, 4531, 4532, 4537, 4544, 4563, 4565, 4566,
4567, 4570, 4572, 4576, 4577, 4579, 4602, 4603,
4604, 4616, 4623, 4706, 4710, 4713, 4714, 4715,
4717, 4718, 4719, 4720, 4721, 4733, 4806, 4811,
4820, 4821, 4822

Engineering, Geological – 1940, 3094, 3095, 3113,
3373, 4383, 4384, 4616, 4811

Engineering, Hydraulic – 3097, 4401

Engineering, Industrial – 1935, 2388, 2422, 2428,
2440, 2470, 2663, 2693, 3015, 3050, 3051, 3063,
3068, 3069, 3074, 3075, 3076, 3077, 3078, 3079,
3080, 3081, 3082, 3083, 3084, 3085, 3106, 3112,
3118, 3171, 3173, 3174, 3186, 3191, 3192, 3203,
3204, 3205, 3206, 3207, 3208, 3209, 3210, 3211,
3212, 3213, 3214, 3977, 3978, 3981, 4001, 4011,
4022, 4095, 4098, 4125, 4140, 4144, 4156, 4184,

4221, 4225, 4228, 4241, 4263, 4266, 4268, 4275,
4277, 4322, 4362, 4464, 4467, 4481, 4486, 4488,
4491, 4519, 4530, 4570, 4576, 4579, 4602, 4604,
4654, 4655, 4656, 4657, 4658, 4659, 4660, 4661,
4662, 4663, 4664, 4665, 4666, 4667, 4668, 4669,
4670, 4671, 4672, 4673, 4674, 4675, 4676, 4677,
4684, 4686, 4687, 4688, 4689, 4690, 4691, 4692,
4693, 4694, 4696, 4710, 4809, 4821, 4822

Engineering, Materials – 2059, 2121, 2122, 2385,
2422, 2428, 3036, 3063, 3068, 3070, 3074, 3075,
3076, 3077, 3078, 3079, 3080, 3081, 3082, 3083,
3084, 3112, 3155, 3191, 3203, 3204, 3205, 3206,
3207, 3208, 3209, 3210, 3211, 3212, 3213, 3242,
3271, 3299, 3955, 3999, 4011, 4061, 4140, 4178,
4260, 4263, 4275, 4299, 4304, 4305, 4306, 4307,
4310, 4313, 4341, 4373, 4420, 4565, 4570, 4602,
4611, 4684, 4685, 4686, 4687, 4688, 4689, 4690,
4691, 4692, 4693, 4694, 4696, 4799, 4820

Engineering, Mechanical – 1935, 1940, 1941, 1943,
1944, 1945, 1946, 1947, 1971, 2055, 2065, 2067,
2100, 2101, 2102, 2103, 2104, 2105, 2128, 2288,
2385, 2389, 2408, 2415, 2422, 2428, 2433, 2440,
2470, 2693, 2953, 3036, 3041, 3050, 3051, 3055,
3058, 3059, 3063, 3068, 3069, 3073, 3074, 3075,
3076, 3077, 3078, 3079, 3080, 3081, 3082, 3083,
3084, 3085, 3086, 3087, 3088, 3089, 3106, 3109,
3112, 3113, 3118, 3142, 3145, 3146, 3147, 3149,
3150, 3155, 3166, 3173, 3174, 3177, 3180,
3182, 3186, 3191, 3192, 3195, 3196, 3203, 3204,
3205, 3206, 3207, 3208, 3209, 3210, 3211, 3212,
3213, 3214, 3215, 3216, 3218, 3219, 3242, 3275,
3373, 3864, 3955, 3977, 3978, 3985, 3992, 3999,
4000, 4001, 4011, 4022, 4024, 4025, 4026, 4028,
4029, 4048, 4061, 4095, 4098, 4104, 4123, 4125,
4140, 4144, 4150, 4156, 4157, 4158, 4160, 4161,
4175, 4178, 4194, 4221, 4225, 4228, 4236, 4241,
4242, 4244, 4260, 4263, 4264, 4266, 4267, 4268,
4275, 4277, 4280, 4286, 4287, 4288, 4290, 4291,
4319, 4322, 4341, 4385, 4397, 4404, 4426, 4428,
4452, 4464, 4467, 4480, 4481, 4486, 4488, 4491,
4527, 4530, 4531, 4537, 4565, 4566, 4570, 4571,
4572, 4576, 4577, 4579, 4602, 4604, 4616, 4623,
4640, 4657, 4659, 4668, 4669, 4674, 4677, 4684,
4686, 4687, 4688, 4689, 4690, 4691, 4692, 4693,
4694, 4696, 4706, 4710, 4713, 4714, 4715, 4717,
4718, 4719, 4720, 4733, 4806, 4811, 4820, 4821,
4822

Engineering, Metallurgical – 1935, 1940, 2470,
2693, 3051, 3106, 3113, 3174, 3326, 3373, 4098,
4228, 4373, 4465, 4491, 4616, 4799, 4811

Engineering, Mining and Mineral – 1940, 2006,
3113, 3114, 3115, 3116, 3344, 3373, 3376, 3377,
3981, 4519, 4616, 4798, 4809, 4810, 4811, 4813,
4814, 4815, 4816, 4817, 4818

Engineering, Nuclear – 1952, 1953, 2408, 3055,
3142, 3177, 3985, 4104, 4236, 4325, 4326, 4327,
4328, 4329, 4330, 4331, 4332, 4527, 4722

Engineering, Ocean – 2105, 2385, 3036, 3155,
3173, 3186, 3242, 3955, 3978, 4001, 4061, 4095,
4125, 4178, 4225, 4266, 4341, 4486, 4576, 4679,
4720, 4820, 4821, 4822, 4823

Engineering, Petroleum – 1935, 2428, 2470, 2693,
3051, 3068, 3106, 3112, 3174, 3191, 3378, 3379,
4011, 4098, 4140, 4228, 4275, 4491, 4514, 4602,
4680, 4681, 4682

English language and literature – 1901, 1917, 2117,
2138, 2161, 2167, 2171, 2187, 2222, 2232, 2239,
2252, 2263, 2277, 2284, 2291, 2296, 2302, 2369,
2555, 2949, 3247, 3336, 3421, 3439, 3448, 3471,
3479, 3488, 3535, 3610, 3624, 3686, 3766, 3812,
3837, 4083, 4113, 4142, 4154, 4771, 4831

Enology – 389

Entomology – 1981, 2015, 2099, 2442, 2465, 2545,
2557, 2577, 2587, 2600, 2610, 2613, 2712, 2982,
3024, 3361, 4252

Environmental conservation – 1900, 1903, 1920,
1948, 1949, 1950, 1951, 1952, 1953, 1954, 1955,
1956, 1957, 1958, 1959, 1960, 1961, 1962, 1963,
1964, 1965, 1966, 1967, 1968, 1969, 1970, 1971,
1972, 1973, 1974, 1975, 1976, 1977, 1978, 1979,
1980, 1981, 1982, 1983, 1984, 1985, 1986, 1987,
1988, 1989, 1990, 1991, 1992, 1993, 1994, 1995,
1996, 1997, 1998, 1999, 2000, 2001, 2002, 2003,
2004, 2005, 2006, 2007, 2008, 2009, 2010, 2011,
2012, 2013, 2014, 2015, 2016, 2017, 2018, 2019,
2021, 2022, 2023, 2025, 2026, 2027, 2028, 2060,

Doctorate

American Society of Podiatric Medical Assistants – 2656

Department of Agriculture – 2680

National Consortium for Graduate Degrees for Minorities in Engineering and Science (GEM) – 2416, 3060, 3183, 4118, 4249

National Institute of General Medical Sciences – 2714, 3259, 4119

Navy Wives Club of America – 2718, 3600

Joanna F. Reed Medical Scholarship Trust – 2723

Texas Space Grant Consortium – 2440, 3085, 3118, 3214, 4022, 4156, 4710

U.S. Air Force – 1688

U.S. Marine Corps – 3735

Vasa Order of America – 2734

Vermont Student Assistance Corporation – 2580, 2736

Walman Optical Company – 2963

Four Year College

25th Infantry Division Association – 5

Academy of Television Arts & Sciences Foundation – 2120, 2312, 2985, 3238, 3398, 3490

ACCEL/Exchange Network – 17

Actuarial Foundation – 18

Adelante! U.S. Education Leadership Fund – 19

Air Traffic Control Association – 3938

Alabama Bankers Association – 3266

Alabama Concrete Industries Association – 2045, 4301

Alabama Council of Teachers of Mathematics – 4055

Alabama Space Grant Consortium – 2380, 3009, 3239, 3267, 3399, 3493, 3669, 3701, 3781, 3949, 4171

Alaska Commission on Postsecondary Education – 3494

Alliance of Black Telecommunications Employees, Inc.-Nation's Capital Chapter – 71

Alpha Omicron Pi Foundation – 81, 82, 86, 87

American Association of Airport Executives Foundation – 3950, 3951

American Association of Airport Executives-Northeast Chapter – 3953

American Association of Women Dentists – 2765

American Business Women's Association – 98

American Ceramic Society – 2121, 4304

American Concrete Institute – 3270, 4312

American Concrete Institute-Greater Michigan Chapter – 3271, 4313

American Concrete Institute-Illinois Chapter – 3272

American Concrete Institute-Nebraska Chapter – 3274, 4314

American Council of Engineering Companies of Colorado – 4316, 4317

American Dental Education Association – 2769

American Dental Hygienists' Association – 2776, 2779, 2780, 2784, 2785, 3790

American Foundation for the Blind – 2201, 2315, 3001, 3500

American Hotel & Lodging Educational Foundation – 135, 136, 4759

American Indian College Fund – 139

American Indian Science and Engineering Society – 2384, 2644, 3013, 4059, 4321

American Institute of Certified Public Accountants – 3886

American Institute of Mining, Metallurgical, and Petroleum Engineers – 4798

American Legion – 155

American Meteorological Society – 3133, 3134, 3135, 3136, 3137, 3138, 4060

American Nephrology Nurses' Association – 2819, 2820, 2821, 2822, 2823, 2824, 2825

American Nuclear Society – 1952, 1953, 3035, 3887, 4327, 4329, 4331, 4332

American Philological Association – 2111

American Physical Society – 3153

American Planning Association – 1954, 3792, 3793, 3857, 3859

American Radio Relay League – 4335, 4339

American Society for Clinical Pathology – 2650, 2651

American Society of Criminology – 3704, 3744

American Society for Engineering Education – 2385, 3036, 3155, 3242, 3955, 4061, 4178, 4341, 4820

American Society of Heating, Refrigerating and Air-Conditioning Engineers, Inc. – 245, 246, 248, 249, 250, 251, 252, 253, 254, 4344

American Society of Podiatric Medical Assistants – 2656

American Society for Quality – 255, 2657, 4347

American Society of Safety Engineers – 1955, 1956, 1957, 1958, 1959, 1960, 1961, 1962, 1963, 1964, 1965, 1966, 4349, 4350, 4351, 4352, 4353, 4354, 4355, 4356, 4357, 4358, 4359, 4360, 4735, 4736, 4737, 4738, 4739, 4740, 4741, 4742, 4743, 4744, 4745, 4746

American Society of Safety Engineers-New Jersey Chapter – 1968

American Society of Women Accountants-St. Louis Chapter – 258

American Water Ski Educational Foundation – 260

Anchor Scholarship Foundation – 268

Appalachian College Association – 2386, 3037, 3505, 3705, 4062, 4063, 4183, 4361

Arizona Commission for Postsecondary Education – 278

Arkansas Community Foundation – 282

Arkansas Department of Higher Education – 3243, 3407, 3506, 3507, 4064

Armed Forces Communications and Electronics Association – 291, 2125, 3157, 3158, 3160, 3162, 3956, 3958, 3960, 4066, 4067, 4069, 4071, 4185, 4186, 4188, 4189, 4190, 4192, 4363, 4364, 4366, 4367, 4368, 4369, 4371

Associated Colleges of Illinois – 304

Association of California Water Agencies – 1969, 2451, 3798, 4377

Association for Education and Rehabilitation of the Blind and Visually Impaired of Ohio – 3003, 3244, 3509

Association of Environmental and Engineering Geologists – 3094, 3095, 4383, 4384

Association of Independent Colleges and Universities of Pennsylvania – 315, 1931, 2053, 2827, 4385, 4386

Association for Iron & Steel Technology – 3282, 4801

Association for Iron & Steel Technology-Northwest Chapter – 3040, 3165, 3286, 4074, 4396, 4805

Association of State Dam Safety Officials – 3097, 4401

Association of Texas Professional Educators – 3511, 3512

Association for Women in Science-Seattle Chapter – 1972, 2393, 2973, 3043, 3100, 3168, 4076, 4405

Boston Society of Civil Engineers – 4407

Boy Scouts of America – 347, 350

Bristol Bay Native Corporation – 353

Brown and Caldwell – 1974, 1975, 2395, 2396, 2665, 2666, 3101, 3102, 4409, 4410

California Alliance for Arts Education – 2132, 2304, 2322, 3676

California Association for Postsecondary Education and Disability – 364

California Environmental Health Association – 1976, 3802

California State Fair – 385, 388, 2454, 2457

California State University – 391, 392, 1890, 2030, 3290, 3761, 3803, 3804

California Table Grape Commission – 394

Canadian Institute of Ukrainian Studies – 1910, 1913, 1915, 2031, 3517

Roy J. Carver Charitable Trust – 403

Catching the Dream – 3518, 4079, 4197, 4416

Center for Education Solutions – 404

Central Intelligence Agency – 410

Chicago Urban League – 417, 418, 419

Chickasaw Foundation – 1891, 3295, 3520, 3709

Chinese American Citizens Alliance – 427, 428

Christermon Foundation – 430

Christian Life Resources – 2226, 2399, 2747, 2987, 3522, 3710, 3762, 3840, 4418

Classical Association of New England – 2113, 3417, 3523

Clayfolk – 2135

Club Foundation – 4762

College Assistance Migrant Program – 448

Colorado Ready Mixed Concrete Association/Colorado Rock Products Association – 2059, 3299, 4420

Communities Foundation of Texas – 2227, 3418, 3964, 3965

Community Foundation for the Fox Valley Region, Inc. – 1977, 2060, 2460, 2582, 2598, 3866

Community Foundation for Greater Atlanta, Inc. – 463, 2228, 3300

Community Foundation of Greater Jackson – 1932, 2400, 3046, 3246, 3711, 3745, 3763, 3805, 4421

Community Foundation of Greater New Britain – 3525

Community Foundation for Greater New Haven – 466

Community Foundation of Louisville – 1978, 2461, 2599

Community Foundation of Middle Tennessee – 469, 2328, 3764

Connecticut Association of Women Police – 3712, 3746

Society for Mining, Metallurgy, and Exploration, Inc.
– 2006, 3114, 3115, 3116, 3376, 3377, 4813,
4814, 4815, 4816, 4817, 4818
Society of Naval Architects and Marine Engineers –
4679, 4823
Society of Physics Students – 3198, 3199, 3200,
3201, 3202, 3618
Society of Plastics Engineers – 3078, 3207, 4685,
4689
Society of Women Engineers-Minnesota Section –
4282, 4702
Sons of Union Veterans of the Civil War – 1558
South Carolina Business Education Association –
3620
South Carolina Commission on Higher Education –
1561, 1563
South Carolina Space Grant Consortium – 2008,
2437, 3623, 4020, 4704, 4705
South Dakota Bankers Association – 3383
South Dakota Board of Regents – 1573
South Dakota Golf Association – 1581
Spina Bifida Association of America – 1585
State University System of Florida – 1593
Commander William S. Stuhr Scholarship Fund –
1598
Surfrider Foundation – 2010, 2439, 3830, 3875
Tau Beta Pi – 4708
Tennessee Student Assistance Corporation – 3630
Texas 4-H Youth Development Foundation – 1621
Texas Extension Association of Family and
Consumer Science – 3232
Texas Higher Education Coordinating Board – 1638,
2800, 2918, 2961, 2969, 2980, 3832
Thornton Sisters Foundation – 1656
Tourism Cares for Tomorrow – 1657, 4783, 4784,
4785, 4786, 4787, 4788, 4789, 4790
Travel Industry Association of America – 1664,
1665, 1666
Harry S. Truman Scholarship Foundation – 2012,
2558, 3030, 3386, 3632, 3664, 3699, 3734, 3777,
3833, 4711
U.S. Air Force – 1688, 1944, 2100, 3086, 3146,
3215, 4025, 4027, 4157, 4287, 4714
U.S. Army – 1695, 1696, 1697, 1699, 1703, 2927
U.S. Army Recruiting Command – 2928
U.S. Coast Guard – 1721
U.S. Navy – 1733, 1736, 1737, 1738, 1739, 1740,
1741, 1742, 2015, 2104, 2442, 2931, 2933, 2982,
3090, 3220, 4162, 4163, 4719, 4723, 4724, 4826
University Aviation Association – 4030
University Interscholastic League – 3635, 3637
US Pan Asian American Chamber of Commerce –
1756
USS Little Rock Association – 1761
Utah Elks Association – 1764
Vasa Order of America – 1775
Vermont Student Assistance Corporation – 3665
Virginia Space Grant Consortium – 2017, 2443,
3031, 3642, 4035, 4037, 4165
Walman Optical Company – 2963
Washington Education Foundation – 1814
Washington Metropolitan Scholars – 1821
Washington State Business Education Association –
1824, 3645, 3646
Washington State FBLA – 1825
Watts Charity Association, Inc. – 1829, 2375, 2742,
3265, 3647, 3779, 3835, 3855
Elie Wiesel Foundation for Humanity – 2301
Wildlife Society-Florida Chapter – 2019, 2028
Wisconsin Foundation for Independent Colleges,
Inc. – 1849, 1850, 1851, 1888, 1904, 2108, 2186,
2187, 2188, 2302, 2999, 3390, 3391, 3392, 3393,
3394, 3487, 3488, 3648, 3649, 3650, 3651, 3667,
3837, 3856, 4169, 4293, 4294, 4295, 4731
Wisconsin Higher Educational Aids Board – 3652,
3653
Women in Federal Law Enforcement – 3741, 3756,
4296

Graduate

The 13th Regional Corporation – 4
Academy of Neonatal Nursing – 2807, 2808
Academy of Television Arts & Sciences Foundation
– 2120, 2312, 2985, 3238, 3398, 3490
Aerospace Illinois Space Grant Consortium – 3937
Air Force Association – 25

Air Force Officers' Wives' Club of Washington, D.C.
– 26, 27
Air Force Services Agency – 2195
Air Traffic Control Association – 3938
Airports Council International-North America – 34
Akademos, Inc. – 2196
Alabama Commission on Higher Education – 38
Alabama Department of Veterans Affairs – 43
Alabama Road Builders Association – 4302
Alaska Commission on Postsecondary Education –
48, 49, 3268, 4755
Alaska Native Tribal Health Consortium – 2616
Alexander Christian Foundation of Indiana – 2313,
3496
Alpha Chi Omega Foundation – 73, 74, 75
Alpha Epsilon Phi Foundation, Inc. – 76
Alpha Mu Tau Fraternity – 2619
Alpha Omicron Pi Foundation – 77, 78, 80, 83, 84,
87, 88, 89, 90
Alpha Phi Alpha Fraternity, Inc. – 91
American Academy of Physician Assistants – 2621,
2622, 2623, 2624, 2625
American Association of Airport Executives
Foundation – 3952
American Association of Airport
Executives-Southwest Chapter – 3954
American Association of Women Dentists – 2765
American Business Women's Association – 98
American Cancer Society-Heartland Division – 103
American Ceramic Society-Southwest Section –
4307
American College of Medical Practice Executives –
2627, 2628, 2629, 2630, 2631, 2632, 2633, 2634,
3782, 3783, 3784, 3785, 3786, 3787, 3788, 3789
American Concrete Institute – 3269, 4311
American Council of the Blind – 112, 113, 114,
2381, 3000, 3034, 3152, 3499, 3703, 4315
American Dental Education Association – 2769
American Dental Hygienists' Association – 2773,
2774, 2779, 2784, 2788, 3703
American Federation of Television and Radio Artists
– 2198, 3400, 3670, 3878
American Foundation for the Blind – 116, 2314,
2382, 3001, 3002, 3011, 3500, 3501, 4173, 4318
American Foundation for Translation and
Interpretation – 3401
American Geological Institute – 3093, 3132, 3502
American Health Information Management
Association – 2637, 2640, 2641, 2642, 3879,
3882, 3883, 3884
American Hellenic Educational Progressive
Association – 121, 123, 126
American Hellenic Educational Progressive
Association-District 1 – 127
American Hellenic Educational Progressive
Association-District 22 – 134
American Holistic Nurses' Association – 2810
American Hungarian Foundation – 1912
American Indian Arts Council, Inc. – 2123, 2303,
3672
American Indian Chamber of Commerce of
California – 137
American Indian Science and Engineering Society –
2383, 2643, 3012, 4058, 4320, 4322
American Institute of Certified Public Accountants –
3886
American Legion Auxiliary – 205, 207
American Legion Baseball – 225
American Nephrology Nurses' Association – 2819,
2820, 2821, 2822, 2823, 2824, 2825
American Nuclear Society – 3035, 3887, 4328,
4330
American Nursery and Landscape Association –
2046, 2047, 2048, 2049, 2445, 2446, 2593, 2594,
2595, 2596
American Planning Association – 3792, 3857, 3858
American Public Power Association – 232
American Radio Relay League – 233, 234, 238,
240, 241, 242, 3402, 3403, 3404, 3405, 3673,
3888, 3889, 3890, 3891, 4337
American Society of Composers, Authors and
Publishers – 2318
American Society for Engineering Education – 2385,
3036, 3155, 3242, 3955, 4061, 4178, 4341, 4820
American Society of Military Comptrollers – 3277,
3794, 4180

American Society for Photogrammetry and Remote
Sensing – 4828
American Society for Quality – 2657, 4347, 4348
American Society of Radiologic Technologists –
2660, 2661
American Society of Safety Engineers – 1957,
1958, 1960, 4351, 4352, 4354, 4737, 4738, 4740
American Society of Safety Engineers-New Jersey
Chapter – 257, 1968
American Water Ski Educational Foundation – 260
AMVETS National Headquarters – 267
Arab American Institute Foundation – 2207, 3406
Arabian Horse Foundation – 270, 271, 272, 274
Arizona Commission for Postsecondary Education –
277
Arizona Planning Association – 3863
Arizona State University – 2208, 3014
Arkansas Department of Higher Education – 287
Armed Forces Communications and Electronics
Association – 2125, 4188, 4367
Army Aviation Association of America – 292
Army Aviation Association of America Scholarship
Foundation – 293
Asian American Journalists Association – 2126,
2209, 2211, 2212, 3409, 3410
Asian American Journalists Association-Portland
Chapter – 2214, 3411
Asian American Journalists Association-Texas
Chapter – 2215, 3412
Association of Cuban Engineers – 4379
Association for Education and Rehabilitation of the
Blind and Visually Impaired of Ohio – 3003, 3244,
3509
Association of Energy Engineers – 4380
Association of Energy Engineers-Georgia Chapter –
4381
Association of Energy Engineers-New England
Chapter – 4382
Association of Environmental and Engineering
Geologists – 3094, 3095, 4383, 4384
Association of Former Intelligence Officers – 312,
313
Association of Information Technology Professionals
– 3892, 3893
Association for Iron & Steel
Technology-Globe-Trotters Chapter – 318
Association of Texas Professional Educators – 3511,
3512
Association of the United States Army-George
Washington Chapter – 322
Association of the Wall and Ceiling Industry – 2054,
4403
Association for Women Geoscientists – 2391, 3099
Lucy C. Ayers Foundation, Inc. – 2829
Alexander Graham Bell Association for the Deaf –
330, 332, 333, 334, 335, 336, 337, 339, 340,
4406
Bristol Bay Native Corporation – 354
Broadcast Music Inc. – 2319, 2321
H. Fletcher Brown Trust – 2790, 2965, 3044, 3707,
4411
Bureau of Maine Veterans' Services – 357
Business and Professional Women of Virginia –
2397, 2667, 2791, 3045, 3169, 3708, 4077, 4196,
4412
California Adolescent Nutrition, Physical Education,
and Culinary Arts Scholarships – 2946, 3514,
3801
California Association for Postsecondary Education
and Disability – 362, 363, 365, 367, 368
California Council of the Blind – 371
California Emergency Nurses Association – 2831
California Japanese American Alumni Association –
381
California Rural Indian Health Board, Inc. – 2671
California State Fair – 389, 2457, 3678
Californians for Disability Rights – 395
Calista Corporation – 396
Canadian Institutes of Health Research – 2792,
2832, 2956, 2974
Cancer Survivors' Fund – 398
Jorge Mas Canosa Freedom Foundation – 2221,
3291, 3415, 3679, 4415
Caremark Rx, Inc. – 401
Catching the Dream – 3245, 3518, 3519, 4079,
4197, 4416

Master's

American Planning Association-California Chapter –
3860, 3861, 3862

Arkansas Department of Higher Education – 2387,
3038, 3156, 3408, 3506, 3508, 4065

Bois Forte Reservation Tribal Council – 346

California Librarians Black Caucus-Greater Los
Angeles Chapter – 382

California State University – 392, 1890, 3290, 3761,
3803

Classical Association of New England – 2113, 3417,
3523

Community Foundation of Middle Tennessee – 469

Conference of Minority Transportation Officials –
479

Connecticut Commission on Culture and Tourism –
489, 4766

Department of Military Affairs – 569

General Federation of Women's Clubs of
Connecticut – 3540, 3541

Georgia Student Finance Commission – 2857

Hawai'i Community Foundation – 743

Healthcare Financial Management
Association-Georgia Chapter – 2688

Healthcare Financial Management Association-New
Hampshire/Vermont Chapter – 2690

Healthcare Financial Management Association-New
Jersey Chapter – 2865

Instrumentation, Systems, and Automation Society –
4518

International Association of Culinary Professionals
Foundation – 826

International Foodservice Editorial Council – 2161,
2252, 2949, 3336, 3439, 3812, 4771, 4831

Kansas-Nebraska Convention of Southern Baptists
– 870

Kentucky Restaurant Association – 4772

La Unidad Latina Foundation, Inc. – 938

Louisiana Baptist Convention – 954

Maryland Higher Education Commission – 2114,
2411, 2701, 3056, 3178, 3446, 3569, 3988, 4106,
4238

Minnesota State University Student Association –
1063

P. Buckley Moss Society – 3581

National Coalition of Ethnic Minority Nurse
Associations – 2886

National Consortium for Graduate Degrees for
Minorities in Engineering and Science (GEM) –
4248, 4551

National Student Nurses' Association – 2889

New England Navy Nurse Corps Association – 2893

New Mexico Department of Veterans' Services –
1308

Oahu Council of Filipino Catholic Clubs – 1356

Oncology Nursing Society – 2906

Pennsylvania National Guard – 1448

Princess Grace Awards – 2173, 3694, 3924

Rhode Island National Guard – 1494

Salem United Methodist Church – 1512

Scholarship Administrative Services, Inc. – 3616

Harold B. & Dorothy A. Snyder Scholarship Fund –
2916, 4624

Tennessee Student Assistance Corporation – 3630

United American Nurses – 3929

U.S. Navy – 2105, 2929, 2930, 4720, 4721

Virginia Space Grant Consortium – 2017, 2443,
3031, 3642, 4037, 4165

Western Catholic Union – 1839

Women in Aviation, International – 4051

World Wide Baraca Philathea Union – 3654

Other

American Legion Auxiliary – 190

Deaf Friends International – 2562

Department of Veterans Affairs – 587

Harry Alan Gregg Foundation – 2563

Lions Clubs International – 2565

Miss Universe Organization – 1068

National Federation of the Blind of Connecticut –
1156

National Federation of Music Clubs – 2345, 2347,
2352

Opportunities for the Blind, Inc. – 2578

Dawn Ramos Productions – 1475

Sunnyside Foundation, Inc. – 1600

Travelers Protective Association of America – 2579

Postdoctoral

Aerospace Illinois Space Grant Consortium – 3937

American Hungarian Foundation – 1912

Department of Transportation – 4443

English-Speaking Union of the United
States-Washington DC Area Branch – 2145,
2377, 3656

Hawai'i Community Foundation – 743

Idaho Space Grant Consortium – 3980

Kansas Space Grant Consortium – 3983

Library of Congress – 1924

Medical Library Association – 2703

National Institute of Allergy and Infectious Diseases
– 2713

National Inventors Hall of Fame – 1995, 2421,
2716, 3061, 3184, 4120, 4254, 4559

National Science Foundation – 4562

Professional

Academy of Neonatal Nursing – 2807, 2808

American College of Medical Practice Executives –
2627, 2629, 2632, 2633, 3782, 3784, 3787, 3788

American Dental Hygienists' Association – 2774

American Holistic Nurses' Association – 2810

American Hotel & Lodging Educational Foundation
– 4758

American Hungarian Foundation – 1912

American Nephrology Nurses' Association – 2819,
2820, 2821, 2822, 2823, 2824, 2825

American Physical Therapy Association – 2746

American Society of Military Comptrollers – 3277,
3794, 4180

American Society of Radiologic Technologists –
2660, 2661

Association of Former Intelligence Officers – 312

H. Fletcher Brown Trust – 2790, 2965, 3044, 3707,
4411

Business and Professional Women of Virginia –
2667, 3708

California State Fair – 3515

Canadian Nurses Foundation – 2833, 2834, 2835,
2836, 2837, 2838, 2839, 2840, 2841, 2842, 2843

Career Transition for Dancers – 400

Catching the Dream – 3245, 3519

Delaware Higher Education Commission – 2850

Delaware Volunteer Firemen's Association – 2678,
4438, 4748

Department of Military and Veterans Affairs – 577

Department of Transportation – 4443

Emergency Nurses Association – 2851, 2852, 2853,
2854, 2855

Engineers' Society of Western Pennsylvania – 4452

English-Speaking Union of the United
States-Washington DC Area Branch – 2145,
2377, 3656

Finance Authority of Maine – 3250

Frameline – 2148, 3225

H.H. Harris Foundation – 3328, 4808

Hawai'i Community Foundation – 743, 744

Healthcare Financial Management
Association-Virginia Chapter – 2692

Hopi Tribe – 789, 791, 792, 793

Idaho State Board of Education – 3556

Illinois Department of Public Health – 2869

Illinois Student Assistance Commission – 2696,
3558

International Association of Culinary Professionals
Foundation – 826

Kentucky Federation of Business and Professional
Women – 891

Knights of Columbus – 914

Kosciuszko Foundation – 2341

Library of Congress – 1924

Maine Roads Scholarship Fund – 3256, 3565, 3850

Maryland Higher Education Commission – 2114,
2411, 2700, 2701, 2879, 3056, 3178, 3237, 3257,
3446, 3566, 3569, 3988, 4106, 4238, 4749

Maryland State Funeral Directors Association –
1002

Massachusetts/Rhode Island League for Nursing –
2881

Medical Library Association – 2703

National Air Transportation Foundation – 3996

National Association of Master Appraisers – 1128

National Association of Railway Business Women –
1129

National Federation of Music Clubs – 2345, 2347,
2352

National FFA Organization – 2485

National Institute of General Medical Sciences –
2714, 3259, 4119

National Student Nurses' Association – 2889

New England Navy Nurse Corps Association – 2893

Newspaper Association of America – 3369

North Carolina State Education Assistance Authority
– 3605

Nursing Foundation of Pennsylvania – 2901, 2902

Ohio Business Teachers Association – 3608

Oncology Nursing Society – 2905, 2906, 2907,
2908

Princess Grace Awards – 2173, 3694, 3924

Recording for the Blind and Dyslexic – 1482

Rhode Island Foundation – 2913, 2914

Screen Actors Guild Foundation – 3696

Siemens Foundation – 2004, 2432, 3072, 3194,
4149, 4279

South Carolina Commission on Higher Education –
2178, 2367, 3381, 3478, 3622, 3662, 3775, 4153

South Dakota Board of Regents – 3627

Student Press Law Center – 2293

Swedish Women's Education Association
International-South Florida Chapter – 1920, 2011,
2180, 2295, 2371, 3384, 3480

Texas Higher Education Coordinating Board – 1635

Texas Women in Law Enforcement – 3733, 3752

United States Bowling Congress – 1716

Washington Higher Education Coordinating Board –
3092, 3221, 3486, 3644, 4166

Women in Aviation, International – 4044, 4049,
4051

Two Year College

Alabama Commission on Higher Education – 36,
37, 3668

American Society for Clinical Laboratory Science –
2647

California Association for Postsecondary Education
and Disability – 366

California State Fair – 387, 2455, 2456

Datatrac Information Systems, Inc. – 538

Electronic Document Systems Foundation – 2141,
3314, 3426, 4205, 4448

Elks National Foundation – 610

Kansas Federation of Business & Professional
Women's Clubs, Inc. – 869

Kentucky Community and Technical College System
– 883, 884, 885, 886, 887, 2875

League for Innovation in the Community College –
4235

Lowe's Companies, Inc. – 2038, 2604, 3342, 3916

Massachusetts Community Colleges – 1003

New Hampshire Charitable Foundation – 1288,
1291

North Carolina Community College System – 1329,
1330, 1331, 3921, 3922

Ohio Space Grant Consortium – 4139, 4274, 4601

Pennsylvania Higher Education Assistance Agency
– 4607

Penobscot Nation – 1450

Scholarship Administrative Services, Inc. – 1515,
1516, 1517, 1518

Scottish Rite Foundation of Wyoming – 1525

Society of Manufacturing Engineers – 4664

South Carolina Commission on Higher Education –
1564

Texas 4-H Youth Development Foundation – 3231

Texas Higher Education Coordinating Board – 1633

Virginia Space Grant Consortium – 4036, 4164,
4292, 4728

Washington Dental Service Foundation – 2802

Undergraduate

10th Mountain Division Descendants, Inc. – 2

11th Armored Cavalry Veterans of Vietnam and
Cambodia – 3

The 13th Regional Corporation – 4

43d Infantry Division Veterans Association – 6

82nd Airborne Division Association – 7

100 Black Men of America, Inc. – 8

South Carolina Center for Educator Recruitment, Retention, and Advancement – 3621

South Carolina Commission on Higher Education – 1560, 1562, 1565, 2178, 2367, 3381, 3478, 3622, 3662, 3775, 4153

South Carolina Higher Education Tuition Grants Commission – 1566

South Carolina Office of Veterans Affairs – 1567

South Carolina Sheriffs' Association – 1568

South Carolina State Department of Education – 2179, 2290, 2310, 2368

South Carolina Student Loan Corporation – 1569, 2117, 2291, 2369, 2555, 3479, 3624, 4154

South Carolina Vocational Rehabilitation Department – 2292

South Dakota Association of Plumbing, Heating, & Cooling Contractors – 3382

South Dakota Association of Towns and Townships – 1570

South Dakota Board of Regents – 1571, 1572, 1574, 1575, 1576, 1577, 1578, 1579, 3625, 3626, 3627

South Dakota Department of Education – 1580

South Dakota National Guard Enlisted Association – 1582

South Dakota Space Grant Consortium – 2009, 2438, 3117, 4021, 4155

Southern Baptist Convention – 2044

Southern Regional Education Board – 1583

Special Operations Warrior Foundation – 1584

SPJST Supreme Lodge – 1586

Sports Turf Managers Association – 1587

State Student Assistance Commission of Indiana – 1588, 1589, 1590, 1591, 1592, 2759, 2917, 3628

Statewide Hispanic Chamber of Commerce of New Jersey – 1594

Student Aid Foundation – 1595

Student Insights – 1596

Student Loan Finance Corporation – 1597

Student Press Law Center – 2293, 2294, 3731

Julius & Esther Stulberg Competition, Inc. – 2370

Sunkist Growers – 1599

Sunnyside Foundation, Inc. – 1600

Sunshine Lady Foundation, Inc. – 1601, 2997, 3263

SuperSibs! – 1602

Supreme Emblem Club of the United States of America – 1603, 1604

Surface Navy Association – 1605

Swedish Women's Education Association International-South Florida Chapter – 1920, 2011, 2180, 2295, 2371, 3384, 3480

Tailhook Educational Foundation – 1606

Mamoru and Aiko Takitani Foundation – 1607

Tanana Chiefs Council, LLC – 4706

Tau Beta Pi – 4707

Technology Student Association – 1608

Tennessee Funeral Directors Association – 1609

Tennessee Student Assistance Corporation – 1610, 1611, 1612, 1613, 1614, 1615, 1616, 3629

Tenth Mountain Division Association – 1618

TET '68, Inc. – 1619

Texas 4-H Youth Development Foundation – 1620, 2556

Texas Asphalt Pavement Association – 4709

Texas Association of Clinical Laboratory Sciences – 2730

Texas Business and Technology Educators Association – 3631, 4284

Texas Classical Association – 2118, 2119, 3481, 3482

Texas DECA – 3385

Texas Electric Cooperatives, Inc. – 1622, 4793

Texas Extension Education Association, Inc. – 4794

Texas Federation of Business and Professional Women's Foundation, Inc. – 1930, 3663, 3732, 3776, 3831

Texas Higher Education Coordinating Board – 1623, 1624, 1625, 1626, 1627, 1628, 1629, 1630, 1631, 1632, 1634, 1635, 1636, 1637, 1639, 1640, 1641, 1642, 1643, 1644, 1645, 1646, 1647, 1648, 1649, 1650, 2731, 2919, 2920, 4797

Texas Motor Transportation Association – 1651

Texas Mutual Insurance Company – 1652

Texas Space Grant Consortium – 2440, 3085, 3118, 3214, 4022, 4156, 4710

Texas Women in Law Enforcement – 3733, 3752

Third Marine Division Association, Inc. – 1653

Third Wave Foundation – 1654, 1655

Tourism Cares for Tomorrow – 4782, 4791

Transport Workers Union of America – 1658

Transportation Clubs International – 1659, 1660, 1661, 1662, 1663

Travelers Protective Association of America – 2579

Travis Officers' Spouses' Club – 1667

Tree Research and Education Endowment Fund – 2099, 2557, 2613

Tuskegee Airmen, Inc. – 1668, 4023

Two/Ten International Footwear Foundation – 1669

UCB Pharma, Inc. – 1670

Morris K. Udall Foundation – 1900, 2013, 2441, 2732, 2299, 3387, 3633, 3778, 3834, 3876

Ulman Cancer Fund for Young Adults – 1671, 1672, 1673, 2921

United American Nurses – 3929

United Companies, Inc. – 1674

United Daughters of the Confederacy – 1675, 1676, 1677, 1678, 1679, 1680, 1681, 1901, 2296, 2922, 2923, 2954, 4285, 4795

United Daughters of the Confederacy-Texas Division – 1682

United Daughters of the Confederacy-Virginia Division – 1683, 1684, 2733, 2924, 4712

United Food and Commercial Workers International Union – 1685

U.S. Air Force – 1686, 1687, 1689, 1690, 1691, 1692, 1693, 1897, 1909, 1914, 1927, 1943, 1945, 1946, 1947, 2101, 2102, 2103, 2760, 2925, 2926, 2962, 2981, 3087, 3088, 3089, 3145, 3147, 3148, 3149, 3150, 3216, 3217, 3218, 3219, 3483, 4024, 4026, 4028, 4029, 4158, 4159, 4160, 4161, 4286, 4288, 4289, 4290, 4291, 4713, 4715, 4716, 4717, 4718

U.S. Army – 1694, 1698, 1700, 1701, 1702, 1704, 1705

U.S. Army National Guard – 1706

U.S. Army Ordnance Corps Association – 1707

United States Army Warrant Officers Association – 1708

U.S. Bancorp – 1709

United States Bowling Congress – 1710, 1711, 1712, 1713, 1714, 1715, 1716, 1717, 1718, 1719

United States Chess Federation – 1720

U.S. Coast Guard Chief Petty Officers Association – 2297

U.S. Coast Guard Institute – 1722

U.S. JCI Senate – 1723

United States Junior Chamber of Commerce – 1724, 1725, 1726

U.S. Marine Corps – 1727, 1728, 1729, 1730, 2014, 2372, 2998, 3634, 3735

U.S. Naval Academy Class of 1963 Foundation – 1731

U.S. Navy – 1732, 1734, 1735, 2105, 2929, 2930, 2932, 4720, 4721, 4722, 4824, 4825, 4827

United States Submarine Veterans, Inc. – 1743

University Aviation Association – 4031, 4032

University Interscholastic League – 1744, 1745, 1746, 2934, 3091, 3636, 4725

University of Texas at Austin – 2298

Urban League of Nebraska, Inc. – 1747, 1748, 1749, 1750

US Pan Asian American Chamber of Commerce – 1751, 1752, 1753, 1754, 1755, 1757, 1911, 3484

USO World Headquarters – 1758

U.S.S. Intrepid Association, Inc. – 1759

USS Lake Champlain Foundation – 1760

Utah Army National Guard – 1762

Utah Association of Independent Insurance Agents – 1763

Utah Elks Association – 1765

Utah Golf Association – 2559

Utah Hemophilia Foundation – 1766

Utah Higher Education Assistance Authority – 1767, 1768, 1769, 1770, 3638

Utah Society of Professional Engineers – 4726

Utah Sports Hall of Fame Foundation – 1771, 1772

Utility Workers Union of America – 1773

Vasa Order of America – 1774, 1776, 1777, 1778, 2734

Vermont Association of Educational Office Professionals – 3639

Vermont Grocers' Association – 1779, 1780, 1781

Vermont Student Assistance Corporation – 1782, 1783, 1784, 1785, 1786, 1787, 1788, 1789, 1790, 2106, 2181, 2182, 2311, 2373, 2560, 2580, 2581, 2589, 2614, 2735, 2736, 2737, 2738, 2801, 2935, 2936, 3388, 3389, 3640, 3736, 3737, 3753, 3754, 3930, 4727

Vertical Flight Foundation – 1791, 4033

Vesalius Trust for Visual Communications in the Health Sciences – 2183, 2739, 3485

Veterans of Foreign Wars of Maine – 2740

Veterans of Foreign Wars of the United States – 1792, 2299, 3264

Veterans of Foreign Wars of the United States of Mexican Ancestry – 1793

Veterans of the Vietnam War, Inc. – 1794

Vietnam Veterans of America – 1795

VietNow National Headquarters – 1796

VII Corps Desert Storm Veterans Association – 1797

Virginia Airport Operators Council – 4034

Virginia Army/Air National Guard Enlisted Association – 1798

Virginia Association for Pupil Transportation – 1799

Virginia Association of School Business Officials – 1800

Virginia Athletic Trainers Association – 1801

Virginia Coalition of Policy and Deputy Sheriffs – 2300

Virginia Congress of Parents and Teachers – 3641

Virginia Daughters of the American Revolution – 1902, 1903, 2016, 2590, 2741, 2937, 3666, 4796

Virginia Department of Veterans' Affairs – 1802

Virginia Future Business Leaders of America-Phi Beta Lambda – 3931

Virginia High School League – 1803, 1804

Virginia National Guard – 1805

Virginia National Guard Association – 1806

Virginia Public Safety Foundation, Inc. – 1807

Virginia Sheriffs' Institute – 3738, 3755

Virginia State Golf Association – 1808

James D. Voelker Foundation – 3739

VSA arts – 2184, 2374, 4834

Dana Walters Scholarship Foundation – 1811

Izaak Walton League of America-Minnesota Division – 2018, 2027, 3643

Wampanoag Tribe of Gay Head – 1812

Washington Council of the Blind – 1813

Washington Education Foundation – 1815, 1816

Washington Higher Education Coordinating Board – 1818, 1819, 1820, 2803, 2938, 2970, 2983, 3092, 3221, 3486, 3644, 4166

Washington NASA Space Grant Consortium – 4038, 4167, 4729

Washington National Guard – 1822, 1823

Washington State Dental Hygienists' Association – 2804

Washington State Federation of Business and Professional Women – 1826

Washington State PTA – 1827

Wasie Foundation – 1828

G.H. Weems Educational Fund – 1830

Wells Fargo Education Financial Services – 1831

Charlie Wells Memorial Scholarship Fund – 4039

Professor Chen Wen-Chen Memorial Foundation – 1832, 1833

West Virginia Division of Veterans' Affairs – 1834

West Virginia Funeral Directors Association – 1835

West Virginia Higher Education Policy Commission – 1836, 1837, 1838, 4730

West Virginia Space Grant Consortium – 4040, 4168

Western Art Association – 2185

Western Catholic Union – 1839

Western Golf Association – 1840

Western Interstate Commission for Higher Education – 1841, 2107, 2761, 2805, 2939, 2964, 2971, 2984, 3836

Wichita and Affiliated Tribes – 1842

Wings Over America Scholarship Foundation – 1843

Winston-Salem Foundation – 1844, 2940, 2941

Wisconsin Council of the Blind – 1845

Wisconsin Department of Veterans Affairs – 1846, 1847, 1848

Wisconsin Funeral Directors Association – 1852

Vocational/Occupational

7th Generation Community Service Corporation – 1
10th Mountain Division Descendants, Inc. – 2
11th Armored Cavalry Veterans of Vietnam and
Cambodia – 3
The 13th Regional Corporation – 4
25th Infantry Division Association – 5
43d Infantry Division Veterans Association – 6
82nd Airborne Division Association – 7
100 Black Men of America, Inc. – 8
100th Infantry Battalion Veterans Club – 9, 10, 11,
3489, 3700, 3758
101st Airborne Division Association – 12
531 Gray Ghost Squadron Association – 13
Acacia Fraternity – 14
Academy of Applied Science – 2194, 4054, 4298
Academy of Model Aeronautics – 15, 16
Academy of Neonatal Nursing – 2807, 2808
Academy of Television Arts & Sciences Foundation
– 2120, 2312, 2985, 3238, 3398, 3490
ACCEL/Exchange Network – 17
Actuarial Foundation – 18
Adelante! U.S. Education Leadership Fund – 19
Adirondack Spintacular – 20
Adjutant General's Department – 21
Aero Club of New England – 3932, 3933, 3934,
3935, 3936
Aerospace Illinois Space Grant Consortium – 3937
African Methodist Episcopal Church – 22
Aggregate Producers of Wisconsin – 4299
AHF, Inc. – 23
Air Force Aid Society – 24
Air Force Association – 25
Air Force Officers' Wives' Club of Washington, D.C.
– 26, 27, 28
Air Force Sergeants Association – 29, 30, 31, 32
Air Force Services Agency – 2195
Air Traffic Control Association – 3938, 3939
Air & Waste Management Association-Connecticut
Chapter – 1948, 3222, 4300
Aircraft Electronics Association – 33, 3940, 3941,
3942, 3943, 3944, 3945, 3946, 3947
Airports Council International-North America – 34
Akademos, Inc. – 2196
Alabama Alliance for Science, Engineering,
Mathematics, and Science Education – 3491
Alabama Bankers Association – 35, 2197, 3266
Alabama Commission on Higher Education – 36,
37, 38, 39, 40, 41, 2809, 3668
Alabama Concrete Industries Association – 2045,
4301
Alabama Council of Teachers of Mathematics –
4055
Alabama Department of Rehabilitation Services –
42
Alabama Department of Veterans Affairs – 43
Alabama Funeral Directors Association – 44
Alabama Golf Course Superintendents Association
– 45
Alabama Indian Affairs Commission – 46
Alabama Law Foundation – 47
Alabama Road Builders Association – 4302
Alabama Space Grant Consortium – 1949, 2379,
2380, 3008, 3009, 3239, 3267, 3399, 3492, 3493,
3669, 3701, 3781, 3948, 3949, 4056, 4171

Alaska Commission on Postsecondary Education –
48, 49, 50, 2615, 2744, 2764, 2955, 2972, 3268,
3494, 3495, 3702, 3743, 3839, 4755
Alaska Independent Blind – 51
Alaska National Guard – 52, 53
Alaska Native Tribal Health Consortium – 2616
Albuquerque Community Foundation – 54, 55
Alexander Christian Foundation of Indiana – 2313,
3496
Horatio Alger Association of Distinguished
Americans, Inc. – 56, 57, 58, 59, 60, 61, 62, 63,
64, 65, 66, 67, 68, 69
All-American Soap Box Derby – 70
Alliance of Black Telecommunications Employees,
Inc.-Nation's Capital Chapter – 71
Allianz Global Investors Distributors LLC – 72
Alpha Chi Omega Foundation – 73, 74, 75
Alpha Delta Kappa – 3497
Alpha Epsilon Phi Foundation, Inc. – 76
Alpha Mu Tau Fraternity – 2617, 2618, 2619, 2620
Alpha Omicron Pi Foundation – 77, 78, 79, 80, 81,
82, 83, 84, 85, 86, 87, 88, 89, 90
Alpha Phi Alpha Fraternity, Inc. – 91
Amalgamated Transit Union – 92
Americal Division Veterans Association – 93
American Academy of Allergy, Asthma &
Immunology – 94
American Academy of Physician Assistants – 2621,
2622, 2623, 2624, 2625
American Association of Airport Executives
Foundation – 3950, 3951, 3952
American Association of Airport
Executives-Northeast Chapter – 3953
American Association of Airport
Executives-Southwest Chapter – 3954
American Association of Blacks in Energy – 3010,
4057, 4303
American Association of Physics Teachers – 3151,
3498
American Association of Women Dentists – 2765
American Atheists – 95, 96
American Brahman Breeders Association – 97,
2444
American Business Women's Association – 98
American Cancer Society-California Division – 99
American Cancer Society-Florida Division – 100
American Cancer Society-Great Lakes Division –
101
American Cancer Society-Great West Division – 102
American Cancer Society-Heartland Division – 103
American Cancer Society-Mid-South Division – 104
American Cancer Society-Midwest Division – 105
American Cancer Society-Ohio Division – 106
American Cancer Society-South Atlantic Division –
107
American Ceramic Society – 2121, 4304
American Ceramic Society-New England Section –
2122, 4305
American Ceramic Society-Southwest Section –
4306, 4307
American Chemical Society – 1950, 2626, 3032,
3033, 4308, 4309
American College of Chiropractic Orthopedists –
2762

American College of Medical Practice Executives –
2627, 2628, 2629, 2630, 2631, 2632, 2633, 2634,
3782, 3783, 3784, 3785, 3786, 3787, 3788, 3789
American College of Nurse-Midwives – 2635, 2636
American Composites Manufacturers Association –
4310
American Concrete Institute – 3269, 3270, 4311,
4312
American Concrete Institute-Greater Michigan
Chapter – 3271, 4313
American Concrete Institute-Illinois Chapter – 3272
American Concrete Institute-Indiana Chapter – 3273
American Concrete Institute-Nebraska Chapter –
3274, 4314
American Council of the Blind – 108, 109, 110, 111,
112, 113, 114, 2381, 3000, 3034, 3152, 3499,
3703, 4172, 4315
American Council of Engineering Companies of
Colorado – 4316, 4317
American Dental Association – 2766, 2767, 2768
American Dental Education Association – 2769
American Dental Hygienists' Association – 2770,
2771, 2772, 2773, 2774, 2775, 2776, 2777, 2778,
2779, 2780, 2781, 2782, 2783, 2784, 2785, 2786,
2787, 2788, 2789, 3790
American Federation of Television and Radio Artists
– 2198, 3400, 3670, 3878
American Fire Sprinkler Association – 2199
American Fire Sprinkler Association-Carolinas
Chapter – 2200
American Flint Glass Workers Union – 115
American Floral Endowment – 2591, 2592
American Foundation for the Blind – 116, 2201,
2314, 2315, 2382, 3001, 3002, 3011, 3500, 3501,
4173, 4318
American Foundation for Translation and
Interpretation – 3401
American Geological Institute – 3093, 3132, 3502
American GI Forum-Mile High Chapter – 117
American Guild of Organists-Greater Bridgeport
Chapter – 2316
American Health Information Management
Association – 2637, 2638, 2639, 2640, 2641,
2642, 3879, 3880, 3881, 3882, 3883, 3884
American Hellenic Educational Progressive
Association – 118, 119, 120, 121, 122, 123, 124,
125, 126, 3655, 3671, 3759
American Hellenic Educational Progressive
Association-District 1 – 127
American Hellenic Educational Progressive
Association-District 4 – 128
American Hellenic Educational Progressive
Association-District 10 – 129
American Hellenic Educational Progressive
Association-District 11 – 130
American Hellenic Educational Progressive
Association-District 13 – 131
American Hellenic Educational Progressive
Association-District 16 – 132
American Hellenic Educational Progressive
Association-District 20 – 133
American Hellenic Educational Progressive
Association-District 22 – 134
American Holistic Nurses' Association – 2810

American Hotel & Lodging Educational Foundation
– 135, 136, 4756, 4757, 4758, 4759
American Hungarian Foundation – 1912
American Indian Arts Council, Inc. – 2123, 2303,
3672
American Indian Chamber of Commerce of
California – 137
American Indian College Fund – 138, 139, 3275,
3276, 3885, 4174, 4175, 4319
American Indian Education Foundation – 140
American Indian Heritage Foundation – 141
American Indian Science and Engineering Society –
1951, 2383, 2384, 2643, 2644, 3012, 3013, 4058,
4059, 4320, 4321, 4322, 4323
American Indian Services – 142
American Institute of Certified Public Accountants –
143, 3886
American Institute of Mining, Metallurgical, and
Petroleum Engineers – 4798
American Institute of Wine & Food-Pacific
Northwest Chapter – 144
American Legion – 145, 146, 147, 148, 149, 150,
151, 152, 153, 154, 155, 156, 157, 158, 159, 160,
161, 162, 163, 164, 165, 166, 167, 168, 169, 170,
171, 172, 173, 174, 175, 176, 177, 178, 179, 180,
181, 182, 183, 184, 185, 186, 2029, 2202, 2317,
2811, 3240, 3241, 3503, 3524
American Legion Auxiliary – 187, 188, 189, 190,
191, 192, 193, 194, 195, 196, 197, 198, 199, 200,
201, 202, 203, 204, 205, 206, 207, 208, 209, 210,
211, 212, 213, 214, 215, 216, 217, 218, 219, 220,
221, 222, 223, 224, 2124, 2645, 2646, 2812,
2813, 2814, 2815, 2816, 2817, 2818, 3504, 3791
American Legion Baseball – 225, 226, 227
American Meteorological Society – 3133, 3134,
3135, 3136, 3137, 3138, 4060
American Military Retirees Association, Inc. – 228
American Military Spouse Education Foundation –
229
American Museum of Natural History – 2203
American Nephrology Nurses' Association – 2819,
2820, 2821, 2822, 2823, 2824, 2825
American Nuclear Society – 1952, 1953, 3035,
3887, 4325, 4326, 4327, 4328, 4329, 4330, 4331,
4332
American Nursery and Landscape Association –
2046, 2047, 2048, 2049, 2445, 2446, 2593, 2594,
2595, 2596
American Philological Association – 2111
American Physical Society – 3153, 3154
American Physical Therapy Association – 2745,
2746
American Planning Association – 1954, 3792, 3793,
3857, 3858, 3859
American Planning Association-California Chapter –
3860, 3861, 3862
American Polish Engineering Association – 4333
American Postal Workers Union – 230, 231
American Psychological Association – 2204, 2986
American Public Power Association – 232
American Radio Relay League – 233, 234, 235,
236, 237, 238, 239, 240, 241, 242, 2205, 2826,
3402, 3403, 3404, 3405, 3673, 3888, 3889, 3890,
3891, 4176, 4177, 4334, 4335, 4336, 4337, 4338,
4339
American Red Cross – 243
American Road and Transportation Builders
Association – 244
American Society of Agricultural and Biological
Engineers – 2447, 2448, 2449, 2450
American Society of Civil Engineers-Maine Section
– 4340
American Society for Clinical Laboratory Science –
2647, 2648
American Society for Clinical Laboratory
Science-Ohio – 2649
American Society for Clinical Pathology – 2650,
2651
American Society of Composers, Authors and
Publishers – 2318
American Society of Criminology – 3704, 3744
American Society for Engineering Education – 2385,
3036, 3155, 3242, 3955, 4061, 4178, 4341, 4820
American Society of Engineers of Indian Origin –
2050, 4179, 4342

American Society of Extra-Corporeal Technology,
Inc. – 2652, 2653, 2654, 2655
American Society of Heating, Refrigerating and
Air-Conditioning Engineers, Inc. – 245, 246, 247,
248, 249, 250, 251, 252, 253, 254, 4343, 4344
American Society of Military Comptrollers – 3277,
3278, 3794, 3795, 4180, 4181
American Society of Military Comptrollers-Mount
Vernon Chapter – 3279, 3796, 4182
American Society of Military
Comptrollers-Washington Chapter – 3280, 3797
American Society for Nondestructive Testing, Inc. –
4345
American Society for Photogrammetry and Remote
Sensing – 4828
American Society of Plumbing Engineers – 4346
American Society of Podiatric Medical Assistants –
2656
American Society for Quality – 255, 256, 2657,
4347, 4348
American Society of Radiologic Technologists –
2658, 2659, 2660, 2661, 2662
American Society of Safety Engineers – 1955,
1956, 1957, 1958, 1959, 1960, 1961, 1962, 1963,
1964, 1965, 1966, 4349, 4350, 4351, 4352, 4353,
4354, 4355, 4356, 4357, 4358, 4359, 4360, 4735,
4736, 4737, 4738, 4739, 4740, 4741, 4742, 4743,
4744, 4745, 4746
American Society of Safety
Engineers-Columbia-Willamette Chapter – 1967
American Society of Safety Engineers-New Jersey
Chapter – 257, 1968
American Society of Women Accountants-St. Louis
Chapter – 258
American Water Ski Educational Foundation – 259,
260
AMVETS-Department of Illinois – 261, 262, 263
AMVETS Ladies Auxiliary – 264
AMVETS National Headquarters – 265, 266, 267
Anchor Scholarship Foundation – 268
Appalachian College Association – 2386, 3037,
3505, 3705, 4062, 4063, 4183, 4361
Aquatrols Corporation – 2051, 2206
Arab American Institute Foundation – 2207, 3406
Arabian Horse Association – 269
Arabian Horse Foundation – 270, 271, 272, 273,
274
Arabian Horse Trust – 275
Arizona Army National Guard – 276
Arizona Commission for Postsecondary Education –
277, 278
Arizona Friends of Foster Children Foundation –
279
Arizona Kidney Foundation – 280
Arizona Planning Association – 3863
Arizona Society Daughters of the American
Revolution – 1889
Arizona State University – 2208, 3014
Arkansas Community Foundation – 281, 282
Arkansas Department of Higher Education – 283,
284, 285, 286, 287, 288, 2387, 3038, 3156, 3243,
3407, 3408, 3506, 3507, 3508, 4064, 4065
Arkansas Department of Workforce Education –
2388, 2663, 3015, 4184, 4362
Arkansas Single Parent Scholarship Fund – 289
Arkansas Student Loan Authority – 290
Armed Forces Communications and Electronics
Association – 291, 2125, 3157, 3158, 3159, 3160,
3161, 3162, 3163, 3956, 3957, 3958, 3959, 3960,
3961, 4066, 4067, 4068, 4069, 4070, 4071, 4072,
4185, 4186, 4187, 4188, 4189, 4190, 4191, 4192,
4193, 4363, 4364, 4365, 4366, 4367, 4368, 4369,
4370, 4371, 4372
Army Aviation Association of America – 292
Army Aviation Association of America Scholarship
Foundation – 293
Army Emergency Relief – 294
Army Engineer Association – 295, 296, 297, 298
Army Engineer Officers Wives Club – 299
Army Officers' Wives' Club of the Greater
Washington Area – 300
Arthritis Foundation-Southern New England Chapter
– 301
Asantewaa – 302
Asian American Journalists Association – 2126,
2209, 2210, 2211, 2212, 3409, 3410

Asian American Journalists Association-Philadelphia
Chapter – 2213
Asian American Journalists Association-Portland
Chapter – 2214, 3411
Asian American Journalists Association-Texas
Chapter – 2215, 3412
Asian & Pacific Islander American Scholarship Fund
– 303
ASM International-Milwaukee Chapter – 4373, 4799
Associated Builders and Contractors – 4374
Associated Colleges of Illinois – 304
Associated Food Dealers of Michigan – 305, 306
Associated General Contractors of Connecticut, Inc.
– 4375
Associated General Contractors of Illinois – 307
Associated General Contractors of Minnesota –
2052, 4376
Associated General Contractors of Vermont – 308
Associated Press Television/Radio Association of
California and Nevada – 2216, 2217, 3413, 3414
Associates of Vietnam Veterans of America – 309
Association of Alaska School Boards – 310
Association of American Editorial Cartoonists –
2127
Association of Blind Citizens – 311
Association of California Water Agencies – 1969,
1970, 2451, 2452, 3798, 3799, 4377, 4378
Association of Cuban Engineers – 4379
Association for Education and Rehabilitation of the
Blind and Visually Impaired of Ohio – 3003, 3244,
3509
Association of Energy Engineers – 4380
Association of Energy Engineers-Georgia Chapter –
4381
Association of Energy Engineers-New England
Chapter – 4382
Association of Environmental and Engineering
Geologists – 3094, 3095, 4383, 4384
Association of Former Intelligence Officers – 312,
313
Association of Graduates – 314
Association of Independent Colleges and
Universities of Pennsylvania – 315, 1931, 2053,
2827, 4385, 4386
Association of Independent Funeral Directors of
Florida – 316
Association of Indians in America-New Jersey
Chapter – 317
Association of Information Technology Professionals
– 3892, 3893
Association of Information Technology
Professionals-Omaha Chapter – 3894
Association for Iron & Steel Technology – 3039,
3096, 3164, 3281, 3282, 3283, 4073, 4387, 4388,
4389, 4800, 4801, 4802
Association for Iron & Steel Technology-Baltimore
Chapter – 3284, 4390, 4803
Association for Iron & Steel Technology-Detroit
Chapter – 3285, 4391, 4804
Association for Iron & Steel
Technology-Globe-Trotters Chapter – 318
Association for Iron & Steel Technology-Midwest
Chapter – 319, 320, 4392, 4393, 4394, 4395
Association for Iron & Steel Technology-Northwest
Chapter – 3040, 3165, 3286, 4074, 4396, 4805
Association for Iron & Steel Technology-Ohio Valley
Chapter – 1971, 2389, 3041, 3166, 4194, 4397,
4806
Association for Iron & Steel Technology-Pittsburgh
Chapter – 3287, 4398, 4807
Association for Iron & Steel Technology-Southeast
Chapter – 3288, 4399
Association of Old Crows – 3167, 4075, 4400
Association of Retired Teachers of Connecticut –
3510
Association of State Dam Safety Officials – 3097,
4401
Association of Texas Professional Educators – 3511,
3512
Association of the United States Army – 321, 4402
Association of the United States Army-George
Washington Chapter – 322
Association of the Wall and Ceiling Industry – 2054,
4403
Association for Women in Architecture – 2055,
2128, 3864, 4404

Title of Awards Index